ANNUAL REGISTER OF
GRANT SUPPORT™

Annual Register of Grant Support™
45th Edition

Publisher
Thomas H. Hogan

Vice President, Content
Dick Kaser

Director, ITI Reference Group
Owen O'Donnell

Managing Editor
Beverley McDonough

Associate Editor
Daniel Bazikian

Manager, Tampa Editorial Operations
Debra James

Project Coordinator, Tampa Editorial
Carolyn Victor

ANNUAL REGISTER OF
GRANT SUPPORT™

A DIRECTORY OF FUNDING SOURCES

45th EDITION 2012

Published by

Information Today, Inc.
143 Old Marlton Pike
Medford, NJ 08055-8750
Phone: (609) 654-6266
Fax: (609) 654-4309
E-mail (Orders): **custserv@infotoday.com**
Web site: http://www.infotoday.com
Copyright 2011, Information Today, Inc. All Rights Reserved.

ISSN 0066-4049
ISBN 978-1-57387-417-5
Library of Congress Catalog Card Number: 69-18307

Information Today, Inc.
143 Old Marlton Pike
Medford, NJ 08055-8750
Phone: 800-300-9868 (Customer Service)
           800-409-4929 (Editorial)
Fax: 609-654-4309
E-mail (orders): custserv@infotoday.com
Web Site: www.infotoday.com

Printed and bound in the United States of America

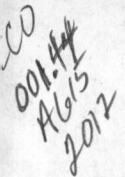

Contents

Continued

Preface

Now in its 45th edition, the *Annual Register of Grant Support™: A Directory of Funding Sources* has achieved a deserved reputation as an authoritative standard reference source on financial support. Known and relied upon by academic scholars and researchers, *Grant Support* also responds to the needs of those in the fields of business, civic improvement, and social welfare. Recognized for its value to the individual, *Grant Support* assists hospitals, arts organizations, community service groups, medical research facilities, and other institutional applicants as well.

The 2012 edition includes details of 2,849 grant support programs of government agencies, public and private foundations, corporations, community trusts, unions, educational and professional associations, and special interest organizations. It covers a broad spectrum of interests from academic and scientific research, project development, travel and exchange programs, and publication support to equipment and construction grants, in-service training, and competitive awards and prizes in a variety of fields.

Each complete program description contains details of the type, purpose, and duration of the grant; amount of funding available for each award and for the entire program or all programs of the organization; eligibility requirements; geographic restrictions; number of applicants and recipients in the most recent year for which statistics are available; representative awards made under the program in the most recent year; application instructions and deadline; personnel of the funding organization as well as its address, founding date, and telephone and fax numbers; e-mail address and web site address if available; data concerning the organization's areas of interest, cooperative funding programs, and consulting or volunteer services; publications available; IRS tax identification number, if applicable; and other pertinent information and special stipulations.

Grant Support attempts to be as comprehensive as possible by including the following forms of financial aid: programs that offer non-repayable financial assistance directly to the grantee or indirectly through payment to the sponsoring institution; programs that accept applicants from the United States or Canada or directly benefit the United States or Canada; study grants and fellowships aimed principally though not exclusively at the graduate or postgraduate levels; grants for construction, facilities, or project costs for education, medical research, health care, civic improvement, etc.; and programs donating consulting services in lieu of a direct monetary grant.

Funding sources are given the opportunity annually to update entry data. Staff research continues to within weeks of *Grant Support*'s publication date to assure information is as current and complete as possible and to identify new funding sources for inclusion. Essential programs for which no updated information has been returned are included, either as they appeared in the last edition, revised where possible, or compiled entirely through secondary research.

Support programs are divided into eleven major areas, further subdivided into more specific subject fields. Each entry contained in *Grant Support* has been placed in the section that reflects its principal interest. If program interests equally emphasize diverse fields, such as communications and business and economics, one full entry and a cross-reference will appear in the respective sections. Similarly, a program for minority political scientists will appear in either "Special Populations" or "Political Science," with a cross-reference in the appropriate section. However, organizations with broad support purposes or interests in three or more well-defined areas are listed in the "Multiple Special Purpose" section.

Four indexes—Subject, Organization and Program, Geographic, and Personnel—facilitate the potential applicant's search for appropriate grant programs. References in each index are to program entry number. While consulting the Subject Index, should the reader wish to know in which chapter a particular entry appears, he or she may consult the Entry Listing by Chapter Index, which precedes the Subject Index.

In the Subject Index, each grant has been indexed in terms of the specific areas to which it may be applied (e.g., Cartography, Mathematics), the type of grant (e.g., Construction and Facilities Projects, Medical Research), and the individuals or organizations eligible for support, if limitations are specified (e.g., Religious Institutions, Women). The Organization and Program Index alphabetically lists grant programs in upper-lower case and funding organizations in upper case. In addition, programs are also listed following the organizations that sponsor them. The Geographic Index groups grantmaking organizations according to the state or country in which they are located. In the Personnel Index, officers of the organizations, Trustees, Directors, and Awards Committee members appear alphabetically.

The editorial staff of *Annual Register of Grant Support*™ strives continually to provide the professional community with the most comprehensive, up-to-date information on existing forms of financial aid from as wide a variety of sources as possible. The staff urges the users of this edition to inform us of any corrections or additions to existing entries and of funding sources not included, and invites suggestions for improvement of future editions.

Introduction

Grant support in America has increased dramatically, both in size and sophistication, since the days when John D. Rockefeller, Sr. walked the streets of New York passing out dimes to the needy.

Today, the support of human services through grants, awards, fellowships, and private gifts is a multibillion-dollar enterprise. Private foundations, corporations, individuals, charitable organizations, and agencies gave an estimated $290.89 billion to charity in 2010, an increase of 3.8 percent compared with the revised estimate of $280.3 billion given in 2009 according to the Giving USA Foundation.

Of the total $290.89 billion given in 2010, $211.77 billion came from individuals and accounts for 73 percent of all estimated giving. Grants from foundations, excluding those affiliated with business enterprises, totalled $41 billion and are estimated at 14 percent. Gifts received through bequests are estimated to be $22.83 billion or 8 percent of the total; corporations contributed $15.29 billion, accounting for 5 percent of the total.

When total charitable giving is analyzed by field, religion received the largest share of 2010 dollars—$100.63 billion—followed by education ($41.67 billion); human services ($26.49 billion); public-society benefit ($24.24 billion); health ($22.83 billion); international affairs ($15.77 billion); arts, culture, and humanities ($13.28 billion); and environment and animals ($6.66 billion).

The 2,849 entries listed in this edition of *Annual Register of Grant Support*™ represent billions of dollars in financial assistance to potential grant seekers.

Part of the success in using the *Annual Register of Grant Support*™ will depend on an understanding of the various types of grantmaking entities, how they differ in their objectives and grantmaking procedures, what they look for in the grant applicant, and how they are approached. It is hoped that the following descriptions of grant-supporting organizations will increase the usability of Grant Support to the potential grant seeker.

PRIVATE FOUNDATIONS

Probably no area of philanthropy is so misunderstood and misused as that of private foundations. According to studies, as many as 80 percent of all applications to private foundations are inappropriate or misdirected. While at least part of the blame for this error must be attributed to private foundations themselves, grant seekers often compound the error by tending to lump all private foundations together as if they shared a common purpose.

Not only do private foundations differ greatly from public funding sources, but there is a wide diversity among private foundations themselves. What may be an appropriate application to the Ford Foundation, for example, may be totally inappropriate to the San Francisco Foundation.

There are more than 37,500 grantmaking foundations in the United States. The reason that an approximate figure must be used is that the federal government defines private foundations more by exclusion than by anything else. If an organization cannot qualify as a charitable, religious, educational, scientific, or governmental organization, it may be classified as a private foundation even if it has never made a grant nor intends to make one. Potential grant seekers should be aware that the mere use of the word "foundation" in the title of an organization is not evidence that the organization will make grants.

Until the tax reform act of 1976, private foundations bore a 4 percent excise tax on net investment income (Section 4940 of the Tax Reform Act of 1969), and annual giving requirements were based on greater of "adjusted net income" or a *variable* percentage of the market value of investment assets—in effect discouraging the foundations from building their assets.

After 1976, the variable percentage was eliminated, and giving requirements were set at 5 percent of market value of assets or of net income. The Economic Recovery Tax Act of 1981 (ERTA) further amended the requirements to a flat 5 percent of market value of assets. In addition, the excise tax on net investment income was reduced to 2 percent in 1978, which further encouraged growth by private foundations.

Several provisions of the Tax Reform Act of 1969 still regulate the activities of foundations. For instance, foundations face restrictions on self-dealing and are limited in the ownership of businesses. One provision of particular interest to the potential grant seeker is a requirement that every private foundation with assets of $5,000 or more (virtually all of them) must submit an annual report that is available for public inspection. These annual reports, printed on special Internal Revenue Service form 990-PF, include the names and addresses of all principal officers of the foundation, the total assets and investments of the foundation and, most important, a complete listing of every grant made during the year of record. Readers of *Grant Support* may wish to review selected 990-PFs of those foundations included in this edition in order to supplement information on current grants.

These 990-PF forms may be obtained directly from the private foundations themselves, or they may be found in over 200 Foundation Center Network member libraries located throughout the country, and are available for public use. (A list of these libraries may be obtained by writing the Foundation Center, 79 Fifth Avenue, New York, NY 10003-3076, or via their web site at www.foundationcenter.org).

A substantial number of private foundations publish their own annual reports over and above the 990-PF requirement mentioned earlier. Copies of these annual reports may be obtained by writing the foundation directly.

TYPES OF FOUNDATIONS

There are certain aspects common to all private foundations in the United States. However, foundations can be broken down into five types, which will assist the grant seeker in understanding their current objectives and grant distribution patterns.

1. National Foundations

Most of the foundations listed in Grant Support are national foundations, meaning that they are not limited to any geographic area in their grant support. National foundations are usually quite large, with assets of $25 million or more. They include all the better-known foundations, such as The Ford Foundation, the Lilly Endowment, The Rockefeller Foundation, and the Carnegie Corporation of New York. Because national foundations may make grants anywhere in the country, it is important to remember that these foundations are usually more attracted to programs and proposals with national, or at least regional, implications. Most of the national foundations are staffed with professional grantmakers, publish their own annual reports, and often have well-defined philanthropic goals.

While national foundations are large enough to fund projects of almost any size—and have been known to make grants of a million dollars or more—it should be remembered that competition for these national foundation grants is extremely fierce. The Ford Foundation, for example, will receive as many as 30,000 proposals every year and will fund only about 2,000.

2. Special-Interest Foundations

Many foundations listed in this edition of Grant Support devote their entire grant efforts to programs within a single field of interest. These special-interest foundations, just as the national foundations, often make grants without any geographic limitations so long as the projects relate to the specific areas. Special-interest foundations range from the massive Robert Wood Johnson Foundation (health) to the Joseph P. Kennedy Foundation (mental retardation) to those supporting research on a single disease.

Some of the larger special-interest foundations employ staff whose purpose is not only to review grants but to stay abreast of information being gathered about that special field of interest. Potential grant seekers, then, should consider special-interest foundations as a potential source of information about a given subject as well as a potential source of funds.

3. Corporate Foundations

During the 1950s, many major corporations created private foundations to serve as the corporate philanthropic arm, although the Tax Reform Act of 1969 greatly slowed the increase in their number. The ExxonMobil Foundation, Inc.

and the Sears-Roebuck Foundation are examples. Readers should be alerted to the fact that while many foundations carry names of large corporations, they are not corporate foundations. The Ford Foundation, for example, is not a corporate foundation; it was created by the Ford family.

Most corporate foundations, while "independent," are very much creatures of the corporations that founded them and fund them. Corporate foundations will, therefore, often be more receptive to proposals that are in line with their corporate interest. Historically, corporate foundations more often have made grants in the fields of education, federated giving (United Way, etc.), minority enterprises, and local social services that demonstrate a benefit to the company employees as well as the community at large.

Most corporate foundations will have relatively small assets in comparison with the amount of grants. This is because once the money has moved from the corporation to the corporate foundation, it can never go back to the corporation. Usually corporations will keep only enough funds in the corporate foundation to sustain the foundation's grant efforts without harming the corporate financial position.

4. Family Foundations

By far, the largest number of private foundations are family foundations. They range in assets from hundreds of millions of dollars, such as those of the several Rockefeller Foundations, to a few thousand dollars.

The grant support pattern of family foundations is very often a personal matter. Often the family foundation will be controlled entirely by family members, and even when these family members have died, the family foundation will often continue to reflect their wishes. Unlike special-interest foundations, family foundations seldom have set fields of interest. Grants more probably will reflect areas of current family interest rather than any recognizable pattern of traditional philanthropy.

Most family foundations are small, and few will have staff or guidelines for submitting proposals. A vast majority of family foundations limit their grants to the city or locality in which the family resides and accumulated its wealth. Unlike national foundations, family foundations are best approached as if they were individual donors, not private foundations.

Because most family foundations are relatively small and have such a limited geographic giving pattern, few are included in Grant Support. These foundations should be explored, however, for modest gifts of a local nature. While the average gift of small family foundations is less than $5,000, the sheer volume of family foundations makes them an important factor in grant support.

5. Community Foundations

In a strictly legal sense, community foundations are not really foundations at all but, rather, public charities. Community foundations maintain this favored tax status by collecting money from the public and directing grants within the community for which they are named. Because community foundations are not private foundations, they have no minimum giving requirements and pay no excise taxes on their net investment income. This is partly responsible for their rapid growth during the past decade, for hundreds of foundations (including some with assets in the many millions of dollars) have given all their money to community foundations.

A number of the larger community foundations, such as the Cleveland Foundation and the New York Community Trust, are listed in *Grant Support*. It is easy to distinguish a community foundation, for it will always be named for the community it serves. The San Francisco Foundation serves San Francisco, the Chicago Community Trust serves Chicago, and so forth. Readers of *Grant Support* should bear in mind that community foundations cannot, by law, make grants outside the geographic regions they serve. The San Francisco Foundation, for example, is not likely to fund a project in Texas, regardless of the merit of the proposal.

For more information about the existence of a community foundation in a given city, readers may wish to consult the local trust bank in that city. (Information can also be obtained by writing the Council on Foundations, Inc., 2121 Crystal Drive, Suite 700, Arlington, VA 22202 or via their web site at www.cof.org.)

CORPORATE GIVING

Although the practice of corporations making grants and gifts to charity is now largely accepted, it was not until 1935 that the Internal Revenue Service allowed a charitable deduction for corporate gifts. In 1982, changes in the tax law enhanced the value of donations of company products, and increased the deduction of corporate contributions from 5 to 10 percent of net income.

Yet while this modest federal government incentive has spurred corporate philanthropy, approximately only one-third of all corporations in the United States make corporate gifts.

Corporations made the largest percentage of their donations to education over the last several years, with health and human services receiving the second largest amounts. Cultural and arts groups, civic and community activities, and various other recipients received the balance of corporate dollars.

Most corporations do not have professional grant reviewers but will often have grant guidelines, specific philanthropic objectives, or well-defined procedures for grant applicants.

An important consideration when approaching corporations is to introduce a benefit, either directly to the company or indirectly through its employees, that grant support can make. A proposal for support of an alcoholism program may be received more readily if the corporation feels alcoholism is a problem among its employees.

Many corporations are willing to provide volunteer service and specific expert assistance as well as money. Corporations also make in-kind contributions, such as free printing, equipment, etc., and will sometimes match gifts made by individual employees.

FEDERATED GIVING

Grant Support lists many grant opportunities from funding sources which, though neither foundations nor corporations, provide many millions of dollars of grant support every year. These funding sources can best be described as federated giving organizations, in that a number of small organizations combine their funding efforts for maximum effect.

The largest and best known federated agency is, of course, United Way. Most United Ways, however, do not make grants so much as they support existing agencies.

There are a number of other federated agencies that do make grants. The Catholic Campaign for Human Development, which is the federated arm of the Catholic Church in America, provides some $8 million in grant support annually. Other federated agencies include the United Negro College Fund, the United Jewish Appeal, the American Association of University Women, and the American Federation of Teachers.

PUBLIC MONEY

Government funding is as complex and confusing as it is big, and the special terms and language of government grants make the subject seem more confusing than it really is. An understanding of the various types of grants and some of the most often used terms may help readers break through the perplexing language of government grants.

Types of Grants

The federal government makes grants in many forms, some of which allow the independent grant seeker an opportunity to be funded, and some which do not. Below are some of the most common types of government grants.

Block Grants: Sometimes called "bloc" grants, these are made from the federal government directly to states or local units of government, such as counties and municipalities. The grant most often comes to the state in a "block," and the state may spend the money as it wishes as long as the funds are being used to fulfill the basic purposes for which they were authorized. Many of the more recent federal grants under what is called "new federalism" have been block grants such as the Housing and Community Development Act money, the Comprehensive Employment and Training Act money, and funds to support programs for older Americans. Under the rules of most block grants, the state must submit an annual "state plan" to the federal government explaining how and where the funds are to be used. This state plan is public information, and potential grant seekers may wish to review it for programs under which they wish to seek grant support. One important aspect of block grants is that while the money is federal, the authority to spend it is local, and the recipients of block grant funds are allowed great flexibility in how they use the money.

Capitation Grants: Stemming from a concept of providing funds per capita of service, capitation grants are awarded based on the actual number of people served, rather than on the task to be performed. For example, an organization may be providing housing for runaway youths. This organization's annual budget is $100,000, and last year it provided housing for 1,000 youths. A capitation grant would provide $100 for each youth housed during the coming year ($100,000 divided by 1,000 youths). Capitation grants are most often used for training grants where payment is based on enrollment, rather than training outcome.

Categorical Grants: Simply stated, funds under a certain "category" must be expended within a certain field of interest, such as mental health, services for the handicapped, or maternity and child care. Although the number of categorical grants provided by the federal government has decreased in the past few years because of an increase in block grants, there are still more than 850 federal grant programs active within the federal government.

Construction Grants: Unless specifically stated, most federal grants will not provide funds for capital purposes, requiring instead that the grantee rent or lease the appropriate facility. Special construction grants, especially in the fields of health and mental health, have been made in the past for construction, renovation, and expansion. Many more important construction grant programs have been severely cut in the past few years, however, and it appears that the federal government is less enamored with this type of grant than in the past.

Demonstration Grants: Among the most common types of grants made in the human services field, demonstration grants, as opposed to basic research grants, are made to agencies in order to illustrate the effectiveness of a certain procedure or methodology, while at the same time providing a direct benefit to a group of clients. Unlike research grants, there is usually a large amount of evidence that the methodology to be demonstrated should prove effective before the grant is awarded. Often, demonstration grants are the second step of research grants, attempting to show that the success of a research grant may have greater applicability or a wider target population than originally envisioned.

Formula Grants: Not so much a type of grant as a method of determining the amount of funds to be made available, formula grants are based most often on the population, income, taxation, and special need of a given area.

The formula for grants will be written into the legislation or regulation that established the fund. The capitation grant mentioned earlier is one type of formula.

Matching Grants: Often confused with formula grants in that there is usually a "formula" for establishing the matching grant requirement, a matching grant means that the agency or individual who is receiving the grant guarantees to provide a certain portion of the total grant funds from sources other than the government. This "match" may be as small as 1 percent to as much as 50 percent with organizations such as the National Endowment for the Arts and National Endowment for the

Humanities. Often there is a "sliding match" requirement, which means that the agency receiving the grant will provide a greater share of the total costs in the second and subsequent years of the award. Matching requirements may be for a "hard" or "soft" match. A "hard" match means that actual dollar matches must be secured, whereas a "soft" match allowed for such donated services as volunteer time and goods or equipment to be counted in lieu of "hard" dollars.

Project Grants: The grants allow the granting agency, usually a department or agency of the federal government, to determine funding based solely on the merits of the project of an individual or organization, rather than by formula requirements mentioned earlier. This is one of the most flexible types of grants in that the granting agency may have complete control in selecting the project, the grant recipient, and the amount of the award.

Research Grants: As opposed to demonstration grants and project grants, research grants are provided to test theories and hypotheses, develop or interpret new information, or revise accepted theories without the requirement that some benefit be immediately passed on to the clients. In fact the term "client" is often replaced with the term "subject" in research grants. There are two types, basic and applied. Basic research, which enjoyed great favor in the 1960s, has found funding harder to obtain lately, while applied research funds have continued to grow, especially in environmental programs.

Staffing Grants: As the phrase implies, these grants are provided for support of salaries of professional and technical staff members, plus in-service training in many cases. Most staffing grants come with a sliding match requirement.

Training Grants: These are awarded to organizations, corporations, or individuals to support the costs of training existing staff, students, or potential staff in the techniques or procedures needed to develop skills in a particular field, such as nursing, paramedical training and legal aid.

Seeking Governmental Sources

In addition to the *Annual Register of Grant Support*™, there are several places potential grant seekers can look for information about federal grants.

Catalog of Federal Domestic Assistance

The most important index for identifying federal resources is the *Catalog of Federal Domestic Assistance* (CFDA). Available online at www.cfda.gov, the catalog gives you access to a database of all Federal programs available to State and local governments (including the District of Columbia); federally-recognized Indian tribal governments; Territories (and possessions) of the United States; domestic public, quasi-public, and private profit and nonprofit organizations and institutions; specialized groups; and individuals.

Available from the web site as a PDF download, the first section contains the indexes. An Agency Index Summary describes the functions and activities of the respective agencies responsible for administering the programs. The Agency

Program Index lists, in numerical order, all programs, titles, the agency responsible, and the kind of assistance being offered—financial, nonfinancial, or combined. The Functional Index Summary lists categories of support, while a Subject Index provides a listing of programs by various topics. The second section provides the Program Descriptions, including detailed information for each program. Also included in the CFDA is a deadlines index and several informational appendices. After you find the program you want, contact the office that administers the program and find out how to apply.

Federal Register

Another valuable source is the *Federal Register*, available at www.gpoaccess.gov. Published by the Office of the Federal Register, National Archives and Records Administration (NARA), the Federal Register is the official daily publication for rules, proposed rules, and notices of Federal agencies and organizations. It includes such items as presidential orders, advisory meetings, program announcements, requests for applications and deadline dates.

Grants.gov

Grants.gov is a central storehouse for information on over 1,000 grant programs and provides access to approximately $500 billion in annual awards. The Department of Health and Human Services is the Grants.gov program's managing partner, and allows access to 26 federal grant-making agencies through the grants.gov web site.

Clearinghouses

Begun in the 1960s on a limited basis, a coordinated grant support process known as clearinghouse review was once required on hundreds of government grants.

As part of this review process, an applicant submits a brief description of the project or activity for which federal support is sought. Some clearinghouses have developed special forms for this "notification of intent," while others ask for a simple program description, along with the name and location of the applicant agency. Clearinghouses then notify the government agencies and elected officials of local governments that might be interested in the project, in order for the departments and agencies to comment.

If the clearinghouse does not identify any problems or possible conflicts, the applicant may complete and submit the proposal to the funding agency unless the clearinghouse specifies that it wants to review the completed proposal.

If there are concerns or unresolved issues, the clearinghouse may arrange a meeting between the applicant and the various departments that have expressed the concern. After any issues have been addressed, the applicant may wish to rewrite the proposal, continue discussions with the departments that are expressing concern, or submit the proposal to the funding source with the comments of the clearinghouse attached.

Program planning and proposal writing

Introductory version

By Norton J. Kiritz and Jerry Mundel

Proposals written for private foundations and those written for government grants (Federal, State, County or City) usually differ in their final form. Foundations often require a brief letter as an initial approach. A full proposal may follow in many situations. Government funding sources almost always require completion of a number of forms along with a detailed proposal narrative. Therefore, proposals to private and government grantmakers look quite different.

The package to a foundation or corporation will usually contain these elements:

1. **The cover letter**
2. **The proposal**
3. **Additional materials.**

1. The cover letter is signed by the Chairperson of the Board of a nonprofit agency, or the top authority in a governmental agency. It briefly describes the program, and tells the grantmaker how important the grant would be to the community served by the applicant agency. It shows strong support of the Board of Directors, which is essential in gaining foundation grants.

2. The body of the proposal may be as modest as one page (in the case of a foundation that limits requests to a page) or voluminous. It may be in letter form or a more formal presentation. In either case, following the instructions in Program Planning & Proposal Writing (PP&PW) will help to assure that the necessary items are included and are presented in a logical manner. Remember one thing: PP&PW can help you structure your thinking and even plan your project or program. It can serve as your proposal format where the funding source has not provided one as often the case with foundation proposals. But it should not be substituted for any format required by a foundation. If they ask you to follow a set format, do it!

3. Additional materials should be limited to those required by the funding source supplemented by only the most important addenda. Reviewers don't grade proposals by the pound, so save your postage.

The proposal package to a government funding source usually contains these elements:

1. **Letter of transmittal**
2. **The proposal**
3. **Additional materials.**

1. The letter of transmittal is a brief statement (2-3 paragraphs) signed by the highest level person within your organization. It briefly describes the request, the amount asked for, and may indicate the significance and importance of the proposed project. It should reflect the Board's support and approval of the request as reflected in the signature of the Board Chairperson (possibly as a dual signature along with the Executive Director/Chief Executive Officer).

2. The proposal going to a government funding source will generally be more lengthy than one going to a private foundation. It will often be 10-20 pages long, and the funding source guidelines will contain the sequence to be followed in writing the narrative portion.

It is a good idea to read the information describing how your proposal will be evaluated. Quite often, government agency guidelines describe exactly how each section of your proposal will be weighed. This tells you what the reviewers look for and helps you to organize your thoughts. If you are told to limit your proposal to 10 single-spaced pages, don't include one or two more thinking that it won't be viewed in a negative light. Follow the guidelines meticulously, because the reviewers will. Proposals can be deemed inappropriate simply because you failed to follow specific instructions.

Proposals going to government funders may also contain unique forms such as fact sheet forms where the entire project, names of key staff, budget, numbers of people impacted by the project, etc. are indicated; assurance forms (addressing issues such as human subjects at risk); equal opportunity policy statements, facility access to the handicapped; and a number of other such forms. It is important to understand which items must be submitted along with your proposal and how they are to be completed, so read the instructions carefully.

3. Additional materials will generally include those items suggested by the funding source. This usually consists of job descriptions, resumes, letters of support or commitment, your IRS tax exemption designation, an annual report, financial statement, and related documents. This section (or Appendix) can be extensive when a funding source requests a great deal of information. There are instances in which the funding source will request copies of certain agency policies and procedures, copies of negotiated indirect cost rates, etc.

Generally, this will happen only once, and for refunding packages to the same public agency, you will probably not need to resubmit the same documents.

We suggest the following as a basic format for planning all of your proposals. Thinking through the various sections should enable you to create virtually all that either a private or government funding source will ask of you. It will also enable you to develop a logical approach to planning and proposal writing.

This is our proposed format:

PROPOSAL SUMMARY
I.   **INTRODUCTION**
II.   **PROBLEM STATEMENT**
III. **PROGRAM GOALS AND OBJECTIVES**
IV.   **METHODS**
V.   **EVALUATION**
VI.   **FUTURE FUNDING**
VII. **BUDGET**
VIII. **APPENDIX**

PROPOSAL SUMMARY

The summary is a very important part of a proposal, not just something you jot down as an afterthought. There may be a box for a summary on the first page of a federal grant application form. It may also be called a proposal abstract. In writing to a foundation, the summary should be the first paragraph of a letter-type proposal, or the first section of a more formal proposal. The summary is probably the first thing that a funding source will read. It should be clear, concise and specific. It should describe who you are, the scope of your project, and the cost. The summary may be all that some in the review process will see, so make it good.

I. INTRODUCTION

In this part of the proposal you introduce your organization as an applicant for funds. More often than not proposals are funded on the reputation of the applicant organization or its key personnel, rather than on the basis of the program's content alone. The Introduction is the section in which you build your credibility, and make the case that your organization should be supported.

Credibility

What gives an organization credibility in the eyes of a funding source? First of all, it depends on the funding source. A traditional, conservative funding source might be more responsive to persons of prominence on your Board of Directors, how long you have been in existence and how many other funding sources have been supporting you. An avant garde funding source might be more interested in a Board of community persons rather than of prominent citizens and in organizations that are new rather than established.

Potential funding sources should be selected because of their possible interest in your type of organization as well as the kind of program you offer. You can use the Introduction to reinforce the connection you see between your interests and those of the funding source.

What are some of the things you can say about your organization in an introductory section?

- How you got started, your purpose and goals
- How long you have been around, how you've grown, and the breadth of your financial support
- Unique aspects of your agency (the fact that you were the first organization of its kind in the nation, etc.)
- Some of your most significant accomplishments as an organization or, if you are a new organization, some of the significant accomplishments of your Board or staff in their previous roles
- Your success with related projects
- The support you have received from other organizations and individuals (accompanied by a few letters of endorsement which can be attached in the Appendix)

We strongly suggest that you start a credibility file which you can use as a basis for the Introduction in your future proposals. In this file you can keep copies of newspaper articles about your organizations, letters of support you receive from other agencies and from your clients. Include statements made by key figures in your field or in the political arena that endorse your kind of program even if they do not mention your agency. For example, by including a presidential commission's statement that the type of program which you are proposing has the most potential of solving the problems with which you deal, you can borrow credibility from those who made the statement (if they have any).

Remember, in terms of getting funded, the credibility you establish in your Introduction may be more important than the rest of your proposal. Build it! But here, as in all of your proposal, be as brief and specific as you can. Avoid jargon and keep it simple.

II. PROBLEM STATEMENT OR ASSESSMENT OF NEED

In the Introduction you have told who you are. From the Introduction we should know your areas of interest—the field in which you are working. Now you will zero in on the specific problem or problems that you want to solve through your proposed program. If the Introduction is the most important part of your proposal in getting funded, the Problem Statement is most important in planning a good program.

The Problem Statement or Needs Assessment describes the situation that caused you to prepare this proposal. It should refer to situation(s) that are outside of your organization (i.e. situations in the life of your clients or community). It does not refer to need internal to your organization, unless you are asking someone to fund an activity to improve your own effectiveness. In particular, the Problem Statement does not describe your lack of money as the problem. Everyone understands that you are asking for money in your solicitation. That is a given. But what external situation will be dealt with if you are awarded the grant? That is what you should describe, and document, in the Problem Statement.

Problem Statements deal with such issues as the homeless, offenders returning to prison with regularity, children who are far behind in their reading skills, youths dropping out of school, and the myriad other problems in contemporary society. Needs Statements are often used when dealing with a less tangible subject. They are especially useful in programs that are artistic, spiritual, or otherwise value-oriented. These are certainly no less important as subjects, but they do not lend themselves as directly to the problem-solving model of PP&PW. You would ordinarily deal with them as Needs and Satisfaction of Needs instead of Problems and Objectives.

You should not assume that "everyone knows this problem is valid." That may be true, but it doesn't give a fund source assurance about your expertise if you fail to demonstrate your knowledge of the problem. Use some appropriate statistics. Augment them with quotes from authorities, especially those in your own community. And make sure that you make the case for the problem in your area of service, not just on a national level. Charts and graphs will probably turn off the reader. If you use excessive statistics, save them for an Appendix, but pull out the key figures for your Problem Statement. And know what the statistics say.

In the Problem Statement, you need to do the following:

- Make a logical connection between your organization's background and the problems and the needs with which you propose to work.
- Clearly define the problem(s) with which you intend to work. Make sure that what you want to do is workable—that it can be done within a reasonable time, by your agency and with a reasonable amount of money.
- Support the existence of the problem by evidence. Statistics, as mentioned above, are but one type of support. You may also use statements from groups in your community concerned about the problem, from prospective clients, and from other organizations working in your community and from professionals in the field.
- Be realistic—don't try and solve all the problems in the world in the next six months.

Note: Many grant applicants fail to understand the difference between problems or needs and methods of solving problems or satisfying needs. For example, an agency working with the elderly in an urban area said that what the community needed were vans to get the elderly to various agencies. They determined that this need existed because not enough seniors were able to get to the social security office, health services, and related human service programs. What they had done was to immediately jump to a method by which the seniors would now be able to readily receive services. The problem with that logic is that the transportation suggested is a method and there are other methods as well. For example, what about the possibility of working with the agencies to decentralize services? Alternatively, volunteer advocates could work with seniors, acting on their behalf with some of these service providers. Ultimately, buying vans might be the best method, but it is clearly a method and not a problem or client need. Be very cautious about this. If you find yourself using lack of statements in the problem section, you are probably saying lack of method. This starts you on a circular reasoning track that will ruin the planning process.

III. PROGRAM GOALS AND OBJECTIVES

A well-prepared proposal has continuity—a logical flow from one section to another. Your Introduction can establish the context for your Problem Statement. Similarly, the Problem Statement will prepare the funding source for your logical Goals and Objectives.

Goals are broad statements such as: Develop additional resources to provide AIDS information to bilingual populations; Reduce underemployment rates among adults; Increase the availability of resources to address the problem of adolescent pregnancies; Create an environment in which folk art is fully appreciated; or Enhance self-images of senior adults.

These types of statements cannot be measured as they are stated. They offer the reader an understanding of the general thrust of a program. They are not the same as objectives.

Objectives are specific, measurable outcomes of your program. Objectives are your promised improvements in the situation you described in the Problem Statement. When you think of Objectives this way, it should be clear in most proposals what your Objective should look like. For example, if the problem was that certain children in your school read at least three grade levels below the norm for their age, then an objective would be that a certain number of those children would read significantly better when you had classmates who had also been reading poorly, but who did not have the benefit of your intervention. These outcome Objectives should state who is to change, what behaviors are to change, in what direction the changes will occur, how much change will occur, and by what time the change will occur.

Another example of a measurable objective would be:

"Within 30 days of completion of the JTPA Classroom Training Program, 75% of the 80 participating welfare recipients will have secured unsubsidized employment at a minimum of $5.25 per hour, and will maintain those positions for a minimum of 90 days."

The Importance of Distinguishing Between Methods and Objectives

Many, if not most, proposals state that the purpose of the program is to establish a program or provide a service. This is consistent with most thinking in the nonprofit sector, which sees the nonprofit organization as a "service provider." This results in Objectives that read like this:

"The objective of this project is to provide counseling and guidance services to delinquent youth between the ages of 8 and 14 in the blank community."

The difficulty with this kind of objective is that it says nothing about outcome. It says nothing about the change in a situation that was described in the Problem. That is, unless the Problem Statement (perish the thought) said that the problem was a "lack of counseling." Presumably the Problem Statement said something about youth being arrested, going to jail, dropping out of school, or whatever.

Objectives should be specific, estimating the amount of benefit to be expected from a program. Some applicants, trying to be as specific as they can, pick a number out of the air. For example, an agency might say that their objective was to decrease unemployment among adults in the XYZ community by 10% within a certain time period. The question you need to ask is: where did that figure come from? Usually it is made up because it sounds good. It sounds like a real achievement. But it should be made of something more substantial than that. Perhaps no program has ever achieved that high a percentage. Perhaps similar programs have resulted in a range of achievement of from 2-6% decrease in unemployment. In that case, 5% would be very good and 6% would be as good as has ever been

done. Ten percent is just plain unrealistic. And it leads one to expect that you don't really know the field very well. Just remember that Objectives should be realistic and attainable. Decide whether the 10% figure is attainable. If not, then it is a poor objective because you cannot achieve it.

If you are having difficulty in defining your Objectives, try projecting your agency a year or two into the future. What differences would you hope to see between then and now? What changes would have occurred? These changed dimensions may be the Objectives of your program.

A Note About Process Objectives

You may be used to seeing Objectives that read like this:

"The objective of this training program is to offer classes in automotive repair three times each week, for a period of 36 weeks, to a group of 40 unemployed individuals,"

or

"The objective of this program is to provide twice-weekly counseling sessions, for a period of 18 weeks, to no less than 50 parents who have been reported to Child and Protective Services for child abuse."

These are Process Objectives, and belong in the Methods section of your proposal. They tell what you will do, and do not address the outcome or benefit of what you will do. It is critically important to distinguish between these process Objectives and true outcome Objectives. If you do not do so, you will end up knowing only what has occurred during your program, and will not have dealt with the changes attributed to your program. Remember, you have proposed your program in order to make some change in the world, not to add one more service to a world already overcrowded with services and service providers.

Process Objectives may be very useful, but they should only appear in the Methods section of your proposal, so they are not confused with the results of your proposed program.

IV. METHODS

You now have told the reviewer who you are, the problems you intend to work with, and your Objectives (which promise a solution to or reduction of the problems). Now you are going to describe the Methods you will use to accomplish your Objectives.

The Methods component of your proposal should describe, in some detail, the activities that will take place in order to achieve the desired results. It is the part of the proposal where the reader should be able to gain a picture in his/her mind of exactly how things work, what your facility looks like, how staff are deployed, how clients are dealt with, what the exhibits look like, how the community center recruits and assigns volunteers, or how the questionnaires will be administered and results interpreted.

There are two basic issues to be dealt with in the Methodology section. What combination of activities and strategy have you selected to employ to bring about the desired results? And why have you selected this particular approach, of all the possible approaches you could have employed?

Justifying your approach requires that you know a good deal about other programs of a similar nature. Who is working on the problem in your community or elsewhere? What Methods have been tried in the past and are being tried now and with what results? In other words, you need to substantiate your choice of Methods.

The consideration of alternatives is an important aspect of describing your methodology. Showing that you are familiar enough with your field to be aware of different program models and showing your reasons for selecting the model you have gives a funding source a feeling of security and adds greatly to your credibility. Obviously then, building credibility only starts in your Introduction, and can be enhanced as you demonstrate that you are knowledgeable throughout your proposal.

Your methodology section should describe who is doing what to whom, and why it is being done that way. Your approach should appear realistic to the reviewer, and not suggest that so much will be performed by so few that the program appears unworkable. A realistic and justified program will be impressive. An unrealistic program will not win you points for good intentions.

V. EVALUATION

Evaluation of your program can serve two purposes. Your program can be evaluated in order to determine how effective it is in reaching its stated Objectives. This concept of Evaluation is aimed at measuring results of your program (outcome Evaluation).

Evaluation can also be used as a tool to provide information necessary to make appropriate changes and adjustments in your program as it proceeds. This concept is focused on the way your program has been conducted (process Evaluation).

Measurable Objectives set the stage for effective outcome Evaluation. If you have difficulty in determining what criteria to use in evaluating your program, better take another look at your Objectives. They probably aren't very specific.

Subjective and Objective Evaluations

Many Evaluation plans are subjective in nature. Subjective Evaluations tell you how people feel about a program, but seldom deal with the concrete results of a program. For example, the Evaluation of an educational program that surveyed students, parents, teachers and administrators of the program would be eliciting attitudes about the program. It would not speak to the tangible improvement in performance attributed to the program.

Subjectivity also allows the introduction of our own biases into an Evaluation. This could easily happen if you evaluate your own programs, especially if you feel that continued funding depends on producing what looks like good results.

One way of obtaining a more objective Evaluation, and sometimes a more professionally prepared Evaluation, is to look to an outside organization to conduct an Evaluation for you. Sometimes it is possible to get an outside organization to develop an Evaluation design that can be submitted to a funding source as part of your proposal. This not only can suggest a more objective Evaluation, but can also add to the credibility of your proposal, since you have added the credibility of the evaluating institution.

It is essential to build an Evaluation plan into your proposal and be prepared to implement your Evaluation at the same time that you start your program. If you want to determine change along some dimension, then you have got to show where your clients have come from. It is very difficult to start an Evaluation at or near the conclusion of the program, for at that time you may not know the characteristics of your clients at the time of their entry into the program.

VI. FUTURE AND OTHER NECESSARY FUNDING

No grantmaker wants to adopt you. Funding sources want to know how you will continue your program when their grant runs out. If you are requesting funds to start a new program, or to expand an existing program, then how will you maintain it after the grant funds have been spent?

A promise to continue looking for alternative sources of support is not sufficient. You should present a plan that will assure the funding source, to the greatest extent possible, that you will be able to maintain this new program after the grant has been completed. Indeed, if you are having difficulty keeping your current operations supported, you will probably have more difficulty in maintaining a level of operation which includes additional programs. The funding source may be doing you no favor by supporting a new project and putting you in the position of having to raise even more money next year than you do now.

At this point in your planning you may realize that there is little likelihood of any other sources of support one or two years hence. This ought to bring you to a decision-making point whether you should even try to implement a new program at this time in your agency's history.

What would constitute a satisfying response in this proposal component? Could you get a local institution or governmental agency to agree to continue to support your program, should it demonstrate the desired results? Can you get such a commitment in writing? Can you generate funds through the project itself—such as fees from services that will build up over a year or two, subscriptions to publications, etc.? Are there third parties available to provide reimbursement for services? Are you expanding your nongrant fundraising activities? The best plan for Future Funding is the plan that does not require continued grant support.

Other Necessary Funding

Other necessary funding refers to what are sometimes called "non-recurring grants." That is, one-time only requests. This could be a request for a vehicle to transport your clientele, or the purchase of a piece of medical equipment for your hospital. While these are not program grants, the funds you request are not all you will need either to utilize the vehicle, or to operate the medical device. For the vehicle to be used, you must cover the costs of a driver, insurance, gas and maintenance. Similarly, the medical equipment must be operated by trained personnel. The funding source will want to know if you are aware of what you need beyond the purchase requested in your grant, and have the funds needed to cover these costs. They surely will not want to fund a bus that will sit in your garage for a year.

VII. BUDGET

Funding source requirements for Budgets vary, with foundations requiring less extensive Budgets than government funding sources. The following Budget design should satisfy most funding sources that allow you to design your own Budget and, with minor changes that the sources will tell you about, can be adapted to fit most government agency requirements. This recommended Budget contains three sections: The first is Personnel, the second is Non-Personnel, and the third is Indirect Costs.

When planning your Budget, it is wise to look closely at your Goals and Objectives to determine the level of activity in the program, and at your Methods section to review the specific plan you have proposed. For example, a Volunteer Senior Peer Counseling program would, one hopes, be less costly to operate than a Senior Peer Counseling program involving paid staff. Budgets should be built from the ground up—that is, based on your Goals and Objectives and the methodology you have proposed. In the context of your program you can begin to itemize such things as the staffing called for, the facilities needed, the equipment required, the supplies necessary, travel costs to be paid, and the range of costs for which your agency must be reimbursed, i.e., time of the CEO, bonding of employees, fundraising, use of space, payroll services, in-service training offered, etc.

It is important to go through this exercise in developing a Budget. Without it, there is a risk of developing unrealistic or impractical requests, where program and Budget are unrelated.

This is how we suggest you structure your Budget:

I. PERSONNEL
A. Salaries & Wages

In this section you can list all full- and part-time staff in the proposed program. We suggest a format which includes the following information:

# of persons per title	Title	Full monthly salary	% of time employed in grant	# of months during grant period	Amount requested	Amount donated or volunteered	Total

How does this look on a completed line item of a Budget? If you are employing a Project Coordinator at a salary of $2,000 per month, working full time (100%) for the entire grant period (12 months) and are asking the funding source to provide the full amount of this salary, then it looks like this:

	Req.	Donated	Total
Proj Coord @ $2,000/ea. 100% x 12 months	$24,000	-0-	$24,000

You can list all of your staff in the same way. If any of your staff are being paid out of another source of funds (for example, a staff person assigned to your project by a County agency), then you total up their salary and put it in the donated column (also referred to as in-kind, local share, or applicant share). Like this:

	Req.	Donated	Total
Soc Workers @ $1500 ea. 50% x 12 months	-0-	$18,000	$18,000

This means that you will have two half-time Social Workers on your staff for the full year and their salaries are being paid by somebody other than the funding source. You take their full salary in the Budget ($1,500/mo.) and halve it ($750) as they are only working 50% time; multiply the $750 by 12 months they will be working (giving you $9,000) and multiply it by 2 (the number of people employed in this capacity). This gives you a total of $18,000 of donated Social Worker services in this project.

What does the $2,000 per month figure for the salary of the Project Coordinator represent? It may represent the actual salary paid the Project Coordinator, but not necessarily. If this is a new project, and if your organization has a typical five-step salary schedule for job classifications, the monthly salary range for the Project Coordinator may look like this:

Step A	Step B	Step C	Step D	Step E
$1,500	$1,750	$2,000	$2,250	$2,500

If you have developed a salary schedule like this for each position, then you should request the mid-point ($2,000) unless you know in advance who will fill that position. In that case, list the actual salary anticipated. If not, the mid-point of the salary schedule allows you to hire someone currently making $1,300/mo., who would welcome the increase even in Step A. You have the flexibility to hire at any point along the range with the assumption that all staff salaries will average out toward the middle of the salary range. (This works if there are a number of positions in your project, not just one or two.)

How do you determine what the salary range of a Project Coordinator ought to be? The federal government prefers that salaries be comparable to the prevailing practice in similar agencies in your community. To justify the salaries you build into your Budget you should obtain information from other local agencies regarding the salaries of persons with job descriptions, qualifications, and responsibilities similar to those of the jobs in your agency. You might go to the local city and/or county government, the school district, or United Way. By comparing the jobs at your agency with the jobs at other local agencies, you plan a salary for each position, and you keep the comparability data on hand, should you be asked by the funding source to justify your staff salaries.

Another final item to be included in your Budget for most public agency applications is the matching support being contributed by your organization, or the donated services. They can either be personnel contributed by you (the applicant organization), or by a third party (another participating agency, a corporation giving you a loaned executive, students, etc.). In many cases this will involve the use of volunteers. You should place a value on the service being performed by that volunteer, e.g. plumber, attorney, carpenter, receptionist, etc. That value is based upon the function being performed by the volunteer, not the professional background or education of the volunteer. A physician volunteering time at a community center where he/she helps out in painting the facility is shown at the hourly wage paid painters, not physicians.

Governmental grantmakers sometimes require financial participation on the part of an applicant, i.e., 10% or 25% match. You may be able to make this contribution in "cash" or in-kind. For example, if you are going to pay the salary of a staff member, that is cash. If you are using volunteers, or receive an executive on loan from a local corporation, that is "in-kind."

If you promise volunteers in your program, you are required to deliver the required volunteer services, just as if the funding source was actually paying their salary. You will be asked to document the work they perform and to keep records of their time. Records may be audited in the case of a government grant. Always be able to document 5-10% more than the required percentage match just in the event that you are audited and some of your volunteer time is disallowed.

Why is it important to develop a match (applicant share) and show the total costs of a project when some of the money or services are not being provided by the funding source? There are several reasons. First the government funding source wants to know that there is a commitment on the part of your agency—a commitment beyond just conducting a program. It helps for them to know there is some likelihood that you have resources with which to continue the program after the funding has ceased. It also provides some clarity as to the exact cost in delivering a service. If the program were to be

replicated elsewhere, and donated services are not available, it tells the funding source what the total cost would be. Finally, when you have local resources (volunteers, cash, staff, equipment, etc.), it reduces the amount of money required of the grantor, thereby allowing additional projects to be funded in other locations.

B. Fringe Benefits

In this section you list the fringe benefits your employees will be receiving, and the dollar cost of these benefits. Some fringe benefits are mandatory, but they vary from state to state, so you will have to determine what they are for your agency in your state. Mandatory fringe benefits may include State Disability Insurance, State Unemployment, FICA, etc. They are usually based on percentages of salaries. For example, if FICA is currently 7.51% of the first $45,000 of each person's salary, an entry for FICA on your Budget might look like this:

	Req.	Donated	Total
FICA @ 7.51% of $90,000	$6,759	-0-	$6,759

$90,000 would be the total of all your salaries, up to $45,000 for any one person.

Some fringe benefits are calculated on a flat amount per month per staff member, and not on a percentage, e.g., health insurance. For example:

	Req.	Donated	Total
Health insurance @ $100/mo. per staff member x 4 staff @ 12 months	$4,800	-0-	$4,800

As with your salary schedule, your fringe benefits should be comparable to the benefits offered in similar agencies in your community.

While you will need to calculate fringe benefits for your own information, in some grant applications you simply indicate the fringe benefit total as a percentage of salary.

C. Consultant and Contract Services

This is the third and final part of the Personnel section of your Budget. In this section you include paid and unpaid consultants (i.e., volunteers). You can differentiate between which items go here and which go in Salaries and Wages on the basis of the manner in which the individual or business normally operates. If a bookkeeping firm generally operates on a fee-for-service basis and is volunteering their service to your organization, that would fit best under Consultant and Contract Services. Essentially, be logical and if a Fed yells at you, change it. (Foundation persons never yell.) Entries might look like these:

	Req.	Donated	Total
Bookkeeping Services @ $200/mo. x 12 mos.	-0-	$2,400	$2,400

Contracted Fundraising Svc. @ $400/day x 10 days	$4,000	-0-	$4,000
Trainer @ $250/day x 8 days	$2,000	-0-	$2,000

II. NON-PERSONNEL

A. Space Costs

In this section, you list all of the facilities you will be using, both those on which you pay rent and those which are being donated for your use. Rent you pay, or the valuation of donated facilities, should be comparable to prevailing rents in the geographic area in which you are located. In addition to the actual rent, you should also include the cost of utilities, maintenance services and renovations, if they are absolutely essential to your program, insurance on the facility, telephones (number of instruments needed, installment costs, and monthly cost of instruments), and out-of-town facilities needed. Include these items in line item fashion like this:

	Req.	Donated	Total
Office Space of 900 sq. feet $1.25/foot/mo. x 12 mos.	$13,500	-0-	$13,500
Facility insurance	-0-	$600	$600

B. Rental, Lease or Purchase of Equipment

Here you list all the equipment, donated or to be purchased, that will be used in the proposed program. This includes office equipment, desks, duplicating machines, word processors, etc. Let discretion be your guide in this section. Try to obtain as much donated equipment as you can. It not only lowers the funding source cost, but it shows the funding source that other people are involved in trying to make the program happen. Be careful to read guidelines closely when working with government grant applications—especially as to their definition of equipment and restrictions which apply. For example, equipment is often defined as something costing more than $500 per unit and/or having a lifetime of greater than one year. Additionally, there may be prohibitions against purchasing equipment, and you may be encouraged to lease rather than purchase.

C. Supplies

This generally means "desk top" supplies such as paper clips, pens, paper, stationery, etc. A reasonable figure to use is $125 per year for each of your staff. If you have any unusual needs for supplies—perhaps you are running an art education program, a sheltered workshop, or some classroom activity requiring a good deal of educational materials—then have a separate line item for such supplies. This component can also include publications, subscriptions, and postage.

D. Travel

All transportation related expenses are included here. Don't put in any big lump sums which will require interpretation or raise a question by the funding source. Include all staff travel, per diem rates approved by your agency and/or the state or federal agency you are applying to, ground transportation, taxi, reimbursement to staff for use of their automobiles, consultant travel costs, use of agency vans or automobiles (if this has not been included under equipment), etc. Examples include the following:

	Req.	Donated	Total
Four round trip air fares LA-NY for workshop on Creative Accounting @ $550/each	$2,000	-0-	$2,000
Reimbursement for staff travel @ .20/mile x average of 400 miles/mo. x 12 mos.	$960	-0-	$960
Per Diem (NY) @ $150/day x 8 days for 4 staff at Creative Accounting Workshop	$1,200	-0-	$1,200

Be sure that you use per diem (hotel and meals) rates which are consistent for the location. Attending a workshop in Weed, California will be considerably less expensive than New York City.

E. Other Costs

This is generally a catch-all category which includes items not reasonable to include elsewhere. For example:

1. Bonding of employees
2. Tuition for classes
3. Professional Association dues
4. Printing (unless you placed this under Consultant and Contract Services)

III. INDIRECT COSTS

The third component of your Budget is called Indirect Costs. The federal government defines indirect costs as those costs of an institution which are not readily identifiable with a particular project or activity, but nevertheless are necessary to the general operation of the institution and the conduct of the activities it performs. The cost of operating and maintaining buildings and equipment, depreciation, administrative salaries, general telephone expenses, general travel and supplies expenses are types of expenses usually considered as indirect costs. While it is possible for all such costs to be charged directly—that is, to the line items listed above—this is often impractical, and you may group them into a common pool. The federal government indicates that "an Indirect Cost Rate is simply a device for determining fairly and expeditiously ... that proportion of an intitution's general expenses each of its projects or activities should bear." An organization or institution can negotiate an Indirect Cost Rate (generally a percentage of Salaries and Wages or Total Direct Costs) with any federal agency from whom it has received funds. This is an important issue since many larger institutions find that every new project undertaken costs the institution money

SAMPLE BUDGET

	Req.	Donated	Total
I. PERSONNEL			
A. Salaries and Wages			
Project Coordinator @$2,000/month @ 100% x 12 months	24,000	-0-	24,000
2 Social Workers @$1,500/month each @50% time x 12 months	-0-	18,000	18,000
20 Volunteer Recreational Aides @50 hours each/year x 7.00/hour	-0-	7,000	7,000
B. Fringe Benefits			
20% of $42,000	4,800	3,600	8,400
C. Consultant and Contract Services			
Bookeeping Services @$200/month x 12 months	-0-	2,400	2,400
Fundraising Services @$400/day x 10 days	4,000	-0-	4,000
Trainer @$250/day x 8 days	2,000	-0-	2,000
Annual Audit	2,000	2,000	4,000
II. NON-PERSONNEL			
A. Space			
900 square feet @$1.25/square foot/month x 12 months	13,500	-0-	13,500
Telephones @$200/month x 12 months	2,400	-0-	2,400
Utilities @$300/month x 12 months	-0-	3,600	3,600
Facility Insurance @$600/year	600	-0-	600
B. Rental, Lease, Purchase of Equipment			
Word Processor/printer	2,000	-0-	2,000
12-passenger van @$400/month x 10 months	4,000	-0-	4,000
3 desk/chair sets @$250/each	750	-0-	750
C. Supplies			
Desk top supplies @$125/year/staff x 3	375	-0-	375
Educational materials @$50/month x 12 months	600	-0-	600
D. Travel			
4 roundtrip airfares LA-NY @$500/each	2,200	-0-	2,200
Reimbursement for staff auto travel @$.20/mile x average of 400 miles/month x 12 months	960	-0-	960
8 days per diem (NY) @$1.50/day	1,200	-0-	1,200
E. Other Costs			
Conference Tuition (Creative Accounting) @$200/each x 4 staff	800	-0-	800
Board Liability Insurance	600	-0-	600
III. INDIRECT COSTS			
15.3% of TADC (Total Allowable Direct Costs) as per att. negot. rate with Dept. of Labor, 1998	10,860	-0-	10,860
TOTAL PROJECT COST:	**77,645**	**36,600**	**114,245**

unless it is reimbursed for the indirect cost associated with operating the institution.

For further clarification of Indirect Cost Rates, contact the Federal Office's Regional Comptroller or your Program Officer for Contract Officer to find out exactly how to go about negotiating Indirect Cost Rates. Once you have such a rate, there may still be instances in which the funding source refuses to pay indirect cost rates or places a cap (a maximum) on the percentage of total direct costs they will pay. Nevertheless, this is an area which should be explored and understood.

VIII. APPENDIX

Addenda to a foundation or corporate proposal should be limited. It is an imposition to suggest that a reviewer plod through many pages of additional material that you decided were important enough to include with your proposal. In the case of a government grant, however, the Appendix may be longer than the body of the proposal. It contains material which needs to be submitted to the funding source, but should not detract from the continuity and flow of the proposal by being included in the narrative. The rationale for any decision about what to include in the body of a proposal should be based on your answering the question, "Do I really want the funding source to read/scan the census runs, flow chart, or job descriptions while reading the proposal?" If the answer is "Yes" then definitely include the item at that juncture. If the answer is "No" then include the item in the Appendix and refer the reader to it.

Funding sources will usually stipulate the attachments they want you to include with your grant application. This will involve a variety of documents, many of which will be required routinely by other funding sources. It is a good idea for Development Officers, Program Planners, Grantwriters, or related personnel to maintain a file of materials which can be included in a proposal package. Such items ought to be accessible to you at all times.

Items which are routinely requested by many funding sources include the following:

1. An Audited Financial Statement

Funding sources generally require an audited financial statement. Many smaller organizations do not routinely have an audit conducted, or cannot afford an audit, and an "unaudited" financial statement is often developed by the agency's accountant or bookkeeper. it is important that the applicants know whether the funding source will accept an unaudited financial statement. A telephone call to the program officer, foundation staff member, or related contact person at the offices of the funding source will provide you with the answer.

2. I.R.S. Documentation Letter

This letter from the I.R.S. indicates that your organization is exempt from federal corporate income taxes. It contains important information regarding the basis for your exemption and the requirements associated with maintaining it. In some cases, individual states may also grant such exemptions, and copies of both letters may be appropriate for submission.

3. Indication of Nonprofit Corporation Status

A copy of the receipt of nonprofit corporation status by the state in which your organization was incorporated may be required by funding sources. In most instances, the favorable determination of tax exemption (above) will be sufficient in that it lists the name of the incorporated nonprofit organization.

4. Roster of Board of Directors

A document more and more requested by funding sources is a roster of board members by affiliation. Of concern is more than simply the names of your board members, but who they represent. By this is meant their job function: minister, doctor, banker, social worker, building contractor, etc. In the cases of retired individuals, indicate their former job or profession.

In situations where organizations have board members who are welfare recipients, housewives, unemployed persons, students, etc., select an area of interest or specialty for such individuals, and indicate that after their name. Don't just list a name without any affiliation.

5. Table of Organization

Another item which may be useful is a table of organization. This table should include the proposed staffing pattern for the project for which funds are being requested, and should also include the larger agency/department/section to whom the new project personnel report. With large organizations, it is not critical that each position be indicated, but units or departments should be shown. In many instances it is more important that the funding source understand how the major "functions" of the organization are carried out, and how boards, committees and staff interrelate. The only problem with these tables is that they often present such a confusing picture that one wonders how the organization could ever work.

6. Organizational Budget

Some funding sources will require submission of an organizational Budget for the current or forthcoming program year. This organizational Budget differs from the Budget for the project itself, previously discussed. This allows the reviewer to put the grant request in a larger context.

7. Summary Chart of Key Events

Most public grant applications will require that you submit some form of timeline for major milestones or activities. This can be done in a variety of formats—Gantt charts, PERT charts, flow charts, etc., and can be done by month, quarterly, or by time elapsed from the initiation of the project. Whatever format you use, it should be clear and easily understood by the funding source.

Other documents are often needed for inclusion as an attachment to a proposal:

8. Negotiated Indirect Cost Rate

A copy of your agency's negotiated indirect cost rate should be included in the Appendix when you are citing a "percentage" amount for indirect costs. This is required when submitting public agency applications where such costs are being charged.

Private foundations may also pay indirect cost rates, but be sure to review foundation guidelines closely in that some place a limit on the percentage they will pay. In some cases this percentage is only ten percent (10%) of total direct costs—considerably less than the negotiated percentage with the federal agency.

9. Letters of Support or Endorsement

Letters from elected officials, other organizations and individuals will need to be submitted as required by a funding source or on the basis of your organization's decision that such indicators of support would be a good idea.

In general, such letters should be addressed to your organization (Executive Director, Board Chairman, etc.) and sent to you for submission along with the proposal. Letters should not be sent under separate cover to the funding source because they may not get there in time or may not be filed appropriately with your proposal. More significantly, many funding sources simply will not accept documents submitted separately.

To aid in the process of securing letters of support, many grantwriters and development officers have developed a procedure designed to aid those individuals and organizations from whom you want such letters. Many elected officials and agency executives are continually asked for such letters of support, but it speeds up the process if they can see an example of the type of letter desired.

It is a good idea to draft letters of support and share them with potential signees. This will ensure that you do not receive a glowing endorsement for your program "to provide a shelter for homeless immigrant families" when you are actually seeking support for "establishing a source of food and shelter for migrating birds." Telephone discussions which summarize project ideas often do not get heard exactly as you think you've transmitted them.

If you plan to include "motherhood letters" along with your proposal, i.e., "As a mother in Centerville with six children, I have nothing but praise for the Headstart program and urge you to continue funding it," try to keep such endorsements to a minimum—no more than two such letters per proposal!

10. Resumes

Whenever possible, resumes/curriculum vitae of key staff should be updated periodically so that you are not submitting the exact resume which was placed in the agency's file ten years ago when the person was hired.

Also, it helps the ease of reading if different resumes are written in the same format, so when updating resumes you might consider developing a similar format for each. With the exclusion of academic and medical personnel, they need be no longer than 2-3 pages.

11. Job Descriptions

While in some instances it is important to create a capsule resume for inclusion in the body of the proposal, in most cases the description of positions ought to be an Appendix item.

Key to entry information

(1) XYZ FOUNDATION (2) **[101]**

(3) One Central Commerce Building
Main and Division Streets
Anytown, IL 60009

(4) (312) 555-5555
Fax: (312) 555-1234
E-Mail Address: abcd@xyzfdn.edu
Web Site Address: www.xyzfdn.edu

(5) FOUNDED: 1990

(6) AREAS OF INTEREST:
Education, medical research, the environment, youth groups, law and social welfare.

(7) CONSULTING OR VOLUNTEER SERVICES:
Technical assistance to community groups, particularly to those providing cultural activities.

(8) NAME OF PROGRAM
John Doe Project Grants Fund

(9) TYPE:
Project/Program grants. Support for a variety of activities in the areas of education, medical research, desert research, atmospheric, earth, and oceanographic sciences, youth organizations, libraries, conservation projects, water pollution studies, fish and game management, preservation, parks and recreation, environmental studies, law, judicial education, crime delinquency, law enforcement, relief and social agencies, museums and historical projects, health, hospitals, and community improvement organizations. Awards are not available for endowment, contingency or reserve purposes.

(10) YEAR PROGRAM STARTED: 1950

(11) PURPOSE:
To support endeavors for the benefit of mankind.

(12) LEGAL BASIS:
Private foundation; tax-exempt under statute 501(c)(3) of the Internal Revenue Code.

(13) ELIGIBILITY: U.S. tax-exempt nonprofit organizations with appropriate interests are eligible to apply. Grants are not made, however, to organizations which distribute them to beneficiaries of their own selection. Priority is given to projects which are not normally financed by public tax funds.

(14) GEOGRAPHIC RESTRICTIONS:
United States.

(15) FINANCIAL DATA:
Grants vary in amount depending upon the needs and nature of the request.

(16) *Amount of support per award:* $1,000 to $500,000.

(17) *Total amount of support:* $6,005,000 for the year ended May 31, 2011.

(18) *Matching fund requirements:* Grants exceeding $25,000 must be matched by an amount not less than one-third the total amount of the grant.

(19) COOPERATIVE FUNDING PROGRAMS:
The Foundation prefers joint funding whenever possible.

(20) NUMBER OF APPLICANTS MOST RECENT YEAR: 512

(21) NUMBER OF AWARDS: 92 for the year ended May 31, 2011.

(22) REPRESENTATIVE AWARDS:
$75,000 to Anytown Hospital, toward facilities and equipment for its new Community Health Center; $25,000 to State University, for development of an interdisciplinary studies program; $15,000 to City Youth Center, toward purchase of equipment for its model reading laboratory program for youths.

(23) APPLICATION INFORMATION:
No official application forms are issued. Interested applicants should submit an informal proposal which briefly includes:
(1) amount requested and an explanation of the necessity or purpose therefore;
(2) aid sought and amounts received from other foundations and sources (include names) during the preceding three years;
(3) aid presently being sought from other sources (or whether such solicitation is contemplated) and, if so, from whom;
(4) copy of tax-exempt letter from the U.S. Treasury and Section 509 classification determination;
(5) latest audited balance sheet and detailed income account and;
(6) signature and approval of the overall head of the applicant institution or organization. Seven copies of application proposals and covering letters should be submitted. Letters of support from appropriate authorities and/or organizations are also encouraged.

(24) *Duration:* Varies according to length of project. Grants may be renewed if continued support can be shown to be beneficial and vital to project success.

(25) *Deadline:* Formal proposals and supporting documents must be received two months prior to board meetings, held in June and December.

(26) PUBLICATIONS:
Annual report; application guidelines.

(27) IRS IDENTIFICATION NUMBER:
00-1234567

(28) BOARD OF TRUSTEES:
John Doe III, Chairman
Margaret Lee, Vice Chairman
Samuel Smith, Treasurer
Robert Johnson, Secretary
Arthur Boyle
Anthony Cates
Phillip Sevoy

(29) OFFICERS:
Phyllis Hartley, Executive Director
David Lisle, President
Susan Banks, Vice President
John Quincy Smith, Project Grants Coordinator

(30) ADDRESS INQUIRIES TO:
John Quincy Smith, Project Grants Coordinator
P.O. Box 777
Neartown, IL 60008

(31) * PLEASE NOTE:
If an applicant is unclear as to the Foundation's current fields of interest, an inquiry directed to it describing the applicant's project may save the trouble or expense of preparing and submitting a formal application.

(1)   Grantmaking organization.

(2)   Entry number, reference corresponding to numbers used in the indexes.

(3)   Address.

(4)   Telephone and fax numbers. E-mail, Web Site addresses, and TDD numbers when available.

(5)   Date organization was founded.

(6)   Major fields of organizational interest.

(7)   Fields in which the organization donates consulting, volunteer, or similar services, if applicable; nature of the service.

(8)   Name(s) of grant program(s).

(9)   Nature of support available under the program(s), e.g., fellowships, project grants, research grants, technical assistance, etc.

(10)   Date program was established.

(11)   Objective of the grant program and/or sponsoring institution.

(12)   Organization's legal status or type (e.g., IRS ruling, state statute, corporate giving program, etc.); legal authority for expenditure of government funds, etc.

(13)   Qualifications required of the applicant individual or project and/or sponsoring institution.

(14)   Restrictions or preferences as to geographic location of the applicant individual or project and/or sponsoring institution.

(15)   Fiscal nature of the grant, including expenses to which it may be applied, restrictions on its use and non-cash benefits.

(16)   Fixed sum, average amount, or range of funds offered for each award.

(17)   Total funding available for the program or, when indicated, for all programs of a grantmaking organization, and the year in question.

(18)   Cost-sharing stipulations.

(19)   Nature of participation with other donors for project support.

(20)   Total applicants, for the most recent year statistics are available.

(21)   Total recipients, and the year in question.

(22)   Representative awards made under the program for the most recent year, including the amount, recipient, and project title or purpose of the award.

(23)   Application requirements and procedures, or references for further information.

(24)   Period for which support is provided; renewal possibilities.

(25)   Closing date(s) for application submission; award announcement date(s).

(26)   Publications that are available from the organization, e.g., annual report, application guidelines, program announcements, etc.

(27)   Internal Revenue Service tax identification number, if applicable.

(28)   Names and titles of principal personnel, e.g., Trustees, Directors, Awards Committee members, etc.

(29)   Names and titles of organization and/or program officers.

(30)   Source of further information and/or recipient of applications.

(31)   Unusual specifications or conditions concerning the program.

An asterisk (*) following an organization name indicates no or incomplete data was received from the source to update or compile the entry. The program listing is then reprinted from the last edition of *Grant Support*, revised where possible, or compiled entirely through staff research.

New listings in 2012 edition

The following is a list of foundations that are offering new grant programs. Bulleted items (•) reflect new program names for the foundation listed.

HUMANITIES

Arts (multiple disciplines)
H. Chase Stone Trust, Colorado Springs, CO

SPECIAL POPULATIONS

Alfred P. Sloan Foundation, New York, NY
  (•) Sloan Indigenous Graduate Partnership

URBAN AND REGIONAL AFFAIRS

Community development and services
Luther T. McCauley Charitable Trust, Colorado Springs, CO

Public health
Freda Maytag-Grace Crawford Trust, Colorado Springs, CO

EDUCATION

Scholar aid programs (all disciplines)
The University of British Columbia, Vancouver, BC, Canada
  (•) Four Year Doctoral Fellowships

SOCIAL SCIENCES

Social sciences (general)
Social Sciences and Humanities Research Council of Canada, Ottawa, ON, Canada
  (•) Banting Postdoctoral Fellowships
  (•) Master's Awards

Sociology and anthropology
National Science Foundation, Arlington, VA
  (•) Archaeology Program
  (•) Archaeometry Program
  (•) Physical Anthropology Program

LIFE SCIENCES

Cardiovascular and pulmonary
American Heart Association, Dallas, TX
  (•) Grant-in-Aid Program
  (•) Great Rivers Affiliate Student Undergraduate Research Fellowship
  (•) Greater Southeast Affiliate Health Sciences Fellowship Program
  (•) National Established Investigator Award
  (•) National Innovative Research Grant

MULTIPLE SPECIAL PURPOSE

Multiple special purpose

ABBOTT FUND [1]
100 Abbott Park Road, D379/AP6D
Abbott Park, IL 60064-3500
(847) 937-7075
Fax: (847) 935-5051

WEB SITE ADDRESS:
www.abbottfund.org

FOUNDED: 1951

AREAS OF INTEREST:
Health and welfare, education, culture and arts, civic and public policy.

NAME(S) OF PROGRAMS:
- **General Grant Program**

TYPE:
General operating grants; Project/program grants. Primary interest in the fields of higher education and human health and welfare. In addition, support of appropriate programs in culture, the arts and civic activities will continue to be a portion of Abbott's program.

YEAR PROGRAM STARTED: 1951

PURPOSE:
To provide support through cash grants to U.S.-based recipients whose areas of interest are consistent with Abbott's basic philanthropic policies and objectives.

LEGAL BASIS:
Corporate nonprofit giving program.

ELIGIBILITY:
Grants will be made only to associations and organizations and not directly to individuals. Grantees must be able to provide evidence of nonprofit, tax-exempt status and must complete the eligibility test to ensure that the organization or program falls within the funding criteria.

Preference is given to requests for one-time contributions and for programmatic and operating purposes. However, grants extending over a defined period of years or directed towards the support of specific building or other capital projects will be considered on an exception basis.

Priority will be given to organizations serving communities in which Abbott has significant operations or employee populations, to organizations whose activities are directed towards the support of professions which provide, directly or indirectly, health care or other services related to Abbott's primary areas of operation.

Grants will not be made to individuals, purely social organizations, political parties or candidates, religious organizations, advertising journals, booklets, symposiums or conferences, social events, for ticket purchases, memberships, business-related purposes or for-profit entities.

FINANCIAL DATA:
Grants vary in amount, depending upon the needs and nature of the request.

APPLICATION INFORMATION:
Online application only.
Duration: One year. Possible multiyear.
Deadline: Applications may be submitted at any time. Most proposals are reviewed within twelve weeks after receipt.

ADDRESS INQUIRIES TO:
Cindy Schwab, Vice President
(See address above.)

THE ABELL FOUNDATION, INC. [2]
111 South Calvert Street
Suite 2300
Baltimore, MD 21202-6174
(410) 547-1300
Fax: (410) 539-6579

E-MAIL ADDRESS:
abell@abell.org

WEB SITE ADDRESS:
www.abell.org

FOUNDED: 1953

AREAS OF INTEREST:
Arts and culture, community development, education, conservation and environment, health and human services, workforce development, criminal justice and addictions.

TYPE:
Capital grants; Challenge/matching grants; Demonstration grants; Development grants; General operating grants; Matching gifts; Project/program grants; Seed money grants.

YEAR PROGRAM STARTED: 1953

PURPOSE:
To improve the quality of life in the area around Baltimore, Maryland.

LEGAL BASIS:
Private foundation.

ELIGIBILITY:
Individuals are not eligible for grants. Qualifying organizations must have IRS 509(a) and 501(c)(3) not-for-profit status. Religious organizations are eligible.

GEOGRAPHIC RESTRICTIONS:
Maryland.

FINANCIAL DATA:
Amount of support per award: $500 to $750,000; average: $43,881.
Total amount of support: Approximately $8,926,069.

REPRESENTATIVE AWARDS:
$20,000 to Banner Neighborhoods Community Corporation, Baltimore, MD, for continued support of the Home Maintenance Program providing minor but necessary repair services for elderly low-income homeowners in southeast Baltimore to enable them to stay in their homes; $75,000 to Druid Heights Community Development, Baltimore, MD, toward the purchase of a six-unit apartment building to provide supportive housing and services to clients in the Maryland Reentry program; $120,000 to The Urban Alliance Foundation, Inc., Baltimore, MD, to provide two-year funding for staffing costs of the Urban Alliance Baltimore Program, a pilot youth employment program for students at Northwestern High School.

APPLICATION INFORMATION:
Foundation application form must be completed and submitted. Applicant organizations must provide IRS 501(c)(3) and 509(a) documentation, the most recently audited financial statement, operating budget, projected budget for each year funding is requested, a list of the board of directors as well as pertinent information regarding the program. Application needs to be preceded by a two-page letter of inquiry.
Duration: Primarily one-year grants; few multiyear awards.
Deadline: Grants will be awarded six times a year; January 1, March 1, May 1, August 1, September 1 and November 1.

IRS IDENTIFICATION NUMBER: 52-6036106

OFFICER:
Robert C. Embry, Jr., President
Sita Culman, Vice President

ADDRESS INQUIRIES TO:
Elizabeth Harber, Senior Program Officer
(See address above.)

THE ABNEY FOUNDATION [3]
100 Vine Street
Anderson, SC 29621
(864) 964-9201
Fax: (864) 964-9209

E-MAIL ADDRESS:
info@abneyfoundation.org

WEB SITE ADDRESS:
www.abneyfoundation.org

FOUNDED: 1957

AREAS OF INTEREST:
Religious, charitable, scientific, literary or educational, including encouragement of art and music.

TYPE:
Capital grants; Development grants; Endowments; Project/program grants; Research grants; Seed money grants.

YEAR PROGRAM STARTED: 1957

PURPOSE:
To make grants for innovative and creative projects and to programs which are responsive to changing community needs in the areas of education, health, social service and cultural affairs.

LEGAL BASIS:
Tax-exempt, private foundation.

ELIGIBILITY:
Applicants must be tax-exempt organizations. No grants to individuals.

GEOGRAPHIC RESTRICTIONS:
South Carolina.

FINANCIAL DATA:
Amount of support per award: $1,000 to $250,000.
Total amount of support: $2,398,000 for the year 2008.

NUMBER OF APPLICANTS MOST RECENT YEAR:
89.

NUMBER OF AWARDS: 45.

APPLICATION INFORMATION:
Applicants must submit a written proposal in accordance with the Foundation's guidelines.
Duration: No grants on a continuing basis. Renewal is possible.
Deadline: November 15.

PUBLICATIONS:
Application guidelines.

IRS IDENTIFICATION NUMBER: 57-6019445

STAFF:
Carl T. Edwards, Executive Director

BOARD OF DIRECTORS:
John R. Fulp, Jr., Chairman, Trustee
Carl T. Edwards, Vice Chairman, Trustee
Johnnye K. Palmer, Treasurer
Lebrena Fulp Campbell, Trustee
John R. Fulp, III, Trustee
David C. King, Trustee
Edd Sheriff, Trustee

ADDRESS INQUIRIES TO:
Carl T. Edwards, Executive Director
(See address above.)

ACADIA UNIVERSITY   [4]
18 University Avenue
Wolfville NS B4P 2R6 Canada
(902) 585-1498
Fax: (902) 585-1096

E-MAIL ADDRESS:
theresa.starratt@acadiau.ca

WEB SITE ADDRESS:
www.acadiau.ca

AREAS OF INTEREST:
English, political science, sociology, biology, chemistry, computer science, geology, psychology, education, recreation management, mathematics, statistics and applied geomatics, and social and political thought.

NAME(S) OF PROGRAMS:
● **Acadia Graduate Awards**

TYPE:
Awards/prizes.

PURPOSE:
To financially support graduate students.

ELIGIBILITY:
Open to registered full-time graduate students at Acadia University. Candidates must possess a 3.0/4.0 grade point average in each of the last two years of undergraduate study in their major.

FINANCIAL DATA:
Amount of support per award: Up to $9,000 for first-year students and a maximum of $8,000 for second-year students.

APPLICATION INFORMATION:
Duration: One or two years.
Deadline: February.

ADDRESS INQUIRIES TO:
Theresa Starratt, Graduate Studies Officer
(See address above.)

*SPECIAL STIPULATIONS:
Recipients should expect to undertake certain duties during the academic year (up to maximum of 10 hours per week and to a maximum of 120 hours per semester) as a condition of tenure of the award. Specific duties will be established by agreement at the beginning of each academic year.

THE ACHELIS FOUNDATION   [5]
767 Third Avenue, 4th Floor
New York, NY 10017-2023
(212) 644-0322
Fax: (212) 759-6510

E-MAIL ADDRESS:
main@achelis-bodman-fnds.org

WEB SITE ADDRESS:
www.foundationcenter.
org/grantmaker/achelis-bodman

FOUNDED: 1940

AREAS OF INTEREST:
Primarily arts and culture, education, employment, health, public policy and youth and families.

TYPE:
Challenge/matching grants; Conferences/seminars; Development grants; General operating grants; Internships; Matching gifts; Project/program grants; Research grants; Scholarships; Technical assistance; Training grants. Over 90% of the Foundation's grants fall into its six program categories.

PURPOSE:
To impact the greater New York City region and enhance the quality of life for its people, especially the disadvantaged; to advance human dignity, inspire personal achievement and foster self-reliance.

LEGAL BASIS:
Private foundation under Section 501(c)(3) of the Internal Revenue Code.

ELIGIBILITY:
The Foundation distributes funds in support of the purposes and programs of duly incorporated, tax-exempt, nonprofit agencies and institutions, in accordance with the Tax Reform Act of 1969, as amended and as they relate to private foundations.

The Foundation generally does not make grants to nonprofit organizations outside of New York, annual appeals, dinner functions and fund-raising events, endowments and capital campaigns, loans and deficit financing, direct grants to individuals (such as scholarships and financial aid), individual day-care and after-school programs, housing, international projects, films and travel, projects for the elderly, small art, dance, music and theater groups, independent or public K-12 schools (except charter schools), national health and mental health organizations, and government agencies and nonprofit programs and services significantly funded or substantially reimbursed by government.

GEOGRAPHIC RESTRICTIONS:
New York, New York.

FINANCIAL DATA:
Net assets of approximately $34,816,759 as of November 30, 2010.

Amount of support per award: $5,000 to $100,000 for the year 2010.

NUMBER OF APPLICANTS MOST RECENT YEAR:
Varies.

NUMBER OF AWARDS: Varies.

APPLICATION INFORMATION:
It is recommended that an organization's initial contact with the Foundation include only the following items:
(1) an inquiry or proposal letter briefly summarizing the history of the project, need, research, objectives, time period, key staff, project budget, and evaluation plan emphasizing measurable outcomes and specific program results;
(2) latest annual report;
(3) current and complete audited financial statements and;
(4) copy of the organization's IRS 501(c)(3) tax-exemption letter.
Duration: One year.

OFFICERS:
John N. Irwin, III, Chairman
Russell P. Pennoyer, President
Peter Frelinghuysen, Vice President
Mary S. Phipps, Vice President
Horace I. Crary, Jr., Treasurer
John B. Krieger, Executive Director and Secretary

BOARD OF TRUSTEES:
Horace I. Crary, Jr.
Walter J.P. Curley, Jr.
Anthony D. Duke
Peter Frelinghuysen
John N. Irwin, III
Leslie Lenkowsky
Russell P. Pennoyer
Mary S. Phipps
Tatiana Pouschine

ADDRESS INQUIRIES TO:
John B. Krieger, Executive Director
(See address above.)

AETNA FOUNDATION, INC.   [6]
151 Farmington Avenue, RC31
Hartford, CT 06156-3180
(860) 273-6382
Fax: (860) 273-7764

E-MAIL ADDRESS:
aetnafoundation@aetna.com

WEB SITE ADDRESS:
www.aetnafoundation.org

FOUNDED: 1972

AREAS OF INTEREST:
Obesity, racial and ethnic health care equity, and integrated health care.

NAME(S) OF PROGRAMS:
● **The Aetna Voice of Conscience Award**
● **Aetna's Employee Programs**
● **Grant Program**

TYPE:
Matching gifts; Project/program grants; Research grants. The Aetna Voice of Conscience Award honors the late Arthur R. Ashe, Jr., a member of Aetna's Board and Chairman of the Foundation at the time of his passing. The annual award honors individual commitment to advancing human rights, opportunity and dignity.

Aetna's Employee Programs have four components, Matching Gifts, Aetna Volunteers Grants, Disaster Response Program and Giving Campaign, to encourage employees, retirees and other eligible individuals affiliated with Aetna to support nonprofit charitable organizations and to serve as volunteers with community agencies.

In the area of obesity, the Foundation supports programs addressing the rising rate of obesity among U.S. adults and children.

In the area of racial and ethnic health care equity, the Foundation supports programs promoting equity in health and health care for common chronic conditions and infant mortality.

In the area of integrated health care, the Foundation supports programs aimed at improving care coordination and promoting cost-effective affordable care.

YEAR PROGRAM STARTED: 1972

PURPOSE:
To promote wellness, health and access to high-quality health care for everyone, while supporting the communities Aetna serves.

LEGAL BASIS:
Corporate giving program.

ELIGIBILITY:
Nonprofit organizations with evidence of IRS 501(c)(3) designation of de facto tax-exempt status may apply for a grant, with the following exceptions:
(1) grants or scholarships to individuals;
(2) religious organizations in support of their sacramental or theological function;
(3) political causes and events;
(4) endowment or capital costs, including construction, renovation or equipment;
(5) direct delivery of reimbursable health care

services;
(6) basic biomedical research;
(7) work for which results and impact cannot be measured;
(8) advertising;
(9) golf tournaments and;
(10) operational expenses/existing deficits.

Grants will be awarded to local, regional and national organizations that can influence local, state or federal policies and programs.

FINANCIAL DATA:
Amount of support per award: Employee Matching Gifts: $300 to $5,000 per year per employee; Grant Program: Varies.

Matching fund requirements: The Foundation has a Matching Gifts component of its Partners in Community Giving program, which matches personal donations from eligible Aetna participants to all eligible educational institutions and tax-exempt charitable groups.

NUMBER OF APPLICANTS MOST RECENT YEAR:
Approximately 2,500.

NUMBER OF AWARDS: 600 to 800.

APPLICATION INFORMATION:
Generally grantmaking is limited to proposals submitted by invitation only. Requests over $50,000 first require a Letter of Inquiry. Complete details are available online.
Duration: Varies.
Deadline: Letters of Inquiry are accepted on a rolling basis. Full proposals must be received by February 15, May 15, August 15, and November 15.

PUBLICATIONS:
Aetna Annual Giving Report.

IRS IDENTIFICATION NUMBER: 23-7241940

STAFF:
Anne C. Beal, M.D., M.P.H., President
Sharon C. Dalton, Vice President
Christopher Montross, Vice President and Assistant Controller
Alyse B. Sabina, M.P.H., Program Officer
Diana M. Hill, Ph.D., Grants Manager
Eileen R. Campbell, Program Consultant
Lynn Ferdman, Program Consultant
Sharon Ions, Program Consultant
Melenie L. Magnotta, Program Consultant

BOARD OF DIRECTORS:
Molly J. Coye
Jeffrey E. Garten
Earl G. Graves
Joseph P. Newhouse

ADDRESS INQUIRIES TO:
See e-mail address above.

*SPECIAL STIPULATIONS:
The Aetna Foundation generally awards only one grant per organization in a calendar year.

THE AHMANSON FOUNDATION   [7]
9215 Wilshire Boulevard
Beverly Hills, CA 90210
(310) 278-0770

E-MAIL ADDRESS:
info@theahmansonfoundation.org

WEB SITE ADDRESS:
www.theahmansonfoundation.org

FOUNDED: 1952

AREAS OF INTEREST:
Arts and humanities, education, human services, medicine and health.

TYPE:
Capital grants; Endowments; Matching gifts; Project/program grants; Scholarships.

PURPOSE:
To support programs that improve the quality of life in southern California.

LEGAL BASIS:
Private family foundation.

ELIGIBILITY:
Grants are made to organizations that have tax-exempt status under Section 501(c)(3) of the Internal Revenue Code. No grants are made to individuals. Nonsectarian religious programs may apply.

GEOGRAPHIC RESTRICTIONS:
Los Angeles County, California.

FINANCIAL DATA:
Amount of support per award: Varies.

NUMBER OF AWARDS: 464.

APPLICATION INFORMATION:
Send letter of inquiry to the Grants Administrator.
Duration: Varies.

ADDRESS INQUIRIES TO:
Yvonne de Beixedon, Grants Administrator
(See address above.)

ALABAMA POWER FOUNDATION, INC.   [8]
600 North 18th Street
Birmingham, AL 35291
(205) 257-2508
Fax: (205) 257-1860

WEB SITE ADDRESS:
alabamapowerfoundation.com

FOUNDED: 1989

AREAS OF INTEREST:
Education, arts and culture, civic and community, health and human services, and environment.

NAME(S) OF PROGRAMS:
- **Alabama Power Service Organization**
- **Educational Grant Program**
- **Energizers**
- **Legacy Endowment Plan**

TYPE:
Capital grants; Challenge/matching grants; Endowments; General operating grants; Project/program grants; Scholarships; Seed money grants.

PURPOSE:
To improve the quality of life of Alabamians and to strengthen the communities in which they live.

LEGAL BASIS:
Corporate foundation.

ELIGIBILITY:
Applicant must be a 501(c)(3) tax-exempt, nonprofit Alabama organization. No grants to individuals, religious or political groups.

GEOGRAPHIC RESTRICTIONS:
Alabama.

FINANCIAL DATA:
Amount of support per award: $2,000 to $200,000; $7,000 average.

Total amount of support: Approximately $8,000,000 annually.

APPLICATION INFORMATION:
Contact office for guidelines. No specific application form required.

Duration: One-time funding.
Deadline: Applications are accepted on a year-round basis.

PUBLICATIONS:
Annual report; information and guidelines.

ADDRESS INQUIRIES TO:
President
(See address above.)

ALCOA FOUNDATION   [9]
201 Isabella Street
Pittsburgh, PA 15212-5858
(412) 553-4545
Fax: (412) 553-4532

WEB SITE ADDRESS:
www.alcoa.com

FOUNDED: 1952

AREAS OF INTEREST:
Environment, empowerment, education and sustainable design.

TYPE:
Project/program grants. Matching of employee gifts to qualified educational institutions. Grants support a variety of special interest programs with emphasis on projects which enhance the environment of communities where Alcoa has a presence.

YEAR PROGRAM STARTED: 1964

PURPOSE:
To strengthen the communities where employees live and in which the company does business.

LEGAL BASIS:
Nonprofit foundation.

ELIGIBILITY:
Organizations classified as public charities and tax-exempt under Section 501(c)(3) of the Internal Revenue Code will be considered. Preference is given to institutions:
(1) located in communities where Alcoa plants or subsidiaries are located;
(2) conducting technical programs and;
(3) capable of exercising great influence in attacking and solving national educational problems.

Unsolicited requests rarely considered.

FINANCIAL DATA:
Amount of support per award: Varies.
Total amount of support: Varies.
Matching fund requirements: Matching gift program allows employees, retirees and directors to contribute money to higher education institutions only.

NUMBER OF APPLICANTS MOST RECENT YEAR:
2,670.

NUMBER OF AWARDS: 110.

APPLICATION INFORMATION:
Applications are accepted on an invitation-only basis.
Duration: Varies.
Deadline: Generally July 31.

GEORGE I. ALDEN TRUST   [10]
c/o Fletcher, Tilton & Whipple, P.C.
370 Main Street
Worcester, MA 01608
(508) 459-8005
Fax: (508) 459-8305

E-MAIL ADDRESS:
trustees@aldentrust.org

WEB SITE ADDRESS:
www.aldentrust.org

FOUNDED: 1912

AREAS OF INTEREST:
Higher education.

TYPE:
Capital grants. Capital projects related to teaching and learning technology, in general, and to the sciences, in particular; some support for need-based scholarship endowment and faculty development.

LEGAL BASIS:
Probate Trust.

ELIGIBILITY:
Principal focus is on independent colleges and universities with full-time, undergraduate enrollments of 1,000 to 3,000 students. Also, educationally related entities in the Worcester (MA) area and at YMCAs in Massachusetts.

GEOGRAPHIC RESTRICTIONS:
New Jersey, New York, Pennsylvania and the six New England states.

FINANCIAL DATA:
Amount of support per award: $5,000 to $5,000,000.
Total amount of support: Approximately $7,000,000.
Matching fund requirements: Usually 1:2 or 1:3 (Alden Trust:matching dollars), with 18-month challenge period. The Trust only pays when the challenge is met in full. The Trust makes no interim or partial payments.

NUMBER OF APPLICANTS MOST RECENT YEAR:
300.

NUMBER OF AWARDS: 42 for the year 2008.

APPLICATION INFORMATION:
Deadline: Trustees meet five times per year to consider proposals.

IRS IDENTIFICATION NUMBER: 04-6023784

TRUSTEES:
Susan B. Woodbury, Chairperson
James E. Collins
Warner S. Fletcher
Gail T. Randall

ADDRESS INQUIRIES TO:
Susan B. Woodbury, Chairperson
(See address above.)

ALEXANDER & BALDWIN FOUNDATION   [11]
822 Bishop Street
Honolulu, HI 96813-3924
(808) 525-6642
Fax: (808) 525-6677

E-MAIL ADDRESS:
lhowe@abinc.com

WEB SITE ADDRESS:
www.alexanderbaldwinfoundation.org

FOUNDED: 1992

AREAS OF INTEREST:
Health and human services, community, education, environment, culture and arts and maritime.

TYPE:
Capital grants; Challenge/matching grants; General operating grants; Project/program grants; Seed money grants.

YEAR PROGRAM STARTED: 1992

PURPOSE:
To support organizations which further the well-being of communities where Alexander & Baldwin employees live and work.

LEGAL BASIS:
Corporate giving foundation.

ELIGIBILITY:
Applicants must be 501(c)(3) organizations.

GEOGRAPHIC RESTRICTIONS:
Hawaii, San Francisco Bay Area and a small percentage of Chicago, Phoenix, Pacific Northwest and southern California.

FINANCIAL DATA:
Amount of support per award: $100 to $100,000.
Total amount of support: $1,600,000 for the year 2010.
Matching fund requirements: Employee with one year of service, a director or a retiree will be matched up to $2,000 for education and up to $1,000 for culture/arts.

NUMBER OF APPLICANTS MOST RECENT YEAR:
Over 700.

NUMBER OF AWARDS: 550 for the year 2010.

REPRESENTATIVE AWARDS:
$240,000 (in total) to United Ways in Hawaii; $75,000 to United Ways in key Mainland areas.

APPLICATION INFORMATION:
Must meet guidelines which include proof of 501(c)(3) status, board of directors list and current budget.
Duration: Varies. Renewal possible.
Deadline: Awards announced on a bimonthly basis.

PUBLICATIONS:
Review of Giving; guidelines.

IRS IDENTIFICATION NUMBER: 99-0291942

DIRECTORS AND OFFICERS:
Meredith J. Ching, President and Director
Christopher J. Benjamin, Vice President, Treasurer and Director
Linda M. Howe, Vice President
Paul K. Ito, Vice President and Assistant Treasurer
Alyson J. Nakamura, Secretary
Vic S. Angoco, Jr.
Norbert M. Buelsing
Grant Y.M. Chun
Stanley M. Kuriyama

ADDRESS INQUIRIES TO:
For Hawaii-based charities:
Linda M. Howe, Vice President
Alexander & Baldwin Foundation
P.O. Box 3440
Honolulu, HI 96801-3440

For Mainland-based charities:
Paul Merwin
Alexander & Baldwin Foundation
c/o Matson Navigation Co.
555 12th Street
Oakland, CA 94607

ALLEGHENY FOUNDATION [12]
One Oxford Centre
301 Grant Street, Suite 3900
Pittsburgh, PA 15219-6401
(412) 392-2900

WEB SITE ADDRESS:
www.scaife.com

AREAS OF INTEREST:
Education, civic development and historic preservation.

TYPE:
General operating grants.

ELIGIBILITY:
Applicant must be a 501(c)(3) nonprofit organization.

GEOGRAPHIC RESTRICTIONS:
Western Pennsylvania.

FINANCIAL DATA:
Amount of support per award: Varies.
Total amount of support: $5,284,000 for the year 2010.

APPLICATION INFORMATION:
Contact Foundation for guidelines.
Duration: Typically one year.
Deadline: The Foundation normally considers grants at an Annual Meeting held in November. However, grant requests may be submitted at any time.

ADDRESS INQUIRIES TO:
Matthew A. Groll, Executive Director
(See address above.)

THE PAUL G. ALLEN FAMILY FOUNDATION   [13]
505 Fifth Avenue South, Suite 900
Seattle, WA 98104
(206) 342-2030
Fax: (206) 342-3030

E-MAIL ADDRESS:
info@pgafamilyfoundation.org

WEB SITE ADDRESS:
www.pgafamilyfoundation.org

FOUNDED: 1988

AREAS OF INTEREST:
Arts and culture, asset building, youth engagement, scientific and technological innovations, and libraries.

TYPE:
Capital grants; Challenge/matching grants; Development grants; Project/program grants.

PURPOSE:
To transform lives and strengthen communities by fostering innovation, creating knowledge and promoting social progress.

LEGAL BASIS:
Private family foundation.

ELIGIBILITY:
Applicants must be organizations organized and operated exclusively for charitable purposes in the Pacific Northwest area, tax-exempt under 501(c)(3) of the IRS code, and not be a private foundation as defined in Section 509(a).

GEOGRAPHIC RESTRICTIONS:
Pacific Northwest which includes Alaska, Idaho, Montana, Oregon and Washington.

FINANCIAL DATA:
Amount of support per award: Varies.
Total amount of support: Varies.
Matching fund requirements: Varies by grant.

NUMBER OF APPLICANTS MOST RECENT YEAR:
230 in 2010.

NUMBER OF AWARDS: 155 grants approved in 2010.

REPRESENTATIVE AWARDS:
Grants approved in 2010: $30,000 to A Contemporary Theatre, Seattle, WA, for production of Yussef El Guindi's Pilgrims Musa and Sheri in the New World; $20,000 to Alberta Bair Theater, Billings, MT, for improving financial performance through technology upgrades; $25,000 to Archie Bray

Foundation, Helena, MT, for ceramics program and exhibition celebrating 60th anniversary; $300,000 to Building Changes, Seattle, WA, for capacity building (employment services and web site enhancements).

APPLICATION INFORMATION:
The Foundation encourages applicants to contact it via its web site if their projects are aligned with Foundation's programs.
Duration: One year. Some multiyear.
Deadline: Varies.

PUBLICATIONS:
Grants List and Anniversary Report (2010), online.

IRS IDENTIFICATION NUMBER: 94-3082532

ADDRESS INQUIRIES TO:
Lisa Arnold, Grants Manager
(See address above.)

ALTRIA GROUP, INC. [14]
6601 West Broad Street
Richmond, VA 23230
(804) 274-2200

WEB SITE ADDRESS:
www.altria.com

FOUNDED: 1956

AREAS OF INTEREST:
Arts and culture, education, environment and youth development.

TYPE:
Project/program grants.

YEAR PROGRAM STARTED: 1956

PURPOSE:
To make strategic and effective grants that strengthen people and communities.

LEGAL BASIS:
Corporate giving program.

ELIGIBILITY:
Grants are only made to organizations that are registered as 501(c)(3) tax-exempt by the Internal Revenue Code. Altria Group does not support individuals.

FINANCIAL DATA:
Amount of support per award: Varies depending on program/initiative.
Matching fund requirements: Must be full-time active employees.

NUMBER OF AWARDS: 4,000.

APPLICATION INFORMATION:
There are specific guidelines for the different grant programs. Detailed instructions are available online.
Duration: One year.

ADDRESS INQUIRIES TO:
Charlie Agee, Director, Contributions
(See address above.)

AMERICAN PHILOSOPHICAL SOCIETY [15]
104 South Fifth Street
Philadelphia, PA 19106-3387
(215) 440-3429

E-MAIL ADDRESS:
lmusumeci@amphilsoc.org

WEB SITE ADDRESS:
www.amphilsoc.org

FOUNDED: 1743

AREAS OF INTEREST:
Scholarly research.

NAME(S) OF PROGRAMS:
● **Franklin Research Grants**

TYPE:
Grants-in-aid; Research grants. Postdoctoral grants toward the cost of scholarly research in all areas of knowledge except those in which support by government or corporate enterprise is more appropriate. Scholarly research covers most kinds of scholarly inquiry by individuals. It does not include journalistic or other writing for general readership; the preparation of textbooks, casebooks, anthologies, or other materials for classroom use by students; or the work of creative and performing artists.

The Society does not have fellowships or scholarships for study, nor does it give grants for travel to conferences.

YEAR PROGRAM STARTED: 1933

PURPOSE:
To support scholarly research by individual scholars.

LEGAL BASIS:
Nonprofit learned society.

ELIGIBILITY:
Applications may be made by residents of the U.S., by American citizens resident abroad and by foreign nationals. American citizens and foreign nationals employed by an American institution may apply for support to carry out work anywhere in the world. Foreign nationals not employed by an American institution may apply for funding to work in the U.S. Applicants expecting to use materials or conduct interviews in a foreign language must possess the necessary competence in the language or languages involved. Grants are never made for predoctoral study or research.

It is the Society's long-standing practice to encourage research by younger and less well-established scholars.

FINANCIAL DATA:
Grants are made payable to the applicant.

The Society offers no funds for conference support, fellowships and scholarships, maintenance work already done, or costs of publication.
Amount of support per award: Funding is offered in multiples of $1,000, up to a maximum of $6,000 for one year.
Total amount of support: Approximately $350,000 per year.

COOPERATIVE FUNDING PROGRAMS: If an applicant receives an award for the same project from another granting insititution, the Society will consider limiting its award to costs that are not covered by the other grant.

NUMBER OF APPLICANTS MOST RECENT YEAR:
454 for the year 2010.

NUMBER OF AWARDS: 73 for the year 2010.

APPLICATION INFORMATION:
Applications are submitted through the Society's online application portal.
Duration: The Committee will seldom approve more than two grants for the same person within any five-year period.
Deadline: October 1 and December 1.

ADDRESS INQUIRIES TO:
Linda Musumeci
Director of Grants and Fellowships
(See address above.)

AMERICAN PHILOSOPHICAL SOCIETY [16]
104 South Fifth Street
Philadelphia, PA 19106-3387
(215) 440-3429

E-MAIL ADDRESS:
lmusumeci@amphilsoc.org

WEB SITE ADDRESS:
www.amphilsoc.org

FOUNDED: 1743

AREAS OF INTEREST:
Scholarly research.

NAME(S) OF PROGRAMS:
● **The Lewis and Clark Fund for Exploration and Field Research**

TYPE:
Research grants. The Lewis and Clark Fund for Exploration and Field Research (initially supported by the Stanford Ascherman/Baruch Blumberg Fund for Basic Science, established by a benefaction from the late Stanford Ascherman, M.D., of San Francisco) encourages exploratory field studies for the collection of specimens and data and to provide the imaginative stimulus that accompanies direct observation. Applications are invited from disciplines with a large dependence on field studies, such as archeology, anthropology, biology, ecology, geography, geology, linguistics, and paleontology, but grants will not be restricted to these fields.

YEAR PROGRAM STARTED: 2005

PURPOSE:
To support scholarly research by individual scholars.

LEGAL BASIS:
Nonprofit learned society.

ELIGIBILITY:
Grants will be available to doctoral students. Postdoctoral fellows, Master's degree candidates, and undergraduates are not eligible. Applicants who have received Lewis and Clark Fund grants may reapply after an interval of two years.

The competition is open to U.S. residents wishing to carry out research anywhere in the world. Foreign applicants must either be based at a U.S. institution or plan to carry out their work in the U.S.

FINANCIAL DATA:
Amount of support per award: Up to $5,000.
Total amount of support: $158,000 for the year 2010.

NUMBER OF APPLICANTS MOST RECENT YEAR:
400 for the year 2010.

NUMBER OF AWARDS: 47 for the year 2010.

APPLICATION INFORMATION:
Applicants should ask their academic advisor to write one of the two letters of recommendation, specifying the student's qualifications to carry out the proposed work and the educational content of the trip. Budgets should be limited to travel and related expenses, including personal field equipment.

When appropriate, the applicant should provide assurances that safety measures will be taken for potentially hazardous projects. When necessary, the applicant and his or her supervisor should discuss the field training that will be provided and the provisions for experienced supervision.

Deadline: February 1, with notification in May, for work in June and beyond.

ADDRESS INQUIRIES TO:
Linda Musumeci
Director of Grants and Fellowships
(See address above.)

AMERICAN SCHLAFHORST FOUNDATION [17]
P.O. Box 240828
Charlotte, NC 28224
(704) 554-0800
Fax: (704) 556-1643

AREAS OF INTEREST:
Arts, children, education, health care, sciences, senior citizens and social services.

TYPE:
Capital grants; Endowments; General operating grants; Research grants; Scholarships; Seed money grants.

PURPOSE:
To improve the quality of life in the community.

LEGAL BASIS:
Corporate foundation.

ELIGIBILITY:
Grants are made to organizations that have tax-exempt status under Section 501(c)(3) of the Internal Revenue Code. No grants are made to individuals.

GEOGRAPHIC RESTRICTIONS:
Greater Charlotte, North Carolina.

FINANCIAL DATA:
Amount of support per award: Varies.

APPLICATION INFORMATION:
Applicants should submit a Letter of Inquiry to the Foundation at the address above.
Duration: Varies.
Deadline: October 15.

ADDRESS INQUIRIES TO:
Dan Loftis, Grant Administrator
(See address above.)

AMGEN FOUNDATION, INC. [18]
One Amgen Center Drive, M.S. 28-1-B
Thousand Oaks, CA 91320
(805) 447-4056
Fax: (805) 376-1258

E-MAIL ADDRESS:
amgenfoundation@amgen.com

WEB SITE ADDRESS:
www.amgen.com/citizenship/foundation.html

FOUNDED: 1991

AREAS OF INTEREST:
Science education, health and human services and community life including arts and culture, social services and environment.

TYPE:
Challenge/matching grants; General operating grants; Grants-in-aid; Matching gifts; Project/program grants. The Foundation funds national-level science education and patient-focused programs.

YEAR PROGRAM STARTED: 1991

PURPOSE:
To advance science education, improve quality of care and access for patients, and

support resources that create sound communities where Amgen staff members live and work.

LEGAL BASIS:
Company-sponsored foundation.

ELIGIBILITY:
The Foundation will consider grant requests from nonprofit organizations that are recognized by the IRS as tax-exempt public charities under Sections 501(c)(3) and 509(a)(1), (2) or (3) of the Internal Revenue Code, located in the U.S. and Puerto Rico. In addition, the Foundation will consider requests for funding from governmental organizations located in the U.S. where the purpose of the grant is to support a charitable, educational, scientific or literary purpose. Thus, eligible grantees may include public elementary and secondary schools, as well as public colleges and universities, public libraries and public hospitals. Successful requests will fall within both the current eligibility guidelines and funding priority areas established by the Foundation. The Foundation has established a grantmaking partnership with United Way Worldwide (UWW) to manage donations to organizations chartered in Europe.

GEOGRAPHIC RESTRICTIONS:
California, Colorado, Massachusetts, Puerto Rico, Rhode Island, Washington, and parts of Europe.

NUMBER OF AWARDS: Grants to nearly 150 organizations for the year 2010.

APPLICATION INFORMATION:
Letter of intent must first be submitted online.
Duration: Typically one year. Possible multiyear funding.
Deadline: Applications are accepted on a rolling basis and reviewed quarterly.

ELMER L. AND ELEANOR J. ANDERSEN FOUNDATION [19]
2424 Territorial Road
St. Paul, MN 55114
(651) 642-0127
Fax: (651) 645-4684

E-MAIL ADDRESS:
eandefdn@mtn.org

FOUNDED: 1957

AREAS OF INTEREST:
Legacy grants: Arts, communications, education, environment, human services, humanities and libraries.

Social Justice grants: Political power and process, environmental justice and civil/human rights.

TYPE:
General operating grants; Project/program grants.

YEAR PROGRAM STARTED: 1957

PURPOSE:
To improve the quality of life through effective family grantmaking, honoring the legacy of its founders and investing in social change.

LEGAL BASIS:
Private family foundation.

ELIGIBILITY:
No applications related to health will be considered. No grants to individuals. Only public charities classified as 501(c)(3) by the IRS should apply.

Unsolicited proposals accepted for Legacy grants only.

Generally, the Foundation does not provide support for:
(1) religious organizations for religious work;
(2) organizations with three consecutive declined requests or;
(3) fund-raisers, one-time events, dinners or telephone solicitations.

GEOGRAPHIC RESTRICTIONS:
Saint Paul and Minneapolis, Minnesota.

FINANCIAL DATA:
Amount of support per award: Legacy grants: $1,000 to $3,000. Social Change grants: $40,000.

Total amount of support: $206,000 for the year 2010.

NUMBER OF AWARDS: 95 for the year 2010.

APPLICATION INFORMATION:
Proposals for Legacy grants should be submitted to the above address. They must include the following:
(1) maximum two-page summary of the proposal, with additional supporting information indicating background of organization, purpose for which funding is sought, constituency served and how it will benefit;
(2) financial information indicating the amount requested, budget for the upcoming year or specific project for which funding is requested, and most recent audited financial statement;
(3) lists of major donors to the organization and Board members of the organization and;
(4) copy of IRS 501(c)(3) exemption letter for organization.

Use of the Minnesota Common Grant form is required.
Duration: One year; some multiyear.
Deadline: May 1 and November 1.

PUBLICATIONS:
Annual report; proposal guidelines.

BOARD OF DIRECTORS:
Julian L. Andersen, President and Director
Amy Andersen, Treasurer and Director
Charles Dayton, Director

ADDRESS INQUIRIES TO:
Mari Oyanagi Eggum
Foundation Administrator
(See address above.)

APPLIED MATERIALS, INC. [20]
3050 Bowers
Mail Stop 0106
Santa Clara, CA 95052
(408) 727-5555
Fax: (408) 986-7115

E-MAIL ADDRESS:
community_affairs@amat.com

WEB SITE ADDRESS:
www.appliedmaterials.com

FOUNDED: 1967

AREAS OF INTEREST:
Arts and culture, community development, education and the environment.

NAME(S) OF PROGRAMS:
• **Applied Materials Corporate Philanthropy Program**

YEAR PROGRAM STARTED: 1990

PURPOSE:
To support the arts and culture, education, community development and the environment.

LEGAL BASIS:
Corporate giving program.

ELIGIBILITY:
Organizations classified as 501(c)(3) by the IRS can apply. Preference is given to areas of company operation. Individuals and religious organizations are ineligible.

FINANCIAL DATA:
Amount of support per award: Varies.
Total amount of support: Varies.

APPLICATION INFORMATION:
Application procedures are available online.
Duration: One year. May be renewed for up to two additional years based on results.

PUBLICATIONS:
Annual report; community report; guidelines.

ADDRESS INQUIRIES TO:
See e-mail address above.

*SPECIAL STIPULATIONS:
Progress is requested to be shared in writing with the Corporate Contribution Committee at least once a year.

APS CORPORATE GIVING PROGRAM [21]

Arizona Public Service Company
400 North 5th Street, 10th Floor
Mail Station 8010
Phoenix, AZ 85004
(602) 250-2702
Fax: (602) 250-2113

E-MAIL ADDRESS:
corporategiving@aps.com

WEB SITE ADDRESS:
www.aps.com

FOUNDED: 1981

AREAS OF INTEREST:
Education, most specifically STEM engineering; community vitality; community and economic development in APS service territories.

TYPE:
Challenge/matching grants; Development grants; Project/program grants. Primary focus is on program support.

YEAR PROGRAM STARTED: 1981

PURPOSE:
To enhance the quality of life in Arizona.

LEGAL BASIS:
Corporate giving program.

ELIGIBILITY:
Applicants must be 501(c) nonprofit organizations. Preference is given to organizations within the APS service territory, although there are exceptions. No funds for individuals, individual scholarships, religious, political, fraternal, legislative or lobbying efforts, travel or hotel expenses.

GEOGRAPHIC RESTRICTIONS:
Arizona.

FINANCIAL DATA:
Amount of support per award: $2,500 to $250,000.
Total amount of support: Over $6,800,000 for the year 2010.

NUMBER OF APPLICANTS MOST RECENT YEAR:
1,000.

NUMBER OF AWARDS: 100.

APPLICATION INFORMATION:
Applications must be submitted online and will require the following documentation:
(1) 501(c) IRS letter of determination;
(2) current list of board members;
(3) list of sponsorship levels (if applicable);
(4) line item budget;
(5) list of other funders and dollar amounts and;
(6) grant evaluation form (if applicable).
Duration: One year. Renewable by reapplication.
Deadline: Applications accepted January to February, April to May, July to August, and October to November.

PUBLICATIONS:
Community Investment Report.

IRS IDENTIFICATION NUMBER: 95-3735903

THE ARCA FOUNDATION [22]

1308 19th Street, N.W.
Washington, DC 20036
(202) 822-9193
Fax: (202) 785-1446

E-MAIL ADDRESS:
proposals@arcafoundation.org

WEB SITE ADDRESS:
www.arcafoundation.org

FOUNDED: 1952

AREAS OF INTEREST:
Wall Street reform, financial regulation, corporate accountability, and advocating for a U.S. foreign policy approach that increases peace and security.

TYPE:
Challenge/matching grants; Conferences/seminars; General operating grants; Project/program grants; Travel grants.

YEAR PROGRAM STARTED: 1952

PURPOSE:
To provide funding for nonprofit organizations working on ways to engage citizens in social change, promote democracy, and reform unjust practices in public policy.

LEGAL BASIS:
Private foundation.

ELIGIBILITY:
Nonprofit organizations.

GEOGRAPHIC RESTRICTIONS:
United States.

FINANCIAL DATA:
Amount of support per award: $50,000.
Total amount of support: Approximately $2,000,000 annually.

NUMBER OF APPLICANTS MOST RECENT YEAR:
500.

NUMBER OF AWARDS: Approximately 60 to 70 annually.

APPLICATION INFORMATION:
Applications must be submitted online. Applications submitted by any other method will not be considered.

The Foundation highly recommends the applicant review the instructions on using the system and online application system FAQs before beginning the application process. The Proposal FAQs outlines the information to be included in the narrative of the proposal, as well as the list of documents that the organization should be prepared to

submit/upload electronically. Documents include the organization's IRS 501(c)(3) letter and Arca's Lobbying Expenditure Form. As always, the Foundation only considers full proposals and does not accept letters of inquiry.
Duration: One year, or the program period.
Deadline: March 1 or September 1 or first business day following if the first falls on a weekend.

PUBLICATIONS:
Annual report with guidelines; past grantee profiles.

STAFF:
Anna Lefer Kuhn, Executive Director
Becca Freedman, Program Associate

BOARD OF DIRECTORS AND OFFICERS:
Nancy R. Bagley, President
Nicole Bagley, Vice President
Mary E. King, Secretary
Rev. Joseph Elderidge
Mike Lux
Janet Shenk
Margery Tabankin

ADDRESS INQUIRIES TO:
See e-mail address above.

ASSISI FOUNDATION OF MEMPHIS INC. [23]

515 Erin Drive
Memphis, TN 38117
(901) 684-1564
Fax: (901) 684-1997

WEB SITE ADDRESS:
www.assisifoundation.org

AREAS OF INTEREST:
Education, health and human services, social justice, ethics and literacy.

TYPE:
Challenge/matching grants; Endowments; General operating grants; Matching gifts; Project/program grants; Research grants; Technical assistance.

YEAR PROGRAM STARTED: 1994

PURPOSE:
To support health, lifelong learning, social justice, and responsible use of resources with respect and compassion for all.

ELIGIBILITY:
Grants are made to organizations that have tax-exempt status under Section 501(c)(3) of the Internal Revenue Code.

GEOGRAPHIC RESTRICTIONS:
Memphis area and Shelby County, Tennessee.

FINANCIAL DATA:
Amount of support per award: Varies.
Total amount of support: Varies.

APPLICATION INFORMATION:
Grant application process and required forms are available to download from the Foundation's web site.
Duration: Varies.

ADDRESS INQUIRIES TO:
Dr. Jan Young, Executive Director
(See address above.)

ATHWIN FOUNDATION [24]

5200 Wilson Road
Suite 307
Minneapolis, MN 55424
(612) 379-3817
Fax: (952) 915-6148

E-MAIL ADDRESS:
jstormcod1@aol.com

WEB SITE ADDRESS:
www.catchcod.com

FOUNDED: 1956

AREAS OF INTEREST:
Arts and humanities, education, human services, environmental enhancement and organizational capacity building.

TYPE:
Capital grants; General operating grants; Project/program grants.

YEAR PROGRAM STARTED: 1956

PURPOSE:
To provide funds for charitable, scientific, literary or educational purposes.

LEGAL BASIS:
Tax-exempt private foundation.

ELIGIBILITY:
Only tax-exempt organizations may apply. No grants are awarded to individuals.

GEOGRAPHIC RESTRICTIONS:
Primarily Minnesota.

FINANCIAL DATA:
Amount of support per award: Varies.

NUMBER OF APPLICANTS MOST RECENT YEAR:
250.

NUMBER OF AWARDS: Varies.

REPRESENTATIVE AWARDS:
$1,000 to American Indian OIC for program support; $25,000 to the American Red Cross-Minneapolis Chapter for a capital campaign; $100,000 to Blake School for a two-year capital campaign.

APPLICATION INFORMATION:
Applicants must submit a letter of inquiry to the Foundation. Early submission is encouraged.
Duration: Varies.
Deadline: Letters of inquiry by March 1 and October 1. Decisions are made two to three months after cutoff.

PUBLICATIONS:
Annual report.

IRS IDENTIFICATION NUMBER: 41-6021773

TRUSTEES:
Bruce W. Bean
Glen Bean
Mary F. Bean
Eleanor Nolan

ADDRESS INQUIRIES TO:
Jim Storm, Administrator
(See address above.)

ATKINSON FOUNDATION   [25]
1720 South Amphlett Boulevard
Suite 100
San Mateo, CA 94402-2710
(650) 357-1101
Fax: (650) 357-1101

E-MAIL ADDRESS:
atkinfdn@aol.com

WEB SITE ADDRESS:
www.atkinsonfdn.org

FOUNDED: 1939

AREAS OF INTEREST:
Social services and education in San Mateo County, California as well as American

private volunteer organizations providing technical assistance and development in Mexico and Central America.

TYPE:
Project/program grants.

YEAR PROGRAM STARTED: 1939

PURPOSE:
To foster the efforts of individuals and families to become socially, economically and physically self-sufficient, and to increase their spiritual, material and social welfare.

LEGAL BASIS:
Private foundation.

ELIGIBILITY:
Applicants must be organizations with Internal Revenue Code 501(c)(3) status.

No loans or grants to individuals or for doctoral study or research. The Foundation does not sponsor nor contribute to one-time events or nationwide appeals from organizations and does not fund publications, films or conferences.

GEOGRAPHIC RESTRICTIONS:
San Mateo County, California, Mexico and Central America.

FINANCIAL DATA:
Amount of support per award: $1,000 to $30,000. Average $8,000.
Total amount of support: $745,403 for the year 2010.

NUMBER OF APPLICANTS MOST RECENT YEAR:
340 for the year 2010.

NUMBER OF AWARDS: 92 for the year 2010.

REPRESENTATIVE AWARDS:
$10,000 to Boys & Girls Club of the Coastside for general program support; $15,000 to Second Harvest Food Bank for mobile pantry program; $9,000 to San Mateo Union High School District for workability program; $10,000 to Adelante Foundation microcredit programs, Honduras.

APPLICATION INFORMATION:
Organizations should submit their request to the administrator using a cover sheet provided by the Foundation. It should include:
(1) a listing of personnel and officials of the agency;
(2) names and primary affiliations of the directors and officers;
(3) brief historical statement;
(4) description of the proposed program, showing the need, population to be served, specific objectives, activities to be carried out, necessary staff, their qualifications and anticipated outcomes;
(5) an organization budget and a project budget;
(6) IRS tax-exempt letter;
(7) indication that request is being made with the approval of the governing body and;
(8) any supplementary information that may strengthen application.
Duration: Usually one year.
Deadline: Call for specific timelines.

PUBLICATIONS:
Annual report; grant guidelines; application procedures.

IRS IDENTIFICATION NUMBER: 94-6075613

OFFICERS AND DIRECTORS:
Linda L. Lanier, President
Ray N. Atkinson, Vice President
Elizabeth H. Curtis, Vice President, Administration

James R. Avedisian, Vice President, Finance
William Crandall, Assistant Treasurer
John E. Herrell, Assistant Treasurer
Jean S. Atkinson, Secretary
Olivia O. Aranda, Director
Dirk Damonte, Director
Shirley Moore, Director

ADDRESS INQUIRIES TO:
Elizabeth H. Curtis, Administrator
(See address above.)

ATRAN FOUNDATION, INC.   [26]
25 East 21st Street
3rd Floor
New York, NY 10010
(212) 505-9677

FOUNDED: 1945

AREAS OF INTEREST:
Jewish and Yiddish culture, labor, medical research in narrow areas of interest and social services.

TYPE:
Fellowships; General operating grants; Project/program grants.

PURPOSE:
To support programs relating to labor and labor relations, Yiddish language and culture, Yiddish literature, medical science and sociology.

LEGAL BASIS:
Tax-exempt under Section 501(c)(3) of the Internal Revenue Code.

ELIGIBILITY:
Grants are made only to 501(c)(3) tax-exempt organizations. No grants to individuals.

GEOGRAPHIC RESTRICTIONS:
United States.

FINANCIAL DATA:
Amount of support per award: Varies.
Total amount of support: Varies.

NUMBER OF APPLICANTS MOST RECENT YEAR:
More than 200 for all programs.

NUMBER OF AWARDS: 35 for the year 2011.

APPLICATION INFORMATION:
No formal application form is required. Application guidelines may be requested from the address above.
Duration: One year.
Deadline: September 30.

PUBLICATIONS:
Guideline letter for application procedure.

IRS IDENTIFICATION NUMBER: 13-5566548

OFFICERS:
Diane Fischer, President
Dr. Barnett Zumoff, Vice President

DIRECTORS:
Leonard Atran
Ruth Atran
Diane Fischer
Sam Norich
Dr. Dominick Purpura
Dr. Barnett Zumoff

ADDRESS INQUIRIES TO:
Diane Fischer, President
(See address above.)

MARY REYNOLDS BABCOCK FOUNDATION [27]

2920 Reynolda Road
Winston-Salem, NC 27106
(336) 748-9222
Fax: (336) 777-0095

E-MAIL ADDRESS:
info@mrbf.org

WEB SITE ADDRESS:
www.mrbf.org

FOUNDED: 1953

AREAS OF INTEREST:
Racism and poverty in the southeastern U.S.

NAME(S) OF PROGRAMS:
● **Moving People and Places Out of Poverty**

TYPE:
General operating grants. Program related investments.

YEAR PROGRAM STARTED: 2005

PURPOSE:
To help to move people and places out of poverty.

LEGAL BASIS:
Private foundation.

ELIGIBILITY:
Applicants must be nonprofit tax-exempt organizations with appropriate interests, located or working in the Southeast.

GEOGRAPHIC RESTRICTIONS:
Southeastern United States.

FINANCIAL DATA:
Amount of support per award: $5,000 to $75,000. Average $50,000.
Total amount of support: Varies.

NUMBER OF APPLICANTS MOST RECENT YEAR: 300.

NUMBER OF AWARDS: 90.

APPLICATION INFORMATION:
Applications must be submitted electronically.
Duration: Three to five years depending on the grant.

PUBLICATIONS:
Application form.

IRS IDENTIFICATION NUMBER: 56-0690140

BOARD OF DIRECTORS:
Laura Mountcastle, President
Wendy Johnson, Vice President
Ken Mountcastle, Treasurer
Dee Davis, Secretary
Bruce Babcock
Victoria Creed
David Dodson
Otis Johnson
Barbara Millhouse
Katharine B. Mountcastle
Katharine R. Mountcastle
Mary Mountcastle
Ivan Kohar Parra
Carol Prejean Zippert

ADDRESS INQUIRIES TO:
Program Officers
(See address above.)

HELEN BADER FOUNDATION, INC. [28]

233 North Water Street, 4th Floor
Milwaukee, WI 53202
(414) 224-6464
Fax: (414) 224-1441

E-MAIL ADDRESS:
info@hbf.org

WEB SITE ADDRESS:
www.hbf.org

FOUNDED: 1991

AREAS OF INTEREST:
Alzheimer's disease and dementia, economic development, children and youth, Jewish education, program-related investments, youth development.

TYPE:
Capital grants; Challenge/matching grants; Conferences/seminars; General operating grants; Matching gifts; Project/program grants; Technical assistance; Training grants.

YEAR PROGRAM STARTED: 1991

PURPOSE:
To fund innovative projects and programs in four primary areas including Alzheimer's disease and dementia, economic development, children and youth, and Jewish education.

LEGAL BASIS:
Family foundation.

ELIGIBILITY:
U.S. organizations must be tax-exempt under Section 501(c)(3) of the IRS or governmental entities. Grants will only be approved for foreign entities which meet specific charitable status requirements.

GEOGRAPHIC RESTRICTIONS:
Alzheimer's and Aging: national. Economic Development and Children and Youth: Milwaukee, Wisconsin. Other areas do not accept unsolicited proposals.

FINANCIAL DATA:
Amount of support per award: $500 to $180,000. Median is $10,000.
Total amount of support: $4,426,447 for the fiscal year 2010.

NUMBER OF APPLICANTS MOST RECENT YEAR: 595.

NUMBER OF AWARDS: 242 for fiscal year 2010.

REPRESENTATIVE AWARDS:
$6,000 to SHARP Literacy, Inc.; $15,000 to Grand Avenue Club; $150,000 to Milwaukee Public Schools.

APPLICATION INFORMATION:
Applicants must submit a one-page letter of application at least 10 weeks prior to the scheduled board of directors meeting. If the Foundation wishes to pursue a grant request, a full proposal and on-site visit are required and a complete application must be submitted within 30 days of the preliminary application.
Duration: Varies. Renewal possible.
Deadline: Applications are accepted at any time.

PUBLICATIONS:
Annual report.

IRS IDENTIFICATION NUMBER: 39-1710914

BOARD OF DIRECTORS:
Jere D. McGaffey, Chairman and Treasurer
Daniel J. Bader, President
David M. Bader, Vice President
Deirdre Britt, Secretary
Linda C. Bader
Frances Wolff

ADDRESS INQUIRIES TO:
Daniel J. Bader, President
(See address above.)

R.C. BAKER FOUNDATION [29]

P.O. Box 6150
Orange, CA 92863-6150
(714) 750-8987
Fax: (714) 750-2057

FOUNDED: 1952

AREAS OF INTEREST:
Education, health, cultural, scientific research, social services for youth and elderly, and crime prevention.

TYPE:
Capital grants; Fellowships; General operating grants; Project/program grants; Scholarships; Technical assistance; Training grants; Work-study programs.

LEGAL BASIS:
Private foundation.

ELIGIBILITY:
Applicant organizations must have IRS tax-exempt status. No grants are made to individuals, endowments or loans. No grants to capital programs of tax-supported institutions.

GEOGRAPHIC RESTRICTIONS:
Western United States.

FINANCIAL DATA:
Amount of support per award: $15,000.
Total amount of support: $1,413,800.

APPLICATION INFORMATION:
Applications should include a description of the proposed project and goals, a recently audited financial statement, amount requested, and a list of other sources of support. In addition, the applicant should include its IRS statement of tax-exempt status. The Foundation does not grant personal interviews.
Duration: One-time grants.
Deadline: May 1 and October 1.

IRS IDENTIFICATION NUMBER: 95-1742283

BOARD OF TRUSTEES:
Frank L. Scott, Chairman
James Benedict
Robert Christiano, Ph.D.
Dennis Cronin
F. Larry Scott, Jr.
Ronald G. Turner

ADDRESS INQUIRIES TO:
Frank L. Scott, Chairman, Board of Trustees
(See address above.)

BALL BROTHERS FOUNDATION [30]

222 South Mulberry
Muncie, IN 47305
(765) 741-5500
Fax: (765) 741-5518

E-MAIL ADDRESS:
donna.munchel@ballfdn.org

WEB SITE ADDRESS:
www.ballfdn.org

FOUNDED: 1926

AREAS OF INTEREST:
Education, arts, culture and humanities, human services, public/society benefit, health and environment.

CONSULTING OR VOLUNTEER SERVICES:
Independent Colleges of Indiana.

TYPE:
Capital grants; Endowments; General operating grants; Matching gifts; Project/program grants; Research grants. The Foundation supports educational programs and actively underwrites a number of challenge or matching grants.

YEAR PROGRAM STARTED: 1926

PURPOSE:
To promote recreational, educational or charitable purposes within the state of Indiana.

LEGAL BASIS:
Private foundation.

ELIGIBILITY:
Indiana not-for-profit organizations or institutions are eligible to apply. No grants to individuals.

GEOGRAPHIC RESTRICTIONS:
Indiana.

FINANCIAL DATA:
Amount of support per award: $1,000 to $1,000,000.

Total amount of support: $5,348,685 for the year 2009.

NUMBER OF APPLICANTS MOST RECENT YEAR:
180 for the year 2009.

NUMBER OF AWARDS: 79.

APPLICATION INFORMATION:
Application must include a description of the project, project staff and budget, IRS determination letter, objective of the proposal, plan of development, expected results and method of evaluation.

Duration: Usually one year. Three years for capital campaigns.

Deadline: April 1 and September 1.

PUBLICATIONS:
Guidelines; annual report.

OFFICERS:
Frank E. Ball, Chairman and Chief Executive Officer
James A. Fisher, Vice Chairman
Douglas J. Foy, Treasurer
Terry L. Walker, Secretary

DIRECTORS:
William Bracken
Stephanie Duckmann
Jud Fisher
Nancy B. Keilty
Judy Oetinger
John J. Pruis
Scott E. Shockley

ADDRESS INQUIRIES TO:
Donna Munchel, Executive Assistant
(See address above.)

GEORGE AND FRANCES BALL FOUNDATION   [31]
222 South Mulberry
Muncie, IN 47305
(765) 741-5500
Fax: (765) 741-5518

E-MAIL ADDRESS:
kmgross@iquest.net

FOUNDED: 1937

AREAS OF INTEREST:
Education, arts and culture, civic community projects, health and human services, environment and conservation.

TYPE:
Capital grants; Challenge/matching grants; Development grants; General operating grants; Project/program grants; Scholarships; Technical assistance.

LEGAL BASIS:
Family foundation.

ELIGIBILITY:
Applicants must be 501(c)(3) organizations or institutes.

GEOGRAPHIC RESTRICTIONS:
East central Indiana, primarily Delaware County.

FINANCIAL DATA:
Amount of support per award: $25,000 median.

Total amount of support: $3,750,000 for the year ended December 31, 2010.

Matching fund requirements: Usually 1:1.

NUMBER OF APPLICANTS MOST RECENT YEAR:
100.

NUMBER OF AWARDS: 45 for the year 2010.

APPLICATION INFORMATION:
General grant request guidelines provided upon request.

Deadline: Applications accepted year-round.

STAFF:
Norman E. Beck, Executive Director
Douglas J. Foy, Treasurer
Tamara S. Phillips, Assistant Treasurer

DIRECTORS:
Frank A. Bracken, President
Joan H. McKee, Secretary
Stefan S. Anderson
Thomas C. Bracken
Ronald K. Fauquher
Jon H. Moll
Robert M. Smitson
Joseph F. Wiese, III

ADDRESS INQUIRIES TO:
Kris Gross, Executive Assistant
(See address above.)

BALTIMORE COMMUNITY FOUNDATION   [32]
2 East Read Street, 9th Floor
Baltimore, MD 21202
(410) 332-4171
Fax: (410) 837-4701

E-MAIL ADDRESS:
info@bcf.org

WEB SITE ADDRESS:
www.bcf.org

FOUNDED: 1972

AREAS OF INTEREST:
Human services, youth, education, transportation, neighborhoods, diversity, environment, arts and culture, and promoting Baltimore.

TYPE:
Project/program grants; Scholarships; Technical assistance.

YEAR PROGRAM STARTED: 1972

PURPOSE:
To work for a healthy productive Baltimore region and to provide a flexible effective way for charitable individuals, corporations and foundations to invest in those efforts.

LEGAL BASIS:
Community foundation.

ELIGIBILITY:
The Foundation welcomes grant applications from organizations in the Greater Baltimore region that are tax-exempt under Section 501(c)(3) of the Internal Revenue Code.

The Foundation will be most likely to fund programs that:
(1) address underlying causes of specific problems and seek long-term systemic solutions;
(2) are preventive rather than remedial;
(3) reach a broad segment of the community;
(4) increase individual access and opportunity;
(5) attract financial or volunteer resources or involve collaboration;
(6) build the capacity of grantee organizations and;
(7) strengthen the private, nonprofit sector.

The Foundation does not make grants for annual fund campaigns, operating support except for start-up, religious or sectarian purposes, capital campaigns, or individuals (including scholarships and fellowships).

GEOGRAPHIC RESTRICTIONS:
Baltimore city and Baltimore County, Maryland.

FINANCIAL DATA:
Amount of support per award: Varies.

Total amount of support: Approximately $22,000,000 for the year 2010.

NUMBER OF AWARDS: 3,160.

REPRESENTATIVE AWARDS:
$15,000 to create a support network for charter schools; $20,000 to increase affordable housing opportunities; $10,000 for consulting services to a growing arts organization.

APPLICATION INFORMATION:
Duration: One year.

Deadline: Letters of inquiry are welcomed throughout the year.

PUBLICATIONS:
The BCF Edge, newsletter; annual report.

OFFICERS:
E. Robert Kent, Jr., Chairman
William C. Baker, Vice Chairman
Susan B. Katzenberg, Vice Chairman
Raymond L. Bank, Treasurer
Juliet A. Eurich, Secretary

STAFF:
Thomas E. Wilcox, President and Chief Executive Officer
Amy Seto, Chief Financial Officer
Cheryl A. Casciani, Director, Community Investments
Laurie Baker Crosley, Director, Philanthropic Services

ADDRESS INQUIRIES TO:
Cheryl A. Casciani
Director, Community Investments
(See address above.)

C.R. BARD FOUNDATION   [33]
730 Central Avenue
Murray Hill, NJ 07974
(908) 277-8182
Fax: (908) 277-8098

E-MAIL ADDRESS:
linda.hrevnack@crbard.com

WEB SITE ADDRESS:
www.crbard.com

FOUNDED: 1988

AREAS OF INTEREST:
Health care, community, employee activities and education.

TYPE:
Matching gifts; Project/program grants; Scholarships. In the area of health care, the Foundation primarily supports organizations or programs specializing in the fields of vascular, urology and oncology. In addition, the Foundation also considers requests from local and national charities in health and medicine. The Foundation does not contribute toward capital campaigns.

In the area of community, cultural and employee activities, the Foundation will consider requests from local civic, youth, art and cultural organizations. Applicants should identify the Bard facility in the community, describe the relationship between the organization and the facility, and explain how Bard employees may participate in its activities. The Foundation will also consider applications from community organizations in which Bard employees are active as volunteers. In such cases, the organization or employee should include a detailed description of his or her participation.

The Foundation is concerned with education, particularly within the health care field. The Foundation will consider requests from institutions of higher education which offer medical curricula, as well as organizations whose programs and services provide benefits to the health care industry.

The Foundation also has a matching gifts program that matches contributions of Bard employees and members of its Board of Directors to accredited colleges, universities, secondary schools and nonprofit medical institutions. In addition, the Foundation matches employee gifts to United Way and similar programs.

YEAR PROGRAM STARTED: 1988

PURPOSE:
To assist nonprofit organizations which improve the quality of life for local communities in areas where Bard has a facility or substantial employee population.

LEGAL BASIS:
Corporate foundation.

ELIGIBILITY:
The Foundation does not contribute to private foundations, individuals, political parties, fraternal groups, religious groups, veterans' organizations or sectarian groups. Organizations receiving major support from the United Way or similar programs are also not eligible. For matching gifts, the individual must be a member of the board of directors or an active U.S. employee of C.R. Bard, Inc., or any of its domestic operating divisions or subsidiaries at the time of the contribution. Nonprofit organizations eligible for matching gifts must be recognized as tax-exempt by the IRS under Section 501(c)(3) of the Internal Revenue Code and must be open to, or operated for the benefit of, the general public.

FINANCIAL DATA:
Amount of support per award: $1,000 to $100,000.
Total amount of support: $2,193,226 for the year 2010.
Matching fund requirements: Bard will match employee gifts of $25 to $15,000 per employee per calendar year and $25 to $5,000 per director per calendar year.

NUMBER OF AWARDS: 180 for the year 2010, excluding matching gifts.

APPLICATION INFORMATION:
Requests for funding must be in writing and include the following:
(1) name, address, history, objectives and description of the organization;
(2) the purpose for which the grant is requested and the amount requested;
(3) a copy of the organization's IRS document indicating 501(c)(3) status;
(4) a copy of the organization's operating budget and its most recent audited financial statement;
(5) a list of the organization's Board of Directors and/or trustees and;
(6) a statement indicating degree of support received from a United Way or similar organization.
Duration: One to five years.

PUBLICATIONS:
Guidelines.

ADDRESS INQUIRIES TO:
Linda Hrevnack
Manager, Community Affairs and Contributions

BARRA FOUNDATION [34]
200 West Lancaster Avenue
Suite 202
Wayne, PA 19087-4046
(610) 964-7601

WEB SITE ADDRESS:
www.barrafoundation.org

FOUNDED: 1963

AREAS OF INTEREST:
Arts and culture, human services, education and health.

TYPE:
Demonstration grants; Project/program grants; Seed money grants.

LEGAL BASIS:
Private foundation.

ELIGIBILITY:
501(c)(3) nonprofit organizations only.

GEOGRAPHIC RESTRICTIONS:
Philadelphia, Pennsylvania metropolitan area.

FINANCIAL DATA:
Amount of support per award: $2,000 to $100,000.
Total amount of support: $2,956,325 for the year 2010.

APPLICATION INFORMATION:
Applications are accepted online only.
Duration: Varies.
Deadline: Applications accepted on a continuous basis.

PUBLICATIONS:
Policy statement.

STAFF:
William Harral, III, President

ADDRESS INQUIRIES TO:
William Harral, III, President
(See address above.)

*SPECIAL STIPULATIONS:
No grants for environmental programs, exhibitions, publications or religious organizations.

BATTLE CREEK COMMUNITY FOUNDATION [35]
34 West Jackson Street
One Riverwalk Center
Battle Creek, MI 49017-3505
(269) 962-2181
Fax: (269) 962-2182

E-MAIL ADDRESS:
bccf@bccfoundation.org

WEB SITE ADDRESS:
www.bccfoundation.org

FOUNDED: 1974

AREAS OF INTEREST:
Education, health, arts, culture, and liveable communities.

TYPE:
Capital grants; Challenge/matching grants; Conferences/seminars; Demonstration grants; Development grants; Exchange programs; General operating grants; Internships; Matching gifts; Project/program grants; Research grants; Scholarships; Seed money grants; Technical assistance; Training grants; Travel grants. Emerging needs grants.

YEAR PROGRAM STARTED: 1974

PURPOSE:
To promote philanthropic giving and the use of endowment funds; to serve as a leader in coordinating local resources to meet the current and future needs of the Battle Creek community.

LEGAL BASIS:
Community foundation.

ELIGIBILITY:
Applicants must be nonprofit organizations whose programs will benefit residents or students of the greater Battle Creek community.

No grants for general operating support, endowments, annual fund-raising programs, or projects outside of the Battle Creek area which do not benefit the local community.

General operating support is only given for arts and culture initiatives.

GEOGRAPHIC RESTRICTIONS:
Battle Creek, Michigan area.

FINANCIAL DATA:
Amount of support per award: Average: $2,000 to $10,000.
Total amount of support: Varies.

NUMBER OF APPLICANTS MOST RECENT YEAR:
3,656.

NUMBER OF AWARDS: 1,380.

APPLICATION INFORMATION:
Prospective grant applicants are encouraged to contact the Foundation staff to discuss their proposals. Applications are available at the Foundation office along with a schedule of dates for reviewing applications and announcing grants.
Duration: One year.
Deadline: Varies by program.

PUBLICATIONS:
Guidelines; annual report.

ADDRESS INQUIRIES TO:
Annette Chapman, Vice President of Grantmaking and Scholarships
(See address above.)

THE BAXTER INTERNATIONAL FOUNDATION   [36]

One Baxter Parkway
Deerfield, IL 60015
(847) 948-4605
Fax: (847) 948-2016

E-MAIL ADDRESS:
fndinfo@baxter.com

WEB SITE ADDRESS:
www.baxter.com

FOUNDED: 1982

AREAS OF INTEREST:
Health care and its enhancement.

TYPE:
Matching gifts; Project/program grants. The
Foundation supports health care awards
programs, including the Foster G. McGaw
Prize, a $100,000 grant awarded annually to
a U.S. hospital that has distinguished itself in
community service and the William Graham
Health Services Research Award, a $50,000
award made annually to an individual who
has made significant contributions to the
improved delivery of medical care through
innovative health-services research.

YEAR PROGRAM STARTED: 1982

PURPOSE:
To increase access to health care services; to
improve the quality and cost-effectiveness of
health care.

LEGAL BASIS:
Corporate foundation.

ELIGIBILITY:
Grants are made to nonprofit 501(c)(3)
organizations with programs or proposals
consistent with the Foundation's priorities. In
evaluating a grant application, the Foundation
looks for eligibility under Foundation
guidelines, evidence that the project is a
response to a valid need and is superior to
other competing projects, and evidence of the
agency's capacity to accomplish its goals.

In general, the Foundation does not make
grants to capital and endowment campaigns,
hospitals, disease-specific organizations,
educational institutions (except in instances
where a grant would help to achieve other
goals, such as increasing the health services
available in a local Baxter community),
individuals, organizations with a limited
constituency such as fraternal, veterans' or
religious organizations, organizations
soliciting contributions for advertising space,
tickets to dinners and fund-raising events and
promotional materials.

FINANCIAL DATA:
Amount of support per award: Varies.
Total amount of support: Approximately
$3,558,191 for the year 2009.

NUMBER OF APPLICANTS MOST RECENT YEAR:
Over 1,000.

NUMBER OF AWARDS: 169 for the year 2009.

REPRESENTATIVE AWARDS:
$50,000 to George Mark Children's Home;
$36,704 to Associacao Pro-Hope Apoio a
Crianca; $46,070 to Hogar Bambi Venezuela;
$60,000 to Family Life Services.

APPLICATION INFORMATION:
An application form is not required; however,
all proposals and requests must include the
following information:
(1) a brief description of the organization, its
purpose, history, programs and achievements;
(2) a statement describing the specific

purpose of the grant requested, including how
the project meets the Foundation priorities;
(3) a plan for measuring results and reporting
periodic progress, as well as for a final
evaluation;
(4) financial information, including the
organization's current operating budget and
the budget for the proposed project;
(5) an audited financial statement;
(6) a copy of the organization's certificate of
tax-exemption from the IRS as a 501(c)(3) or
equivalent organization;
(7) a list of officers and board members and
their affiliations and;
(8) sources of income, including support
from corporate donors (with amounts noted),
the United Way, foundations and the
government.
Duration: Typically one year.
Deadline: Varies.

BOARD OF DIRECTORS:
Donna Namath, Executive Director
Katherine Azuara
Alice J. Campbell
Robert Davis
Robert Hombach
Shaun Newlon
Peter Nicklin
John Park
Charles W. Thurman

EXECUTIVE DIRECTOR:
Donna Namath

ADDRESS INQUIRIES TO:
See e-mail address above.

ADELAIDE BREED BAYRD FOUNDATION   [37]

350 Main Street
Malden, MA 02148
(781) 324-0322
Fax: (781) 397-0531

E-MAIL ADDRESS:
kezer@kezer.com

FOUNDED: 1927

AREAS OF INTEREST:
Community services, education and cultural
projects, health-related projects and
youth-related projects.

TYPE:
Capital grants; Project/program grants; Seed
money grants.

PURPOSE:
To support organizations whose activities are
centered in the Malden, MA, area, and to
support organizations elsewhere, whose
activities give substantial benefit to the
citizens of Malden.

LEGAL BASIS:
Private foundation.

ELIGIBILITY:
Grants are made to nonprofit, 501(c)(3)
organizations in the Foundation's areas of
interest. Requests from individuals,
endowment funds, performing arts (excepting
educational projects and programs) and
research will generally be excluded.

In general, the Foundation favors grants
toward project services over capital
expenditures.

GEOGRAPHIC RESTRICTIONS:
Boston area, with emphasis on Malden and
vicinity.

FINANCIAL DATA:
Amount of support per award: Varies.

Total amount of support: Average $700,000
annually.

REPRESENTATIVE AWARDS:
$33,000 to ABBF New Scholarships; $5,000
to Agassiz Village; $10,000 to American Red
Cross; $3,000 to Boston Ballet.

APPLICATION INFORMATION:
No particular form of request is required. A
letter stating the need, the purpose of the
organization and other salient matters will
suffice. Copies of summaries of current
budget or recent financial statements may be
helpful. Organizations should be prepared to
furnish a copy of IRS tax form 501(c)(3) or
another tax-exempt certificate.
Duration: Typically one year.
Deadline: Second Tuesday in February,
except for emergency situations.

PUBLICATIONS:
Annual report.

IRS IDENTIFICATION NUMBER: 04-6051258

TRUSTEES:
C. Henry Kezer, President
Susan C. Mansur, Treasurer
Francis K. Brown, II
Richard R. Burns, Jr.
Rev. Paul C. McPheeters
H. Allen Stevens
Dorothy Whittier

ADDRESS INQUIRIES TO:
C. Henry Kezer, President
(See address above.)

BECHTEL GROUP FOUNDATION   [38]

50 Beale Street
San Francisco, CA 94105
(415) 768-7158
Fax: (415) 768-0263

E-MAIL ADDRESS:
becfoun@bechtel.com

WEB SITE ADDRESS:
www.bechtel.com/foundation.html

FOUNDED: 1954

AREAS OF INTEREST:
Colleges and universities, primarily schools
of engineering at selected universities
worldwide; charities in communities with
Bechtel offices and projects.

NAME(S) OF PROGRAMS:
• **Bechtel Global Scholar Grants**
• **Building Positive Community
  Relationships Grants**
• **Improving the Pipeline of Engineering
  and Construction Talent Grants**
• **Matching Gift Grants**

TYPE:
Matching gifts; Project/program grants;
Scholarships. Employee matching gifts; The
majority of grants are initiated internally by
employees to support organizations where
they contribute and serve as volunteers.

YEAR PROGRAM STARTED: 1954

PURPOSE:
To support employee involvement in
communities with Bechtel offices or projects;
to support engineering education programs
worldwide.

LEGAL BASIS:
Corporate Foundation.

ELIGIBILITY:
Grants are initiated internally by employees based on involvement in nonprofits. Most grants go to communities with Bechtel office or project.

FINANCIAL DATA:
Amount of support per award: Building Positive Community Relationship: under $5,000; Bechtel Global Scholar: one-time scholarship of $3,000; Matching Gifts: up to $1,000 annually.
Total amount of support: $2,020,000 for the year 2009.
Matching fund requirements: Must go to U.S. college; maximum match is $1,000 per employee per year.

APPLICATION INFORMATION:
Deadline: Applications reviewed as received.

ADDRESS INQUIRIES TO:
LeeAnne Lang, Assistant Secretary
(See address above.)

THE BELK FOUNDATION [39]
2801 West Tyvola Road
Charlotte, NC 28217-4500
(704) 426-8396
Fax: (704) 357-1896
E-MAIL ADDRESS:
susan_blount@belk.com
WEB SITE ADDRESS:
www.belkfoundation.org
FOUNDED: 1928
AREAS OF INTEREST:
Education.
TYPE:
Capital grants; Endowments; General operating grants; Professorships; Project/program grants; Scholarships. Educational grants from kindergarten through college.
PURPOSE:
To increase the number of children and youth who perform at or above grade level in core subjects; to increase the number of youth to graduate high school in four years; to increase the number of youth who have an intentional path forward after high school through post-secondary education or training or meaningful employment.
ELIGIBILITY:
501(3)(c) organizations located in the southeastern states where Belk department stores do business, with an emphasis on North Carolina and South Carolina. No grants made to individuals.
FINANCIAL DATA:
Amount of support per award: $5,000 to $100,000.
Total amount of support: Varies.
APPLICATION INFORMATION:
Unsolicited grants proposals are not accepted.
Deadline: April 1 and October 1.
STAFF:
Susan Blount, Foundation Administrator
ADDRESS INQUIRIES TO:
Susan Blount, Foundation Administrator
(See address above.)

THE BELO FOUNDATION [40]
400 South Record Street
Dallas, TX 75202
(214) 977-6661
Fax: (214) 977-6620
E-MAIL ADDRESS:
ameadows@belo.com
WEB SITE ADDRESS:
www.belo.com/about/foundation
FOUNDED: 1952
AREAS OF INTEREST:
College-level journalism education; urban parks and green space.
TYPE:
Capital grants; Endowments; General operating grants; Professorships; Project/program grants; Scholarships.
YEAR PROGRAM STARTED: 1952
PURPOSE:
To provide funds for the development of urban parks and green space; to support college-level journalism education.
LEGAL BASIS:
Corporate foundation.
ELIGIBILITY:
Eligible organizations must have IRS 501(c)(3) status and be located in Dallas-Fort Worth, Texas and other cities where Belo Corporation and A.H. Belo Corporation have operating companies.
FINANCIAL DATA:
Amount of support per award: Typically $1,000 to $50,000.
Total amount of support: Varies.
NUMBER OF AWARDS: 6 for fiscal year 2011.
APPLICATION INFORMATION:
Initial requests should be in the form of a letter with a minimum of background material to support the request. Include information on your organization's officers and directors and a copy of the 501(c)(3) tax-exemption letter from the IRS.

The Foundation also encourages telephone calls or letters of inquiry before submission of a complete proposal.
Duration: Varies.
Deadline: Applications are accepted throughout the year.
PUBLICATIONS:
Handout (FAQ Sheet).
TRUSTEES:
Robert W. Decherd, Chairman
Marian Spitzberg, President
Guy H. Kerr
Dunia A. Shive
ADDRESS INQUIRIES TO:
Amy M. Meadows
Vice President and Executive Director
(See address above.)

BEMIS COMPANY FOUNDATION [41]
One Neenah Center
P.O. Box 669
Neenah, WI 54957
(920) 527-5300
Fax: (920) 527-7600
E-MAIL ADDRESS:
slebel@bemis.com
WEB SITE ADDRESS:
www.bemis.com
FOUNDED: 1959
AREAS OF INTEREST:
Education, social welfare and health, cultural and civic needs.
NAME(S) OF PROGRAMS:
● **Bemis Scholarship Program**
● **Educational Gift Matching**
● **FoodShare Program**
● **Nonprofit Gift Matching Program**
● **United Way Program**
TYPE:
Capital grants; Challenge/matching grants; General operating grants; Matching gifts; Project/program grants. Grants to tax-exempt organizations in the communities in which the Bemis Company operates. Scholarships, matching educational and matching nonprofit gifts are for employees only.

The Bemis Scholarship Program provides financial aid to sons and daughters of employees of the company and its subsidiaries. The Program is open to the sons and daughters under age 25 who wish to attend community colleges, four-year colleges, universities or vocational schools.

The Educational Gift Matching program gives employees an opportunity to have their personal contributions to eligible secondary schools, vocational/technical schools, colleges and universities double-matched by the Bemis Company.

Through the Bemis FoodShare Program, employees have the opportunity to have their contributions to local food banks and food shelves matched by the company.

In the United Way program, Bemis contributes to the United Way in communities where the company has facilities.
YEAR PROGRAM STARTED: 1959
PURPOSE:
To match available funds with those public needs where the interests of the company and its employees are inseparable.
LEGAL BASIS:
Corporate foundation.
ELIGIBILITY:
Grants are made to tax-exempt, U.S.-based organizations only. Priorities in grants will be given to those organizations and/or programs that will contribute the most to advancing the quality of life for all peoples in the communities in which the Bemis Company operates. Emphasis will be on those programs that encourage the development of our human resources, education programs and, in a lesser degree, civic and art institutions that encourage participation by the general public. Special consideration will be given to those programs in which the company's employees actively participate or are directly benefited.

The Foundation will not make grants to individuals or to organizations for religious purposes or for political purposes, either for lobbying efforts or campaigns. The Foundation prefers not to make grants for educational capital funds programs, endowment purposes or to support trips or tours. Grants will not exceed 5% of the total requirements of any organization or specific campaign goal.

Educational Gift Matching:
(1) an eligible employee is any regular hourly or salaried employee or retiree of the Bemis Company or any of its subsidiaries or any person serving on the Bemis Company Board of Directors and;
(2) an eligible educational institution is an

accredited independent secondary school, junior college, community college or degree-granting college or university; all education institutions eligible for this program must be located in the U.S. and have a U.S. Treasury Department ruling that contributions are deductible by the donor for federal income tax purposes.

Nonprofit Gift Matching:
(1) an eligible employee is any regular hourly or salaried employee or retiree of the Bemis Company or any of its subsidiaries or any person serving on the Bemis Company Board of Directors and;
(2) the institution receiving the funds must be a 501(c)(3) organization.

FINANCIAL DATA:
Amount of support per award: Varies.
Total amount of support: $3,250,000 per year.
Matching fund requirements: Educational Gift Matching: The Plan provides that the employee's contribution to an eligible educational institution will be double-matched.

REPRESENTATIVE AWARDS:
$135,298 to FoodShare Program; $347,056 to the Educational Gift Matching Program; $636,034 to Scholarships; $416,177 to United Way Program.

APPLICATION INFORMATION:
Grant proposals need not follow a specific format, but all proposals should include:
(1) name of the organization and amount requested;
(2) brief description of the objectives for which the grant is sought;
(3) details as to how the objectives are to be attained;
(4) budget, including information about existing and other possible sources of income;
(5) officers and board members and;
(6) statement that the organization has tax-exempt status under Section 501(c)(3) of the Internal Revenue Code and that contributions to it are tax deductible.
It is preferred that all initial inquiries be by mail and not by telephone or personal visits.
Duration: Varies.
Deadline: February, May, August and November.

PUBLICATIONS:
Application guidelines.

IRS IDENTIFICATION NUMBER: 41-6038616

ADDRESS INQUIRIES TO:
Sandy Ebel, Foundation Secretary
(See address above.)

*SPECIAL STIPULATIONS:
All initial inquiries should be made by mail.

H.N. AND FRANCES C. BERGER FOUNDATION   [42]
P.O. Box 13390
Palm Desert, CA 92255
(760) 341-5293
Fax: (760) 341-3518

WEB SITE ADDRESS:
www.hnberger.org

FOUNDED: 1961

AREAS OF INTEREST:
Arts, culture, children, education, environment, health, human services and youth.

TYPE:
Project/program grants.

PURPOSE:
To provide people with the opportunity to improve their own situations.

LEGAL BASIS:
Private family foundation.

ELIGIBILITY:
Grants are made to organizations that have tax-exempt status under Section 501(c)(3) of the Internal Revenue Code. No grants are made to individuals. Nonsectarian religious programs may apply.

GEOGRAPHIC RESTRICTIONS:
United States, primarily southern California.

FINANCIAL DATA:
Amount of support per award: Grants vary in amount, depending upon the needs and nature of the request.

APPLICATION INFORMATION:
Submit a one- to two-page request for consideration. This should include a concise statement of intent as well as a brief history of the organization and its activities.

ADDRESS INQUIRIES TO:
Christopher McGuire
Vice President of Programs
(See address above.)

THE GRACE AND FRANKLIN BERNSEN FOUNDATION   [43]
15 West 6th Street, Suite 1308
Tulsa, OK 74119-5407
(918) 584-4711
Fax: (918) 584-4713

E-MAIL ADDRESS:
gfbernsen@aol.com

WEB SITE ADDRESS:
www.bernsen.org

FOUNDED: 1968

AREAS OF INTEREST:
Arts, civic, education, medical, religious, United Way, and children.

TYPE:
Capital grants; Challenge/matching grants; Matching gifts.

YEAR PROGRAM STARTED: 1968

PURPOSE:
To provide grants in support of religious, charitable, scientific, literary or educational purposes, or for the prevention of cruelty to children.

LEGAL BASIS:
Private family foundation.

ELIGIBILITY:
The Foundation gives priority to applications from nonprofit organizations with clearly defined benefits, such as those for building and capital funding purposes, and other special program needs. Education programs, including those in the arts, higher education, human services and community programs, religious causes and youth programs are eligible for support.

Grants may require matching funds to be raised by the recipient.

No grants are made to elementary or secondary education institutions unless they involve programs for at-risk, handicapped or learning-disabled children. No grants are made to individuals, or for the benefit of specific individuals.

GEOGRAPHIC RESTRICTIONS:
Tulsa, Oklahoma area.

FINANCIAL DATA:
Amount of support per award: Average: $5,000.
Total amount of support: $1,200,000.
Matching fund requirements: Typically one half.

NUMBER OF APPLICANTS MOST RECENT YEAR: 135.

NUMBER OF AWARDS: 45.

APPLICATION INFORMATION:
Applications should be submitted in writing by the chief executive officer of the applicant organization. They must include a brief description of the organization, an explanation of its importance, a clear statement of its goals, financial need including the other sources of funds and copies of a tax-exemption letter from the IRS.

Additional information required with summary letter:
(1) list of current officers and Board of Trustees;
(2) most recent audited financial statement or last year's IRS Form 990;
(3) current year-to-date financial statements and budget and;
(4) project budget (if applicable) and plans to support the project after the grant period.

If additional information is required, the organization making application will be notified of the additional submittal requirements.

Deadline: Grant applications must be received before the 12th day of any given month in order to be considered for the next trustee meeting.

IRS IDENTIFICATION NUMBER: 23-7009414

TRUSTEES:
Donald F. Marlar
Donald E. Pray
John D. Strong, Jr.
W. Bland Williamson

ADDRESS INQUIRIES TO:
Margaret Skyles, Administrator
(See address above.)

BERRIEN COMMUNITY FOUNDATION   [44]
2900 South State Street
Suite 2 East
St. Joseph, MI 49085
(269) 983-3486
Fax: (269) 983-4939

E-MAIL ADDRESS:
bcf@berriencommunity.org

WEB SITE ADDRESS:
www.berriencommunity.org

FOUNDED: 1952

AREAS OF INTEREST:
Building spirit of community/arts and culture, nurturing our children, encouraging youth leadership and development.

TYPE:
Challenge/matching grants; Demonstration grants; Development grants; Project/program grants; Scholarships; Seed money grants.

PURPOSE:
To promote philanthropy, build a spirit of community and enhance the quality of life in Berrien County, MI.

ELIGIBILITY:
501(c)(3) or equivalent.

GEOGRAPHIC RESTRICTIONS:
Berrien County, Michigan.

FINANCIAL DATA:
Amount of support per award: Varies.
Total amount of support: More than $1,900,000 for the year 2009.

APPLICATION INFORMATION:
Deadline: September 1.

ADDRESS INQUIRIES TO:
Nanette Keiser, President
(See address above.)

THE LOWELL BERRY FOUNDATION [45]
3685 Mount Diablo Boulevard
Suite 269
Lafayette, CA 94549
(925) 284-4427
Fax: (925) 284-4332

E-MAIL ADDRESS:
info@lowellberryfoundation.org

WEB SITE ADDRESS:
www.lowellberryfoundation.org

FOUNDED: 1950

AREAS OF INTEREST:
Christian ministry, social service and educational programs.

TYPE:
General operating grants; Project/program grants.

YEAR PROGRAM STARTED: 1950

PURPOSE:
To strengthen the leadership of the local Christian church ministry; to assist social services organizations in Alameda and Contra Costa counties, CA.

LEGAL BASIS:
Private nonprofit corporation.

ELIGIBILITY:
Most grants are restricted to programs in California's Contra Costa and Alameda counties. No grants to individuals, capital funding programs, or equipment.

GEOGRAPHIC RESTRICTIONS:
Contra Costa and Alameda counties, California.

FINANCIAL DATA:
Amount of support per award: Varies.
Total amount of support: $1,000,000 for the year 2009.

NUMBER OF AWARDS: Varies.

REPRESENTATIVE AWARDS:
Religious Grants: $25,000 to City Team Ministries for general operations; Social Services Grants: $5,000 to Loaves and Fishes of Contra Costa to support winter needs.

APPLICATION INFORMATION:
Proposal should contain the following elements:
(1) summary statement and background information;
(2) names of the individuals on the board of directors, including a brief biography of each member;
(3) specific monetary amount requested with

a budget listing how the funds will be spent;
(4) copy of the organization's annual operating budget in detail;
(5) copy of the organization's most recent IRS 990 tax form and;
(6) copy of IRS 501(c)(3) tax-exempt status letter.
Duration: One year.
Deadline: Varies.

BOARD OF DIRECTORS:
Larry R. Langdon, President
Patricia Berry Conklin, Vice President
Gary L. Depolo, Treasurer
Barbara Berry Corneille, Secretary
John D. Asher, Director
Jami S. Kane, Director
Jayne S. Mordell, Director
Annette S. Robison, Director

ADDRESS INQUIRIES TO:
Katherine Sanders, Office Manager
(See address above.)

BERWIND CORPORATION [46]
3000 Centre Square West
1500 Market Street
Philadelphia, PA 19102
(215) 575-2306
Fax: (215) 606-1849

E-MAIL ADDRESS:
requests@berwind.com

WEB SITE ADDRESS:
www.berwind.com

FOUNDED: 1886

AREAS OF INTEREST:
Animal welfare, after-school education and urban revitalization.

TYPE:
General operating grants; Matching gifts; Project/program grants.

ELIGIBILITY:
Applicants must be 501(c)(3) organizations within Berwind operating areas.

GEOGRAPHIC RESTRICTIONS:
Primarily Philadelphia area, Pennsylvania.

FINANCIAL DATA:
Amount of support per award: Varies.
Total amount of support: $1,000,000 for the year 2010.
Matching fund requirements: Dollar-for-dollar up to $5,000 for employee grants only.

APPLICATION INFORMATION:
Duration: One year.
Deadline: Varies.

ADDRESS INQUIRIES TO:
Catherine Murphy, Managing Director
Berwind Family Office
(See address above.)

BING FUND [47]
9700 West Pico Boulevard
Los Angeles, CA 90035
(310) 277-5711
Fax: (310) 277-6368

FOUNDED: 1920

AREAS OF INTEREST:
Museums, higher education, performing arts, population control, and hospitals.

TYPE:
Project/program grants.

PURPOSE:
To fund a variety of worthwhile projects in the community.

LEGAL BASIS:
501(c)(3) tax-exempt organizations.

ELIGIBILITY:
Must be a tax-exempt organization under Section 501(c)(3) of the Internal Revenue Code. Funding is at the discretion of the Directors.

GEOGRAPHIC RESTRICTIONS:
Southern California.

FINANCIAL DATA:
Amount of support per award: Varies.
Total amount of support: Varies.

NUMBER OF APPLICANTS MOST RECENT YEAR: 100.

NUMBER OF AWARDS: Varies.

APPLICATION INFORMATION:
Duration: Varies. Renewal possible.
Deadline: Varies.

ADDRESS INQUIRIES TO:
Sue Porto, Office Manager
(See address above.)

THE WILLIAM BINGHAM FOUNDATION [48]
20325 Center Ridge Road
Suite 629
Rocky River, OH 44116
(440) 331-6350

E-MAIL ADDRESS:
info@wbinghamfoundation.org

WEB SITE ADDRESS:
www.wbinghamfoundation.org

FOUNDED: 1955

AREAS OF INTEREST:
Education, science, health and human services, and the arts.

TYPE:
Capital grants; Challenge/matching grants; Endowments; General operating grants; Project/program grants.

YEAR PROGRAM STARTED: 1955

PURPOSE:
To provide funding to nonprofit organizations that sponsor programs in the areas of education, science, health and human services, and the arts.

LEGAL BASIS:
Private family foundation.

ELIGIBILITY:
Grants are made only to public charities. Grants are not made to individuals or to organizations located outside of the U.S.

GEOGRAPHIC RESTRICTIONS:
United States.

FINANCIAL DATA:
Amount of support per award: $10,000 to $20,000 average.

NUMBER OF APPLICANTS MOST RECENT YEAR: 600.

NUMBER OF AWARDS: 20 grants average.

REPRESENTATIVE AWARDS:
$50,000 to Environmental Learning Center, Inc., Vero Beach, FL, for purchase and installation of solar equipment systems and signage; $50,000 to University Hospitals of Cleveland, Cleveland, OH, for accreditation of Chest Pain Center at Geauga Medical Center; $63,853 to Catholic Charities of the

Archdiocese of Washington, Washington, DC, for support of a development coordinator for the Archdiocesan Legal Network.

APPLICATION INFORMATION:
The Foundation is not accepting unsolicited proposals.
Duration: Generally one year.

ADDRESS INQUIRIES TO:
Laura H. Gilbertson, Director
(See address above.)

A.G. BISHOP CHARITABLE TRUST [49]

JPMorgan Chase Bank, N.A.
1116 West Long Lake Road
Bloomfield Hills, MI 48302
Fax: (248) 645-8448

WEB SITE ADDRESS:
www.jpmorgan.com/onlinegrants

FOUNDED: 1942

AREAS OF INTEREST:
Religious, charitable, scientific, literary and educational programs.

TYPE:
Capital grants; General operating grants; Project/program grants; Research grants.

YEAR PROGRAM STARTED: 1942

PURPOSE:
Grants for organized public charities within the community of Flint-Genesee County, MI.

LEGAL BASIS:
501(c)(3).

ELIGIBILITY:
No grants are made to individuals or private foundations. Grants made to tax-exempt organizations only. Applicants must be located within the Flint-Genesee County, MI area.

GEOGRAPHIC RESTRICTIONS:
Flint-Genesee County, Michigan.

FINANCIAL DATA:
Amount of support per award: Varies.
Total amount of support: Varies.

NUMBER OF AWARDS: 31.

APPLICATION INFORMATION:
Applicants are required to submit the following:
(1) an IRS tax-exemption letter;
(2) four copies of a brief communication for purpose of requesting a grant;
(3) last two fiscal year-end financial statements;
(4) list of current officers and board of directors and;
(5) list of other organizations that have pledged money or are being solicited for the same purposes.
Duration: Varies.
Deadline: Award announcements made within four months after receipt of application.

ADDRESS INQUIRIES TO:
Nayda Schwartz
Vice President and Trust Officer
(See address above.)

MORTON K. AND JANE BLAUSTEIN FOUNDATION [50]

10 East Baltimore Street, Suite 1111
Baltimore, MD 21202
(410) 347-7201
Fax: (410) 347-7210

E-MAIL ADDRESS:
info@blaufund.org

WEB SITE ADDRESS:
www.blaufund.org

AREAS OF INTEREST:
Educational opportunity, health and human rights.

TYPE:
General operating grants; Project/program grants. Project and general support grants.

PURPOSE:
To promote educational opportunity, access to health and human rights for underserved people.

ELIGIBILITY:
501(c)(3) organizations.

GEOGRAPHIC RESTRICTIONS:
Baltimore, Maryland and New York, New York.

FINANCIAL DATA:
Amount of support per award: $20,000 to $50,000.

APPLICATION INFORMATION:
Send two- to three-page letter of intent or application. IRS tax status determination letter is required. Faxed and e-mailed letters of intent are not accepted.
Duration: One to two years. Prior grantee organizations may be renewable.

ADDRESS INQUIRIES TO:
Betsy F. Ringel, Executive Director
(See address above.)

THE BLUESCOPE FOUNDATION NORTH AMERICA [51]

1540 Genessee
P.O. Box 419917
Kansas City, MO 64141-0917
(816) 968-3208
Fax: (816) 627-8993

E-MAIL ADDRESS:
jcharmon@butlermfg.com

WEB SITE ADDRESS:
www.butlermfg.com

FOUNDED: 1952

AREAS OF INTEREST:
United charities, scholarship program, aid to education, community needs, youth and civic cultural activities, hospitals and health and minorities.

TYPE:
Capital grants; General operating grants; Matching gifts; Project/program grants; Scholarships. Scholarship program available to children of Company employees only. Matching gift program for employee contributions to eligible educational or cultural institutions.

In the area of community needs, support is given to organizations which serve broadly the communities in which the Company has employees and significant capital investment. Programs falling within this category include United Way organizations in Company plant cities, minority assistance limited to nonprofit agencies that help provide jobs or job training for the disadvantaged, foster the movement of minorities into the mainstream of economic life and enable minorities to improve their level of educational attainment, and neighborhood and non-residential building programs utilizing the company's products.

In the area of education, grants are made to colleges and universities which supply significant numbers of employees to the Company and/or which provide opportunities for continuing education to employees, help disadvantaged students who demonstrate ability and desire to prepare for and remain in colleges and universities, have programs which have the objective of providing education to residents of Company plant locations and provide educational opportunities which advance minorities, women and individuals with disabilities.

In the area of culture, the Foundation considers programs which help broaden the cultural experience of the residents of local communities through the support of visual and performing arts organizations, demonstrate concern for excellence and innovation in the arts, and bring cultural opportunity to the economically disadvantaged.

In the area of public affairs, the Foundation helps promote strong relationships between the public and private sectors to assist in the solution to urban problems, reinforce the efforts of groups formed to gather and disseminate information that is in the general public interest, encourage community volunteerism, and promote economic education and the merits of the free enterprise system.

YEAR PROGRAM STARTED: 1952

PURPOSE:
To provide sustained financial assistance to worthy charitable, educational, health and welfare programs in the U.S.; to enhance the quality of life in those communities where employees of Butler Manufacturing Company reside.

LEGAL BASIS:
A nonprofit, benevolent and charitable corporation under the laws of the State of Missouri. A 501(c)(3) private foundation under IRS code.

ELIGIBILITY:
Grants are made only to nonprofit organizations located in areas where the company has facilities. Organizations must have a clear statement of purpose in the public interest, a program consistent with the organization's stated purpose, evidence of interagency cooperation to avoid duplication of services, an active and responsive governing body of volunteers holding regular meetings, evidence of professional program management and reasonable fund-raising expenses, maintenance of ethical publicity and promotion of the program that excludes exaggerated or misleading claims, and fund solicitation policies which prohibit the payment of commission or other compensation based on total funds raised or undue pressures.

Grants are not normally made to individuals, political organizations, religious organizations for sectarian purposes, pre-school, primary and secondary educational institutions, fraternal or veteran's organizations, organizations receiving United Way support for operating expenses, national health organizations, including local or regional chapters, hospitals (except those providing unique services, burn centers or children's services), tours, conferences, seminars, workshops, testimonial dinners, tables, tickets, advertisements, walk-a-thons, endowment funds, and other foundations of any type providing grants to not-for-profits or programs beyond the Foundation's stated geographic areas of interest.

FINANCIAL DATA:
Amount of support per award: $1,000 to $10,000.

Total amount of support: $300,000 annually.

Matching fund requirements: The minimum single gift the Foundation will match per eligible donor is $25. The maximum single gift or total of annual gifts to be matched per eligible donor for full-time employees is $2,000 per calendar year.

NUMBER OF APPLICANTS MOST RECENT YEAR: Over 500.

NUMBER OF AWARDS: 50 for fiscal year 2009, excluding matching gifts.

REPRESENTATIVE AWARDS:
$7,500 to Harvesters, Kansas City, MO; $1,500 to River City Dance Theatre, San Marcos, TX; $4,000 to Genesis School, Kansas City, MO.

APPLICATION INFORMATION:
Initial contact should be made by phone, e-mail or letter addressed to the Foundation Administrator or, in non-Kansas City locations, to the plant or division manager describing the need, purpose and general activities of the requesting charitable organization. The letter will be reviewed by the plant or division manager to assure compliance with the policies established by the Foundation Trustees with a recommendation and forwarded to the Foundation Administrator.

Applicants must provide evidence of compliance with eligibility requirements, plus an annual report describing program activities and supporting services including financial statements, detailed annual budget and copy of IRS not-for-profit determination.

Duration: One year.

Deadline: Announcements are made after quarterly Trustee meetings.

PUBLICATIONS:
Annual report; contributions policy; application guidelines.

IRS IDENTIFICATION NUMBER: 44-0663648

TRUSTEES:
Harry Yeatman, President
Dan Kumm, Vice President and Secretary
Natalie Treff, Treasurer
Tanya Bennett
Gary Coder
D.J. Schmidt
Mishca Waliczek

ADDRESS INQUIRIES TO:
Jill Harmon, Foundation Director
(See address above.)

THE BODMAN FOUNDATION [52]

767 Third Avenue, 4th Floor
New York, NY 10017-2023
(212) 644-0322
Fax: (212) 759-6510

E-MAIL ADDRESS:
main@achelis-bodman-fnds.org

WEB SITE ADDRESS:
www.foundationcenter.org/grantmaker/achelis-bodman

FOUNDED: 1945

AREAS OF INTEREST:
Primarily arts and culture, education, employment, health, public policy and youth and families.

TYPE:
Challenge/matching grants; Conferences/seminars; Development grants; General operating grants; Internships; Matching gifts; Project/program grants; Research grants; Scholarships; Technical assistance; Training grants. Over 90% of the Foundation's grants fall into its six program areas.

PURPOSE:
To impact the greater New York City region and enhance the quality of life for its people, especially the disadvantaged; to advance human dignity, inspire personal achievement and foster self-reliance.

LEGAL BASIS:
Private foundation under Section 501(c)(3) of the Internal Revenue Code.

ELIGIBILITY:
The Foundation distributes funds in support of the purposes and programs of duly incorporated, 501(c)(3) tax-exempt nonprofit agencies and institutions, in accordance with the Tax Reform Act of 1969, as amended and as they relate to private foundations.

The Foundation generally does not make grants to nonprofit organizations outside of New York and New Jersey; annual appeals, dinner functions and fund-raising events; endowments and capital campaigns; loans and deficit financing; direct grants to individuals (such as scholarships and financial aid); individual day-care and after-school programs; housing; international projects; films and travel; projects for the elderly; small art, dance, music and theater groups; independent or public K-12 schools (except charter schools); national health and mental health organizations and; government agencies and nonprofit programs and services significantly funded or substantially reimbursed by government.

GEOGRAPHIC RESTRICTIONS:
Primarily New York City, but also northern New Jersey.

FINANCIAL DATA:
Net assets of approximately $53,822,423 as of November 30, 2010.

Amount of support per award: $10,000 to $100,000 for the year 2010.

NUMBER OF APPLICANTS MOST RECENT YEAR: Varies.

NUMBER OF AWARDS: Varies.

APPLICATION INFORMATION:
It is recommended that an organization's initial contact with the Foundation include only the following items:
(1) an inquiry or proposal letter briefly summarizing the history of the project, need, research, objectives, time period, key staff, project budget, and evaluation plan emphasizing measurable outcomes and specific program results;
(2) latest annual report;
(3) current and complete audited financial statements and;
(4) copy of the organization's IRS 501(c)(3) tax-exemption letter.

Duration: One year. Renewal does not generally follow the year of a grant.

OFFICERS:
John N. Irwin, III, Chairman
Russell P. Pennoyer, President
Peter Frelinghuysen, Vice President
Mary S. Phipps, Vice President
Horace I. Crary, Jr., Treasurer
John B. Krieger, Executive Director and Secretary

BOARD OF TRUSTEES:
Horace I. Crary, Jr.
Walter J.P. Curley, Jr.
Anthony D. Duke
Peter Frelinghuysen
John N. Irwin, III
Leslie Lenkowsky
Russell P. Pennoyer
Mary S. Phipps
Tatiana Pouschine

ADDRESS INQUIRIES TO:
John B. Krieger, Executive Director
(See address above.)

THE BOEING COMPANY [53]

100 North Riverside
Chicago, IL 60606-1596
(312) 544-2000
Fax: (312) 544-2074

WEB SITE ADDRESS:
www.boeing.com/community

FOUNDED: 1914

AREAS OF INTEREST:
Education (including early learning and primary and secondary education), health and human services, arts and culture, civic, and environment.

TYPE:
Challenge/matching grants; Development grants; Matching gifts; Project/program grants; Research grants; Scholarships; Seed money grants; Technical assistance. In the area of education, Boeing focuses on raising the quality of U.S. schools, as measured by student achievement, to world-class standards. This support is limited to schools and districts near major Boeing sites that are committed to implementing systemic change that embraces the philosophy that schools must have clear learning objectives and be held accountable for results.

In the area of health and human services, support is available for seed money (one-time grants) for new programs/projects addressing community need and priority and one-time grants to support equipment purchases, facilities enhancement and special projects.

In the area of arts and culture, the Foundation invests in programs that promote participation in arts and cultural activities and experiences.

In the area of civic initiatives, support is available for seed money (one-time grants) for new projects/programs addressing community need and priority and one-time grants to support equipment purchases, facilities enhancement and special projects.

In the area of environment, the Foundation invests in programs that protect and conserve the natural environment.

Also, Boeing donates surplus goods (e.g., computers, office equipment) to four major categories, including education, health and human services, arts and culture and civic initiatives. However, Boeing requires a prioritized list of items being requested to determine the level of donation to be provided.

YEAR PROGRAM STARTED: 1964

PURPOSE:
To continually improve the effectiveness of Boeing's philanthropic resources applied toward enhancing the quality of life in communities where our employees live and work.

LEGAL BASIS:
Company contributions program.

ELIGIBILITY:
Boeing encourages proposals that involve collaboration between multiple organizations to address community needs. Boeing discourages requests that involve such elements as endowments, as well as programs whose beneficiaries are not located in areas where Boeing employees live and/or work. Boeing will not consider personal requests, grants for political candidates, committees or organizations, requests in support of travel expenses for individuals or groups, requests from religious organizations or institutions, support to hospital or medical research organizations, applications from athletic organizations for events or agency-sponsored walks, runs and golf tournaments.

FINANCIAL DATA:
Amount of support per award: Varies.

Total amount of support: Varies.

Matching fund requirements: All gifts from The Boeing Company Employee Gift Matching Program will be matched on a dollar-for-dollar basis, except for gifts by retirees which will be matched $.50 to the dollar.

APPLICATION INFORMATION:
Application procedures and requirements are available online.

Duration: Varies.

Deadline: Varies.

PUBLICATIONS:
Community Involvement Report; guidelines; annual report.

EXECUTIVE COUNCIL:
W. James McNerney, Jr., Chairman, President and Chief Executive Officer
James F. Albaugh, Executive Vice President
James A. Bell, Executive Vice President
J. Michael Luttig, Executive Vice President and General Counsel
Dennis A. Muilenburg, Executive Vice President
Michael J. Cave, Senior Vice President
Thomas J. Downey, Senior Vice President, Communications
Timothy Keating, Senior Vice President, Government Operations
Richard Stephens, Senior Vice President, Human Resources and Administration
Wanda K. Denson-Low, Senior Vice President, Office of Internal Governance
Shephard W. Hill, President, Boeing International
John J. Tracy, Chief Technology Officer

ADDRESS INQUIRIES TO:
Global Corporate Citizenship
(See address above.)

*SPECIAL STIPULATIONS:
Applicant must be a 501(c)(3) organization in communities where Boeing employees live and/or work.

THE BOOTH-BRICKER FUND   [54]
826 Union Street
Suite 300
New Orleans, LA 70112
(504) 581-2430
Fax: (504) 566-4785

FOUNDED: 1966

AREAS OF INTEREST:
The Fund makes contributions for the purposes of promoting, developing and fostering religious, charitable, scientific, literary and educational nonprofit organizations.

TYPE:
Capital grants; Development grants; Project/program grants.

PURPOSE:
To promote, develop and foster religious, charitable, scientific, literary and educational nonprofit organizations. Starting in 2006, the Fund's program of charitable distributions has focused exclusively on taking advantage of the historic opportunity to reform public education in New Orleans.

ELIGIBILITY:
The Fund generally does not provide sustaining (operations and maintenance) funding. Requests are welcomed for capital needs, special projects and other one-time requirements. No grants are made to individuals or supporting organizations–i.e., a Section 501(c)(3) organization with further designation under Section 509(a)(3).

GEOGRAPHIC RESTRICTIONS:
Louisiana, with priority given to the New Orleans area.

FINANCIAL DATA:
Market value of assets as of December 31, 2010: $35,770,079.

Amount of support per award: Varies.

Total amount of support: Charitable distributions of $1,495,382 for the year 2010. Since its inception, the Fund has made charitable contributions exceeding $28,000,000.

NUMBER OF AWARDS: 78 gifts made in 2010.

APPLICATION INFORMATION:
Applications, which should be made by letter, are considered by the board of trustees at its quarterly meetings. There are no forms or deadlines. Requests should include complete information about the applicant organization, including its history, purpose, finances, current operations, governing board and tax status. A detailed explanation of the proposed use of the funds must be provided. Videotapes or DVDs should not be submitted.

Duration: Varies.

BOARD OF TRUSTEES:
Henry N. Kuechler, III
Charles B. Mayer
Gray S. Parker
Mary Kay Parker
Nathaniel P. Phillips, Jr.
H. Hunter White, Jr.

OFFICERS:
Gray S. Parker, Chairman
Ingrid C. Laffont, Treasurer
Heather A. Riley, Secretary

ADDRESS INQUIRIES TO:
Gray S. Parker, Chairman
(See address above.)

BRISTOL-MYERS SQUIBB FOUNDATION, INC.   [55]
345 Park Avenue
New York, NY 10154-0037
(212) 546-4331
Fax: (212) 546-9574

WEB SITE ADDRESS:
www.bms.com/foundation

FOUNDED: 1953

AREAS OF INTEREST:
HIV/AIDS in Africa, hepatitis in Asia, serious mental illness in the U.S. and cancer in Europe.

TYPE:
Project/program grants; Research grants.

PURPOSE:
To reduce health disparities by strengthening community-based health care worker capacity, integrating medical care and community-based supportive services, and mobilizing communities in the fight against disease; to strengthen the health and well-being of the communities where Bristol-Myers Squibb employees live and work.

LEGAL BASIS:
Corporate foundation.

ELIGIBILITY:
The Foundation considers requests for support only from tax-exempt organizations that satisfy the requirements of Section 501(c)(3) of the Internal Revenue Code. Preferential consideration is given to proposals that most directly and effectively address themselves to advancing the specific priorities within each of the areas of interest listed above.

No grants are made to individuals, political, fraternal, social or veterans' organizations, religious or sectarian organizations, unless engaged in a significant project benefiting the entire community, organizations receiving the Foundation's support through United Way or other federated campaigns, endowments, or courtesy advertising.

FINANCIAL DATA:
Amount of support per award: Varies.
Total amount of support: Varies.

APPLICATION INFORMATION:
Detailed application information and guidelines are available from the Foundation.
Duration: One year.

STAFF:
John L. Damonti, President

BOARD OF DIRECTORS:
Lamberto Andreotti, Chairman
Beatrice Cazala
John E. Celentano
John L. Damonti
Anthony C. Hooper
Sandra Leung
Elliott Sigal, M.D., Ph.D.

ADDRESS INQUIRIES TO:
Foundation Coordinator
(See address above.)

JAMES GRAHAM BROWN FOUNDATION, INC.   [56]
4350 Brownsboro Road
Suite 200
Louisville, KY 40207
(502) 896-2440
Fax: (502) 896-1774

E-MAIL ADDRESS:
grants@jgbf.org

WEB SITE ADDRESS:
www.jgbf.org

FOUNDED: 1943

AREAS OF INTEREST:
Education, economic development, cultural and human services.

TYPE:
Capital grants; Project/program grants.

YEAR PROGRAM STARTED: 1943

PURPOSE:
To foster the well-being, quality of life and image of Louisville and Kentucky.

LEGAL BASIS:
Private foundation.

ELIGIBILITY:
Only Kentucky organizations that have a tax-exempt designation under Section 501(c)(3) of the IRS Code can apply.

GEOGRAPHIC RESTRICTIONS:
Kentucky, with emphasis on Louisville.

FINANCIAL DATA:
Amount of support per award: $25,000 and up.

NUMBER OF AWARDS: 70.

REPRESENTATIVE AWARDS:
$200,000 to Brescia College, Owensboro, KY, for a project to make five buildings accessible to the handicapped; $500,000 to Georgetown College, Georgetown, KY, to construct an addition to the college's Cooke Memorial Library.

APPLICATION INFORMATION:
Duration: One year.

PUBLICATIONS:
Annual report.

ADDRESS INQUIRIES TO:
Dodie McKenzie, Grants Director
(See address above.)

THE JOE W. AND DOROTHY DORSETT BROWN FOUNDATION   [57]

320 Hammond Highway, Suite 500
Metairie, LA 70005
(504) 834-3433
Fax: (504) 834-3441

E-MAIL ADDRESS:
bethbuscher@thebrownfoundation.org

WEB SITE ADDRESS:
www.thebrownfoundation.org

FOUNDED: 1959

AREAS OF INTEREST:
Health and science, community benefit, human services, religion and education, conservation, environment and the arts.

TYPE:
General operating grants; Project/program grants; Research grants; Training grants.

PURPOSE:
To alleviate human suffering.

ELIGIBILITY:
Applicants must be nonprofit 501(c)(3). Religious organizations are eligible to apply. The Foundation favors requests for funds where funds are generally unavailable from most other sources. Within the five focus areas, the focus is primarily on relieving

human suffering, secondary interest includes cultural, spiritual, educational or scientific initiatives. No grants are made to individuals.

GEOGRAPHIC RESTRICTIONS:
Louisiana and Mississippi. Preference is given to the greater New Orleans area and Mississippi gulf coast.

FINANCIAL DATA:
Amount of support per award: Varies.

APPLICATION INFORMATION:
Duration: One year. Must reapply.
Deadline: September 30.

ADDRESS INQUIRIES TO:
Beth Buscher
Secretary to Board President
(See address above.)

*SPECIAL STIPULATIONS:
No grants are made to individuals.

BROWN SHOE COMPANY, INC. CHARITABLE TRUST   [58]

8300 Maryland Avenue
St. Louis, MO 63105
(314) 854-4000
Fax: (314) 854-4205

E-MAIL ADDRESS:
bberberich@brownshoe.com

WEB SITE ADDRESS:
www.brownshoe.com

FOUNDED: 1951

AREAS OF INTEREST:
Culture and education.

TYPE:
Capital grants; General operating grants; Matching gifts.

YEAR PROGRAM STARTED: 1951

PURPOSE:
To help fund worthwhile ongoing programs in the areas of education, health and human services.

LEGAL BASIS:
Corporate contributions program.

ELIGIBILITY:
Grants are restricted to major 501(c)(3) organizations participating in the health, cultural and educational areas. Educational institutions must be private and above the secondary school level. All organizations must be geographically located in areas of employee concentration and with expenditures restricted to the U.S.

GEOGRAPHIC RESTRICTIONS:
Primarily St. Louis, Missouri.

FINANCIAL DATA:
Amount of support per award: Varies.
Total amount of support: Varies.
Matching fund requirements: Matches gifts from full-time salaried employees and directors to educational institutions and cultural organizations, $50 to $2,500 per employee per year, and are matched on a 2:1 basis, up to $5,000.

APPLICATION INFORMATION:
The Foundation requires no formal application form, but applicants must provide a copy of their 501(c)(3) exemption letter, audited financial statement, a proposed budget for the project and a list of the organization's directors.
Duration: One year.
Deadline: Varies.

ADDRESS INQUIRIES TO:
Ann Joos, Executive Assistant
(See address above.)

*SPECIAL STIPULATIONS:
No grants are made to individuals.

THE MARGARET E. BURNHAM CHARITABLE TRUST   [59]

c/o H.M. Payson & Co.
P.O. Box 31
Portland, ME 04112-0031
(207) 772-3761
Fax: (207) 871-7508

E-MAIL ADDRESS:
jbe@hmpayson.com

WEB SITE ADDRESS:
www.megrants.org/burnham.html

AREAS OF INTEREST:
Community/social services, medical, educational, arts and culture, and environment.

TYPE:
Grants-in-aid; Project/program grants. Annual grant dedicated to responding to the needs of the Maine communities served.

PURPOSE:
To benefit nonprofit organizations located or operating in the state of Maine and serving within the state of Maine.

ELIGIBILITY:
Organizations must be 501(c)(3) and must operate in and serve the state of Maine. Individuals, private foundations under Section 509, and religious organizations are not eligible.

GEOGRAPHIC RESTRICTIONS:
Maine.

FINANCIAL DATA:
Amount of support per award: $1,000 to $20,000.

APPLICATION INFORMATION:
A completed application consists of the following:
(1) certification, application, project description, and budget pages;
(2) copy of the organization's most recent 501(c)(3) IRS ruling;
(3) copy of the organization's most recent financial statement or tax return and;
(4) list of the organization's officers and directors.
Duration: One year.
Deadline: October 1.

ADDRESS INQUIRIES TO:
Thomas M. Pierce, Trustee
(See address above.)

EDYTH BUSH CHARITABLE FOUNDATION, INC.   [60]

199 East Welbourne Avenue, Suite 100
Winter Park, FL 32789
(407) 647-4322
(888) 647-4322 (Florida only)
Fax: (407) 647-7716

E-MAIL ADDRESS:
dhessler@edythbush.org

WEB SITE ADDRESS:
www.edythbush.org

FOUNDED: 1973

AREAS OF INTEREST:
Children, youth and families, education, health care, limited interest in the arts, improvement of nonprofit organizations, and human services.

TYPE:
Capital grants; Challenge/matching grants; Demonstration grants; Development grants; Matching gifts; Project/program grants; Technical assistance; Training grants.

PURPOSE:
To provide nonprofit programs and grantmaking designed to help people help themselves.

LEGAL BASIS:
Private foundation.

ELIGIBILITY:
The Foundation welcomes grant applications from nonprofit organizations that have secured their 501(c)(3) and 509(a) IRS rulings. The Foundation has elected to focus its resources within Lake, Orange, Seminole and Osceola counties, Florida. Other grant requests should have support from one of our Board of Directors. The Foundation will not fund organizations that are chiefly tax-supported nor does it fund individual scholarships, individual research (even if through an exempt or otherwise qualified educational organization), alcoholism or drug abuse programs or facilities, routine operating expenses, the pay-off of deficits or pre-existing debt, foreign organizations or foreign expenditures, travel projects or fellowships, chiefly church, sacramental, denominational or inter-denominational purposes (except those outreach programs for elderly, indigents, needy, youth or homeless, regardless of belief, race, color, creed, or sex); endowment funds, advocacy organizations, cultural or arts organizations or organizations that have receipts or revenues from memberships and/or contributions of less than $25,000.

GEOGRAPHIC RESTRICTIONS:
Lake, Orange, Osceola and Seminole counties, Florida.

FINANCIAL DATA:
Amount of support per award: Typically $5,000 to $50,000. Maximum grant has been $450,000 spread over three years. Large grants are typically spread over two or three years.
Total amount of support: $2,480,837 for the year 2008.
Matching fund requirements: Must be new or increased cash contributions or pledges.

NUMBER OF AWARDS: 55 new for the year 2008.

REPRESENTATIVE AWARDS:
Civic and Community: $2,500 to Black History Committee of Orange County, Inc., Orlando, FL, to support Sixth Annual Black History Month Gala and Celebration; Cultural: $70,000 to Micheele Puppets, Inc., Orlando, FL, to provide new and increased office and workshop space and to purchase computer hardware and software; Education: $25,000 to U.S. Catholic Conference-Diocese of Orlando, Orlando, FL, for the Jerry and Peggy Hilbrich Scholarship Fund; Health Care: $25,500 to Hospice of Michigan Inc., Detroit, MI, in support of the documentary "Except for Six" and a public awareness campaign "Have You Had the Talk?"; Human Services: $25,000 to Foundation for Foster Children, Orlando, FL, to provide a fund-raising challenge to local high-net worth

individuals, increasing philanthropic giving for the healthy development of over 1,500 foster youth in the Central Florida region.

APPLICATION INFORMATION:
Letter of inquiry stating the amount sought, the purpose of the grant and nature of the organization. No proposals will be accepted by facsimile.
Duration: One to three years. Renewal by reapplication.
Deadline: Applications are accepted year-round.

PUBLICATIONS:
Guidelines; brochure.

IRS IDENTIFICATION NUMBER: 23-7318041

OFFICERS:
David A. Odahowski, President and Chief Executive Officer
Mary Ellen Hutcheson, CPA, Vice President and Treasurer
Deborah J. Hessler, Program Officer and Corporate Secretary

BOARD OF DIRECTORS:
Gerald F. Hilbrich, Chairman
Mary Gretchen Belloff, Vice Chairman
Matthew W. Certo
Deborah C. German, M.D.
Herbert F. Holm
David A. Odahowski
Richard J. Walsh

ADDRESS INQUIRIES TO:
Deborah J. Hessler, Program Officer and Corporate Secretary
(See address above.)

CABOT FAMILY CHARITABLE TRUST [61]
70 Federal Street
Boston, MA 02110
(617) 226-7505
Fax: (617) 451-1724

E-MAIL ADDRESS:
kmchugh@cabwel.com

WEB SITE ADDRESS:
www.cabwel.com

FOUNDED: 1942

AREAS OF INTEREST:
Arts and culture, education and youth development, environment and conservation, health and human services, and for the public benefit.

TYPE:
Capital grants; Challenge/matching grants; Endowments; General operating grants; Project/program grants. Capital campaigns.

YEAR PROGRAM STARTED: 1942

PURPOSE:
To provide funding for nonprofit organizations working in the arts, environment, youth development, education, health and human services.

LEGAL BASIS:
Charitable trust.

ELIGIBILITY:
The Trust supports only nonprofit organizations holding active 501(c)(3) status under the IRS code. The Trust does not make contributions to individuals, political organizations, religious institutions, advertising, sponsorship or fraternal organizations.

Applicants must meet the following criteria:
(1) reflect Cabot family interests and provide benefits to communities and organizations that have been supported by family philanthropy;
(2) extend important services to individuals and groups not served adequately through other programs and institutions;
(3) manage change by assessing community needs and developing programs to meet emerging needs;
(4) promote productive cooperation and full use of resources by nonprofit organizations and community groups and;
(5) test new approaches to problems or adapt solutions that have been successful elsewhere.

GEOGRAPHIC RESTRICTIONS:
Boston and other nearby areas.

FINANCIAL DATA:
Amount of support per award: $5,000 to $50,000 per year.
Total amount of support: Estimated giving about $1,400,000.

NUMBER OF APPLICANTS MOST RECENT YEAR:
350 for the year 2010.

NUMBER OF AWARDS: Approximately 40.

REPRESENTATIVE AWARDS:
$30,000 to Generations Inc. for intergenerational tutoring progam that matches 2,700 children in the Boston Public Schools to mentors who are local residents; $15,000 to Boston Area Rape Crisis Center for programs and services for victims of sexual assault in 27 communities; $25,000 to the Boston Ballet for new work and performances.

APPLICATION INFORMATION:
Applicants should submit a concept paper of three pages plus cover sheet and budget. Application form is available on the web site.
Duration: Usually, one year.
Deadline: February 1 and September 1.

PUBLICATIONS:
Annual report.

IRS IDENTIFICATION NUMBER: 04-6035446

TRUSTEES:
Frank Bradley
Jane C. Bradley
Edmund B. Cabot
John G.L. Cabot
Mary Schneider Enriquez
Greenfield Sluder

EXECUTIVE DIRECTOR:
Katherine S. McHugh

ADDRESS INQUIRIES TO:
Katherine S. McHugh, Executive Director
(See address above.)

THE MORRIS AND GWENDOLYN CAFRITZ FOUNDATION [62]
1825 K Street, N.W.
Suite 1400
Washington, DC 20006
(202) 223-3100
Fax: (202) 296-7567

E-MAIL ADDRESS:
info@cafritzfoundation.org

WEB SITE ADDRESS:
www.cafritzfoundation.org

FOUNDED: 1948

AREAS OF INTEREST:
Community services, arts and humanities, education, health and the environment.

TYPE:
Challenge/matching grants; General operating grants; Project/program grants; Scholarships; Technical assistance.

YEAR PROGRAM STARTED: 1948

PURPOSE:
To build a stronger community for residents of the Washington, DC area through support of programs in arts and humanities, community services, education, health and the environment.

LEGAL BASIS:
Private foundation.

ELIGIBILITY:
Grants are made only to charitable, educational and cultural institutions exempt from taxation under the Internal Revenue Code. IRS-registered, tax-exempt, 501(c)(3) organizations with a public charity status of 509(a)(1) or 509(a)(2) only. The general policy is to concentrate grants to organizations, operating within the greater Washington metropolitan area, with projects of direct assistance to the District of Columbia and its environs. Grants are not made for capital purposes, endowments or to individuals.

GEOGRAPHIC RESTRICTIONS:
District of Columbia; Montgomery and Prince George's counties in Maryland; Arlington and Fairfax counties, and the cities of Alexandria and Falls Church in Virginia.

FINANCIAL DATA:
Amount of support per award: Varies.
Total amount of support: $16,393,750 awarded for the fiscal year ended April 30, 2011.

NUMBER OF APPLICANTS MOST RECENT YEAR: 700.

NUMBER OF AWARDS: 376.

REPRESENTATIVE AWARDS:
$15,000 to City Arts, Inc., Washington, DC for general support; $20,000 to Clean Water Fund, Washington, DC for the Anacostia Watershed Initiative; $25,000 to Family Services, Inc., Gaithersburg, MD for the Healthy Families Montgomery Program; $50,000 to The Nonprofit Roundtable of Greater Washington, Washington, DC for the Think Twice Before You Slice Campaign; $30,000 to Playworks, Washington DC for general support; $50,000 outright and $25,000 as a 1:1 match to Alexandria Neighborhood Health Services, Alexandria, VA for general support.

APPLICATION INFORMATION:
To be considered for funding, an organization must submit a complete proposal, not a Letter of Inquiry (LOI). LOIs are not required. Organizations may submit a proposal for only one deadline within a 12-month period. The Foundation requires that all organizations use the Washington Grantmakers' Common Grant Application.
Duration: One year.
Deadline: November 1, March 1 and July 1.

PUBLICATIONS:
Annual report; application guidelines.

OFFICERS:
Calvin Cafritz, President and Chief Executive Officer

Daniel J. Callahan, III, Vice Chairman and Treasurer
Ed McGeogh, Vice President, Asset Management

STAFF:
Rose Ann Cleveland, Executive Director

DIRECTORS:
Calvin Cafritz, Chairman of the Board
Daniel J. Callahan, III
Robert Peck
Earl A. Powell, III
Alice M. Rivlin, Ph.D.

ADVISORY BOARD:
Anne Allen
Anthony W. Cafritz
Elliot S. Cafritz
Jane Lipton Cafritz
Kate D. Clark
Carolyn J. Deaver
The Hon. Robert W. Duemling
The Hon. Constance A. Morella
Elizabeth M. Peltekian
Julia Sparkman Shepard

ADDRESS INQUIRIES TO:
Rose Ann Cleveland, Executive Director
(See address above.)

CAMPBELL SOUP FOUNDATION [63]
One Campbell Place
Camden, NJ 08103-1799
(856) 342-6423
Fax: (856) 541-8185

E-MAIL ADDRESS:
wendy_milanese@campbellsoup.com

WEB SITE ADDRESS:
www.campbellsoup.com

FOUNDED: 1954

AREAS OF INTEREST:
Quality of life in plant communities, home community of Camden, NJ.

NAME(S) OF PROGRAMS:
- **Campbell Summer Program**
- **Dollars for Doers Fund**

TYPE:
Challenge/matching grants; Project/program grants. The Dollars for Doers Fund is a program designed to fund nonprofit organizations where Campbell employees volunteer in communities.

Campbell Summer Program funds organizations that provide summer employment, recreation, academic and cultural programs in the city of Camden.

YEAR PROGRAM STARTED: 1954

PURPOSE:
To improve the quality of life in those communities where Campbell Soup Company has a presence.

LEGAL BASIS:
Tax-exempt private foundation.

ELIGIBILITY:
Grants are made to tax-exempt organizations providing service consistent with Fund objectives. The Fund does not make grants to individuals for any purpose, nor does it make grants to organizations outside the U.S. and its possessions.

GEOGRAPHIC RESTRICTIONS:
United States.

FINANCIAL DATA:
Amount of support per award: Varies.

Total amount of support: $1,600,000 for the year ended June 30, 2009.
Matching fund requirements: Active employee and directors; $100 to $3,000 per person per year to higher education facilities only.

APPLICATION INFORMATION:
Foundation guidelines are available online.
Duration: Usually one-time grants.
Deadline: Written requests are accepted and reviewed throughout the year.

PUBLICATIONS:
Community Giving Report.

OFFICERS:
Jerry S. Buckley, Chairman
Anthony DiSilvestro, Controller

TRUSTEES:
Jerry S. Buckley
Mark Cacciatore
Carlos M. del Sol
Karen Lewis
Maureen Linder
Steve White

ADDRESS INQUIRIES TO:
Wendy Milanese, Grant Administrator
(See address above.)

THE CANNON FOUNDATION, INC. [64]
52 Spring Street
Concord, NC 28025
(704) 786-8216
Fax: (704) 782-2812

E-MAIL ADDRESS:
fdavis@cannonfoundation.org

WEB SITE ADDRESS:
www.cannonfoundation.org

FOUNDED: 1943

AREAS OF INTEREST:
Health care, higher education, human services, culture, history and religion.

TYPE:
Capital grants; Project/program grants.

YEAR PROGRAM STARTED: 1943

ELIGIBILITY:
Applicant must be 501(c)(3) nonprofit organization. No grants to individuals.

GEOGRAPHIC RESTRICTIONS:
North Carolina.

FINANCIAL DATA:
Amount of support per award: $5,000 to $2,000,000.
Total amount of support: Approximately $6,130,273 for fiscal year ended September 30, 2010.

NUMBER OF APPLICANTS MOST RECENT YEAR: 163.

NUMBER OF AWARDS: 128.

APPLICATION INFORMATION:
Initially, send a letter or e-mail of inquiry outlining the organization's goal and purposes, and the intended use and amount of the grant requested.
Duration: One year.
Deadline: January 5, April 5, July 5 and October 5. Notification within two months of deadlines.

PUBLICATIONS:
Guidelines brochure.

STAFF:
Frank Davis, Executive Director

ADDRESS INQUIRIES TO:
Frank Davis, Executive Director
(See address above.)

CARNEGIE CORPORATION OF NEW YORK [65]
437 Madison Avenue
New York, NY 10022
(212) 371-3200
Fax: (212) 754-4073

WEB SITE ADDRESS:
www.carnegie.org

FOUNDED: 1911

AREAS OF INTEREST:
Education, international peace and security, international development, and strengthening U.S. democracy.

TYPE:
Conferences/seminars; Development grants; Project/program grants; Research grants; Seed money grants.

YEAR PROGRAM STARTED: 1911

PURPOSE:
To promote the advancement and diffusion of knowledge and understanding.

LEGAL BASIS:
Private foundation.

ELIGIBILITY:
Grants are made primarily to academic institutions and national or regional organizations.

The Foundation does not fund basic operating expenses, endowments, facilities, scholarships, travel, individual schools or preschools, or curriculum projects. The Foundation does not accept unsolicited requests to improve understanding among other countries or policymakers in the U.S., or proposals concerned with private sector development in Africa.

FINANCIAL DATA:
Amount of support per award: Varies.
Total amount of support: Approximately $126,200,000 for the year 2010.

NUMBER OF AWARDS: Varies.

APPLICATION INFORMATION:
No official application forms are issued. Application information is available on the web site.
Duration: Varies.

PUBLICATIONS:
Program guidelines; pamphlet; meeting and occasional papers; *Carnegie Reporter,* magazine; annual report.

IRS IDENTIFICATION NUMBER: 13-1628151

ADDRESS INQUIRIES TO:
E-mail: grantsinfo@carnegie.org

AMON G. CARTER FOUNDATION [66]
201 Main Street, Suite 1945
Fort Worth, TX 76102
(817) 332-2783
Fax: (817) 332-2787

WEB SITE ADDRESS:
www.agcf.org

FOUNDED: 1945

AREAS OF INTEREST:
The arts, health and medical services, youth and elderly, and human and social services.

TYPE:
Capital grants; Challenge/matching grants; Development grants; Matching gifts; Project/program grants; Seed money grants.

LEGAL BASIS:
Private foundation.

ELIGIBILITY:
Applicants must be 501(c)(3) organizations. Board focus on Fort Worth and Tarrant County, TX.

No loans. No grants to individuals.

FINANCIAL DATA:
Amount of support per award: $10,000 to $500,000.

NUMBER OF APPLICANTS MOST RECENT YEAR: 400 for the year 2008.

NUMBER OF AWARDS: 200 for the year 2008.

REPRESENTATIVE AWARDS:
$7,557,570 to Amon Carter Museum; $2,500,000 to Texas Christian University.

APPLICATION INFORMATION:
Send brief letter request supplemented with project budget and/or other pertinent information in support of request.
Duration: Three years maximum. Renewal rare.

PUBLICATIONS:
Grant policy and guideline statement.

OFFICERS:
Ruth Carter Stevenson, President
Robert W. Brown, M.D., Vice President
W. Patrick Harris, Executive Vice President, Finances
John H. Robinson, Executive Vice President, Grant Administration
Kathy King, Controller

BOARD OF DIRECTORS:
Ruth Carter Stevenson, Chairperson
Robert W. Brown, M.D.
Kate L. Johnson
Mark L. Johnson
Sheila B. Johnson

ADDRESS INQUIRIES TO:
John H. Robinson
Executive Vice President, Grant Administration
(See address above.)

HAROLD K.L. CASTLE FOUNDATION [67]
1197 Auloa Road
Kailua, HI 96734-4606
(808) 263-7073
Fax: (808) 261-6918

E-MAIL ADDRESS:
bmurph@castlefoundation.org

WEB SITE ADDRESS:
www.castlefoundation.org

FOUNDED: 1962

AREAS OF INTEREST:
Hawaii's public education redesign and enhancement, Hawaii's nearshore marine resource conservation, strengthening the communities of Windward Oahu, and other areas of focus when the Foundation sees a special opportunity to make a difference with limited resources.

TYPE:
Capital grants; Project/program grants; Seed money grants.

PURPOSE:
To benefit the people of Hawaii.

LEGAL BASIS:
Family foundation.

ELIGIBILITY:
Nonprofit organizations serving the state of Hawaii with Internal Revenue Code Sections 501(c)(3) and 509(a) public charity status and public schools in Hawaii.

GEOGRAPHIC RESTRICTIONS:
Hawaii.

FINANCIAL DATA:
Amount of support per award: $150 to $2,000,000 for fiscal year 2010.
Total amount of support: $5,206,166.21 for fiscal year 2010.

COOPERATIVE FUNDING PROGRAMS: Hawaii Community Stabilization Initiative.

NUMBER OF APPLICANTS MOST RECENT YEAR: 123.

NUMBER OF AWARDS: 51.

REPRESENTATIVE AWARDS:
$1,000,000 to Hawaii Pacific University; $750,000 to Maui Arts and Cultural Center; $1,000,000 to Seabury Hall; $1,500,000 to YMCA-Windward Branch.

APPLICATION INFORMATION:
Prospective grant applicants must submit an Online Inquiry Form, which is the first step in requesting funds from the Foundation. The Foundation will contact applicants within one month to request more information, invite the submission or a full proposal, or to inform you that the Foundation will be unable to consider a full proposal due to limited resources and/or a mismatch with Foundation priorities.
Duration: Program grants: Up to five years.
Deadline: Applications accepted on a rolling basis. Capital support requests due each year by October 1.

PUBLICATIONS:
Application guidelines; annual report.

IRS IDENTIFICATION NUMBER: 99-6005445

STAFF:
Terrence R. George, Executive Vice President and Chief Operating Officer
Carlton K.C. Au, Chief Financial Officer and Treasurer
Elizabeth Murph, Grants Manager
Ann Matsukado, Accounting Manager

BOARD OF DIRECTORS:
James C. McIntosh, Chairman of the Board
H. Mitchell D'Olier, President and Chief Executive Officer
Dr. Claire L. Asam
Corbett A.K. Kalama
Randolph G. Moore
Eric K. Yeaman

ADDRESS INQUIRIES TO:
Elizabeth Murph, Grants Manager
(See address above.)

HUGH STUART CENTER CHARITABLE TRUST [68]
96 North Third Street
Suite 500
San Jose, CA 95112
(408) 293-0463
Fax: (408) 293-9514

FOUNDED: 1977

AREAS OF INTEREST:
Churches and civic organizations, hospitals and schools.

TYPE:
Capital grants; Development grants; General operating grants; Project/program grants; Scholarships.

YEAR PROGRAM STARTED: 1977

PURPOSE:
To make funds and scholarships available to churches, hospitals, schools and civic organizations.

LEGAL BASIS:
Private foundation under Section 501(c)(3) of the Internal Revenue Code.

ELIGIBILITY:
501(c)(3) civic and religious organizations that work for the betterment of Santa Clara County and schools. On occasion, donations are made out of county.

GEOGRAPHIC RESTRICTIONS:
California, primarily Santa Clara County.

FINANCIAL DATA:
Amount of support per award: $2,000 to $50,000 for the year 2010.
Total amount of support: $355,292 for the year 2010.

NUMBER OF APPLICANTS MOST RECENT YEAR:
150 to 300 annually.

NUMBER OF AWARDS: 36 for the year 2010.

APPLICATION INFORMATION:
Applicants must submit letter of request to the Trust and proof of 501(c)(3).
Duration: One year. Renewal possible.
Deadline: Requests are reviewed continuously. Funding is year-round and there are no time limits.

IRS IDENTIFICATION NUMBER: 94-2455308

ADDRESS INQUIRIES TO:
Arthur K. Lund and Shirley Oneal
Co-Trustees
(See address above.)

CENTRAL MAINE POWER COMPANY   [69]

83 Edison Drive
Augusta, ME 04336
(800) 565-0121 ext. 2967
(207) 629-1067
Fax: (207) 623-5908

WEB SITE ADDRESS:
www.cmpco.com

AREAS OF INTEREST:
Education, civic, science, technology education and economic development.

NAME(S) OF PROGRAMS:
• **Central Maine Power Company Corporate Contributions Program**

TYPE:
Capital grants; Challenge/matching grants; Demonstration grants; General operating grants; Project/program grants; Research grants.

LEGAL BASIS:
Corporation giving program.

ELIGIBILITY:
Applicants must be nonprofit organizations, limited to the area serviced by Central Maine Power.

GEOGRAPHIC RESTRICTIONS:
Maine.

FINANCIAL DATA:
Amount of support per award: $100 to $1,000.

NUMBER OF APPLICANTS MOST RECENT YEAR:
500.

NUMBER OF AWARDS: 100.

APPLICATION INFORMATION:
Applicants should send a proposal letter.
Duration: Typically one year. Some multiyear funding.
Deadline: Applications accepted throughout the year. Grants announced monthly.

STAFF:
John H. Carroll, Manager of Public Affairs

ADDRESS INQUIRIES TO:
Shelley Morris
Public Affairs Department
(See address above.)

*SPECIAL STIPULATIONS:
Only available to schools and nonprofits within company's service territory in Maine.

THE CHAMPLIN FOUNDATIONS   [70]

300 Centerville Road, Suite 300 S
Warwick, RI 02886-0226
(401) 736-0370
Fax: (401) 736-7248

WEB SITE ADDRESS:
fdncenter.org/grantmaker/champlin

FOUNDED: 1932

AREAS OF INTEREST:
Conservation, environment, education, health, cultural programs, youth, social service, historic preservation and libraries.

TYPE:
Capital grants; Scholarships. Direct grants for capital needs including the purchase of equipment, real estate, renovations, construction and reduction of mortgage indebtedness.

YEAR PROGRAM STARTED: 1932

PURPOSE:
To make grants to qualified charitable organizations to promote the general well-being of humanity, with preference to Rhode Island.

LEGAL BASIS:
Tax-exempt private foundation.

ELIGIBILITY:
Tax-exempt organizations, preferably in Rhode Island, may apply. No grants are awarded to individuals. Scholarships are limited to Rhode Island public high school graduates accepted at Brown University.

GEOGRAPHIC RESTRICTIONS:
Rhode Island.

FINANCIAL DATA:
Amount of support per award: Average: $25,000 to $65,000.
Total amount of support: $17,074,565 for the year 2010.

NUMBER OF APPLICANTS MOST RECENT YEAR:
278 for the year 2010.

NUMBER OF AWARDS: 174 for the year 2010.

REPRESENTATIVE AWARDS:
Open Space/Environment: $775,000 to The Nature Conservancy; Hospitals: $850,000 to Rhode Island Hospital; Youth: $425,000 to Boys & Girls Club of Providence; Libraries:

$666,565 to Ocean State Libraries; Social Services: $456,185 to Salvation Army of Pawtucket; Education: $1,700,000 to Brown University.

APPLICATION INFORMATION:
Applicants must submit a brief letter concisely describing the project and its intended purpose, status of any fund-raising effort and other sources of funds available. Copies of IRS 501(c)(3) tax-exemption and 509(a) letters must be furnished. Audited financial statements may be required on request.
Duration: No grants are awarded on a continuing basis. Applicants must apply for renewal.
Deadline: April 30. Grants awarded in November; checks issued in December.

PUBLICATIONS:
Annual report; guidelines; Report on Open Space and Recreation Grants.

IRS IDENTIFICATION NUMBER: 51-0165988

EXECUTIVE COMMITTEE:
John Gorham, Chairman
Keith H. Lang, Executive Director
Timothy N. Gorham, Associate Director

ADDRESS INQUIRIES TO:
Keith H. Lang, Executive Director
(See address above.)

*SPECIAL STIPULATIONS:
Preference is given to Rhode Island tax-exempt organizations.

All initial inquiries must be made by mail.

BEN B. CHENEY FOUNDATION   [71]

3110 Ruston Way, Suite A
Tacoma, WA 98402
(253) 572-2442

E-MAIL ADDRESS:
info@benbcheneyfoundation.org

WEB SITE ADDRESS:
www.benbcheneyfoundation.org

AREAS OF INTEREST:
Charity, civic affairs, culture, education, the elderly, health, social services and youth.

TYPE:
Capital grants; Project/program grants; Seed money grants.

PURPOSE:
To improve the quality of life in communities where the Cheney Lumber Company operated.

LEGAL BASIS:
Foundation.

ELIGIBILITY:
Applicants must be 501(c)(3) tax-exempt organizations.

GEOGRAPHIC RESTRICTIONS:
Southwestern Washington, southwestern Oregon and the seven northernmost counties in California.

FINANCIAL DATA:
Amount of support per award: $1,000 to $15,000 for small grants; $16,000 to $50,000 for regular grants.
Total amount of support: Varies.

APPLICATION INFORMATION:
Begin with a query letter; projects of interest will be contacted for a follow-up interview.
Duration: Typically one to two years. No renewals.

ADDRESS INQUIRIES TO:
Brad Cheney, Executive Director
(See address above.)

CHEVRON CORPORATION [72]

6001 Bollinger Canyon Road
San Ramon, CA 94583
(925) 842-0600

WEB SITE ADDRESS:
www.chevron.com

FOUNDED: 1879

AREAS OF INTEREST:
Health, education and economic
development.

TYPE:
General operating grants; Matching gifts;
Project/program grants; Research grants;
Scholarships; Seed money grants; Technical
assistance.

YEAR PROGRAM STARTED: 2001

PURPOSE:
To help communities where the Company
operates; to support a variety of programs
from health, human rights and the arts to
education.

LEGAL BASIS:
Corporate giving program.

ELIGIBILITY:
The Corporation does not accept unsolicited
funding requests, grant applications or project
proposals. Most partnerships are formed from
existing relationships in communities where
Chevron operates. On occasion, new
partnerships are sought which uniquely
address community needs and deliver
meaningful results.

FINANCIAL DATA:
Amount of support per award: Varies.
Total amount of support: Up to $100,000,000
annually to U.S. nonprofit organizations.

REPRESENTATIVE AWARDS:
World Wildlife Fund, The Nature
Conservancy, The World Business Council
for Sustainable Development.

APPLICATION INFORMATION:
Duration: Varies.

ADDRESS INQUIRIES TO:
Corporate Contributions and Programs
(See address above.)

CHICAGO TRIBUNE FOUNDATION [73]

435 North Michigan Avenue, 2nd Floor
Chicago, IL 60611-4041
(312) 222-4300
Fax: (312) 222-3751

E-MAIL ADDRESS:
ctcommunityrelations@tribune.com

WEB SITE ADDRESS:
www.chicagotribune.com/communityrelations

FOUNDED: 1958

AREAS OF INTEREST:
Civic, culture, employee matching gifts and
journalism.

TYPE:
General operating grants; Internships;
Matching gifts; Project/program grants.
Civic: Grants in this program area support
business, nonprofit or educational initiatives.
Grant requests in the civic program area will
be considered by invitation only.

Culture: Grants support cultural organizations
within the Chicago metropolitan area that
foster diverse art or provide educational
programs in the arts for children from
low-income communities.

Journalism: The Foundation strives for
journalistic excellence by building a broad
and diverse pool of journalists to serve
readers in Chicago and around the nation. It
seeks to focus its resources on local and
national programs that will help train
journalists who might otherwise not enter the
field, and help them thrive in newsrooms.
The Foundation provides support in three
categories: (1) internships; (2) training and
education programs and; (3) training and
networking programs for journalism
educators or advisors in colleges within the
Chicago metropolitan area.

PURPOSE:
To promote public knowledge and strengthen
the Chicago metropolitan community by
encouraging journalistic excellence and
diversity, supporting diverse cultural
institutions, and promoting civic efforts; to
provide Chicago Tribune employees the
opportunity to direct the Foundation's
contributions via a matching gift program.

LEGAL BASIS:
Corporate private foundation.

ELIGIBILITY:
All grant requests must fall within the
described geographic and program areas in
order to be considered for either general
support or program support. The Foundation
does not fund individual, capital or
international grants. The grant requests must
be received by the required dates described
in the program area.

GEOGRAPHIC RESTRICTIONS:
City of Chicago, Illinois and the Chicago
metropolitan area.

FINANCIAL DATA:
Amount of support per award: $2,500 to
$5,000.
Total amount of support: Approximately
$330,000 for the year 2010.

REPRESENTATIVE AWARDS:
Civic: $5,000 to Rock for Reading, Chicago,
IL, to distribute books to low-income
communities; Culture: $5,000 to Black
Ensemble Theater Corporation, Chicago, IL,
for African-American theater productions and
education programs in schools; Journalism:
$7,500 to Sports Journalism Institute to
provide summer internships and training for
diverse or female journalism students.

APPLICATION INFORMATION:
The Foundation accepts, but does not require,
the Chicago Area Grant Application Form.
Use the information requested on the
Chicago Area Grant Application Form as a
guide for the proposal. Provide the
information requested on the Form in a two-
to five-page narrative. The following
attachments must be included with the
proposal:
(1) a one-sided, one-page list of one's board
of directors and their business affiliation and
title;
(2) a copy of the most recent IRS tax-exempt
status form;
(3) audited financial statements or Form 990
from the most recent fiscal year;
(4) organization budget for year in which
funding is sought;
(5) sources of support listing which funds

have been committed and;
(6) annual report or other literature on the
organization's programmatic, financial and
strategic accomplishments.

PUBLICATIONS:
Corporate contributions guidelines; annual
report.

STAFF:
Jan Ellen Woelffer, Grant and Charitable
Programs Specialist

BOARD OF DIRECTORS AND OFFICERS:
Tony Hunter, Chairman
Kathleen O'Hara, President
Janice Jacobs
Sheila Solomon

ADDRESS INQUIRIES TO:
Jan Ellen Woelffer, Grant and Charitable
Programs Specialist
(See address above.)

THE CHRISTENSEN FUND [74]

260 Townsend Street
Suite 600
San Francisco, CA 94107
(415) 644-1630
Fax: (415) 644-1670

E-MAIL ADDRESS:
info@christensenfund.org

WEB SITE ADDRESS:
www.christensenfund.org

FOUNDED: 1957

AREAS OF INTEREST:
Supporting organizations working on
biological and cultural diversity.

NAME(S) OF PROGRAMS:
- **African Rift Valley**
- **Central Asia**
- **Global**
- **Greater Southwest**
- **Melanesia**
- **Northern Australia**

TYPE:
Conferences/seminars; Exchange programs;
General operating grants; Project/program
grants; Research grants; Seed money grants;
Technical assistance; Training grants; Travel
grants.

YEAR PROGRAM STARTED: 2003

PURPOSE:
To buttress the indigenous and traditional
stewards of bio-cultural diversity in the
landscapes which have provided their cultural
and ecological heritages.

LEGAL BASIS:
Private, independent foundation.

ELIGIBILITY:
Must have nonprofit 501(c)(3) status or
similar not-for-profit organization based
outside U.S.

GEOGRAPHIC RESTRICTIONS:
Greater southwestern United States and
northwestern Mexico, Northern Australia,
Central Asia; Melanesia, and the Africa Rift
Valley (Southwest Ethiopia/Northern Kenya).

FINANCIAL DATA:
Amount of support per award: Up to
$200,000.
Total amount of support: $11,000,000.

NUMBER OF APPLICANTS MOST RECENT YEAR:
715.

NUMBER OF AWARDS: 161 for the year 2010.

APPLICATION INFORMATION:
Information may be obtained from the Fund's web site.

Duration: Varies.

Deadline: August 31.

TRUSTEES:
C. Diane Christensen, President and Chairperson
Thomas Seligman, Vice President
Kenneth Kirshenbaum, Treasurer
Dr. Kenneth Wilson, Executive Director
Walter Coward, Jr.
Rodolfo Dirzo
Winona LaDuke
Peter Liu
John Robinson
Atossa Soltani
Tara Diann Stein
Michael Nicoll Yahgulanaas

ADDRESS INQUIRIES TO:
Lourdes Inga
Manager of Grants Administration
(See address above.)

THE CHRYSLER FOUNDATION [75]
1000 Chrysler Drive
CIMS 485-13-35
Auburn Hills, MI 48326-2766
(248) 512-2500
Fax: (248) 512-2503

WEB SITE ADDRESS:
thechryslerfoundation.com

FOUNDED: 1953

AREAS OF INTEREST:
Higher education, pre-college education, civic and community affairs, culture and the arts, and public policy/marketplace issues.

TYPE:
Development grants; General operating grants; Project/program grants; Research grants; Scholarships. The Chrysler Foundation Scholarship Program provides scholarships to children of regular, full-time employees of Chrysler LLC subsidiaries operating in the U.S. that contribute to The Chrysler Foundation and its U.S.-based subsidiaries.

YEAR PROGRAM STARTED: 1953

PURPOSE:
To strengthen Chrysler's ability to support and enhance the well-being of the many communities in which the company operates and to provide a means of support for selected national nonprofit organizations.

LEGAL BASIS:
Company-sponsored foundation.

ELIGIBILITY:
Grants are made to nonprofit, tax-exempt, 501(c)(3) educational, civic and cultural organizations primarily in locations where the greatest number of employees of Chrysler LLC subsidiaries live and work, that operate in the U.S. and that contribute to The Chrysler Foundation. Some support is targeted for national organizations as well.

No grants are made to individuals or for endowment funds. The Foundation makes no loans.

Neither the Foundation nor Corporation donates vehicles for on-road use. No capital campaigns (includes funding for building programs, equipment or vehicles).

GEOGRAPHIC RESTRICTIONS:
Arizona, California, Colorado, Florida, Illinois, Indiana, Metropolitan Detroit, Michigan, New York, Ohio, Texas and Washington, DC.

FINANCIAL DATA:
Amount of support per award: Varies.

APPLICATION INFORMATION:
Grants are made by invitation only; unsolicited requests will not be accepted.

Duration: One year. Renewal upon application by invitation.

Deadline: October 1 for decision by year-end. Requests for funding in the next year received after October 1 will not be reviewed until January.

PUBLICATIONS:
Annual report.

OFFICERS:
Jody Trapasso, President and Trustee
Brian G. Glowiak, Vice President and Secretary
Sarah Elliott, Assistant Vice President

TRUSTEES:
Fred Diaz
Scott Garberding
Scott Kunselman
Nancy Rae
Gualberto Ranieri
Jody Trapasso

CITIZENS BANK FOUNDATION [76]
28 State Street
Boston, MA 02109
(617) 994-7702
Fax: (617) 725-5790

E-MAIL ADDRESS:
christine.m.johnson@citizensbank.com

WEB SITE ADDRESS:
www.citizensbank.com

FOUNDED: 1967

AREAS OF INTEREST:
Affordable housing, health and human services, and economic development, including financial literacy.

TYPE:
Charitable grants. Citizens gives priority consideration for charitable grants to programs that:
(1) promote affordable housing;
(2) encourage the development of innovative responses to basic human needs;
(3) encourage community-based services targeted to low- and moderate-income families and individuals;
(4) support community development initiatives that are catalysts for economically distressed areas and;
(5) promote new ways to address issues of economic self-sufficiency.

YEAR PROGRAM STARTED: 1971

PURPOSE:
To sustain and advance the quality of life in the communities in which Citizens Bank operates.

LEGAL BASIS:
Corporate foundation.

ELIGIBILITY:
Funding priority is given to those projects which:
(1) support community-based programs that directly relate to the business of banking;

(2) positively impact low- and moderate-income populations;
(3) are one year in duration;
(4) directly affect the people served;
(5) are multicultural;
(6) show a high likelihood of success and potential to be replicated;
(7) are focused on long-range solutions to broad-based urban issues, including community development or redevelopment activities and;
(8) assist in promoting financial education and credit-service information to the community.

In addition, Citizens generally does not sponsor annual appeals, individuals, single disease/issue information and research organizations, religious organizations, including restoration of church buildings, labor, fraternal and veterans organizations (including fraternal orders of police/firefighters), political organizations or projects, operating deficits, underwriting of conferences and seminars, governmental and quasi-governmental public agencies or organizations, endowment, annual operating support, trips and tours, including transportation costs, payment on bank loans (including loans from Citizens Bank), advertising and fund-raising activities, foundations, historic preservation or public or private educational institutions.

GEOGRAPHIC RESTRICTIONS:
Connecticut, Delaware, Massachusetts, New Hampshire, New Jersey, New York, Pennsylvania, Rhode Island and Vermont.

FINANCIAL DATA:
Amount of support per award: Varies.
Total amount of support: Varies.

APPLICATION INFORMATION:
Information is available online.

Duration: Typically one year.

Deadline: It will take up to eight weeks for a grant request to be reviewed by the appropriate State Contributions Committee. A site visit and additional information may be required prior to a final determination.

You will be notified of a grant approval or denial by letter.

BOARD OF DIRECTORS:
Ellen Alemany, Chairperson

ADDRESS INQUIRIES TO:
Citizens Bank Foundation
(See address above.)

*SPECIAL STIPULATIONS:
Grants are made only in states where Citizens Bank operates.

LIZ CLAIBORNE FOUNDATION [77]
1441 Broadway, 16th Floor
New York, NY 10018
(212) 626-5704

WEB SITE ADDRESS:
www.lizclaiborneinc.com/web/guest/lizclaibornefoundation

FOUNDED: 1981

AREAS OF INTEREST:
Women's programs only, specifically economic independence.

TYPE:
Challenge/matching grants; General operating grants; Matching gifts; Project/program grants; Seed money grants; Technical assistance.

YEAR PROGRAM STARTED: 1981

LEGAL BASIS:
Corporate foundation.

ELIGIBILITY:
Organizations classified as 501(c)(3) by the
IRS can apply. Individuals and religious,
political and fraternal organizations are
ineligible.

GEOGRAPHIC RESTRICTIONS:
Los Angeles County, California; Hudson
County, New Jersey; New York, New York;
Butler County, Ohio.

FINANCIAL DATA:
Amount of support per award: $10,000 to
$50,000.

Matching fund requirements: 1:1; $25
minimum, $2,000 maximum to one
organization per employee per year; $10,000
annual total per employee; includes arts,
education, health, human services and the
environment.

REPRESENTATIVE AWARDS:
$30,000 to New York City Employment
Training Coalition, New York, New York;
$50,000 to WomenRising, Jersey City, NJ;
$25,000 to Women in Non Traditional
Employment Roles, Los Angeles, CA.

APPLICATION INFORMATION:
Proposals must include the following:
(1) statement of goals, history and
accomplishments;
(2) statement of purpose or objective of
proposal;
(3) description of how the program or project
is to be carried out, and the qualifications of
the staff involved; number of clients to be
served, and specific, quantifiable outcomes
projected for those clients in the next year as
a result of the program or project;
(4) amount requested;
(5) current organization-wide budget with
proposed project's budget, showing both
expenses and income; also include the
following year's budgets if proposal is
submitted within three months of the
organization's new fiscal year;
(6) most recent audited financial statements;
(7) for both the current and previous year,
list of applicable funding sources, public and
private, and amounts contributed, including
(for the current year) those pending approval;
for projects, show the amount supplied from
the organization's general funds;
(8) number of professional and support staff,
and their titles;
(9) list of board members, with their
affiliations and;
(10) copy of the U.S. Department of the
Treasury letter establishing the organization's
501(c)(3) status.
Duration: One year. Grants are renewable.
Deadline: Applications are accepted
throughout the year.

PUBLICATIONS:
Application guidelines.

IRS IDENTIFICATION NUMBER: 13-3060673

ADDRESS INQUIRIES TO:
Sheila M. Renovitch, Director
(See address above.)

*SPECIAL STIPULATIONS:
The Foundation does not accept proposals for
programs relating to the arts or the
environment. No scholarships (except for
children of Liz Claiborne Inc. employees) or
courtesy advertising.

EDNA MCCONNELL CLARK FOUNDATION [78]
415 Madison Avenue, 10th Floor
New York, NY 10017
(212) 551-9100
Fax: (212) 421-9325

E-MAIL ADDRESS:
info@emcf.org

WEB SITE ADDRESS:
www.emcf.org

FOUNDED: 1970

AREAS OF INTEREST:
Youth development.

NAME(S) OF PROGRAMS:
● **Youth Development Fund**

TYPE:
General operating grants. Business planning
grants. Focus areas for the Youth
Development Fund are academic
achievement, preparation for work force, and
avoidance of risky behavior.

PURPOSE:
To support efforts by high-performing
nonprofit organizations to increase their
capacity to serve more kids (ages 9 to 24)
with proven programs during the non-school
hours.

LEGAL BASIS:
Private foundation.

GEOGRAPHIC RESTRICTIONS:
United States.

FINANCIAL DATA:
Amount of support per award: Varies.

COOPERATIVE FUNDING PROGRAMS: When
foundation interests are shared with other
organizations.

APPLICATION INFORMATION:
Organizations need to complete survey
online.
Duration: Varies.
Deadline: No official deadlines. Board meets
four times a year, plus standing committee
meetings.

PUBLICATIONS:
Annual report.

IRS IDENTIFICATION NUMBER: 23-7047034

OFFICERS:
Nancy Roob, President
Ralph Stefano, Vice President, Director of
Finance and Administration
Woodrow McCutchen, Vice President, Senior
Portfolio Manager

TRUSTEES:
James McConnell Clark, Jr., Chairman
H. Lawrence Clark
Alice F. Emerson
Janice C. Kreamer
Theodore E. Martin
James E. Moltz
Nancy Roob
Joyce Shields
Ellen Shuman

ADDRESS INQUIRIES TO:
Albert Chung
Director of Communications Operations
(See address above.)

*PLEASE NOTE:
The Foundation does not accept unsolicited
proposals.

THE CLIFFS FOUNDATION [79]
1100 Superior Avenue
Cleveland, OH 44114-2589
(216) 694-5700
Fax: (216) 694-4880

WEB SITE ADDRESS:
www.cliffsnaturalresources.com

FOUNDED: 1962

AREAS OF INTEREST:
Education, health, welfare, civic affairs,
cultural affairs and the arts.

TYPE:
General operating grants.

PURPOSE:
To enhance the quality of life of the
Company's employees and communities in
which the Company operates.

ELIGIBILITY:
Nonprofit organizations may apply.

GEOGRAPHIC RESTRICTIONS:
Adger, Alabama; Upper Peninsula of
Michigan; northeastern Minnesota; Cleveland,
Ohio; and Pineville, West Virginia.

FINANCIAL DATA:
Amount of support per award: $250 to
$5,000.
Matching fund requirements: Education only.
Employees, retired officers and active
directors are eligible.

APPLICATION INFORMATION:
All requests for support must be in writing.
Duration: One year.
Deadline: Applications accepted throughout
the year.

PUBLICATIONS:
Guidelines.

STAFF:
Dana W. Byrne, Vice President and Assistant
Treasurer

ADDRESS INQUIRIES TO:
Dana W. Byrne
Vice President and Assistant Treasurer
(See address above.)

*SPECIAL STIPULATIONS:
No consideration will be given to any
solicitation made by telephone or e-mail.

COASTAL BEND COMMUNITY FOUNDATION [80]
600 Leopard Street, Suite 1716
Corpus Christi, TX 78401
(361) 882-9745
Fax: (361) 882-2865

E-MAIL ADDRESS:
kwilliams@cbcfoundation.org

WEB SITE ADDRESS:
www.cbcfoundation.org

FOUNDED: 1981

AREAS OF INTEREST:
Arts, children and youth, community
development, crime prevention, elderly,
environment, health, social welfare, education
and human services.

TYPE:
Capital grants; Challenge/matching grants;
Development grants; General operating
grants; Project/program grants; Scholarships;
Seed money grants; Training grants.

YEAR PROGRAM STARTED: 1981

PURPOSE:
To improve the quality of life in the Coastal Bend area.

LEGAL BASIS:
Community foundation.

ELIGIBILITY:
Grants are made to organizations that have tax-exempt status under Section 501(c)(3) of the Internal Revenue Code. No grants are made to individuals.

GEOGRAPHIC RESTRICTIONS:
Aransas, Bee, Jim Wells, Kleberg, Nueces, Refugio and San Patricio counties, Texas.

FINANCIAL DATA:
Amount of support per award: Varies.

Total amount of support: $3,238,968 for the year 2009.

Matching fund requirements: Determined on individual basis.

COOPERATIVE FUNDING PROGRAMS: Coastal Bend Day of Giving.

NUMBER OF APPLICANTS MOST RECENT YEAR: 1,594.

NUMBER OF AWARDS: 1,321.

APPLICATION INFORMATION:
Organizations should submit application with requested documentation by the application deadline. Applications that do not conform to the required format will not be considered.

Duration: Must be completed in the following calendar year.

Deadline: Deadlines are posted online.

IRS IDENTIFICATION NUMBER: 74-2190039

ADDRESS INQUIRIES TO:
Karen W. Selim
President and Chief Executive Officer
(See address above.)

THE COCKRELL FOUNDATION [81]

1000 Main Street
Suite 3250
Houston, TX 77002
(713) 209-7500 ext. 7505
Fax: (713) 209-7599

E-MAIL ADDRESS:
foundation@cockrell.com

WEB SITE ADDRESS:
www.cockrell.com

FOUNDED: 1957

AREAS OF INTEREST:
Education, arts, health care, youth activities and medical research.

TYPE:
Capital grants; Fellowships; General operating grants; Professorships; Project/program grants; Scholarships.

YEAR PROGRAM STARTED: 1966

PURPOSE:
To provide financial support for charitable organizations in the Houston area in support of education, health, civic, religious and social services.

LEGAL BASIS:
Private foundation.

ELIGIBILITY:
Fellowships, professorships and scholarships to the University of Texas School of Engineering only.

In general, the Foundation gives support for annual and capital campaigns, building funds, endowment funds, general purposes, matching funds, and special projects. Grants are made only to nonprofit, tax-exempt organizations. To be eligible, an organization must have a determination letter from the IRS indicating that it is an organization described in Section 501(c)(3) of the Internal Revenue Code and is not a private foundation within the meaning of Section 509(a) of the code.

GEOGRAPHIC RESTRICTIONS:
Primarily Houston, Texas.

FINANCIAL DATA:
Amount of support per award: Varies.

Total amount of support: $7,299,787 in grants for the year 2009.

Matching fund requirements: Successful fund-raising per match requirement.

NUMBER OF AWARDS: 35 grants for the year 2009.

REPRESENTATIVE AWARDS:
$50,000 to Boy Scouts of America, Sam Houston Area Council; $3,077,806 to University of Texas Engineering Foundation; $15,000 to Free Enterprise Institute; $20,000 to M.D. Anderson Cancer Center.

APPLICATION INFORMATION:
The Foundation supplies no application form. Applicants should submit a written description, no longer than five pages, of how the grant money will be used, covering the following items:
(1) description of the need or problem;
(2) a simple statement of what is hoped to be accomplished;
(3) a budget for the project, giving the total cost, the amount raised to date toward the project or program, the sources from which it has come, including private, religious organizations and/or government sources, and, in particular, the amount contributed by the individuals on the Board of Directors;
(4) plans for raising any uncovered balance;
(5) an explanation of why it is necessary to seek outside support;
(6) the current status of the project-where it stands now and how long it will take to complete;
(7) the specific sum being requested of the Foundation;
(8) plans for putting continuing projects on a self-sustaining basis and an estimate of when this will occur;
(9) name and address of tax-exempt organization which will be the recipient if a donation is made and a copy of the exemption letter from the U.S. Treasury Department;
(10) copy of the organization's current annual budget;
(11) copy of the organization's latest IRS-990;
(12) copy of the organization's latest audited financials;
(13) a list of the members of the Board of Directors;
(14) a list of the officers of the organization and;
(15) an Executive Summary Sheet.
Duration: One year. Occasionally multiple years.

PUBLICATIONS:
The Cockrell Foundation Fact Sheet.

IRS IDENTIFICATION NUMBER: 74-6076993

OFFICERS AND DIRECTORS:
Ernest H. Cockrell, President and Director

M. Nancy Williams, Executive Vice President
Milton T. Graves, Vice President and Director
Wendy W. Randolph, Assistant Secretary and Treasurer
David A. Cockrell, Director
Ernest D. Cockrell, Director
Janet S. Cockrell, Director
Carol Cockrell Curran, Director
Richard B. Curran, Director
J. Webb Jennings, III, Director
Laura Jennings Turner, Director

ADDRESS INQUIRIES TO:
M. Nancy Williams
Executive Vice President
(See address above.)

THE OGDEN CODMAN TRUST [82]

c/o Rackemann, Sawyer & Brewster
160 Federal Street, 15th Floor
Boston, MA 02110-1700
(617) 951-1108
Fax: (617) 542-7437

E-MAIL ADDRESS:
smonahan@rackemann.com

FOUNDED: 1968

AREAS OF INTEREST:
Environment, conservation, historic preservation, cultural, health and social services in the town of Lincoln, MA.

TYPE:
Project/program grants. Support for special programs.

PURPOSE:
To improve the quality of life in Lincoln.

LEGAL BASIS:
Private independent foundation.

ELIGIBILITY:
The Foundation does not generally fund operating expenses.

GEOGRAPHIC RESTRICTIONS:
Lincoln, Massachusetts.

FINANCIAL DATA:
Amount of support per award: $2,000 to $50,000.

Total amount of support: Approximately $156,400 for the year 2010.

Matching fund requirements: Case-by-case basis.

NUMBER OF APPLICANTS MOST RECENT YEAR: 10 for the year 2010.

NUMBER OF AWARDS: 10 for the year 2010.

REPRESENTATIVE AWARDS:
Town of Lincoln; Codman Community Farm.

APPLICATION INFORMATION:
Contact Grants Coordinator prior to submitting an application.

Duration: Varies.

Deadline: Quarterly.

PUBLICATIONS:
Application guidelines.

TRUSTEES:
Daniel W. Fawcett
William B. Tyler, Esq.
Walter G. Van Dorn

ADDRESS INQUIRIES TO:
Susan T. Monahan, Grants Coordinator
(See e-mail address above.)

THE GEORGE W. CODRINGTON CHARITABLE FOUNDATION [83]

3900 Key Center
127 Public Square
Cleveland, OH 44114-1291
(216) 566-5699
Fax: (216) 566-5800

E-MAIL ADDRESS:
craig.martahus@thompsonhine.com

FOUNDED: 1955

AREAS OF INTEREST:
Humanitarian projects.

TYPE:
Capital grants; Challenge/matching grants; Endowments; General operating grants; Matching gifts. Annual grants to public charitable or educational projects.

YEAR PROGRAM STARTED: 1955

PURPOSE:
To assist, encourage and promote the well-being of mankind, regardless of race, color or creed.

LEGAL BASIS:
Private foundation.

ELIGIBILITY:
The Foundation's supportive services are limited to public charitable or educational projects. No grants are made to individuals.

GEOGRAPHIC RESTRICTIONS:
Cuyahoga County, Ohio and immediately adjacent areas.

FINANCIAL DATA:
Amount of support per award: $500 to $200,000.
Total amount of support: Varies.

REPRESENTATIVE AWARDS:
$8,000 to the Cleveland Society for the Blind; $3,000 to the Lyric Opera Cleveland; $60,000 to the Free Medical Clinic of Greater Cleveland.

APPLICATION INFORMATION:
Applications should be directed to The Supervisory Board of the Foundation. The application should state fully but briefly the amount requested, the need for the grant, the area served by the applicant, a brief history of the applicant's organization, description of the applicant's contributions to the area and listing of the applicant's officers and trustees. Original plus two copies should be submitted.
Deadline: Pending applications are considered at meetings of the Supervisory Board held in April, June, September and December.

PUBLICATIONS:
Annual report.

IRS IDENTIFICATION NUMBER: 34-6507457

SUPERVISORY BOARD:
Craig R. Martahus, Esq., Chairman
William R. Seelbach, Vice Chairman
Raymond T. Sawyer, Esq., Secretary

ADDRESS INQUIRIES TO:
Craig R. Martahus, Esq.
Chairman, Supervisory Board
(See address above.)

THE COLEMAN FOUNDATION, INC. [84]

651 West Washington Boulevard
Suite 306
Chicago, IL 60661-2134
(312) 902-7120
Fax: (312) 902-7124

E-MAIL ADDRESS:
info@colemanfoundation.org

WEB SITE ADDRESS:
www.colemanfoundation.org

FOUNDED: 1951

AREAS OF INTEREST:
Entrepreneurship education, cancer care, and developmental disability services.

TYPE:
Capital grants; Challenge/matching grants; Conferences/seminars; Project/program grants. The major areas of grantmaking include:
(1) education, with a strong emphasis on entrepreneurship education (national in scope, with focus in Chicago);
(2) cancer care and treatment in the Chicago metropolitan area and;
(3) services for the disabled in the Chicago metropolitan area, with a strong emphasis on developmental disabilities.

ELIGIBILITY:
Grants are only made to IRS-certified tax-exempt nonprofit organizations, 501(c)(3) or 509(a)(1), (2) or (3) and that are not private foundations. Funding is prohibited to individuals, for-profit businesses, advertising books and tickets. General solicitations and annual appeals will not be considered.

Only programs within the U.S. will be considered.

GEOGRAPHIC RESTRICTIONS:
Primarily metropolitan Chicago and other select parts of the Midwest.

FINANCIAL DATA:
Amount of support per award: Varies.

NUMBER OF AWARDS: Approximately 100.

APPLICATION INFORMATION:
A two-page letter of inquiry should be sent by the applicant which includes the following:
(1) brief description of the organization;
(2) synopsis of the program to be proposed;
(3) clear statement of program/grant objectives and how they will be evaluated;
(4) estimate of the size grant to be proposed or range of proposed funding;
(5) statement of how the program/project will be sustained following the grant period and;
(6) contact name and information, including e-mail address of the project manager, for further communication.

Brochures, video tapes, CDs and other attachments should not be sent with the letter of inquiry. Any such attachments will not be considered at this stage of review.
Deadline: Letters of Inquiry are accepted on a continuing basis.

ADDRESS INQUIRIES TO:
Rosa Berardi, Program Officer
(See address above.)

THE COLLINS FOUNDATION [85]

1618 S.W. First Avenue
Suite 505
Portland, OR 97201
(503) 227-7171
Fax: (503) 295-3794

E-MAIL ADDRESS:
information@collinsfoundation.org

WEB SITE ADDRESS:
www.collinsfoundation.org

FOUNDED: 1947

AREAS OF INTEREST:
Quality of life issues. Projects that will have an immediate and long-term impact on life in the community.

TYPE:
Challenge/matching grants; Project/program grants. Grants made to agencies exclusively in the state of Oregon to improve, enrich and give greater expression to its religious, educational, cultural and scientific endeavors. Also, to assist in improving the quality of life in the state.

YEAR PROGRAM STARTED: 1947

PURPOSE:
To help fund programs or projects that will make life better in the community.

LEGAL BASIS:
Private, nonprofit foundation.

ELIGIBILITY:
The Foundation is organized in the state of Oregon for projects within the state. All applicant agencies must be tax-exempt, as established by the Treasury Department of the United States. No support is given to private foundations.

GEOGRAPHIC RESTRICTIONS:
Agencies must be domiciled in Oregon.

FINANCIAL DATA:
Amount of support per award: Varies.
Matching fund requirements: The Foundation looks favorably on grants which must be matched.

APPLICATION INFORMATION:
A folder describing application information is available on request.
Duration: Varies.
Deadline: Deadline is not specified. Awards are announced periodically throughout the year.

OFFICERS:
Truman W. Collins, President
Cynthia G. Addams, Executive Vice President
Ralph Bolliger, Vice President
Maribeth W. Collins, Vice President
Cherida C. Smith, Vice President
Timothy R. Bishop, Treasurer

BOARD OF TRUSTEES:
Ralph Bolliger
Maribeth W. Collins
Truman W. Collins
Lee Diane Collins-Vest
Jerry E. Hudson
Cherida C. Smith

ADDRESS INQUIRIES TO:
Cynthia G. Addams, Executive Vice President
(See address above.)

COMMUNITIES FOUNDATION OF TEXAS, INC. [86]

Grants Department
5500 Caruth Haven Lane
Dallas, TX 75225
(214) 750-4222
Fax: (214) 750-4210

E-MAIL ADDRESS:
grants@cftexas.org

WEB SITE ADDRESS:
www.cftexas.org

AREAS OF INTEREST:
Arts, community improvement, disaster relief, education, health, housing, religion, scientific research, social services and youth.

TYPE:
Project/program grants.

YEAR PROGRAM STARTED: 1953

LEGAL BASIS:
Public charity.

FINANCIAL DATA:
Amount of support per award: Varies.
Total amount of support: Varies.

APPLICATION INFORMATION:
Duration: One year.

ADDRESS INQUIRIES TO:
Grants Processing
(See address above.)

THE COMMUNITY FOUNDATION [87]

7501 Boulders View Drive, Suite 110
Richmond, VA 23225
(804) 330-7400
Fax: (804) 330-5992

E-MAIL ADDRESS:
info@tcfrichmond.org

WEB SITE ADDRESS:
www.tcfrichmond.org

FOUNDED: 1968

AREAS OF INTEREST:
Basic human needs for children and families, child and youth development, community and economic development, community enrichment and promoting philanthropy/strengthening nonprofit capacity.

NAME(S) OF PROGRAMS:
● **Strengthening Families - Strengthening Communities**

TYPE:
Awards/prizes; Capital grants; Challenge/matching grants; Conferences/seminars; Development grants; General operating grants; Project/program grants; Research grants; Scholarships; Seed money grants; Technical assistance; Training grants.

YEAR PROGRAM STARTED: 1995

PURPOSE:
To give financial assistance to worthwhile charitable organizations serving people in the community.

LEGAL BASIS:
Community foundation.

ELIGIBILITY:
Proposals will be accepted from charitable organizations which serve the city of Richmond, outlying counties or the Tri-Cities.

GEOGRAPHIC RESTRICTIONS:
Richmond, Virginia metropolitan area and the Tri-Cities, Colonial Heights, Goochland, Hopewell and Petersburg.

FINANCIAL DATA:
Amount of support per award: $5,000 to $100,000. Average $25,000.
Total amount of support: $3,700,000 for the year 2008.

NUMBER OF APPLICANTS MOST RECENT YEAR:
379 organizations for the year 2008.

NUMBER OF AWARDS: 342 for the year 2008.

REPRESENTATIVE AWARDS:
$50,000 to Central Virginia Food Bank to support the new community kitchen; $92,500 to Friends Association for Children to support the Music Education Program; $25,000 to the Phoenix Project to support the University-Community Partnership Program in Petersburg.

APPLICATION INFORMATION:
Send letters of intent (maximum two pages) prior to submission of full proposal (by invitation only). Full proposal requires board list, 501(c)(3) tax determination letter, project and operating budgets, financial statements or 990 and grant form. Grantees must submit an outcome evaluation plan form, as well as a signed annual quid pro quo compliance statement.
Duration: Usually one year. Renewal possible.
Deadline: May 5 and November 5. Announcement in September and March.

PUBLICATIONS:
Annual report; policy and guidelines for grant requests.

IRS IDENTIFICATION NUMBER: 23-7009135

OFFICERS:
John Sherman, Chairperson

ADDRESS INQUIRIES TO:
Susan H. Hallett or
Elaine Summerfield
Program Officers
(See address above.)

COMMUNITY FOUNDATION FOR SOUTHEAST MICHIGAN [88]

333 West Fort Street
Suite 2010
Detroit, MI 48226
(313) 961-6675
Fax: (313) 961-2886

E-MAIL ADDRESS:
cfsem@cfsem.org

WEB SITE ADDRESS:
www.cfsem.org

FOUNDED: 1984

AREAS OF INTEREST:
Environment, health, arts and culture, economic development, human services and civic affairs.

TYPE:
Development grants; Project/program grants; Seed money grants.

LEGAL BASIS:
Public Foundation.

ELIGIBILITY:
No grants for buildings, equipment, religious programs, fund-raising, individuals, conferences or annual meetings.

GEOGRAPHIC RESTRICTIONS:
The seven counties of Southeast Michigan: Livingston, Macomb, Monroe, Oakland, St. Clair, Washtenaw and Wayne.

FINANCIAL DATA:
Amount of support per award: Varies.
Total amount of support: In 2010, more than $52,000,000 in grants was awarded. Since inception, CFSEM has awarded more than $450,000,000.

NUMBER OF AWARDS: Nearly 2,900 grants were awarded for the year 2010.

APPLICATION INFORMATION:
Telephone Foundation to discuss proposal before submitting application.
Duration: One year.
Deadline: Generally quarterly: March, June, September and December.

PUBLICATIONS:
Annual report, newsletters - available at the web site.

STAFF:
Mariam C. Noland, President
Elizabeth C. Sullivan, Vice President, Community Investment
Karen L. Leppanen, Vice President, Finance and Administration
Robin D. Ferriby, Vice President, Philanthropic Services
Theresa Fraley, Communications Director and Special Assistant to the President
Randall Ross, Manager, Philanthropic Services
Katie G. Brisson, Senior Program Officer
Christopher B. Smith, Program Officer

OFFICERS OF THE TRUSTEES:
Allan D. Gilmour, Chairman
Joseph L. Hudson, Jr., Founding Chairperson
Alfred R. Glancy, III, Vice Chairman
Alan E. Schwartz, Vice Chairman
Barbara C. Van Dusen, Vice Chairman
Michael T. Monahan, Treasurer
W. Frank Fountain, Secretary
Vivian Day Stroh, Program and Distribution Committee Chair

ADDRESS INQUIRIES TO:
Mariam C. Noland, President
(See address above.)

COMMUNITY FOUNDATION OF DELAWARE COUNTY

3954 North Hampton Drive
Powell, OH 43065
(614) 764-2332
Fax: (614) 764-2333

E-MAIL ADDRESS:
cfdc@midohio.net

WEB SITE ADDRESS:
www.delawarecf.org

TYPE:
Scholarships.

See entry 1304 for full listing.

COMMUNITY FOUNDATION OF EASTERN CONNECTICUT

147 State Street
New London, CT 06320
(860) 442-3572
Fax: (860) 442-0584

E-MAIL ADDRESS:
jennob@cfect.org

WEB SITE ADDRESS:
www.cfect.org

TYPE:
General operating grants; Project/program grants; Scholarships.

See entry 1305 for full listing.

COMMUNITY FOUNDATION OF GREATER MEMPHIS [89]

1900 Union Avenue
Memphis, TN 38104
(901) 728-4600
Fax: (901) 722-0010

E-MAIL ADDRESS:
mwolowicz@cfgm.org

WEB SITE ADDRESS:
www.cfgm.org

FOUNDED: 1969

AREAS OF INTEREST:
Grants administered for charitable purposes
in metropolitan Memphis.

NAME(S) OF PROGRAMS:
- **Nonprofit Capacity Building Grants**
- **Scholarship Funds**

TYPE:
Challenge/matching grants; Project/program
grants; Scholarships; Technical assistance.

YEAR PROGRAM STARTED: 1974

PURPOSE:
To provide support for the benefit of the
geographic area that the Foundation serves;
to strengthen the community through
philanthropy.

LEGAL BASIS:
Community foundation.

ELIGIBILITY:
Applicants must be charitable and nonprofit
under IRS regulations, holding a 501(c)(3)
tax-exempt status. Applicants must be located
in the geographic area that the Foundation
serves.

GEOGRAPHIC RESTRICTIONS:
Metropolitan Memphis, Tennessee.

FINANCIAL DATA:
Amount of support per award: $250 to
$75,000.
Total amount of support: $500,000 for the
fiscal year 2011-12.
Matching fund requirements: Stipulated with
some grant awards.

NUMBER OF APPLICANTS MOST RECENT YEAR:
Varies.

NUMBER OF AWARDS: Approximately 30 for the
fiscal year 2010-11.

REPRESENTATIVE AWARDS:
Community Grants: $25,000 to South
Memphis Alliance, which, in partnership with
Memphis Area Neighborhood Development
Corporation and the Works, Inc., launched a
community-based organizing project to
address issues of community organization in
the urban neighborhoods of South Memphis.
Nonprofit Capacity Building Grants: $20,000
to Synergy Foundation, Inc., Bridge Grant to
help Synergy regain financial stability.
Research and Initiatives: $250,000 to Seedco
for "EarnBenefits," a three-year
demonstration project that assists low-wage
workers in retaining their jobs and continuing
to be even more productive members of
society.

APPLICATION INFORMATION:
Grant guidelines and application forms are
available on request.
Duration: One year. Some grants are
awarded on a multiyear basis.
Deadline: Varies.

PUBLICATIONS:
Newsletters; annual report.

IRS IDENTIFICATION NUMBER: 58-1723645

ADDRESS INQUIRIES TO:
Melissa Wolowicz
Director of Grants and Initiatives
(See address above.)

THE COMMUNITY FOUNDATION OF MOUNT VERNON & KNOX COUNTY [90]

One South Main Street
Mount Vernon, OH 43050
(740) 392-3270
Fax: (740) 399-5296

E-MAIL ADDRESS:
sbarone@mvkcfoundation.org

WEB SITE ADDRESS:
www.mvkcfoundation.org

FOUNDED: 1944

AREAS OF INTEREST:
New projects in educational, charitable and
civic fields.

TYPE:
Capital grants; Challenge/matching grants;
Matching gifts; Project/program grants;
Scholarships; Seed money grants.

YEAR PROGRAM STARTED: 1944

PURPOSE:
To improve the quality of life for the people
of Mount Vernon and Knox County, OH.

LEGAL BASIS:
Nonprofit, community foundation.

ELIGIBILITY:
Grants from unrestricted funds generally
limited to projects in Knox County, OH.

GEOGRAPHIC RESTRICTIONS:
Knox County, Ohio.

FINANCIAL DATA:
Amount of support per award: Varies.
Total amount of support: $750,000.

REPRESENTATIVE AWARDS:
$65,000 to Central Ohio Technical College;
$65,000 to Mount Vernon Nazarene
University; $50,000 to YMCA of Mount
Vernon; $45,000 to Interchurch Social
Services.

APPLICATION INFORMATION:
Application forms are available online.
Personal presentations only at invitation of
Distribution Committee.

PUBLICATIONS:
Annual report.

IRS IDENTIFICATION NUMBER: 23-7002871

BOARD OF DIRECTORS:
Bruce Hawkins, Chairman
Douglas Brenneman, Vice Chairman
Sally Nelson, Treasurer
Robert L. Rauzi, Secretary
R. Leroy Bumpus
Terry Divelbiss
Marc Hawk
Gene Jackson
Dr. Amy Murnen
Marsha Rinehart
Karen Buchwald Wright
Gordon Yance

ADDRESS INQUIRIES TO:
Sam Barone, Executive Director
(See address above.)

COMMUNITY FOUNDATION OF THE EASTERN SHORE

1324 Belmont Avenue, Suite 401
Salisbury, MD 21804
(410) 742-9911
Fax: (410) 742-6638

E-MAIL ADDRESS:
cfes@cfes.org

WEB SITE ADDRESS:
www.cfes.org

TYPE:
Awards/prizes; Challenge/matching grants;
Demonstration grants; Project/program
grants; Scholarships; Seed money grants;
Technical assistance; Training grants.

See entry 1319 for full listing.

THE COMMUNITY FOUNDATION OF THE HOLLAND/ZEELAND AREA [91]

70 West 8th Street
Suite 100
Holland, MI 49423
(616) 396-6590
Fax: (616) 396-3573

E-MAIL ADDRESS:
info@cfhz.org

WEB SITE ADDRESS:
www.cfhz.org

FOUNDED: 1951

AREAS OF INTEREST:
Education, the arts, recreation, community
development, the needs of youth and the
elderly, and health and human services.

TYPE:
Capital grants; Matching gifts;
Project/program grants; Scholarships; Seed
money grants.

YEAR PROGRAM STARTED: 1951

PURPOSE:
To make the greater Holland Zeeland Area a
better place in which to live and work by
enhancing the quality of life for all its
citizens.

LEGAL BASIS:
Corporation and public charity, 509(a)(1) and
170(b)(1)(A)(vi).

ELIGIBILITY:
Grants are made to organizations that have
tax-exempt status under Section 501(c)(3) of
the Internal Revenue Code or governmental
agencies. No grants are made to individuals.
Nonsectarian religious programs may apply.

GEOGRAPHIC RESTRICTIONS:
Holland and Zeeland, Michigan area only.

FINANCIAL DATA:
Amount of support per award: $500 to
$15,000.

NUMBER OF APPLICANTS MOST RECENT YEAR:
78.

NUMBER OF AWARDS: 64 for the year 2009.

REPRESENTATIVE AWARDS:
Community Action House; Zeeland Historical
Society; Latin Americans United for
Progress; Outdoor Discovery Center.

APPLICATION INFORMATION:
Grant applicants are strongly encouraged to
call the Foundation to discuss a proposal
prior to submitting an application.

Completed scholarship applications must be
submitted to the high school guidance office.
Guidance officers will provide the application
materials and an official transcript to the
Foundation. Applicant should check with the
counseling office for their internal deadline.
Duration: One year.

PUBLICATIONS:
Annual report; application guidelines.

IRS IDENTIFICATION NUMBER: 38-6095283

STAFF:
Elizabeth Kidd, Program Director

ADDRESS INQUIRIES TO:
Program Director
(See address above.)

THE COMMUNITY FOUNDATION OF WESTERN NORTH CAROLINA [92]

P.O. Box 1888
Asheville, NC 28802
(828) 254-4960
Fax: (828) 251-2258

E-MAIL ADDRESS:
info@cfwnc.org

WEB SITE ADDRESS:
www.cfwnc.org

FOUNDED: 1978

AREAS OF INTEREST:
Economic development, assisting people in
need, planned development, and livable
communities.

TYPE:
Project/program grants; Scholarships.
Program areas:
(1) assisting people in need;
(2) building communities and economic
vitality;
(3) improving educational opportunities;
(4) promoting quality health;
(5) enhancing the environment and;
(6) advancing the arts.

YEAR PROGRAM STARTED: 1978

PURPOSE:
To promote philanthropy; to build mountain
communities in western North Carolina.

ELIGIBILITY:
501(c)(3) required for grants. Eligibility
varies by program.

GEOGRAPHIC RESTRICTIONS:
Western North Carolina.

FINANCIAL DATA:
Total amount of support: $346,500 in
scholarships, $1,774,457 in competitive
grants and $8,904,040 in donor advised
grants for fiscal year 2009-10.

NUMBER OF AWARDS: 220 Competitive Grants
and 165 Scholarships for the year 2009-10.

APPLICATION INFORMATION:
Duration: Varies.

PUBLICATIONS:
Good Works, quarterly newsletter; annual
report.

ADDRESS INQUIRIES TO:
Virginia Dollar, Program Administrator
(See address above.)

COMPTON FOUNDATION, INC. [93]

255 Shoreline Drive, Suite 540
Redwood City, CA 94065
(650) 508-1181
Fax: (650) 508-1191

WEB SITE ADDRESS:
www.comptonfoundation.org

FOUNDED: 1946

AREAS OF INTEREST:
Peace and security, environment and
sustainability, population and reproductive
health, family advisory board and campaign
finance.

TYPE:
Project/program grants.

PURPOSE:
To foster human and ecological security by
addressing contemporary threats to these
inalienable rights; to support responsible
stewardship that respects the rights of future
generations to a balanced and healthy
ecology, both personal and global, allowing
for the full richness of human experience.

ELIGIBILITY:
Organizations classified as 501(c)(3) by the
IRS. Individuals and religious organizations
are ineligible.

FINANCIAL DATA:
Amount of support per award: Varies.
Total amount of support: $4,225,628 for the
year 2010.

APPLICATION INFORMATION:
Application procedures are available online.
Duration: One year. Grants are renewable.
Deadline: Varies.

PUBLICATIONS:
Environmental and Social Sustainability
Policy brochure; Grant Highlights (both
available on web site).

STAFF:
Ellen Friedman, Executive Director
Roger Fuse Brown, Director of Grants
Management and Investment Accounting
Deborah K. Daughtry, Director of
Communications and Office Management
Jennifer L. Sokolove, Senior Program Officer
for the Environment and Family Advisory
Board
Nancy C. Flynn-Silva, Grants Management
Associate and Peace and Security Associate
Nicole Lopez-Hagen, Program Assistant

BOARD OF DIRECTORS:
Rebecca DiDomenico, President
Vanessa Compton, Vice President
Marty Krasney, Treasurer
W. Danforth Compton, Secretary
Betty L. Farrell
J. Martin Goebel
Stephen Perry
Steven M. Riskin
Terry Tempest Williams

ADDRESS INQUIRIES TO:
Deborah K. Daughtry, Director of
Communications and Office Management
(See address above.)

*SPECIAL STIPULATIONS:
The Foundation does not accept proposals
sent by fax or e-mail.

THE CONNELLY FOUNDATION [94]

One Tower Bridge, Suite 1450
West Conshohocken, PA 19428
(610) 834-3222
Fax: (610) 834-0866

E-MAIL ADDRESS:
eawilcox@connellyfdn.org

WEB SITE ADDRESS:
www.connellyfdn.org

FOUNDED: 1955

AREAS OF INTEREST:
Educational, civic and cultural institutions,
health with emphasis on human services. A
significant portion of funding is directed
toward organizations affiliated with the
Catholic Church.

TYPE:
Capital grants; General operating grants;
Project/program grants; Scholarships;
Technical assistance.

PURPOSE:
To enhance the quality of life in the
Delaware Valley.

LEGAL BASIS:
Private foundation.

ELIGIBILITY:
No grants to individuals, political or national
organizations or other foundations, nor does
the Foundation respond to annual appeals or
general letters of solicitation. Foundation
guidelines restrict funding any organization
more than once during a 12-month period.
Applicants who have received previous grants
from the Foundation should submit final
reports under separate cover.

GEOGRAPHIC RESTRICTIONS:
Camden, New Jersey; Bucks, Chester,
Delaware and Montgomery counties and city
of Philadelphia, Pennsylvania.

FINANCIAL DATA:
Amount of support per award: $5,000 to
$50,000.
Total amount of support: $9,565,058 for the
year 2009.

NUMBER OF AWARDS: 528.

APPLICATION INFORMATION:
A single copy of the proposal must include:
(1) executive summary of the project, its
goals, financial requirements and present
status. A specific grant amount must be
requested;
(2) brief history of the organization, an
annual report, two most recent audited
financial statements along with IRS Forms
990 (with all schedules);
(3) detailed proposal including projects
objectives, budget, timetable for
implementation and target population. For
capital projects (construction, renovation,
equipment), expenses must be documented as
follows:
(a) for new construction or renovation to
existing space - a complete breakdown of all
costs including professional fees and
expenses, a visual rendering of the project,
square footage, copies of preliminary or final
bids, and financing arrangements (if
applicable);
(b) for acquisition of equipment - a copy of
the most appropriate of three bids, costs of
installation and financing arrangements (if
applicable);
(4) anticipated outcomes and a plan for
assessing them;
(5) committed and prospective financial
support for this project (sources and
amounts), also plans to fund the project on
an ongoing basis;
(6) names and occupations of all directors or
trustees, a listing of key staff and their
qualifications, and resume of project officer
and;
(7) copy of the Internal Revenue Service
determination letter granting tax exemption
status.
Duration: One year.

Deadline: Written proposals are accepted and reviewed by the Foundation throughout the year. With the exception of Foundation initiatives, there are no deadlines. Applicants receive a response within approximately three months.

PUBLICATIONS:
Application guidelines.

OFFICERS:
Josephine C. Mandeville, President
Emily C. Riley, Executive Vice President
Lewis W. Bluemle, Senior Vice President
Victoria K. Flaville, Senior Vice President of Programs and Chief Operating Officer
Amy M. Snyder, Chief Financial Officer

ADDRESS INQUIRIES TO:
E. Ann Wilcox
Associate Vice President, Administration
(See address above.)

*PLEASE NOTE:
Visits to the Foundation office or contacts with its staff initiated by applicants during the proposal review process are discouraged.

CONSTELLATION ENERGY GROUP   [95]
Community Partnerships
100 Constellation Way
Baltimore, MD 21202

E-MAIL ADDRESS:
corporate.contributions@constellation.com

WEB SITE ADDRESS:
www.cemarketing.com

FOUNDED: 1816

AREAS OF INTEREST:
Economic development, energy assistance, poverty solutions, education and environment.

TYPE:
Capital grants; Challenge/matching grants; Conferences/seminars; General operating grants; Matching gifts; Project/program grants; Scholarships. Sponsorships and in-kind grants. Matching gifts for institutions of higher education.

PURPOSE:
To assist nonprofit organizations that play significant roles in education, environmental improvement and economic development where Constellation Energy has significant business interests.

LEGAL BASIS:
Corporate giving program and foundation.

ELIGIBILITY:
Organizations must be classified as 501(c)(3) tax-exempt nonprofit.

GEOGRAPHIC RESTRICTIONS:
Central Maryland, New England, Great Lakes region, Texas region and Western region.

FINANCIAL DATA:
Amount of support per award: Average $4,000 to $6,000.
Total amount of support: $8,200,000.
Matching fund requirements: For accredited institutions of higher education.

APPLICATION INFORMATION:
Applicants must submit a full proposal following the contributions guidelines on the web site.
Deadline: Year-round for event sponsorships or grant requests less than $10,000; for grant requests of $10,000 and up: April 1 and September 1.

PUBLICATIONS:
Application guidelines.

ADDRESS INQUIRIES TO:
Stacey Ullrich, Executive Director
Community Partnerships
(See address above.)

CONSUMERS ENERGY FOUNDATION   [96]
One Energy Plaza, Room EP8-210
Jackson, MI 49201-2276
(517) 788-0432
(877) 501-4952
Fax: (517) 788-2281

E-MAIL ADDRESS:
foundation@consumersenergy.com

WEB SITE ADDRESS:
www.consumersenergy.com/foundation

FOUNDED: 1989

AREAS OF INTEREST:
Social welfare, education, culture and arts, community and civic affairs, Michigan growth and environmental enhancement.

CONSULTING OR VOLUNTEER SERVICES:
Employee volunteer program.

TYPE:
Capital grants; General operating grants; Internships; Matching gifts; Project/program grants; Scholarships; Seed money grants; Technical assistance.

YEAR PROGRAM STARTED: 1992

PURPOSE:
To encourage employees to volunteer their time to nonprofit organizations.

LEGAL BASIS:
Corporate program.

ELIGIBILITY:
501(c)(3) tax-exempt status, nonprofit organizations are eligible for support. The Foundation will not fund individuals, political, religious, labor or veteran's organizations or agencies supported by United Way.

Requests will be considered from organizations elsewhere for programs or projects that significantly benefit the state of Michigan.

GEOGRAPHIC RESTRICTIONS:
Michigan.

FINANCIAL DATA:
Employees are encouraged to volunteer 45 hours per year to nonprofit organizations. The Foundation will fund up to $500 per organization.
Amount of support per award: $1,000 to $10,000.
Total amount of support: $1,000,000 for the year 2011.
Matching fund requirements: Foundation will match employee and retiree contributions to education, Michigan Food Banks and community foundations. Minimum $25 and maximum $1,000 per year per employee and retiree.

NUMBER OF APPLICANTS MOST RECENT YEAR:
1,200.

REPRESENTATIVE AWARDS:
$50,000 to Salvation Army, west Michigan; $40,000 to Jackson Symphony Orchestra; $20,000 to Food Bank of Eastern Michigan; $10,000 to Senior Services of Kalamazoo; $15,000 to Bay Area Family YMCA.

APPLICATION INFORMATION:
Cover letter and completed grant application required by mail only. See guidelines brochure for information.
Duration: Varies. Renewal unlikely.

PUBLICATIONS:
Guidelines brochure.

DIRECTORS:
J.G. Russell, Chairman
David G. Mengebier, President
Carolyn A. Bloodworth, Secretary and Treasurer
James E. Brunner
John M. Butler
William E. Garrity
Jackson L. Hanson
Daniel J. Malone
Ronn J. Rasmussen
T.J. Webb

ADDRESS INQUIRIES TO:
Carolyn A. Bloodworth
Secretary and Treasurer
(See address above.)

V.V. COOKE FOUNDATION   [97]
220 Mount Mercy Drive
Suite 2
Pewee Valley, KY 40056
(502) 241-0303

E-MAIL ADDRESS:
merhoff@bellsouth.net

FOUNDED: 1947

AREAS OF INTEREST:
Civic affairs, education, religion and humanitarianism.

TYPE:
Capital grants; Endowments; General operating grants; Scholarships; Seed money grants.

LEGAL BASIS:
Private foundation.

ELIGIBILITY:
Grants are made to organizations that have tax-exempt status under Section 501(c)(3) and are not described in Section 509(a)(3) of the Internal Revenue Code. Grants are made for religious, educational, humanitarian and civic purposes. No grants are made to individuals.

GEOGRAPHIC RESTRICTIONS:
Louisville, Kentucky.

FINANCIAL DATA:
Amount of support per award: $100 to $25,000.
Total amount of support: $178,300 for the year ended August 31, 2010.

NUMBER OF APPLICANTS MOST RECENT YEAR:
42.

NUMBER OF AWARDS: 60.

REPRESENTATIVE AWARDS:
$1,500 to Alice Lloyd College; $25,000 to Georgetown College.

APPLICATION INFORMATION:
Applications should be in letter form, outlining the organization's goals and purposes, and the intended use and amount of the grant requested. Eight copies of the application are required.
Deadline: Applications are considered in mid-January, April, July and October.

PUBLICATIONS:
Application guidelines.

IRS IDENTIFICATION NUMBER: 61-6033714

STAFF:
Theodore L. Merhoff, Executive Director

ADDRESS INQUIRIES TO:
Theodore L. Merhoff, Executive Director
(See address above.)

COOPER FOUNDATION   [98]
1248 O Street, No. 870
Lincoln, NE 68508-1493
(402) 476-7571
Fax: (402) 476-2356

E-MAIL ADDRESS:
info@cooperfoundation.org

WEB SITE ADDRESS:
www.cooperfoundation.org

FOUNDED: 1934

AREAS OF INTEREST:
Education, human services, arts and
humanities, and the environment.

TYPE:
Challenge/matching grants; Demonstration
grants.

PURPOSE:
To support the operations and core programs
of strong, well-managed and effective
nonprofit organizations located in and
working in Lancaster County, NE.

LEGAL BASIS:
Private foundation.

ELIGIBILITY:
Most grants are made to organizations
located in and impacting residents of
Lancaster County, NE.

The Foundation does not fund individuals,
businesses, health organizations or issues,
churches, religious organizations or issues,
travel, memberships, endowments,
non-501(c)(3) organizations, 509(a)(3)
supporting organizations, fiscal agents, or
private foundations.

GEOGRAPHIC RESTRICTIONS:
Nebraska.

FINANCIAL DATA:
Amount of support per award: $1,000 to
$15,000; Average: $5,000.
Total amount of support: $800,000 for the
year 2010.

NUMBER OF AWARDS: 60.

APPLICATION INFORMATION:
The Foundation accepts formal applications
only from organizations that have already
communicated with them and have been
asked to complete an application form. The
initial communication may be in person, by
phone, by mail or by facsimile. The
Foundation staff is available for consultation
at any stage in the process.

Applications must include:
(1) amount of the request;
(2) project budget, including sources and
amounts of income and detailed expenses;
(3) development plan explaining how, from
whom and in what amounts funds will be
raised and how the project will be sustained
after the grant period;
(4) plan to evaluate the effectiveness of the
project during the grant period and;
(5) clear, complete financial information that
matches the supporting documentation.
Accuracy and evidence of good financial
management is important.

Reapplication cannot be made sooner than 12
months after grant approval or decline, or the
final payment date, whichever is later.
Organizations submitting a collaborative
grant may apply on their own, but not during
the same grant application cycle.

Duration: One year. Must reapply annually.

Deadline: January 15, April 1, August 1 and
October 1.

ADDRESS INQUIRIES TO:
Victoria Kovar, Program Officer
(See address above.)

THE MARY S. AND DAVID C. CORBIN FOUNDATION   [99]
910 Key Building
159 South Main Street
Akron, OH 44308
(330) 762-6427
Fax: (330) 762-6428

E-MAIL ADDRESS:
corbin@nls.net

WEB SITE ADDRESS:
www.foundationcenter.org/grantmaker/corbin

AREAS OF INTEREST:
Arts, culture, environment, health, housing,
human services, education, youth and
medical research.

TYPE:
Project/program grants.

PURPOSE:
To benefit charities in the Akron and Summit
County, OH areas and national charities that
have a presence in the Akron and Summit
County, OH areas.

ELIGIBILITY:
Organizations classified as 501(c)(3) by the
IRS and non-private foundations can apply.
The Foundation gives primary consideration
to the City of Akron and Summit County,
OH charitable organizations and/or local
chapters of national charities located in the
Akron, Summit County, OH area.

The Foundation does not fund individuals,
annual fund-raising campaigns, ongoing
requests for general operating support,
operating deficits, or organizations which in
turn make grants to others. The Foundation
generally does not fund religious
organizations.

GEOGRAPHIC RESTRICTIONS:
City of Akron and Summit County, Ohio.

FINANCIAL DATA:
Amount of support per award: $150 to
$2,000,000.
Total amount of support: $816,491 for the
year 2008.

APPLICATION INFORMATION:
Contact the Foundation for application
procedures. The Foundation application can
also be downloaded from the web site.
Organizations should send a brief letter on
their letterhead and should submit one
original and one copy of all application
materials. Letter should include:
(1) a brief description of the organization
and;
(2) a description of the proposed project,
proposed accomplishments, duration, the total
cost of the project and the specific amount
requested from the Foundation.

Duration: One year.

Deadline: March 1 and September 1.

ADDRESS INQUIRIES TO:
Erika J. May, Grants Administrator
(See address above.)

*SPECIAL STIPULATIONS:
Only written applications will be considered.
Both telephone and personal interviews are
discouraged unless requested by the
Foundation.

MARION STEDMAN COVINGTON FOUNDATION [100]
P.O. Box 29304
Greensboro, NC 27429-9304
(336) 282-0480

E-MAIL ADDRESS:
info@mscovingtonfoundation.org

WEB SITE ADDRESS:
www.mscovingtonfoundation.org

AREAS OF INTEREST:
Historic preservation, arts and culture, and
education as related to historic presentation.

TYPE:
Capital grants; Challenge/matching grants;
Conferences/seminars; General operating
grants; Project/program grants; Research
grants; Seed money grants.

YEAR PROGRAM STARTED: 1986

PURPOSE:
To provide grants to nonprofit organizations
operating in the area of historic preservation.

ELIGIBILITY:
Grants are made to federally tax-exempt,
nonprofit organizations.

GEOGRAPHIC RESTRICTIONS:
Primarily North Carolina.

FINANCIAL DATA:
Funds are also provided for
construction/renovation projects, equipment
and materials, operating support, program
support and publications.
Amount of support per award: $10,000
average.
Total amount of support: $342,000.

NUMBER OF APPLICANTS MOST RECENT YEAR:
32.

NUMBER OF AWARDS: 17.

APPLICATION INFORMATION:
Contact the Foundation for application
procedures.
Deadline: September 1 and March 1.
Announcement approximately six weeks after
the deadline.

PUBLICATIONS:
Annual report; guidelines.

IRS IDENTIFICATION NUMBER: 56-6286555

TRUSTEES:
Kathleen H. Crockett
Steven J. Frost
Jane C. Hilderbrand
John C. Larson
Rodney L. Swink
Donald O. Tise, Jr.

ADDRESS INQUIRIES TO:
Alexa S. Aycock, Grants Coordinator
(See address above.)

*SPECIAL STIPULATIONS:
Challenge grants may be requested or the
Foundation may designate a grant as such. In
either event, there will be a specified time
period in which the matching funds are to be
raised.

S.H. COWELL FOUNDATION [101]

100 Montgomery Street, Suite 2570
San Francisco, CA 94104
(415) 397-0285
Fax: (415) 986-6786

E-MAIL ADDRESS:
info@shcowell.org

WEB SITE ADDRESS:
www.shcowell.org

FOUNDED: 1955

AREAS OF INTEREST:
Affordable housing, children and families
at-risk and education.

TYPE:
Capital grants; Challenge/matching grants;
Project/program grants. Community building.

YEAR PROGRAM STARTED: 1955

PURPOSE:
To improve the quality of life of children
living in poverty in northern California by
making grants that support and strengthen
their families and the neighborhoods where
they live.

LEGAL BASIS:
Independent nonprofit foundation.

ELIGIBILITY:
Organization must be tax-exempt and must
submit evidence that a grant would qualify
under the Tax Reform Act of 1969. Grants
are restricted to organizations, projects and
programs in northern California, except by
invitation of the Foundation.

As a matter of policy, the Foundation
typically does not make grants to hospitals
for construction or research, sectarian
religious groups, individuals for scholarships
or financial aid and rarely for operating
expenses.

GEOGRAPHIC RESTRICTIONS:
Northern California.

FINANCIAL DATA:
Amount of support per award: $20,000 to
$200,000.
Total amount of support: $9,500,000 for the
year 2009.

REPRESENTATIVE AWARDS:
$200,000 to Bay Area Partnership for
Children and Youth, Oakland, CA, for
coaching and technical support for
after-school programs; $316,000 to Sanger
Unified School District, Sanger, CA, to build
on a literacy program in four elementary
schools; $20,500 to California Family
Resource Association for leadership
development.

APPLICATION INFORMATION:
The application process is rigorous, and
prospective grantees should expect to work
with Cowell staff before, during, and after a
formal proposal is submitted. There are five
steps to the process:
(1) make sure that your project meets
Foundation funding criteria;
(2) call the Foundation;
(3) if asked to do so, submit a letter of
inquiry;
(4) if asked to do so, submit a full proposal.
Please do not send a formal proposal unless a
program officer requests one. If you are
asked to submit a proposal, staff will give
you a list of required information and;
(5) plan on at least one site visit.
Duration: Varies.

Deadline: The Directors meet to make grants
bimonthly throughout the year.

PUBLICATIONS:
Annual report; application guidelines.

OFFICERS AND BOARD OF DIRECTORS:
Ann Alpers, President
Donald D. Roberts, Secretary and General
Counsel
Cora M. Tellez, Vice President
Lisa Backus
Jack W. Chu
Charles E. Ellwein
Dr. Mikiko Huang
Scott Mosher
Deborah Oritz
Lydia Tan

ADDRESS INQUIRIES TO:
Lise Maisano
Vice President of Grant Programs
(See address above.)

*SPECIAL STIPULATIONS:
No grants to individuals, for media projects,
conferences, seminars, to sectarian
organizations, hospitals or
public/governmental agencies.

JESSIE B. COX CHARITABLE TRUST [102]

c/o GMA Foundations, Inc.
77 Summer Street, 8th Floor
Boston, MA 02110
(617) 391-3094
Fax: (617) 426-7087

E-MAIL ADDRESS:
jbcoxtrust@gmafoundations.com

WEB SITE ADDRESS:
www.jbcoxtrust.org

FOUNDED: 1982

AREAS OF INTEREST:
Health care (access), education (early
learning and out-of-school time), and
environment (habitat conservation).

TYPE:
Challenge/matching grants; Demonstration
grants; Development grants; Project/program
grants; Seed money grants. These grants are
offered to organizations to help develop
programs for health care, education and
environment.

YEAR PROGRAM STARTED: 1982

PURPOSE:
To support organizations in New England
working on important societal issues in the
Trust's fields of interest, for which adequate
funding cannot be obtained from other
sources, with a particular interest in projects
which primarily benefit underserved
populations and disadvantaged communities.

LEGAL BASIS:
Charitable Lead annuity trust.

ELIGIBILITY:
Support will not be provided for buildings,
equipment or land purchases, endowments,
scholarship funds, fund-raising, deficits,
normal operating budgets, individuals,
sectarian religious activity, organizations
outside of New England, recent grantees or
projects usually supported by the public
sector.

GEOGRAPHIC RESTRICTIONS:
New England states including Connecticut,
Maine, Massachusetts, New Hampshire,
Rhode Island and Vermont.

FINANCIAL DATA:
Amount of support per award: $20,000 to
$75,000; average $35,000.
Total amount of support: $1,911,082 for the
year 2010.

NUMBER OF APPLICANTS MOST RECENT YEAR:
300 average per year.

APPLICATION INFORMATION:
Concept paper, cover sheet, IRS letter of
501(c)(3) status and preliminary budget are
required.
Duration: One to two years. Renewals
seldom.
Deadline: March 15 and September 15.

IRS IDENTIFICATION NUMBER: 04-6478024

ADDRESS INQUIRIES TO:
Grants Administrator
(See address above.)

HENRY P. AND SUSAN C. CROWELL TRUST [103]

1880 Office Club Pointe, Suite 2200
Colorado Springs, CO 80920
(719) 272-8300
Fax: (719) 272-8305

E-MAIL ADDRESS:
info@crowelltrust.org

WEB SITE ADDRESS:
www.crowelltrust.org

FOUNDED: 1927

AREAS OF INTEREST:
Higher Christian education and evangelical
foreign missions.

TYPE:
General operating grants; Project/program
grants.

YEAR PROGRAM STARTED: 1927

PURPOSE:
To aid evangelical Christianity by support to
organizations having for their purposes its
teaching, advancement and active extension
at home and abroad.

LEGAL BASIS:
Private foundation.

ELIGIBILITY:
No grants to churches, individuals or for
endowment funds or research. No loans.

GEOGRAPHIC RESTRICTIONS:
United States.

FINANCIAL DATA:
Amount of support per award: Average
$35,000.
Total amount of support: $3,500,000.

NUMBER OF APPLICANTS MOST RECENT YEAR:
375.

NUMBER OF AWARDS: 100.

APPLICATION INFORMATION:
Applicants must ensure the project fits the
guidelines of the Trust by completing the
online Self-Screening Aid to determine
eligibility and begin the application process.
If the organization and project fit the
minimum requirements, applicants should
complete the New Applicant Datasheet and
submit a proposal of no more than three
pages. Organizations previously funded by
the Trust should go to the Organizations
Previously Funded page.
Duration: One year only; may resubmit
annually.

Deadline: The Board meets in the spring and fall to consider grant requests. Proposals should be submitted by February 28 and July 31 for consideration. Proposals received after the deadline may be held over for the following grant cycle.

PUBLICATIONS:
Application guidelines.

IRS IDENTIFICATION NUMBER: 36-6038028

STAFF:
Candace Sparks, Chief Executive Officer

ADDRESS INQUIRIES TO:
Mark Gradin, Grant Administrator
(See address above.)

THE CULLEN FOUNDATION [104]
601 Jefferson, 40th Floor
Houston, TX 77002
(713) 651-8837
Fax: (713) 651-2374

E-MAIL ADDRESS:
salexander@cullenfdn.org

WEB SITE ADDRESS:
www.cullenfdn.org

FOUNDED: 1947

AREAS OF INTEREST:
Arts, education, medicine, science, handicapped and public service.

TYPE:
Capital grants; Challenge/matching grants; Development grants; Endowments; Fellowships; General operating grants; Professorships; Project/program grants; Research grants; Scholarships.

PURPOSE:
To provide charitable, educational and medical grants for hospitals, medical research, higher education and music and the performing arts; to provide aid to the handicapped and community funds.

LEGAL BASIS:
Tax-exempt, private foundation.

ELIGIBILITY:
Grants are limited to the state of Texas by indenture. No grants are made to individuals or businesses.

GEOGRAPHIC RESTRICTIONS:
Texas, primarily Houston.

FINANCIAL DATA:
Amount of support per award: $1,000 to $5,000,000.
Total amount of support: $5,825,000.

NUMBER OF APPLICANTS MOST RECENT YEAR:
110 proposals.

NUMBER OF AWARDS: 32 new grants awarded for the year 2009.

REPRESENTATIVE AWARDS:
$137,500 to Alley Theatre; $25,000 to Project Grad; $40,000 to W. Oscar Neuhaus Memorial Foundation; $30,000 to Wellsprings Village; $20,000 to Open Door Mission.

APPLICATION INFORMATION:
A brief letter describing concisely the project and its purpose together with pertinent brochures, etc. No formal application forms, but a check list of suggested format is available on request and on the Foundation's web site.

Duration: No grants are awarded on a continuing basis.
Deadline: Rotating and ongoing.

PUBLICATIONS:
Application guidelines.

IRS IDENTIFICATION NUMBER: 76-0647361

DIRECTORS AND OFFICERS:
Roy H. Cullen, President and Director
Isaac Arnold, Jr., Vice President and Director
Alan M. Stewart, Treasurer and Executive Director
Wilhemina E. Robertson, Secretary and Director
Bert L. Campbell, Director
William H. Drushel, Jr., Director

ADDRESS INQUIRIES TO:
Sue Alexander, Grant Administrator
(See address above.)

*SPECIAL STIPULATIONS:
Grants are made to qualified charities in the state of Texas, primarily in the Houston area. No grants to individuals or businesses.

THE NATHAN CUMMINGS FOUNDATION, INC. [105]
475 10th Ave, 14th Floor
New York, NY 10018
(212) 787-7300
Fax: (212) 787-7377

E-MAIL ADDRESS:
contact@nathancummings.org

WEB SITE ADDRESS:
www.nathancummings.org

FOUNDED: 1949

AREAS OF INTEREST:
The arts, the environment, health and Jewish life.

NAME(S) OF PROGRAMS:
- **Arts & Culture**
- **Collaborative Initiatives for Social and Economic Justice**
- **Contemplative Practice**
- **Ecological Innovation**
- **Health**
- **Jewish Life and Values**

TYPE:
General operating grants; Project/program grants.

YEAR PROGRAM STARTED: 1989

PURPOSE:
To promote democratic values and social justice, including fairness, diversity and community; to build a socially and economically just society that values and protects the ecological balance for future generations; to promote humane health care; to foster arts and culture that enrich communities.

LEGAL BASIS:
Private foundation.

ELIGIBILITY:
Grants to U.S.-based organizations only.

GEOGRAPHIC RESTRICTIONS:
United States.

FINANCIAL DATA:
Amount of support per award: Varies.
Total amount of support: $19,758,485 for the year 2010.

NUMBER OF APPLICANTS MOST RECENT YEAR:
1,038 Letters of Inquiry for the year 2010.

NUMBER OF AWARDS: 313 grants for the year 2010.

APPLICATION INFORMATION:
The application process is very competitive; only those organizations whose projects fit most closely with the Foundation's programmatic goals will be invited to submit a Foundation Application Form.
Duration: Varies.
Deadline: Letters of Inquiry are accepted throughout the year. The Board of Trustees meets in April and November.

IRS IDENTIFICATION NUMBER: 23-7093201

STAFF:
Lance E. Lindblom, President and Chief Executive Officer
Caroline Williams, Executive Vice President
Laura Shaffer, Director of Shareholder Activities
M. Annette Ensley, Director of Administration and Human Resources
Armanda Famiglietti, Director of Grants Management
Maurine Knighton, Program Director, Arts & Culture
Peter Teague, Program Director, Environment/Contemplative Practice
Sara C. Kay, Program Director, Health
Rabbi Jennie Rosenn, Program Director, Jewish Life and Values

ADDRESS INQUIRIES TO:
Lance E. Lindblom
President and Chief Executive Officer
(See address above.)

*SPECIAL STIPULATIONS:
Before submitting a Letter of Inquiry, please note that the Foundation's core programs do not provide funding for: individuals; academic scholarships; capital, building or endowment campaigns; sponsorships; fund-raising events or dinners; foreign-based organizations; projects addressing specific diseases; social services; local projects without national or regional impact.

THE CUMMINS FOUNDATION [106]
500 Jackson Street, MC 60633
Columbus, IN 47201
(812) 377-3114
Fax: (812) 377-7897

WEB SITE ADDRESS:
www.cummins.com

FOUNDED: 1954

AREAS OF INTEREST:
Focus on environment, education and social justice.

TYPE:
Project/program grants.

YEAR PROGRAM STARTED: 1954

PURPOSE:
To improve the quality of life in communities where Cummins has manufacturing operations and subsidiaries; to promote the Foundation's philanthropic objectives through grants in priority areas as well as projects of special interest in Columbus and subsidiary communities.

LEGAL BASIS:
Corporate foundation.

ELIGIBILITY:
Grantees must be tax-exempt organizations or institutions located in areas where Cummins

has a presence. No grants are made to individuals or for denominational religious organizations. No scholarships are granted.

FINANCIAL DATA:
Amount of support per award: Varies.

NUMBER OF AWARDS: Varies.

APPLICATION INFORMATION:
Duration: Varies.

PUBLICATIONS:
Sustainability report.

DIRECTORS:
T.M. Solso, Chairman
J. Blackwell
T. Linebarger
W.I. Miller

MARGARET A. DARRIN FOUNDATION   [107]

120 Columbia Turnpike
Florham Park, NJ 07932
(973) 822-2995
Fax: (973) 822-8200

FOUNDED: 1987

AREAS OF INTEREST:
Arts, humanities, civic affairs, education, health, social services and women's issues.

TYPE:
General operating grants.

YEAR PROGRAM STARTED: 1987

ELIGIBILITY:
No restrictions or limitations on funding. Grants made to nonprofit 501(c)(3) organizations only.

GEOGRAPHIC RESTRICTIONS:
Northeastern United States.

FINANCIAL DATA:
Amount of support per award: Maximum approximately $500 to $15,000.

REPRESENTATIVE AWARDS:
$41,000 to Hague Adirondacks Historical Museum; $10,000 to Williston Northampton School, Easthampton, MA; $1,000 to Hutchinson Island Fire Department.

APPLICATION INFORMATION:
Applications should take the form of a brief letter describing the charity, its background and the purpose of the contribution.
Duration: One year. Must reapply for additional funding.
Deadline: October 31.

IRS IDENTIFICATION NUMBER: 22-6426771

STAFF:
Michael Hanifin, President

ADDRESS INQUIRIES TO:
Charitable Contributions
(See address above.)

THE ARTHUR VINING DAVIS FOUNDATIONS   [108]

225 Water Street
Suite 1510
Jacksonville, FL 32202
(904) 359-0670
Fax: (904) 359-0675

E-MAIL ADDRESS:
office@avdf.org

WEB SITE ADDRESS:
www.avdf.org

FOUNDED: 1952

AREAS OF INTEREST:
Private higher education, health care (caring attitudes), graduate theological education (seminaries fully accredited by the Association of Theological Schools), public television (major educational series for viewing nationally on PBS), secondary education (professional development programs that strengthen teachers and teaching in grades nine-12), and programs that promote and strengthen caring attitudes in health care.

TYPE:
Project/program grants.

LEGAL BASIS:
Privately endowed foundation established by the will of Arthur Vining Davis.

ELIGIBILITY:
Grants are limited to institutions in the U.S. and its territories. Activities and functions not supported include assistance to individuals (except as participants in an organized institutional scholarship program), voter registration drives and voter education, efforts to influence elections or legislation, expenditures for noncharitable purposes and projects incurring obligations extending over many years. Support is not granted to institutions primarily supported by government funds except medical institutions and secondary education programs.

GEOGRAPHIC RESTRICTIONS:
United States.

FINANCIAL DATA:
Amount of support per award: $150,000 to $400,000, depending on program area.
Total amount of support: $8,814,716 for the year 2010.

COOPERATIVE FUNDING PROGRAMS: As a policy, the Foundations' support increased cooperation among foundations and expanded communication with the public. The staff has taken an active part in national and regional efforts in this direction.

NUMBER OF AWARDS: 40 for the year 2010.

REPRESENTATIVE AWARDS:
$250,000 to Private Higher Education; $200,000 to Graduate Theological Education; $150,000 to Secondary Education.

APPLICATION INFORMATION:
No application forms are used and elaborate presentations are unnecessary. Preliminary inquiry should take the form of a letter stating the proposal's purpose, methods and expected results, together with a brief budget. This request should come from the head of the institution. If the proposal seems to fall within the Foundation's areas of interest and capability, the staff may request further data, discussion and the opportunity to visit the institution, as necessary. Proposals are not accepted via fax or e-mail.
Duration: Re-grants in higher education and religion generally are not considered until at least four years after a previous grant.
Deadline: Proposals may be submitted at any time.

PUBLICATIONS:
Guideline brochure; annual report.

OFFICERS:
Dr. Jonathan T. Howe, Executive Director
Jane M. Estes, Chief Financial Officer
Doreen Flippin, Vice President for Administration
William C. Keator, Vice President for Programs

Cheryl Tupper, Program Director
Dr. James L. Waits, Consultant

TRUSTEES:
J.H. Dow Davis, Chairman
Haley T. Davis
Holbrook R. Davis
Joel P. Davis
Maynard K. Davis
Serena Davis Hall
Mrs. John L. Kee, Jr.
John L. Kee, III

ADDRESS INQUIRIES TO:
Dr. Jonathan T. Howe, Executive Director
(See address above.)

EDWIN W. AND CATHERINE M. DAVIS FOUNDATION   [109]

30 East 7th Street, Suite 2000
St. Paul, MN 55101-1394
(651) 228-0935

FOUNDED: 1956

AREAS OF INTEREST:
The Foundation's program is directed to the amelioration of social problems and to increasing the opportunities available to disadvantaged peoples. Grants are given in the fields of education, social welfare, mental health, the arts, and environmental problems.

TYPE:
General operating grants; Project/program grants.

YEAR PROGRAM STARTED: 1956

PURPOSE:
To receive, manage and apply a fund or funds exclusively for charitable, religious, scientific or educational purposes.

LEGAL BASIS:
Founded as a nonprofit corporation under Chapter 317, Minnesota Statutes.

ELIGIBILITY:
Grants are made to nonprofit, 501(c)(3) organizations.

The Foundation does not usually make grants to individuals, capital campaigns for buildings or equipment or endowment campaigns.

The Foundation also does not make loans to organizations or individuals.

In general, the Foundation prefers not to make long-term commitments, in order to preserve flexibility in its program to meet changing conditions from year to year.

FINANCIAL DATA:
Amount of support per award: Varies.
Total amount of support: $977,388 for the year 2009.

APPLICATION INFORMATION:
Applications to the Foundation are to be in the form of a letter, no longer than three pages, which includes the background of the organization, the need for the services or specified project, the plan to address the need, the benefits provided by the services or project, the plans for evaluation of results and the program and/or organizational budget.

Applications must include a copy of the applicant's letters concerning federal income tax exemption issued by the IRS.

PUBLICATIONS:
Annual report.

OFFICERS:
Bette D. Moorman, President
Lisa M. Fremont, Treasurer
John L. Davis, Secretary
Jay A. Narverud, Assistant Treasurer
Carol R. Caruthers, Assistant Secretary

ADDRESS INQUIRIES TO:
Gayle Roth, Grants Administrator
(See address above.)

JOHN DEERE FOUNDATION [110]

One John Deere Place
Moline, IL 61265
(309) 748-7960
Fax: (309) 748-7953

WEB SITE ADDRESS:
www.deere.com

FOUNDED: 1948

AREAS OF INTEREST:
Higher education, community, and solutions for world hunger.

TYPE:
Project/program grants.

PURPOSE:
To support programs and activities that responsibly seek to build a better future for everyone.

LEGAL BASIS:
Corporate foundation.

ELIGIBILITY:
The Foundation only considers grant requests from tax-exempt, nonprofit organizations located in the U.S. or its possessions. No grants to individuals.

GEOGRAPHIC RESTRICTIONS:
United States and its territories.

FINANCIAL DATA:
Amount of support per award: Varies.
Total amount of support: $12,250,000.

APPLICATION INFORMATION:
Deadline: One to two years, with review.

OFFICERS:
John Bustle, Vice President

DELUXE CORPORATION FOUNDATION [111]

3680 Victoria Street North
Shoreview, MN 55126-2966
(651) 787-5124
(651) 483-7842
Fax: (651) 481-4371

E-MAIL ADDRESS:
pam.bridger@deluxe.com

WEB SITE ADDRESS:
www.deluxe.com

FOUNDED: 1952

AREAS OF INTEREST:
Human services, culture and the arts, K-12 economic education programs, tutoring programs, employment programs, and small business coaching.

TYPE:
Capital grants; General operating grants; Matching gifts; Project/program grants. Volunteer match on behalf of employee volunteerism at 501(c)(3) nonprofit.

LEGAL BASIS:
Corporate foundation.

ELIGIBILITY:
The Foundation will generally not make grants to organizations that are not exempt under Sections 501(c)(3) or 509(a)(1), (2) or (3), individuals, colleges and universities, religious organizations, organizations designed primarily for lobbying, seminars, conferences, workshops or fund-raisers, endowments, research projects, tours and travel expenses, start-up organizations, athletic events or sponsorships.

It is not a common practice of the Foundation to consider requests for multiyear commitments.

GEOGRAPHIC RESTRICTIONS:
United States.

FINANCIAL DATA:
Amount of support per award: $5,000 to $10,000 average.
Total amount of support: Varies.
Matching fund requirements: Varies.

COOPERATIVE FUNDING PROGRAMS: United Way.

REPRESENTATIVE AWARDS:
Junior Achievement of Eastern Massachusetts for program that teaches youth about the economics of life; Reading Recovery Council of North America to train teachers so that they can help students who struggle with reading; HomeBase Youth Services, Phoenix, AZ, for teaching homeless youth how to live independent lives.

APPLICATION INFORMATION:
Grant applications should include the following information:
(1) evidence of tax-exempt status under Section 501(c)(3) or under Section 509(a)(1), (2) or (3) of the Internal Revenue Code;
(2) intended purpose of funds requested;
(3) number of persons and types of groups served;
(4) history, purpose and brief description of the organization;
(5) budget for the fiscal year and recent audited financial statement;
(6) sources and amounts of secured corporate support;
(7) list of others being solicited for support and;
(8) copy of 990-PF (complete with schedules and statements).
Duration: One year.
Deadline: The Foundation accepts grant requests outside of Minnesota March 1 to November 1, but applicants should not repeat requests during a calendar year. Within Minnesota, applications are accepted February 1 through November 1. Minnesota-based nonprofit arts organizations' applications are accepted February 1 through April 1. Minnesota-based nonprofit youth organizations' applications are accepted May 1 through June 30.

BOARD OF DIRECTORS:
Lee J. Schram, President
Jennifer A. Anderson, Director of Foundations and Community Affairs
Julie Loosbrock
Terry Peterson
Anthony C. Scarfone

ADDRESS INQUIRIES TO:
Pamela G. Bridger, Foundations and Community Affairs Administrator
(See address above.)

DICKSON FOUNDATION [112]

301 South Tryon Street
Suite 1800
Charlotte, NC 28202
(704) 372-5404

FOUNDED: 1944

AREAS OF INTEREST:
Education and health care.

TYPE:
Capital grants; Project/program grants.

YEAR PROGRAM STARTED: 1944

PURPOSE:
To support programs that meet the needs of and improve the quality of life in the Southeast.

LEGAL BASIS:
Private foundation.

ELIGIBILITY:
Grants are made to organizations that have tax-exempt status under Section 501(c)(3) of the Internal Revenue Code. No grants are made to individuals.

GEOGRAPHIC RESTRICTIONS:
Southeastern United States.

FINANCIAL DATA:
Amount of support per award: Varies.
Total amount of support: Varies.

APPLICATION INFORMATION:
Send a letter of inquiry outlining the organization's goal and purposes, and the intended use and amount of the grant requested. Further information may be obtained from the Foundation.

ADDRESS INQUIRIES TO:
Alan T. Dickson, President
(See address above.)

GERALDINE R. DODGE FOUNDATION [113]

14 Maple Avenue
Morristown, NJ 07960
(973) 540-8442
Fax: (973) 540-1211

E-MAIL ADDRESS:
info@grdodge.org

WEB SITE ADDRESS:
www.grdodge.org

FOUNDED: 1974

AREAS OF INTEREST:
The arts, environment, education, and Morris County projects.

TYPE:
General operating grants; Project/program grants. Grants in four key areas through the use of traditional and new media to educate the public about issues in the Foundation's areas of interest and to promote new paradigms towards a creative, sustainable New Jersey.

Art grants enhance the cultural richness of the community in which citizens reside and contribute to New Jersey's creative economy.

Educational grants provide transformational experiential educational opportunities both inside and outside of the classroom for young people who have limited access to educational excellence.

Environmental grants help to achieve ecosystem resilience and sustainable community solutions.

Morris County Grants support a wide range of nonprofit organizations working together to enhance the quality of life for an increasingly diverse part of the state. This funding fosters meaningful connections among people of diverse ethnicities, cultures and classes.

PURPOSE:
To support and encourage those educational, cultural, social and environmental values that contribute to making our society more humane and our world more livable.

LEGAL BASIS:
Private foundation.

ELIGIBILITY:
Applicants must be nonprofit, 501(c)(3) tax-exempt organizations located in or providing benefits to the residents of the state of New Jersey. No grants in areas of higher education, health and religion. No support for capital programs, endowments, equipment purchases, scholarships, indirect costs or deficit reduction. No direct awards to individuals nor grants to conduit organizations, nor is funding made for lobbying efforts.

GEOGRAPHIC RESTRICTIONS:
New Jersey.

APPLICATION INFORMATION:
Unsolicited requests for scholarships and grants are not accepted. New applicants should submit a one-page letter of inquiry to determine if a project falls within the Foundation's guidelines. Letters of inquiry may be submitted throughout the year, but must be received at least two weeks prior to the corresponding submission deadline. Letters of inquiry must be submitted online or e-mailed, without attachments. Following staff review of initial inquiries, applicants will be notified whether or not to submit a full proposal.

Applicants invited to apply are then required to submit an electronic copy of their proposal.
Duration: Typically 12 months.
Deadline: Letter of Inquiry: February 15 and August 1; Application: March 1 and September 1. Notification early July and mid-December, respectively.

PUBLICATIONS:
Application guidelines; biannual report.

IRS IDENTIFICATION NUMBER: 23-7406010

STAFF:
Christopher J. Daggett, President and Chief Executive Officer

ADDRESS INQUIRIES TO:
Rose Ann DeBois, Grants Manager
Tel: (973) 540-8442 ext. 109
E-mail: rdebois@grdodge.org

*SPECIAL STIPULATIONS:
The Foundation does not accept fax proposals or proposals sent via express mail carriers.

DOMINION FOUNDATION   [114]
D.L. Clark Building, Suite 400
501 Martindale Street
Pittsburgh, PA 15212-5835
(412) 237-2972
Fax: (412) 237-4782

WEB SITE ADDRESS:
www.dom.com

FOUNDED: 1985

AREAS OF INTEREST:
United Way, health and human services, culture and the arts, civic and community development, the environment, and education.

TYPE:
Matching gifts.

PURPOSE:
To invest in communities in states where Dominion provides electricity and natural gas service: North Carolina, Ohio, West Virginia and Virginia; to support selected charitable endeavors in locations where it has facilities and business interests, including Connecticut, Illinois, Indiana, Maryland, Massachusetts, New York, Pennsylvania, Rhode Island and Wisconsin.

ELIGIBILITY:
Applicants must be 501(c)(3) organizations. No grants to individuals, sectarian purposes, fraternal, political, advocacy or labor organizations, religious programs of churches, or operating funds of individual United Way agencies.

FINANCIAL DATA:
Amount of support per award: Generally $1,000 to $15,000.
Total amount of support: Over $15,000,000 annually.

APPLICATION INFORMATION:
Application requires description of organization, purpose of request, amount requested and list of other sources of support, most recent audited financial statement and IRS 501(c)(3) letter. The narrative statement should pay particular attention to the project's objectives, the need(s) addressed by the project, the impact on the community and the method of accomplishing the objectives.

PUBLICATIONS:
Grant guidelines.

EXECUTIVE DIRECTOR:
James C. Mesloh

*SPECIAL STIPULATIONS:
Organizations seeking support should direct their requests to the operating company in their area.

GAYLORD AND DOROTHY DONNELLEY FOUNDATION [115]
35 East Wacker Drive, Suite 2600
Chicago, IL 60601
(312) 977-2700
Fax: (312) 977-1686

E-MAIL ADDRESS:
gddf@gddf.org

WEB SITE ADDRESS:
www.gddf.org

FOUNDED: 1952

AREAS OF INTEREST:
Artistic vitality and land conservation in the Chicago region and the low country of South Carolina.

TYPE:
Challenge/matching grants; Exchange programs; General operating grants; Project/program grants.

YEAR PROGRAM STARTED: 1952

PURPOSE:
The promotion of artistic vitality and land conservation.

LEGAL BASIS:
Tax-exempt, private foundation.

ELIGIBILITY:
Grants are made to tax-exempt, nonprofit 501(c)(3) organizations. Grants are not made to individuals, for community welfare, education, benefits, conferences, loans or pledges.

GEOGRAPHIC RESTRICTIONS:
Chicago region and South Carolina's low country.

FINANCIAL DATA:
Amount of support per award: Varies.
Total amount of support: Varies.

NUMBER OF APPLICANTS MOST RECENT YEAR:
349.

NUMBER OF AWARDS: 315.

APPLICATION INFORMATION:
Proposals should be submitted in response to guidelines, if projects are applicable.
Duration: Typically one year.
Deadline: Varies.

PUBLICATIONS:
Application guidelines; annual report.

OFFICERS AND DIRECTORS:
Laura Donnelley, Chairman
Judith Stockdale, Executive Director
Elliott R. Donnelley, Life Director
Jane Rishel, Life Director
Sir Peter Crane, Director
Ceara Donnelley, Director
Shawn M. Donnelley, Director
Charles Lane, Director
Cheryl Mayberry McKissack, Director
Dr. John Rashford, Director
Max Wheeler, Director
Mimi Wheeler, Director
Tom Trinley, Director of Finance and Administration

ADDRESS INQUIRIES TO:
Program Director
(See address above.)

R.R. DONNELLEY   [116]
111 South Wacker Drive
Chicago, IL 60606
(312) 326-7302
(312) 326-7626
Fax: (312) 326-8387

E-MAIL ADDRESS:
communityrelations@rrd.com

WEB SITE ADDRESS:
www.rrdonnelley.com

FOUNDED: 1864

AREAS OF INTEREST:
Education, literacy, welfare, children at risk, support of the written word, and children and youth.

NAME(S) OF PROGRAMS:
● Corporate Contributions Program

TYPE:
General operating grants; Project/program grants. Scholarships are for children of employees only. Geographical focus on communities with manufacturing operations.

YEAR PROGRAM STARTED: 1964

PURPOSE:
To exercise corporate social responsibility, with special emphasis on enhancing the Company's manufacturing communities.

LEGAL BASIS:
Corporate contributions program.

ELIGIBILITY:
Grants are made only to nonprofit organizations. No grants are made to individuals.

FINANCIAL DATA:
Amount of support per award: Varies.
Total amount of support: Varies.

NUMBER OF APPLICANTS MOST RECENT YEAR:
Varies.

NUMBER OF AWARDS: Varies.

APPLICATION INFORMATION:
Requests should be in the form of a short proposal containing a description of the organization, its activities and its clients, a clear statement of what the organization wants from R.R. Donnelley and an explanation of what it plans to accomplish with such assistance. Attach a copy of the organization's IRS status letter, a list of board members and an audited financial statement. A limited amount of other supporting materials, such as an annual report, brochure or newsletter, is also welcome.
Duration: One year. Must reapply for additional funding.
Deadline: Proposals are accepted from January 1 to November 1 and referred to the next Contributions Committee meeting.

PUBLICATIONS:
Corporate Social Responsibility Report.

ADDRESS INQUIRIES TO:
Dr. Damayanti Vasudeven
Vice President, Diversity and Inclusion
(See address above.)

THE DOUTY FOUNDATION [117]
P.O. Box 540
Plymouth Meeting, PA 19462
(610) 828-8145
Fax: (610) 834-8175

E-MAIL ADDRESS:
judy1@aol.com

WEB SITE ADDRESS:
www.grants-info.org/douty
www.douty.org

FOUNDED: 1968

AREAS OF INTEREST:
Economic and educational opportunities to disadvantaged people, especially children.

TYPE:
General operating grants; Project/program grants. Projects with social impact, innovative projects and general operations.

YEAR PROGRAM STARTED: 1969

PURPOSE:
To support programs that provide either educational opportunities for the disadvantaged or local innovative social services.

LEGAL BASIS:
Tax-exempt private foundation.

ELIGIBILITY:
Qualifying tax-exempt organizations are eligible. Grants are not made for capital expenditures, agency promotions, annual reports, renovations or to organizations with annual budgets of more than $2,000,000. Grants are not made to individuals or for religious or political purposes.

GEOGRAPHIC RESTRICTIONS:
Greater Philadelphia, Pennsylvania area with preference to Montgomery and Philadelphia counties.

FINANCIAL DATA:
Amount of support per award: Up to $5,000.
Total amount of support: $240,453 for the year 2009.

NUMBER OF APPLICANTS MOST RECENT YEAR:
150 for the year 2009.

NUMBER OF AWARDS: 96 for the year 2009.

APPLICATION INFORMATION:
One copy of the proposal and seven copies of the proposal cover sheet are requested. No more than one application should be submitted within one year except under special circumstances.

The following information should be included in the application:
(1) name and purpose of organization;
(2) purpose of the grant;
(3) special nature of the project;
(4) estimated number of people to be served;
(5) leadership involved in the project;
(6) amount of funds requested;
(7) total funds needed;
(8) other funds available;
(9) Board of Trustees list;
(10) financial report, including annual budget and balance sheet and;
(11) determination letter showing tax-exempt status.

Applications may also be submitted online.
Duration: One year. Renewals are usually limited to four years.
Deadline: February 15, May 15 and October 15. Request for summer programs should be submitted by March 15 deadline.

IRS IDENTIFICATION NUMBER: 23-6463709

TRUSTEES:
Judith L. Bardes
Carrolle Perry Devonish
Thomas B. Harvey, Esq.
Steve Honeyman
Sylvie Gallier Howard
Nancy J. Kirby

STAFF:
Judith L. Bardes, Executive Director

ADDRESS INQUIRIES TO:
Judith L. Bardes, Executive Director
(See address above.)

*SPECIAL STIPULATIONS:
Organizations that have been funded for a five-year period may not reapply until at least two years have passed.

THE HERBERT H. AND GRACE A. DOW FOUNDATION [118]
1018 West Main Street
Midland, MI 48640-4292
(989) 631-3699
Fax: (989) 631-0675

E-MAIL ADDRESS:
info@hhdowfoundation.org

WEB SITE ADDRESS:
www.hhdowfdn.org

FOUNDED: 1936

AREAS OF INTEREST:
Education, science, community life, and arts and culture within the state of Michigan.

TYPE:
Capital grants; Matching gifts;
Project/program grants; Seed money grants.

Grants for religious, charitable, scientific, literary or educational purposes for the public benefaction of the inhabitants of the city of Midland and the people of the state of Michigan.

PURPOSE:
To improve the educational, religious, economic and cultural lives of Michigan's people as their lives, needs and wants can be defined in a world which constantly presents new or different challenges and opportunities.

LEGAL BASIS:
Private foundation.

ELIGIBILITY:
The Foundation does not make grants directly to individuals. Its charter limits its grants to Michigan organizations. In addition, it cannot legally support organizations to which contributions are not tax-deductible, according to IRS regulations, organizations that practice discrimination by race, sex, creed, age or national origin, political organizations or organizations whose purposes are to influence legislation other than by legislative means, or sectarian religious organizations or programs, other than churches in the Midland community.

The Trustees tend to support organizations that have clearly stated objectives, strong and purposeful management and are publicly accountable as to existing finances and expenditure of proposed grants, have needs which are not easily recognizable by or susceptible of governmental or public financing, are not hesitant to explore, initiate, volunteer or execute new, original ideas or concepts in the place of the traditional or customary, are willing to collaborate with other persons or organizations to give synergy to a common objective or goal and have purposes which tend to advance private enterprise and the preservation of a free, open and self-resourceful society.

GEOGRAPHIC RESTRICTIONS:
Michigan.

FINANCIAL DATA:
Amount of support per award: Usually larger awards for major projects: $100,000 to $5,000,000.
Matching fund requirements: Determined on a case-by-case basis.

COOPERATIVE FUNDING PROGRAMS: This Foundation often cooperates with other Midland foundations.

NUMBER OF AWARDS: Approximately 65 large awards; many smaller and miscellaneous grants.

APPLICATION INFORMATION:
There is no formal application form. Applicants should submit a letter setting forth the nature and potential results of a program for which funding is sought, the institutions and personnel responsible for the work, the total cost of the project, including endowment for operations, the amount of the grant sought from the Foundation, and how and over what period of time the grant may be disbursed. The letter should be accompanied by evidence of tax-exempt status, the latest audited financial statement, current budget and the names of management and the names and occupations of voluntary trustees or directors of the organization. Proposals should include provisions and procedures for continuing evaluation of programs for which support is requested.

Duration: One to three years. Large grants: Three years or more.

Deadline: The Board meets periodically during the year to make final grant decisions. Grants and installments of grants are usually disbursed late in December.

PUBLICATIONS:
Annual report (available online).

IRS IDENTIFICATION NUMBER: 38-1437485

STAFF:
Jenee Velasquez, Executive Director

OFFICERS AND TRUSTEES:
Margaret Ann Riecker, President
Michael L. Dow, Vice President
Macauley Whiting, Jr., Treasurer
Margaret E. Thompson, Secretary
Julie Arbury
Ruth A. Doan
Diane Dow Hullet
Bonnie Buchanan Matheson
Willard Mott
John Carras, Associate Trustee
Suzanna McCuan, Associate Trustee
Charles Riecker, Associate Trustee

ADDRESS INQUIRIES TO:
Margaret Ann Riecker, President
(See address above.)

*PLEASE NOTE:
Grant funds are often committed for years ahead.

*SPECIAL STIPULATIONS:
The Foundation's charter limits its grants to Michigan organizations.

DOW JONES FOUNDATION [119]
P.O. Box 300
Princeton, NJ 08543
(609) 520-4765
Fax: (609) 520-5180

E-MAIL ADDRESS:
howard.hoffman@dowjones.com

FOUNDED: 1954

AREAS OF INTEREST:
Promotion and protection of journalism, literacy and education.

TYPE:
General operating grants; Scholarships.

PURPOSE:
To support causes engaged in the promotion and protection of journalism, as well as causes devoted specifically to literacy and education.

LEGAL BASIS:
Corporate foundation.

ELIGIBILITY:
The Foundation does not currently make grants in medical and scientific research.

FINANCIAL DATA:
Amount of support per award: Varies.

APPLICATION INFORMATION:
All requests for Foundation support must be submitted in writing. Each request must indicate IRS tax-exemption certificate number.

Deadline: Normally, requests received will be considered by the board of directors only at their annual meeting in June for distribution in the next fiscal year.

PUBLICATIONS:
Application guidelines.

IRS IDENTIFICATION NUMBER: 13-6070158

OFFICERS:
Les Hinton, Chairman of the Advisory Committee
Howard Hoffman, Secretary

ADDRESS INQUIRIES TO:
Howard Hoffman, Secretary
(See address above.)

THE DRISCOLL FOUNDATION [120]
30 East 7th Street
Suite 2000
St. Paul, MN 55101
(651) 228-0935
Fax: (651) 228-0776

FOUNDED: 1963

AREAS OF INTEREST:
Arts and humanities, conservation of natural resources, education, health, religion and social welfare.

TYPE:
Project/program grants. Foundation policy restricts grants to organizations in the metropolitan areas of St. Paul and Minneapolis, MN, and San Francisco, CA.

Note: The Driscoll Foundation does not offer scholarships, operate any institution, or conduct studies, research or experimental projects. It is a grantmaking foundation, contributing to the support of programs of established, private, tax-exempt organizations.

YEAR PROGRAM STARTED: 1963

PURPOSE:
To support activities and programs of established, nonprofit organizations.

LEGAL BASIS:
Nonprofit corporation. Private, grantmaking foundation.

ELIGIBILITY:
Grants may be made in support of educational television organizations generally, or for one or more of their specific educational programs which may be videotaped.

The Foundation may support research on and studies of important problems of public concern, but solely for the purpose of gathering and presenting facts which may assist the public in better understanding such problems and arriving at realistic and effective solutions to them.

Grants are not made to individuals, organizations which conduct propaganda and lobbying programs, voter registration programs, conferences and seminars, travel by individuals or groups, publication of books, periodicals and monographs or production of films.

Grants usually are not made to other private foundations and as a rule are not made to operating foundations. Preference is given to those voluntary organizations that are classified under the "Tax Reform Act of 1969" as "public charities" or "non-private foundations."

GEOGRAPHIC RESTRICTIONS:
Generally confined to metropolitan areas of St. Paul and Minneapolis, Minnesota, and San Francisco, California.

FINANCIAL DATA:
Amount of support per award: Grants vary in amount, depending upon the needs and nature of the request.

COOPERATIVE FUNDING PROGRAMS: The Foundation prefers, if it contributes at all, to participate with other donors to a reasonable extent, but not to assume a major portion of the amount to be raised.

REPRESENTATIVE AWARDS:
$10,000 to Command and Staff College Foundation, Quantico, VA, for operating support.

APPLICATION INFORMATION:
There is no set form of application for grants. All applications should be delivered by mail to the Foundation's corporate headquarters at the address above.
Duration: One year.

PUBLICATIONS:
Annual report.

OFFICERS AND DIRECTORS:
W. John Driscoll, President
Elizabeth S. Driscoll

ADDRESS INQUIRIES TO:
W. John Driscoll, President
(See address above.)

JOSEPH DROWN FOUNDATION [121]
1999 Avenue of the Stars, Suite 2330
Los Angeles, CA 90067
(310) 277-4488
Fax: (310) 277-4573

E-MAIL ADDRESS:
staff@jdrown.org

WEB SITE ADDRESS:
www.jdrown.org

FOUNDED: 1953

AREAS OF INTEREST:
Education.

TYPE:
General operating grants; Project/program grants.

YEAR PROGRAM STARTED: 1953

PURPOSE:
To assist individuals in becoming successful, self-sustaining and contributing members of society.

ELIGIBILITY:
No funds to individuals, endowments, capital campaigns or building funds. The Foundation will not underwrite annual meeting or conferences. No funding for religious programs and special events.

In the area of medical research, the Foundation does not accept unsolicited requests.

GEOGRAPHIC RESTRICTIONS:
Los Angeles, California.

FINANCIAL DATA:
Amount of support per award: $5,000 to $50,000.

Total amount of support: Approximately $4,000,000 for the fiscal year ended March 31, 2011.

COOPERATIVE FUNDING PROGRAMS: LAUF.

NUMBER OF APPLICANTS MOST RECENT YEAR: 1,200.

NUMBER OF AWARDS: 150.

APPLICATION INFORMATION:
No special application form is required. Proposals should include a letter with information about both the organization as a whole and the project in particular, a

501(c)(3) tax determination letter from the IRS, a budget for both the organization as a whole and the project in particular, the most recent audited financial statements, a copy of the most recent Form 990 filed with the IRS and a list of the current board of directors. Any additional materials, such as an annual report, may be attached.

Duration: One year.

Deadline: January 15, April 15, July 15 and October 15 (postmark).

PUBLICATIONS:
Application guidelines.

OFFICERS AND STAFF:
Norman C. Obrow, Chairman
Wendy Wachtell, President
Ann T. Miller, Chief Financial Officer
Alyssa Ichelberger, Program Administrator

ADDRESS INQUIRIES TO:
Wendy Wachtell, President
(See address above.)

*SPECIAL STIPULATIONS:
In the area of medical research, the Foundation does not accept unsolicited requests.

THE DUCHOSSOIS FAMILY FOUNDATION   [122]
333 North Michigan, Suite 510
Chicago, IL 60601
(312) 641-5765
Fax: (312) 641-5736

FOUNDED: 1984

AREAS OF INTEREST:
Cancer research and mental illness.

TYPE:
Project/program grants; Research grants.

YEAR PROGRAM STARTED: 1984

PURPOSE:
To provide funding to nonprofit organizations to conduct research in the treatment of cancer, as well as funding for research into mental illness.

LEGAL BASIS:
Corporate foundation.

ELIGIBILITY:
Grants are made to nonprofit organizations that are IRS 501(c)(3) tax-exempt. Selection is based on the organization's value and performance. The Foundation does not provide support for individuals, including scholarships or fellowships, sectarian institutions or organizations or programs for which grants would be used primarily for the study and/or propagation of a particular field and/or organizations which are not recognized by the IRS as tax-exempt public charities.

GEOGRAPHIC RESTRICTIONS:
Chicago, Illinois metropolitan area.

FINANCIAL DATA:
Amount of support per award: Grants vary in amount, depending upon the needs and nature of the request.

Total amount of support: Approximately $1,000,000 for the year 2008.

APPLICATION INFORMATION:
Submit one-page summary request letter describing the organization, its needs and purposes and the amount of support requested. Also include a list of the board of directors and their business or professional affiliations.

Duration: One year. Renewals possible.

Deadline: Contact Foundation.

OFFICER:
Kimberly Duchossois, President

ADDRESS INQUIRIES TO:
Iris Krieg, Executive Director
(See address above.)

*SPECIAL STIPULATIONS:
The Foundation does not accept unsolicited proposals.

DORIS DUKE CHARITABLE FOUNDATION   [123]
650 Fifth Avenue, 19th Floor
New York, NY 10019
(212) 974-7000
Fax: (212) 974-7590

WEB SITE ADDRESS:
www.ddcf.org

FOUNDED: 1996

AREAS OF INTEREST:
Environment, performing arts, child abuse prevention and clinical research.

NAME(S) OF PROGRAMS:
- **Arts Program**
- **Child Abuse Prevention Program**
- **Environment Program**
- **Medical Research Program**

TYPE:
Grants-in-aid. The Arts Program supports performing artists with the creation and public performance of their work. DDCF supports artists and presenters in dance, jazz, theatre and multi-disciplinary performing arts.

The Child Abuse Prevention Program protects children from abuse and neglect in order to promote their healthy development. The Program's primary goal is to improve parent-child interactions and to increase parents' access to information and services that help prevent child maltreatment before it occurs.

The Environment Program preserves wildlife in the U.S., both flora and fauna. The Program seeks to accomplish its mission through two strategic initiatives:
(1) habitat conservation and;
(2) climate change.

The Medical Research Program supports the prevention, treatment and cure of human disease. The goal of the Program is to strengthen and support clinical research to help advance the translation of basic biomedical discoveries into new treatments, preventions and cures for human diseases.

YEAR PROGRAM STARTED: 1997

PURPOSE:
To improve the quality of people's lives by nurturing the arts, protecting and restoring the environment, seeking cures for diseases and helping to protect children from abuse and neglect.

LEGAL BASIS:
Nonprofit foundation.

APPLICATION INFORMATION:
Grants are initiated by the Foundation or are competitively awarded through Request for Proposal (RFP) processes. Foundation staff welcome two-page letters of inquiry from qualifying organizations which succinctly describe its mission and strategy and also

outline how its objectives relate to those of the Foundation. Fax applications to number above.

In selecting projects for Foundation support, consideration is given to the following questions:
Does the project address a significant funding gap or support a critical opportunity?
Is the project designed to achieve both the objectives of the applicant organization and the program goals of the Foundation?
What is the project's potential for long-term impact in terms of replication, reach or visibility in the field?
Does the applicant organization have the capacity to effectively execute the project?
What opportunity exists to leverage additional resources as a result of Foundation funding?

Applying organizations are requested not to send binders, books, CDs, videotapes or audiotapes.

Duration: Multiyear grants are awarded.

TRUSTEES:
Nannerl O. Keohane, Chairperson
Harry B. Demopoulos
Anthony S. Fauci
James F. Gill
Ann Hawley
John H.T. Wilson
John E. Zuccotti

STAFF:
Edward P. Henry, President
Linda Diamond, Program Associate for Grants Administration

ADDRESS INQUIRIES TO:
Office of Grants Administration
(See address above.)

THE DUKE ENDOWMENT   [124]
100 North Tryon Street
Suite 3500
Charlotte, NC 28202-4012
(704) 376-0291
Fax: (704) 376-9336

E-MAIL ADDRESS:
gcochrane@tde.org

WEB SITE ADDRESS:
www.dukeendowment.org

FOUNDED: 1924

AREAS OF INTEREST:
Not-for-profit hospitals in North Carolina and South Carolina; children's welfare and adoption assistance institutions in North Carolina and South Carolina; rural United Methodist churches and retired ministers in North Carolina and four colleges: Duke, Furman and Johnson C. Smith universities and Davidson College.

TYPE:
Capital grants; Challenge/matching grants; Conferences/seminars; Endowments; General operating grants; Matching gifts; Project/program grants; Scholarships.

YEAR PROGRAM STARTED: 1924

PURPOSE:
To carry out the terms of the Trust Indenture, as written by James B. Duke, by supporting four institutions in higher education, not-for-profit hospitals and children's homes in North Carolina and South Carolina, retired pastors of the United Methodist Church and programs and projects of rural United Methodist Churches in North Carolina.

LEGAL BASIS:
Charitable trust.

ELIGIBILITY:
North and South Carolina organizations and institutions with appropriate interests and activities are eligible.

GEOGRAPHIC RESTRICTIONS:
North Carolina and South Carolina.

FINANCIAL DATA:
Amount of support per award: Varies.
Total amount of support: $152,000,000 for the year 2010.
Matching fund requirements: Varies with grant.

NUMBER OF APPLICANTS MOST RECENT YEAR:
Varies.

NUMBER OF AWARDS: Varies.

REPRESENTATIVE AWARDS:
$12,000,000 multiyear grant to improve the health of United Methodist clergy in rural North Carolina; $15,000,000 to Duke University for a new program that makes civic engagement an integral part of an undergraduate's education.

APPLICATION INFORMATION:
Inquiries about grant disbursement policies may be directed to the address above.
Duration: Typically one year. All eligible beneficiaries may request continued and renewed support.
Deadline: Applications are accepted at any time. Grant decisions are made by trustees who meet 10 times per year.

PUBLICATIONS:
Annual report; occasional papers and reports on projects and programs.

IRS IDENTIFICATION NUMBER: 56-0529965

TRUSTEES AND OFFICERS:
L. Neil Williams, Jr., Chairman
Mary Duke Trent Jones, Vice Chairman
Minor Mickel Shaw, Vice Chairman
Eugene W. Cochrane, Jr., President
Rhett N. Mabry, Vice President
Mary L. Piepenbring, Vice President
Karen H. Rogers, Treasurer
Terri W. Honeycutt, Corporate Secretary
Arthur E. Morehead, IV, Staff Counsel
Todd Walker, Director Investments
William G. Anlyan, M.D.
William Barnet, III
Dennis M. Campbell, Ph.D.
Ravenel B. Curry, III
Constance F. Gray
Thomas S. Kenan, III
Charles C. Lucas, III
Wilhelmina Reuben-Cooke, J.D.
Russell M. Robinson, II
Mary D.B.T. Semans
Jean G. Spaulding, M.D.
Kenneth D. Weeks, Jr., M.D.

ADDRESS INQUIRIES TO:
Eugene W. Cochrane, Jr., President
(See address above.)

THE CALEB C. AND JULIA W. DULA EDUCATIONAL AND CHARITABLE FOUNDATION [125]
112 South Hanley Road, 2nd Floor
St. Louis, MO 63105-3418
(314) 726-2800
Fax: (314) 863-3821

FOUNDED: 1939

AREAS OF INTEREST:
Higher and secondary education, libraries, hospitals, social service, church support, cultural programs and historic preservation.

TYPE:
General operating grants; Project/program grants. Grants for projects and, to a lesser degree, general support.

PURPOSE:
To provide funding to projects of interest to the Foundation.

LEGAL BASIS:
Missouri nonprofit corporation; educational and charitable foundation.

ELIGIBILITY:
501(c)(3) tax-exempt organizations in the Foundation's areas of interest are eligible to apply. No grants are made to individuals.

GEOGRAPHIC RESTRICTIONS:
United States.

FINANCIAL DATA:
Amount of support per award: $5,000 to $100,000.

APPLICATION INFORMATION:
There are no set requirements. A letter/proposal describing the organization and the project along with the amount requested should be sent to the Trustees in care of James F. Mauze, Esq. Requests are forwarded to the Trustees who meet in the spring and the fall.
Duration: Varies.
Deadline: March 15 and October 15.

ADDRESS INQUIRIES TO:
James F. Mauze, Esq.
(See address above.)

DUNSPAUGH DALTON FOUNDATION [126]
1500 San Remo Avenue, Suite 103
Coral Gables, FL 33146
(305) 668-4192
Fax: (305) 668-4247

E-MAIL ADDRESS:
dunspaughdalton@aol.com

WEB SITE ADDRESS:
dunspaughdalton.com

AREAS OF INTEREST:
Higher, secondary, and elementary education; social services; youth; health associations and hospitals; cultural programs; and civic affairs.

TYPE:
Capital grants; Endowments; General operating grants; Professorships; Project/program grants.

ELIGIBILITY:
Grants are made to organizations that have tax-exempt status under Section 501(c)(3) of the Internal Revenue Code. No grants are made to individuals.

GEOGRAPHIC RESTRICTIONS:
Monterey Peninsula and northern California, Miami-Dade County, Florida and North Carolina.

FINANCIAL DATA:
Amount of support per award: $10,000 average.

APPLICATION INFORMATION:
Applicant must submit:
(1) proposal summary (not to exceed one-half page) explaining why the grant is requested, what outcomes are hoped to be achieved and how funds will be spent;
(2) narrative including background, funding requirements and evaluation (not to exceed five pages);
(3) completed Grant Application Form and;
(4) the most recent financial statements used as the basis for filing IRS Form 990.

Mail, e-mail or fax all application documents to either office listed on the Grant Application Form.
Duration: One year. Can reapply.
Deadline: The board meets every one to two months to consider requests.

ADDRESS INQUIRIES TO:
Leslie W. Buchanan, Secretary/Treasurer or Alexina Lane, Vice-President
(See address above.)

If living in northern California:
Sarah Bonner, President
P.O. Box 1437
Pebble Beach, CA 93953

JESSIE BALL DUPONT FUND [127]
One Independent Drive
Suite 1400
Jacksonville, FL 32202-5011
(904) 353-0890
(800) 252-3452
Fax: (904) 353-3870

E-MAIL ADDRESS:
contactus@dupontfund.org

WEB SITE ADDRESS:
www.dupontfund.org

FOUNDED: 1976

AREAS OF INTEREST:
Education, religion, health and human services, arts and culture, juvenile delinquency, environment, women and children's issues, historic preservation, economic and community development, nonprofit development and asset building.

TYPE:
Challenge/matching grants; General operating grants; Project/program grants; Seed money grants; Technical assistance. Organizational capacity building.

Geared to nonprofit, religious organizations and small liberal arts colleges.

YEAR PROGRAM STARTED: 1976

PURPOSE:
To assist eligible institutions in developing the capacity to meet the present and future needs of their specialized constituencies and local communities.

LEGAL BASIS:
Private foundation.

ELIGIBILITY:
Applicant organizations must have received a contribution from Mrs. duPont between January 1, 1960 and December 31, 1964. No grants to individuals.

GEOGRAPHIC RESTRICTIONS:
Primarily the South, especially Delaware, Florida, and Virginia.

FINANCIAL DATA:
Amount of support per award: $98 to $500,000 for the year 2009. Average: $10,000.
Total amount of support: $10,788,157 in grants paid for the year 2009.

NUMBER OF APPLICANTS MOST RECENT YEAR: 350 for the year ended December 31, 2009.

NUMBER OF AWARDS: 314 grants for the year ended December 31, 2009.

APPLICATION INFORMATION:
The Fund makes grants only to a defined universe of organizations. Proof of eligibility is determined by examining Mrs. duPont's personal or tax records or by the applicant presenting written, verifiable evidence of having received a contribution during the eligibility period.
Duration: Usually one year, but may extend up to five years.
Deadline: Trustees meet quarterly in February, May, August and November to consider grant applications. Awards are announced immediately after the meetings.

PUBLICATIONS:
Annual report; application form; brochures, "Notes from the Field."

IRS IDENTIFICATION NUMBER: 59-6368632

TRUSTEES:
Thomas H. Jeavons, Chairperson
Mary Lynn Huntley, Vice Chairperson
David Llewellyn, Representing Corporate Co-Trustee, Northern Trust
Rev. Eddie E. Jones, Jr., Clerical Trustee
Leroy Davis
Audrey McKibbin Moran
Mary K. Phillips

STAFF:
Sherry P. Magill, Ph.D., President
Mark Constantine, Vice President for Strategy, Policy and Learning
Sally Douglass, Director of Programs
Barbara Roole, Senior Policy Director
Katie Ensign, Senior Program Officer
Edward King, Jr., Senior Program Officer

*PLEASE NOTE:
Guidelines must be followed carefully when submitting proposal.

EASTERN BANK CHARITABLE FOUNDATION [128]

195 Market Street
Lynn, MA 01901
(781) 598-7595
Fax: (781) 596-4445

E-MAIL ADDRESS:
l.kurzrok@easternbank.com

WEB SITE ADDRESS:
www.easternbank.com

FOUNDED: 1994

AREAS OF INTEREST:
Human services, family and children, affordable housing, community health.

TYPE:
Capital grants; Endowments; Project/program grants. Community grants; Partnership grants.

YEAR PROGRAM STARTED: 1994

PURPOSE:
To contribute, in a meaningful way, to the health and vitality of the various communities which are served by Eastern Bank, by providing financial support to selected nonprofit organizations operating within these communities.

LEGAL BASIS:
Corporate foundation.

ELIGIBILITY:
Applicants must be nonprofit 501(c)(3) organizations and be located in the market area served by Eastern Bank. The Foundation does not accept applications from organizations with 509(a)(3) designation or private foundations.

GEOGRAPHIC RESTRICTIONS:
Eastern Massachusetts area.

FINANCIAL DATA:
Amount of support per award: $50 to $50,000.
Total amount of support: $2,465,937 for the year 2010.
Matching fund requirements: Full-time employees, trustees and directors: Minimum $50, maximum $1,000 per year.

NUMBER OF APPLICANTS MOST RECENT YEAR: 2,000.

NUMBER OF AWARDS: 900.

APPLICATION INFORMATION:
Applications are only accepted through the online application site.
Deadline: Ongoing for requests up to $10,000. Requests for Eastern Bank grants ($10,000 to $50,000): March 1 and September 1.

PUBLICATIONS:
Annual report, available online.

IRS IDENTIFICATION NUMBER: 22-3317340

ADDRESS INQUIRIES TO:
Laura Kurzrok, Executive Director
(See address above.)

EATON CORPORATION [129]

Eaton Center
1111 Superior Avenue
Cleveland, OH 44114-2584
(216) 523-4944
Fax: (216) 479-7013

E-MAIL ADDRESS:
barrydoggett@eaton.com

WEB SITE ADDRESS:
www.eaton.com

FOUNDED: 1953

AREAS OF INTEREST:
Education, arts and culture, children at-risk, community improvement and neighborhood development.

TYPE:
Capital grants; Challenge/matching grants; Matching gifts; Product donations; Project/program grants. The Corporation places a priority on contributing to those organizations in which Eaton employees are personally involved and which serve their needs. Contributions are made to health, human service, civic, arts and cultural organizations and educational institutions.

Support of capital campaigns at educational institutions is generally limited to programs of direct interest to Eaton, which prefers to invest in engineering, scientific, technological and business-related projects.

YEAR PROGRAM STARTED: 1953

PURPOSE:
To contribute to the betterment of life in communities where Eaton employees live and work; to support employee involvement and investment; to promote self-sufficiency; to sustain arts and cultural institutions; to enhance education.

LEGAL BASIS:
Corporate foundation.

ELIGIBILITY:
501(c)(3) organizations within the Corporation's areas of interest are eligible for support. Grants are not made to religious, fraternal or labor organizations; to individuals or individual endeavors; debt retirement; medical research; endowment funds; fund-raising benefits, sponsorships or other events; or annual operating budgets of United Way agencies or hospitals.

FINANCIAL DATA:
Amount of support per award: Typically, $1,000 to $100,000. Average: $5,000 to $15,000.
Total amount of support: U.S.: $6,864,000 for the year 2008; U.S. and international: $7,948,000 for the year 2008. These cash grants are mainly from the Charitable Fund, but also from the company.
Matching fund requirements: The Corporation single-matches employee contributions to nationally accredited educational institutions and arts and cultural organizations approved by the Corporate Contributions Committee.

REPRESENTATIVE AWARDS:
$20,000 to Rhode Island Mentoring Partnership, Warwick, RI; $5,000 to Lakewood Ranch YMCA, Sarasota, FL; $13,600 to Manavya Home, Pune, India; $16,225 to Belmond Area United Way, Belmond, IA.

APPLICATION INFORMATION:
Send requests to the nearest company facility. All requests for contributions must be in writing. Each should include a one-page cover letter (on organization letterhead), a one- to three-page description of organization's program, and an attached description of the organization's history and purpose, identification of other organizations (including corporations) involved in funding the program and gift amounts committed, names of Eaton employees and a description of their involvement (if applicable), copies of the most recently audited financial statements and the current budget, a roster of officers and directors or trustees of the organization and their affiliations, and official government documentation of the organization's 501(c)(3) tax-exempt IRS status (or its non-U.S. equivalent).

Grants are generally limited to one grant per organization in a given year. Previous grants are not considered as precedent for additional support. Proposals should not be submitted in binders or with videotapes, CD-ROMs and/or in other costly manners.
Duration: Grants are typically given for one year. Multiyear commitments are usually capital grants.
Deadline: Grant requests are accepted and reviewed throughout the year.

PUBLICATIONS:
Annual report; guidelines.

STAFF:
Veronica M. Runcis, Manager, Public Affairs
Emily A. Stitt, Administrator, Gift Matching Program

CONTRIBUTIONS COMMITTEE:
W.B. Doggett, Chairman
Craig Arnold
Bill Blausey
Thomas Gross
James McGill
Kurt McMaken

ADDRESS INQUIRIES TO:
W.B. Doggett, Senior Vice President
Public and Community Affairs
(See address above.)

EDISON INTERNATIONAL   [130]
2244 Walnut Grove Avenue, Quad 4A G.O. 1
Rosemead, CA 91770
(626) 302-5538
Fax: (626) 302-7985

E-MAIL ADDRESS:
tammy.tumbling@sce.com

WEB SITE ADDRESS:
www.sce.com

FOUNDED: 1996

AREAS OF INTEREST:
Education, environment and the underserved.

CONSULTING OR VOLUNTEER SERVICES:
Volunteer Program, Energy in Action.

NAME(S) OF PROGRAMS:
● **Corporate Contributions Program**
● **Employee Matching Gifts Program**

TYPE:
Challenge/matching grants; General operating
grants; Matching gifts; Project/program
grants; Scholarships. Matching gifts and
employees for education only: private and
public schools (K-University).

YEAR PROGRAM STARTED: 1986

PURPOSE:
To promote the economic prosperity and
overall quality of life in the areas where its
employees live and work by supporting
numerous community initiatives and
historically supporting a variety of effective
educational, civic and charitable activities.

LEGAL BASIS:
Nonprofit 501(c)(3) organization.

ELIGIBILITY:
Focus on Southern California and areas with
a concentration of employees.

No grants to individuals, political
organizations or candidates, veterans
organizations, fraternal orders, labor groups,
commercial profit-making enterprises,
religious or sectarian organizations or any
group whose activities are not in the best
interests of Edison International, its
employees, shareholders, customers or the
communities it serves.

FINANCIAL DATA:
Amount of support per award: Average
$10,000 or less.
Matching fund requirements: Equal match to
$2,000 for accredited public and private
educational institutions.

NUMBER OF APPLICANTS MOST RECENT YEAR:
Varies.

NUMBER OF AWARDS: Varies.

REPRESENTATIVE AWARDS:
$250,000 to Aquarium of the Pacific;
$10,000 to Women's Foundation of
California; $40,000 to Walking Shield
American Indian Society.

APPLICATION INFORMATION:
Applications for Edison grants and
sponsorships must be submitted online during
Edison's funding cycles. Application links
are active only during funding cycles.
Deadline: Funding cycles are during the
months of February, May and August.

PUBLICATIONS:
Annual report; contributions policy;
application guidelines.

OFFICERS:
John E. Bryson, Chairman

ADDRESS INQUIRIES TO:
Tammy Tumbling
Manager of Community Involvement
(See address above.)

EL POMAR FOUNDATION   [131]
10 Lake Circle
Colorado Springs, CO 80906
(719) 633-7733
Fax: (719) 577-7010

E-MAIL ADDRESS:
fellowship@elpomar.org; grants@elpomar.org

WEB SITE ADDRESS:
www.elpomar.org

FOUNDED: 1937

AREAS OF INTEREST:
Health, education, welfare, arts and culture,
humanities, civic and community, and
leadership.

NAME(S) OF PROGRAMS:
● **Fellowship Program**
● **Grants Program**

TYPE:
Capital grants; Challenge/matching grants;
Fellowships; General operating grants;
Matching gifts; Project/program grants;
Scholarships; Technical assistance. The
Fellowship Program brings highly qualified
college graduates with diverse backgrounds
and interests to the Foundation. This program
focuses on professional development and
prepares Fellows for positions of leadership
in Colorado and the nation. Grants Program
is to support construction, development and
acquisition of buildings and equipment and
other projects in education, health,
humanities, resources, environment and
welfare in the state of Colorado.

PURPOSE:
To support general-purpose grantmaking,
civic collaboration, projects of major
community importance and initiatives that
provide various kinds of assistance to
nonprofit organizations; to provide leadership
development opportunities for a range of
individuals, from those just out of college to
those responsible for the state's most
important nonprofits; to help those least able
to help themselves.

LEGAL BASIS:
Private nonprofit charitable foundation.

ELIGIBILITY:
Colorado organizations with appropriate
interests may apply. Fully tax-supported
institutions are not eligible, but requests from
municipalities will be considered if funds are
required for a specific project. Scholarships
and fellowships are not granted directly.

The Foundation does not make grants under
the following conditions:
(1) to another foundation or organization
which distributes money to recipients of its
own selection;
(2) to organizations that practice
discrimination of any kind;
(3) to cover deficits, debt elimination or for
endowment;
(4) for the making of films or other media
projects;

(5) for primary or secondary education
(K-12), although the Foundation will
consider, on a limited basis, capital requests
from nonpublicly funded secondary schools;
(6) for research or studies;
(7) to organizations which do not have fiscal
responsibility for the proposed project;
(8) to nonprofit organizations that do not
have an active 501(c)(3) nonprofit
determination letter from the IRS;
(9) to individuals;
(10) for travel, conferences, conventions,
group meetings or seminars;
(11) for camps, camp programs or other
seasonal activities;
(12) to religious organizations for support of
religious programs and;
(13) for grants intended to influence
legislation or support candidates for political
office.

Because of the tremendous needs throughout
the state of Colorado, grant requests of more
than $100,000 will be considered only in
exceptional circumstances.

GEOGRAPHIC RESTRICTIONS:
Colorado.

FINANCIAL DATA:
Amount of support per award: Fellowship
Program: $29,000; Grants Program: $2,500 to
$50,000.
Total amount of support: Approximately
$20,000,000 annually.

NUMBER OF AWARDS: 708 for the year 2009.

APPLICATION INFORMATION:
All inquiries to the Foundation should be in
writing and no interviews are granted until
after an application is received.
Duration: Fellowship Program: Two years;
Grant Program: Typically one year.

PUBLICATIONS:
Annual report; application guidelines.

IRS IDENTIFICATION NUMBER: 84-6002373

OFFICERS:
William J. Hybl, Chairman and Chief
Executive Officer
R. Thayer Tutt, Jr., President and Chief
Investment Officer
Robert J. Hilbert, Secretary, Treasurer and
Senior Vice President, Administration
David J. Palenchar, Senior Vice President,
Operations

TRUSTEES:
Judy Bell
Robert J. Hilbert
William J. Hybl
David J. Palenchar
Brenda J. Smith
R. Thayer Tutt, Jr.
William R. Ward

ADDRESS INQUIRIES TO:
William J. Hybl
Chairman and Chief Executive Officer
(See address above.)

RUTH H. AND WARREN A. ELLSWORTH FOUNDATION   [132]
c/o Fletcher Tilton-Whipple
370 Main Street, 11th Floor
Worcester, MA 01608
(508) 459-8000
(508) 459-8042
Fax: (508) 459-8342

E-MAIL ADDRESS:
stilton@ftwlaw.com

AREAS OF INTEREST:
Culture, education, health and human services.

TYPE:
Project/program grants.

PURPOSE:
To support organizations that are providing solutions to or preventing problems within the immediate community.

ELIGIBILITY:
Grants are made to organizations that have tax-exempt status under Section 501(c)(3) of the Internal Revenue Code. No grants are made to individuals. Nonsectarian religious programs may apply.

The Foundation does not usually fund grants for general operating expense.

GEOGRAPHIC RESTRICTIONS:
Worcester, Massachusetts and surrounding area.

FINANCIAL DATA:
Amount of support per award: $500 to $25,000.

APPLICATION INFORMATION:
Submit a proposal in a letter form and a grant application summary.
Deadline: June 1.

ADDRESS INQUIRIES TO:
Karen Brady, Administrator
(See address above.)

EMERSON   [133]
8000 West Florissant Avenue
St. Louis, MO 63136
(314) 553-2000
(314) 553-3621

WEB SITE ADDRESS:
www.emerson.com

FOUNDED: 1944

AREAS OF INTEREST:
Education; youth, culture and the arts; health, welfare and civic needs.

TYPE:
Capital grants; Challenge/matching grants; Development grants; Endowments; General operating grants; Matching gifts; Project/program grants.

YEAR PROGRAM STARTED: 1950

PURPOSE:
To encourage sound, innovative programs that enrich human lives, promote volunteerism, provide services directly to those in need and increase the overall impact of contributed funds.

LEGAL BASIS:
Corporate contributions program.

ELIGIBILITY:
Grants are made to organizations having IRS 501(c)(3) tax-exempt status, located in areas where Emerson has facilities. The Trust does not contribute to organizations that practice discrimination by race, color, creed, sex, age or national origin, religious or politically partisan organizations, projects requiring funding directly to an organization located outside the U.S. or its territories, loans or investment funds, fraternal, veterans' or labor groups unless they furnish services benefiting the general public, aid to individuals, underwriting of deficits or post-event funding.

FINANCIAL DATA:
Amount of support per award: Varies.
Total amount of support: Approximately $23,000,000 for the year 2010.

REPRESENTATIVE AWARDS:
Arkansas College; Work Force 2000, IA; AIDS Foundation of St. Louis, MO; Bach Society of St. Louis, MO; Cypress Pops Orchestra, CA.

APPLICATION INFORMATION:
Proposals should be submitted in writing and include the following information:
(1) brief description and history of the organization submitting the proposal;
(2) a clear statement of the purpose and objectives of the project or program (including expected results), the program budget, the amount requested, a statement of how the funds will be used and a timetable of project completion;
(3) statement of the relationship of the project's goals to the priorities of the Emerson Charitable Trust;
(4) annual report or audited financial statement of the requesting organization showing income and expenses, operational budget and which may include a copy of the most recent IRS 990 report;
(5) supporting factual information that may be useful as a basis of evaluation, such as a list of sources providing support to the organization;
(6) copy of the organization's IRS 501(c)(3) tax-exemption statement;
(7) listing of the organization's Board of Directors and a statement regarding staff who will manage the project and;
(8) statement of general plans for sustaining activities and post-grant evaluation of the project.
Applicants should expect a 30- to 60-day turnaround on all written proposals.
Duration: One year. Must reapply, unless multiyear funding at outset.

PUBLICATIONS:
Annual report; guidelines.

ADDRESS INQUIRIES TO:
Robert M. Cox, Jr., Senior Vice President
(See address above.)

ERION FOUNDATION   [134]
P.O. Box 732
Loveland, CO 80539
(970) 667-4549
Fax: (970) 663-6187

E-MAIL ADDRESS:
contact@erionfoundation.org

WEB SITE ADDRESS:
www.erionfoundation.org

FOUNDED: 1986

AREAS OF INTEREST:
Education, health, welfare, and culture.

TYPE:
Capital grants; Challenge/matching grants; Development grants; Endowments.

YEAR PROGRAM STARTED: 1986

PURPOSE:
To support the Loveland, CO community.

LEGAL BASIS:
Private foundation.

ELIGIBILITY:
Eligible organizations must be IRS 501(c)(3) tax-exempt.

GEOGRAPHIC RESTRICTIONS:
Loveland, Colorado and the immediate surrounding area.

FINANCIAL DATA:
Amount of support per award: Varies.

APPLICATION INFORMATION:
Applicants must submit via mail:
(1) completed application form;
(2) a copy of the organization's 501(c)(3) designation letter and;
(3) page one of the organization's most recent IRS Form 990.
Duration: Varies.

ADDRESS INQUIRIES TO:
Doug Erion, Grants Administrator
(See address above.)

EXELON CORPORATION   [135]
Corporate Relations
10 South Dearborn, 53rd Floor
Chicago, IL 60603
(312) 394-4361

E-MAIL ADDRESS:
steve.solomon@exeloncorp.com

WEB SITE ADDRESS:
www.exeloncorp.com

FOUNDED: 1888

AREAS OF INTEREST:
Math and science, environmental education, arts and culture, and neighborhood development.

NAME(S) OF PROGRAMS:
● **Corporate Giving Program**

TYPE:
General operating grants; Project/program grants; Scholarships.

PURPOSE:
To strengthen customer and community relations by promoting the advancement of math, science and energy education, contributing to charitable organizations that promote efficiency and renewable energy, promoting economic and community development, and contributing to organizations that promote diversity in the workplace and community.

LEGAL BASIS:
Corporate contributions program.

ELIGIBILITY:
Grants are made to institutions, organizations and agencies located in Exelon's service area (northern Illinois and southeastern Pennsylvania). Educational giving is limited to private colleges and universities. The company does not purchase ads in benefit programs. No contributions are made to religious organizations for religious purposes, political organizations, or to individuals.

GEOGRAPHIC RESTRICTIONS:
Northern Illinois and Southeastern Pennsylvania.

FINANCIAL DATA:
Amount of support per award: Average: $12,000.
Total amount of support: $17,900,000 for the year 2010.
Matching fund requirements: Education only.

NUMBER OF AWARDS: 300.

APPLICATION INFORMATION:
A letter briefly outlining the proposal should be addressed to Steve Solomon, Director of Corporate Relations, at the address above. The company accepts the Chicago Area Common Application Form.

Duration: One year.

Deadline: Applications are reviewed on an ongoing basis.

PUBLICATIONS:
Guidelines.

STAFF:
John W. Rowe, Chairman and Chief Executive Officer of Exelon Corp.
Frank Clark, Chairman and Chief Executive Officer of ComEd
Denis O'Brien, President and Chief Executive Officer of PECO Energy

ADDRESS INQUIRIES TO:
Steve Solomon
Director of Corporate Relations
(See address above.)

EXXONMOBIL CORPORATION [136]

5959 Las Colinas Boulevard
Irving, TX 75039-2298
(972) 444-1106
Fax: (972) 444-1405

E-MAIL ADDRESS:
contributions@exxonmobil.com

WEB SITE ADDRESS:
www.exxonmobil.com/community

FOUNDED: 1998

AREAS OF INTEREST:
Environment, public information and policy research, higher education and pre-college education, health, minority and women-oriented service organizations.

CONSULTING OR VOLUNTEER SERVICES:
The corporation encourages its employees and annuitants to volunteer at nonprofit agencies which serve their local communities with Volunteer Involvement Fund (VIF) grants of up to $500 each.

TYPE:
Capital grants; General operating grants; Matching gifts; Project/program grants.

YEAR PROGRAM STARTED: 1998

PURPOSE:
To provide funding to worthwhile organizations with interests that mirror those of the company.

LEGAL BASIS:
Corporate contributions program.

ELIGIBILITY:
ExxonMobil makes grants to organizations which have tax-deductible status under Section 501(c)(3) of the Internal Revenue Code. In general, ExxonMobil contributes to organizations and activities which are national or international in scope or significance and to local agencies only in geographic areas where there is a significant concentration of ExxonMobil employees or facilities.

ExxonMobil does not provide funds to be used for religious or political purposes or to individuals. Generally excluded from the grants program are contributions to endowments, organizations formed to combat a single disease and operating support to agencies funded by United Way.

GEOGRAPHIC RESTRICTIONS:
Baldwin and Mobile counties, Alabama; Anchorage, Fairbanks, Juneau and North Slope, Alaska; Santa Barbara County and Torrance, California; District of Columbia; LaGrange, Georgia; Joliet and vicinity, Illinois; Kingman and Stevens County, Kansas; Baton Rouge, Chalmette, Louisiana; Detroit, Michigan; Billings, Montana; Clinton and Paulsboro, New Jersey; Lea County, New Mexico; Rochester, New York; Akron, Ohio; Shawnee and Texas County, Oklahoma; Baytown, Beaumont, Dallas/Fort Worth, Houston and vicinity, Midland/Odessa and Tyler/Longview, Texas; San Juan County, Utah; Fairfax County and northern Virginia; Lincoln, Sublette and Sweetwater counties, Wyoming.

FINANCIAL DATA:
Amount of support per award: Varies.

APPLICATION INFORMATION:
ExxonMobil does not seek, and rarely funds, unsolicited applications and project proposals.

PUBLICATIONS:
Annual report.

ADDRESS INQUIRIES TO:
Larry Harlan, Manager
Corporate Citizenship and Community Investments
(See address above.)

FARGO-MOORHEAD AREA FOUNDATION [137]

502 First Avenue North, Suite 202
Fargo, ND 58102
(701) 234-0756
Fax: (701) 234-9724

E-MAIL ADDRESS:
office@areafoundation.org

WEB SITE ADDRESS:
www.areafoundation.org

FOUNDED: 1960

AREAS OF INTEREST:
Arts; education; human, youth, civic and health services.

TYPE:
Project/program grants; Scholarships.

PURPOSE:
To encourage philanthropy; to develop a permanent endowment to assess and respond to emerging and changing community needs; to provide a permanent charitable trust to donors with varied interests and giving capacities.

ELIGIBILITY:
Must be 501(c)(3) nonprofit organization.

GEOGRAPHIC RESTRICTIONS:
Cass and Clay counties, Minnesota and North Dakota.

FINANCIAL DATA:
Amount of support per award: Varies per award.

Total amount of support: Approximately $2,300,000 annually.

NUMBER OF AWARDS: Varies.

APPLICATION INFORMATION:
Organizations applying for funds are required to use the Foundation Grant Proposal Forms available online, by regular mail, phone or e-mail (cher@areafoundation.org).

Duration: One year.

Deadline: Grant Proposals will be accepted anytime before 4:30 P.M., on April 20. Applicants will be notified on or before May 31.

ADDRESS INQUIRIES TO:
Cher Hersrud, Advancement Officer
(See address above.)

FIELD FOUNDATION OF ILLINOIS [138]

200 South Wacker Drive, Suite 3860
Chicago, IL 60606
(312) 831-0910
Fax: (312) 831-0961

E-MAIL ADDRESS:
apennick@fieldfoundation.org

WEB SITE ADDRESS:
www.fieldfoundation.org

FOUNDED: 1960

AREAS OF INTEREST:
Education, health, culture, the environment, community welfare and urban and community affairs, primarily serving Chicago.

TYPE:
Capital grants; Challenge/matching grants; General operating grants; Matching gifts; Project/program grants; Research grants; Technical assistance; Training grants. Support is available for general and capital support and special programs.

Requests from major cultural institutions for capital gifts is restricted to repairs/maintenance or replacement.

Urban affairs grants are made for programs that strengthen, unify and build urban communities' metropolitan areas or neighborhoods.

Through its grants program in primary and secondary education, the Foundation is interested in supporting individual public schools or clusters of schools in three areas:
(1) curriculum development;
(2) teaching quality and;
(3) parental involvement.

YEAR PROGRAM STARTED: 1962

PURPOSE:
To provide support for community, civic and cultural organizations in the Chicago area, enabling both new and established programs to test innovations, to expand proven strengths or to address specific, time-limited operational needs.

LEGAL BASIS:
Private foundation.

ELIGIBILITY:
Support is limited to programs primarily serving Chicago residents. Grants are made to nonprofit institutions. Grants are not made directly to individuals.

GEOGRAPHIC RESTRICTIONS:
Chicago, Illinois.

FINANCIAL DATA:
Amount of support per award:
Programs/projects: $10,000 to $25,000.
Grants to individual schools do not exceed $20,000 a year.

Total amount of support: Approximately $3,000,000 annually.

NUMBER OF APPLICANTS MOST RECENT YEAR: 300.

APPLICATION INFORMATION:
Letter of application should include a brief description of the project, the proposed budget, history and background of the applying organization and certification of the organization's IRS status.

Duration: One year. Project/program and capital funding: Possible renewals up to three years.

Deadline: May 15, September 15 and January 15.

OFFICERS:
Judy Block, Chairman
Aurie Pennick, Executive Director and Treasurer
Sarah Linsley, Secretary and General Counsel

BOARD OF DIRECTORS:
Judy Block
Gloria Castillo
Marshall Field
Lyle Logan
F. Oliver Nicklin
George A. Ranney, Jr.

ADDRESS INQUIRIES TO:
Grants Manager
(See address above.)

FIRMAN FUND [139]

1422 Euclid Avenue
Hanna Building, Suite 1030
Cleveland, OH 44115-2004
(216) 363-1030
Fax: (216) 363-1038

AREAS OF INTEREST:
Medicine, education, culture, youth, welfare, conservation and community funds.

TYPE:
Capital grants; Endowments; General operating grants; Project/program grants; Research grants.

LEGAL BASIS:
Tax-exempt, private foundation.

ELIGIBILITY:
Tax-exempt organizations may apply. No grants are awarded to individuals. No unsolicited requests accepted.

GEOGRAPHIC RESTRICTIONS:
Colorado and Florida.

FINANCIAL DATA:
Amount of support per award: $1,000 to $250,000.

Total amount of support: Approximately $450,000 for the year 2010.

NUMBER OF APPLICANTS MOST RECENT YEAR:
50.

NUMBER OF AWARDS: 30.

APPLICATION INFORMATION:
A letter should be submitted concisely describing the project and its intended purpose, including a budget and projected needs.

Duration: Grants awarded are not to be considered on a continuing basis. Yearly renewal on request.

Deadline: March, June and September.

TRUSTEES:
Royal Firman, III
Stephanie Firman
Cynthia F. Webster
Robert C. Webster, Jr.

ADDRESS INQUIRIES TO:
Neil A. Brown, Secretary
(See address above.)

FIRST COMMUNITY FOUNDATION OF PENNSYLVANIA [140]

330 Pine Street, Suite 400
Williamsport, PA 17701
(570) 321-1500
Fax: (570) 321-6434

E-MAIL ADDRESS:
bettyg@fcfpa.org

WEB SITE ADDRESS:
www.fcfpa.org

FOUNDED: 1916

AREAS OF INTEREST:
Arts and culture, education, recreation and environment, health, human services, economic and community development.

CONSULTING OR VOLUNTEER SERVICES:
Estate planning seminars, grant applicant training.

NAME(S) OF PROGRAMS:
● **The Ralph and Josephine Smith Fund for Northumberland County**
● **The Margaret Waldron Memorial Trust Fund**
● **The Williamsport-Lycoming Community Foundation Grants**

TYPE:
Project/program grants.

YEAR PROGRAM STARTED: 1998

PURPOSE:
To improve the quality of life in Williamsport and Lycoming County, PA.

LEGAL BASIS:
Community foundation.

ELIGIBILITY:
Central and northcentral Pennsylvania qualified 501(c)(3) organizations only.

GEOGRAPHIC RESTRICTIONS:
Bradford, Lycoming, Montour, Northumberland, Sullivan and Union counties, Pennsylvania.

FINANCIAL DATA:
Amount of support per award: Varies.
Total amount of support: Varies.

COOPERATIVE FUNDING PROGRAMS:
Scholarships in combination with donor-advised funds.

APPLICATION INFORMATION:
Application must include a copy of the IRS tax determination letter.

PUBLICATIONS:
Annual report; grants and loans policy; *Insights in Estate and Financial Planning*; other tax and estate planning brochures.

IRS IDENTIFICATION NUMBER: 24-6013117

FIRSTENERGY FOUNDATION [141]

76 South Main Street
Akron, OH 44308
(330) 761-4246
Fax: (330) 761-4203

WEB SITE ADDRESS:
www.firstenergycorp.com

FOUNDED: 1961

AREAS OF INTEREST:
Principally education, the arts, community improvements, and overall health of the community.

TYPE:
Capital grants; General operating grants; Matching gifts; Project/program grants.

PURPOSE:
To improve the vitality of our communities and support key safety initiatives; to promote local and regional economic development and revitalization efforts; to support FirstEnergy employees' community leadership and volunteer interests.

LEGAL BASIS:
Corporate foundation.

ELIGIBILITY:
Organizations must qualify as nonprofit, tax-exempt under 501(c)(3) of the IRS code. Organizations must be located within the FirstEnergy operating companies' services area and comply with the basic Standards in Philanthropy as set by the National Information Bureau.

Generally, no grants are made to individuals or for political organizations, endowment funds, deficit financing, research, scholarships or fellowships. No loans.

FINANCIAL DATA:
Amount of support per award: Grants vary in amount, depending upon the needs and nature of the request.

Matching fund requirements: Employees only.

APPLICATION INFORMATION:
Guidelines available at the Foundation web site.

Deadline: Proposals are accepted throughout the year. Decisions may take up to 12 weeks.

ADDRESS INQUIRIES TO:
Mary Beth Carroll, President
(See address above.)

*SPECIAL STIPULATIONS:
Currently, unsolicited grant applications are not accepted.

A.J. FLETCHER FOUNDATION [142]

400 Cedarview Court
Raleigh, NC 27609
(919) 573-4647
Fax: (919) 573-4660

E-MAIL ADDRESS:
djohnson@ajf.org

WEB SITE ADDRESS:
www.ajf.org

AREAS OF INTEREST:
Arts, technology, adolescent pregnancy, public education, human services, and statewide service needs.

TYPE:
General operating grants.

PURPOSE:
To support nonprofit organizations in their endeavors to improve the quality of life in North Carolina.

ELIGIBILITY:
Eligible organizations must be IRS 501(c)(3) tax-exempt.

GEOGRAPHIC RESTRICTIONS:
North Carolina.

FINANCIAL DATA:
Amount of support per award: Varies.
Total amount of support: Varies.

APPLICATION INFORMATION:
Applicant organizations must include a copy of the IRS tax-exempt determination letter.

ADDRESS INQUIRIES TO:
Deremia Johnson, Director of
Administration and Programs
(See address above.)

THE FLINN FOUNDATION [143]
1802 North Central Avenue
Phoenix, AZ 85004
(602) 744-6800
Fax: (602) 744-6815

E-MAIL ADDRESS:
info@flinn.org

WEB SITE ADDRESS:
www.flinn.org

FOUNDED: 1965

AREAS OF INTEREST:
Health, medical science and education in
Arizona.

TYPE:
Demonstration grants; Project/program
grants; Scholarships; Seed money grants. The
Foundation's grants primarily support the
planning and start-up of new initiatives.
Ongoing or general operating support of
established programs is not provided. Grants
support a specific activity addressing a
problem of interest to the Foundation. Each
project is of a specified duration, with a
defined operating budget.

YEAR PROGRAM STARTED: 1981

PURPOSE:
To improve the quality of life in Arizona by
strengthening medical education and
biomedical research programs, enhancing the
effectiveness of health care services,
especially for children and youth,
strengthening Arizona's universities through
an undergraduate scholarship program for
outstanding Arizona high school students,
and enhancing the visibility and long-term
artistic mission of Arizona's principal and
mid-sized visual and performing arts
organizations.

LEGAL BASIS:
Tax-exempt private foundation.

ELIGIBILITY:
Grant applicants must be tax-exempt,
nonprofit organizations which have qualified
for exemption under Section 501(c)(3) of the
IRS code and, generally, are not those
classified as private foundations.

Grants are made only for charitable purposes
that support organizations and activities in
Arizona. The Foundation generally does not
make grants to support individuals, building
and equipment projects, endowment or
annual fund-raising campaigns or to meet
ongoing operating costs or deficits.

GEOGRAPHIC RESTRICTIONS:
Arizona.

FINANCIAL DATA:
Amount of support per award: $70,000
average.
Total amount of support: Approximately
$5,600,000 annually.

NUMBER OF APPLICANTS MOST RECENT YEAR:
Approximately 450.

REPRESENTATIVE AWARDS:
$200,000 to the University of Arizona for
cognitive neuroscience research; $194,500 to
the Phoenix Art Museum for educational
programs of the "Splendors of Egypt"

exhibition; $25,000 to the Cochise County
Department of Health to develop a managed
care health plan for seniors.

APPLICATION INFORMATION:
There is no standard application form, except
for those proposals submitted in response to
a Foundation-initiated program. A
preliminary letter of inquiry or phone call
may be helpful in determining the
appropriateness of a full submission. Only
those projects which clearly fall within one
of the Foundation's three specified fields of
activity and meet the Foundation's three
funding objectives are given serious
consideration. No unsolicited applications
accepted.

PUBLICATIONS:
Annual report; application guidelines; special
reports; grants list.

ADMINISTRATIVE STAFF:
Jack B. Jewett, President and Chief Executive
Officer
Catherine McGonigle, Executive Vice
President
Michael Cochise Young, Ph.D., Assistant
Vice President, Scholarship Programs
Felecia Clack, Grants Coordinator
Christa Thompson, Scholarship Program
Coordinator

ADDRESS INQUIRIES TO:
Grants Coordinator or
Scholarship Program Coordinator
(See address above.)

*SPECIAL STIPULATIONS:
No unsolicited applications accepted.

THE FORD FOUNDATION [144]
320 East 43rd Street
New York, NY 10017
(212) 573-5000
Fax: (212) 351-3677

E-MAIL ADDRESS:
office-secretary@fordfoundation.org

WEB SITE ADDRESS:
www.fordfoundation.org

FOUNDED: 1936

NAME(S) OF PROGRAMS:
- **Democracy, Rights and Justice
  Program**
- **Economic Opportunity and Assets
  Program**
- **Education, Creativity and Free
  Expression Program**

TYPE:
Conferences/seminars; Endowments;
Fellowships; General operating grants;
Matching gifts; Project/program grants;
Research grants; Seed money grants;
Technical assistance. General purposes,
publications, program-related investments,
special projects, individual grants.

Democracy, Rights and Justice Program deals
with the issues of democratic and
accountable government, human rights, and
social justice philanthropy.

Economic Opportunity and Assets Program
deals with the issues of economic fairness,
metropolitan opportunity, and sustainable
development.

Education, Creativity and Free Expression
Program deals with the issues of educational
opportunity and scholarship, freedom of
expression, and sexuality and reproductive
health and rights.

PURPOSE:
To reduce poverty and injustice and to
promote democratic values, international
cooperation and human achievement.

LEGAL BASIS:
Private foundation.

ELIGIBILITY:
Qualified institutions, individuals and
communities with appropriate interests are
eligible to apply. Most of the Foundation's
grant funds are given to organizations.
Although the Foundation also makes grants
to individuals, such grants are few in number
relative to demand. These are limited to
research, training and other activities related
to the Foundation's program interests and
subject to certain limitations and procedural
requirements under the U.S. Internal Revenue
Code.

The Foundation does not award
undergraduate scholarships or make grants
for purely personal or local needs. Support
for graduate fellowships is generally funneled
through grants to universities and other
organizations, which are responsible for the
selection of recipients. Support is not
normally given for routine operating costs of
institutions or for religious activities. Except
in rare cases, funding is not available for the
construction or maintenance of buildings.

FINANCIAL DATA:
Grants vary in amount, depending upon the
needs and nature of the request. Through
2009, the Foundation has spent over $15
billion on programs and grants in the U.S.
and other countries around the world.

Amount of support per award: For fiscal year
ending September 30, 2009: Median grant
size to organizations: $200,000; Median grant
size to individuals: $97,695.

Total amount of support: Total of grants,
program-related investments and
Foundation-administered projects for fiscal
year ending September 30, 2009:
$510,688,255.

NUMBER OF AWARDS: For fiscal year ending
September 30, 2009: Grants to organizations:
1,728; Grants to individuals: 7.

APPLICATION INFORMATION:
Prospective applicants should, as a first step,
submit a brief letter of inquiry in order to
determine whether the Foundation's present
interests and funds permit consideration as a
proposal.

There is no application form. Proposals
should set forth objectives, the proposed
program for pursuing objectives,
qualifications of persons engaged in the
work, a detailed budget, present means of
support and status of applications to other
funding sources and legal and tax status.

Deadline: Applications are considered
throughout the year.

PUBLICATIONS:
Annual report; program policy statement
including application guidelines; *Ford
Foundation Report*, issued quarterly.

IRS IDENTIFICATION NUMBER: 13-1684331

OFFICERS:
Luis A. Ubinas, President
Barron M. Tenny, Executive Vice President,
Secretary and General Counsel
Eric Doppstadt, Vice President and Chief
Investment Officer
Pablo J. Farias, Vice President, Economic
Opportunity and Assets

Alison R. Bernstein, Vice President,
Education, Creativity and Free Expression
Maya Harris, Vice President, Democracy,
Rights and Justice
Marta Lourdes Tellado, Vice President for
Communications
Jacob Gayle, Deputy Vice President for the
Special Initiative on HIV/AIDS
David Chiel, Deputy Vice President, Program
Management
Nicholas M. Gabriel, Treasurer and Chief
Financial Officer
Nancy P. Feller, Associate General Counsel
and Assistant Secretary

BOARD OF TRUSTEES:
Kathryn S. Fuller, Chairperson of the Board
Kofi Appenteng
Afsaneh M. Beschloss
Anke A. Ehrhardt
Juliet Villarreal Garcia
Irene Y. Hirano
J. Clifford Hudson
Yolanda Kakabadse
Robert S. Kaplan
Thurgood Marshall, Jr.
Richard Moe
N.R. Narayana Murthy
Peter A. Nadosy
Cecile Richards
Luis A. Ubinas
W. Richard West, Jr.

FORD MOTOR COMPANY FUND & COMMUNITY SERVICES [145]
One American Road, 11th Floor
Dearborn, MI 48126-2798
(313) 248-7210
Fax: (313) 337-1713

E-MAIL ADDRESS:
fordfund@ford.com

WEB SITE ADDRESS:
www.community.ford.com

FOUNDED: 1949

AREAS OF INTEREST:
Innovation and education, community
development and American legacy, and
auto-related safety education.

NAME(S) OF PROGRAMS:
● **Community Grants Program**

TYPE:
Project/program grants. Support largely for
education, including basic research grants,
community funds and urban affairs, and civic
and cultural programs.

PURPOSE:
To support initiatives and institutions that
enhance and/or improve opportunities for
those who live in communities where Ford
Motor Company operates.

LEGAL BASIS:
Corporate foundation.

ELIGIBILITY:
No grants are made directly to individuals.
Not-for-profit organizations with 501(c)(3)
tax-exempt status may apply.

GEOGRAPHIC RESTRICTIONS:
United States.

FINANCIAL DATA:
Amount of support per award: Varies.
Total amount of support: $29,306,000 for the
year 2009.

APPLICATION INFORMATION:
Application form available online. Paper
proposals not accepted.

ADDRESS INQUIRIES TO:
Jim Vella, President
(See address above.)

FREEMAN FOUNDATION [146]
c/o The Rockefeller Trust Company
30 Rockefeller Plaza
New York, NY 10112
(212) 649-5853
Fax: (212) 549-5519

FOUNDED: 1978

AREAS OF INTEREST:
Asian studies, environmental conservation
and preservation, Vermont programs.

TYPE:
Challenge/matching grants; Exchange
programs; Fellowships; General operating
grants; Professorships; Project/program
grants; Research grants; Scholarships; Seed
money grants; Technical assistance; Training
grants; Travel grants; Visiting scholars.

PURPOSE:
To support a range of charitable
organizations.

ELIGIBILITY:
Eligible organizations must be IRS 501(c)(3)
tax-exempt.

GEOGRAPHIC RESTRICTIONS:
Hawaii, Vermont and Asia.

FINANCIAL DATA:
Amount of support per award: $5,000 to
$1,000,000.

NUMBER OF APPLICANTS MOST RECENT YEAR:
50.

NUMBER OF AWARDS: 200.

APPLICATION INFORMATION:
Applicants should submit a letter describing
the program and financial needs.
Duration: Varies by the program. Renewal
possible.
Deadline: Applications must be received at
least one month prior to quarterly Trustee's
meetings.

PUBLICATIONS:
Annual report.

IRS IDENTIFICATION NUMBER: 13-2965090

TRUSTEES AND OFFICERS:
Graeme Freeman, Executive Director and
President
Doreen Freeman
George Snell

ADDRESS INQUIRIES TO:
The Rockefeller Trust Company
George S. Tsandikos, Managing Director
(See address above.)

FREEPORT-MCMORAN COPPER & GOLD FOUNDATION [147]
333 North Central Avenue
Phoenix, AZ 85004
(602) 366-8018
(602) 366-8100
Fax: (602) 366-7368

E-MAIL ADDRESS:
foundation@fmi.com

WEB SITE ADDRESS:
www.fcx.com

FOUNDED: 1953

AREAS OF INTEREST:
Community safety, health and wellness,
environment, cultural preservation and the
arts, economic development, and education
and training.

NAME(S) OF PROGRAMS:
● **Matching Gifts Program**
● **Social Investment Program**

TYPE:
Matching gifts; Project/program grants.

YEAR PROGRAM STARTED: 1932

PURPOSE:
To serve as a catalyst of positive change in
the communities where the company has
major facilities and update the quality of life.

LEGAL BASIS:
Corporate foundation.

ELIGIBILITY:
Nonprofit programs and organizations aligned
with the core values of the company. Must be
located in communities where the company
has a presence.

GEOGRAPHIC RESTRICTIONS:
United States.

FINANCIAL DATA:
Amount of support per award: Varies.
Matching fund requirements: Minimum $25.
First $500 is matched 2:1; above $500 is
matched dollar-for-dollar.

APPLICATION INFORMATION:
Guidelines and application is available on the
Foundation web site.
Duration: One year. Renewable.
Deadline: Proposals are accepted throughout
the year. Social Investment Program: August
30 for grant award the following year.

OFFICERS:
Tracy Bame, Director of Social
Responsibility and Community Development

ADDRESS INQUIRIES TO:
Contributions Administrator
(See address above.)

FRESNO REGIONAL FOUNDATION [148]
5250 North Palm Avenue
Suite 424
Fresno, CA 93704
(559) 226-5600
Fax: (559) 230-2078

E-MAIL ADDRESS:
info@fresnoregfoundation.org

WEB SITE ADDRESS:
fresnoregfoundation.org

FOUNDED: 1966

AREAS OF INTEREST:
Primarily arts and culture, health and human
services, and youth services, with a lesser
emphasis on environment, parks and music.

NAME(S) OF PROGRAMS:
● **Arts and Culture**
● **Human Services**
● **Youth Grants**

TYPE:
General operating grants; Project/program
grants.

LEGAL BASIS:
Community foundation.

ELIGIBILITY:
Generally, applicants must be exempt under
Internal Revenue Code Section 501(c)(3).
However, if it is found that a grant to an
agency or organization presents an

opportunity to be of substantial service to the community, and there are no others that provide the program or activity within the applicant's service area, such proposals will be considered.

GEOGRAPHIC RESTRICTIONS:
Central San Joaquin Valley, California; primarily the counties of Fresno, Kings, Madera, Mariposa, Merced, and Tulare.

FINANCIAL DATA:
Amount of support per award: Varies.
Total amount of support: $4,200,000 for the year 2009.

NUMBER OF AWARDS: 560.

APPLICATION INFORMATION:
Organizations should submit a statement of purpose and history of organization, budget, sources of support, goals and specifics regarding the program to be funded, annual report (if available) and copy of the organization's tax-exempt letter.
Duration: One year. Renewal possible.

STAFF:
Daniel DeSantis, Chief Executive Officer
Sandra Flores, Senior Program Officer

ADDRESS INQUIRIES TO:
Sandra Flores, Senior Program Officer
(See address above.)

FREY FOUNDATION   [149]
40 Pearl Street, N.W.
Suite 1100
Grand Rapids, MI 49503-3028
(616) 451-0303
Fax: (616) 451-8481

E-MAIL ADDRESS:
freyfdn@freyfdn.org

WEB SITE ADDRESS:
www.freyfdn.org

FOUNDED: 1974

AREAS OF INTEREST:
Children and their families, environment, community arts, civic progress, and philanthropy.

NAME(S) OF PROGRAMS:
- **Community Capital Projects**
- **Encouraging Civic Progress**
- **Enhancing the Lives of Children and Their Families**
- **Nurturing Community Arts**
- **Protecting the Environment**
- **Strengthening Philanthropy**

TYPE:
Capital grants; Demonstration grants; Project/program grants; Seed money grants; Technical assistance. Grants are available for special one-time only or time-limited purposes, such as "start-up" or program expansion, demonstration projects, planning or other forms of technical assistance, evaluation, advocacy, and applied research. Capital is available in some program areas.

YEAR PROGRAM STARTED: 1974

PURPOSE:
To promote healthy development of children and their families, particularly infants and children under the age of six and their parents, with special attention to traditionally disadvantaged populations; to protect, preserve and improve the ecological health of natural resources; to stimulate vitality, effectiveness and growth of community-based arts; to encourage civic action to improve the

livability of cities and communities; to improve the effectiveness of organized philanthropy and stimulate its growth.

LEGAL BASIS:
Private family foundation.

ELIGIBILITY:
Applicants must be public institutions and 501(c)(3) nonprofit organizations. No grants to individuals, endowment funds, debt retirement, general operating expenses, scholarships, travel, to cover routine, current or emergency expenses and/or sectarian charitable activities.

GEOGRAPHIC RESTRICTIONS:
Grand Rapids area, Emmet or Charlevoix counties, Michigan.

FINANCIAL DATA:
Amount of support per award: Varies upon nature of request.
Total amount of support: Approximately $4,500,000 for the year 2010.

NUMBER OF AWARDS: Average 85 per year.

APPLICATION INFORMATION:
Eligible applicants are encouraged to contact the Foundation to discuss prospective proposals and to receive a set of guidelines and application materials.
Duration: One year.
Deadline: February 15, May 15, August 15 and November 15.

PUBLICATIONS:
Annual report; *Taking Care of Civic Business*; *Charting the Course; Today's Winners, Tomorrow's Losers.*

STAFF:
Milton W. Rohwer, President
Joyce Bobolts, Director of Finance and Administration
Lynne J. Ferrell, Program Officer
Kristine L. Huizen, Program Officer
Teresa J. Crawford, Grants Manager

BOARD OF TRUSTEES:
David G. Frey, Chairman
John M. Frey, Vice Chairman
Edward J. Frey, Jr., Secretary, Treasurer and Trustee

ADDRESS INQUIRIES TO:
Milton W. Rohwer, President
(See address above.)

THE FROST FOUNDATION, LTD.   [150]
511 Armijo Street, Suite A
Santa Fe, NM 87501
(505) 986-0208
Fax: (505) 986-0430

E-MAIL ADDRESS:
frost0729@aol.com
info@frostfound.org

WEB SITE ADDRESS:
www.frostfound.org

FOUNDED: 1959

AREAS OF INTEREST:
Social service and humanitarian needs, the environment and education.

CONSULTING OR VOLUNTEER SERVICES:
Professional services of staff are offered for special projects.

TYPE:
Challenge/matching grants; Project/program grants; Research grants; Seed money grants.

YEAR PROGRAM STARTED: 1959

PURPOSE:
To seek and assist innovative projects that will have positive impact beyond the boundaries of a single state.

LEGAL BASIS:
Tax-exempt private foundation.

ELIGIBILITY:
The Foundation encourages self-reliance, creativity and ingenuity on the part of prospective recipients.

Its efforts are directed primarily to support exemplary organizations and programs which can generate positive change beyond traditional boundaries, to encourage creativity which recognizes emerging needs, and to assist innovation which addresses current urgent problems.

Within these parameters, it provides initial impetus to exemplary organizations and programs, to operating funds, to pioneering organizations and programs which other institutions might simularly use, and to programs which have potential for wider service or educational exposure than an individual community.

The Foundation encourages collaborations, mergers and the formation of alliances among agencies within the community to reduce duplication of effort and to promote a maximum effective use of funds. The Foundation also considers requests for operating. It is prepared to review applications of human service needs, environmental and education programs in New Mexico and Louisiana from organizations which have an IRS 501(c)(3) determination.

GEOGRAPHIC RESTRICTIONS:
Louisiana and New Mexico.

FINANCIAL DATA:
Amount of support per award: $15,000 average per award.
Total amount of support: Approximately $2,000,000 annually.

NUMBER OF APPLICANTS MOST RECENT YEAR:
Approximately 500.

NUMBER OF AWARDS: Approximately 65.

APPLICATION INFORMATION:
A brief description of the institution/organization, including its mission, must be submitted along with evidence of tax-exempt status, the amount requested, a statement of the specific need(s) to be met by the project, a budget projection with the time frame expected and the qualifications of the staff members selected to serve the project. Faxed summaries are not accepted.
Duration: Generally limited to three years. On rare occasions, because of special circumstances, grants will be renewed.
Deadline: December 1 for March Board meeting and June 1 for September Board meeting.

PUBLICATIONS:
Annual report; application guidelines.

OFFICERS:
Mary Amelia Whited-Howell, President
Philip B. Howell, Executive Vice President and Treasurer
Taylor F. Moore, Secretary

BOARD OF DIRECTORS:
Ann Rogers Gerber
Philip B. Howell
John A. LeVan

Taylor F. Moore
Mary Amelia Whited-Howell

EXECUTIVE COMMITTEE:
Philip B. Howell
John A. LeVan
Mary Amelia Whited-Howell

ADDRESS INQUIRIES TO:
Mary Amelia Whited-Howell, President
(See address above.)

LLOYD A. FRY FOUNDATION [151]

120 South LaSalle Street
Suite 1950
Chicago, IL 60603
(312) 580-0310
Fax: (312) 580-0980

E-MAIL ADDRESS:
usong@fryfoundation.org

WEB SITE ADDRESS:
www.fryfoundation.org

FOUNDED: 1983

AREAS OF INTEREST:
Education, arts and culture education, access
to health care, and employment, with special
emphasis on support of inner-city projects.

TYPE:
Project/program grants.

LEGAL BASIS:
Private foundation.

ELIGIBILITY:
501(c)(3).

GEOGRAPHIC RESTRICTIONS:
Inner-city Chicago, Illinois.

FINANCIAL DATA:
Amount of support per award: $15,000 to
$50,000 average.
Total amount of support: $6,833,415 for
fiscal year 2010.

NUMBER OF AWARDS: 350.

APPLICATION INFORMATION:
Application and guidelines are available at
the web site.
Duration: One year.
Deadline: December 1, March 1, June 1 and
September 1.

PUBLICATIONS:
Annual report.

IRS IDENTIFICATION NUMBER: 36-6108775

STAFF:
Unmi Song, Executive Director
Diane Sotiros, C.P.A., Controller
Sydney R. Sidwell, Senior Program Officer
Sharon Bush, Program Officer
Regina Dixon-Reeves, Ph.D., Program
Officer
Soo Na, Program Officer
Nicholas Burt, Grants Administrator
Lisa Torres, Program Assistant

ADDRESS INQUIRIES TO:
Unmi Song, Executive Director
(See address above.)

GANNETT FOUNDATION [152]

7950 Jones Branch Drive
McLean, VA 22107-0150
(703) 854-6047
(703) 854-6000
Fax: (703) 854-2167

E-MAIL ADDRESS:
foundation@gannett.com

WEB SITE ADDRESS:
www.gannettfoundation.org

FOUNDED: 1991

AREAS OF INTEREST:
Education and neighborhood improvement,
economic development, youth development,
community problem-solving, assistance to
disadvantaged people, environmental
conservation and cultural enrichment.

TYPE:
General operating grants; Matching gifts;
Project/program grants.

PURPOSE:
To improve the education, health and
advancement of the people who live in
Gannett communities.

LEGAL BASIS:
Corporate foundation.

ELIGIBILITY:
Local organizations determined by the IRS to
be tax-exempt under 501(c)(3) in
communities where the Gannett Company,
Inc. owns a daily newspaper or broadcast
station.

FINANCIAL DATA:
Amount of support per award: $4,000 to
$6,000.
Matching fund requirements: Gifts for
programs or initiatives where the primary
purpose is the promotion of religious doctrine
or tenets are excluded.

NUMBER OF AWARDS: 1,200.

APPLICATION INFORMATION:
Application form and guidelines are available
online.
Duration: One year. Renewal possible.

ADDRESS INQUIRIES TO:
Pat Lyle, Program Administrator
(See address above.)

GATX CORPORATION [153]

222 West Adams Street
Chicago, IL 60606
(312) 621-6200
Fax: (312) 621-6648

E-MAIL ADDRESS:
community@gatx.com
contactgatx@gatx.com

WEB SITE ADDRESS:
www.gatx.com

FOUNDED: 1898

AREAS OF INTEREST:
Education, family and environment, cultural,
health care, and social service issues.

NAME(S) OF PROGRAMS:
● **Dollars-for-Doers**
● **Employee Matching Gifts**

TYPE:
Challenge/matching grants; Development
grants; General operating grants;
Grants-in-aid; Internships; Matching gifts;
Project/program grants; Seed money grants;
Technical assistance. United Way support,
employee matching gift program for
501(c)(3) organizations, education, family
issues, and environment.

YEAR PROGRAM STARTED: 1953

PURPOSE:
To improve communities by proactively
supporting significant issues relevant to the
economic viability of the Corporation's local
communities through initiatives that are
consistent with the Corporation's business
interests.

LEGAL BASIS:
Corporate contributions program.

ELIGIBILITY:
Applicants must be nonprofit tax-exempt
organizations with a 501(c)(3) tax-exempt
status. The Corporation will not fund
individuals, political or religious
organizations, foundations, capital campaigns
or endowment funds.

GEOGRAPHIC RESTRICTIONS:
Chicago neighborhoods of Englewood, Grand
Boulevard and Humboldt Park.

FINANCIAL DATA:
Amount of support per award: $5,000 to
$50,000.
Matching fund requirements: $50 minimum
and $2,000 maximum per employee and
calendar year.

NUMBER OF APPLICANTS MOST RECENT YEAR:
295.

NUMBER OF AWARDS: 75.

REPRESENTATIVE AWARDS:
Education: $20,000 to Chicago Communities
in Schools; $53,000 to Waterford Institute;
Families: $14,600 to the Robert Crown
Center for Health Education; Environment:
$25,000 to Wildlife Habitat Council.

APPLICATION INFORMATION:
All applicants must use the Chicago Area
Grant Application. A complete application
includes the following materials:
(1) Chicago Area Grant Application
(CAGA);
(2) application narrative as described in the
CAGA;
(3) itemized budget for the project;
(4) itemized organizational budget for the
current fiscal year;
(5) audited financial statement for the most
recently completed fiscal year;
(6) brief biographies of key organizational
staff, including job description and
professional qualifications;
(7) list of institutional funding for the current
fiscal year, including amounts;
(8) a list of members of the board of
directors, including affiliations;
(9) annual report for the most recently
completed fiscal year, if available, and;
(10) IRS tax determination letter indicating
the applicant's status as a 501(c)(3) nonprofit
organization or equivalent.
Duration: One year. Renewals are possible
after formal request has been received.
Deadline: January 15, April 15, July 15 and
October 15. Announcement approximately
three weeks after committee meeting.

PUBLICATIONS:
Application guidelines; grant application
form.

*PLEASE NOTE:
Guidelines must be followed carefully when
submitting proposals.

*SPECIAL STIPULATIONS:
Only one grant request per calendar year and
applicant.

If an organization received funding in the
previous year, a final report using the
Chicago Area Common Report must be
received prior to review of any subsequent
proposals.

CARL GELLERT AND CELIA BERTA GELLERT FOUNDATION [154]

2171 Junipero Serra Boulevard, Suite 310
Daly City, CA 94014
(650) 985-2080
Fax: (650) 985-2084

E-MAIL ADDRESS:
info@gellertfoundation.org

WEB SITE ADDRESS:
www.gellertfoundation.org

FOUNDED: 1958

AREAS OF INTEREST:
Religious, charitable, scientific, literary or educational purposes.

TYPE:
Capital grants; Development grants; Endowments; General operating grants; Project/program grants; Scholarships; Technical assistance.

YEAR PROGRAM STARTED: 1958

LEGAL BASIS:
Private foundation.

ELIGIBILITY:
No grants to individuals. Grants are available for nonprofit tax-exempt organizations which are not private foundations, that have and can prove 501(c)(3) and 509(a)170(b) status.

GEOGRAPHIC RESTRICTIONS:
Alameda, Contra Costa, Marin, Napa, San Francisco, San Mateo, Santa Clara, Solano and Sonoma, the nine counties of the Greater San Francisco Bay area, California.

FINANCIAL DATA:
Total amount of support: $1,606,647.66 in new grants and prior commitments for fiscal year ended December 31, 2009.

NUMBER OF APPLICANTS MOST RECENT YEAR:
289 for fiscal year ended December 31, 2009.

NUMBER OF AWARDS: 150 for fiscal year ended December 31, 2009.

APPLICATION INFORMATION:
One copy of the following items are to be submitted to the Foundation:
(1) Grant Request Application with an original signature and all line items on the form completed;
(2) documentation of 501(c)(3) tax-exempt classification;
(3) documentation of 509(a)(1) and 170(b)(1)(A) status;
(4) an unbound copy of the most recently filed Form 990 and;
(5) one unbound proposal, five pages or less, to include a brief history and statement of the current goals and activities of the organization and a brief outline of the project and phase of project for which the organization seeks funding, showing demonstration of need, population served, specific objectives and outcomes, time line of the project, amount of funding required for the project, and the specific amount of funding (no ranges) requested from the Foundation.

Name of the organization applying for a grant must be consistent on all required documentation (application, letterhead, IRS letters, Form 990). Tax ID number/EIN must also be the same. All documentation must show the address of the organization to be within one of the nine counties of the San Francisco Bay area.

Electronic submissions will not be accepted.

Deadline: August 15, annually or following Monday if 15th falls on a weekend.

IRS IDENTIFICATION NUMBER: 94-6062858

DIRECTORS:
Marie C. Bentley
Andrew A. Cresci
Lorraine D'Elia
Jack Fitzpatrick
Robert J. Grassilli, Jr.
Michael J. King
J. Malcolm Visbal

ADDRESS INQUIRIES TO:
Jack Fitzpatrick, Executive Director
(See address above.)

THE FRED GELLERT FAMILY FOUNDATION [155]

95 Harriet Way
Tiburon, CA 94920
(415) 381-7575
Fax: (415) 381-8526

E-MAIL ADDRESS:
foundation@fredgellert.com

WEB SITE ADDRESS:
www.fdncenter.org/grantmaker/fredgellert

FOUNDED: 1958

AREAS OF INTEREST:
Arts, education, youth and family services, green planning, environmental health, sustainable agriculture, sustainable consumption and reproductive choice, with primary focus on health and environment.

NAME(S) OF PROGRAMS:
- **Arts & Humanities**
- **Education**
- **Environment**
- **Health**
- **Youth, Seniors & Family Service**

TYPE:
Capital grants; Challenge/matching grants; Conferences/seminars; General operating grants; Matching gifts; Project/program grants; Seed money grants; Technical assistance.

YEAR PROGRAM STARTED: 1958

PURPOSE:
To advance positive forces for social change to ensure quality of life for future generations.

LEGAL BASIS:
Private family foundation.

ELIGIBILITY:
Applicants must be 501(c)(3) organizations. No grants to individuals or for purchasing development rights or land. No unsolicited grant proposals are accepted.

FINANCIAL DATA:
Amount of support per award: $1,000 to $40,000; Average: $3,000.
Total amount of support: $650,000 for the year 2008.
Matching fund requirements: Provide information on challenge grant.

NUMBER OF APPLICANTS MOST RECENT YEAR:
Approximately 120 for the year 2008.

REPRESENTATIVE AWARDS:
$3,000 to Richardson Bay Audubon; $4,000 to Campaign to Safeguard America's Waters; $20,000 to Resource Renewal Institute.

APPLICATION INFORMATION:
The Foundation does not accept unsolicited inquiries.

PUBLICATIONS:
Annual report; application guidelines.

ADDRESS INQUIRIES TO:
Leslie Leslie, Grant Director
(See address above.)

*SPECIAL STIPULATIONS:
All organizations must submit a report of work accomplished to date, due at end of funding cycle, or before receiving upcoming year's installment. No unsolicited inquiries are accepted.

GENERAL SERVICE FOUNDATION [156]

557 North Mill Street
Suite 201
Aspen, CO 81611
(970) 920-6834
Fax: (970) 920-4578

E-MAIL ADDRESS:
info@generalservice.org

WEB SITE ADDRESS:
www.generalservice.org

FOUNDED: 1946

AREAS OF INTEREST:
Human rights and economic justice, reproductive justice, and Colorado.

NAME(S) OF PROGRAMS:
- **Colorado Program**
- **Human Rights and Economic Justice**
- **Reproductive Justice**

TYPE:
Challenge/matching grants; Demonstration grants; Development grants; General operating grants; Project/program grants; Seed money grants; Technical assistance; Travel grants. The goal of the Human Rights and Economic Justice program is to advance and strengthen human rights, democratic reform, and economic justice in Mexico, Central America and Cuba.

The goal of the Reproductive Justice program is to ensure that women and girls in the U.S. have the power and resources to make healthy decisions about their bodies, sexuality and reproduction.

The goal of the Foundation's grantmaking program in Colorado is to (a) build the capacity of key base-building organizations committed to justice and equity in the state, and (b) to facilitate collaboration among its grantees and also between its grantees and other sectors (including media, research, leadership, policy and issue-advocacy groups) to create a powerful, permanent infrastructure capable of affecting statewide policy change over the long term.

YEAR PROGRAM STARTED: 1946

PURPOSE:
To address some of the world's basic long-term problems; to bring about a more just and sustainable world; to nurture and learn from strategic partnerships, embracing risk and possibility; to align every aspect of Foundation's organization with its deeply held values which include a commitment to leadership, integrity, diversity, experimentation, accountability, justice and excellence.

LEGAL BASIS:
Private foundation, tax-exempt under IRS statute 501(c)(3).

ELIGIBILITY:
Organizations must be tax-exempt under U.S. law.

In general, the Foundation does not contribute to annual campaigns, nor to capital campaigns, to individuals or for relief.

Because the Foundation's areas of concern are broad, the Board has determined guidelines within each area. All applicants are urged only to submit applications falling within the Foundation's Contribution Policy and Guidelines.

GEOGRAPHIC RESTRICTIONS:
Mexico, Central America and Cuba for Human Rights and Democracy. United States for Reproductive Health and Rights.

FINANCIAL DATA:
Amount of support per award: $2,000 to $50,000.

NUMBER OF APPLICANTS MOST RECENT YEAR:
Approximately 167 annually.

NUMBER OF AWARDS: 87.

APPLICATION INFORMATION:
The Foundation requests that applications for contributions be in line with the approved Guidelines and be submitted online.

Duration: One to two years.

Deadline: February 1 and September 1 for letters of inquiry.

IRS IDENTIFICATION NUMBER: 36-6018535

OFFICERS:
Robin Snidow, Board Chairperson
Zoe Estrin, Vice Chairperson
Will Halby, Treasurer
Marcie J. Musser, Secretary
Sara Samuels, Assistant Secretary

DIRECTORS:
Mary Lloyd Estrin
Eliot Estrin
Robert L. Estrin
Zoe L. Foxley
Peter Halby
Will Halby
Cleo Hill
Marcie J. Musser
Robert W. Musser
Robin Snidow

THE GEORGE FOUNDATION [157]

215 Morton Street
Richmond, TX 77469
(281) 342-6109
Fax: (281) 341-7635

E-MAIL ADDRESS:
dkoch@thegeorgefoundation.org

WEB SITE ADDRESS:
www.thegeorgefoundation.org

FOUNDED: 1945

AREAS OF INTEREST:
Basic human needs and education.

TYPE:
Capital grants; General operating grants; Project/program grants; Scholarships. Preventative programs for children and families.

YEAR PROGRAM STARTED: 1947

PURPOSE:
To support organizations and programs that assist in developing strong, stable families with emphasis on the economically disadvantaged.

ELIGIBILITY:
Applicants must be 501(c)(3) nonprofit organizations. No grants to individuals.

GEOGRAPHIC RESTRICTIONS:
Fort Bend County area, Texas.

FINANCIAL DATA:
Amount of support per award: Varies.

APPLICATION INFORMATION:
Guidelines and application is available at the web site.

Duration: One year. Reapplication must be made for additional funding.

Deadline: January 15, April 15, July 15 and October 15.

TRUSTEES:
William Jameson
Pat McDonald
Thomas McNutt
John Null
Michael Wells

ADDRESS INQUIRIES TO:
Dee Koch, Grants Officer
(See address and e-mail above.)

GEORGIA POWER FOUNDATION, INC. [158]

241 Ralph McGill Boulevard
Bin 10131
Atlanta, GA 30308
(404) 506-6784
Fax: (404) 506-1485

E-MAIL ADDRESS:
gpfoundation@southernco.com

WEB SITE ADDRESS:
www.georgiapower.com

FOUNDED: 1986

AREAS OF INTEREST:
Quality of education in Georgia, protecting the environment, workforce planning, and health and human services, primarily through United Way and Salvation Army.

CONSULTING OR VOLUNTEER SERVICES:
Employees and retirees volunteer to support educational, environmental, community and developmental initiatives in our communities.

TYPE:
Capital grants; General operating grants; Matching gifts; Project/program grants; Scholarships. Matching gifts in educational area only.

YEAR PROGRAM STARTED: 1987

PURPOSE:
To support the company's tradition of community involvement and to improve and enrich the communities in which it serves.

LEGAL BASIS:
Corporate foundation.

ELIGIBILITY:
The foundation makes grants to 501(c)3 organizations that seek to improve the quality of life for Georgia residents.

No grants to individuals, private schools or religious organizations.

GEOGRAPHIC RESTRICTIONS:
Georgia.

FINANCIAL DATA:
Amount of support per award: $14,477 average grant for the year 2009.

Total amount of support: $7,308,000 for the year 2009.

Matching fund requirements: In the area of education, matching funds are required from degree granting graduate and professional schools, universities, two- and four-year colleges and technical schools located in the U.S. that are regionally or professionally accredited and are public charities and recognized by the IRS as 501(c)(3) tax-exempt organizations.

NUMBER OF APPLICANTS MOST RECENT YEAR:
1,033 for the year 2009.

NUMBER OF AWARDS: 494 paid by Foundation and 153 paid by Company for the year 2009.

APPLICATION INFORMATION:
Application should be submitted online and include:
(1) a brief description of the organization requesting support and a list of its officers and board members;
(2) statement of amount requested, the purpose for which the grant is sought, and explanation of the measurements that will demonstrate successful implementation;
(3) sources of other support and the amounts of assured or anticipated support for the project proposed;
(4) evidence of the organization's current tax-exempt status and;
(5) current audited financial statements.

Duration: Renewal annually.

Deadline: February 15, May 15, August 15 and November 15.

PUBLICATIONS:
Contributions guidelines.

IRS IDENTIFICATION NUMBER: 58-1709417

DIRECTORS:
Mike K. Anderson, President and Chief Executive Officer
W. Craig Barrs
Mickey A. Brown
Ronnie R. Labrato

ADDRESS INQUIRIES TO:
Susan M. Carter, Executive Director
(See address above.)

*SPECIAL STIPULATIONS:
No grants to individuals, private elementary and secondary schools, and religious or sectarian organizations.

GEORGIA-PACIFIC FOUNDATION [159]

133 Peachtree Street, N.E.
32nd Floor
Atlanta, GA 30303
(404) 652-4182
Fax: (404) 749-2754

WEB SITE ADDRESS:
www.gp.com/gpfoundation

FOUNDED: 1927

AREAS OF INTEREST:
Education, environment, entrepreneurship, community enrichment and employee involvement.

TYPE:
Project/program grants; Scholarships.

PURPOSE:
To make investments that improve the quality of life in communities where Georgia-Pacific employees live and work.

LEGAL BASIS:
Corporate foundation.

ELIGIBILITY:
Organizations must have 501(c)(3) tax-exemption status from the IRS.

The Foundation does not support organizations that discriminate on the basis of race, color, creed, national origin or gender; private organizations; "bail-out" funds given to provide emergency assistance to organizations for general operating purposes; individuals, other than through scholarship and community service programs; political causes, candidates and legislative lobbying or advocacy efforts of any type; churches or religious denominations, religious or theological schools; general operating support for United Way member agencies; operating support for colleges and universities; fund-raising events such as raffles, telethons, walk-a-thons and auctions; and for trips and tours.

FINANCIAL DATA:
Amount of support per award: Minimum $1,000.

APPLICATION INFORMATION:
Send a written proposal including the project goals, budget and anticipated results.
Deadline: January 1 through October 31. Within 45 days of receipt of the request with the appropriate documentation, the Foundation will respond with written notification as to whether the grant is accepted.

GHEENS FOUNDATION   [160]
One Riverfront Plaza, Suite 705
401 West Main Street
Louisville, KY 40202
(502) 584-4650
Fax: (502) 584-4652

E-MAIL ADDRESS:
carl@gheensfoundation.org

WEB SITE ADDRESS:
gheensfoundation.org

FOUNDED: 1957

AREAS OF INTEREST:
Culture, education and health.

TYPE:
Capital grants; Challenge/matching grants; Development grants; General operating grants; Project/program grants; Research grants; Scholarships; Technical assistance.

YEAR PROGRAM STARTED: 1957

PURPOSE:
To support programs that meet the needs of society and improve the quality of life in the community.

LEGAL BASIS:
501(c)(3), private foundation.

ELIGIBILITY:
Grants are made to organizations that have tax-exempt status under Section 501(c)(3) of the Internal Revenue Code. No grants are made to individuals.

GEOGRAPHIC RESTRICTIONS:
Louisville, Kentucky and Terrebone and Lafourche parishes in Louisiana.

FINANCIAL DATA:
Amount of support per award: Varies depending on the nature of the request.
Total amount of support: Varies.

NUMBER OF APPLICANTS MOST RECENT YEAR:
219.

NUMBER OF AWARDS: 100.

APPLICATION INFORMATION:
All applications must have written approval from the President, Chief Executive Officer, or Head of the nonprofit applicant.

The following items must be included in the application package:
(1) seven copies of the application form (pages 1 and 2, program and financial summaries, questions 1 to 7);
(2) one copy of the IRS tax determination letter and certificate;
(3) one copy of the Annual Federal Return (Form 990) and;
(4) seven copies of any supporting materials, such as a larger proposal, brochures, needs assessment, or letters of support.
Duration: One year. May reapply.

ADDRESS INQUIRIES TO:
Carl M. Thomas, Executive Director
(See address above.)

HERMAN GOLDMAN
FOUNDATION   [161]
44 Wall Street
Suite 1212
New York, NY 10005
(212) 461-2132
Fax: (212) 461-2223

E-MAIL ADDRESS:
goldfound@aol.com

FOUNDED: 1942

AREAS OF INTEREST:
Arts, health, social justice and education.

TYPE:
General operating grants; Grants-in-aid; Project/program grants.

YEAR PROGRAM STARTED: 1943

PURPOSE:
To benefit those in need.

LEGAL BASIS:
Private foundation.

ELIGIBILITY:
Grants for individuals are not considered. It is not possible to respond to emergency requests, nor to financial needs of crash programs because of the time the Foundation requires to study grant proposals. Applicants must be tax-exempt organizations.

GEOGRAPHIC RESTRICTIONS:
Primarily, New York City metropolitan area.

FINANCIAL DATA:
Amount of support per award: $1,000 to $50,000.
Total amount of support: Varies.

APPLICATION INFORMATION:
Applicants should submit one copy only of a written proposal and/or can use the New York-New Jersey area Common Grant Application Form. No letter of inquiry required. Applicants must provide IRS tax-exempt documentation.
Duration: One year.
Deadline: Applications accepted throughout the year.

PUBLICATIONS:
Annual report.

ADDRESS INQUIRIES TO:
Richard K. Baron, Executive Director
(See address above.)

THE GOODYEAR TIRE &
RUBBER COMPANY   [162]
1144 East Market Street, D/798
Akron, OH 44316-0001
(330) 796-8928
Fax: (330) 796-2202

WEB SITE ADDRESS:
www.goodyear.com
www.goodyear.com/corporate/about/about_community.html

FOUNDED: 1898

AREAS OF INTEREST:
Safety, health and human services, culture and the arts, education, civic and community improvement.

TYPE:
Project/program grants.

PURPOSE:
To promote healthy, high functioning communities in locations where Company major plants and offices reside; to be a socially aware and responsive global citizen wherever the Company operates or does business.

LEGAL BASIS:
Corporate contributions program.

ELIGIBILITY:
Grants are made to nonprofit, tax-exempt organizations in communities where Goodyear plants and headquarters offices are located. No grants are made to individuals.

Requests are required to meet guidelines of strategic giving based on safety by focusing on safety programs plus at least one additional category noted below and/or provide volunteer opportunities for Company associates which are appropriately aligned with Company strategy:
(1) Civic and Community and Other: Grant awards will depend on local needs and customs in the communities in which the Company operates;
(2) Culture and the Arts: Requests from organizations and institutions serving plant communities and selected national arts organizations will be considered provided they comply with the connection to safety;
(3) Education: Requests for support from colleges, universities, and other educational institutions serving the areas in which Company plants and principal offices are located must demonstrate a connection with safety and/or must be a source of subsidized educational opportunities for Company associates and their families; a limited number of private and public universities of national or regional significance whose programs are of special interest or those that provide a continuing source of associates to the Company may also receive priority and;
(4) Health and Human Services: Highest priority is given to United Way campaigns in communities where Company plants and principal offices are located; organizations receiving United Way support may not be eligible for additional funding.
A limited number of traditional grants will be honored at the Company's discretion.

FINANCIAL DATA:
Amount of support per award: Varies.

APPLICATION INFORMATION:
Applicants should request the application package by letter, on the organization's letterhead, and signed by a representative employee/director of the grant seeker who is authorized to submit a request on behalf of the organization. All materials should be in

letter-sized format; over-sized documents will be discarded. Provide the following documents and information in the package: (1) the purpose, amount and community need that will be met by the request; (2) the program's potential connection to safety for priority consideration; (3) the geographical area and audience served by the applicant's organization and the request; (4) a board of trustees list; (5) a copy of the organization's 501(c)(3) IRS Letter of Determination proving tax-exempt status or equivalent; (6) the most recent organizational financial statement and income-and-expense budget; (7) a list of other current and projected sources of funding for the program; (8) a breakdown, by percentage, of how grant funds are utilized by the organization (i.e., administration, services, research, etc.) and; (9) the nature of Goodyear goods and services utilized by the organization.

Organizations in the greater Akron, OH area should send requests to the address listed above. Those located in U.S. communities where Goodyear has plants and major facilities should contact the local plant manager's office for mailing instructions.

Deadline: November 15 for consideration in following year.

PUBLICATIONS:
Overview.

ADDRESS INQUIRIES TO:
Faith S. Stewart
Director, Global Community Enterprise
(See address above.)

*PLEASE NOTE:
The Company does not accept grant requests by telephone or e-mail.

W. R. GRACE FOUNDATION, INC. [163]
7500 Grace Drive
Columbia, MD 21044
(410) 531-4000
Fax: (410) 531-4233

WEB SITE ADDRESS:
www.grace.com

FOUNDED: 1961

AREAS OF INTEREST:
Higher education, civic, youth development, cultural programs, community funds, health and human services.

TYPE:
Challenge/matching grants; Matching gifts; Project/program grants.

YEAR PROGRAM STARTED: 1961

PURPOSE:
To provide primary support for education, particularly programs emphasizing math, sciences and chemistry.

LEGAL BASIS:
Company-sponsored foundation.

ELIGIBILITY:
Nonprofit, tax-exempt organizations with a 501(c)(3) tax-exempt status are eligible for support. The Foundation will not support individuals, political or religious organizations.

Grants to organizations in communities where W. R. Grace & Co. has significant employee population.

GEOGRAPHIC RESTRICTIONS:
United States and Canada.

FINANCIAL DATA:
Amount of support per award: Grants vary in amount based on the needs and nature of the request; Average: $1,000.

NUMBER OF AWARDS: Approximately 200 each year.

APPLICATION INFORMATION:
Application is made by letter including a statement of purpose, sources of support, specifics regarding particular project to be funded, 501(c)(3) tax-exempt letter, audited financial statements and annual report.
Duration: Usually one year. Multiyear commitments possible.

DIRECTORS:
W. B. McGowan, Chairman

ADDRESS INQUIRIES TO:
Janet Davis, Administrator
(See address above.)

PHILIP L. GRAHAM FUND [164]
c/o The Washington Post Company
1150 Fifteenth Street, N.W.
Washington, DC 20071
(202) 334-6640
Fax: (202) 334-4498

E-MAIL ADDRESS:
plgfund@washpost.com

WEB SITE ADDRESS:
www.plgrahamfund.org

FOUNDED: 1963

AREAS OF INTEREST:
Primarily health and human services, education, arts and humanities, and community endeavors in the Washington, DC metropolitan area. Secondly, journalism and communications.

TYPE:
Capital grants; Development grants; Project/program grants. Technology enhancement. Other infrastructure investments.

YEAR PROGRAM STARTED: 1963

PURPOSE:
To use resources for the betterment of the Washington, DC metropolitan area; to provide assistance to activities in the field of journalism and communication.

LEGAL BASIS:
General interest foundation.

ELIGIBILITY:
Applicants must be 501(c)(3) organizations located in the Washington, DC metropolitan area. No grants to individuals, for religious or political purposes, research, conferences, travel, fund-raising, event sponsorships, hospitals or publications.

GEOGRAPHIC RESTRICTIONS:
Washington, DC metropolitan area.

FINANCIAL DATA:
Amount of support per award: $2,500 to $300,000. Average grant approximately $25,000.
Total amount of support: $4,900,000 for the year 2008.

NUMBER OF APPLICANTS MOST RECENT YEAR:
Approximately 400.

NUMBER OF AWARDS: Approximately 130 for the year 2008.

REPRESENTATIVE AWARDS:
$20,000 to The African Continuum Theatre Company, Washington, DC to build and stabilize the organizational infrastructure required for a professional theatre company; $60,000 to The Children's Inn at NIH, Bethesda, MD to support the capital campaign to add 22 resident rooms and new public spaces; $25,000 to Northern Virginia Urban League, Alexandria, VA to rehabilitate the basement of Freedom House headquarters as a museum preserving the legacy of the slaves once held there.

APPLICATION INFORMATION:
Organizations interested in applying for funding must first submit a letter of inquiry (LOI) through their online application system prior to one of the three deadlines each year.
Duration: Varies.
Deadline: March 15, July 15 and December 7.

IRS IDENTIFICATION NUMBER: 52-6051781

TRUSTEES:
Martin Cohen
Donald E. Graham
Theodore C. Lutz
Pinkie Mayfield
Carol Melamed

ADDRESS INQUIRIES TO:
Eileen Daly, President
(See address above.)

*SPECIAL STIPULATIONS:
Proposals accepted only through the Fund web site.

GRAND RAPIDS COMMUNITY FOUNDATION [165]
185 Oakes Street, S.W.
Grand Rapids, MI 49503
(616) 454-1751
Fax: (616) 454-6455

E-MAIL ADDRESS:
grfound@grfoundation.org

WEB SITE ADDRESS:
www.grfoundation.org

FOUNDED: 1922

AREAS OF INTEREST:
Academic achievement, economic prosperity, healthy ecosystems, healthy people, social enrichment and vibrant neighborhoods.

NAME(S) OF PROGRAMS:
● **Access Camps**
● **Good Schools and Good Classrooms**

TYPE:
Capital grants; Challenge/matching grants; Demonstration grants; Development grants; Project/program grants; Scholarships; Seed money grants; Technical assistance. The Foundation also administers scholarship programs. Education mini-grants.

PURPOSE:
To build and manage our community's permanent endowment and lead the community to strengthen the lives of its people.

LEGAL BASIS:
Nonprofit organization established by resolution and declaration of trust. Incorporated in 1989.

ELIGIBILITY:
Applicant must have a current 501(c)(3) nonprofit designation from the IRS or be a governmental organization located in Kent

County and serve local residents. No grants to individuals except through the scholarship program.

GEOGRAPHIC RESTRICTIONS:
Grand Rapids, Michigan and surrounding communities.

FINANCIAL DATA:
Amount of support per award: Access Camps: $5,000 to $10,000; Good Schools and Good Classrooms: Varies.

Total amount of support: $9,753,200 in grants for fiscal year ended June 30, 2010.

NUMBER OF APPLICANTS MOST RECENT YEAR: 2,513.

NUMBER OF AWARDS: 1,485.

REPRESENTATIVE AWARDS:
Kent Intermediate School District to continue the work of a school-based program that will coordinate and deliver health and human services to students and their families.

APPLICATION INFORMATION:
For the general fund, applicants fill out an online preapplication on the Foundation's web site. After committee review, applicants may be asked to submit a Full Proposal, with final grant disposition determined by the Board of Trustees.

Duration: Generally, one-time grants. Foundation will, under certain circumstances, award multiyear grants.

Deadline: Varies by Fund. No deadline for the General Fund; preapplications are reviewed every two weeks.

PUBLICATIONS:
Annual report; quarterly newsletter.

IRS IDENTIFICATION NUMBER: 38-2877959

OFFICERS:
Carol J. Karr, Chairperson
Diana R. Sieger, President
Marilyn Zack, Vice President of Development
Lynne Black, Vice President of Finance and Administration
Marcia L. Rapp, Vice President of Programs
Roberta F. King, Vice President of Public Relations and Marketing

ADDRESS INQUIRIES TO:
Ann Puckett, Grants Administrator
(See address above.)

THE GREENWALL FOUNDATION   [166]

420 Lexington Avenue
Suite 2500
New York, NY 10170-0020
(212) 679-7266
Fax: (212) 679-7269

E-MAIL ADDRESS:
admin@greenwall.org

WEB SITE ADDRESS:
www.greenwall.org

FOUNDED: 1949

AREAS OF INTEREST:
Bioethics.

NAME(S) OF PROGRAMS:
● **Bioethics**

TYPE:
Project/program grants; Research grants. Through its Interdisciplinary Program in Bioethics, the Foundation provides funding for physicians, lawyers, philosophers, economists, theologians and other

professionals to address micro and macro issues in bioethics, providing guidance for those engaged in decision making at the bedside as well as those responsible for shaping institutional and public policy.

LEGAL BASIS:
Private, independent foundation according to Sections 501(c)(3) and 509(a) of the Internal Revenue Code.

ELIGIBILITY:
The Foundation makes philanthropic grants to support work in bioethics and invites proposals for funding new or continuing programs of institutions that are IRS tax-exempt under Section 501(c)(3) of the Internal Revenue Code. Special attention is given to proposals demonstrating innovative approaches to the specific concerns outlined in the Foundation's guidelines. One of the Foundation's goals is to put in place programs which can become self-sustaining and thus continue to serve the needs of society far beyond the limited term of its funding.

The approval of applications is based on the merit of a specific application and not the reputation of the applicant. The Foundation normally does not provide funds for equipment purchase, facility construction or renovation, general operating expenses, or for grants to private foundations, endowment funds and individual applicants.

Although the Foundation welcomes proposals for projects continuing beyond one year, funding beyond the first year is contingent on meeting first-year objectives and submitting a timely written report to the Foundation. Satisfactory site visits may also be a condition precedent to initial funding or renewals.

GEOGRAPHIC RESTRICTIONS:
New York City, New York.

FINANCIAL DATA:
Total amount of support: $2,725,656 in grants paid for the year ended December 31, 2008.

REPRESENTATIVE AWARDS:
$99,630 to Children's Hospital Boston, MA, for research support; $15,000 to The Esopus Foundation, New York, NY, to support emerging artists' projects in two issues of *Esopus* magazine; $15,000 to Smack Mellon Studios, Brooklyn, NY, to support the Exhibition Program and Artist Studio Program.

APPLICATION INFORMATION:
Requests for support should include an original and three copies of a program description, a one-page executive summary, a summary budget (expense and income), NIH-type CVs, and other relevant material.

Deadline: February 1 and August 1. Renewal possible.

IRS IDENTIFICATION NUMBER: 13-6082277

STAFF:
William C. Stubing, President
Fredrica Jarcho, Ph.D., Vice President for Program
Sam D. Teigen, Grants Administrator

ADDRESS INQUIRIES TO:
William C. Stubing, President
(See address above.)

JOHN SIMON GUGGENHEIM MEMORIAL FOUNDATION   [167]

90 Park Avenue
New York, NY 10016
(212) 687-4470
Fax: (212) 697-3248

E-MAIL ADDRESS:
fellowships@gf.org

WEB SITE ADDRESS:
www.gf.org

FOUNDED: 1925

AREAS OF INTEREST:
Sciences, social sciences, humanities and the creative arts.

NAME(S) OF PROGRAMS:
● **Guggenheim Fellowships**

TYPE:
Fellowships.

YEAR PROGRAM STARTED: 1925

PURPOSE:
To further the development of scholars and artists by assisting them to engage in research in any field of knowledge and creation in any of the arts.

LEGAL BASIS:
Private foundation.

ELIGIBILITY:
The Fellowships are awarded to men and women who have already demonstrated exceptional capacity for productive scholarship or exceptional creative ability in the arts.

Fellowships are awarded through two annual competitions: one open to citizens and permanent residents of the U.S. and Canada, and the other open to citizens and permanent residents of Latin America and the Caribbean. The Fellowships will be awarded by the Trustees upon nominations made by a Committee of Selection.

FINANCIAL DATA:
The amounts of the grants will be adjusted to the needs of the Fellows, considering their other resources and the purpose and scope of their plans, in accord with the Foundation's annual fellowship budget.

Amount of support per award: Varies.

Total amount of support: Approximately $8,800,000 annually.

NUMBER OF AWARDS: Approximately 187 annually.

APPLICATION INFORMATION:
Online application is available at the Foundation web site.

Duration: Appointments must be from six to 12 months. Fellows of the Foundation, until further notice from the Board of Trustees, may no longer seek renewed assistance.

Deadline: Applications must be submitted on or before September 15 for U.S. and Canadian competition. Fellowships to be announced the following April for U.S. competition. Latin American competition: December 1, with fellowship awards to be announced the following June. Applicants should check online for up-to-date deadlines.

PUBLICATIONS:
Annual report; announcement of Fellowship competition and recipients; application guidelines.

IRS IDENTIFICATION NUMBER: 13-5673173

OFFICERS:
Edward Hirsch, President

Coleen P. Higgins-Jacob, Vice President,
Chief Financial Officer and Treasurer
Andre Bernard, Vice President and Secretary
Richard V. Hatter, Director, Development and
Public Relations

TRUSTEES:
Robert A. Caro
Joel Conarroe
Michael Hegarty
Edward Hirsch
William P. Kelly
Joyce Carol Oates
A. Alex Porter
Joseph A. Rice
Richard A. Rifkind
Charles P. Stevenson, Jr.
Waddell W. Stillman
Patrick J. Waide, Jr.
Ellen Taaffe Zwilich

ADDRESS INQUIRIES TO:
Fellowships Program
(See address above.)

THE GEORGE GUND FOUNDATION [168]

1845 Guildhall Building
45 Prospect Avenue West
Cleveland, OH 44115
(216) 241-3114
Fax: (216) 241-6560

E-MAIL ADDRESS:
info@gundfdn.org

WEB SITE ADDRESS:
www.gundfoundation.org

FOUNDED: 1952

AREAS OF INTEREST:
Education, economic development and
community revitalization, human services,
arts and environment.

TYPE:
General operating grants; Project/program
grants.

YEAR PROGRAM STARTED: 1952

PURPOSE:
To enhance the quality of life, particularly for
those living in the greater Cleveland area; to
solve community problems; to improve living
conditions, particularly for the poor and
underprivileged; to provide opportunities for
all people to live constructive lives in a
peaceful world.

LEGAL BASIS:
Private foundation.

ELIGIBILITY:
Grants are made only to nonprofit,
tax-exempt educational and philanthropic
organizations. No awards are made to
individuals. Grants for operating budget
support will be considered only if the need is
for limited duration and will accomplish
some important purpose which will
strengthen the future position of the
institution. Preference will be given to pilot
projects, innovative programs and research
which hold promise of significant benefits of
broad applicability. Approximately 65% of
funds are allocated to grants in the fields of
education, human services and economic
revitalization.

GEOGRAPHIC RESTRICTIONS:
Primarily greater Cleveland and Cuyahoga
County, Ohio.

FINANCIAL DATA:
Amount of support per award: $500 to over
$2,000,000.

Total amount of support: $18,280,729 for the
year 2009.

NUMBER OF AWARDS: 201 for the year 2009.

APPLICATION INFORMATION:
No special forms are required and the
application should normally be a letter or
formal statement, including a brief history of
the institution or organization, a description
of its nature, the objectives of the request,
qualifications of key personnel, significant
and innovative features and a projected
budget showing how grant funds will be
utilized and over what period of time.
Duration: One year to multiyear.
Deadline: March 15, July 15 and November
15, for board meetings to be held in July,
November and February, respectively.

PUBLICATIONS:
Annual report; Guidelines for Grant
Applicants.

TRUSTEES:
Geoffrey Gund, President and Treasurer
Llura A. Gund, Vice President
Ann L. Gund, Secretary
David Goodman
Catherine Gund
George Gund, III
George Gund, IV
Zachary Gund
Cathy M. Lewis
Anna Traggio

ADMINISTRATIVE STAFF:
David T. Abbott, Executive Director
Robert B. Jaquay, Associate Director
Marcia Egbert, Senior Program Officer,
Human Services
Deena M. Epstein, Senior Program Officer,
Arts
John Mitterholzer, Senior Program Officer,
Environment
Ann K. Mullin, Senior Program Officer,
Education
Jeffrey Grimes, Fellow

ADDRESS INQUIRIES TO:
David Abbott, Executive Director or
Alice Cardillo, Office Manager
(See address above.)

HANCOCK COUNTY COMMUNITY FOUNDATION

312 East Main Street
Greenfield, IN 46140
(317) 462-8870
Fax: (317) 467-3330

E-MAIL ADDRESS:
mgibble@hccf.cc

WEB SITE ADDRESS:
www.hccf.cc

TYPE:
Project/program grants; Scholarships.

See entry 1379 for full listing.

HARDEN FOUNDATION [169]

1636 Ercia Street
Salinas, CA 93906
(831) 442-3005
Fax: (831) 443-1429

E-MAIL ADDRESS:
jgrainger@hardenfoundation.org

WEB SITE ADDRESS:
www.hardenfoundation.org

FOUNDED: 1963

AREAS OF INTEREST:
Children, youth and family, senior citizens,
animal welfare and the environment,
agriculture, education, arts and culture, and
health.

TYPE:
Capital grants; General operating grants;
Project/program grants.

YEAR PROGRAM STARTED: 1963

PURPOSE:
To fund groups working in the Foundation's
areas of interest.

LEGAL BASIS:
Private foundation.

ELIGIBILITY:
The Foundation does not fund schools,
churches or religious activities, or individuals
for endowments or fund-raising. Eligible
organizations must be of a 501(c)(3),
not-for-profit character.

GEOGRAPHIC RESTRICTIONS:
Monterey County, California.

FINANCIAL DATA:
Amount of support per award: $5,000 to
$100,000.

APPLICATION INFORMATION:
Guidelines and application forms are
available online.
Duration: Grants are biannual. Capital grants
are given on a one-time basis.
Deadline: March 1 and September 1.

PUBLICATIONS:
Application form, including guidelines.

ADDRESS INQUIRIES TO:
Joseph Grainger, Executive Director
(See address above.)

THE JOHN A. HARTFORD FOUNDATION, INC. [170]

55 East 59th Street
New York, NY 10022
(212) 832-7788
Fax: (212) 593-4913

E-MAIL ADDRESS:
mail@jhartfound.org

WEB SITE ADDRESS:
www.jhartfound.org

FOUNDED: 1929

AREAS OF INTEREST:
Aging and health.

NAME(S) OF PROGRAMS:
● **Aging and Health Program**

TYPE:
Demonstration grants; Fellowships; Matching
gifts; Project/program grants; Research
grants.

YEAR PROGRAM STARTED: 1979

PURPOSE:
To enhance the capacity of the health care
system to accommodate the nation's growing
elderly population.

LEGAL BASIS:
Private foundation.

ELIGIBILITY:
Grantee organizations must be located in the
U.S. and must have 501(c)(3) IRS tax exempt
designation.

The majority of the Foundation's current grantmaking relates to enhancing geriatric research and training and integrating and improving health-related services to the elderly.

The Foundation awards both single and multiple-year grants. No support for general purposes, endowment funds or capital budgets.

GEOGRAPHIC RESTRICTIONS:
United States.

FINANCIAL DATA:
Amount of support per award: $12,526 to $1,912,590 for the year 2010.
Total amount of support: $24,184,226 for the year 2010.

NUMBER OF APPLICANTS MOST RECENT YEAR:
364 for the year 2010.

NUMBER OF AWARDS: 24 for the year 2010.

APPLICATION INFORMATION:
All proposals are by invitation only from one of the Foundation's program officers, program director, or the executive director.
Duration: One to three years.

PUBLICATIONS:
Annual report.

TRUSTEES:
Norman H. Volk, Chairman
Kathryn D. Wriston, President
William T. Comfort, Jr., Secretary
John H. Allen
Anson M. Beard, Jr.
John J. Curley
Lile R. Gibbons
James G. Kenan, III
Christopher T.H. Pell
Barbara Paul Robinson
Margaret L. Wolff

STAFF:
Corinne H. Reider, Executive Director and Treasurer
Eva Cheng, Finance Director and Controller
Christopher A. Langston, Program Director
Amy J. Berman, Senior Program Officer
Nora O'Brien-Suric, Senior Program Officer
Rachael A. Watman, Senior Program Officer
Marcus R. Escobedo, Program Officer
Francisco J. Doll, Grants Manager

ADDRESS INQUIRIES TO:
Francisco J. Doll, Grants Manager
(See address above.)

HAWAIIAN ELECTRIC INDUSTRIES CHARITABLE FOUNDATION   [171]
P.O. Box 730
Honolulu, HI 96808-0730
(808) 543-7601
Fax: (808) 543-7602

E-MAIL ADDRESS:
heicf@hei.com

WEB SITE ADDRESS:
www.hei.com/heicf/heicf.html

FOUNDED: 1984

AREAS OF INTEREST:
Community development, education, the environment and family services.

TYPE:
Capital grants; Challenge/matching grants; Project/program grants.

YEAR PROGRAM STARTED: 1984

PURPOSE:
To assume leadership in making our community a better place to live.

LEGAL BASIS:
Corporate foundation.

ELIGIBILITY:
Applicant organizations must be IRS 501(c)(3). Contributions will not be provided for companies outside of HEICF area, government-supported activities, religious activities, veteran or fraternal organizations, political funds, program advertising or individuals.

GEOGRAPHIC RESTRICTIONS:
Hawaii.

FINANCIAL DATA:
Amount of support per award: $500 to $100,000.
Total amount of support: $1,500,000 for the year 2010.
Matching fund requirements: Full-time, regular employee, 501(c)(3) educational and family service organizations.

APPLICATION INFORMATION:
Applications must include a description of the organization, goals and objectives of the proposed project, amount requested, budget, current audited financial statements of the organization, other sources of funding, list of Board of Directors and HEI employees involved with the project, copy of IRS letter of tax-exempt status, the chief executive officer's compensation and benefits, number of paid staff and volunteers, and plans for acknowledging HEI contribution.
Duration: One year.
Deadline: Quarterly: January 1, April 1, July 1 and October 1.

ADDRESS INQUIRIES TO:
Rena Hwang, Administrator
(See address above.)

ROBERT M. HEARIN FOUNDATION   [172]
P.O. Box 16505
Jackson, MS 39236-6505
(601) 366-8363
Fax: (601) 366-8364

AREAS OF INTEREST:
Higher education and arts.

TYPE:
Scholarships.

PURPOSE:
To provide support to four-year colleges and art organizations.

ELIGIBILITY:
Scholarships are given through the four-year colleges and universities within the state of Mississippi.

GEOGRAPHIC RESTRICTIONS:
Mississippi.

FINANCIAL DATA:
Amount of support per award: Varies.

ADDRESS INQUIRIES TO:
Daisy Blackwell, Trustee
(See address above.)

H.J. HEINZ COMPANY FOUNDATION   [173]
One PPG Place, Suite 3100
Pittsburgh, PA 15222
(412) 456-5773
Fax: (412) 442-3227

E-MAIL ADDRESS:
heinz.foundation@us.hjheinz.com

WEB SITE ADDRESS:
www.heinz.com/foundation

FOUNDED: 1951

AREAS OF INTEREST:
Nutrition, diversity and fostering healthy communities.

CONSULTING OR VOLUNTEER SERVICES:
Employee volunteer program.

TYPE:
Matching gifts; Project/program grants. Matching gifts: Accredited education institutions; Arts and Culture, including public radio and television, performing arts companies, museums, libraries and art galleries.

YEAR PROGRAM STARTED: 1951

PURPOSE:
To fulfill corporate responsibility through philanthropic giving in communities with Heinz operating companies and in cities where Heinz holds a major corporate presence.

LEGAL BASIS:
Corporate foundation.

ELIGIBILITY:
All organizations seeking funding must be tax-exempt under 501(c)(3) of the Internal Revenue Code.

The Foundation does not make grants for loans or assistance to individuals, general scholarships, fellowships, travel grants, political campaigns either local or national and/or sectarian religious purposes.

FINANCIAL DATA:
Amount of support per award: Varies.
Total amount of support: Varies.
Matching fund requirements: The Foundation will match gifts in amounts of no less than $25 and no more than $5,000 for employees. A personal gift must be made to an eligible organization in the form of cash or securities and must be paid, not merely pledged. The market value of the securities will be the closing price on the day the gift was made or if there was no sale on that day, the most recently published closing price preceding the date of the gift.

The Foundation will not match payments made for services, tuition, membership dues, subscriptions, preferential seating or any type of payment not made as a direct contribution. In addition, the Foundation will not match any payment to the extent that the match would satisfy a pledge which the individual has made.

REPRESENTATIVE AWARDS:
Extra Mile Education Foundation; Make-A-Wish Foundation of Western Pennsylvania.

APPLICATION INFORMATION:
A written project summary may be sent including the goals of the applying organization, the specific purpose for which funds are requested, how the objective will be accomplished, to whom and where the program will be offered and whether the project is a single project or one that requires additional phases. A letter of intent is recommended to approach the H.J. Heinz Company Foundation.
Duration: Mostly one year. Renewal requests are considered.

TRUSTEES:
John Runkel, Chairman
Ted Bobby
Kristen Clark
Beth Eckenrode
Michael Mullen
Michael Okoroafer

ADDRESS INQUIRIES TO:
Tammy B. Aupperle, Director
(See address above.)

HENDERSON FOUNDATION [174]

P.O. Box 420
Sudbury, MA 01776-0420
(978) 443-4646
Fax: (978) 443-9510

FOUNDED: 1947

AREAS OF INTEREST:
Charitable, educational, religious and health.

TYPE:
General operating grants.

PURPOSE:
To continue support to general operations of those organizations now supported.

LEGAL BASIS:
Nonprofit foundation.

ELIGIBILITY:
Funding limited to public charities with a nonprofit 501(c)(3) tax-exempt status. The Foundation does not support activities for which the IRS requires grantor's responsibility and reports.

FINANCIAL DATA:
Amount of support per award: Minimum $500.
Total amount of support: $458,000 for the year 2008.

APPLICATION INFORMATION:
Send letter of inquiry with documentation of nonprofit 501(c)(3) tax-exempt status.
Duration: Up to three years.

TRUSTEES:
Barclay G. Henderson
Ernest Henderson, III
Roberta Henderson
Joseph C. Petrone

B. KEITH & NORMA F. HEUERMANN FOUNDATION [175]

Whitney, Newman, Mersch and Otto
1228 L Street
Aurora, NE 68818
(402) 694-3161

FOUNDED: 1994

AREAS OF INTEREST:
Children, the aged, the developmentally challenged, disabled, physically impaired, youth education and agriculturally related activites.

TYPE:
Capital grants; Matching gifts; Project/program grants; Research grants; Technical assistance.

YEAR PROGRAM STARTED: 1994

PURPOSE:
To support programs that meet the needs of society and improve the quality of life preferably in communities in rural Nebraska.

LEGAL BASIS:
Private foundation.

ELIGIBILITY:
Grants are made to organizations that have tax-exempt status under Section 501(c)(3) of the Internal Revenue Code. No grants are made to individuals. The Foundation does not loan funds to grant applicants.

GEOGRAPHIC RESTRICTIONS:
Rural areas in Nebraska.

FINANCIAL DATA:
Amount of support per award: $1,000 to $25,000.

NUMBER OF APPLICANTS MOST RECENT YEAR:
100.

NUMBER OF AWARDS: 50 for the year 2007-08.

APPLICATION INFORMATION:
The Foundation does not have an application form. The Grant Proposal should identify a special need or project to which funds will be applied including the objectives to be attained, people or groups who will benefit, work plans or timetables for achieving the stated objectives, and any other means of support. A copy of the 501(c)(3) letter from the IRS should accompany the application. Please provide the grant applicant's federal ID number.
Grant Proposal should be limited to two pages. Supporting documents such as project budget, other resources, names of supporters, and background information about the organization may be attached to the proposal. Stapled proposals are favored over bound ones. Brevity is appreciated.

Applicants must submit five original copies of the proposal.
Duration: Proposal may be for a project which extends over several years; however, the Foundation may review and make grants only on an annual basis.
Deadline: Proposals may be submitted at any time. The Directors convene at least three times per year at meetings to be scheduled in its discretion to review requests for grants.

PUBLICATIONS:
Guidelines.

IRS IDENTIFICATION NUMBER: 47-0748466

ADDRESS INQUIRIES TO:
Timothy J. Otto
(See address above.)

THE WILLIAM AND FLORA HEWLETT FOUNDATION [176]

2121 Sand Hill Road
Menlo Park, CA 94025
(650) 234-4500
Fax: (650) 234-4501

WEB SITE ADDRESS:
www.hewlett.org

FOUNDED: 1966

AREAS OF INTEREST:
Education, the environment, performing arts and population.

NAME(S) OF PROGRAMS:
- **Education**
- **Environment**
- **Global Development**
- **Performing Arts**
- **Philanthropy**
- **Population**

TYPE:
Capital grants; Challenge/matching grants; General operating grants; Matching gifts; Project/program grants.

YEAR PROGRAM STARTED: 1966

PURPOSE:
To provide grants to solve social and environmental problems at home and around the world.

LEGAL BASIS:
Private foundation.

ELIGIBILITY:
The Foundation does not fund individuals and generally does not fund:
(1) scholarships;
(2) endowments;
(3) capital campaigns;
(4) building construction;
(5) for-profit organizations or;
(6) unincorporated associations or groups.

Requirements vary by area of interest and are available on the Foundation web site.

FINANCIAL DATA:
Amount of support per award: $393,900 average for the year 2010.
Total amount of support: $345,190,721 for the year ended December 31, 2009.
Matching fund requirements: Foundation matches eligible employees' contributions to qualifying organizations.

NUMBER OF AWARDS: 596.

APPLICATION INFORMATION:
Information may be obtained at the Foundation web site.
Duration: Generally, one to three years.
Deadline: Varies according to program.

PUBLICATIONS:
Annual report; application guidelines; newsletter.

BOARD OF DIRECTORS:
Walter B. Hewlett, Chairman
Byron Auguste
Paul Brest
Harvey Fineberg
Eleanor H. Gimon
Marianne Gimon
Patricia A. House
Koh Boon Hwee
Mary H. Jaffe
Richard Levin
Stephen C. Neal
Jean G. Stromberg

ADMINISTRATIVE STAFF:
Paul Brest, President
Susan Bell, Vice President
Laurance R. Hoagland, Jr., Vice President and Chief Investment Officer
Susan Ketcham, Chief Financial Officer and Corporate Secretary
Sara Davis, Director of Grants Administration
Barbara Chow, Program Director, Education
Ruth Levine, Program Director, Global Development and Population
John McGuirk, Program Director, Performing Arts
Eric Brown, Communications Director
Jean McCall, Director of Human Resources
Lucy Ellis, Controller

HEWLETT-PACKARD COMPANY [177]

3000 Hanover Street, MS 1046
Palo Alto, CA 94304-1185
(650) 857-1501
(800) 752-0900

WEB SITE ADDRESS:
www.hp.com/hpinfo/socialinnovation/index.
html

AREAS OF INTEREST:
HP focuses its Social Innovations in four
areas: HP Education, HP Entrepreneurship,
HP in health, and HP in the Community.

TYPE:
Matching gifts; Product donations. Primarily
HP equipment donations. Employee matching
cash and product donation programs for
middle schools, high schools, universities and
tax-exempt organizations.

The Company has two main areas of focus
for philanthropy donations: education and
health. Education grants are targeted to
middle schools, high schools and universities
with a focus on math, science and technology
education, as well as increasing numbers and
diversity in the engineering pipeline.

The Company distributes Requests for
Proposals (RFPs) for grant programs it offers
in the education area. These grant programs
have very specific goals, awards and
application timelines.

Company employees can participate in cash
and product-matching grant programs
targeted middle schools, high schools,
universities and tax-exempt organizations. HP
encourages employees to volunteer in their
communities.

PURPOSE:
To create information products that accelerate
the advancement of knowledge and
fundamentally improve the effectiveness of
people and organizations.

LEGAL BASIS:
Corporation.

ELIGIBILITY:
Support is limited to nonprofit organizational
partners that align with the Company's
annually developed philanthropy initiatives.
The Company does not take unsolicited
requests from educational institutions,
nonprofit organizations or individuals.

GEOGRAPHIC RESTRICTIONS:
Asia, Pacific and Japan; Europe, the Middle
East, Africa, Latin America, and United
States (including Puerto Rico.)

FINANCIAL DATA:
Amount of support per award: Grants vary in
amount, depending upon the program.

CORINA HIGGINSON
TRUST   [178]
3400 Bryan Point Road
Accokeek, MD 20607
(301) 283-2113

E-MAIL ADDRESS:
info@corinahigginsontrust.org

WEB SITE ADDRESS:
www.corinahigginsontrust.org

AREAS OF INTEREST:
Education and human services.

TYPE:
General operating grants.

PURPOSE:
To improve the quality of life in the
mid-Atlantic region.

ELIGIBILITY:
Eligible organizations must be IRS 501(c)(3)
tax-exempt. An organization cannot be
awarded more than one grant per year.

GEOGRAPHIC RESTRICTIONS:
Maryland, Virginia and Washington, DC.

FINANCIAL DATA:
Amount of support per award: Typically
$5,000.

APPLICATION INFORMATION:
Applicants must include a copy of the
tax-exempt determination letter with the
application.
Duration: One year.
Deadline: Spring and fall for Letters of
Inquiry. Full proposals by invitation only.

ADDRESS INQUIRIES TO:
Wilton Corkern, Jr., President
(See address above.)

HILLMAN FOUNDATION   [179]
330 Grant Street, Suite 2000
Pittsburgh, PA 15219
(412) 338-3466
Fax: (412) 338-3463

E-MAIL ADDRESS:
foundation@hillmanfo.com

WEB SITE ADDRESS:
www.hillmanfdn.org

FOUNDED: 1951

AREAS OF INTEREST:
Community and civic affairs, human and
social services, cultural advancement and the
arts, all levels of education, youth and youth
services and health and medicine.

TYPE:
Capital grants; Endowments; Project/program
grants.

PURPOSE:
To support programs designed to improve
and enrich the quality of life within the city
of Pittsburgh and the southwestern
Pennsylvania region.

LEGAL BASIS:
Private foundation.

ELIGIBILITY:
Limited to organizations qualifying for
charitable, 501(c)(3) tax-exempt status. No
contributions are made to individuals or to
organizations outside the U.S., for travel
expenses of groups or for meetings, such as
conferences and seminars.

GEOGRAPHIC RESTRICTIONS:
Pittsburgh, Pennsylvania and southwestern
Pennsylvania.

FINANCIAL DATA:
Amount of support per award: Varies.
Total amount of support: $6,136,500 as of
October 25, 2009.

REPRESENTATIVE AWARDS:
$50,000 to Pittsburgh Habitat for Humanity
toward construction of duplex housing units;
$35,000 to Regional Family YMCA of
Laurel Highlands toward construction of new
program/administrative facility; $15,000 to
Pittsburgh Film Office toward purchase of
computer hardware and software; $3,000 to
Greater Pittsburgh Community Food Bank
toward disaster relief services to assist flood
victims in southwestern Pennsylvania.

APPLICATION INFORMATION:
Applicants wanting to submit a proposal to
Hillman Foundation should complete the
Grant Inquiry Form which can be found at
the Foundation web site.

Applications should include an annual budget
of the organization, a listing of the
organization's directors/trustees, detailed
information concerning costs of the project or
program to be funded and a time schedule (if
appropriate). Evidence of the applicant's
tax-exempt status is also required. Additional
information deemed necessary by the
applicant is welcomed.
Duration: Typically one year; some multiyear
funding.

PUBLICATIONS:
Annual report.

OFFICERS:
Henry L. Hillman, Chairman
David K. Roger, President
C.G. Grefenstette, Vice President
Eric C. Johnson, Vice President, Investments
Lisa R. Johns, Treasurer and Secretary

TRUSTEES:
Bruce I. Crocker
C.G. Grefenstette
Elsie H. Hillman
Henry L. Hillman
Juliet Lea Hillman Simonds
Eric C. Johnson
David K. Roger

ADDRESS INQUIRIES TO:
Lauri Fink, Program Officer
(See address above.)

HILLSDALE FUND, INC.   [180]
701 Green Valley Road, Suite 300
Greensboro, NC 27408
(336) 574-8696

TYPE:
Project/program grants.

LEGAL BASIS:
Family foundation.

ELIGIBILITY:
Must have 501(c)(3) status of Internal
Revenue Code to be eligible. Grants will not
be made available for indirect costs or
overhead as opposed to direct funding,
routine, recurring operating expenses,
conferences and seminars, travel and study,
or individuals for any purpose.

FINANCIAL DATA:
Amount of support per award: Varies.
Total amount of support: Varies.

APPLICATION INFORMATION:
Applicants should submit the Hillsdale Fund
application, which is available with
guidelines from the address above, and
include a copy of the IRS tax-exempt letter.
Deadline: Varies.

ADDRESS INQUIRIES TO:
Mary Scott, Executive Director
P.O. Box 20124
Greensboro, NC 27420

HIRSCHFELD FAMILY
FOUNDATION, INC.   [181]
c/o Jeff Orr
P.O. Box 1060
Kearney, NE 68848-1060
(308) 236-4455
Fax: (308) 236-4493

FOUNDED: 1990

AREAS OF INTEREST:
Aging centers/services; higher education,
hospitals (general), human services;
museums, YM/YWCAs and YM/YWHAs.

TYPE:
Project/program grants.

PURPOSE:
To support education and human services.

ELIGIBILITY:
No grants to individuals.

FINANCIAL DATA:
Amount of support per award: $1,000 to $1,000,000.

Total amount of support: Varies from year to year.

NUMBER OF APPLICANTS MOST RECENT YEAR:
57.

NUMBER OF AWARDS: 39.

APPLICATION INFORMATION:
Initial approach must be by letter requesting an application form.

IRS IDENTIFICATION NUMBER: 47-0762188.

STAFF:
Daniel J. Hirschfeld, President

ADDRESS INQUIRIES TO:
Jeff Orr
(See address above.)

THE HITACHI FOUNDATION [182]
1215 17th Street, N.W.
Washington, DC 20036
(202) 457-0588
Fax: (202) 296-1098

WEB SITE ADDRESS:
www.hitachifoundation.org

FOUNDED: 1985

AREAS OF INTEREST:
Education, community development and corporate citizenship.

NAME(S) OF PROGRAMS:
- **Business and Work Program**
- **Hitachi Community Action Partnership**
- **Yoshiyama Young Entrepreneurs Program**

TYPE:
Challenge/matching grants; Project/program grants. The Hitachi Community Action Partnership works with teams of Hitachi corporate employees to identify issues facing their communities and actions the company and employees can take in response.

The Yoshiyama Young Entrepreneurs Program identifies and supports inspiring young entrepreneurs who are operating businesses that create greater economic opportunity and help to improve the lives of low-wealth individuals in America.

YEAR PROGRAM STARTED: 1985

PURPOSE:
To improve the ability of individuals, institutions and communities to participate in a global society, one which manifests itself in every aspect of our lives, including environmental, economic, cultural and social. The Foundation's mission is societal capacity building, which fosters greater participation and leadership by citizens in government, education and community.

LEGAL BASIS:
Private foundation.

ELIGIBILITY:
Grant applicants must be nonprofit 501(c)(3) organizations.

Yoshiyama Young Entrepreneurs Program: Businesses that are one to five years old and have been generating revenue for a minimum of the past 12 months.

GEOGRAPHIC RESTRICTIONS:
United States.

FINANCIAL DATA:
Yoshiyama Young Entrepreneurs receive a cash prize and technical resources to support their business, and benefit from a partnership with Investors Circle.

Amount of support per award: Varies.

Total amount of support: Varies.

APPLICATION INFORMATION:
Guidelines and application is available on the Foundation web site.

Duration: Varies.

Deadline: Varies.

STAFF:
Mark G. Popovich, Senior Program Officer
Katrinka Hall, Manager of Executive Operations

OFFICERS AND BOARD OF DIRECTORS:
Bruce MacLaury, Ph.D., Chairman
Barbara Dyer, President and Chief Executive Officer
Melissa L. Bradley
Tony Brown
Adm. Bruce DeMars
Albert Fuller
Hon. Frances Garcia
Maurice Lim Miller
Louise Woerner

HOBLITZELLE FOUNDATION [183]
5556 Caruth Haven Lane, Suite 200
Dallas, TX 75225
(214) 373-0462
Fax: (214) 750-7412

E-MAIL ADDRESS:
pharris@hoblitzelle.org

WEB SITE ADDRESS:
www.hoblitzelle.org

FOUNDED: 1942

AREAS OF INTEREST:
Education, cultural affairs, social welfare and health.

TYPE:
Capital grants; Challenge/matching grants; Matching gifts; Project/program grants.

YEAR PROGRAM STARTED: 1942

LEGAL BASIS:
Private foundation.

ELIGIBILITY:
Educational institutions, hospitals, community agencies, youth and other welfare programs and organizations with appropriate interests are eligible.

GEOGRAPHIC RESTRICTIONS:
Texas, primarily Dallas.

FINANCIAL DATA:
Amount of support per award: $60,000 average.

Total amount of support: $4,652,732 for fiscal year 2009-10.

NUMBER OF APPLICANTS MOST RECENT YEAR:
600.

NUMBER OF AWARDS: 65.

REPRESENTATIVE AWARDS:
University of Texas Southwestern Medical Center; Carter Bloodcare World Affairs Council of Greater Dallas.

APPLICATION INFORMATION:
Applications for grants should be made in writing to the Foundation. Oral presentations will not be entertained.

Duration: One year and multiyear.

Deadline: April 15 for May meeting, August 15 for September meeting and December 15 for January meeting. If holiday weekend, next business day.

PUBLICATIONS:
Annual report; application guidelines.

IRS IDENTIFICATION NUMBER: 75-6003984

OFFICERS:
William T. Solomon, Chairman
Caren H. Prothro, Vice Chairman
Paul W. Harris, President
J. McDonald Williams, Treasurer
Donna C. Berry, Corporation Secretary

DIRECTORS:
Rafael M. Anchia
Linda P. Custard
John Dayton
Deedie Rose
Kern Wildenthal, M.D.

ADDRESS INQUIRIES TO:
Paul W. Harris, President and Chief Executive Officer
(See address above.)

HOUSTON ENDOWMENT INC. [184]
600 Travis, Suite 6400
Houston, TX 77002-3000
(713) 238-8100
Fax: (713) 238-8102

E-MAIL ADDRESS:
info@houstonendowment.org

WEB SITE ADDRESS:
www.houstonendowment.org

FOUNDED: 1937

AREAS OF INTEREST:
Arts, education, environment, health, human services, neighborhood development and community enhancement.

TYPE:
Capital grants; Challenge/matching grants; Conferences/seminars; Development grants; Fellowships; General operating grants; Internships; Matching gifts; Project/program grants; Scholarships; Technical assistance. Program support.

LEGAL BASIS:
Private foundation.

ELIGIBILITY:
Organizations exempt under Section 501(c)(3). No grants are made directly to individuals. All scholarship funds are disbursed through recipient institutions. No grants made outside the U.S.

GEOGRAPHIC RESTRICTIONS:
Harris County and contiguous counties (Brazoria, Chambers, Fort Bend, Galveston, Liberty, Montgomery and Waller).

FINANCIAL DATA:
Amount of support per award: Varies.

Total amount of support: Approximately $111,900,000 for the year 2009.

APPLICATION INFORMATION:
Only written applications are considered. No special form is required. Scholarships are never awarded directly on the basis of personal inquiry but are administered by colleges and universities. A list of recipient institutions is available on request.
Duration: One year to multiyear.

PUBLICATIONS:
Annual report.

ADDRESS INQUIRIES TO:
Grant Department
(See address above.)

MABEL Y. HUGHES CHARITABLE TRUST   [185]

Wells Fargo Bank
MAC No. C7300-493
1740 Broadway
Denver, CO 80274
(720) 947-6755
Fax: (720) 947-6804

FOUNDED: 1969

AREAS OF INTEREST:
Youth, health, education, culture and human services in the state of Colorado, with emphasis on Denver metropolitan area.

TYPE:
General operating grants; Project/program grants.

PURPOSE:
To provide funding to nonprofit and educational institutions that address vital community needs especially, but not limited to, human services.

LEGAL BASIS:
Private tax-exempt foundation.

ELIGIBILITY:
501(c)(3) tax-exempt organizations in Colorado only may apply. No grants are awarded to individuals.

GEOGRAPHIC RESTRICTIONS:
Colorado.

FINANCIAL DATA:
Amount of support per award: $5,000 to $10,000.
Total amount of support: Approximately $500,000 per year.

NUMBER OF APPLICANTS MOST RECENT YEAR:
Approximately 300.

APPLICATION INFORMATION:
Submit a brief letter describing project, why needed, population to be served, brief line item budget, information about organization seeking funds and its accomplishments to date, starting and ending dates, plans for post-grant funding and project evaluation, and a copy of latest 501(c)(3) exemption.
Duration: No grants awarded on a continuing basis. Renewals are possible.

TRUSTEES:
W.R. Alexander

ADDRESS INQUIRIES TO:
Peggy Toal, Vice President
(See address above.)

THE HUMANA FOUNDATION   [186]

500 West Main Street
Louisville, KY 40202
(502) 580-3041
Fax: (502) 580-1256

E-MAIL ADDRESS:
bwright@humana.com

WEB SITE ADDRESS:
www.humanafoundation.org

FOUNDED: 1981

AREAS OF INTEREST:
Domestic and international health care, education and civic and cultural development in communities that the corporation serves.

TYPE:
Capital grants; Challenge/matching grants; General operating grants; Internships; Professorships; Project/program grants; Scholarships. General program grants, capital campaigns and scholarships for children of employees.

YEAR PROGRAM STARTED: 1981

PURPOSE:
To act as the philanthropic arm of Humana Inc.

LEGAL BASIS:
Corporate foundation.

ELIGIBILITY:
The Humana Foundation supports and nurtures charitable activities that promote healthy lives and healthy communities.

FINANCIAL DATA:
Amount of support per award: Varies.
Matching fund requirements: Restricted to Humana Inc. officers and board of directors.

REPRESENTATIVE AWARDS:
$339,200 to Fund for the Arts; $561,000 to Humana Foundation Scholarship Program; $439,500 to Metro United Way.

APPLICATION INFORMATION:
Contact the Foundation for guidelines. Scholarship applications become available online November 16.
Duration: One year.
Deadline: Scholarships: January 15. Grant deadlines vary based on geographic location.

IRS IDENTIFICATION NUMBER: 61-1004763

ADDRESS INQUIRIES TO:
Virginia K. Judd, Executive Director
(See address above.)

THE HYDE AND WATSON FOUNDATION   [187]

31-F Mountain Boulevard
Warren, NJ 07059
(908) 753-3700
Fax: (908) 753-0004

WEB SITE ADDRESS:
www.fdncenter.
org/grantmaker/hydeandwatson

FOUNDED: 1983

AREAS OF INTEREST:
Broad fields include education, social services, arts, health, religion and humanities.

TYPE:
Capital grants; Challenge/matching grants. The Foundation supports capital projects such as hard costs related to purchase and relocation of facilities and/or building improvements, purchase of capital equipment, and other one-time capital needs.

LEGAL BASIS:
Private.

ELIGIBILITY:
Grants are made to nonprofit organizations that have received 501(c)(3) and 509(a)(1) or

509(a)(2) status from the IRS. In general, the Foundation does not accept applications for endowment, operating support, benefit fund-raisers, annual fund appeals, or from fiscal agents.

GEOGRAPHIC RESTRICTIONS:
Primarily the five boroughs of New York City, and Essex, Morris and Union counties in New Jersey.

FINANCIAL DATA:
Amount of support per award: Typical grant $5,000 to $25,000.
Total amount of support: $4,594,250 in grants paid for the year ended December 31, 2009.

NUMBER OF APPLICANTS MOST RECENT YEAR:
691 for the year 2009.

NUMBER OF AWARDS: 377 for the year 2009.

APPLICATION INFORMATION:
Applicants must submit the following:
(1) a completed Grant Application Form;
(2) a brief narrative (no longer than three pages), signed by an authorized official, summarizing the background of the organization and constituency served, the purpose of the appeal, project total and amount requested, and anticipated time frame for the project;
(3) a project budget with line items, including amount raised and balance needed;
(4) an operating budget for the current fiscal year;
(5) a list of supporters for the most recent fiscal year;
(6) a list of the board of directors/trustees and their business affiliations;
(7) a copy of the most recent audited financial report or Form 990 (if not available, call the Foundation to discuss);
(8) a copy of the organization's annual report (if available) and;
(9) a copy of the organization's most recent 501(c)(3) and 509(a)(1) or 509(a)(2) IRS ruling letter(s).

If your organization is a former grantee, in accordance with current guidelines, the Foundation will not consider any future proposals from your organization until a report is provided for any previous grants received from the Foundation. You may use the "Grant Report Form" available on the web site.

Appeals or inquiries submitted by e-mail will not be considered.
Deadline: Applications should be received no later than February 15 for the Spring meeting and no later than September 15 for the Fall meeting.

PUBLICATIONS:
Program policy statement and grant application guidelines.

OFFICERS:
Hunter W. Corbin, Chairman
William V. Engel, President
Brunilda Moriarty, Executive Vice President
Thomas W. Berry, Treasurer
Robert W. Parsons, Jr., Secretary
John W. Holman, III, Assistant Treasurer
Anke Lofrese, Assistant Treasurer
Sarah A. Kalra, Assistant Secretary

DIRECTORS:
Thomas W. Berry
Hunter W. Corbin
Elizabeth R. Curry
Hans Dekker

William V. Engel
Jennifer Chandler Hauge
John W. Holman, Jr.
John W. Holman, III
Thomas H. MacCowatt
Robert W. Parsons, Jr.
Anita V. Spivey
Kate B. Wood

ADDRESS INQUIRIES TO:
William V. Engel, President
(See address above.)

*PLEASE NOTE:
Appeals or inquiries submitted by e-mail will
not be considered.

IDAHO COMMUNITY FOUNDATION [188]
210 West State Street
Boise, ID 83702
(208) 342-3535
Fax: (208) 342-3577

E-MAIL ADDRESS:
info@idcomfdn.org

WEB SITE ADDRESS:
www.idcomfdn.org

FOUNDED: 1988

AREAS OF INTEREST:
Arts, civic affairs, community, conservation,
culture, education, environment, health and
human services.

NAME(S) OF PROGRAMS:
• **Deer Creek Fund Grants**
• **Geography Grants**
• **IFFT Fund Grants**
• **Northern, Eastern and Southwestern
  Region Competitive Grants**
• **Perc H. Shelton and Gladys A. Pospisil
  Shelton Foundation Advised Fund
  Grants**

TYPE:
Project/program grants; Scholarships; Seed
money grants.

YEAR PROGRAM STARTED: 1988

PURPOSE:
To enrich the quality of life throughout
Idaho.

LEGAL BASIS:
Community foundation; 501(c)(3) public
charity.

ELIGIBILITY:
Grants are made to organizations that are
nonprofit. Nonsectarian religious programs
and government entities may apply. No
grants are made to individuals.

FINANCIAL DATA:
Amount of support per award: Competitive
grants to $5,000. Others unlimited.
Total amount of support: Approximately
$4,800,000 for the year 2010.

COOPERATIVE FUNDING PROGRAMS:
Steele-Reese Foundation Fund.

NUMBER OF APPLICANTS MOST RECENT YEAR:
1,500.

NUMBER OF AWARDS: Approximately 900.

APPLICATION INFORMATION:
Form can be downloaded from the
Foundation web site.
Duration: Varies.
Deadline: Northern Region: January 15;
Eastern Region: April 1; Southwestern
Region: July 1.

PUBLICATIONS:
Annual report; monthly e-newsletters;
Techniques, quarterly estate planning
newsletter.

IRS IDENTIFICATION NUMBER: 82-0425063

ADMINISTRATION:
Robert A. Hoover, President and Chief
Executive Officer
Holly Motes, Controller
Lauren Carlson, Donor Development Officer

ADDRESS INQUIRIES TO:
Holly Motes, Controller
(See address above.)

IDDINGS BENEVOLENT TRUST [189]
Kettering Tower, 40 North Main Street
Suite 1620
Dayton, OH 45423-2490
(937) 224-1773
Fax: (937) 224-1871

FOUNDED: 1973

AREAS OF INTEREST:
The needs of youth and human services
within the greater Dayton area only with
limited consideration for all other interest
areas.

TYPE:
Capital grants; Challenge/matching grants;
Demonstration grants; Project/program
grants; Seed money grants. Funds for
development of new projects, emerging social
needs of youth, human services and capital
improvements. Grants are made only in Ohio,
with a special focus on the greater Dayton
area. No consideration for endowment funds
or grants to individuals.

YEAR PROGRAM STARTED: 1973

PURPOSE:
To improve community environment and
lives of citizens.

LEGAL BASIS:
Private, tax-exempt trust.

ELIGIBILITY:
Applicants must be nonprofit organizations.
Proof of tax exemption required. Primary
area of interest is greater Dayton area, but is
legally limited to Ohio-based organizations.
No consideration for endowment funds,
grants to individuals, or sponsorship of
fund-raiser events.

GEOGRAPHIC RESTRICTIONS:
Ohio, with emphasis on Montgomery County
(Dayton) and adjacent counties.

FINANCIAL DATA:
Amount of support per award: Usually
$1,000 to $50,000.
Total amount of support: $450,000 in grants
for the year 2010.
Matching fund requirements: Stipulated in
specific grants.

COOPERATIVE FUNDING PROGRAMS: On special
projects.

NUMBER OF APPLICANTS MOST RECENT YEAR:
Approximately 60 for the year 2010.

NUMBER OF AWARDS: Approximately 45 for the
year 2010.

REPRESENTATIVE AWARDS:
$5,000 to YWCA to help with new phone
system; $300,000 to Dayton Public Schools
for the first year of a three-year commitment

for the Positive Behavior Project; $15,000 to
AIDS Resource Center for "Protecting our
Youth" project.

APPLICATION INFORMATION:
Contact the Foundation office prior to
submitting a proposal.
Applicants must submit:
(1) proof of tax-exempt 501(c)(3) status
(single copy);
(2) seven copies of Foundation's official
application form which includes a synopsis
page, a budget page for the specific project,
and three pages describing the purpose and
benefits of grant and;
(3) single copies of the organization's annual
budget, income sources, Board of Trustees
and supportive information as requested.
Duration: Usually one year. Projects may be
considered for a one-year renewal after
proper evaluation. Three-year maximum for
capital campaigns.
Deadline: March 1, June 1, September 1 and
November 1. Award announcements are
made within 10 days following board
meeting in month after deadline.

PUBLICATIONS:
Information brochure; application guidelines
and form.

OFFICERS:
Kenneth Kent, Vice President, Trust
Department
Maribeth A. Graham, Administrator

ADDRESS INQUIRIES TO:
Maribeth A. Graham, Administrator
(See address above.)

*PLEASE NOTE:
Applications through bank are not acceptable.

*SPECIAL STIPULATIONS:
Recipients of grants must submit quarterly
evaluations as long as the project is funded
by the Foundation. A final report must be
submitted on completion of the project.
Unable to consider proposals outside Ohio.

INDEPENDENCE FOUNDATION
Offices at the Bellevue
200 South Broad Street, Suite 1101
Philadelphia, PA 19102
(215) 985-4009
Fax: (215) 985-3989

E-MAIL ADDRESS:
ssherman@independencefoundation.org

WEB SITE ADDRESS:
www.independencefoundation.org

TYPE:
Challenge/matching grants; Fellowships;
General operating grants; Project/program
grants.

See entry 2650 for full listing.

INTEL FOUNDATION [190]
JF3-165
5200 Northeast Elam Young Parkway
Hillsboro, OR 97124-6497
(503) 712-3355

E-MAIL ADDRESS:
intel.foundation@intel.com

WEB SITE ADDRESS:
www.intel.com/education

FOUNDED: 1989

AREAS OF INTEREST:
K-12 education; math, science and
engineering education; women and

underrepresented minorities in science and engineering; and public understanding of technology and its impact on contemporary life. Additional areas of interest in communities where Intel is located.

CONSULTING OR VOLUNTEER SERVICES:
Volunteer programs at sites where Intel has facilities.

NAME(S) OF PROGRAMS:
● **Community Grants**

TYPE:
Matching gifts; Project/program grants. Community grants are awarded to programs which are located in a community where Intel has a major facility.

YEAR PROGRAM STARTED: 1989

PURPOSE:
To advance math, science and engineering education; to promote the entrance of women and underrepresented minorities into careers in science and engineering; to promote public understanding of technology and its impact on contemporary life.

ELIGIBILITY:
Foundation awards cash grants to nonprofit, tax-exempt organizations for specific projects. The Foundation does not fund individuals, events such as dinners and auctions, advertising, annual fund drives, endowment or capital improvement campaigns, lobbying activities, private foundations, organizations which promote discrimination or religious, fraternal or political organizations. The Foundation does not consider funding for local programs outside Intel site communities.

If a request is received and the applicant's program does not fit the definition of a Community Grant, it will be denied.

The Foundation does not accept unsolicited requests.

GEOGRAPHIC RESTRICTIONS:
Arizona; Folsom and Santa Clara, California; Hudson, Massachusetts; Rio Rancho, New Mexico; Hillsboro, Oregon; DuPont, Washington.

FINANCIAL DATA:
Amount of support per award: Varies.

APPLICATION INFORMATION:
Organizations must apply online for any community grants. The Intel Foundation does not accept unsolicited requests for national grants.
Duration: Varies.
Deadline: Applications are reviewed throughout the year.

*SPECIAL STIPULATIONS:
If a request is received and the applicant's program does not fit the definition of a Community Grant, it will be denied.

ANN JACKSON FAMILY FOUNDATION [191]
P.O. Box 5580
Santa Barbara, CA 93150-5580
(805) 969-2258
Fax: (805) 969-0315

WEB SITE ADDRESS:
www.annjacksonfamilyfoundation.org

AREAS OF INTEREST:
Community infrastructure, art, human services and health.

TYPE:
Capital grants; General operating grants.

PURPOSE:
To enhance the community.

LEGAL BASIS:
Private foundation.

ELIGIBILITY:
Grants are made to organizations that have tax-exempt status under Section 501(c)(3) of the Internal Revenue Code. No grants are made to individuals.

GEOGRAPHIC RESTRICTIONS:
Primarily Santa Barbara County, California.

FINANCIAL DATA:
Amount of support per award: Typically $1,000 to $10,000 for general operating grants.

APPLICATION INFORMATION:
The Foundation encourages applicants to use the Common Grant Application form, a link to which is available on the web site.
Duration: One year, with occasional multiyear. Renewal by reapplication.

ADDRESS INQUIRIES TO:
Palmer G. Jackson, Sr., President
(See address above.)

THE JACKSON FOUNDATION [192]
c/o U.S. Bank, NA
P.O. Box 3168
Portland, OR 97208
(503) 275-4414
(503) 275-4400
Fax: (503) 274-4177

WEB SITE ADDRESS:
www.thejacksonfoundation.com

FOUNDED: 1960

AREAS OF INTEREST:
Arts/performing arts, economic development, substance abuse, human services, minorities, housing, disabilities, humanities, education, environment, health, children/youth, aged and women.

TYPE:
Capital grants; Challenge/matching grants; Development grants; General operating grants; Matching gifts; Project/program grants; Research grants.

YEAR PROGRAM STARTED: 1963

PURPOSE:
Net income for use within the state of Oregon for charitable and educational purposes and for the advancement of public welfare.

LEGAL BASIS:
Private foundation.

ELIGIBILITY:
Grants are made to 501(c)(3) organizations. Priority is given to one-time special projects and development projects. No grants to individuals.

GEOGRAPHIC RESTRICTIONS:
Oregon.

FINANCIAL DATA:
Amount of support per award: $1,000 to $10,000.
Total amount of support: $680,013 for fiscal year ended June 2008.

NUMBER OF APPLICANTS MOST RECENT YEAR:
250.

NUMBER OF AWARDS: 125.

REPRESENTATIVE AWARDS:
$5,000 to Portland Community College Foundation; $5,000 to High Desert Museum; $3,500 to Wallowa Medical Memorial; $1,000 to Sisters of the Road Cafe; $10,000 to William Temple House; $7,500 to Nature Conservancy.

APPLICATION INFORMATION:
Eligible organizations should request an application form.
Duration: One year.
Deadline: March 31, June 30, September 30 and December 31.

OFFICERS AND DIRECTORS:
Milo E. Ormseth
Julie S. Vigeland

ADDRESS INQUIRIES TO:
Robert H. Depew, Vice President
U.S. Bank, NA
(See address above.)

HENRY M. JACKSON FOUNDATION [193]
1501 Fourth Avenue
Suite 1580
Seattle, WA 98101
(206) 682-8565
Fax: (206) 682-8961

E-MAIL ADDRESS:
foundation@hmjackson.org

WEB SITE ADDRESS:
www.hmjackson.org

FOUNDED: 1983

AREAS OF INTEREST:
International affairs, public service, environment/natural resources and human rights.

NAME(S) OF PROGRAMS:
● **Environmental and Natural Resources Management Program**
● **Human Rights Program**
● **International Affairs Education Program**
● **Public Service Program**

TYPE:
Challenge/matching grants; Conferences/seminars; Internships; Professorships; Project/program grants; Seed money grants.

YEAR PROGRAM STARTED: 1983

PURPOSE:
To advance education and public understanding of critical public policy issues in the four priority areas above.

LEGAL BASIS:
Publicly supported foundation.

ELIGIBILITY:
Grants are made to private, nonprofit, tax-exempt organizations under 501(c)(3) and public, tax-exempt entities under 170(c). No grants are made to individuals.

No grants for capital or general operating expenses.

GEOGRAPHIC RESTRICTIONS:
Public service grants are limited to applicants in the Northwest (Washington, Oregon, Idaho, Alaska). Human Rights grants are limited to Russia and United States organizations working in Russia.

FINANCIAL DATA:
Amount of support per award: $1,000 to $125,000.

Total amount of support: Average: $500,000.

REPRESENTATIVE AWARDS:
$71,000 to support guest faculty on topics of current foreign policy concerns for senior-level courses at the University of Washington's Jackson School of International Studies; $15,000 to support the publication and dissemination of a report on urban sprawl's toll on open space and farmland; $10,000 to create two new exhibits representing gulag life during different epochs of Soviet history on the site of a former prison labor camp; $34,536 for a program that places young adults on city boards and commissions.

APPLICATION INFORMATION:
Proposals should include:
(1) a cover letter summarizing the project and amount requested;
(2) a detailed budget, implementation strategy, identification of board and/or those responsible for the project and plans for evaluation;
(3) IRS tax-exempt status determination letter and;
(4) most recent financial statements (preferred audited).
Duration: Varies.
Deadline: December 1, March 1, June 1 and September 1, for awards announced in March, June, September and December, respectively.

PUBLICATIONS:
Application guidelines; annual report; newsletter; memorial lecture.

IRS IDENTIFICATION NUMBER: 52-1313011

OFFICERS:
Helen H. Jackson, Chairman
John Hempelmann, President
Craig Gannett, Vice President
Linda Mason Wilgis, Vice President
David Rostov, Treasurer
Anna Marie Laurence, Secretary
Joel C. Merkel, General Counsel

ADDRESS INQUIRIES TO:
Lara Iglitzin, Executive Director
(See address above.)

JACKSONVILLE JAGUARS FOUNDATION [194]

One Everbank Field Drive
Jacksonville, FL 32202
(904) 633-5437
Fax: (904) 633-5683

WEB SITE ADDRESS:
www.jaguars.com

FOUNDED: 1993

AREAS OF INTEREST:
Social welfare for disadvantaged youths.

TYPE:
General operating grants; Project/program grants. Limited capital grants that target economically and socially "at-risk" youths in northeast Florida.

YEAR PROGRAM STARTED: 1994

PURPOSE:
To help meet the needs of disadvantaged youths (prenatal through teens), striving to address the causes of those needs through enhanced participation of parents, legal guardians and local mentors in northeast Florida.

LEGAL BASIS:
Corporation foundation.

ELIGIBILITY:
Organizations in northeast Florida that work for disadvantaged youths on a non-sectarian nature. Must have 501(c)(3) IRS documentation.

No grants to individuals, schools or single-disease organizations.

GEOGRAPHIC RESTRICTIONS:
Baker, Clay, Duval, Nassau, and Saint Johns counties, Florida.

FINANCIAL DATA:
Amount of support per award: Varies.
Total amount of support: $1,000,000 annually.

COOPERATIVE FUNDING PROGRAMS: Youth Anti-Obesity Grants with Baptist Health; Teen Pregnancy Prevention Grants with Weaver Family Foundation and Blue Cross Blue Shield of Florida.

NUMBER OF APPLICANTS MOST RECENT YEAR: 42.

NUMBER OF AWARDS: 37.

APPLICATION INFORMATION:
Submit a one-page summary that includes the specific goals, objectives, proposed activities and results expected to the Foundation.
Duration: One year. Renewal by reapplication.
Deadline: July and February.

ADDRESS INQUIRIES TO:
Peter Racine, Executive Director
(See address above.)

GEORGE FREDERICK JEWETT FOUNDATION [195]

The Russ Building
235 Montgomery Street, Suite 612
San Francisco, CA 94104
(415) 421-1351
Fax: (415) 421-0721

E-MAIL ADDRESS:
tfbjewettf@aol.com

FOUNDED: 1957

AREAS OF INTEREST:
Arts and humanities, conservation and preservation, education, medical services and research, population and social welfare.

TYPE:
Capital grants; Challenge/matching grants; Endowments; General operating grants; Project/program grants; Scholarships; Technical assistance. Priority interests include education, libraries, music, preservation, protection of environment, including population issues and scientific research. The Fund focuses on grants largely in geographic areas in which Trustees and family members have knowledge of particular needs.

YEAR PROGRAM STARTED: 1957

PURPOSE:
To stimulate, encourage and support activities of established, voluntary and nonprofit organizations which are of importance to human welfare.

LEGAL BASIS:
Family foundation in perpetual trust, exempted from Federal Income Tax by Section 501(c)(3) and classified under Section 509 of such Code.

ELIGIBILITY:
Private, tax-exempt organizations which provide services to help meet the human needs in their respective communities are supported. No grants are made to individuals. No grants for tickets or fund-raising events.

No unsolicited proposals will be accepted.

GEOGRAPHIC RESTRICTIONS:
Washington, DC and Massachusetts.

FINANCIAL DATA:
Amount of support per award: $5,000 to $50,000. Average grant: $20,000.
Total amount of support: $1,548,705 for the year 2010.

COOPERATIVE FUNDING PROGRAMS: The Foundation prefers to participate with other donors.

NUMBER OF APPLICANTS MOST RECENT YEAR: 224.

NUMBER OF AWARDS: 71.

REPRESENTATIVE AWARDS:
$25,000 to Salt Pond Areas Bird Sanctuaries; $40,000 to Planned Parenthood of the Inland Northwest; $7,500 to Project Open Hand.

APPLICATION INFORMATION:
Letters of inquiry only.
Duration: Most grants are given for one year.
Deadline: Grants are awarded quarterly: March, June, September and December.

PUBLICATIONS:
Annual report; guidelines.

TRUSTEES:
George Frederick Jewett, III, Chairman
Margaret Jewett Greer
William Hershey Greer, Jr.
Lucille McIntyre Jewett

ADDRESS INQUIRIES TO:
Toni Bermudez
Program Grants Officer
(See address above.)

JFK LIBRARY FOUNDATION [196]

Columbia Point
Boston, MA 02125-3313
(617) 514-1654
Fax: (617) 514-1652

E-MAIL ADDRESS:
kennedy.library@nara.gov

WEB SITE ADDRESS:
www.jfklibrary.org

FOUNDED: 1964

AREAS OF INTEREST:
History, government, archival administration and library science, journalism, communications and other related disciplines.

NAME(S) OF PROGRAMS:
• **Kennedy Library Archival Internships**

TYPE:
Internships. Awarded to undergraduate and graduate students majoring in history, government, archival administration, library science, journalism, communications and related disciplines for on-site work with the staff at the Kennedy Library.

YEAR PROGRAM STARTED: 1970

LEGAL BASIS:
Private foundation in cooperation with a U.S. government agency.

FINANCIAL DATA:
Amount of support per award: Interns are paid at a rate of $12.50 per hour; minimum commitment of 12 hours per week.

APPLICATION INFORMATION:
Candidate must complete application form, submit a copy of current college transcript, and a letter of reference.
Duration: Varies.

JOHNSON & JOHNSON FAMILY OF COMPANIES   [197]

One Johnson & Johnson Plaza
New Brunswick, NJ 08933
(732) 524-0400
Fax: (732) 524-3300

WEB SITE ADDRESS:
www.jnj.com

FOUNDED: 1953

AREAS OF INTEREST:
Health care.

TYPE:
Matching gifts; Project/program grants; Research grants. International programs, product donation, cash grants. Emphasis on health care, with a special interest in maternal and child health care issues. The Company administers major programs in partnership with selected nonprofit organizations. Grants largely extended through these programs on a Request for Proposal basis.

The Corporation conducts extensive product giving program but only through established partnerships with selected nonprofit organizations. No unsolicited requests accepted.

The Corporation also conducts large matching gifts program in areas of higher education, hospitals, disease-specific organizations, cultural organizations and prevention and treatment of substance abuse.

PURPOSE:
To make life-changing, long-term differences in human health by targeting the world's major health-related issues through community-based partnerships.

ELIGIBILITY:
Grants are made to organizations with 501(c)(3) status. Grants are not made for endowments, appeals for unrestricted funds, tours, fund-raising galas and sporting events, political, fraternal or athletic groups, sectarian or religious organizations, capital expenditures, individuals or loans. Priority is given to activities and needs in locations where the company has a presence in the U.S. and Puerto Rico.

FINANCIAL DATA:
Amount of support per award: Varies.
Total amount of support: Varies.

NUMBER OF AWARDS: More than 600.

APPLICATION INFORMATION:
No unsolicited requests are accepted.
Duration: Varies.

PUBLICATIONS:
Corporate Contributions report; application guidelines, policy statement.

STAFF:
Michael J. Bzdak, Director, Corporate Contributions
Anu Gupta, M.D., Director, Corporate Contributions
William Lin, Ph.D., Director, Corporate Contributions
Joy Marini, Director, Corporate Contributions

Rick Martinez, M.D., Director, Corporate Contributions
Conrad Person, Director, Corporate Contributions
Bonnie J. Petrauskas, Director, Corporate Contributions

ADDRESS INQUIRIES TO:
William Lin, Ph.D., Director
Corporate Contributions
(See address above.)

JOHNSON CONTROLS FOUNDATION   [198]

5757 North Green Bay Avenue
Milwaukee, WI 53209
(414) 524-2296
Fax: (414) 524-2077

WEB SITE ADDRESS:
www.johnsoncontrols.com

FOUNDED: 1952

AREAS OF INTEREST:
Higher education, health and social services, civic activities, culture and arts.

TYPE:
Matching gifts; Project/program grants. The Foundation matches the personal gifts of employees, retirees and directors to accredited colleges and universities, community arts and cultural organizations and to United Way in the aggregate from its U.S. company units.

PURPOSE:
To be operated for charitable purposes which include the distribution and application of financial support to soundly managed and operated organizations or causes which are fundamentally philanthropic.

LEGAL BASIS:
Corporate foundation.

ELIGIBILITY:
Contributions are limited to organizations which are exempt from taxation under the Internal Revenue Code. No gifts will be made to any municipal, state, federal agency or department or to any organization established to influence legislation. No distribution will be made to a private individual. No gifts will be made to sectarian institutions or programs whose services are limited to members of any one religious group or whose funds are used primarily for the propagation of religion. Grants are not usually given to public or private pre-schools, elementary or secondary institutions, but are limited to colleges and universities.

GEOGRAPHIC RESTRICTIONS:
United States.

FINANCIAL DATA:
Amount of support per award: $50 to $100,000.
Total amount of support: $14,800,000 including matching gifts for the year 2008.

NUMBER OF AWARDS: Up to 40.

REPRESENTATIVE AWARDS:
$50,000 to Discovery World Museum; $75,000 to Milwaukee Symphony Orchestra; $50,000 to Milwaukee Performing Arts; $125,000 to the University of Wisconsin, Milwaukee.

APPLICATION INFORMATION:
Proposals, preferably in concise letter form, should include statement regarding tax-exempt status, description of the structure, governing board, purpose, history

and programs of the organization, summary of the need for support and how it will be used, geographic areas served by the organization, budget information about the organization and statement regarding other sources of income from corporations and foundations, community support and involvement. Must include 501(c)(3) letter.

ADDRESS INQUIRIES TO:
Johnson Controls Foundation
P.O. Box 591
Milwaukee, WI 53201-0591

THE JOHNSON FOUNDATION, INC.   [199]

33 East Four Mile Road
Racine, WI 53402
(262) 681-3331
Fax: (262) 681-3325

E-MAIL ADDRESS:
rdower@johnsonfdn.org

WEB SITE ADDRESS:
www.johnsonfdn.org

FOUNDED: 1959

AREAS OF INTEREST:
Conferences (relatively brief, intensive meetings of a small number of experts gathered to address a well-defined issue or problem, consonant with the Foundation's mission).

TYPE:
Conferences/seminars.

YEAR PROGRAM STARTED: 1960

PURPOSE:
To improve society by identifying and addressing important national or international issues and by developing appropriate strategies for their resolution.

LEGAL BASIS:
Exempt operating foundation.

ELIGIBILITY:
Tax-exempt charitable and educational organizations may apply. Basic eligibility requirements include:
(1) 501(c)(3) and 509(a)(1), (2), or (3) status documentation;
(2) proposed conference topic aligns with the Foundation's Environment and Community program areas;
(3) proposed conference topic is nonpartisan and nonsectarian in nature and;
(4) co-sponsor and other involved parties are willing to collaborate with the Foundation on conference design, implementation, and evaluation strategies.

The Foundation does not make grants. The Foundation does not sponsor regular meetings of single organizations, staff retreats, training programs, or fund-raising events. In no case is the facility available for a fee or for use by organizations other than those with educational/charitable status.

FINANCIAL DATA:
When the Foundation supports a conference sponsored by another organization, its usual contribution consists of the provision of the full conference facilities of Wingspread, planning and logistical support by the staff, meals and other amenities and local transportation.

NUMBER OF APPLICANTS MOST RECENT YEAR:
Approximately 100.

IRS IDENTIFICATION NUMBER: 38-3675289

EXECUTIVE OFFICERS:
Roger C. Dower, President
Lois Y. Berg, Director of Administrative
Services

TRUSTEES AND OFFICERS:
Helen Johnson-Leipold, Chairman of the
Board
Roger C. Dower, President
Mike Dombeck
James D. Ericson
Imogene Powers Johnson
Janice C. Kreamer
Winifred J. Marquart
Paul R. Portney
Paula Wolff
Kate Wolford

ADDRESS INQUIRIES TO:
Wendy Butler
Special Initiatives Coordinator
(See address above.)
Tel: (262) 681-3321
E-mail: wbutler@johnsonfdn.org

MAGIC JOHNSON FOUNDATION, INC. [200]

9100 Wilshire Boulevard
Suite 700, East Tower
Beverly Hills, CA 90212
(310) 246-4400
Fax: (310) 246-1106

WEB SITE ADDRESS:
www.magicjohnson.org

FOUNDED: 1991

AREAS OF INTEREST:
HIV/AIDS education, prevention and care;
also youth.

NAME(S) OF PROGRAMS:
- **Magic Johnson Foundation HIV/AIDS Grant**
- **Taylor Michaels Scholarship**

TYPE:
Project/program grants; Scholarships;
Technical assistance.

PURPOSE:
To support organizations and programs
specializing in HIV/AIDS education,
prevention and care, and in the areas of
education, social needs and health issues of
young people.

LEGAL BASIS:
National public charity.

ELIGIBILITY:
Organizations classified as 501(c)(3) by the
IRS can apply. Funding will not be
considered for projects by individuals and
families. Advertising or sponsorship for other
funding events are not eligible to receive
funds. Research grants, conferences, travel,
videos and capital acquisitions are also
excluded.

GEOGRAPHIC RESTRICTIONS:
Northern and southern California;
Washington, DC; Atlanta, Georgia; Chicago,
Illinois; Baltimore, Maryland; New York,
New York; Cleveland, Ohio; Houston, Texas.

FINANCIAL DATA:
Amount of support per award: Grants: $5,000
to $25,000; Scholarships: Varies by need.
Total amount of support: Varies.

APPLICATION INFORMATION:
By invitation only, but do accept letters of
intent on an ongoing basis. Applicants should
request in writing (maximum two pages) to
be placed on the Magic Johnson Foundation's
database. Requests must contain the name of
the organization, address, telephone and fax
numbers, e-mail address, contact person, a
brief explanation of specific funding needs
and a history of services provided.
Deadline: Letters of Intent accepted on an
ongoing basis.

PUBLICATIONS:
Annual report; grant guidelines.

ADDRESS INQUIRIES TO:
Shane Jenkins, Director of HIV and
Social Programs
(See address above.)

DAISY MARQUIS JONES FOUNDATION [201]

1600 South Avenue
Suite 250
Rochester, NY 14620-3921
(585) 461-4950
Fax: (585) 461-9752

E-MAIL ADDRESS:
mail@dmjf.org

WEB SITE ADDRESS:
www.dmjf.org

FOUNDED: 1968

AREAS OF INTEREST:
Disadvantaged children and families, access
to health care, assistance to senior citizens
and economic security for families.

TYPE:
Capital grants; Challenge/matching grants;
Demonstration grants; Development grants;
General operating grants; Matching gifts;
Project/program grants; Seed money grants.

YEAR PROGRAM STARTED: 1968

PURPOSE:
To improve the well-being of residents of
Monroe and Yates counties, New York,
particularly within the city of Rochester; to
meet the needs of the disadvantaged,
focusing on prevention; to develop children
and families to their maximum potential.

LEGAL BASIS:
Not-for-profit, private foundation.

ELIGIBILITY:
Applicants must be nonprofit, tax-exempt
organizations in Monroe and Yates counties,
New York. The Foundation does not consider
requests for aid for basic research, private
schools, the arts, or religious purposes. The
Foundation does not make grants to
individuals.

GEOGRAPHIC RESTRICTIONS:
Monroe and Yates counties, New York.

FINANCIAL DATA:
Amount of support per award: Varies.
Total amount of support: $1,105,660 for the
year 2009.
Matching fund requirements: Stipulated with
specific programs.

NUMBER OF AWARDS: 51.

REPRESENTATIVE AWARDS:
$8,000 to City of Rochester Police
Department to help support a public
recognition program for city youths; $25,000
to International Museum of Photography at
George Eastman House to support a program
celebrating the life of Dr. Martin Luther
King, Jr.; $15,000 to Flower City Habitat for
Humanity for construction of a house built
totally by women; $45,000 to Anthony L.

Jordan Health Corporation to maintain
comprehensive health care for inner city
teens.

APPLICATION INFORMATION:
A short letter of inquiry is the preferred form
of initial contact. The letter should include a
brief description of the proposal, the amount
requested and the intended starting date. If
the proposed project is consistent with the
Foundation's objectives and areas of interest,
the applicant will be sent an application form
to be completed and returned to the
Foundation.

PUBLICATIONS:
Annual report.

STAFF:
Donald W. Whitney, President
Marless A. Honan, Secretary

TRUSTEES AND OFFICERS:
Donald W. Whitney, President
Roger L. Gardner

ADDRESS INQUIRIES TO:
Donald W. Whitney, President
(See address above.)

THE JOYCE FOUNDATION [202]

70 West Madison Street
Suite 2750
Chicago, IL 60602
(312) 782-2464
Fax: (312) 782-4160

E-MAIL ADDRESS:
info@joycefdn.org

WEB SITE ADDRESS:
www.joycefdn.org

FOUNDED: 1948

AREAS OF INTEREST:
Education, employment, environment, gun
violence, money and politics, and culture.

TYPE:
Awards/prizes; Demonstration grants;
Development grants; General operating
grants; Matching gifts; Project/program
grants; Research grants; Seed money grants.
Employee matching gifts.

YEAR PROGRAM STARTED: 1948

PURPOSE:
To support efforts to protect the natural
environment of the Great Lakes; to reduce
poverty and violence in the region; to ensure
that its people have access to good schools,
decent jobs, and a diverse and thriving
culture; to reform the system of financing
elections campaigns to ensure that public
policies truly reflect public rather than private
interests.

LEGAL BASIS:
Private foundation.

ELIGIBILITY:
Applicants must be tax-exempt, charitable
organizations that are based or have a
program in the Midwest, which the
Foundation defines as including Illinois,
Indiana, Michigan, Minnesota, Ohio and
Wisconsin. A limited number of environment
grants are made to organizations in Canada.
The Foundation generally does not support
capital proposals, endowment campaigns,
religious activities, commercial ventures,
direct service programs or scholarships.

GEOGRAPHIC RESTRICTIONS:
Midwest, including Illinois, Indiana,
Michigan, Minnesota, Ohio and Wisconsin.

FINANCIAL DATA:
Amount of support per award: Up to
$1,900,000 over three years; average grant:
$140,000.

Total amount of support: $36,000,000 for the
year 2009.

NUMBER OF APPLICANTS MOST RECENT YEAR:
713.

NUMBER OF AWARDS: 280.

REPRESENTATIVE AWARDS:
$1,000,000 to the Illinois Community
College Board, Springfield, IL, to test new
programs and policies aimed at increasing the
number of adult basic and developmental
education students who transition to
postsecondary occupational education and
ultimately to better jobs in Illinois; $350,000
to William J. Brennan, Jr. Center for Justice,
New York, NY, to support its campaign
finance and judicial reform initiatives,
particularly in the Midwest; $50,000 to the
Cuyahoga Community College Foundation,
Cleveland, OH, to support a multiyear
collaborative that includes a long-term
residency and commissioning of a new work
by African-American jazz artist and
composer, Cecilia Smith.

APPLICATION INFORMATION:
Guidelines on how to apply and other details
are available on the web site.

Duration: The majority of awards are for one
year, although multiyear grants are also
considered. Renewal of funding is primarily
based on grantee's fulfillment of terms and
goals of the previous grant and the program's
continued advancement of Foundation
priorities.

Deadline: April 12 for July; August 17 for
December; December 7 for April.

PUBLICATIONS:
Program and Grant Proposal Guidelines
(online); newsletters; annual report.

IRS IDENTIFICATION NUMBER: 36-6079185

STAFF:
Ellen S. Alberding, President
Deborah Gillespie, Vice President of Finance
and Administration
Gretchen Crosby Sims, Vice President of
Programs
Jane R. Patterson, Chief Investment Officer
Michelle T. Boone, Program Officer, Culture
Nina Vinik, Program Officer, Gun Violence
John Luczak, Program Manager, Education
Edmund Miller, Program Manager,
Environment
Whitney Smith, Employment Program
Manager
Gil M. Sarmiento, Controller
Veronica Salter, Grants Manager

BOARD OF DIRECTORS:
John T. Anderson, Chairman
Charles U. Daly, Vice Chairman
Ellen S. Alberding
Jose B. Alvarez
Robert G. Bottoms
Anthony S. Earl
Roger R. Fross
Carlton L. Guthrie
Daniel P. Kearney
Tracey L. Meares
Margot M. Rogers
Paula Wolff

ADDRESS INQUIRIES TO:
E-mail: applications@joycefdn.org

THE JPMORGAN CHASE
FOUNDATION   [203]
270 Park Avenue, 37th Floor
New York, NY 10017-2014
(212) 270-6000

E-MAIL ADDRESS:
gale.jennings@jpmorgan.com

WEB SITE ADDRESS:
www.jpmorganchase.com/grants

FOUNDED: 1969

AREAS OF INTEREST:
Community development, education, arts and
culture.

TYPE:
Challenge/matching grants; Matching gifts;
Project/program grants; Technical assistance.

YEAR PROGRAM STARTED: 1969

LEGAL BASIS:
Corporate foundation.

ELIGIBILITY:
Charitable, not-for-profit organizations as
defined by section 501(c)(3) of the IRS tax
code.

GEOGRAPHIC RESTRICTIONS:
United States.

FINANCIAL DATA:
Amount of support per award: Varies.

APPLICATION INFORMATION:
Potential grantee must first submit an online
Letter of Inquiry. Complete details and
instructions are available on the Foundation
web site.

Duration: Varies.
Deadline: Grant applications may be
submitted throughout the year.

PUBLICATIONS:
Annual report; *Community Partnership
Report.*

IRS IDENTIFICATION NUMBER: 23-7049738

ALICE AND JULIUS KANTOR
CHARITABLE TRUST   [204]
809 North Bedford Drive
Beverly Hills, CA 90210
(310) 360-7541
Fax: (310) 360-7580

FOUNDED: 1977

AREAS OF INTEREST:
Medical research, arts and cultural programs,
education and human services.

TYPE:
Development grants; Project/program grants;
Research grants.

YEAR PROGRAM STARTED: 1977

PURPOSE:
To find cures for diseases and aid mankind.

LEGAL BASIS:
Trust.

ELIGIBILITY:
Grants are made to organizations that have
tax-exempt status under Section 501(c)(3) of
the Internal Revenue Code. No grants are
made to individuals, religious organizations
or political organizations.

FINANCIAL DATA:
Amount of support per award: Varies.

APPLICATION INFORMATION:
Applicants must submit a brief letter
outlining the purpose of the grant, as well as
a letter certifying the organization's 501(c)(3)
status under the Internal Revenue Code.

Duration: Varies.

ADDRESS INQUIRIES TO:
Arnold Seidel, Trustee
(See address above.)

THE J.M. KAPLAN FUND,
INC.   [205]
261 Madison Avenue
19th Floor
New York, NY 10016
(212) 767-0630
Fax: (212) 767-0639

E-MAIL ADDRESS:
info@jmkfund.org

WEB SITE ADDRESS:
www.jmkfund.org

FOUNDED: 1945

AREAS OF INTEREST:
Marine conservation, historic preservation
and migrations, public spaces and public
services.

NAME(S) OF PROGRAMS:
● **City Life Grant**
● **Discretionary Grants**
● **Environment Program Grant**
● **Furthermore Grant**
● **Historic Preservation Grant**
● **Migrations Grant**

TYPE:
General operating grants; Project/program
grants.

YEAR PROGRAM STARTED: 1945

PURPOSE:
To support programs that meet the needs of
society and improve the quality of life.

LEGAL BASIS:
Tax-exempt private foundation under
provisions of Section 501(c)(3) of the
Internal Revenue Code.

ELIGIBILITY:
Grants are made to organizations that have
tax-exempt status under Section 501(c)(3) of
the Internal Revenue Code. No grants are
made to individuals. Non-sectarian religious
programs may apply.

GEOGRAPHIC RESTRICTIONS:
United States.

FINANCIAL DATA:
Amount of support per award: $30,000 to
$200,000 for program grants; $2,500 to
$100,000 for discretionary grants.

Total amount of support: $8,000,000 for the
year 2010.

NUMBER OF APPLICANTS MOST RECENT YEAR:
Over 750.

APPLICATION INFORMATION:
Organizations should submit a brief letter, no
more than two pages, describing their work
and its relevance to the specific program
interests of the Fund.

Duration: 12 to 18 months.

TRUSTEES:
Peter Davidson, Chairman
Joan K. Davidson, President Emeritus
Betsy Davidson
Bradford Davidson
Matthew Davidson
Caio Fonseca
Elizabeth K. Fonseca
Isabel Fonseca
Quina Fonseca

Mary E. Kaplan
Richard D. Kaplan

STAFF:
Conn Nugent, Executive Director
Laura Hansen, Director, City Life Program
William Falahee, Controller
Angela Carabine, Grants Manager
Ann Birckmayer, Program Associate,
Furthermore Grants
Suzette Brooks Masters, Program Consultant,
Migrations
Ken Lustbader, Program Consultant, Historic
Preservation

ADDRESS INQUIRIES TO:
Angela Carabine, Grants Manager
(See address above.)

MAY GORDON LATHAM KELLENBERGER HISTORICAL FOUNDATION [206]
610 Pollock Street
New Bern, NC 28562
(252) 639-3500
Fax: (252) 514-4876

FOUNDED: 1978

AREAS OF INTEREST:
Historic preservation in the city of New Bern
and Craven County, NC.

TYPE:
Project/program grants.

YEAR PROGRAM STARTED: 1978

PURPOSE:
To aid in the preservation of significant
structures in New Bern as well as to assist in
historical research and study pertaining to the
city of New Bern and Craven County, NC.

LEGAL BASIS:
Special-interest foundation.

ELIGIBILITY:
Applicants must be organizations, agencies
and institutions which are tax-exempt under
the provisions of the U.S. Internal Revenue
Code.

GEOGRAPHIC RESTRICTIONS:
Craven County and New Bern, North
Carolina.

APPLICATION INFORMATION:
Contact Foundation for application form and
guidelines.
Duration: One year. Can be renewed for one
additional year.
Deadline: June 10 and December 10.
Announcement on August 1 and February 1.

PUBLICATIONS:
Application guidelines.

OFFICERS:
Dr. Jeffrey J. Crow, Chairman
Bob Mattocks, Secretary and Treasurer
Dr. Jerry C. Cashion, Project Review
Committee Chairman

ADDRESS INQUIRIES TO:
Nancy Perlman, Administrative Support
(See address above.)

W.K. KELLOGG FOUNDATION [207]
One Michigan Avenue East
Battle Creek, MI 49017-4012
(269) 968-1611
Fax: (269) 968-0413

E-MAIL ADDRESS:
proposalsprocessing@wkkf.org

WEB SITE ADDRESS:
www.wkkf.org

FOUNDED: 1930

AREAS OF INTEREST:
Family economic security; education and
learning; food, health and well-being; civic
engagement; and racial equity.

TYPE:
Challenge/matching grants; Project/program
grants; Seed money grants. Grants for pilot
projects to improve human well-being are
made in the U.S., Latin America, the
Caribbean and southern Africa.

The Foundation encourages grant seekers to
review the latest information on its web site
regarding its focus areas of educated kids,
healthy kids, secure families, racial equity,
and civic engagement before beginning the
application process. This will assist in
determining if/how grant seeker's idea might
be a fit with the Foundation's current
programming framework.

YEAR PROGRAM STARTED: 1930

PURPOSE:
To support children, families and
communities as they strengthen and create
conditions that propel vulnerable children to
achieve success as individuals and as
contributors to the larger community and
society.

LEGAL BASIS:
Independent private foundation.

ELIGIBILITY:
To be eligible for support, applying
organization or institution, as well as the
purpose of the proposed project, must qualify
under the regulations of the U.S. IRS.
Grantees must have the financial potential to
sustain the project on a continuing basis after
Foundation funding is ended. The Foundation
is not able to provide funding directly to
individuals.

GEOGRAPHIC RESTRICTIONS:
United States, Latin America, the Caribbean
and southern Africa.

FINANCIAL DATA:
As of August 31, 2010, the Foundation held
total assets of $7.2 billion.
Amount of support per award: Varies.
Total amount of support: As of August 31,
2010: New commitments of $360,000,857;
total grant expenditures of $289,147,404.

NUMBER OF AWARDS: As of August 31, 2010:
674 total new commitments; 2,299 total
active grants.

APPLICATION INFORMATION:
The preferred method for grant submissions
is the Foundation's online application. Grant
applicants who are not able to apply
electronically may submit their grant request
via regular mail. The Foundation will give
prompt consideration to all preproposal
submissions. The initial review may take up
to three months to complete. If the proposed
project falls within the Foundation's priorities
and available resources, applicants may be
asked to develop a more detailed proposal.

Letters not submitted online should be
directed to Central Proposal Processing, at
the address above.
Duration: Varies.

Deadline: The Foundation accepts proposals
on an ongoing basis, and staff members
review them as they are received.

PUBLICATIONS:
Annual report.

OFFICERS:
Sterling Speirn, President and Chief
Executive Officer
La June Montgomery-Tabron, Chief
Operating Officer and Treasurer
James McHale, Chief of Staff
Joel Wittenburg, Vice President and Chief
Investment Officer
Joanne Krell, Vice President for
Communications
Gail Christopher, Vice President for Program
Strategy
Gregory Taylor, Vice President for Program
Strategy
Susan Katz Froning, Corporate Secretary and
General Counsel

BOARD OF TRUSTEES:
Fred Keller, Chairman
Roderick Gillum
Dorothy Johnson
Hanmin Liu
Cynthia Milligan
Wenda Weekes Moore
Bobby Moser
Ramon Murguia
Sterling Speirn
Joseph Stewart
Richard Tsoumas

ADDRESS INQUIRIES TO:
Central Proposal Processing
(See address above.)

*PLEASE NOTE:
Grants are concentrated in the U.S., Latin
America, the Caribbean and southern Africa.

HARRIS AND ELIZA KEMPNER FUND [208]
2201 Market Street, Suite 1250
Galveston, TX 77550-1529
(409) 762-1603 ext. 123
Fax: (409) 762-5435

E-MAIL ADDRESS:
information@kempnerfund.org

WEB SITE ADDRESS:
www.kempnerfund.org

FOUNDED: 1946

AREAS OF INTEREST:
Arts, historic preservation, community
development, education, and health and
human services. Broad general interests, with
no specific limitations; preference is for
support of local projects in Galveston, TX.

NAME(S) OF PROGRAMS:
● **Matching Gifts Program**
● **Primary Grant Program**
● **Program Related Investments**

TYPE:
Capital grants; Challenge/matching grants;
Conferences/seminars; Demonstration grants;
Endowments; Exchange programs;
Fellowships; General operating grants;
Project/program grants; Seed money grants;
Visiting scholars. Primary Grant Program
provides grants to qualifying organizations in
the greater Galveston, TX area in the arts
and historic preservation, community
development, education, and health and
human services.

Program Related Investments are recommended by Fund trustees for Galveston projects.

YEAR PROGRAM STARTED: 1946

PURPOSE:
To support a wide range of innovative as well as traditional programs for the enhancement of the local community.

LEGAL BASIS:
Independent private foundation.

ELIGIBILITY:
Primary Grant Program: Preferred applicants are programs/projects that benefit the greater Galveston, TX community. Seed money, operating funds, small capital needs and special projects, and partnering with other funding sources are supported. Proposals will not be considered for fund-raising benefits, direct-mail solicitations, grants to individuals, or grants to non-U.S.-based organizations.

Matching Gifts Program: Restricted to Kempner family members and trustees of the Kempner Fund.

GEOGRAPHIC RESTRICTIONS:
Galveston, Texas.

FINANCIAL DATA:
Amount of support per award: Grants: $1,000 to $60,000 for the year ended December 31, 2010.

Total amount of support: $981,357 in grants, plus $299,231 in matching gifts for the year ended December 31, 2010.

Matching fund requirements: Restricted to descendants of Harris and Eliza Kempner.

NUMBER OF APPLICANTS MOST RECENT YEAR:
79 for the year 2010.

NUMBER OF AWARDS: 45 for the year 2010.

REPRESENTATIVE AWARDS:
$60,000 to Sugarland Heritage Foundation; $3,000 to Galveston Ballet; $1,500 to Galveston Island Nature Tourism Council; $9,500 to Ambassador Academy; $37,500 to Teen Health Center.

APPLICATION INFORMATION:
Applicants should submit a brief cover letter, signed by the Executive Director and Board Chairman, stating the need and amount being requested. Complete guidelines and forms are available at the web site.

The following project/program information also needs to be submitted:
(1) name and telephone number of contact person;
(2) description;
(3) timeline;
(4) budget (income and expenses);
(5) list of sources and amounts being solicited and/or received or pledged;
(6) future funding plans (for new and continuing programs) and;
(7) plans for evaluating program's progress and/or results.

The following organization information should be attached:
(1) statement of purpose and brief history;
(2) names of present officers and board members;
(3) operating budget (revenue and expenses) for year for which funds are sought;
(4) financial statements (year-to-date), audit, and/or Tax Form 990 for most recent fiscal year;
(5) copy of post-1969 IRS determination letter to document tax-exempt status and;

(6) statement on organization letterhead that there has been no change in IRS status since issuance of ruling letter.

Duration: Varies.

Deadline: Primary Grant Program: March 15 and October 15.

IRS IDENTIFICATION NUMBER: 74-6042458

STAFF:
Anne Brasier, Executive Director

DIRECTORS:
Arthur Alpert, Honorary Director
John Currie, Honorary Director
Barbara W. Sasser, Honorary Director

OFFICERS AND TRUSTEES:
Lyda Ann Thomas, President
Robert K. Lynch, Vice President
Daniel Thorne, Treasurer
Eliza K. Quigley, Secretary
John H. Campbell
Rhoda T. Ezell
Patricia Gray
Daniel Hamilton
Hetta T. Kempner
Randall T. Kempner
Elizabeth K. McFarland

THE KERR FOUNDATION, INC.   [209]
12501 North May Avenue
Oklahoma City, OK 73120
(405) 749-7991
Fax: (405) 749-2877

WEB SITE ADDRESS:
www.thekerrfoundation.org

FOUNDED: 1963

AREAS OF INTEREST:
Education, cultural activities and health.

TYPE:
Capital grants; Challenge/matching grants; Conferences/seminars; Development grants; Matching gifts; Professorships; Project/program grants.

YEAR PROGRAM STARTED: 1986

PURPOSE:
To support programs of interest to the Foundation in the areas of health, education, youth services and cultural activities.

LEGAL BASIS:
Private, charitable foundation.

ELIGIBILITY:
Application is limited to nonprofit, 501(c)(3) tax-exempt organizations. No grants to individuals.

GEOGRAPHIC RESTRICTIONS:
Arkansas, Colorado, Kansas, Missouri, New Mexico, Oklahoma, Texas, and Washington, D.C.

FINANCIAL DATA:
Grant-seeking organizations must first raise a specified amount in actual donations or up-to-three-year pledges. The grant will be paid upon successful raising of the funds or pledges, which must occur within one year or a mutually agreed-upon time limit.

Amount of support per award: $5,000 to $50,000.

COOPERATIVE FUNDING PROGRAMS: All Oklahoma foundations.

NUMBER OF APPLICANTS MOST RECENT YEAR:
65.

NUMBER OF AWARDS: 20.

REPRESENTATIVE AWARDS:
Grants to Tulsa Ballet Theatre, Tulsa, OK; University of Oklahoma for Natural History Museum and special projects.

APPLICATION INFORMATION:
Forms and guidelines are available online.

Duration: Most grants awarded on a one-time basis.

OFFICERS AND TRUSTEES:
Mrs. Robert S. Kerr, Jr., President and Chairperson
Steven Kerr, Treasurer
Laura Kerr Ogle, Secretary
Cody T. Kerr
Ray Kline

ADDRESS INQUIRIES TO:
Mrs. Robert S. Kerr, Jr.
President and Chairman of the Board
(See address above.)

GRAYCE B. KERR FUND, INC.   [210]
117 Bay Street
Easton, MD 21601
(410) 822-6652
Fax: (410) 822-4546

E-MAIL ADDRESS:
office@gbkf.org

WEB SITE ADDRESS:
www.gbkf.org

FOUNDED: 1986

AREAS OF INTEREST:
Education, cultural programs, public policy research. Major emphasis is education.

TYPE:
Project/program grants. Grants to nonprofit organizations. Grants are not limited to any one specific area of interest or geographical location. Currently, the Fund's principal areas of interest include nurturing educational achievement and excellence, fostering life skills critical to self-sufficiency, and encouraging cultural growth. The Fund supports research and other activities directed toward improving the information base available to the public.

YEAR PROGRAM STARTED: 1986

PURPOSE:
To provide financial support to worthy nonprofit organizations that enhance the quality of life, significantly impact and sustain long-term change and growth in organizations and institutions.

LEGAL BASIS:
Private, charitable foundation.

ELIGIBILITY:
Applicants must be nonprofit, 501(c)(3) tax-exempt organizations. No grants to individuals.

GEOGRAPHIC RESTRICTIONS:
United States.

FINANCIAL DATA:
Grant minimums and maximums are not designated. Preference may be given, in some years, to large grants where a genuine impact may be accomplished.

Amount of support per award: Varies.

Total amount of support: Varies.

APPLICATION INFORMATION:
Forms are available online.

Duration: Usually one year.

PUBLICATIONS:
Annual report; application.

IRS IDENTIFICATION NUMBER: 73-1256124

BOARD OF TRUSTEES:
Sheryl V. Kerr, Chairperson
John R. Valliant, President and Trustee
James S. Maffitt, Secretary and Treasurer
Marcy Kerr Yuknat, Family Trustee

ADDRESS INQUIRIES TO:
John R. Valliant, President
(See address above.)

KIMBERLY-CLARK FOUNDATION, INC. [211]

P.O. Box 619100
Dallas, TX 75261-9100
(972) 281-1477

E-MAIL ADDRESS:
kcfoundation@kcc.com

WEB SITE ADDRESS:
www.kimberly-clark.com

FOUNDED: 1952

AREAS OF INTEREST:
Social welfare, medicine and health.

TYPE:
Project/program grants.

YEAR PROGRAM STARTED: 1952

PURPOSE:
To support organizations that strengthen today's families.

LEGAL BASIS:
Corporate foundation.

ELIGIBILITY:
Grants are made to tax-exempt, charitable, 501(c)(3) nonprofit organizations in communities where Kimberly-Clark has operations. There are a limited number of contributions to national organizations.

FINANCIAL DATA:
Amount of support per award: Varies.
Total amount of support: $12,600,000 for the year 2009.

REPRESENTATIVE AWARDS:
$1,300,000 to Boys and Girls Clubs of America; $20,000 to Susan G. Komen Foundation; $50,000 to Catalyst for Women; $200,000 to American Red Cross.

APPLICATION INFORMATION:
Written requests must be sent to the Foundation. Please call before sending requests.
Duration: One to five years.

PUBLICATIONS:
Annual report.

OFFICERS:
Tony Palmer, President
Mark A. Buthman, Vice President
Jenny Lewis, Vice President
Steve Voskuil, Treasurer
John Wesley, Secretary

DIRECTORS:
Mark A. Buthman
Thomas J. Falk
Tony Palmer

ADDRESS INQUIRIES TO:
Jenny Lewis, Vice President
(See address above.)

STEPHEN AND TABITHA KING FOUNDATION [212]

49 Florida Avenue
Bangor, ME 04401
(207) 990-2910
Fax: (207) 990-2975

E-MAIL ADDRESS:
info@stkfoundation.org

WEB SITE ADDRESS:
www.stkfoundation.org

FOUNDED: 1985

AREAS OF INTEREST:
Arts, children/youth, health, education, libraries, recovery, women's issues, human rights and literacy.

TYPE:
Awards/prizes; Capital grants; Challenge/matching grants; Demonstration grants; Development grants; Endowments; General operating grants; Matching gifts; Project/program grants; Seed money grants; Training grants.

YEAR PROGRAM STARTED: 1985

PURPOSE:
To improve the quality of life in Maine.

LEGAL BASIS:
Private family foundation.

ELIGIBILITY:
Organizations classified as 501(c)(3) by the IRS and located in Maine can apply. Grants are only awarded to nonprofit organizations operating in the state of Maine. Individuals and religious organizations are ineligible.

GEOGRAPHIC RESTRICTIONS:
Maine.

FINANCIAL DATA:
Amount of support per award: $50,000 maximum request.
Total amount of support: Varies, dependent on investment revenue.
Matching fund requirements: Must be met through grassroots local community funding.

NUMBER OF APPLICANTS MOST RECENT YEAR: 1,000.

NUMBER OF AWARDS: Approximately 250.

APPLICATION INFORMATION:
Contact the Foundation for application procedures.
Duration: Foundation prefers one-time grants. Multiyear commitments occasionally.
Deadline: June 30 and December 31.

IRS IDENTIFICATION NUMBER: 13-3364647

STAFF:
Stephanie Leonard, Administrator

ADDRESS INQUIRIES TO:
Stephanie Leonard, Administrator
(See address above.)

F.M. KIRBY FOUNDATION, INC. [213]

17 DeHart Street
Morristown, NJ 07963-0151
(973) 538-4800

WEB SITE ADDRESS:
www.fmkirbyfoundation.org

FOUNDED: 1931

AREAS OF INTEREST:
General charitable support.

TYPE:
Capital grants; Challenge/matching grants; Endowments; Fellowships; General operating grants; Professorships; Project/program grants; Research grants; Scholarships. Grants usually are reflective of personal interest by

one or more members of the Kirby family who are, or have been, active in the affairs of the Foundation.

YEAR PROGRAM STARTED: 1931

LEGAL BASIS:
Private foundation.

ELIGIBILITY:
Organizations must be tax-exempt under applicable provisions of the IRS code and not private foundations. No grants are made to individuals. No grants are made to public foundations which would, as a result thereof, become private foundations. No grants for fund-raising activities such as benefits, charitable dinners, sports or theater events, etc. No loans are made.

GEOGRAPHIC RESTRICTIONS:
Morris County, New Jersey; Hillsborough, North Carolina area and Wilkes-Barre, Pennsylvania area.

FINANCIAL DATA:
Amount of support per award: Varies.
Total amount of support: $18,142,166 for the year 2010.
Matching fund requirements: Determined on a case-by-case basis.

NUMBER OF APPLICANTS MOST RECENT YEAR:
Approximately 610 for the year 2010.

NUMBER OF AWARDS: 318 for the year 2010.

APPLICATION INFORMATION:
The preferred method of initial contact is a full proposal with a cover letter. The Foundation provides no formal application forms and sets down no specific guidelines. Proposals should include:
(1) a report on the use of previous grants if applicable;
(2) a description of the organization, its purpose and the project, if any;
(3) an indication of the budget for which financial support is requested;
(4) roster of directors and principal officers;
(5) copy of the current audited financial statement;
(6) copy of the valid IRS tax determination letter and;
(7) copy of current annual budget.
Duration: One year. Renewal possible.
Deadline: October 31. Solicitations received after deadline will be held over to following year.

PUBLICATIONS:
Application guidelines.

IRS IDENTIFICATION NUMBER: 51-6017929

STAFF:
William H. Byrnes, Program Officer

DIRECTORS AND OFFICERS:
S. Dillard Kirby, President and Director
Jefferson W. Kirby, Vice President and Director
Thomas Bianchini, Secretary and Treasurer
Alice K. Horton, Director
F. M. Kirby, Director
Walker D. Kirby, Director
Laura H. Virkler, Director

ADDRESS INQUIRIES TO:
S. Dillard Kirby, President
(See address above.)

KITSAP COMMUNITY FOUNDATION

9657 Levin Road, N.W.
Suite 260
Silverdale, WA 98383
(360) 698-3622
Fax: (360) 698-6043

E-MAIL ADDRESS:
kcf@kitsapfoundation.org

WEB SITE ADDRESS:
www.kitsapfoundation.org

TYPE:
General operating grants; Project/program grants; Scholarships.

See entry 1399 for full listing.

JOSIAH W. AND BESSIE H. KLINE FOUNDATION, INC.   [214]

515 South 29th Street
Harrisburg, PA 17104
(717) 561-4373
Fax: (717) 561-0826

FOUNDED: 1952

AREAS OF INTEREST:
Medical, academic, benevolent, community and cultural.

NAME(S) OF PROGRAMS:
● **Kline Foundation Grants**

TYPE:
Project/program grants; Research grants.

YEAR PROGRAM STARTED: 1952

PURPOSE:
To aid blind or incapacitated persons or crippled children in need of financial assistance; to make grants to Pennsylvania colleges and universities, to hospitals and institutions for crippled children or to any other benevolent or charitable institution; to make grants for scientific or medical research to be performed by scientific persons or by colleges, universities or research institutions.

LEGAL BASIS:
Community foundation.

ELIGIBILITY:
The Foundation does not make loans and does not make grants to individuals and generally does not make grants for normal operational phases of established programs or to national organizations or religious programs.

Normally grants are not made to state-affiliated schools, colleges, or universities.

GEOGRAPHIC RESTRICTIONS:
Cumberland and Dauphin counties, Pennsylvania.

FINANCIAL DATA:
Amount of support per award: $500 to $250,000.
Total amount of support: $848,131 for the year 2010.

NUMBER OF AWARDS: 32 for the year 2010.

APPLICATION INFORMATION:
To be considered for Foundation aid, a copy of the Foundation's completed application form must be submitted and the following information must be fully stated:
(1) a description of the need and purpose, the qualifications of the requesting organization and the location as to where and how the support will be used;
(2) a budget for the project and any support

that will be received from other sources;
(3) the amount of the request from the Foundation and the dates the funds are needed and;
(4) a copy of a letter from the IRS showing that the organization is exempt from federal income tax under Section 501(c)(3) of the Internal Revenue Code and that the organization is not a private foundation under Section 509(a).

Duration: One-time grant.

Deadline: April and October. Some grants are awarded in June, while others are generally awarded after December 1 of each year.

PUBLICATIONS:
Annual report; application guidelines; application.

ADDRESS INQUIRIES TO:
John A. Obrock, C.P.A.
(See address above.)

JOHN S. AND JAMES L. KNIGHT FOUNDATION   [215]

Wachovia Financial Center
200 South Biscayne Boulevard, Suite 3300
Miami, FL 33131-2349
(305) 908-2600
Fax: (305) 908-2698

E-MAIL ADDRESS:
grants@knightfoundation.org

WEB SITE ADDRESS:
www.knightfoundation.org

FOUNDED: 1950

AREAS OF INTEREST:
Journalism and engaged and informed communities.

NAME(S) OF PROGRAMS:
● **Arts Program**
● **Communities Program**
● **Journalism Program**
● **National Program**

TYPE:
Capital grants; Challenge/matching grants; Development grants; Endowments; Matching gifts; Project/program grants; Seed money grants; Technical assistance. The Foundation promotes excellence in journalism worldwide and invests in the vitality of 26 U.S. communities.

The Foundation focuses on three areas:
(1) Innovating Media and Journalism: The Foundation aims to help sustain democracy by leading journalism to its best possible future in the 21st century;
(2) Engaging Communities: To sustain healthy communities in a democracy, the Foundation's community engagement initiatives aim to give all residents a strong sense of belonging and caring, timely access to relevant information, the ability to understand that information, and the motivation to take sustainable action on the issues that matter most to them and;
(3) Fostering the Arts: Through its national arts program, the Foundation seeks to weave the arts into the fabric of the Knight resident communities to engage and inspire their residents; the Foundation believes that the arts are a catalyst for public dialogue, and that shared cultural experiences contribute to a sense of place and communal identity.

YEAR PROGRAM STARTED: 1950

PURPOSE:
To sustain democracy in the digital age by fostering informed and engaged communities; to back transformational ideas at the intersection of media, journalism, community engagement and the arts; to advance media innovation with a wide range of initiatives; to support projects, including in the arts, that increase community engagement through the use of technology and other innovative approaches.

LEGAL BASIS:
Private non-operating foundation.

ELIGIBILITY:
An applicant organization must have received a letter of determination from the Internal Revenue Service granting it 501(c)(3) tax-exempt status and stating that it is not a private foundation according to the definition in Section 509(a) of the Internal Revenue Code.

The Knight News Challenge permits for-profit entities and individuals to apply from anywhere in the world.

The Knight Community Information Challenge accepts applications from community and place-based foundations in the U.S. and its territories, as well as Mexico and Canada.

The Knight Arts Challenge accepts applications from South Florida and Greater Philadelphia individuals, for-profit and nonprofit organizations.

GEOGRAPHIC RESTRICTIONS:
A segment of the Foundation's activities focuses on 26 communities where the Knight brothers owned newspapers, with donor-advised programs in 18 and program director-led programs in the eight "resident Knight communities" (San Jose, California; Miami, Florida; Macon, Georgia; Detroit, Michigan; St. Paul, Minnesota; Charlotte, North Carolina; Akron, Ohio; and Philadelphia, Pennsylvania).

FINANCIAL DATA:
Amount of support per award: $5,000 minimum.
Total amount of support: $98,014,645 for the year 2010.
Matching fund requirements: Some but not all of Knight's funding options require matching funds. This includes the Knight Arts Challenge in Miami and Philadelphia.

NUMBER OF APPLICANTS MOST RECENT YEAR: 4,525 for the year 2010.

NUMBER OF AWARDS: 318 for the year 2010.

APPLICATION INFORMATION:
Applicants must submit an online letter of inquiry. If the inquiry is determined to fall into Knight Foundation funding priorities, applicants are asked to submit a full proposal.
Duration: Varies per project; usually from one to five years.

PUBLICATIONS:
Evaluation and Assessment publications; Reporter Analysis evaluation articles; KnightBlog posts.

IRS IDENTIFICATION NUMBER: 65-0464177

STAFF:
Jorge Martinez, Director of Information Systems
Belinda Turner Lawrence, Vice President and Chief Administrative Officer
Marc Fest, Vice President of Communications

Trabian Shorters, Vice
President/Communities
Paula Ellis, Vice President/Strategic
Initiatives
Juan Martinez, Vice President and Chief
Financial Officer
Eric Newton, Senior Adviser to the President
Dennis Scholl, Vice President/Arts and
Miami Program Director
Michael Maness, Vice President/Journalism
Program
Mayur Patel, Vice President/Strategy and
Assessment

TRUSTEES AND OFFICERS:
Robert W. Briggs, Chairman
Alberto Ibarguen, President and Chief
Executive Officer
Cesar L. Alvarez
Mary Sue Coleman
Marjorie Knight Crane
James N. Crutchfield
Paul S. Grogan
Rolfe Neill
Mariam C. Noland
Beverly Knight Olson
Earl W. Powell
Ray Rodriguez
John W. Rogers, Jr.
E. Roe Stamps, IV
Paul E. Steiger

ADDRESS INQUIRIES TO:
Grants Administrator
(See address above.)

MARION I. AND HENRY J.
KNOTT FOUNDATION, INC. [216]

3904 Hickory Avenue
Baltimore, MD 21211
(410) 235-7068
Fax: (410) 889-2577

E-MAIL ADDRESS:
choffman@knottfoundation.org

WEB SITE ADDRESS:
www.knottfoundation.org

FOUNDED: 1977

AREAS OF INTEREST:
Education (private and Catholic schools
only), health care, human and social services,
arts and humanities.

TYPE:
Challenge/matching grants; General operating
grants; Matching gifts; Technical assistance;
Training grants.

YEAR PROGRAM STARTED: 1977

PURPOSE:
To further Roman Catholic activities and
other charitable, cultural, educational, health
care and human service activities within the
meaning of Section 501(c)(3) of the Internal
Revenue Code.

LEGAL BASIS:
Private family foundation.

ELIGIBILITY:
Applicants must be nonprofit, charitable
organizations with evidence of tax-exemption
ruling under Section 501(c)(3) of the Internal
Revenue Code. No grants pertaining to
scholarships, individuals, annual giving,
pro-choice causes, public education or
institutions, or politically oriented activities.

The Foundation does not favor multiyear
requests.

GEOGRAPHIC RESTRICTIONS:
All counties in the state of Maryland
excluding the entire Eastern Shore, Calvert,
Cecil, Charles, Montgomery, Prince George's,
and St. Mary's counties.

FINANCIAL DATA:
Amount of support per award: $10,000 to
$100,000. Average $30,000.
Total amount of support: $1,889,147 for the
year 2009.
Matching fund requirements: Specific to
grantee. Usually matched within a six-month
period.

NUMBER OF APPLICANTS MOST RECENT YEAR:
150.

NUMBER OF AWARDS: 48.

REPRESENTATIVE AWARDS:
$30,000 to Casa of Baltimore; $40,000 to
Baltimore Reads; $35,000 to Shepherd's
Clinic; $20,000 to Art with a Heart; $50,000
to St. Elizabeth of Hungary Church.

APPLICATION INFORMATION:
Required documentation includes proof of
501(c)(3) status, brief narrative of objective
of proposal, history of requesting agency, list
of trustees and officers, administrating
personnel with resume, budget for project,
most recent audited report and list of
foundations and corporations that have
supported previous requests and are being
solicited for this request. Must call Executive
Director before submitting a proposal.
Duration: Usually one year.
Deadline: Letters of Inquiry and Financials:
February, June and October. Full Proposal:
March 28, July 25 and November 28,
respectively.

IRS IDENTIFICATION NUMBER: 52-1517876

TRUSTEES AND OFFICERS:
Owen M. Knott, President
Lindsay R. Gallagher
Marty Voelkel Hanssen
E.B. Harris
Kelly L. Harris
Thomas Harris
Erin Knott
Marion I. Knott
Martin G. Knott, Jr.
Martin G. Knott, Sr.
Teresa A. Knott
Brian McDonald
Meghan McDonald
Peter McGill
David L. Porter
Joanna O. Porter
Margie Riehl
Michael Riehl
Brooke Rodgers
Patrick Rodgers
Geralynn D. Smyth
John Smyth
Patrick Smyth
Peggy Smyth
Jan Steendam
Alice Voelkel
Emmett Voelkel

ADDRESS INQUIRIES TO:
M. Gregory Cantori, Executive Director
(See address above.)

KORET FOUNDATION [217]

33 New Montgomery Street
Suite 1090
San Francisco, CA 94105-4526
(415) 882-7740
Fax: (415) 882-7775

E-MAIL ADDRESS:
koret@koretfoundation.org

WEB SITE ADDRESS:
www.koretfoundation.org

FOUNDED: 1979

AREAS OF INTEREST:
Arts, community service and volunteerism,
Jewish community services, education and
employment for youth, elderly, hunger and
homelessness.

TYPE:
Capital grants; General operating grants;
Project/program grants; Seed money grants.

YEAR PROGRAM STARTED: 1979

PURPOSE:
To address societal challenges and strengthen
Bay Area life; to invest in strategic, local
solutions that help to inspire a multiplier
effect, encouraging collaborative funding and
developing model initiatives.

LEGAL BASIS:
Private foundation.

ELIGIBILITY:
Grant applicants must be 501(c)(3)
organizations. Private foundations are not
eligible to apply.

Although the majority of funding is granted
to six of nine bay area counties, the
Foundation will consider national and Israeli
projects.

GEOGRAPHIC RESTRICTIONS:
Alameda, Contra Costa, Marin, San
Francisco, San Mateo and Santa Clara
counties, California.

FINANCIAL DATA:
Amount of support per award: Grants vary in
amount, depending upon the needs and
nature of the request.
Total amount of support: $25,000,000 to
$30,000,000.

APPLICATION INFORMATION:
Contact the Foundation for application
guidelines.
Duration: Varies.

PUBLICATIONS:
Annual report; application guidelines.

IRS IDENTIFICATION NUMBER: 94-1624987

OFFICERS:
Jeff Farber, Chief Executive Officer

ADDRESS INQUIRIES TO:
Tina Frank
Director of Grant Operations
(See address above.)

KRAFT FOODS, INC. [218]

3 Lakes Drive
Northfield, IL 60093-2758
(847) 646-2000
(847) 646-2696
Fax: (847) 646-5241

E-MAIL ADDRESS:
nrobinson@kraftfoods.com

WEB SITE ADDRESS:
www.kraftfoods.com

AREAS OF INTEREST:
Hunger, children's nutrition and fitness.

TYPE:
Project/program grants.

LEGAL BASIS:
Corporate giving program.

ELIGIBILITY:
Grants are made only to tax-exempt organizations qualifying under Section 501(c)(3) of the Internal Revenue Code or for hunger and hungry lifestyle programs.

Kraft supports organizations which are national in scope or serve those communities where Kraft Foods principal operations are located.

Generally, Kraft will not consider requests for funding individuals, organizations with a limited constituency, such as fraternal or veterans' groups, organizations which restrict their services to members of one religious group, political organizations, travel, tuition and registration fees, membership dues, goodwill advertisements for benefit purposes, loans of any kind and/or product donations.

FINANCIAL DATA:
Amount of support per award: Varies.
Total amount of support: $19,300,000 for fiscal year 2008-09.
Matching fund requirements: Employees only.

NUMBER OF APPLICANTS MOST RECENT YEAR:
Varies.

NUMBER OF AWARDS: Varies with requests.

APPLICATION INFORMATION:
Contact Kraft for guidelines and application.
Duration: One year or multiyear.

PUBLICATIONS:
Guidelines.

ADDRESS INQUIRIES TO:
Nicole Robinson, Director
Corporate Community Involvement
(See address above.)

THE KRESGE FOUNDATION   [219]
3215 West Big Beaver Road
Troy, MI 48084
(248) 643-9630
Fax: (248) 643-0588

E-MAIL ADDRESS:
info@kresge.org

WEB SITE ADDRESS:
www.kresge.org

FOUNDED: 1924

AREAS OF INTEREST:
Arts and culture, Detroit/community development, education, environment, and health and human services.

TYPE:
Capital grants; Challenge/matching grants; General operating grants; Project/program grants; Technical assistance. Facilities capital; Growth capital grants; Planning grants; Program-related investments.

Challenge grants only for construction or renovation of facilities, purchase of major capital equipment or an integrated system at a cost of at least $300,000 and the acquisition of real estate.

YEAR PROGRAM STARTED: 1924

PURPOSE:
To promote the well-being of mankind.

LEGAL BASIS:
Independent private foundation.

ELIGIBILITY:
Tax-exempt charitable organizations operating in the fields of higher education (including

community colleges), health care and long-term care, human services, science and the environment, arts and humanities and public affairs. Governmental agencies are also eligible to apply. Full accreditation is required for higher education and hospital applicants and preferred in all other fields that offer it. Evidence of initial funding for the requested project is considered essential.

The following projects are eligible:
(1) construction of facilities;
(2) renovation of facilities;
(3) purchase of major equipment or an integrated system at a cost of at least $300,000; equipment costs may include computer software expenses, if applicable and;
(4) purchase of real estate.

Religious organizations, elementary and secondary schools, private foundations and individuals are not eligible to apply. However, accredited seminaries are eligible to apply. Also, agencies operated by religious organizations that serve secular needs may be eligible if the programs have financial and governing autonomy separate from the parent organization. They must also have space formally dedicated to their programs.

Some elementary and secondary schools may be eligible in the Foundation's Human Services category, if they predominantly serve individuals with physical and/or developmental disabilities.

FINANCIAL DATA:
Amount of support per award: Varies.
Total amount of support: $197,000,000 for the year 2009.

NUMBER OF AWARDS: 404 for the year 2009.

APPLICATION INFORMATION:
Only electronic application is accepted. Detailed guidelines and form are available on the Foundation web site.
Duration: Varies.

PUBLICATIONS:
Annual report.

ADDRESS INQUIRIES TO:
Grants Inquiry Coordinator
(See address above.)

ALBERT AND BESSIE MAE KRONKOSKY CHARITABLE FOUNDATION   [220]
112 East Pecan, Suite 830
San Antonio, TX 78205
(210) 475-9000
Fax: (210) 354-2204

E-MAIL ADDRESS:
kronfndn@kronkosky.org

WEB SITE ADDRESS:
www.kronkosky.org

FOUNDED: 1991

AREAS OF INTEREST:
Elderly, youth, child abuse and neglect, persons with disabilities, culture and the arts, museums, libraries, prevention of cruelty to animals, health, parks, zoos and wildlife sanctuaries.

NAME(S) OF PROGRAMS:
● **Precious Minds, New Connections**

TYPE:
Capital grants; Challenge/matching grants; Endowments; General operating grants; Matching gifts; Project/program grants;

Research grants; Seed money grants; Technical assistance; Training grants; Research contracts.

YEAR PROGRAM STARTED: 1999

PURPOSE:
To produce profound good that is tangible and measurable in Bandera, Bexar, Comal, and Kendall counties in Texas by implementing the Kronkoskys' charitable purposes.

LEGAL BASIS:
Private foundation.

ELIGIBILITY:
Corporate organizations that are exempt under Section 501(c)(3) of the Internal Revenue Code. The Foundation will not make grants to individuals or for-profit organizations. In addition, the Foundation has a geographic limitation that requires that grant funds be used in the specific counties listed below.

GEOGRAPHIC RESTRICTIONS:
Bandera, Bexar, Comal and Kendall counties, Texas.

FINANCIAL DATA:
Amount of support per award: $1,750 to $500,000 for the year 2010. Average grant: $80,000.
Total amount of support: $9,728,915 for the year 2010.

NUMBER OF APPLICANTS MOST RECENT YEAR:
140 for the year 2010.

NUMBER OF AWARDS: 117 grants for the year 2010.

REPRESENTATIVE AWARDS:
Parenting Education Programs.

APPLICATION INFORMATION:
Send a Letter of Inquiry to the address above. If the Letter of Inquiry meets requirements, it will be reviewed by Foundation's staff within 10 days of receipt. If the proposal is accepted, an application package as well as a timeline for submission of the grant proposal will be forwarded. If proposal is not accepted, notification in writing will be sent. Please note geographic requirement.
Duration: Usually one year.
Deadline: Letters of Inquiry will be accepted throughout the year and reviewed on a rolling basis.

PUBLICATIONS:
Program guidelines; annual report (online only).

IRS IDENTIFICATION NUMBER: 74-6385152

ADDRESS INQUIRIES TO:
Palmer Moe, Managing Director
(See address above.)

THE JEAN AND E. FLOYD KVAMME FOUNDATION
P.O. Box 2494
Saratoga, CA 95070
(408) 395-2829
Fax: (408) 354-0804

TYPE:
Capital grants; Development grants; General operating grants; Project/program grants.

See entry 1667 for full listing.

LAIDLAW FOUNDATION [221]

365 Bloor Street East
Suite 2000
Toronto ON M4W 3L4 Canada
(416) 964-3614 ext. 307
Fax: (416) 975-1428

E-MAIL ADDRESS:
askinner@laidlawfdn.org

WEB SITE ADDRESS:
www.laidlawfdn.org

FOUNDED: 1949

AREAS OF INTEREST:
Youth engagement, youth social
infrastructure, institutional change and policy
development.

NAME(S) OF PROGRAMS:
- **Youth Organizing**

TYPE:
Project/program grants; Seed money grants.

YEAR PROGRAM STARTED: 1949

PURPOSE:
To invest in innovative ideas, convene
interested parties, share learning and
advocate for change in support of young
people becoming healthy, creative and fully
engaged citizens.

LEGAL BASIS:
Private family foundation.

ELIGIBILITY:
The Foundation will fund youth-led
initiatives through two different streams:
Catalyst Grants and Project Grants.
Applicants must be young people 14 to 25
years of age.

GEOGRAPHIC RESTRICTIONS:
Greater Golden Horseshoe area of Canada.

FINANCIAL DATA:
Amount of support per award: Catalyst
Grants: Up to $5,000; Project Grants: Up to
$25,000.

APPLICATION INFORMATION:
Applicants must submit:
(1) Grant Application Cover Sheet;
(2) three- to five-page proposal;
(3) work plan;
(4) budget;
(5) contact information for other community
groups, agencies or individuals that will play
a role in the proposal, if applicable;
(6) partnership agreement between main
applicant and administrative partner and/or
letter from administrative partner, if
applicable;
(7) list of board of directors or governing
committee members, if applicable;
(8) current operating budget for the
group/organization, if applicable;
(9) most recent audited financial statements,
if applicable and;
(10) most recent final report if applicant has
been previously funded from Laidlaw.

Submit 12 hard copies and one electronic
copy (by e-mail). Confirmation will be sent
by e-mail when proposal is received.
Deadline: Fall and winter.

ADDRESS INQUIRIES TO:
Ana Skinner
Program Manager, Youth Organizing
(See address and e-mail above.)

LAMB FOUNDATION [222]

P.O. Box 1705
Lake Oswego, OR 97035
(503) 635-8010
Fax: (503) 635-6544

E-MAIL ADDRESS:
lambfnd@thelambfoundation.org

WEB SITE ADDRESS:
www.thelambfoundation.org

FOUNDED: 1971

AREAS OF INTEREST:
Social services for youth and children, arts,
and environment.

TYPE:
Challenge/matching grants; Project/program
grants; Seed money grants.

LEGAL BASIS:
Private foundation.

ELIGIBILITY:
Applicants must be nonprofit 501(c)(3) public
charity organizations.

GEOGRAPHIC RESTRICTIONS:
Pacific Northwest.

FINANCIAL DATA:
Amount of support per award: Typical grants:
$5,000 to $15,000.
Total amount of support: Approximately
$200,000.

NUMBER OF APPLICANTS MOST RECENT YEAR:
14.

NUMBER OF AWARDS: 18.

REPRESENTATIVE AWARDS:
$15,000 to Farmers Ending Hunger; $15,000
to Growing Gardens; $15,000 to Outside In.

APPLICATION INFORMATION:
The Foundation is not currently accepting
unsolicited applications. Upon invitation,
application information will be sent to the
prospective applicant.
Duration: One year.
Deadline: Included in application materials
sent to invited applicants.

PUBLICATIONS:
Brochure.

IRS IDENTIFICATION NUMBER: 23-7120564

STAFF:
Debra Iguchi, Administrator

ADDRESS INQUIRIES TO:
Debra Iguchi, Administrator
(See address above.)

*SPECIAL STIPULATIONS:
Prospective applicants are encouraged to
contact the office periodically for changes.

LAND O'LAKES FOUNDATION [223]

4001 Lexington Avenue North
Arden Hills, MN 55126
(651) 481-2123
Fax: (651) 481-2000

E-MAIL ADDRESS:
lrbotham@landolakes.com

WEB SITE ADDRESS:
www.foundation.landolakes.com

FOUNDED: 1997

AREAS OF INTEREST:
Human services, education, youth, civic
affairs, the arts and hunger.

CONSULTING OR VOLUNTEER SERVICES:
Group projects.

NAME(S) OF PROGRAMS:
- **California Regions Grant Program**
- **Community Grants Program**
- **Dollars for Doers Program**
- **Matching Gifts to Education Program**
- **Member Co-op Match Program**
- **Mid-Atlantic Grant Program**

TYPE:
Capital grants; Challenge/matching grants;
Endowments; General operating grants;
Matching gifts; Project/program grants; Seed
money grants; Technical assistance. Major
support is in the form of cash contributions,
supplemented with food and product
donations to Feeding America National Food
Bank Network only.

California Regions Grant Program funds
community projects in three areas of
California: Orland, Tulare/Kings/Bakersfield
and Ontario, initiated by Land O'Lakes dairy
member-leaders.

Community Grants Program provides support
through cash grants to nonprofit organizations
that are working to improve communities
where Land O'Lakes has a significant
concentration of members or employees.
Foundation's primary focus area is hunger
and hunger-related issues.

Dollars for Doers Program recognizes
employee and retiree volunteerism with
financial contributions ($100 to $500
annually) to 501(c)(3) nonprofit organizations
based on volunteer hours.

Matching Gifts to Education Program
matches gifts by full- and part-time
employees, Board of Directors members and
Leadership Council members (from $25 to
$1,000 per donor) to grades K-12,
postsecondary education, and public radio
and public television stations.

Member Co-op Match Program matches
dollar-for-dollar the cash donations of
member cooperatives, thus doubling the
funds available for hometown projects.

Mid-Atlantic Grant Program funds
community projects in Maryland, New York,
Pennsylvania and Virginia, initiated by Land
O'Lakes dairy member-leaders.

YEAR PROGRAM STARTED: 1981

PURPOSE:
To demonstrate a commitment to improving
and enhancing the quality of life in
communities where Land O'Lakes has
facilities, plants, members and employees; to
invest and participate in community programs
that strengthen and preserve the quality of
rural life; to encourage and support employee
volunteerism.

LEGAL BASIS:
Corporate foundation.

ELIGIBILITY:
Contributions are generally restricted to
organizations which have been granted
501(c)(3) tax-exempt status and are working
to improve communities where Land
O'Lakes has a significant concentration of
members or employees. Contributions are
focused in the western, north central and
eastern states. Of our donations, 85% will be
made in rural areas and 15% in urban areas
within those states.

Funds generally will not be used for
lobbying, political and religious
organizations, veteran, fraternal and labor
organizations, fund-raising events, benefits or
advertising, national groups, individuals,

scholarships, private colleges and universities, disease/medical research or treatment or racing/sports sponsorships.

Matching Gift recipient organizations must be located in the U.S. and be tax-exempt under Section 501(c)(3) of the Internal Revenue Code. Eligible institutions include the following:
(1) elementary and secondary schools that are fully accredited by the Department of Education;
(2) public or private colleges, universities, junior colleges, technical/vocational institutes, community colleges and graduate professional schools with appropriate regional or professional accreditation, or tax-exempt alumni funds, foundations or associations that collect funds exclusively for the direct benefit of an eligible institution and;
(3) public radio and television stations that meet the criteria established by the Corporation for Public Broadcasting.

FINANCIAL DATA:
Amount of support per award: California Regions Grant Program and Mid-Atlantic Grant Program: $500 to $5,000. Dollars for Doers Program: $100 to $500. Matching Gifts to Education Program: $25 to $1,000 per eligible donor. Member Co-op Match Program: $500 to $10,000 per year.

Total amount of support: Approximately $2,100,000 for the year 2010.

Matching fund requirements: Cash only.

COOPERATIVE FUNDING PROGRAMS: Through the Member Co-op Match Program, Land O'Lakes member cooperatives may request that the Foundation match their donations to local nonprofits, within the parameters of the program.

NUMBER OF APPLICANTS MOST RECENT YEAR: More than 6,000.

NUMBER OF AWARDS: 1,126 for the year 2011.

REPRESENTATIVE AWARDS:
Feeding America National Food Bank Network.

APPLICATION INFORMATION:
Completed Cash Contribution Application Form is required which should include the following information:
(1) a copy of the organization's most recent annual report with financial information included or a brief history and current activities of the organization;
(2) a current operating budget and proposed budget if the project will occur during the following fiscal year and;
(3) a copy of the organization's tax-exempt ruling under Section 501(c)(3) of the Internal Revenue Code or a description of the organization's ownership and/or management.

Applications should be sent to the Executive Director, Land O'Lakes Foundation, P.O. Box 64150, St. Paul, MN 55164-0150.

Duration: One grant per organization per calendar year.

Deadline: No deadline for requests for $25,000 or less; review by staff with announcement within three months. For requests for more than $25,000: January 2, May 1 (arts only), July 1 and November 1.

PUBLICATIONS:
Contributions program guidelines; CSR report is available online at web site.

IRS IDENTIFICATION NUMBER: 41-1864977

ADDRESS INQUIRIES TO:
Executive Director
Land O'Lakes Foundation
P.O. Box 64150
St. Paul, MN 55164-0150

*PLEASE NOTE:
The Foundation is accepting limited applications in 2011.

LAND O'LAKES FOUNDATION [224]
4001 Lexington Avenue North
Arden Hills, MN 55126
(651) 481-2123
Fax: (651) 481-2000

E-MAIL ADDRESS:
lrbotham@landolakes.com

WEB SITE ADDRESS:
www.foundation.landolakes.com

AREAS OF INTEREST:
Dairy science or dairy manufacturing/marketing.

NAME(S) OF PROGRAMS:
● **John Brandt Memorial Scholarship Fund**

TYPE:
Scholarships. John Brandt Memorial Scholarship Program is a $25,000 scholarship available to graduate students pursuing dairy-related degrees at Iowa State University, South Dakota State University, the University of Minnesota, Twin Cities, or the University of Wisconsin, Madison. One or two scholarships are awarded annually to deserving candidates who have demonstrated exceptional commitment and aptitude toward their field of study.

PURPOSE:
To encourage graduate study in dairy science or dairy marketing/manufacturing.

LEGAL BASIS:
Corporate foundation.

ELIGIBILITY:
Applicants must be pursuing a program of study leading to a Master's or Doctor of Philosophy degree in dairy cattle nutrition, genetics, physiology or management, or the manufacturing, processing or marketing of milk and dairy products at one of the four following institutions: University of Minnesota, University of Wisconsin, Iowa State University and South Dakota State University. Such factors as personal recommendations, scholastic record, planned program of study and research and future plans for working in the dairy industry or closely related fields shall be considered in making the award.

FINANCIAL DATA:
Amount of support per award: Approximately $25,000.

Total amount of support: Approximately $25,000, depending on need and endowment market performance.

NUMBER OF APPLICANTS MOST RECENT YEAR: Over 450.

NUMBER OF AWARDS: 1-2 annually.

APPLICATION INFORMATION:
The Foundation sends out Requests for Proposals (RFPs) to the qualifying schools to begin the application process. Those with recommendations should send an application form including personal history, transcripts of scholastic record, and a plan of study and

research to be followed in pursuit of an advanced degree. Applications should be sent to the Executive Director, Land O'Lakes Foundation, P.O. Box 64150, St. Paul, MN 55164-0150.

Duration: One academic year. No renewals.

Deadline: Applications must be postmarked by April 30. Notification by early June.

ADDRESS INQUIRIES TO:
Executive Director
Land O'Lakes Foundation
P.O. Box 64150
St. Paul, MN 55164-0150

*SPECIAL STIPULATIONS:
Scholarships for graduate-level studies.

HERBERT AND GERTRUDE LATKIN CHARITABLE FOUNDATION [225]
1002 Anacapa
Santa Barbara, CA 93101
(805) 564-6211
Fax: (805) 884-1404

FOUNDED: 1991

AREAS OF INTEREST:
Animal cruelty, child abuse, emergency medical services, health and welfare to elderly and needy people, scholarships to deserving college students.

TYPE:
Project/program grants; Scholarships.

YEAR PROGRAM STARTED: 1991

PURPOSE:
To promote the health and welfare of the elderly; to prevent cruelty to animals; to provide emergency medical service for persons suffering as a result of calamity or disaster; to prevent child abuse; to provide assistance to the needy.

LEGAL BASIS:
Private family foundation.

ELIGIBILITY:
Grants are made to organizations that have tax-exempt status under Section 501(c)(3) of the Internal Revenue Code. No grants are made to individuals or religious organizations.

GEOGRAPHIC RESTRICTIONS:
Santa Barbara County, California.

FINANCIAL DATA:
Amount of support per award: Varies.

Total amount of support: $214,000 for the year 2009.

NUMBER OF APPLICANTS MOST RECENT YEAR: 80.

NUMBER OF AWARDS: 66.

APPLICATION INFORMATION:
Send a letter of inquiry outlining the organization's goal and purposes, and the intended use and amount of the grant requested.

Duration: One year. Renewal possible.

Deadline: April 1 and October 1.

IRS IDENTIFICATION NUMBER: 77-6070540

ADDRESS INQUIRIES TO:
Janice Gibbons, Trust Officer
(See address above.)

THE BLANCHE AND IRVING LAURIE FOUNDATION [226]
P.O. Box 53
Roseland, NJ 07068-5788
(973) 993-1743
Fax: (973) 993-3146

AREAS OF INTEREST:
Arts, children, needs of the elderly, education, medical care and needs of the Jewish community.

TYPE:
Capital grants; Project/program grants.

LEGAL BASIS:
Private foundation.

ELIGIBILITY:
No funds for general organization endowments, nor to meet general operating expenses or budget deficits. Funds given for specific projects only.

GEOGRAPHIC RESTRICTIONS:
Middlesex County, New Jersey.

FINANCIAL DATA:
Amount of support per award: $25,000 to $50,000.

APPLICATION INFORMATION:
Submit seven copies of proposal including statement of program objectives, project budget, plans for publicizing the project, background information about the organization and copy of IRS tax-exemption letter.
Duration: Varies.
Deadline: Proposals accepted year-round.

PUBLICATIONS:
Informational brochure.

BOARD OF TRUSTEES:
Laura Barron
Gene R. Korf, Esq.
Scott Korf
Richard A. Patt
Harvey Rich
Adelaide Marcus Zagoren

ADDRESS INQUIRIES TO:
Gene R. Korf, Esq., Executive Director
(See address above.)

JACOB AND CHARLOTTE LEHRMAN FOUNDATION, INC. [227]
1836 Columbia Road, N.W.
Washington, DC 20009
(202) 328-8400
Fax: (202) 328-8405

E-MAIL ADDRESS:
info@lehrmanfoundation.org

WEB SITE ADDRESS:
lehrmanfoundation.org

FOUNDED: 1971

AREAS OF INTEREST:
Jewish life in Washington, DC; Israel; arts; education; underserved children; health and environment.

NAME(S) OF PROGRAMS:
- **Impact Award**

TYPE:
Awards/prizes; Project/program grants. Recognizes a Washington, DC, emerging nonprofit organization that supports education and underserved children by making an extraordinary difference in their lives.

YEAR PROGRAM STARTED: 2001

GEOGRAPHIC RESTRICTIONS:
Primarily greater Washington, DC area.

FINANCIAL DATA:
Total amount of support: $25,000.

ADDRESS INQUIRIES TO:
Robert Lehrman, Vice President
(See address above.)

*PLEASE NOTE:
The Foundation is not accepting unsolicited proposals for the 2011 grant cycle.

LEVI STRAUSS FOUNDATION [228]
Levi's Plaza
1155 Battery Street
San Francisco, CA 94111
(415) 501-6000
Fax: (415) 501-6575

WEB SITE ADDRESS:
www.levistrauss.com

FOUNDED: 1952

AREAS OF INTEREST:
HIV/AIDS prevention and care, economic development and access to education.

CONSULTING OR VOLUNTEER SERVICES:
Each Levi Strauss & Co. production facility has a Community Involvement Team (CIT) which does volunteer work in the local community.

NAME(S) OF PROGRAMS:
- **Community Involvement Team (CIT) Grants**

TYPE:
Conferences/seminars; Demonstration grants; General operating grants; Matching gifts; Product donations; Project/program grants; Seed money grants; Technical assistance; Training grants. The Foundation has the following program issue areas:
(1) preventing the spread of HIV/AIDS through prevention-related programs targeting women and youth, particularly where local policymakers are seeking compassionate alternatives and/or where social bias about HIV/AIDS remains strong;
(2) increasing economic development opportunities by supporting work force development, microenterprise programs and asset-building initiatives for youth and women and;
(3) ensuring access to an education through support of two alternative approaches: (a) where universal education is provided but certain youth lack access to a quality education, the Foundation will fund art and creative expression programs aimed at reconnecting them with school and learning and (b) where youth, in particular girls, are denied access to any education, the Foundation will fund programs that seek to build support for providing access, overcoming obstacles and creating self-sustaining schools when appropriate and necessary.

YEAR PROGRAM STARTED: 1952

PURPOSE:
To act as catalysts for positive change in local communities where Levi Strauss & Co. has a business presence by awarding grants, encouraging employees to volunteer their time and standing behind critical, controversial issues; to help alleviate poverty on behalf of youth (7 to 25 years of age) and women.

LEGAL BASIS:
Corporate foundation.

ELIGIBILITY:
The Foundation does not fund:
(1) individuals (stipends or fellowships);
(2) capital or endowment campaigns/building funds;
(3) equipment or devices for individual users;
(4) sports teams or athletic competitions;
(5) advertising;
(6) sectarian or religious activities;
(7) political campaigns or causes and;
(8) organizations that do not meet the Foundation's nondiscrimination policy.

FINANCIAL DATA:
Total amount of support: Over $13,000,000 annually.
Matching fund requirements: Levi Strauss & Co. employees; agency must sign non-discrimination policy.

APPLICATION INFORMATION:
The Foundation invites letters of inquiry from single organizations or for collaboration among organizations. These letters can be up to three pages in length, should include a brief description of the program or project and the amount of funding requested, as well as proof of nonprofit status. U.S.-based organizations should include a copy of their IRS letter confirming their 501(c)(3) tax-exempt status.
Duration: Varies.

PUBLICATIONS:
Application guidelines.

IRS IDENTIFICATION NUMBER: 94-6064702

LIBRA FOUNDATION [229]
3 Canal Plaza
Portland, ME 04112
(207) 879-6280
Fax: (207) 879-6281

E-MAIL ADDRESS:
liz@librafoundation.org

WEB SITE ADDRESS:
www.librafoundation.org

FOUNDED: 1989

AREAS OF INTEREST:
Arts, culture and humanities, education, environment, health, human services, justice, public/society benefit and religion.

TYPE:
Grants-in-aid; Project/program grants.

PURPOSE:
To strive for innovative ways to enrich Maine, empower communities, and enhance the quality of life of all Maine citizens.

ELIGIBILITY:
Charitable nonprofit organizations whose activities, operations, or purposes take place only within the state of Maine. Religious organizations are eligible. Organizations must supply a copy of tax-exempt 501(c)(3) letter. Grants are not made to individuals.

GEOGRAPHIC RESTRICTIONS:
Maine.

FINANCIAL DATA:
Amount of support per award: Up to $25,000.
Total amount of support: Approximately $8,000,000 for the year 2009.

APPLICATION INFORMATION:
Applicants are asked to complete a two-paged application in accordance with the

Foundation's guidelines, both of which may be obtained from the Foundation by contacting the Executive Assistant.

Duration: One year. Must reapply after expiration of one year.

Deadline: February 15, May 15, August 15 and November 15.

ADDRESS INQUIRIES TO:
Elizabeth C. Flaherty
Executive Assistant
(See address above.)

LILLY ENDOWMENT INC. [230]

2801 North Meridian Street
Indianapolis, IN 46208
(317) 924-5471
Fax: (317) 926-4431

E-MAIL ADDRESS:
wolframg@lei.org

WEB SITE ADDRESS:
www.lillyendowment.org

FOUNDED: 1937

AREAS OF INTEREST:
Religion, education and community development.

TYPE:
Awards/prizes; Capital grants; Challenge/matching grants; Conferences/seminars; Development grants; General operating grants; Internships; Matching gifts; Project/program grants; Research grants; Scholarships; Technical assistance; Training grants. In the area of religion, support for programs that enrich the religious lives of American Christians, mainly by supporting efforts to call, support and educate a new generation of talented pastors and to strengthen current pastors in their capacities for excellence in ministry; support for programs that seek to help congregations be healthy communities of faith; support for theological seminaries and other educational and religious institutions that share these aims; support for projects which strengthen the contributions that religious ideas, practices, values and institutions make to the common good.

In the area of education, support for initiatives and programs that improve education in Indiana, with special emphasis on higher education and on programs designed to increase the number of Indiana residents with Bachelor's degrees; support for a number of invitational grant programs, many of which are aimed at Indiana's colleges' and universities' abilities to increase the state's educational attainment level; support on an invitational basis for minority his/her education.

In the area of youth, support for direct-service organizations in central Indiana; support for building capacity of intermediary organizations throughout the state; support for professional development for the staffs and volunteer leadership of these organizations.

In the area of leadership education, support for projects that nurture good stewardship among the trustees and executives of charitable organizations; support for scholarship on the characteristics of able trusteeship and good governance of nonprofit organizations.

In the area of fund-raising and philanthropy, support for programs (nationally and in Indiana) to increase the charitable giving among Americans; support for efforts to create a body of reliable knowledge about giving and fund-raising; support for scholarly pursuit of the subject.

In the areas of community development, support is available for programs that involve Indianapolis initiatives in the arts, culture and preservation, human services and community development and revitalization. Indiana initiatives include Indiana United Ways and community foundations. Economic public-policy general support grants are offered on an invitational basis limited to a limited number of organizations that promote free market and democratic principles.

YEAR PROGRAM STARTED: 1937

PURPOSE:
To support the causes of religion, education and community development.

LEGAL BASIS:
Private foundation.

ELIGIBILITY:
Applicants must be 501(c)(3) tax-exempt organizations and institutions with appropriate interests in targeted geographic areas. General grantmaking prohibitions include loans or cash to individuals, health care/biological science projects, mass media projects, endowments, libraries, student scholarships (except in Indiana), general operating support/capital campaigns for organizations outside of Indiana.

GEOGRAPHIC RESTRICTIONS:
Indiana.

FINANCIAL DATA:
Grants vary in amount depending on the needs and nature of the request.

Amount of support per award: Varies.

Total amount of support: $276,100,000 paid for the year 2009.

Matching fund requirements: Varies.

APPLICATION INFORMATION:
Except for specialized programs, no official application forms are required. The usual first step is a two-page letter outlining the project and budget and a description of the applicant organization, including a statement of federal tax-exempt status.

Duration: Typically one year.

Deadline: Applications accepted on an ongoing basis.

PUBLICATIONS:
Application guidelines; annual report.

IRS IDENTIFICATION NUMBER: 35-0868122

OFFICERS:
Thomas M. Lofton, Chairman
N. Clay Robbins, President
Craig Dykstra, Senior Vice President, Religion
Sara B. Cobb, Vice President, Education
E.G. White, Vice President, Finance
Diane M. Stenson, Treasurer and Vice President
David D. Biber, Secretary

DIRECTORS:
Otis R. Bowen
Daniel P. Carmichael
William G. Enright
Charles E. Golden
Eli Lilly, II
Mary K. Lisher
Thomas M. Lofton
N. Clay Robbins

ADDRESS INQUIRIES TO:
Program Office
(See address above.)

*SPECIAL STIPULATIONS:
Awards are made to 501(c)(3) groups only.

LINCOLN FINANCIAL FOUNDATION [231]

1300 South Clinton Street
Fort Wayne, IN 46802
(260) 455-3879
Fax: (260) 455-4004

E-MAIL ADDRESS:
sandi.kemmish@lfg.com

WEB SITE ADDRESS:
www.lincolnfinancial.com

FOUNDED: 1962

AREAS OF INTEREST:
Arts and culture, education/workforce and youth development, human services.

CONSULTING OR VOLUNTEER SERVICES:
Volunteer Involvement Program for employees of Lincoln Financial Group.

TYPE:
Matching gifts; Project/program grants; Technical assistance.

YEAR PROGRAM STARTED: 1962

PURPOSE:
To encourage nonprofit projects that will enhance the quality of life in communities where Lincoln Financial Group has a business presence.

LEGAL BASIS:
Corporate Foundation.

ELIGIBILITY:
Applicants must be 501(c)(3) organizations.

No grants to individuals, for endowments, for sponsorship of sporting events or for the purchase of tickets. Multiyear grants are not accepted.

GEOGRAPHIC RESTRICTIONS:
Hartford, Connecticut; Fort Wayne, Indiana; Omaha, Nebraska; Concord, New Hampshire; Greensboro, North Carolina; Philadelphia, Pennsylvania.

FINANCIAL DATA:
Amount of support per award: Varies.

Total amount of support: Up to 2% of the corporation's pre-tax earnings annually.

Matching fund requirements: Qualified 501(c)(3).

NUMBER OF APPLICANTS MOST RECENT YEAR: 563.

NUMBER OF AWARDS: 464.

APPLICATION INFORMATION:
Online application form required. Some attachments requested.

Duration: Quarterly.

Deadline: Varies.

PUBLICATIONS:
Guidelines.

IRS IDENTIFICATION NUMBER: 35-6042099

ADDRESS INQUIRIES TO:
Program Officer
(See address above.)

THE LOATS FOUNDATION, INC. [232]

35 East Church Street
Frederick, MD 21701
(301) 663-6361
Fax: (301) 663-7747

FOUNDED: 1979

AREAS OF INTEREST:
Scholarship for Frederick County residents only and charitable organizations of Frederick County, MD.

TYPE:
Scholarships.

YEAR PROGRAM STARTED: 1979

PURPOSE:
To help residents of Frederick County, MD go on to higher education by providing financial aid.

LEGAL BASIS:
Nonprofit foundation.

ELIGIBILITY:
Residents of Frederick County, MD only. Distributed by colleges on a need basis.

GEOGRAPHIC RESTRICTIONS:
Frederick County, Maryland.

FINANCIAL DATA:
Amount of support per award: $3,000 cap.
Total amount of support: Varies.

APPLICATION INFORMATION:
Applications for scholarships are available at all Maryland colleges and universities.
Duration: One year. Renewable on need basis.

ADDRESS INQUIRIES TO:
Helen Hahn, Secretary
(See address above.)

THE LUBRIZOL FOUNDATION [233]

29400 Lakeland Boulevard, Suite 053A
Wickliffe, OH 44092-2298
(440) 347-5080
Fax: (440) 347-1858

E-MAIL ADDRESS:
kal@lubrizol.com

WEB SITE ADDRESS:
www.lubrizol.com

FOUNDED: 1952

AREAS OF INTEREST:
Education, health and human services, civic, cultural, environmental and youth activities.

NAME(S) OF PROGRAMS:
- **Community Connection Employee Volunteer Gift Program**
- **Matching Gift Program**

TYPE:
Capital grants; Fellowships; General operating grants; Matching gifts; Project/program grants; Scholarships. The Foundation has scholarship programs at 38 selected colleges and universities. It also matches gifts of Lubrizol employees to most charitable organizations on a dollar-for-dollar basis.

In the area of education, support is given for scholarships, fellowships and awards in selected fields of study through selected colleges and universities, with major emphasis on the study of chemistry and chemical and mechanical engineering, capital and operating grants to colleges, universities, schools, educational programs and combined educational funds.

In the area of health and human services, support is provided for combined funds, direct grants to health and human service activities.

In the area of civic and cultural, support is provided for public television stations, performing arts organizations, schools of fine arts and museums.

In the area of youth activities, support is given to programs that contribute to character-building, such as those which promote good citizenship, self-reliance, an understanding of free enterprise and an appreciation of nature and the environment.

In the environmental area, support is given to parks, nature centers, conservancies and local environmental education efforts.

YEAR PROGRAM STARTED: 1952

PURPOSE:
To support educational, youth, health, human services, civic and cultural and environmental activities of a tax-exempt, charitable nature.

LEGAL BASIS:
Private, tax-exempt foundation.

ELIGIBILITY:
Grants are made to U.S. nonprofit, educational or other charitable tax-exempt organizations. Grants are not generally made to endowments, religious or political purposes or individuals.

GEOGRAPHIC RESTRICTIONS:
Primarily Greater Cleveland, Ohio and Houston, Texas.

FINANCIAL DATA:
Amount of support per award: Grants vary in amount, depending upon the needs and nature of the request.
Total amount of support: $2,546,016, including matching gifts for the year 2010.
Matching fund requirements: 1:1 match; $25 minimum; $5,000 maximum, and 10 gifts maximum.

NUMBER OF APPLICANTS MOST RECENT YEAR: 320.

NUMBER OF AWARDS: 38 discretionary grants; 235 total awards including operating, capital and discretionary.

REPRESENTATIVE AWARDS:
$110,200 to the United Way of Lake County, Inc. for general operating support; $84,800 to the United Way of the Texas Gulf Coast for general operating support; $183,300 to the United Way Services of Cleveland for general operating support.

APPLICATION INFORMATION:
Grant proposals should include the following: (1) a cover letter that summarizes the purpose of the request signed by the executive officer of the organization; (2) a narrative of specific information related to the subject of the request; (3) current audited financial statements and a specific project budget, if applicable and; (4) documentation of the organization's Federal tax-exempt status.

Additional descriptive literature (annual report, brochures, etc.) that accurately characterizes the overall activities of the organization is appreciated. Upon review, further information may be requested including an interview or site visit.

Applicants will receive written notification of the decision on their proposal. An organization whose request has been declined should not submit another proposal for at least 12 months after such notification. Applicants are welcome to contact the Foundation office for further clarification of the foregoing requirements.
Duration: One year, with possible renewal. Some grants are ongoing.

PUBLICATIONS:
Annual report.

IRS IDENTIFICATION NUMBER: 34-6500595

OFFICERS:
J.L. Hambrick, Chairman
D.J. Enzerra, President
B.A. Valentine, Treasurer
K.A. Lerchbacher, Secretary

TRUSTEES:
D.J. Enzerra
R.T. Graf
J.L. Hambrick
K.L. Jethrow
K.A. Lerchbacher
B.A. Valentine

ADDRESS INQUIRIES TO:
Karen A. Lerchbacher
Foundation Administrator
(See address above.)

THE HENRY LUCE FOUNDATION, INC. [234]

51 Madison Avenue, 30th Floor
New York, NY 10010
(212) 489-7700
Fax: (212) 581-9541

E-MAIL ADDRESS:
hlf1@hluce.org

WEB SITE ADDRESS:
www.hluce.org

FOUNDED: 1936

AREAS OF INTEREST:
Interdisciplinary exploration of higher education; increased understanding between Asia and the U.S.; the study of religion and theology; scholarship in American art; opportunities for women in science and engineering; environmental and public policy programs.

NAME(S) OF PROGRAMS:
- **American Art Program**
- **Clare Boothe Luce Program**
- **Luce Foundation Theology Program**
- **Henry Luce III Fellows in Theology Program**
- **Luce Scholars Program**

TYPE:
Fellowships; Internships; Project/program grants; Scholarships. American Art Program focuses on the American fine and decorative arts and is committed to scholarship and the overall enhancement of this field. The program is national in scope and provides support for all periods and genres of American art history.

The Clare Boothe Luce Program promotes the advancement of American women through higher education in the sciences, engineering and mathematics.

The Luce Foundation's Theology program encourages the development of leadership for religious communities through theological education, and fosters scholarship that links the academy to churches and the wider public. The program provides funding for seminary education, leadership, ecumenical and interreligious programs, and religion and the arts.

The Henry Luce III Fellows in Theology program, administered by the Association of Theological Schools, supports innovative research and publication by full-time seminary faculty.

The Luce Scholars Program provides stipends and internships for young Americans to live and work in Asia each year.

PURPOSE:
To promote interdisciplinary exploration of higher education, increased understanding between Asia and the U.S., the study of religion and theology, scholarship in American art, opportunities for women in science and engineering, environmental and public policy programs.

ELIGIBILITY:
The Foundation does not support health care or medical projects and does not fund development assistance work overseas. It does not normally assist journalism, media and film projects or the performing arts.

APPLICATION INFORMATION:
No special forms are required although separate guidelines and deadlines exist for specific programs. In most cases, an initial letter of inquiry, to determine whether a project falls within the Foundation's guidelines, can be addressed to the appropriate program director or officer.

LYNDHURST FOUNDATION [235]

517 East Fifth Street
Chattanooga, TN 37403-1826
(423) 756-0767
Fax: (423) 756-0770

E-MAIL ADDRESS:
bclark@lyndhurstfoundation.org

WEB SITE ADDRESS:
www.lyndhurstfoundation.org

FOUNDED: 1938

AREAS OF INTEREST:
Enhancing the quality of Chattanooga's public gathering places in downtown and along the riverfront, plus its public schools, its diverse arts and cultural organizations and its natural environment. Beyond the city's boundaries, the Foundation wants to be involved in projects that protect and enhance the natural environment of the southern Appalachian region.

TYPE:
Challenge/matching grants; Conferences/seminars; Demonstration grants; Development grants; Endowments; General operating grants; Matching gifts; Project/program grants; Seed money grants; Technical assistance. The Foundation intends to focus upon continued development of the Tennessee Riverpark, redevelopment of the Southside as a live-and-work urban neighborhood, facilitation of historic preservation, stimulation of downtown housing development, strengthening of the city's arts and cultural life, protection and enhancement of the community's natural environment, the reform of the community's public schools, the continued development of improved housing opportunities for people of modest means and innovations in social service programs that provide genuine

progress against social problems and genuine enhancement of community strengths in Chattanooga.

YEAR PROGRAM STARTED: 1978

PURPOSE:
To support a variety of nonprofit programs to make life better within the city of Chattanooga.

LEGAL BASIS:
Private foundation.

ELIGIBILITY:
Applicants must be 501(c)(3) organizations in the southeastern U.S.

GEOGRAPHIC RESTRICTIONS:
Southeast, with special consideration given to certain developments in Chattanooga, Tennessee.

FINANCIAL DATA:
Amount of support per award:
Approximately $30,000 average grant.
Total amount of support: $11,138,800 for the year 2008.

NUMBER OF AWARDS: 74.

REPRESENTATIVE AWARDS:
$10,000 to Cumberland Trail Conference for the construction of a foot bridge; $100,000 to Public Education Foundation in support of an education data analyst for the Hamilton County Department of Education; $55,000 to Chattanooga Neighborhood Enterprise for technical assistance and neighborhood revitalization activities.

APPLICATION INFORMATION:
A grant request should be initiated by a brief letter of two or three pages describing the organization and the specific project for which support is being sought. Included should be an estimated project budget, a copy of the organization's tax-exempt ruling from the IRS and a list of directors and staff members. Further information and an interview or visit may be requested.
Duration: One year. Renewal possible for up to three years.
Deadline: July 5 for August meeting, September 30 for November meeting.

PUBLICATIONS:
Annual report.

OFFICERS:
Allen L. McCallie, Chairman of the Board
Benic M. Clark, III, President/Treasurer
Tom Montague, Secretary

TRUSTEES:
Nelson D. Campbell
George Fontaine
Meg Gerber
Kate Juett
Cartter Lupton
Allen L. McCallie
Tom Montague
Alice Smith

STAFF:
Benic M. Clark, III, President/Treasurer
Margaret Stakely, Controller
Sarah Morgan, Program Officer
Karen Rudolph, Program Officer

ADDRESS INQUIRIES TO:
Benic M. Clark, III, President/Treasurer
(See address above.)

*PLEASE NOTE:
Most of the Foundation's grants are distributed solely at the Foundation's initiative. This means that, in most categories, the Foundation does not seek or fund unsolicited requests.

M & M AREA COMMUNITY FOUNDATION

1101 11th Avenue
Menominee, MI 49858
(906) 864-3599
Fax: (906) 864-3657

E-MAIL ADDRESS:
mmfoundation@czwireless.net

WEB SITE ADDRESS:
www.mmcommunityfoundation.org

TYPE:
Project/program grants; Scholarships; Training grants.

See entry 1408 for full listing.

THE J.E. AND L.E. MABEE FOUNDATION, INC.   [236]

401 South Boston Avenue
Suite 3001
Tulsa, OK 74103-4017
(918) 584-4286
Fax: (918) 585-5540

WEB SITE ADDRESS:
www.mabeefoundation.com

FOUNDED: 1948

AREAS OF INTEREST:
Education, scientific and medical research, religion and charities.

TYPE:
Capital grants; Project/program grants.

PURPOSE:
To assist religious, charitable and educational organizations.

LEGAL BASIS:
Nonprofit foundation.

ELIGIBILITY:
Grants are awarded to nonprofit, tax-exempt, non-tax-supported, established institutions which combine sound character and stability with progressiveness and purpose. The Foundation does not generally favor deficit financing and debt retirement, operating or program funds, annual fund-raising campaigns, endowments, government-owned or operated institutions, educational institutions below the college level, furnishings or equipment (except major medical equipment) or grants to a church.

Grants are made toward building and facility construction, renovation projects and the purchase of major capital grants.

GEOGRAPHIC RESTRICTIONS:
Arkansas, Kansas, Missouri, New Mexico, Oklahoma and Texas.

FINANCIAL DATA:
Amount of support per award: $25,000 to $1,000,000.
Total amount of support: $25,000 to $30,000,000.

NUMBER OF AWARDS: 100.

APPLICATION INFORMATION:
There is no application form. Proposals must contain the following items:
(1) the legal name and address of the organization;
(2) name, title, address and telephone number of the primary contact person;
(3) brief description of the organization;
(4) description of the project, with goals and objectives;
(5) description of the population expected to

benefit from the project;
(6) detailed budget for the project;
(7) a list of funding sources including those received and any pending or pledged;
(8) the cut-off date for a challenge grant;
(9) a time schedule for start of construction;
(10) indicate how the project will be sustained after the grant expires;
(11) verification of IRS tax-exempt status under Section 501(c)(3) and not a private foundation under Section 509(a);
(12) the organization's most recent audited financial statement and interim financial statement for the current fiscal period and;
(13) a list of officers with titles and names of the governing body with primary professional affiliations.

Duration: Varies.

Deadline: March 1, June 1, September 1 and December 1.

PUBLICATIONS:
Program announcement; proposal guidelines.

ADDRESS INQUIRIES TO:
Ray Tullius, Vice Chairman
(See address above.)

JOHN D. AND CATHERINE T. MACARTHUR FOUNDATION [237]

140 South Dearborn Street
Suite 1200
Chicago, IL 60603-5285
(312) 726-8000
Fax: (312) 920-6258

E-MAIL ADDRESS:
4answers@macfound.org

WEB SITE ADDRESS:
www.macfound.org

FOUNDED: 1978

AREAS OF INTEREST:
Housing, human rights, mental health, peace, urban affairs, population and conservation.

NAME(S) OF PROGRAMS:
- **General Program**
- **MacArthur Fellows Program**
- **Program on Global Security and Sustainability**
- **Program on Human and Community Development**

TYPE:
General operating grants; Project/program grants; Research grants. The Program on Human and Community Development supports national research and policy work and - in Chicago and nationally - direct local efforts.

The Program on Global Security and Sustainability provides support in core areas of interest: international peace and security; population; conservation and sustainable development; and human rights and international justice. The Foundation also supports work in selected geographic regions, such as but not limited to India, Mexico, Nigeria and Russia.

The MacArthur Fellows Program awards fellowships to exceptionally creative individuals, regardless of field. Applications or nominations are not accepted.

YEAR PROGRAM STARTED: 1979

PURPOSE:
To support creative people and effective institutions committed to building a just and peaceful world.

LEGAL BASIS:
Private, independent foundation.

ELIGIBILITY:
The Foundation does not support capital campaigns, political activities, programs and activities that are among routine or accepted responsibilities of government, organizations that support humanitarian or disaster relief, or attempts to influence specific legislation. The Foundation does not provide scholarships or tuition assistance for undergraduate, graduate, or postgraduate studies, nor does it provide support to annual fund-raising drives, institutional benefits, honorary functions, or similar appeals.

FINANCIAL DATA:
Assets of $6.1 billion estimated for the year 2008.

Amount of support per award: $553,000.

Total amount of support: $311,280,837 for the year 2008.

NUMBER OF APPLICANTS MOST RECENT YEAR:
6,400.

NUMBER OF AWARDS: 601.

APPLICATION INFORMATION:
Grant seekers should submit a two- to three-page letter of inquiry addressed to the Foundation's Office of Grants Management, Research and Information. The letter should include:
(1) a brief statement of purpose;
(2) the significance of the issue addressed by the project, and how it relates to the Foundation's interests and goals;
(3) how the project will address the issue;
(4) how the issue relates to your organization, and why your organization is qualified to undertake the project;
(5) the audiences who will be interested in your work, and some thoughts on how you might communicate with them and;
(6) a rough estimate of the cost of the project, and the amount requested from the Foundation, and other sources of support.

Your letter should also provide contact information including name, address, telephone and fax numbers of applicant's organization, the name and title of the principal contact person, and the name of the parent organization.

Duration: One to five years. Renewals by reapplication.

PUBLICATIONS:
Annual report.

BOARD OF DIRECTORS:
Robert E. Denham, Chairperson
Lloyd Axworthy
John Seely Brown
Jack Fuller
Robert L. Gallucci
Jamie S. Gorelick
Mary Graham
Donald R. Hopkins, M.D.
Daniel Huttenlocher
Will Miller
Mario J. Molina
Marjorie M. Scardino
Claude M. Steele

OFFICERS AND DIRECTORS:
Robert E. Denham, Chairperson
Robert L. Gallucci, President
Marc Yanchura, Vice President and Chief Financial Officer
Susan S. Manske, Vice President and Chief Investment Officer
Joshua J. Mintz, Vice President and General Counsel

Elspeth Revere, Vice President, General Program
Barry Lowenkron, Vice President, Global Security and Sustainability
Julia Stasch, Vice President, Human and Community Development
David S. Chernoff, Associate General Counsel
Elizabeth Kane, Secretary

ADDRESS INQUIRIES TO:
Richard J. Kaplan
Associate Vice President for Institutional Research and Grants Management
(See address above.)

THE MACLELLAN FOUNDATION, INC. [238]

820 Broad Street, Suite 300
Chattanooga, TN 37402
(423) 294-1366
Fax: (423) 755-1640

E-MAIL ADDRESS:
info@maclellan.net

WEB SITE ADDRESS:
www.maclellan.net

FOUNDED: 1945

AREAS OF INTEREST:
Youth agencies, selected schools of higher education and theological seminaries and Protestant religious associations working in the U.S. and abroad.

TYPE:
Challenge/matching grants; General operating grants; Grants-in-aid; Seed money grants.

YEAR PROGRAM STARTED: 1954

PURPOSE:
To serve national and international organizations committed to furthering the Kingdom of Christ and select local organizations, which foster the spiritual welfare of the community, by providing financial and leadership resources to extend the Kingdom of God to every tribe, nation, people and tongue.

LEGAL BASIS:
Tax-exempt private foundation.

ELIGIBILITY:
The Foundation only provides grants to nonprofit Christian organizations.

APPLICATION INFORMATION:
Application forms and guidelines are available online.

Duration: Varies.

Deadline: Proposals are accepted throughout the year.

OFFICER:
Hugh O. Maclellan, Jr., Chairman

ADDRESS INQUIRIES TO:
Bethany Rowe, Grants Manager
E-mail: bethany@maclellan.net

MARBROOK FOUNDATION [239]

730 Second Avenue South
Suite 1300
Minneapolis, MN 55402
(612) 752-1783
Fax: (612) 752-1780

E-MAIL ADDRESS:
jhara@marbrookfoundation.org

WEB SITE ADDRESS:
www.marbrookfoundation.org

FOUNDED: 1948

AREAS OF INTEREST:
The Foundation's primary interest is in initiatives or organizations that create equal opportunity for immigrants and refugees in the Twin Cities metro area.

TYPE:
Capital grants; Endowments; General operating grants; Project/program grants; Scholarships; Technical assistance. As the immigrant and refugee populations grow and become increasingly diverse, so does the potential for enrichment and transformation in our communities. The Foundation believes that addressing the opportunities and challenges that come with blending cultures, languages and beliefs will help to revitalize our communities and contribute to our well-being.

YEAR PROGRAM STARTED: 1948

PURPOSE:
To promote the values of the Brooks Family by making grants and focusing involvement in designated charitable areas and causes that reflect those values.

LEGAL BASIS:
Tax-exempt, private foundation.

ELIGIBILITY:
The Foundation will give priority to projects or organizations that address at least one of the following areas:
(1) initiatives working to create equal opportunity or to empower immigrants and refugees (e.g., affordable housing, job training, life skills);
(2) environmental justice and advocacy for neighborhoods with a high concentration of immigrants and refugees;
(3) expanding access to healthy food for neighborhoods with a high concentration of immigrants and refugees;
(4) academic success for children of immigrants and refugees;
(5) English language instruction for immigrants and refugees;
(6) cultural preservation for new Americans;
(7) integrating a comprehensive approach (of body, mind and spirit) to the well-being of immigrants and refugees, with a special interest in programs honoring the inherent spiritual and cultural richness of immigrant communities and;
(8) arts organizations/projects that highlight cultural awareness or address social issues of immigrants and refugees.

The Foundation does not fund:
(1) start-up organizations;
(2) programs for the elderly;
(3) domestic abuse programs;
(4) disease-related organizations;
(5) homeless shelters;
(6) food shelves;
(7) conferences and events;
(8) programs serving the physically or mentally disabled or;
(9) individuals or organizations which attempt to influence legislation or to intervene in any political campaign.

GEOGRAPHIC RESTRICTIONS:
Minnesota, with emphasis on Minneapolis and St. Paul.

FINANCIAL DATA:
Amount of support per award: Grants vary in amount, depending upon the needs and nature of the request.

Total amount of support: $650,000 for the year 2010.

NUMBER OF APPLICANTS MOST RECENT YEAR:
190 for the year 2010.

NUMBER OF AWARDS: 90 for the year 2010.

REPRESENTATIVE AWARDS:
$10,000 to LearningWorks at Blake: A Breakthrough Program for general operating support; $10,000 to the Somali Success School for general operating support; $3,000 to the English Learning Center for general operating support; $3,000 to Project for Pride in Living for general operating support.

APPLICATION INFORMATION:
A formal application form is not required; however, written proposals should include a description of the objectives, specific details on how the objectives are to be attained, a budget, and a proposed method of evaluation to determine the eventual extent to which the proposed objectives are met. Also included should be a description of the organization and a statement showing 501(c)(3) status. The organization should also state whether or not it has been classified as a nonprivate foundation or a private operating foundation under the provisions of the Tax Reform Act of 1969.

Deadline: May 15 and November 15.

PUBLICATIONS:
Annual report; application guidelines.

TRUSTEES:
Conley Brooks
Conley Brooks, Jr.
Markell Brooks
Sarah Brooks
Stephen B. Brooks
Markell Kiefer
Katherine M. Leighton
Julie Zelle

EXECUTIVE DIRECTOR:
Julia S. Hara

MARDAG FOUNDATION   [240]
55 Fifth Street East, Suite 600
St. Paul, MN 55101-1797
(651) 224-5463
Fax: (651) 224-8123

E-MAIL ADDRESS:
inbox@mardag.org

WEB SITE ADDRESS:
www.mardag.org

FOUNDED: 1969

AREAS OF INTEREST:
Children, seniors and other at-risk populations, education and the arts.

TYPE:
Capital grants; Challenge/matching grants; Project/program grants; Seed money grants.

YEAR PROGRAM STARTED: 1969

PURPOSE:
To make grants to qualified nonprofit organizations within the state of Minnesota that help to enhance and improve the quality of life.

LEGAL BASIS:
Private foundation.

ELIGIBILITY:
Applicants must be 501(c)(3) nonprofit corporations or public entities. The Foundation does not make grants through fiscal agents or for ongoing annual operating purposes.

The Foundation will consider grants applications for:
(1) capital projects, program expansion, or special projects of a time-limited nature;
(2) start-up costs for promising new programs that demonstrate sound management and clear goals relevant to community needs;
(3) support for established agencies that have temporary or transition needs and;
(4) funds to match contributions received from other sources or to provide a challenge to help raise new contributions.

The Foundation will not consider grant applications for:
(1) programs serving Minneapolis and the surrounding West Metro area;
(2) scholarships and grants to individuals;
(3) annual operating expenses;
(4) sectarian religious programs;
(5) medical research;
(6) federated campaigns;
(7) conservation or environmental programs;
(8) events and conferences;
(9) programs serving the physically, developmentally and mentally disabled;
(10) capital campaigns of private secondary schools or;
(11) capital and endowment campaigns of private colleges and universities.

GEOGRAPHIC RESTRICTIONS:
East Metro area of Dakota, Ramsey and Washington counties, as well as greater Minnesota.

FINANCIAL DATA:
Amount of support per award: Varies.

APPLICATION INFORMATION:
Applicants are encouraged to request the Foundation's application form, narrative guidelines and evaluation plan summary form prior to submission. The applicant may wish to submit a two- or three-page letter of inquiry describing the proposal prior to preparation of a full proposal to see if the project fits the interests and guidelines of the Foundation. Both letters of inquiry and full proposals (one copy) must be in writing. Proposals will not be returned to the applicant. Do not send applications in binders or folders, or include videotapes or audio tapes. Acceptance of either a letter of inquiry or a proposal for review does not assure that a grant will be awarded.

Duration: Typically one year.

Deadline: Applications must be postmarked by December 31 for April board meeting, May 1 for August board meeting, or August 1 for November board meeting.

PUBLICATIONS:
Application; narrative guidelines; annual report.

IRS IDENTIFICATION NUMBER: 41-1698990

OFFICERS:
Timothy M. Ober, President
Gretchen D. Davidson, Vice President
Richard B. Ober, Treasurer
Phyllis Rawls Goff, Secretary

TRUSTEES:
Janice K. Angell
Gretchen D. Davidson
Cornelia M. Eberhart
Phyllis Rawls Goff
Patrick Medure
Gayle M. Ober
Hon. Wilhelmina M. Wright

ADDRESS INQUIRIES TO:
Lisa Hansen, Grants Manager
(See address above.)

MARIN COMMUNITY FOUNDATION [241]

5 Hamilton Landing, Suite 200
Novato, CA 94949
(415) 464-2500
Fax: (415) 464-2555

E-MAIL ADDRESS:
info@marincf.org

WEB SITE ADDRESS:
www.marincf.org

FOUNDED: 1986

AREAS OF INTEREST:
Human needs, education, community
development, religion, environment and the
arts.

TYPE:
Awards/prizes; Capital grants;
Challenge/matching grants;
Conferences/seminars; General operating
grants; Project/program grants; Scholarships;
Technical assistance.

YEAR PROGRAM STARTED: 1987

PURPOSE:
To encourage and apply philanthropic
contributions to help improve the human
condition, embrace diversity, promote a
humane and democratic society, and enhance
the community's quality of life, now and for
future generations.

LEGAL BASIS:
Community foundation.

ELIGIBILITY:
Proposals must be consistent with the
Foundation's program goals and must meet
two additional requirements. First, the
applicant must be a public or nonprofit
organization and, second, the proposed
project must be conducted in and/or benefit
the residents of Marin County, CA. Projects
with a regional or multi-county benefit may
be funded only in proportion to the extent
that they benefit the Marin County
community.

Ineligible activities include for-profit
purposes, basic research, the start-up of new
nonprofit organizations that will
unnecessarily duplicate existing programs or
services or undertake services that can be
more effectively provided by other
organizations and grants to individuals. Other
limitations specific to each program area are
outlined in the funding guidelines. No grants
are made to individuals.

Buck Trust grants are limited to Marin
County.

GEOGRAPHIC RESTRICTIONS:
Marin County, California.

FINANCIAL DATA:
Amount of support per award: $50,000 to
$150,000.
Total amount of support: $54,850,000 for the
year 2010.

APPLICATION INFORMATION:
Applicants are encouraged to contact a
program officer to determine if a proposed
project or program is consistent with
Foundation goals. Following a discussion
with the program officer, applicants may
submit a letter of intent through its online
Grant Application Center.

Duration: Varies. Renewal possible.
Deadline: Applications are accepted
according to a schedule posted by the
Foundation on their web site.

PUBLICATIONS:
General information brochure.

IRS IDENTIFICATION NUMBER: 94-3007979

OFFICERS:
Thomas Peters, President
Sid Hartman, Chief Financial and Operating
Officer

BOARD OF TRUSTEES:
Ann Mathieson, Chairperson
Robert Reynolds, Vice Chairperson
Sara Barnes
George Bull
Gary Giacomini
Jay L. Paxton
Kerry Peirson
Maria Ramos-Chertok
Margaret Van Camp

MARRIOTT INTERNATIONAL, INC. [242]

10400 Fernwood Road
Bethesda, MD 20817
(301) 380-5875
Fax: (301) 380-2843

E-MAIL ADDRESS:
community.engagement@marriott.com

WEB SITE ADDRESS:
www.marriott.com/socialresponsibility

FOUNDED: 1927

AREAS OF INTEREST:
Shelter and food, environment, readiness for
hotel careers, vitality of children, and
embracing diversity and people with
disabilities.

TYPE:
Project/program grants. In the area of health
and human services, contributions are
allocated to United Way agencies in most
communities where Marriott has operations.
Emphasis on programs and activities that
provide opportunities for people with
disabilities or that pertain to hunger relief.

In the area of education, contributions are
generally limited to institutions and
organizations at the college or university
level which offer programs relevant to the
hospitality industry or where the company
has an active involvement. Emphasis is
placed on institutions or programs that
promote cultural diversity or serve minority
or disadvantaged students.

In the area of civic, contributions support a
range of organizations generally in Marriott's
headquarters area and select organizations
that are national in scope. Emphasis on
programs and activities that address cultural
diversity, urban problems or increased
minority participation.

In the area of cultural, contributions are
made to a limited number of cultural
organizations, mostly in the company's
headquarters area and select organizations
that are national in scope.

LEGAL BASIS:
Corporate contributions program.

ELIGIBILITY:
Grants are made to tax-exempt 501(c)(3)
organizations which fill important community
needs.

GEOGRAPHIC RESTRICTIONS:
United States.

FINANCIAL DATA:
Amount of support per award: Varies.
Total amount of support: Over $2,000,000.

APPLICATION INFORMATION:
Applicant organizations must submit an
e-mail to
community.engagement@marriott.com
detailing their specific financial needs and
organizational background. Included in the
background information should be the current
budget, list of sources of past and current
funds and the most recent independent audit.
Written requests should be received six
weeks prior to any deadline.
Duration: Varies.
Deadline: Before end of October.

PUBLICATIONS:
Application guidelines.

ADDRESS INQUIRIES TO:
Niki Zoli, Manager, Social Responsibility
and Community Engagement
(See address above.)

*PLEASE NOTE:
Phone calls cannot be accepted from
organizations soliciting support, nor can
appointments be made.

MCCORMICK FOUNDATION [243]

205 North Michigan Avenue
Suite 4300
Chicago, IL 60601-5927
(312) 445-5000
Fax: (312) 445-5001

E-MAIL ADDRESS:
info@mccormickfoundation.org

WEB SITE ADDRESS:
www.mccormickfoundation.org

FOUNDED: 1955

AREAS OF INTEREST:
Community strengthening, civic education,
civic engagement, news literacy, youth
media, early childhood education, and
veterans affairs.

NAME(S) OF PROGRAMS:
- **Civic Program**
- **Communities Program**
- **Education Program**
- **Journalism Program**
- **Veterans Program**

TYPE:
General operating grants; Project/program
grants.

YEAR PROGRAM STARTED: 1955

PURPOSE:
To foster communities of educated, informed
and engaged citizens.

FINANCIAL DATA:
Total amount of support: $76,700,000 for the
year 2010.

PUBLICATIONS:
Annual report; program brochures;
conference reports.

J.M. MCDONALD FOUNDATION, INC. [244]

P.O. Box 3219
Evergreen, CO 80437-3219
(303) 674-9300
Fax: (303) 674-9216

E-MAIL ADDRESS:
info@jmmcdonaldfoundation.org

WEB SITE ADDRESS:
jmmcdonaldfoundation.org

FOUNDED: 1952

AREAS OF INTEREST:
Education, humanities, health, and a variety
of social and human services.

TYPE:
Capital grants; Development grants;
Project/program grants.

YEAR PROGRAM STARTED: 1952

LEGAL BASIS:
Private foundation.

ELIGIBILITY:
Nonprofit organizations with appropriate
interests are eligible for support. Applicants
must be located in the U.S. and have
IRS-509A and 501(c)(3) letter. No grants are
made to individuals.

GEOGRAPHIC RESTRICTIONS:
Primarily upstate New York.

FINANCIAL DATA:
Amount of support per award: Grants vary in
amount, depending upon the needs and
nature of the request.

APPLICATION INFORMATION:
Application for funding through online
granting process is available at the
Foundation web site.
Duration: One year.
Deadline: April 15 and September 15.

PUBLICATIONS:
Application guidelines.

OFFICERS AND TRUSTEES:
Donald R. McJunkin, President
Nancy J. Palmer, Vice President
Donald C. Berry, Jr., Treasurer
Janet E. Stanton, Secretary
Dana Amundson
Pamela Criswell
Scott Palmer

JAMES S. MCDONNELL
FOUNDATION   [245]
1034 South Brentwood Boulevard
Suite 1850
St. Louis, MO 63117
(314) 721-1532
Fax: (314) 721-7421

E-MAIL ADDRESS:
info@jsmf.org

WEB SITE ADDRESS:
www.jsmf.org

FOUNDED: 1950

AREAS OF INTEREST:
Brain cancer research, studying complex
systems and understanding human cognition.

NAME(S) OF PROGRAMS:
• **Collaborative Activity Awards**
• **Postdoctoral Fellowship Awards in
  Studying Complex Systems**
• **Scholar Awards**
• **21st Century Research Awards**

TYPE:
Research grants. The Foundation provides
funding for grants in four program areas. The
four program areas are:

Collaborative Activity Awards is to initiate
interdisciplinary discussions on problems or
issues, to help launch interdisciplinary

research networks, or to fund communities of
researches dedicated to developing new
methods, tools and application of basic
research.

Postdoctoral Fellowship Awards in intended
to provide students in the final stages of
completing a Ph.D. degree more leeway in
identifying and securing postdoctoral training
opportunities in complex systems research.

21st Century Research Awards is designed to
support research projects with a high
probability of generating new knowledge and
insights.

Scholar Awards is for funding provided in
the area of Understanding Human Cognition.

YEAR PROGRAM STARTED: 2000

PURPOSE:
To encourage investigators to engage difficult
problems; to support ideas and approaches
departing from conventional wisdom; to fund
novel or interdisciplinary proposals.

LEGAL BASIS:
Private foundation.

FINANCIAL DATA:
Amount of support per award: Collaborative
Activity Awards: Varies; Postdoctoral
Fellowship: $200,000; 21st Century Research
Awards: Up to $450,000; Scholar Awards:
Up to $600,000.

NUMBER OF APPLICANTS MOST RECENT YEAR:
200 for the year 2010.

NUMBER OF AWARDS: 38 grants approved for
the year 2010.

APPLICATION INFORMATION:
Guidelines and application for all programs is
available on the Foundation web site.
Deadline: Research Awards: March; Scholars
Awards: February; Postdoctoral: July. There
are no deadlines for Collaborative Activity
Awards.

Letters of inquiry are accepted year-round for
collaborative fund seekers.

IRS IDENTIFICATION NUMBER: 54-2074788

OFFICERS:
Dr. John T. Bruer, President
Dr. Susan Fitzpatrick, Vice President

BOARD OF DIRECTORS:
Jeanne M. Champer
Holly M. James
Alicia S. McDonnell
James S. McDonnell, III
Jeffrey M. McDonnell
John F. McDonnell
Marcella M. Stevens

MCGREGOR FUND   [246]
333 West Fort Street, Suite 2090
Detroit, MI 48226-3134
(313) 963-3495
Fax: (313) 963-3512

E-MAIL ADDRESS:
info@mcgregorfund.org

WEB SITE ADDRESS:
www.mcgregorfund.org

FOUNDED: 1925

AREAS OF INTEREST:
Human services, education, health, the arts
and public benefit in metropolitan Detroit.

TYPE:
General operating grants; Project/program
grants. Limited capital grants; program and

operational support. The Fund also supports
aid to private liberal arts colleges and
universities in Michigan.

YEAR PROGRAM STARTED: 1925

PURPOSE:
To relieve misfortunes and promote the
well-being of mankind.

LEGAL BASIS:
Tax-exempt private foundation.

ELIGIBILITY:
Tax-exempt, Internal Revenue Code 501(c)(3)
organizations in the Detroit metropolitan
area.

The Fund does not provide loan funds, make
direct grants to students for scholarships,
make grants for travel, conferences, seminars
or workshops or make grants to individuals.

GEOGRAPHIC RESTRICTIONS:
Metropolitan Detroit, Michigan and Ohio.

FINANCIAL DATA:
Amount of support per award: $25,000 to
$50,000.
Total amount of support: $7,000,000 for the
year ended June 30, 2010.

NUMBER OF APPLICANTS MOST RECENT YEAR:
Approximately 200.

NUMBER OF AWARDS: 150.

REPRESENTATIVE AWARDS:
$250,000 to Coalition on Temporary Shelter
to support homeless shelters; $200,000 to
Forgotten Harvest to support the campaign to
acquire and retrofit a new facility for food
rescue operations.

APPLICATION INFORMATION:
Guidelines available on the Fund web site.
Duration: No grants are made on a
continuing basis.
Deadline: Submit applications three months
prior to Board meeting dates in March, June,
September and December.

PUBLICATIONS:
Annual report; guidelines; application
procedures.

IRS IDENTIFICATION NUMBER: 38-0808800

OFFICERS:
James B. Nicholson, Chairman
Ruth R. Glancy, Vice Chairman

BOARD OF TRUSTEES:
C. David Campbell, President
Gerard Anderson
Cynthia N. Ford
Ruth R. Glancy
Ira J. Jaffe
Denise J. Lewis
James B. Nicholson
Susan Schooley, M.D.
William W. Shelden, Jr.

ADDRESS INQUIRIES TO:
C. David Campbell, President
(See address above.)

THE MCLEAN
CONTRIBUTIONSHIP   [247]
945 Haverford Road, Suite A
Bryn Mawr, PA 19010
(610) 527-6330 ext. 1
Fax: (610) 527-9733

WEB SITE ADDRESS:
foundationcenter.org/grantmaker/mclean

FOUNDED: 1951

AREAS OF INTEREST:
Education, environment, health and hospitals, care of the elderly and youth development.

TYPE:
Capital grants; Endowments. The Contributionship makes a relatively limited number of grants for projects of long-term benefit. Its trustees focus on capital projects: bricks and mortar, endowment, or provision of seed money; they may make grants in ways to encourage the successful funding of projects.

PURPOSE:
To support understanding and preserving the environment; to encourage compassionate and cost-effective healthcare; to improve the quality of life through education and through support of the communities' cultural assets usually in the form of capital projects.

LEGAL BASIS:
Private foundation.

ELIGIBILITY:
Organizations, including some religious, classified as 501(c)(3) by the IRS can apply. Individuals are ineligible.

The Contributionship favors projects that:
(1) stimulate a better understanding of the natural environment, and encourage the preservation of its important features;
(2) encourage more compassionate and cost-effective care for the ill and aging, in an atmosphere of dignity and self-respect and;
(3) promote education, or medical, scientific or (on occasion) cultural developments enhancing the quality of life.

In addition, the trustees from time to time support projects which:
(1) motivate promising young people to assess and develop their talents despite social and economic obstacles and;
(2) encourage those in newspaper and related fields to become more effective and responsible in helping people understand better how, events in their communities and around the world affect them.

GEOGRAPHIC RESTRICTIONS:
Mainly in the Greater Philadelphia area. Some grants to Lake, Osceola and Pasco counties, Florida; Nashua, New Hampshire; and DuBois, Pennsylvania.

FINANCIAL DATA:
Amount of support per award: $1,000 to $100,000.

Total amount of support: $2,114,120 for the year 2010.

NUMBER OF APPLICANTS MOST RECENT YEAR:
151 for the year 2010.

NUMBER OF AWARDS: 95 for the year 2010.

REPRESENTATIVE AWARDS:
$50,000 to Bryn Mawr Rehab Hospital, Malvern, PA, towards overhead lifts for the Patient Safe Handling Initiative; $20,000 to Fairmount Park Conservancy, Philadelphia, PA, towards revitalizing Hunting Park in eastern North Philadelphia; $75,000 to The Pennsylvania School for the Deaf, Philadelphia, PA, towards the Maguire Student-Community Learning Center.

APPLICATION INFORMATION:
The Contributionship accepts the common grant application form of the Delaware Valley Grantmakers Association. Application should include:
(1) a letter, which describes and justifies the project;
(2) a budget and timetable, strategy for

securing funding and latest financial statement;
(3) interim operating statements or budgets for future periods if appropriate;
(4) evidence of tax-exempt status and;
(5) a list of officers and directors.

Mail applications to Sandra L. McLean, Executive Director, at the address above.
Duration: One to three years.

PUBLICATIONS:
Application guidelines.

IRS IDENTIFICATION NUMBER: 23-6396940

TRUSTEES:
Will McLean, Chairman
Sandra L. McLean, Executive Director and Trustee
Jean G. Bodine
Carolyn M. Raymond
William L. McLean, III
John F. Bales, Advisory Trustee
Diana L. McLean, Advisory Trustee

ADDRESS INQUIRIES TO:
Sandra L. McLean
Executive Director and Trustee
(See address above.)

THE JOSEPH R. MCMICKING FOUNDATION [248]

500 Sansome Street
Suite 608
San Francisco, CA 94111
(415) 732-7890
Fax: (415) 732-7895

E-MAIL ADDRESS:
miriam@mcmickingfoundation.org

WEB SITE ADDRESS:
mcmickingfoundation.org

AREAS OF INTEREST:
Arts, computer science, education and science.

TYPE:
Project/program grants.

ELIGIBILITY:
The Foundation makes grants only to organizations that are exempt from federal tax under section 501(c)(3) of the Internal Revenue Code and are not classified as private foundations under section 509(a) of the Code.

The Foundation does not provide support for grants to individuals or loans.

GEOGRAPHIC RESTRICTIONS:
San Francisco Bay Area, California.

FINANCIAL DATA:
Amount of support per award: $1,000 to $20,000.

Total amount of support: $500,000 annually.

NUMBER OF AWARDS: 45.

APPLICATION INFORMATION:
Organizations seeking information should direct inquiries by mailing a letter and application to the Executive Director. The Foundation will not accept proposals sent by facsimile.
Duration: Applicants can reapply on a yearly basis, unless original proposal was for extended time.
Deadline: Proposals are accepted throughout the year.

ADDRESS INQUIRIES TO:
Miriam White, Executive Director
(See address above.)

MEADOWS FOUNDATION, INC. [249]

Wilson Historic District
3003 Swiss Avenue
Dallas, TX 75204-6049
(214) 826-9431
(800) 826-9431
Fax: (214) 827-7042

E-MAIL ADDRESS:
grants@mfi.org

WEB SITE ADDRESS:
www.mfi.org

FOUNDED: 1948

AREAS OF INTEREST:
Arts and culture, civic and public affairs (including the natural environment), education, health (including mental health), and human services.

NAME(S) OF PROGRAMS:
● **CCC Community Cooperation**
● **Charitable Schools Program**
● **Executive Suites Program**
● **Preservation Dallas**
● **Wilson Historic District Project**

TYPE:
Awards/prizes; Capital grants; Challenge/matching grants; Demonstration grants; Development grants; Endowments; General operating grants; Matching gifts; Project/program grants; Research grants; Seed money grants; Technical assistance; Training grants; Loan forgiveness programs. Program-related investments. Support for organizations, agencies, programs and projects within the areas of the Foundation's interest. Areas of high interest: environment, mental health and public education.

YEAR PROGRAM STARTED: 1948

PURPOSE:
To assist people and institutions of Texas improve the quality and circumstances of life for themselves and future generations.

LEGAL BASIS:
Tax-exempt, private foundation.

ELIGIBILITY:
Applicants must be tax-exempt organizations, benefitting Texas. No grants are awarded to individuals. Generally, no contributions for church or seminary construction, annual fund-raising drives, out of state travel, or professional conferences/symposia.

GEOGRAPHIC RESTRICTIONS:
Texas.

FINANCIAL DATA:
Amount of support per award: $25,000 to $500,000.

Total amount of support: $34,124,435 in grants paid and $44,115,047 in qualifying distributions for the year 2008.

Matching fund requirements: Stipulated with specific grants.

NUMBER OF APPLICANTS MOST RECENT YEAR:
791 for the year 2008.

NUMBER OF AWARDS: 230 for the year 2008.

REPRESENTATIVE AWARDS:
$390,000 to ACCION Texas toward creating a special loan fund for individuals with delinquent mortgage payments caused by current economic and credit conditions; $120,000 to Caddo Lake Institute toward determining the amount of river flow needed

to keep Caddo Lake healthy; $400,500 to Communities Foundation of Texas for the Texas High School Project toward creating an early college high school to increase the number of low-income students in Brownsville who will attend college; $250,000 to Kid Net Foundation dba Jonathan's Place toward constructing four facilities to serve abused, abandoned and neglected children in Dallas County; $201,000 to Patriot Paws Service Dogs toward a pilot program to prepare prison inmates to become trainers of service dogs to assist disabled veterans and other persons with mobile disabilities.

APPLICATION INFORMATION:
Application/proposal should include:
(1) a brief history of the organization, its current focus and recent accomplishments;
(2) a copy of the latest verification of tax-exempt status from the IRS;
(3) certified audits for the last three years, current operating budget and year-to-date financial statements;
(4) statement of need for the proposed project, to include population served, and how project will address need;
(5) a list of trustees or directors, corporate officers and key staff;
(6) the specific dollar amount requested and the date payment is needed;
(7) a list of all entities asked to give financial support and their responses;
(8) project line-item budget (include income and expenses);
(9) plans to evaluate the project (include measurable, time-specific goals) and;
(10) support for the project after the grant period.
Duration: No grants are awarded on a continuing basis. Multiyear grants are utilized on occasion.
Deadline: Proposals are accepted throughout the year.

PUBLICATIONS:
Annual report; guidelines.

IRS IDENTIFICATION NUMBER: 75-6015322

STAFF:
Cynthia A. Cass, Grants Administrator
Carol Stabler, Director of Communications
Adrianna Cuellar Rojas, Senior Program Officer
Michael K. McCoy, Senior Program Officer
Cindy Patrick, Senior Program Officer
Kathy Smith, Senior Program Officer
Brittani Trusty, Research Analyst

OFFICERS AND DIRECTORS:
Robert A. Meadows, Chairman, Board of Trustees, Director and Vice President
Linda P. Evans, President and Chief Executive Officer, Trustee and Director
Paula Herring, Vice President and Treasurer
Bruce H. Esterline, Vice President for Grants
Robert E. Weiss, Vice President for Administration
Gregory C. Dowell, Assistant Vice President and Chief Investment Officer
Chere St. Clair, Corporate Secretary
Olin Lancaster, III, Director
Peter Miller, Director
G. Tomas Rhodus, Jr., Director
Dudley L. Rouse, Jr., Director
Jean B. Silvertooth, Director
Daniel H. Chapman, Trustee and Director
John A. Hammack, Trustee and Director
Margaret Macdonald, Trustee and Director
P. Mike McCullough, Trustee and Director
Karen L. Meadows, Trustee and Director
Kimberly C. Morris, Trustee and Director

William Nesbitt, Trustee and Director
Elizabeth Meadows Rouse, Trustee and Director
Andrew C. Wilson, Trustee and Director

ADDRESS INQUIRIES TO:
Bruce H. Esterline
Vice President for Grants
(See address above.)

MEDICAL LIBRARY ASSOCIATION   [250]
65 East Wacker Place
Suite 1900
Chicago, IL 60601-7298
(312) 419-9094
Fax: (312) 419-8950

E-MAIL ADDRESS:
mlapd2@mlahq.org

WEB SITE ADDRESS:
www.mlanet.org

FOUNDED: 1898

AREAS OF INTEREST:
Health sciences librarianship.

NAME(S) OF PROGRAMS:
• **MLA Continuing Education Grants**

TYPE:
Grants-in-aid. The Continuing Education Grants are designed to aid in the study of the theoretical, administrative and technical aspects of library and information science.

PURPOSE:
To provide professional health science librarians with the opportunity to continue their education.

ELIGIBILITY:
Candidates must be U.S. or Canadian citizens, or permanent residents who are mid-level librarians with a graduate degree in library science and at least two years of work experience at the professional level.

FINANCIAL DATA:
Amount of support per award: $100 to $500.

NUMBER OF AWARDS: 1.

APPLICATION INFORMATION:
Applicants must complete and submit an application form which is available online. Candidates should also identify a continuing education program.
Duration: One year.
Deadline: December 1.

ADDRESS INQUIRIES TO:
Lisa Fried, Coordinator
Professional Development Department
(See address above.)

*SPECIAL STIPULATIONS:
The award is not to support work towards a degree or certificate.

MEDTRONIC FOUNDATION [251]
710 Medtronic Parkway, MSLC110
Minneapolis, MN 55432-5604
(763) 505-2639
(866) 632-1410
Fax: (763) 505-2648

WEB SITE ADDRESS:
www.medtronic.com/foundation

FOUNDED: 1979

AREAS OF INTEREST:
Health, education, arts, civic affairs, culture and human services.

NAME(S) OF PROGRAMS:
• **CommunityLink**
• **HeartRescue**
• **Medtronic Fellows**
• **Patient Link**
• **Strengthening Health Systems**

TYPE:
Challenge/matching grants; Fellowships; Matching gifts; Scholarships. Matching Gifts to Education involves employees.

YEAR PROGRAM STARTED: 1979

PURPOSE:
To benefit the socioeconomically disadvantaged of Medtronic communities in the areas of education, health, human services, and arts, civic affairs and culture.

LEGAL BASIS:
Corporate foundation.

ELIGIBILITY:
Grants are made to 501(c)(3) tax-exempt organizations, schools or government agencies for specific projects or programs. The Foundation does not support individuals, continuing medical education, religious groups for religious purposes, fund-raising and social events, general operating support, political or fraternal activities, reimbursable health treatment, or scientific research.

GEOGRAPHIC RESTRICTIONS:
Primarily Tempe/Greater Phoenix, Arizona; Goleta, Santa Ana, Santa Rosa and Sunnyvale California; Louisville and Metro Denver, Colorado; Jacksonville, Florida; Warsaw, Indiana; Beverly and Danvers, Massachusetts; Twin Cities and seven-county metropolitan area, Minnesota; Memphis, Tennessee; Fort Worth and San Antonio, Texas; Redmond, Washington; and Humacao and Villalba, Puerto Rico.

FINANCIAL DATA:
Amount of support per award: $500.00 to $2,239,222.
Total amount of support: $27,466,871 (unaudited).

NUMBER OF APPLICANTS MOST RECENT YEAR: 867.

NUMBER OF AWARDS: 544.

APPLICATION INFORMATION:
Applicants should review the General Foundation Guidelines to ensure eligibility. Each grant program has its own set of guidelines and deadlines. U.S organizations must apply via the online application process. In addition to the completion of the online application, the following documents are required:
(1) budget form;
(2) interim/final report on the organization's most recent Medtronic Foundation Grant (if funding has previously been received);
(3) list of officers and directors and their affiliations;
(4) IRS tax exemption letter;
(5) latest annual report (only required if available electronically) and;
(6) financial statement from most recently completed fiscal year (whether audited or not).

Organizations based outside the U.S. must first complete a Letter of Inquiry. Upon receiving the letter, a Foundation representative may recommend the organization submit a full application.
Duration: Varies.
Deadline: Grants are generally reviewed within 90 days.

IRS IDENTIFICATION NUMBER: 41-1306950

STAFF:
Heather Hudnut Page, Director, Foundation
and Community Affairs
Kris Fortman, Manager
Deb Anderson, Grants Administration
Mary Cade, Foundation Attorney
Wendy Bennett, Foundation Consultant
Paige Bingham, Foundation Consultant
Joan Mellor, Foundation Consultant
Luc Giraud

ADDRESS INQUIRIES TO:
Deb Anderson
Grants Administration
(See address above.)

THE ANDREW W. MELLON FOUNDATION [252]
140 East 62nd Street
New York, NY 10065
(212) 838-8400
Fax: (212) 500-2302

E-MAIL ADDRESS:
bj@mellon.org

WEB SITE ADDRESS:
www.mellon.org

FOUNDED: 1969

AREAS OF INTEREST:
Higher education and scholarship, scholarly
communications, museums and art
conservation, performing arts, conservation
and the environment.

TYPE:
Challenge/matching grants; Endowments;
General operating grants; Project/program
grants; Research grants. Grants on a selective
basis to institutions in the Foundation's areas
of interest.

PURPOSE:
To build, strengthen and sustain institutions
and their core capacities, rather than be a
source for narrowly defined projects.

LEGAL BASIS:
Not-for-profit corporation.

ELIGIBILITY:
Organizations and institutions with
appropriate interests are eligible. The
Foundation does not award fellowships or
grants to individuals or make grants to
primarily local organizations.

FINANCIAL DATA:
Amount of support per award: Varies.

APPLICATION INFORMATION:
Applications are considered throughout the
year and no special forms are required.
Ordinarily a simple letter setting forth the
need, the nature and the amount of the
request and the justification for it, together
with evidence of suitable classification by the
IRS and any supplementary exhibits an
applicant may wish to submit, will suffice to
assure consideration. Unsolicited applications
are rarely funded.
Duration: Varies.

PUBLICATIONS:
Annual report.

OFFICERS:
Don Michael Randel, President
Philip E. Lewis, Vice President
Mariet Westermann, Vice President
Michele S. Warman, General Counsel and
Secretary
John E. Hull, Financial Vice President

TRUSTEES:
Anne M. Tatlock, Chairman
Danielle S. Allen
Lewis Bernard
Paul LeClerc
Sir Colin Lucas
Walter E. Massey
Don Michael Randel
W. Taylor Reveley, III
Lawrence R. Ricciardi

ADDRESS INQUIRIES TO:
Michele S. Warman
General Counsel and Secretary
(See address above.)

*PLEASE NOTE:
The Foundation rarely funds unsolicited
proposals.

MERCK FAMILY FUND [253]
95 Eliot Street, Suite 2
Milton, MA 02186
(617) 696-3580
Fax: (617) 696-7262

E-MAIL ADDRESS:
merck@merckff.org

WEB SITE ADDRESS:
www.merckff.org

FOUNDED: 1954

AREAS OF INTEREST:
Protecting the natural environment, meeting
human needs and addressing the root causes
of problems faced by social and
economically disadvantaged people.

TYPE:
General operating grants; Project/program
grants; Seed money grants. Eastern
Ecosystems programs support increasing the
sustainable use of forests, rivers and
wetlands; participation of people living in the
area; and addressing conflicts between
environmental preservation and economic
development.

The Sustainable Economics projects work to
challenge taxpayer subsidies to industries
harming the environment, create state and
federal "green" tax programs, redefine
indicators of national economic progress and
quality of natural resources, and encourage
households or the business community to
move towards sustainability.

The Green and Open Space program supports
greening projects to empower local residents,
build grassroots organizations, result in a
healthier environment plus provide additional
benefits: healthy food for gardeners, job
training programs, improved links between
rural and urban, or coordination with schools.

Youth Organizing Projects enable
disadvantaged youth to take positive action
for their communities, are designed and
implemented by young people and have the
potential to make lasting change after
completion of the project.

YEAR PROGRAM STARTED: 1993

PURPOSE:
To protect and restore vital eastern
ecosystems and promote economic practices
for a sustainable environment.

LEGAL BASIS:
Tax-exempt corporation.

ELIGIBILITY:
Eastern Ecosystems restricted to Southern
Appalachians, Northern Forest, and the
coastal wetlands of South Carolina.

GEOGRAPHIC RESTRICTIONS:
United States.

FINANCIAL DATA:
Amount of support per award: $10,000 to
$50,000.

APPLICATION INFORMATION:
New requests for support should be made by
letter of inquiry rather than with a full
proposal or a request for a personal meeting.
The letter should not exceed three pages and
should describe the project, its purpose and
its likely impact. The letter should also
briefly describe the organization and its goals
and specify the amount of funds requested.
Applicants will be contacted if a full
proposal is warranted. Unsolicited proposals
will not be acknowledged.
Duration: Grants may be from one to three
years. Progress reports must be received
before continuation or renewal support will
be considered.

PUBLICATIONS:
Annual report; grants list; guidelines.

IRS IDENTIFICATION NUMBER: 22-6063382

STAFF:
Jenny D. Russell, Executive Director
James Maguire, Director of Grants
Management and Investment Accounting
Brinda Maira, Program Officer

OFFICERS AND TRUSTEES:
Nathaniel Chamberlin, President
Eliza Hatch, Vice President
Wilhelm Merck, Treasurer
Max Abeles
Katie Chamberlin
Patience M. Chamberlin
Oona Coy
Elliott Merck

ADDRESS INQUIRIES TO:
Jenny D. Russell, Executive Director
(See address above.)

METLIFE FOUNDATION [254]
1095 Avenue of the Americas, 40th Floor
New York, NY 10036
(212) 578-6272
Fax: (212) 578-0617

E-MAIL ADDRESS:
metlifefoundation@metlife.com

WEB SITE ADDRESS:
www.metlife.org

FOUNDED: 1976

AREAS OF INTEREST:
Health, United Way, education, civic affairs,
culture and program-related investments.

CONSULTING OR VOLUNTEER SERVICES:
Employee volunteer programs.

TYPE:
General operating grants; Matching gifts;
Project/program grants; Research grants;
Scholarships. Program-related investments.
Grants are made in the areas of health,
education, civic affairs, culture and United
Way.

To encourage healthy lifestyles, grants are
directed toward health promotion and
organizations, particularly for young people
and other groups at risk due to poor
economic or social conditions, as well as
toward research on Alzheimer's disease.

To strengthen the quality of education, grants
are made to national programs and
organizations that recruit and train teachers,

increase opportunities for minorities, improve basic skills, and work to prevent youth violence. Business, insurance and higher education are also supported.

To increase access to the arts, grants are made to support traveling exhibitions and the touring initiatives of performing arts groups. Arts education and cultural programs that further the understanding of our country's diversity are also emphasized.

To strengthen the social and economic fabric of our nation's communities, grants are made to promote affordable housing and economic development, improve social services, strengthen the family unit, and increase opportunities for young people and the socially and economically disadvantaged. Volunteer activity, particularly among young people, is also encouraged.

MetLife and the Foundation make below-market rate investments with groups and projects working to improve communities across the country. Either directly or through relending with nonprofit intermediaries, social investments reach every major city in the nation and over 30 states. Loans support affordable housing developments with social services, organizations serving the homeless and mentally ill, health care services and community-based economic development.

YEAR PROGRAM STARTED: 1976

PURPOSE:
To support nonprofit organizations and to help them meet the complex challenges facing our communities; to make these challenges more manageable and enhance the quality of life for all of us.

LEGAL BASIS:
The Foundation is a tax-exempt organization under Section 501(c)(3) and is classified as a private foundation as defined by Section 509(a) of the Internal Revenue Code.

ELIGIBILITY:
Applicants must be 501(c)(3) tax-exempt organizations in the Foundation's areas of interest.

No grants are made to private foundations or religious, fraternal, political, athletic, social or veterans organizations, organizations receiving support from United Way, hospital capital fund campaigns, local chapters of national organizations, disease-specific organizations, labor groups, organizations whose activities are mainly international, organizations primarily engaged in patient care or direct treatment, drug treatment centers and community health clinics, elementary and secondary schools, courtesy advertising or festival participation or individuals. Generally, no support is given for endowment funds.

FINANCIAL DATA:
Amount of support per award: $1,000 to $100,000.
Total amount of support: $39,465,498 for the year 2009.
Matching fund requirements: Employee contributions to colleges and universities.

NUMBER OF AWARDS: Varies.

REPRESENTATIVE AWARDS:
$50,000 to Brooklyn Academy of Music; $5,000 to Children's Defense Fund; $100,000 to National Council of La Raza; $50,000 to Recruiting New Teachers; $500,000 to Trust for Public Land.

APPLICATION INFORMATION:
The Foundation only accepts online grant proposals. Details available on the web site.
Duration: Generally one year. Two or three years occasionally.
Deadline: Requests and applications are reviewed throughout the year.

PUBLICATIONS:
Annual report of contributions; guidelines (available online).

BOARD OF DIRECTORS:
Gwenn Carr, Chairman of the Board
A. Dennis White, President and Chief Executive Officer
Jonathan Rosenthal, Treasurer
Maria Morris
William Mullaney
William J. Toppeta
Michael Vietri

ADDRESS INQUIRIES TO:
A. Dennis White
President and Chief Executive Officer
(See address above.)

*SPECIAL STIPULATIONS:
Requests for proposals are used on occasion.

MEYER MEMORIAL TRUST   [255]
425 N.W. 10th Avenue, Suite 400
Portland, OR 97209
(503) 228-5512

E-MAIL ADDRESS:
mmt@mmt.org

WEB SITE ADDRESS:
www.mmt.org

FOUNDED: 1978

AREAS OF INTEREST:
Arts and humanities, education, health and human services, conservation and environment, public affairs/social benefit.

NAME(S) OF PROGRAMS:
- **Capacity Building Grants**
- **Grassroots Grants**
- **Responsive Grants**

TYPE:
Capital grants; Challenge/matching grants; Demonstration grants; Development grants; General operating grants; Matching gifts; Project/program grants; Seed money grants; Technical assistance. Capacity Building Grants help nonprofit organizations increase contributed or earned income, realize new efficiencies, or otherwise build capacity to advance their missions.

Under the Grassroots Grants program, the Trust funds a wide variety of small projects in Oregon.

Responsive Grants are awarded in the areas of social services, health, affordable housing, community development, conservation and environment, public affairs and social benefit, arts and culture, and education. They are given for a wide variety of projects, expansions, capacity building, capital projects, and start-ups. The Trust also makes grants for special purposes.

YEAR PROGRAM STARTED: 1982

PURPOSE:
To invest in people, ideas and efforts that deliver significant social benefit to Oregon and southwest Washington.

LEGAL BASIS:
Private, independent foundation.

ELIGIBILITY:
Applicants must:
(1) be an IRS-sanctioned tax-exempt organization;
(2) be requesting support for a program that operates in Oregon and/or Clark County, WA (considered part of the Portland metropolitan area);
(3) provide equal opportunity in leadership, staffing and service regardless of age, gender, race, ethnicity, sexual orientation, disability, national origin, political affiliation or religious belief and;
(4) be current on all reports owed to the Trust on previous grants.

Generally, the Trust does not fund:
(1) direct grants, scholarships, or loans to individuals;
(2) endowments;
(3) general fund drives, annual appeals, special events or sponsorships;
(4) elimination of operating deficits;
(5) projects of sectarian or religious organizations that principally benefit their own members or adherents;
(6) direct replacement funding for activities previously supported by federal, state or local public sources;
(7) acquisition of land for conservation purposes (except through Program Related Investments);
(8) hospital capital construction projects (except through Program Related Investments);
(9) animal welfare organizations (both domestic and wild animals);
(10) projects that primarily benefit students of a single K-12 school, unless the school is an independent alternative school primarily serving low-income and/or special needs populations and;
(11) projects for purposes of influencing legislation, and the grantee cannot expend any part of the grant in a way that violates its tax-exempt status.

GEOGRAPHIC RESTRICTIONS:
Oregon and Clark County, Washington.

FINANCIAL DATA:
Amount of support per award: Varies.
Total amount of support: Approximately $21,881,000 for the fiscal year 2009.

NUMBER OF APPLICANTS MOST RECENT YEAR: 669.

NUMBER OF AWARDS: 350.

APPLICATION INFORMATION:
Organizations must register on the Trust's online system to complete and submit the application.
Duration: One or multiple years. Usually nonrenewable.
Deadline: There are no deadlines for Responsive Grants. The Trust accepts proposals throughout the year. Grassroots Grants: February 15, March 15, July 15 and November 15.

TRUSTEES:
Debbie F. Craig
John Emrick
Orcillia Z. Forbes
Gerry Pratt
George Puentes

STAFF:
Doug Stamm, Chief Executive Officer
Wayne Pierson, Chief Financial Officer and Treasurer

Marie Deatherage, Director, Communications and Learning
Barbara Gibbs, Director, Policy and Strategy
Paul Reich, Director, Program-Related Investing
Candy Solovjovs, Program Officer
Kim Thomas, Program Officer
Sally Yee, Program Officer
Terry DeBruyne, Comptroller

ADDRESS INQUIRIES TO:
Doug Stamm, Executive Director
(See address above.)

ROBERT R. MEYER FOUNDATION   [256]

1901 6th Avenue North, Suite 300
Birmingham, AL 35203
(205) 326-5382
Fax: (205) 264-7052

E-MAIL ADDRESS:
carla.gale@regions.com

FOUNDED: 1942

AREAS OF INTEREST:
Arts, education, humanities, civic affairs, health and human services, and charitable work.

TYPE:
Assistantships; Challenge/matching grants; Conferences/seminars; Development grants; General operating grants; Matching gifts; Project/program grants; Research grants; Technical assistance; Training grants; Work-study programs.

YEAR PROGRAM STARTED: 1942

PURPOSE:
To help in community affairs.

LEGAL BASIS:
Private foundation.

ELIGIBILITY:
Grants restricted to charitable organizations in the Birmingham, AL area only. No grants to individuals or corporations.

GEOGRAPHIC RESTRICTIONS:
Birmingham, Alabama area.

FINANCIAL DATA:
Amount of support per award: $2,500 to $200,000; Average: $30,000.
Total amount of support: Approximately $1,900,000 for the year 2010.

NUMBER OF APPLICANTS MOST RECENT YEAR:
Approximately 120 for the year 2010.

NUMBER OF AWARDS: Approximately 60.

APPLICATION INFORMATION:
Call for grant guidelines and application.
Duration: One year.
Deadline: March 1 and September 1.

PUBLICATIONS:
Application form.

ADVISORY COMMITTEE:
Beverly Baker
Sharon L. Blackburn
Raymond Harbert
Elmer B. Harris

TRUSTEE:
Regions Bank

ADDRESS INQUIRIES TO:
Carla B. Gale, Vice President
(See address above.)

THE MIAMI FOUNDATION   [257]

200 South Biscayne Boulevard, Suite 505
Miami, FL 33131-2343
(305) 371-2711
Fax: (305) 371-5342

E-MAIL ADDRESS:
gewing-chow@miamifoundation.org

WEB SITE ADDRESS:
www.miamifoundation.org

FOUNDED: 1967

AREAS OF INTEREST:
Education, health and human services, arts and culture, the environment, economic development and community.

NAME(S) OF PROGRAMS:
- **Community Grants Program**
- **GLBT Community Projects Fund**
- **Miracle Loan Program**
- **Safe Passage: Youth Transitioning from Foster Care**

TYPE:
Project/program grants. Special initiative grants.

YEAR PROGRAM STARTED: 1967

PURPOSE:
To enhance the quality of life for all the residents of Greater Miami.

LEGAL BASIS:
Community foundation.

ELIGIBILITY:
Applicants must be 501(c)(3) organizations as well as some grassroots organizations.

No grants to individuals. No grants for memberships, fund-raising events or memorials.

GEOGRAPHIC RESTRICTIONS:
Miami-Dade County, Florida.

FINANCIAL DATA:
Amount of support per award: Community Grants Programs: Average $10,000; Special Initiative Grants: $10,000 to $60,000, depending on grants program.

NUMBER OF APPLICANTS MOST RECENT YEAR:
600.

NUMBER OF AWARDS: 130.

APPLICATION INFORMATION:
Application includes cover letter with the purpose of the grant and the amount requested as well as a narrative about the applicant organization and budget. Attachments should include IRS determination letter, board list, and current fiscal year operating budget. Slight variations per grant program may apply.
Duration: Typically one year. Possible renewal.

PUBLICATIONS:
Annual report; quarterly newsletter; grant guidelines; professional advisors guides.

STAFF:
Javier Alberto Soto, President
Charisse Grant, Vice President for Programs
Betty Alonso, Director of Programs
Gianne Ewing-Chow, J.D., Senior Program Officer
Pamela Cirimele, Program Assistant

ADDRESS INQUIRIES TO:
Gianne Ewing-Chow, Senior Program Officer
(See address above.)

MICROSOFT CORPORATION   [258]

One Microsoft Way
Redmond, WA 98052-6399
(425) 882-8080
(425) 706-8185
Fax: (425) 706-7329

E-MAIL ADDRESS:
upinfo@microsoft.com

WEB SITE ADDRESS:
www.microsoft.com/giving

FOUNDED: 1983

AREAS OF INTEREST:
U.S. Program Areas: Expanding opportunities through technology access, strengthening nonprofits through technology, developing a diverse technology workforce and building community through corporate funding and through matching our employees' individual giving.

International Program Areas: Improving the quality of life for people in countries and communities where Corporation employees live and do business.

NAME(S) OF PROGRAMS:
- **Disaster Response and Humanitarian Relief**
- **Employee Giving and Volunteer Programs**
- **Microsoft Grants and Programs in Puget Sound**
- **Microsoft Unlimited Potential-Community Technology Skills Program**
- **Nongovernmental Organization Capacity Building**
- **Software Donations**

TYPE:
Grants-in-aid; Matching gifts; Product donations; Scholarships; Technical assistance.

YEAR PROGRAM STARTED: 1983

PURPOSE:
To bring the benefits of information technology to underserved people and communities who do not have access to this technology; to support organizations in the communities in which Microsoft employees live and work; to support Microsoft employees taking an active role in their community through volunteer and matching gift programs.

LEGAL BASIS:
Corporate giving program.

ELIGIBILITY:
Grants are restricted to nonprofit organizations with tax-exempt 501(c)(3) status.

Microsoft does not make charitable grants to individuals; private foundations; political, labor, religious or fraternal organizations; amateur or professional sports groups, teams or events; conferences or symposia; hospitals or medical clinics; sponsorship of events, tables, exhibitions or performances; fund-raising events such as luncheons, dinners, walks, runs or sports tournaments; programs serving people and communities outside the U.S. (exceptions may be made for pilot programs initiated by a Microsoft subsidiary in another country).

FINANCIAL DATA:
Contributes cash and software.
Matching fund requirements: Employee donations to eligible organizations are matched up to $12,000 per employee per year.

APPLICATION INFORMATION:
All proposals should include:
(1) a copy of the organization's tax-exempt notification letter from the IRS;
(2) a description of the organization (including its mission, accomplishments, governance, area and population served);
(3) the operating budget for the current fiscal year including funding sources and;
(4) lists of current board members and key organizational staff.

Additional information may be requested by Microsoft. Proposal materials, including photographs, videos and special binders cannot be returned.

Proposals over e-mail or fax lines or by phone will not be accepted.

Funding proposals are accepted through Microsoft subsidiary offices throughout the world. Locations can be found online.

Deadline: Proposals are reviewed February 15, May 15, and October 30. Award announcement approximately six weeks following deadline.

PUBLICATIONS:
Program brochure; annual report of giving.

ADDRESS INQUIRIES TO:
Community Affairs
(See address above.)

MID-NEBRASKA COMMUNITY FOUNDATION, INC.   [259]
120 North Dewey
North Platte, NE 69101
(308) 534-3315
Fax: (308) 534-6117

E-MAIL ADDRESS:
mncf@hamilton.net

WEB SITE ADDRESS:
www.midnebraskafoundation.org

FOUNDED: 1978

AREAS OF INTEREST:
Arts, education, civic development, environment, health and welfare.

TYPE:
Capital grants; Demonstration grants; Development grants; Endowments; Project/program grants; Scholarships.

PURPOSE:
To serve charitable people and nonprofit causes in North Platte and the surrounding area.

GEOGRAPHIC RESTRICTIONS:
Custer, Dawson, Frontier, Hayes, Keith, Lincoln, Logan, McPherson, and Perkins counties, Nebraska.

APPLICATION INFORMATION:
Application form required. Initial approach by letter or telephone.
Deadline: April 15, July 15, October 15 and January 15.

IRS IDENTIFICATION NUMBER: 47-0604965

ADDRESS INQUIRIES TO:
Eric Seacrest, Executive Director
(See address above.)

ADAH K. MILLARD CHARITABLE TRUST   [260]
Northern Trust Company
One Oakbrook Terrace
Oakbrook Terrace, IL 60181
(630) 932-6929
Fax: (630) 932-6950

E-MAIL ADDRESS:
trm@ntrs.com

FOUNDED: 1976

AREAS OF INTEREST:
Youth agencies, arts, cultural programs and hospitals.

TYPE:
Capital grants; Project/program grants. Project grants in areas of the Foundation's interest.

YEAR PROGRAM STARTED: 1976

PURPOSE:
To make grants to charitable agencies in Omaha and Douglas County, NE.

LEGAL BASIS:
Tax-exempt.

ELIGIBILITY:
Tax-exempt organizations in Omaha and Douglas County, NE. No grants are awarded to individuals.

GEOGRAPHIC RESTRICTIONS:
Douglas County and Omaha, Nebraska.

FINANCIAL DATA:
Amount of support per award: Average $15,000.
Total amount of support: $50,000.
Matching fund requirements: Stipulated with specific programs.

NUMBER OF AWARDS: 35.

REPRESENTATIVE AWARDS:
Salvation Army; United Way; Nebraska Food Bank.

APPLICATION INFORMATION:
A request should be made for guidelines to submit grant applications. Six copies of the application are required.
Duration: No grants are awarded on a continuing basis.
Deadline: March 20 and October 1. Announcements in May and November.

PUBLICATIONS:
Application guidelines.

ADDRESS INQUIRIES TO:
Thomas R. Mitchell, Senior Vice President
(See address above.)

MILLIPORE CORPORATE GIVING PROGRAM   [261]
290 Concord Road
Billerica, MA 01821-7037
(978) 715-1268
Fax: (978) 715-1385

E-MAIL ADDRESS:
tara_duplaga@millipore.com

WEB SITE ADDRESS:
www.millipore.com/corporategiving

FOUNDED: 1985

AREAS OF INTEREST:
Science, education (K-12), and sustainability.

TYPE:
Capital grants; Challenge/matching grants; Matching gifts; Project/program grants; Research grants; Scholarships.

YEAR PROGRAM STARTED: 1985

PURPOSE:
To serve the public interest in ways that are meaningful to the company and its employees.

ELIGIBILITY:
Organizations, excluding religious, classified as 501(c)(3) by the IRS can apply. Individuals are ineligible.

GEOGRAPHIC RESTRICTIONS:
United States.

FINANCIAL DATA:
Since inception, over $20,000,000 has been distributed to deserving nonprofit programs on a local and national level.
Amount of support per award: $5,000 average grant.
Matching fund requirements: $25 minimum gift.

APPLICATION INFORMATION:
Eligible programs may submit a copy of the 501(c)(3) certificate, tax identification number, and a letter of inquiry no more than two pages in length briefly describing the organization, the program for which funding is sought, and the amount of funding requested. Those organizations whose programs are of interest to Millipore will be invited to submit full proposals.

Millipore also accepts the Associated Grant Makers Common Proposal Form.
Duration: One year. Grants are renewable.
Deadline: Proposals are considered every 10 to 12 weeks at Review Committee meetings.

ADDRESS INQUIRIES TO:
Tara Duplaga
Corporate Giving Representative
(See address above.)

THE MOODY FOUNDATION [262]
2302 Post Office Street, Suite 704
Galveston, TX 77550
(409) 797-1500
Fax: (409) 763-5564

E-MAIL ADDRESS:
pmmoore@moodyf.org

WEB SITE ADDRESS:
www.moodyf.org

FOUNDED: 1942

AREAS OF INTEREST:
Arts, education, medical research, community and economic development, environment and youth programs.

TYPE:
Capital grants; Challenge/matching grants; Research grants; Scholarships. Capital campaigns; Equipment; Matching funds; Building/renovation; Program development and research.

YEAR PROGRAM STARTED: 1942

PURPOSE:
To assist in supporting activities that are directed toward improving the general well-being of the citizens of the state of Texas, especially Galveston.

LEGAL BASIS:
Private family foundation.

ELIGIBILITY:
Tax-exempt organizations in the state of Texas only are eligible to apply. The Foundation generally does not make grant awards for deficit financing, operational expenses of established organizations, or grants for any activities considered a taxable expenditure under the 1969 Tax Reform Act. No grants to individuals (except for one scholarship program). No loans.

GEOGRAPHIC RESTRICTIONS:
Texas.

FINANCIAL DATA:
Amount of support per award: Average $10,000.
Total amount of support: Varies.
Matching fund requirements: Organizations must generally "raise balance" for project.

NUMBER OF AWARDS: 20 to 30.

REPRESENTATIVE AWARDS:
$30,000 to American Cancer Society Inc./Cattle Baron's Ball, Dallas, TX; $15,000 to Community Schools in Dallas; $5,000 to Garland Family Outreach, Inc., Garland, TX.

APPLICATION INFORMATION:
Prospective candidates should write or call the Foundation to ascertain if appropriate to request guidelines for making application.
Duration: Generally, grants are awarded for one year at a time.

PUBLICATIONS:
Annual report; application guidelines.

IRS IDENTIFICATION NUMBER: 74-1403105

STAFF:
Frances Anne Moody-Dahlberg, Executive Director
E. Douglas McLeod, Director of Development
Garrik Addison, Chief Financial Officer
Allan Mathews, Scholarship Administrator
Gerald Smith, Program Officer
Peter M. Moore, Grants Director
Bernice C. Torregrossa, Grants Analyst

BOARD OF TRUSTEES:
Robert L. Moody, Sr., Chairman
Ross R. Moody, Treasurer
Frances Anne Moody-Dahlberg

FOUNDERS:
Libbie Shearn Moody
W.L. Moody, Jr.

ADDRESS INQUIRIES TO:
Peter M. Moore, Grants Director
(See address above.)

THE MOTOROLA MOBILITY FOUNDATION [263]
600 N U.S. Highway 45
Libertyville, IL 60048
(847) 523-3597

E-MAIL ADDRESS:
giving@motorola.com

WEB SITE ADDRESS:
www.motorola.com/giving

FOUNDED: 1953

AREAS OF INTEREST:
Concentration in the fields of science; technology, engineering and math education.

TYPE:
Matching gifts; Project/program grants.

PURPOSE:
To support systemic change or impact of science, math, computer and engineering programs; to increase the number of underrepresented populations who pursue engineering and science as a career.

LEGAL BASIS:
Corporate foundation.

FINANCIAL DATA:
Amount of support per award: Varies.
Matching fund requirements: $50 minimum, $10,000 maximum.

NUMBER OF APPLICANTS MOST RECENT YEAR:
1,000.

NUMBER OF AWARDS: 200.

APPLICATION INFORMATION:
Contact the Foundation.
Duration: Grants are made on a calendar year basis. No automatic renewals.

IRS IDENTIFICATION NUMBER: 36-6109323

ADDRESS INQUIRIES TO:
Eileen Sweeney, Director
(See e-mail address above.)

THE CLARENCE E. MULFORD TRUST [264]
P.O. Box 290
Fryeburg, ME 04037
(207) 935-2061
Fax: (207) 935-3939

AREAS OF INTEREST:
Animals, education, literature, religion, science and youth.

TYPE:
Project/program grants.

PURPOSE:
To support charitable organizations that are working to improve the quality of life for Maine residents.

LEGAL BASIS:
Trust fund.

ELIGIBILITY:
Grants are made to organizations that have tax-exempt status under Section 501(c)(3) of the Internal Revenue Code. No grants are made to individuals. Religious organizations may apply.

GEOGRAPHIC RESTRICTIONS:
Fryeburg, Maine and adjoining towns.

FINANCIAL DATA:
Amount of support per award: $500 to $10,000.
Total amount of support: $540,000 for the year 2010.

APPLICATION INFORMATION:
Organizations should submit IRS tax exemption letter under 501(c)(3) of the Internal Revenue Code.
Duration: One year. Renewal by reapplication.

TRUSTEES:
David R. Hastings, III
Peter Hastings

ADDRESS INQUIRIES TO:
Peter Hastings, Trustee
(See address above.)

M.J. MURDOCK CHARITABLE TRUST [265]
703 Broadway, Suite 710
Vancouver, WA 98660
(360) 694-8415
Fax: (360) 694-1819

E-MAIL ADDRESS:
stevem@murdock-trust.org

WEB SITE ADDRESS:
www.murdock-trust.org

FOUNDED: 1975

AREAS OF INTEREST:
Education, science, health and human services, arts and culture.

TYPE:
Capital grants; Challenge/matching grants; Development grants; Project/program grants; Research grants. In addition to a special interest in education and scientific research, the Trust partners with a wide variety of organizations that serve the arts, public affairs, health and medicine, human services, leadership development and persons with disabilities.

PURPOSE:
To enrich the quality of life in the Pacific Northwest by providing grants and enrichment programs to organizations seeking to strengthen the region's educational, spiritual and cultural base in creative and sustainable ways.

LEGAL BASIS:
Private foundation.

ELIGIBILITY:
Applications for grants are considered only from organizations which have been ruled to be tax-exempt under Section 501(c)(3) of the Internal Revenue Code and are not private foundations. Primary attention is given to applications for the support of projects and programs conducted by qualified institutions within five states of the Pacific Northwest, including Alaska, Idaho, Montana, Oregon and Washington. Priority is given to organizations and projects which are not primarily or normally financed by public tax funds.

Applications are not considered for loans, endowment, debt retirement, operational deficits, contributions to general fund drives or annual charitable appeals, continuation of programs previously financed from external sources or emergency funding.

GEOGRAPHIC RESTRICTIONS:
Pacific Northwest.

FINANCIAL DATA:
Assets of approximately $700,000,000 as of December 31, 2010.
Amount of support per award: Average $180,000.
Total amount of support: $30,000,000 for the year 2010.

NUMBER OF APPLICANTS MOST RECENT YEAR:
303.

NUMBER OF AWARDS: 196 for the year 2010.

APPLICATION INFORMATION:
Submit a letter of inquiry and request for guidelines to loi@murdock-trust.org or:
P.O. Box 1618
Vancouver, WA 98668-1618.

PUBLICATIONS:
Annual report; *Grants Proposal Guidelines*; proposal form.

TRUSTEES:
John W. Castles
Lynwood W. Swanson
Neal O. Thorpe

OFFICERS AND STAFF:
Steven G.W. Moore, Executive Director
Terry Stokesbary, Senior Program Director for Enrichment Programs
Dana L. Miller, Senior Program Director for Grant Programs
John Van Zytveld, Senior Fellow
Dave Coleman, Program Director
Christopher Gillem, Program Director
Barton A. Hadder, Program Director
Jan Kennedy, Program Director
Jill Tatum, Program Director

ADDRESS INQUIRIES TO:
Dana L. Miller, Senior Program Director
for Grant Programs
(See address above.)

NATIONWIDE FOUNDATION [266]

One Nationwide Plaza
Mail Drop 1.20.301
Columbus, OH 43215-2220
(614) 249-4310
Fax: (866) 212-7960

E-MAIL ADDRESS:
blicklk@nationwide.com

WEB SITE ADDRESS:
www.nationwide.com/foundation

FOUNDED: 1959

AREAS OF INTEREST:
Health and welfare, education, culture and
the arts and civic and community affairs.

TYPE:
Capital grants; Challenge/matching grants;
General operating grants; Matching gifts;
Project/program grants.

YEAR PROGRAM STARTED: 1959

PURPOSE:
To provide financial support for qualified
tax-exempt organizations whose programs
address basic human needs.

LEGAL BASIS:
Corporate foundation.

ELIGIBILITY:
Qualified, tax-exempt organizations in
Columbus, OH and locations with a large
number of Nationwide associates are eligible.

FINANCIAL DATA:
Amount of support per award: $5,000 to
$7,000 average.
Total amount of support: $28,268,931 for the
year 2009 (Foundation only).
Matching fund requirements: Matching gifts
to educational institutions.

NUMBER OF AWARDS: 268 for the year 2008.

APPLICATION INFORMATION:
Guidelines and application form is available
at the Foundation web site.
Duration: One year. Renewal possible.
Deadline: September 1. Announcement in
mid-March.

PUBLICATIONS:
Contributions guidelines.

ADDRESS INQUIRIES TO:
Karen H. Blickley, Director
(See address above.)

*SPECIAL STIPULATIONS:
Preference is given to organizations in
Columbus, OH or those recommended by a
state office.

NEW ENGLAND BIOLABS FOUNDATION [267]

240 County Road
Ipswich, MA 01938
(978) 998-7990
Fax: (978) 356-3250

E-MAIL ADDRESS:
fosters@nebf.org

WEB SITE ADDRESS:
www.nebf.org

FOUNDED: 1982

AREAS OF INTEREST:
Environmental issues.

TYPE:
Grants-in-aid; Project/program grants; Seed
money grants. The Foundation prefers to help
organizations start their projects with the
understanding that once they are established,
funding from other sources will be sought.

YEAR PROGRAM STARTED: 1982

PURPOSE:
To support grassroots organizations working
with the environment.

ELIGIBILITY:
The Foundation prefers to fund grassroots
organizations and/or projects (i.e., those
conceived, developed and managed by the
community). Grassroots organizations,
emerging support groups, charitable
organizations and individuals (primarily for
small environmental research projects, or
those representing a nonprofit organization)
may apply. Grants are not made to religious
organizations.

FINANCIAL DATA:
Amount of support per award: Average
$7,000 per year, maximum of $10,000.
Total amount of support: $300,000 annually.

NUMBER OF APPLICANTS MOST RECENT YEAR:
100.

NUMBER OF AWARDS: 30.

APPLICATION INFORMATION:
Make a preliminary inquiry to the Foundation
with a one-page letter, a phone call or e-mail,
briefly describing the project. Those accepted
will be asked for a proposal.
Duration: Maximum of four years.
Deadline: Proposals must be postmarked by
either March 1 or September 1 to be
accepted.

ADDRESS INQUIRIES TO:
Susan Foster, Assistant Director
(See address above.)

NEW YORK LIFE FOUNDATION [268]

51 Madison Avenue
New York, NY 10010-1655
(212) 576-7341
Fax: (212) 576-6220

E-MAIL ADDRESS:
nylfoundation@newyorklife.com

WEB SITE ADDRESS:
www.newyorklifefoundation.org

AREAS OF INTEREST:
Nurturing the children.

TYPE:
Grants-in-aid.

YEAR PROGRAM STARTED: 1979

ELIGIBILITY:
Grants are made only to private, nonprofit
organizations which have tax-exempt status
under Section 501(c)(3) of the IRS and
which are not private foundations. Priority is
given to requests from organizations that are
national in scope and from those that focus
on issues and problems in New York City,
NY, where the Company's home office is
located.

The Foundation does not make grants to
individuals or government agencies. The
Foundation also does not give to sectarian or
religious organizations or to activities whose
services are limited to members of a religious
group, fraternal, social, professional, athletic
or veterans' organizations, for seminars,
conferences or trips, pre-school, primary or
secondary educational institutions,
endowments, memorials, or capital
campaigns, organizations which are members
of United Ways already supported by the
Foundation, fund-raising events, telethons,
races or other benefits, goodwill advertising,
organizations whose programs are principally
international, basic or applied research or to
organizations that discriminate on the basis
of race, color, creed, gender or national
origin.

GEOGRAPHIC RESTRICTIONS:
New York City and Westchester County, New
York.

FINANCIAL DATA:
Amount of support per award: Varies.
Total amount of support: $10,500,000 for the
year ended December 31, 2009.

NUMBER OF AWARDS: 200.

APPLICATION INFORMATION:
All requests must be submitted online
through the Foundation's web site.
Duration: One-year to multiyear grants.

THE NISSAN FOUNDATION [269]

One Nissan Way
Franklin, TN 37067
(615) 725-3406
Fax: (615) 725-8535

E-MAIL ADDRESS:
nissanfoundation@nissan-usa.com

WEB SITE ADDRESS:
www.nissanusa.com

FOUNDED: 1992

AREAS OF INTEREST:
Cultural diversity/cultural heritage, cultural
traditions and beliefs, and education.

TYPE:
Development grants; Project/program grants;
Training grants.

YEAR PROGRAM STARTED: 1992

PURPOSE:
To celebrate diverse cultural heritage.

LEGAL BASIS:
Private, corporate foundation.

ELIGIBILITY:
Eligible organizations must be IRS 501(c)(3)
tax-exempt. The Foundation does not fund
capital campaigns.

GEOGRAPHIC RESTRICTIONS:
Southern California (Los Angeles to San
Diego); Atlanta, Georgia; Metro Detroit,
Michigan; south central Mississippi; New
York, New York; middle Tennessee and north
central Texas.

FINANCIAL DATA:
Amount of support per award: $5,000 to
$50,000.
Total amount of support: $575,000 for the
year 2008.

APPLICATION INFORMATION:
Applicants must first submit a letter of
inquiry. Selected organizations are then
invited to submit a letter of intent and full
proposal. All applications must be submitted
online.

Duration: One year. Renewal by reapplication.

Deadline: November.

PUBLICATIONS:
Contributions policy; application guidelines.

ADDRESS INQUIRIES TO:
The Nissan Foundation
P.O. Box 685001
Mailstop B5B
Franklin, TN 37076-5001

*SPECIAL STIPULATIONS:
Grants are provided only to programs or projects that support cultural heritage within the geographic areas listed above.

THE NORCLIFFE FOUNDATION   [270]
Wells Fargo Center
999 Third Avenue, Suite 1006
Seattle, WA 98104
(206) 682-4820
Fax: (206) 682-4821

E-MAIL ADDRESS:
arline@thenorcliffefoundation.com

WEB SITE ADDRESS:
www.thenorcliffefoundation.com

FOUNDED: 1952

AREAS OF INTEREST:
Health, education, social services, civic improvement, religion, historic preservation, culture and the arts, youth programs, and environment.

TYPE:
Capital grants; Challenge/matching grants; Conferences/seminars; Endowments; General operating grants; Research grants; Seed money grants.

YEAR PROGRAM STARTED: 1952

PURPOSE:
To improve the lives of people.

LEGAL BASIS:
Private foundation.

ELIGIBILITY:
Eligible organizations must be of IRS 501(c)(3), not-for-profit status. Grants are not given to individuals.

GEOGRAPHIC RESTRICTIONS:
Puget Sound area of Washington state.

FINANCIAL DATA:
Amount of support per award: Varies.
Total amount of support: $9,528,000 for the year 2010.

NUMBER OF AWARDS: Over 300 for the year 2009.

APPLICATION INFORMATION:
An application form or letter of proposal is requested. Applying organizations must provide IRS 501(c)(3) documentation, a list of the board of directors, a financial statement and budget information, and background information on the agency applying.
Duration: Varies by project. Grants are generally not renewable.
Deadline: Applications are accepted throughout the year.

ADDRESS INQUIRIES TO:
Arline Hefferline, Foundation Manager
(See address above.)

THE NORDSON CORPORATION FOUNDATION   [271]
28601 Clemens Road
Westlake, OH 44145-1148
(440) 892-1580
Fax: (440) 414-5751

E-MAIL ADDRESS:
crender@nordson.com

WEB SITE ADDRESS:
www.nordson.com

FOUNDED: 1952

AREAS OF INTEREST:
Education, human welfare, civic, arts and culture.

CONSULTING OR VOLUNTEER SERVICES:
Corporate volunteer program.

TYPE:
Capital grants; Challenge/matching grants; General operating grants; Matching gifts; Project/program grants; Technical assistance.

YEAR PROGRAM STARTED: 1988

PURPOSE:
Dedicated to improving the quality of life in our communities by improving educational outcomes that enable individuals to become self-sufficient, active participants in the community.

LEGAL BASIS:
Corporate foundation.

ELIGIBILITY:
Grants are made to tax-exempt organizations, as defined in Section 501(c)(3) of the Internal Revenue Code. No grants to religious organizations.

GEOGRAPHIC RESTRICTIONS:
Mainly San Diego County, California; Greater Atlanta area, Georgia; Mercer County, New Jersey; Lorain County, Ohio; and Providence, Rhode Island.

FINANCIAL DATA:
Amount of support per award: $5,000 to $25,000.
Total amount of support: $2,700,000 for the year 2010.
Matching fund requirements: Foundation will match minimum contributions of $25 to a maximum of $6,000 for any calendar year.

NUMBER OF APPLICANTS MOST RECENT YEAR:
250 for the year 2008.

NUMBER OF AWARDS: 157 for the year 2008.

APPLICATION INFORMATION:
Nonprofit organizations should contact NCF staff to obtain the application form. Proposals submitted in any other form will not be accepted.
Duration: Typically one year.
Deadline: February 15, May 15, August 15 and November 15 for meetings held in January, April, July and October, respectively.

PUBLICATIONS:
Annual report.

TRUSTEES:
Doug Bloomfield
Beverly Coen
Michael Hilton
John Keane
Peter Lambert
Shelly Peet
Greg Thaxton

STAFF:
Maggie Combs, Manager, Community Affairs

Kathy Ladiner, Grants Manager and Matching Gifts Coordinator
Jennifer Kuhn, Community Relations Liaison/New Jersey
Elizabeth Cabral, Community Relations Liaison/Rhode Island
Ray McHenry, Community Relations Liaison/San Diego County
Joan Szczepanik, Program Assistant

ADDRESS INQUIRIES TO:
Cecilia H. Render, Tel: (440) 892-1580
Kathy Ladiner, Tel: (440) 892-1580 (Matching Gifts)
Maggie Combs, Tel: (770) 497-3400 (Greater Atlanta)
Ray McHenry, Tel: (760) 930-7258 (San Diego)
Elizabeth Cabral, Tel: (401) 431-7105 (Providence, RI)
Jennifer Kuhn, Tel: (609) 259-9222 (NJ)

KENNETH T. AND EILEEN L. NORRIS FOUNDATION   [272]
11 Golden Shore, Suite 450
Long Beach, CA 90802
(562) 435-8444
Fax: (562) 436-0584

E-MAIL ADDRESS:
grants@norrisfoundation.org

WEB SITE ADDRESS:
www.norrisfoundation.org

FOUNDED: 1963

AREAS OF INTEREST:
Funding categories include medicine, education and science, youth, community and culture.

TYPE:
Capital grants; Challenge/matching grants; Endowments; General operating grants; Project/program grants; Research grants.

YEAR PROGRAM STARTED: 1963

PURPOSE:
To support programs that advance better health and intellectual enlightenment through education, cultivation of the arts, individual responsibility, freedom and dignity.

LEGAL BASIS:
Family foundation.

ELIGIBILITY:
Applicants must be nonprofit, tax-exempt organizations. The Foundation does not support individuals and/or political or religious organizations.

GEOGRAPHIC RESTRICTIONS:
Southern California.

FINANCIAL DATA:
Amount of support per award: Grants vary in amount, depending upon the needs and nature of the request.
Total amount of support: Varies.

APPLICATION INFORMATION:
Potential applicants should contact the Foundation for guidelines and application form.
Duration: Varies. Most grants are for one year.
Deadline: Education and Medical: May 1 to June 30; decision in October. Youth: February 15 to March 31; decision in August. Community and Cultural: December 1 to January 31; decision in May.

PUBLICATIONS:
Biannual report.

ADDRESS INQUIRIES TO:
Ronald R. Barnes, Executive Director
(See address above.)

NORTH CAROLINA COMMUNITY FOUNDATION   [273]

4601 Six Forks Road, Suite 524
Raleigh, NC 27609-5286
(919) 828-4387
(800) 201-9533
Fax: (919) 828-5495

E-MAIL ADDRESS:
smigliore@nccommunityfoundation.org

WEB SITE ADDRESS:
www.nccommunityfoundation.org

FOUNDED: 1988

AREAS OF INTEREST:
Arts and conservation, education, health, historical and culture resources, preservation of environmental and social services.

TYPE:
General operating grants; Project/program grants; Scholarships.

PURPOSE:
To inspire North Carolinians to make lasting and meaningful contributions to their communities.

LEGAL BASIS:
501(c)(3).

ELIGIBILITY:
Nonprofit, tax-exempt organizations. No grants are made to individuals.

GEOGRAPHIC RESTRICTIONS:
North Carolina.

FINANCIAL DATA:
Amount of support per award: Varies.
Total amount of support: $5,750,772 for fiscal year ended March 31, 2010.

ADDRESS INQUIRIES TO:
Sally Migliore
Director of Community Leadership
(See address above.)

THE NORTHWEST MINNESOTA FOUNDATION

4225 Technology Drive, N.W.
Bemidji, MN 56601
(218) 759-2057
Fax: (218) 759-2328

E-MAIL ADDRESS:
nwmf@nwmf.org

WEB SITE ADDRESS:
www.nwmf.org

TYPE:
Development grants; Endowments; Project/program grants; Training grants.

See entry 1426 for full listing.

NSTAR FOUNDATION   [274]

One NSTAR Way
SW300
Westwood, MA 02090
(781) 441-3587

E-MAIL ADDRESS:
kristin.slater@nstar.com

WEB SITE ADDRESS:
www.nstar.com

FOUNDED: 1981

AREAS OF INTEREST:
Youth programs, quality of life services, and the economically disenfranchised.

TYPE:
Awards/prizes; Challenge/matching grants; Development grants; Endowments; Grants-in-aid; Matching gifts; Project/program grants; Research grants; Scholarships; Seed money grants; Technical assistance; Training grants. Financial support to qualified organizations serving communities within the Foundation's service territory.

YEAR PROGRAM STARTED: 1981

PURPOSE:
To be involved in and aware of the concern and needs facing the communities of which the Company is a part.

LEGAL BASIS:
Corporate foundation.

ELIGIBILITY:
Applicants must be institutions and organizations with a 501(c)(3) tax-exempt designation.

The Foundation does not support capital campaigns (building as well as renovation). Foundations and religiously focused groups do not qualify for funding.

FINANCIAL DATA:
Amount of support per award: $1,000 to $100,000. $2,500 average.
Total amount of support: $1,000,000 to $1,500,000.
Matching fund requirements: The Foundation matches dollar-for-dollar employee gifts to approved educational or cultural organizations and homeless shelters. Minimum of $100 and maximum of $2,500 in any calendar year.

REPRESENTATIVE AWARDS:
$5,000 to North End Against Drugs; $5,000 to Plymouth Philharmonic Orchestra.

APPLICATION INFORMATION:
Guidelines are available from the Foundation. All proposals must be submitted in writing and should be addressed to the Foundation Administrator in advance of any personal or telephone contact. All proposals should include letter from the IRS showing 501(c)(3) tax-exemption and 509(a)(1) or (2) designation, annual report of organization, budget and detailed costs for projects, specific amount being requested, other funding support, provisions for accountability and progress reports to project funders. All applicants must use the AGM Common Proposal Format which is forwarded with guidelines.
Duration: Usually one year.

PUBLICATIONS:
Guidelines; matching grants program brochure.

TRUSTEES:
T.J. May, Chairman

ADDRESS INQUIRIES TO:
Ann Cardello, Administrator
(See address above.)

WILLIAM J. AND DOROTHY K. O'NEILL FOUNDATION   [275]

30195 Chagrin Boulevard
Suite 106
Cleveland, OH 44124
(216) 831-4134
Fax: (216) 378-0594

E-MAIL ADDRESS:
info@oneillfdn.org

WEB SITE ADDRESS:
www.oneillfdn.org

FOUNDED: 1987

AREAS OF INTEREST:
Capacity building - all program areas.

TYPE:
Matching gifts. Capacity building; Proactive grants; Gifts in recognition of service; Youth Philanthropy grants. In the area of capacity building, the Foundation funds projects that create and implement strategic plans, governance and board development, leadership succession planning, planning and implementing technology systems, fund development, and communications and marketing strategies.

Proactive grants are only solicited by O'Neill Family members.

Matching gifts and gifts in recognition of service are directed by O'Neill Family members.

Youth Philanthropy grants are made by O'Neill Family youth.

YEAR PROGRAM STARTED: 1987

PURPOSE:
To fund programs that address root causes of family strength and family disintegration, capacity building for nonprofits and areas of interest to individual family members.

LEGAL BASIS:
Family foundation.

ELIGIBILITY:
Nonprofit organizations with IRS 501(c)(3) tax-exempt status are eligible for support. No grants to individuals or to organizations which operate wholly outside the U.S. No grants in response to annual appeal form letters.

In order to be eligible, you must have either received a grant from the Foundation already and/or be notified that you are eligible.

GEOGRAPHIC RESTRICTIONS:
Cleveland, Columbus and Licking counties, Ohio; Washington, DC; Bonita Springs and Naples, Florida; Big Island, Hawaii; Annapolis and Baltimore, Maryland; New York, New York; Houston, Texas; and Richmond, Virginia.

FINANCIAL DATA:
Amount of support per award: Average: $35,000.
Total amount of support: $2,963,810 for the year 2010.

NUMBER OF APPLICANTS MOST RECENT YEAR:
218 for the year 2008.

NUMBER OF AWARDS: 90 for the year 2008.

REPRESENTATIVE AWARDS:
$25,000 to America Scores; $44,500 to Cleveland Botanical Garden; $28,000 to Eliza Bryant Village; $25,000 to Legal Aid Bureau; $35,000 to Zvi Dance.

APPLICATION INFORMATION:
Call for guidelines.
Duration: One year.
Deadline: Letters of Inquiry: April 1, August 1, and December 1.

PUBLICATIONS:
Annual report; application guidelines.

IRS IDENTIFICATION NUMBER: 34-1560893

OFFICERS:
Leah S. Gary, President and Chief Executive Officer
Robert W. Donahey, Treasurer

TRUSTEES:
Timothy M. O'Neill, Chairperson
Leah S. Gary, President and Chief Executive Officer
Linda France Clifford
Robert W. Donahey
Kelly Sweeney McShane
John H. O'Neill
Sara O'Neill Sullivan

ADDRESS INQUIRIES TO:
Cynthia Drennan, Director
Grants Management and Foundation Operations
(See address above.)

THE JOHN R. OISHEI FOUNDATION [276]

One HSBC Center
Suite 3650
Buffalo, NY 14203-2805
(716) 856-9490
Fax: (716) 856-9493

E-MAIL ADDRESS:
info@oishei.org

WEB SITE ADDRESS:
www.oishei.org

FOUNDED: 1940

AREAS OF INTEREST:
Strengthening neighborhoods and building communities, self-sufficiency, education and employment, community health and medical research, expanding the impact of regional assets, and building organizational strength through operational improvements.

TYPE:
Challenge/matching grants; Professorships; Project/program grants; Research grants; Seed money grants.

PURPOSE:
To be a catalyst for change; to enhance the economic vitality and the quality of life for the Buffalo Niagara region.

LEGAL BASIS:
Private foundation.

ELIGIBILITY:
An organization seeking support must be determined by the Internal Revenue Code to be tax-exempt under Section 501(c)(3). Private Foundations, as defined in Section 509(a) of the Internal Revenue Code, will not be eligible for Foundation support. To receive Foundation support, an organization must be

well managed, including an active board drawn from a cross section of the community. It must have a consistent record of sound fiscal management and a demonstrated track record of efficient operations and effective programming. The Foundation does not make grants to governmental institutions, agencies or projects. Organizations that rely heavily on government funding are eligible to apply, but must be able to demonstrate that a grant from the Foundation would supplement rather than supplant public funding.

GEOGRAPHIC RESTRICTIONS:
Buffalo Niagara region, NY.

FINANCIAL DATA:
Amount of support per award: $10,000 to $3,500,000.
Total amount of support: $19,100,000 for the year 2010.

NUMBER OF AWARDS: 137 for the year 2010.

REPRESENTATIVE AWARDS:
$2,000,000 to Canisius College Science Center; $525,000 to Community Health Center of Buffalo; $360,000 to Erie Community College Foundation; $300,000 to Riviera Theatre & Organ Preservation Society.

APPLICATION INFORMATION:
Detailed information is available in the "How to Apply" section on the Foundation web site.
Deadline: The Foundation accepts and processes applications throughout the year. Notification within three months.

PUBLICATIONS:
Catalyst for Change, annual report and guidelines.

OFFICERS:
James M. Wadsworth, Chairman and Director
Mary S. Martino, Vice Chairman
Robert D. Gioia, President
Allan R. Wiegley, Treasurer and Director
Gayle L. Houck, Secretary

DIRECTORS:
Thomas E. Baker
Robert M. Bennett
Ruth D. Bryant
Christopher T. Dunstan
Mary S. Martino
Ann M. McCarthy
James M. Wadsworth
Edward F. Walsh, Jr.
Allan R. Wiegley

ADDRESS INQUIRIES TO:
Robert D. Gioia, President
(See address above.)

OMAHA COMMUNITY FOUNDATION [277]

302 South 36th Street
Suite 100
Omaha, NE 68131
(402) 342-3458
Fax: (402) 342-3582

E-MAIL ADDRESS:
sarah@omahafoundation.org

WEB SITE ADDRESS:
www.omahafoundation.org

FOUNDED: 1982

AREAS OF INTEREST:
General philanthropy.

CONSULTING OR VOLUNTEER SERVICES:
Nonprofit Capacity Building Initiative.

NAME(S) OF PROGRAMS:
● **African American Unity Fund**
● **Endowment Funds of Southwest Iowa**
● **Fund for Omaha**
● **Futuro Latino Fund**
● **Youth in Philanthropy**

TYPE:
Capital grants; Project/program grants; Scholarships. Donors can contribute through the Omaha Community Foundation to any nonprofit agency. The OCF also has five discretionary grant programs.

PURPOSE:
To facilitate charitable giving and serve as a vehicle for community improvement; to improve the quality of life in Greater Omaha by supporting needs not being met in the areas of civic, cultural, health, education and social service.

LEGAL BASIS:
Public foundation.

ELIGIBILITY:
Organizations applying for grants must be tax-exempt as defined by IRS 501(c)(3) status. Except under unusual circumstances, no grants for endowments, capital campaigns, deficit financing, annual fund drives or fund-raising activities. The grant request must have the approval of the governing board of the requesting organization.

GEOGRAPHIC RESTRICTIONS:
Greater Omaha area. Endowment funds of Southwest Iowa limited to the counties of: Audubon, Cass, Crawford, Fremont, Harrison, Mills, Montgomery, Page and Shelby.

FINANCIAL DATA:
Amount of support per award: $5,000 to $15,000.

NUMBER OF AWARDS: Approximately 425.

APPLICATION INFORMATION:
Contact the Foundation for details.
Duration: Varies.
Deadline: African American Unity Fund and Futuro Latino Fund: August 1; Endowment Funds: February 1; Fund for Omaha: March 1 and September 1; Scholarships: March 31.

PUBLICATIONS:
Newsletter, available on web site.

IRS IDENTIFICATION NUMBER: 47-0645958

STAFF:
Sarah Gilbert, Director of Philanthropic Services

ADDRESS INQUIRIES TO:
Sarah Gilbert
Director of Philanthropic Services
(See address above.)

ORANGE COUNTY COMMUNITY FOUNDATION [278]

4041 MacArthur Boulevard
Suite 510
Newport Beach, CA 92660-2503
(949) 553-4202
Fax: (949) 553-4211

E-MAIL ADDRESS:
mconner@oc-cf.org

WEB SITE ADDRESS:
www.oc-cf.org

FOUNDED: 1989

AREAS OF INTEREST:
Children and youth, family relationships, diverse communities, music education and performance, classical music and education, health, environment and education.

TYPE:
Endowments; General operating grants; Project/program grants; Scholarships; Technical assistance. Community Services.

The Foundation offers several grant programs throughout the year in human services, education, health, arts and culture, and the environment. Other special grant competitions also occur throughout the year.

YEAR PROGRAM STARTED: 1990

PURPOSE:
To encourage, support and facilitate philanthropy in Orange County.

LEGAL BASIS:
Community foundation.

ELIGIBILITY:
Applicant agencies must be tax-exempt, serve its residents, and operate without discrimination on the basis of race, religion, gender, sexual orientation, age, national origin or disability.

GEOGRAPHIC RESTRICTIONS:
Orange County, California.

FINANCIAL DATA:
Amount of support per award: Average grant: $5,000 to $25,000.
Total amount of support: $22,300,000 for fiscal year 2009-10.

COOPERATIVE FUNDING PROGRAMS: ReachOut OC; OC Founders Roundtable.

APPLICATION INFORMATION:
Applications are reviewed by a committee appointed by the Community Foundation's Board of Governors.
Duration: Generally one year for unrestricted grants. Renewal occasionally possible for scholarships.
Deadline: Varies.

PUBLICATIONS:
Annual report; newsletters; guidelines.

IRS IDENTIFICATION NUMBER: 33-0378778

ADDRESS INQUIRIES TO:
Todd Hanson, Vice President of Donor Relations and Programs
(See address above.)

THE BERNARD OSHER FOUNDATION   [279]

One Ferry Building, Suite 255
San Francisco, CA 94111
(415) 861-5587
Fax: (415) 677-5972

E-MAIL ADDRESS:
info@osherfoundation.org

WEB SITE ADDRESS:
www.osherfoundation.org

FOUNDED: 1977

AREAS OF INTEREST:
Scholarship funding to selected colleges and universities, integrative medicine, lifelong learning for seasoned adults, arts and humanities.

TYPE:
Project/program grants; Scholarships. The Foundation provides scholarship funding nationally to selected colleges and

universities and funds integrative medicine centers at Harvard University, the University of California at San Francisco, and the Karolinska Institute in Stockholm. It also supports a growing network of lifelong learning institutes for seasoned adults located at over 120 colleges and universities from Maine to Hawaii. Arts and humanities grants are made to nonprofit organizations principally in the Greater San Francisco Bay Area, specifically Alameda and San Francisco counties, as well as the state of Maine.

YEAR PROGRAM STARTED: 1977

PURPOSE:
To provide scholarship funding nationally to selected colleges and universities and to fund integrative medicine centers; to support a network of lifelong learning institutes for seasoned adults; to support the arts and humanities.

ELIGIBILITY:
Requests will be accepted only from organizations which are classified by the IRS as nonprofit and designated as IRS 501(c)(3). Organizations seeking funds should have experience which is relevant to the proposed project.

The Foundation is precluded by its policies from making direct grants to individuals.

FINANCIAL DATA:
Amount of support per award: Varies.
Total amount of support: Varies.

APPLICATION INFORMATION:
A letter of inquiry is invited as the first step in communicating with the Foundation. If proposal is invited, it should include the following:
(1) a brief background of the applicant, including qualifications of people involved;
(2) description of the nature and scope of the proposed program and the anticipated results;
(3) preliminary timetable;
(4) preliminary budget outline;
(5) financial statement covering the most recent year of operation;
(6) evidence of tax-exempt status and;
(7) names of appropriate governing authority and evidence of request approval.
Duration: One year.

STAFF:
Mary G.F. Bitterman, President
Thomas Moffett, Chief Financial Officer/Chief Investment Officer
David Blazevich, Senior Program Officer
Andrew Lynch, Program Officer
Jeanie Hirokane, Executive Administrator/Corporate Secretary

BOARD OF DIRECTORS:
Barbro Osher, Chairman
Bernard Osher, Founder and Treasurer
Mary G.F. Bitterman, President
David Agger
Phyllis Cook
Robert Friend
John Gallo
Laura Lauder
John Pritzker

ADDRESS INQUIRIES TO:
Mary G.F. Bitterman, President
(See address above.)

PACCAR FOUNDATION   [280]

P.O. Box 1518
Bellevue, WA 98009

E-MAIL ADDRESS:
ken.hastings@paccar.com

WEB SITE ADDRESS:
www.paccar.com/foundation.asp

FOUNDED: 1951

AREAS OF INTEREST:
Education, science, arts and humanities.

TYPE:
Capital grants.

LEGAL BASIS:
Private foundation.

ELIGIBILITY:
No grants to individuals, political or lobbying groups, fraternal organizations or religious organizations for sectarian purposes.

GEOGRAPHIC RESTRICTIONS:
Columbus, Mississippi; Chillicothe, Ohio; Broken Arrow, Oklahoma; Denton, Texas; Bellevue, Kirkland, Renton, Seattle and Skagit, Washington.

FINANCIAL DATA:
Amount of support per award: $10,000 to $250,000.
Total amount of support: $5,000,000.

APPLICATION INFORMATION:
Send proposal with proof of IRS 501(c)(3) status, description of goals and programs, background data on key personnel, amount requested and the purpose for which it is needed.
Duration: One year. Must reapply for continued funding.
Deadline: Applications accepted throughout the year. Decisions made semi-annually.

STAFF:
Ken Hastings, Vice President and General Manager

ADDRESS INQUIRIES TO:
Ken Hastings
Vice President and General Manager
(See address above.)

PACIFIC GAS AND ELECTRIC COMPANY   [281]

77 Beale Street
San Francisco, CA 94105
(415) 973-4743
Fax: (415) 973-5411

E-MAIL ADDRESS:
s2sy@pge.com

WEB SITE ADDRESS:
www.pge.com/giving

AREAS OF INTEREST:
Education, environmental stewardship, and community vitality.

CONSULTING OR VOLUNTEER SERVICES:
Volunteer program.

TYPE:
Project/program grants; Scholarships. Signature programs.

YEAR PROGRAM STARTED: 2001

LEGAL BASIS:
Corporate contributions program.

ELIGIBILITY:
Applicants must have tax-deductible status from the IRS under Section 501(c)(3) or be a unit of government (including a public school). Contributions are not made to: individuals; tickets for contests, raffles or other prize-oriented activities; religious organizations (unless for a program offered

to the public on a nondiscriminatory basis and without regard to the recipient's religious affiliation); endowments; debt-reduction campaigns; films; or political or partisan organizations or events.

The most successful grant applications are those that:
(1) address a demonstrated community need;
(2) link a nonprofit or government program to the Company's business goals and employee presence in the community and;
(3) can provide the grantee and the Company with recognition in the community.

GEOGRAPHIC RESTRICTIONS:
Northern and central California.

FINANCIAL DATA:
Amount of support per award: $1,000 to $25,000. Most grants are under $5,000.
Total amount of support: $19,300,000 for the year 2010.
Matching fund requirements: 1:1 basis: $25 to $2,500 per calendar year, per employee.

NUMBER OF APPLICANTS MOST RECENT YEAR:
Over 2,500.

NUMBER OF AWARDS: Over 1,300 in 2010.

REPRESENTATIVE AWARDS:
$7,000 to Burris Park Foundation, Hanford, CA, for projects that assist in green building efforts, energy efficiency programs, brownfields, and/or urban park projects; $10,000 to the Western Regional Office, Ducks Unlimited, Rancho Cordova, CA, for protection, conservation and restoration of natural resources, habitats, non-urban parks, tree planting/replanting, fire protection and restoration; $17,500 to Paramount Theatre of the Arts, Inc., Oakland, CA; $45,000 to The Alliance to Save Energy, Washington, DC, to support organizations and projects in the realms of public policy and environmental justice organizations, and all other projects.

APPLICATION INFORMATION:
Prior to applying for a grant, applicants should contact the local PG&E representative in their project area to discuss the grant proposal. All applicants must use the online grant application. PG&E will neither accept nor process grant proposals in any other format. Please submit only a fully-completed application. Incomplete applications will not be considered.
Duration: Generally one year.
Deadline: Applications are preferred before September 30 of each year.

ADDRESS INQUIRIES TO:
Sarah Sasaki
Manager, Community Investments
(See address above.)

PACIFIC LIFE FOUNDATION/PACIFIC LIFE   [282]
700 Newport Center Drive
Newport Beach, CA 92660-6397
(949) 219-3787
Fax: (949) 219-7614

E-MAIL ADDRESS:
bhardwig@pacificlife.com

WEB SITE ADDRESS:
www.pacificlifefoundation.com

FOUNDED: 1984

NAME(S) OF PROGRAMS:
● **Arts and Culture**
● **Civic, Community, and Environment**
● **Education**
● **Health and Human Services**

TYPE:
Capital grants; General operating grants; Matching gifts; Product donations; Project/program grants. Arts and Culture: Funds nonprofit agencies that provide the public with a broad spectrum of arts and cultural initiatives (e.g., workshops, performances) to help build the public's appreciation of and participation in dance, music, and theater.

Civic, Community, and Environment: Funding is directed to a wide range of programs that enhance communities through leadership development and environmental protection, as well as fund research to learn more about marine mammals.

Education: Funds nonprofit agencies committed to providing quality educational programs for youth and adults (e.g., mentoring, tutoring, literacy) to help them excel academically and in life.

Health and Human Services: Contributions are allocated to agencies that seek to improve the quality of life of those in need, including the working poor, the homeless, and individuals with physical or developmental disabilities.

PURPOSE:
To recognize and support employees' varied interests and community involvement and, through focus programs, to identify and respond to particular community needs so that, whenever possible, funds may be channeled to those areas in which the most good can be accomplished with the funds available.

LEGAL BASIS:
Corporate foundation and corporate contributions program.

ELIGIBILITY:
Grants are made to nonprofit, tax-exempt, 501(c)(3) organizations. The Foundation does not provide support for individuals; political parties, candidates or partisan political organizations; labor organizations, fraternal organizations, athletic clubs or social clubs; K-12 schools, school districts, or school foundations (contact Foundation for exceptions); sectarian or denominational religious organizations, except for programs which are broadly promoted, available to anyone, and free from religious orientation; fund-raising events (e.g., membership drives, luncheons/dinners, tournaments and benefits); or advertising sponsorships.

GEOGRAPHIC RESTRICTIONS:
The Greater Orange County, California area and other areas, such as Omaha, Nebraska.

FINANCIAL DATA:
Amount of support per award: General grants: $5,000 to $10,000 for a one-year period of funding; Capital grants: $10,000 to $100,000, paid out over multiple years; Matching Gift Program for Higher Education: Up to $2,000; Matching Gift Program to Nonprofits: Up to $500.00
Total amount of support: Matching Gift Program for Higher Education: $146,735 for the year 2010. Pacific Life Charitable Contributions and Pacific Life Foundation Charitable Grants: $5,500,000 for the year 2010.

NUMBER OF AWARDS: Matching Gift Program for Higher Education: 56 colleges and universities in 2010.

APPLICATION INFORMATION:
Grant guidelines and application form is available online.
Duration: Agencies may reapply annually for funding; however, grants are made to any one agency for no more than three consecutive years. Support may again be requested after a two-year interim period.
Deadline: Submissions accepted July 15 to August 15.

PUBLICATIONS:
Annual report.

OFFICERS:
James T. Morris, Chairman
Robert G. Haskell, President
Tennyson S. Oyler, Vice President
Michele A. Townsend, Vice President
Edward R. Byrd, Chief Financial Officer
Joseph J. Tortorelli, General Counsel
Jane M. Guon, Secretary
Brenda K. Hardwig, Assistant Secretary

BOARD OF DIRECTORS:
Jennifer S. Annala
Sharon A. Cheever
Alyssa C. Dowding
R. Stephen Hannahs
Robert G. Haskell
James T. Morris
John C. Mulvihill
Tennyson S. Oyler
Cathy L. Schwartz
Alice P. Terlecky
Michele A. Townsend
Christine A. Tucker

ADDRESS INQUIRIES TO:
Robert G. Haskell, President
(See address above.)

THE DAVID AND LUCILE PACKARD FOUNDATION   [283]
300 Second Street
Los Altos, CA 94022
(650) 948-7658
Fax: (650) 948-5793

E-MAIL ADDRESS:
inquiries@packard.org

WEB SITE ADDRESS:
www.packard.org

FOUNDED: 1964

AREAS OF INTEREST:
Arts; children, families and communities; conservation and sciences; organizational effectiveness; philanthropy; and Pueblo, CO.

NAME(S) OF PROGRAMS:
● **Children, Families and Communities**
● **Conservation and Science**
● **Population and Reproductive Health**

TYPE:
Capital grants; Challenge/matching grants; Conferences/seminars; Demonstration grants; Development grants; Fellowships; General operating grants; Matching gifts; Project/program grants; Research grants; Scholarships; Seed money grants; Technical assistance. Grants are made to provide support in the local five-county area for organizational development, arts education and traditional performing arts, as well as for areas of wetlands preservation and restoration, marine fisheries protection and restoration.

Funds are also provided to support fellowships for 20 young professors in science and engineering.

In addition, the Foundation supports children's health programs through children, families, and communities programs, population and family planning services.

Support is given for research of the deep ocean in the Monterey, California area and community grants in Pueblo County, CO.

YEAR PROGRAM STARTED: 1964

PURPOSE:
To support private, voluntary charities.

LEGAL BASIS:
Private foundation incorporated under California law.

ELIGIBILITY:
Applicants must be qualified tax-exempt charitable organizations. Most community-oriented grants are made to organizations that serve the people of Santa Cruz, Santa Clara, San Mateo and Monterey counties. Requests for support of community and local activities outside of these geographical areas will rarely be considered. Grants are also made in Pueblo (CO) and for national and international programs in conservation, population, public policy and children's health. No proposals may be accepted that benefit individuals or that are for religious purposes.

FINANCIAL DATA:
Amount of support per award: $500 to $30,000,000.

Total amount of support: Approximately $265,000,000 for the year 2010.

APPLICATION INFORMATION:
Contact the Foundation for guidelines.
Duration: Grants are made for one year, with occasional multiyear grants.

PUBLICATIONS:
Annual report; guideline brochures.

OFFICERS:
Susan Packard Orr, Chairperson
Nancy Packard Burnett, Vice Chairperson
Julie E. Packard, Vice Chairperson
Carol S. Larson, President and Chief Executive Officer
George Vera, Vice President and Chief Financial Officer
Mary Anne Rodgers, Secretary and General Counsel

BOARD OF TRUSTEES:
Ned Barnholt
Jason Burnett
Nancy Packard Burnett
Linda Griego
Don Kennedy
Carol S. Larson
Franklin M. Orr, Jr.
Katy Orr
Susan Packard Orr
Arianna Packard
Julie E. Packard
William K. Reilly
Colburn S. Wilbur

PARK BANK FOUNDATION, INC.   [284]
330 East Kilbourn Avenue
Milwaukee, WI 53202
(414) 270-3209
Fax: (414) 223-3022

E-MAIL ADDRESS:
susanb@parkbankonline.com

FOUNDED: 1980

AREAS OF INTEREST:
Arts and culture, community development, conservation, education, health, historic preservation and social services.

TYPE:
Capital grants; Development grants; General operating grants.

YEAR PROGRAM STARTED: 1980

PURPOSE:
To fund qualifying organizations in the Milwaukee Metropolitan area as well as surrounding communities.

ELIGIBILITY:
Must have 501(c)(3) status and be located in the Milwaukee area and surrounding communities. No grants are made to individuals. Non-sectarian religious programs may apply.

GEOGRAPHIC RESTRICTIONS:
Milwaukee, Wisconsin metropolitan area.

FINANCIAL DATA:
Amount of support per award: $50 to $6,000.

APPLICATION INFORMATION:
Send a request on organization's letterhead along with a copy of the 501(c)(3) status and a current financial statement of the organization.
Duration: One year.
Deadline: Request needs to be received six weeks prior to meeting dates to be held March 30, July 31 and November 30.

THE PARKER FOUNDATION   [285]
2604-B El Camino Real
Suite 244
Carlsbad, CA 92008
(760) 720-0630
Fax: (760) 720-1239

WEB SITE ADDRESS:
www.theparkerfoundation.org

FOUNDED: 1971

AREAS OF INTEREST:
Adult and youth services, visual and performing arts, museums and zoos, education, medical purposes and community activities.

TYPE:
Capital grants; Challenge/matching grants; Matching gifts; Project/program grants. Programs and capital funding.

YEAR PROGRAM STARTED: 1971

PURPOSE:
To improve all aspects of life of the people of San Diego County, CA.

LEGAL BASIS:
Tax-exempt, independent private foundation.

ELIGIBILITY:
Applicants must be organizations operating in San Diego County, CA, qualified under IRS 501(c)(3). No grants to individuals or for support of conferences or symposia. No support provided for any project to the extent that it becomes dependent on the Foundation for continued existence.

GEOGRAPHIC RESTRICTIONS:
San Diego County, California.

FINANCIAL DATA:
Amount of support per award: Varies.
Total amount of support: $1,874,339 in grants paid in fiscal year 2010.

PUBLICATIONS:
Annual report.

ADDRESS INQUIRIES TO:
Robbin C. Powell, Assistant Secretary
(See address above.)

*SPECIAL STIPULATIONS:
Limited by governing documents to San Diego County, CA.

PARKER HANNIFIN CORPORATION FOUNDATION   [286]
6035 Parkland Boulevard
Cleveland, OH 44124
(216) 896-3000
Fax: (216) 896-4057

E-MAIL ADDRESS:
tpiraino@parker.com

WEB SITE ADDRESS:
www.parker.com

AREAS OF INTEREST:
Educational, health, welfare, youth and other charitable organizations.

TYPE:
Capital grants; Matching gifts; Project/program grants. Through the National Merit Scholarship for Parker employee children only.

LEGAL BASIS:
Corporate foundation.

ELIGIBILITY:
Grants are made to nonprofit organizations. Emphasis will be placed on organizations that benefit Parker employees and shareholders by improving services in communities with Parker operations and educational opportunities for current and potential employees.

Contributions will not be made to fraternal or labor organizations. Donations to religious organizations are limited to organizations serving the general public on a non-denominational basis, such as the Y's, Salvation Army, educational institutions, hospitals, etc.

FINANCIAL DATA:
Amount of support per award: $20 to $600,000.

Total amount of support: $4,000,000.

APPLICATION INFORMATION:
Applicants should submit a proposal stating needs and what the grant will be used for.
Duration: One-time award.
Deadline: June 30.

ADDRESS INQUIRIES TO:
Thomas A. Piraino
Vice President, Secretary
and General Counsel
(See address above.)

THE RALPH M. PARSONS FOUNDATION   [287]
888 West 6th Street, 7th Floor
Los Angeles, CA 90017
(213) 362-7600
Fax: (213) 362-7601

WEB SITE ADDRESS:
www.rmpf.org

FOUNDED: 1961

AREAS OF INTEREST:
Social impact, health, civic and cultural affairs, and higher education in Los Angeles County.

TYPE:
General operating grants; Project/program grants.

YEAR PROGRAM STARTED: 1978

LEGAL BASIS:
Not-for-profit corporation.

ELIGIBILITY:
Applicants must be 501(c)(3) organizations not classified under 509(a). Grants limited to organizations providing services in Los Angeles County.

No funding for mass mailings, fund-raisers, individuals, conferences, religious or political activities and/or dinners or endowments.

GEOGRAPHIC RESTRICTIONS:
Los Angeles County, California.

FINANCIAL DATA:
Amount of support per award: Varies.
Total amount of support: Varies.

REPRESENTATIVE AWARDS:
$25,000 to Bet Tzedek, Los Angeles, CA, to train, recruit and evaluate the work of pro bono attorneys.

APPLICATION INFORMATION:
Submit preliminary letter outlining project and amount requested. Program staff will determine whether applicant is qualified and may request additional information.
Duration: One year.

PUBLICATIONS:
Annual report.

STAFF:
Wendy Garen, President and Chief Executive Officer
Astra Galang, Chief Financial Officer
Mary Christian, Program Officer
Jinhee Pai Kim, Program Officer
Ricardo Lima, Grants Administrator

BOARD OF DIRECTORS:
William R. Bamattre
Elizabeth Lowe
Walter B. Rose
Karen Hill Scott
James A. Thomas
Robert Tranquada, M.D.
Franklin Ulf
Gayle Wilson

ADDRESS INQUIRIES TO:
Wendy Garen
President and Chief Executive Officer
(See address above.)

AMELIA PEABODY CHARITABLE FUND [288]

185 Devonshire Street
Suite 600
Boston, MA 02110
(617) 451-6178

WEB SITE ADDRESS:
apcfund.org

FOUNDED: 1984

AREAS OF INTEREST:
Social service and youth services in Massachusetts; environment, health and historic preservation.

TYPE:
Capital grants; Challenge/matching grants.

PURPOSE:
To support organizations that work to improve the quality of life in New England.

LEGAL BASIS:
Private foundation.

ELIGIBILITY:
Eligible organizations must be IRS 501(c)(3) tax-exempt and classified as a public charity under Section 509(a)(1) or 509(a)(2) of the Internal Revenue Code. No grants to individuals or religious organizations. No funding is provided for operating costs, start-ups or salaries, or education.

GEOGRAPHIC RESTRICTIONS:
New England states, primarily Massachusetts.

FINANCIAL DATA:
Amount of support per award: Varies per program.
Total amount of support: Approximately $8,000,000.

NUMBER OF APPLICANTS MOST RECENT YEAR:
Approximately 300.

NUMBER OF AWARDS: 100.

APPLICATION INFORMATION:
A complete proposal should have the following:
(1) Grant Request Summary Form;
(2) proposal checklist;
(3) proposal narrative which provides a clear description of the need, what the applicant is proposing to do about the need, what the organization is requesting, and what results are expected, including a detailed budget of how funds will be spent;
(4) a copy of the determination letter from the IRS classifying the organization as a nonprofit organization under Section 501(c)(3) and as a public charity under Section 509(a)(1) or 509(a)(2) of the Internal Revenue Code;
(5) a letter, dated and signed by the director on the organization's letterhead, affirming that the organization's determination letter from the IRS continues in full force and effect and that a grant from the Fund as applied for would not adversely affect the public charity status;
(6) a copy of the most recent IRS Form 990 and Schedule A;
(7) financial statement, clearly showing all income sources and expenses for the organization for the most recent tax year and;
(8) a list of the Board of Directors/Trustees.

Additionally, include four separate copies of the proposal narrative with the Grant Request Summary Form stapled to the front of each set.
Duration: Renewal possible after three years; four years for major grants.
Deadline: February 1 and July 1.

PUBLICATIONS:
Guidelines.

IRS IDENTIFICATION NUMBER: 23-7364949

ADDRESS INQUIRIES TO:
Cheryl Gideon, Executive Assistant
Business and Grants Coordinator
(See address above.)

PEACOCK FOUNDATION, INC. [289]

100 S.E. Second Street, Suite 2370
Miami, FL 33131-2145
(305) 373-1386
Fax: (305) 375-0660

WEB SITE ADDRESS:
peacockfoundationinc.org

AREAS OF INTEREST:
Elderly, children, youth, art for educational purposes, environmental education, disabilities, health and hospitals, medical research and human services.

TYPE:
General operating grants; Project/program grants. Support is provided for projects/programs and limited operating funds.

ELIGIBILITY:
Organizations classified as 501(c)(3) by the IRS can apply. Individuals are ineligible.

GEOGRAPHIC RESTRICTIONS:
Broward, Miami-Dade and Monroe counties, Florida.

FINANCIAL DATA:
Amount of support per award: Average $25,000.

NUMBER OF AWARDS: 65.

APPLICATION INFORMATION:
Applicants must initially submit letter of inquiry.
Duration: One year.

ADDRESS INQUIRIES TO:
Joelle Allen, Executive Director
(See address above.)

THE WILLIAM PENN FOUNDATION [290]

Two Logan Square, 11th Floor
100 North 18th Street
Philadelphia, PA 19103-2757
(215) 988-1830
Fax: (215) 988-1823

E-MAIL ADDRESS:
moreinfo@williampennfoundation.org

WEB SITE ADDRESS:
www.williampennfoundation.org

FOUNDED: 1945

AREAS OF INTEREST:
Art, communities, culture, environment, children, youth and families.

NAME(S) OF PROGRAMS:
- **Arts and Culture**
- **Children, Youth and Families**
- **Environment and Communities**

TYPE:
Capital grants; Challenge/matching grants; Demonstration grants; Development grants; General operating grants; Project/program grants; Research grants; Seed money grants; Technical assistance. In the areas of children, youth and families, grants are made to promote a better early care and education system, more effective and equitable education policies, networks of developmental opportunities for older youth, and improvements to the systems supporting families. The program focuses on critical transitions in the lives of children as they progress from birth, through early childhood, and into young adulthood.

In the area of environment and communities, grants are made to foster greater cross-sector collaborations that build on the assets of our region through revitalization of its urban core and protection and restoration of watersheds, with a focus on key waterways. Investments are intended to catalyze innovation and leadership in the region.

In the area of arts and culture, the Foundation provides various types of core operating support for arts groups and cultural institutions, enabling them to pursue their creative missions. Work is also funded that broadly advances the region's cultural sector.

YEAR PROGRAM STARTED: 1945

PURPOSE:
To improve the quality of life in the Greater Philadelphia area, particularly for its economically disadvantaged residents; to serve nonprofit organizations that help people improve their lives within a more just and caring society.

LEGAL BASIS:
Private foundation.

ELIGIBILITY:
Applicants must be organizations which are defined as tax-exempt under Section 501(c)(3) of the Internal Revenue Code and which are not private foundations. Grants may be made to religious institutions for non-sectarian purposes, to governments and national organizations in support of policy and advocacy projects.

The Foundation does not fund scholarships, fellowships, or grants to individuals; loans or investment programs; debt reduction; sectarian religious activities; housing capital projects; exempt organizations that pass funds to non-exempt groups; profit-making enterprises; non-public schools; programs for rehabilitation or research; programs to replace discontinued government support or national or international grants.

GEOGRAPHIC RESTRICTIONS:
Philadelphia area (Bucks, Chester, Delaware and Montgomery counties), Pennsylvania and Camden, New Jersey.

FINANCIAL DATA:
Amount of support per award: Varies.
Total amount of support: $80,000,000 for the year 2010.

COOPERATIVE FUNDING PROGRAMS: The Foundation regularly joins with other foundations and institutions to fund projects.

NUMBER OF APPLICANTS MOST RECENT YEAR: 325.

NUMBER OF AWARDS: Varies.

APPLICATION INFORMATION:
All applicants must first submit a letter of inquiry.
Duration: Varies.

PUBLICATIONS:
Annual report.

IRS IDENTIFICATION NUMBER: 23-1503488

BOARD OF DIRECTORS:
Michael Bailin
James Gately
David Haas
Frederick R. Haas
Janet Haas
William D. Haas
Christine James-Brown
Daniel Meyer
Howard Meyers
Jo-Anna J. Moore

OFFICERS AND STAFF:
Feather Houstoun, President
Olive Mosier, Director, Arts and Culture
Ronnie Bloom, Director, Children, Youth and Families
Brent Thompson, Director, Communications

Geraldine Wang, Director, Environment and Communities
Helen Davis Picher, Director, Evaluation and Planning

ADDRESS INQUIRIES TO:
Proposal Intake Department
(See address above.)

PEPSICO FOUNDATION   [291]
700 Anderson Hill Road
Purchase, NY 10577
(914) 253-2000
Fax: (914) 253-2070

WEB SITE ADDRESS:
www.pepsico.com

FOUNDED: 1962

AREAS OF INTEREST:
The support of nonprofit organizations where purchase-based employees are personally involved as volunteers.

NAME(S) OF PROGRAMS:
● **Employee Matching Gifts Program**

TYPE:
Matching gifts. The Matching Gifts Program offers PepsiCo employees, their spouses and retired employees the opportunity of having their gifts to nonprofit organizations matched by the PepsiCo Foundation.

LEGAL BASIS:
Nonprofit under 501(c)(3).

ELIGIBILITY:
Contributions are generally limited to tax-exempt, nonprofit organizations that are qualified to receive contributions under the Internal Revenue Code.

FINANCIAL DATA:
Amount of support per award: $25 to $10,000.
Total amount of support: Varies.

NUMBER OF APPLICANTS MOST RECENT YEAR: 7,500.

NUMBER OF AWARDS: Varies.

APPLICATION INFORMATION:
A request for funds should include a statement of objectives, a history of achievements, the roster of officers, written evidence of tax-exempt status and a financial statement.
Deadline: Varies.

PUBLICATIONS:
Application guidelines.

OFFICERS:
Indra Nooyi, Chairman
Jacqueline R. Millan, Vice President
Matthew McKenna, Treasurer

ADDRESS INQUIRIES TO:
Program Manager
Corporate Contributions
(See address above.)

THE CARL AND LILY PFORZHEIMER FOUNDATION, INC.   [292]
950 Third Avenue, 30th Floor
New York, NY 10022
(212) 223-6500
Fax: (212) 223-2222

FOUNDED: 1942

AREAS OF INTEREST:
Education, primarily early 19th century English literature.

TYPE:
Grants-in-aid; Project/program grants.

PURPOSE:
To provide resources for the in-depth study of 19th century English literature.

LEGAL BASIS:
Private foundation.

ELIGIBILITY:
Grants are awarded only to IRS 501(c)(3) tax-exempt organizations. No grants are made directly to individuals.

GEOGRAPHIC RESTRICTIONS:
Primarily United States.

FINANCIAL DATA:
Amount of support per award: Average: $25,000 to $50,000.

APPLICATION INFORMATION:
Organizations may submit a proposal.
Duration: Varies.

ADDRESS INQUIRIES TO:
Carl H. Pforzheimer III, President
(See address above.)

THE PHILLIPS FOUNDATION   [293]
One Massachusetts Avenue, N.W.
Suite 620
Washington, DC 20001
(202) 250-3887 ext. 628
Fax: (202) 216-9188

E-MAIL ADDRESS:
jhollingsworth@thephillipsfoundation.org

WEB SITE ADDRESS:
www.thephillipsfoundation.org

FOUNDED: 1990

AREAS OF INTEREST:
Promotion of a constitutional, democratic and free-market society.

NAME(S) OF PROGRAMS:
● **Ronald Reagan College Leaders Scholarship Program**

TYPE:
Scholarships. Renewable scholarships to college undergraduates who demonstrate leadership on behalf of the cause of freedom, American values and Constitutional principles.

YEAR PROGRAM STARTED: 1999

PURPOSE:
To recognize outstanding college undergraduate activists who are promoting American values on college campuses; to alleviate the financial burdens associated with higher education, permitting the winners to devote more time both to pursuing their academic goals and advancing their leadership initiatives.

ELIGIBILITY:
Applicants must be U.S. citizens enrolled full-time in good standing at any accredited four-year degree-granting institution in the U.S. or its territories. Applicants may apply during their sophomore year and may reapply before their senior year.

GEOGRAPHIC RESTRICTIONS:
United States.

FINANCIAL DATA:
Amount of support per award: $1,000 to $10,000.

NUMBER OF AWARDS: Varies.

APPLICATION INFORMATION:
Students submit an application form accompanied by a 500- to 750-word essay introducing themselves, discussing their perspectives on freedom, American values and Constitutional principles, and summarizing their leadership initiatives, activism and accomplishments. Supporting documentation on leadership achievements and official school certification of enrollment in good standing must accompany the application.

Duration: Up to two years. Renewals for sophomores applying.

Deadline: January 15.

TRUSTEES AND OFFICERS:
Thomas L. Phillips, Chairman
Jon A. Heimerman, Treasurer
D. Jeffrey Hollingsworth, Assistant Secretary
Kellyanne E. Conway
Becky Norton Dunlop
Thomas A. Fuentes
Alfred S. Regnery
Ronald E. Robinson

EXECUTIVE DIRECTOR:
John W. Farley

ADDRESS INQUIRIES TO:
Jeff Hollingsworth, Assistant Secretary
(See address above.)

THE ALBERT PICK, JR. FUND [294]

30 North Michigan Avenue
Suite 1002
Chicago, IL 60602-3502
(312) 236-1192
Fax: (312) 236-1209

E-MAIL ADDRESS:
cleopatra@albertpickjrfund.org

WEB SITE ADDRESS:
www.albertpickjrfund.org

FOUNDED: 1947

AREAS OF INTEREST:
Civic and community, culture, education, health and human services.

TYPE:
General operating grants; Project/program grants.

YEAR PROGRAM STARTED: 1947

PURPOSE:
To offer a hand when help is needed.

LEGAL BASIS:
Private family foundation.

ELIGIBILITY:
Grants are awarded to 501(c)(3) nonprofit organizations. The Fund restricts or prohibits support to individuals, nonprofits whose location and program emphasis are outside the city of Chicago, nonprofit organizations with exemptions other than Section 501(c)(3) of the Internal Revenue Code, fraternal, veteran, labor, athletic or religious organizations serving a limited constituency, coalitions, alliances or similar umbrella organizations, professional groups with volunteer service programs, local chapters of state, regional or national organizations, except those with Chicago-based projects which otherwise meet the guidelines and advance the goals of the Fund, hospitals, local chapters of single-disease agencies, building programs, endowment funds or capital campaigns, campaigns for the reduction or liquidation of debts, student aid

or scholarship programs, political, lobbying or voter registration programs or those supporting the candidacy of a particular individual, funds to support travel, group or individual, fund-raising events or benefits including sponsorship, tickets or courtesy advertising and organizations which might in any way pose a conflict with the Fund's goals, programs or employees.

An exception to this policy applies for those few grant relationships which fulfill the intent or philanthropic obligations of the Fund, or its founders.

In the area of civic and community, the Fund will consider applications from civic and community-based organizations working to stabilize and improve their neighborhoods. While the Fund does not support physical rehabilitation efforts, it will consider general operating requests and projects offering needed community services. Additionally, programs which enhance the environment, address the needs of minorities and the physically disabled and/or promote good government and human relations will be considered.

In the area of culture, the Fund supports the efforts of Chicago's cultural organizations, both large and small. It considers applications from the full spectrum of arts endeavors. The Fund is particularly interested in projects which seek to expand audience access or educate new audiences through outreach activities.

In the area of education, the Fund believes that its resources can have the greatest impact for educational improvement and reform at the pre-collegiate level. Therefore, the majority of its resources for this program category will be allocated to organizations with programs and services in early childhood education, tutoring, at-risk intervention and in-job training and re-training. A small number of grants may be made to postsecondary institutions designed to support the educational advancement and special needs of minorities, women and the disabled.

In the area of health and human services, the Fund values the efforts of Chicago-based nonprofits involved in the direct delivery of health and human service programs. Grants will not be made to hospitals or local chapters of single-disease agencies. Eligible nonprofits with programs in wellness, community-based health care delivery, youth, family planning or geriatric services, mental health, physical rehabilitation and crisis and shelter care services will be considered.

GEOGRAPHIC RESTRICTIONS:
Chicago, Illinois.

FINANCIAL DATA:
Amount of support per award: Minimum $3,000.

APPLICATION INFORMATION:
Eligible nonprofits are requested to complete an application form, available from the Fund. Only those proposals which completely meet the requirements outlined in the guidelines will be reviewed.

Duration: Generally, one year.

Deadline: January 21 for the Spring quarter, April 1 for the Summer quarter, July 1 for Fall quarter and October 1 for Winter quarter.

PUBLICATIONS:
Guidelines; grant application form.

OFFICERS:
Robert B. Lifton, Chairman
Albert Pick, III, Vice President
Burton Kaplan, Treasurer
Gregory M. Darnieder, Secretary

BOARD OF DIRECTORS:
Gregory M. Darnieder
Janet Diedericks
Burton Kaplan
Robert B. Lifton
Albert Pick, III
Gwendolyn M. Rice
Nadine Van Sant

ADDRESS INQUIRIES TO:
Cleopatra B. Alexander, Executive Director
(See address above.)

THE HAROLD WHITWORTH PIERCE CHARITABLE TRUST [295]

c/o Nichols and Pratt
50 Congress Street
Boston, MA 02109
(617) 523-8368
Fax: (617) 523-8949

E-MAIL ADDRESS:
piercetrust@nichols-pratt.com

WEB SITE ADDRESS:
www.piercetrust.org

AREAS OF INTEREST:
Education, green and public spaces, capital projects and arts education.

TYPE:
Capital grants; Project/program grants.

PURPOSE:
To support projects that will bring long-range benefits to Boston's citizens.

ELIGIBILITY:
Eligible organizations must be IRS 501(c)(3) tax-exempt.

No grants are made for scholarships to individuals. In addition, no grants are made for fund-raising events, films, videos, travel, fund-raising training or advocacy.

GEOGRAPHIC RESTRICTIONS:
Boston, Massachusetts area.

FINANCIAL DATA:
Amount of support per award: $10,000 to $60,000.

Total amount of support: Varies.

NUMBER OF AWARDS: Varies.

REPRESENTATIVE AWARDS:
Education: $20,000 to Associated Day Care Services, Boston, MA, to train and mentor teachers of infants and toddlers in an intensive Literacy Curriculum specifically designed for infants and toddlers; Capital Projects: $50,000 to Ballet Theatre of Boston, Cambridge, MA, for a capital grant to help make possible the construction of a new home for the Ballet Theater within a church in Cambridge; Green and Public Spaces: $10,000 to Boston GreenSpace Alliance for a second installment of a two-year grant for operating support for the Alliance.

APPLICATION INFORMATION:
Applications are available at the address above and must include a copy of the IRS tax determination letter. The application process consists of three steps:
(1) a telephone call to the Trust's grant administrator to determine eligibility;
(2) a concept letter describing the applicant

organization and its mission, etc., and; (3) after review of concept letters by the trustees, they will invite full proposals from a limited number of applicants. They will then decide which proposals to fund.

Duration: Varies.

Deadline: Concept letter due (postmarked) March 1 and September 15; Invited proposals: mid-April and mid-October.

PUBLICATIONS:
Application guidelines.

ADDRESS INQUIRIES TO:
Elizabeth D. Nichols, Program Director
(See address above.)

IRWIN ANDREW PORTER FOUNDATION   [296]

P.O. Box 580057
Minneapolis, MN 55458-0057

E-MAIL ADDRESS:
iapfound@hotmail.com

WEB SITE ADDRESS:
www.iapfoundation.org

FOUNDED: 1996

AREAS OF INTEREST:
Arts, education, environment and social programs.

TYPE:
Challenge/matching grants; Grants-in-aid; Project/program grants.

PURPOSE:
To fund innovative projects that foster connections between individuals, communities, the environment and the world at large.

ELIGIBILITY:
The Foundation provides funding for a variety of interest areas. The quality, innovation, thoughtfulness and effectiveness of a project are of more importance than the specific interest area. However, its areas of interest are the arts, education, environment and social programs.

International projects should be applicable to, and repeatable in, other regions. The Foundation gives funding to nonprofit organizations with U.S. IRS tax-exempt status only. International organizations must have a fiscal agent incorporated in the U.S. with an appropriate U.S. IRS tax-exempt designation.

The Foundation does not provide financial support for:
(1) general operating expenses;
(2) capital projects;
(3) endowments;
(4) scholarships;
(5) fund-raising events or activities, social events, goodwill advertising or marketing;
(6) lobbying, political, fraternal, athletic, social or veterans organizations;
(7) religious programs;
(8) travel for individuals or groups;
(9) individuals or;
(10) ordinary school funding.

GEOGRAPHIC RESTRICTIONS:
Illinois, Iowa, Michigan, Minnesota, North Dakota, South Dakota and Wisconsin.

FINANCIAL DATA:
Amount of support per award: Grants: $500 to $30,000 annually.

APPLICATION INFORMATION:
Two phase application. Phase I is a short online application. Phase II is a full written

proposal, due within 30 days of notification that the project was selected for further consideration.

Duration: Generally, one year.

Deadline: Phase I: March 31; Phase II: Within 30 days of notification.

ADDRESS INQUIRIES TO:
Amy L. Hubbard, Chairman
(See address above.)

PPG INDUSTRIES FOUNDATION   [297]

One PPG Place
Pittsburgh, PA 15272
(412) 434-2453 (voice mail)

E-MAIL ADDRESS:
foundation@ppg.com

WEB SITE ADDRESS:
www.ppg.com
www.ppgfoundation.com

FOUNDED: 1951

AREAS OF INTEREST:
Education, human services, culture and the arts, civic and community affairs.

NAME(S) OF PROGRAMS:
● **American Chemical Society Scholarships Plus Program**
● **Grant Incentives for Volunteerism by PPG Employees and Retirees (GIVE)**
● **Matching Gifts Program**
● **National Merit Scholarships**
● **PPG CARE Fund**
● **Public Education Leadership Community Grants (PELC)**

TYPE:
Capital grants; General operating grants; Project/program grants; Scholarships. American Chemical Society Scholarships Plus Program is designed for underrepresented minorities who will study chemistry or chemical engineering in college.

Grant Incentives for Volunteerism by PPG Employees and Retirees (GIVE) is a program to encourage PPG employee involvement in volunteerism. The GIVE Program recognizes personal involvement by active PPG employees and retirees who volunteer on their own time by providing grants to eligible institutions in the U.S.

Matching Gifts Program matches gifts of PPG employees and directors to qualified institutions.

National Merit Scholarships: the Foundation has three National Merit Scholarship Program categories. The Employee-Child Scholarship Program is for sons and daughters of PPG Industries, Inc. employees. The Plant Community Scholarship Program offers a community scholarship program to major PPG facilities. The National Achievement Scholarship Program awards two scholarships per year to outstanding African-American students in this program.

Public Education Leadership Community Grants (PELC) provides financial resources to public schools where employees are involved.

YEAR PROGRAM STARTED: 1951

PURPOSE:
To enhance the quality of life in those communities within the U.S. where PPG Industries has a major presence; to develop human potential.

LEGAL BASIS:
Corporate, nonprofit foundation.

ELIGIBILITY:
Grants are made to tax-exempt organizations in the Foundation's areas of interest. Priority is given to applications from organizations dedicated to enhancing the welfare of communities in which PPG Industries is a resident. It gives consideration to those organizations whose activities either enhance individual opportunities or help to strengthen the nation's human services, educational, or economic systems on a regional or nationwide basis.

In general, the Foundation will not award grants to advertisement sponsorship for benefit purposes, endowments, individuals, organizations established to influence legislation or support political activities, organizations outside of the U.S. or its territories, projects which would directly benefit PPG Industries, Inc., religious groups solely for religious purposes, special events and telephone solicitations or United Way agencies for operating support.

GEOGRAPHIC RESTRICTIONS:
United States.

FINANCIAL DATA:
Amount of support per award: Varies.

Total amount of support: $4,700,000 in grants paid for the year 2009.

Matching fund requirements: Contributions by PPG employees and members of the board of directors of the company are matched on a 1:1 basis by the Foundation; $25 minimum, $10,000 maximum per year per donor.

NUMBER OF AWARDS: 275 direct grants for the year 2009.

APPLICATION INFORMATION:
To apply for a Foundation grant, submit a proposal which includes:
(1) verification of Internal Revenue Code Section 501(c)(3) government instrumentalities tax-exempt status;
(2) organization's mission statement;
(3) purpose/objectives of the grant;
(4) summary of the project;
(5) amount requested and rationale;
(6) schedule of implementation;
(7) description of the benefits to be achieved and the population to be served;
(8) plans for evaluating and reporting results;
(9) most recent audited financial report of the organization;
(10) financial analysis of the project;
(11) person in charge of the project and qualifications and;
(12) names and affiliations of trustees or board of directors.

Proposals should be clear and brief. A member of the Foundation staff will contact the organization if more information is needed.

Duration: Varies.

Deadline: Requests for funding are accepted year-round.

STAFF:
Sue Sloan, Executive Director, PPG Industries Foundation
Leah Swiger, Program Administrator

BOARD OF DIRECTORS:
Charles E. Bunch, Chairman and Chief Executive Officer
James C. Diggs, Senior Vice President, General Counsel and Secretary

Robert J. Dellinger, Senior Vice President, Finance
Charles W. Wise, Vice President, Human Resources

PRINCIPAL FINANCIAL GROUP FOUNDATION INC.   [298]
711 High Street
Des Moines, IA 50392-0150
(515) 247-7227
Fax: (515) 246-5475

E-MAIL ADDRESS:
allen.andrew@principal.com

WEB SITE ADDRESS:
www.principal.com/about/giving

FOUNDED: 1987

AREAS OF INTEREST:
Health and human services, education, arts and culture, civic and community, and environment.

CONSULTING OR VOLUNTEER SERVICES:
The mission of the Principal Volunteer Network is to be the primary volunteer network for community service to educate and recruit employees, agents and retirees of the Principal Financial Group; thus enhancing the company's social responsibility goals and business objectives.

NAME(S) OF PROGRAMS:
● **The Charitable Giving Program**

TYPE:
Capital grants; General operating grants; Project/program grants.

YEAR PROGRAM STARTED: 1987

PURPOSE:
To support various educational, health and welfare, and civic and cultural organizations.

LEGAL BASIS:
Corporate foundation.

ELIGIBILITY:
Applicants must be nonprofit IRS 501(c)(3) organizations.

Grants are generally not made to athletes or athletic organizations, conference or seminar attendance, goodwill advertising, endowments or memorials, festival participation, fraternal organizations, hospital or health care facility capital fund drives, individuals, K-12 schools, libraries, organizations/projects or programs outside the U.S., partisan political organizations, private foundations, sectarian, religious or denominational organizations, social organizations, tax-supported organizations, or United Way organizations seeking funds for United Way-funded programs.

GEOGRAPHIC RESTRICTIONS:
Wilmington, Delaware; Cedar Falls, Greater Des Moines, Mason City and Waterloo, Iowa; Grand Island, Nebraska; Spokane, Washington; Appleton, Wisconsin.

FINANCIAL DATA:
Amount of support per award: Varies.
Total amount of support: Varies.

NUMBER OF APPLICANTS MOST RECENT YEAR:
744.

APPLICATION INFORMATION:
Proposals should include:
(1) a grant request form;
(2) cover letter with amount requested, background and mission of organization, purpose of funding, desired outcome and how measured;
(3) evaluation of previous funding;
(4) budget;
(5) board list;
(6) IRS exemption letter of 501(c)(3) status;
(7) one audit 990 form and;
(8) annual report.

10 copies of proposal should be sent if request is more than $10,000.
Deadline: March 1 for health and human services grants, June 1 for education grants, September 1 for arts and culture grants, and December 1 for civic and community grants and environment grants.

PUBLICATIONS:
Guidelines.

ADDRESS INQUIRIES TO:
Andrew Allen
Community Investment Consultant
(See address above.)

PROGRESS ENERGY   [299]
410 South Wilmington Street
Raleigh, NC 27601
(919) 546-6880
Fax: (919) 546-4338

E-MAIL ADDRESS:
woody.dicus@pgnmail.com

WEB SITE ADDRESS:
www.progress-energy.com

FOUNDED: 1908

AREAS OF INTEREST:
Education (primarily energy education), economic development and the environment, with an emphasis on carbon reduction and workforce development.

CONSULTING OR VOLUNTEER SERVICES:
Volunteer programs are linked to Employee Giving Campaign partners.

TYPE:
Challenge/matching grants; Development grants; Project/program grants; Scholarships.

YEAR PROGRAM STARTED: 1992

PURPOSE:
To provide financial support to a variety of organizations whose programs and activities benefit the company's customers and employees as well as Progress Energy operations.

LEGAL BASIS:
Corporate contributions program and foundation.

ELIGIBILITY:
Applicants should be tax-exempt organizations with a responsible and active governing board, serving without compensation and having no material conflicts of interest. If affiliated with United Way, applicants must have United Way approval for separate or additional fund-raising. Organizations should have a clear statement of purpose and no avoidable duplication of services of other organizations in the same area. No grants will be made to individuals, political candidates or fraternal, veterans or labor organizations. No funding for religious purposes, courtesy advertising, memberships or to athletic teams or programs when the purpose is not primarily charitable.

GEOGRAPHIC RESTRICTIONS:
Florida, North Carolina and South Carolina.

FINANCIAL DATA:
Amount of support per award: Varies.

Total amount of support: $4,000,000 Corporate and $7,000,000 Foundation average annually.
Matching fund requirements: Company will match employee contributions to approved charitable organizations/higher education.

APPLICATION INFORMATION:
Request proposal including cover letter, mission statement, purpose of funding, and IRS letter. Applications also accepted online.
Duration: One year. Renewal possible after a formal renewal request is received and evaluated.
Deadline: Varies.

PUBLICATIONS:
Annual report.

ADDRESS INQUIRIES TO:
Jennifer Pittman, Contributions Specialist
(See address above.)

THE PROSPECT HILL FOUNDATION   [300]
99 Park Avenue, Suite 2220
New York, NY 10016-1601
(212) 370-1165
Fax: (212) 599-6282

E-MAIL ADDRESS:
grants@prospect-hill.org

WEB SITE ADDRESS:
www.prospect-hill.org

FOUNDED: 1960

AREAS OF INTEREST:
Environmental conservation, nuclear weapons control, reproductive health, social services, and arts, cultural and educational institutions.

TYPE:
Endowments; Project/program grants. Environmental Conservation: Priorities include conservation of significant private and public lands, improvement of water quality, and protection of coastal areas.

Nuclear Weapons Policy: Priorities include reduction of nuclear weapons proliferation through multilateral agreements and use of international institutions, reduction of dependency on nuclear weapons through long-term cooperative security initiatives, and U.S. policymakers and citizens who are informed and thoughtful on issues of nonproliferation.

Reproductive Health: Priorities include the right of men and women to be informed of and have access to safe, effective, affordable and acceptable methods of fertility regulation of their choice; geographically, grants support activities in the U.S. and in Latin America.

Social Services: Support is directed to a range of programs seeking to improve people's quality of life.

YEAR PROGRAM STARTED: 1960

PURPOSE:
To advance the human experience while ensuring the well-being of the earth.

LEGAL BASIS:
Private foundation.

ELIGIBILITY:
Applicants must be nonprofit 501(c)(3) tax-exempt organizations. The Foundation does not consider grants for individuals, basic research, sectarian religious activities or organizations that lack tax exemption under U.S. law.

GEOGRAPHIC RESTRICTIONS:
United States, with a particular regional focus in Massachusetts, New Jersey, New York and Rhode Island.

FINANCIAL DATA:
Market value of endowment as of June 30, 2009: $53,000,000.
Amount of support per award: $10,000 to $50,000.
Total amount of support: $2,859,500 in grants for the year 2008 09. Matching contributions awarded: $314,207.

APPLICATION INFORMATION:
Unsolicited requests for support are not normally considered. Invited applicants may submit proposals. Two hard copies of the full application containing all the elements listed below should be provided:
(1) organization background and history;
(2) proposed grant activity including timeframe;
(3) description of how success will be measured for the proposed activity;
(4) biographies of key staff;
(5) list of board members;
(6) most recent three years of audited financial statements;
(7) organization budget (current and upcoming fiscal years);
(8) budget for proposed grant activities;
(9) list of other key funders including levels of support and;
(10) copy of IRS determination letter.

In addition, the narrative portion of the application should be sent to the e-mail address above.
Duration: Varies.

PUBLICATIONS:
Grants & Guidelines, brochure.

IRS IDENTIFICATION NUMBER: 13-6075567

STAFF:
Penny Fujiko Willgerodt, E.D.
Summer Greenstein, Grants Administrator

DIRECTORS AND OFFICERS:
John B. Beinecke, President and Director
William S. Beinecke, Director and Chairman
Frederick W. Beinecke, Vice President and Secretary
Robert J. Barletta, Treasurer
Frances G. Beinecke, Director
Sarah Beinecke Richardson, Director

ADDRESS INQUIRIES TO:
Penny Fujiko Willgerodt, E.D.
(See address above.)

PUBLIC WELFARE FOUNDATION, INC. [301]
1200 U Street, N.W.
Washington, DC 20009-4443
(202) 965-1800
Fax: (202) 265-8851

E-MAIL ADDRESS:
info@publicwelfare.org

WEB SITE ADDRESS:
www.publicwelfare.org

FOUNDED: 1947

AREAS OF INTEREST:
Workers' rights and criminal and juvenile justice.

NAME(S) OF PROGRAMS:
● **Criminal and Juvenile Justice**
● **Workers' Rights**

TYPE:
General operating grants; Project/program grants.

YEAR PROGRAM STARTED: 1947

PURPOSE:
To support efforts to ensure fundamental rights and opportunities for people in need; to look for carefully defined points where the Foundation's funds can make a difference in bringing about systemic changes that can improve the lives of countless people.

LEGAL BASIS:
Private foundation.

ELIGIBILITY:
Applicants' requests must adhere to the Foundation's funding guidelines.

GEOGRAPHIC RESTRICTIONS:
United States.

FINANCIAL DATA:
Amount of support per award: Varies.
Total amount of support: $22,500,000 allocated for grants for fiscal year 2010.

NUMBER OF APPLICANTS MOST RECENT YEAR:
1,106 for fiscal year 2008.

NUMBER OF AWARDS: 320 approved grants for fiscal year 2008.

APPLICATION INFORMATION:
Applicants should submit letters of inquiry, up to five pages long, four to six weeks before proposal deadlines. This letter should contain facts and figures about the organization, describe its mission and explain the purpose of the request, including the Program under which a grant is being requested. Applicants will be invited by e-mail to submit full proposals. The Foundation cannot consider full proposals which have not been invited.
Duration: Grants usually one or two years. Renewal possible.
Deadline: Letters of Inquiry should be received by November, February and June.

PUBLICATIONS:
Annual report.

IRS IDENTIFICATION NUMBER: 54-0597601

OFFICERS:
Peter Edelman, Chairperson
Michael C. Williams, Secretary/Treasurer

BOARD OF DIRECTORS:
Jackie Clegg
Peter Edelman
Thomas Ehrlich
Juliet Villarreal Garcia
Robert H. Haskell
Brent L. Henry
Goodwin Liu
Thomas J. Scanlon
Thomas W. Scoville
C. Elizabeth Warner
Michael C. Williams

PUBLIX SUPER MARKETS CHARITIES, INC. [302]
3300 Publix Corporate Parkway
Lakeland, FL 33811
(863) 688-7407

FOUNDED: 1966

AREAS OF INTEREST:
Youth, formal education and United Way.

TYPE:
Challenge/matching grants; General operating grants; Project/program grants. Youth and education programs.

YEAR PROGRAM STARTED: 1966

PURPOSE:
To give back to communities within the southeastern states.

LEGAL BASIS:
Private foundation.

ELIGIBILITY:
Applicants should be 501(c)(3) organizations in operation longer than one year. Broad community support. No grants to individuals.

GEOGRAPHIC RESTRICTIONS:
Alabama, Florida, Georgia, South Carolina and Tennessee.

FINANCIAL DATA:
Amount of support per award: $100 to $100,000.
Matching fund requirements: Only through Publix associates for education.

NUMBER OF APPLICANTS MOST RECENT YEAR:
4,772.

NUMBER OF AWARDS: 3,400.

REPRESENTATIVE AWARDS:
$50,000 to Salvation Army for a capital campaign (over five years); $6,000 to Atlanta-Fulton County Zoo; $5,000 to Camp Fire Boys and Girls.

APPLICATION INFORMATION:
Applicants should send in a formal request on the organization's letterhead. Attach a copy of current 501(c)(3) Determination Letter. Applicant's 501(c)(3) should be in effect in excess of one year. Request should fall within the Charity's focus of youth, formal education and United Way. An application will be sent to be completed and returned with the requested information (per the application). Notification by letter six to eight weeks after submission.

IRS IDENTIFICATION NUMBER: 59-6194119

OFFICERS:
Carol Jenkins Barnett, President
Hoyt R. Barnett, Vice President
Tina Johnson, Treasurer
John Attaway, Secretary
Sharon Miller, Executive Director
Barbara Hart, Director

ADDRESS INQUIRIES TO:
Sharon Miller, Executive Director
(See address above.)

*SPECIAL STIPULATIONS:
Telephone requests, faxes and e-mails will not be accepted and are strongly discouraged; please make all inquiries in writing. 501(c)(3) determination letter from IRS required.

THE QUAKER CHEMICAL FOUNDATION [303]
901 Hector Street
Conshohocken, PA 19428-0809
(610) 832-4301

WEB SITE ADDRESS:
www.quakerchem.com

FOUNDED: 1962

AREAS OF INTEREST:
Civic and community, cultural, health and welfare, and education.

TYPE:
Matching gifts; Project/program grants. The Foundation matches employee gifts to qualified educational institutions, health and

welfare organizations, civic and arts or cultural institutions which are operated for the benefit of the general public.

YEAR PROGRAM STARTED: 1964

PURPOSE:
To help community projects where the company has domestic operations.

LEGAL BASIS:
Corporate foundation.

ELIGIBILITY:
Applicants must be IRS 501(c)(3) tax-exempt organizations. As a general rule, the Foundation does not support national organizations, limiting its interest to those organizations that are active in the areas in which the Quaker Chemical Corporation has operations.

FINANCIAL DATA:
Amount of support per award: Average grant: $1,500.
Matching fund requirements: Minimum $25 and maximum $1,000 per employee, retiree, director or spouse thereof per fiscal year.

NUMBER OF APPLICANTS MOST RECENT YEAR: 126.

NUMBER OF AWARDS: 52.

REPRESENTATIVE AWARDS:
Bartram's Garden; Conshohocken Fellowship House; Philadelphia Zoo; Delaware Valley Science Fairs.

APPLICATION INFORMATION:
The following information be included in the application:
(1) project description;
(2) budget and;
(3) list of board of directors and officers.
Duration: One year.
Deadline: April 30.

PUBLICATIONS:
Guidelines.

IRS IDENTIFICATION NUMBER: 23-6245803

TRUSTEES:
Craig E. Bush
Katherine N. Coughenour
Irene M. Kisleiko
Christian Scholund
Jane L. Williams

ADDRESS INQUIRIES TO:
Secretary to Foundation
(See address above.)

THE NELL J. REDFIELD FOUNDATION [304]
P.O. Box 61
Reno, NV 89504
(775) 323-1373
Fax: (775) 323-4476

E-MAIL ADDRESS:
redfieldfoundation@yahoo.com

FOUNDED: 1974

AREAS OF INTEREST:
Aged, disadvantaged children, education, religion, health care and the homeless poor.

TYPE:
Capital grants; Challenge/matching grants; Development grants; Matching gifts; Project/program grants. Grants for higher education. Medical and social welfare for disadvantaged children and seniors.

PURPOSE:
To promote education, health care and care for the homeless poor.

LEGAL BASIS:
Nonprofit foundation.

ELIGIBILITY:
Grants are made to organizations that have tax-exempt status under Section 501(c)(3) of the Internal Revenue Code. Nonsectarian religious programs may apply. No grants are made to individuals or private foundations.

Grants are restricted to organizations in northern Nevada.

GEOGRAPHIC RESTRICTIONS:
Northern Nevada.

FINANCIAL DATA:
Amount of support per award: Varies.
Total amount of support: Varies.

APPLICATION INFORMATION:
Initially, contact the fund with a two-page summary that includes the specific goals, objectives, proposed activities and results expected.
Duration: One year. Renewal possible.
Deadline: Quarterly during each calendar year.

ADDRESS INQUIRIES TO:
Gerald C. Smith, Director
(See address above.)

THE REEBOK FOUNDATION [305]
1895 J.W. Foster Boulevard
Canton, MA 02072
(781) 401-5000
Fax: (781) 401-4744

WEB SITE ADDRESS:
www.reebok.com

FOUNDED: 1986

AREAS OF INTEREST:
Programs for underserved youth in the greater Boston, MA area.

TYPE:
General operating grants; Matching gifts.

YEAR PROGRAM STARTED: 1986

PURPOSE:
To help children fulfill their potential.

LEGAL BASIS:
Corporate foundation.

ELIGIBILITY:
Grant applicants must be nonprofit organizations that provide equal access to funding and equal opportunity, and do not discriminate based on race, religion or sex. Grants are not made to individuals, political or fraternal organizations, or for advertising in program books or medical research.

GEOGRAPHIC RESTRICTIONS:
Greater Boston, Massachusetts area.

FINANCIAL DATA:
Amount of support per award: $500 to $10,000.
Total amount of support: $369,576 for the year 2008.
Matching fund requirements: Employees of Reebok International Ltd, its subsidiaries and divisions. Organizations must be IRS 501(c)(3). Employee contributions to qualified organizations are matched dollar-for-dollar, up to $1,500 maximum.

NUMBER OF AWARDS: 695 for the year 2008.

APPLICATION INFORMATION:
An initial letter is requested to determine the interest and appropriateness of a full proposal.

Deadline: Applications accepted throughout the year.

PUBLICATIONS:
Guidelines.

IRS IDENTIFICATION NUMBER: 04-3073548

STAFF:
Geri Noonan, Executive Director

BOARD OF TRUSTEES:
Joe Keane, Chief Financial Officer and Chief Operating Officer

ADDRESS INQUIRIES TO:
Meghan Grimaldi, Global Philanthropy
(See address above.)

THE REGENSTEIN FOUNDATION [306]
401 South LaSalle Street
Suite 205
Chicago, IL 60605
(312) 362-0535
Fax: (312) 362-0537

E-MAIL ADDRESS:
regfound@aol.com

FOUNDED: 1950

TYPE:
Capital grants; Endowments; General operating grants. Support for numerous fields including education, community services, medicine and health, urban affairs, arts and music. In general, most grants are made to organizations located in and directly serving the residents of Illinois, basically in the metropolitan Chicago area.

YEAR PROGRAM STARTED: 1950

PURPOSE:
To help improve life and the community in and around Chicago.

LEGAL BASIS:
Private foundation.

ELIGIBILITY:
Any charitable organization other than private foundations for exempt purposes. No grants are made to individuals or for the benefit of designated individuals.

GEOGRAPHIC RESTRICTIONS:
Chicago, Illinois.

FINANCIAL DATA:
Only a small number of applicants will receive funds due to the relatively limited amount available and the number of organizations funded on trustee initiative.
Amount of support per award: Varies.
Total amount of support: Varies.

NUMBER OF APPLICANTS MOST RECENT YEAR: 45.

NUMBER OF AWARDS: 35.

APPLICATION INFORMATION:
Contact the Foundation in writing for an application.
Duration: One year. Renewable.
Deadline: March 31 and September 30.

OFFICERS:
Susan Regenstein, Chairperson
Thomas Stazak, Vice President and Treasurer

ADDRESS INQUIRIES TO:
Susan Regenstein, Chairperson
(See address above.)

THE CHARLES H. REVSON FOUNDATION [307]

55 East 59th Street
23rd Floor
New York, NY 10022
(212) 935-3340
Fax: (212) 688-0633

E-MAIL ADDRESS:
info@revsonfoundation.org

WEB SITE ADDRESS:
www.revsonfoundation.org

FOUNDED: 1956

AREAS OF INTEREST:
Urban affairs, with emphasis on New York City, education, biomedical research policy and Jewish philanthropy and education.

TYPE:
Fellowships; Project/program grants; Research grants. The Foundation supports a number of ongoing fellowship programs in public policy, biomedical research and Jewish education.

YEAR PROGRAM STARTED: 1978

PURPOSE:
To make a commitment to spread knowledge and to improve human life.

LEGAL BASIS:
Private foundation.

ELIGIBILITY:
Grants are made to nonprofit, tax-exempt organizations. The Foundation does not make grants to individuals or for endowments, local health appeals, direct service programs, building or construction funds, or routine budgetary support.

GEOGRAPHIC RESTRICTIONS:
New York, New York and Israel.

FINANCIAL DATA:
Amount of support per award: $1,000 to $500,000.

REPRESENTATIVE AWARDS:
$1,727,700 to New York University to support the Charles H. Revson Law Students Public Interest Fellowship Program (LSPIN) for 75 internships for New York-area law students in each of the next three summers; $900,000 to the Center on Budget and Policy Priorities to support its monitoring and public education activities related to the federal budget.

APPLICATION INFORMATION:
The Foundation welcomes letters of inquiry from prospective grantees. Letters should be no longer than two pages and include:
(1) Revson program area of proposed project;
(2) brief description of project and of sponsoring organization and;
(3) amount requested.

Allow up to 90 days for a response from the Foundation.

In response to a letter of inquiry, the Foundation may invite the submission of a complete proposal.

No proposals accepted by fax.
Duration: Varies.

PUBLICATIONS:
Biennial report; application guidelines; 20-year report.

IRS IDENTIFICATION NUMBER: 13-6126105

STAFF:
Julie Sandorf, President
Azade Ardali, Administrative Officer
Nessa Rapoport, Senior Program Officer
Yulian Ramos, Program Officer
Karen Yu, Accountant
Maria Marcantonio, Grants Administrator
Jacob Taber, Program Assistant in Jewish Philanthropy and Education

BOARD OF DIRECTORS:
Martha Minow, Chairman
Charles H. Revson, Jr., Secretary and Treasurer
Stacy Dick
Cheryl Cohen Effron
Suzanne Gluck
Jeffrey Goldberg
Jerome Groopman
Reynold Levy
Gerald Rosenfeld
Clifford Tabin

ADDRESS INQUIRIES TO:
See e-mail address above.

Z. SMITH REYNOLDS FOUNDATION, INC. [308]

147 South Cherry Street
Suite 200
Winston-Salem, NC 27101-5287
(336) 725-7541 ext. 105
(800) 443-8319
Fax: (336) 725-6069

E-MAIL ADDRESS:
lwinner@zsr.org

WEB SITE ADDRESS:
www.zsr.org

FOUNDED: 1936

AREAS OF INTEREST:
Community and economic development, environment, pre-collegiate education, social justice and equity, and democracy and civic engagement.

TYPE:
Challenge/matching grants; General operating grants; Project/program grants; Seed money grants. Sabbatical Program.

YEAR PROGRAM STARTED: 1936

PURPOSE:
To support charitable causes within the state of North Carolina.

LEGAL BASIS:
Family foundation.

ELIGIBILITY:
North Carolina public and nonprofit private institutions and organizations are eligible. No grants are made to individuals for any purpose.

GEOGRAPHIC RESTRICTIONS:
North Carolina.

FINANCIAL DATA:
Amount of support per award: $500 to $1,200,000.

Total amount of support: Approximately $20,522,736 for year ending December 2010.

NUMBER OF APPLICANTS MOST RECENT YEAR:
Approximately 362 in 2010.

NUMBER OF AWARDS: Approximately 190 in 2010.

APPLICATION INFORMATION:
Application information can be downloaded from the web site.
Deadline: February for the spring meeting and August for the fall meeting.

PUBLICATIONS:
Annual report.

IRS IDENTIFICATION NUMBER: 58-6038145

OFFICERS:
David L. Neal, President
Nancy R. Bagley, Vice President
John O. McNairy, Treasurer
Terry Lockamy, Assistant Treasurer
Leslie J. Winner, Secretary
Patricia B. Williamson, Assistant Secretary

TRUSTEES:
Nancy R. Bagley
Anita Brown-Graham
Daniel G. Clodfelter
Ilana Dubester
John O. McNairy
Katharine B. Mountcastle, Life Trustee
Mary Mountcastle
Stephen L. Neal
Jane S. Patterson
Virgil Smith
Lloyd P. Tate, Jr.

ADDRESS INQUIRIES TO:
Leslie J. Winner, Secretary
(See address above.)

THE RHODE ISLAND FOUNDATION/RHODE ISLAND COMMUNITY FOUNDATION [309]

One Union Station
Providence, RI 02903-1746
(401) 274-4564
Fax: (401) 331-8085

E-MAIL ADDRESS:
oheleen@rifoundation.org

WEB SITE ADDRESS:
www.rifoundation.org

FOUNDED: 1916

TYPE:
Challenge/matching grants; Conferences/seminars; Demonstration grants; Development grants; Fellowships; General operating grants; Project/program grants; Research grants; Scholarships; Seed money grants; Technical assistance; Travel grants; Loan forgiveness programs.

YEAR PROGRAM STARTED: 1916

PURPOSE:
To improve the living conditions and well-being of the inhabitants of Rhode Island.

LEGAL BASIS:
Community foundation.

ELIGIBILITY:
Grants are not generally made directly to individuals. Programs must primarily benefit Rhode Island.

GEOGRAPHIC RESTRICTIONS:
Rhode Island.

FINANCIAL DATA:
Amount of support per award: Varies.

Total amount of support: $29,000,000 for the year 2010.

Matching fund requirements: Varies.

NUMBER OF APPLICANTS MOST RECENT YEAR:
1,400.

NUMBER OF AWARDS: 850 from discretionary funds.

APPLICATION INFORMATION:
Guidelines available at the Foundation web site.
Duration: Varies.

Deadline: Varies.

PUBLICATIONS:
Annual report; newsletter; guidelines; reports.

BOARD OF DIRECTORS:
David M. Hirsch, Chairman
Lorne Adrain
Stephanie Chaffee
Patricia J. Flanagan, M.D.
Cynthia Garcia-Coll, Ph.D.
Marie Langlois
Hon. Ronald K. Machtley
Hon. Maureen McKenna Goldberg
Cynthia Reed
Keith Stokes
Anne Szostak

ADDRESS INQUIRIES TO:
Owen Heleen, Vice President for
Grant Programs
(See address above.)

SID W. RICHARDSON
FOUNDATION   [310]
309 Main Street
Fort Worth, TX 76102
(817) 336-0494
Fax: (817) 332-2176

E-MAIL ADDRESS:
cjohns@sidrichardson.org

WEB SITE ADDRESS:
www.sidrichardson.org

FOUNDED: 1947

AREAS OF INTEREST:
Education, health, human service, and the
arts and humanities.

TYPE:
Capital grants; Challenge/matching grants;
Development grants; General operating
grants; Matching gifts; Professorships;
Project/program grants; Research grants.

PURPOSE:
To support organizations that serve the
people of Texas.

LEGAL BASIS:
Private foundation.

ELIGIBILITY:
All funds must be limited to the state of
Texas for IRS 501(c)(3) tax-exempt
institutions and organizations or 509(a)
organizations (other than a private foundation
under the latter code). An organization also
may qualify if it falls within the terms of
Section 170(c)(1) and the contribution
requested is to be used exclusively for public
purposes. No grants are made to individuals.

GEOGRAPHIC RESTRICTIONS:
Texas.

FINANCIAL DATA:
Amount of support per award: $1,000 to
$1,650,000.

NUMBER OF APPLICANTS MOST RECENT YEAR:
Approximately 400.

REPRESENTATIVE AWARDS:
Education: $200,000 to the University of
Texas at Dallas for the UTeach Dallas
Program; Health: $100,000 to Fort Worth
Northside Community Health Center, Inc. for
general support; Human Services: $135,000
to Safe Haven of Tarrant County for general
support; Cultural: $50,000 to Performing Arts
Fort Worth for the Children's Education
Program.

APPLICATION INFORMATION:
Initial contact should be by letter briefly
explaining project or program. If the project
is within areas of current activity, an
application will be provided.
Duration: Up to four years.
Deadline: January 15.

PUBLICATIONS:
Annual report.

IRS IDENTIFICATION NUMBER: 75-6015828

BOARD OF DIRECTORS:
Edward P. Bass, Chairman
Lee M. Bass, Vice President
Sid R. Bass, Vice President

ADDRESS INQUIRIES TO:
Pete Geren, President
(See address above.)

ROCKEFELLER FAMILY
FUND   [311]
475 Riverside Drive
Room 900
New York, NY 10115-0066
(212) 812-4252
Fax: (212) 812-4299

E-MAIL ADDRESS:
ccaddle-steele@rffund.org

WEB SITE ADDRESS:
www.rffund.org

FOUNDED: 1967

NAME(S) OF PROGRAMS:
● **Citizen Participation and Government
  Accountability**
● **Economic Justice for Women**
● **Environment**
● **Institutional Responsiveness**

TYPE:
Challenge/matching grants; General operating
grants. The Citizen Participation and
Government Accountability program supports
nonpartisan organizations that help citizens
exercise the right to vote and navigate
government processes and institutions. It
advocate for more effective oversight of
public officials and public expenditures. The
program looks for ways to increase citizen
participation in the formation of public
policy.

Economic Justice for Women program seeks
to improve the quality of life for working
women and their families by advocating for
equitable employment opportunities and
updated employment standards.

Initiatives under the Environment program
are designed to enact aggressive policies at
the state and national levels to reduce carbon
emissions; highlight the risks of coal-burning
power plants and mountaintop removal
coal-mining; and sound climate science,
while exposing those who distort it.

The Institutional Responsiveness program
area helps to provide organizations with the
means to effect the policies and actions of
public and private institutions.

YEAR PROGRAM STARTED: 1967

PURPOSE:
To make grants to nonprofit organizations in
the areas of economic justice for women, the
environment, institutional responsiveness,
citizen participation and government
accountability.

LEGAL BASIS:
A not-for-profit charitable corporation
existing under the New York state
not-for-profit corporation law.

ELIGIBILITY:
Tax-exempt organizations engaged in
educational and charitable activities of
national significance are eligible for support.

The Fund does not ordinarily consider
projects that pertain to a single community,
except in the rare instance where a project is
unique, strategically placed to advance a
national issue, or is likely to serve as a
national model. Grants are rarely made to
organizations which traditionally enjoy
popular support, such as universities,
museums, hospitals or endowed institutions.

The Family Fund does not make grants for
academic or scholarly research or social or
human service programs. Grants are also not
made to support individuals, scholarships,
international programs, domestic programs
dealing with international issues,
profit-making businesses, construction or
restoration projects, or to reduce an
organization's debt. Instead, support is
offered for advocacy efforts that are
action-oriented and likely to yield tangible
public policy results.

GEOGRAPHIC RESTRICTIONS:
United States.

FINANCIAL DATA:
Total net assets of $76,083,100 as of
December 31, 2008.
Amount of support per award: $40,000
average for the year ended December 31,
2008.
Total amount of support: $1,920,000 core
grants funding for the year ended December
31, 2008.
Matching fund requirements: Fund will
match employee contributions.

NUMBER OF AWARDS: 49 core grants funded for
the year ended December 31, 2008.

REPRESENTATIVE AWARDS:
Citizen Participation and Government
Accountability: $40,000 to Voter Action,
Seattle, WA, to prevent disenfranchisement of
eligible voters by challenging the use of
unreliable voting machines; Economic Justice
for Women: $40,000 to the Women's Law
Project, Philadelphia, PA for the WomenVote
PA project to undertake voter education,
increase voter participation, and develop a
statewide agenda designed to improve the
economic status of women in PA;
Environment: $4000 to Appalachian Voices,
Boone, NC to fight the development of new
coal-fired power plants; Institutional
Responsiveness: $30,000 to Project on
Government Oversight, Washington, DC to
investigate federal contract abuses and make
recommendations for reform.

APPLICATION INFORMATION:
Contact the Fund for guidelines.
Duration: Grants are normally given for no
more than two years at a time and are
normally not given for more than three or
four consecutive years.
Deadline: Letters of inquiry are accepted
throughout the year.

PUBLICATIONS:
Annual report.

OFFICERS:
Peter Gill Case, President
Paul Growald, Vice President

David Kaiser, Vice President
Miranda Kaiser, Vice President
Emily Rockefeller, Vice President
Geoffrey Strawbridge, Vice President
Lee Wasserman, Director and Secretary
Leah D'Angelo, Treasurer
James Sligar, Counsel

BOARD OF TRUSTEES:
Peter Gill Case
Julia D'Amico
Eric Dayton
Paul Growald
David Kaiser
Miranda Kaiser
Renee Lambert
Emily Rockefeller
Justin Rockefeller
Rebecca Rockefeller
Wendy Rockefeller
Geoffrey Strawbridge

ADDRESS INQUIRIES TO:
Carolyn Caddle-Steele, Grants Manager
(See address above.)

ROCKWELL FUND, INC.   [312]
770 South Post Oak Lane
Suite 525
Houston, TX 77056
(713) 629-9022
Fax: (713) 629-7702

E-MAIL ADDRESS:
info@rockfund.org

WEB SITE ADDRESS:
www.rockfund.org

FOUNDED: 1931

AREAS OF INTEREST:
Community health, human services and
public education.

NAME(S) OF PROGRAMS:
 • **Operating Funds**
 • **Program/Project Support**

TYPE:
Capital grants; Challenge/matching grants;
Development grants; Endowments;
Fellowships; General operating grants;
Professorships; Project/program grants;
Scholarships; Seed money grants; Technical
assistance. Capacity building grants.

YEAR PROGRAM STARTED: 1949

PURPOSE:
To improve the quality of life in the greater
Houston area.

LEGAL BASIS:
Nonprofit organization.

ELIGIBILITY:
Grants are not made to individuals. Eligible
organizations must have IRS 501(c)(3)
not-for-profit status. Religious organizations
are eligible.

GEOGRAPHIC RESTRICTIONS:
Greater Houston, Texas area.

FINANCIAL DATA:
Amount of support per award: Varies.
Total amount of support: Varies.

APPLICATION INFORMATION:
Proposals should be made using Rockwell's
Grant Application Form, which can be
downloaded from the Fund web site.
Applying organizations must have IRS Form
990 and Internal Revenue Code 501(c)(3)
documentation.
Duration: One year. Renewable by
reapplication.

IRS IDENTIFICATION NUMBER: 74-6040258

STAFF:
R. Terry Bell, President and Chief Investment
Officer
Margaret E. McConn, C.P.A., Vice President
and Chief Financial Officer
Judy Ahlgrim, Grants Administrator
Quynh-Anh McMahan, Research and
Evaluation Manager
Jana Mullins, Program Officer
Carolyn Watson, Program Officer
Kerri Washburn, Accounting

ADDRESS INQUIRIES TO:
Judy Ahlgrim, Grants Administrator
(See address above.)

ROLEX SA   [313]
665 Fifth Avenue
New York, NY 10022-5385
(212) 758-7700
Fax: (212) 371-0371

WEB SITE ADDRESS:
www.rolexawards.com

FOUNDED: 1976

AREAS OF INTEREST:
Science and medicine, technology,
exploration, environment and cultural
heritage.

NAME(S) OF PROGRAMS:
 • **Rolex Awards for Enterprise Program**

TYPE:
Awards/prizes; Project/program grants; Seed
money grants. Awards are given biennially.

YEAR PROGRAM STARTED: 1976

PURPOSE:
To encourage groundbreaking personal
enterprise and initiative; to improve the
quality of life and expand the knowledge of
the world.

ELIGIBILITY:
Awards given for original and innovative
projects in the areas of science and medicine,
technology and innovation, exploration and
discovery, the environment and cultural
heritage. Given to an individual based on
originality, feasibility and potential impact
and exceptional spirit of enterprise.

NUMBER OF APPLICANTS MOST RECENT YEAR:
1,500 to 2,500.

PUBLICATIONS:
Applications; winners publication; journal.

ADDRESS INQUIRIES TO:
The Secretariat
(See address above.)

SAINT CROIX VALLEY
FOUNDATION
516 Second Street, Suite 214
Hudson, WI 54016
(715) 386-9490
Fax: (715) 386-1250

E-MAIL ADDRESS:
info@scvfoundation.org

WEB SITE ADDRESS:
www.scvfoundation.org

TYPE:
Project/program grants; Scholarships.

See entry 1455 for full listing.

SALISBURY COMMUNITY
FOUNDATION   [314]
220 North Tryon
Charlotte, NC 28202
(704) 973-4559
Fax: (704) 973-4959

E-MAIL ADDRESS:
kcoppadge@fftc.org

WEB SITE ADDRESS:
www.salisbury-cf.org

FOUNDED: 1944

TYPE:
Challenge/matching grants; Project/program
grants; Seed money grants. These grants are
offered to support charitable organizations.

YEAR PROGRAM STARTED: 1944

PURPOSE:
To support charitable organizations in the
Salisbury and Rowan County areas.

LEGAL BASIS:
Community foundation.

ELIGIBILITY:
Applicants must be 501(c)(3) organizations.

GEOGRAPHIC RESTRICTIONS:
Rowan County, North Carolina.

FINANCIAL DATA:
Amount of support per award: Varies.

APPLICATION INFORMATION:
Contact the Foundation for guidelines.
Duration: One year.
Deadline: September 9.

PUBLICATIONS:
Annual report.

IRS IDENTIFICATION NUMBER: 56-0772117

BOARD OF TRUSTEES:
Tom E. Smith, Chairperson
Dwight F. Messinger, Vice Chairperson
J. Steven Fisher, Treasurer
Greg Alcorn
Kathleen S. Boyd, D.D.S.
Sarah Busby
Larry T. Cloninger
Shari Graham
Judy S. Grissom, Ed.D.
Carol Herndon
Richard Huffman
Catrelia Steele Hunter, Ed.D.
Susan W. Kluttz
Edward P. Norvell
Patricia P. Rendleman

ADDRESS INQUIRIES TO:
Karen Coppadge, Grants Specialist
(See address above.)

THE FAN FOX AND LESLIE R.
SAMUELS FOUNDATION,
INC.   [315]
350 Fifth Avenue
Suite 4301
New York, NY 10118
(212) 239-3030
Fax: (212) 239-3039

E-MAIL ADDRESS:
info@samuels.org

WEB SITE ADDRESS:
www.samuels.org

FOUNDED: 1959

AREAS OF INTEREST:
The arts and health care for the elderly.

NAME(S) OF PROGRAMS:
 • **Performing Arts**

TYPE:
Development grants; Project/program grants. General operating grants for performing artists only.

The majority of the Foundation's funding in the arts is for the performing arts. In the area of health care, the Foundation will consider funding direct health care and social service programs to improve quality of life for New York City elderly.

The Foundation realizes that it cannot support an organization indefinitely and expects the programs it funds to become self-supporting within a few years.

YEAR PROGRAM STARTED: 1959

PURPOSE:
To provide funding in the arts, mainly for the performing arts; to improve, in the area of health, the quality of life of the elderly in New York, NY.

LEGAL BASIS:
Private foundation.

ELIGIBILITY:
Grants are made to organizations that are tax-exempt under Section 501(c)(3) of the Internal Revenue Code. The Foundation does not give grants to individuals or for scholarships. General operating support is for performing arts only.

GEOGRAPHIC RESTRICTIONS:
New York City.

FINANCIAL DATA:
Amount of support per award: $2,000 to $300,000.
Total amount of support: Varies.

APPLICATION INFORMATION:
A letter should briefly summarize the proposal and state the amount of the grant being requested. A copy of the organization's tax exemption letter issued by the IRS, most recent audited financial report, and organization brochure (if available) should be included. Also, Board of Directors list, project budget and current contributors list.
Duration: Health Care: One to two years; Performing Arts: One year.
Deadline: December 1, March 1, June 1 and September 1.

IRS IDENTIFICATION NUMBER: 13-3124818

STAFF:
Alexandra Francis, Program Associate

OFFICERS AND DIRECTORS:
Marvin A. Kaufman, Chairman
Joseph C. Mitchell, President
Rob Marx, Vice President

ADDRESS INQUIRIES TO:
Alexandra Francis, Program Associate
(See address above.)

THE SAN FRANCISCO FOUNDATION [316]

225 Bush Street
Suite 500
San Francisco, CA 94104
(415) 733-8500
Fax: (415) 477-2783

E-MAIL ADDRESS:
info@sff.org

WEB SITE ADDRESS:
www.sff.org

FOUNDED: 1948

AREAS OF INTEREST:
Community health, education, arts and culture, community development, and the environment.

NAME(S) OF PROGRAMS:
● **Bay Area Grants Program**

TYPE:
Project/program grants. The Foundation has a variety of special projects, mini-grant programs and initiatives. These grantmaking efforts are narrowly tailored to promote change around a particular issue or geographic area.

PURPOSE:
To promote change in the areas of community health, education, arts and culture, community development, and the environment.

LEGAL BASIS:
Community foundation.

GEOGRAPHIC RESTRICTIONS:
Alameda, Contra Costa, Marin, San Francisco and San Mateo counties, California.

APPLICATION INFORMATION:
Requests for Proposals are released and publicized periodically through the Foundation's web site and through targeted communications.

ADDRESS INQUIRIES TO:
Bay Area Grants Program
(See address above.)

SARA LEE FOUNDATION [317]

3500 Lacey Road
Downers Grove, IL 60515
(630) 598-8459
Fax: (630) 598-7364

WEB SITE ADDRESS:
www.saraleefoundation.org

FOUNDED: 1981

AREAS OF INTEREST:
Community organizations focusing on food-related programs such as food insecurity, nutrition and healthy lifestyles, women's self-sufficiency and diversity through highly visible cultural initiatives in the Chicago area.

TYPE:
Matching gifts; Project/program grants. Direct services grants/matching grants. Support for special projects and matching grants in the Foundation's areas of interest. The Foundation awards both single and very few multiyear grants.

The Foundation seeks to form partnerships with groups whose integrity, expertise and accomplishments enhance the overall chances of lasting success.

YEAR PROGRAM STARTED: 1981

LEGAL BASIS:
Corporate foundation.

ELIGIBILITY:
Nonprofit, 501(c)(3) organizations are eligible for support. Grants are made in the Chicago area, as well as selected communities where Sara Lee has a presence.

The following are not eligible for direct grants:
(1) capital and endowment campaigns;
(2) individuals;
(3) organizations with a limited constituency, such as fraternities or veterans' groups;
(4) organizations which limit their services to members of one religious group or those whose purpose is to propagate a particular religious faith or creed;
(5) political organizations, or those having the primary purpose of influencing legislation or promoting a particular ideological point of view;
(6) health organizations concentrating their research and treatment in one area of human disease;
(7) tickets to dinners and other fund-raising events as well as goodwill advertising in yearbooks or dinner programs;
(8) groups that discriminate on the basis of age, race, gender, religion, national origin, sexual orientation, disability or other legally protected classification;
(9) units of government and;
(10) organizations whose most recent audit shows an accumulated deficit.

GEOGRAPHIC RESTRICTIONS:
Metropolitan Chicago.

FINANCIAL DATA:
Amount of support per award: Varies.
Matching fund requirements: Full-time active Sara Lee employees, minimum $25 donation.

APPLICATION INFORMATION:
The Foundation utilizes an online Letter of Intent (LOI) and invitational Request for Proposal (RFP) system. Paper applications will not be accepted.
Duration: Primarily one year.

IRS IDENTIFICATION NUMBER: 36-3150460

OFFICERS:
Stephen J. Cerrone, President
Marcel Smits, Vice President and Treasurer
Paulette Dodson, Vice President and Secretary
Judy E. Schaefer, Vice President
Robert K. Chan, Assistant Treasurer
Helen N. Kaminski, Assistant Secretary
Mary Kay Phee Schenfeld, Assistant Secretary

STAFF:
Judy E. Schaefer, Director
Robert Rizzo, Senior Manager-Grants Program
Emily Wittenberg, Finance Administrator

BOARD OF DIRECTORS:
Stephen J. Cerrone
Paulette Dodson
Jon Harris
Marcel Smits

ADDRESS INQUIRIES TO:
Judy Schaefer, Director
(See address above.)

SARKEYS FOUNDATION [318]

530 East Main Street
Norman, OK 73071
(405) 364-3703
Fax: (405) 364-8191

E-MAIL ADDRESS:
sarkeys@sarkeys.org

WEB SITE ADDRESS:
www.sarkeys.org

FOUNDED: 1962

AREAS OF INTEREST:
Education, health care and medical research, cultural and humanitarian programs of regional interest.

TYPE:
Capital grants; Challenge/matching grants; Development grants; Endowments; Matching gifts; Professorships; Project/program grants; Research grants; Technical assistance; Training grants.

YEAR PROGRAM STARTED: 1962

PURPOSE:
To improve the quality of life in Oklahoma.

LEGAL BASIS:
Private charitable foundation.

ELIGIBILITY:
Applicants must be 501(c)(3) organizations which are not private foundations under 509(a) of the Internal Revenue Code.

GEOGRAPHIC RESTRICTIONS:
Oklahoma.

FINANCIAL DATA:
Amount of support per award: Varies.
Total amount of support: $2,861,748 for the year 2009.

NUMBER OF AWARDS: Approximately 62 for the year 2009.

APPLICATION INFORMATION:
The application form should be typed and all space limitations observed. The attachments should also be typed, unbound and printed on one side only. The Foundation does not accept faxed or e-mail proposals. A new application form should be requested each year.
Duration: Varies.
Deadline: February 1 and August 1. Notification following April and October board meetings.

PUBLICATIONS:
Application guidelines; annual report.

OFFICERS AND TRUSTEES:
Fred Gipson, President
Dan Little, Vice President
Joseph Morris, Secretary-Treasurer
Teresa B. Adwan
Richard Bell
Fred Gipson
Terry West

ADDRESS INQUIRIES TO:
Kim Henry, Executive Director
Susan Frantz, Senior Program Officer
Linda English Weeks, Senior Program Officer
Diana Hartley, Program Officer
(See address above.)

*SPECIAL STIPULATIONS:
The recipient must sign an agreement outlining the terms of the award and provide reports as requested.

DR. SCHOLL FOUNDATION [319]
1033 Skokie Boulevard
Suite 230
Northbrook, IL 60062-4109
(847) 559-7430
Fax: (847) 559-7439

WEB SITE ADDRESS:
www.drschollfoundation.com

FOUNDED: 1947

AREAS OF INTEREST:
Private education at all levels, including elementary and secondary schools, colleges and universities and medical and nursing institutions; general charitable programs, including grants to hospitals and programs

for children, developmentally disabled and senior citizens, civic, cultural, social services, health care, economic and religious activities.

TYPE:
Project/program grants.

YEAR PROGRAM STARTED: 1947

PURPOSE:
To help support worthwhile projects and activities.

LEGAL BASIS:
Private foundation.

ELIGIBILITY:
Organization must submit copy of tax-exemption letter from the IRS identifying that the applicant is a tax-exempt organization under Internal Revenue Code 501(c)(3), but is not a private foundation under 509(a) of the Internal Revenue Code. All grant requests should be in the form of a special project or program.

GEOGRAPHIC RESTRICTIONS:
United States.

FINANCIAL DATA:
Amount of support per award: $1,000 to $25,000.
Total amount of support: Varies.

APPLICATION INFORMATION:
A formal application form is required together with the tax-exemption letter, budget, financial statements and details about the organization, its officers, directors and specialized personnel.
Duration: Usually one year.
Deadline: March 1. Notification in November and distribution in December.

OFFICERS AND TRUSTEES:
Pamela Scholl, President
Anne Moseley, Vice President
Jeanne M. Scholl, Vice President
John Nitschke, Treasurer
Mary Ann Hynes
Stephen Meer
Richard B. Patterson
Daniel Scholl
Susan Scholl

ADDRESS INQUIRIES TO:
Pamela Scholl, President
(See address above.)

CHARLES AND HELEN SCHWAB FOUNDATION [320]
530 Lytton Avenue, Suite 200
Palo Alto, CA 94301
(650) 617-3476
Fax: (650) 617-3469

E-MAIL ADDRESS:
info@schwabfoundation.org

WEB SITE ADDRESS:
www.schwabfoundation.org

FOUNDED: 1987

AREAS OF INTEREST:
K-12 education, human services and culture and community.

NAME(S) OF PROGRAMS:
● **Foundation Initiative Grants**

TYPE:
Project/program grants; Technical assistance. Capacity building and human services programs.

YEAR PROGRAM STARTED: 2001

PURPOSE:
To support program development and funding in key social issues that have clear points of intersection and represent a continuum of interventions toward individual self-sufficiency.

LEGAL BASIS:
Private foundation.

GEOGRAPHIC RESTRICTIONS:
San Francisco Bay area, California.

FINANCIAL DATA:
Amount of support per award: Varies.
Total amount of support: $15,800,000 in grants for the year ended June 30, 2009.

NUMBER OF AWARDS: 120.

APPLICATION INFORMATION:
The Foundation does not accept unsolicited grant applications, grant proposals or letters of inquiry.
Duration: Varies.

PUBLICATIONS:
Foundation brochure; program reports.

IRS IDENTIFICATION NUMBER: 94-3188972

STAFF:
Ana Thompson, Executive Director
Dianne Barney, Administrative Director

BOARD OF DIRECTORS AND OFFICERS:
Charles R. Schwab, Chairman
Helen O. Schwab, President
Nancy Bechtle, Director
Sally Bowles, Director
Katie Schwab, Director

ADDRESS INQUIRIES TO:
Human Services Program
(See address above.)

THE ELLEN BROWNING SCRIPPS FOUNDATION [321]
6121 Terryhill Drive
La Jolla, CA 92037
(858) 212-3311
Fax: (858) 459-4809

E-MAIL ADDRESS:
dougdawson46@yahoo.com

FOUNDED: 1935

AREAS OF INTEREST:
Health care, medical research, education, conservation, recreation, family, youth and child welfare agencies, wildlife and animals, libraries and literacy.

TYPE:
Project/program grants; Research grants; Scholarships; Technical assistance.

YEAR PROGRAM STARTED: 1935

PURPOSE:
To provide funding for a number of social causes including medical research, health care, the arts, conservation and programs to help children.

LEGAL BASIS:
Private foundation.

ELIGIBILITY:
Applicant must be a tax-exempt, 501(c)(3) organization within San Diego County, CA.

GEOGRAPHIC RESTRICTIONS:
San Diego County, California.

FINANCIAL DATA:
Amount of support per award: $5,000 to $125,000.
Total amount of support: $1,125,000.

NUMBER OF AWARDS: 54.

APPLICATION INFORMATION:
Information is available from the Foundation.
Deadline: May 1.

ADDRESS INQUIRIES TO:
E. Douglas Dawson, Executive Director
(See address above.)

THE SEATTLE FOUNDATION [322]
1200 Fifth Avenue, Suite 1300
Seattle, WA 98101-3151
(206) 515-2131
Fax: (206) 622-7673

E-MAIL ADDRESS:
c.erickson@seattlefoundation.org

WEB SITE ADDRESS:
www.seattlefoundation.org

FOUNDED: 1946

AREAS OF INTEREST:
Arts and culture, education, basic needs,
environment, economy, health and wellness,
neighborhoods and communities.

NAME(S) OF PROGRAMS:
● **Community Grantmaking Program**

TYPE:
Capital grants; Development grants; General
operating grants; Technical assistance.
Equipment purchases; Facility renovation
grants.

YEAR PROGRAM STARTED: 1946

PURPOSE:
To improve the quality of life in the Puget
Sound area.

LEGAL BASIS:
Community foundation.

ELIGIBILITY:
Organizations must be IRS 501(c)(3)
tax-exempt. No grants to individuals.

GEOGRAPHIC RESTRICTIONS:
King County, Washington.

FINANCIAL DATA:
Amount of support per award: $1,000 to
$150,000.

NUMBER OF APPLICANTS MOST RECENT YEAR:
400.

NUMBER OF AWARDS: 183 for the year 2009.

APPLICATION INFORMATION:
Applications must include a copy of the IRS
tax determination letter and form 990.
Duration: One-time grants.
Deadline: February 15, May 15, August 15
and November 15.

PUBLICATIONS:
Annual report; *Healthy Communities Report.*

STAFF:
Ceil Erickson, Program Director

ADDRESS INQUIRIES TO:
Ceil Erickson, Program Director
(See address above.)

THE SEAVER INSTITUTE [323]
11611 San Vicente Boulevard
Suite 545
Los Angeles, CA 90049
(310) 979-0298
Fax: (310) 979-0297

E-MAIL ADDRESS:
vsd@theseaverinstitute.org

FOUNDED: 1955

AREAS OF INTEREST:
Arts and the sciences.

TYPE:
Project/program grants; Research grants;
Seed money grants.

YEAR PROGRAM STARTED: 1955

PURPOSE:
To provide seed money to highly regarded
organizations for particular projects which
offer the potential for significant
advancement in their fields.

LEGAL BASIS:
Tax-exempt private foundation.

ELIGIBILITY:
Applicant must be a legally tax-exempt
organization. The Institute does not support
endowments, scholarships, construction,
ongoing projects or deficit grants.

GEOGRAPHIC RESTRICTIONS:
United States.

FINANCIAL DATA:
Amount of support per award: $25,000 to
$400,000.

NUMBER OF APPLICANTS MOST RECENT YEAR:
250.

NUMBER OF AWARDS: 20.

REPRESENTATIVE AWARDS:
Woods Hole Oceanographic Institute for
brown tides; California Institute of
Technology for genetics and genes in cancer
cells; Nature Conservatory for plant
conservation; The Juilliard School
Conductors Program.

APPLICATION INFORMATION:
A written request is required. No formal
guidelines.
Duration: One year. Renewal is possible.
Deadline: Early April and early October.

PUBLICATIONS:
Official guidelines letter; annual report.

BOARD OF TRUSTEES:
Dr. David Alexander
Nancy Bekavac
Dr. Richard Call
Victoria Seaver Dean
Robert Flick
Myron E. Harpole
Margaret Keene
Carlton Seaver
Christopher Seaver
Martha Seaver
Patrick Seaver
Roxanne Wilson

ADDRESS INQUIRIES TO:
Victoria Seaver Dean, President
(See address above.)

SIMMONS FAMILY FOUNDATION [324]
722 West Shepard Lane
Suite 103
Farmington, UT 84025
(801) 550-5026
Fax: (801) 323-9314

E-MAIL ADDRESS:
elizabeth@simmonsfoundation.org

WEB SITE ADDRESS:
www.simmonsfoundation.org

FOUNDED: 1986

AREAS OF INTEREST:
Religion, community enhancement,
education, art and medicine.

TYPE:
Challenge/matching grants; Development
grants; General operating grants; Matching
gifts; Project/program grants; Research
grants; Scholarships; Seed money grants.

PURPOSE:
To foster virtues of good citizenship through
religious, medical, community, art and
educational purposes.

LEGAL BASIS:
Private family foundation.

ELIGIBILITY:
Grants to nonprofit organizations that are
tax-exempt under Section 501(c)(3) or
Section 170(c) of the Internal Revenue Code.
No grants to individuals.

GEOGRAPHIC RESTRICTIONS:
Utah.

FINANCIAL DATA:
Amount of support per award: Varies.
Total amount of support: $797,029 for the
year 2008.

NUMBER OF APPLICANTS MOST RECENT YEAR:
80.

NUMBER OF AWARDS: 29 for the year 2008.

REPRESENTATIVE AWARDS:
$15,000 to Caring Foundation for Children
for general support; $50,000 to Mothers
Against Drunk Driving for Strengthening
Families DVD; $10,000 to Utah Botanical
Center for Wetland Discovery Point.

APPLICATION INFORMATION:
Applications should consist of a letter and
other supporting documents, including:

Letter of Application. Organizations
requesting a grant should submit a letter on
the letterhead of the organization. This letter
must be signed by the chief executive officer
(e.g., President, Executive Director, etc.) and
should include a statement that the chief
executive officer approves the request and
endorses it as a strong priority of the
organization for Foundation support.

The letter must include the following
information:
(1) a brief description of the history and
mission of the organization and its current
activities;
(2) a statement that explains the problem or
issues the project addresses, how the project
will respond to or resolve the problem, and
why the strategy will be effective. If statistics
or opinions are included, the source or
reference should be cited;
(3) a statement of the specific population that
will benefit from the project;
(4) a description of the activities and
timetable for their accomplishment;
(5) a detailed budget of the overall cost of
the project, the amount of funding requested
from the Foundation and how the funds will
be used. The statement should discuss how
the project would be funded after the
Foundation's funding ceases;
(6) a list of all other sources of support that
have committed funding for the proposed
project, including the amount of support
committed;
(7) a list of all other sources of support from
which the organization has requested funding
for the project, including the amount
requested, and for which a response is
pending as of the date of application;
(8) the proposed method for evaluating the

project's effectiveness;

(9) the name, title and telephone number of the person with whom the Foundation should communicate regarding the request, if other than the chief executive officer;

(10) a photocopy of the latest determination letter issued by the IRS regarding the organization's current tax-exempt status under Section 501(c)(3) or Section 170(c);

(11) the organization's most recent audited financial statements. If the organization's financial statements are not audited, reviewed, or compiled by an independent accountant, the organization should submit internally prepared financial statements, including a balance sheet and a statement of revenues and expenses, marked unaudited;

(12) a complete copy of the organization's most recently filed IRS Form 990, including Schedule A and all supporting schedules;

(13) the organization's current annual operating budget, including revenues and expenses and;

(14) a current list of the organization's board of directors or trustees. If the project has a separate advisory group, the organization should submit these names in addition to the board list.

Deadline: August 15.

PUBLICATIONS:
Application guidelines.

IRS IDENTIFICATION NUMBER: 13-3420599

BOARD OF TRUSTEES:
Elizabeth S. Hoke
David E. Simmons
Harris H. Simmons
L.E. Simmons
Matthew R. Simmons
Julia S. Watkins

ADDRESS INQUIRIES TO:
Elizabeth W. Gerner, M.A., M.P.A.
Executive Director
(See address above.)

J. MARION SIMS FOUNDATION   [325]
800 North White Street
Lancaster, SC 29720
(803) 286-8772
Fax: (803) 286-8774

E-MAIL ADDRESS:
jmorton@jmsims.org

WEB SITE ADDRESS:
www.jmsims.org

FOUNDED: 1995

AREAS OF INTEREST:
Education, community health and wellness and adult literacy.

TYPE:
Challenge/matching grants; General operating grants; Project/program grants; Seed money grants; Technical assistance.

YEAR PROGRAM STARTED: 1995

PURPOSE:
To provide community support.

LEGAL BASIS:
Private foundation.

ELIGIBILITY:
Organizations and agencies classified as 501(c)(3) by the IRS can apply. Individuals are ineligible.

GEOGRAPHIC RESTRICTIONS:
Fort Lawn, Great Falls and Lancaster County, South Carolina.

FINANCIAL DATA:
Amount of support per award: $102,657.
Total amount of support: $3,105,442 for fiscal year ended September 30, 2009.

NUMBER OF APPLICANTS MOST RECENT YEAR:
40 for fiscal year ended September 30, 2009.

NUMBER OF AWARDS: 26 for fiscal year ended September 30, 2009.

APPLICATION INFORMATION:
Contact the Foundation for guidelines.
Duration: Grants are renewable.
Deadline: April 15 and October 15.

PUBLICATIONS:
Annual report.

IRS IDENTIFICATION NUMBER: 57-0355295

ADDRESS INQUIRIES TO:
James T. Morton, President
(See address above.)

THE SIRAGUSA FOUNDATION   [326]
One East Wacker Drive
Suite 2910
Chicago, IL 60601
(312) 755-0064
Fax: (312) 755-0069

E-MAIL ADDRESS:
info@siragusa.org

WEB SITE ADDRESS:
www.siragusa.org

FOUNDED: 1950

AREAS OF INTEREST:
Arts and culture, education, environment, health and human services.

TYPE:
General operating grants; Matching gifts; Project/program grants; Scholarships. Project grants or unrestricted support.

YEAR PROGRAM STARTED: 1950

PURPOSE:
To help people help themselves with the ultimate goal of improving their quality of life.

LEGAL BASIS:
Tax-exempt private foundation, incorporated in Illinois.

ELIGIBILITY:
No grants are made to individuals. Only tax-exempt organizations are eligible.

GEOGRAPHIC RESTRICTIONS:
Greater Chicago, Illinois area.

FINANCIAL DATA:
Amount of support per award: Varies.

NUMBER OF AWARDS: 136 for the year 2010.

APPLICATION INFORMATION:
Unsolicited letters of inquiry and proposals are not currently accepted.
Duration: Varies.

PUBLICATIONS:
Annual report; guidelines.

STAFF:
Irene S. Phelps, President and Chief Executive Officer

BOARD OF DIRECTORS:
Richard D. Siragusa, Chairman of the Board
James Durkan
Caitlyn Hicks
Jennifer I. Hicks
John E. Hicks, Jr.

Alisa Perrotte
Melvyn H. Schneider
Alexander Siragusa
Isabel Siragusa
John R. Siragusa, III
Mrs. Ross D. Siragusa
Ross D. Siragusa, III
Sinclair C. Siragusa

ADDRESS INQUIRIES TO:
Irene S. Phelps
President and Chief Executive Officer
(See address above.)

THE SKILLMAN FOUNDATION   [327]
100 Talon Centre Drive
Suite 100
Detroit, MI 48207
(313) 393-1185
Fax: (313) 393-1187

E-MAIL ADDRESS:
info@skillman.org

WEB SITE ADDRESS:
www.skillman.org

FOUNDED: 1960

AREAS OF INTEREST:
Children's relationships: parent and child relationship, family support and child care. Learning opportunities: early childhood education, public school improvement. Home and community: recreation and leisure, community building, capacity building, culture and the arts.

TYPE:
Capital grants; General operating grants; Matching gifts; Project/program grants; Technical assistance. In the area of Children's Relationships, the Foundation supports programs that foster positive, nurturing and sustained relationships between children and adults, especially parents.

In the area of Learning Opportunities, the Foundation supports programs that promote high-quality learning opportunities so that children acquire skills necessary to achieve, reach their full potential and lead productive lives.

In the area of Home and Community, the Foundation supports programs that strengthen healthy, safe and supportive homes and communities and contribute to the cultural enrichment and full development of children.

YEAR PROGRAM STARTED: 1960

PURPOSE:
To improve the lives of children in metropolitan Detroit; to apply its resources to foster positive relationships between children and adults; to support high-quality learning opportunities and to strengthen healthy, safe and supportive homes and communities.

LEGAL BASIS:
Private foundation.

ELIGIBILITY:
The Foundation considers proposals only from organizations which have been ruled to be tax-exempt under Section 501(c)(3) of the Internal Revenue Code and which are not private foundations as defined in Section 509(a) of the Code. Applications from government and public-sector entities will be considered, both for projects within the program areas and for planning, training,

technical assistance and evaluation to improve the way government entities deliver services.

GEOGRAPHIC RESTRICTIONS:
Detroit, Michigan metropolitan area, Macomb, Oakland and Wayne counties.

FINANCIAL DATA:
Amount of support per award: $10,000 minimum.

REPRESENTATIVE AWARDS:
$80,000 to City of Detroit-Health Department to implement the Nurse-Family Partnership home visiting project to improve the health and life-course of low-income, first-time mothers and their children in two Detroit neighborhoods; $160,000 to Detroit Area Pre-College Engineering Program to expand the math, science and engineering program to serve more students in grades 4-12 and their parents; $242,000 to The Yes Foundation for YES for PREP program, which identifies, develops and prepares gifted and talented minority youth in the city of Detroit to achieve their fullest potential as scholars and leaders in school and in the community; $180,000 to Girl Scouts of Metro Detroit for Studio B (Become, Belong, Believe and Build) program to meet the needs of preteen and teen minority girls linking them with young adult mentors in economically disadvantaged communities.

APPLICATION INFORMATION:
Send a letter of intent, and upon invitation, a full application. Applications should be clear and concise. When applying for a one-year grant or the first year of a multiyear grant, applicants should send one complete application.
Duration: Generally one year.

PUBLICATIONS:
Annual report; application guidelines.

IRS IDENTIFICATION NUMBER: 38-1675780

TRUSTEES:
David Baker Lewis, Chairman
Lizabeth Ardisana, Vice Chairman
Lillian Bauder
William M. Brodhead
Stephen E. Ewing
Edsel B. Ford, II
Carol Goss
Herman B. Gray
Denise Ilitch
Mary L. Kramer
Amyre Makupson
Eddie R. Munson
Robert S. Taubman

OFFICERS AND STAFF:
Carol Goss, President and Chief Executive Officer
Danielle Olekszyk, Chief Financial Officer and Treasurer
Alan Harris, Vice President and Chief Investment Officer
Tonya Allen, Vice President of Programs
Ed Egnatios, Senior Program Officer, Good Neighborhoods
Sharnita Johnson, Senior Program Officer, Changemaking
Kristen McDonald, Senior Program Officer, Education
Robert Thornton, Program Officer
Suzanne Moran, Grants Manager
Shirley Ingraham, Operations and Technology Manager
Steve Catallo, Investment Officer
Bill Hanson, Director, Communications and Technology

ADDRESS INQUIRIES TO:
Program Office
(See address above.)

ALFRED P. SLOAN FOUNDATION [328]
630 Fifth Avenue, Suite 2550
New York, NY 10111-0242
(212) 649-1649
Fax: (212) 246-7585

E-MAIL ADDRESS:
lin@sloan.org

WEB SITE ADDRESS:
www.sloan.org

FOUNDED: 1934

AREAS OF INTEREST:
Research and related programs in science and technology, education in science, technology, management, economic growth, industrial competitiveness and selected national issues.

TYPE:
Fellowships; Project/program grants; Research grants. Grants for imaginative and constructive projects in the Foundation's areas of interest.

YEAR PROGRAM STARTED: 1934

PURPOSE:
To support imaginative and constructive approaches to problems of domestic needs and uses.

LEGAL BASIS:
Private foundation.

ELIGIBILITY:
Recognized tax-exempt educational and research institutions with appropriate interests are eligible to apply. The Foundation's activities do not extend to primary or secondary education, religion, the creative or performing arts, medical research, health care or to the humanities. Grants are not made for endowments, buildings or equipment and are very rarely made for general support or for activities outside the U.S.

GEOGRAPHIC RESTRICTIONS:
United States.

FINANCIAL DATA:
Amount of support per award: Varies.
Total amount of support: $78,000,000 in grants annually.

APPLICATION INFORMATION:
A brief letter of inquiry, rather than a fully developed proposal, is an advisable first step for an applicant, conserving his or her time and allowing the Foundation to make a preliminary response as to the possibility of support.
Duration: One to three years. Extensions or renewals are possible.

PUBLICATIONS:
Annual report.

BOARD OF TRUSTEES:
Stephen L. Brown, Chairman
Leisle Lin, Secretary
Richard Bernstein
Mary Schmidt Campbell
Frederick Henderson
Freeman A. Hrabowski, III
Paul L. Joskow
Peter S. Kim, Ph.D.
Robert Litterman
Sandra O. Moose
James Poterba

Marta Tienda
Shelia E. Widnall

ADMINISTRATIVE OFFICERS AND STAFF:
Paul L. Joskow, President
William Petersen, Vice President and Chief Investment Officer
Christopher T. Sia, Treasurer and Chief Technology Officer
Leisle Lin, Vice President, Finance
Gail Pesyna, Vice President, Human Resources and Program Management
Jesse H. Ausubel, Vice President, Programs
Doron Weber, Vice President, Programs
Deborah Collins, Director, Administration
Anne McKissick, Director, Grants Administration
Kathleen E. Christensen, Program Director
Daniel L. Goroff, Program Director
Joshua M. Greenberg, Program Director
Ted Greenwood, Program Director
Paula J. Olsiewski, Program Director

A.O. SMITH FOUNDATION [329]
11270 West Park Place
Milwaukee, WI 53224-3690
(414) 359-4107
Fax: (414) 359-4180

WEB SITE ADDRESS:
www.aosmith.com

FOUNDED: 1955

AREAS OF INTEREST:
Education, civic and cultural affairs, human services, health and hospital, and United Way.

TYPE:
Project/program grants. Employee Education Matching Gift to secondary, four-year colleges and universities, junior colleges, community colleges, graduate and professional schools, technical and specialized schools.

YEAR PROGRAM STARTED: 1955

PURPOSE:
To strengthen higher education throughout the country; to promote the civic, cultural and social welfare of communities; to advance medical research and improve local health services where A.O. Smith plants are located.

LEGAL BASIS:
Corporate foundation.

ELIGIBILITY:
The Foundation does not make contributions to politically active organizations or any other organization whose chief purpose is to influence legislation.

FINANCIAL DATA:
Amount of support per award: $500 minimum.

NUMBER OF AWARDS: 229.

APPLICATION INFORMATION:
No specific application form is required. Inquiries should be made on your organization's letterhead and include the following information:
(1) the exact name and location of the organization;
(2) a description of the organization, including its objectives and purpose;
(3) verification of IRS 501(c)(3) tax-exempt status;
(4) the geographic area served by the organization;
(5) an explanation of the activity for which support is being requested;
(6) the amount of support being requested;

(7) a description of the benefits to be achieved and who will receive them;
(8) budget information about the organization, including other sources of income and;
(9) plans for reporting results.
Duration: Varies.
Deadline: October 31.

PUBLICATIONS:
Annual report.

ADDRESS INQUIRIES TO:
Roger S. Smith
(See address above.)

THE ETHEL SERGEANT CLARK SMITH MEMORIAL FUND   [330]

Wells Fargo Bank, N.A.
123 South Broad Street
Philadelphia, PA 19109
(215) 670-4226
Fax: (610) 436-7807

E-MAIL ADDRESS:
reginald.j.middleton@wellsfargo.com

FOUNDED: 1977

AREAS OF INTEREST:
Arts and culture, hospitals, education, libraries, social services, women's programs and people with disabilities in Delaware County, PA.

TYPE:
Capital grants; Challenge/matching grants; Development grants; Project/program grants. Grants and challenge grants to community interest organizations in southeastern Pennsylvania. Grants to hospitals, colleges and schools for program and capital projects. Grants for social services, arts/cultural events and centers.

YEAR PROGRAM STARTED: 1977

PURPOSE:
To promote the public welfare in Delaware County, PA.

LEGAL BASIS:
Private foundation.

ELIGIBILITY:
Candidates must be tax-exempt organizations not classified as private foundations or private operating foundations within the terms of the Tax Reform Act of 1969. Primary emphasis is on those serving community needs in Delaware County, the former home of Ethel Sergeant Clark Smith. Grants will be made for capital projects, operating expenses and special programs that are meaningful to the success of the individual endeavors of the organizations. As a general rule, requests for funds on a long-term basis or for deficit financing will not be considered.

GEOGRAPHIC RESTRICTIONS:
Southeastern Pennsylvania.

FINANCIAL DATA:
Amount of support per award: $5,000 to $50,000.
Total amount of support: Approximately $600,000 annually.
Matching fund requirements: Varies.

NUMBER OF APPLICANTS MOST RECENT YEAR:
Approximately 200.

NUMBER OF AWARDS: Approximately 60 annually.

APPLICATION INFORMATION:
Contact the Fund for application form.
Duration: Three consecutive years maximum.
Deadline: March 1 and September 1.

PUBLICATIONS:
Biennial report.

IRS IDENTIFICATION NUMBER: 23-6648857

ADVISORY COMMITTEE:
Diane R. Bricker
Jack Holefelder
Dr. Joseph E. Pappano, Jr.
Sen. Dominic Pileggi
Alice Strine, Esq.

ADDRESS INQUIRIES TO:
Reginald J. Middleton, Administrator
(See address above.)

THE W.W. SMITH CHARITABLE TRUST   [331]

200 Four Falls Corporate Center
Suite 300
West Conshohocken, PA 19428
(610) 397-1844
Fax: (610) 397-1680

E-MAIL ADDRESS:
mmontgomery@wwsmithcharitabletrust.org

WEB SITE ADDRESS:
www.wwsmithcharitabletrust.org

FOUNDED: 1976

AREAS OF INTEREST:
Basic medical research protocols dealing with cancer, AIDS and heart disease, financial aid programs for qualified needy undergraduate students at accredited four-year universities and colleges, and programs providing shelter, food and clothing for children and needy families with children and the elderly.

NAME(S) OF PROGRAMS:
- **College Scholarships**
- **Food, Clothing and Shelter**
- **Medical Research**

TYPE:
Project/program grants; Research grants; Scholarships. By invitation only, these grants are offered to provide financial aid programs for qualified needy undergraduate students at accredited four-year universities and colleges and also provide shelter, food and clothing for children and needy families with children and the elderly.

YEAR PROGRAM STARTED: 1978

PURPOSE:
To enhance medical excellence; to enable children, families and the elderly to improve their lives; to assure students of a college education.

LEGAL BASIS:
Private foundation.

ELIGIBILITY:
Grants are limited to nonprofit organizations within the Delaware Valley area: Bucks, Chester, Delaware, Montgomery and Philadelphia (PA), as well as the city of Camden (NJ). Grants are made only to tax-exempt, 501(c)(3) organizations, not classified as private foundations or private operating foundations within the terms of the Tax Reform Act of 1969.

Grants will be made for programs or organizations with proven or prudently predictable records of performance; never directly to individuals. Renovation projects,

special programs that deal with food, clothing and shelter for children and the elderly may be funded, but requests for general operating expenses, deficit financing and capital campaigns are not considered.

As a rule, under the Basic Needs Grants, the further away any request is from direct provision of literal food, clothing or shelter, the less likely funding may be granted.

The Trust budgets no funds to purchase charity tables, program advertisements, golf tournament sponsorships, organizational memberships or analogous fund-raising events.

GEOGRAPHIC RESTRICTIONS:
Bucks, Chester, Delaware, Montgomery and Philadelphia counties, Pennsylvania and Camden, New Jersey.

FINANCIAL DATA:
Amount of support per award: $5,000 to $142,000 for the year 2009-10.
Total amount of support: Program grants of $4,010,492 for fiscal year 2009-10.

NUMBER OF APPLICANTS MOST RECENT YEAR:
133 for fiscal year 2009-10.

NUMBER OF AWARDS: 98 for fiscal year 2009-10.

APPLICATION INFORMATION:
Proposals will be considered only for the following purposes:
(1) specific, basic medical research projects dealing with cancer, heart disease or AIDS;
(2) by invitation of the Trust only, accredited, four-year university and college financial aid programs for needy, worthy, full-time undergraduate students (no requests ever accepted directly from individual students) and;
(3) providing shelter, food or clothing for children age 18 or under (including needy families with dependent children) or the elderly age 60 and above.

The trustees endeavor to keep abreast of the needs and conditions in the area served by the Trust and variations from these policies may be made at their discretion.

Duration: Scholarship and Food, Clothing and Shelter grants: One year; Medical Research grant: Multiyear funding possible.

Deadline: Cancer and AIDS Research: June 15. Scholarships: May 1. Food, Clothing and Shelter: December 15 and June 15. Heart Research: September 15.

PUBLICATIONS:
Biennial report (includes application guidelines).

IRS IDENTIFICATION NUMBER: 23-6648841

TRUSTEES:
Mary L. Smith

ADMINISTRATORS:
Louise A. Havens, Grant Administrator, Medical Research
Deborah J. McKenna, Advisor
Michelle Montgomery, Grant Administrator, Food, Clothing and Shelter/Scholarships

ADDRESS INQUIRIES TO:
Michelle Montgomery, Grants Administrator
(See address above.)

THE JOHN BEN SNOW FOUNDATION, INC. [332]

50 Presidential Plaza
Suite 106
Syracuse, NY 13202
(315) 471-5256
Fax: (315) 471-5256

E-MAIL ADDRESS:
johnbensnow@verizon.net

WEB SITE ADDRESS:
www.johnbensnow.com

FOUNDED: 1948

AREAS OF INTEREST:
Arts and culture, community initiatives, education, environment, journalism, special grants, youth programs and historic preservation.

TYPE:
Capital grants; Challenge/matching grants; Development grants; Fellowships; Project/program grants; Scholarships; Seed money grants; Technical assistance.

YEAR PROGRAM STARTED: 1948

PURPOSE:
To grant funds for educational, cultural and humanitarian purposes.

LEGAL BASIS:
Corporation.

ELIGIBILITY:
Applicants must be IRS 501(c)(3) organizations primarily in central and northern New York state. Grants are made to qualified organizations for educational and humanitarian purposes.

The general policy of the Board of Directors gives preference to proposals seeking one-year funding of program-related grants, matching grants, startup grants and capital grants and to reject proposals from individuals, religious organizations, government agencies, or for endowments, contingency funding, or general operating support.

GEOGRAPHIC RESTRICTIONS:
Central and northern New York state.

FINANCIAL DATA:
Amount of support per award: Typically $5,000 to $15,000.

Total amount of support: $338,650 in total grants for the year ended December 31, 2008.

NUMBER OF APPLICANTS MOST RECENT YEAR:
More than 60.

NUMBER OF AWARDS: 36.

REPRESENTATIVE AWARDS:
Community Initiatives: $25,000 to WCNY Public Broadcasting, Syracuse, NY; Education: $25,000 to On Point for College to assist at-risk youth to attend college; Journalism: $12,000 to School Press Institute, Syracuse University, Syracuse, NY.

APPLICATION INFORMATION:
The Foundation is pro-active in seeking grant proposals from qualifying 501(c)(3) organizations. Additionally, the Foundation accepts unsolicited proposals from qualifying organizations.

Applicants should inquire about funding first. Foundation will then supply guidelines and a formal application to be filled out. The inquiry should include:
(1) the name and complete address of the organization;
(2) a brief summary of the project to be funded;
(3) the name and address of the person responsible for the use of funds and;
(4) a photocopy of the organization's IRS tax-exemption letter.

If the proposal meets the stated guidelines and priorities of the Foundation, a grant application will be forwarded. All grant applications must be submitted using the Foundation grant application form and must be received by April 1 of the year in which a grant is requested.
Duration: One year. Renewals depend on the project.
Deadline: Letter of inquiry: No later than January 1 of the year in which the grant is requested. Grant application: April 1. Final or progress report: March 1 of the year following grant.

PUBLICATIONS:
Guidelines; annual report.

BOARD MEMBERS:
David H. Snow, President
Jonathan L. Snow, Vice President and Treasurer
Emelie Melton Williams, Secretary
Angus M. Burton
Valerie A. MacFie
Allen R. Malcolm
Marilyn R. Melton

ADDRESS INQUIRIES TO:
Jonathan L. Snow
Vice President and Treasurer
(See address above.)

SOUTHWEST FLORIDA COMMUNITY FOUNDATION

8260 College Parkway
Suite 101
Fort Myers, FL 33919
(239) 274-5900
Fax: (239) 274-5930

E-MAIL ADDRESS:
info@floridacommunity.com

WEB SITE ADDRESS:
www.floridacommunity.com

TYPE:
Capital grants; Challenge/matching grants; Conferences/seminars; Demonstration grants; Project/program grants; Scholarships; Seed money grants; Technical assistance; Training grants.

See entry 1468 for full listing.

SOWERS CLUB OF NEBRASKA FOUNDATION [333]

1701 South 17th Street
Suite 1H
Lincoln, NE 68502
(402) 438-2244
Fax: (402) 438-2426

E-MAIL ADDRESS:
sowersclub@windstream.net

WEB SITE ADDRESS:
www.thesowersclub.com

FOUNDED: 1986

AREAS OF INTEREST:
Charity and education.

TYPE:
Project/program grants; Scholarships.

PURPOSE:
To offer assistance to organizations that serve and educate the community.

ELIGIBILITY:
Agency must have been in existence for a minimum of five years and must qualify as exempt under Section 501(c)(3) of the Internal Revenue Code. Grant requests will not be considered for individuals, promoting religious purposes or for political purposes.

GEOGRAPHIC RESTRICTIONS:
Lincoln, Nebraska and surrounding communities.

FINANCIAL DATA:
Total amount of support: $75,000 per year.

APPLICATION INFORMATION:
Grant request must include eight copies of the following:
(1) "Letter of Determination" from the IRS regarding 501(c)(3) status and;
(2) annual report or current Balance Sheet outlining your administrative costs. All information will be treated with strict confidentiality.

All Blanks on the Grant Request form must be completed. Do not answer a question on the Request form by reference to another question, document or party.
Deadline: February 15, June 15 and September 15.

BOARD OF DIRECTORS AND OFFICERS:
Dean Petersen, President
Stan Dinges, Vice President
Roger Zajicek, Treasurer
Lee Arellano, Secretary
Charlie Decker
Bradford Kistler
Dick Stephenson

ADDRESS INQUIRIES TO:
Lee Arellano, Secretary
(See address above.)

SETH SPRAGUE EDUCATIONAL AND CHARITABLE FOUNDATION [334]

c/o Bank of America
NY1-100-28-05
One Bryant Park
New York, NY 10036
(646) 855-1011
Fax: (646) 855-5463

AREAS OF INTEREST:
Hospitals, educational institutions and social agencies.

TYPE:
Project/program grants.

ELIGIBILITY:
The Foundation makes grants to hospitals, educational institutions, social agencies and other charitable organizations. No grants to individuals.

GEOGRAPHIC RESTRICTIONS:
San Diego, California; Maine; Boston area, Massachusetts; and metropolitan New York City, New York.

FINANCIAL DATA:
Amount of support per award: $10,000 to $20,000.

Total amount of support: $1,000,000 for the year 2009.

APPLICATION INFORMATION:
Contact the Foundation for application information.

Deadline: April 1 and September 1. Award announcement in June and December.

ADDRESS INQUIRIES TO:
Christine O'Donnell, Vice President
(See address above.)

THE STATE STREET FOUNDATION   [335]
State Street Financial Center
One Lincoln Street
Boston, MA 02111-2900
(617) 664-8720
Fax: (617) 664-8759

E-MAIL ADDRESS:
jamcgrail@statestreet.com

WEB SITE ADDRESS:
www.statestreet.com

FOUNDED: 1804

AREAS OF INTEREST:
Providing economically disadvantaged citizens with the skills they need to be successful, with a focus on initiatives that seek to achieve systemic change and address core problems affecting local communities.

NAME(S) OF PROGRAMS:
● **Global Philanthropy Program**

TYPE:
General operating grants; Project/program grants. Particular emphasis is on programs that help the poor in the Greater Boston inner-city neighborhoods and communities where State Street has a presence. The Foundation supports public/private partnerships that serve this need, build community capabilities and promote collaborations between community institutions to increase effectiveness.

YEAR PROGRAM STARTED: 1977

PURPOSE:
To channel funds back into the communities where State Street employees work and live.

LEGAL BASIS:
Corporate foundation.

ELIGIBILITY:
Grant applicants must be tax-exempt, 501(c)(3) organizations. The Foundation does not make individual scholarships grants, nor does it fund research, having a preference for programs emphasizing direct delivery of services. It does not support organizations by purchasing advertisements, tables or tickets at dinners or other functions.

FINANCIAL DATA:
Each year the Corporation allocates a minimum of one and a half percent for a three-year rolling average of the company's pre-tax income.
Amount of support per award: $3,000 to $25,000.
Total amount of support: $17,800,000 for the year 2010.

APPLICATION INFORMATION:
Grant Proposal Summary Form and instructions are available at the Foundation web site.
Duration: One year.
Deadline: April 1, August 1 and December 1. Notification of decision mid-July, mid-November and mid-March, respectively.

PUBLICATIONS:
Contributions guidelines.

JOHN STAUFFER CHARITABLE TRUST   [336]
301 North Lake Avenue, 10th Floor
Pasadena, CA 91101
(626) 793-9400
Fax: (626) 793-5900

E-MAIL ADDRESS:
jsenecal@lagerlof.com

FOUNDED: 1974

AREAS OF INTEREST:
Colleges, universities and hospitals within California.

TYPE:
Capital grants; Challenge/matching grants; Endowments; Fellowships; Matching gifts; Professorships; Project/program grants; Scholarships. All within the state of California.

YEAR PROGRAM STARTED: 1974

PURPOSE:
To support U.S. universities, colleges and hospitals in acquiring land, erecting buildings and other facilities, obtaining equipment, instruments, books, furnishings and providing scholarships, fellowships and professorships.

LEGAL BASIS:
Tax-exempt private foundation founded in 1974 as a Testamentary Trust under will of John Stauffer by Order of the Superior Court of the State of California in and for the County of Los Angeles.

ELIGIBILITY:
Tax-exempt hospitals, colleges and universities with a preference given to those which maintain balanced operating budgets.

GEOGRAPHIC RESTRICTIONS:
California.

FINANCIAL DATA:
Amount of support per award: $100,000 to $3,000,000.

NUMBER OF APPLICANTS MOST RECENT YEAR:
Approximately 200.

REPRESENTATIVE AWARDS:
$3,000,000 to Huntington Hospital; $300,000 to Claremont McKenna College; $500,000 to Stanford University; $2,500,000 to California Institute of Technology.

APPLICATION INFORMATION:
Applicants must submit three copies of a letter to the Office of the Trust setting forth the amount requested, the need for the subject of the grant, objective to be achieved and manner in which John Stauffer's name may be memorialized. If deemed appropriate, the Trustees will request supplemental information. Papers establishing tax-exempt status will be required. Requests for personal interviews are discouraged.

PUBLICATIONS:
Application guidelines.

IRS IDENTIFICATION NUMBER: 23-7434707

TRUSTEES:
John F. Bradley, Sr.
H. Jess Senecal, Esq.
Michael S. Whalen, Esq.

ADDRESS INQUIRIES TO:
H. Jess Senecal, Esq.
(See address above.)

STEELCASE FOUNDATION   [337]
P.O. Box 1967 GH-4E
Grand Rapids, MI 49501-1967
(616) 246-4695
Fax: (616) 475-2200

E-MAIL ADDRESS:
sbroman@steelcase.com

WEB SITE ADDRESS:
www.steelcasefoundation.org

FOUNDED: 1951

AREAS OF INTEREST:
Human service, health, education, social welfare, the arts and culture, and the environment in the areas of Steelcase, Inc. manufacturing plants. Particular concern is given to people who are disadvantaged, disabled, and young or elderly in an attempt to improve the quality of their lives.

TYPE:
Capital grants; Challenge/matching grants; Demonstration grants; Development grants; Matching gifts; Project/program grants; Seed money grants. Special projects, startup, capital and capacity building.

YEAR PROGRAM STARTED: 1951

PURPOSE:
To improve the quality of life in the communities where Steelcase employees live.

LEGAL BASIS:
Corporate foundation.

ELIGIBILITY:
The Foundation makes grants to IRS-certified non-profit organizations in areas where Steelcase manufacturing plants are located.

GEOGRAPHIC RESTRICTIONS:
Athens, Alabama; Grand Rapids, Michigan; Markham, Ontario.

FINANCIAL DATA:
Amount of support per award: $1,000 to $1,000,000.
Total amount of support: $4,395,582 for the year ended November 30, 2009.

NUMBER OF APPLICANTS MOST RECENT YEAR:
300.

NUMBER OF AWARDS: 50.

APPLICATION INFORMATION:
To obtain a grant application, send a letter on your organization letterhead and signed by the chief executive officer. Include the following items with the letter:
(1) Description of your organization or project;
(2) Expected results of the project;
(3) Amount of grant funds requested and;
(4) Copy of your IRS 501(c)(3) non-profit certification.

  If the proposal meets the Foundation criteria, a detailed application form will be sent to the organization.
Duration: Varies.
Deadline: Grant requests are reviewed quarterly.

PUBLICATIONS:
Annual report; application; guidelines.

IRS IDENTIFICATION NUMBER: 38-6050470

TRUSTEES:
Kate Pew Wolters, Chairperson
James P. Hackett
Earl D. Holton
Mary Anne Hunting
Mary Goodwillie Nelson
Robert C. Pew, III

STAFF:
Susan K. Broman, President
Phyllis A. Gebben, Coordinator, Steelcase Donations

ADDRESS INQUIRIES TO:
Susan K. Broman, President
(See address above.)

THE WILLIAM B. STOKELY, JR. FOUNDATION   [338]
620 Campbell Station Road, Station West
Suite 27
Knoxville, TN 37934
(865) 966-4878
Fax: (865) 675-5095

FOUNDED: 1951

AREAS OF INTEREST:
College and university scholarship programs
and cultural, educational, religious and health
service organizations.

TYPE:
General operating grants; Matching gifts;
Scholarships.

YEAR PROGRAM STARTED: 1951

PURPOSE:
To provide funds for colleges and universities
for scholarships.

LEGAL BASIS:
Tax-exempt private foundation.

ELIGIBILITY:
The Foundation does not extend funds to
individuals but rather to colleges and
universities in the form of scholarships to
disburse under the guidelines of their
particular program. Also considered are the
needs of cultural, educational, religious
(Christian) and health service organizations
in areas where the Stokely family has ties.
Regional priority is given to the southeastern
U.S. and eastern Tennessee.

Organizations requesting funds must be
approved, listed nonprofit organizations with
501(c)(3) status. All proposals must be
submitted in writing for review by the Board
of Directors.

GEOGRAPHIC RESTRICTIONS:
Southeastern United States and Eastern
Tennessee.

FINANCIAL DATA:
Amount of support per award: $25 to
$100,000.

APPLICATION INFORMATION:
All proposals must be submitted in writing
for review by the Board of Directors.
Duration: Varies.
Deadline: Proposals are reviewed on an
ongoing basis.

IRS IDENTIFICATION NUMBER: 35-6016402

BOARD OF DIRECTORS:
William B. Stokely, III, President
Kay H. Stokely, Executive Vice President
Andrea White, Vice President, Treasurer and
Secretary
Stacy S. Byerly
Shelley S. Przewrocki
Clayton F. Stokely
William B. Stokely, IV

ADDRESS INQUIRIES TO:
William B. Stokely, III, President
(See address above.)

ROY AND CHRISTINE STURGIS CHARITABLE AND EDUCATIONAL TRUST   [339]
c/o Bank of America, N.A.
901 Main Street, 19th Floor
Dallas, TX 75202-3714
(214) 209-1965

E-MAIL ADDRESS:
debi.allen@baml.com
tx.philanthropic@baml.com

WEB SITE ADDRESS:
www.bankofamerica.com

FOUNDED: 1981

AREAS OF INTEREST:
Education, arts and culture, youth and social
services, science and health.

TYPE:
Capital grants; Challenge/matching grants;
Matching gifts; Project/program grants.

LEGAL BASIS:
Private foundation (charitable trust).

ELIGIBILITY:
Applications must have a 501(c)(3) exempt
status from federal income tax as determined
by the IRS before applying for a grant.

Charitable organizations which receive a
one-payment grant must skip a year before
applying again. Charitable organizations
which receive multiyear payments cannot
apply again while receiving payments and
must skip a year after the last payment is
received.

Trustee will consider grant requests for
supplements for capital improvements,
special projects, medical research and
equipment, grants to meet challenges,
endowments, start-up funds (extraordinary
review), limited general operating expenses
and construction or renovation of facilities.

The Trustee may favorably consider
proposals which are unique, necessary and of
high priority for the charitable organizations
and which do not duplicate other services
which are available, proposals for which
funding may not be readily available from
other sources and essential projects which are
sufficiently described as worthwhile,
important and of a substantive nature.

The Trustee will not consider providing
support for political organizations, loans,
scholarships for individuals, tuition for
individuals or for seminars. No grants to
individuals or for mass appeals for funding.

GEOGRAPHIC RESTRICTIONS:
Arkansas and Dallas area in Texas.

FINANCIAL DATA:
Amount of support per award: $5,000 to
$200,000 for multiyear payments. Average:
$23,500.
Total amount of support: $2,396,000 for the
year 2008.

NUMBER OF AWARDS: 51 for the year 2008.

REPRESENTATIVE AWARDS:
$30,000 to the Daughters of Charity Services,
Dumas and Gould, for purchase of medical
equipment for primary health care clinics;
$50,000 to Greenhill School, Dallas, TX, for
construction of fine arts center and sciences
building.

APPLICATION INFORMATION:
The following documents are required:
(1) copy of organization's 501(c)(3) IRS
letter;

(2) a one-page history of organization
describing when it was founded, its purpose
and the people it serves;
(3) a one-page budget outline for the
program or project for which the grant is
requested;
(4) list of organization's board of directors
(name, address and phone number) and;
(5) organization's previous year's audited
financial statement.
Deadline: December 31.

PUBLICATIONS:
Guidelines.

IRS IDENTIFICATION NUMBER: 75-6331832

STAFF:
David T. Ross, Senior Philanthropic Officer

ADDRESS INQUIRIES TO:
David T. Ross, Senior Philanthropic Officer
(See address above.)

SUNTRUST FOUNDATION   [340]
919 East Main Street
Richmond, VA 23219
(804) 782-7907
Fax: (804) 782-5191

E-MAIL ADDRESS:
jane.markins@suntrust.com

WEB SITE ADDRESS:
www.suntrust.com

AREAS OF INTEREST:
Education, health and human services, culture
and art, civic and community.

TYPE:
General operating grants; Matching gifts;
Project/program grants. Employee matching
gifts program is designed to encourage
SunTrust employees to support educational
institutions and cultural organizations.

PURPOSE:
To improve the quality of life in the
communities in which SunTrust operates.

LEGAL BASIS:
Corporate giving program.

ELIGIBILITY:
Applicants must be 501(c)(3) organizations.

When considering a specific contribution
request, the following are among the criteria
that SunTrust applies:
(1) does the cause fall under one or more of
the areas of interest of the Foundation?;
(2) does SunTrust have a business presence
in the geographic area in which the
contribution will have impact?;
(3) will the contribution support programs
and activities for improvement of the quality
of life in the community served? and;
(4) will the organization requesting financial
support have good management and active
involvement of community leaders?

No grants to individuals.

GEOGRAPHIC RESTRICTIONS:
Florida, Georgia, Maryland, North Carolina,
South Carolina, Tennessee, Virginia and
Washington, DC.

FINANCIAL DATA:
Amount of support per award: Varies.
Total amount of support: Varies.
Matching fund requirements: SunTrust will
match any employee contribution to
educational institutions and for arts and
culture.

APPLICATION INFORMATION:
Well-organized, fully documented requests for aid will facilitate the review process. The proposal must be in writing with appropriate documentation. The documentation should include project and/or operating budgets and a full description of the area of need and the reasons for the request. The applicant should give special attention to the guidelines applied by the Foundation when considering a proposal.
Duration: Varies. Renewal possible.
Deadline: September 1.

PUBLICATIONS:
Guidelines.

ADDRESS INQUIRIES TO:
Regional Headquarters or
SunTrust Foundation
(See address above.)

SURDNA FOUNDATION INC.   [341]
330 Madison Avenue, 30th Floor
New York, NY 10017-5001
(212) 557-0010 ext. 237
Fax: (212) 557-0003

E-MAIL ADDRESS:
request@surdna.org

WEB SITE ADDRESS:
www.surdna.org

FOUNDED: 1917

AREAS OF INTEREST:
Environment, community revitalization, effective citizenry, arts and the nonprofit sector.

NAME(S) OF PROGRAMS:
● **Strong Local Economy**
● **Sustainable Environment**
● **Thriving Cultures**

TYPE:
General operating grants; Project/program grants.

YEAR PROGRAM STARTED: 1917

PURPOSE:
To foster catalytic, entrepreneurial programs which offer viable solutions to difficult systemic problems.

ELIGIBILITY:
Grants are not generally given to individuals or to fund capital campaigns or building construction, or for internationally based or focused projects.

GEOGRAPHIC RESTRICTIONS:
United States.

FINANCIAL DATA:
Amount of support per award: Varies.
Total amount of support: $8,525,000 for the year 2009.

NUMBER OF AWARDS: 73 for the year 2009.

APPLICATION INFORMATION:
Application guidelines are available online.

PUBLICATIONS:
Annual report.

ADDRESS INQUIRIES TO:
Phillip Henderson, President
(See address above.)

TAHOE TRUCKEE COMMUNITY FOUNDATION   [342]
11071 Donner Pass Road
Truckee, CA 96161
(530) 587-1776
Fax: (530) 550-7985

E-MAIL ADDRESS:
foundation@ttcf.net

WEB SITE ADDRESS:
www.ttcf.net

AREAS OF INTEREST:
Education, environment, arts and culture, civic benefits, health, human services, youth development, recreation and animal welfare.

TYPE:
Project/program grants.

YEAR PROGRAM STARTED: 1998

PURPOSE:
To enhance the quality of life in the Truckee Tahoe community.

ELIGIBILITY:
Grants are made to organizations that have tax-exempt status under Section 501(c)(3) of the Internal Revenue Code. No grants are made to individuals.

GEOGRAPHIC RESTRICTIONS:
Truckee and Tahoe region, California.

FINANCIAL DATA:
Amount of support per award: $5,000 to $10,000.
Total amount of support: $1,100,000 to $1,500,000.

APPLICATION INFORMATION:
Contact the Foundation for application procedures.
Duration: One year.
Deadline: Varies.

ADMINISTRATIVE STAFF:
Ed Bokinskie, Administration Director
Phebe Bell, Program Officer

EXECUTIVE OFFICERS:
Lisa Dobey, Chief Executive Officer

ADDRESS INQUIRIES TO:
Phebe Bell, Program Officer
(See address above.)

S. MARK TAPER FOUNDATION   [343]
12011 San Vicente Boulevard, Suite 400
Los Angeles, CA 90049
(310) 476-5413
Fax: (310) 471-4993

E-MAIL ADDRESS:
questions@smtfoundation.org

WEB SITE ADDRESS:
www.smtfoundation.org

FOUNDED: 1989

AREAS OF INTEREST:
Including, but not limited to, environment, independent living for the disabled, children, hunger, AIDS, teenage pregnancy prevention, economic revitalization, the arts, public education and civic affairs.

TYPE:
Capital grants; Challenge/matching grants; Demonstration grants; Development grants; Endowments; General operating grants; Matching gifts; Project/program grants; Scholarships; Seed money grants; Technical assistance; Training grants. Specific project grants.

YEAR PROGRAM STARTED: 1989

PURPOSE:
To enhance the quality of people's lives.

LEGAL BASIS:
Independent foundation.

ELIGIBILITY:
No grants to individuals. Applicants must be certified tax-exempt under Section 501(c)(3) of the Internal Revenue Code.

Previously funded nonprofit organizations are not eligible for another grant until after three full cycles have elapsed following the grant cycle during which previous grant was made.

GEOGRAPHIC RESTRICTIONS:
Southern California, primarily Los Angeles County.

FINANCIAL DATA:
Amount of support per award: Small grants: up to $50,000; medium grants: $50,001 to $250,000; large grants: over $250,000.
Total amount of support: Varies.

NUMBER OF APPLICANTS MOST RECENT YEAR:
400.

NUMBER OF AWARDS: 80.

APPLICATION INFORMATION:
Application form required. Make initial contact by way of Letter of Inquiry. Letter must include organization background information, purpose of project, amount requested and anticipated results. Documentation of 501(c)(3) status required. Letters of Inquiry submitted by e-mail or fax will not be accepted.
Duration: One year unless paid in installments.
Deadline: December 1 through February 25 only.

PUBLICATIONS:
Letter of Inquiry Guidelines.

OFFICERS:
Janice Taper Lazarof, President

ADDRESS INQUIRIES TO:
Adrienne Wittenberg, Grants Director
(See address above.)

*PLEASE NOTE:
Check web site for Guidelines before sending Letter of Inquiry. Guidelines are updated in mid-November.

JOHN TEMPLETON FOUNDATION   [344]
300 Conshohocken State Road
Suite 500
West Conshohocken, PA 19428
(610) 941-2828
Fax: (610) 825-1730

WEB SITE ADDRESS:
www.templeton.org

FOUNDED: 1987

AREAS OF INTEREST:
Higher education, science and religion, theology, medicine, philosophy, spirituality and health, character development and free enterprise education.

TYPE:
Awards/prizes; Challenge/matching grants; Project/program grants; Research grants. Awards are financial in nature.

PURPOSE:
To promote and support relationships and progress between science and religion.

LEGAL BASIS:
Private foundation.

ELIGIBILITY:
Organizations classified as 501(c)(3) by the IRS can apply.

FINANCIAL DATA:
Amount of support per award: Varies.
Total amount of support: Varies.
Matching fund requirements: Defined on an individual grant basis.

NUMBER OF APPLICANTS MOST RECENT YEAR:
560 for the year 2009.

NUMBER OF AWARDS: 204 for the year 2009.

APPLICATION INFORMATION:
Funding guidelines can be found at web site.

PUBLICATIONS:
Brochures; newsletter; articles.

IRS IDENTIFICATION NUMBER: 62-1322826

TEXAS INSTRUMENTS FOUNDATION [345]
12500 TI Boulevard
Dallas, TX 75243
(972) 995-2011

E-MAIL ADDRESS:
giving@ti.com

WEB SITE ADDRESS:
www.ti.com/giving

FOUNDED: 1964

AREAS OF INTEREST:
Education, arts and culture, and community investment.

TYPE:
Matching gifts; Project/program grants. Education grants; Capital campaign grants.

YEAR PROGRAM STARTED: 1965

PURPOSE:
To better the communities in which Texas Instruments operates.

LEGAL BASIS:
Nonprofit foundation.

ELIGIBILITY:
Organization must be 501(c)(3) and tax exempt. No grants to individuals, student scholarships, good will advertising or for contributions of Texas Instruments products.

GEOGRAPHIC RESTRICTIONS:
Texas.

FINANCIAL DATA:
Matching fund requirements: Up to $10,000 per person per category each year.

REPRESENTATIVE AWARDS:
Laying the Foundation; SMU School of Engineering-Caruth Institute; United Way; Eisemann Center for the Performing Arts.

APPLICATION INFORMATION:
All requests for funding should be submitted online.
Duration: Varies. Renewals possible.

PUBLICATIONS:
Guidelines.

IRS IDENTIFICATION NUMBER: 75-6038519

STAFF:
Ann Pomykal, Executive Director

TEXTRON CHARITABLE TRUST [346]
40 Westminster Street
Providence, RI 02903
(401) 457-3172
Fax: (401) 457-3598

WEB SITE ADDRESS:
www.textron.com

FOUNDED: 1969

AREAS OF INTEREST:
Culture and the arts, education, job training, health care, minorities and women, United Way, environment/conservation and youth groups.

TYPE:
Capital grants; Matching gifts; Project/program grants; Scholarships. Employee matching gift programs for cultural, educational, hospital, environmental, conservation and wildlife institutions. Scholarships for children of Textron employees.

YEAR PROGRAM STARTED: 1969

PURPOSE:
To support organizations, institutions and programs that contribute significantly to the quality of life in the communities where Textron employees live and work.

LEGAL BASIS:
Corporate contributions program.

ELIGIBILITY:
Grants are made to nonprofit, tax-exempt organizations. The Trust cannot contribute to organizations which are not determined to be a tax-exempt public charity as defined by the Internal Revenue Code 501(c)(3), separate appeals for operating funds by local United Way agencies, however, capital fund campaigns approved by local United Ways can be considered for support, fund-raising appeals from, or matching program contributions to churches, seminaries or other directly related religious organizations, individuals, including political candidates, endowment funds, or requests that intend to reduce operating deficits.

FINANCIAL DATA:
Amount of support per award: Employee Matching Gifts: $25 to $7,500 per employee annually.
Total amount of support: Varies.

APPLICATION INFORMATION:
Grant requests should be submitted in writing. Special forms and multiple copies are not required. Proposals should include:
(1) a statement of the purposes and objectives of the organization;
(2) a history of previous programs;
(3) a list of the organization's officers, board of directors and staff;
(4) an annual operating budget for the year in which the project will occur;
(5) audited financial statements for the most recently completed year;
(6) the subject of the proposal and how it relates to the needs of the community;
(7) a budget for the program or project;
(8) the dollar level of support requested;
(9) a copy of tax-exempt determination letter from the IRS and;
(10) a list of other sources approached for financial assistance with the project and dollar level received from each source.
Duration: Generally one year. Multiyear commitments are kept to a minimum.
Deadline: March 1 and September 1.

PUBLICATIONS:
Policy statement; guidelines.

ADDRESS INQUIRIES TO:
Karen Warfield
Community Affairs Manager
(See address above.)

3M FOUNDATION, INC. [347]
Community Affairs
3M Center Building 225-01-S-23
St. Paul, MN 55144-1000
(651) 733-1721
(651) 733-0144
Fax: (651) 737-3061

E-MAIL ADDRESS:
cfkleven@mmm.com

WEB SITE ADDRESS:
www.3mgiving.com

FOUNDED: 1953

AREAS OF INTEREST:
Education, arts and culture, health and human services and environment.

TYPE:
Capital grants; General operating grants; Matching gifts; Product donations; Project/program grants. The Contributions Program of 3M consists of gifts by the 3M Foundation, cash and product donations by 3M and employee/retiree volunteerism.

YEAR PROGRAM STARTED: 1953

PURPOSE:
To positively impact communities and prepare individuals and families for success.

LEGAL BASIS:
Corporate contributions program.

ELIGIBILITY:
Grants are made in the program areas of interest to established, well-managed organizations which have an IRS 501(c)(3) nonprofit status, and which are located in and serving 3M communities. Essential qualities are programs with broad-based community support, a reputation for leadership and high-quality service delivery and measurable results.

The 3M Foundation will not fund organizations in non-3M communities, individuals, for-profit organizations, disease-related organizations, hospitals, (in general) individual K-12 schools, organizations with a limited constituency, such as religious, fraternal, social, veterans or military organizations, and scholarship funds or organizations.

Grants are not awarded for advocacy and lobbying efforts to influence legislation; conferences, seminars, workshops or publications of their proceedings; endowments; film/video production; fund-raising, testimonial, athletic and special events; purchase of equipment that has not been manufactured by 3M; and travel for individuals or groups.

3M Community Giving generally will not consider organizations or causes that do not impact 3M communities, lease, conferences, seminars, workshops, symposia, publication of proceedings and all aspects relating to conferences, fund-raising and testimonial events/dinners, grants to individual K-12 schools, including tickets, silent auctions, raffles, telethons, etc., not more than 10% of the organization's campaign goal or annual budget, whichever is smaller, programs or projects beyond three years.

FINANCIAL DATA:
Amount of support per award: Varies.

Total amount of support: $58,800,000 for the year 2010.

Matching fund requirements: Limited to 3M employees and retirees.

NUMBER OF APPLICANTS MOST RECENT YEAR: 10,000.

NUMBER OF AWARDS: Approximately 3,000.

APPLICATION INFORMATION:
Applications are by invitation only.
Duration: Generally one year, and not more than three years.
Deadline: April and October.

PUBLICATIONS:
Annual report; contributions guidelines.

IRS IDENTIFICATION NUMBER: 41-6038262

BOARD:
R.D. MacDonald, President
R.J. Torgerson, Vice President
J.L. Yeomans, Treasurer
C.F. Kleven, Secretary
A.H. Janusz, Recording Secretary
G.W. Buckley
J.L. Bushman
M.P. Delkoski
B.W. Kaufmann
J.R. Lavers
R.M. Miller
M.I. Smith
J.B. Sweeney
S.K. Tokach
S.C. Webster
J.K. Woodworth

JOHN H. AND H. NAOMI TOMFOHRDE FOUNDATION   [348]

c/o Rackemann, Sawyer & Brewster
160 Federal Street, 15th Floor
Boston, MA 02110-1700
(617) 951-1108
Fax: (617) 542-7437

E-MAIL ADDRESS:
smonahan@rackemann.com

WEB SITE ADDRESS:
www.cybergrants.com/tomfohrde

FOUNDED: 1996

AREAS OF INTEREST:
Cultural, social and civic betterment, community health, higher education, scientific research within the New England area with a special focus on Greater Boston.

TYPE:
Capital grants; Conferences/seminars; Matching gifts; Product donations; Project/program grants; Seed money grants; Technical assistance. The Foundation's particular focus is on supporting the work of charitable institutions, organizations and agencies in the New England area and particularly in Greater Boston, which are dedicated to the cultural, social and civic betterment of the community and particularly which foster the advancement of higher education, the classic arts, scientific research in biomedicine and the improvement of community health.

PURPOSE:
To bring about the cultural, social and civic betterment of the community and particularly to foster the advancement of higher education, the classic arts, scientific research in biomedicine and the improvement of community health.

LEGAL BASIS:
Private, independent foundation.

ELIGIBILITY:
The Foundation supports nonprofit 501(c)(3) organizations only.

GEOGRAPHIC RESTRICTIONS:
New England, with a preference for Greater Boston.

FINANCIAL DATA:
Amount of support per award: $5,000 to $10,000.
Total amount of support: $210,000 for the year 2010.
Matching fund requirements: Determined on a case-by-case basis.

NUMBER OF APPLICANTS MOST RECENT YEAR: 100 for the year 2010.

NUMBER OF AWARDS: 27 for the year 2010.

REPRESENTATIVE AWARDS:
Boston Health Care for the Homeless; Boston History Center and Museum.

APPLICATION INFORMATION:
Applicants are required to submit a Preliminary Application-Concept Cover Letter. Only applicants whose preliminary application has been approved will be invited to submit a full proposal.
Deadline: January, April and August for trustees meetings in February, June and October, respectively.

IRS IDENTIFICATION NUMBER: 04-3338742

TRUSTEES:
Albert M. Fortier, Jr., Esq.
William B. Tyler, Esq.

STAFF:
Susan T. Monahan, Grants Coordinator

ADDRESS INQUIRIES TO:
Susan T. Monahan, Grants Coordinator
(See e-mail address above.)

TOPFER FAMILY FOUNDATION   [349]

3600 North Capital of Texas Highway
Building B, Suite 310
Austin, TX 78746
(512) 329-0009
(866) 897-0298
Fax: (512) 329-6462

E-MAIL ADDRESS:
info@topferfoundation.org

WEB SITE ADDRESS:
www.topferfoundation.org

FOUNDED: 2000

AREAS OF INTEREST:
Child abuse prevention and treatment, youth enrichment, job training and support services, children's health, and aging in place.

TYPE:
Project/program grants.

PURPOSE:
To help people connect to the tools and resources needed to build self-sufficient and fulfilling lives; to address the needs of the communities in which the Topfer family resides.

ELIGIBILITY:
Organizations must be nonprofit, classified 501(c)(3). No grants to individuals.

GEOGRAPHIC RESTRICTIONS:
Greater Chicago, Illinois and greater Austin, Texas metropolitan areas. In Illinois, preference is given to Cook, DuPage and Lake counties.

FINANCIAL DATA:
Amount of support per award: $5,000 to $100,000.
Total amount of support: $2,800,000.

APPLICATION INFORMATION:
Application should be submitted online.
Duration: One year. Must reapply.
Deadline: Varies.

ADDRESS INQUIRIES TO:
Erica Gustafson, Grants Administrator
(See address above.)

TOTAL PETROCHEMICALS USA FOUNDATION   [350]

1201 Lousiana, Suite 1800
Houston, TX 77002
(713) 483-5000
Fax: (713) 483-5429

WEB SITE ADDRESS:
www.totalpetrochemicalsusa.com

FOUNDED: 1974

AREAS OF INTEREST:
Education.

TYPE:
Development grants; Matching gifts; Project/program grants.

LEGAL BASIS:
Corporate foundation.

ELIGIBILITY:
Grants are made to organizations which are tax-exempt under Section 501(c)(3) of the Internal Revenue Code. Grants may not be made to individuals nor are grants made to private foundations as defined in Section 509(a) of the Internal Revenue Code.

GEOGRAPHIC RESTRICTIONS:
Primarily Houston, Texas.

FINANCIAL DATA:
Total amount of support: Varies.
Matching fund requirements: All gifts from Total Petrochemicals USA, Inc. full-time employees are matched to four-year educational institutions from which the donor received a degree. The minimum gift that will be matched is $25 and the maximum gift per person per calendar year is $5,000. The contribution must be a personal gift of the eligible donor and cannot include resources from other people or institutions.

NUMBER OF APPLICANTS MOST RECENT YEAR: Approximately 500.

NUMBER OF AWARDS: Varies.

APPLICATION INFORMATION:
No form is prescribed for submitting grant applications; however, budgets and statements of financial condition will assist the Foundation in acting upon any request for funds. A categorized statement regarding the expected sources of funds, excluding individual contributors and specifically whether the organization is supported by the United Way, are also of interest. Prior to issuance of a grant, an organization will be requested to furnish documentation of its status under the Code and a statement regarding its present operation and sources of support.
Duration: Varies.

OFFICERS:
Geoffroy Petit, Chief Executive Officer
Karyn Grace, Secretary

ADDRESS INQUIRIES TO:
Karyn Grace, Manager
Public Affairs and Corporate
Communications
(See address above.)

THE HARRY A. AND MARGARET D. TOWSLEY FOUNDATION [351]

P.O. Box 349
Midland, MI 48640-0349
(989) 837-1100
Fax: (989) 837-3240

FOUNDED: 1959

AREAS OF INTEREST:
Education, cultural arts, religion, health and community service.

TYPE:
Project/program grants.

YEAR PROGRAM STARTED: 1959

PURPOSE:
To assist religious, educational, charitable and scientific organizations with their programs; to prevent cruelty to children.

LEGAL BASIS:
Private foundation.

ELIGIBILITY:
The Foundation does not make direct grants to individuals, provide loan funds, fund travel or conferences, or make grants to students for scholarships, books or other media. Grants are not made to institutions which in policy or practice unfairly discriminate against age, race, color, creed or sex.

GEOGRAPHIC RESTRICTIONS:
Primarily Michigan.

APPLICATION INFORMATION:
Organizations seeking aid should submit verification of tax-exempt and nonprofit status, amount of requested funds, explanation of need, and most recent financial statement along with operating budget and other funding sources.
Duration: Varies. Renewal possible.
Deadline: Application should be made within the first three months of the year. Announcement will be made during the third quarter of the year.

PUBLICATIONS:
Brochure; annual report.

IRS IDENTIFICATION NUMBER: 38-6091798

OFFICERS:
Margaret Ann Riecker, Chairperson
Lynn T. White, President
Judith D. Rumelhart, Vice President/Secretary
Wendell Dunbar, Treasurer

ADDRESS INQUIRIES TO:
Lynn T. White, President
(See address above.)

TRUST FUNDS INCORPORATED [352]

100 Broadway, Third Floor
San Francisco, CA 94111
(415) 434-3323
Fax: (415) 434-2936

FOUNDED: 1934

AREAS OF INTEREST:
Elementary, secondary and graduate Catholic education, Catholic religious and social service organizations and programs, and religious arts.

TYPE:
Project/program grants.

YEAR PROGRAM STARTED: 1934

PURPOSE:
To support worthwhile projects and programs that share the interests of the Foundation.

LEGAL BASIS:
Private foundation.

ELIGIBILITY:
Grants are usually limited to the San Francisco Bay area. No grants to individuals. No grants for buildings or endowments, annual campaigns, or to organizations which draw substantial public support.

GEOGRAPHIC RESTRICTIONS:
San Francisco, California and surrounding area.

FINANCIAL DATA:
Amount of support per award: $1,000 to $10,000.

APPLICATION INFORMATION:
Application forms provided for all grant proposals complying with guidelines. Write or call first.
Deadline: Quarterly.

PUBLICATIONS:
Applications and guidelines.

IRS IDENTIFICATION NUMBER: 94-6062952

DIRECTORS:
James T. Healy, President
Thomas F. Kubasak, Chief Finance Officer
Joan C. O'Rourke, Secretary
Thomas Kelley, Director
John Strain, Director

ADDRESS INQUIRIES TO:
James T. Healy, President
(See address above.)

TULL CHARITABLE FOUNDATION, INC. [353]

50 Hurt Plaza
Suite 1245
Atlanta, GA 30303
(404) 659-7079
Fax: (404) 659-1223

E-MAIL ADDRESS:
carol@tullfoundation.org

WEB SITE ADDRESS:
www.tullfoundation.org

FOUNDED: 1952

AREAS OF INTEREST:
Education, health and human services, youth development and the arts.

TYPE:
Capital grants; Challenge/matching grants; Endowments.

YEAR PROGRAM STARTED: 1952

PURPOSE:
To respond to charitable and community needs in the Atlanta metropolitan area and in Georgia.

LEGAL BASIS:
Converted from Trust to Nonprofit Corporation of Georgia.

ELIGIBILITY:
Nonprofit 501(c)(3) organizations located within Georgia are eligible for support.

The Foundation does not make grants to individuals or churches and does not participate in the operation of a project other than that of providing start-up funds.

The Foundation's trustees prefer to make grants that will have a significant and lasting impact on an organization, as well as the community. Priority is given to grant requests that:
(1) are strategically important to an organization's growth and capacity;
(2) enable the organization to more effectively address important community needs and;
(3) are cost-effective.

Proposals that address education, health and human services, youth development, and the arts are given priority by Foundation trustees.

GEOGRAPHIC RESTRICTIONS:
Georgia.

FINANCIAL DATA:
Total amount of support: $2,600,000 for the year 2010.

APPLICATION INFORMATION:
Prior to receiving a full proposal, the Foundation prefers a concise letter-of-intent providing a brief description of the applicant organization, the project for which funding is being requested, the total cost of the project and the amount being requested and a copy of the organization's 501(c)(3) certification. If the Foundation determines that further consideration is to be given to the proposed project, additional information will be requested.
Deadline: December 1, March 1, June 1 and September 1.

PUBLICATIONS:
Guidelines; policies.

TRUSTEES AND OFFICERS:
Larry Prince, Chairman
Sylvia Looney Dick
Lillian Giornelli
Jack Guynn
B. Harvey Hill, Jr.
Warren Jobe
Solon Patterson

ADDRESS INQUIRIES TO:
Barbara T. Cleveland, Executive Director
Carol Aiken, Assistant
(See address above.)

THE TUSCHMAN FOUNDATION [354]

4544 Post Oak Place
Suite 392
Houston, TX 77027
(713) 706-4000
Fax: (713) 963-9954

E-MAIL ADDRESS:
j.tusch@att.net

FOUNDED: 1983

AREAS OF INTEREST:
Education, medicine, science, sports community service and welfare needs.

TYPE:
Capital grants; Challenge/matching grants; Development grants; Exchange programs; Internships; Matching gifts; Seed money grants.

YEAR PROGRAM STARTED: 1983

PURPOSE:
To provide funds on a matching basis to charitable institutions or as seed monies for fund-raising; to provide reoccurring benefits to recipients attending to the needs of others.

LEGAL BASIS:
Private foundation.

ELIGIBILITY:
Recipients must be 501(c)(3) qualified institutions and have BBB satisfactory ratings. No funds are provided for operational purposes.

GEOGRAPHIC RESTRICTIONS:
Colorado and Texas.

FINANCIAL DATA:
Amount of support per award: $1,500 to $3,000.

Matching fund requirements: Funds are provided on a matching basis, 1:1 to 1:3, except for seed monies for fund-raising campaigns.

APPLICATION INFORMATION:
Grant requests should include the following: (1) name, address and phone number of organization and the contact person; (2) most recent annual report and information materials; (3) explanation of need for the funds, including purposes, budgets, benefits to the organization and community, timing, and alternative funding; (4) financial information including current year budget and year-to-date figures; (5) copy of IRS determination letter on 501(c)(3) status; (6) potential sources of matching funds and; (7) satisfactory rating from the Charity Watch section of the local Better Business Bureau.

PUBLICATIONS:
Annual report.

OFFICER:
John S. Tuschman, President

UNION PACIFIC FOUNDATION   [355]
1400 Douglas, Stop 1560
Omaha, NE 68179
(402) 544-5600
Fax: (402) 501-0011

E-MAIL ADDRESS:
upf@up.com

WEB SITE ADDRESS:
www.up.com/found

FOUNDED: 1955

AREAS OF INTEREST:
Health and human services; community and civic; fine arts in communities served by Union Pacific.

TYPE:
Capital grants; General operating grants; Project/program grants. Support generally for capital campaigns, building funds, equipment and materials, renovation and operating support.

YEAR PROGRAM STARTED: 1959

PURPOSE:
To improve the quality of life in the communities served by Union Pacific and where its employees live and work.

LEGAL BASIS:
Incorporated in Utah, May 13, 1955.

ELIGIBILITY:
Organization must be private, nonprofit, 501(c)(3) tax-exempt and located in a community served by Union Pacific.

GEOGRAPHIC RESTRICTIONS:
Arizona, Arkansas, California, Colorado, Idaho, Illinois, Iowa, Kansas, Louisiana, Minnesota, Missouri, Montana, Nebraska, Nevada, New Mexico, Oklahoma, Oregon, Texas, Utah, Washington, Wisconsin and Wyoming.

FINANCIAL DATA:
Amount of support per award: Varies.
Total amount of support: $7,000,000 for the year 2010.

NUMBER OF APPLICANTS MOST RECENT YEAR: 1,600.

NUMBER OF AWARDS: 600 for the year 2010.

APPLICATION INFORMATION:
Details may be obtained from the Foundation web site.
Duration: Most grants are awarded annually.
Deadline: August 15 for consideration for the following year's budget.

TRUSTEES:
J.M. Hemmer
R.M. Knight, Jr.
J.J. Koraleski
R.W. Turner
J.R. Young

THE UPS FOUNDATION   [356]
55 Glenlake Parkway, N.E.
Atlanta, GA 30328
(404) 828-6374
Fax: (404) 828-7435

E-MAIL ADDRESS:
community@ups.com

WEB SITE ADDRESS:
www.community.ups.com

FOUNDED: 1951

AREAS OF INTEREST:
Economic and global literacy, environmental sustainability, nonprofit effectiveness, encouraging diversity and community safety.

NAME(S) OF PROGRAMS:
● **James E. Casey Scholarship Program**
● **Neighbor to Neighbor**
● **George D. Smith Scholarship Program**

TYPE:
Project/program grants; Scholarships. James E. Casey Scholarship Program provides the opportunity for children of UPS employees to earn four-year scholarships at colleges and universities.

Neighbor-to-Neighbor program mobilizes UPS employees and their families to serve as volunteers in their communities.

George D. Smith Scholarship Program provides scholarships for children of full- and part-time UPS employees enrolled in a full-time study program of up to two years.

YEAR PROGRAM STARTED: 1951

PURPOSE:
To improve lives and strengthen the capacity of nonprofits through volunteerism, community grants and creative programs.

LEGAL BASIS:
Corporate foundation.

ELIGIBILITY:
Applicants must be any worthy philanthropic, nonprofit project or organization that is

tax-exempt under 501(c)(3). The Foundation does not fund annual campaigns, building or endowment funds, deficit financing, emergency funds, individuals, land acquisition, loans, operating costs or capital expenses, publications, or religious organizations or theological functions.

FINANCIAL DATA:
Amount of support per award: Varies per award.
Total amount of support: Varies.

APPLICATION INFORMATION:
The Foundation does not accept unsolicited proposals, but does invite leading organizations in focus areas to submit proposals.

PUBLICATIONS:
Annual report.

USG FOUNDATION, INC.   [357]
550 West Adams Street
Chicago, IL 60661
(312) 436-4021
(312) 436-4000
Fax: (312) 672-3706

WEB SITE ADDRESS:
www.usg.com

FOUNDED: 1978

AREAS OF INTEREST:
Homelessness and shelter, health and welfare, education, arts and culture, and civic activities.

TYPE:
Project/program grants.

YEAR PROGRAM STARTED: 1978

PURPOSE:
To provide assistance to nonprofit organizations seeking solutions to educational, social or health problems or whose work contributes to cultural enrichment.

LEGAL BASIS:
Tax-exempt, corporate foundation.

ELIGIBILITY:
Applicants must be tax-exempt 501(c)(3) organizations. The Foundation supports the creation of economic opportunity through grants to organizations that provide affordable housing/shelter, encourage self-sufficiency and assist economic development.

The Foundation does not contribute to organizations without IRS tax-exempt 501(c)(3) status, sectarian organizations having an exclusively religious nature, individuals, political parties, offices or candidates, fraternal or veterans' organizations, primary or secondary schools, organizations that cannot provide adequate accounting records, procedures or courtesy advertising.

GEOGRAPHIC RESTRICTIONS:
Primarily Chicago, Illinois.

FINANCIAL DATA:
Amount of support per award: Varies.
Total amount of support: Varies.

APPLICATION INFORMATION:
Grant proposals should be submitted in writing to receive consideration. The Foundation does not use a printed application form; however, the proposal should include the following:
(1) cover letter briefly outlining a statement of the need or problem and a background

summary of the need or problem with specific reasoning why the USG Foundation would be interested in the proposal;
(2) the amount requested and how it will be used;
(3) copy of the organization's 501(c)(3) tax-exemption letter from the IRS;
(4) copy of the organization's most recent financial statements;
(5) list of the members of the organization's governing board;
(6) statement of the program's purpose describing why the organization is involved in the project and a notation indicating any special qualifications the organization may possess for obtaining its stated objectives;
(7) detailed description of any proposed special project;
(8) program's measurable goals;
(9) itemized plan outlining how the organization intends to achieve those goals and;
(10) any additional literature that further defines the organization's goals and achievements such as an annual report, fund-raising literature, auditor's report, etc.
Duration: One year. Renewal possible upon reapplication.

PUBLICATIONS:
Guidelines.

ADDRESS INQUIRIES TO:
Jeffrey P. Rodewald, President
(See address above.)

VERIZON FOUNDATION [358]

One Verizon Way
Basking Ridge, NJ 07920
(866) 247-2687 (volunteers program)
Fax: (908) 630-2660

E-MAIL ADDRESS:
verizon.foundation@verizon.com

WEB SITE ADDRESS:
foundation.verizon.com

FOUNDED: 2001

NAME(S) OF PROGRAMS:
- **Domestic Violence Prevention**
- **Education**
- **Healthcare and Accessibility**
- **Internet Safety**
- **Literacy**

TYPE:
Matching gifts; Project/program grants.

PURPOSE:
To ensure that technology touches peoples' lives; to support initiatives that improve literacy, knowledge and readiness; to support domestic violence prevention; to support technology to improve health care; to help people understand how to use the technology of the Internet safely.

LEGAL BASIS:
Private, nonprofit organization.

ELIGIBILITY:
Proposals will be considered from eligible tax-exempt organizations in certain 501(c)(3) subsections as defined by IRS.

Proposals will also be considered from elementary and secondary schools (public and private) that are registered with the National Center for Education Statistics (NCES).

GEOGRAPHIC RESTRICTIONS:
United States.

FINANCIAL DATA:
Amount of support per award: Average $5,000 to $10,000.

Total amount of support: Approximately $68,000,000 in grants for the year 2009.

APPLICATION INFORMATION:
The Foundation only accepts electronic proposals through its Apply Online process.
Deadline: The Foundation reviews proposals January 1 through October 31.

ADDRESS INQUIRIES TO:
See e-mail address above.

THE WALLACE FOUNDATION [359]

5 Penn Plaza, 7th Floor
New York, NY 10001
(212) 251-9700
Fax: (212) 679-6990

E-MAIL ADDRESS:
info@wallacefoundation.org

WEB SITE ADDRESS:
www.wallacefoundation.org

FOUNDED: 1965

AREAS OF INTEREST:
Education leadership, arts participation and out-of-school learning.

NAME(S) OF PROGRAMS:
- **Arts for Young People**
- **Wallace Excellence Awards**

TYPE:
Awards/prizes; Challenge/matching grants; Conferences/seminars; Development grants; Endowments; Project/program grants; Research grants; Technical assistance; Research contracts.

YEAR PROGRAM STARTED: 2000

PURPOSE:
To enable institutions to expand learning and enrichment opportunities for all people by supporting and sharing effective ideas and practices.

LEGAL BASIS:
Private foundation.

ELIGIBILITY:
Grant applicants must be 501(c)(3) tax-exempt organizations. No grants are made to individuals.

GEOGRAPHIC RESTRICTIONS:
United States.

FINANCIAL DATA:
Estimated assets of $750,000,000 as of December 31, 2009.

Amount of support per award: Varies depending on needs and nature of request.

Total amount of support: $49,800,502 in grants paid for calendar year 2009.

NUMBER OF APPLICANTS MOST RECENT YEAR:
563 for calendar year 2008.

NUMBER OF AWARDS: 94 grants approved for calendar year 2008.

APPLICATION INFORMATION:
In most cases, the Foundation evaluates prospective grantees through the issuance of Requests for Proposals or other careful screening processes. Nevertheless, an organization may submit an inquiry by e-mail briefly describing the project, the organization, the estimated total for the project, and the portion requiring funding.
Duration: Varies.

PUBLICATIONS:
Annual report.

IRS IDENTIFICATION NUMBER: 13-6183757

OFFICERS AND BOARD OF DIRECTORS:
Kevin W. Kennedy, Chairman
M. Christine DeVita, President
Rob D. Nagel, Director of Investments and Treasurer
Mary E. Geras, Director of Finance and Assistant Treasurer
Holly Dodge, Secretary
Lawrence T. Babbio, Jr., Director
Candace K. Beinecke, Director
W. Don Cornwell, Director
Augusta Souza Kappner, Director
Susan J. Kropf, Director
Peter C. Marzio, Director
Ann S. Moore, Director

ADDRESS INQUIRIES TO:
General Management
(See address above.)

*PLEASE NOTE:
Grants are rarely made to unsolicited projects, especially from local organizations.

THE WASHINGTON POST COMPANY [360]

1150 15th Street, N.W.
Washington, DC 20071
(202) 334-6617
Fax: (202) 334-4536

E-MAIL ADDRESS:
calderonr@washpost.com

WEB SITE ADDRESS:
www.washpostco.com

FOUNDED: 1947

AREAS OF INTEREST:
Civic and community, education and cultural programs.

TYPE:
General operating grants. Employee Matching Gifts Program.

PURPOSE:
To support communities where the Washington Post Company operates.

ELIGIBILITY:
Applicants must be nonprofit 501(c)(3) organizations.

FINANCIAL DATA:
Amount of support per award: Average $500 to $2,500.

Total amount of support: Varies.

Matching fund requirements: $25 minimum, $2,000 per year/per employee maximum. 1:1 or 1:2 for schools or where employee is an active volunteer.

REPRESENTATIVE AWARDS:
The Phillips Collection; Washington Ballet; Capital Area Food Bank; Samaritan Inns; Inner City-Inner Child; Children's Charities.

APPLICATION INFORMATION:
Send short letter describing proposed program and budget.
Duration: One year. Renewal possible.

ADDRESS INQUIRIES TO:
Rima Calderon, Vice President-Communications and External Relations
(See address above.)

THE WASIE FOUNDATION   [361]

230 Manitoba Avenue South
Suite 110
Wayzata, MN 55391-1612
(952) 955-8500
Fax: (952) 955-8509

WEB SITE ADDRESS:
www.wasie.org

FOUNDED: 1966

AREAS OF INTEREST:
Postsecondary educational scholarship
programs for people of Polish ancestry in
Minnesota; care, treatment and research
regarding schizophrenia and arthritis;
children's health; and organizations providing
services and programs to people living with
cancer.

NAME(S) OF PROGRAMS:
- **Arthritis Grants**
- **Cancer Grants**
- **Children's Medical Health Grants**
- **Schizophrenia Grants**
- **Scholarship Program**

TYPE:
Capital grants; Challenge/matching grants;
Conferences/seminars; Development grants;
General operating grants; Matching gifts;
Project/program grants; Research grants. The
grant program provides funding in four
specific health areas schizophrenia, arthritis,
cancer, and children with medical problems.

YEAR PROGRAM STARTED: 1966

LEGAL BASIS:
Private foundation.

ELIGIBILITY:
Grants are made to 501(c)(3) nonprofit
organizations.

GEOGRAPHIC RESTRICTIONS:
Minnesota and south Florida (Broward,
Miami-Dade, and Palm Beach counties).

FINANCIAL DATA:
Amount of support per award: Varies.
Total amount of support: $1,400,000 for the
year 2009.

NUMBER OF AWARDS: 42 grants paid for the
year 2009.

REPRESENTATIVE AWARDS:
2009: $25,000 program support for people
with schizophrenia; $125,000 program
support for pediatric rheumatology; $25,000
for program (camp) for children with chronic
disease; $10,000 program support for
children with cancer.

APPLICATION INFORMATION:
The Foundation encourage organizations
which believe they fall within their funding
guidelines, to initiate contact through a
telephone call to one of the program staff
who will gather information and assist with
the proposal process.

Proposal submission is by invitation only.

Duration: One to three years. Renewal
possible.

Deadline: Submissions are invited throughout
the year.

STAFF:
Gregg D. Sjoquist, President and Chief
Executive Officer
Jen Klaassens, Vice President of Programs,
Florida
Jan Preble, Vice President of Programs
Dani Levenson, Vice President of Operations

ADDRESS INQUIRIES TO:
Jan Preble
Vice President of Programs
(See address above.)

EDWIN S. WEBSTER FOUNDATION   [362]

c/o GMA
77 Summer Street, Suite 800
Boston, MA 02110-1006
(617) 391-3087
Fax: (617) 426-7087

E-MAIL ADDRESS:
mjenney@gmafoundations.com

WEB SITE ADDRESS:
www.gmafoundations.com

FOUNDED: 1948

AREAS OF INTEREST:
Charitable purposes, with emphasis on
hospitals, medical research and education,
youth agencies, cultural activities and
programs addressing the needs of minorities.

TYPE:
Capital grants; Challenge/matching grants;
Endowments; General operating grants.

YEAR PROGRAM STARTED: 1982

PURPOSE:
To work towards a better society by giving
grants to organizations trying to help people
with serious needs not otherwise being
addressed.

LEGAL BASIS:
Nonprofit foundation.

ELIGIBILITY:
No grants are given to individuals or
organizations outside the U.S. The majority
of contributions are made to organizations in
the New England area. It is the policy of the
Foundation to support charitable
organizations that are well known to the
Trustees, with emphasis on hospitals, medical
research, education, youth agencies, cultural
activities and programs addressing the needs
of minorities. Grantees must have tax-exempt
status.

GEOGRAPHIC RESTRICTIONS:
Primarily New England.

FINANCIAL DATA:
Amount of support per award: $5,000 to
$50,000.

APPLICATION INFORMATION:
A written letter presenting the need, the
amount requested and copy of IRS letter of
tax-exempt status should be presented. All
other application information is available
from the Foundation.

Duration: One year.

Deadline: For consideration at spring
meeting, proposals should arrive by May 1.
For consideration at the fall meeting,
proposals should arrive by November 1.

PUBLICATIONS:
Guidelines.

TRUSTEES:
Henry U. Harris, III
Alexander Hiam
Suzanne Harte Sears

ADDRESS INQUIRIES TO:
Michelle Jenney, Administrator
(See address above.)

WEINGART FOUNDATION   [363]

1055 West 7th Street
Suite 3050
Los Angeles, CA 90017-2305
(213) 688-7799
Fax: (213) 688-1515

E-MAIL ADDRESS:
info@weingartfnd.org

WEB SITE ADDRESS:
www.weingartfnd.org

FOUNDED: 1951

AREAS OF INTEREST:
Human services, health, education, with
emphasis on projects that benefit children and
youth.

NAME(S) OF PROGRAMS:
- **Capacity Building**
- **Capital Support**
- **Core Support**
- **Program Support**
- **Small Grant Program**

TYPE:
Capital grants; Challenge/matching grants;
Development grants; Project/program grants;
Technical assistance. The Foundation makes
grants to assist organizations that work in the
areas of health, human services and
education. The Foundation gives highest
priority to activities that provide greater
access to people who are economically
disadvantaged and underserved. Of particular
interest to it are applications that specifically
address the needs of low-income children and
youth, older adults and people affected by
disabilities and homelessness. The
Foundation also funds activities that benefit
the general community and improve the
quality of life for all individuals in southern
California.

Core Support: Unrestricted funding that
enables an organization to carry out its
mission. It can be used to underwrite
administrative infrastructure and/or to
maintain core programs and essential staff.

Capacity Building: For new or enhanced
activities aimed at strengthening an
organization's programmatic and/or
administrative capacity. Projects must
evidence a credible plan for sustaining costs.

Capital Support: For specific projects with
capital expenditures. Funding is available to
support land, facility, equipment purchases,
renovations or new construction.

Program Support: For new, expansion or
enhancement program requests. Projects must
evidence a viable fund-raising and
sustainability plan.

Small Grant Program: For increasing access
to funding and strengthening the capacity of
small, community-based, and developing
organizations, with priority given to
organizations with operating budgets under
$1,500,000. The Program also supports small
capital projects for organizations of any size.

PURPOSE:
To assist credible agencies and institutions
serving children and youth, the aged, the
disabled, the homeless, the sick, the poor or
otherwise disadvantaged and projects
benefiting the general community.

ELIGIBILITY:
An organization that is certified as
tax-exempt under Section 501(c)(3) of the
U.S. Internal Revenue Code and is not a
private foundation as defined in Section
509(a) of that Code is eligible for

consideration. The Foundation does not fund Section 509(a)(3) Type III nonfunctionally integrated supporting organizations.

Grants are not made:
(1) to organizations that discriminate against certain groups or individuals in the delivery of programs and services on the basis of race, religion, national origin, gender, age, sexual orientation or disability;
(2) for propagandizing, influencing legislation and/or elections, promoting voter registration; for political candidates, political campaigns; for litigation;
(3) for social or political issues outside the U.S.;
(4) to individuals;
(5) to federated appeals or for the collection of funds for redistribution to other nonprofit groups;
(6) for conferences, workshops, temporary exhibits, travel, surveys, films or publishing activities;
(7) for endowment funds;
(8) for contingencies, deficits or debt reduction;
(9) for fund-raising dinners or events or;
(10) for research.

Grants generally are not approved for:
(1) national organizations that do not have local chapters operating in the geographic area of grant focus;
(2) projects or programs normally financed by government sources;
(3) refugee or religious programs, consumer interest or environmental advocacy or;
(4) feasibility studies.

GEOGRAPHIC RESTRICTIONS:
Southern California, with priority given to Los Angeles, Orange, Riverside, San Bernardino, San Diego, Santa Barbara, and Ventura counties.

FINANCIAL DATA:
Assets of $635,679,121 for the year ended June 30, 2010.
Amount of support per award: $5,000 to $750,000.
Total amount of support: $37,667,990 paid out for the fiscal year ended June 30, 2010.
Matching fund requirements: Organization matches 1:1.

NUMBER OF AWARDS: 546 approved grants for the fiscal year ended June 30, 2010.

APPLICATION INFORMATION:
It is recommended that all applicants apply to the Regular Grant Program using the online LOI process. If submitting the request online is not an option, applicants may also submit a letter via regular mail. The letter, which should be limited to two pages, should include a brief description of the organization's mission and activities, a brief explanation of how the funds would be used, and the total amount of funding requested from the Foundation. If the request is for a specific project or activity (capital, capacity building, or program), the applicant should also include the total cost of the project for which funding is sought and the amount raised to date.

If it is determined from the Letter of Inquiry that the request meets the Foundation's priorities and interests, the applicant will be provided with the instructions and forms required to prepare and submit a formal application.

There is no Letter of Inquiry required for the Small Grant Program.

Duration: Mostly, one-two years. Core Support grants are generally made for a two-year period.
Deadline: The Foundation accepts applications throughout the year.

PUBLICATIONS:
Annual report, only available on web site.

IRS IDENTIFICATION NUMBER: 95-6054814

OFFICERS:
Steve L. Soboroff, Chairman of the Board
Fred J. Ali, President and Chief Executive Officer
Deborah M. Ives, Vice President and Treasurer
Laurence A. Wolfe, Vice President, Administration and Real Estate and Corporate Secretary
Belen Vargas, Vice President Grant Operations

BOARD OF DIRECTORS:
William C. Allen
Andrew E. Bogen
Steven D. Broidy
Murray L. Galinson
Monica L. Lozano
John W. Mack
Miriam Muscarolas
Steve L. Soboroff

ADDRESS INQUIRIES TO:
President and Chief Executive Officer
Weingart Foundation
(See address above.)

HERMAN O. WEST FOUNDATION   [364]
101 Gordon Drive
Lionville, PA 19341
(610) 594-2900
Fax: (610) 594-3000

WEB SITE ADDRESS:
www.westpharma.com

FOUNDED: 1972

AREAS OF INTEREST:
Funding of nonprofit organizations serving cultural, health and public service needs of the areas/communities where West Pharmaceutical Services maintains operations. To fund the company's employee scholarship program and to encourage financial support to education through its matching gifts to education programs.

TYPE:
Capital grants; Challenge/matching grants; General operating grants; Matching gifts; Project/program grants; Scholarships.

YEAR PROGRAM STARTED: 1972

PURPOSE:
To fund nonprofit organizations, provide employee scholarship programs and employee matching gifts program.

LEGAL BASIS:
Corporate contributions program.

ELIGIBILITY:
Organizations with tax-exempt status and employees of West Pharmaceutical Services (for employee matching gifts program and scholarship program for children).

FINANCIAL DATA:
Amount of support per award: $500 to $150,000.
Total amount of support: Approximately $672,351 for the year 2010.

APPLICATION INFORMATION:
Application includes description of service provided, financial statement, including sources of funding and how dispersed, list of future needs and services of program and documentation of tax-exempt status.
Duration: Varies. Renewal possible.

PUBLICATIONS:
Application guidelines.

OFFICERS AND TRUSTEES:
George R. Bennyhoff, Chairman
Paula Johnson, M.D., Trustee
Richard D. Luzzi, Trustee

ADDRESS INQUIRIES TO:
Maureen B. Goebel, Administrator
(See address above.)
Tel: (610) 594-2945

WESTERN INTERSTATE COMMISSION FOR HIGHER EDUCATION   [365]
3035 Center Green Drive
Boulder, CO 80301
(303) 541-0270
Fax: (303) 541-0226

E-MAIL ADDRESS:
info-sep@wiche.edu

WEB SITE ADDRESS:
www.wiche.edu/psep

FOUNDED: 1953

AREAS OF INTEREST:
Allopathic medicine, dentistry, physical and occupational therapy, optometry, podiatry, osteopathy, veterinary medicine, physician assistant and pharmacy.

NAME(S) OF PROGRAMS:
● **Professional Student Exchange Program (PSEP)**

TYPE:
Scholarships. Tuition assistance/loan for service.

YEAR PROGRAM STARTED: 1953

PURPOSE:
To provide affordable access to professional health care education.

ELIGIBILITY:
Must be a resident of a state listed below. Rules vary by state.

GEOGRAPHIC RESTRICTIONS:
Alaska, Arizona, Colorado, Hawaii, Idaho, Montana, Nevada, New Mexico, North Dakota, Utah, Washington and Wyoming.

FINANCIAL DATA:
Amount of support per award: Varies.
Total amount of support: Varies.

NUMBER OF APPLICANTS MOST RECENT YEAR: Varies by state and field.

NUMBER OF AWARDS: 700 for the year 2010-11.

APPLICATION INFORMATION:
Contact the state higher education office in your state of residency for an application.
Duration: One year. Grants are renewable for course of study; subject to available funding.
Deadline: October 15 of the year prior to admission.

PUBLICATIONS:
Brochure.

ADDRESS INQUIRIES TO:
Margo Colalancia, Director
(See address above.)

*SPECIAL STIPULATIONS:
Grant is for residents of one western state making applications to participating schools in another western state.

E. L. WIEGAND FOUNDATION [366]

Wiegand Center
165 West Liberty Street, Suite 200
Reno, NV 89501
(775) 333-0310
Fax: (775) 333-0314

FOUNDED: 1982

AREAS OF INTEREST:
Education, medical research, civic and community affairs, arts and cultural affairs, and public affairs.

TYPE:
Capital grants; Professorships; Project/program grants; Research grants.

YEAR PROGRAM STARTED: 1982

PURPOSE:
To support charitable organizations and Roman Catholic charitable institutions.

LEGAL BASIS:
Private charitable trust.

ELIGIBILITY:
The Foundation will consider applications from institutions that are tax-exempt under Section 501(c)(3) of the IRS, and which are not private foundations as defined in Section 509.

The review process by the Foundation will consider institutions that:
(1) are exemplary in their field;
(2) have a history of high achievement and sound management;
(3) demonstrate a stable financial condition;
(4) have the potential to be self-supporting after the stage of initial funding by the Foundation;
(5) focus on strengthening traditional values essential to the preservation of a democratic society nurtured by free market principles (in the area of public affairs) and;
(6) are developing programs and projects that have a significant impact in the area for which the grant is requested.

GEOGRAPHIC RESTRICTIONS:
Arizona, Idaho, Montana, Nevada, Oregon, Utah and Washington; grants in the classification of Public Policy also consider New York City and Washington, DC.

FINANCIAL DATA:
Amount of support per award: $1,000 to $1,000,000.
Total amount of support: $2,187,703 for the year 2010.

NUMBER OF APPLICANTS MOST RECENT YEAR: 60.

NUMBER OF AWARDS: 28 for the year 2010.

APPLICATION INFORMATION:
A prospective applicant should describe the highlights of the proposal (including data regarding the organization, sources of funding, a brief description of the project or program, estimated budget and timeline) in a letter addressed to the Foundation. If, after staff consideration, it is determined that the program or project complies with the preliminary review, a prospective applicant shall receive an application for grant form which shall be assigned numerically to such

applicant. The Foundation is only able to support a small percentage of the proposals it receives.
Deadline: Letters of Inquiry accepted throughout the year.

IRS IDENTIFICATION NUMBER: 94-2839372

ADDRESS INQUIRIES TO:
Kristen A. Avansino
President and Executive Director
Grants Program
(See address above.)

MATILDA R. WILSON FUND [367]

6th Floor at Ford Field
1901 St. Antoine Street
Detroit, MI 48226
(313) 259-7777
Fax: (313) 393-7579

E-MAIL ADDRESS:
roosterveen@bodmanllp.com

FOUNDED: 1944

AREAS OF INTEREST:
Arts, education, health and human services.

TYPE:
Capital grants; Project/program grants.

ELIGIBILITY:
Applicants must be 501(c)(3) organizations. No grants to individuals.

GEOGRAPHIC RESTRICTIONS:
Southeast Michigan.

FINANCIAL DATA:
Amount of support per award: $500 to $50,000.

NUMBER OF APPLICANTS MOST RECENT YEAR:
Approximately 150.

NUMBER OF AWARDS: 50.

REPRESENTATIVE AWARDS:
$7,000,000 to Oakland University, Rochester, MI, for exterior restoration projects at Meadow Brook Hall.

APPLICATION INFORMATION:
No application form. Applicants must submit tax-exempt documentation.
Duration: One year, some multiyear.
Deadline: January, April and August.

IRS IDENTIFICATION NUMBER: 38-6087665

STAFF:
Robin L. Oosterveen, Program Director

ADDRESS INQUIRIES TO:
David P. Larsen, Secretary
(See address above.)

*PLEASE NOTE:
Priority given to organizations that Mrs. Wilson supported during her lifetime, or with which the Fund has a long-standing commitment.

WOLFE ASSOCIATES, INC. [368]

34 South Third Street
Columbus, OH 43215
(614) 460-3782
Fax: (614) 469-6173

E-MAIL ADDRESS:
rwolfe@10tv.com

FOUNDED: 1973

AREAS OF INTEREST:
Health and medicine, religion, education, culture, community service and environment.

TYPE:
Project/program grants.

YEAR PROGRAM STARTED: 1973

PURPOSE:
To support a variety of organizations actively involved in the pursuit of religious, charitable, scientific, literary or education goals in their respective communities.

LEGAL BASIS:
Private foundation.

ELIGIBILITY:
Grants are made to tax-exempt public foundations and charities.

GEOGRAPHIC RESTRICTIONS:
Primarily the central Ohio area.

FINANCIAL DATA:
Amount of support per award: Varies.

APPLICATION INFORMATION:
Applicants should submit a cover letter with a brief summary of the proposal and amount requested.
Deadline: The Foundation accepts and reviews applications throughout the year.

ADDRESS INQUIRIES TO:
Rita J. Wolfe, Vice President
(See address above.)

THE ROBERT W. WOODRUFF FOUNDATION [369]

50 Hurt Plaza, Suite 1200
Atlanta, GA 30303
(404) 522-6755
Fax: (404) 522-7026

E-MAIL ADDRESS:
fdns@woodruff.org

WEB SITE ADDRESS:
www.woodruff.org

FOUNDED: 1937

AREAS OF INTEREST:
Elementary, secondary and higher education; health care and education; human services, particularly for children and youth; economic development and civic affairs; art and cultural activities; conservation and environmental education.

TYPE:
Capital grants; Project/program grants.

YEAR PROGRAM STARTED: 1937

PURPOSE:
To support charitable, scientific and educational activities to achieve systemic improvement in public education, health care access, and family, children and youth services at the state and local levels.

LEGAL BASIS:
Independent, private foundation with a broad charter to support charitable, scientific and educational activities.

ELIGIBILITY:
Grants generally are limited to tax-exempt public charities located and operating in Georgia. Preference is given to one-time capital projects. Grants to organizations for basic operating support are avoided. No grants made to individuals. The Foundation does not give out loans.

GEOGRAPHIC RESTRICTIONS:
Georgia.

FINANCIAL DATA:
Amount of support per award: Generally $50,000 to $1,000,000.

Total amount of support: $106,387,538 for the year 2009.

NUMBER OF APPLICANTS MOST RECENT YEAR: 500 for the year 2008.

NUMBER OF AWARDS: 36 for the year 2010.

APPLICATION INFORMATION:
Application form not required. Proposal (one copy) should be made in letter form and should include the following information: (1) a description of the organization, its purposes, programs, staffing and governing board; (2) the organization's latest financial statements, including the most recent audit report; (3) a description of the proposed project and full justification for its funding; (4) an itemized project budget, including other sources of support in hand or anticipated and; (5) evidence from the IRS of the organization's tax-exempt status and that the applying organization itself is not a private foundation.
Deadline: September 1 and February 1.

PUBLICATIONS:
Application guidelines.

OFFICERS:
P. Russell Hardin, President
J. Lee Tribble, Treasurer
Erik S. Johnson, Secretary

TRUSTEES:
James B. Williams, Chairman
James M. Sibley, Vice Chairman
Wilton D. Looney
Charles H. McTier
E. Jenner Wood, III

ADDRESS INQUIRIES TO:
P. Russell Hardin, President
(See address above.)

WORLD BANK FAMILY NETWORK (WBFN) [370]
1818 H Street, N.W.
MSN H2-204
Washington, DC 20433
(202) 473-8751
Fax: (202) 522-3142

E-MAIL ADDRESS:
mmmf@worldbank.org

WEB SITE ADDRESS:
mmmf-grants.org

FOUNDED: 1981

AREAS OF INTEREST:
Agriculture, architecture and urban planning, civil engineering, education, foresty, journalism, nursing, nutrition, pediatrics, public administration, public health, social sciences, social work and others.

NAME(S) OF PROGRAMS:
● **Margaret McNamara Memorial Fund**

TYPE:
Grants-in-aid.

YEAR PROGRAM STARTED: 1981

PURPOSE:
To support the education of women from developing countries who are committed to improving the lives of women and children in their home countries.

ELIGIBILITY:
Applicants must be nationals of developing countries that are currently eligible to borrow

from the World Bank. The U.S./Canada program is open to women residing in the U.S., but not as permanent residents. Candidates must also be enrolled in an accredited educational institution in the U.S. where the grant will be used. They must be at least 25 years old and must not be related to any World Bank Group staff member or their spouse. They must return to their home country, or another developing country, within two years of program completion.

The South Africa program draws students worldwide.

FINANCIAL DATA:
Amount of support per award: $15,000 in U.S./Canada; $4,000 in South Africa.

NUMBER OF APPLICANTS MOST RECENT YEAR: 175 for the year 2010.

NUMBER OF AWARDS: 16 for the year 2010.

APPLICATION INFORMATION:
The application can only be completed and submitted online. Two recommendations from professors/supervisors must also be submitted electronically. At least one recommendation must be from a professor/advisor at the applicant's current institution and one must have known the applicant for at least one year.

The following documents are required for the U.S./Canada program and must be mailed: (1) copy of Fall registration; (2) official copy of transcript for Fall in a sealed envelope from the Registrar; (3) official estimate of annual expenses for students published by applicant's institution; (4) one passport-size photograph; (5) copy of U.S./Canadian Visa; (6) for applicants at U.S. universities, copy of I-20/DC-2019 (formally IAP-66); (7) for applicants at Canadian universities, copy of study permit and; (8) copy of curriculum vitae/resume (maximum two pages).

Requirements for the South Africa program are available online.
Duration: One year.
Deadline: February 28.

ADDRESS INQUIRIES TO:
Coordinator Grants
(See address above.)

WYMAN-GORDON FOUNDATION [371]
c/o Fletcher, Tilton & Whipple, P.C.
370 Main Street
Worcester, MA 01608
(508) 798-8621
(508) 459-8000
Fax: (508) 791-1201

FOUNDED: 1966

AREAS OF INTEREST:
Health and human services, education, civic and community affairs, culture and arts.

TYPE:
Grants-in-aid. The Foundation focuses its grantmaking in non-operating areas (i.e., capital campaigns, equipment).

YEAR PROGRAM STARTED: 1966

PURPOSE:
To operate exclusively for charitable, scientific and/or educational purposes.

LEGAL BASIS:
Corporate contributions program.

ELIGIBILITY:
Applicants must be nonprofit organizations with a 501(c)(3) tax-exempt status.

GEOGRAPHIC RESTRICTIONS:
Primarily Worcester area, Massachusetts.

FINANCIAL DATA:
Amount of support per award: $100 to $150,000.

NUMBER OF APPLICANTS MOST RECENT YEAR: 200.

REPRESENTATIVE AWARDS:
$150,000 to United Way of Central Massachusetts; $10,000 to Worcester Public Library; $3,000 to Mechanics Hall; $20,000 to Grafton Soccer Club; $3,500 to Worcester Municipal Research Bureau.

APPLICATION INFORMATION:
Application includes 501(c)(3) tax-exempt letter, statement of purpose and specifics regarding project or program to be funded.

IRS IDENTIFICATION NUMBER: 04-6142600

OFFICERS AND TRUSTEES:
David P. Gruber, President
Wallace F. Whitney, Jr., Secretary and Treasurer
Warner S. Fletcher, Trustee

ADDRESS INQUIRIES TO:
Warner S. Fletcher, Trustee
(See address above.)

THE WYOMISSING FOUNDATION, INC. [372]
960 Old Mill Road
Wyomissing, PA 19610-2522
(610) 376-7496
Fax: (610) 372-7626

E-MAIL ADDRESS:
pswavely@wyofound.org

WEB SITE ADDRESS:
www.wyofound.org

FOUNDED: 1929

AREAS OF INTEREST:
Charitable purposes, primarily local giving, with emphasis on hospitals, higher education, youth agencies and community funds, conservation and music.

TYPE:
Capital grants; Challenge/matching grants; Development grants; Grants-in-aid; Project/program grants; Research grants; Seed money grants.

YEAR PROGRAM STARTED: 1929

LEGAL BASIS:
Private donor foundation.

ELIGIBILITY:
No grants to individuals. Applicants must be 501(c)(3) organizations.

GEOGRAPHIC RESTRICTIONS:
Primarily Berks County, Pennsylvania.

FINANCIAL DATA:
No fiscal restrictions; non-cash benefits have been made.
Amount of support per award: $1,000 to $300,000.
Total amount of support: Varies.

NUMBER OF APPLICANTS MOST RECENT YEAR: Varies.

APPLICATION INFORMATION:
Guidelines available at the web site.
Duration: Varies.

Deadline: March, June and September.

IRS IDENTIFICATION NUMBER: 23-1980570

OFFICERS:
John Weidenhammer, President
Daniel Scheffey, Vice President
Paul R. Roedel, Treasurer

EXECUTIVE DIRECTOR:
Karen A. Rightmire

ADDRESS INQUIRIES TO:
Karen A. Rightmire, Executive Director
(See address above.)

*SPECIAL STIPULATIONS:
The Foundation does not grant interviews
either in person or by telephone.

XCEL ENERGY FOUNDATION [373]
414 Nicollet Mall
Minneapolis, MN 55401-1993
(800) 328-8226
Fax: (612) 215-4522

E-MAIL ADDRESS:
foundation@xcelenergy.com

WEB SITE ADDRESS:
www.xcelenergy.com

FOUNDED: 2001

AREAS OF INTEREST:
Environment, education, community
development, arts and culture.

TYPE:
Conferences/seminars; Endowments; General
operating grants; Matching gifts;
Project/program grants; Scholarships;
Training grants.

YEAR PROGRAM STARTED: 2001

PURPOSE:
To help promote a desirable, healthy
environment in those areas served by Xcel
Energy.

ELIGIBILITY:
Applicants must be 501(c)(3) nonprofit
organizations in the service area. Grants will
not be made to individuals, political parties,
national organizations, research programs or
government agencies. Grants are made to
religious organizations only if program
sponsored has a direct benefit to the
community and not the religious
organization.

GEOGRAPHIC RESTRICTIONS:
Colorado, Michigan, Minnesota, New
Mexico, North Dakota, South Dakota, Texas
and Wisconsin.

FINANCIAL DATA:
Amount of support per award: $1,000 to
$25,000 specific to the geographic area.
Total amount of support: Maximum $750.
Matching fund requirements: 501(c)(3)
nonprofits. Minimum donation $25,
maximum $500.

NUMBER OF APPLICANTS MOST RECENT YEAR:
1,098.

NUMBER OF AWARDS: 481.

APPLICATION INFORMATION:
The Foundation has an online grant
application system. No later than three weeks
after the deadline for submitting a Letter of
Intent, organizations will be notified whether
or not they have been selected to submit a
full proposal. Full proposals will be due
within three weeks of notification.
(Notification e-mail will contain the
deadline.) Applicants being granted funds
from the Foundation will be required to
return a signed tax receipt form, stating that
no goods or services have been received in
exchange for the grant. Organizations also
will be required to provide a final report on
the grant at the end of their fiscal year, or at
the end of the funded program/project
through Foundation's online system.
Deadline: Environment: January 18 and
August 20. Education: January 18. Economic
Sustainability: April 29. Arts and Culture:
August 20.

STAFF:
Shanda Vangas, Grants Manager
Jim Garness, Senior Foundation
Representative
Terry Price, Senior Foundation
Representative

ADDRESS INQUIRIES TO:
Jim Garness
Senior Foundation Representative
(See address above.)

THE XEROX FOUNDATION [374]
45 Glover Avenue
Norwalk, CT 06856
(203) 849-2453
Fax: (203) 849-2479

FOUNDED: 1978

AREAS OF INTEREST:
Education and workforce preparedness,
science and technology, employee and
community affairs, cultural affairs, and
national affairs.

TYPE:
Assistantships; Challenge/matching grants;
Development grants; Fellowships; General
operating grants; Grants-in-aid; Internships;
Matching gifts; Professorships;
Project/program grants; Research grants;
Scholarships; Seed money grants; Technical
assistance; Training grants.

YEAR PROGRAM STARTED: 1974

PURPOSE:
To assist a variety of social, civic, and
cultural organizations that provide
broad-based community programs and
services in the cities where our employees
live and work; to support higher education to
prepare qualified men and women for careers

in business, government and education; to
advance knowledge in science and
technology; to enhance learning opportunities
for minorities and disadvantaged; to foster
debate on major national public policy issues;
to support national leadership efforts around
major social problems, education,
employability and cultural affairs.

LEGAL BASIS:
Corporate foundation.

ELIGIBILITY:
Grants are made only to organizations that
have been granted exemption from Federal
Income Tax under Section 501(c)(3) and
ruled to be publicly supported under Section
509(a) of the Internal Revenue Code. No
grants for individuals; capital grants (except
for special circumstances and approved by
Board of Trustees); endowments or endowed
chairs; political organizations or candidates;
religious or sectarian groups; municipal,
county, state, federal or quasi-government
agencies.

GEOGRAPHIC RESTRICTIONS:
United States.

FINANCIAL DATA:
Amount of support per award: Grants vary in
amount, depending upon the needs and
nature of the request.
Total amount of support: $12,600,000 for the
year 2010.

APPLICATION INFORMATION:
No specific application form is used.
Applications must be submitted in letter
form. The letter should contain:
(1) the legal name of the organization;
(2) the official contact person;
(3) its tax-exempt status;
(4) a brief description of its activities and
programs;
(5) the purpose for which the grant is being
requested;
(6) the benefits expected;
(7) the plans for evaluation;
(8) the projected budget and;
(9) the expected sources and amount of funds
needed.

Any additional factual material related to the
organization or the request that may be
useful for evaluation, plus a copy of the
latest annual financial statement, if available,
should also be included.
Duration: The Foundation usually does not
make grants for continuing support without a
follow-up request. Large grants may be
approved for one year or on a multiyear
basis.
Deadline: Grant reviews take place monthly.

OFFICERS:
Dr. Joseph M. Cahalan, President

ADDRESS INQUIRIES TO:
Dr. Joseph M. Cahalan, President
The Xerox Foundation
(See address above.)

HUMANITIES

Humanities (general)

AMERICAN ACADEMY IN ROME [375]

7 East 60th Street
New York, NY 10022-1001
(212) 751-7200
Fax: (212) 751-7220

E-MAIL ADDRESS:
info@aarome.org

WEB SITE ADDRESS:
www.aarome.org

FOUNDED: 1894

AREAS OF INTEREST:
Arts and humanities.

NAME(S) OF PROGRAMS:
● **Rome Prize Fellowships**

TYPE:
Awards/prizes; Fellowships; Residencies.
Fellowships for independent work in
architecture, landscape architecture, design,
musical composition, visual arts, historic
preservation/conservation, ancient studies,
medieval studies, renaissance and early
modern studies, and modern Italian studies.
Supported projects must be conducted at
American Academy in Rome facilities.

YEAR PROGRAM STARTED: 1894

PURPOSE:
To support emerging artists and scholars in
the early or middle stages of their careers; to
refine and expand their professional, artistic
or scholarly aptitudes, drawing on their
colleagues' erudition and experience, as well
as on the inestimable resources of the Italian
capital of Rome, Europe and the
Mediterranean.

LEGAL BASIS:
Private, not-for-profit.

ELIGIBILITY:
Must be U.S. citizen at the time of
application. U.S. citizens and those foreign
nationals who have lived in the U.S. for the
three years immediately preceding the
application deadline may apply for the NEH
Postdoctoral Fellowships. Graduate students
in the humanities may apply only for
Predoctoral Fellowships. Previous winners of
the Rome Prize are not eligible to reapply.
Undergraduate students are not eligible for
Rome Prize Fellowships.

FINANCIAL DATA:
Rome Prize includes stipend, meals, a
bedroom with private bath, and a study or
studio. Winners of six-month and 11-month
fellowships receive stipends.
Amount of support per award: Fellowships
provide stipends of $14,000 (six-month) and
$26,000 (11-month).
Total amount of support: $2,700,000.

COOPERATIVE FUNDING PROGRAMS: National
Endowment for the Arts, National
Endowment for the Humanities, Andrew W.
Mellon Foundation, Samuel Kress Foundation
and American Academy of Arts and Letters.

NUMBER OF APPLICANTS MOST RECENT YEAR:
900.

NUMBER OF AWARDS: 30.

APPLICATION INFORMATION:
Application forms are available online.
Duration: Six-month and 11-month
fellowships depending on field of application.
Predoctoral awards in the humanities include
11-month and two-year fellowships.

Deadline: November 1.

STAFF:
Shawn Miller, Program Director

ADDRESS INQUIRIES TO:
Programs Department
(See address above.)

AMERICAN ANTIQUARIAN SOCIETY (AAS) [376]

185 Salisbury Street
Worcester, MA 01609-1634
(508) 755-5221
Fax: (508) 754-9069

E-MAIL ADDRESS:
perickson@mwa.org

WEB SITE ADDRESS:
www.americanantiquarian.org

FOUNDED: 1812

AREAS OF INTEREST:
American history and culture through 1876.

NAME(S) OF PROGRAMS:
● **AAS American Society for Eighteenth
Century Studies Fellowship**
● **AAS National Endowment for the
Humanities Fellowships**
● **AAS-Northeast Modern Language
Association Fellowship**
● **American Historical Print Collectors
Fellowship**
● **Stephen Botein Fellowships**
● **The "Drawn to Art" Fellowship**
● **Jay and Deborah Last Fellowship**
● **The Legacy Fellowship**
● **Kate B. and Hall J. Peterson
Fellowships**
● **The Reese Fellowship**
● **Joyce A. Tracy Fellowship**

TYPE:
Conferences/seminars; Fellowships.
Fellowships provide support for residence at
the Society's library for research on any topic
supported by the collections. All awards are
for research and writing using the library's
resources.

YEAR PROGRAM STARTED: 1972

PURPOSE:
To enable scholars to come to Worcester for
an extended period to do research in the
Society's collections.

LEGAL BASIS:
AAS was incorporated by the legislature of
Massachusetts, October 24, 1812.

ELIGIBILITY:
Fellows are selected on the basis of the
applicant's scholarly qualifications, the
scholarly significance of the project, and the
appropriateness of the proposed study to the
Society's collections.

The National Endowment for the Humanities
Fellowships are intended for scholars beyond
the Doctorate, for which senior and
mid-career scholars are encouraged to apply.

Short-term fellowships are available for
scholars holding Ph.D. and for doctoral
candidates engaged in dissertation research.

GEOGRAPHIC RESTRICTIONS:
United States.

FINANCIAL DATA:
Amount of support per award: Long-term
fellowships carry stipends up to $50,400.
Short-term fellowships are $1,850 per month.

NUMBER OF APPLICANTS MOST RECENT YEAR:
170.

NUMBER OF AWARDS: 40.

APPLICATION INFORMATION:
Duration: One month for short-term
fellowships. Four to 12 months for long-term
fellowships.
Deadline: January 15. Announcement by
March 15.

ADDRESS INQUIRIES TO:
Paul Erickson
Director of Academic Programs
(See address above.)

*SPECIAL STIPULATIONS:
Recipient must maintain regular and
continuous residence at the Society during
his or her period of tenure.

AMERICAN ANTIQUARIAN SOCIETY (AAS) [377]

185 Salisbury Street
Worcester, MA 01609-1634
(508) 755-5221
Fax: (508) 753-3311

E-MAIL ADDRESS:
cmcrell@mwa.org

WEB SITE ADDRESS:
www.americanantiquarian.org

AREAS OF INTEREST:
American history, literature and culture
through 1876.

NAME(S) OF PROGRAMS:
● **AAS Fellowship for Creative and
Performing Artists and Writers**

TYPE:
Fellowships. Visiting fellowship for historical
research by creative and performing artists,
writers, filmmakers and journalists.

YEAR PROGRAM STARTED: 1995

PURPOSE:
To multiply and improve ways in which an
understanding of history is communicated to
the American people.

ELIGIBILITY:
Creative and performing artists, writers,
filmmakers, journalists, and others whose
goals are to produce imaginative,
non-formulaic works dealing with pre-20th
century American history. Works are for the
general public, rather than for academic or
educational audiences.

FINANCIAL DATA:
Amount of support per award: Stipend of
$1,350 for Fellows living on campus; $1,850
for Fellows residing off-campus.

NUMBER OF APPLICANTS MOST RECENT YEAR:
40.

NUMBER OF AWARDS: 4.

APPLICATION INFORMATION:
A complete fellowship application consists of
the following materials:
(1) cover sheet;
(2) current resume, including a list of any
awards, scholarships or grants received;
(3) a statement of not more than five typed,
double-spaced pages briefly summarizing the
applicant's educational and professional
background and goals, describing the
research for the project including readings in
primary and secondary sources, and
indicating the nature of the research program
proposed for the AAS fellowship;

(4) 10 copies of representative samples of previous works must be included for distribution to the selection committee. Written works (play and video scripts; prose and poetry; works of nonfiction, etc.) cannot exceed 25 pages in length. Applicants are welcome to send two or three copies of full, completed works in addition to the 25-page sample. If submitting samples of films, videos, audio and music recordings, or reproductions (digital versions and/or photographs) of paintings, sculptures, prints and other art works, please send only three copies or sets with the completed application. Applicants are encouraged to include any relevant reviews of their work by professional critics. If the applicant wishes to have any of these samples returned, please enclose a self-addressed, stamped envelope and;

(5) two letters of reference should be sent directly to AAS by individuals familiar with the applicant's career accomplishments and goals.

Duration: Four-week residency.

Deadline: October 5, with notification on or about December 5.

ADDRESS INQUIRIES TO:
James David Moran
Director of Outreach
(See address above.)

AMERICAN COUNCIL OF LEARNED SOCIETIES   [378]
633 Third Avenue, 8th Floor
New York, NY 10017-6795
(212) 697-1505 ext. 136 or 138

E-MAIL ADDRESS:
fellowships@acls.org

WEB SITE ADDRESS:
www.acls.org

FOUNDED: 1919

AREAS OF INTEREST:
The humanities and related social sciences.

NAME(S) OF PROGRAMS:
● **ACLS Fellowship**

TYPE:
Fellowships. Postdoctoral fellowships to support research in the humanities or research projects with a predominantly humanities-related emphasis in the social sciences.

PURPOSE:
To provide opportunities for scholars to engage in humanities research.

LEGAL BASIS:
Nonprofit.

ELIGIBILITY:
U.S. citizens or permanent residents holding a Ph.D. degree conferred two years before application deadline or its equivalent (taken to mean scholarly maturity as demonstrated by professional experience and publications) may apply. Applicant must not have held a "supported research leave" during the two years ending July 1, 2012, including any supported research leave to be initiated during the 2011-12 academic year.

FINANCIAL DATA:
Amount of support per award: Fellowships are up to $60,000 for full professor (and career equivalent), up to $40,000 for associate professor (and career equivalent), and up to $35,000 for assistant professor (and career equivalent).

NUMBER OF APPLICANTS MOST RECENT YEAR: 926.

NUMBER OF AWARDS: Approximately 20 fellowships for each level.

APPLICATION INFORMATION:
Applications must be submitted through the ACLS Online Fellowship Application system.
Duration: Fellows must devote six to 12 continuous months to full-time work on supported projects.
Deadline: September 28.

THE AMERICAN NUMISMATIC SOCIETY   [379]
75 Varick Street, 11th Floor
New York, NY 10013
(212) 571-4470 ext. 153
Fax: (212) 571-4479

E-MAIL ADDRESS:
isaac@numismatics.org

WEB SITE ADDRESS:
www.numismatics.org

FOUNDED: 1858

AREAS OF INTEREST:
Numismatics (coins and medals), history and archeology.

NAME(S) OF PROGRAMS:
● **The Eric P. Newman Graduate Summer Seminar**

TYPE:
Grants-in-aid. Grants for graduate students and junior faculty to attend the Society's summer seminar held at its museum in New York. The Graduate Seminar in Numismatics is an intensive program of study including lectures and conferences conducted by specialists in various fields, preparation and oral delivery of a research paper and actual contact with the coinage in the Society's collection. Curatorial staff and other experts from the U.S. and abroad will participate in the seminar.

YEAR PROGRAM STARTED: 1952

PURPOSE:
To familiarize students with numismatic methodology and scholarship; to provide a deeper understanding of the contributions made by numismatics to other fields of study.

ELIGIBILITY:
Applications are accepted from students of demonstrated competence who will have completed at least one year of graduate work in history, classical studies, economic history or other related fields. Applications are also encouraged from junior faculty members with an advanced degree in one of these fields.

Applications are also accepted from outstanding students from foreign institutions who have completed at least one year of graduate work and are able to demonstrate fluency in English; however, no financial aid for them is offered.

FINANCIAL DATA:
Stipends are available to qualified applicants who are citizens or permanent residents of the U.S. or Canada.

Amount of support per award: Stipends of $4,000 are available to qualified applicants.

Total amount of support: Varies.

COOPERATIVE FUNDING PROGRAMS: Support of attendance at the Seminar is made possible by a generous donation from Mr. and Mrs. Eric P. Newman.

NUMBER OF APPLICANTS MOST RECENT YEAR: 50.

NUMBER OF AWARDS: Up to 6.

APPLICATION INFORMATION:
Applications must be supported by three letters of recommendation. Additional information and application forms will be provided upon request.
Duration: Seven to eight weeks, June through July.
Deadline: February 15.

OFFICERS:
Dr. Peter Van Alfen, Director
Richard Witschonke, Co-Director

ADDRESS INQUIRIES TO:
Dr. Peter Van Alfen, Director
(See address above.)

AMERICAN PHILOSOPHICAL SOCIETY   [380]
c/o American Philosophical Society Library
105 South Fifth Street
Philadelphia, PA 19106-3386
(215) 440-3400
Fax: (215) 440-3423

E-MAIL ADDRESS:
espamer@amphilsoc.org

WEB SITE ADDRESS:
www.amphilsoc.org

FOUNDED: 1743

AREAS OF INTEREST:
Scholarly research.

NAME(S) OF PROGRAMS:
● **The Library Resident Research Fellowships**

TYPE:
Fellowships; Grants-in-aid; Research grants. Short-term residential fellowships for conducting research in the Library's collections.

YEAR PROGRAM STARTED: 1991

PURPOSE:
To encourage research by scholars in the Library's collections.

LEGAL BASIS:
Nonprofit learned society.

ELIGIBILITY:
Open to both U.S. citizens and foreign nationals who are holders of a Ph.D. or the equivalent, Ph.D. candidates who have passed their preliminary exams and independent scholars. Applicants in any relevant field of scholarship may apply.

FINANCIAL DATA:
Amount of support per award: $2,000 per month.

NUMBER OF APPLICANTS MOST RECENT YEAR: 60.

NUMBER OF AWARDS: 23.

APPLICATION INFORMATION:
Application forms may be downloaded from the web site. Applicants should submit cover sheet stating name, title of project, expected period of residence, institutional affiliation, mailing address, telephone numbers, social security number, a letter (not to exceed three single-spaced pages) which briefly describes the project, states the specific relevance of the American Philosophical Society's collections to the project and indicates expected results of the research (such as

publications), a curriculum vitae or resume and two letters of reference (doctoral candidates must use their dissertation advisor).

Duration: One to three months, taken between June 1 and May 31.

Deadline: March 1. Notification by May 1.

PUBLICATIONS:
Program announcement; list of guides to the Society's collections.

ADDRESS INQUIRIES TO:
Earle Spamer
The Library Resident Research Fellowships
(See address above.)

*SPECIAL STIPULATIONS:
Fellows are expected to be in residence during the period of their award.

THE AMERICAN SCHOOL OF CLASSICAL STUDIES AT ATHENS

6-8 Charlton Street
Princeton, NJ 08540-5232
(609) 683-0800
Fax: (609) 924-0578

E-MAIL ADDRESS:
application@ascsa.org; ascsa@ascsa.org

WEB SITE ADDRESS:
www.ascsa.edu.gr

TYPE:
Fellowships. Fellowships for postdoctoral scholars and professionals in the humanities.

See entry 934 for full listing.

THE AMERICAN SCHOOL OF CLASSICAL STUDIES AT ATHENS

6-8 Charlton Street
Princeton, NJ 08540-5232
(609) 683-0800
Fax: (609) 924-0578

E-MAIL ADDRESS:
application@ascsa.org; ascsa@ascsa.org

WEB SITE ADDRESS:
www.ascsa.edu.gr

TYPE:
Fellowships. The M. Alison Frantz Fellowship and The Jacob Hirsch Fellowship are part of the Student Associate Program, which is open to advanced graduate students in the same fields as the Regular Academic Program (classical studies and ancient Mediterranean studies and related fields such as history of art, anthropology, prehistory, studies in postclassical Greece, etc.), who plan to pursue independent research projects and who do not wish to commit to the full Regular Academic Program.

The Jacob Hirsch Fellowship is also open to students from Israel.

See entry 935 for full listing.

THE AMERICAN SCHOOL OF CLASSICAL STUDIES AT ATHENS

6-8 Charlton Street
Princeton, NJ 08540-5232
(609) 683-0800
Fax: (609) 924-0578

E-MAIL ADDRESS:
application@ascsa.org; ascsa@ascsa.org

WEB SITE ADDRESS:
www.ascsa.edu.gr

TYPE:
Fellowships. Several Fellowships awarded by the School for the full academic year: the Samuel H. Kress Fellowship in art and architecture of antiquity; the Gorham Phillips Stevens Fellowship in the history of architecture; the Ione Mylonas Shear Fellowship in Mycenaean archaeology or Athenian architecture and/or archaeology; the Homer A. and Dorothy B. Thompson Fellowship in the study of pottery. Additionally, three Fellowships are unrestricted as to field: the Edward Capps, the Doreen Canaday Spitzer, and the Eugene Vanderpool Fellowships.

See entry 936 for full listing.

THE AMERICAN SCHOOL OF CLASSICAL STUDIES AT ATHENS

6-8 Charlton Street
Princeton, NJ 08540-5232
(609) 683-0800
Fax: (609) 924-0578

E-MAIL ADDRESS:
application@ascsa.org; ascsa@ascsa.org

WEB SITE ADDRESS:
www.ascsa.edu.gr

TYPE:
Fellowships. Traveling fellowship awarded annually and held in Athens and Rome in alternate years. Fellows will use either the American Academy in Rome or the American School of Classical Studies at Athens as a base.

See entry 938 for full listing.

THE AMERICAN SCHOOL OF CLASSICAL STUDIES AT ATHENS

6-8 Charlton Street
Princeton, NJ 08540-5232
(609) 683-0800
Fax: (609) 924-0578

E-MAIL ADDRESS:
application@ascsa.org; ascsa@ascsa.org

WEB SITE ADDRESS:
www.ascsa.edu.gr

TYPE:
Scholarships. Four-week program in intermediate-level Medieval Greek language and philology at the Gennadius Library, with site and museum trips. Seminar given every other year. Next seminar to be held in 2013.

See entry 940 for full listing.

ARCHAEOLOGICAL INSTITUTE OF AMERICA   [381]

656 Beacon Street, 6th Floor
Boston, MA 02215
(617) 358-4184
Fax: (617) 353-6550

E-MAIL ADDRESS:
lsparks@aia.bu.edu

WEB SITE ADDRESS:
www.archaeological.org

FOUNDED: 1879

AREAS OF INTEREST:
Archaeological research and publication.

NAME(S) OF PROGRAMS:
● **Jane C. Waldbaum Archaeological Field School Scholarship**

TYPE:
Scholarships. Award to support participation in an archaeological excavation or survey project.

YEAR PROGRAM STARTED: 2006

ELIGIBILITY:
Open to junior and senior undergraduates or first-year graduate students. Applicants cannot previously have participated in archaeological excavation and must be at least a junior at the time of application. Applicants must be enrolled in a college or university in the U.S. or Canada, but do not have to be U.S. citizens or residents.

FINANCIAL DATA:
Amount of support per award: $1,000.

NUMBER OF APPLICANTS MOST RECENT YEAR:
150.

NUMBER OF AWARDS: 7.

APPLICATION INFORMATION:
All applications must be submitted electronically through the AIA web site. Required materials include the application form, two letters of reference, official transcript(s) and a letter of acceptance from the field school. All application materials must be received by the deadline.

Duration: Minimum one-month stay at the field school. Nonrenewable.

Deadline: Sunday closest to a week after March 1.

ADDRESS INQUIRIES TO:
Laurel Nilsen Sparks
Lecture and Fellowship Coordinator
(See address above.)

ARCHAEOLOGICAL INSTITUTE OF AMERICA   [382]

656 Beacon Street, 6th Floor
Boston, MA 02215
(617) 358-4184
Fax: (617) 353-6550

E-MAIL ADDRESS:
lsparks@aia.bu.edu

WEB SITE ADDRESS:
www.archaeological.org

FOUNDED: 1879

AREAS OF INTEREST:
Archaeological research and publication.

NAME(S) OF PROGRAMS:
● **Anna C. and Oliver C. Colburn Fellowship**

TYPE:
Fellowships. Awarded to an applicant every other year contingent upon his or her acceptance as an incoming Associate Member or Student Associate Member of the American School of Classical Studies at Athens, Greece.

YEAR PROGRAM STARTED: 1991

PURPOSE:
To support studies at the American School of Classical Studies at Athens, Greece.

LEGAL BASIS:
Nonprofit, scientific and educational organization.

ELIGIBILITY:

Applicants must be U.S. or Canadian citizens or permanent residents, or those who are actively pursuing an advanced degree at a North American college or university, who are at the predoctoral stage or who have recently received the Ph.D. degree (within five years of the date of application). They must apply concurrently to the American School for Senior Associate Membership or Student Associate Membership. Applicants may not be Members of the American School during the year of application.

Other major fellowships may not be held during the requested tenure of the fellowship award.

The fellowship recipient is required to submit a report on the use of the stipend both to the President of the Archaeological Institute of America and to the Director of the American School of Classical Studies at Athens at the conclusion of the tenure of the fellowship.

FINANCIAL DATA:

Amount of support per award: $11,000.

Total amount of support: $11,000.

NUMBER OF APPLICANTS MOST RECENT YEAR: 5.

NUMBER OF AWARDS: 1.

APPLICATION INFORMATION:

Official application materials are available on the web site. Graduate transcript(s), three letters of reference, and a summary statement of the proposed project are required. Candidates must apply concurrently to the American School for Senior Associate Membership or Student Associate Membership.

Duration: One academic year.

Deadline: January 15, 2012 and every other year thereafter.

OFFICERS:

Elizabeth Bartman, President

ADDRESS INQUIRIES TO:

Laurel Nilsen Sparks
Lecture and Fellowship Coordinator
(See address above.)

*SPECIAL STIPULATIONS:

After the tenure of their fellowship, all fellows are expected to submit an abstract to the Program Committee within two years, in accordance with that committee's guidelines, in order to present a paper on their research at the Institute annual meeting.
Other major fellowships may not be held during the requested tenure of the Colburn award.

ARCHAEOLOGICAL INSTITUTE OF AMERICA [383]

656 Beacon Street, 6th Floor
Boston, MA 02215
(617) 358-4184
Fax: (617) 353-6550

E-MAIL ADDRESS:
lsparks@aia.bu.edu

WEB SITE ADDRESS:
www.archaeological.org

FOUNDED: 1879

AREAS OF INTEREST:
Archaeological research and publication.

NAME(S) OF PROGRAMS:
- **Olivia James Traveling Fellowship**

TYPE:

Fellowships. Awarded, preferably, to individuals engaged in dissertation research or to recent recipients of the Ph.D. (within five years of the application deadline) for travel and study in Greece, the Aegean Islands, Cyprus, Sicily, Southern Italy, Asia Minor or Mesopotamia to conduct a project in (most suitably) classics, sculpture, architecture, archaeology or history.

YEAR PROGRAM STARTED: 1961

PURPOSE:
To encourage the continued study of archaeological sites; to provide fellowships for travel and study in Greece, the Aegean Islands, Cyprus, Sicily, Southern Italy, Asia Minor or Mesopotamia.

LEGAL BASIS:
Nonprofit, scientific and educational organization.

ELIGIBILITY:

Applicants must be U.S. citizens. Preference is given to individuals engaged in dissertation research or to recent Ph.D. recipients (within five years of application deadline). Preference is also given to projects of at least a half-year's duration. The award is for travel and study in Greece, the Aegean Islands, Cyprus, Sicily, Southern Italy, Asia Minor or Mesopotamia and is not intended to support field excavation projects. Recipients may not hold other major fellowships during the requested tenure.

FINANCIAL DATA:

Amount of support per award: $25,000.

Total amount of support: $25,000.

NUMBER OF APPLICANTS MOST RECENT YEAR: 18.

NUMBER OF AWARDS: 1.

APPLICATION INFORMATION:

Official application materials are available August of each year, on the web site. Graduate transcript(s), three letters of reference, and a summary statement of proposed project are required. Applications for the fellowship can now be submitted electronically.

Duration: Single fellowship for work to be conducted between July 1 and the following June 30.

Deadline: November 1. Announcement by February 1.

OFFICERS:

Elizabeth Bartman, President

ADDRESS INQUIRIES TO:

Laurel Nilsen Sparks
Lecture and Fellowship Coordinator
(See address above.)

ARCHAEOLOGICAL INSTITUTE OF AMERICA [384]

656 Beacon Street, 6th Floor
Boston, MA 02215
(617) 358-4184
Fax: (617) 353-6550

E-MAIL ADDRESS:
lsparks@aia.bu.edu

WEB SITE ADDRESS:
www.archaeological.org

FOUNDED: 1879

AREAS OF INTEREST:
Archaeological research and publication.

NAME(S) OF PROGRAMS:
- **Harriet and Leon Pomerance Fellowship**

TYPE:
Fellowships. Awarded to support a person on an individual project of a scholarly nature relating to Aegean Bronze Age Archaeology. Preference will be given to candidates whose project requires travel to the Mediterranean for the purpose stated above.

YEAR PROGRAM STARTED: 1972

PURPOSE:
To promote serious scholarly study of Aegean Bronze Age Archaeology.

LEGAL BASIS:
Nonprofit, scientific and educational organization.

ELIGIBILITY:

Applicants must be citizens or permanent residents of the U.S. or Canada, or be actively pursuing an advanced degree at a North American college or university. Previous Harriet Pomerance Fellows are not eligible. At the conclusion of the fellowship tenure, the recipient must submit a report on the use of the stipend to the president of the Institute.

FINANCIAL DATA:

Amount of support per award: $5,000.

Total amount of support: $5,000.

NUMBER OF APPLICANTS MOST RECENT YEAR: 7.

NUMBER OF AWARDS: 1.

APPLICATION INFORMATION:

Official application materials are available in August of each year, on the web site. Graduate transcript(s), three letters of reference, and a summary statement of proposed project are required. Applications for the fellowship can be submitted electronically.

Duration: One academic year or less.

Deadline: November 1. Announcement by February 1.

OFFICERS:

Elizabeth Bartman, President

ADDRESS INQUIRIES TO:

Laurel Nilsen Sparks
Lecture and Fellowship Coordinator
(See address above.)

THE AUSTRALIAN NATIONAL UNIVERSITY [385]

Humanities Research Centre, RSHA
Sir Roland Wilson Building, No. 120
McCoy Circuit
Australian National University
Canberra, ACT 0200 Australia
61 2 612 54357
Fax: 61 2 612 51380

E-MAIL ADDRESS:
leena.messina@anu.edu.au

WEB SITE ADDRESS:
hrc.anu.edu.au

FOUNDED: 1973

AREAS OF INTEREST:
European thought and culture, their influence overseas, any area of research in the humanities (broadly interpreted), and human rights.

NAME(S) OF PROGRAMS:
- **Visiting Fellowships**

TYPE:
Conferences/seminars; Fellowships. Visiting Fellowships are offered with a grant, without a grant or with a partial grant.

YEAR PROGRAM STARTED: 1973

PURPOSE:
To stimulate research in the humanities throughout Australia.

LEGAL BASIS:
Integral part of the Australian National University, Research School of Humanities.

ELIGIBILITY:
Applicants are usually established academics and must have a higher degree. Relevance of project proposed to research platforms, publications.

FINANCIAL DATA:
Amount of support per award: Visiting Fellowships provide accommodation for 12 weeks plus airfares up to $3,000.
Total amount of support: Approximately $150,000 (AUD) annually.

NUMBER OF APPLICANTS MOST RECENT YEAR:
Approximately 60.

NUMBER OF AWARDS: Approximately 8 to 12.

APPLICATION INFORMATION:
Application form, curriculum vitae, and three reports from referees are required.
Duration: One year. Not usually renewable.
Deadline: Late February. Award announcement around June.

PUBLICATIONS:
Annual report; descriptive brochure; journal; application guidelines; forms and HRC bulletin.

ADDRESS INQUIRIES TO:
Leena Messina, Programs Manager
(See address above.)

JOHN CARTER BROWN LIBRARY

P.O. Box 1894
Providence, RI 02912
(401) 863-2725
Fax: (401) 863-3477

E-MAIL ADDRESS:
jcbl_fellowships@brown.edu

WEB SITE ADDRESS:
www.jcbl.org

TYPE:
Fellowships; Research grants.
See entry 622 for full listing.

CANADIAN FEDERATION FOR THE HUMANITIES AND SOCIAL SCIENCES

275 Bank Street, Suite 300
Ottawa ON K2P 2L6 Canada
(613) 238-6112 ext. 352
Fax: (613) 238-6114

E-MAIL ADDRESS:
secaspp@fedcan.ca

WEB SITE ADDRESS:
www.fedcan.ca/english/aspp/aspp.html

TYPE:
Grants-in-aid. Grants to aid the publication of scholarly manuscripts in the social sciences and humanities.
See entry 1971 for full listing.

CANADIAN INSTITUTE IN GREECE/L'INSTITUT CANADIEN EN GRECE [386]

330 Albert Street
Waterloo ON N2L 3T8 Canada
(519) 886-4428

E-MAIL ADDRESS:
gschaus@wlu.ca

WEB SITE ADDRESS:
www.cig-icg.gr

FOUNDED: 1974

AREAS OF INTEREST:
Modern Greek, classical languages and literatures, history, archaeology, history of art and music.

NAME(S) OF PROGRAMS:
● **Elizabeth Alfodi-Rosenbaum Fellowship**
● **Franz and Neda Leipen Fellowship**
● **Homer and Dorothy Thompson Fellowship**

TYPE:
Conferences/seminars; Endowments; Fellowships; Internships. Intended to support the graduate work of a person who needs to study in Greece.

YEAR PROGRAM STARTED: 1974

PURPOSE:
To promote the study of modern Greek, classical languages and literatures, history, archaeology, history of art and music.

LEGAL BASIS:
Incorporated in Canada and Greece.

ELIGIBILITY:
Open to Canadian citizens or landed immigrants.

FINANCIAL DATA:
Amount of support per award: $9,000 (CAN) plus $4,000 for housing support in Athens.

NUMBER OF APPLICANTS MOST RECENT YEAR: 4 to 6.

NUMBER OF AWARDS: 2.

APPLICATION INFORMATION:
Applicants must write, enclosing a curriculum vitae and an outline of the proposed research. Applicants must also arrange for three referees to send letters to the Canadian address.
Duration: Nine months.
Deadline: March 1.

ADDRESS INQUIRIES TO:
E-mail: cig-icg@cig-icg.gr

CENTER FOR HELLENIC STUDIES [387]

3100 Whitehaven Street, N.W.
Washington, DC 20008
(202) 745-4400
Fax: (202) 332-8688

E-MAIL ADDRESS:
chs@chs.harvard.edu
fellowships@chs.harvard.edu

WEB SITE ADDRESS:
www.chs.harvard.edu

FOUNDED: 1961

AREAS OF INTEREST:
Postgraduate ancient Greek studies.

NAME(S) OF PROGRAMS:
● **Junior Fellowships**

TYPE:
Fellowships; Residencies; Visiting scholars. The Center offers both Residential and Non-Residential Fellowships to scholars working on various aspects of ancient Greek civilization. Eligible fields of research include archaeology, art history, epigraphy, history, literary criticism, philology, philosophy, pedagogical applications and interdisciplinary research.

YEAR PROGRAM STARTED: 1961

PURPOSE:
To encourage research in Hellenic studies.

LEGAL BASIS:
A unit of Harvard University.

ELIGIBILITY:
Investigators holding a Ph.D. degree or equivalent are eligible to apply. Professional competence in ancient Greek, as evidenced by publication, is essential.

FINANCIAL DATA:
Residential Fellowships provide a stipend plus lodging. Non-Residential Fellowships provide a stipend. The Residential Fellowships stipend (maximum $34,000) is adjusted according to the number of dependents and the amount of outside funding. Travel and research assistance available ($1,000).
Non-Residential Fellowship stipend supports travel and research (maximum $5,000).

NUMBER OF APPLICANTS MOST RECENT YEAR:
Fellowships: 92.

NUMBER OF AWARDS: Residential Fellowships: full year 6, semester 4; Non-Residential Fellowships: 9.

APPLICATION INFORMATION:
Official application materials are available at the web site.
Duration: Support is available for a nine-month period beginning September 1 and ending May 31.
Deadline: October.

PUBLICATIONS:
Application form and guidelines.

DIRECTORS:
Gregory Nagy
Douglas Frame, Associate Director

ADDRESS INQUIRIES TO:
Fellowships and Curricular Development
(See address above.)

CENTER FOR MEDIEVAL AND RENAISSANCE STUDIES [388]

University of California, Los Angeles
302 Royce Hall
Box 951485
Los Angeles, CA 90095-1485
(310) 825-1880
Fax: (310) 825-0655

E-MAIL ADDRESS:
cmrs@humnet.ucla.edu

WEB SITE ADDRESS:
www.cmrs.ucla.edu

FOUNDED: 1963

AREAS OF INTEREST:
All aspects related to the Medieval and Renaissance periods.

NAME(S) OF PROGRAMS:
● **Fredi Chiappelli Travel Fellowships in Italian Studies**
● **CMRS Travel Grants**

- **Interdisciplinary Research Grants**
- **Research Assistantships in Medieval and Renaissance Studies**
- **The George T. and Margaret W. Romani Fellowships**
- **Summer Fellowships in Medieval and Renaissance Studies**
- **Lynn and Maude White Fellowship**

TYPE:
Assistantships; Awards/prizes; Conferences/seminars; Fellowships; Project/program grants; Research grants; Travel grants; Visiting scholars.

PURPOSE:
To promote interdisciplinary and cross-cultural studies of modern civilization in its formative period between the fourth and mid-17th centuries and to provide added research opportunities, facilities and assistance.

LEGAL BASIS:
Nonprofit university research organization.

ELIGIBILITY:
For the CMRS Travel Grants, applicant must be a UCLA graduate student attending conferences, symposia, meetings of professional organizations to present research papers on any topic in the field of Medieval and Renaissance Studies.

For Research Assistantships, the applicant must expect to be a registered graduate student at UCLA and must have the goal of obtaining a Ph.D. in the field of Medieval and Renaissance Studies.

For Romani Fellowships, students must be nominated by their academic departments, pursuing studies in an aspect of the Middle Ages or Renaissance under mentorship of an active CMRS faculty member.

For Summer Fellowships, the applicant must hold a Ph.D.

For the Lynn and Maude White Fellowship, the applicant must be a graduate student advanced to candidacy for the Ph.D. at UCLA in a department associated with the Center for Medieval and Renaissance Studies.

For the Fredi Chiappelli Travel Fellowship, the applicant must be a graduate student at UCLA and have a need to travel to pursue research in any aspect of medieval or Renaissance Italian studies.

For Interdisciplinary Research grants, the applicant team must be UCLA faculty or graduate students and represent more than one academic discipline.

FINANCIAL DATA:
Amount of support per award: Chiappelli Travel Fellowship: $2,500. CMRS Travel Grants: Varies. Interdisciplinary Research: Up to $2,000 per year. Romani Fellowships: $20,000 per year. Summer Fellowships: $500 stipend. Lynn and Maude White Fellowship: $15,000.

NUMBER OF AWARDS: Chiappelli Travel Fellowships: Up to 4. CMRS Travel Grants: Varies. Research Assistantships: 3. Romani Fellowships: 1-2. Summer Fellowships: 2. Lynn and Maude White Fellowship: 1.

APPLICATION INFORMATION:
For CMRS Travel Grants, submit letter of request with conference or meeting name, date and place; title of paper or research project being presented; travel expense budget; conference program.

For Research Assistantships, applicant must submit a curriculum vitae, transcripts, statement of purpose and three letters of recommendation.

For Romani Fellowships, nominated by department, pursuing study in Middle Ages or Renaissance topic, under CMRS faculty member mentorship in four categories: (1) graduate students newly admitted to UCLA; (2) continuing UCLA graduate students; (3) graduate or postdoctoral students from other universities who have been invited to study at UCLA for a full academic year and; (4) postdoctoral students studying at UCLA for a full academic year.

For Summer Fellowships, applicant must submit a curriculum vitae and a letter stating research project and a letter of recommendation.

For the Lynn and Maude White Fellowship, applicant must submit a curriculum vitae, a research proposal, three current letters of recommendation and a letter from the student's dissertation director.

Duration: Research Assistantships: Nine months, October through June annually. Summer Fellowship: Mid-June to end of September. Lynn and Maude White Fellowship: One year.

Deadline: Research Assistantships and Lynn and Maude White Fellowship: Early April with announcement in May. Summer Fellowship: Early February with announcement in March. Chiappelli Travel Fellowship: Late February with announcement in late March. Interdisciplinary Research grants: Applications accepted at any time.

PUBLICATIONS:
Viator, annual journal; *Comitatus*, graduate journal; *Cursor Mundi*, book series.

STAFF:
Prof. Brian Copenhaver, Director
Karen E. Burgess, Assistant Director
Benay Furtivo, Administrative Analyst
Brett Landenberger, Webmaster and Project Assistant
Blair Sullivan, Publications Director

ADDRESS INQUIRIES TO:
Prof. Brian Copenhaver, Director
(See address above.)

CENTER FOR 17TH AND 18TH CENTURY STUDIES   [389]
University of California, Los Angeles
10745 Dickson Plaza, 310 Royce Hall
Los Angeles, CA 90095-1404
(310) 206-8552
Fax: (310) 206-8577

E-MAIL ADDRESS:
c1718cs@humnet.ucla.edu

WEB SITE ADDRESS:
www.c1718cs.ucla.edu

FOUNDED: 1985

AREAS OF INTEREST:
England between 1640 and 1830: history, language and literature, religion and theology; Oscar Wilde and the 1890s; modern fine printing.

NAME(S) OF PROGRAMS:
- **Clark Predoctoral Fellowships**

TYPE:
Fellowships. Offered for three consecutive months during the period July 1 through June

30 to registered University of California doctoral candidates whose dissertation project is on a specific subject relevant to the collections and interests of the Clark Library.

YEAR PROGRAM STARTED: 1990

PURPOSE:
To provide support for research in the humanities.

LEGAL BASIS:
University.

ELIGIBILITY:
Advanced, registered University of California doctoral candidates are eligible.

GEOGRAPHIC RESTRICTIONS:
California.

FINANCIAL DATA:
Amount of support per award: Stipends are $7,500 for three months.
Total amount of support: $7,500 to $22,500 per academic year.

NUMBER OF APPLICANTS MOST RECENT YEAR:
100 for academic year 2008-09.

APPLICATION INFORMATION:
Applicants must submit:
(1) a curriculum vitae (maximum of two pages);
(2) a bibliography of scholarly works (published and unpublished) and;
(3) a statement of research plans (maximum 1,000 words, double-spaced).

In addition to the information provided on the application form, applicants must submit three scholarly references with required reference cover sheets.
Duration: Three months. Nonrenewable.
Deadline: February 1 of each year.

PUBLICATIONS:
Application guidelines; brochure on the Center and Library and its holdings; biennial newsletters; proceedings of conferences.

OFFICERS:
Peter H. Reill, Director of the Center and Clark Library
Candis Snoddy, Assistant Director

ADDRESS INQUIRIES TO:
Myrna Ortiz, Fellowship Coordinator
(See address above.)

CENTER FOR 17TH AND 18TH CENTURY STUDIES   [390]
University of California, Los Angeles
10745 Dickson Plaza, 310 Royce Hall
Los Angeles, CA 90095-1404
(310) 206-8552
Fax: (310) 206-8577

E-MAIL ADDRESS:
c1718cs@humnet.ucla.edu

WEB SITE ADDRESS:
www.c1718cs.ucla.edu

FOUNDED: 1985

AREAS OF INTEREST:
England between 1640 and 1750: history, language and literature, religion and theology; Oscar Wilde and the 1890s; modern fine printing.

NAME(S) OF PROGRAMS:
- **ASECS/Clark Library Fellowships**

TYPE:
Fellowships. Postdoctoral fellowships for research in residence for a period of one month any time from July 1 through June 30

at the William Andrews Clark Memorial Library on a project in The Restoration or eighteenth century.

YEAR PROGRAM STARTED: 1985

PURPOSE:
To provide support for research in the humanities.

LEGAL BASIS:
University.

ELIGIBILITY:
Candidates must:
(1) have received the Doctorate prior to appointment;
(2) be members in good standing of the American Society for Eighteenth-Century Studies and;
(3) be working on a project in The Restoration or the eighteenth century.

FINANCIAL DATA:
Amount of support per award: $2,500 for one month.

NUMBER OF APPLICANTS MOST RECENT YEAR: 8 for academic year 2007-08.

NUMBER OF AWARDS: 1 for academic year 2007-08.

APPLICATION INFORMATION:
Application information may be obtained from the Center.
Duration: One month. Nonrenewable.
Deadline: February 1 of each year.

PUBLICATIONS:
Application guidelines; brochure on the Center and Library and its holdings; biennial newsletters; proceedings of conferences.

OFFICERS:
Peter H. Reill, Director of the Center and Clark Library
Candis Snoddy, Assistant Director

ADDRESS INQUIRIES TO:
Myrna Ortiz, Fellowship Coordinator
(See address above.)

CENTER FOR 17TH AND 18TH CENTURY STUDIES [391]
University of California, Los Angeles
10745 Dickson Plaza, 310 Royce Hall
Los Angeles, CA 90095-1404
(310) 206-8552
Fax: (310) 206-8577

E-MAIL ADDRESS:
c1718cs@humnet.ucla.edu

WEB SITE ADDRESS:
www.c1718cs.ucla.edu

FOUNDED: 1985

AREAS OF INTEREST:
England between 1640 and 1830: history, language and literature, religion and theology; Oscar Wilde and the 1890s; modern fine printing.

NAME(S) OF PROGRAMS:
● **Ahmanson and Getty Postdoctoral Fellowships**

TYPE:
Fellowships. With the support of the Ahmanson Foundation of Los Angeles and the J. Paul Getty Trust, the UCLA Center for 17th and 18th-Century Studies and the William Andrews Clark Memorial Library have a theme-based fellowship program to encourage the participation of junior scholars in the Center's cross-disciplinary,

comparative research projects. The major theme for a given year is announced the preceding fall.

Participating fellows will be expected to make a substantive contribution to program seminars.

YEAR PROGRAM STARTED: 1992

PURPOSE:
To provide support for research in the humanities.

LEGAL BASIS:
University.

ELIGIBILITY:
Candidates must have received their Ph.D. in the last six years prior to application and be engaged in research pertaining to the theme.

FINANCIAL DATA:
Amount of support per award: Stipends are $37,740 for the academic year.
Total amount of support: $150,000 for the year 2009-10.

APPLICATION INFORMATION:
Applicants must submit:
(1) a curriculum vitae (maximum of two pages);
(2) a bibliography of scholarly works (published and unpublished) and;
(3) a statement of research plans (maximum 1,000 words, double-spaced).

In addition to the information provided on the application form, applicants must submit three scholarly references with required reference cover sheets.
Duration: Three academic quarters. Nonrenewable.
Deadline: February 1 of each year preceding the award.

PUBLICATIONS:
Application guidelines; brochure on the Center and Library and its holdings; fellowships brochure; biennial newsletters; proceedings of conferences.

OFFICERS:
Peter H. Reill, Director of the Clark Library and Director, Center for 17th- and 18th-Century Studies
Candis Snoddy, Assistant Director

ADDRESS INQUIRIES TO:
Myrna Ortiz, Fellowship Coordinator
(See address above.)

CENTER FOR 17TH AND 18TH CENTURY STUDIES [392]
University of California, Los Angeles
405 Hilgard Avenue, 310 Royce Hall
Los Angeles, CA 90095-1404
(310) 206-8552
Fax: (310) 206-8577

E-MAIL ADDRESS:
c1718cs@humnet.ucla.edu

WEB SITE ADDRESS:
www.c1718cs.ucla.edu

FOUNDED: 1985

AREAS OF INTEREST:
England between 1640 and 1830: history, language and literature, religion and theology; Oscar Wilde and the 1890s; modern fine printing.

NAME(S) OF PROGRAMS:
● **Short-Term Research Fellowships**

TYPE:
Fellowships. Short-term (one to three months) postdoctoral fellowships for research in residence for any period of the year (July 1 through June 30) at the William Andrews Clark Memorial Library on specific subjects relevant to the collections and interests of the Library.

YEAR PROGRAM STARTED: 1985

PURPOSE:
To provide support for research in the humanities.

LEGAL BASIS:
University.

ELIGIBILITY:
Candidates must have received the Doctorate prior to appointment. Preference will be given to applicants outside the southern California area.

FINANCIAL DATA:
Amount of support per award: $2,500 per month.
Total amount of support: Approximately $60,000 for academic year 2009-10.

APPLICATION INFORMATION:
Application information may be obtained from the Center.
Duration: One to three months. Nonrenewable.
Deadline: February 1 of each year.

PUBLICATIONS:
Application guidelines; brochure on the Center and Library and its holdings; biennial newsletters; proceedings of conferences.

OFFICERS:
Peter H. Reill, Director of the Center and Clark Library
Candis Snoddy, Assistant Director

ADDRESS INQUIRIES TO:
Myrna Ortiz, Fellowship Coordinator
(See address above.)

CENTER FOR THE HUMANITIES [393]
Mellon Postdoctoral Fellowship Program
Wesleyan University
95 Pearl Street
Middletown, CT 06459-0069
(860) 685-3044
Fax: (860) 685-2171

E-MAIL ADDRESS:
kroberts@wesleyan.edu

WEB SITE ADDRESS:
www.wesleyan.edu/chum

FOUNDED: 1959

AREAS OF INTEREST:
The Center aims to explore fresh and vital aspects of the humanities, to realize an interdisciplinary response to human problems and to generate new possibilities for curricular reform. In fulfilling these aims, the Center must also examine the assumptions that underlie academic disciplines and humanistic theories. It must encourage research as well as the fundamental discourse of teachers and students.

These aims are reflected in its constituency which includes scholars, artists, public figures and students. Fellows range in age and achievement from undergraduates to the most eminent humanists. Departments at Wesleyan University participating in the Center include Classics, Modern Languages and Literatures,

English, the College of Letters, Philosophy,
History, Religion, Anthropology, Psychology
and the Fine Arts.

NAME(S) OF PROGRAMS:
- **Andrew W. Mellon Postdoctoral Fellowship**

TYPE:
Fellowships.

PURPOSE:
To promote advanced study and research in
the humanities, arts and qualitative social
sciences; to provide scholars who have lately
completed their Ph.Ds. with free time to
further their own work in a cross-disciplinary
setting, and to associate them with a
distinguished faculty.

LEGAL BASIS:
Grant from Andrew W. Mellon Foundation to
Wesleyan University.

ELIGIBILITY:
Scholars who have received their Ph.D.
degree after June 2009 in any field of inquiry
in the humanities or humanistic social
sciences - broadly conceived - are invited to
apply.

Fellows will be expected to participate in the
lectures, colloquia and discussion groups that
are organized each semester around a specific
theme chosen for its theoretical interest and
its pertinence to crucial problems in related
disciplines of the humanities, the qualitative
social sciences or the arts. Additional duties
of the fellows will be to teach one course
and to give one public lecture.

Fellow must reside in Middletown,
Connecticut for tenure of fellowship.

FINANCIAL DATA:
Amount of support per award: $40,000.

COOPERATIVE FUNDING PROGRAMS: Andrew W.
Mellon Foundation.

NUMBER OF APPLICANTS MOST RECENT YEAR:
250.

NUMBER OF AWARDS: 1 to 2 each year.

APPLICATION INFORMATION:
There is no official application form.
Applications should include:
(1) a letter from the applicant, including a
statement of current research interests and a
brief proposal for a one-semester
undergraduate course related to the Center
for the Humanities theme;
(2) a full curriculum vitae;
(3) three letters of recommendation and;
(4) copies of published work, extracts from
the dissertation, or drafts of work in progress
(not to exceed 25 pages).
Duration: One year.

PUBLICATIONS:
Brochure.

ADDRESS INQUIRIES TO:
Jill Morawski, Director
(See address above.)

CENTURYONE FOUNDATION, INC.   [394]
235 Bellefontaine Street
Pasadena, CA 91105
(626) 441-2024
(888) 932-7123
Fax: (626) 441-2694

E-MAIL ADDRESS:
foundation@centuryone.org

WEB SITE ADDRESS:
www.centuryone.org

FOUNDED: 1996

AREAS OF INTEREST:
Archaeological, historical and biblical
research pertaining to the first century A.D.

TYPE:
Project/program grants.

YEAR PROGRAM STARTED: 1996

PURPOSE:
To fund in whole and/or in part
archaeological projects, historical and biblical
research, lectures and symposiums,
publications and education on subjects
pertaining to the time of the first century
C.E./A.D.

LEGAL BASIS:
Nonprofit, public California corporation.

FINANCIAL DATA:
Amount of support per award: Varies.

NUMBER OF AWARDS: 3.

OFFICERS:
Michael D. McKinney, President

ADDRESS INQUIRIES TO:
Michael D. McKinney, President
(See address above.)

CONNECTICUT HUMANITIES COUNCIL   [395]
37 Broad Street
Middletown, CT 06457
(860) 685-2260
Fax: (860) 685-7597

E-MAIL ADDRESS:
info@ctculture.org

WEB SITE ADDRESS:
www.ctculture.org

FOUNDED: 1973

AREAS OF INTEREST:
Humanities in Connecticut, heritage and
reading.

NAME(S) OF PROGRAMS:
- **Book Voyagers**
- **Wilbur Cross Awards**
- **Heritage Resource Center and Field Services**
- **Heritage Revitalization Fund**
- **Reading for a Lifetime**

TYPE:
Awards/prizes; Challenge/matching grants;
Conferences/seminars; Development grants;
General operating grants; Project/program
grants; Research grants; Technical assistance.

YEAR PROGRAM STARTED: 1973

PURPOSE:
To conduct research on Connecticut history
and to thoughtfully present it.

ELIGIBILITY:
Applicants must be incorporated as private,
nonprofit organizations or cities or
municipalities in Connecticut, and must
regularly provide service to the public.

GEOGRAPHIC RESTRICTIONS:
Connecticut.

FINANCIAL DATA:
Amount of support per award: Up to $10,000
for discretionary funding; Up to $50,000 for
major grants.
Total amount of support: Varies.

Matching fund requirements: 50% of request
for implementation support over $25,000.

COOPERATIVE FUNDING PROGRAMS: Greater
Hartford Arts Council, Hartford Foundation
for Public Giving, Middlesex Community
Foundation, Northwest Connecticut
Foundation.

NUMBER OF APPLICANTS MOST RECENT YEAR:
51.

NUMBER OF AWARDS: 51.

REPRESENTATIVE AWARDS:
$19,507 to New Haven Museum and
Historical Society for an orientation
exhibition for the rotunda; $12,530 to the
Antiquarian and Landmarks Society to
develop an interpretive plan for the Nathan
Hale Homestead.

APPLICATION INFORMATION:
Preapplication discussion with CHC staff is
strongly urged two months before submission
of formal application. Specify the grant line
and program category when submitting
proposal.
Duration: One year and multiyear grants.
Deadline: For grants up to $10,000: March 1,
April 1, June 1, July 1, September 1, October
1 and December 1; For grants over $10,000:
February 1, May 1 and November 1.

STAFF:
Stuart Parnes, Executive Director
Brett Thompson, Director of
Communications
Laurie MacCallum Rayner, Director of
Heritage Revitalization Fund
Sandra Santy, Director of Reading
Susan Muro, Book Voyagers Program
Director
Scott Wands, Heritage Resource Center and
Field Services Program Director
Carolyn Buchholz, Financial Manager

ADDRESS INQUIRIES TO:
Laurie MacCallum Rayner
Director of Heritage Revitalization Fund
(See address above.)

CORNELL UNIVERSITY   [396]
Society for the Humanities
A.D. White House
27 East Avenue
Ithaca, NY 14853-1101
(607) 255-9274
Fax: (607) 255-1422

E-MAIL ADDRESS:
humctr-mailbox@cornell.edu

WEB SITE ADDRESS:
www.arts.cornell.edu/sochum

FOUNDED: 1966

AREAS OF INTEREST:
Postdoctoral fellowships in the humanities.

NAME(S) OF PROGRAMS:
- **Mellon Postdoctoral Fellowships**

TYPE:
Fellowships. Postdoctoral teaching-research
fellowships in the humanities, each awarded
for a two-year period. While in residence at
Cornell, postdoctoral fellows hold department
affiliation and have limited teaching duties
and the opportunity for scholarly work.

PURPOSE:
To encourage the academic growth of
promising humanists with recent Ph.D.
degrees.

LEGAL BASIS:
University.

ELIGIBILITY:
Applicant must have received the Ph.D. degree one year prior to application. Applicants who will receive the Ph.D. degree by June 30 of the beginning program year are eligible to apply. Such applicants must include a letter of confirmation.

FINANCIAL DATA:
Fellows receive stipend while in residence.
Amount of support per award: $45,000 per year.
Total amount of support: Varies.

COOPERATIVE FUNDING PROGRAMS: Funded by a grant from the Andrew W. Mellon Foundation.

NUMBER OF AWARDS: 2 to 3 each year.

APPLICATION INFORMATION:
If the applicant does not have a Ph.D. in hand at the time of application, a letter of confirmation must be received from applicant's committee chair or department stating that applicant will have the Ph.D. degree before the term of the fellowship begins on July 1 of the beginning program year. Faxed applications will not be accepted.
Duration: Two years.

ADDRESS INQUIRIES TO:
Program Administrator
Mellon Postdoctoral Fellowships
(See address above.)

CORNELL UNIVERSITY   [397]
Society for the Humanities
A.D. White House
27 East Avenue
Ithaca, NY 14853-1101
(607) 255-9274
Fax: (607) 255-1422

E-MAIL ADDRESS:
humctr-mailbox@cornell.edu

WEB SITE ADDRESS:
www.arts.cornell.edu/sochum

FOUNDED: 1966

AREAS OF INTEREST:
Humanities studies.

NAME(S) OF PROGRAMS:
● **Society for the Humanities Fellowships**

TYPE:
Fellowships. Yearly fellowships with a new focal theme each year. Fellows include scholars from other universities and members of the Cornell faculty released from regular duties.

PURPOSE:
To support research and encourage imaginative teaching in the humanities.

LEGAL BASIS:
University.

ELIGIBILITY:
Applicants must have received the Ph.D. degree before January 1 of the year of their application. They must have one or more years of teaching experience which may include teaching as a graduate student. Fellows should be working on topics related to the year's theme. Their approach to humanities should be broad enough to appeal to students and scholars in several humanistic disciplines.

FINANCIAL DATA:
Fellows receive a stipend and spend most of their time in research and writing but are encouraged to offer an informal seminar related to their research.

Amount of support per award: $45,000.
Total amount of support: Varies.

NUMBER OF APPLICANTS MOST RECENT YEAR:
150.

NUMBER OF AWARDS: 6 to 8 each year.

APPLICATION INFORMATION:
Candidates should inform the Society of their intention to apply. The following materials must be submitted:
(1) a curriculum vitae;
(2) a copy of one scholarly paper (no more than 35 pages in length);
(3) a one-page abstract and a detailed statement of the research project the applicant would like to pursue during the term of the fellowship (1,000 to 3,000 words);
(4) a two-page proposal for a seminar related to the applicant's research and;
(5) two letters of recommendation from senior colleagues to whom candidates should send their research proposal and teaching proposal.

Referees should send their letters of recommendation directly to the Society before the closing date. Faxed applications will not be accepted.
Duration: One year.
Deadline: October 1.

PUBLICATIONS:
Brochure.

ADDRESS INQUIRIES TO:
Megan Dirks, Program Administrator
Society for the Humanities
(See address above.)

GLADYS KRIEBLE DELMAS
FOUNDATION   [398]
275 Madison Avenue, 33rd Floor
New York, NY 10016-1101
(212) 687-0011
Fax: (212) 687-8877

E-MAIL ADDRESS:
info@delmas.org

WEB SITE ADDRESS:
www.delmas.org

FOUNDED: 1976

AREAS OF INTEREST:
Humanities, research libraries, performing arts and research in the history and culture of Venice and the Veneto.

NAME(S) OF PROGRAMS:
● **Humanities Program**
● **Performing Arts Program**
● **Research Library Program**
● **Venetian Research Program**

TYPE:
Conferences/seminars; Fellowships; General operating grants; Project/program grants; Research grants.

YEAR PROGRAM STARTED: 1977

PURPOSE:
To provide grants for research projects in Venice and the Veneto; to support performing arts organizations in New York and research libraries and humanities projects.

LEGAL BASIS:
Private foundation.

ELIGIBILITY:
For Venetian Research Program, applicants must be U.S. citizens or permanent residents at the predoctoral and postdoctoral levels. If graduate students, applicants must have fulfilled all doctoral requirements except for completion of the dissertation at the time of application.

GEOGRAPHIC RESTRICTIONS:
Performing Arts Grants to New York City only.

FINANCIAL DATA:
Amount of support per award: Varies.

REPRESENTATIVE AWARDS:
$210,000 over three years to the New York Public Library for the Performing Arts; $25,000 to the American Philological Association for the Classical Atlas Project; $4,200 for "Theatrical Dance in 17th Century Venetian Opera;" $7,000 for "Pseudo-Dionysius and the Mathematical Culture of 16th Century Venice."

APPLICATION INFORMATION:
Duration: Varies.
Deadline: Venetian Research Program: December 15.

TRUSTEES:
George Labalme, Jr.
Joseph C. Mitchell
Dr. David H. Stam

DUMBARTON OAKS   [399]
1703 32nd Street, N.W.
Washington, DC 20007
(202) 339-6410
(202) 339-6414
Fax: (202) 339-6419

E-MAIL ADDRESS:
fellowshipprogram2011@doaks.org

WEB SITE ADDRESS:
www.doaks.org

FOUNDED: 1940

AREAS OF INTEREST:
Archaeology, gardens, history, history of art, philosophy, landscape, language, literature, religion and theology.

NAME(S) OF PROGRAMS:
● **Fellowships and Project Grants in Byzantine Studies, Pre-Columbian Studies and Garden and Landscape Studies**

TYPE:
Awards/prizes; Fellowships; Internships; Project/program grants; Residencies. Residential fellowships and project support in the area of Byzantine studies (including related aspects of late Roman, early Christian, western medieval, Slavic and Near Eastern studies), Pre-Columbian studies (of Mexico, Central America and Andean South America), and Garden and Landscape studies (including garden history, landscape architecture and related disciplines).

YEAR PROGRAM STARTED: 1941

PURPOSE:
To promote research in Byzantine studies, Pre-Columbian studies, and Garden and Landscape studies.

LEGAL BASIS:
Research institute affiliated with Harvard University.

ELIGIBILITY:
Fellowships are awarded on the basis of demonstrated scholarly ability and preparation of the candidate, including knowledge of the requisite languages, interest

and value of the study or project and the project's relevance to the resources of Dumbarton Oaks.

Junior Fellowships are awarded to degree candidates who at the time of application have fulfilled all preliminary requirements for a Ph.D. or appropriate final degree and plan to work on a dissertation or final project at Dumbarton Oaks under the direction of a faculty member from their own university.

Fellowships are awarded to scholars who hold a Ph.D. or appropriate final degree or have established themselves in their field and wish to pursue their own research. Graduate students who expect to have a Ph.D. prior to taking up residence at Dumbarton Oaks may also apply.

Summer Fellowships are awarded to Byzantine, Pre-Columbian, or Garden and Landscape scholars on any level beyond the first year of graduate (postbaccalaureate) study.

FINANCIAL DATA:
Fellowships and Junior Fellowships: Award includes stipend, housing (with the exception of residents from the greater Washington, DC metropolitan area), a dependent allowance, a research expense allowance, lunch on weekdays, and a health insurance contribution from Dumbarton Oaks. Travel expense reimbursement may be provided for Fellows and Junior Fellows if support cannot be obtained from other sources.

Summer Fellowships: Besides maintenance allowance, support includes housing in a Dumbarton Oaks apartment, lunch on weekdays, Dumbarton Oaks's health insurance contribution, and travel expense reimbursement if other travel support cannot be obtained. No housing allowances or dependents' allowances for families are available in the summer.

Amount of support per award: Fellowship awards for 2011-12 are approximately $27,000 for an unmarried Junior Fellow to a maximum of $47,000 for a Fellow from outside the U.S. accompanied by family members. This includes a stipend of approximately $15,000 for a Junior Fellow; $28,000 stipend for a Fellow for the full academic year.

A maintenance allowance of $250 per week for Summer Fellowships.

NUMBER OF APPLICANTS MOST RECENT YEAR: 141.

NUMBER OF AWARDS: 6 Junior Fellowships; 13 Fellowships; 16 Summer Fellowships.

APPLICATION INFORMATION:
Applications must be submitted electronically(www.doaks.org/research/info_fellowships.html). A brochure is available upon request to the Director's office.

Duration: Fellowships are usually awarded for a full academic year (mid-September to mid-May); however, requests for a single term of support (mid-September to early January; mid-January to mid-May) are also considered. Summer Fellowships are awarded for periods of six to nine weeks, beginning early June and ending early August.

Deadline: Applications must be received on or before November 1 preceding the academic year for which support is sought. Applicants are informed in mid-February.

PUBLICATIONS:
Fellowship and Project award brochure; application guidelines.

OFFICERS:
Jan Ziolkowski, Director

ADDRESS INQUIRIES TO:
See address and e-mail above.

*SPECIAL STIPULATIONS:
Fellowships are tenable only for full-time resident work.

EARTHWATCH INSTITUTE
114 Western Avenue
Boston, MA 02134
(978) 461-0081
(800) 776-0188
Fax: (978) 461-2332

E-MAIL ADDRESS:
research@earthwatch.org

WEB SITE ADDRESS:
www.earthwatch.org/research

TYPE:
Research grants. Both personnel and financial support to field research projects. Volunteers pay to support the project and also work as research assistants to the scholars, usually for two to three-week periods. Teams range in size from four to 20, with the average expedition using three to five teams. Since numbers of dollars vary directly with numbers of volunteers, applicants are urged to pay close attention to that relationship in their research design.

See entry 1937 for full listing.

EMORY COLLEGE OF ARTS AND SCIENCES   [400]
Mellon Fellowship Committee
Emory College Office
550 Asbury Circle, 400 Candler Library
Atlanta, GA 30322
(404) 727-6059
Fax: (404) 727-9360

E-MAIL ADDRESS:
mellio2@emory.edu

WEB SITE ADDRESS:
www.college.emory.edu

FOUNDED: 1836

AREAS OF INTEREST:
Topics appropriate to humanities disciplines.

NAME(S) OF PROGRAMS:
● **Andrew W. Mellon Faculty Fellowships in the Humanities**

TYPE:
Fellowships. A two-year fellowship awarded to a nontenured, postdoctoral scholar capable of initiating thoughtful and attractive approaches to teaching and developing his or her own scholarly research.

The host department for each fellowship is selected from among the humanities on a rotating basis. Within the departments, the area of specialization is also rotated. The department and specialization for each fellowship is announced in the appropriate field's employment publication several months prior to the application deadline. In addition to work on his or her research proposal, the fellow will teach one course per semester.

YEAR PROGRAM STARTED: 1976

NUMBER OF APPLICANTS MOST RECENT YEAR: 65.

NUMBER OF AWARDS: One or two annually, on a rotating basis, for two-year terms.

APPLICATION INFORMATION:
Applicants must submit:
(1) curriculum vitae;
(2) a 500-word description of the proposed research;
(3) a brief description of two courses related to the research that would likely be taught during tenure as a Mellon fellow and;
(4) at least two letters of recommendation evaluating the applicant's teaching and research.
Duration: Two years. Nonrenewable.

THE FIELDSTONE FOUNDATION   [401]
2 Ada, Suite 200
Irvine, CA 92618
(949) 790-7496
Fax: (949) 453-0944

E-MAIL ADDRESS:
janinem@fieldstonefoundation.org

WEB SITE ADDRESS:
www.fieldstonefoundation.org

FOUNDED: 1983

AREAS OF INTEREST:
Educational, humanitarian, and Christian ministries and cultural arts.

CONSULTING OR VOLUNTEER SERVICES:
Nonprofit executive leadership training and peer coaching.

TYPE:
Challenge/matching grants; General operating grants; Project/program grants. Grants are awarded to improve the quality of life for children and families.

YEAR PROGRAM STARTED: 1983

PURPOSE:
To improve the quality of life for children and families.

ELIGIBILITY:
Eligible organizations must be IRS 501(c)(3) tax-exempt. The Foundation does not fund grants to individuals or churches.

GEOGRAPHIC RESTRICTIONS:
Orange and San Diego counties, California.

FINANCIAL DATA:
Amount of support per award: Varies.
Total amount of support: Varies.

NUMBER OF APPLICANTS MOST RECENT YEAR: 60.

NUMBER OF AWARDS: 56.

APPLICATION INFORMATION:
The application must include a copy of the IRS tax determination letter. Proposals by invitation only. Foundation staff will initiate all grant considerations.
Duration: One year.
Deadline: June 1 to June 30.

STAFF:
Marcos Ramirez
Robin Stropko

ADDRESS INQUIRIES TO:
Janine Mason
(See address above.)

THE FOLGER INSTITUTE   [402]

Folger Shakespeare Library
201 East Capitol Street, S.E.
Washington, DC 20003-1094
(202) 675-0333
Fax: (202) 544-4623

E-MAIL ADDRESS:
institute@folger.edu

WEB SITE ADDRESS:
www.folger.edu/institute

FOUNDED: 1970

AREAS OF INTEREST:
Early modern history, literature, political
science, art and cultural studies.

NAME(S) OF PROGRAMS:
● **Early Modern Studies**

TYPE:
Conferences/seminars; Grants-in-aid;
Internships; Travel grants. Fall and Spring
seminars and workshops. Yearlong colloquia.
Stipends for institutes. Grants for travel and
lodging expenses, according to need, for
workshops and seminars.

YEAR PROGRAM STARTED: 1986

PURPOSE:
To advance the teachings and study of
Shakespeare and the early modern period.

LEGAL BASIS:
Research center at an independent research
library.

ELIGIBILITY:
Grants in support of program participation
are available to affiliates of the member
universities. The Folger Institute does not
offer grants-in-aid support of scholars from
outside of the consortium.

APPLICATION INFORMATION:
Potential interns, screened on an individual
basis, should send a resume, cover letter, and
a letter from their institution's internship
office stating the requirements for credit (if it
is to be requested). Letters of
recommendation may be solicited after a
preliminary screening.
Duration: Six to nine months.
Deadline: Long term research fellowships:
November 1. Short-term fellowships: March
1.

OFFICERS:
David Schalkwyk, Director of Research
Kathleen Lynch, Executive Director
Owen Williams, Assistant Director

ADDRESS INQUIRIES TO:
Adrienne Shevchuk, Program Assistant
(See address above.)

*PLEASE NOTE:
Scholars wishing to apply for long or
short-term fellowships should contact Carol
Brobeck, Fellowships Coordinator (see
address above) or call (202) 675-0348;
e-mail: brobeck@folger.edu.

FOUNDATION FOR JEWISH CULTURE   [403]

330 Seventh Avenue, 21st Floor
New York, NY 10001
(212) 629-0500 ext. 209 (Kroll Film Fund)
(212) 629-0500 ext. 212 (Paul Zakrzewski)
Fax: (212) 629-0508

E-MAIL ADDRESS:
grants@jewishculture.org

WEB SITE ADDRESS:
www.jewishculture.org

FOUNDED: 1960

AREAS OF INTEREST:
Jewish arts and humanities.

NAME(S) OF PROGRAMS:
● **The Maurice and Marilyn Cohen Fund
for Doctoral Dissertation Fellowships in
Jewish Studies**
● **The Lynn and Jules Kroll Fund for
Jewish Documentary Film**

TYPE:
Fellowships; Project/program grants;
Research grants. Cohen Fund for Doctoral
Dissertation Fellowships is intended to
support the final stages of completing a
dissertation, encouraging scholarly research,
publication and teaching in the various
disciplines of Jewish studies.

Kroll Fund for Jewish Documentary Film
supports the completion of original
documentaries that explore the Jewish
experience in all its complexity. The priority
of the Fund is to support projects that
address significant subjects; offer fresh,
challenging perspectives; engage audiences
across cultural lines; and expand the
understanding of Jewish experiences.

YEAR PROGRAM STARTED: 1996

ELIGIBILITY:
Cohen Fund for Doctoral Dissertation
Fellowships: Applicants must be citizens or
permanent residents of the U.S. and must
have completed all academic requirements
except the dissertation. Proficiency in a
Jewish language is required. Applicants will
be judged on the basis of their potential
contribution to the field of Jewish
scholarship.

Kroll Fund for Jewish Documentary Film:
Director or producer of the film must be a
U.S. citizen. The film must be in
postproduction.

FINANCIAL DATA:
Amount of support per award: Cohen Fund
for Doctoral Dissertation Fellowships:
Amount determined by selection committee.
Kroll Fund for Jewish Documentary Film:
No grant exceeds $50,000 or 50% total
budget, whichever is less; awards are usually
between $15,000 and $35,000.

Total amount of support: Cohen Fund for
Doctoral Dissertation Fellowships: $80,000.
Kroll Fund for Jewish Documentary Film:
$150,000.

NUMBER OF APPLICANTS MOST RECENT YEAR:
Cohen Fund for Doctoral Dissertation
Fellowships: 40. Kroll Fund for Jewish
Documentary Film: 100.

NUMBER OF AWARDS: Cohen Fund for Doctoral
Dissertation Fellowships: 5 for the year
2010-11. Kroll Fund for Jewish Documentary
Film: Up to 6.

APPLICATION INFORMATION:
Duration: One year. Nonrenewable.
Deadline: Cohen Fund: April 1. Kroll Fund:
Late July.

ADDRESS INQUIRIES TO:
Paul Zakrzewski, Program Officer,
Literature and Scholarship
(See address above.)

Andy Ingall, Program Officer
Kroll Fund for Jewish Documentary Film
(See address above.)

THE GWATHMEY MEMORIAL TRUST   [404]

Bank of America
VA2-300-12-99
P.O. Box 26688
Richmond, VA 23261-6688
(804) 788-3698
Fax: (804) 788-2700

FOUNDED: 1982

AREAS OF INTEREST:
History, literature, art and architecture, and
direct services.

TYPE:
Capital grants; Development grants.

YEAR PROGRAM STARTED: 1982

ELIGIBILITY:
Grants are made to Virginia institutions and
organizations which are tax-exempt 501(c)(3)
organizations and operate for charitable,
scientific, literary, or educational purposes.
Preference is given to specific, well-defined
projects and programs whose results can be
evaluated.

Grants are not made to private foundations,
national or community organizations, or to
individuals.

GEOGRAPHIC RESTRICTIONS:
Virginia.

FINANCIAL DATA:
Amount of support per award: $5,000 to
$100,000; Average: $20,000 to $25,000.
Total amount of support: $700,000 for the
year 2010.

APPLICATION INFORMATION:
All applicants must submit a description of
the organization, evidence of the
organization's tax-exempt and private
foundation status, financial statements, and
names and affiliations of the organization's
trustees, directors, advisors and principal
staff. In addition, a concise description of the
project including the needs and anticipated
benefits to be met, detailed financial plan,
brief biographical background of the person
who will conduct or supervise the proposed
program, plans for evaluation of the project's
results, and covering letter from an official of
the organization stating that the organization
has formally approved the proposed program
are required.
Duration: One year.
Deadline: March 1 and September 1.

PUBLICATIONS:
Guidelines for applicants.

ADDRESS INQUIRIES TO:
Richard B. Brandt, Ph.D., Advisor
(See address above.)

THE HASTINGS CENTER

21 Malcolm Gordon Road
Garrison, NY 10524
(845) 424-4040
Fax: (845) 424-4545

E-MAIL ADDRESS:
visitors@thehastingscenter.org

WEB SITE ADDRESS:
www.thehastingscenter.org

TYPE:
Internships; Residencies; Visiting scholars.
Independent study. Some financial aid is
available.

See entry 2239 for full listing.

HAWAII STATE FOUNDATION ON CULTURE AND THE ARTS

250 South Hotel Street
Second Floor
Honolulu, HI 96813
(808) 586-0300
Fax: (808) 586-0308
TTY: (808) 586-0740

WEB SITE ADDRESS:
  hawaii.gov/sfca

TYPE:
  Project/program grants.

See entry 488 for full listing.

HIRSCHFELD FAMILY FOUNDATION, INC.

c/o Jeff Orr
P.O. Box 1060
Kearney, NE 68848-1060
(308) 236-4455
Fax: (308) 236-4493

TYPE:
  Project/program grants.

See entry 181 for full listing.

THE GEORGE A. AND ELIZA GARDNER HOWARD FOUNDATION

194 Meeting Street
Providence, RI 02912
(401) 863-2640
Fax: (401) 863-6280

E-MAIL ADDRESS:
  howard_foundation@brown.edu

WEB SITE ADDRESS:
  www.brown.edu/Howard_Foundation

TYPE:
  Fellowships. The Foundation awards a
  limited number of fellowships each year for
  independent projects in fields selected on a
  rotational basis.

See entry 1749 for full listing.

THE HUNTINGTON FOUNDATION, INC.   [405]

401 11th Street, Suite 306
Huntington, WV 25701
(304) 522-0611

FOUNDED: 1986

AREAS OF INTEREST:
  Charitable, religious, educational and
  scientific pursuits.

TYPE:
  Challenge/matching grants.

YEAR PROGRAM STARTED: 1986

PURPOSE:
  To encourage institutional change or to help
  grant recipients make more effective use of
  resources they generate from other sources
  (challenge grants); to promote strong
  public/private collaborative efforts to meet
  community needs and to foster volunteer
  efforts wherever possible.

ELIGIBILITY:
  The Foundation does not make grants for
  salaries and normal operating expenses.
  Grants are made only to organizations
  qualifying for tax exemption under Section
  501(c)(3) of the Internal Revenue Code.

Current priorities for grants include:
  (1) health care programs;
  (2) medical education and research;
  (3) youth programs for educational, religious
  and physical development and;
  (4) cultural, educational and recreational
  programs that enhance the quality of life in
  the community.

Construction grants are not accepted.

GEOGRAPHIC RESTRICTIONS:
  Areas of Cabell and Wayne counties, West
  Virginia.

APPLICATION INFORMATION:
  A standard application form is required,
  which will be sent upon request. Six copies
  of the application should be sent to the
  president of the Foundation at the address
  above. Receipt of every application will be
  acknowledged by mail.
  Deadline: January, April, July and October.

PUBLICATIONS:
  Guidelines.

BOARD OF DIRECTORS:
  Frank E. Hanshaw, Jr.
  Kermit E. McGinnis
  Leon K. Oxley
  Joseph B. Touma

ADMINISTRATIVE STAFF:
  Glenna J. Smoot, Executive Secretary

ADDRESS INQUIRIES TO:
  Glenna J. Smoot, Executive Secretary
  P.O. Box 2548
  Huntington, WV 25726

HENRY E. HUNTINGTON LIBRARY AND ART GALLERY   [406]

1151 Oxford Road
San Marino, CA 91108
(626) 405-2194
Fax: (626) 449-5703

E-MAIL ADDRESS:
  cpowell@huntington.org

WEB SITE ADDRESS:
  www.huntington.org

FOUNDED: 1919

AREAS OF INTEREST:
  British and American art history, history,
  literature and history of science.

NAME(S) OF PROGRAMS:
  ● **Research Awards at the Huntington
    Library and Art Gallery**

TYPE:
  Fellowships; Research grants; Visiting
  scholars. Grants for studies in American or
  British literature, history, art history and
  history of science.

YEAR PROGRAM STARTED: 1927

PURPOSE:
  To encourage significant scholarship in the
  areas of the Huntington collections.

LEGAL BASIS:
  Private, nonprofit.

ELIGIBILITY:
  Persons who have demonstrated unusual
  abilities as scholars are encouraged to apply.
  Consideration is given to the value of the
  candidate's project and the degree to which
  the Huntington Library will be used. Projects
  to be used for doctoral dissertations will be
  considered.

FINANCIAL DATA:
  Amount of support per award: Short-term:
  $2,500 per month; Long-term: $50,000 for
  the academic year.
  Total amount of support: Varies.

NUMBER OF APPLICANTS MOST RECENT YEAR:
  Short-term: 337; Long-term: 143.

NUMBER OF AWARDS: Short-term: 125;
  Long-term: 11.

APPLICATION INFORMATION:
  Duration: Short-term grants: One to five
  months. Long-term awards: Minimum of nine
  months.
  Deadline: December 15 for commencement
  on July 1.

IRS IDENTIFICATION NUMBER: 95-1644589

OFFICERS:
  Steven Koblik, President
  George Abdo, Vice President, Advancement
  Alison Sowden, Vice President, Financial
  Affairs
  James Folsom, Director, Botanical Gardens
  John Murdoch, Director, Art Collections
  Robert C. Ritchie, Director, Research
  David Zeidberg, Director, Library

TRUSTEES:
  Stewart Smith, Chairman
  Paul Haaga
  Anne Rothenberg
  Loren Rothschild
  Geneva Thornton

ADDRESS INQUIRIES TO:
  Robert C. Ritchie
  Director of Research
  (See address above.)

*SPECIAL STIPULATIONS:
  Recipients of all fellowships are expected to
  be in continuous residence at the Huntington.

INSTITUT FRANCAIS D'AMERIQUE   [407]

Romance Language Department CB 3170
University of North Carolina
Chapel Hill, NC 27599-3170
(919) 929-6919
(919) 962-9824
Fax: (919) 962-1403

E-MAIL ADDRESS:
  cmaley@email.unc.edu

WEB SITE ADDRESS:
  www.unc.edu/depts/institut

FOUNDED: 1926

AREAS OF INTEREST:
  Franco-American studies in art, economics,
  history, history of science, linguistics,
  literature and social sciences.

NAME(S) OF PROGRAMS:
  ● **Gilbert Chinard Fellowships and
    Awards**
  ● **Edouard Morot-Sir Fellowship in
    Literature**
  ● **Harmon Chadbourn Rorison
    Fellowship**

TYPE:
  Awards/prizes; Fellowships; Research grants.
  Fellowships available consist of four annual
  supporting grants for Ph.D. candidates or
  assistant professors to pursue research in
  France.

YEAR PROGRAM STARTED: 1926

PURPOSE:
  To help young researchers in the specified
  fields.

LEGAL BASIS:
Nonprofit association, chartered in Washington, D.C.

ELIGIBILITY:
Applicants must be students at the Ph.D. level (working on the dissertation) or Ph.D. held no longer than three years before deadline.

GEOGRAPHIC RESTRICTIONS:
North America.

FINANCIAL DATA:
Amount of support per award: Fellowship is valued at $1,500, subject to annual re-evaluation.
Total amount of support: $6,000 allocated annually.

NUMBER OF APPLICANTS MOST RECENT YEAR:
55.

NUMBER OF AWARDS: 4 annually.

APPLICATION INFORMATION:
No application form. Applicants write two pages (maximum) describing research project, planned trip and curriculum vitae. A letter of recommendation from dissertation director or expert in the field (for assistant professors) is required.
Duration: One-month minimum.
Deadline: January 15. Notification in mid-March.

ADDRESS INQUIRIES TO:
Dr. Catherine A. Maley, President
(See address above.)

THE INSTITUTE FOR ADVANCED STUDIES IN THE HUMANITIES [408]
The University of Edinburgh
Hope Park Square
Edinburgh EH8 9NW Scotland
44 (0)131 650 4671
Fax: 44 (0)131 668 2252

E-MAIL ADDRESS:
iash@ed.ac.uk

WEB SITE ADDRESS:
www.iash.ed.ac.uk/index.html

FOUNDED: 1969

AREAS OF INTEREST:
Any discipline within humanities and social science. Priority will be given to projects relevant to current institute research themes. (See www.iash.ed.ac.uk/themes.html.)

CONSULTING OR VOLUNTEER SERVICES:
Institute has connections with and is within easy reach of the National Library of Scotland, the National Archives of Scotland, the Royal Museum of Scotland and the Edinburgh University Library.

NAME(S) OF PROGRAMS:
● **Visiting Research Fellowships**

TYPE:
Fellowships. Visiting Research Fellowships with the use of a private office in the Institute with all the usual research facilities. Recipients of the Fellowships are expected to play a full part in the activities of the Institute.

YEAR PROGRAM STARTED: 1970

PURPOSE:
To further advanced studies in the humanities, broadly conceived.

LEGAL BASIS:
Institution of University of Edinburgh.

ELIGIBILITY:
Applicants should be scholars of established reputation or younger scholars holding a Doctorate or offering equivalent evidence of aptitude for advanced study.

The Election Committee will consider the academic record and the publications of all applicants, their capacity to disseminate their views effectively in public and the likelihood of completing the proposed research by task by the end of the fellowship or shortly afterwards. Students who have not completed their studies for a particular degree are not eligible.

No teaching is required of Fellows in the project, but each Fellow will be expected to make at least one public presentation of his or her research activities.

NUMBER OF APPLICANTS MOST RECENT YEAR:
23.

NUMBER OF AWARDS: 13 for the year 2006-07.

APPLICATION INFORMATION:
Forms can be downloaded from the web site. The Election Committee will only consider applications accompanied by full documentation and supported by a minimum of two and a maximum of three referees reports. It is the responsibility of each applicant to ensure that their referees submit their reports directly to Edinburgh. Candidates may like to submit a copy of an article or publication relevant to their application. The Institute will not return any documents to applicants. Airmail should be used for all communications from outside the U.K.
Duration: Fellowships are tenable for two to six months. Nonrenewable.
Deadline: February 26.

PUBLICATIONS:
Application guidelines.

OFFICERS:
Prof. Susan Manning, Director

ADDRESS INQUIRIES TO:
Prof. Susan Manning, Director
(See address above.)

*SPECIAL STIPULATIONS:
Fellows, as well as carrying out research, are required to live in or near Edinburgh and may be asked to give one seminar.

INSTITUTE FOR ADVANCED STUDY
Einstein Drive
Princeton, NJ 08540
(609) 734-8250
Fax: (609) 951-4457

E-MAIL ADDRESS:
donne@ias.edu

WEB SITE ADDRESS:
www.sss.ias.edu

TYPE:
Fellowships. Postdoctoral research fellowships at the School of Social Science. In 2012-13, the thematic focus will be "Economics and Politics."

See entry 1979 for full listing.

INSTITUTE FOR HUMANE STUDIES (IHS)
3301 North Fairfax Drive, Suite 440
Arlington, VA 22201-4432
(703) 993-4880
Fax: (703) 993-4890

E-MAIL ADDRESS:
ihs@ihs.gmu.edu

WEB SITE ADDRESS:
www.theihs.org

TYPE:
Awards/prizes; Fellowships. Humane Studies Fellowships cover the fields of arts and humanities, fine and applied art, law, mass communication and information, religion and theology, or social and behavioral science.

Charles G. Koch Summer Fellowship deals with current public policy issues, career development workshops, writing projects with a professional editor, and the experience of spending a summer in a Washington, DC, or state-based policy community.

See entry 2126 for full listing.

JEROME FOUNDATION, INC. [409]
400 Sibley Street, Suite 125
St. Paul, MN 55101
(651) 224-9431
(800) 995-3766 (MN and NYC only)
Fax: (651) 224-3439

E-MAIL ADDRESS:
info@jeromefdn.org

WEB SITE ADDRESS:
www.jeromefdn.org

FOUNDED: 1964

AREAS OF INTEREST:
Arts with a focus on media arts, literature, dance, music, theater and visual arts and arts criticism. Emphasis is on discovery and promotion of emerging creative artists.

TYPE:
Awards/prizes; Demonstration grants; Fellowships; General operating grants; Project/program grants; Research grants; Residencies; Seed money grants; Travel grants.

YEAR PROGRAM STARTED: 1964

PURPOSE:
To contribute to a dynamic and evolving culture by supporting the creation, development and production of new works by emerging artists.

LEGAL BASIS:
Tax-exempt, private foundation.

ELIGIBILITY:
Foundation grants are made primarily to not-for-profit arts organizations and to individual professional artists through specific programs. The Foundation accepts requests from new organizations. It also supports not-for-profit fiscal sponsors that apply on behalf of artists. The Foundation is flexible and will consider various funding mechanisms if they provide significant assistance to emerging artists.

The Foundation does not support capital (building and endowment) campaigns, nor does it offer travel grants other than the specific Travel and Study Grant Program it administers.

Foundation support is restricted to emerging artists who are legal residents of Minnesota and/or New York City, New York.

GEOGRAPHIC RESTRICTIONS:
Minnesota and the five boroughs of New York City, New York.

FINANCIAL DATA:
Amount of support per award: $22,000.

Total amount of support: Average $2,900,000 annually.

NUMBER OF APPLICANTS MOST RECENT YEAR:
650.

REPRESENTATIVE AWARDS:
$20,000 to Aaron Davis Hall, New York, NY, for fund for new works; $10,000 to All Out Arts, New York, NY, for development and production of new plays.

APPLICATION INFORMATION:
Applicants should include the following items in their proposal:
(1) Organizational history - briefly describe the organization's history, mission and major accomplishments, particularly as they pertain to Foundation mission;
(2) Overview of current programs - describe current year's activities, including geographic area(s) served and artists served. Specify to what degree current programs address the Foundation's focus;
(3) Proposed program/project - describe proposed program including background information on its history, purpose, size and evolution over time;
(4) provide information on key artistic and administrative personnel involved in the proposed program, including the qualifications of the person(s) who will provide overall direction. Complete resumes for emerging creative artists involved in the program must be submitted. Work samples should also be submitted;
(5) provide a detailed description of how emerging creative artists are identified and selected, including announcement, submission and review procedures, the qualifications of who is entrusted with making selections and the criteria for selection;
(6) submit a detailed program budget showing estimated expenses and income. Identify committed, pending and projected funding sources. The Foundation will support the direct costs of programs serving emerging artists. Support for indirect costs/overhead may be requested if the figure is 15% or less of the project budget;
(7) provide information on the applicant's history of and plans for addressing issues of cultural diversity in governance (board) and operations (staff), artist selection, programming and audience development. Applicants should identify accomplishments and set forth the areas that need attention in the future, explaining how these challenges will be addressed;
(8) provide the names, addresses, e-mails and telephone numbers of five to seven knowledgeable individual references who are not affiliated with the applicant and who can speak to the artistic strengths of the program, the organization and the artists. Provide names, addresses, e-mails and telephone numbers of artists who participated in the previous year in the program(s) for which support is requested;
(9) describe the method(s) to be used to evaluate program effectiveness;
(10) evidence of applicant organization or fiscal sponsor not-for-profit and tax-exempt status in the form of a letter ruling from the IRS;
(11) letter from chief artistic and/or administrative officer endorsing the proposal

and agreeing that the organization will assume the full responsibility for the proper fiscal management of and accounting for any grant received, and will make certain that reports required by the Foundation are submitted on a timely basis;
(12) list of board members with occupations, number of years served, number of meetings per year and average attendance. Identify the board chair and;
(13) an audited financial statement or IRS Form 990 for the most recently completed fiscal year, a total operating budget for the current year and operating budgets for the year(s) for which grant support is requested. Budgets should include projected expenses and income.
Duration: One to two years. Renewal possible.
Deadline: Applications are accepted on an ongoing basis. Applicants should allow four to five months for evaluation of proposals.

PUBLICATIONS:
Annual report.

STAFF:
Cynthia A. Gehrig, President
Eleanor Savage, Vice President
Robert Byrd, Program Director

DIRECTORS:
Catherine Jordan, Chairperson
Philip Bither
Carlyle Brown
Cynthia Mayeda
Barbara McLanahan
Gary Nan Tie
Calogero Salvo
Charles Zelle

ADDRESS INQUIRIES TO:
Cynthia A. Gehrig, President
(See address above.)

MASSACHUSETTS FOUNDATION FOR THE HUMANITIES [410]
66 Bridge Street
Northampton, MA 01060-2406
(413) 584-8440
Fax: (413) 584-8454

E-MAIL ADDRESS:
info@masshumanities.org

WEB SITE ADDRESS:
www.masshumanities.org

FOUNDED: 1974

AREAS OF INTEREST:
Humanities and areas of special concern in Massachusetts, historic societies and libraries.

NAME(S) OF PROGRAMS:
- **Project Grants**
- **Reading and Discussion Grants**
- **Research Inventory Grants**
- **Scholar in Residence Grants**

TYPE:
Project/program grants.

PURPOSE:
To identify and develop major initiatives in areas of special interest or concern.

LEGAL BASIS:
Private, nonprofit corporation.

ELIGIBILITY:
Applicants must be nonprofit organizations. The Foundation does not fund staff salaries, refreshments, travel expenses, or indirect costs.

GEOGRAPHIC RESTRICTIONS:
Massachusetts.

FINANCIAL DATA:
Amount of support per award: Up to $10,000.

Total amount of support: $350,000.

Matching fund requirements: Outright Funds must be matched equally by your organization through cost-sharing.

REPRESENTATIVE AWARDS:
"Shifting Gears: The Changing Meaning of Work in Massachusetts," for study of economic change; "Understanding the AIDS Challenge;" "Knowing Our Place: Humanistic Aspects of Environmental Issues;" "Seeing Through the Media: The Crisis of our Cultural Environment," for studying the impact of the media on American society.

APPLICATION INFORMATION:
Applicants should speak to a program officer four weeks before deadline and submit a draft proposal two weeks before deadline. The application should include cover page, project summary, project description, budget and budget explanation, schedule of grant-related activities, one-page resumes of project personnel, statements by humanities scholars, and letters of support from collaborating organizations.
Duration: Typically one year.
Deadline: Proposal deadlines are on or before the first business day of November, February and May.

PUBLICATIONS:
Newsletter; application guidelines; brochure.

OFFICERS:
John Burgess, President

STAFF:
David Tebaldi, Executive Director
Pleun Bouricius, Assistant Director
John Sieracki, Director of Development and Communications
Anne Rogers, Systems Manager
Hayley Wood, Senior Program Officer
Rose Sackey-Milligan, Program Officer
Melissa Wheatons, Grants Administrator

ADDRESS INQUIRIES TO:
Pleun Bouricius, Assistant Director
(See address above.)

ALLETTA MORRIS MCBEAN CHARITABLE TRUST [411]
1200 Central Boulevard
Suite B
Brentwood, CA 94513
(925) 516-6212
Fax: (925) 516-4496

E-MAIL ADDRESS:
mcbeanproperties@worldnet.att.net

FOUNDED: 1986

AREAS OF INTEREST:
Historic and land preservation in and around Newport, RI.

TYPE:
Capital grants; Challenge/matching grants; Endowments; General operating grants; Project/program grants.

YEAR PROGRAM STARTED: 1986

PURPOSE:
To enhance the quality of life in and around Newport and Aquidneck Island, RI.

LEGAL BASIS:
Private charitable trust.

ELIGIBILITY:
Applicants must be tax-exempt organizations.

GEOGRAPHIC RESTRICTIONS:
Aquidneck Island, Rhode Island.

FINANCIAL DATA:
Amount of support per award: $25,000 to $100,000.

Total amount of support: $3,200,000 per year.

Matching fund requirements: Varies.

NUMBER OF APPLICANTS MOST RECENT YEAR:
20 to 25.

REPRESENTATIVE AWARDS:
$50,000 to Edward King House Senior Citizens Center for building renovations; $6,000 to Lucy's Hearth for kitchen renovation; $250,000 to Newport Performing Arts Center Task Group for acquisition and facade restoration of the opera house.

APPLICATION INFORMATION:
Six formal proposals with budgets are preferred, as well as other sources of funding for project, tax-exempt status and other background material.
Deadline: February 28 and July 31.

IRS IDENTIFICATION NUMBER: 94-3019660

OFFICERS:
Donald C. Christ, Chairman
John J. Slocum, Jr., Secretary
Charlene C. Kleiner, Assistant Secretary
Noreen S. Drexel
Gladys V. Szapary
John A. van Beuren

ADDRESS INQUIRIES TO:
Donald C. Christ, Chairman
Charlene C. Kleiner, Assistant Secretary
(See address above.)

MICHIGAN SOCIETY OF FELLOWS [412]

University of Michigan
0540 Rackham Building
915 East Washington Street
Ann Arbor, MI 48109-1070
(734) 763-1259

E-MAIL ADDRESS:
society.of.fellows@umich.edu

WEB SITE ADDRESS:
www.rackham.umich.edu/sof

FOUNDED: 1970

AREAS OF INTEREST:
All schools and colleges at the University of Michigan.

NAME(S) OF PROGRAMS:
● **Postdoctoral Fellowships in the Humanities and the Arts, Sciences and Professions**

TYPE:
Fellowships. Fellows are appointed as Assistant Professors or Research Scientists in appropriate departments and as Postdoctoral Scholars in the Michigan Society of Fellows. They are expected to be in residence in Ann Arbor during the academic years of the fellowship, to teach for the equivalent of one academic year, to participate in the informal intellectual life of the Society, and to devote time to their independent research or artistic projects.

YEAR PROGRAM STARTED: 1970

PURPOSE:
To recognize and support academic and creative excellence in humanities and the arts, the social, physical, and life sciences, and the professions.

LEGAL BASIS:
Nonprofit, tax-exempt organization.

ELIGIBILITY:
Candidates should be near the beginning of their professional careers, but not more than three years beyond completion of their degrees. The Ph.D. degree or comparable professional or artistic degree, received prior to appointment, is required.

Applications from degree candidates and recipients of the Ph.D. from the University of Michigan will not be considered.

FINANCIAL DATA:
Amount of support per award: $52,000 annually for three years plus health benefits for 2011-14 fellowships. $1,500 per year allowance toward travel and research expenses.

COOPERATIVE FUNDING PROGRAMS: Mellon Foundation.

NUMBER OF APPLICANTS MOST RECENT YEAR:
1,062 for the year 2011.

NUMBER OF AWARDS: 8 each year.

APPLICATION INFORMATION:
Applications will be reviewed by members of the Society of Fellows and by faculty in appropriate University of Michigan departments. Final selection of candidates will be made by the senior fellows of the Society.
Duration: Three years.
Deadline: October 1. Final selections made end of January.

PUBLICATIONS:
Application guidelines.

OFFICERS:
Donald S. Lopez, Jr., Chairperson of Society

*SPECIAL STIPULATIONS:
Fellows are expected to reside in Ann Arbor during the academic years of the fellowship.

NATIONAL ENDOWMENT FOR THE HUMANITIES [413]

1100 Pennsylvania Avenue, N.W.
Room 510
Washington, DC 20506
(202) 606-8400
Fax: (202) 606-8240

E-MAIL ADDRESS:
info@neh.gov

WEB SITE ADDRESS:
www.neh.gov

FOUNDED: 1965

AREAS OF INTEREST:
Scholarship, research, education and public programs in the humanities. In the act that established the Endowment, the term humanities includes, but is not limited to, the study of history, philosophy, languages, linguistics, literature, archaeology, jurisprudence, the history, theory and criticism of the arts, ethics, comparative religion and those aspects of the social sciences that employ historical or philosophical approaches.

NAME(S) OF PROGRAMS:
● **Research Program**

TYPE:
Research grants. Grants provide support for collaborative research in the preparation for publication of editions, translations and other important works in the humanities and in the conduct of large or complex interpretive studies including archaeology projects and the humanities studies of science and technology. Grants also support research opportunities offered through independent research centers and scholarly organizations and international research centers.

YEAR PROGRAM STARTED: 1967

PURPOSE:
To provide funding for research and the publication of that research. The work must be in a field of interest to the National Endowment.

LEGAL BASIS:
Federal agency, established by act of Congress: The National Foundation on the Arts and Humanities Act of 1965, Public Law 89-209, as amended.

ELIGIBILITY:
Applicants can be individuals, institutions of higher education, nonprofit professional associations, scholarly societies and other nonprofit organizations.

GEOGRAPHIC RESTRICTIONS:
United States.

FINANCIAL DATA:
Amount of support per award: Varies.
Total amount of support: Varies.

APPLICATION INFORMATION:
Application can be downloaded at www.grants.gov.
Duration: One year.
Deadline: November 5.

PUBLICATIONS:
Annual report; *Grant Programs*; *Humanities Magazine*.

IRS IDENTIFICATION NUMBER: 52-1098584

ADDRESS INQUIRIES TO:
Paula Wasley, Public Affairs Specialist
(See address above.)

NATIONAL ENDOWMENT FOR THE HUMANITIES [414]

1100 Pennsylvania Avenue, N.W.
Room 510
Washington, DC 20506
(202) 606-8400
Fax: (202) 606-8240

E-MAIL ADDRESS:
info@neh.gov

WEB SITE ADDRESS:
www.neh.gov

FOUNDED: 1965

AREAS OF INTEREST:
Scholarship, research, education and public programs in the humanities. In the act that established the Endowment, the term humanities includes, but is not limited to, the study of history, philosophy, languages, linguistics, literature, archaeology, jurisprudence, the history, theory and criticism of the arts, ethics, comparative religion and those aspects of the social sciences that employ historical or philosophical approaches.

NAME(S) OF PROGRAMS:
● **Office of Challenge Grants**

TYPE:
Capital grants; Challenge/matching grants; Professorships; Residencies; Visiting scholars. Nonprofit institutions interested in developing new sources of long-term support for educational, scholarly, preservation and public programs in the humanities may be assisted in these efforts by an NEH Challenge Grant. Grantees are required to raise three or four dollars in new or increased donations for every federal dollar offered.

Both federal and nonfederal funds may be used to establish or increase institutional endowments and thus guarantee long-term support for a variety of humanities needs. Funds may also be used for limited direct capital expenditures where such needs are compelling and clearly related to improvements in the humanities.

YEAR PROGRAM STARTED: 1977

PURPOSE:
To encourage long-range financial and program planning within humanities institutions and organizations; to provide means for humanities organizations and institutions to increase levels and kinds of continuing financial support; to sustain or develop high-quality work within the humanities; to join federal with nonfederal support so that those institutions in which teaching, learning and research of the humanities occur may achieve greater financial stability.

LEGAL BASIS:
Federal agency, established by act of Congress: The National Foundation on the Arts and Humanities Act of 1965, Public Law 89-209, as amended.

ELIGIBILITY:
Nonprofit postsecondary, educational, research or cultural institutions and organizations working within the humanities are eligible for support.

GEOGRAPHIC RESTRICTIONS:
United States.

FINANCIAL DATA:
All funds may be used to establish or increase institutional endowments.
Amount of support per award: Varies.
Total amount of support: Varies.
Matching fund requirements: A minimum of three nonfederal dollars must match each federal dollar received.

REPRESENTATIVE AWARDS:
$75,000 to Lenox Library Association, Lenox, MA, to support construction of a special collections research area, renovation of archival storage facilities, collection preservation, automation of acquisitions, circulation and endowment expansion; $150,000 to Saint Louis University, St. Louis, MO, to support an endowment for Saint Louis University's Center for Medieval and Renaissance Studies that will provide library materials, fellowships and a professorship in Byzantine and classical studies; $125,000 to Historical Society of Cheshire County, Keene, NH, to support renovation and expansion of a new site for a consolidated museum and archival center.

APPLICATION INFORMATION:
A narrative proposal in addition to other information requested in the program's guidelines.
Duration: Varies.
Deadline: Late Winter or early Spring.

PUBLICATIONS:
Annual report; *Grant Programs*; *Humanities Magazine*.

IRS IDENTIFICATION NUMBER: 52-1098584

ADDRESS INQUIRIES TO:
Paula Wasley, Public Affairs Specialist
(See address above.)

NATIONAL ENDOWMENT FOR THE HUMANITIES   [415]
1100 Pennsylvania Avenue, N.W.
Room 510
Washington, DC 20506
(202) 606-8400
Fax: (202) 606-8240

E-MAIL ADDRESS:
info@neh.gov

WEB SITE ADDRESS:
www.neh.gov

FOUNDED: 1965

AREAS OF INTEREST:
Scholarship, research, education and public programs in the humanities.

NAME(S) OF PROGRAMS:
● **Fellowships**
● **Summer Stipends**

TYPE:
Awards/prizes; Fellowships. Grants provide support for scholars to undertake full-time independent research and writing in the humanities. Grants are available for a maximum of one year and a minimum of six weeks to two months of summer study.

Grants also provide support for historically Black college and university faculty to undertake one year of full-time study leading to a doctoral degree in the humanities with preference given to those individuals who are at the dissertation stage of their work.

YEAR PROGRAM STARTED: 1967

PURPOSE:
To encourage continued research and study in the humanities discipline.

LEGAL BASIS:
Federal agency, established by act of Congress: The National Foundation on the Arts and Humanities Act of 1965, Public Law 89-209, as amended.

GEOGRAPHIC RESTRICTIONS:
United States.

FINANCIAL DATA:
Amount of support per award: Varies.
Total amount of support: Varies.

APPLICATION INFORMATION:
Application can be downloaded from www.grants.gov.
Duration: Up to one year.
Deadline: Fellowships: May 1; Summer Stipends: Late September.

PUBLICATIONS:
Annual report; *Grant Programs*; *Humanities Magazine*.

IRS IDENTIFICATION NUMBER: 52-1098584

ADDRESS INQUIRIES TO:
Paula Wasley, Public Affairs Specialist
(See address above.)

NATIONAL ENDOWMENT FOR THE HUMANITIES   [416]
1100 Pennsylvania Avenue, N.W.
Room 510
Washington, DC 20506
(202) 606-8400
Fax: (202) 606-8240

E-MAIL ADDRESS:
info@neh.gov

WEB SITE ADDRESS:
www.neh.gov

FOUNDED: 1965

AREAS OF INTEREST:
Scholarship, research, education and public programs in the humanities. In the act that established the Endowment, the term humanities includes, but is not limited to, the study of history, philosophy, languages, linguistics, literature, archaeology, jurisprudence, the history, theory and criticism of the arts, ethics, comparative religion and those aspects of the social sciences that employ historical or philosophical approaches.

NAME(S) OF PROGRAMS:
● **Seminars and Institutes Program**

TYPE:
Conferences/seminars. Grants support summer seminars and national institutes in the humanities for college and school teachers. These faculty development activities are conducted at colleges and universities across the country. Lists of pending seminars and institutes are available from the program.

YEAR PROGRAM STARTED: 1983

PURPOSE:
To provide opportunities for teachers to study under the direction of a master teacher and distinguished scholar in an area of mutual interest at a college or university during the summer.

LEGAL BASIS:
Federal agency, established by act of Congress: The National Foundation on the Arts and Humanities Act of 1965, Public Law 89-209, as amended.

ELIGIBILITY:
Applicants can be individuals or institutions of higher learning.

GEOGRAPHIC RESTRICTIONS:
United States.

FINANCIAL DATA:
Amount of support per award: Varies.
Total amount of support: Varies.

APPLICATION INFORMATION:
Participant application forms and instructions can be obtained from seminar directors at the host institutions. Those wishing to participate in seminars should submit their applications to the seminar director. Information about the program is publicized in the fall preceding the summer in question.
Duration: Seminars last four, five, or six weeks, depending on the choice of the director.
Deadline: Late February to early March.

PUBLICATIONS:
Annual report; *Grant Programs*; *Humanities Magazine*.

IRS IDENTIFICATION NUMBER: 52-1098584

ADDRESS INQUIRIES TO:
Paula Wasley, Public Affairs Specialist
(See address above.)

NATIONAL ENDOWMENT FOR THE HUMANITIES [417]

1100 Pennsylvania Avenue, N.W.
Room 510
Washington, DC 20506
(202) 606-8400
Fax: (202) 606-8240

E-MAIL ADDRESS:
info@neh.gov

WEB SITE ADDRESS:
www.neh.gov

FOUNDED: 1965

AREAS OF INTEREST:
Scholarship, research, education and public programs in the humanities. In the act that established the Endowment, the term humanities includes, but is not limited to, the study of history, philosophy, languages, linguistics, literature, archaeology, jurisprudence, the history, theory and criticism of the arts, ethics, comparative religion and those aspects of the social sciences that employ historical or philosophical approaches.

NAME(S) OF PROGRAMS:
● **Preservation and Access**

TYPE:
Project/program grants. Support may be sought to preserve the intellectual content and aid bibliographic control of collections, to compile bibliographies, descriptive catalogs and guides to cultural holdings, to create dictionaries, encyclopedias, databases and other types of research tools and reference works and to stabilize material culture collections through the appropriate housing and storing of objects, improved environmental control and the installation of security, lighting and fire-prevention systems.

Applications may also be submitted for national and regional education and training projects, regional preservation field service programs and research and demonstration projects that are intended to enhance institutional practice and the use of technology for preservation and access.

YEAR PROGRAM STARTED: 1985

PURPOSE:
To advance study in the area indicated.

LEGAL BASIS:
Federal agency, established by act of Congress: The National Foundation on the Arts and Humanities Act of 1965, Public Law 89-209, as amended.

ELIGIBILITY:
For the Preservation and Guides Programs, institutions and individuals are eligible to apply. For the U.S. newspaper program, state agencies, organizations, institutions and libraries are eligible.

FINANCIAL DATA:
Amount of support per award: Varies.
Total amount of support: Varies.

REPRESENTATIVE AWARDS:
$90,000 to Atlanta University Center, Atlanta, GA, to support a project to arrange and describe archival collections that document the African-American experience in the arts, religion, education, race relations and civil rights; $138,914 to Baltimore Museum of Industry, Baltimore, MD, to support the arrangement, description and preservation microfilming of the corporate records of the Canton Company of Baltimore, Maryland, dating from 1836 to

1981; $110,281 to Santa Barbara Museum of Natural History, Santa Barbara, CA, to support the computerization of the catalog and accession records of the museum's archaeological and ethnographic collections.

APPLICATION INFORMATION:
Contact NEH.
Duration: Usually one year.

PUBLICATIONS:
Annual report; *Grant Programs*; *Humanities Magazine*.

IRS IDENTIFICATION NUMBER: 52-1098584

ADDRESS INQUIRIES TO:
Paula Wasley, Public Affairs Specialist
(See address above.)

NATIONAL ENDOWMENT FOR THE HUMANITIES

1100 Pennsylvania Avenue, N.W.
Washington, DC 20506
(202) 606-8269
Fax: (202) 606-8557

E-MAIL ADDRESS:
publicpgms@neh.gov

WEB SITE ADDRESS:
www.neh.gov

TYPE:
Project/program grants. Grants support the planning and production of television and radio programs in the humanities intended for general audiences; the planning and implementation of exhibitions, the interpretation of historic sites and the production of related publications; multimedia components and educational programs and the planning and implementation of projects through the use of books, new technologies and other resources in the collections of libraries and archives in formats such as reading and discussion programs, lectures, symposia and interpretive exhibitions.

See entry 2075 for full listing.

NATIONAL HUMANITIES CENTER [418]

7 T.W. Alexander Drive
Research Triangle Park, NC 27709
(919) 549-0661
Fax: (919) 990-8535

E-MAIL ADDRESS:
nhc@nationalhumanitiescenter.org

WEB SITE ADDRESS:
www.nationalhumanitiescenter.org

FOUNDED: 1976

AREAS OF INTEREST:
History, literature, philosophy, classics, political theory, law, religion, anthropology, art history, folklore and other humanistic fields.

NAME(S) OF PROGRAMS:
● **National Humanities Center Fellowships**

TYPE:
Fellowships; Visiting scholars. Awards for advanced study in the humanities in residence at the Center.

YEAR PROGRAM STARTED: 1978

PURPOSE:
To support advanced study in the humanities; to encourage the exchange of ideas among humanist scholars; to enhance the influence of the humanities in the U.S.

LEGAL BASIS:
Privately incorporated nonprofit institute for advanced study.

ELIGIBILITY:
Open to scholars in the humanities. As a rule, the Center does not consider applications from candidates who have not yet completed the Doctorate. Fellowships for younger scholars are not intended for an immediate postdoctoral year but are awarded to individuals who have begun their professional careers and are undertaking research significantly beyond their dissertations.

FINANCIAL DATA:
Fellows receive travel expenses to and from the Center for themselves and their families.
Amount of support per award: Stipends up to $60,000; $50,000 average.
Matching fund requirements: Stipulated with specific grants.

COOPERATIVE FUNDING PROGRAMS: Scholars who have financial support from university or other funding agencies are welcome to apply and receive from the Center the difference between that support and their normal academic salaries.

APPLICATION INFORMATION:
Application forms are available upon request, to be submitted with five copies of the applicant's curriculum vitae, project proposal and financial statement. Neither application requests nor application materials are accepted via fax.
Duration: One academic year, September through May.
Deadline: October 15. Announcement in March.

PUBLICATIONS:
Annual report; application guidelines; semiannual newsletter.

IRS IDENTIFICATION NUMBER: 59-1735367

OFFICERS AND TRUSTEES:
Alan Brinkley, Chairman of the Board
William C. Jordin, Chairperson, Committee on Scholarly Programs

ADDRESS INQUIRIES TO:
Lois Whittington, Program Coordinator
Fellowship Program
(See address above.)

NEW YORK COUNCIL FOR THE HUMANITIES [419]

150 Broadway
Suite 1700
New York, NY 10038
(212) 233-1131
Fax: (212) 233-4607

E-MAIL ADDRESS:
nych@nyhumanities.org

WEB SITE ADDRESS:
www.nyhumanities.org

FOUNDED: 1975

AREAS OF INTEREST:
Humanities, public programs and education.

NAME(S) OF PROGRAMS:
● **Major Grants**
● **Mini Grants**
● **Speakers in the Humanities Program**

TYPE:
Challenge/matching grants; Project/program grants; Seed money grants. Major Project Grants are generally awarded for large-scale projects in the form of matching grants.

Mini Grants are designed for humanities programs of modest scale or for exhibition planning.

Speakers in the Humanities Program allows local organizations to present distinguished lectures by a select group of scholars and professionals to community audiences on various topics.

YEAR PROGRAM STARTED: 1975

PURPOSE:
To bring broad-based humanities programming to New York state audiences.

LEGAL BASIS:
State humanities council, nonprofit under Internal Revenue Code 501(c)(3).

ELIGIBILITY:
Nonprofit 501(c)(3) organizations in New York state.

GEOGRAPHIC RESTRICTIONS:
New York state.

FINANCIAL DATA:
Amount of support per award: Major Grants: Typically $2,500 to $20,000; Mini Grants: $250 to $2,500.
Total amount of support: $750,000.
Matching fund requirements: All program grants must be matched (at least dollar-for-dollar) with cash and/or in-kind contributions.

NUMBER OF APPLICANTS MOST RECENT YEAR:
Major and Mini Grants: 170; Speakers in the Humanities Awards: 350.

NUMBER OF AWARDS: Major and Mini Grants: 105; Speakers in the Humanities Awards: 349.

APPLICATION INFORMATION:
All applications are available online.
Deadline: March 15 and September 15 for Major Grants. Announcement in end of June and end of January, respectively. Mini Grants and Speakers in the Humanities Awards may be applied for throughout the year.

PUBLICATIONS:
Application guidelines.

IRS IDENTIFICATION NUMBER: 51-0152266

ADDRESS INQUIRIES TO:
Jane McNamara, Director of Grants
(See address and e-mail above.)

*SPECIAL STIPULATIONS:
Grants available only to New York-based, nonprofit organizations.

THE NEWBERRY LIBRARY [420]
Office of Research and Academic Programs
60 West Walton Street
Chicago, IL 60610-7324
(312) 255-3662
Fax: (312) 255-3680

E-MAIL ADDRESS:
research@newberry.org

WEB SITE ADDRESS:
www.newberry.
org/research/felshp/fellowshome.html

FOUNDED: 1887

AREAS OF INTEREST:
The humanities of Western Europe, England and the Americas from the late Middle Ages to the early 20th century.

NAME(S) OF PROGRAMS:
- **Newberry Library Short-Term Fellowships**

TYPE:
Fellowships; Residencies. Fellowships of one week to two months for advanced research, including doctoral dissertations, in history and the humanities. Fellowships provide access to the Newberry's collections for those who live and work beyond commuting distance from Chicago.

YEAR PROGRAM STARTED: 1942

PURPOSE:
To give scholars engaged in research in the fields listed above the opportunity to utilize the specialized collections of the Newberry Library.

LEGAL BASIS:
Private research library.

ELIGIBILITY:
Applicants must have the Ph.D. or equivalent or have completed all requirements except the dissertation. Preference will be given to applicants from outside the greater Chicago area whose research particularly requires study at the Newberry.

FINANCIAL DATA:
Amount of support per award: $1,600 per month.

NUMBER OF APPLICANTS MOST RECENT YEAR:
123.

NUMBER OF AWARDS: Varies.

APPLICATION INFORMATION:
Duration: One to two months.
Deadline: March 2.

STAFF:
Diane Dillon, Director of Scholarly and Undergraduate Programs

ADDRESS INQUIRIES TO:
Committee on Awards
(See address above.)

THE NEWBERRY LIBRARY [421]
Office of Research and Academic Programs
60 West Walton Street
Chicago, IL 60610-7324
(312) 255-3662
Fax: (312) 255-3680

E-MAIL ADDRESS:
research@newberry.org

WEB SITE ADDRESS:
www.newberry.
org/research/felshp/fellowshome.html

FOUNDED: 1887

AREAS OF INTEREST:
Late Medieval and Renaissance studies.

NAME(S) OF PROGRAMS:
- **The Audrey Lumsden-Kouvel Fellowship**
- **The Newberry Library-Ecole Nationale des Chartes Exchange Fellowship**

TYPE:
Conferences/seminars; Exchange programs; Fellowships; Visiting scholars. The Audrey Lumsden-Kouvel Fellowship is for postdoctoral scholars conducting extended research in residence at the Newberry Library for six months.

The Newberry Library-Ecole Nationale des Chartes Exchange Fellowship is granted to a graduate student to study at the Ecole Nationale des Chartes in Paris. The recipient must be a candidate for a Ph.D. degree.

Funds are also available for graduate students and postdoctoral scholars from affiliated institutions to participate in any of the Center's seminars and programs.

LEGAL BASIS:
Private research library.

ELIGIBILITY:
Audrey Lumsden-Kouvel Fellowship: Open to postdoctoral scholars. Applicants must plan to be in continuous residence for at least three months. Preference will be given to those who plan longer stays during the academic year or who wish to use the Fellowship to extend a sabbatical. Applicants for this fellowship need not be from outside the Chicago area. Project focus should be on Romance cultures.

Ecole Nationale des Chartes Exchange Fellowship: Applicant must be American or Canadian graduate student. Preference will be given to students from schools supporting the Center for Renaissance Studies.

FINANCIAL DATA:
Amount of support per award: Audrey Lumsden-Kouvel Fellowship: Stipend up to $25,500 for six months. Ecole Nationale des Chartes Exchange Fellowship: Varies and is determined by Ecole Nationale des Chartes (has been approximately $1,200).

NUMBER OF APPLICANTS MOST RECENT YEAR:
10.

NUMBER OF AWARDS: 1 each.

APPLICATION INFORMATION:
Full fellowship and program information and a list of affiliated institutions is available from the address above.
Duration: Varies.
Deadline: Audrey Lumsden-Kouvel Fellowship: March 2. Ecole Nationale des Chartes Exchange Fellowship: January 12.

STAFF:
Diane Dillon, Director of Scholarly and Undergraduate Programs

ADDRESS INQUIRIES TO:
Committee on Awards
(See address above.)

THE NEWBERRY LIBRARY [422]
Office of Research and Academic Programs
60 West Walton Street
Chicago, IL 60610-7324
(312) 255-3662
Fax: (312) 255-3680

E-MAIL ADDRESS:
research@newberry.org

WEB SITE ADDRESS:
www.newberry.
org/research/felshp/fellowshome.html

FOUNDED: 1887

AREAS OF INTEREST:
The humanities of Western Europe, England and the Americas from the late Middle Ages to the early 20th century.

NAME(S) OF PROGRAMS:
- **National Endowment for the Humanities Fellowships**

TYPE:
Fellowships; Research grants; Residencies. Support for projects in any field appropriate to the Library's collections.

YEAR PROGRAM STARTED: 1975

PURPOSE:
To encourage the individual scholar's research and to deepen and enrich the opportunities for serious intellectual exchange.

LEGAL BASIS:
Private research library.

ELIGIBILITY:
Established scholars at the postdoctoral level or its equivalent may apply. Awards are open to U.S. citizens and foreign nationals who have been living in the U.S. for at least three years. Preference is given to applicants who have not held major fellowships for three years preceding the proposed period of residency. An established scholar, as defined by the Awards Committee, is generally someone who has at least two published articles in refereed journals or the equivalent at the time of application.

FINANCIAL DATA:
Applicants may combine grants with sabbaticals or other stipendiary support.
Amount of support per award: Up to $50,400.
Total amount of support: Varies.

NUMBER OF APPLICANTS MOST RECENT YEAR: 61.

NUMBER OF AWARDS: Approximately 3.

APPLICATION INFORMATION:
Duration: Six to 11 months.
Deadline: January 12.

STAFF:
Diane Dillon, Director of Scholarly and Undergraduate Programs

ADDRESS INQUIRIES TO:
Committee on Awards
(See address above.)

THE NEWBERRY LIBRARY [423]
Office of Research and Academic Programs
60 West Walton Street
Chicago, IL 60610-7324
(312) 255-3662
Fax: (312) 255-3680

E-MAIL ADDRESS:
research@newberry.org

WEB SITE ADDRESS:
www.newberry.
org/research/felshp/fellowshome.html

FOUNDED: 1887

AREAS OF INTEREST:
The humanities of Western Europe, England and the Americas from the late Middle Ages to the early 20th century.

NAME(S) OF PROGRAMS:
● **Newberry-British Academy Fellowship for Study in Great Britain**

TYPE:
Exchange programs; Fellowships; Travel grants; Research contracts. In cooperation with the British Academy, the Newberry Library offers an exchange fellowship for study up to three months in Great Britain in any field in the humanities in which the Newberry's collections are strong.

YEAR PROGRAM STARTED: 1972

LEGAL BASIS:
Private research library.

ELIGIBILITY:
Applicants must be established scholars at the postdoctoral level or its equivalent. Preference is given to readers and staff of the Newberry and to scholars who have previously used the Newberry.

FINANCIAL DATA:
Fellow's home institution is expected to continue to pay his or her salary.
Amount of support per award: GBP 1,350 per month.

NUMBER OF APPLICANTS MOST RECENT YEAR: 6.

NUMBER OF AWARDS: Varies.

APPLICATION INFORMATION:
Duration: Three months.
Deadline: January 12.

OFFICERS:
Diane Dillon, Director of Scholarly and Undergraduate Programs

ADDRESS INQUIRIES TO:
Committee on Awards
(See address above.)

THE NEWBERRY LIBRARY [424]
Office of Research and Academic Programs
60 West Walton Street
Chicago, IL 60610-7324
(312) 255-3662
Fax: (312) 255-3680

E-MAIL ADDRESS:
dillond@newberry.org

WEB SITE ADDRESS:
www.newberry.
org/research/felshp/fellowshome.html

FOUNDED: 1887

AREAS OF INTEREST:
The Newberry Library specializes in the humanities of Western Europe, England and the Americas from the late Middle Ages to the early 20th century.

NAME(S) OF PROGRAMS:
● **Arthur Weinberg Fellowship for Independent Scholars**

TYPE:
Fellowships; Residencies. Weinberg Fellowship is for scholars working outside the academy who have demonstrated excellence through publishing and are working in a field appropriate to the Newberry's collections.

LEGAL BASIS:
Private research library.

ELIGIBILITY:
Applicants must be scholars who are not employed professionally as such. Candidates must have demonstrated excellence through publishing and are working in a field appropriate to the Newberry collections. Preference is given to scholars working on historical issues related to social justice and reform. Applicants for this fellowship need not be from outside the Chicago area.

FINANCIAL DATA:
Amount of support per award: $1,600 per month stipend, pro-rated for shorter periods.

NUMBER OF APPLICANTS MOST RECENT YEAR: 2.

NUMBER OF AWARDS: 1.

APPLICATION INFORMATION:
Duration: Nine months to one year.
Deadline: March 2.

STAFF:
Diane Dillon, Director of Scholarly and Undergraduate Programs

ADDRESS INQUIRIES TO:
Committee on Awards
(See address above.)

THE PHI BETA KAPPA SOCIETY
1606 New Hampshire Avenue, N.W.
Washington, DC 20009
(202) 745-3235
Fax: (202) 986-1601

E-MAIL ADDRESS:
awards@pbk.org

WEB SITE ADDRESS:
www.pbk.org

TYPE:
Awards/prizes; Fellowships; Project/program grants; Research grants; Scholarships; Travel grants. Grant to women scholars made in alternate years for advanced research dealing with Greek language, literature, history or archaeology (odd-numbered years) or with French language or literature (even-numbered years).

See entry 1157 for full listing.

THE SCHOMBURG CENTER FOR RESEARCH IN BLACK CULTURE [425]
515 Malcolm X Boulevard
New York, NY 10037-1801
(212) 491-2228
Fax: (212) 491-2098

WEB SITE ADDRESS:
www.nypl.org/locations/tid/64/node/131

FOUNDED: 1925

AREAS OF INTEREST:
African, African-American and Afro-Caribbean history and culture.

NAME(S) OF PROGRAMS:
● **Scholars-in-Residence**

TYPE:
Fellowships. Awarded to scholars and professionals whose research in the Black experience can benefit from extended access to the Center's collections. Seminars, colloquia, forums, symposia and conferences complement the residency program.

YEAR PROGRAM STARTED: 1986

PURPOSE:
To encourage research and writing in Black history and culture. To facilitate interaction among the participants, including fellows funded by other sources, and to provide for widespread dissemination of findings through lectures, publications and the Schomburg Center Seminars.

ELIGIBILITY:
Applicants must be professionals and/or scholars in the humanities studying Black history and culture and fields related to the Schomburg Center's collections and program activities, including librarianship, archives and museum administration, special collections, photographs, audiovisual materials and publications. Studies in the social sciences, the arts, science and technology, psychology, education and

religion are also eligible if they utilize a humanistic approach and contribute to humanistic knowledge. Creative writing projects (works of poetry and fiction) and projects that result in a performance are not eligible.

Persons seeking support for research leading to degrees are not eligible under this program. Candidates for advanced degrees must have received the degree or completed all requirements for it by the application deadline. Foreign nationals are ineligible unless they will have resided in the U.S. for three years immediately preceding the award date of the fellowship.

FINANCIAL DATA:
Amount of support per award: Stipend of $30,000 for six months and up to $60,000 for one year.

COOPERATIVE FUNDING PROGRAMS: Funded by the National Endowment for the Humanities, the Ford Foundation, and the Samuel I. Newhouse Foundation.

NUMBER OF APPLICANTS MOST RECENT YEAR: 130.

APPLICATION INFORMATION:
Application form may be requested from the Center.
Duration: Six or 12 consecutive months.
Deadline: December 1.

PUBLICATIONS:
Program announcement.

STAFF:
Colin Palmer, Director

ADDRESS INQUIRIES TO:
Scholars-in-Residence Program
(See address above.)

*PLEASE NOTE:
The Center will assist scholars in locating housing.

*SPECIAL STIPULATIONS:
Fellows may not be employed or hold other major fellowships or grants during period of residency.

SOCIAL SCIENCES AND HUMANITIES RESEARCH COUNCIL OF CANADA
350 Albert Street
Ottawa ON K1P 6G4 Canada
(613) 943-7777
Fax: (613) 943-1329

E-MAIL ADDRESS:
fellowships@sshrc-crsh.gc.ca

WEB SITE ADDRESS:
www.sshrc-crsh.gc.ca

TYPE:
Awards/prizes; Fellowships; Scholarships. Through its Doctoral Awards program, SSHRC offers two types of funding for doctoral students:
(1) SSHRC Doctoral Fellowships and;
(2) Joseph-Armand Bombardier (JAB) Canada Graduate Scholarships (CGS) program–Doctoral Scholarships.

See entry 1995 for full listing.

SOCIAL SCIENCES AND HUMANITIES RESEARCH COUNCIL OF CANADA
350 Albert Street
Ottawa ON K1P 6G4 Canada
(613) 943-7777
Fax: (613) 943-1329

E-MAIL ADDRESS:
fellowships@sshrc-crsh.gc.ca

WEB SITE ADDRESS:
www.sshrc-crsh.gc.ca

TYPE:
Fellowships; Scholarships. Award is offered to one outstanding successful doctoral award holder who intends to enter a Canadian Studies program at a Canadian university.

See entry 1996 for full listing.

SOCIAL SCIENCES AND HUMANITIES RESEARCH COUNCIL OF CANADA
350 Albert Street
Ottawa ON K1P 6G4 Canada
(613) 943-7777
Fax: (613) 943-1329

E-MAIL ADDRESS:
fellowships@sshrc-crsh.gc.ca

WEB SITE ADDRESS:
www.sshrc-crsh.gc.ca

TYPE:
Fellowships. For Canadian citizens or permanent residents of Canada, to support postdoctoral research in the humanities and social sciences.

See entry 1997 for full listing.

SOCIAL SCIENCES AND HUMANITIES RESEARCH COUNCIL OF CANADA
350 Albert Street, 16th Floor
Ottawa ON K1P 6G4 Canada
(613) 992-3027
Fax: (613) 947-0223

E-MAIL ADDRESS:
strategic@sshrc-crsh.gc.ca

WEB SITE ADDRESS:
www.sshrc.ca

TYPE:
Research grants. Strategic research grants. Assistance for research or training of researchers in areas of national importance to establish a knowledge base on identified social needs or problems. Grants are available for strategic research, strategic research networks, strategic research workshops and strategic partnership development.

See entry 1998 for full listing.

SOCIAL SCIENCES AND HUMANITIES RESEARCH COUNCIL OF CANADA
350 Albert Street
Ottawa ON K1P 6G4 Canada
(613) 943-7777
Fax: (613) 943-1329

E-MAIL ADDRESS:
fellowships@sshrc-crsh.gc.ca

WEB SITE ADDRESS:
www.vanier.gc.ca

TYPE:
Awards/prizes; Fellowships; Scholarships. For full-time doctoral students in the humanities and social sciences.

See entry 1999 for full listing.

SOCIAL SCIENCES AND HUMANITIES RESEARCH COUNCIL OF CANADA
350 Albert Street
Ottawa ON K1P 6G4 Canada
(613) 943-7777
Fax: (613) 943-1329

E-MAIL ADDRESS:
fellowships@sshrc-crsh.gc.ca

WEB SITE ADDRESS:
www.sshrc-crsh.gc.ca

TYPE:
Fellowships. Banting Postdoctoral Fellowships are for Canadian citizens, permanent residents of Canada and foreign citizens to support postdoctoral research in the humanities and social sciences.

See entry 2000 for full listing.

SOCIAL SCIENCES AND HUMANITIES RESEARCH COUNCIL OF CANADA
350 Albert Street
Ottawa ON K1P 6G4 Canada
(613) 943-7777
Fax: (613) 943-1329

E-MAIL ADDRESS:
scholfin@sshrc-crsh.gc.ca

WEB SITE ADDRESS:
www.sshrc-crsh.gc.ca

TYPE:
Awards/prizes; Fellowships; Scholarships.

See entry 2001 for full listing.

STANFORD HUMANITIES CENTER [426]
Stanford University
424 Santa Teresa Street
Stanford, CA 94305-4015
(650) 723-3052
Fax: (650) 723-1895

E-MAIL ADDRESS:
shc-fellowships@stanford.edu

WEB SITE ADDRESS:
shc.stanford.edu

FOUNDED: 1980

AREAS OF INTEREST:
History, literature, philosophy, classics, languages, social theory, political theory, law, religion, anthropology, art history, folklore and other areas of the humanities.

NAME(S) OF PROGRAMS:
● **External Faculty Fellowships**

TYPE:
Fellowships. Fellowships are awarded to support research projects in the humanities; creative arts projects are not eligible. The Humanities Center seeks candidates whose research is likely to contribute to intellectual exchange among a diverse group of scholars within the disciplines of the humanities.

YEAR PROGRAM STARTED: 1982

PURPOSE:
To promote the humanities and humanistic study at Stanford and nationally, primarily through a research fellowship program.

LEGAL BASIS:
Private, nonprofit research center at Stanford University.

ELIGIBILITY:
Postdoctoral level research in the humanities. Applicants are expected to be at least three years beyond receipt of their Ph.D. at the start of their fellowship year.

FINANCIAL DATA:
Amount of support per award: Stipend of $60,000, plus a moving and housing allowance.

Matching fund requirements: Applicants are encouraged to seek supplementary financial support.

NUMBER OF APPLICANTS MOST RECENT YEAR: 300.

NUMBER OF AWARDS: 8 for the year 2011-12.

APPLICATION INFORMATION:
Application is required and may be obtained directly from the Humanities Center web site.

Duration: Academic year. Normally September 15 to June 15. No renewals.

Deadline: October. Award announcement by late March.

ADVISORY BOARD:
Sandra Barnes, Anthropology, University of Pennsylvania
Coit Blacker, Political Science
Al Camarillo, History
Hester Gelber, Religious Studies
Jonathan Holloway, African American Studies and History, Yale University
Wilfred Jager
Roberta Katz, Associate Vice President for Strategic Planning
Barbara Koenig
Nancy Kollmann, History
Linda R. Meier, Community Volunteer
Alex Nemerov, Art History, Yale University
Walter Robb
James Spohrer
Patrick Suppes, Philosophy
William M. Todd, III, Slavic Languages and Literatures, Harvard University
David Wellbery, Germanic Studies, University of Chicago
Sylvia Yanagisako, Cultural and Social Anthropology

ADDRESS INQUIRIES TO:
See e-mail address above.

STIFTELSEN RIKSBANKENS JUBILEUMSFOND   [427]
Kungstradgardsg. 18
SE-114 86 Stockholm Sweden
46 08-50 62 64 00
Fax: 46 08-50 62 64 31

E-MAIL ADDRESS:
rj@rj.se

FOUNDED: 1964

AREAS OF INTEREST:
Scientific research in humanities and social sciences.

NAME(S) OF PROGRAMS:
● **Europe and Global Challenges**
● **Pro Futura**

TYPE:
Conferences/seminars; Exchange programs; Fellowships; General operating grants; Project/program grants; Research grants; Travel grants; Visiting scholars.

YEAR PROGRAM STARTED: 1965

PURPOSE:
To support and promote scientific research.

LEGAL BASIS:
Independent, non-governmental foundation.

ELIGIBILITY:
Open to single researchers or research groups. The Foundation is interested in supporting multidisciplinary or interdisciplinary research projects in which researchers from different disciplines, faculties, localities or countries collaborate with Swedish scholars.

FINANCIAL DATA:
Amount of support per award: Average SEK 2,000,000.

Total amount of support: SEK 350,000,000.

COOPERATIVE FUNDING PROGRAMS: Occasional co-financing for large projects.

NUMBER OF APPLICANTS MOST RECENT YEAR: 780.

APPLICATION INFORMATION:
Applicants should first submit a short outline sketch and a publication list. If the preliminary proposal is accepted, applicants will be required to send a complete application.

Duration: Two to four years average for projects; six to eight years for programs.

Deadline: February 10.

PUBLICATIONS:
Annual report; Information to Grant Applicants; yearbook.

STAFF:
Goran Blomquist, Managing Director
Bjorn Olsson, Finance Director
Dr. Jenny Bjorkman, Public Relations Officer
Kerstin Stigmark, Research Secretary, Economics, Law, and Political Science
Dr. Britta Lovgren, Research Secretary, Humanities
Dr. Maria Wikse, Research Secretary, Humanities
Dr. Torbjorn Eng, Research Secretary, Social Science
Dr. Fredrik Lundmark, Research Secretary, Social Science

ADDRESS INQUIRIES TO:
Dr. Jenny Bjorkman
Public Relations Officer
(See address above.)

SWANN FOUNDATION FOR CARICATURE AND CARTOON   [428]
Prints and Photographs Division
Library of Congress
101 Independence Avenue, S.E.
Washington, DC 20540-4730
(202) 707-9115
Fax: (202) 707-6647

E-MAIL ADDRESS:
swann@loc.gov

WEB SITE ADDRESS:
www.loc.gov/rr/print/swann/swann-fellow.html

FOUNDED: 1967

AREAS OF INTEREST:
Caricature and cartoons.

NAME(S) OF PROGRAMS:
● **Swann Foundation Fellowships**

TYPE:
Conferences/seminars; Fellowships; Internships; Project/program grants; Visiting scholars. Small grants. Annual fellowship awarded to candidate for a Ph.D. or Master's degree.

YEAR PROGRAM STARTED: 1995

PURPOSE:
To support the documentation and understanding of caricature and cartoon as art, considering how theory developed in relation to other visual arts, social history and intellectual history.

LEGAL BASIS:
Nonprofit, federal agency.

ELIGIBILITY:
Fellowships are awarded to active Ph.D. candidates, M.A. candidates and those people who have received an advanced degree within the last three years.

GEOGRAPHIC RESTRICTIONS:
North America.

FINANCIAL DATA:
Amount of support per award: Up to $15,000.

Total amount of support: $15,000 for the 2011-12 academic year.

NUMBER OF APPLICANTS MOST RECENT YEAR: Approximately 20.

NUMBER OF AWARDS: Varies.

APPLICATION INFORMATION:
Applicants should submit a project proposal and budget.

Duration: One academic year, generally fall through following late spring.

Deadline: February 15.

ADDRESS INQUIRIES TO:
Martha Kennedy
Curator, Popular and Applied Graphic Art
(See address above.)

*SPECIAL STIPULATIONS:
Must be a graduate student or a postgraduate within three years of receiving an M.A. or Ph.D. from a university in the U.S., Canada, or Mexico.

U.S. DEPARTMENT OF EDUCATION   [429]
Jacob K. Javits Fellowships Program
1990 K Street, N.W., Suite 6018
Washington, DC 20006-8524
(202) 219-7138
Fax: (202) 502-7859

E-MAIL ADDRESS:
ope_javits_program@ed.gov

WEB SITE ADDRESS:
www.ed.gov/programs/jacobjavits/index.html

FOUNDED: 1985

AREAS OF INTEREST:
Specified subfields of the arts, humanities and social sciences.

NAME(S) OF PROGRAMS:
● **Jacob K. Javits Fellowship Program**

TYPE:
Fellowships.

YEAR PROGRAM STARTED: 1985

PURPOSE:
To provide financial assistance to students who have demonstrated superior academic ability and achievement, exceptional promise and financial need to undertake graduate study at the doctoral and Master of Fine Arts level in selected fields of arts, humanities, and social sciences.

LEGAL BASIS:
Government agency.

ELIGIBILITY:
Eligibility is limited to U.S. citizens or nationals, permanent residents of the U.S., or citizens of any one of the Freely Associated States.

Undergraduate students about to enter graduate school and graduate students who have not yet completed their first year of graduate study and who intend to pursue a doctoral or Master's degree, if the Master's degree is the terminal or highest degree awarded in an approved field, may apply; 20% of the fellowships shall be awarded in the social sciences, 20% in the arts, and 60% in the humanities. A minimum of 60% of the awards shall be made to students who have no graduate credits.

Applicants must be eligible to be accepted to or currently attending a graduate program leading to a Doctorate or a terminal Master's degree in an eligible field of study at an institution of higher education approved by an accrediting agency recognized by the Secretary of the Department of Education. Applicants attending a foreign institution are ineligible.

Students who have already received a Javits fellowship in previous years are not eligible.

FINANCIAL DATA:
Amount of support per award: Stipend up to $30,000 per academic year, depending upon financial need. In addition, $13,755 is awarded to the Fellow's institution for tuition and fees in lieu of normal charges to the student.
Total amount of support: $9,687,000 for the year 2010.

NUMBER OF APPLICANTS MOST RECENT YEAR:
800 for fiscal year 2010.

NUMBER OF AWARDS: 67 new; 173 continuing (estimated).

APPLICATION INFORMATION:
Application should be submitted in hardcopy only.
Duration: One academic year. Renewal up to a maximum of three years, pending funding availability and academic performance.
Deadline: September 30.

PUBLICATIONS:
Application guidelines.

ADDRESS INQUIRIES TO:
Carmen Gordon, Program Manager
(See e-mail address above.)

UCLA CHICANO STUDIES RESEARCH CENTER

193 Haines Hall
Box 951544
Los Angeles, CA 90095
(310) 794-9646
Fax: (310) 206-1784

E-MAIL ADDRESS:
csrcinfo@chicano.ucla.edu

WEB SITE ADDRESS:
www.chicano.ucla.edu

TYPE:
Fellowships; Visiting scholars.

See entry 1132 for full listing.

UNIVERSITY OF PENNSYLVANIA, PENN HUMANITIES FORUM [430]

3260 South Street
Penn Museum
Philadelphia, PA 19104-6324
(215) 898-8220
Fax: (215) 746-5946

E-MAIL ADDRESS:
phf@sas.upenn.edu

WEB SITE ADDRESS:
www.phf.upenn.edu

FOUNDED: 1999

AREAS OF INTEREST:
Humanities.

NAME(S) OF PROGRAMS:
● Andrew W. Mellon Postdoctoral Fellowships in the Humanities

TYPE:
Fellowships. Fellows conduct research and teach one course in the fall term.

YEAR PROGRAM STARTED: 1976

PURPOSE:
To support and encourage the intellectual development of untenured scholars in the humanities.

LEGAL BASIS:
Nonprofit, non-taxable university.

ELIGIBILITY:
Candidates must have research interests that relate to the forum's topic of study for the year of the fellowship ("Adaptation" for 2011-12). Preference is given to proposals that are interdisciplinary and to candidates who have not previously used the resources of the University of Pennsylvania and whose work would allow them to take advantage of the research strengths of the institution and to make a contribution to its intellectual life. Research proposals are invited in all areas of humanistic studies except educational curriculum-building and performing arts.

FINANCIAL DATA:
Fellowships include health insurance.
Amount of support per award: $46,500.

NUMBER OF AWARDS: 5.

APPLICATION INFORMATION:
Applications are available commencing in June at the web site above. Applicants are expected to submit the application, which includes a description of their proposed project, as well as recommendations.
Duration: One year in residence at University of Pennsylvania.
Deadline: October 15 of the year preceding the fellowship. Announcement in January of the fellowship year.

STAFF:
Gary Tomlinson, Director
Jennifer Conway, Associate Director
Sara Varney, Administrative Coordinator

ADDRESS INQUIRIES TO:
Jennifer Conway, Associate Director
(See address above.)

VILLA I TATTI: THE HARVARD UNIVERSITY CENTER FOR ITALIAN RENAISSANCE STUDIES

Via di Vincigliata, 26
50135 Florence Italy
(39 055) 603 251
(39 055) 608 909
Fax: (39 055) 603 383

E-MAIL ADDRESS:
info@itatti.it

WEB SITE ADDRESS:
www.itatti.it

TYPE:
Fellowships. Stipendiary and non-stipendiary fellowships for the academic year July 1 through June 30 in residence in Florence for study on any aspect of the Italian Renaissance. There are a limited number of short-term Outreach Visiting Fellowships designed to reach out to Italian Renaissance scholars from areas that have been underrepresented at Villa I Tatti, especially those from Asia, Latin America, the Iberian Peninsula and the Mediterranean basin (except Italy).There are also a limited number of short-term Craig Hugh Smyth Visiting Fellowships mainly for museum and library professionals, but academic administrators and conservators are welcome to apply, and mothers engaged in some aspect of Italian Renaissance studies.

See entry 1003 for full listing.

LEWIS WALPOLE LIBRARY [431]

Yale University
P.O. Box 1408
Farmington, CT 06034
(860) 677-2140
Fax: (860) 677-6369

E-MAIL ADDRESS:
walpole@yale.edu

WEB SITE ADDRESS:
www.library.yale.edu/walpole

AREAS OF INTEREST:
18th century studies (mainly British), the study of Horace Walpole and Strawberry Hill.

NAME(S) OF PROGRAMS:
● Visiting Research Fellowship Program

TYPE:
Internships; Travel grants. 18th century studies (mainly British), including history, literature, theatre, drama, art, architecture, politics, philosophy or social history.

PURPOSE:
To fund study into any aspect of British 18th century studies in the Library's collection of 18th century British prints, paintings, books and manuscripts.

ELIGIBILITY:
Applicants should normally be pursuing an advanced degree or must be engaged in postdoctoral research or equivalent research. Level of study is at doctoral, postdoctoral, postgraduate and research levels.

FINANCIAL DATA:
Amount of support per award: Fellowship: $2,000, plus travel to and from the Library, and free accommodations on site.
Total amount of support: Varies.

NUMBER OF AWARDS: Up to 12.

APPLICATION INFORMATION:
Applicants must submit a curriculum vitae, a brief outline of research proposal of up to three pages and two confidential letters of recommendation.
Duration: One month.
Deadline: January 15.

ADDRESS INQUIRIES TO:
Margaret K. Powell, Librarian
(See address above.)

WEGE FOUNDATION   [432]
P.O. Box 6388
Grand Rapids, MI 49516-6388
(616) 957-0480
Fax: (616) 957-0616

E-MAIL ADDRESS:
tmccarthy@wegefoundation.org

WEB SITE ADDRESS:
www.wegefoundation.org

FOUNDED: 1968

AREAS OF INTEREST:
Education, environment, health care, human services and the arts in west Michigan.

TYPE:
Capital grants; Challenge/matching grants; Endowments; General operating grants; Internships; Matching gifts; Project/program grants; Scholarships.

PURPOSE:
To assist programs and projects in the areas of education, environment, health care, arts and culture, and human services.

ELIGIBILITY:
Grants are made to tax-exempt, nonprofit organizations which meet the Foundation's current program priorities and are located in the west Michigan area.

GEOGRAPHIC RESTRICTIONS:
Greater Grand Rapids and west Michigan.

FINANCIAL DATA:
Amount of support per award: $500 to $40,000.
Total amount of support: Approximately $10,000,000 annually.

NUMBER OF APPLICANTS MOST RECENT YEAR:
175.

NUMBER OF AWARDS: 55.

APPLICATION INFORMATION:
Duration: One year. Renewal possible.
Deadline: Apply as early as possible in the year.

BOARD OF DIRECTORS:
Peter M. Wege, Chairman
Peter M. Wege, II, President
Ellen Satterlee, Treasurer and Executive Director
W. Michael Van Haren, Secretary
Mary Goodwillie Nelson, Trustee
Christopher Wege, Trustee
Diana Wege, Trustee
Jonathan Wege, Trustee

ADDRESS INQUIRIES TO:
Terri McCarthy
Vice President of Programs
(See address above.)

WOODROW WILSON INTERNATIONAL CENTER FOR SCHOLARS   [433]
One Woodrow Wilson Plaza
1300 Pennsylvania Avenue, N.W.
Washington, DC 20004-3027
(202) 691-4170
Fax: (202) 691-4001

E-MAIL ADDRESS:
fellowships@wilsoncenter.org

WEB SITE ADDRESS:
www.wilsoncenter.org

FOUNDED: 1968

AREAS OF INTEREST:
Social sciences and humanities.

NAME(S) OF PROGRAMS:
● **Fellowship Program at the Woodrow Wilson International Center for Scholars**

TYPE:
Fellowships; Research grants; Residencies; Scholarships; Visiting scholars. The Center seeks to commemorate, through its residential fellowship program of advanced research, both the scholarly depth and the public concerns of Woodrow Wilson. The Center welcomes outstanding project proposals in the social sciences and humanities on national and/or international issues - topics that intersect with questions of public policy or provide the historical framework to illume policy issues of contemporary importance. The Center especially welcomes projects likely to foster communication between the world of ideas and the world of public affairs.

Projects should have relevance to the world of public policy. Fellows should be prepared to interact with policymakers in Washington and with the Center's staff working on similar areas.

Fellowships are tenable in residence only at the Woodrow Wilson International Center for Scholars. The Center will not provide support for research to be carried out elsewhere. Fellows devote their full time to research and writing.

YEAR PROGRAM STARTED: 1970

LEGAL BASIS:
Government agency.

ELIGIBILITY:
The Center seeks individuals from throughout the world with superior projects representing diverse scholarly interests in the social sciences and humanities - topics that intersect with questions of public policy.

Academic participants are normally established scholars at the postdoctoral level but cannot be currently working on a Ph.D.

For non-academic participants, namely those from careers in government, journalism, business, diplomacy and other professions, an equivalent degree of professional achievement is required.

Criteria for selection include scholarly capabilities, promise and achievements, the importance and originality of the proposed research, and the likelihood of the applicant being able to accomplish what he or she proposes.

Applicants should have a very good command of spoken English, since the Center is designed to encourage the exchange of ideas among its Fellows.

FINANCIAL DATA:
The Center tries to ensure that the stipend provided under the fellowship, together with fellow's other sources of funding (e.g., grants secured by applicant and sabbatical allowances), approximate a fellow's regular salary (up to a maximum of $85,000).
Total amount of support: $1,496,000 for the year 2009.

NUMBER OF APPLICANTS MOST RECENT YEAR:
300.

NUMBER OF AWARDS: 25.

REPRESENTATIVE AWARDS:
"Business, Politics and Social Responsibility in Latin America;" "Fads and Fashions in Economic Policy Reform;" "Questions of Precedence: History, Ownership and Value in Contemporary West African Political Economies."

APPLICATION INFORMATION:
Applicant must submit:
(1) the two-page, single-sided Fellowship Application Form (preferably typed);
(2) a list of publications that includes exact titles, names of publishers, dates of publication and status of forthcoming publications (not to exceed three pages);
(3) a Project Proposal (not to exceed five single-spaced typed pages, using 12-point type). The Center reserves the right to omit from review applications that are longer than the requested page length;
(4) a bibliography for the project that includes primary sources and relevant secondary sources (not to exceed three pages) and;
(5) the one-page Financial Information Form.

All application materials must be submitted in English. Applications submitted via fax will not be considered.
Duration: Fellowships of usually nine months are tenable September 1 of the fellowship year.
Deadline: October 1 for receipt of applications. Decisions announced by early April of the following year.

PUBLICATIONS:
Annual report; application guidelines.

OFFICERS:
Lee H. Hamilton, Director
Michael Van Dusen, Senior Vice President
Steve Lagerfeld, Editor, Wilson Quarterly
John Milewski, Producer of Radio Dialogue
Janet Spikes, Librarian
Lucy Jilka, Director, Scholar Administration Office
Cynthia Arnson, Director, Latin American Program
Blair A. Ruble, Director, Kennan Institute for Advanced Russian Studies
Robert S. Litwak, Director, Division of International Studies
Robert Hathaway, Director, Asia Program
Barbara Hall, Director, Development
Sharon McCarter, Director, Public Affairs
David Biette, Director, Canada Institute

TRUSTEES:
Joseph Gildenhorn, Chairman
Sander Gerber, Vice Chairman
John Casteen, III
Charles Glazer
Carlos Gutierrez

ADDRESS INQUIRIES TO:
Lucy Jilka, Director
Scholar Administration Office
(See address above.)

WINTERTHUR MUSEUM, GARDEN & LIBRARY   [434]

Route 52
Winterthur, DE 19735
(302) 888-4600
(302) 888-4637
Fax: (302) 888-4870

E-MAIL ADDRESS:
rkrill@winterthur.org

WEB SITE ADDRESS:
www.winterthur.org

FOUNDED: 1951

AREAS OF INTEREST:
American decorative arts, American art,
American cultural and social history and
horticulture.

NAME(S) OF PROGRAMS:
- **Dissertation Fellowships**
- **NEH Fellowships**
- **Winterthur Fellowships**

TYPE:
Fellowships; Research grants; Visiting
scholars. Long-term and short-term
fellowships to be held in residence at
Winterthur Museum.

The Dissertation Fellowships are for doctoral
candidates. The award is a nine-month
fellowship or a semester-length fellowship.

NEH Fellowships consist of four- to
12-month fellowships for advanced research
in American life into the early 20th century.

Winterthur Fellowships consist of one- to
three-month fellowships designed to promote
research and study in topics of relevance to
Winterthur's collections.

All fellowships are residential, requiring
research and writing at Winterthur.

YEAR PROGRAM STARTED: 1977

PURPOSE:
To promote research in any humanistic field,
work of an interdisciplinary nature and/or
research with both objects and documents.

LEGAL BASIS:
Tax-exempt, public charitable organization.

ELIGIBILITY:
Winterthur Fellowships are available to
academic, museum and independent scholars
and to support dissertation research.
NEH Fellowships are available to scholars,
holding the Ph.D., pursuing advanced
research. Must be U.S. citizen or resident of
the U.S. three years prior to application.
Applicants for a Dissertation Fellowship must
have completed coursework, passed
qualifying exams, fulfilled language
requirements, and have an approved
prospectus. The fellowship is open to
students in departments of history,
anthropology, folklore, art history, American
studies, African-American history, historic
preservation, and related fields.

FINANCIAL DATA:
Applicants may hold sabbaticals and grants
from their own institutions, but may not
simultaneously hold other major fellowships.
Housing is available in a cottage on the
museum grounds (full housekeeping facilities
and furnished rooms).
Amount of support per award: Dissertation
Fellowships: $7,000 per semester; NEH
Fellowships: Up to $40,000 for two
semesters; Winterthur Fellowships: $1,500
per month.
Total amount of support: Varies.

REPRESENTATIVE AWARDS:
John Lardas Modern, Professor of Religious
Studies, Franklin & Marshall College,
Lancaster, PA, "Haunted Modernity; or, the
Metaphysics of Secularism in Antebellum
America;" Julia A. Sienkewicz, University of
Illinois, *Citizenship by Design: the Creation
of Identity through Art, Architecture and
Landscape in the Early Republic*; Sarah
Carter, Harvard University, *A Basket, A
Needle, A Penknife: Object Lessons in
Nineteenth-Century American Material and
Visual Culture.*

APPLICATION INFORMATION:
Application instructions and materials are
available online. Applicants for each
fellowship should submit a three- to
five-page statement of purpose, a curriculum
vitae and three letters of recommendation.
Supporting materials for dissertation research
must include the dissertation prospectus and
a letter from the dissertation advisor.
Duration: NEH Fellowships: Four to 12
months; Winterthur Fellowships: One to three
months.
Deadline: January 15. Announcement by
April 30.

IRS IDENTIFICATION NUMBER: 51-0066038

ADDRESS INQUIRIES TO:
Research Fellowship Program
Academic Programs Department
5105 Kennett Pike
Wilmington, DE 19735
(See e-mail address above.)

CARTER G. WOODSON INSTITUTE FOR AFRICAN-AMERICAN AND AFRICAN STUDIES   [435]

University of Virginia
McCormick Road, 108 Minor Hall
Charlottesville, VA 22903
(434) 924-3109
Fax: (434) 924-8820

E-MAIL ADDRESS:
woodson@virginia.edu

WEB SITE ADDRESS:
www.virginia.edu/~woodson

FOUNDED: 1981

AREAS OF INTEREST:
Those disciplines of the humanities and
social sciences which concern themselves
with Afro-American and African Studies.

NAME(S) OF PROGRAMS:
- **African-American and African Studies
Fellowships**

TYPE:
Fellowships. The Woodson Institute offers
residential fellowships to predoctoral and
postdoctoral scholars. These fellowships are
designed to facilitate the completion of works
in progress by providing scholars with
unencumbered leave.

Afro-American and African Studies is
considered to cover Africa, Africans and
peoples of African descent in North, Central
and South America and the Caribbean, past
and present.

YEAR PROGRAM STARTED: 1981

PURPOSE:
To help researchers complete dissertations,
books and other research projects focusing on
the Black experience.

LEGAL BASIS:
University.

ELIGIBILITY:
Open to qualified candidates without
restriction as to citizenship or current
residence except for employees of the
University of Virginia who may not apply.
Applicants for the predoctoral fellowships
must have completed all requirements for the
Ph.D. except the dissertation prior to August
1. Applicants for the postdoctoral fellowship
must have been awarded their Ph.D. by the
time of application or furnish proof that it
will have been received prior to June 30.

Proposals will be judged on the basis of the
significance of the proposed work, the
applicant's qualifications, familiarity with
existing relevant research literature, the
research design of the project and the
promise of completion within the award
period. Preference will be given to projects
whose field research is already substantially
completed.

Fellowship recipients must be in residence at
the University of Virginia for the duration of
the award period and are expected to
contribute to the intellectual life of the
University. In pursuit of these goals,
predoctoral fellows will become visiting
graduate students attached to their respective
disciplinary departments, and postdoctoral
fellows will receive the status of visiting
scholars in their respective fields.

FINANCIAL DATA:
Amount of support per award: Predoctoral
Fellowship: $20,000 per year; Postdoctoral
Fellowship: $45,000.

NUMBER OF APPLICANTS MOST RECENT YEAR:
127; 51 predoctoral and 76 postdoctoral.

NUMBER OF AWARDS: 5.

REPRESENTATIVE AWARDS:
Y.H. Affinnih, doctoral candidate, Sociology,
New York University, for "Occupational
Commitment and the Myth of
Self-Employment Among Lagos Port and
Dock Workers;" Melvin Patrick Ely,
Postdoctoral Fellow, History, Princeton
University, for "Amos 'n' Andy: Their
Lineage, Life and Legacy, 1890-1966."

APPLICATION INFORMATION:
Complete guidelines are available by written
request to: P.O. Box 400162, Charlottesville,
VA 22904-4162. The following materials
must be submitted in the number of copies
indicated:
(1) a completed summary sheet (original
only);
(2) a letter of application stating interest in
the fellowship program (eight copies);
(3) curriculum vitae (eight copies);
(4) a project description not to exceed seven
double-spaced pages indicating the nature of
the research to be completed during the
period of the fellowship award as well as the
significance of this work for Afro-American
and/or African Studies. This description
should have a title and should include a
detailed research plan giving concrete
objectives to be achieved during the award
period. For predoctoral candidates, these
objectives must include award of the Ph.D.
For postdoctoral applicants, the objectives
should include a statement of plans for
publication of the results of the proposed
research and writing (eight copies);
(5) graduate school transcript(s) (predoctoral
candidates only) (eight copies) and;

(6) three confidential letters of reference to be sent directly to the Woodson Institute by persons qualified to evaluate the specific proposal for which support is being sought (original only).

Applicants cannot apply for both fellowships (predoctoral and postdoctoral) in the same year.

Duration: Predoctoral Fellowships: Two years; Postdoctoral Fellowships: One year.

Deadline: December 5. Notification by mail early March.

PUBLICATIONS:
Program guidelines.

STAFF:
Deborah E. McDowell, Director

ADDRESS INQUIRIES TO:
Program Administrator
(See address above.)

*SPECIAL STIPULATIONS:
Fellows are required to present a formal paper to the University community at least once a year.

YALE CENTER FOR BRITISH ART   [436]
1080 Chapel Street
New Haven, CT 06520-8280
(203) 432-2824
Fax: (203) 432-4538

E-MAIL ADDRESS:
ycba.research@yale.edu

WEB SITE ADDRESS:
www.yale.edu/ycba

FOUNDED: 1977

AREAS OF INTEREST:
British art, history and literature.

NAME(S) OF PROGRAMS:
● **Visiting Scholar Awards**

TYPE:
Fellowships; Research grants; Residencies; Visiting scholars. Short-term resident fellowships for scholars of literature, history, the history of art or related fields. The Center also offers predoctoral residential awards.

YEAR PROGRAM STARTED: 1978

PURPOSE:
To allow scholars of literature, history, the history of art or related fields to study the Center's holdings of paintings, drawings, prints and rare books and to make use of its research facilities (photograph archive and reference library).

LEGAL BASIS:
University-affiliated museum and research center.

ELIGIBILITY:
Open to scholars engaged in predoctoral and postdoctoral or equivalent research related to British art and to museum professionals whose responsibilities and research interests include British art.

FINANCIAL DATA:
Fellowships include the cost of travel to and from New Haven and also provide accommodation and a living allowance. Recipients will be required to be in residence in New Haven during the Fellowship period.
Amount of support per award: $1,800 plus travel expenses.

COOPERATIVE FUNDING PROGRAMS: One fellowship per annum is reserved for members of the American Society for Eighteenth-Century Studies; by arrangement with the Huntington Library and the Delaware Art Museum, scholars may apply for tandem awards.

NUMBER OF APPLICANTS MOST RECENT YEAR:
32 for the year 2010-11.

NUMBER OF AWARDS: 20.

REPRESENTATIVE AWARDS:
Denis Longchamps, Ph.D. in Art History, "Mary Anne Burges's scientific and literary achievements;" Jennifer Ferng, Ph.D. candidate, Massachusetts Institute of Technology, "On Stone: Constructing Architecture, Materiality, and Victorian Representations of the Geological Landscape in Nineteenth-Century Britain;" Nathaniel Stein, doctoral candidate, Brown University, "Colonial Encounter and Corporeal Vulnerability: British Masculinity and the Representation of India, 1857-1879;" Dipti Khera, Ph.D. candidate, Columbia University, "Picturing India's 'Land of Princes' between the Mughal and British Empires: Topographical Imaginings of Udaipur and its Environs."

APPLICATION INFORMATION:
There are no application forms. However, candidates should submit name, address and telephone number, curriculum vitae listing educational background, professional experience and publications, a brief outline of research proposal not to exceed three pages and two confidential letters of recommendation to arrive by the application deadline to the Associate Head of Research, Lisa Ford, at ycba.visitingscholars@yale.edu. Candidates should also indicate preferred dates.
Duration: One to four months.
Deadline: Mid-January.

PUBLICATIONS:
Brochure.

STAFF:
Amy Meyers, Director
Martina Droth, Head of Research
Lisa Ford, Associate Head of Research

ADDRESS INQUIRIES TO:
Lisa Ford, Associate Head of Research
P.O. Box 208280
New Haven, CT 06520
E-mail: lisa.ford@yale.edu

*SPECIAL STIPULATIONS:
Inquiries and application submissions must be by e-mail only.

Architecture

THE AMERICAN ARCHITECTURAL FOUNDATION   [437]
c/o AAF-RMHF
1799 New York Avenue, N.W.
Washington, DC 20006-5207
(202) 626-7550
Fax: (202) 626-7420

E-MAIL ADDRESS:
info@archfoundation.org

WEB SITE ADDRESS:
www.archfoundation.org
www.rmhf.org

FOUNDED: 1942

AREAS OF INTEREST:
Architecture; urban design; leadership development.

NAME(S) OF PROGRAMS:
● **The Richard Morris Hunt Fellowship**

TYPE:
Awards/prizes; Exchange programs; Fellowships; Research grants; Travel grants. Six-month professional study in France awarded in alternate years to midcareer American architects and urbanists pursuing careers with an emphasis on historic preservation topics.

YEAR PROGRAM STARTED: 1990

PURPOSE:
To study American and French architecture heritage.

ELIGIBILITY:
Open to architects and urban design professionals who have written and oral proficiency in French and are pursuing a career in historic preservation. In alternate years, open to French architects.

GEOGRAPHIC RESTRICTIONS:
United States and French citizens only.

FINANCIAL DATA:
Amount of support per award: $25,000.
Total amount of support: $25,000.

COOPERATIVE FUNDING PROGRAMS:
Co-sponsored by the AAF and the French Heritage Society.

NUMBER OF APPLICANTS MOST RECENT YEAR:
9.

NUMBER OF AWARDS: 1.

APPLICATION INFORMATION:
Applicants should submit a recent biography, three letters of recommendation, examples of professional work such as slides, sketches or photographs, a statement explaining how academic background and work experience relate to the Fellowship and how the Fellowship will benefit professionally. Applicants must demonstrate French language proficiency.
Duration: Six months.
Deadline: Mid-September.

PUBLICATIONS:
Program announcement.

STAFF:
Elizabeth Blazevich, Program Manager

THE AMERICAN INSTITUTE OF ARCHITECTS   [438]
1735 New York Avenue, N.W.
Washington, DC 20006-5292
(202) 626-7539
Fax: (202) 626-7399

E-MAIL ADDRESS:
rhayes@aia.org
infocentral@aia.org

WEB SITE ADDRESS:
www.aia.org/aah

FOUNDED: 1952

AREAS OF INTEREST:
Health care, facility planning, design and construction, facilities management, clinical engineering, and safety and security.

NAME(S) OF PROGRAMS:
- **AIA Arthur N. Tuttle, Jr. Graduate Fellowship in Health Facility Planning and Design**

TYPE:
Fellowships; Research grants. The American Institute of Architects and the American Hospital Association sponsor this program with additional support from the Steris Corporation, which offers one or more graduate fellowships.

YEAR PROGRAM STARTED: 1952

PURPOSE:
To increase the amount of research being done in the area of health care facility design and planning.

LEGAL BASIS:
Nonprofit organization.

ELIGIBILITY:
Open to graduate and postgraduate students enrolled at an accredited school of architecture. Applicants must be citizens of Canada, Mexico or the U.S.

FINANCIAL DATA:
Amount of support per award: Varies.

APPLICATION INFORMATION:
Duration: One to two years depending on proposal.
Deadline: Last Friday in April.

PUBLICATIONS:
Guidelines.

ADDRESS INQUIRIES TO:
Richard L. Hayes, Ph.D., AIA
AIA Academy of Architecture for Health
(See address above.)

THE AMERICAN INSTITUTE OF ARCHITECTS   [439]
1735 New York Avenue, N.W.
Washington, DC 20006-5292
(202) 626-7529
Fax: (202) 626-7399

E-MAIL ADDRESS:
scholarships@aia.org

WEB SITE ADDRESS:
www.aia.org

FOUNDED: 1943

AREAS OF INTEREST:
Architecture.

NAME(S) OF PROGRAMS:
- **American Institute of Architects (AIA) Minority/Disadvantaged Scholarship Program**

TYPE:
Scholarships. Awards to provide an opportunity for financially disadvantaged and/or minority groups to pursue a professional degree in architecture.

YEAR PROGRAM STARTED: 1973

PURPOSE:
To provide scholarships for those who would not otherwise have the opportunity to be enrolled in professional architecture studies.

ELIGIBILITY:
Applicants must be residents of the U.S. High school seniors, technical school/junior college students transferring to an NAAB school of architecture or college freshmen who are entering a program leading to a professional degree (Bachelor, Master's of Architecture or D.Arch.) are eligible to apply.

Students who have completed the first year of a standard four-year curriculum are not eligible.

GEOGRAPHIC RESTRICTIONS:
United States.

FINANCIAL DATA:
Scholarship awards vary according to financial need. The amount of the award is determined based on the financial information and consultation with the Director of Financial Aid at the student's school.
Amount of support per award: Approximately $4,000.

NUMBER OF AWARDS: Approximately 4 to 5.

APPLICATION INFORMATION:
Candidates may begin the application process in January and must submit:
(1) a letter of recommendation completed by an architect, an AIA component, a community design center representative, a guidance counselor or teacher, a director of a community, civic, or religious organization, or the dean, administrative head, or professor at an NAAB-accredited professional program;
(2) a completed application form;
(3) a copy of transcripts of all high school and college records, including SAT or ACT scores;
(4) a copy of a written acceptance from an NAAB-accredited professional program in architecture (can be provided at time of acceptance);
(5) a personal statement outlining interests, experience, and career plans related to architecture;
(6) a statement describing the applicant's disadvantaged circumstances;
(7) one freehand drawing on an 8 1/2 x 11-inch page depicting any subject; cannot be drafted or done using computer-aided design and;
(8) completed portion of the last page of the application by the high school guidance counselor or the administrative head at the NAAB-accredited professional program.
Duration: One academic year, renewable up to five years until the applicant's degreed program is complete, provided the student remains in good standing at an NAAB-accredited school of architecture, has a continued financial need and adheres to all program requirements.
Deadline: April.

OFFICERS:
Robert Ivey, Executive Vice President and Chief Executive Officer, American Institute of Architects

ADDRESS INQUIRIES TO:
Jamie Yeung, Manager
Professional Development Resources
(See address above.)

THE AMERICAN SCHOOL OF CLASSICAL STUDIES AT ATHENS
6-8 Charlton Street
Princeton, NJ 08540-5232
(609) 683-0800
Fax: (609) 924-0578

E-MAIL ADDRESS:
application@ascsa.org; ascsa@ascsa.org

WEB SITE ADDRESS:
www.ascsa.edu.gr

TYPE:
Fellowships.
See entry 460 for full listing.

AMERICAN SOCIETY OF INTERIOR DESIGNERS EDUCATIONAL FOUNDATION   [440]
608 Massachusetts Avenue, N.E.
Washington, DC 20002-6006
(202) 675-2351
Fax: (202) 546-3240

E-MAIL ADDRESS:
foundation@asid.org

WEB SITE ADDRESS:
www.asidfoundation.org

FOUNDED: 1931

AREAS OF INTEREST:
Interior design (commercial and residential) and interior design-related industry.

NAME(S) OF PROGRAMS:
- **ASID Foundation Legacy Scholarship for Graduate Students**
- **ASID Foundation Legacy Scholarship for Undergraduates**
- **Irene Winifred Eno Grant**
- **Joel Polsky Academic Achievement Award**
- **Joel Polsky Prize**

TYPE:
Awards/prizes; Conferences/seminars; Fellowships; Project/program grants; Research grants; Scholarships; Seed money grants. Irene Winifred Eno Grant provides financial assistance to individuals or groups engaged in the creation of an educational program(s) or an interior design research project dedicated to health, safety and welfare.

The Legacy Scholarship for Graduate Students is awarded on the basis of academic/creative accomplishment.

The Legacy Scholarship for Undergraduates is given to a creatively outstanding student as demonstrated through their portfolio.

The Polsky Academic Achievement Award is given annually to recognize an outstanding undergraduate or graduate student's interior design research or thesis project.

The Joel Polsky Prize recognizes outstanding academic contributions to the discipline of interior design through literature or visual communication.

PURPOSE:
To encourage excellence in the field of interior design.

LEGAL BASIS:
Nonprofit foundation.

ELIGIBILITY:
The Legacy Scholarship for Graduate Students is open to students who are enrolled in or have applied for admission to a graduate-level interior design program at a degree-granting institution.

The Legacy Scholarship for Undergraduates is open to all students in their junior or senior year of undergraduate study and enrolled in at least a three-year program of interior design. The Irene Winifred Eno Grant is open to students, educators, interior design practitioners, institutions or other interior design related groups.

The Joel Polsky Academic Achievement Award judges interior design research or doctoral and Master's thesis projects.

The Joel Polsky Prize entrants should address the needs of the public, designers and students on such topics as educational research, behavioral science, business practice, design process, theory or other technical subjects.

High school students and college freshmen are not eligible.

GEOGRAPHIC RESTRICTIONS:
United States.

FINANCIAL DATA:
Amount of support per award: Irene Winifred Eno Grant: $5,000; Joel Polsky Academic Achievement Award and Joel Polsky Prize: $1,000; Legacy Scholarship for graduate and undergraduate students: $4,000.

APPLICATION INFORMATION:
Complete details available online.
Duration: One-time award.

PUBLICATIONS:
ASID Professional Designer, magazine; *Access*, the student newsletter; application guidelines; Press Releases; Newsflash.

OFFICERS:
Valerie O'Keefe, Foundation Manager

ADDRESS INQUIRIES TO:
Valerie O'Keefe
Foundation Manager
(See address above.)

ARCHITECTURAL LEAGUE OF NEW YORK [441]
594 Broadway, Suite 607
New York, NY 10012
(212) 753-1722
Fax: (212) 486-9173

E-MAIL ADDRESS:
info@archleague.org

WEB SITE ADDRESS:
www.archleague.org

FOUNDED: 1881

AREAS OF INTEREST:
Architecture, architectural history and urban studies.

NAME(S) OF PROGRAMS:
● **Deborah J. Norden Fund**

TYPE:
Research grants; Travel grants. The Deborah J. Norden Fund, established in 1995 in memory of architect and arts administrator Deborah Norden, awards travel/study grants to students and recent graduates in the field of architecture, architectural history, and urban studies.

YEAR PROGRAM STARTED: 1995

PURPOSE:
To support genuinely independent projects that require travel.

ELIGIBILITY:
Students or recent graduates in the fields of architecture, architectural history and urban studies.

The intention of the fund is to support genuinely independent projects. Grant funds cannot be used for tuition or for participation in an organized program, such as a university's summer abroad program.

FINANCIAL DATA:
Amount of support per award: Up to $5,000.
Total amount of support: $5,000.

APPLICATION INFORMATION:
Applicants should submit in letter form, a brief proposal, no more than three pages, which succinctly describes the objectives of the grant request and how it will assist the applicant's intellectual and creative development. The grant amount requested must be specified. The submission should also include a resume of not more than two pages, project schedule, and budget for travel and other project costs. Two letters of recommendation must be requested from individuals who are knowledgeable about the applicant's ability and project. Applicants must submit six copies of their proposal, resume, schedule, and budget. The applicant's name and brief project title must appear on the first page of the proposal.
Deadline: Mid-March. Announcement in April.

ADDRESS INQUIRIES TO:
Rosalie Genevro, Executive Director
(See address above.)

ARCHITECTURAL LEAGUE OF NEW YORK [442]
594 Broadway, Suite 607
New York, NY 10012
(212) 753-1722
Fax: (212) 486-9173

E-MAIL ADDRESS:
info@archleague.org

WEB SITE ADDRESS:
www.archleague.org

AREAS OF INTEREST:
Young architects.

NAME(S) OF PROGRAMS:
● **The League Prize for Young Architects and Designers**

TYPE:
Research grants; Travel grants. A poster of the winning entries will be published and distributed nationally, as will a catalogue of winning work published by the Architectural League and Princeton Architectural Press. An exhibition of the work will be held at the Architectural League each spring.

PURPOSE:
To recognize specific works of high quality and to encourage the exchange of ideas among young architects and designers who might otherwise not have a forum; to focus on the aesthetic, cultural, and social concerns of architecture and the allied arts; to help architects, artists, and the public enrich their understanding of the purposes and importance of the art of architecture.

ELIGIBILITY:
Entrants may submit work done independently, or as an employee, or as a teacher. Entrants must be ten years or less out of graduate or undergraduate school; students are not eligible for this competition. Work completed for fulfillment of course requirements at academic institutions is not eligible.

GEOGRAPHIC RESTRICTIONS:
United States, Canada and Mexico.

FINANCIAL DATA:
Amount of support per award: $1,000.

NUMBER OF AWARDS: 6 per year.

APPLICATION INFORMATION:
A written statement (not to exceed 250 words) is requested, which defines and considers the work under the rubric of the competition theme. Significant weight is given to how an applicant's work addresses the theme. A single portfolio, which may include several projects, must be bound and no larger than 11 x 14 inches. The portfolio may not contain more than 30 double-sided pages. CDs, models, slides and transparencies will not be accepted.

Each submission must include an entry form and $25 entry fee. Insert form, intact, into an unsealed envelope attached to the inside back cover of the submission. To maintain anonymity, no identification of the entrant may appear on any part of the submission, except on the entry form and return envelope.

Portfolios will be returned by mail only if a self-addressed envelope with postage is also enclosed. The Architectural League assumes no liability for original drawings. The League will take every precaution to return submissions intact, but can assume no responsibility for loss or damage. Portfolios may be discarded after six months if no return envelope is provided.

ADDRESS INQUIRIES TO:
Anne Rieselbach, Program Director
(See address above.)

THE COMMUNITY FOUNDATION OF LOUISVILLE, INC.
325 West Main Street, Suite 1110
Louisville, KY 40202
(502) 585-4649
Fax: (502) 587-7484

E-MAIL ADDRESS:
alexs@cflouisville.org

WEB SITE ADDRESS:
www.cflouisville.org

TYPE:
Endowments; Grants-in-aid; Scholarships.

See entry 472 for full listing.

ENTERPRISE COMMUNITY PARTNERS [443]
10227 Wincopin Circle, Suite 500
American City Building
Columbia, MD 21044
(410) 964-1230
(434) 960-2484
Fax: (410) 964-1376

WEB SITE ADDRESS:
www.enterprisecommunity.org

AREAS OF INTEREST:
Architecture and community development.

NAME(S) OF PROGRAMS:
● **Rose Architectural Fellowship**

TYPE:
Fellowships.

YEAR PROGRAM STARTED: 2000

PURPOSE:
To promote architectural and community design in low-income communities and to encourage architects to become lifelong leaders in public service and community development.

ELIGIBILITY:
Applicants must possess a professional Baccalaureate degree in architecture from an

accredited college or university, or expect to graduate from an accredited school of architecture before the Fellowship begins. A professional graduate degree in architecture from an accredited university is preferred. The expected minimum grade point average is "B" or 3.0 on a 4.0 scale for all undergraduate and graduate work.

Applicants with diverse educational, professional, and personal backgrounds are encouraged to apply.

GEOGRAPHIC RESTRICTIONS:
United States.

FINANCIAL DATA:
Compensation is provided to the partner organization to pay for its share of health insurance and payroll taxes which are paid on behalf of the employee.
Amount of support per award: $46,000 annual stipend.
Matching fund requirements: Community based organizations must match Rose Fellowship funds 2:1.

NUMBER OF APPLICANTS MOST RECENT YEAR:
25.

NUMBER OF AWARDS: 3.

ADDRESS INQUIRIES TO:
Katie Swenson
Director, Rose Architectural Fellowship
Tel: (781) 235-4189
(See address above.)

THE JAMES MARSTON FITCH CHARITABLE FOUNDATION [444]
c/o The Neighborhood Preservation Center
232 East 11th Street
New York, NY 10003
(212) 252-6809
Fax: (212) 471-9987

E-MAIL ADDRESS:
info@fitchfoundation.org

WEB SITE ADDRESS:
www.fitchfoundation.org

FOUNDED: 1988

AREAS OF INTEREST:
Architecture, engineering, environmental planning, and historic preservation.

NAME(S) OF PROGRAMS:
• **Richard Blinder Award**
• **Mid-Career Grant**

TYPE:
Research grants. Richard Blinder Award was created to promote studies that explore the architecture of cultural buildings which integrate historic preservation and new construction–past, present and future; presented biennially.

Mid-Career Grant Program: This grant is the primary mission and the signature grant of this Foundation. The grants are intended to support projects of innovative original research or creative design that advance the practice of historic preservation in the U.S.

PURPOSE:
To advance the study and practice of the preservation of the historic architectural heritage of the U.S.; to support preservation through a research grant program as well as through such educational activities as publications, seminars and lectures.

ELIGIBILITY:
Richard Blinder Award proposal must demonstrate that it fosters architectural preservation in the U.S. Applicant must be an architect holding a professional degree or a valid license to practice architecture. Grants are awarded only to individuals, not organizations or university-sponsored research projects. Grants are not awarded for professional fees.

Mid-Career Grant is for college graduates with a postgraduate degree and at least 10 years of professional experience.

GEOGRAPHIC RESTRICTIONS:
United States.

FINANCIAL DATA:
Amount of support per award: Up to $15,000.

NUMBER OF AWARDS: Richard Blinder Award: 1; Mid-Career Grant: 1 to 3.

APPLICATION INFORMATION:
Contact the Foundation for guidelines and application.
Duration: One year.
Deadline: Mid-September.

ADDRESS INQUIRIES TO:
See e-mail address above.

GRAHAM FOUNDATION FOR ADVANCED STUDIES IN THE FINE ARTS [445]
4 West Burton Place
Chicago, IL 60610
(312) 787-4071

E-MAIL ADDRESS:
grantprograms@grahamfoundation.org

WEB SITE ADDRESS:
www.grahamfoundation.org

FOUNDED: 1956

AREAS OF INTEREST:
Architecture and related spatial practices that engage a wide range of cultural, social, political, technological, environmental and aesthetic issues. The Foundation is interested in projects that investigate the contemporary condition, expand historical perspectives, or explore the future of architecture and the designed environment.

NAME(S) OF PROGRAMS:
• **Carter Manny Award**
• **Production and Presentation Grants**
• **Research and Development Grants**

TYPE:
Awards/prizes; Project/program grants; Research grants. Grants to organizations, individuals and public programs.

Carter Manny Award: To support research for academic dissertations by promising scholars who are presently candidates for a doctoral degree, and whose dissertations focus on areas traditionally supported by the Foundation. Students must be nominated by their department to apply for this Award.

Production and Presentation Grants: To assist individuals and organizations with the production-related expenses that are necessary to take a project from conceptualization to realization and public presentation. These projects may include, but are not limited to, publications, exhibitions, installations, conferences, films, new-media projects, and other public programs.

Research and Development Grants: To assist individuals with seed money for research-related expenses such as travel, documentation, materials, supplies and other development costs.

YEAR PROGRAM STARTED: 1956

PURPOSE:
To make project-based grants to individuals and organizations and to produce public programs to foster the development and exchange of diverse and challenging ideas about architecture and its role in the arts, culture and society.

LEGAL BASIS:
Private foundation.

ELIGIBILITY:
Giving in the U.S. and internationally. No grants for endowments, general operating expenses, capital projects, scholarship aid or for work in pursuit of an academic degree (except for the Carter Manny Award), debt or expenses incurred prior to the date of grant request. Both individuals and institutions may apply.

APPLICATION INFORMATION:
Application to the Foundation involves a two-stage process and is open submission.

Stage One/Inquiry Form: Eligible candidates interested in applying for a grant must first submit an Inquiry Form. The Inquiry Form is available on the Foundation web site with each grant cycle and must be submitted online.

Stage Two/Proposal Form: Applicants whose projects best match the Foundation's priorities and interests are invited to submit a Proposal Form and supplementary materials. Applicants not invited to submit a Proposal Form are sent a decline letter at this stage. An invitation to submit a Proposal Form does not guarantee eventual funding.

Award Decision: Funding recommendations are presented to the Board of Trustees for consideration. If a grant is awarded, applicant will be asked to sign a Grant Agreement that outlines the conditions of the award, such as annual reporting. Funding decisions at all stages of the review are based on: Priority of the proposed project as related to the Foundation's mission and interests; the project's fulfillment of the Foundation's criteria for evaluation; availability of Foundation funds.
Duration: Varies.
Deadline: February 25 for organizations; September 15 for individuals.

PUBLICATIONS:
Annual report; guidelines.

OFFICERS:
Sarah Herda, Director
Ellen Hartwell Alderman, Program Coordinator
Maureen Kaucher, Finance and Business Manager
Carolyn T. Kelly, Grants Manager
Sarah Rogers, Communications and Outreach Coordinator
Stephanie Whitlock, Program Officer

TRUSTEES:
Samuel Assefa
Rena Conti
Jeanne Gang
Chandra Goldsmith
Jeffrey Jahns
Sean Keller
Bruce Sagan

Linda Searl
Elizabeth Smith
Hamza Walker
Ross Wimer

ADDRESS INQUIRIES TO:
See e-mail address above.

THE LEF FOUNDATION   [446]
121 Circle Road
San Rafael, CA 94903
(415) 499-9591 (CA)
(617) 492-5333 (New England)
Fax: (617) 868-5603 (New England)

E-MAIL ADDRESS:
marina@lef-foundation.org

WEB SITE ADDRESS:
www.lef-foundation.org

FOUNDED: 1985

AREAS OF INTEREST:
Performing arts, visual arts, architecture and
design, film and video, and intermedia.

NAME(S) OF PROGRAMS:
● **Moving Image Fund**

TYPE:
Awards/prizes; Project/program grants; Seed
money grants. Program development.

PURPOSE:
To support the creation and presentation of
contemporary work.

ELIGIBILITY:
Grants are made to organizations that have
tax-exempt status under Section 501(c)(3) of
the Internal Revenue Code, as well as
individuals with 501(c)(3) fiscal sponsors.

GEOGRAPHIC RESTRICTIONS:
Northern California and New England.

NUMBER OF AWARDS: 300.

APPLICATION INFORMATION:
Application form and guidelines are available
on the Foundation web site.
Duration: Varies.

ADDRESS INQUIRIES TO:
Marina Drummer
Grants Advisor-California
(See address above.)

THE PAUL MELLON CENTRE FOR STUDIES IN BRITISH ART   [447]
16 Bedford Square
London WC1B 3JA England
44 (0) 20 7580 0311
Fax: 44 (0) 20 7636 6730

E-MAIL ADDRESS:
info@paul-mellon-centre.ac.uk

WEB SITE ADDRESS:
www.paul-mellon-centre.ac.uk

FOUNDED: 1970

AREAS OF INTEREST:
British art and architectural history.

NAME(S) OF PROGRAMS:
● **Educational Programme Grants**
● **Junior Fellowships**
● **Paul Mellon Centre Rome Fellowship**
● **Postdoctoral Fellowships**
● **Research Support Grants**
● **Senior Fellowships**

TYPE:
Conferences/seminars; Fellowships;
Project/program grants; Research grants.

Educational Programme Grants for lectures,
symposia, seminars or conferences on British
art and architecture.

The Junior Fellowship is to pursue ongoing
doctoral research at an American or British
university.

The Paul Mellon Centre Rome Fellowship
offers fellowships to scholars working on
Grand Tour subjects or in the field of
Anglo-Italian cultural and artistic relations.

The Postdoctoral Fellowship works to
transform doctoral research into publishable
form such as a book, series of articles, or
exhibition catalogues.

Research Support Grants are for expenses in
pursuit of research.

The Senior Fellowship supports an
established scholar in the field of British art
and architectural history to complete a
manuscript or book for immediate
publication.

YEAR PROGRAM STARTED: 1998

PURPOSE:
To promote scholarship and publications.

LEGAL BASIS:
University-affiliated research center.

ELIGIBILITY:
Candidates for the Junior Fellowship may be
of any nationality but must be enrolled in a
graduate program at an American or other
non-British university for study in the U.K.
or at a non-American university for study in
the U.S.

The Postdoctoral fellowship is awarded
within four years of an applicant's doctoral
award. Applicants must have had their
doctoral theses successfully examined.

Applicants for the Rome Fellowship should,
preferably, be competent in spoken and
written Italian.

FINANCIAL DATA:
Amount of support per award: Varies.

APPLICATION INFORMATION:
Full details and application forms are
available online.
Duration: Junior Fellowship: three months.
Postdoctoral Fellowship: six months. Rome
Fellowship: four months. Senior Fellowship:
12 months.
Deadline: Fellowships: January 15. Grants:
September 15.

ADDRESS INQUIRIES TO:
Grants Administrator
(See address above.)

NATIONAL SOCIETY DAUGHTERS OF THE AMERICAN REVOLUTION   [448]
1776 D Street, N.W.
Washington, DC 20006-5303
(202) 879-3292

WEB SITE ADDRESS:
www.dar.org

FOUNDED: 1895

AREAS OF INTEREST:
Historic preservation.

NAME(S) OF PROGRAMS:
● **J.E. Caldwell Centennial Scholarship**

TYPE:
Scholarships.

YEAR PROGRAM STARTED: 1985

PURPOSE:
To provide ways and means to aid students
in attaining higher education.

LEGAL BASIS:
Incorporated historical society.

ELIGIBILITY:
Applicants must be enrolled in the junior or
senior year of a fully accredited college or
university in the U.S. and pursuing a degree
in the field of historic preservation, may
reside in any state, and must be a U.S.
citizen. All applicants must be sponsored by
a local DAR chapter.

GEOGRAPHIC RESTRICTIONS:
United States.

FINANCIAL DATA:
Amount of support per award: $2,000.

APPLICATION INFORMATION:
To obtain a scholarship application packet,
send a self-addressed, stamped #10
business-size envelope to the Office of the
Reporter General, DAR Scholarship
Committee at the address listed above.

Included with the application packet is the
list of DAR State Scholarship Chairmen. All
scholarship applicants are required to have a
letter of sponsorship from a chapter.
Individuals interested in obtaining a letter of
sponsorship from a local chapter are
encouraged to contact the DAR State
Chairman.
Deadline: February 15.

PUBLICATIONS:
American Spirit, magazine.

ADDRESS INQUIRIES TO:
Office of the Reporter General
DAR Scholarship Committee
(See address above.)

ROTCH TRAVELLING SCHOLARSHIP IN ARCHITECTURE   [449]
c/o Boston Society of Architects
52 Broad Street
Boston, MA 02109
(617) 951-1433
Fax: (617) 951-0845

E-MAIL ADDRESS:
bsa@architects.org

WEB SITE ADDRESS:
www.rotch.org

FOUNDED: 1883

AREAS OF INTEREST:
Architecture.

NAME(S) OF PROGRAMS:
● **Rotch Travelling Scholarship**
● **Rotch Travelling Studio**

TYPE:
Fellowships. Traveling Fellowships. Rotch
Travelling Scholarship awards a minimum of
eight months of foreign travel and study in
the field of architecture and allied subjects.

Rotch Travelling Studio allows faculty to
take architecture students for a one-month
travelling program.

YEAR PROGRAM STARTED: 1883

PURPOSE:
To provide young architects with the
opportunity to gain experience with other
cultures; to augment the architectural

education of students of architecture at the highest level of scholarship within a studio format.

LEGAL BASIS:
Private trust.

ELIGIBILITY:
Rotch Travelling Scholarship: Applicants must be U.S. citizens no more than 35 years of age who have a degree from an accredited school of architecture plus at least one year of experience in an architectural office in Massachusetts, or a degree from an accredited Massachusetts school of architecture and one year of experience in an architectural office not necessarily in Massachusetts.

Rotch Travelling Studio: Applicants are invited from faculty members in all NAAB accredited schools of architecture in the U.S. for travel anywhere in the world during the following calendar year.

GEOGRAPHIC RESTRICTIONS:
United States.

FINANCIAL DATA:
Amount of support per award: Travelling Scholarship: $35,000 up; Travelling Studio: $20,000.

APPLICATION INFORMATION:
Official application forms are available online.
Duration: Travelling Scholarship: Minimum eight months; Travelling Studio: One month.
Deadline: Travelling Scholarship: January; Travelling Studio: October.

TRUSTEES:
Robert Holoway, President
Steven Foote, Vice President
Doug Burden, Treasurer
Peter Weiderspahn, Secretary

*SPECIAL STIPULATIONS:
No Rotch scholar may hold simultaneously another travelling scholarship, nor may he or she be employed during the period of the scholarship without special permission.

ROYAL INSTITUTE OF BRITISH ARCHITECTS   [450]
RIBA Research Trusts
Education Department
66 Portland Place
London W1B 1AD England
44 (0) 20 7580 5533
Fax: 44 (0) 20 7307 3754

E-MAIL ADDRESS:
education@inst.riba.org

WEB SITE ADDRESS:
www.architecture.com

FOUNDED: 1834

AREAS OF INTEREST:
Architecture, and the arts and sciences connected therewith, in the U.K.

NAME(S) OF PROGRAMS:
● **RIBA Research Trusts Awards**

TYPE:
Research grants. Merit-based award to support recent architecture graduates who are pursuing research in the field of architecture.

PURPOSE:
To support recent graduates, whether or not they are graduates from an RIBA-validated course of architectural studies, who are pursuing an area of study in modern

architecture, town planning or historical research to develop their interest and abilities as researchers.

ELIGIBILITY:
Open to applicants interested in a wide range of subject matter relevant to the advancement of architecture, and the arts and sciences connected therewith, in the U.K. Non-architects and overseas applications will be considered. Applications from outside of the U.K. must be for research mainly undertaken within the U.K. The supervisor must be domiciled in the U.K. Project proposals where research is carried out outside the U.K. will be accepted only in exceptional circumstances.

GEOGRAPHIC RESTRICTIONS:
United Kingdom.

FINANCIAL DATA:
The value of an award will be determined by the estimated requirements of the project.
Amount of support per award: Maximum award not to exceed GBP 7,500.

COOPERATIVE FUNDING PROGRAMS: A candidate may have funding from other sources.

NUMBER OF AWARDS: Up to 4.

APPLICATION INFORMATION:
All applications must be made on the application forms available from the above address. Applications for up to GBP 7,500 will be considered.
Duration: Up to two years.
Deadline: Varies.

OFFICER:
Harry Rich, Chief Executive

ADDRESS INQUIRIES TO:
RIBA Education Projects
(See address above.)
E-mail: joanna.scott@inst.riba.org

SIR JOHN SOANE MUSEUM FOUNDATION   [451]
1040 First Avenue, Suite 311
New York, NY 10022
(212) 223-2012
Fax: (860) 435-8019

E-MAIL ADDRESS:
info@soanefoundation.com

WEB SITE ADDRESS:
www.soanefoundation.com

AREAS OF INTEREST:
Education of the public in architecture and the fine and decorative arts.

NAME(S) OF PROGRAMS:
● **Sir John Soane Museum Foundation Traveling Fellowship**

TYPE:
Fellowships. Designed to help graduate students and scholars pursue research projects related to the work of Sir John Soane's Museum and its collections.

PURPOSE:
To educate and inspire the general and professional public in architecture and the fine and decorative arts.

ELIGIBILITY:
Applicants must be enrolled in a graduate degree program in a field appropriate to the Foundation's purpose. Level of study is postgraduate.

FINANCIAL DATA:
Amount of support per award: $5,000.

NUMBER OF APPLICANTS MOST RECENT YEAR: 16.

NUMBER OF AWARDS: 1.

APPLICATION INFORMATION:
Applicants must submit a formal proposal of not more than one page describing the goal, scope and purpose of the research project, in addition to three letters of recommendation.
Duration: One year.
Deadline: March 1.

ADDRESS INQUIRIES TO:
Chas Miller, Executive Director
(See address above.)

SOCIETY OF ARCHITECTURAL HISTORIANS   [452]
1365 North Astor Street
Chicago, IL 60610-2144
(312) 573-1365
Fax: (312) 573-1141

E-MAIL ADDRESS:
beifrig@sah.org

WEB SITE ADDRESS:
www.sah.org

FOUNDED: 1940

AREAS OF INTEREST:
Architecture and its related arts.

NAME(S) OF PROGRAMS:
● **Sally Kress Tompkins Fellowship**

TYPE:
Fellowships; Internships; Travel grants. The Sally Kress Tompkins Fellowship, a joint program of the Society of Architectural Historians and the National Park Service's Historic American Buildings Survey, permits an architectural historian to work on a 12-week project during the summer. The Fellow will prepare a written history to become part of the permanent collection focusing on either a specific nationally significant building/site, or a broader architectural history topic. The Fellow will be stationed in the field working in conjunction with a measured drawings team, or in the Washington, DC office. The Fellow will be selected by a jury of two SAH members and one HABS representative.

PURPOSE:
To advance the knowledge and understanding of architecture, design, landscape and urbanism worldwide.

LEGAL BASIS:
Nonprofit professional organization.

ELIGIBILITY:
Graduate students and member of SAH.

FINANCIAL DATA:
Amount of support per award: $500 to $9,200.
Total amount of support: $10,000.

COOPERATIVE FUNDING PROGRAMS: National Park Service's Historic American Buildings Survey (HABS).

NUMBER OF APPLICANTS MOST RECENT YEAR: 5.

NUMBER OF AWARDS: 1.

APPLICATION INFORMATION:
Details are available online, for members.
Duration: One year.

PUBLICATIONS:
Newsletter; *Journal of the Society of Architectural Historians.*

ADDRESS INQUIRIES TO:
Beth Eifrig, Administrative Assistant to
Director of Programs
(See address above.)

THE SOCIETY OF NAVAL ARCHITECTS AND MARINE ENGINEERS

601 Pavonia Avenue, Suite 400
Jersey City, NJ 07306
(201) 499-5056
Fax: (201) 798-4975

E-MAIL ADDRESS:
efaustino@sname.org

WEB SITE ADDRESS:
www.sname.org

TYPE:
Scholarships. The Society annually awards
both graduate and undergraduate scholarships
to encourage study in naval architecture,
marine engineering, ocean engineering or
marine industry-related fields.

Graduate Scholarships are made for one year
of study leading to a Master's in naval
architecture, marine engineering, ocean
engineering or in fields directly related to the
marine industry.

Undergraduate Scholarships are administered
by schools offering undergraduate programs
on grants given to the schools.

See entry 2829 for full listing.

VIRGINIA POLYTECHNIC INSTITUTE AND STATE UNIVERSITY

MAOP Office
110 Femoyer Hall
Blacksburg, VA 24061
(540) 231-5023
Fax: (540) 231-2618

E-MAIL ADDRESS:
maop@vt.edu

WEB SITE ADDRESS:
www.maop.vt.edu

TYPE:
Assistantships; Fellowships; Internships;
Scholarships. The program assists with
graduate school financing in exchange for
assistance to MAOP administration. Graduate
students assist with programming
implementation such as mentoring to
undergraduate students.

See entry 1086 for full listing.

WASHINGTON UNIVERSITY   [453]

School of Architecture
Campus Box 1079
One Brookings Drive
St. Louis, MO 63130-4899
(314) 935-6200
Fax: (314) 935-7656

WEB SITE ADDRESS:
www.steedmancompetition.com

FOUNDED: 1925

AREAS OF INTEREST:
Architectural education.

NAME(S) OF PROGRAMS:
● **James Harrison Steedman Memorial
Fellowship in Architecture**

TYPE:
Awards/prizes; Fellowships; Travel grants. An
award made on the basis of a design
competition that requires the recipient to
travel and study abroad for nine months. Not
to be used towards tuition.

YEAR PROGRAM STARTED: 1925

PURPOSE:
To assist well-qualified architectural
graduates to benefit by travel and study of
architecture in foreign countries.

ELIGIBILITY:
Open to graduates of an accredited school of
architecture, regardless of age, for a period
up to eight years after the receipt of their
first professional degree. Candidates must
have at least one year of practical experience
in the office of a practicing architect. Citizens
of all countries are eligible.

FINANCIAL DATA:
Amount of support per award: $30,000
stipend for nine months of travel abroad.
Total amount of support: $30,000.

NUMBER OF APPLICANTS MOST RECENT YEAR:
125.

NUMBER OF AWARDS: 1 awarded biennially.

APPLICATION INFORMATION:
Registration forms are available online.
Applications are available in late October
every odd year and fellowships are awarded
in the spring every even year.
Duration: Nine months.

PUBLICATIONS:
Application guidelines.

GOVERNING BOARD:
William Wischmeyer

ADDRESS INQUIRIES TO:
Executive Director
Steedman Governing Committee
(See address above.)

Arts (multiple disciplines)

ACADEMY FOUNDATION OF THE ACADEMY OF MOTION PICTURE ARTS AND SCIENCES

8949 Wilshire Boulevard
Beverly Hills, CA 90211-1972
(310) 247-3000 ext. 131
Fax: (310) 859-9619

E-MAIL ADDRESS:
rmiller@oscars.org

WEB SITE ADDRESS:
www.oscars.org

TYPE:
Awards/prizes.

See entry 576 for full listing.

ALABAMA STATE COUNCIL ON THE ARTS   [454]

201 Monroe Street
Montgomery, AL 36104
(334) 242-4076
Fax: (334) 240-3269

E-MAIL ADDRESS:
staff@arts.alabama.gov

WEB SITE ADDRESS:
www.arts.alabama.gov

FOUNDED: 1966

AREAS OF INTEREST:
Architecture, literature, fine arts, arts in
education, museums and libraries, music, and
creative and performing arts.

CONSULTING OR VOLUNTEER SERVICES:
Strengthens cultural activities already in
existence, assists in formation of new cultural
activities, works towards improving the
quality of presentations by both professional
and amateur organizations and offers
assistance to culturally oriented groups.

NAME(S) OF PROGRAMS:
● **Arts-in-Education**
● **Community Arts Development**
● **Cultural Facilities**
● **Folk Arts**
● **Literary Art**
● **Performing Arts**
● **Visual Arts and Crafts**

TYPE:
Awards/prizes; Challenge/matching grants;
Conferences/seminars; Development grants;
Fellowships; General operating grants;
Internships; Project/program grants;
Residencies; Technical assistance. Grants to
various disciplines comprising technical and
financial assistance to local organizations in
sponsoring activities of quality and promise
in the various arts disciplines of the visual
and performing arts within communities
throughout Alabama.

YEAR PROGRAM STARTED: 1967

PURPOSE:
To increase interest, participation and support
in the arts by supplementing local initiatives
and local funds in order to enable a greater
number of quality activities to be seen or
heard throughout the state.

LEGAL BASIS:
Alabama Law, Act No. 551, Regular Session
1967 and Act No. 1065, Regular Session,
1969.

ELIGIBILITY:
Applicants must be qualified organizations
sponsoring arts events or programs for
communities. Such groups include local arts
councils, arts associations, museums, literary
associations, colleges and universities, dance
and theatre groups. Evidence of nonprofit
status is required.

GEOGRAPHIC RESTRICTIONS:
Alabama.

FINANCIAL DATA:
Amount of support per award: $500 to
$300,000.
Total amount of support: $5,500,000 for the
year ended September 30, 2009.
Matching fund requirements: Equal amounts
from other sources with exception of Artists
Fellowships.

APPLICATION INFORMATION:
A special application form can be obtained
and submitted by using the Council eGRANT
system which is available on their web site.
Duration: One year. Renewal by
reapplication.
Deadline: March 1, June 1 and September 1.

PUBLICATIONS:
Guide to Programs; *Alabama Arts*, magazine;
Touring & Presenting Guide.

IRS IDENTIFICATION NUMBER: 63-6000619

EXECUTIVE COUNCIL:
Julie Hall Friedman, Chairman

Jim Harrison, III, Vice Chairman
Dora Hanson James, Secretary

ADDRESS INQUIRIES TO:
Albert B. Head, Executive Director
(See address above.)

ALASKA STATE COUNCIL ON THE ARTS   [455]

161 Klevin Street
Suite 102
Anchorage, AK 99508-1508
(907) 269-6610
Fax: (907) 269-6601

E-MAIL ADDRESS:
charlotte.fox@alaska.gov

WEB SITE ADDRESS:
www.eed.state.ak.us/aksca

FOUNDED: 1966

AREAS OF INTEREST:
Alaska native arts, visual, literary and
performing arts.

CONSULTING OR VOLUNTEER SERVICES:
Technical assistance for grantees.

TYPE:
Conferences/seminars; General operating
grants; Project/program grants; Residencies;
Technical assistance; Travel grants. Services
provided to arts organizations and individual
artists statewide. Also, workshop grants and
Master Artist/Apprentice grants.

Eight specific grant categories, responding to
a variety of arts needs, are available to
Alaskan nonprofit arts organizations and
qualified individual artists.

YEAR PROGRAM STARTED: 1966

PURPOSE:
To promote general support of the arts in
Alaska.

LEGAL BASIS:
State agency.

ELIGIBILITY:
Grant applicants must be Alaskan nonprofit
organizations or individuals.

GEOGRAPHIC RESTRICTIONS:
Alaska.

FINANCIAL DATA:
Amount of support per award: Varies
according to program.
Total amount of support: $600,000 total
grants budget.
Matching fund requirements: All
organizational grants require at least 1:1
match (cash).

APPLICATION INFORMATION:
Specific guidelines and applications are
available online.
Duration: One year.
Deadline: Varies according to program.

PUBLICATIONS:
Annual report; individual grant program
guidelines.

STAFF:
Charlotte Fox, Executive Director
Andrea Noble-Pelant, Grants Administrator

ADDRESS INQUIRIES TO:
Charlotte Fox, Executive Director
(See address above.)

THE ALLIANCE FOR YOUNG ARTISTS & WRITERS   [456]

557 Broadway, 2nd Floor
New York, NY 10012
(212) 343-7717
Fax: (212) 389-3939

E-MAIL ADDRESS:
vmatthews@scholastic.com

WEB SITE ADDRESS:
www.artandwriting.org

FOUNDED: 1923

AREAS OF INTEREST:
Art and writing.

NAME(S) OF PROGRAMS:
● **The Scholastic Art and Writing
   Awards**

TYPE:
Awards/prizes; Scholarships. Scholarship
grants offered through Scholastic Awards
programs to college-bound high school
seniors demonstrating outstanding creative
ability.

YEAR PROGRAM STARTED: 1923

PURPOSE:
To provide guidance and support for the next
generation of artists and writers and reward
outstanding achievement in the creative arts.

LEGAL BASIS:
Nonprofit.

ELIGIBILITY:
Individual awards are offered for students in
grades 7-12. Scholarships are offered for
seniors submitting portfolios.

GEOGRAPHIC RESTRICTIONS:
United States and Canada.

FINANCIAL DATA:
Scholarship recipients are additionally
eligible for school-specific, tuition
scholarships at more than 50 colleges.
Amount of support per award: $10,000.
Total amount of support: Varies.

NUMBER OF APPLICANTS MOST RECENT YEAR:
50,075.

NUMBER OF AWARDS: 15.

APPLICATION INFORMATION:
Duration: One year.
Deadline: January.

IRS IDENTIFICATION NUMBER: 13-3780998

ADDRESS INQUIRIES TO:
Venas Matthews
Senior Manager of External Relations
(See address above.)

AMERICA-ISRAEL CULTURAL FOUNDATION

20 East 46th Street, 15th Floor
New York, NY 10017
(212) 557-1600
Fax: (212) 557-1611

E-MAIL ADDRESS:
info@aicf.org

WEB SITE ADDRESS:
www.aicf.org

TYPE:
Awards/prizes; Endowments; Fellowships;
Project/program grants; Scholarships. For
study in the arts of music, painting and

sculpture, dance and drama, film and
television, to be pursued either in Israel or in
other countries.
See entry 1006 for full listing.

THE AMERICAN CERAMIC SOCIETY   [457]

600 North Cleveland Avenue, Suite 210
Westerville, OH 43082
(614) 890-4700
Fax: (614) 794-5882

E-MAIL ADDRESS:
tnicol@ceramics.org

WEB SITE ADDRESS:
www.ceramics.org

FOUNDED: 1898

AREAS OF INTEREST:
Ceramic education and glass.

NAME(S) OF PROGRAMS:
● **Graduate Student Poster Contest**
● **Outstanding Educator Award**
● **Student Speaking Contest**
● **Undergraduate Student Poster Contest**

TYPE:
Awards/prizes.

PURPOSE:
To promote and encourage materials science
and engineering studies in the discipline of
glass and ceramics.

FINANCIAL DATA:
Amount of support per award: Varies.
Total amount of support: $2,000 for the year
2010.

ADDRESS INQUIRIES TO:
Tricia Nicol, Membership Services Manager
(See address and e-mail above.)

AMERICAN CUSTOM GUNMAKERS GUILD EDUCATION FOUNDATION [458]

22 Vista View Lane
Cody, WY 82414-9606
(307) 587-4297
Fax: (307) 587-4297

E-MAIL ADDRESS:
foundation@acgg.org

WEB SITE ADDRESS:
www.acgg.org/foundation

FOUNDED: 2006

AREAS OF INTEREST:
Custom gunmaking and gunsmithing.

NAME(S) OF PROGRAMS:
● **Gunsmithing Student Grant-in-Aid**
● **Trinidad State Gunsmithing
   Scholarship**

TYPE:
Conferences/seminars; Grants-in-aid.

PURPOSE:
To further the education and development of
gunmakers.

LEGAL BASIS:
501(c)(3).

ELIGIBILITY:
Open to applicants that are gunsmithing
students. Grant is to help attend association
annual seminars and exhibition of work.

FINANCIAL DATA:
Amount of support per award: Gunsmithing
Student Grant-in-Aid: $500; Trinidad State
Gunsmithing Scholarship: $300.

Total amount of support: Gunsmithing
Student Grant-in-Aid: $2,000; Trinidad State
Gunsmithing Scholarship: $600.

NUMBER OF AWARDS: Gunsmithing Student
Grant-in-Aid: 4; Trinidad State Gunsmithing
Scholarship: 2.

APPLICATION INFORMATION:
Completed Grant-in-Aid application must be
submitted to the applicant's sponsor. At least
one gunsmithing faculty sponsor is required.
Additional sponsors are encouraged and can
represent anyone especially knowledgeable
about the applicant's interests and abilities.
Student form and sponsor forms can be
submitted together or separately.

Deadline: Gunsmithing Student Grant-in-Aid:
October 1; Trinidad State Gunsmithing
Scholarship: June 1.

PUBLICATIONS:
Gunmaker: Journal of Fine Gunmaking.

ADDRESS INQUIRIES TO:
Jan Billeb, Executive Director
(See address above.)

AMERICAN FIDELITY
FOUNDATION   [459]
2000 North Classen, Suite 7N
Oklahoma City, OK 73106
(405) 523-5111
Fax: (405) 523-5421

WEB SITE ADDRESS:
americanfidelityfoundation.org

AREAS OF INTEREST:
Education, arts, culture, health and human
services, and civic and economic
development.

TYPE:
Endowments; General operating grants;
Research grants. Employment Matching
Gifts.

ELIGIBILITY:
Organizations with 501(c)(3) status.

GEOGRAPHIC RESTRICTIONS:
Oklahoma County, Oklahoma.

FINANCIAL DATA:
Amount of support per award: Grants to a
single charity are typically $500 to $5,000.
Total amount of support: Varies.

APPLICATION INFORMATION:
Organizations that wish to be considered for
a grant are asked to submit a letter of
interest. If the Foundation chooses to pursue
the project or program described, a formal
application will be sent for completion to the
organization within two weeks.

ADDRESS INQUIRIES TO:
Jo Ella Ramsey, Administrator
(See address above.)

THE AMERICAN SCHOOL OF
CLASSICAL STUDIES AT
ATHENS   [460]
6-8 Charlton Street
Princeton, NJ 08540-5232
(609) 683-0800
Fax: (609) 924-0578

E-MAIL ADDRESS:
application@ascsa.org; ascsa@ascsa.org

WEB SITE ADDRESS:
www.ascsa.edu.gr

FOUNDED: 1881

AREAS OF INTEREST:
Financial support for individuals involved in
research.

NAME(S) OF PROGRAMS:
● **CAORC Multi-Country Research
Fellowships**

TYPE:
Fellowships.

PURPOSE:
To provide support for individuals whose
research has regional significance and
requires travel to multiple countries, at least
one of which hosts an American overseas
research center such as the American School.

ELIGIBILITY:
Fellowship is limited to U.S. citizens. Open
to Ph.D. candidates and postdoctoral scholars
at all levels with research requiring travel to
several countries with an American overseas
research center. Master's degree candidates
must meet membership eligibility
requirements of the American School.

FINANCIAL DATA:
School fees are to be paid out of the
fellowship stipend by the recipient.
Fellowship does not include travel costs,
housing, board, and other living expenses.

Amount of support per award: Doctoral
candidates/postdoctoral scholars: $12,000 for
all centers; Master's students: $8,000.

COOPERATIVE FUNDING PROGRAMS: Fellowships
for Multi-Country Research are funded by
the Bureau of Educational and Cultural
Affairs of the U.S. Department of State
through a grant to the Council of American
Overseas Research Centers.

APPLICATION INFORMATION:
Guidelines for applying is available on the
web site.

Duration: Doctoral and postdoctoral scholars:
Minimum of 90 days; Master's students:
Minimum of 60 days.

Deadline: January 12. Awards announced on
April 15.

STAFF:
Jack Davis, Director

ADDRESS INQUIRIES TO:
Committee Chair
(See address above.)

*SPECIAL STIPULATIONS:
Research and reporting must be completed by
October 31, 2012. Recipients may not hold
any other federally funded grant at the same
time, such as a Fulbright or NEH Fellowship.

A final report is due at the end of the award
period, and the ASCSA expects that copies
of all publications that result from research
conducted as a Fellow of the ASCSA be
contributed to the relevant library of the
School.

ARIZONA COMMISSION ON
THE ARTS   [461]
417 West Roosevelt Street
Phoenix, AZ 85003
(602) 771-6501
Fax: (602) 256-0282

E-MAIL ADDRESS:
info@azarts.gov

WEB SITE ADDRESS:
www.azarts.gov

FOUNDED: 1967

AREAS OF INTEREST:
Performing arts, visual arts and literary arts.

TYPE:
Capital grants; Challenge/matching grants;
Conferences/seminars; Demonstration grants;
Development grants; Formula grants; General
operating grants; Grants-in-aid; Internships;
Project/program grants; Research grants;
Residencies; Technical assistance; Training
grants; Travel grants; Visiting scholars.
Specialized library services to artists and arts
organizations.

YEAR PROGRAM STARTED: 1967

PURPOSE:
To stimulate and encourage public interest in
the arts. Dedicated to making quality arts
opportunities available to its citizens, the Arts
Commission takes a leadership role in
broadening the support systems for the arts
and demonstrating how the arts are integral
to the vitality of our communities and
citizens.

Commission goals are to increase
opportunities for all residents of Arizona to
experience the arts; assist individual artists
and arts organizations in Arizona; stimulate
support and visibility for the arts in Arizona;
foster the preservation, promotion and
availability of Arizona's diverse ethnic arts;
make the arts fundamental to education.

LEGAL BASIS:
State agency.

GEOGRAPHIC RESTRICTIONS:
Arizona.

FINANCIAL DATA:
Amount of support per award: Varies.
Total amount of support: Varies.

APPLICATION INFORMATION:
Call for application or download from web
site.
Duration: Varies.
Deadline: Varies.

PUBLICATIONS:
Annual report; guide to programs for arts
organizations and schools; artist guide to
programs.

ADDRESS INQUIRIES TO:
Robert C. Booker, Executive Director
(See address above.)

ARTS COUNCIL SILICON
VALLEY   [462]
4 North Second Street
Suite 500
San Jose, CA 95113-1305
(408) 998-2787
Fax: (408) 971-9458

E-MAIL ADDRESS:
djones@artscouncil.org

WEB SITE ADDRESS:
www.artscouncil.org

FOUNDED: 1982

AREAS OF INTEREST:
Arts organizations, individual artists and
community arts.

NAME(S) OF PROGRAMS:
● **AEG Grants Program**
● **Applied Materials Excellence in the
Arts**
● **Artist Fellowships**
● **Community Arts Fund**
● **Regional Arts Fund**

TYPE:
Awards/prizes; Conferences/seminars; Fellowships; General operating grants; Project/program grants; Residencies; Technical assistance. The AEG Grants Program provides support for artists and arts organizations to provide arts immersion activities for pre-schoolers and their families.

Artist Fellowships provide awards to recognize the accomplishments of individual artists.

The Community Arts Fund provides funding for community arts activities reflective of our multicultural region, with emphasis on encouraging community-based, volunteer-driven organizations.

The Regional Arts Fund provides funding for the organizational and artistic development of arts organizations, with emphasis on support for mid-sized professional and semi-professional groups.

LEGAL BASIS:
Private, nonprofit arts council.

GEOGRAPHIC RESTRICTIONS:
Santa Clara County, California.

FINANCIAL DATA:
Amount of support per award: AEG Grants Program: $5,000 to $10,000; Applied Materials Excellence in the Arts: $2,500 to $5,000; Artist Fellowships: $4,000; Community Arts Fund: Up to $4,000; Regional Arts Fund: $5,500 to $10,000.
Total amount of support: $562,897 for fiscal year 2009-10.

COOPERATIVE FUNDING PROGRAMS: Applied Materials Excellence in the Arts.

NUMBER OF APPLICANTS MOST RECENT YEAR:
225 for the year 2009-10.

NUMBER OF AWARDS: AEG Grants: 10; Applied Materials Excellence in the Arts: 30; Artist Fellowships: 6; Community Arts: 41; Regional Arts: 35.

PUBLICATIONS:
Annual report.

IRS IDENTIFICATION NUMBER: 94-2825213

ADDRESS INQUIRIES TO:
Diem Jones, Deputy Director
(See address above.)

ASIAN AMERICAN ARTS ALLIANCE   [463]
20 Jay Street, Suite 740
Brooklyn, NY 11201
(212) 941-9208
Fax: (212) 366-1778

E-MAIL ADDRESS:
a4@aaartsalliance.org

WEB SITE ADDRESS:
www.aaartsalliance.org

FOUNDED: 1983

AREAS OF INTEREST:
Art and artists.

TYPE:
Internships.

YEAR PROGRAM STARTED: 1983

PURPOSE:
To increase access, visibility and financial support for the Asian American community's rich and diverse cultural contributions to American society.

LEGAL BASIS:
Nonprofit organization.

ELIGIBILITY:
Individuals interested in Asian-American issues and the nonprofit world may apply.

APPLICATION INFORMATION:
Guidelines and application form is available on the web site.
Duration: One semester. Renewable.

STAFF:
Andrea Louie, Executive Director
Nico Daswani, Program Director
Mariko Masaoka-Drew, Programs and Communication Associate

ADDRESS INQUIRIES TO:
Mariko Masaoka-Drew
Programs and Communication Associate
(See address above.)

*PLEASE NOTE:
Internship takes place in New York City.

ASIAN CULTURAL COUNCIL   [464]
6 West 48th Street, 12th Floor
New York, NY 10036-1802
(212) 843-0403
Fax: (212) 843-0343

E-MAIL ADDRESS:
acc@accny.org

WEB SITE ADDRESS:
www.asianculturalcouncil.org

FOUNDED: 1980

AREAS OF INTEREST:
Visual and performing arts of Asia.

TYPE:
Exchange programs; Fellowships; Project/program grants; Research grants; Residencies; Travel grants; Visiting scholars. Support of cultural exchange in the visual and performing arts between the U.S. and those countries of Asia extending from Afghanistan through Japan.

YEAR PROGRAM STARTED: 1980

LEGAL BASIS:
Public foundation organized under Section 501(c)(3).

ELIGIBILITY:
Applicants must be individuals or institutions involved in projects related to the Council's interests and should write to inquire about specific requirements.

GEOGRAPHIC RESTRICTIONS:
East and Southeast Asia.

FINANCIAL DATA:
The Asian Cultural Council's grant programs are supported by endowment income and annual contributions from foundations, corporations, and individuals in the U.S. and Asia. Levels of grant activity are based on financial resources available.
Amount of support per award: Varies.
Total amount of support: Varies.

APPLICATION INFORMATION:
Grant applicants must first submit the appropriate online Individual or Organization Inquiry form.
Duration: Three months to one year. Renewals are rare.
Deadline: Letter of Inquiry: September 15; Full application: November 15 (postmarked).

PUBLICATIONS:
Annual report; application guidelines.

IRS IDENTIFICATION NUMBER: 13-3018822

OFFICERS:
Elizabeth J. McCormack, Chairman
Valerie Rockefeller Wayne, Vice Chairman
Richard S. Lanier, President
Stephen B. Heintz, Vice President
Pauline R. Yu, Secretary

TRUSTEES:
John H. Foster
Kenneth H. C. Fung
Douglas Tong Hsu
Hans Michael Jebsen
J. Christopher Kojima
Erh-fei Liu
Josie Cruz Natori
Abby M. O'Neill
Russell A. Phillips, Jr.
David Rockefeller, Jr.
Isaac Shapiro
Michael I. Sovern
Seiji Tsutsumi

ASTRAEA LESBIAN FOUNDATION FOR JUSTICE
116 East 16th Street, 7th Floor
New York, NY 10003
(212) 529-8021
Fax: (212) 982-3321

E-MAIL ADDRESS:
grants@astraeafoundation.org

WEB SITE ADDRESS:
www.astraeafoundation.org

TYPE:
Awards/prizes.
See entry 1033 for full listing.

THE WILLIAM G. BAKER, JR. MEMORIAL FUND   [465]
2 East Read Street, Ninth Floor
Baltimore, MD 21202
(410) 332-4171
Fax: (410) 837-4701

E-MAIL ADDRESS:
mwarlow@bakerfund.org

WEB SITE ADDRESS:
www.bcf.org

FOUNDED: 1964

AREAS OF INTEREST:
Arts and culture.

TYPE:
Project/program grants.

YEAR PROGRAM STARTED: 1964

PURPOSE:
To improve the quality of life in the Greater Baltimore area.

LEGAL BASIS:
Private, nonprofit foundation.

ELIGIBILITY:
Cultural organizations (or their fiscal agents) serving the Baltimore area that qualify as public charities under Section 501(c)(3) of the Internal Revenue Code.

The fund does not normally make grants to annual appeals, event sponsorships or services outside the greater Baltimore area.

GEOGRAPHIC RESTRICTIONS:
Greater Baltimore area.

FINANCIAL DATA:
Amount of support per award: $2,500 to $50,000.

Total amount of support: $932,546 for the year 2010.

NUMBER OF APPLICANTS MOST RECENT YEAR: Over 50.

NUMBER OF AWARDS: 40 for the year 2010.

APPLICATION INFORMATION:
Applicants must complete the online application and evaluation chart. Maryland Cultural Data Project data profile is required.
Duration: Varies.
Deadline: Varies.

IRS IDENTIFICATION NUMBER: 52-6057178

GOVERNING BOARD:
Connie E. Imboden, Chairperson
Louis R. Cestello
Gwen Davidson
Steven G. Ziger

ADDRESS INQUIRIES TO:
Melissa Warlow, Executive Director
(See address above.)

BATON ROUGE AREA FOUNDATION [466]
402 North Fourth Street
Baton Rouge, LA 70802
(225) 387-6126
Fax: (225) 387-6153

E-MAIL ADDRESS:
ghobdy@braf.org

WEB SITE ADDRESS:
www.braf.org

AREAS OF INTEREST:
Arts, cultural programs, education, community development, human services, environment, scholarships, medical and health.

TYPE:
Capital grants; Challenge/matching grants; Conferences/seminars; Demonstration grants; Development grants; Matching gifts; Project/program grants; Scholarships; Seed money grants; Technical assistance; Training grants; Visiting scholars.

PURPOSE:
To connect philanthropists with capable nonprofits to make sure the needs of the community are met; to invest in and manage pivotal projects that can change the community.

ELIGIBILITY:
Eligible organizations must be IRS 501(c)(3) tax-exempt.

GEOGRAPHIC RESTRICTIONS:
Baton Rouge area, Louisiana.

FINANCIAL DATA:
Amount of support per award: Varies.
Total amount of support: Varies.

APPLICATION INFORMATION:
Application details are available online. All applications must include a copy of the IRS tax determination letter.
Duration: One year. Must reapply for additional funding.

ADDRESS INQUIRIES TO:
Gerri Hobdy, Director of Grantmaking
(See address above.)

CALIFORNIA ARTS COUNCIL [467]
1300 I Street, Suite 930
Sacramento, CA 95814
(916) 322-6555
(800) 201-6201
Fax: (916) 322-6575

E-MAIL ADDRESS:
mbarber@cac.ca.gov

WEB SITE ADDRESS:
www.cac.ca.gov

FOUNDED: 1976

AREAS OF INTEREST:
Operating and creative support to art organizations, artists, visual and performing arts programs in schools and after-school programs.

CONSULTING OR VOLUNTEER SERVICES:
Sponsor conferences and technical assistance to art organizations.

NAME(S) OF PROGRAMS:
- **Artists in Schools**
- **Creating Public Value**
- **State-Local Partnership Program in the Arts**
- **Statewide Service Networks in the Arts**

TYPE:
Challenge/matching grants; General operating grants; Project/program grants.

YEAR PROGRAM STARTED: 1976

PURPOSE:
To advance California in the arts and creativity.

LEGAL BASIS:
State arts agency, funded by state budget and other sources.

ELIGIBILITY:
To be eligible for funding, a California-based group or organization should be an incorporated nonprofit and have been in existence at least two years and be able to demonstrate fiscal and managerial responsibility. Grants are given to provide in-school and after-school arts educational activities, assistance for specific artistic services such as events, exhibitions and publications, to expand participation by segments of the public who have had limited access to cultural events, and to encourage and enhance communication among artists, organizations and the general public.

GEOGRAPHIC RESTRICTIONS:
California.

FINANCIAL DATA:
Amount of support per award: Varies according to program.
Total amount of support: Varies.

NUMBER OF APPLICANTS MOST RECENT YEAR: 300.

NUMBER OF AWARDS: Approximately 200.

APPLICATION INFORMATION:
Duration: Six months to one year.
Deadline: Varies according to program.

PUBLICATIONS:
Guide to programs; applications; newsletters.

COUNCIL MEMBERS:
Malissa Feruzzi Schriver, Chairperson
Marilyn Nielsen, Interim Director
Wylie Aitken
Michael Alexander
Andrew Green
Adam Hubbard

Charmaine Jefferson
Terry Lenihan
Karen Skelton
Susan Steinhauser
William Turner

ADDRESS INQUIRIES TO:
Mary Beth Barber, Information Officer
(See address above.)

CANADA COUNCIL FOR THE ARTS [468]
350 Albert Street
Ottawa ON K1P 5V8 Canada
(800) 263-5588 ext. 5060 (CAN only)
(613) 566-4414 ext. 5060
Fax: (613) 566-4390
TTY: (866) 585-5559

E-MAIL ADDRESS:
info@canadacouncil.ca

WEB SITE ADDRESS:
www.canadacouncil.ca/grants

FOUNDED: 1957

AREAS OF INTEREST:
The arts in Canada (dance, music, inter-arts, theatre, visual arts, media arts, creative writing and publishing).

NAME(S) OF PROGRAMS:
- **Grants to Professional Canadian Artists and Arts Organizations**

TYPE:
Awards/prizes; Development grants; General operating grants; Grants-in-aid; Project/program grants; Residencies; Travel grants. Several programs of support providing grants and services to professional Canadian artists and nonprofit arts organizations.

PURPOSE:
To provide grants and services to professional Canadian artists and arts organizations in dance, music, theatre, media arts (film video, audio, new media), inter-arts (including contemporary circus art), visual arts and creative writing to help them pursue professional development, independent artistic creation or production.

LEGAL BASIS:
Independent agency established by the Parliament of Canada in 1957.

ELIGIBILITY:
Individual professional artists must be Canadian citizens or permanent residents of Canada. The Canada Council defines a professional artist as someone who has specialized training in the field (not necessarily in academic institutions), who is recognized as such by her or his peers (artists working in the same artistic tradition) and who has a history of public presentation or publication.

Canadian arts organizations, such as theatre companies, art museums, public galleries, artist-run centres, dance companies, orchestras and film cooperatives, that are staffed by arts professionals who create artistic works or present them to the Canadian public, are also eligible, as are professional publishing houses.

Canadian arts organizations are assessed on the basis of criteria such as professionalism, artistic excellence, community acceptance, stability and sound financial management.

GEOGRAPHIC RESTRICTIONS:
Canada.

FINANCIAL DATA:
Grants for Professional Artists contribute towards living expenses, cost of materials related to the project, professional development, or independent artistic creation or production. Funds may not be used for capital costs.

Amount of support per award: Grants for Professional Artists: $3,000 to $20,000 (CAN) in increments of $1,000 (CAN); Travel grants: $500 to $2,500 (CAN), depending on need.

Total amount of support: Varies.

NUMBER OF APPLICANTS MOST RECENT YEAR:
16,000.

NUMBER OF AWARDS: 6,200.

APPLICATION INFORMATION:
Prospective applicants should specify their citizenship and their field of interest and indicate whether they are professional. Further information and brochures are available on request.

The Council does not accept applications that are sent by fax or e-mail.

PUBLICATIONS:
Program information sheets.

ADDRESS INQUIRIES TO:
Christian Mondor, Information Officer
(See address above.)

CAUZ GROUP   [469]
P.O. Box 229
Pymble BC N.S.W. 2073 Australia
(61)(2) 9928-1552

E-MAIL ADDRESS:
trustawards@trust.com.au

WEB SITE ADDRESS:
www.trust.com.au

FOUNDED: 1961

AREAS OF INTEREST:
Portrait painting.

NAME(S) OF PROGRAMS:
● **Portia Geach Memorial Award**

TYPE:
Awards/prizes. Cash award for the best portrait painted from life of a man or woman distinguished in Art, Letters or the Sciences, by any female artist resident in Australia.

YEAR PROGRAM STARTED: 1965

PURPOSE:
To recognize the portrait painted from life of the highest artistic merit.

LEGAL BASIS:
Trustees of the Portia Geach Memorial Fund.

ELIGIBILITY:
Entrants must be female Australian residents who are either Australian-born, naturalized, or British-born. Entries must be the original work of the competitor. Works must have been executed entirely during the commenced year previously. Each entry must be a portrait painted from life of a man or woman distinguished in Art, Letters or the Sciences. Self-portraits are accepted. Works must be two-dimensional and must use the medium of paint.

Sculptures, photographic and video works are not eligible. There is no limit to the number of entries an artist can submit.

GEOGRAPHIC RESTRICTIONS:
Australia.

FINANCIAL DATA:
Amount of support per award: $18,000 (AUD) annually.

NUMBER OF APPLICANTS MOST RECENT YEAR:
312.

NUMBER OF AWARDS: 1.

APPLICATION INFORMATION:
Complete application information is available from Cauz.

Duration: One year.

Deadline: Last Friday in August.

ADDRESS INQUIRIES TO:
Kate Brodie
(See address above.)

CINTAS FOUNDATION   [470]
c/o Morrison, Brown, Argiz & Farra LLP
1001 Brickell Bay Drive
Miami, FL 33131
(305) 373-5500 ext. 2202
Fax: (305) 373-0056

E-MAIL ADDRESS:
fgonzalez@mbafcpa.com

WEB SITE ADDRESS:
www.cintasfoundation.org

FOUNDED: 1981

AREAS OF INTEREST:
Architecture, creative writing, music composition and the visual arts.

NAME(S) OF PROGRAMS:
● **Cintas Fellowships in the Arts**

TYPE:
Fellowships. Awarded to persons of Cuban citizenship or lineage residing outside Cuba for achievement of a creative nature in architecture, painting, sculpture, printmaking, music composition and literature.

YEAR PROGRAM STARTED: 1964

PURPOSE:
To recognize outstanding creative work done by a person from Cuba or a person of Cuban descent.

LEGAL BASIS:
Private, not-for-profit agency.

ELIGIBILITY:
Applications are open to professionals in the creative arts, of Cuban citizenship or lineage, who can give evidence of their creative production by records of exhibitions, performances or (when appropriate) by published books or scores. Students wishing to pursue academic programs are not eligible for awards nor are performing artists as opposed to creative artists. Although there is no fixed age limit, the Fellowships are intended for young professionals in the arts who have completed their academic and technical training. The program focuses on one creative genre per grant cycle.

FINANCIAL DATA:
Amount of support per award: $10,000, paid in four equal quarterly stipends.

Total amount of support: Varies.

NUMBER OF APPLICANTS MOST RECENT YEAR:
150.

NUMBER OF AWARDS: 2 to 5 annually.

APPLICATION INFORMATION:
Eligible candidates may request application forms and letter of reference forms from the Foundation. Applications should be in English and should be accompanied by

supporting documentation of an appropriate nature, such as published books or music scores or photographs and color slides of paintings or sculpture.

Duration: 12 consecutive months beginning September 1.

ADDRESS INQUIRIES TO:
Cintas Fellows Collection
(See address above.)

ROBERT STERLING CLARK FOUNDATION
135 East 64th Street
New York, NY 10065
(212) 288-8900
Fax: (212) 288-1033

E-MAIL ADDRESS:
rscf@rsclark.org

WEB SITE ADDRESS:
www.rsclark.org

TYPE:
Project/program grants; Research grants.

See entry 1285 for full listing.

COLORADO CREATIVE INDUSTRIES   [471]
1625 Broadway, Suite 2700
Denver, CO 80202
(303) 892-3802
Fax: (303) 892-3848
TDD: (303) 894-2664

E-MAIL ADDRESS:
coloarts@state.co.us

WEB SITE ADDRESS:
www.coloarts.org

FOUNDED: 1967

AREAS OF INTEREST:
Visual arts, literature, performing arts, folk arts and media arts, youth-at-risk and economic benefits.

NAME(S) OF PROGRAMS:
● **Colorado Creates**
● **Colorado Masterpieces**
● **Small Step Awards**
● **Start Schools**
● **Youthreach**

TYPE:
Awards/prizes; Challenge/matching grants; General operating grants; Internships; Project/program grants; Technical assistance.

PURPOSE:
To promote the cultural, educational and economic growth of Colorado through development of its arts and cultural heritage.

LEGAL BASIS:
State government agency.

ELIGIBILITY:
Colorado artists and nonprofit tax-exempt organizations.

GEOGRAPHIC RESTRICTIONS:
Colorado.

FINANCIAL DATA:
Amount of support per award: Colorado Creates: $4,000 to $10,000; Colorado Masterpieces: $55,000; Small Step Awards: $500 to $1,000; Start Schools: $2,000 to $15,000; Youthreach: Up to $17,000 for a two-year grant.

Total amount of support: Varies.

Matching fund requirements: 1:1 match; 50% can be cash and 50% can be in-kind donations.

NUMBER OF APPLICANTS MOST RECENT YEAR: 250.

NUMBER OF AWARDS: 120.

APPLICATION INFORMATION:
Duration: Colorado Creates: Three years on, one year off. Other programs: Generally one year.

PUBLICATIONS:
Annual report; guidelines; press releases; news clips; strategic plan.

OFFICERS:
John Hickenlooper, Governor
Chris Castilian, Chairperson
Elaine Mariner, Director

ADDRESS INQUIRIES TO:
Elaine Mariner, Director
(See address above.)

THE COMMUNITY FOUNDATION OF LOUISVILLE, INC.   [472]
325 West Main Street, Suite 1110
Louisville, KY 40202
(502) 585-4649
Fax: (502) 587-7484

E-MAIL ADDRESS:
alexs@cflouisville.org

WEB SITE ADDRESS:
www.cflouisville.org

AREAS OF INTEREST:
Visual arts, crafts, theatre and historic preservation.

TYPE:
Endowments; Grants-in-aid; Scholarships.

PURPOSE:
To enrich the quality of life for all citizens in the Louisville area and to serve as a catalyst for promoting philanthropy within the local community.

ELIGIBILITY:
Grants are made to organizations that have tax-exempt status under Section 501(c)(3) of the Internal Revenue Code.

GEOGRAPHIC RESTRICTIONS:
Louisville, Kentucky and surrounding communities.

APPLICATION INFORMATION:
Deadline: October 1.

ADDRESS INQUIRIES TO:
Alexandra M. Spoelker
Vice President, Community Leadership
(See address above.)

CONGRESSIONAL BLACK CAUCUS FOUNDATION, INC.
1720 Massachusetts Avenue, N.W.
Washington, DC 20036
(202) 263-2800
Fax: (202) 775-0773

E-MAIL ADDRESS:
info@cbcfinc.org

WEB SITE ADDRESS:
www.cbcfinc.org

TYPE:
Scholarships. CBCS Performing Arts Scholarship, developed in honor of the late Curtis Mayfield, is intended to ensure that

students pursuing a career in the performing arts receive the financial assistance to achieve their goals.

CBCS Visual Arts Scholarship was established for students who are pursuing a career in the visual arts.

See entry 1091 for full listing.

CONNECTICUT COMMISSION ON CULTURE AND TOURISM   [473]
One Constitution Plaza, 2nd Floor
Hartford, CT 06103
(860) 256-2722
(860) 256-2800
Fax: (860) 256-2811

E-MAIL ADDRESS:
an-ming.truxes@ct.gov

WEB SITE ADDRESS:
www.cultureandtourism.org

FOUNDED: 1965

AREAS OF INTEREST:
Fine arts, literature, museums and libraries, music, creative and performing arts, theatre, dance, arts in education, community arts programs, artist slide bank, art in public spaces, history, tourism and colleges/universities.

CONSULTING OR VOLUNTEER SERVICES:
Volunteer Lawyers for the Arts program.

NAME(S) OF PROGRAMS:
● **Arts-in-Education Program**
● **Support of the Arts in Connecticut**

TYPE:
Awards/prizes; Challenge/matching grants; Conferences/seminars; Endowments; Fellowships; General operating grants; Internships; Project/program grants; Residencies; Technical assistance; Training grants. Grants are available to Connecticut artists, arts institutions, arts organizations and nonprofit arts-sponsoring organizations for program support and technical assistance.

YEAR PROGRAM STARTED: 1965

PURPOSE:
To support artistic excellence and foster cultural development through the arts and to increase public understanding of, participation in and support for the arts in Connecticut.

LEGAL BASIS:
The State of Connecticut Enabling Legislation, Public Act No. 78-187 created the original Connecticut Commission on the Arts.

ELIGIBILITY:
Connecticut artists, art institutions, units of state or local government, art organizations and nonprofit arts-sponsoring associations whose principle residence is in Connecticut. Ineligible programs are those which take place out of state, student projects, fund-raising benefits, social activities, membership activities, scholarships, underwriting of past deficits or capital expenditures.

GEOGRAPHIC RESTRICTIONS:
Connecticut.

FINANCIAL DATA:
Amount of support per award: Varies.

Matching fund requirements: Funds to organizations require a minimum one-to-one cash match. Funds to artists do not require a match.

COOPERATIVE FUNDING PROGRAMS: Matching funds, Federal-state partnership and regional development projects.

NUMBER OF APPLICANTS MOST RECENT YEAR: 1,100.

REPRESENTATIVE AWARDS:
$134,266 to Goodspeed Opera House for operating costs associated with a public program.

APPLICATION INFORMATION:
A guidelines brochure may be requested from the Commission three to four months in advance to the project.
Duration: Varies.
Deadline: Varies.

PUBLICATIONS:
Copyright Law; Non-Profit Incorporation-A Guide for Artists and Organizations; Contract Law for Artists and Organizations; Culture and Tourism Newsletter; Bi-Monthly Bulletin; *Art in Public Spaces Program Guide; Hot Schools Transform Education; Economic Impact of the Nonprofit Arts Industry in Connecticut; Performing Artists,* online directories.

STAFF:
Christopher Bergstrom, Executive Director
An-Ming Truxes, Arts Division Director
David Bahlman, History Division Director
Randal Fiveash, Tourism Division Director

ADDRESS INQUIRIES TO:
Rhonda Olisky, Program Associate
(See address above.)

CONSEIL DES ARTS DE MONTREAL   [474]
1210 East Sherbrooke Street
First Floor
Montreal QC H2L 2L9 Canada
(514) 280-3582
Fax: (514) 280-3784

E-MAIL ADDRESS:
dsauvage@ville.montreal.qc.ca

WEB SITE ADDRESS:
www.artsmontreal.org

FOUNDED: 1956

AREAS OF INTEREST:
Visual arts, dance, theatre, music, literature, cinema, new artistic practices, video and electronic arts.

NAME(S) OF PROGRAMS:
● **Programme de tournees**
● **Programme General**

TYPE:
Awards/prizes; Development grants; Exchange programs; General operating grants; Project/program grants; Technical assistance. Grants to nonprofit professional organizations having their head offices in Montreal.

YEAR PROGRAM STARTED: 1956

PURPOSE:
To assist Montreal's artistic and cultural organizations.

LEGAL BASIS:
Regional organization.

ELIGIBILITY:
Professional, nonprofit organizations in Montreal.

GEOGRAPHIC RESTRICTIONS:
Montreal, Quebec.

FINANCIAL DATA:
Amount of support per award: Varies.
Total amount of support: $9,649,455 (CAN) for the year 2010.

NUMBER OF APPLICANTS MOST RECENT YEAR:
400.

NUMBER OF AWARDS: 329 for the year 2010.

APPLICATION INFORMATION:
Duration: One fiscal year.
Deadline: Programme de tournees: September. Programme General: Varies by type of grant.

PUBLICATIONS:
Annual report.

STAFF:
Sylviane Martineau, Cultural Advisor, Dance
Rejane Bouge, Cultural Advisor, Literature, Cinema
Claire Metras, Cultural Advisor, Music
Claude Des Landes, Cultural Advisor, Theatre
Marie-Michele Cron, Cultural Advisor, Visual Arts, Media Arts and New Artist Practices

ADDRESS INQUIRIES TO:
Cultural Advisor
(See address above.)

THE CORPORATION OF YADDO [475]

312 Union Avenue
Saratoga Springs, NY 12866
(518) 584-0746
Fax: (518) 584-1312

E-MAIL ADDRESS:
chwait@yaddo.org

WEB SITE ADDRESS:
www.yaddo.org

FOUNDED: 1900

AREAS OF INTEREST:
Literature, visual arts, music composition, filmmaking, choreography, performance art and other creative arts.

NAME(S) OF PROGRAMS:
- **Artist Residencies**

TYPE:
Residencies; Travel grants.

YEAR PROGRAM STARTED: 1926

PURPOSE:
To enable artists to work in a quiet, protected and supportive environment.

LEGAL BASIS:
A publicly supported charity.

ELIGIBILITY:
For creative artists working at a professional level in their field.

FINANCIAL DATA:
No cash grants. The award covers room, board and studio costs. A small fund exists to provide limited help towards the expenses of travel or renting equipment to invited guests of any discipline who otherwise might not be able to visit.

NUMBER OF APPLICANTS MOST RECENT YEAR:
1,084 for the year 2009.

NUMBER OF AWARDS: 222 for the year 2009.

APPLICATION INFORMATION:
Applicants should apply to the Admissions Panel that best represents the project they wish to undertake should they be invited for a residency. Applicants may apply to only one admissions panel, in one genre, at a time. Applicants with concerns about choice of panel should contact the Program Director.

All application materials must be assembled according to the instructions for each discipline and physically mailed to Yaddo. Yaddo does not accept letters of recommendation by fax or e-mail.
Duration: Up to two months.
Deadline: January 1 and August 1.

PUBLICATIONS:
Annual report; application guidelines; newsletter; case statement.

IRS IDENTIFICATION NUMBER: 14-1343055

OFFICERS:
Peter C. Gould, Chairman of the Board
Peter Kayafas, Vice Chairman
Elaina Richardson, President
Patricia Sopp, Vice President, Finance and Assistant Treasurer
Candace Weir, Treasurer
Gardner McFall, Corporate Secretary
Susan Brynteson, Recording Secretary

ADDRESS INQUIRIES TO:
Candace Wait, Program Director
The Corporation of Yaddo
P.O. Box 395
Saratoga Springs, NY 12886

THE COSTUME SOCIETY OF AMERICA [476]

390 Amwell Road, Suite 402
Hillsborough, NJ 08844
(908) 359-1471
(800) 272-9447 (U.S.)
Fax: (908) 450-1118

E-MAIL ADDRESS:
national.office@costumesocietyamerica.com

WEB SITE ADDRESS:
www.costumesocietyamerica.com

FOUNDED: 1973

AREAS OF INTEREST:
Costume, art history, research, textile and fashion design, museum studies and anthropology.

NAME(S) OF PROGRAMS:
- **Stella Blum Research Grant**
- **CSA Travel Research Grant**
- **Adele Filene Travel Award**

TYPE:
Awards/prizes; Conferences/seminars; Development grants; Fellowships; General operating grants; Project/program grants; Research grants; Scholarships; Travel grants. Stella Blum Research Grant is a merit award for a student researching a North American costume topic.

CSA Travel Research Grant aids in travel to collections to any library, archive, museum or site for research to further an ongoing project.

Adele Filene Travel Award assists the travel of a CSA student member to that year's CSA national symposium to present either a juried paper or poster.

YEAR PROGRAM STARTED: 1987

PURPOSE:
To advance the global understanding of all aspects of dress and appearance.

ELIGIBILITY:
Must be a Costume Society of America member for all awards.

CSA Travel Research Grant: Must be a CSA non-student member. Proof must be given that work on the project is already underway.

Adele Filene Travel Award: Must be currently enrolled as a student with a juried paper or poster accepted by the CSA symposium.

FINANCIAL DATA:
Amount of support per award: Stella Blum Research Grant: Up to $3,500; CSA Travel Research Grant: $1,500; Adele Filene Travel Award: Up to $500.

NUMBER OF APPLICANTS MOST RECENT YEAR:
6.

NUMBER OF AWARDS: Varies.

APPLICATION INFORMATION:
Information is available, under "Opportunities," on the Society's web site.
Duration: One year.
Deadline: Stella Blum Research Grant: May 1; CSA Travel Research Grant: September 1; Adele Filene Travel Award: March 1.

ADDRESS INQUIRIES TO:
Amanda Tate, Member Services Director
(See address above.)

DELAWARE DIVISION OF THE ARTS [477]

Carvel State Office Building
820 North French Street
Wilmington, DE 19801
(302) 577-8278
Fax: (302) 577-6561

E-MAIL ADDRESS:
delarts@state.de.us

WEB SITE ADDRESS:
www.artsdel.org

FOUNDED: 1969

AREAS OF INTEREST:
Performing arts, visual arts, literature and media.

CONSULTING OR VOLUNTEER SERVICES:
Technical assistance to community groups and arts organizations.

NAME(S) OF PROGRAMS:
- **Arts in Education**
- **Arts Organizations Grants**
- **Community Based Organizations Grants**
- **Gallery Program**
- **Individual Artist Fellowships**
- **Opportunity Grants**

TYPE:
Awards/prizes; Challenge/matching grants; Conferences/seminars; Fellowships; General operating grants; Project/program grants; Residencies; Technical assistance. Grants to Delaware nonprofit, tax-exempt organizations for projects in the arts. Fellowships program for individual creative artists who reside in Delaware.

YEAR PROGRAM STARTED: 1970

PURPOSE:
To nurture and support the arts to enhance the quality of life for all Delawareans.

LEGAL BASIS:
State agency.

ELIGIBILITY:
Applicants must be nonprofit, tax-exempt organizations in the state of Delaware. Fellowship applicants are individual creative artists who reside in Delaware.

GEOGRAPHIC RESTRICTIONS:
Delaware.

FINANCIAL DATA:
Amount of funds available is determined by state appropriation and funding from the National Endowment for the Arts.
Amount of support per award: Variable according to program.
Total amount of support: $1,850,000.
Matching fund requirements: Organization grants matching requirements vary according to program.

NUMBER OF APPLICANTS MOST RECENT YEAR:
250.

NUMBER OF AWARDS: 176.

APPLICATION INFORMATION:
Application must be made on forms available on the web site.
Duration: Varies.
Deadline: March 1 for most grants. Announcement July 1 for most grants.

PUBLICATIONS:
Artline, semiannual.

ADDRESS INQUIRIES TO:
Paul Weagraff, Director
(See address above.)

DISTRICT OF COLUMBIA COMMISSION ON THE ARTS AND HUMANITIES   [478]
1371 Harvard Street, N.W.
Washington, DC 20009
(202) 724-5613
Fax: (202) 727-4135
TDD: (202) 727-3148

E-MAIL ADDRESS:
cah@dcarts.dc.gov

WEB SITE ADDRESS:
www.dcarts.dc.gov

FOUNDED: 1968

AREAS OF INTEREST:
The arts in the District of Columbia.

NAME(S) OF PROGRAMS:
- **Artist Fellowship Program**
- **Arts Education Projects**
- **City Arts Projects**
- **Cultural Facilities Program**
- **DCARTS International**
- **East of the River Arts Initiative**
- **Elders Learning Through the Arts**
- **Festivals DC**
- **Folk and Traditional Arts Mini-Grant Program**
- **Hip Hop Community Arts Initiative**
- **Public Art Building Communities**
- **Small Projects Program**
- **UPSTART Program**
- **Young Artist Program**

TYPE:
Awards/prizes; Challenge/matching grants; Conferences/seminars; Fellowships; General operating grants; Grants-in-aid; Project/program grants; Technical assistance; Training grants. Services provided to arts institutions and individual artists including inquiry services, technical assistance and funding.

YEAR PROGRAM STARTED: 1968

PURPOSE:
To administer funds to arts organizations, community organizations and individual artists to support arts endeavors within the District of Columbia.

LEGAL BASIS:
State arts agency authorized by executive order.

ELIGIBILITY:
Applicants must be residents of Washington, DC. Organizations must be located in Washington, DC and be nonprofit IRS 501(c)(3) arts organizations within the District of Columbia at least two years prior to application in some programs and one year in most others.

GEOGRAPHIC RESTRICTIONS:
Washington, DC.

FINANCIAL DATA:
Amount of support per award: Individual Artist Fellowships: $5,000.
Total amount of support: $1,000 to $30,000. For capital funding projects and for organizations: Up to $100,000.
Matching fund requirements: Most organizational grant awards must be matched by the applicant.

PUBLICATIONS:
Application guidelines.

STAFF:
Gloria Nauden, Executive Director

ADDRESS INQUIRIES TO:
Moshe Adams
Acting Legislative and Grants Manager
(See address above.)

EAST TENNESSEE FOUNDATION
625 Market Street
Suite 1400
Knoxville, TN 37902
(865) 524-1223
(877) 524-1223
Fax: (865) 637-6039

E-MAIL ADDRESS:
etf@etf.org

WEB SITE ADDRESS:
www.easttennesseefoundation.org

TYPE:
Project/program grants; Scholarships; Seed money grants; Technical assistance.

See entry 1188 for full listing.

THE FIELDSTONE FOUNDATION
2 Ada, Suite 200
Irvine, CA 92618
(949) 790-7496
Fax: (949) 453-0944

E-MAIL ADDRESS:
janinem@fieldstonefoundation.org

WEB SITE ADDRESS:
www.fieldstonefoundation.org

TYPE:
Challenge/matching grants; General operating grants; Project/program grants. Grants are awarded to improve the quality of life for children and families.

See entry 401 for full listing.

FLORIDA DEPARTMENT OF STATE, DIVISION OF CULTURAL AFFAIRS   [479]
500 South Bronough Street
Tallahassee, FL 32399-0250
(850) 245-6470
Fax: (850) 245-6497

E-MAIL ADDRESS:
info@florida-arts.org

WEB SITE ADDRESS:
www.florida-arts.org

FOUNDED: 1969

AREAS OF INTEREST:
The Division of Cultural Affairs administers the cultural grant programs of the Department of State and is responsible for planning and implementing arts programs statewide, providing technical assistance to artists and arts organizations, awarding, administering, monitoring and evaluating the grants program, disseminating arts-related information and encouraging cultural development in Florida.

CONSULTING OR VOLUNTEER SERVICES:
Facilitative services in all areas are available.

NAME(S) OF PROGRAMS:
- **Capitol Complex Exhibition Program**
- **Cultural Facilities Program**
- **Florida Cultural Endowment Program**
- **Florida Individual Artist Fellowship Program**
- **General Program Support Grants Program**
- **Specific Cultural Projects Grants Program**
- **State Touring Program**

TYPE:
Awards/prizes; Capital grants; Challenge/matching grants; Conferences/seminars; Development grants; Endowments; Exchange programs; Fellowships; General operating grants; Grants-in-aid; Project/program grants; Seed money grants; Technical assistance; Training grants; Travel grants. Fellowships to individual artists residing in the state of Florida. Program provides a limited number of unmatched fellowships for creative artists in dance, folk arts, inter-disciplinary, literature, media arts, music, theatre and visual arts.

YEAR PROGRAM STARTED: 1971

PURPOSE:
To encourage the creation of projects that promote excellence in the arts and that strive to bring arts to a community-wide audience.

LEGAL BASIS:
State government agency.

ELIGIBILITY:
To apply for a grant, an organization must qualify as a political subdivision of a municipal, county or state government in Florida or be a not-for-profit, tax-exempt Florida corporation, meet specific budgetary and program requirements as outlined for the appropriate artistic disciplines, special programs and funding categories, match

dollar-for-dollar, in most cases, the grant amount requested from the Division and meet all legal and financial requirements described in the *Guide to Cultural Programs*.

To apply for and retain a fellowship, an applicant must be a Florida citizen, at least 18 years old, and maintain Florida residency for the duration of the grant period. The applicant must not be a degree-seeking student at the time of application or at any time during the grant period. Applicant must not have received a Division fellowship during the past four years at the time of the application.

GEOGRAPHIC RESTRICTIONS:
Florida.

FINANCIAL DATA:
Cash grants are for program expenses rather than for capital improvements.
Amount of support per award: Varies depending upon grant program and specific eligibility.
Matching fund requirements: Fellowships: Unmatched. In most cases, Grants are matched 1:1.

NUMBER OF APPLICANTS MOST RECENT YEAR:
More than 1,800.

NUMBER OF AWARDS: More than 100 awards for fiscal year 2009-10.

APPLICATION INFORMATION:
Program guidelines can be downloaded from the web site.
Duration: One year.
Deadline: June for General Program Support and Specific Cultural Projects grants. July for fellowships.

OFFICERS:
Sandy Shaughnessy, Director, Division of Cultural Affairs

STAFF:
Gaylen Phillips, Associate Director of Arts Resources and Services

ADDRESS INQUIRIES TO:
Jennifer Hoesing, Arts Consultant
(See address above.)

FONDATION DES ETATS-UNIS   [480]
15, boulevard Jourdan
75014 Paris France
(33 1) 53 80 68 87
Fax: (33 1) 53 80 68 99

E-MAIL ADDRESS:
culture@feusa.org

WEB SITE ADDRESS:
www.feusa.org

FOUNDED: 1929

NAME(S) OF PROGRAMS:
● **Harriet Hale Woolley Scholarships**

TYPE:
Scholarships. The Woolley Scholarship is a private grant awarded annually to graduate and postgraduate American students in the visual fine arts (painting, graphic design, printmaking, sculpture, photography) and music (instrumental or vocal performance). The Scholarship is not intended for research in art history, musicology or composition, nor for dance or theatre.

Grantees live at the Fondation des Etats-Unis, which is one of the student residencies of the "Cite internationale universitaire de Paris."

They are expected to participate in the cultural and social activities of the Fondation. A serious project for graduate study in Paris must be approved by the director of the Fondation des Etats-Unis.

YEAR PROGRAM STARTED: 1933

PURPOSE:
To promote artistic and cultural exchange between the U.S. and France.

ELIGIBILITY:
Requirements include:
(1) American citizenship;
(2) between 21 and 35 years of age (only single applicants can be considered, as the Fondation has no accommodations for couples);
(3) graduation with high academic standing from an American college, university, or professional school of recognized standing. Preference is given to mature students who have already done some graduate study;
(4) evidence of high-level artistic or musical accomplishment and;
(5) good moral character, personality and adaptability, plus good physical health and emotional stability.

Scholarship recipient must reside at the Fondation des Etats-Unis for the academic year.

FINANCIAL DATA:
The Scholarship is designed to assist with living expenses while in Paris. In addition, scholars are offered rent during the nine-month academic year.
Amount of support per award: Stipend of EUR 8,500, payable in five installments during the academic year (October 1 to June 30).
Total amount of support: EUR 12,000 or over $17,000 (USD).

NUMBER OF AWARDS: Up to 4 annually.

APPLICATION INFORMATION:
Application should be made to the address above, accompanied by seven international postal coupons (available at the post office). Documents to be submitted include:
(1) a short yet detailed statement of the foreign study project including the Paris school and/or instructor preferred by the candidate (candidates in the visual arts should be especially attentive to this point);
(2) a Harriet Hale Woolley application (found on web site); all entries must be complete and accurate;
(3) attestation of proficiency in the French language by a qualified teacher of French;
(4) three letters of recommendation from professors familiar with the applicant's general qualifications, artistic ability and accomplishment (letters should be original copies on letterhead paper, and mailed by the issuer); it is highly recommended that candidates include a letter of admission to study at a French institution;
(5) complete transcript of college or university record with embossed seal of the issuing institution;
(6) a simple medical certificate of general health (successful candidates will be required to show proof of paid-up accident and health insurance before arrival);
(7) four small identification photographs 1 inch x 1-1/4 inch (3 x 4 cm.), with applicant's name printed on the back of each one and;
(8) examples of the applicant's work; for visual artists, a CD or DVD of works and/or photographs are suggested; for musicians, 10

to 15 minutes of music on audio CD showcasing three contrasting styles is suggested.

Application materials will not be returned. Please send all materials by mail. Faxes and e-mail attachments will not be accepted.
Duration: One academic year.
Deadline: All application dossiers and their supporting materials must be received no later than January 31, for the following academic year.

PUBLICATIONS:
Application guidelines.

OFFICER:
Terence Murphy, Director

ADDRESS INQUIRIES TO:
Elizabeth Askren-Brie, Cultural Attache Harriet Hale Woolley Scholarship
(See address above.)
E-mail: elizabeth.askren-brie@feusa.org

*SPECIAL STIPULATIONS:
As this project should include enrollment in a recognized French art school or music conservatory, it is strongly suggested that the candidate establish a significant contact with a teacher or institution prior to arriving in France and to show evidence of this contact in his or her application dossier.

FORECAST PUBLIC ARTWORKS   [481]
2300 Myrtle Avenue
Suite 160
St. Paul, MN 55114
(651) 641-1128
Fax: (651) 641-1983

E-MAIL ADDRESS:
info@forecastart.org

WEB SITE ADDRESS:
www.forecastart.org

FOUNDED: 1978

AREAS OF INTEREST:
Public art.

CONSULTING OR VOLUNTEER SERVICES:
Consulting for public artists and communities.

NAME(S) OF PROGRAMS:
● **Forecast Public Art Annual Grant Program**
● **MN Regional Grant Program**

TYPE:
Project/program grants; Research grants.

YEAR PROGRAM STARTED: 1988

PURPOSE:
To fund emerging artists of all disciplines to develop and/or produce public art projects.

LEGAL BASIS:
Private nonprofit corporation.

ELIGIBILITY:
Open to emerging artists of all disciplines. Minnesota residents only.

GEOGRAPHIC RESTRICTIONS:
Minnesota.

FINANCIAL DATA:
Amount of support per award: Up to $2,000 for research and development; up to $7,000 for public projects.

NUMBER OF APPLICANTS MOST RECENT YEAR:
50 to 100 per competition.

NUMBER OF AWARDS: 18 for the year 2010.

APPLICATION INFORMATION:
Proposal forms available in September. There is no fee for the form. Generally five to 10 slides plus proposal for new work required.
Duration: Up to one year.
Deadline: November 15. Announcement February 15.

PUBLICATIONS:
Public Art Review, a semi-annual publication focusing on public art projects and issues.

IRS IDENTIFICATION NUMBER: 41-1361351

STAFF:
Jack Becker, Executive Director
Melinda Childs, Program Manager
Nichole Goodwell, Program Manager
Kaitlin Frick, Program Assistant

ADDRESS INQUIRIES TO:
Melinda Childs, Program Manager
(See address above.)

FOUNDATION FOR JEWISH CULTURE

330 Seventh Avenue, 21st Floor
New York, NY 10001
(212) 629-0500 ext. 209 (Kroll Film Fund)
(212) 629-0500 ext. 212 (Paul Zakrzewski)
Fax: (212) 629-0508

E-MAIL ADDRESS:
grants@jewishculture.org

WEB SITE ADDRESS:
www.jewishculture.org

TYPE:
Fellowships; Project/program grants; Research grants. Cohen Fund for Doctoral Dissertation Fellowships is intended to support the final stages of completing a dissertation, encouraging scholarly research, publication and teaching in the various disciplines of Jewish studies.

Kroll Fund for Jewish Documentary Film supports the completion of original documentaries that explore the Jewish experience in all its complexity. The priority of the Fund is to support projects that address significant subjects; offer fresh, challenging perspectives; engage audiences across cultural lines; and expand the understanding of Jewish experiences.

See entry 403 for full listing.

FOUNDATION FOR JEWISH CULTURE [482]

330 Seventh Avenue, 21st Floor
New York, NY 10001
(212) 629-0500 ext. 212 (Paul Zakrzewski)
(212) 629-0500 ext. 216 (Ester Bloom)
Fax: (212) 629-0508

E-MAIL ADDRESS:
info@jewishculture.org

WEB SITE ADDRESS:
www.jewishculture.org

FOUNDED: 1960

AREAS OF INTEREST:
Jewish arts, theater and academic study.

NAME(S) OF PROGRAMS:
● **Sidney and Hadassah Musher Publication Prize**

TYPE:
Awards/prizes. Biennial award to facilitate the publication of doctoral dissertations relating to Jewish life in Israel or America, 1880 to the present.

PURPOSE:
To facilitate the publication of doctoral dissertations relating to New life in Israel or America.

ELIGIBILITY:
Applicants must have completed their dissertation and defense and have a commitment for publication from an academic or university press. All relevant fields and departments are eligible.

GEOGRAPHIC RESTRICTIONS:
North America.

FINANCIAL DATA:
Amount of support per award: $3,000.

NUMBER OF AWARDS: 1 every other year.

PUBLICATIONS:
Guidelines.

ADDRESS INQUIRIES TO:
Paul Zakrzewski, Program Officer
Literature and Scholarship
(See address above.)

*SPECIAL STIPULATIONS:
Must be a U.S. citizen or permanent resident.

CARL M. FREEMAN FOUNDATION [483]

18330 Village Center Drive
Second Floor
Olney, MD 20832
(302) 436-3555
Fax: (302) 436-3080

E-MAIL ADDRESS:
info@freemanfoundation.org

WEB SITE ADDRESS:
www.freemanfoundation.org

FOUNDED: 1960

AREAS OF INTEREST:
Facilitating, supporting and promoting innovative community-based leadership and giving.

NAME(S) OF PROGRAMS:
● **FACES Grant**

TYPE:
Capital grants; Challenge/matching grants; General operating grants.

PURPOSE:
To provide funding and capacity-building support to nonprofit organizations in the communities served by the Carl M. Freeman Companies.

ELIGIBILITY:
Must be IRS-recognized 501(c)(3) tax-exempt, nonprofit organizations or public agencies serving the residents of the Companies' funding areas.

GEOGRAPHIC RESTRICTIONS:
Sussex County, Delaware and Montgomery County, Maryland.

FINANCIAL DATA:
Amount of support per award: $2,500 or $5,000.
Total amount of support: Varies.

APPLICATION INFORMATION:
Guidelines available on the web site.

ADDRESS INQUIRIES TO:
Trish Schechtman
Operations Manager/Grants Manager
(See address above.)

FREER GALLERY OF ART AND ARTHUR M. SACKLER GALLERY [484]

Smithsonian Institution, MRC 707
1050 Independence Avenue, S.W.
Washington, DC 20560
(202) 633-0401
Fax: (202) 357-4911

WEB SITE ADDRESS:
www.asia.si.edu

FOUNDED: 1923

AREAS OF INTEREST:
Asian art, 19th and early 20th century American art.

CONSULTING OR VOLUNTEER SERVICES:
Docent tours for the public through Freer Gallery of Art and Arthur M. Sackler Gallery.

NAME(S) OF PROGRAMS:
● **Forbes Fellowship**
● **Smithsonian Fellowship**
● **Stern Fund**

TYPE:
Awards/prizes; Fellowships; Internships; Project/program grants; Research grants; Technical assistance; Visiting scholars. Forbes Fellowship is a competitive grant to further the scientific study of care, conservation and protection of works of art related to the Freer Collection.

The Stern Fund is designed to increase the appreciation and understanding of Japanese art.

YEAR PROGRAM STARTED: 1923

PURPOSE:
To advance scholarship of Asian art and 19th and early 20th century American art.

LEGAL BASIS:
U.S. government agency.

ELIGIBILITY:
Varies with each fellowship.

FINANCIAL DATA:
Amount of support per award: Senior and Postdoctoral: Up to $45,000 per year; Predoctoral: $30,000 per year.
Total amount of support: Varies.

COOPERATIVE FUNDING PROGRAMS:
Smithsonian Office of Fellowships and Grants, University of Michigan.

APPLICATION INFORMATION:
For Smithsonian Fellowship, write to Office of Fellowships and Grants at the Smithsonian. For Forbes Fellowship, write to Department of Conservation and Scientific Research, Freer/Sackler Galleries at the above address. For the Stern Fund, the fellowship for a senior scholar from Japan is by invitation only.

PUBLICATIONS:
Annual report.

OFFICERS:
Dr. Julian Raby, Director
Dr. James Ulak, Deputy Director

FUNDING EXCHANGE

666 Broadway, Suite 500
New York, NY 10012
(212) 529-5300 ext. 320
Fax: (212) 982-9272

E-MAIL ADDRESS:
grants@fex.org

WEB SITE ADDRESS:
www.fex.org

TYPE:
Grants-in-aid.

See entry 2059 for full listing.

THE DAVID GEFFEN FOUNDATION

12011 San Vicente Boulevard
Suite 606
Los Angeles, CA 90049
(310) 581-5955
Fax: (310) 581-5949

E-MAIL ADDRESS:
ddishman@geffenco.com

TYPE:
Capital grants; General operating grants;
Project/program grants.

See entry 1529 for full listing.

GEORGIA COUNCIL FOR THE ARTS   [485]

75 Fifth Street, N.W.
Suite 1200
Atlanta, GA 30308
(404) 962-4839

E-MAIL ADDRESS:
gaarts@gaarts.org

WEB SITE ADDRESS:
www.gaarts.org

FOUNDED: 1968

AREAS OF INTEREST:
The arts.

CONSULTING OR VOLUNTEER SERVICES:
Extensive technical assistance to nonprofit
arts organizations in all disciplines on matters
of artistic, administrative or technical
concern, including community arts councils,
municipal arts agencies, literary guilds, visual
arts organizations and performing groups
such as orchestras, dance and theatre
companies. Also, for arts activities sponsored
by art and history museums, cultural support
groups, public libraries, school systems,
agencies such as parks/recreation departments
and other presenter groups.

NAME(S) OF PROGRAMS:
● **Arts Services**
● **Community Arts Development**
● **Traditional Arts**

TYPE:
Awards/prizes; Challenge/matching grants;
Conferences/seminars; Demonstration grants;
Development grants; Formula grants; General
operating grants; Grants-in-aid; Internships;
Matching gifts; Project/program grants;
Research grants; Residencies; Seed money
grants; Technical assistance; Training grants;
Visiting scholars; Research contracts.
Capacity building; Poetry competitions;
Traditional arts apprenticeships. Technical
assistance and grants in categories including,
but not limited to, architecture/environmental
arts, dance, education (arts related),
filmmaking, folk arts/heritage arts and crafts,
historic preservation (arts-related), literary
arts, multi-media, museums, music,
photography, public radio, television, theatre
and visual arts.

YEAR PROGRAM STARTED: 1968

PURPOSE:
To promote and provide access to the arts for
residents of the state of Georgia.

LEGAL BASIS:
Government agency.

ELIGIBILITY:
Grants are made to nonprofit, tax-exempt arts
organizations or units of government which
are incorporated in the state of Georgia.

GEOGRAPHIC RESTRICTIONS:
Georgia.

FINANCIAL DATA:
Amount of support per award: $2,250 to
$50,000.
Total amount of support: $5,000,000.
Matching fund requirements: Varies.

NUMBER OF APPLICANTS MOST RECENT YEAR:
700.

NUMBER OF AWARDS: 500.

APPLICATION INFORMATION:
Grant applications are available online.
Duration: One year. Must reapply for
additional funding.

PUBLICATIONS:
Application guidelines; quarterly newsletter.

ADDRESS INQUIRIES TO:
Public Information Officer
(See address above.)

NANCY GRAVES FOUNDATION   [486]

450 West 31st Street, 2nd Floor
New York, NY 10001
(212) 560-0602
Fax: (212) 560-0604

E-MAIL ADDRESS:
mail@nancygravesfoundation.org

WEB SITE ADDRESS:
www.nancygravesfoundation.org

FOUNDED: 1996

AREAS OF INTEREST:
Visual arts.

NAME(S) OF PROGRAMS:
● **Grants for Visual Artists**

TYPE:
Grant for nominated visual artists for work in
any medium other than their own.

YEAR PROGRAM STARTED: 2000

PURPOSE:
To give assistance to individual artists; to
maintain an archive of the Founder's life and
work and organize exhibitions of her art.

ELIGIBILITY:
Grantees must be residents of the U.S. who
have been working as artists for at least five
years beyond his or her schooling. Grants
will not be awarded to students. Applications
will be solicited from nominated visual artists
who wish to have the opportunity to master a
technique, medium or discipline that is
different from the one in which he or she is
primarily recognized.

FINANCIAL DATA:
Amount of support per award: $5,000.

NUMBER OF AWARDS: 2 annually.

APPLICATION INFORMATION:
Artist applicants must be nominated by
Foundation nominators and will subsequently
receive an application for consideration by a
second panel of jurors.

STAFF:
Jennifer Farrell, Director

ADDRESS INQUIRIES TO:
Jennifer Farrell, Director
(See address above.)

HAMBIDGE   [487]

P.O. Box 339
Rabun Gap, GA 30568
(706) 746-5718
Fax: (706) 746-9933

E-MAIL ADDRESS:
center@hambidge.org

WEB SITE ADDRESS:
www.hambidge.org

FOUNDED: 1934

AREAS OF INTEREST:
Artist residency program.

NAME(S) OF PROGRAMS:
● **Hambidge Residency Program Fellowships**

TYPE:
Fellowships. Fellowships apply to any field
or discipline of creative work. They consist
of the:
(1) Nellie Mae Rowe Fellowship;
(2) Fulton County Arts Council Fellowship
and;
(3)NEA Fellowship.

PURPOSE:
To provide applicants with an environment
for creative work in the arts and sciences.

ELIGIBILITY:
Open to qualified applicants in all disciplines
who can demonstrate seriousness, dedication
and professionalism. International residents
are welcome.

FINANCIAL DATA:
Nellie Mae Rowe Fellowship is awarded as a
two-week paid residency.
Amount of support per award: Fulton County
Arts Council Fellowship and NEA
Fellowship: Stipend of $700, plus two-week
residency.

APPLICATION INFORMATION:
Applicants should submit:
(1) completed application form (three pages);
(2) applicant statement;
(3) resume/professional summary;
(4) work examples (CDs and hard copies as
outlined in the instruction pages);
(5) bio;
(6) two letters of reference included with the
application or e-mailed by the application
deadline (does not apply to returning
Fellows);
(7) $30 check/processing fee (all applicants)
and;
(8) stamped, self-addressed envelope for
return of work samples (if desired).
Envelope should be marked "Attention
Residency Program."
Duration: Two weeks to two months.
Deadline: January 15, April 15 and
September 15.

ADDRESS INQUIRIES TO:
Debra Sanders, Office Manager
(See address above.)

HANNAFORD CHARITABLE FOUNDATION

145 Pleasant Hill Road
Scarborough, ME 04074
(207) 885-3834
Fax: (207) 885-3051

WEB SITE ADDRESS:
www.hannaford.com

TYPE:
Scholarships.

See entry 1654 for full listing.

HAWAII STATE FOUNDATION ON CULTURE AND THE ARTS [488]

250 South Hotel Street
Second Floor
Honolulu, HI 96813
(808) 586-0300
Fax: (808) 586-0308
TTY: (808) 586-0740

WEB SITE ADDRESS:
hawaii.gov/sfca

FOUNDED: 1965

AREAS OF INTEREST:
Arts education, community arts, heritage and preservation, presentation, folk arts and community arts.

NAME(S) OF PROGRAMS:
● **SFCA Grants Programs**

TYPE:
Project/program grants.

YEAR PROGRAM STARTED: 1965

PURPOSE:
To stimulate, encourage and promote culture, the arts and humanities throughout the state of Hawaii.

LEGAL BASIS:
State arts agency.

ELIGIBILITY:
Hawaii Revised Statutes for organizations and individuals as defined in section 9-11.

GEOGRAPHIC RESTRICTIONS:
Hawaii.

FINANCIAL DATA:
Limits on the amount of funding for any one project are established by the SFCA Board. Certain costs are not allowable for SFCA funding.
Amount of support per award: Varies.
Total amount of support: $1,300,000 for the year 2010.
Matching fund requirements: 1:1 match required.

NUMBER OF AWARDS: 115 for the year 2010.

APPLICATION INFORMATION:
Applicants must complete the required application forms and attachments.
Duration: Funds are awarded on a biennial basis. No funds are awarded on a continuing basis.
Deadline: Varies.

PUBLICATIONS:
Annual Report; application guidelines.

BOARD MEMBERS:
Lori Thomas, Chairperson
Sandra Albano
Mary Begier
Leonard Chow
Sandra Fong
Teri Gorman
James Jennings
Peter Rosegg
Sheryl Seaman

ADDRESS INQUIRIES TO:
Ronald K. Yamakawa, Executive Director
(See address above.)

HAYSTACK MOUNTAIN SCHOOL OF CRAFTS [489]

22 Church Street
Deer Isle, ME 04627
(207) 348-2306
Fax: (207) 348-2307

E-MAIL ADDRESS:
haystack@haystack-mtn.org

WEB SITE ADDRESS:
www.haystack-mtn.org

FOUNDED: 1950

AREAS OF INTEREST:
Craft education in ceramics, metals, wood, fibers, graphics, glass and blacksmithing.

TYPE:
Conferences/seminars; Fellowships; Scholarships; Visiting scholars; Work-study programs. Minority scholarships; Technical Assistant and Work Study Scholarships. Awards for study in diverse craft media and workshops in six studios including ceramics, metals, wood, fibers, graphics, glass and blacksmithing.

YEAR PROGRAM STARTED: 1950

PURPOSE:
To offer professional instruction and demonstration in crafts.

LEGAL BASIS:
Nonprofit educational organization.

ELIGIBILITY:
U.S. and foreign citizens who are capable of doing graduate-level work are eligible for technical assistant scholarships. Candidates must be at least 18 years of age.

FINANCIAL DATA:
Annual scholarships cover the cost of tuition, or tuition and room and board.
Amount of support per award: $1,080.
Total amount of support: $120,000.

NUMBER OF APPLICANTS MOST RECENT YEAR: 237.

NUMBER OF AWARDS: 121 (60 work-study students; 61 technical assistants).

APPLICATION INFORMATION:
Guidelines and application form is available at the web site.
Duration: One- to two-week sessions.
Deadline: Scholarship applications: March 1; Regular applications: April 1.

PUBLICATIONS:
Catalog; newsletter; scholarly monographs; regional program brochures; eNewsletters.

TRUSTEES:
Lissa Hunter, President
Claire Sanford, Vice President
W. Arnold Yasinski, Treasurer

ADDRESS INQUIRIES TO:
Stuart Kestenbaum, Director
Haystack Mountain School of Crafts
22 Church Street (November to April)
89 Haystack School Drive (May to October)
Deer Isle, ME 04627

MAXIMILIAN E. & MARION O. HOFFMAN FOUNDATION, INC.

970 Farmington Avenue, Suite 203
West Hartford, CT 06107
(860) 521-2949
Fax: (860) 561-5082

E-MAIL ADDRESS:
kwhoffman@snet.net

TYPE:
Project/program grants.

See entry 2418 for full listing.

HUTCHINSON COMMUNITY FOUNDATION [490]

One North Main Street
Suite 501
Hutchinson, KS 67501
(620) 663-5293
Fax: (620) 663-9277

E-MAIL ADDRESS:
info@hutchcf.org

WEB SITE ADDRESS:
www.hutchcf.org

FOUNDED: 1989

AREAS OF INTEREST:
Arts, civic improvements, education, health and human services.

TYPE:
Project/program grants; Seed money grants.

YEAR PROGRAM STARTED: 1989

PURPOSE:
To make Hutchinson area a better place to work and live.

LEGAL BASIS:
501(c)(3) public foundation.

ELIGIBILITY:
Organizations that support innovative projects located in Reno County, KS, and government units that work in the Foundation's objective.

GEOGRAPHIC RESTRICTIONS:
Reno County, Kansas.

NUMBER OF APPLICANTS MOST RECENT YEAR: 50.

NUMBER OF AWARDS: 23.

APPLICATION INFORMATION:
One copy of the applicant's current IRS determination letter Section 501(c)(3) or 509(a) is required. Contact the Foundation for application procedures.
Duration: One year. Reapplication possible.
Deadline: The last Monday in August.

PUBLICATIONS:
Annual report; application guidelines.

OFFICERS AND STAFF:
Aubrey Patterson, President and Executive Director
Terri L. Eisiminger, Vice President of Administration
Kare Van Cantfort, Community Investment Officer

ADDRESS INQUIRIES TO:
Aubrey A. Patterson
President and Executive Director
(See address above.)

IDAHO COMMISSION ON THE ARTS [491]

2410 Old Penitentiary Road
Boise, ID 83712
(208) 334-2119
Fax: (208) 334-2488

E-MAIL ADDRESS:
info@arts.idaho.gov

WEB SITE ADDRESS:
www.arts.idaho.gov

FOUNDED: 1966

AREAS OF INTEREST:
All disciplines in the arts.

CONSULTING OR VOLUNTEER SERVICES:
Technical assistance in arts management.

NAME(S) OF PROGRAMS:
- **Arts Education Projects**
- **Directory of Teaching Artists**
- **Entry Track**
- **Fellowships**
- **Public Programs in the Arts**
- **Quick Fund$**
- **Traditional Arts Apprenticeship Program**
- **Tumblewords**
- **Writer-in-Residence Program**

TYPE:
Conferences/seminars; Fellowships; General operating grants; Project/program grants; Residencies; Technical assistance. Fellowship/apprenticeship, touring/sponsorship, immediate assistance.

YEAR PROGRAM STARTED: 1966

PURPOSE:
To develop the artistic and cultural life of Idaho.

LEGAL BASIS:
State agency.

ELIGIBILITY:
Applicants must be nonprofit, tax-exempt organizations or artists living in Idaho.

GEOGRAPHIC RESTRICTIONS:
Idaho.

FINANCIAL DATA:
Fiscal restrictions, non-cash benefits.
Amount of support per award: Up to $25,000.
Total amount of support: $612,365 for fiscal year 2010.
Matching fund requirements: 50:50, cash or in-kind.

NUMBER OF APPLICANTS MOST RECENT YEAR:
232 for fiscal year 2010.

APPLICATION INFORMATION:
Applications must be on the appropriate form, typed in 12-point, or neatly handwritten. Do not use applications forms from previous years. Review the checklist carefully because the panel will review the application as submitted. Answer the required narrative questions, paying close attention to the page limitations, and check to see that the application is complete, signed and dated. Incomplete applications are subject to return.
Duration: 12 months.
Deadline: Varies.

PUBLICATIONS:
Application guidelines.

IRS IDENTIFICATION NUMBER: 82-6000952

OFFICERS:
Mark Hofflund, Chairman
Ruth Piispanen, Education Program Director
Cort Conley, Literature Director
Barbara Robinson, Director of Artist Services
Maria Carmen Gambliel, Folk Arts Program Director
Michelle Coleman, Community Development Director

ADDRESS INQUIRIES TO:
Executive Director
(See address above.)

ILLINOIS ARTS COUNCIL   [492]

James R. Thompson Center
100 West Randolph, Suite 10-500
Chicago, IL 60601
(312) 814-6750
Fax: (312) 814-1471

E-MAIL ADDRESS:
iac.info@illinois.gov

WEB SITE ADDRESS:
www.arts.state.il.us/agency/iac
www.arts.illinois.gov

FOUNDED: 1965

AREAS OF INTEREST:
The arts.

NAME(S) OF PROGRAMS:
- **Local Arts Agency Grants**
- **Organizational Development Division Program Grants**

TYPE:
General operating grants; Grants-in-aid; Project/program grants. Local Arts Agency Grants to community arts councils, including project grants for specific programs.

The Organizational Development Division Program provides financial assistance to strengthen nonprofit organizations in the fields of architecture, dance, film, literature, music, public media, theater, and the visual arts.

PURPOSE:
To make the arts more widely available to Illinois residents; to promote an environment that is beneficial to artistic activities; to aid the continuing development of the state's cultural resources.

ELIGIBILITY:
Any nonprofit organization which has been actively servicing the Illinois public for at least one year prior to the date of application is eligible. Applicant organizations should be involved in the above-mentioned fields, although public and private higher educational institutions may apply for art programs that serve the wider community and cannot be funded entirely with regular institutional funds.

GEOGRAPHIC RESTRICTIONS:
Illinois.

FINANCIAL DATA:
Amount of support per award: Varies depending on needs and nature of the request.

APPLICATION INFORMATION:
Guidelines available on the Council web site.
Duration: Up to one year.

OFFICERS:
Shirley R. Madigan, Chairperson
Rhoda A. Pierce, Vice Chairperson
Andy Van Meter, Secretary

INDIANA ARTS COMMISSION   [493]

100 North Senate Avenue
Room 505
Indianapolis, IN 46204
(317) 232-1268
Fax: (317) 232-5595
TDD: (317) 233-3001

E-MAIL ADDRESS:
GrantsAdmin@iac.in.gov

WEB SITE ADDRESS:
www.in.gov/arts

FOUNDED: 1969

AREAS OF INTEREST:
The arts including crafts, dance, design, education, expansion arts, folk, literature, media, multiarts, museums, music, presenters, statewide arts service organizations, theatre and visual and local arts agencies.

CONSULTING OR VOLUNTEER SERVICES:
Consultation on a limited basis to Indiana organizations and artists.

TYPE:
Block grants; Conferences/seminars; Development grants; General operating grants; Project/program grants; Technical assistance. Arts in education; Arts organizations and services; Capacity building; Individual artist projects. Most grants are awarded through a network of regional partners which serve all 92 counties.

YEAR PROGRAM STARTED: 1969

PURPOSE:
To act as public catalyst, partner and investor that serves the citizens of Indiana by funding, encouraging, promoting and expanding all the arts.

LEGAL BASIS:
State agency.

ELIGIBILITY:
Applicants must be private tax-exempt, not-for-profit arts organizations or public agencies or individual artists. Eligible organizations without tax-exempt status should submit a fiscal year budget. IAC does not fund capital improvements, purchase of permanent equipment, costs of receptions, foods or beverages or agents fees for programs contracted through commercial agencies.

GEOGRAPHIC RESTRICTIONS:
Indiana.

FINANCIAL DATA:
Amount of support per award: Varies.
Total amount of support: $3,600,000.
Matching fund requirements: Matching funds may include in-kind as well as cash.

APPLICATION INFORMATION:
Applicants must complete an application, grant agreement and any reporting required by the program guidelines. Program guidelines are available from the Commission. Potential applicants should contact the agency before applying.
Duration: July 1 through June 30, fiscal year.

PUBLICATIONS:
Monthy newsletters; press releases; grant/program guidelines.

IRS IDENTIFICATION NUMBER: 35-6000158

COMMISSION MEMBERS:
Jeanne E. Mirro, Chairperson
Karen Ellerbrook, Vice Chairperson
Judy Hess, Secretary
Gilberto Cardenas
John Ford
Linda W. Goad
Pam Hicks
Jeffrey Kirk
Linda S. Levell
Suzanne Rentschler
Kelly B. Schreckengast
Irene Smith-King
Richard Q. Stifel
Earl R. Williams
Trevor Yager

ADDRESS INQUIRIES TO:
Executive Director
(See address above.)

*SPECIAL STIPULATIONS:
Must have impact on the state of Indiana.

INSTITUTE OF AMERICAN INDIAN ARTS (IAIA)
83 Avan Nu Po Road
Santa Fe, NM 87508
(505) 424-2331
(800) 804-6422
Fax: (505) 424-4500

E-MAIL ADDRESS:
enrollment@iaia.edu

WEB SITE ADDRESS:
www.iaia.edu

TYPE:
Awards/prizes; Scholarships.

See entry 1117 for full listing.

INTERNATIONAL DOCUMENTARY ASSOCIATION [494]
1201 West 5th Street
Suite M270
Los Angeles, CA 90017-1461
(213) 534-3600
Fax: (213) 534-3610

E-MAIL ADDRESS:
info@documentary.org

WEB SITE ADDRESS:
www.documentary.org

FOUNDED: 1982

AREAS OF INTEREST:
Documentary film.

NAME(S) OF PROGRAMS:
● **IDA Music Documentary Award**
● **IDA/ABC News Videosource Award**
● **IDA/David L. Wolper Student Documentary Achievement Award**
● **Pare Lorentz Award**

TYPE:
Awards/prizes; Internships. IDA Music Documentary Award is given to a filmmaker for an outstanding documentary communicating the cultural importance of music and its power to enrich the human spirit.

IDA/ABC News Videosource Award is awarded for the best use of news footage as an integral component in a documentary.

IDA/David L. Wolper Student Documentary Achievement Award recognizes exceptional achievement in non-fiction film and video production at the university level and brings greater public and industry awareness to the work of students in the documentary field.

The Pare Lorentz Award winner will demonstrate one or more of Lorentz's central concerns: the appropriate use of the natural environment, justice for all and the illumination of pressing social problems, presented as a compelling story by skillful filmmaking.

YEAR PROGRAM STARTED: 1984

PURPOSE:
To promote nonfiction film and video around the world by supporting and recognizing the efforts of documentary film and video makers, increasing public appreciation and demand for the documentary, and providing a forum for documentary makers, their supporters and suppliers.

LEGAL BASIS:
501(c)(3).

FINANCIAL DATA:
Amount of support per award: IDA Music Documentary Award: $5,000; IDA/ABC News Videosource Award: $2,000 honorarium and $2,000 worth of research time at the ABC News Videosource; IDA/David L. Wolper Student Documentary Achievement Award: $1,000 honorarium, production of 1,000 DVDs courtesy of Magic Rock Entertainment and $1,000 certificate toward purchase of Kodak motion picture film; Pare Lorentz Award: $2,500 honorarium.

COOPERATIVE FUNDING PROGRAMS: Eastman Kodak Company.

NUMBER OF APPLICANTS MOST RECENT YEAR: 120.

NUMBER OF AWARDS: 4.

APPLICATION INFORMATION:
Guidelines and application form is available on the Association web site.
Duration: Annual awards.

IRS IDENTIFICATION NUMBER: 95-3911227

ADDRESS INQUIRIES TO:
Michael Lumpkin, Executive Director
(See address above.)

IOWA ARTS COUNCIL [495]
600 East Locust Street
Des Moines, IA 50319-0290
(515) 281-4641
Fax: (515) 242-6498

E-MAIL ADDRESS:
matthew.harris@iowa.gov

WEB SITE ADDRESS:
www.iowaartscouncil.org

FOUNDED: 1967

AREAS OF INTEREST:
All arts disciplines, primarily in Iowa.

CONSULTING OR VOLUNTEER SERVICES:
Technical assistance in a variety of disciplines and subject areas, including information.

NAME(S) OF PROGRAMS:
● **Arts Resources and Artists Programs**
● **Funding and Arts in Education Programs**
● **Technical Assistance and Community Development Programs**

TYPE:
Challenge/matching grants; Conferences/seminars; Development grants; General operating grants; Project/program grants; Residencies; Scholarships; Technical assistance; Training grants. Seminars, technical assistance and funding. Services provided to institutions and individuals statewide.

YEAR PROGRAM STARTED: 1967

PURPOSE:
To enrich the quality of life for Iowans through support of the arts.

LEGAL BASIS:
State agency established under Chapter 304A, Code of Iowa.

ELIGIBILITY:
Applicants must be nonprofit, tax-exempt organizations or Iowa individuals, age 18 or older (and not a student, artist or arts educator), who have resided in Iowa at least one year prior to application deadline.

Nonprofit organizations located in states bordering Iowa are eligible for support if the project clearly demonstrates that Iowans are being served.

GEOGRAPHIC RESTRICTIONS:
Iowa.

FINANCIAL DATA:
Amount of support per award: Varies.
Matching fund requirements: One-to-one cash or in-kind match for most grant programs.

REPRESENTATIVE AWARDS:
$1,800 to University of Iowa, Hancher Auditorium to host a residency with the Ying Quartet to introduce chamber music to patients, visitors, staff and students at the University of Iowa Hospitals and Clinics; $3,600 to the Fort Madison Area Arts Association to design an Iowa Sesquicentennial mural of Fort Madison and Lee County incorporating ideas from 250 area school children and to be painted by community volunteers.

APPLICATION INFORMATION:
Completed application form must be submitted. Applicants must prepare a narrative section for all applications.
Duration: 12 months or less.

PUBLICATIONS:
Online e-newsletter (monthly); Online Teaching Artists Roster; Online Performing Artists Roster; Online Folk Arts Directory; Online Directory of Iowa Artists and Performing Groups.

IRS IDENTIFICATION NUMBER: 42-6004812

STAFF:
Matthew Harris, Division Administrator
Sarah Ekstrand, Rosters and Special Projects
Linda Lee, Grants Administrator
Dawn Martinez Oropeza, Arts Education/Community Programs
Riki Saltzman, Folk and Traditional Arts
Bruce Williams, Public Art and Operating Support

ADDRESS INQUIRIES TO:
Matthew Harris
Division Administrator
(See address above.)

KENTUCKY ARTS COUNCIL [496]
500 Mero Street, 21st Floor
Frankfort, KY 40601-1987
(502) 564-8110 ext. 469
Fax: (502) 564-2839

E-MAIL ADDRESS:
kyarts@ky.gov

WEB SITE ADDRESS:
artscouncil.ky.gov

FOUNDED: 1966

AREAS OF INTEREST:
Arts development (visual arts, performing arts, literature and media), community development, artists-in-education and individual artists.

CONSULTING OR VOLUNTEER SERVICES:
Staff available for assistance in planning in above areas and in applying for grants.

NAME(S) OF PROGRAMS:
- **Arts Education Programs**
- **Arts Organizations**
- **Community Arts**
- **Individual Artists**

TYPE:
Awards/prizes; Fellowships; General
operating grants; Project/program grants;
Technical assistance. Arts development and
artist support.

YEAR PROGRAM STARTED: 1966

PURPOSE:
Grants are intended to help sponsoring
organizations and artists reach and develop
new audiences or strengthen themselves
artistically or managerially. The agency acts
as the funding and program coordinating
organization for the arts in Kentucky.

LEGAL BASIS:
State Arts Agency of the Commonwealth of
Kentucky.

ELIGIBILITY:
Nonprofit organizations incorporated in the
state of Kentucky or Kentucky artists. Most
grant programs require IRS tax-exempt
status.

GEOGRAPHIC RESTRICTIONS:
Kentucky.

FINANCIAL DATA:
Amount of support per award: $200 to
$135,000.
Total amount of support: $2,600,000
annually.
Matching fund requirements: Most programs
are dollar-for-dollar.

NUMBER OF APPLICANTS MOST RECENT YEAR:
500.

NUMBER OF AWARDS: 350.

APPLICATION INFORMATION:
Contact the Council to request application
information and forms.
Duration: One fiscal year, July 1 through
June 30.
Deadline: Varies.

PUBLICATIONS:
Bimonthly newsletter; guide to programs;
Kentucky Performing Arts on Tour Directory.

IRS IDENTIFICATION NUMBER: 61-0600439

OFFICERS:
Lori Meadows, Executive Director

ADDRESS INQUIRIES TO:
Lori Meadows, Executive Director
(See address above.)

LANNAN FOUNDATION
313 Read Street
Santa Fe, NM 87501-2628
(505) 986-8160
Fax: (505) 986-8195

WEB SITE ADDRESS:
www.lannan.org

TYPE:
Awards/prizes; Challenge/matching grants;
Demonstration grants; Development grants;
Fellowships; General operating grants;
Project/program grants. The Lannan Literary
Awards recognize established writers of
fiction, nonfiction and poetry. Awards are
given to writers whom the Foundation
believes to have made a significant
contribution to English-language literature

and to writers of distinctive literary merit
who demonstrate potential for outstanding
future work.

The Prize for Cultural Freedom was
established to recognize people whose
extraordinary and courageous work celebrates
the human right to freedom of imagination,
inquiry and expression. As defined by the
Foundation, cultural freedom is the right of
individuals and communities to define and
protect valued and diverse ways of life
currently threatened by globalization.

Visual Art Grants fund organizations which
support contemporary art.

Indigenous Communities Grants funds a
national grant program limited to the urgent
needs of rural Native American communities.
Funding priority is given to indigenous
projects for education, the revival and
preservation of languages and cultures, legal
rights, environmental protection and
economic development which is sustainable
and consistent with traditional values.

See entry 720 for full listing.

THE LEEWAY FOUNDATION
1315 Walnut Street
Suite 832
Philadelphia, PA 19107
(215) 545-4078
Fax: (215) 545-4021

E-MAIL ADDRESS:
info@leeway.org

WEB SITE ADDRESS:
www.leeway.org

TYPE:
Project/program grants. Art and Change
Grant: Semiannual award for women and
trans artists who engage in art and social
change work and have financial need.

Leeway Transformation Award: Celebrates
women and trans artists who create art and
social change and have done so for the past
five years or more, demonstrating a
commitment to art for social change work.

See entry 1151 for full listing.

LEHIGH VALLEY COMMUNITY FOUNDATION   [497]
961 Marcon Boulevard
Suite 300
Allentown, PA 18109-9521
(610) 266-4284
Fax: (610) 266-4285

E-MAIL ADDRESS:
lvcf@lehighvalleyfoundation.org

WEB SITE ADDRESS:
www.lehighvalleyfoundation.org

FOUNDED: 1967

AREAS OF INTEREST:
Arts and culture, community development,
education, environment, health care, history
and heritage, human services and science.

TYPE:
Project/program grants.

PURPOSE:
To promote philanthropy in order to improve
the quality of life in the Foundation's region.

LEGAL BASIS:
Nonprofit, tax-exempt 501(c)(3) organization.

ELIGIBILITY:
Limited to nonprofit, tax-exempt
organizations serving citizens within the
geographic limits of its outreach.

GEOGRAPHIC RESTRICTIONS:
Lehigh and Northampton counties,
Pennsylvania, with limited funding also
available for Monroe and upper Bucks
counties, Pennsylvania.

FINANCIAL DATA:
Amount of support per award: Average
discretionary grant: $5,000.
Total amount of support: $1,034,813 from
both discretionary and non-discretionary
funds for fiscal year ended June 30, 2010.

NUMBER OF APPLICANTS MOST RECENT YEAR:
30 for the year 2010.

NUMBER OF AWARDS: 15 for the year 2010.

APPLICATION INFORMATION:
Application can be downloaded from the
Foundation's web site. Financial sheet must
be submitted with grant application.
Deadline: July 1. Notification December 15.

STAFF:
Carol Henn, Executive Director

ADDRESS INQUIRIES TO:
Carol Henn, Executive Director
(See address above.)

THE JOHN J. LEIDY FOUNDATION
305 West Chesapeake Avenue
Suite 308
Towson, MD 21204
(410) 821-3006
Fax: (410) 821-3007

E-MAIL ADDRESS:
info@leidyfoundation.org

WEB SITE ADDRESS:
www.leidyfoundation.org

TYPE:
General operating grants; Scholarships.

See entry 1403 for full listing.

THE LIBERACE FOUNDATION FOR THE PERFORMING AND CREATIVE ARTS   [498]
1775 East Tropicana Avenue
Las Vegas, NV 89119-6529
(702) 798-5595
Fax: (702) 798-7386

E-MAIL ADDRESS:
scholarship@liberace.org

WEB SITE ADDRESS:
www.liberace.org

FOUNDED: 1976

AREAS OF INTEREST:
College education in performing and creative
arts.

NAME(S) OF PROGRAMS:
- **Liberace Scholars**

TYPE:
Challenge/matching grants; Scholarships.
Scholarships and awards to colleges that
prepare students for careers in the arts.

YEAR PROGRAM STARTED: 1976

PURPOSE:
To provide grants to accredited colleges and
universities that offer degrees in the
performing and creative arts.

LEGAL BASIS:
501(c)(3) organization.

ELIGIBILITY:
Accredited colleges, universities or conservatories that offer degrees in the creative or performing arts. Limited to juniors, seniors and graduate students.

FINANCIAL DATA:
The grant is solely for tuition.
Amount of support per award: Varies.
Total amount of support: $200,000 for the year 2008-09.
Matching fund requirements: 1:1.

NUMBER OF APPLICANTS MOST RECENT YEAR:
70.

APPLICATION INFORMATION:
Deadline: March 15.

IRS IDENTIFICATION NUMBER: 95-3044116

ADDRESS INQUIRIES TO:
E-mail: dan@joshuatreetv.com

*SPECIAL STIPULATIONS:
Awards are limited to college juniors and seniors or graduate students.

LOUISIANA DIVISION OF THE ARTS, DEPARTMENT OF CULTURE, RECREATION AND TOURISM [499]
1051 North Third Street, Room 420
Baton Rouge, LA 70802
(225) 342-8180
(225) 342-6083 (grants line)
Fax: (225) 342-8173

E-MAIL ADDRESS:
arts@crt.state.la.us

WEB SITE ADDRESS:
www.crt.state.la.us/arts

FOUNDED: 1976

AREAS OF INTEREST:
Arts education.

NAME(S) OF PROGRAMS:
● **Arts-in-Education**

TYPE:
General operating grants. Categories:
(1) Artists in Residence;
(2) General Program Support;
(3) Planning and;
(4) Implementation.

YEAR PROGRAM STARTED: 1976

PURPOSE:
To ensure the arts are a part of the basic curriculum for every student in Louisiana schools.

ELIGIBILITY:
All categories of arts-in-education grants are open to all artists who have a fiscal agent and partnership with a school and arts organizations with a 501(c)(3) status. Other 501(c)(3) organizations are eligible for all categories except General Program Support.

GEOGRAPHIC RESTRICTIONS:
Louisiana.

FINANCIAL DATA:
Amount of support per award: Varies.
Total amount of support: Varies.

APPLICATION INFORMATION:
Guidelines are available online.
Deadline: First business day in March.

STAFF:
Bethany France, Director of Arts-in-Education Services

ADDRESS INQUIRIES TO:
Bethany France, Director of Arts-in-Education Services
Tel: (225) 342-8209
E-mail: bfrance@crt.state.la.us

LOUISIANA DIVISION OF THE ARTS, DEPARTMENT OF CULTURE, RECREATION AND TOURISM [500]
1051 North Third Street, Room 420
Baton Rouge, LA 70802
(225) 342-8180
Fax: (225) 342-8173

E-MAIL ADDRESS:
arts@crt.state.la.us

WEB SITE ADDRESS:
www.crt.state.la.us/arts

FOUNDED: 1976

AREAS OF INTEREST:
Dance, design, folklife, literature, media, music, theater, visual arts and crafts, arts-in-education, and arts service organizations.

CONSULTING OR VOLUNTEER SERVICES:
Grants writing, program development, community development, and alternate funding sources.

NAME(S) OF PROGRAMS:
● **Decentralized Arts Funding Program**
● **Statewide Arts Grants Programs**

TYPE:
Awards/prizes; Conferences/seminars; Training grants. Stabilization grants. Grants in a variety of programs are offered to arts organizations across the state.

Stabilization grants are offered in four levels of operating support to nonprofit arts organizations.

YEAR PROGRAM STARTED: 1977

PURPOSE:
To support established and emerging arts organizations; to stimulate public participation in the arts.

LEGAL BASIS:
Government agency (the official state arts agency of Louisiana).

ELIGIBILITY:
Grants are available for nonprofit arts organizations, traditional Louisiana cultures and arts-in-education programming. Organizations domiciled in Louisiana are eligible to apply for grants to support arts activities taking place in Louisiana.

Eligible applicants generally fall into one of the following categories: nonprofit 501(c)(3) organizations, public or private educational institutions, colleges or universities sponsoring arts activities intended for community participation (not academic, credit-producing, or curriculum-oriented projects), agencies of local, parish, or state government such as state or parish libraries, units of municipal government, parish police juries and agencies of state government.

GEOGRAPHIC RESTRICTIONS:
Louisiana.

FINANCIAL DATA:
Amount of support per award: Decentralized Arts Funding Program: $500 to $15,000; Local Arts Agencies: $3,600 to $123,600; Stabilization: $2,500 to $45,000.
Matching fund requirements: Decentralized Arts Funding Program: No minimum match requirement; Stabilization and Local Arts Agencies: Dollar-for-dollar or as high as 3:1.

APPLICATION INFORMATION:
Applications are available online.
Duration: One year.
Deadline: First business day in March.

ADDRESS INQUIRIES TO:
Kelly Pepper, Director of Organization and Community Development
Tel: (225) 342-8175
E-mail: kpepper@crt.state.la.us

THE MACDOWELL COLONY [501]
100 High Street
Peterborough, NH 03458
(603) 924-3886
(212) 535-9690
Fax: (603) 924-9142; (212) 737-3803

E-MAIL ADDRESS:
info@macdowellcolony.org
admissions@macdowellcolony.org

WEB SITE ADDRESS:
www.macdowellcolony.org

FOUNDED: 1907

AREAS OF INTEREST:
Writing, theatre, visual art, music composition, filmmaking, architecture and interdisciplinary art.

NAME(S) OF PROGRAMS:
● **Artist Residency Program**

TYPE:
Fellowships; Residencies; Travel grants. Residency fellowships for established and emerging writers and playwrights, visual artists (painters, photographers, printmakers, sculptors, etc.), composers, filmmakers, architects and interdisciplinary artists to support periods of creative work from two weeks to two months in an inspiring environment at The MacDowell Colony in New Hampshire.

YEAR PROGRAM STARTED: 1907

PURPOSE:
To nurture the arts by offering creative individuals of the highest talent an inspiring environment in which they can produce enduring works of the imagination.

LEGAL BASIS:
Nonprofit corporation, certified by IRS as falling under Code Section 509(a)(2).

ELIGIBILITY:
Talent is the sole criterion for acceptance. Established artists as well as emerging artists of promising talent are encouraged to apply.

FINANCIAL DATA:
Fellowships defray the costs of room, board and the use of an independent studio. Limited travel funds are available. There are no residency fees. Artist stipends available for artists-in-residence, based on need.
Amount of support per award: Fellowships equivalent to the cost of residency ($10,000). Stipends and travel grants up to $1,000.
Total amount of support: $2,600,000.

NUMBER OF APPLICANTS MOST RECENT YEAR: 2,534.

NUMBER OF AWARDS: Approximately 250 artists-in-residence.

APPLICATION INFORMATION:
Application forms accompanied by specified work samples and a $30 application fee are required before seasonal deadlines. Read guidelines before completing application.
Duration: Residence periods are from two weeks to two months. No more than one admission per 12-month period.
Deadline: January 15, April 15 and September 15, four to seven months in advance of residency.

PUBLICATIONS:
Application guidelines.

OFFICERS AND STAFF:
Michael Chabon, Chairman, Board of Directors
Susan Davenport Austin, President
Cheryl A. Young, Executive Director

ADDRESS INQUIRIES TO:
Admissions Director
(See address above.)

MAINE ARTS COMMISSION   [502]

193 State Street
25 State House Station
Augusta, ME 04333-0025
(207) 287-2724
(207) 287-2750
Fax: (207) 287-2725
TTY: (877) 887-3878

E-MAIL ADDRESS:
kathy.shaw@maine.gov

WEB SITE ADDRESS:
www.mainearts.com

FOUNDED: 1966

AREAS OF INTEREST:
Arts.

CONSULTING OR VOLUNTEER SERVICES:
Opportunities for artists and arts organization.

NAME(S) OF PROGRAMS:
- **Artists in Maine Communities**
- **Arts and Humanities Grants**
- **Arts Visibility**
- **Celebrating the Traditional Arts**
- **Creative Communities = Economic Development**
- **Good Idea Grants: Contemporary**
- **Great Work(s)**
- **Individual Artist Fellowships**
- **Innovative Production Grant**
- **Jane Morrison Film Scholarship**
- **SMART**
- **Ticket to Ride**
- **Traditional Arts Apprenticeships**
- **Traditional Arts Fellowships**

TYPE:
Block grants; Fellowships; Project/program grants; Residencies. Traditional arts apprenticeships.

YEAR PROGRAM STARTED: 1966

PURPOSE:
To encourage and stimulate public interest and participation in the cultural heritage and cultural programs of our state; to expand the state's cultural resources; to encourage and

assist freedom of artistic expression for the well-being of the arts; to meet the needs and aspirations of persons in all parts of the state.

LEGAL BASIS:
Government agency.

ELIGIBILITY:
Applicants must be nonprofit Maine arts organizations, individual artists, schools and/or certain units of city/state or tribal government.

GEOGRAPHIC RESTRICTIONS:
Maine.

FINANCIAL DATA:
Amount of support per award: Generally $1,500 to $50,000.
Total amount of support: $712,813 for the year 2009.
Matching fund requirements: 1:1, cash or in-kind for most grants. No matching requirement for grants to individual artists.

COOPERATIVE FUNDING PROGRAMS: Maine Community Foundation; Maine Humanities Council.

NUMBER OF APPLICANTS MOST RECENT YEAR: 595.

NUMBER OF AWARDS: 123 for the year 2009.

APPLICATION INFORMATION:
Applicant must speak with a staff member about the project before submitting an application. Failure to do so will disqualify the applicant.

Application forms must be submitted electronically through e-grants program.
Duration: Varies from 30 days to a full fiscal year period.
Deadline: Varies for all programs.

PUBLICATIONS:
Maine arts magazine; various program brochures.

IRS IDENTIFICATION NUMBER: 01-6000001

COMMISSION MEMBERS:
John M. Rohman, Chairperson
Owen Smith, Vice Chairperson

ADDRESS INQUIRIES TO:
Kathy Ann Shaw
Senior Grants Associate
(See address above.)

ROBERT MAPPLETHORPE FOUNDATION, INC.   [503]

477 Madison Avenue, 15th Floor
New York, NY 10022-5835
(212) 755-3025
Fax: (212) 941-4764

E-MAIL ADDRESS:
joree@mapplethorpe.org

WEB SITE ADDRESS:
www.mapplethorpe.org

FOUNDED: 1988

AREAS OF INTEREST:
Photography as an art form; scientific study of AIDS and AIDS-related research in order to help find a cure.

NAME(S) OF PROGRAMS:
- **Photography Program**

TYPE:
Project/program grants. Assists in creation or expansion of photography departments in museums and other public institutions.

Emphasis is on the acquisition of photographs or the support for study and exhibition facilities.

YEAR PROGRAM STARTED: 1988

ELIGIBILITY:
The Foundation will not provide grants or scholarships to individual photographers. The Foundation will supply museums and other public institutions by assisting in the creation or expansion of photographic departments.

FINANCIAL DATA:
Amount of support per award: Varies.
Total amount of support: Varies.

APPLICATION INFORMATION:
There is no formal application form.
Duration: Varies.
Deadline: Proposals are accepted on a continuing basis.

ADDRESS INQUIRIES TO:
Joree Adilman, Foundation Manager
(See address above.)

EDWARD AND BETTY MARCUS FOUNDATION   [504]

P.O. Box 227437
Dallas, TX 75222-7437
(214) 361-4681
Fax: (214) 941-3103

E-MAIL ADDRESS:
bancroft@marcusfoundation.net

FOUNDED: 1984

AREAS OF INTEREST:
Visual arts and visual arts education in Texas.

TYPE:
Project/program grants. The project/program grants are in visual arts education.

PURPOSE:
To increase understanding and appreciation of visual arts through direct support of visual arts institutions and education.

LEGAL BASIS:
Private foundation.

ELIGIBILITY:
Applicants must be tax-exempt IRS 501(c)(3) organizations located and operating in Texas. The Foundation will not fund capital campaigns, individuals, scholarships, religious organizations, annual drives and operating funds.

GEOGRAPHIC RESTRICTIONS:
Texas.

FINANCIAL DATA:
Amount of support per award: Varies.

APPLICATION INFORMATION:
Guidelines available on request.
Duration: One to three years possible.

PUBLICATIONS:
Guidelines; annual report.

ADDRESS INQUIRIES TO:
M'Lou Bancroft, Executive Director
(See address above.)

MARYLAND STATE ARTS COUNCIL   [505]

175 West Ostend Street
Suite E
Baltimore, MD 21230
(410) 767-6555
Fax: (410) 333-1062
TDD/TTY: (410) 333-4519

E-MAIL ADDRESS:
msac@msac.org

WEB SITE ADDRESS:
www.msac.org

FOUNDED: 1967

AREAS OF INTEREST:
Arts.

NAME(S) OF PROGRAMS:
- **Artists in Education**
- **Arts and Entertainment Districts Program**
- **Arts in Communities**
- **Community Arts Development**
- **Grants for Organizations**
- **Individual Artist Awards**
- **Maryland Folklife Program**
- **Public Art Program**

TYPE:
Awards/prizes; Block grants; Challenge/matching grants; General operating grants; Project/program grants; Residencies; Technical assistance. Arts program, arts project grants. Individual artist awards. The Council awards grants to county arts councils in Maryland through its Community Arts Development program.

The Maryland Folklife program is dedicated to the identification, documentation and presentation of Maryland traditional artists to general audiences through public life and educational activities.

The Artists in Education program is designed to increase access to a range of artistic disciplines and to assist schools in integrating the arts into the curriculum. Projects vary in length from one-day visits to four-week residencies.

The Arts in Communities program awards grants for up to $1,000 for arts activities undertaken by organizations not currently receiving MSAC funding.

The Grants for Organizations Program provides support to those who produce or present the arts to the public.

YEAR PROGRAM STARTED: 1967

PURPOSE:
To make the arts more widely available to all Maryland residents, to strengthen the state's cultural institutions and to encourage the development of resident artistic activity throughout the state.

LEGAL BASIS:
Article 41 of the Annotated Code of Maryland as amended, Sections 387 to 395, inclusive.

ELIGIBILITY:
Applying organizations must be not-for-profit, tax-exempt and incorporated in the state of Maryland. Individuals must be 18 years of age or older and a Maryland resident.

Funding is not provided for acquisition of capital assets, capital improvements, depreciation, deficits, capital debt reduction and contributions to endowments.

GEOGRAPHIC RESTRICTIONS:
Maryland.

FINANCIAL DATA:
Amount of support per award: Varies.
Total amount of support: Varies.
Matching fund requirements: 1:1

APPLICATION INFORMATION:
Guidelines and grant application forms may be acquired by writing to the Council office.
Duration: Up to one year. No grants are automatically renewable.

EXECUTIVE DIRECTOR:
Theresa Colvin

ADDRESS INQUIRIES TO:
Theresa Colvin, Executive Director
(See address above.)

MASSACHUSETTS CULTURAL COUNCIL [506]
10 St. James Avenue
3rd Floor
Boston, MA 02116-3803
(617) 727-3668
(800) 232-0960
Fax: (617) 727-0044
TTY: (617) 338-9153

E-MAIL ADDRESS:
mcc@art.state.ma.us

WEB SITE ADDRESS:
www.massculturalcouncil.org

FOUNDED: 1966

AREAS OF INTEREST:
The arts, humanities and interpretive sciences in Massachusetts.

NAME(S) OF PROGRAMS:
- **John and Abigail Adams Arts Program for Cultural Economic Development**
- **Artist Grants**
- **The Big Yellow School Bus**
- **Cultural Investment Portfolio**
- **Local Cultural Council Program**
- **Massachusetts Cultural Facilities Fund**
- **STARS Residencies**
- **Traditional Arts Apprenticeship**
- **YouthReach Initiative**

TYPE:
Conferences/seminars; Fellowships; Formula grants; General operating grants; Project/program grants; Technical assistance.

LEGAL BASIS:
State agency.

ELIGIBILITY:
Applicants need to be either a nonprofit organization in Massachusetts or a legal resident of the state. Additional requirements vary per program.

GEOGRAPHIC RESTRICTIONS:
Massachusetts.

FINANCIAL DATA:
Amount of support per award: Varies according to program.

NUMBER OF APPLICANTS MOST RECENT YEAR:
Approximately 10,500.

NUMBER OF AWARDS: Approximately 5,000.

APPLICATION INFORMATION:
Duration: One or three years, depending on program.
Deadline: Varies by program.

PUBLICATIONS:
Application guidelines.

STAFF:
Anita Walker, Executive Director
Charlie McDermott, Deputy Director

BOARD:
Ira Lapidus, Chairperson
Barbara W. Grossman, Vice Chairperson

ADDRESS INQUIRIES TO:
Tel: (617) 727-3668

THE METROPOLITAN MUSEUM OF ART [507]
1000 Fifth Avenue
New York, NY 10028-0198
(212) 650-2763
Fax: (212) 396-5168

E-MAIL ADDRESS:
education.grants@metmuseum.org

WEB SITE ADDRESS:
www.metmuseum.org

FOUNDED: 1870

AREAS OF INTEREST:
Study or research in American visual and decorative arts.

NAME(S) OF PROGRAMS:
- **The Douglass Foundation Fellowship in American Art**

TYPE:
Fellowships. Fellowship is awarded in honor of John K. Howat. It is given to a promising young scholar for one year's study or research in the American Wing (in either the Department of American Paintings and Sculpture or the Department of American Decorative Arts) on an aspect of the Museum's collection.

PURPOSE:
To promote study and research in American visual and decorative arts.

ELIGIBILITY:
Applicants should have been enrolled for at least one year in an advanced degree program in the field of American art or culture.

FINANCIAL DATA:
Amount of support per award: $30,000, plus up to $5,000 for travel and miscellaneous expenses.
Total amount of support: Varies.

APPLICATION INFORMATION:
Fellowship applications must be submitted in English. Three letters of recommendation are required, none of which may be from current Metropolitan Museum of Art staff. The submission of the required letters of recommendation in English is encouraged. Applicants must submit a typed application in triplicate including the following, in the order listed below:
(1) name, home and present address, telephone number and e-mail address;
(2) full resume of education and employment;
(3) a two-part statement, not to exceed 1,000 words, specifying what the applicant wishes to accomplish during the fellowship period and detailing how the Museum's resources can be utilized to accomplish the applicant's goals;
(4) tentative schedule of work to be accomplished during the fellowship period;
(5) tentative schedule of travel required during the fellowship period;
(6) three letters of recommendation (at least one academic and one professional); these should be sent directly to the above address;
(7) list of other applications for fellowships or grants applied for in same period and;
(8) for predoctoral applicants only, official undergraduate and graduate transcripts (original plus two copies).
Deadline: First Friday in November.

ADDRESS INQUIRIES TO:
Marcie Karp, Managing Museum Educator
Academic Programs Education Department
(See address above.)

MICHIGAN COUNCIL FOR ARTS AND CULTURAL AFFAIRS   [508]

300 North Washington Square
Lansing, MI 48913
(517) 241-4011
Fax: (517) 241-3979

E-MAIL ADDRESS:
   braceyj@michigan.org

WEB SITE ADDRESS:
   www.themedc.org/arts

FOUNDED: 1966

AREAS OF INTEREST:
   Arts.

CONSULTING OR VOLUNTEER SERVICES:
   Consulting services in the arts, management, development, consultations and workshops, conferences, communications, media development and artist services.

NAME(S) OF PROGRAMS:
   • **Program for Operational and Projects Support**
   • **School Bus Grants**

TYPE:
   General operating grants; Project/program grants. Grants and services to organizations for the production, development, promotion and support of the arts in Michigan.

   School Bus Grants assist in covering school bus transportation costs to visit museums, musical or theatrical performances, zoos, science centers, etc.

PURPOSE:
   To develop and encourage programs and projects that make music, painting, literature, cinema, dance, sculpture, crafts, architecture and all the arts available to the people of Michigan, regardless of their age, location, background or economic status; to support activities of Michigan artists.

LEGAL BASIS:
   State agency.

ELIGIBILITY:
   Generally, grants will be awarded only for activities within the state of Michigan. For most programs, applicants should be Michigan-based nonprofit tax-exempt organizations residing in Michigan. The Council ordinarily does not finance an existing deficit, capital improvements, curriculum-oriented activities or permanent equipment.

GEOGRAPHIC RESTRICTIONS:
   Michigan.

FINANCIAL DATA:
   Amount of support per award: Varies.
   Total amount of support: $2,300,000 for the year 2011.
   Matching fund requirements: Varies with program.

COOPERATIVE FUNDING PROGRAMS:
   Re-Granting and Partnership programs.

NUMBER OF APPLICANTS MOST RECENT YEAR:
   310 for the year 2009.

NUMBER OF AWARDS: 290 for the year 2009.

APPLICATION INFORMATION:
   Guidelines and application forms for each program are revised in the early fall each year and are available upon request.
   Duration: One year, October 1 through September 30.

PUBLICATIONS:
   Program guidelines; factsheet.

IRS IDENTIFICATION NUMBER: 38-6000134

OFFICERS:
   Nheena Ittner, Chairman
   John Bracey, Executive Director

ADDRESS INQUIRIES TO:
   John Bracey, Executive Director
   (See address above.)

MID ATLANTIC ARTS FOUNDATION   [509]

201 North Charles Street
Suite 401
Baltimore, MD 21201
(410) 539-6656 ext. 104
Fax: (410) 837-5517

E-MAIL ADDRESS:
   maaf@midatlanticarts.org

WEB SITE ADDRESS:
   www.midatlanticarts.org

FOUNDED: 1979

AREAS OF INTEREST:
   Regional arts activities crossing state lines in Delaware, District of Columbia, Maryland, New Jersey, New York, Pennsylvania, Virginia, West Virginia and the U.S. Virgin Islands; international funding through USArtists International.

NAME(S) OF PROGRAMS:
   • **American Masterpieces**
   • **Arts Information Exchange Program (AIEX)**
   • **ArtsConnect**
   • **French-American Jazz Exchange**
   • **jazz.NEXT**
   • **Jazz Touring Network**
   • **Living Legacy Jazz Award**
   • **Mid Atlantic Creative Fellowships**
   • **Mid Atlantic Folk Arts Outreach Program**
   • **Mid Atlantic Tours**
   • **On Screen/In Person**
   • **Pennsylvania Performing Arts on Tour**
   • **Special Presenter Initiatives**
   • **USArtists International**

TYPE:
   Fellowships; Project/program grants; Residencies; Technical assistance.

YEAR PROGRAM STARTED: 1979

PURPOSE:
   To promote the sharing of arts resources among the Foundation's partner states.

LEGAL BASIS:
   Private, not-for-profit organization.

ELIGIBILITY:
   Individuals and organizations must be based in the region for most programs. Other requirements vary according to the specific program.

   American Masterpieces and Mid Atlantic Tours provide fee support for foundation-initiated performing arts tours.

   ArtsConnect provides artist fee support to not-for-profit presenting networks comprised of at least three Mid Atlantic-based organizations.

   French-American Jazz Exchange supports projects between French and American jazz artists.

   Mid Atlantic Creative Fellowships places an artist from each member state in residence at selected organizations. A different artistic discipline is selected each year for foundation support.

On Screen/In Person provides fee subsidy to film series host sites.

   USArtists International supports music, dance, and theatre artists at international festivals.

GEOGRAPHIC RESTRICTIONS:
   Delaware, District of Columbia, Maryland, New Jersey, New York, North Carolina, Ohio, Pennsylvania, Virginia, West Virginia and the U.S. Virgin Islands.

FINANCIAL DATA:
   Amount of support per award: $1,000 to $15,000.
   Matching fund requirements: Varies according to program.

COOPERATIVE FUNDING PROGRAMS:
   Pennsylvania Performing Arts on Tour.

NUMBER OF APPLICANTS MOST RECENT YEAR:
   More than 1,000.

NUMBER OF AWARDS: More than 500.

APPLICATION INFORMATION:
   Guidelines available on the web site.
   Duration: Varies.
   Deadline: Varies.

PUBLICATIONS:
   Guidelines; monthly e-mail newsletter; biennial report.

IRS IDENTIFICATION NUMBER: 52-1169382

STAFF:
   Alan W. Cooper, Executive Director

MID-AMERICA ARTS ALLIANCE   [510]

2018 Baltimore Avenue
Kansas City, MO 64108
(816) 421-1388
Fax: (816) 421-3918

E-MAIL ADDRESS:
   lindag@maaa.org

WEB SITE ADDRESS:
   www.maaa.org

FOUNDED: 1972

AREAS OF INTEREST:
   Performing and visual arts (traveling exhibits) throughout the U.S.

CONSULTING OR VOLUNTEER SERVICES:
   Consulting on sponsorship in all phases of performing and visual arts.

NAME(S) OF PROGRAMS:
   • **Regional Touring Program**
   • **Touring Exhibits through ExhibitsUSA**

TYPE:
   Project/program grants; Technical assistance. Support and project/program grants for community arts projects and touring performing arts.

YEAR PROGRAM STARTED: 1973

PURPOSE:
   To increase the access to high quality arts programs and to sponsor competency.

LEGAL BASIS:
   Missouri corporation, 501(c)(3).

ELIGIBILITY:
   Nonprofit organizations presenting M-AAA touring programs in Arkansas, Kansas, Missouri, Nebraska, Oklahoma and Texas may apply. Visual arts exhibitors throughout the country may request traveling exhibits.

GEOGRAPHIC RESTRICTIONS:
Arkansas, Kansas, Missouri, Nebraska, Oklahoma and Texas.

FINANCIAL DATA:
Amount of support per award: Varies.
Total amount of support: Varies.
Matching fund requirements: Presenters must pay unsubsidized portion of program cost.

COOPERATIVE FUNDING PROGRAMS: State arts agencies of Arkansas, Kansas, Missouri, Nebraska, Oklahoma, Texas, corporations and foundations, and the National Endowment for the Arts.

PUBLICATIONS:
Biannual report; annual touring program books for performing arts and ExhibitsUSA; exhibit catalogs.

IRS IDENTIFICATION NUMBER: 23-7303693

OFFICERS:
Mary Kennedy McCabe, Executive Director

ADDRESS INQUIRIES TO:
Linda Gramse, Executive Assistant
(See address above.)

THE MILLAY COLONY FOR THE ARTS, INC. [511]
454 East Hill Road
Austerlitz, NY 12017-0003
(518) 392-3103
Fax: (518) 392-4144 (call first)

E-MAIL ADDRESS:
apply@millaycolony.org

WEB SITE ADDRESS:
www.millaycolony.org

FOUNDED: 1973

AREAS OF INTEREST:
Writing, composing, music and visual arts.

TYPE:
Residencies. The Millay Colony offers one-month residencies from the months of April through November for visual artists, writers and composers in order to immerse themselves in creative work. The Colony accommodates a multidisciplinary group of six to seven artists each month. The Colony's Main Building is fully accessible for artists with disabilities.

YEAR PROGRAM STARTED: 1974

PURPOSE:
To provide space, studio and time for writers and composers to immerse themselves in their work.

ELIGIBILITY:
Residents are selected after undergoing an application and juried process. Juries make selections anonymously.

FINANCIAL DATA:
No cash grant is made, nor is any residency fee required. Meals are provided.

NUMBER OF APPLICANTS MOST RECENT YEAR:
625 for the year 2009.

NUMBER OF AWARDS: 48 to 50 per year.

APPLICATION INFORMATION:
Online application process is available. An application form may also be requested by sending a self-addressed, stamped envelope to the address above.

An application fee of $35 is required for U.S. applicants, and a $60 application fee is required for international applicants.

Duration: Residencies are for one month.

Deadline: October 1 for the following April through November.

DIRECTORS:
Caroline Crumpacker, Executive Director

ADDRESS INQUIRIES TO:
Calliope Nicholas, Residency Director
(See address above.)

JOAN MITCHELL FOUNDATION [512]
545 West 25th Street, 15th Floor
New York, NY 10001
(212) 524-0100
Fax: (212) 524-0101

E-MAIL ADDRESS:
info@joanmitchellfoundation.org

WEB SITE ADDRESS:
www.joanmitchellfoundation.org

AREAS OF INTEREST:
Art: painting and sculpture.

NAME(S) OF PROGRAMS:
● **MFA Grant Program**
● **Painters and Sculptors Grant Program**

TYPE:
Emerging grants. Stipends. Awarded in recognition of artistic merit and financial need, to further artistic careers.

PURPOSE:
To demonstrate that painting and sculpture are significant cultural necessities; to encourage the ambitions of developing artists.

ELIGIBILITY:
By nomination only.

FINANCIAL DATA:
Amount of support per award: MFA Grants: $15,000; Painters and Sculptors Grants: $25,000.

NUMBER OF AWARDS: MFA Grants: 15; Painters and Sculptors Grants: 25.

APPLICATION INFORMATION:
Candidates are nominated and contacted by the Foundation.
Duration: One-time award.

ADDRESS INQUIRIES TO:
Allison Hawkins, Grants Program Director
(See address above.)

THE MOODY FOUNDATION
2302 Post Office Street, Suite 704
Galveston, TX 77550
(409) 797-1500
Fax: (409) 763-5564

E-MAIL ADDRESS:
pmmoore@moodyf.org

WEB SITE ADDRESS:
www.moodyf.org

TYPE:
Capital grants; Challenge/matching grants; Research grants; Scholarships. Capital campaigns; Equipment; Matching funds; Building/renovation; Program development and research.

See entry 262 for full listing.

MARIETTA MCNEILL MORGAN AND SAMUEL TATE MORGAN, JR. FOUNDATION
Bank of America
Philanthropic Management VA2-300-12-99
1111 East Main Street, 12th Floor
P.O. Box 26688
Richmond, VA 23261-6688
(804) 788-2963
Fax: (804) 788-2700

TYPE:
Capital grants; Challenge/matching grants. Grants for capital only. No grants to individuals, for endowment funds or operating funds.

See entry 1599 for full listing.

WILLIAM MORRIS SOCIETY IN THE U.S. [513]
P.O. Box 53263
Washington, DC 20009

E-MAIL ADDRESS:
us@morrissociety.org

WEB SITE ADDRESS:
www.morrissociety.org

FOUNDED: 1957

AREAS OF INTEREST:
The life and work of William Morris as a craftsman, designer and writer.

NAME(S) OF PROGRAMS:
● **Joseph R. Dunlap Memorial Fellowship**
● **William Morris Society Award**

TYPE:
Fellowships; Research grants; Scholarships; Travel grants; Visiting scholars; Research contracts. Supports scholarly, creative, and translation projects about William Morris and his designs, writings and other work.

YEAR PROGRAM STARTED: 1995

PURPOSE:
To support research projects that deal with any subject relating to William Morris.

LEGAL BASIS:
Society.

ELIGIBILITY:
Projects may deal with any subject - biographical, literary, historical, social, artistic, political, typographical - relating to Morris. They may be scholarly or creative, and may include translations or the preparation of educational materials. Applicants for all awards may be from any country. Applications are particularly encouraged from younger members of the Society and from those at the beginning of their careers. Recipients need not have an academic or institutional appointment and the Ph.D. is not required.

FINANCIAL DATA:
Amount of support per award: Up to $1,000.

APPLICATION INFORMATION:
Applicants are asked to submit a resume and a two-page description of their projects, including a timeline and an indication of where the results might be published. At least one recommendation should be sent separately. Submissions will not be accepted via e-mail.

For translation submissions, send one copy of the translation (of the published version, if relevant), with a letter of reference from someone acquainted with both languages assessing the quality of the translation. Translations should have been completed within the past five years.

For teaching materials, no letters of recommendation are needed, but enclose a cover letter describing the ways in which the materials might be (or already have been) used in learning situations.

Duration: One year.

Deadline: December 15. Announcement by January 15.

PUBLICATIONS:
Announcement.

ADDRESS INQUIRIES TO:
Florence Boos, Vice President
(See address above.)

NATIONAL ENDOWMENT FOR THE ARTS   [514]

1100 Pennsylvania Avenue, N.W.
Washington, DC 20506
(202) 682-5400

WEB SITE ADDRESS:
www.arts.gov

FOUNDED: 1965

AREAS OF INTEREST:
National artistic accomplishments of the past, present and future.

TYPE:
Fellowships; Project/program grants. The Arts Endowment offers assistance for a full range of arts disciplines, and types and sizes of organizations involved in the arts.

YEAR PROGRAM STARTED: 1966

PURPOSE:
To support artists, art forms, art events, art education, and to conserve highly significant works of art.

LEGAL BASIS:
The National Foundation on the Arts and Humanities Act of 1965, Public Law 89-209, as amended.

ELIGIBILITY:
Individuals who apply must be published (not self-published) authors or poets.

Grants are awarded only for specific projects. A project may consist of one or more specific events or activities. All phases of a project, from planning to implementation, are eligible. A project does not have to be new; existing projects are competitive. An organization must be nonprofit, 501(c)(3) tax-exempt, have a three-year history of programming (except for applicants for folk and traditional art projects), and have staff dedicated specifically to the project. The endowment welcomes projects that assist and involve individual artists or have national, regional or field-wide impact or availability or that provide an unusual or especially valuable contribution because of geographic location.

Assistance is not available for elementary or secondary schools directly, avocational or student groups, new organizations, or for the purpose of construction, purchase or renovation of facilities. The endowment does not provide seasonal or general operating support.

GEOGRAPHIC RESTRICTIONS:
United States, American Samoa, Guam, the Northern Marianas, Puerto Rico or the U.S. Virgin Islands.

FINANCIAL DATA:
Amount of support per award: Varies.

Total amount of support: Varies.

Matching fund requirements: Grantee organizations must match with nonfederal funds on at least a one-to-one basis.

APPLICATION INFORMATION:
Each organization may apply on its own behalf only once, and under only one of the goals, each year. In addition to its own application, an organization may be part of a consortium application or as an independent component of a parent organization such as a university or cultural complex. Applications will be reviewed on the basis of artistic excellence and artistic merit.

Duration: One year.

PUBLICATIONS:
The Grants to Organizations Guidelines.

NATIONAL FOUNDATION FOR ADVANCEMENT IN THE ARTS   [515]

777 Brickell Avenue, Suite 370
Miami, FL 33131
(305) 377-1140
(800) 970-2787
Fax: (305) 377-1149

E-MAIL ADDRESS:
hillc@youngarts.org

WEB SITE ADDRESS:
www.youngarts.org

FOUNDED: 1981

AREAS OF INTEREST:
To identify emerging artists and assist them at critical junctures in their educational and professional development; to raise the appreciation for, and support of, the arts in American society.

CONSULTING OR VOLUNTEER SERVICES:
Offers the names of registrants and awardees of its YoungArts® program nationally to colleges, universities and performing arts institutions which subscribe to the Foundation's Scholarship List Service (SLS).

NAME(S) OF PROGRAMS:
● **Alumni Grant**
● **In the Studio/Out of the Studio**
● **YoungArts Miami**
● **YoungArts New York**
● **YoungArts Week**

TYPE:
Awards/prizes; Conferences/seminars; Endowments; Fellowships; Internships; Project/program grants; Scholarships. Cash grants and scholarship opportunities to young artists.

YEAR PROGRAM STARTED: 1981

PURPOSE:
To recognize and support aspiring artists in their formative years and provide career entry opportunities.

LEGAL BASIS:
Private nonprofit, 501(c)(3), operating national foundation.

ELIGIBILITY:
YoungArts is open to all high school seniors or, if student has already graduated from high school, must be 17 or 18 years old on December 1, 2011 to participate in YoungArts 2012. Participants must be U.S. citizens or permanent residents.

NFAA does not make grants in response to unsolicited requests from individuals or organizations, but welcomes proposals for creation of formal or pilot programs in areas of its interest.

NFAA offers a conference for high school arts educators on preparing students for college auditions.

20 U.S. Presidential Scholars in the Arts are selected exclusively from YoungArts participants by the White House Commission on Presidential Scholars.

GEOGRAPHIC RESTRICTIONS:
United States.

FINANCIAL DATA:
Up to 150 national finalists attend YoungArts week in Miami, all expenses paid.

Amount of support per award: YoungArts Gold Awards: $10,000 each; YoungArts Silver Awards: $5,000; YoungArts Award: Level I, $3,000; Level II, $1,500; Level III, $1,000; Level IV, $500; Level V, $250; Honorable Mention, $250.

Total amount of support: Over $525,000 annually.

COOPERATIVE FUNDING PROGRAMS: NFAA works in partnership with other arts organizations to offer workshops, internships and residencies to students in advanced stages of their arts training.

NUMBER OF APPLICANTS MOST RECENT YEAR:
YoungArts: 7,000 for the 2010 program.

NUMBER OF AWARDS: Approximately 800 cash awards per year.

APPLICATION INFORMATION:
There is a $35 registration fee per category. There is a $10 discount for registering early before June 30.

Deadline: YoungArts: early registration June 30, regular registration through October 14. Audition/portfolio materials due October 29, 2011.

IRS IDENTIFICATION NUMBER: 59-2141837

ADDRESS INQUIRIES TO:
Carla Hill
Director of National Programs
Tel: (800) 970-2787 ext. 219
(See e-mail address above.)

NEBRASKA ARTS COUNCIL   [516]

1004 Farnam Street
Omaha, NE 68102
(402) 595-2122
Fax: (402) 595-2334

E-MAIL ADDRESS:
nac.grants@nebraska.gov

WEB SITE ADDRESS:
www.nebraskaartscouncil.org

FOUNDED: 1965

AREAS OF INTEREST:
Architecture, visual arts, artists, art organizations, literature, museums and libraries, performing arts, aged, children and youth, community and rural development and services and education.

CONSULTING OR VOLUNTEER SERVICES:
Technical (staff) services for requesting organizations who desire assistance in arts programming efforts. Developmental aspects of assistance to arts organizations and/or individuals is predominant.

NAME(S) OF PROGRAMS:
- **Artists-in-Schools/Communities Grants**
- **Arts Access Project Grants**
- **Arts Project Grants**
- **Basic Support Grants**
- **Individual Artist Fellowships**
- **Mini Grants**
- **Nebraska Touring Program**
- **Professional Development Grants**
- **School Partnership Projects**

TYPE:
Fellowships; General operating grants; Project/program grants. Grants to encourage growth and activity in the arts for the citizens of the state of Nebraska.

YEAR PROGRAM STARTED: 1965

PURPOSE:
To stimulate and encourage, throughout the state, the study and presentation of the visual and performing arts and public interest and participation therein; to promote the arts, cultivate resources and support excellence in artistic endeavors for all Nebraskans.

LEGAL BASIS:
Government agency under state legislation. Agency also accepts federal funds (from the National Endowment for the Arts) and private funds for purposes of its intent.

ELIGIBILITY:
Nonprofit, incorporated status is required of applying organizations. Applicant organizations must have federal tax-exempt status or proof of application for that status at the time of application. Individuals not connected with nonprofit organizations are eligible only for Individual Artist Fellowships and must be Nebraska residents. The NAC does not provide funding for capital expenditures or existing deficits.

GEOGRAPHIC RESTRICTIONS:
Nebraska.

FINANCIAL DATA:
Amount of support per award: Up to $7,500.
Total amount of support: $1,200,000.
Matching fund requirements: 1:1, at least half of the applicant match must be in cash, while the other may be in-kind.

COOPERATIVE FUNDING PROGRAMS: Support is provided for organizations desiring programming in the Mid-America Arts Alliance (six-state consortium consisting of Arkansas, Kansas, Missouri, Nebraska, Oklahoma and Texas).

NUMBER OF APPLICANTS MOST RECENT YEAR: 400.

APPLICATION INFORMATION:
Application form is available on the web site.
Duration: One year.
Deadline: March 1 and October 1.

PUBLICATIONS:
Guide to Programs and Services; Artist Directory.

ADDRESS INQUIRIES TO:
See e-mail address above.

NEVADA ARTS COUNCIL   [517]
716 North Carson Street
Suite A
Carson City, NV 89701
(775) 687-6680
Fax: (775) 687-6688

E-MAIL ADDRESS:
sboskoff@nevadaculture.org

WEB SITE ADDRESS:
nac.nevadaculture.org

FOUNDED: 1967

AREAS OF INTEREST:
Visual, literary, performing, design and folk arts, as well as community development.

CONSULTING OR VOLUNTEER SERVICES:
Consulting on arts management, resources in the arts, grants workshops, community arts and professional arts needs.

NAME(S) OF PROGRAMS:
- **Artist Services Program**
- **Arts Education**
- **Community Arts Development**
- **Folklife Program**
- **Governor's Arts Awards**
- **Grants Program**

TYPE:
Awards/prizes; Challenge/matching grants; Conferences/seminars; Development grants; Fellowships; General operating grants; Project/program grants; Residencies; Technical assistance; Training grants; Work-study programs. Grants to Nevada nonprofit groups, individual artists, public institutions and for arts in education.

YEAR PROGRAM STARTED: 1967

PURPOSE:
To enrich the cultural life of the state through leadership that preserves, supports, strengthens and makes accessible excellence in the arts to all Nevadans.

LEGAL BASIS:
Government agency.

ELIGIBILITY:
Nevada nonprofit organizations with IRS tax-exempt status and individual artists with one-year minimum residency may apply for grants. Artists may also apply for artist residencies. Fellowships require residency.

GEOGRAPHIC RESTRICTIONS:
Nevada.

FINANCIAL DATA:
Amount of support per award: $250 to $10,000.
Matching fund requirements: Usually 1:1. Challenge grants 3:1.

APPLICATION INFORMATION:
Interested individuals or groups should check with the Council office for the latest information on grants policies and other programs. Applications also available on the web site.
Duration: Length of project can usually be no longer than one fiscal year, July 1 to June 30, except for challenge grants and quarterly grants.
Deadline: Call for specific dates.

PUBLICATIONS:
Guide to Grants Program; *Artists' Fellowship Program*; *Arts in Education Program*; *Folk Arts Apprenticeships*; *Nevada Art News*; *Neon*, arts letter, annual report.

IRS IDENTIFICATION NUMBER: 88-6000022

OFFICERS:
Tim Jones, Chairperson
Susan Boskoff, Executive Director
Linda Ficklin, Administrative Services Officer

ADDRESS INQUIRIES TO:
Susan Boskoff, Executive Director
(See address above.)

NEW ENGLAND FOUNDATION FOR THE ARTS   [518]
145 Tremont Street
Seventh Floor
Boston, MA 02111-1254
(617) 951-0010
Fax: (617) 951-0016

E-MAIL ADDRESS:
info@nefa.org

WEB SITE ADDRESS:
www.nefa.org

FOUNDED: 1975

AREAS OF INTEREST:
Performing artists, ensembles, literary artists, composers, public art and Native American art.

NAME(S) OF PROGRAMS:
- **Expeditions**
- **Fund for the Arts**
- **Meet the Composer/New England**
- **National Dance Project**
- **Native Arts @ NEFA**
- **New England States Touring Program**
- **Presenter Travel Fund**

TYPE:
Project/program grants; Travel grants. Production and touring grants.

PURPOSE:
To facilitate the movement of people, ideas and resources in the arts within New England and beyond; to make vital connections between artists and audiences; to build the strength, knowledge and leadership of the region's creative sector.

LEGAL BASIS:
Public/private partnership.

GEOGRAPHIC RESTRICTIONS:
Primarily New England.

FINANCIAL DATA:
Amount of support per award: Varies by program.
Total amount of support: Varies.

NUMBER OF AWARDS: 450.

NEW HAMPSHIRE STATE COUNCIL ON THE ARTS   [519]
19 Pillsbury Street
Concord, NH 03301
(603) 271-2789
Fax: (603) 271-3584

E-MAIL ADDRESS:
cassandra.mason@dcr.nh.gov

WEB SITE ADDRESS:
www.nh.gov/nharts

FOUNDED: 1965

AREAS OF INTEREST:
The arts in New Hampshire.

CONSULTING OR VOLUNTEER SERVICES:
Artists as Entrepreneurs Workshops, Fall Arts in Education Partnership Conference and Grants Information Services Workshops.

NAME(S) OF PROGRAMS:
- **Apprenticeships**
- **Artist Entrepreneurial Workshops**
- **Artist in Residence**
- **Artist Services**
- **Arts in Education**
- **Arts in Health Care Project Grants**
- **Cultural Conservation**
- **Cultural Facilities Grants**
- **General Project Grants**

- **Individual Artist Fellowship**
- **Operating Grants**
- **Percent for Art**
- **Traditional Arts Apprenticeship**
- **Youth Arts Project Grants**

TYPE:
Awards/prizes; Challenge/matching grants; Conferences/seminars; Development grants; Fellowships; General operating grants; Project/program grants; Residencies; Technical assistance. Grant assistance to New Hampshire organizations and individual artists.

YEAR PROGRAM STARTED: 1965

PURPOSE:
To support and promote excellence, education and community investment in the arts for people in New Hampshire.

LEGAL BASIS:
Agency of the state of New Hampshire.

ELIGIBILITY:
Organizations must be incorporated in New Hampshire. Individual artists must reside in New Hampshire for at least one year.

GEOGRAPHIC RESTRICTIONS:
New Hampshire.

FINANCIAL DATA:
Amount of support per award: $250 to $20,000.
Total amount of support: $1,000,000 for fiscal year 2010.
Matching fund requirements: Varies.

APPLICATION INFORMATION:
A completed application form is required for all grants. Support materials are required from all applicants; work sample required from individual artists. IRS tax-exempt 501(c)(3) letter is required from nonprofit organizations.
Deadline: Varies.

PUBLICATIONS:
NH Art News, newsletter; *E-News*; *E-Opps*; biennial report.

STAFF:
Lynn Graton, Acting Director

*SPECIAL STIPULATIONS:
Funding is restricted to New Hampshire artists, organizations, schools, libraries, branches of government and communities.

NEW JERSEY STATE COUNCIL ON THE ARTS   [520]
225 West State Street, 4th Floor
Trenton, NJ 08625
(609) 292-6130
Fax: (609) 989-1440

E-MAIL ADDRESS:
julie@arts.sos.state.nj.us

WEB SITE ADDRESS:
www.njartscouncil.org

FOUNDED: 1966

AREAS OF INTEREST:
Dance, music, opera, musical theatre, theatre, visual arts, design arts, crafts, media arts, presenters, multi and interdisciplinary, arts education, folk art, local arts, literary arts, stabilization and advancement.

NAME(S) OF PROGRAMS:
- **Arts Education Special Initiative Grants**
- **Arts in Communities Grants**
- **Arts Project Grants**

- **Folk Arts Apprenticeships**
- **General Operating Support Grants**
- **General Program Support Grants**
- **Long-Term Residencies**
- **Projects Serving Artists Grants**
- **Short-Term Residencies/Arts Education**
- **Special Project Grants**

TYPE:
Fellowships; General operating grants; Internships; Project/program grants; Residencies; Technical assistance. Apprenticeships; local arts grants. Fellowships and matching grants to provide money to New Jersey artists and organizations. Local arts grants (for local arts) are available to designated county arts agencies only.

General Operating Support Grants: awarded every three years to New Jersey-based, nonprofit arts organizations to help underwrite the expense of their total operation including their expense of producing and presenting arts events.

General Program Support Grants: awarded every three years to other New Jersey-based, nonprofit organizations to help underwrite the expense of presenting major, ongoing arts programs.

Long-term Residencies: offered in several different arts disciplines and are applied for by the school or other sponsoring agency.

Short-term Residencies/Arts Education: offered in prose, poetry and playwriting with Council funds providing the artists' fees.

Arts Project Grants: awarded annually to New Jersey-based, nonprofit organizations and agencies to help support specific public arts events.

Arts Education Special Initiative Grants: awarded every three years to build arts organizations' capacities to make the arts a basic part of education in schools.

Projects Serving Artists Grants: awarded annually to New Jersey-based nonprofits to support projects that serve New Jersey artists' needs.

Arts in Communities Grants: awarded annually to New Jersey-based nonprofits to support projects that connect the arts to people and communities in deep and meaningful ways, encourage participation and demonstrate the public value of the arts.

Folk Arts Apprenticeships: awarded to New Jersey residents to support an apprentice learning a traditional art form from a master in their shared community.

YEAR PROGRAM STARTED: 1966

PURPOSE:
To improve the quality of life of New Jersey, its people and communities by helping the arts to flourish.

LEGAL BASIS:
State governmental agency.

ELIGIBILITY:
The Council awards grants on a highly competitive basis, employing standardized criteria for eligibility and evaluation published in guidelines and convening panels of independent experts in the various fields of endeavor for objective feedback and recommendations. A New Jersey resident or a nonprofit organization incorporated in the State of New Jersey committed to professionalism in the arts may apply.

GEOGRAPHIC RESTRICTIONS:
New Jersey.

FINANCIAL DATA:
Amount of support per award: Varies.
Total amount of support: $16,000,000 for fiscal year 2010.
Matching fund requirements: Fellowships are non-matching. Matching grants to organizations must be on a basis of at least 1:1, 3:1 for operating and program support grants.

NUMBER OF APPLICANTS MOST RECENT YEAR:
Approximately 400 fellowship applications and 300 organization/project applications for fiscal year 2010.

APPLICATION INFORMATION:
Details available on the Council web site.
Duration: Annual.

PUBLICATIONS:
Guide to Programs & Services, brochure; *Arts Plan New Jersey*; *NJ Resource Guide*; *Jersey Arts E-News*.

STAFF:
Steve Runk, Executive Director
Julie Ellen Prusinowski, Director of Programs and Services

ADDRESS INQUIRIES TO:
Julie Ellen Prusinowski, Director of Programs and Services
(See address above.)

NEW YORK FOUNDATION FOR THE ARTS   [521]
20 Jay Street, Suite 740
Brooklyn, NY 11201
(212) 366-6900
Fax: (212) 366-1778

E-MAIL ADDRESS:
sball@nyfa.org

WEB SITE ADDRESS:
www.nyfa.org

FOUNDED: 1971

AREAS OF INTEREST:
The arts, with a primary focus on New York state.

NAME(S) OF PROGRAMS:
- **Artists' Fellowships**
- **Strategic Opportunity Stipends**

TYPE:
Awards/prizes; Development grants; Fellowships; Grants-in-aid. Artists' Fellowships: Cash awards made to individual or pairs of originating artists living and working in the state of New York for use in career development. Funds are unrestricted.

Strategic Opportunity Stipends (SOS): Literary, media, visual, music and performing artists may request support for specific, forthcoming opportunities that are distinct from work in progress.

PURPOSE:
To provide the time and resources for the creative mind and the artistic spirit to think, work and prosper.

ELIGIBILITY:
18 years of age or older. Cannot be enrolled in graduate or undergraduate degree program.

GEOGRAPHIC RESTRICTIONS:
New York State.

FINANCIAL DATA:
Amount of support per award: Artists' Fellowships: $7,000 cash awards; Strategic Opportunity Stipends: $200 to $1,500.

Total amount of support: Artists'
Fellowships: Varies; Strategic Opportunity
Stipends: $80,000 to $85,000 annually.

NUMBER OF APPLICANTS MOST RECENT YEAR:
Varies.

NUMBER OF AWARDS: Varies.

APPLICATION INFORMATION:
Deadline: Artists' Fellowships: Usually fall;
Strategic Opportunity Stipends: September
29, February 2 and May 24.

STAFF:
Michael Royce, Executive Director

*PLEASE NOTE:
Strategic Opportunity Stipends are not
available to artists living in the five boroughs
of New York City.

NEW YORK STATE COUNCIL
ON THE ARTS   [522]
175 Varick Street, 3rd Floor
New York, NY 10014
(212) 627-4455
(800) 895-9838 (New York only)
Fax: (212) 620-5911

E-MAIL ADDRESS:
public.affairs@nysca.org

WEB SITE ADDRESS:
www.nysca.org

FOUNDED: 1960

AREAS OF INTEREST:
Public support for the arts in New York state.

CONSULTING OR VOLUNTEER SERVICES:
Technical assistance is available for eligible
nonprofit arts organizations.

TYPE:
Awards/prizes; Capital grants;
Challenge/matching grants;
Conferences/seminars; Development grants;
General operating grants; Internships;
Residencies; Technical assistance. Grants are
awarded to eligible New York state nonprofit
organizations through 14 discipline-based
funding programs: Architecture, Design and
Planning (includes capital projects); Arts
Education; Dance; Electronic Media and
Film; Folk Arts; Individual Artists;
Literature; Museum; Music; Presenting;
Special Arts Services; State and Local
Partnerships; Theatre; and Visual Arts. In
addition, NYSCA support reaches an
additional 1,500 community-based
organizations each year in the form of
regrants, which are administered by a
statewide network of Local Arts Councils
through NYSCA's Decentralization program.

YEAR PROGRAM STARTED: 1960

PURPOSE:
To ensure that the role of the arts in New
York's communities will continue to grow
and play a more significant part in the
welfare and education of New York's
citizens.

LEGAL BASIS:
State agency.

ELIGIBILITY:
Grants are awarded to nonprofit organizations
incorporated in New York state, Indian tribes,
and units of local government. Individuals
and unincorporated groups may only apply
through an eligible nonprofit organization.

GEOGRAPHIC RESTRICTIONS:
New York state.

FINANCIAL DATA:
Amount of support per award: Varies by
program.
Matching fund requirements: Varies by
program.

NUMBER OF AWARDS: Over 2,400 annually.

APPLICATION INFORMATION:
Applications and guidelines are available
online. New applicants (except municipalities
and Indian tribes) must submit proof of
nonprofit status. Returning applicants who
have applied in the past three years must
certify that their nonprofit status remains
valid.
Duration: One calendar year. Organizations
may reapply each year.

PUBLICATIONS:
Program guidelines.

STAFF:
Danny Simmons, Chairperson
Dr. Barbaralee Diamonstein-Spielvogel, Vice
Chairperson
Jeff Soref, Vice Chairperson
Heather A. Hitchens, Executive Director
Tracy Hamilton Thompson, Director of
Administration
Megan White, Deputy Director of Programs

ADDRESS INQUIRIES TO:
Office of Public and Governmental Affairs
(See address above.)

NEW YORK STATE HISTORICAL
ASSOCIATION   [523]
Lake Road
Cooperstown, NY 13326
(607) 547-1400
Fax: (607) 547-1404

E-MAIL ADDRESS:
info@nysha.org

WEB SITE ADDRESS:
www.nysha.org

FOUNDED: 1899

AREAS OF INTEREST:
New York state and culture.

NAME(S) OF PROGRAMS:
● Henry Allen Moe Prize

TYPE:
Awards/prizes. Prizes for published
catalogues treating collections located or
exhibited in New York state.

YEAR PROGRAM STARTED: 1983

PURPOSE:
To foster and recognize scholarship in art
history and decorative arts studies in the
form of published catalogues located or
exhibited in New York state.

LEGAL BASIS:
Private.

ELIGIBILITY:
Entries should add new information to what
is known about the subject and may
completely document an exhibition. Only
catalogues treating collections located or
exhibited in New York state qualify.

FINANCIAL DATA:
Amount of support per award: $250 to
$3,000.

NUMBER OF APPLICANTS MOST RECENT YEAR:
11 for the year 2010.

NUMBER OF AWARDS: 1 for the year 2010.

APPLICATION INFORMATION:
Entries published in the previous two years
only should be submitted in four copies
accompanied by a letter of transmittal.
Deadline: On or before February 15 for
awards in the current year.

PUBLICATIONS:
New York History; Heritage Magazine.

OFFICERS:
Dr. Douglas E. Evelyn, Chairman of the
Board
Robert Irwin, Vice Chairman
Stephen M. Duff, Treasurer
Glenn A. Perrone, Assistant Secretary

ADDRESS INQUIRIES TO:
Paul D'Ambrosio
Vice President and Chief Curator
(See address above.)

NORTH CAROLINA ARTS
COUNCIL   [524]
Department of Cultural Resources
109 East Jones Street
Raleigh, NC 27601
(919) 807-6500
Fax: (919) 807-6532

E-MAIL ADDRESS:
ncarts@ncdcr.gov

WEB SITE ADDRESS:
www.ncarts.org

FOUNDED: 1964

AREAS OF INTEREST:
Arts development throughout North Carolina.

CONSULTING OR VOLUNTEER SERVICES:
Consulting services to arts organizations.

NAME(S) OF PROGRAMS:
● **Artist Fellowships**
● **Arts and Audiences**
● **Arts in Education Grants**
● **Grassroots Arts Program**
● **Organizational Development**
● **Outreach Program**
● **Regional Artist Project Grants**
● **State Arts Resources**
● **Statewide Service Organizations**

TYPE:
Challenge/matching grants; Development
grants; Fellowships; General operating grants;
Internships; Project/program grants;
Residencies; Technical assistance. Per capita
distribution of funds for arts development,
general operating support, project grants,
local government challenge grants,
arts-in-education grants, new works grants,
discipline-development grants, individual
artist fellowships, fee subsidy for touring
groups, consultant grants, scholarship grants
and workshops.

Artist Fellowships: To support the creative
development of North Carolina artists. In
even years, fellowships are awarded to
writers, songwriters, composers, playwrights
and screenwriters. In odd years, fellowships
are awarded in the areas of visual art, craft,
film/video and choreography.

Arts and Audiences: To help arts
organizations broaden, deepen and diversify
participation in their arts programs.

Arts in Education Grants: For schools and
nonprofit organizations to strengthen the use
of the arts in pre-K-through-12 settings.

Grassroots Arts Program: Distributes funds
for arts programming, primarily through local
arts councils, to all 100 North Carolina
counties using a per capita-based formula.

Organizational Development: Grants for short-term technical assistance and long-term organizational development through the New Realities program.

Outreach Program: Provides funds to develop and sustain the administration and artistic programs of community-based African-American, Asian-American, Latino and Native American arts organizations.

Regional Artist Project Grants: For regional consortia of local arts councils, which award project grants to artists in their regions.

State Arts Resources: For mature arts organizations that, over time, have consistently produced strong arts programs and demonstrated strong management and financial accountability.

Statewide Service Organizations: Support is provided to organizations that provide programs and services to the arts community on a statewide or regional basis.

YEAR PROGRAM STARTED: 1967

PURPOSE:
To enrich cultural life in North Carolina by nurturing and supporting excellence in the arts and by providing opportunities for every North Carolinian to experience the arts.

LEGAL BASIS:
Agency of the state of North Carolina.

ELIGIBILITY:
Except for fellowships to individual artists who are North Carolina residents, the Council awards grants only to North Carolina organizations which qualify as tax-exempt and nonprofit under Section 501(c)(3) of the Internal Revenue Code of 1954.

GEOGRAPHIC RESTRICTIONS:
North Carolina.

FINANCIAL DATA:
Amount of support per award: $20,000 average grant. Project and challenge grants generally do not exceed $10,000. General operating support as much as $95,000, per capita distribution as much as $217,000 per grant and artist fellowships as much as $10,000.
Total amount of support: Varies.
Matching fund requirements: 1:1 cash match, except for fellowships.

NUMBER OF APPLICANTS MOST RECENT YEAR: 1,801.

NUMBER OF AWARDS: 1,102 total (individuals: 154; organizations: 948; subgrants: 532) for fiscal year 2009-10.

APPLICATION INFORMATION:
Application form is available online.
Deadline: Organizational grant applications: March 1. Individuals: November 1.

STAFF:
Mary B. Regan, Executive Director

ADDRESS INQUIRIES TO:
Bridgette Lacy, Media Relations Manager (See address above.)

*PLEASE NOTE:
Creating Place and Folklife Grant programs are temporarily suspended.

NORTH DAKOTA COUNCIL ON THE ARTS [525]
1600 East Century Avenue
Suite 6
Bismarck, ND 58503
(701) 328-7590
Fax: (701) 328-7595

E-MAIL ADDRESS:
comserv@nd.gov

WEB SITE ADDRESS:
www.nd.gov/arts

FOUNDED: 1967

AREAS OF INTEREST:
Arts.

NAME(S) OF PROGRAMS:
- **Arts-in-Education/Artists in Residence**
- **Arts-in-Education/S.A.L.T.**
- **Arts-in-Education/Teacher Incentive**
- **Community Arts Access**
- **Individual Artists Fellowships**
- **Institutional Support**
- **Presenter Support**
- **Professional Development**
- **Special Projects**
- **Technology**
- **Traditional Arts Apprenticeships**

TYPE:
Challenge/matching grants; Conferences/seminars; Exchange programs; Fellowships; General operating grants; Grants-in-aid; Project/program grants; Residencies; Technical assistance. Funding and technical assistance provided to institutions and organizations statewide for special projects and administration of special projects.

YEAR PROGRAM STARTED: 1967

PURPOSE:
To stimulate and encourage the study and presentation of and public participation in the performing and visual arts in North Dakota.

LEGAL BASIS:
North Dakota Legislative Assembly.

ELIGIBILITY:
Grants are awarded only to nonprofit organizations, schools, government subdivisions and individuals in North Dakota. Requirements vary according to program.

GEOGRAPHIC RESTRICTIONS:
North Dakota.

FINANCIAL DATA:
Amount of support per award: Varies by program.
Total amount of support: $1,315,594 for fiscal year 2010.
Matching fund requirements: Varies by grant.

COOPERATIVE FUNDING PROGRAMS: Institutional Support and Arts-in-Education.

NUMBER OF APPLICANTS MOST RECENT YEAR: 395 for the year 2010.

NUMBER OF AWARDS: 360 funded for the year 2010.

APPLICATION INFORMATION:
Duration: Up to one year.
Deadline: Varies.

PUBLICATIONS:
Newsletter; guidelines; brochures.

OFFICER:
David Trottier, Chairperson

ADDRESS INQUIRIES TO:
Executive Director
(See address above.)

OHIO ARTS COUNCIL [526]
30 East Broad Street
33rd Floor
Columbus, OH 43215
(614) 466-2613
Fax: (614) 466-4494
TDD: (800) 750-0750

E-MAIL ADDRESS:
mary.campbell-zopf@oac.state.oh.us

WEB SITE ADDRESS:
www.oac.state.oh.us

FOUNDED: 1965

AREAS OF INTEREST:
Arts.

CONSULTING OR VOLUNTEER SERVICES:
Staff assistance related to applications and program development.

NAME(S) OF PROGRAMS:
- **Artists with Disabilities Access**
- **Arts Access**
- **Arts Learning: Artist Express**
- **Arts Learning: Artist in Residence/Artists**
- **Arts Learning: Artist in Residence/Sponsors**
- **Arts Learning: Arts Partnership**
- **Building Cultural Diversity**
- **Individual Artist Grants and Services: Traditional Arts Apprenticeships**
- **Ohio Artists on Tour**
- **Ohio Heritage Fellowship Awards**
- **Project Support**
- **Sustainability**

TYPE:
Assistantships; Awards/prizes; Conferences/seminars; Fellowships; Formula grants; General operating grants; Internships; Matching gifts; Project/program grants; Residencies; Technical assistance. Special projects and general programming.

YEAR PROGRAM STARTED: 1965

PURPOSE:
To fund and support quality arts experiences to strengthen Ohio communities culturally, educationally and economically.

LEGAL BASIS:
State agency.

ELIGIBILITY:
All applicants for grants must meet the following legal requirements including intending your project to be nonprofit, having the fact that every tax-exempt organization must have an Employer Identification Number, every applicant having to be an Ohio resident or Ohio-based to receive direct grant support, producing projects of high aesthetic quality and artistic merit, providing at least one-half of the activity cost, preferably in dollars (in-kind services may be used as a part of the required match), submitting accurate budgets that are appropriate to the proposed project or creative work, demonstrating financial responsibility and methods to provide community access and involvement.

No person or persons shall, on the grounds of race, color, national origin, handicap, age, sex or religion, be excluded from participation in, be denied benefits of or be otherwise subjected to discrimination under any program, service or benefit advocated, authorized or provided by the state of Ohio.

GEOGRAPHIC RESTRICTIONS:
Ohio.

FINANCIAL DATA:
Amount of support per award: $200 to $400,000.

Total amount of support: $7,600,000 for fiscal year 2009.

Matching fund requirements: Generally, 1:1 cash match.

COOPERATIVE FUNDING PROGRAMS: Ohio River Border Initiative with West Virginia Arts Commission.

NUMBER OF APPLICANTS MOST RECENT YEAR: 1,391 for fiscal year 2009.

NUMBER OF AWARDS: 608 for fiscal year 2009.

REPRESENTATIVE AWARDS:
Cleveland Orchestra, Cleveland, OH; Worthington Arts Council, Worthington, OH; Lima Symphony Orchestra, Lima, OH; Actor's Summer Theatre, Columbus, OH; Southern Ohio Museum, Portsmouth, OH.

APPLICATION INFORMATION:
Applicants must use OAC's web-based application system to submit an application.
Duration: June 30.
Deadline: Artists with Disabilities Access: Application accepted anytime; Arts Access: March 1; Arts Learning-Artist Express: Application due in six weeks prior to the date of the visit; Arts Learning-Artist in Residence/Artists: July 1; Arts Learning-Artist in Residence/Sponsors: March 1; Arts Learning-Arts Partnership: March 1; Building Cultural Diversity: June 1; Individual Artist Grants and Services: January 15; Ohio Artists on Tour: May 15; Ohio Heritage Fellowship Awards: January 15; Project Support: April 1; Sustainability: February 1.

PUBLICATIONS:
Guidelines; *Arts Ohio*; *Arts Perspective*; *Ohio Festivals & Competitions Guide*; *Focusing the Light: The Arts and Practice of Planning*; *Appreciative Journey: A Guide to Developing International Cultural Exchange*.

IRS IDENTIFICATION NUMBER: 31-1334820

OFFICERS:
Julie S. Henahan, Executive Director
Mary Campbell-Zopf, Deputy Director
Dia Foley, Grants Office Director

ADDRESS INQUIRIES TO:
Mary Campbell-Zopf, Deputy Director
(See address above.)

OKLAHOMA ARTS COUNCIL   [527]
Jim Thorpe Building, Room 640
2101 North Lincoln Boulevard
Oklahoma City, OK 73105
(405) 521-2931
Fax: (405) 521-6418

E-MAIL ADDRESS:
okarts@arts.ok.gov

WEB SITE ADDRESS:
www.arts.ok.gov

FOUNDED: 1965

AREAS OF INTEREST:
Arts.

NAME(S) OF PROGRAMS:
● **Arts in Alternative Education Grants**
● **Local Government Challenge Grants**
● **Major Grant Support**
● **Organizational Support**
● **Small Grant Support**

TYPE:
Challenge/matching grants; Conferences/seminars; General operating

grants; Project/program grants; Residencies; Technical assistance. State-appropriated funds and federal funds from the National Endowment for the Arts are disbursed to nonprofit, tax-exempt and nonreligious organizations for arts projects statewide.

YEAR PROGRAM STARTED: 1965

PURPOSE:
To further the arts in the state of Oklahoma.

LEGAL BASIS:
State agency.

ELIGIBILITY:
Nonprofit, tax-exempt and nonreligious Oklahoma organizations are eligible to apply.

GEOGRAPHIC RESTRICTIONS:
Oklahoma.

FINANCIAL DATA:
Amount of support per award: Varies.
Total amount of support: Varies.

NUMBER OF APPLICANTS MOST RECENT YEAR: Approximately 550.

APPLICATION INFORMATION:
Duration: Projects receiving funding must be completed during the fiscal year.

PUBLICATIONS:
Program Guidelines; general brochures.

OFFICERS:
Kym Koch Thompson, Chairperson
Suzanne Tate, Executive Director

ADDRESS INQUIRIES TO:
Suzanne Tate, Executive Director
(See address above.)

OREGON ARTS COMMISSION   [528]
775 Summer Street, N.E.
Suite 200
Salem, OR 97301-1280
(503) 986-0082
Fax: (503) 986-0260

E-MAIL ADDRESS:
oregon.artscomm@state.or.us

WEB SITE ADDRESS:
www.oregonartscommission.org

FOUNDED: 1967

AREAS OF INTEREST:
Arts.

NAME(S) OF PROGRAMS:
● **Arts Build Communities**
● **Arts Recognition Grants**
● **Arts Services Grants**
● **Career Opportunity Grants**
● **Cultural Tourism Grants**
● **Grants for Arts Learning**
● **Individual Artists Fellowship Grants**
● **Operating Support Grants**
● **Oregon Media Arts Fellowship**

TYPE:
Awards/prizes; Conferences/seminars; Fellowships; General operating grants; Project/program grants; Technical assistance; Training grants; Travel grants. Services provided to arts institutions statewide.

YEAR PROGRAM STARTED: 1967

PURPOSE:
To provide grants and services to the arts, offer developmental, consultative and technical assistance, provide public information and serve as a central resource

for the arts and collaborate in the fiscal/financial management of arts organizations.

LEGAL BASIS:
Agency of the state of Oregon.

ELIGIBILITY:
Grants are available to nonprofit organizations and professional, nonstudent artists.

GEOGRAPHIC RESTRICTIONS:
Oregon.

FINANCIAL DATA:
Amount of support per award: Varies.
Total amount of support: $1,700,000 for the year 2010.
Matching fund requirements: Minimum 1:1.

NUMBER OF APPLICANTS MOST RECENT YEAR:
Varies.

NUMBER OF AWARDS: Varies.

APPLICATION INFORMATION:
Duration: One year.
Deadline: Varies.

PUBLICATIONS:
Program guide; monographs of Arts Build Communities Program, Arts Learning Program and Percent for Art Program; guidelines for various grant programs; Creative Vitality Index Report.

IRS IDENTIFICATION NUMBER: 93-0563386

STAFF:
Christine D'Arcy, Executive Director
Shannon Planchon, Assistant Director

ADDRESS INQUIRIES TO:
Shannon Planchon, Assistant Director
(See address above.)

PENNSYLVANIA COUNCIL ON THE ARTS   [529]
216 Finance Building
Harrisburg, PA 17120
(717) 787-6883
Fax: (717) 783-2539

E-MAIL ADDRESS:
phorn@state.pa.us

WEB SITE ADDRESS:
www.pacouncilonthearts.org

FOUNDED: 1966

AREAS OF INTEREST:
Arts.

NAME(S) OF PROGRAMS:
● **Arts Organization Grants**

TYPE:
Block grants; Challenge/matching grants; General operating grants; Grants-in-aid; Internships; Project/program grants; Residencies; Technical assistance; Travel grants. General support grants, specific support grants, and peer to peer consultation.

YEAR PROGRAM STARTED: 1966

PURPOSE:
To foster the excellence, diversity and vitality of the arts in Pennsylvania; to broaden the availability and appreciation of those arts throughout the state.

LEGAL BASIS:
State agency.

ELIGIBILITY:
Incorporated nonprofit organizations located in Pennsylvania and serving residents of the state may apply.

GEOGRAPHIC RESTRICTIONS:
Pennsylvania.

FINANCIAL DATA:
Funding comes from state-appropriated funds and federal grants.

Amount of support per award: $250 to $300,000 for grants.

Total amount of support: Varies.

Matching fund requirements: Usually a dollar-for-dollar match for organizations.

NUMBER OF APPLICANTS MOST RECENT YEAR:
2,077 project and organization; 1,768 fellowships.

NUMBER OF AWARDS: 1,986 project and organization; 176 fellowships.

APPLICATION INFORMATION:
Duration: One year.
Deadline: Varies.

PUBLICATIONS:
Guide to Fellowship Programs; Guide to Programs and Services; Guide to the Arts-in-Education Program.

STAFF:
Jewel Jones-Fulp, Program Associate
Marcella Shoffner, Program Associate

ADMINISTRATIVE STAFF:
Bryan K. Holtzapple, Grants and Fiscal Officer

DIRECTORS:
Philip Horn, Executive Director
Brian Rogers, Deputy Executive Director
Heather Doughty, Deputy Director for Communications
Charon Battles, Dance, Preserving Diverse Cultures and Challenge Program
Jamie Dunlap, Arts in Education
Lori Schmelz, Arts, Film and Electronic Media

ADDRESS INQUIRIES TO:
Program Director of Pertinent Arts Discipline (See address above.)

RAGDALE FOUNDATION   [530]
1260 North Green Bay Road
Lake Forest, IL 60045
(847) 234-1063 ext. 206
Fax: (847) 234-1063

E-MAIL ADDRESS:
admissions@ragdale.org

WEB SITE ADDRESS:
www.ragdale.org

FOUNDED: 1976

AREAS OF INTEREST:
Visual arts, poetry, fiction, nonfiction writing, music composition, performance art, play/screenwriting and interdisciplinary arts.

NAME(S) OF PROGRAMS:
● **Residencies at Ragdale Foundation**

TYPE:
Residencies. Low-cost subsidized residencies at Ragdale Foundation, an artist's community, providing a place to work undisturbed on creative projects. One-half and full-fee waivers are also available after acceptance, based upon financial need.

YEAR PROGRAM STARTED: 1976

PURPOSE:
To provide a place for artists to work undisturbed on creative projects.

LEGAL BASIS:
Not-for-profit, tax-exempt foundation.

ELIGIBILITY:
Residents are chosen by selections committees composed of professionals in the

arts. Writers, composers, visual artists and artists of other disciplines are accepted. Couples are not accepted unless each qualifies independently.

FINANCIAL DATA:
Amount of support per award: Residencies with room and board provided. Standard fee is $25 per day. Some half- and full-fee waivers are available, based upon financial need.

Total amount of support: Varies.

NUMBER OF APPLICANTS MOST RECENT YEAR:
Approximately 400.

NUMBER OF AWARDS: 150.

APPLICATION INFORMATION:
Completed application must be submitted along with references, resume, work samples and project description. A $40 application fee is required. Financial aid application must be completed after acceptance.

Duration: Two to six weeks.

Deadline: January 15 for residencies June through early September. May 15 for residencies September through December. September 15 for residencies January through May.

PUBLICATIONS:
Application guidelines; two newsletters annually.

IRS IDENTIFICATION NUMBER: 36-2937927

TRUSTEES:
Phoebe Turner, President
Annette Dezelan, Vice President
Roland Kulla, Vice President
Jay Owen, Treasurer
Fred Klein, Secretary
Susan Page Tillett, Executive Director
Cindy Broten
Donna Coffin
Sandy Deromedi
Stuart Emanuel
Roberta Haebler
Anne LeClaire
Ann Merritt
John Merritt, Life Trustee
Audrey Niffenegger
Philip Rosborough
Roberta Rubin
Mike Rummel
David Woodhouse

ADDRESS INQUIRIES TO:
Regin Igloria
Director of Artists-in-Residence
Ragdale Foundation
(See address above.)

RHODE ISLAND STATE COUNCIL ON THE ARTS   [531]
One Capitol Hill, 3rd Floor
Providence, RI 02908
(401) 222-3882
(401) 222-6996
Fax: (401) 222-3018

E-MAIL ADDRESS:
info@arts.ri.gov

WEB SITE ADDRESS:
www.arts.ri.gov

FOUNDED: 1967

AREAS OF INTEREST:
Arts.

NAME(S) OF PROGRAMS:
● **Fellowships**
● **Folk Arts Apprenticeships**

● **General Operating Support**
● **Project Grants**

TYPE:
Fellowships; General operating grants; Project/program grants. Funding for Rhode Island nonprofit organizations doing arts programming and for Rhode Island artists. Individual artist support includes Fellowships and Folk Arts Apprenticeships. Organizational support includes General Operating Support.

YEAR PROGRAM STARTED: 1967

PURPOSE:
To support and develop increased and substantial arts opportunities for Rhode Island.

LEGAL BASIS:
Agency of the state of Rhode Island.

ELIGIBILITY:
Varies with each grant category.

GEOGRAPHIC RESTRICTIONS:
Rhode Island.

FINANCIAL DATA:
Amount of support per award: Varies.

Total amount of support: $1,861,824 for fiscal year 2008.

Matching fund requirements: Matching funds required for all grants, except for individual artists.

COOPERATIVE FUNDING PROGRAMS: State and local cooperative programs.

REPRESENTATIVE AWARDS:
$30,000 in general operating support to a theatre company; $5,000 fellowship in film/video; $1,000 for folk arts apprenticeship in Yoruba drumming.

APPLICATION INFORMATION:
Duration: Varies with program.
Deadline: April 1 and October 1.

IRS IDENTIFICATION NUMBER: 05-6000523

OFFICERS:
Randall Rosenbaum, Executive Director
Sherilyn Brown, Arts-in-Education Director (Education Partnerships)
Daniel L. Kahn, Arts-in-Education Assistant (Grants)
Elizabeth Keithline, Grants Coordinator
Cristina DiChiera, Individual Artists Coordinator

THE SAN FRANCISCO FOUNDATION   [532]
225 Bush Street
Suite 500
San Francisco, CA 94104
(415) 733-8500
Fax: (415) 477-2783

E-MAIL ADDRESS:
info@sff.org

WEB SITE ADDRESS:
www.sff.org

FOUNDED: 1948

AREAS OF INTEREST:
Arts and artists.

NAME(S) OF PROGRAMS:
● **Art Awards**

TYPE:
Awards/prizes.

PURPOSE:
To foster individual artistic growth within the community.

LEGAL BASIS:
Community foundation.

ELIGIBILITY:
Poets, writers, sculptors, painters, filmmakers, media artists, photographers, printmakers and performing artists are eligible.

GEOGRAPHIC RESTRICTIONS:
Alameda, Contra Costa, Marin, San Francisco and San Mateo counties, California.

FINANCIAL DATA:
Amount of support per award: $2,000 to $10,000.

ADDRESS INQUIRIES TO:
Art Awards Program
(See address above.)

THE GEORGE AND HELEN SEGAL FOUNDATION [533]
136 Davidson Mill Road
North Brunswick, NJ 08902
(732) 951-0950
Fax: (732) 821-5877

E-MAIL ADDRESS:
segalfoundation@comcast.net

WEB SITE ADDRESS:
www.segalfoundation.org

FOUNDED: 2000

AREAS OF INTEREST:
Financial support to artists and sculptors.

TYPE:
Grants-in-aid. Biennial grant.

YEAR PROGRAM STARTED: 2000

PURPOSE:
To exhibit and display the works of George Segal, and to award grants to artists in order to enable them to pursue their artistic endeavors.

ELIGIBILITY:
Open New Jersey sculptors only. Applicant must be 21 years of age or older. No students.

GEOGRAPHIC RESTRICTIONS:
New Jersey.

FINANCIAL DATA:
Amount of support per award: $5,000 to $10,000.

NUMBER OF AWARDS: Either ten $5,000 or five $10,000 awards.

APPLICATION INFORMATION:
The following items must be included with the application:
(1) cover letter describing how the grant funds will be used and how they will advance the applicant's artistic career;
(2) six images of current work on a CD. Place name, year the work was done, title, dimensions and medium used on the CD. The Foundation will not be returning any material and;
(3) current resume, including dates, listing exhibition record, grants, awards and other professional activities.

ADDRESS INQUIRIES TO:
Susan Kutliroff, Secretary/Treasurer
(See address above.)

SMITHSONIAN INSTITUTION
Office of Fellowships and Internships
470 L'Enfant Plaza, S.W., Suite 7102
MRC 902, P.O. Box 37012
Washington, DC 20013-7012
(202) 633-7070
Fax: (202) 633-7069

E-MAIL ADDRESS:
siofg@si.edu

WEB SITE ADDRESS:
www.si.edu/research+study

TYPE:
Fellowships. Offered to qualified scholars for research to be conducted in residence at the Smithsonian in association with the staff, using collections and research facilities.

See entry 1962 for full listing.

SOUTH CAROLINA ARTS COMMISSION [534]
1800 Gervais Street
Columbia, SC 29201-3585
(803) 734-8696
Fax: (803) 734-8526

WEB SITE ADDRESS:
www.southcarolinaarts.com

FOUNDED: 1967

AREAS OF INTEREST:
Arts programming for all art forms reaching all strata of South Carolina population.

NAME(S) OF PROGRAMS:
• Artist Fellowship Program

TYPE:
Fellowships.

YEAR PROGRAM STARTED: 1980

PURPOSE:
To offer financial assistance to visual, literary and performing artists in South Carolina who show significant potential within their art form and to provide an opportunity for a more intensive individual development rather than short-term project support.

LEGAL BASIS:
State arts agency.

GEOGRAPHIC RESTRICTIONS:
South Carolina.

FINANCIAL DATA:
Amount of support per award: $5,000.
Total amount of support: $30,000.

NUMBER OF AWARDS: 6.

APPLICATION INFORMATION:
Detailed information is available from the Commission.
Duration: One fiscal year only.
Deadline: October 1.

STAFF:
Ken May, Interim Executive Director

ADDRESS INQUIRIES TO:
Clay Burnette
Director of Grants and Contracts
(See address above.)

*PLEASE NOTE:
Funding is dependent on state appropriation and federal grants.

SOUTH DAKOTA ARTS COUNCIL [535]
711 East Wells Avenue
Pierre, SD 57501-3369
(605) 773-3301
Fax: (605) 773-5977

E-MAIL ADDRESS:
sdac@state.sd.us

WEB SITE ADDRESS:
www.artscouncil.sd.gov

FOUNDED: 1966

AREAS OF INTEREST:
Statewide arts programming in all arts disciplines.

NAME(S) OF PROGRAMS:
• Artist Grants
• Artist-in-Schools
• Arts Organization Challenge Grants
• Professional Development
• Project Grants
• SOSS (Season Support)
• Technical Assistance
• Touring Arts

TYPE:
Challenge/matching grants; Fellowships; General operating grants; Grants-in-aid; Project/program grants; Residencies; Seed money grants; Technical assistance. Artist grants; arts challenge grants/general operating support.

YEAR PROGRAM STARTED: 1968

PURPOSE:
To support development of the arts.

LEGAL BASIS:
State agency.

ELIGIBILITY:
Requirements vary with projects. Most grants are available to South Dakota residents only, with the exception of Touring Arts and Artist-in-Schools.

GEOGRAPHIC RESTRICTIONS:
South Dakota.

FINANCIAL DATA:
Amount of support per award: $100 to $45,000.
Total amount of support: $1,163,000.
Matching fund requirements: Required except for Artist Grants.

NUMBER OF AWARDS: 500.

APPLICATION INFORMATION:
Applications are accepted through an online e-grant system.
Duration: Generally one fiscal year. Renewable.
Deadline: March 1 for Organizations and Artist Grants. September 1 for Touring Arts and Artist-in-Schools.

PUBLICATIONS:
Quarterly newsletter; *Touring Arts and Artist in Schools,* brochure; Guide to Grants.

STAFF:
Michael Pangburn, Director
Rebecca DallaGrana, Assistant Director
Sharon Winckler, Program Coordinator

ADDRESS INQUIRIES TO:
Michael Pangburn, Director
(See address above.)

H. CHASE STONE TRUST [536]
c/o JPMorgan Private Client Services
402 North Tejon Street, Suite 200
Colorado Springs, CO 80903
(719) 227-6445
Fax: (719) 227-6448

E-MAIL ADDRESS:
julie.golden@jpmorgan.com

WEB SITE ADDRESS:
www.jpmorgan.com/onlinegrants

AREAS OF INTEREST:
Primarily performing, literary and fine arts.

TYPE:
Project/program grants.

PURPOSE:
To support, sustain and develop charitable
organizations operating in the El Paso
County community.

ELIGIBILITY:
Performing, literary and fine arts
organizations serving the entire El Paso
County community are eligible to apply.
Must have 501(c)(3) not-for-profit status. No
grants to individuals.

FINANCIAL DATA:
Amount of support per award: $3,000 to
$10,000.

APPLICATION INFORMATION:
Application and guidelines are available
online. Organization must provide current
copy of IRS determination letter showing
tax-exempt status under Section 501(c)(3)
and public charity status under Section
509(a).

Duration: One year. No renewals.

Deadline: March 31, June 30 and October
31.

ADDRESS INQUIRIES TO:
Julie Golden, Trust Advisor
(See address above.)

THE FRANK M. TAIT
FOUNDATION

1530 Kettering Tower
40 North Main Street
Dayton, OH 45423
(937) 222-2401
Fax: (937) 224-6015

E-MAIL ADDRESS:
taitfdn@earthlink.net

TYPE:
Project/program grants. Focus on youth
development, particularly early childhood
development.

See entry 1221 for full listing.

TENNESSEE ARTS
COMMISSION   [537]

401 Charlotte Avenue
Nashville, TN 37243-0780
(615) 741-1701
Fax: (615) 741-8559

E-MAIL ADDRESS:
rod.reiner@tn.gov

WEB SITE ADDRESS:
www.arts.state.tn.us

FOUNDED: 1967

AREAS OF INTEREST:
All arts disciplines in Tennessee.

CONSULTING OR VOLUNTEER SERVICES:
Consultant, informational and developmental
services are offered to arts groups, individual
artists, museums and arts councils throughout
the state.

NAME(S) OF PROGRAMS:
● **Division of Arts Programs**
● **Division of Communications,
  Information & Technology**

TYPE:
Challenge/matching grants;
Conferences/seminars; Fellowships; General
operating grants; Project/program grants;
Residencies; Technical assistance; Training
grants. Professional development.

Arts Programs consist of grants to
institutions, individuals, coordinating
agencies and entities of government.
Consultation information and development
assistance to state arts constituency is also
provided.

Grant Programs: Funds may not be used for
capital improvements or for permanent
equipment.

YEAR PROGRAM STARTED: 1967

PURPOSE:
To support and encourage the life and growth
of the arts and craft in the state of Tennessee
and preservation of the state's cultural
heritage.

LEGAL BASIS:
Independent state agency.

ELIGIBILITY:
Applicant organization must have nonprofit,
tax-exempt status and be chartered in
Tennessee or an entity of government.

GEOGRAPHIC RESTRICTIONS:
Tennessee.

FINANCIAL DATA:
Amount of support per award: $200 to
$100,000.

Matching fund requirements: Most grant
awards require a 1:1 match.

NUMBER OF APPLICANTS MOST RECENT YEAR:
850.

NUMBER OF AWARDS: 800.

APPLICATION INFORMATION:
Details available on the web site.

Duration: One fiscal year, July to June.

Deadline: Varies.

PUBLICATIONS:
Quarterly newsletters; weekly online
newsletter.

COMMISSION MEMBERS:
Ellen M. Hays, Chairperson
Budd Bishop, Vice Chairperson
Kurt Winstead, Secretary
Gale Jones Carson
Donna Chase
Rhea Condra
Lanis Cope
Ed Gerace
Lucia Gilliland
Ann K. Looney
Carol L. McCoy
Carol W. Prentiss
Barry Scott
Ginger Terry
Bob Wormsley

ADDRESS INQUIRIES TO:
Rod Reiner, Deputy Director
(See address above.)

*SPECIAL STIPULATIONS:
Grants categories are limited to residents,
artists and organizations of Tennessee. Grants
are made to individuals, nonprofit
organizations and/or entities of government.

TEXAS COMMISSION ON THE
ARTS   [538]

E.O. Thompson Building
920 Colorado, 5th Floor
Austin, TX 78701
(512) 463-5535
(800) 252-9415 (in Texas only)
Fax: (512) 475-2699

E-MAIL ADDRESS:
laura@arts.state.tx.us

WEB SITE ADDRESS:
www.arts.state.tx.us

FOUNDED: 1965

AREAS OF INTEREST:
Operational support and project support to
nonprofit Texas arts organizations for
ongoing programs and/or arts education,
health and human services, economic
development, public safety and criminal
justice, and natural resources and agriculture;
performance support for civic, cultural and
other nonprofit organizations.

CONSULTING OR VOLUNTEER SERVICES:
Seminars, information services, technical
assistance and funding. Services provided to
institutions statewide.

NAME(S) OF PROGRAMS:
● **TCA Grant Programs**

TYPE:
Block grants; Challenge/matching grants;
Conferences/seminars; Exchange programs;
General operating grants; Project/program
grants; Residencies; Technical assistance;
Training grants; Travel grants; Visiting
scholars. Organizational support, project
support and touring support.

YEAR PROGRAM STARTED: 1965

PURPOSE:
To foster the development of a receptive
climate for the arts that will culturally enrich
and benefit the citizens of Texas.

LEGAL BASIS:
H.B. 273 and H.B. 1784.

ELIGIBILITY:
Any 501(c)(3) organization, educational
institution, or form of government may apply.
Presenters and producers of performing arts
whose programs are designed to stimulate
artistic activity and to heighten awareness of
and broaden public access to the arts in rural
and underserved areas of the state are eligible
to apply.

Award made according to project cost,
program limits, ability to meet funding
criteria and available funds.

GEOGRAPHIC RESTRICTIONS:
Texas.

FINANCIAL DATA:
Matching fund requirements: Funds provided
by the state through the grants process must
be matched by the application organization.
Matching funds are generally expected to be
in cash or in cash and in kind.

APPLICATION INFORMATION:
Guidelines available online. All applications
submitted electronically. Contact TCA staff
to obtain user ID and password.

Duration: Up to one year.

Deadline: Varies.

PUBLICATIONS:
Guide to Programs and Services.

STAFF:
Dr. Gary Gibbs, Executive Director

COMMISSION MEMBERS:
Patty A. Bryant, Chairperson
Polly Sowell, Vice Chairperson
Jeanne Parker, Treasurer
Paul Kellam McCash, Jr., Secretary
S. Shawn Stephens, Parliamentarian
David Garza, At-Large
Dale Brock
Alphonse A. Dotson
Linda Hatchel
Molly Hipp Hubbard
Patty Huffines
Liza Lewis
Billye Proctor Shaw

ADDRESS INQUIRIES TO:
Laura Wiegand
Director of Programs and Technology
(See address above.)

TOURISM CARES
275 Turnpike Street
Suite 307
Canton, MA 02021
(781) 821-5990 ext. 208
Fax: (781) 821-8949

E-MAIL ADDRESS:
carolynv@tourismcares.org

WEB SITE ADDRESS:
www.tourismcares.org/grants

TYPE:
Project/program grants. Grants to nonprofit, tax-exempt organizations.

As part of its mission, Tourism Cares distributes charitable grants to worthy tourism-related 501(c)(3) nonprofit organizations worldwide to conserve, preserve or restore sites of exceptional cultural, historic or natural significance. The program goals call for a balanced distribution to U.S. and non-U.S. recipients.

See entry 2348 for full listing.

TWO TEN FOOTWEAR FOUNDATION
1466 Main Street
Waltham, MA 02451
(800) 346-3210 ext. 1512
Fax: (781) 736-1555

E-MAIL ADDRESS:
scholarship@twoten.org

WEB SITE ADDRESS:
www.twoten.org

TYPE:
Scholarships. Intended for students who are interested in pursuing a career in footwear design.

See entry 1889 for full listing.

UNITARIAN UNIVERSALIST ASSOCIATION OF CONGREGATIONS   [539]
UU Funding Program
P.O. Box 301149
Jamaica Plain, MA 02130
(617) 971-9600
Fax: (617) 971-0029

E-MAIL ADDRESS:
uufp@aol.com

WEB SITE ADDRESS:
www.uua.org/awards

FOUNDED: 1986

AREAS OF INTEREST:
Limited to the fine arts of painting, drawing, enameling, printmaking, photography and sculpture.

NAME(S) OF PROGRAMS:
- **Stanfield and D'Orlando Art Scholarship**

TYPE:
Scholarships. Annual scholarship to be awarded to an applicant majoring in art, for further study in that major, at an accredited school.

YEAR PROGRAM STARTED: 1980

PURPOSE:
To aid a Unitarian Universalist student majoring in art.

LEGAL BASIS:
Religious organization.

ELIGIBILITY:
Applicants must be members in good standing for at least one year before date of application or sponsored by a member of a Unitarian Universalist Congregation and must be enrolled in an accredited school. Eligible art fields include drawing, painting, enameling and printmaking.

GEOGRAPHIC RESTRICTIONS:
United States.

FINANCIAL DATA:
Payment is made directly to the recipient.
Amount of support per award: Average $1,000.
Total amount of support: Varies.

NUMBER OF APPLICANTS MOST RECENT YEAR:
18.

NUMBER OF AWARDS: Varies.

APPLICATION INFORMATION:
Applications should include a short essay on applicant, photos or slides of at least six works by applicant, a letter of recommendation, statement of tuition costs where applicant is enrolled and an application which has been signed. Scholarship brochures and application forms available upon receipt of written request.
Duration: One academic year.
Deadline: February 15. Announcements by May 15.

UNITED ARTS COUNCIL OF RALEIGH AND WAKE COUNTY, INC.   [540]
110 South Blount Street
Raleigh, NC 27601
(919) 839-1498 ext. 226
Fax: (919) 839-6002

E-MAIL ADDRESS:
eoakley@unitedarts.org

WEB SITE ADDRESS:
www.unitedarts.org

FOUNDED: 1990

AREAS OF INTEREST:
Arts, arts education, music education, theatre arts education, humanities-community development, and teacher-preparation education.

NAME(S) OF PROGRAMS:
- **Artists-in-the-Schools Grants Program**
- **Community Arts Reach Program**
- **Program Support Grants**
- **Regional Artist Grants**

TYPE:
Project/program grants; Seed money grants; Training grants.

PURPOSE:
To enhance and strengthen arts and arts education in Wake County, North Carolina.

ELIGIBILITY:
Funds are available to Wake County (NC) schools, individual artists, arts organizations and agencies with specific arts programming.

GEOGRAPHIC RESTRICTIONS:
Raleigh and Wake County, North Carolina.

FINANCIAL DATA:
Amount of support per award: $1,000 to $30,000.
Total amount of support: Varies.
Matching fund requirements: Required for some programs.

NUMBER OF APPLICANTS MOST RECENT YEAR:
200.

NUMBER OF AWARDS: Over 400 for the year 2010-11.

PUBLICATIONS:
Guidelines.

IRS IDENTIFICATION NUMBER: 56-0770175

UNIVERSITY OF MINNESOTA
Room 113, Andersen Library
222 21st Avenue South
Minneapolis, MN 55455
(612) 624-4576

E-MAIL ADDRESS:
clrc@umn.edu

WEB SITE ADDRESS:
special.lib.umn.edu/clrc/

TYPE:
Travel grants. Award to travel to Kerlan Collection, University of Minnesota, plus per diem.

See entry 745 for full listing.

UNIVERSITY OF MINNESOTA   [541]
Room 113, Andersen Library
222 21st Avenue South
Minneapolis, MN 55455
(612) 624-4576
Fax: (612) 625-5525

E-MAIL ADDRESS:
clrc@umn.edu

WEB SITE ADDRESS:
special.lib.umn.edu/clrc/

AREAS OF INTEREST:
Research and children's literature.

NAME(S) OF PROGRAMS:
- **Marilyn Hollinshead Fellowship**

TYPE:
Travel grants.

PURPOSE:
To fund children's literature research with manuscripts and/or original illustrations.

FINANCIAL DATA:
Award to travel to Kerlan Collection, University of Minnesota, as well as per diem.
Amount of support per award: $1,500.
Total amount of support: $1,500.

NUMBER OF AWARDS: 1.

APPLICATION INFORMATION:
Electronic application acceptable by deadline.

Duration: Grants are awarded annually and are nonrenewable.

Deadline: January 30 of research year.

ADDRESS INQUIRIES TO:
Fellowship Committee
(See address above.)

THE UNIVERSITY OF TEXAS AT AUSTIN AND THE TEXAS INSTITUTE OF LETTERS   [542]

The Graduate School
Main 101
Austin, TX 78705
(512) 232-3609
Fax: (512) 471-7620

E-MAIL ADDRESS:
adameve@mail.utexas.edu

WEB SITE ADDRESS:
www.utexas.edu/ogs/Paisano

NAME(S) OF PROGRAMS:
• **The Dobie Paisano Fellowship Program**

TYPE:
Project/program grants. Provides an opportunity for creative or nonfiction writers to live and write for an extended period in an environment that offers isolation and tranquility.

Ralph A. Johnston Memorial Fellowship is aimed at writers who have demonstrated some publishing and critical success.

Jesse H. Jones Writing Fellowship is aimed at, but not limited to, writers who are early in their careers.

Both fellowships provide and require free residence at the ranch.

YEAR PROGRAM STARTED: 1967

PURPOSE:
To stimulate creative writing by making it possible for a person to work without distractions in an environment that offers isolation and tranquility.

ELIGIBILITY:
Criteria for making the awards include quality of work, character of the proposed project, and suitability of the applicant for life at Paisano, the late J. Frank Dobie's ranch near Austin, TX.

At the time of application, the applicant must meet one of the following:
(1) be a native Texan;
(2) have lived in Texas at some time for at least three years or;
(3) have published significant work with a Texas subject.

FINANCIAL DATA:
Amount of support per award: Ralph A. Johnston Memorial Fellowship: $20,000 over four months; Jesse H. Jones Writing Fellowship: $18,000 over five and a half months.

NUMBER OF APPLICANTS MOST RECENT YEAR:
Ralph A. Johnston Memorial Fellowship: 33; Jesse H. Jones Writing Fellowship: 73.

NUMBER OF AWARDS: 1 each annually.

APPLICATION INFORMATION:
Application fee of $20 for one fellowship or $30 for both fellowships is required. If applying for both fellowships, include the fee with the Johnston Memorial Fellowship application and check the appropriate box at the top of the Johnston application form. Application fees are non-refundable.

Applicants must submit each application and its accompanying materials in separate packets. Make checks or money orders payable to The University of Texas at Austin.

Both application forms can be downloaded and printed from the web site. To request a printed copy of either application, send a self-addressed, stamped envelope (2 ounces postage) to the address above.

Duration: Ralph A. Johnston Memorial Fellowship: Four months. Jesse H. Jones Writing Fellowship: Five and a half months. Both nonrenewable.

Deadline: Mid-January.

ADDRESS INQUIRIES TO:
Michael Adams
(See address above.)

*SPECIAL STIPULATIONS:
Fellows must reside at Paisano Ranch.

VCCA (VIRGINIA CENTER FOR THE CREATIVE ARTS)   [543]

154 San Angelo Drive
Amherst, VA 24521
(434) 946-7236
Fax: (434) 946-7239

E-MAIL ADDRESS:
vcca@vcca.com

WEB SITE ADDRESS:
www.vcca.com

FOUNDED: 1971

TYPE:
Exchange programs; Fellowships; Residencies. VCCA is a creative space offering exchange programs, fellowships and residencies. It is open to writers, visual artists and composers. VCCA enables these artists, both professional and upcoming, to concentrate on their work and take it to new heights.

YEAR PROGRAM STARTED: 1971

PURPOSE:
To provide visual artists, writers and composers with a creative space so they can pursue their projects with a minds-wide-open focus, free from the distractions and responsibilities of daily life.

LEGAL BASIS:
Nonprofit corporation.

ELIGIBILITY:
Achievement or outstanding promise within a field of art must be demonstrated.

FINANCIAL DATA:
All fellowships are for periods of residency. No cash awards, stipends, etc., are offered.

NUMBER OF APPLICANTS MOST RECENT YEAR:
650 for all programs.

NUMBER OF AWARDS: Over 360.

APPLICATION INFORMATION:
Application must include two references from professionals in one's field, samples of one's work and a curriculum vitae. Residencies available for three composers, nine visual artists and 11 writers at any time.

Duration: Two to eight weeks.

Deadline: January 15 for fellowships running from June to October. May 15 for fellowships running from October to January. September 15 for fellowships running from February to May.

PUBLICATIONS:
Application form; annual report; newsletters.

STAFF:
Sheila Gulley Pleasants, Artists Services Director
Craig Pleasants, Program Director
Lexie Boris, Communications Director

EXECUTIVE DIRECTOR:
Suny Monk

ADDRESS INQUIRIES TO:
Sheila Gulley Pleasants, Artists Services Director
(See address above.)

VERMONT ARTS COUNCIL [544]

136 State Street
Montpelier, VT 05602
(802) 828-3293
Fax: (802) 828-3363

E-MAIL ADDRESS:
info@vermontartscouncil.org

WEB SITE ADDRESS:
www.vermontartscouncil.org

FOUNDED: 1964

AREAS OF INTEREST:
Visual arts including painting, sculpture, drawing, printmaking, architectural and cultural facilities design, crafts, film and photography; performing arts in music, theatre and dance; literature.

CONSULTING OR VOLUNTEER SERVICES:
Staff members may counsel and assist individuals and organizations in the development of arts projects and activities.

NAME(S) OF PROGRAMS:
• **Artist Development Grants**
• **Arts Learning Grants**
• **Arts Partnership Grants**
• **Community Arts Grants**
• **Creation Grants**
• **Cultural Facilities Grants**
• **Cultural Routes Grants**
• **Teaching Artist Express Grants**
• **Teaching Artist Residency Grants**
• **Technical Assistance Grants**

TYPE:
Challenge/matching grants; Conferences/seminars; Development grants; Project/program grants; Residencies; Technical assistance; Travel grants. Professional development grants; Cultural facilities improvements; Arts partnerships.

YEAR PROGRAM STARTED: 1966

PURPOSE:
To advance and preserve the arts at the center of Vermont communities.

LEGAL BASIS:
Official state arts agency and a nonprofit membership corporation.

ELIGIBILITY:
Applicants must be nonprofit organizations, agencies of town, county, state government and/or individual artists of demonstrated ability who are residents of Vermont for at least one year.

Funding is not available for:
(1) academic tuition;
(2) activities in which artists are not appropriately compensated;
(3) construction of new facilities, renovation of existing facilities, or other capital improvements (exceptions in cases that comply with Cultural Facilities Grants);
(4) deficits and debts incurred from past activities;

(5) events that present faculty members on the campus of their own institutions;

(6) events which are predominantly religious or sectarian;

(7) events whose sponsors are not in compliance with the requirements of the Americans with Disabilities Act of 1990 and Section 504 of the Rehabilitation Act of 1973;

(8) food and beverages;

(9) for-profit organizations;

(10) fund-raising events;

(11) international travel (airline tickets);

(12) lobbying expenses;

(13) private events to which the public is not invited and;

(14) purchase of permanent equipment (exceptions in cases that comply with Cultural Facilities Grants).

GEOGRAPHIC RESTRICTIONS:
Vermont.

FINANCIAL DATA:
Amount of support per award: Varies according to each program.

Total amount of support: $1,528,794 in grants and services and $841,030 in grants only for the year 2009.

Matching fund requirements: Generally 1:1.

COOPERATIVE FUNDING PROGRAMS: Cultural Facilities Grants with the state of Vermont.

NUMBER OF APPLICANTS MOST RECENT YEAR:
250.

NUMBER OF AWARDS: 135.

APPLICATION INFORMATION:
Interested applicants can view the *Arts Council Grant Guidelines* and application online. Individual artists are required to submit samples of work. All applications must be submitted online and a signed hard copy postmarked by the deadline date.

Duration: Typically one year.

Deadline: Varies.

PUBLICATIONS:
Grant guidelines; *Art Directory*; *ArtMail*.

IRS IDENTIFICATION NUMBER: 03-0218115

ADDRESS INQUIRIES TO:
Sonia Rae, Artist and Community Services Manager or
Stacy Raphael, Education and Community Programs Manager
(See address above.)

VIRGIN ISLANDS COUNCIL ON THE ARTS   [545]

41-42 Norre Gade
St. Thomas, VI 00802
(340) 774-5984
Fax: (340) 774-6206

E-MAIL ADDRESS:
blmahoney@smartnet.vi

WEB SITE ADDRESS:
www.vicouncilonarts.org

FOUNDED: 1966

AREAS OF INTEREST:
Fine arts, language and literature, music, creative, visual and performing arts and crafts.

NAME(S) OF PROGRAMS:
● **Expanding Opportunities for Participation in the Arts**

TYPE:
General operating grants; Project/program grants; Residencies; Technical assistance.

Professional Development. Grants and technical assistance to individual artists, arts organizations and arts institutions in the Virgin Islands.

YEAR PROGRAM STARTED: 1966

PURPOSE:
To encourage wider participation in the arts by means of individual creative development and the strengthening of cultural organizations.

LEGAL BASIS:
Government agency.

ELIGIBILITY:
Applicants must be residents of the Virgin Islands for at least two years. Grants are made to Virgin Island-based projects or applicants.

GEOGRAPHIC RESTRICTIONS:
Virgin Islands.

FINANCIAL DATA:
Amount of support per award: Up to approximately $10,000. Organizations can receive a maximum of $10,000 and individuals can receive a maximum of $5,000.

Total amount of support: Depends on government, local and federal funding.

Matching fund requirements: The amount varies depending on category of grant. Usually 1:1.

NUMBER OF APPLICANTS MOST RECENT YEAR:
164.

NUMBER OF AWARDS: 153.

REPRESENTATIVE AWARDS:
$10,000 to Reichhold Center for the Performing Arts; $5,000 to the Farmers Association.

APPLICATION INFORMATION:
Official application information is available from the Council.

Duration: One year. Renewable on reapplication and reconsideration by the Board of Directors.

Deadline: January 31 and August 31.

STAFF:
Betty L. Mahoney, Executive Director

ADDRESS INQUIRIES TO:
Monique Walters, Grants Officer
(See address above.)

VIRGINIA COMMISSION FOR THE ARTS   [546]

Lewis House
223 Governor Street
Richmond, VA 23219
(804) 225-3132
Fax: (804) 225-4327

E-MAIL ADDRESS:
peggy.baggett@arts.virginia.gov

WEB SITE ADDRESS:
www.arts.virginia.gov

FOUNDED: 1968

AREAS OF INTEREST:
Arts activities including but not limited to performances, exhibitions, demonstrations, workshops, readings and other presentations or participatory experiences in the fields of crafts, dance, folk arts, literature, museum work, music, public media, theatre and visual arts, provided by artists or arts organizations located in the state of Virginia.

TYPE:
Challenge/matching grants; Conferences/seminars; Fellowships; General operating grants; Project/program grants; Residencies; Technical assistance. Arts in Education grants; Technology enhancement grants; Touring grants; Writers grants.

YEAR PROGRAM STARTED: 1968

PURPOSE:
To support and stimulate excellence in all the arts for all of the people of Virginia.

LEGAL BASIS:
State agency.

ELIGIBILITY:
Applicants must be nonprofit, tax-exempt organizations, schools or professional artists, government units.

GEOGRAPHIC RESTRICTIONS:
Virginia.

FINANCIAL DATA:
Amount of support per award: Varies.

Total amount of support: Approximately $5,100,000 for fiscal year 2009-10.

Matching fund requirements: Generally half or more.

NUMBER OF APPLICANTS MOST RECENT YEAR:
1,065 for fiscal year 2008-09.

NUMBER OF AWARDS: 829 for fiscal year 2008-09.

APPLICATION INFORMATION:
Duration: One year for most.

Deadline: March 1, April 1 and August 1 for most programs. Year-round for other programs.

PUBLICATIONS:
Program guidelines.

IRS IDENTIFICATION NUMBER: 54-0843105

STAFF:
Peggy J. Baggett, Executive Director

ADDRESS INQUIRIES TO:
Peggy J. Baggett, Executive Director
(See address above.)

VIRGINIA MUSEUM OF FINE ARTS   [547]

Art and Education Division
200 North Boulevard
Richmond, VA 23220-4007
(804) 204-2685
Fax: (804) 204-2675

E-MAIL ADDRESS:
elizabeth.cruickshanks@vmfa.museum

WEB SITE ADDRESS:
www.vmfa.museum/fellowships

FOUNDED: 1932

AREAS OF INTEREST:
Education and careers in the visual arts.

NAME(S) OF PROGRAMS:
● **Professional Fellowship Program**
● **Student Fellowship Program**

TYPE:
Awards/prizes; Fellowships. Awards for undergraduate students, graduate students and professionals in the visual arts including painting, sculpture, crafts, photography, filmmaking, video, printmaking and drawing. Art history is for graduate students only.

YEAR PROGRAM STARTED: 1940

PURPOSE:
To aid Virginians who seek financial aid for additional education or experience in the arts.

LEGAL BASIS:
State agency administering funds from an endowment and a private foundation.

ELIGIBILITY:
All Applicants: Persons must be citizens or permanent residents of the U.S. and current legal residents of Virginia. A legal resident has a valid Virginia driver's license and/or pays income taxes in Virginia and/or is a registered Virginia voter. Applicants must be able to provide verification of residency upon request.

Student Applicants: Persons must be current legal residents of Virginia, and must have been legal residents for at least 12 consecutive months prior to the application deadline. Students paying in-state tuition to an accredited Virginia college, university or school of the arts qualify as legal residents of Virginia. Students must be enrolled full-time at an accredited college, university or school of the arts for the grant period of August 2012-May 2013. Half-year fall semester Fellowship awards will be considered on a case-by-case basis for full-time students in the final year of a degree program who plan to graduate in December 2012.

Professional Applicants: Persons must be current legal residents of Virginia, and must have been legal residents for at least 24 consecutive months prior to the application deadline. Professional applicants must not be degree-seeking students at the time of the application deadline nor during the grant period of August 2012-May 2013.

GEOGRAPHIC RESTRICTIONS:
Virginia.

FINANCIAL DATA:
Amount of support per award: Professional Fellowships: $8,000; Undergraduate Fellowships: $4,000; Graduate Fellowships: $6,000.
Total amount of support: $258,000 for the year 2011.

NUMBER OF APPLICANTS MOST RECENT YEAR:
642.

NUMBER OF AWARDS: 43.

APPLICATION INFORMATION:
Duration: August 2012 to May 2013. No renewals.
Deadline: November 10, 2011. Notification in mid-February.

STAFF:
Elizabeth Cruickshanks, Coordinator, Fellowship Program

ADDRESS INQUIRIES TO:
Fellowship Program
(See address above.)

*PLEASE NOTE:
Awards are made to applicants of highest artistic merit whose careers will benefit from financial assistance.

KURT WEILL FOUNDATION FOR MUSIC [548]
7 East 20th Street
New York, NY 10003-1106
(212) 505-5240
Fax: (212) 353-9663

E-MAIL ADDRESS:
kwfinfo@kwf.org

WEB SITE ADDRESS:
www.kwf.org

FOUNDED: 1962

AREAS OF INTEREST:
The study and performance of music by Kurt Weill.

TYPE:
Grants-in-aid; Research grants; Travel grants. Research Grants support specific research expenses on a topic related to Kurt Weill and/or Lotte Lenya. Travel grants support Kurt Weill projects, and reimburse reasonable travel expenses to locations of primary source material.

Symposia: Support of direct expenses for performing and educational organizations.

Publication Assistance aids in expenses related to preparing manuscripts for publication in a recognized scholarly medium.

Dissertation Fellowships assist Ph.D. candidates in research activities.

College/University Performance and Production Grants - Stage Works: Grants to colleges and universities in support of general production expenses for performances of Kurt Weill's stage works (including The Threepenny Opera); Concert Works: Assistance for performances of concert works.

Broadcasts: Given to producers and not-for-profit broadcasters to support programs that feature Kurt Weill's life and/or music.

Professional Performance and Production Grants: Support to professional and regional opera companies, theater companies, and concert groups to enhance the musical qualities of a performance.

PURPOSE:
To preserve and perpetuate the legacies of composer Kurt Weill (1900-1950) and actress-singer Lotte Lenya (1898-1981).

ELIGIBILITY:
Grant support is strictly limited to projects directly related to Kurt Weill.

Research and Travel Grants: Applicants must be researching a topic related to Kurt Weill and/or Lotte Lenya. Travel grants should be requested, in support of Kurt Weill projects, to reimburse reasonable travel expenses to locations of primary source material.

Symposia: Performing and educational organizations may apply for support of direct expenses, including speakers' honoraria and travel expenses.

Publication Assistance: Funds may be requested for activities including, but not limited to, editing, indexing, design, and reproduction fees. Not-for-profit publishing companies are encouraged to apply. All proposals must have been subject to peer review; such reviews must be submitted in support of the application. Normally conference proceedings are ineligible unless the essays have undergone significant revision as components of a book.

College/University Performance and Production Grants - Stage Works: All works must be presented in fully staged versions using Weill's original orchestrations; Concert Works: Expenses can include, but are not limited to, increased rehearsal time, guest artist fees and promotion.

Broadcasts: Proposals are welcome from producers and not-for-profit broadcasters. A complete description of the project must accompany a commitment to broadcast.

Professional Performance and Production Grants Requests: Proposals from professional and regional opera companies, theater companies, and concert groups should substantiate that requested funds will be used to enhance the musical qualities of the performance. Appropriate requests include funds for soloists, orchestra fees, and extra rehearsals. If more than 50% of the performing forces in a production are students or volunteers, the application must be submitted under the College/University category.

FINANCIAL DATA:
Amount of support per award: Varies.
Total amount of support: Varies.

APPLICATION INFORMATION:
Research and Travel grant applicants must submit a detailed outline of the proposed project.

Dissertation Fellowship applications must include a copy of the dissertation proposal and two letters of recommendation, one of which must be from the faculty advisor.
Deadline: November 1 for the following academic year.

ADDRESS INQUIRIES TO:
Carolyn Weber, Director
(See address above.)

WEST VIRGINIA DIVISION OF CULTURE AND HISTORY [549]
The Culture Center
State Capitol Complex
1900 Kanawha Boulevard East
Charleston, WV 25305-0300
(304) 558-0220
Fax: (304) 558-3560

E-MAIL ADDRESS:
jeff.a.pierson@wv.gov

WEB SITE ADDRESS:
www.wvculture.org

FOUNDED: 1967

AREAS OF INTEREST:
Artists and arts organizations, including community and development, touring, institutions, special projects and support for artists, cultural facilities purchase and rehabilitation.

CONSULTING OR VOLUNTEER SERVICES:
Consultation in a variety of fields is available.

TYPE:
Capital grants; Challenge/matching grants; Fellowships; General operating grants; Internships; Project/program grants; Residencies; Technical assistance; Training grants; Travel grants. Long-range planning. Individual artists grants.

YEAR PROGRAM STARTED: 1967

PURPOSE:
To provide financial and technical assistance to further the promotion, presentation and development of the arts throughout the state of West Virginia.

LEGAL BASIS:
Government agency.

ELIGIBILITY:
Nonprofit organizations and public agencies may apply. Nonprofits must have been based

in West Virginia one year prior to application. Individual artists must be residents of West Virginia one year prior to application.

GEOGRAPHIC RESTRICTIONS:
West Virginia.

FINANCIAL DATA:
Generally, grants cover 50% of project cost.
Amount of support per award: $125 to $100,000.
Total amount of support: Approximately $2,000,000 for the year 2011.
Matching fund requirements: Dollar-for-dollar.

COOPERATIVE FUNDING PROGRAMS: Ohio River Border Initiative (ORBI) with Ohio Arts Council.

APPLICATION INFORMATION:
Copies of application guidelines and application forms are available upon request to the Commission.
Duration: One year. Must reapply for additional funding.
Deadline: Varies.

PUBLICATIONS:
Annual report; application guidelines; *ArtWorks,* newsletter.

OFFICERS:
Randall Reid-Smith, Commissioner
Karen Gresham, Deputy Commissioner
Susan Stevenson Landis, Chairman, West Virginia Commission on the Arts
Jeff Pierson, Director of Arts, West Virginia Commission on the Arts

ADDRESS INQUIRIES TO:
Jeff Pierson, Director of Arts
West Virginia Commission on the Arts
(See address above.)

WHITAKER FOUNDATION [550]
308 North 21st Street
Suite 400
St. Louis, MO 63103
(314) 241-4352
Fax: (314) 241-4381

WEB SITE ADDRESS:
www.thewhitakerfoundation.org

FOUNDED: 1975

AREAS OF INTEREST:
The arts, the use of and preservation of parks.

TYPE:
Project/program grants. Project/program grants are for urban parks and the arts.

PURPOSE:
To enrich lives through the arts; to encourage the preservation and use of parks.

LEGAL BASIS:
Private foundation.

ELIGIBILITY:
Organizations must be tax-exempt 501(c)(3). Project support is preferred. No support for social events.

GEOGRAPHIC RESTRICTIONS:
Metropolitan area of St. Louis, Missouri.

FINANCIAL DATA:
Amount of support per award: Varies.
Total amount of support: $1,460,000 for fiscal year 2008.

NUMBER OF APPLICANTS MOST RECENT YEAR:
150.

NUMBER OF AWARDS: 41 for fiscal year 2008.

APPLICATION INFORMATION:
Detailed guidelines and application form can be obtained from the address above.
Deadline: October, January and April.

PUBLICATIONS:
Guidelines.

ADDRESS INQUIRIES TO:
Christy Gray, Executive Director
(See address above.)

WISCONSIN ARTS BOARD [551]
101 East Wilson Street
1st Floor
Madison, WI 53702
(608) 266-0190
Fax: (608) 267-0380

E-MAIL ADDRESS:
artsboard@wisconsin.gov

WEB SITE ADDRESS:
www.artsboard.wisconsin.gov

FOUNDED: 1973

AREAS OF INTEREST:
All arts disciplines in Wisconsin.

CONSULTING OR VOLUNTEER SERVICES:
Workshops and individual consultations.

NAME(S) OF PROGRAMS:
- **Artist and Community Collaborations Grant**
- **Artists Fellowships/Individual Artist Program**
- **Creation & Presentation**
- **Creative Communities**
- **Cultural Facilities Assistance Program**
- **Folk Arts Apprenticeship Program**
- **Percent for Art**
- **Wisconsin Regranting Program**

TYPE:
Challenge/matching grants; Fellowships; Internships; Project/program grants; Technical assistance. Inquiry services, research and funding. Services provided to institutions and individuals statewide in Wisconsin.

Creative Communities Grants include Artists Education, Local Arts and Folk Arts.

PURPOSE:
To provide support of arts projects and activities in the state of Wisconsin.

LEGAL BASIS:
Agency of the state of Wisconsin.

ELIGIBILITY:
Applicants must be organizations located in Wisconsin, operating for three years and have 501(c)(3) tax-exempt status. Individual applicants must be residents of Wisconsin for at least one year prior to application and for duration of project.

GEOGRAPHIC RESTRICTIONS:
Wisconsin.

FINANCIAL DATA:
Amount of support per award: $1,000 to $40,000 depending on the program.
Total amount of support: $2,300,000 for fiscal year 2009.
Matching fund requirements: All grants must be matched with the exception of Fellowships.

NUMBER OF AWARDS: 205 for fiscal year 2008.

APPLICATION INFORMATION:
Application form is available online.
Duration: One year.

Deadline: Varies.

PUBLICATIONS:
Arts and Crafts Fairs Directory, available online.

STAFF:
George Tzougros, Executive Director

ADDRESS INQUIRIES TO:
Karen Goeschko, Assistant Director Programs and Services
(See address above.)

WOMEN IN FILM
6100 Wilshire Boulevard
Suite 710
Los Angeles, CA 90048
(323) 935-2211
Fax: (323) 935-2212

E-MAIL ADDRESS:
foundation@wif.org

WEB SITE ADDRESS:
www.wif.org/foundation

TYPE:
Project/program grants. Awards for completion of films or videotapes on subjects that meet the stated guidelines of WIF on an annual basis.

See entry 1165 for full listing.

WOMEN'S STUDIO WORKSHOP (WSW) [552]
722 Binnewater Lane
Rosendale, NY 12472
(845) 658-9133
Fax: (845) 658-9031

E-MAIL ADDRESS:
info@wsworkshop.org

WEB SITE ADDRESS:
www.wsworkshop.org

FOUNDED: 1974

AREAS OF INTEREST:
Book arts.

NAME(S) OF PROGRAMS:
- **Artists' Book Residency Grants**

TYPE:
Project/program grants; Residencies.

YEAR PROGRAM STARTED: 1979

PURPOSE:
To enable artists to produce a limited edition artists' book while in residence at the Women's Studio Workshop.

FINANCIAL DATA:
Amount of support per award: $2,000 to $2,700 stipend for six- to eight-week residency, materials up to $750, access to all studios, and housing.

NUMBER OF APPLICANTS MOST RECENT YEAR:
100.

NUMBER OF AWARDS: 3 to 5.

APPLICATION INFORMATION:
Application must include:
(1) application form;
(2) one-page description of the project (send three copies);
(3) structural dummy to demonstrate how the book will be bound. It does not have to be a complete representation of the finished piece. However, please include one to two spreads that are fully sketched out. Dummy should be actual-size. (The Workshop anticipates ideas will be refined before residency);

(4) media/studios needed to produce the book, as well as a materials budget (send three copies);
(5) resume (send three copies);
(6) ten images of recent work with a slide script, which should include title, media, dimension and date. Individual slides must be marked clearly. Check the FAQ sheet for slide/digital specifications. (Submit slides of work other than the proposed book. Slides should reflect the direction of the applicant's work in their primary medium) and;
(7) self-addressed, stamped envelope for return of materials.

Duration: Six to eight weeks. Nonrenewable.
Deadline: November 15.

ADDRESS INQUIRIES TO:
Ann Kalmbach, Executive Director
(See address above.)

WOMEN'S STUDIO WORKSHOP (WSW)   [553]

722 Binnewater Lane
Rosendale, NY 12472
(845) 658-9133
Fax: (845) 658-9031

E-MAIL ADDRESS:
info@wsworkshop.org

WEB SITE ADDRESS:
www.wsworkshop.org

FOUNDED: 1974

AREAS OF INTEREST:
Art-in-education.

NAME(S) OF PROGRAMS:
● **Arts-in-Education**

TYPE:
Residencies. With National Endowment for the Arts (NEA) support, WSW awards two eight-week residencies to artists in the book arts.

PURPOSE:
To help grantees create new work while they simultaneously teach young people through the workshop's studio-based art-in-education program.

ELIGIBILITY:
Artists working in the book arts.

FINANCIAL DATA:
Amount of support per award: $400 per week stipend, $750 materials budget, housing, travel costs (within the Continental U.S.) and unlimited studio access.

APPLICATION INFORMATION:
Two-step juried RFP. Submit initially to WSW; WSW then applies to the NEA.
Duration: Eight weeks.
Deadline: November 15.

ADDRESS INQUIRIES TO:
Ann Kalmbach, Executive Director
(See address above.)

*PLEASE NOTE:
Normally, residencies are September to October and March to April. Specific dates are determined by the academic calendar and vary annually.

WOMEN'S STUDIO WORKSHOP (WSW)   [554]

722 Binnewater Lane
Rosendale, NY 12472
(845) 658-9133
Fax: (845) 658-9031

E-MAIL ADDRESS:
info@wsworkshop.org

WEB SITE ADDRESS:
www.wsworkshop.org

FOUNDED: 1974

AREAS OF INTEREST:
Visual artists.

NAME(S) OF PROGRAMS:
● **Studio Residency**

TYPE:
Residencies.

YEAR PROGRAM STARTED: 1999

PURPOSE:
To provide artists with time and resources to create a new body of work.

ELIGIBILITY:
Women printmakers, papermakers, book artists, ceramists, photographers or artist collaborators can apply.

FINANCIAL DATA:
Amount of support per award: $2,000 artist stipend, $750 material budget, travel stipend, housing and unlimited studio use.

APPLICATION INFORMATION:
Applicants should submit:
(1) application form;
(2) one-page project description on a separate sheet;
(3) resume;
(4) 10 numbered images of recent work, including script and;
(5) self-addressed, stamped envelope for return of materials.
Duration: Six to eight weeks. Nonrenewable.
Deadline: April 1.

ADDRESS INQUIRIES TO:
Ann Kalmbach, Executive Director
(See address above.)

THE HELENE WURLITZER FOUNDATION OF NEW MEXICO   [555]

218 Los Pandos Road
Taos, NM 87571
(575) 758-2413
Fax: (575) 758-2559

E-MAIL ADDRESS:
hwf@taosnet.com

WEB SITE ADDRESS:
www.wurlitzerfoundation.org

FOUNDED: 1954

AREAS OF INTEREST:
Creative, not interpretive, work in all media and allied fields.

TYPE:
Residencies. Residence grants for national and international artists involved in creative work, including writing, painting, sculpture and musical composition.

YEAR PROGRAM STARTED: 1954

PURPOSE:
To encourage and stimulate creative work in all media, including visual arts, literary arts and musical composition.

LEGAL BASIS:
Tax-exempt under Section 501(c)(3) and Section 4945(j)(3), (g)(3) and (g)(1).

ELIGIBILITY:
No restrictions are made on the basis of race, sex, age or religious or ethnic background or national origin.

FINANCIAL DATA:
No direct monetary grants are made. Residences are located in Taos, NM and are furnished with free utilities and rent.
Amount of support per award: Varies.
Total amount of support: Varies.

COOPERATIVE FUNDING PROGRAMS: Robert Chesley Foundation.

NUMBER OF APPLICANTS MOST RECENT YEAR: 160.

NUMBER OF AWARDS: 33.

APPLICATION INFORMATION:
Application must include five samples maximum (slides, photographs, or digital images) from visual artists (please list medium and dimensions), writing sample not to exceed 35 double-spaced pages or six poems from literary artists, or one CD/DVD from composers. Failure to comply with the guidelines will result in elimination from the review process. The Foundation will not retain samples of work and recommends a self-addressed, stamped envelope be included with samples if applicant wishes to have samples returned.

Applicant should also send self-addressed, stamped envelope if requesting application via mail.
Duration: Three-month residencies preferred. Grants can be shortened or extended under special circumstances.
Deadline: January 18.

IRS IDENTIFICATION NUMBER: 85-0128634

OFFICERS AND BOARD OF DIRECTORS:
Rena Rosequist, President
Peggy Nelson, Vice President
Bill Ebie, Treasurer
Harold Hahn, Secretary
Michael A. Knight, Executive Director
Mary Alexander
Joseph Caldwell
Tito Naranjo

ADDRESS INQUIRIES TO:
Michael A. Knight, Executive Director
(See address above.)

*SPECIAL STIPULATIONS:
Single occupancy only, no pets, no smoking, no outside employment while in residence.

WYOMING ARTS COUNCIL [556]

2320 Capitol Avenue
Cheyenne, WY 82002
(307) 777-7742
Fax: (307) 777-5499

E-MAIL ADDRESS:
ebratt@state.wy.us

WEB SITE ADDRESS:
wyoarts.state.wy.us

FOUNDED: 1967

AREAS OF INTEREST:
Arts within the state of Wyoming.

CONSULTING OR VOLUNTEER SERVICES:
Technical assistance for 501(c)(3) nonprofit and government organizations.

NAME(S) OF PROGRAMS:
● **Art Festival Grants**
● **Arts Access Grants**
● **Arts Across Wyoming Grants**
● **Arts in Education Grants**
● **Community Arts Partners Grants**
● **Folk Arts Grants**

- **Grants to Organizations Grants**
- **Individual Artist Professional Development Grants**
- **Literary Arts Fellowships**
- **Open Door Grants**
- **Operating Support Grants**
- **Performing Arts Fellowships**
- **Technology in the Arts Grants**
- **Visual Arts Fellowships**

TYPE:
Development grants; Fellowships; Formula grants; General operating grants; Project/program grants; Residencies. Grants and fellowships are for individual artists. General operating and project/program grants are for 501(c)(3) nonprofit and government organizations.

YEAR PROGRAM STARTED: 1967

PURPOSE:
To assist artistic programs of outstanding quality that serve the needs of Wyoming citizens, further public interest in the state's cultural heritage and resources and encourage artistic expression, essential for the well-being of the arts.

LEGAL BASIS:
Agency of the state of Wyoming.

ELIGIBILITY:
Grants are provided to 501(c)(3) nonprofit organizations, educational institutions and governmental entities within the state, including arts centers, museums, symphonies, schools, dance workshops, theatre and local arts councils. Fellowships provided in visual arts, literature, performing arts and to Wyoming residents.

GEOGRAPHIC RESTRICTIONS:
Wyoming.

FINANCIAL DATA:
Amount of support per award: Varies.
Total amount of support: Varies.
Matching fund requirements: A one-to-one cash match is required on all grants.

NUMBER OF APPLICANTS MOST RECENT YEAR:
More than 400.

NUMBER OF AWARDS: Over 300 grants are awarded each year.

APPLICATION INFORMATION:
Apply online for most grant programs.
Duration: One fiscal year (July 1 to the following June 30).
Deadline: Varies.

PUBLICATIONS:
Application guidelines; artist roster; newsletter.

STAFF:
Rita Basom, Manager
Camilla El-Antably, Arts in Education/Deputy Manager
Karen Merklin, Grant Manager
Marirose Morris, Arts Access Specialist
Randy Oestman, Community Development Specialist
Annie Hatch, Folk Arts Specialist
Michael Shay, Individual Arts Specialist

ADDRESS INQUIRIES TO:
Karen Merklin, Grant Manager
(See address above.)

XERIC FOUNDATION   [557]
351 Pleasant Street, No. 214
Northampton, MA 01060
(413) 585-0671

E-MAIL ADDRESS:
xericgrant@aol.com

WEB SITE ADDRESS:
www.xericfoundation.org

FOUNDED: 1991

AREAS OF INTEREST:
Comic books.

NAME(S) OF PROGRAMS:
- **Grants for Comic Book Creators**
- **Grants for Nonprofit Organizations**

TYPE:
Project/program grants; Scholarships; Seed money grants. Funds for charitable and nonprofit organizations for unique projects or services and where possible to leverage other funds. Grant for comic book creators to assist with the physical production and distribution of comic books including printing, color separation, solicitation and shipping.

YEAR PROGRAM STARTED: 1991

PURPOSE:
To encourage comic book creators to experience the learning process involved in self-publishing.

LEGAL BASIS:
Private, nonprofit corporation.

ELIGIBILITY:
Grants for comic book creators cannot be used for creative or living expenses, nor can they be used to obtain professional services from existing publishers. Organizations applying for grants must be charitable and nonprofit organizations with their own IRS letter of 501(c)(3) tax-exempt status. No funds for operating budgets or capital costs.

GEOGRAPHIC RESTRICTIONS:
United States or Canada for comic book artists and western Massachusetts for nonprofit organization grants.

FINANCIAL DATA:
Amount of support per award: Generally not over $5,000.
Total amount of support: Over $2,500,000 awarded to date.

NUMBER OF APPLICANTS MOST RECENT YEAR:
Varies.

NUMBER OF AWARDS: Varies.

APPLICATION INFORMATION:
There is no formal application form. Grant proposals must be submitted in the form of a written request.

Comic book artists must include in their submissions a cover letter, resume, statement of purpose, financial statement, proposed budget and a presentation of the work. Six copies are required.

Nonprofit organizations must include with their grant request a cover letter, history of the organization, description of the project, personnel list, projected calendar, budget and financial statements in addition to a copy of the organization's tax-exemption letter from the IRS. Six copies are required.
Duration: One year.
Deadline: March 31 and September 30 for comic book artists. January 31 for nonprofit organizations.

PUBLICATIONS:
Grant guidelines.

IRS IDENTIFICATION NUMBER: 22-3149258

ADDRESS INQUIRIES TO:
See e-mail address above.

*PLEASE NOTE:
Applications will not be returned. Applicants may reapply the following year.

Performing arts

ACADEMY FOUNDATION OF THE ACADEMY OF MOTION PICTURE ARTS AND SCIENCES   [558]
1313 North Vine Street
Los Angeles, CA 90028
(310) 247-3010
Fax: (310) 247-3794

E-MAIL ADDRESS:
nicholl@oscars.org

WEB SITE ADDRESS:
www.oscars.org/nicholl

FOUNDED: 1927

AREAS OF INTEREST:
Motion picture arts and sciences.

NAME(S) OF PROGRAMS:
- **The Don and Gee Nicholl Fellowships in Screenwriting**

TYPE:
Awards/prizes; Fellowships. Awards provide a portion of living expenses for one year for promising new writers so that they may concentrate during that period on writing for the screen.

YEAR PROGRAM STARTED: 1985

PURPOSE:
To foster the development of the art of motion picture screenwriting.

LEGAL BASIS:
Non-public foundation.

ELIGIBILITY:
Applicants may not have earned more than $5,000 or any other consideration as a screenwriter for theatrical films or television or sold or optioned screen or television rights to any original story, treatment, outline screenplay or teleplay.

FINANCIAL DATA:
Amount of support per award: $30,000 each.
Total amount of support: $150,000 for the year 2010.

NUMBER OF APPLICANTS MOST RECENT YEAR:
6,304 for the year 2010.

NUMBER OF AWARDS: Up to 5 fellowships each year.

APPLICATION INFORMATION:
Applicants must submit one copy of an original screenplay in PDF format, approximately 100 to 130 pages in length, written in screenplay format standard to the U.S. motion picture industry. Submissions must have been written originally in English; translations will not be accepted. Submissions must be the original work of the applicant and may not be based, in whole or in part, on any other person's or persons' fictional or nonfictional material, published or unpublished, produced or unproduced. Sequels utilizing characters or storylines from produced motion pictures, television shows or published fiction are not eligible. Nor are adaptations eligible, unless the source material is solely the entrant's original work.

Applicants must also fill out an application form via an online account, completed in its entirety and pay a nonrefundable entry fee. This fee will be applied against judging and administrative costs. Applications and screenplays are accepted online only. Submitted materials will not be returned.

Duration: One year. Commencing on or about November 15.

Deadline: Uploaded by 11:59 P.M., May 1. Announcement in late October.

PUBLICATIONS:
Guidelines.

FELLOWSHIP COMMITTEE:
Gale Anne Hurd, Chairperson
John Bailey
Naomi Foner
Ron Mardigian
Bill Mechanic
Dan Petrie, Jr.
Steven Poster
Tom Rickman
Eva Marie Saint
Peter Samuelson
Robert Shapiro
Dana Stevens

ADDRESS INQUIRIES TO:
Nicholl Fellowships
(See address above.)

*PLEASE NOTE:
Each fellowship is payable quarterly for one year. The first payment will be made at the start of the fellowship year. The second, third, fourth and final payments will be made subject to satisfactory progress of the recipient's work, as judged by the Academy's Nicholl Fellowship Committee. The Academy reserves the right to grant no awards if, in the opinion of the Nicholl Fellowship Committee, no application is of sufficient merit.

*SPECIAL STIPULATIONS:
Nicholl Fellowships may not be held concurrently with other fellowships. During the fellowship year, Nicholl Fellows are expected to complete an original screenplay 100 to 130 pages in length.

AMERICAN DANCE FESTIVAL [559]

Box 90772
Durham, NC 27708-0772
(919) 684-6402
Fax: (919) 684-5459

E-MAIL ADDRESS:
adf@americandancefestival.org

WEB SITE ADDRESS:
www.americandancefestival.org

NAME(S) OF PROGRAMS:
• **Tuition Scholarships**

TYPE:
Scholarships.

PURPOSE:
To offer assistance to promising students.

ELIGIBILITY:
Open to promising students who have a high level of technical ability, creative potential and who have experience in either performing and/or choreography.

FINANCIAL DATA:
Amount of support per award: Quarter to full tuition.

APPLICATION INFORMATION:
Students must either submit their application before their audition date or be prepared to turn it in at the audition site. Students unable to attend an audition may submit a DVD containing two minutes of technique and a one-and-a-half-minute solo.

ADDRESS INQUIRIES TO:
Nicolle Wasserman
Director of School Administration and Student Affairs
(See address above.)

AMERICAN SOCIETY FOR THEATRE RESEARCH [560]

Texas Tech University
Department of Theatre and Dance
Box 42061
Lubbock, TX 79409-2061
(806) 742-3601 ext. 241
Fax: (806) 742-1338

E-MAIL ADDRESS:
dorothy_chansky@yahoo.com

WEB SITE ADDRESS:
www.astr.org

FOUNDED: 1956

AREAS OF INTEREST:
Theatre history, criticism and theory.

NAME(S) OF PROGRAMS:
• **The ASTR Collaborative Research Award**
• **Biennial Sally Banes Publication Prize**
• **Oscar G. Brockett Essay Award**
• **Helen Krich Chinoy Dissertation Research Fellowships**
• **Co-sponsored Events Awards**
• **Selma Jeanne Cohen Conference Presentation Award**
• **Distinguished Scholar Award**
• **Grants for Researchers with Heavy Teaching Loads**
• **Barnard Hewitt Award**
• **Errol Hill Award**
• **Gerald Kahan Scholar's Prize**
• **David Keller Travel Grants**
• **Thomas F. Marshall Graduate Student Awards**
• **The Brooks McNamara Publishing Subvention**
• **Research Fellowships**
• **Targeted Research Areas Grants**

TYPE:
Awards/prizes; Conferences/seminars; Exchange programs; Fellowships; Research grants; Residencies; Scholarships; Seed money grants; Travel grants; Visiting scholars. The ASTR Collaborative Research Award aims to foster the exchange of research across different academic and community contexts within the U.S. or between U.S. scholars and those abroad; to foster long-term relationships benefiting faculty who work in different types of institutional environments; and to foster the exchange of research in subject areas underrepresented in U.S. theatre scholarship, pedagogy, and performance practice.

Biennial Sally Banes Publication Prize: Award (given on even-numbered years) to the publication (book or essay) that best explores the intersections of theatre and dance/movement in the previous two calendar years.

Oscar G. Brockett Essay Award: A plaque is awarded for the best essay written by a senior scholar and published in English in a

refereed scholarly journal or volume published by an academic press. The subject can be on any subject in theatre research, broadly construed.

Helen Krich Chinoy Dissertation Research Fellowships assist Ph.D. candidates with travel to national and international collections connected with their dissertations.

Co-sponsored Events Awards assist with events that fulfill ASTR's purpose through collaboration with other organizations and institutions and increase the visibility of the work of both ASTR and the award recipient within a wider professional context.

Selma Jeanne Cohen Conference Presentation Award goes to a scholar to participate in a plenary or working session at the ASTR conference.

Distinguished Scholar Award is given each year to a scholar whose body of work has made a significant contribution to the field of theatre, dance, opera, and/or performance studies.

Grants for Researchers with Heavy Teaching Loads promote scholarly and practical exchange among theatre historians by providing research opportunities to scholars at institutions with heavy teaching loads and limited support for scholarship.

Barnard Hewitt Award: The Barnard Hewitt Award for Outstanding Research in Theatre History is awarded each year to the best book in "theatre history or cognate disciplines" published during the previous calendar year.

Errol Hill Award: A plaque is awarded for the best book-length manuscript or scholarly essay in recognition of outstanding scholarship in African American theater, drama, and/or performance studies. The book or essay must be published during the year in question (2010 for the 2011 award), and deal with African American theater history, dramatic literature, or performance studies.

Gerald Kahan Scholar's Prize: A plaque is awarded for the best essay written by a junior scholar and published in English in a refereed scholarly journal on any subject in theater research. The Kahan Prize presentation at the ASTR annual meeting includes an acknowledgement of the editor's contribution to scholarship.

David Keller Travel Grants, honoring the late David Mathias Keller (1936-1994), encourage untenured scholars with terminal degrees to become active members of the Society by helping them to meet the expenses of attending the ASTR annual meeting in November.

Thomas F. Marshall Graduate Student Awards, honoring the late Thomas F. Marshall, encourage active student membership of the Society by helping to meet the expenses of attending the ASTR annual meeting.

The Brooks McNamara Publishing Subvention supports the costs of securing rights to reproduce illustrations for publication, costs of acquiring illustrations, and/or the costs of reproducing illustrations in conjunction with a book under contract for publication. (Electronic publications will also be considered.)

Research Fellowships underwrite some of the expenses associated with projects in the field of theatre and/or performance studies.

Targeted Research Areas Grants are intended to support specific projects in areas currently underrepresented. Such areas include but are not limited to pre-1900 research; Asian, African, Latin American, and Middle Eastern theatre, dance and performance; and little known repertoires; translations of important theatre documents, including plays, will also be considered.

YEAR PROGRAM STARTED: 1976

LEGAL BASIS:
Nonprofit learned society.

ELIGIBILITY:
The ASTR Collaborative Research Award: At least one participant from a host institution must be a current ASTR member; all participants must hold a terminal degree. Biennial Sally Banes Publication Prize: Any independent, tenured or untenured scholar; eligible books and articles must have been published in the previous two calendar years. Oscar G. Brockett Essay Award: Author must have been a member of ASTR for at least three years and be at least seven years beyond the Ph.D. Helen Krich Chinoy Dissertation Research Fellowships: Ph.D. candidates who have passed their qualifying exams within the last two years (or will have passed their qualifying exams by June of the current year) and have begun working on their dissertations. The project must be part of the dissertation research. Selma Jeanne Cohen Conference Presentation Award: Any independent, tenured or untenured scholar (graduate students, postdoctorates and faculty are eligible to apply). Grants for Researchers with Heavy Teaching Loads: Any scholar who holds full-time faculty appointments at institutions where their teaching load is at least four courses a semester (or the equivalent). Gerald Kahan Scholar's Prize: The author must be untenured and within seven years of the Doctorate, or must be enrolled in a doctoral program, at the time the essay is published. Eligible articles must have appeared in 2010. David Keller Travel Grants: Any untenured scholars with terminal degrees, including independent scholars and tenure-track and adjunct faculty. Thomas F. Marshall Graduate Student Awards: Any student majoring in theatre/performance studies in any academic department at any level of higher education. Research Fellowships: Anyone who holds a terminal degree and who has been a member of the Society for at least three years is eligible to apply. Targeted Research Areas Grants: Any independent, tenured or untenured scholar who is currently a member of the Society and holds a terminal degree, or any graduate student who is applying in support of a project that is not directly related to her/his dissertation and is an area that is currently underrepresented.

FINANCIAL DATA:
Amount of support per award: The ASTR Collaborative Research Award: $1,750; Biennial Sally Banes Publication Prize: $500; Helen Krich Chinoy Dissertation Research Fellowships: $3,000 (typically divided into three equal awards); Co-sponsored Events Awards: Up to $1,500; Selma Jeanne Cohen Conference Presentation Award: Up to $1,000; Grants for Researchers with Heavy Teaching Loads: Up to $1,000; Barnard Hewitt Award: $1,000; David Keller Travel Grants and Thomas F. Marshall Graduate Student Awards: $800; The Brooks McNamara Publishing Subvention: Up to $600; Research Fellowships: $4,000 (which

can be divided among multiple winners); Targeted Research Areas Grants: Up to $4,000 total per annum (which may be split among more than one award).
Total amount of support: Varies.

NUMBER OF AWARDS: Dissertation Research Fellowship: Usually 3; David Keller Travel Grants and Thomas F. Marshall Travel Grants: Up to 3.

APPLICATION INFORMATION:
Contact the Society.
Duration: Varies.
Deadline: Spring.

ADDRESS INQUIRIES TO:
Dorothy Chansky, Chairperson
Awards and Fellowships Committees
(See address above.)

ARTS MIDWEST [561]
2908 Hennepin Avenue, Suite 200
Minneapolis, MN 55408-1954
(612) 341-0755
Fax: (612) 341-0902

E-MAIL ADDRESS:
christy@artsmidwest.org

WEB SITE ADDRESS:
www.artsmidwest.org

FOUNDED: 1985

AREAS OF INTEREST:
Performing arts booking conference and performing arts grants to presenting organizations.

NAME(S) OF PROGRAMS:
● **Midwest Arts Conference**
● **Performing Arts Fund**

TYPE:
Conferences/seminars. Performing arts grants.

YEAR PROGRAM STARTED: 1985

PURPOSE:
To connect people throughout the Midwest and the world to meaningful arts opportunities, sharing creativity, knowledge, and understanding across boundaries.

LEGAL BASIS:
Nonprofit.

ELIGIBILITY:
Nonprofit performing arts presenters within our nine-state region.

GEOGRAPHIC RESTRICTIONS:
Illinois, Indiana, Iowa, Michigan, Minnesota, North Dakota, Ohio, South Dakota and Wisconsin.

FINANCIAL DATA:
Amount of support per award: Up to 20% of the artist's contracted fee, $500 to $5,000.

APPLICATION INFORMATION:
Both an eGRANT application and a hard-copy application package must be submitted. Up to two separate applications may be submitted.
Deadline: eGRANT: March 30.

THE BANFF CENTRE [562]
107 Tunnel Mountain Drive
Banff AB T1L 1H5 Canada
(403) 762-6180
Fax: (403) 762-6345

E-MAIL ADDRESS:
arts_info@banffcentre.ca

WEB SITE ADDRESS:
www.banffcentre.ca

FOUNDED: 1933

AREAS OF INTEREST:
Studio art, photography, ceramics, performance art, video art, theatre production and design, stage management and opera.

TYPE:
Conferences/seminars; Project/program grants; Residencies; Work-study programs.

PURPOSE:
To provide financial assistance to deserving artists for a residency at The Banff Centre.

ELIGIBILITY:
Open to advanced students who have been accepted for a residency at The Banff Centre.

FINANCIAL DATA:
Amount of support per award: Varies.
Total amount of support: Varies.

APPLICATION INFORMATION:
Applicants must submit a completed application form, accompanied by requested documentation.

CAPEZIO/BALLET MAKERS DANCE FOUNDATION, INC. [563]
One Campus Road
Totowa, NJ 07512
(973) 595-9000 ext. 6203
Fax: (973) 595-0341

WEB SITE ADDRESS:
www.capeziodance.com

FOUNDED: 1952

AREAS OF INTEREST:
National, state and some local dance profession service organizations. Annual Capezio Dance Award in recognition of significant contribution to the art form.

NAME(S) OF PROGRAMS:
● **Capezio Dance Award**
● **Grants Program**

TYPE:
Awards/prizes; Development grants; General operating grants; Project/program grants. Grants to national, state and some local dance service organizations such as dance alliances, dance festivals and other organizations having a major impact on the field.

Awards are not open to the public.

Capezio Dance Award is given annually by the Trustees to an individual, company or organization that brings respect, stature and distinction to dance in America.

YEAR PROGRAM STARTED: 1952

PURPOSE:
To create a greater awareness and appreciation of dance as an art form and support efforts which service and increase interest in the dance field.

LEGAL BASIS:
Private tax-exempt, corporate foundation.

ELIGIBILITY:
Service or other organization with significant impact on the dance field. No support for individual dancers, companies or schools.

GEOGRAPHIC RESTRICTIONS:
United States.

FINANCIAL DATA:
Amount of support per award: $1,000 to $10,000.

Total amount of support: $50,000 to $100,000.

NUMBER OF APPLICANTS MOST RECENT YEAR: 200.

NUMBER OF AWARDS: 70 average.

APPLICATION INFORMATION:
Send letter explaining services and requesting guidelines.
Duration: No limitations.
Deadline: April 1.

PUBLICATIONS:
Brochure of guidelines and criteria; listing of grantees and Capezio Award winners.

IRS IDENTIFICATION NUMBER: 13-6161198

TRUSTEES:
Lawrence Freedman
Anthony Giacoio
Donald Terlizzi
Michael Terlizzi
Nicholas P. Terlizzi, Jr.

ADDRESS INQUIRIES TO:
Jane Remer, Executive Director
(See address above.)

*SPECIAL STIPULATIONS:
Does not fund individuals, schools, colleges or universities, films or media or dance companies.

CAUZ GROUP   [564]
P.O. Box 229
Pymble BC N.S.W. 2073 Australia
(61)(2) 8295-8100

E-MAIL ADDRESS:
trustawards@trust.com.au

WEB SITE ADDRESS:
www.trust.com.au

FOUNDED: 1979

AREAS OF INTEREST:
Personal management and furtherance of education of classical musicians in the arts (i.e., music, visual arts, literature, performing arts, etc.).

NAME(S) OF PROGRAMS:
● **Lady Mollie Askin Ballet Travelling Scholarship**
● **Sir Robert Askin Operatic Travelling Scholarship**
● **Kathleen Mitchell Award**

TYPE:
Awards/prizes; Scholarships; Travel grants. The scholarships shall be used for study, maintenance and travel either in Australia or overseas.

The Lady Mollie Askin Scholarship is awarded for outstanding ability and promise in Ballet.

The Sir Robert Askin Scholarship is awarded for outstanding ability and promise as a male operatic singer.

The Kathleen Mitchell Award is awarded to young Australian writers aged under 30 at the time their novel is published.

The above scholarships and award are entirely separate and are from separate charitable bequests.

YEAR PROGRAM STARTED: 1996

PURPOSE:
Lady Mollie Askin Ballet Travelling Scholarship and Sir Robert Askin Operatic Travelling Scholarship: To augment a

scholar's own resources affording him or her a cultural education by means of a travelling scholarship. Kathleen Mitchell Award: To advance the improvement of Australian literature; to improve the educational style of young authors, and to provide them with additional amounts to improve their literary efforts.

LEGAL BASIS:
Trust.

ELIGIBILITY:
Robert Askin: Must be male Australian citizen 18 to 29 years of age; Mollie Askin: Must be Australian citizen 17 to 29 years of age; Kathleen Mitchell Award: Born in Australia, British born or naturalised Australian who has been a resident in Australia for the 12 months preceding close of entries date, and 29 years of age or less.

FINANCIAL DATA:
Amount of support per award: Sir Robert Askin Operatic Travelling Scholarship and Lady Mollie Askin Ballet Travelling Scholarship: $20,000 (AUD); Kathleen Mitchell Award: $7,500 (AUD).

APPLICATION INFORMATION:
Applications must include a birth certificate, Australian citizenship certificate, a curriculum vitae, three references, work samples, and a summary of proposed aims and activities. Complete application information may be obtained from the address above.
Duration: Biennial.
Deadline: Robert Askin and Mollie Askin Scholarships: Last Friday in November of preceding year. Kathleen Mitchell Award: Third Friday in February.

PUBLICATIONS:
Application guidelines.

ADDRESS INQUIRIES TO:
Jane Ryan
(See address above.)

CHOPIN FOUNDATION OF THE U.S.
1440 79th Street Causeway, Suite 117
Miami, FL 33141
(305) 868-0624
Fax: (305) 865-5150

E-MAIL ADDRESS:
info@chopin.org

WEB SITE ADDRESS:
www.chopin.org

TYPE:
Scholarships. Scholarship program supporting young American pianists, 14 to 17 years of age.

See entry 802 for full listing.

COLONIAL PLAYERS, INC. THEATER-IN-THE-ROUND   [565]
108 East Street
Annapolis, MD 21401
(410) 268-7373 (Box Office)
(410) 263-0533 (Lobby)

E-MAIL ADDRESS:
treasurer@cplayers.com

WEB SITE ADDRESS:
www.cplayers.com
www.thecolonialplayers.org

FOUNDED: 1949

AREAS OF INTEREST:
Theatre and the arts.

NAME(S) OF PROGRAMS:
● **Biennial Promising Playwright Award**

TYPE:
Awards/prizes. Monetary award and showcase for an outstanding script by an aspiring playwright.

YEAR PROGRAM STARTED: 1973

PURPOSE:
To foster the arts and to encourage aspiring playwrights and promising talent in every aspect of the theatre.

LEGAL BASIS:
501(c)(3) nonprofit.

ELIGIBILITY:
Competition is open to any aspiring playwright residing in any of the states descendant from the original 13 colonies (Connecticut, Delaware, Georgia, Maryland, Massachusetts, New Hampshire, New Jersey, New York, North Carolina, Pennsylvania, Rhode Island, South Carolina and Virginia), West Virginia and the District of Columbia.

Only full-length plays, suitable for arena production, with up to two settings, and running not less than 90 minutes and not more than two hours, excluding intermission, will be considered. Cast sizes are limited to 10 actors or fewer. Musicals and adaptations in copyright will not be considered. In addition, plays that have been previously produced professionally will not be considered.

Plays submitted must be free of royalty and copyright restrictions which would prevent Colonial Players from producing the play. Collaborations of two or more authors are acceptable. Musicals and adaptations in copyright will not be considered. The play must not have been professionally produced elsewhere at the time of submission. Nonprofessional productions, staged readings and/or workshop productions prior to submission are permitted. (Please list places and dates along with name, address, phone number of the playwright in a sealed envelope attached to the manuscript.) Only plays which receive Honorable Mention from previous Colonial Players' contests may be resubmitted for consideration.

GEOGRAPHIC RESTRICTIONS:
Connecticut, Delaware, District of Columbia, Georgia, Maryland, Massachusetts, New Hampshire, New Jersey, New York, North Carolina, Pennsylvania, Rhode Island, South Carolina, Virginia and West Virginia.

FINANCIAL DATA:
Amount of support per award: $1,000 and workshop reading of the play.

NUMBER OF APPLICANTS MOST RECENT YEAR: 21.

NUMBER OF AWARDS: 1.

APPLICATION INFORMATION:
Scripts must be typewritten and firmly bound in a cover (no brads, no staples and no ring binders). The first sheet must include only the title of the play. The second sheet must contain a description of the setting(s), characters and the time of action. In a separate packet, author should submit the same first two pages bound with a one-page synopsis of the play and a 10-page sample from the play. The author's name, address and phone number may not appear anywhere on the manuscripts (no headers or footers)

but must be attached to the manuscript in a sealed envelope. Scripts will be numbered for judging.

Duration: Colonial Players reserves the right to work with the Director in a workshop production of the play within two years after the award is announced. Subsequent productions of the play at other theaters must give credit to Colonial Players, Inc. for premiering the play.

Deadline: Manuscripts will be accepted only if they bear postmarks between September 1 and December 31. Those received before or after will not be considered. Final decision of the judges will be announced no later than June 30 of the following year.

PUBLICATIONS:
Contest rules.

IRS IDENTIFICATION NUMBER: 23-7074203

OFFICERS:
Terry Averill, President

ADDRESS INQUIRIES TO:
Coordinator
The Colonial Players, Inc.
Promising Playwright Contest
(See address above.)

Manuscripts must be sent to
The Colonial Players, Inc.
Promising Playwright Contest
(See address above.)

*SPECIAL STIPULATIONS:
The award-winning playwright will be invited to a weekend workshop devoted entirely to the winning play the summer after the contest winner is announced. The workshop will include intensive discussions with directors, designers and actors, and a rehearsed reading in front of an audience.

MARTHA GRAHAM SCHOOL OF CONTEMPORARY DANCE, INC. [566]

316 East 63rd Street
New York, NY 10065
(212) 838-5886
Fax: (212) 838-0339

E-MAIL ADDRESS:
info@marthagraham.org

WEB SITE ADDRESS:
www.marthagraham.org

FOUNDED: 1926

AREAS OF INTEREST:
Training professional dancers.

NAME(S) OF PROGRAMS:
- **Independent Program**
- **Professional Trainee Program**
- **Summer Intensive**
- **Teens Program**
- **Third Year Post Certificate Program**
- **Winter Intensive**

TYPE:
Conferences/seminars; General operating grants; Internships; Matching gifts; Project/program grants; Research grants; Residencies; Scholarships; Work-study programs. Awards for class tuition.

Scholarship students work at the school.

YEAR PROGRAM STARTED: 1966

PURPOSE:
To provide help to the most promising dance students who are studying at the Martha Graham School.

LEGAL BASIS:
Nonprofit private school.

ELIGIBILITY:
Proficiency in dancing with special proficiency in the Martha Graham Technique is required. On-site scholarship auditions.

FINANCIAL DATA:
Scholarships are full (minimum of eight classes a week) or partial (student pays approximately half tuition per quarter for a minimum of eight classes a week). Scholarships require regular attendance.
Amount of support per award: Full $5,000; Half $2,500. Both for a 10-month school year.
Total amount of support: Varies.

NUMBER OF APPLICANTS MOST RECENT YEAR: 210.

NUMBER OF AWARDS: 24.

APPLICATION INFORMATION:
Applicants are students at the School at the time they apply. Award is by competition judged by the School faculty.
Duration: Normally awarded on a 12-month basis, on the basis of competition.

IRS IDENTIFICATION NUMBER: 13-1834089

BOARD OF TRUSTEES:
Judith Schlosser, Chairman
Inger Witter, President
LaRue Allen
Amy Blumenthal
Audra Cohen
Inga Golay
Laura Gordon
Patrick Leonard
Lorraine Oler
Neila Radtke
Paul Szlard
Calvin Tsao
Ronald Windisch

ADDRESS INQUIRIES TO:
Tami Alesson, Director of Education
(See address above.)

JACOB'S PILLOW DANCE FESTIVAL, INC. [567]

358 George Carter Road
Becket, MA 01223
(413) 243-9919
Fax: (413) 243-4744

E-MAIL ADDRESS:
info@jacobspillow.org

WEB SITE ADDRESS:
www.jacobspillow.org

FOUNDED: 1932

AREAS OF INTEREST:
Nurturing and sustaining artistic creation, presentation, education and preservation as well as engaging and deepening public appreciation and support for dance.

NAME(S) OF PROGRAMS:
- **The Intern Program at Jacob's Pillow**
- **The School at Jacob's Pillow**

TYPE:
Assistantships; Awards/prizes; Exchange programs; Fellowships; Internships; Residencies; Scholarships; Training grants; Visiting scholars. The Intern Program at Jacob's Pillow has training in arts administration and technical theater production. The School at Jacob's Pillow has five intensive programs: Ballet, Cultural

Traditions, Contemporary, Jazz/Musical Theatre Dance and Choreographers Lab, all including awards/prizes/scholarships.

There are creative development residencies available.

PURPOSE:
The Intern Program at Jacob's Pillow: To train aspiring young professionals and career-changers in arts administration and technical theater production during the Festival season and in arts administrations during the fall/winter/spring. The School at Jacob's Pillow: To provide professional development training to advanced dancers in summer dance programs.

ELIGIBILITY:
The Intern Program at Jacob's Pillow provides professional training experience in arts administration and technical theater production to aspiring young professionals and career-changers. The School at Jacob's Pillow is open to U.S. and foreign nationals who are 16 years of age or older and complete application requirements for the program(s) selected.

FINANCIAL DATA:
The School at Jacob's Pillow provides scholarships applicable toward tuition, room and board. Festival performances are an integral part of The School programs.
Amount of support per award: The School at Jacob's Pillow: Varies.
Total amount of support: Varies.

NUMBER OF APPLICANTS MOST RECENT YEAR:
Over 1,000 for both programs.

NUMBER OF AWARDS: 140 per year.

APPLICATION INFORMATION:
Intern Program at Jacob's Pillow: Applicants must write a cover letter explaining why they wish to intern at Jacob's Pillow, what position(s) they are applying for and in what priority order, their qualifications and interests, their goals and expectations for the internship and dates and days of the week they are available. The complete application must be assembled in the following order:
(1) Intern application form;
(2) cover letter;
(3) resume;
(4) at least two work-related references with names, titles, relationships, phone numbers, and e-mail addresses;
(5) two letters of recommendation and;
(6) if applicable, support materials specified in position descriptions.

Copies should be mailed together in one envelope to the attention of Intern Coordinator.

The School at Jacob's Pillow: All applicants must audition. Initially, applicants must submit a complete, legible program application, assembled and mailed as instructed on the Application Checklist. Enclosures vary by program.
Duration: The Intern Program at Jacob's Pillow: Up to three months. The School at Jacob's Pillow: One to three weeks.

ADDRESS INQUIRIES TO:
See e-mail address above.

THE JAPANESE AMERICAN CITIZENS LEAGUE (JACL) [568]

New York JACL
75 Grove Street
Bloomfield, NJ 07003
(973) 680-1441

E-MAIL ADDRESS:
lckimura@att.net

WEB SITE ADDRESS:
www.jacl.org

AREAS OF INTEREST:
Theatrical works of the Japanese
American/Canadian experience.

NAME(S) OF PROGRAMS:
- **Ruby Yoshino Schaar Playwright Award**

TYPE:
Awards/prizes. Biennial playwright award.

YEAR PROGRAM STARTED: 1984

PURPOSE:
To encourage talented playwrights to tell the
story of the Japanese American or Japanese
Canadian experience in North America.

ELIGIBILITY:
Applicant must be a playwright of Japanese
descent with American or Canadian
citizenship, sponsored by an active member
of JACL or a chapter of JACL, and have had
at least one of his or her plays presented in a
public forum, such as established theater,
workshop or formal reading. Play submitted
must not have been theatrically produced
before January 1 of the two previous years.
Manuscripts will be judged for dramatic
excellence and insight into the Japanese
American or Japanese Canadian experience.

FINANCIAL DATA:
Amount of support per award:
Approximately $3,000.

NUMBER OF AWARDS: 1 biennially.

APPLICATION INFORMATION:
Manuscripts are restricted to one per
applicant. A clear copy of the typed
manuscript in a professional format should be
accompanied by a completed application
form. Do not send an original manuscript.
Deadline: April 1.

ADDRESS INQUIRIES TO:
Lillian Kimura
(See address above.)

MEET THE COMPOSER, INC.

90 John Street, Suite 312
New York, NY 10038
(212) 645-6949
Fax: (212) 645-9669

E-MAIL ADDRESS:
mtc@meetthecomposer.org

WEB SITE ADDRESS:
www.meetthecomposer.org

TYPE:
Awards/prizes; Fellowships; Residencies.

See entry 820 for full listing.

NATIONAL OPERA ASSOCIATION, INC.

2403 Russell Long Boulevard
Canyon, TX 79016
(806) 651-2857
Fax: (806) 651-2958

E-MAIL ADDRESS:
rhansen@noa.org

WEB SITE ADDRESS:
www.noa.org

TYPE:
Awards/prizes. Cash prizes awarded to Artist
Division winners and Scholarship Division

winners. Also scholarships to AIMS, awarded
in both divisions. Productions of winning
operas in Chamber Opera Competition will
be scheduled for annual convention.

See entry 827 for full listing.

NEW DRAMATISTS [569]

424 West 44th Street
New York, NY 10036
(212) 757-6960
Fax: (212) 265-4738

E-MAIL ADDRESS:
newdramatists@newdramatists.org

WEB SITE ADDRESS:
www.newdramatists.org

FOUNDED: 1949

AREAS OF INTEREST:
Service organization for member playwrights.
Work with member writers on new plays,
providing them with workshops, readings and
staged readings. Involves directors and
dramaturges in workshops.

TYPE:
Awards/prizes; Internships; Residencies.
Resident playwrights are selected by an
admissions panel which consists of current
resident playwrights, alumni playwrights, and
other theatre professionals. The panel
changes completely from year to year.

YEAR PROGRAM STARTED: 1949

PURPOSE:
To provide playwrights with the tools and
freedom to make lasting contributions to the
theatre.

LEGAL BASIS:
Not-for-profit corporation.

ELIGIBILITY:
Open to U.S. citizens.

GEOGRAPHIC RESTRICTIONS:
United States.

FINANCIAL DATA:
Internships include college credit, where
available.
Amount of support per award: Full-time
interns work 40 hours per week with a
stipend of $50 to cover transportation and
lunch. Part-time interns work a minimum of
15 hours per week with a stipend of $25.

NUMBER OF APPLICANTS MOST RECENT YEAR:
331 for the year 2008.

NUMBER OF AWARDS: 5 to 8 residencies per
year.

PUBLICATIONS:
Application guidelines; brochure.

OFFICERS:
Seth Gelblum, Chairman
Isobel Robins Konecky, President

ADDRESS INQUIRIES TO:
Erin Detrick, Artistic Programs Administrator
(See address above.)

PEN AMERICAN CENTER [570]

588 Broadway, Suite 303
New York, NY 10012-5246
(212) 334-1660 ext. 122
Fax: (212) 334-2181

E-MAIL ADDRESS:
awards@pen.org

WEB SITE ADDRESS:
www.pen.org

FOUNDED: 1922

AREAS OF INTEREST:
American theater.

NAME(S) OF PROGRAMS:
- **PEN/Laura Pels Foundation Awards for Drama**

TYPE:
Awards/prizes. Honors both a Grand Master
of American Theater as well as an
outstanding new voice.

PURPOSE:
To honor the accomplishments of American
playwrights.

ELIGIBILITY:
Candidates for the award to a senior
American playwright are proposed by the
judges. Candidates for the award to an
American playwright in mid-career must be
playwrights writing in English who have had
a professional production of at least two
full-length works mounted in a theatre of at
least 299 seats and contracted specifically for
either limited or open runs.

FINANCIAL DATA:
Amount of support per award: Master
American Dramatist: a specially
commissioned art object; Mid-Career
American Playwright: cash prize of $7,500.

APPLICATION INFORMATION:
Playwrights may not apply on their own
behalf. They must be nominated by their
peers - producers, agents, critics, or other
playwrights who are expected to write a
letter of support, describing in some detail
the literary character of the candidate's work,
accompanied by a list of the candidate's
produced work. Do not send scripts.
Deadline: February 3.

PEW FELLOWSHIPS IN THE ARTS

1608 Walnut Street, 18th Floor
Philadelphia, PA 19103
(267) 350-4920
Fax: (267) 350-4997

E-MAIL ADDRESS:
pfa@pcah.us
mfranklin@pcah.us

WEB SITE ADDRESS:
www.pcah.us/fellowships

TYPE:
Fellowships. Opportunities for contemporary
artists in the Philadelphia five-county area to
concentrate on the development and creation
of art. Fellowships to support artists at
critical junctures in any stage of their career
development. Fellows will be expected to
participate annually in at least two meetings
with other fellowship recipients.

See entry 600 for full listing.

PRINCESS GRACE FOUNDATION-USA [571]

150 East 58th Street, 25th Floor
New York, NY 10155
(212) 317-1470
Fax: (212) 317-1473

E-MAIL ADDRESS:
grants@pgfusa.org

WEB SITE ADDRESS:
www.pgfusa.org

FOUNDED: 1982

AREAS OF INTEREST:
Theater, dance, choreography, film and playwriting.

NAME(S) OF PROGRAMS:
- **Princess Grace Awards**

TYPE:
Fellowships; Scholarships. Apprenticeships. Dedicated to identifying and assisting emerging artists in theater, dance and film through grants.

YEAR PROGRAM STARTED: 1984

PURPOSE:
To identify and assist emerging young artists in the fields of dance, theater and film within the U.S.

LEGAL BASIS:
Not-for-profit, tax-exempt, publicly supported charity.

ELIGIBILITY:
Must be a U.S. citizen or permanent resident.

GEOGRAPHIC RESTRICTIONS:
United States.

FINANCIAL DATA:
Amount of support per award: Theater, Dance and Film Awards: $5,000 to $25,000 average; Playwright Awards: $7,500.
Total amount of support: More than $7,000,000 since inception.

NUMBER OF AWARDS: Over 600 since inception.

APPLICATION INFORMATION:
All applicants, except playwrights, must be nominated by a school department chair/dean or company artistic director. The nominating organization must be a registered 501(c)(3). Detailed information is available online.
Duration: September 1 to August 31.
Deadline: Must be postmarked by March 31 for theater and playwriting; April 30 for dance and choreography; June 1 for film.

PUBLICATIONS:
Fact sheet; mission statement; press releases; newsletter.

IRS IDENTIFICATION NUMBER: 23-2218331

OFFICERS:
Hon. John F. Lehman, Chairman
Robert O. Marx, Vice Chairman
Toby E. Boshak, Secretary and Treasurer
Amy B. Desmond, Assistant Treasurer

ADDRESS INQUIRIES TO:
Diana Kemppainen, Program Manager
(See address above.)

FOREST ROBERTS THEATRE [572]
Northern Michigan University
1401 Presque Isle Avenue
Marquette, MI 49855-5364
(906) 227-2559
Fax: (906) 227-2567

E-MAIL ADDRESS:
newplays@nmu.edu

WEB SITE ADDRESS:
www.nmu.edu/theatre

FOUNDED: 1899

AREAS OF INTEREST:
Performing arts and playwriting.

NAME(S) OF PROGRAMS:
- **Mildred and Albert Panowski Playwriting Award**

TYPE:
Awards/prizes; Residencies.

YEAR PROGRAM STARTED: 1977

PURPOSE:
To encourage and stimulate artistic growth among educational and professional playwrights. Also to provide students with the creative opportunity to produce an original work on the university stage.

LEGAL BASIS:
Tax-exempt, nonprofit.

FINANCIAL DATA:
The award will include a fully mounted production and a trip to Marquette to act as Artist-in-Residence during the four-day run of the show. Room and board will be provided. Conducting informal seminars and workshops will be a part of this residency. A professional dramaturge will respond to the script and work with the playwright and director.
Amount of support per award: $2,000.

NUMBER OF APPLICANTS MOST RECENT YEAR:
160.

NUMBER OF AWARDS: Generally 1 award per school year.

APPLICATION INFORMATION:
Applications are to be submitted online.
Duration: One year. Renewal possibilities on a year-to-year basis.
Deadline: Entries must be received on or before September 1 to be considered for the current theme. Winner will be announced in December.

PUBLICATIONS:
Brochure.

ADDRESS INQUIRIES TO:
Playwrighting Coordinator
(See address above.)

EMMA A. SHEAFER CHARITABLE TRUST [573]
TX1-2963
P.O. Box 227237
Dallas, TX 75222-7237
Fax: (212) 464-2305

E-MAIL ADDRESS:
philp_lisa@jpmorgan.com

WEB SITE ADDRESS:
www.fdncenter.org/grantmaker/sheafer/

AREAS OF INTEREST:
Performing arts organizations in New York City, primarily for capacity-building initiatives, including capital and special projects.

TYPE:
Capital grants. Support provided for capacity building and special projects.

LEGAL BASIS:
Private organization.

ELIGIBILITY:
A minimum of three years must elapse between grant awards. No grants to individuals, private foundations, governmental organizations or for matching gifts or loans.

Organizations must be classified by the IRS as public charities and tax-exempt under Section 501(c)(3) of the Internal Revenue Code of 1986.

GEOGRAPHIC RESTRICTIONS:
New York, New York.

FINANCIAL DATA:
Amount of support per award: $15,000 to $25,000.

NUMBER OF AWARDS: Approximately 20 grants are made annually.

REPRESENTATIVE AWARDS:
$32,000 to the Abingdon Theatre Company, New York, NY, for its marketing initiative; $27,000 to Amas Musical Theatre, New York, NY, for the New Era Marketing Initiative; $27,000 to The Builders Association, Inc., New York, NY, for its expanded marketing initiative; $25,000 to Dance Works, Inc., aka, Pentacle, New York, NY, for the ARC Initiative; $20,000 to Dance Theatre of Harlem, Inc., New York, NY, for technology improvements.

APPLICATION INFORMATION:
Proposals should include:
(1) the primary goals of the organization including, as appropriate, the need or problem that the organization works to address and the segments of the population to which efforts are primarily directed;
(2) the most recent annual report, if available;
(3) a brief history of the organization, if not contained in the annual report;
(4) a list of the directors or trustees and their affiliations;
(5) the most recent financial audit;
(6) the current operating budget (if proposal is for two-year funding, provide this information for each year to which the grant would apply);
(7) a list of foundation and corporate support with amounts each has given, for the most recently completed fiscal year and the current fiscal year (if proposal is for two-year funding, provide this information for each year to which the grant would apply);
(8) a copy of the IRS 501(c)(3) determination letter and a complete copy of latest IRS Form 990, including salary information;
(9) a description of the project for which support is being sought including (a) a statement of its primary purpose and the need or problem to be addressed, (b) the population planned to be served and how this population will benefit from the project, (c) its anticipated duration, (d) its current budget (if proposal is for two-year funding, provide this information for each year to which the grant would apply), and (e) a list of foundation, corporate and other support applied to the current budget and the previous year's budget, with respect to the project (if proposal is for two-year funding, provide this information for each year to which the grant would apply) and;
(10) whether the organization has an endowment (if so, the value of the corpus as of the close of the most recently completed fiscal year, and whether the endowment is permanently restricted, board restricted, etc.).

Number all attachments and indicate the dates covered by each document, as appropriate.

Organizations must allow three years to elapse following a grant award, before submitting a subsequent proposal.

Duration: One year.

Deadline: Proposals: May 1. Grants are paid in June and December.

PUBLICATIONS:
Grants list.

ADDRESS INQUIRIES TO:
Lisa Philp, Managing Director
Emma A. Sheafer Charitable Trust
c/o JPMorgan Chase Bank, N.A.
Philanthropic Services
(See address above.)

THE SHUBERT FOUNDATION, INC.   [574]

234 West 44th Street
New York, NY 10036
(212) 944-3777
Fax: (212) 944-3767

WEB SITE ADDRESS:
www.shubertfoundation.org

FOUNDED: 1945

AREAS OF INTEREST:
Arts-related organizations, dance, education, human services and theatre.

TYPE:
General operating grants.

YEAR PROGRAM STARTED: 1945

PURPOSE:
To sustain and advance the live performing arts, in particular the American theatre and secondarily dance.

LEGAL BASIS:
Private foundation.

ELIGIBILITY:
The Foundation supports not-for-profit theatre and dance companies, as well as some arts-related organizations that assist in the development of the theatre. Applicants must be nonprofit organizations with Internal Revenue Code 501(c)(3) status. Organizations must submit audited financial statements. No grants to individuals.

GEOGRAPHIC RESTRICTIONS:
United States.

FINANCIAL DATA:
All grants cover general operating support only.
Amount of support per award: $10,000 to $275,000.
Total amount of support: $18,200,000 for the year 2010.

NUMBER OF APPLICANTS MOST RECENT YEAR:
500.

REPRESENTATIVE AWARDS:
$20,000 to Open Stage of Harrisburg, Harrisburg, PA; $145,000 to La Jolla Playhouse, La Jolla, CA; $210,000 to Manhattan Theatre Club.

APPLICATION INFORMATION:
A comprehensive application form, including audited financial data, must be submitted to the Foundation in duplicate. Applications, guidelines and instructions can be downloaded from the web site August to December; however, applications cannot be requested or submitted via e-mail.
Duration: One year. Renewal only with reapplication.
Deadline: December 1 for theatre category; October 15 for dance and other categories. Announcement in May each year.

PUBLICATIONS:
Annual report with application guidelines.

OFFICERS:
Philip J. Smith, Chairman of the Board
Michael I. Sovern, President
Wyche Fowler, Jr.

Lee J. Seidler
Stuart Subotnick
Robert E. Wankel

ADDRESS INQUIRIES TO:
Vicki Reiss, Executive Director
(See address above.)

WAGNER COLLEGE   [575]

Wagner College Theater
One Campus Road
Staten Island, NY 10301
(718) 390-3223
Fax: (718) 390-3323

E-MAIL ADDRESS:
todd.price@wagner.edu

WEB SITE ADDRESS:
www.wagner.edu

FOUNDED: 1957

AREAS OF INTEREST:
Playwriting.

NAME(S) OF PROGRAMS:
● **Stanley Drama Award**

TYPE:
Awards/prizes; Project/program grants. Annual award for the best play or musical submitted to the competition.

YEAR PROGRAM STARTED: 1957

PURPOSE:
To call attention to and encourage new playwrights.

LEGAL BASIS:
University.

ELIGIBILITY:
The Award is offered for an original full-length play, musical or one-act play sequence that has not been professionally produced or received tradebook publication. Writers of musicals are urged to submit music on cassette tapes or CDs.

The Stanley Award competition will consider only one submission (a single full-length play, musical or one-act sequence) per playwright. Plays entered previously in the competition may not be resubmitted. Former Stanley Award winners are not eligible to compete.

FINANCIAL DATA:
Amount of support per award: $2,000.

NUMBER OF APPLICANTS MOST RECENT YEAR:
67.

NUMBER OF AWARDS: 1 each year.

APPLICATION INFORMATION:
Applications may be obtained by sending a self-addressed, stamped envelope to the address above or on the web site. All scripts must be accompanied by a completed application. A reading fee of $30 must accompany the manuscript.
Deadline: October 1. Announcement the following April.

PUBLICATIONS:
Application guidelines.

ADDRESS INQUIRIES TO:
Todd Alan Price
Stanley Drama Award
(See address above.)

*SPECIAL STIPULATIONS:
Previous winners are ineligible.

THE LOREN L. ZACHARY SOCIETY FOR THE PERFORMING ARTS

2250 Gloaming Way
Beverly Hills, CA 90210-1717
(310) 276-2731
Fax: (310) 275-8245

E-MAIL ADDRESS:
peterhubner@earthlink.net

WEB SITE ADDRESS:
www.zacharysociety.org

TYPE:
Awards/prizes.

See entry 844 for full listing.

Fine arts

ACADEMY FOUNDATION OF THE ACADEMY OF MOTION PICTURE ARTS AND SCIENCES   [576]

8949 Wilshire Boulevard
Beverly Hills, CA 90211-1972
(310) 247-3000 ext. 131
Fax: (310) 859-9619

E-MAIL ADDRESS:
rmiller@oscars.org

WEB SITE ADDRESS:
www.oscars.org

AREAS OF INTEREST:
Filmmakers.

NAME(S) OF PROGRAMS:
● **Student Academy Awards Competition**

TYPE:
Awards/prizes.

PURPOSE:
To recognize outstanding achievements in student filmmaking; to support and encourage filmmakers with no previous professional experience who are enrolled in accredited colleges and universities.

ELIGIBILITY:
To be eligible, the filmmaker must be a full-time student at an accredited U.S. college, university, film school or art school. The film must have been made in a teacher-student relationship within the curricular structure of that institution. The film must be in one of the following categories: Alternative, Animated, Documentary and Narrative.

FINANCIAL DATA:
Amount of support per award: $5,000 Gold Award, $3,000 Silver Award, and $2,000 Bronze Award.

NUMBER OF AWARDS: 12 maximum.

APPLICATION INFORMATION:
Regional juries have sole responsibility for the determination of final selections for submission to the Academy. Each regional jury may consider only films from schools within its own region.
Deadline: April 1.

ADDRESS INQUIRIES TO:
Richard Miller
Awards Administration Director
(See address above.)

AMERICAN ORIENTAL SOCIETY [577]

Hatcher Graduate Library, Room 110
University of Michigan
Ann Arbor, MI 48109-1205
(734) 647-4760
Fax: (734) 763-6743

E-MAIL ADDRESS:
  jrodgers@umich.edu

WEB SITE ADDRESS:
  www.umich.edu/~aos

FOUNDED: 1842

AREAS OF INTEREST:
  Archaeology, fine arts, history, philosophy,
  language, literature, religion and theology.

NAME(S) OF PROGRAMS:
  ● **Louise Wallace Hackney Fellowship**

TYPE:
  Fellowships. Fellowship for the study of
  Chinese art with special relation to painting.

YEAR PROGRAM STARTED: 1946

PURPOSE:
  To encourage basic research in the languages
  and literatures of Asia.

LEGAL BASIS:
  Nonprofit.

ELIGIBILITY:
  Graduate students who have successfully
  completed at least three years of Chinese
  language study at a recognized university and
  have some knowledge or training in art.
  Students must have completed all
  requirements for the Ph.D. except research,
  travel and the written dissertation. Applicants
  should have the sponsorship of recognized
  scholars in the fields of Chinese language
  and culture.

  U.S. citizenship is required.

GEOGRAPHIC RESTRICTIONS:
  United States.

FINANCIAL DATA:
  Amount of support per award: $8,000.
  Total amount of support: $8,000 annually.

NUMBER OF APPLICANTS MOST RECENT YEAR:
  Approximately 3.

NUMBER OF AWARDS: 1 annually.

APPLICATION INFORMATION:
  Applicants should write to the secretary, at
  the address given above, outlining the
  proposed plan of study and accompany this
  letter with a curriculum vitae, an academic
  record and no less than three letters of
  recommendation.

  Duration: Renewals of appointment are
  possible but not usually considered.

  Deadline: Applications should be submitted
  no later than March 1. Announcement at the
  end of April.

PUBLICATIONS:
  Application guidelines.

DIRECTORS AND OFFICERS:
  Jonathan Rodgers, Secretary and Treasurer
  Edwin Gerow, Editor

ADDRESS INQUIRIES TO:
  Jonathan Rodgers, Secretary and Treasurer
  (See address above.)

*SPECIAL STIPULATIONS:
  All materials must be submitted in duplicate
  or application will be considered incomplete.

BRUCEBO FINE ART SCHOLARSHIP FOUNDATION [578]

Department of Geography
McGill University
805 Sherbrooke West
Montreal QC H3A 2K6 Canada
(450) 672-6096
Fax: (514) 398-7437

E-MAIL ADDRESS:
  jan.lundgren@mcgill.ca

FOUNDED: 1971

AREAS OF INTEREST:
  Promotion of fine arts; Canada-Sweden
  relationships.

NAME(S) OF PROGRAMS:
  ● **W.B. Bruce European Fine Art Travel
    Scholarship**
  ● **Brucebo Fine Art Summer Residency
    Scholarship**

TYPE:
  Scholarships; Travel grants. Grant principally
  in the fields of fine arts, visual art and
  design. Grant is either for stay at the
  Brucebo Studio on the Island of Hanseatic
  Gotland, Sweden, in the Baltic Sea, for three
  months during the summer annually, or for
  undertaking a European Fine Art
  Travel-Study journey during a period of the
  fall term, or the following winter/spring term.

YEAR PROGRAM STARTED: 1971

PURPOSE:
  To support talented Canadian fine arts
  graduated students and fine arts practitioners,
  B.F.A. or M.F.A. persons, in the early years
  of their respective careers.

LEGAL BASIS:
  Private.

ELIGIBILITY:
  Qualified Canadian artists (preferably
  painters) with appropriate project plans are
  eligible to apply.

GEOGRAPHIC RESTRICTIONS:
  Gotland, Sweden or Europe.

FINANCIAL DATA:
  Amount of support per award: SEK 30,000,
  the equivalent of approximately $5,000
  (CAN).
  Total amount of support: SEK 60,000.

NUMBER OF APPLICANTS MOST RECENT YEAR:
  40.

NUMBER OF AWARDS: 2.

APPLICATION INFORMATION:
  Application form and guidelines can be
  found on the Embassy of Sweden Ottawa
  web site: www.swedenabroad.com.

  Duration: Three months.

  Deadline: January 31.

STAFF:
  Dr. Jan Lundgren, Liaison Officer, Brucebo
  Fine Art Scholarship Foundation of Gotland,
  Sweden

ADDRESS INQUIRIES TO:
  Dr. Jan Lundgren, Liaison Officer
  (See address above.)

*SPECIAL STIPULATIONS:
  Canadian citizens and landed immigrants.

  Recipient submits a report on his or her
  activities engaged in after return to Canada.

THE CENTER FOR PHOTOGRAPHY AT WOODSTOCK [579]

59 Tinker Street
Woodstock, NY 12498
(845) 679-9957
Fax: (845) 679-6337

E-MAIL ADDRESS:
  info@cpw.org

WEB SITE ADDRESS:
  www.cpw.org

FOUNDED: 1977

AREAS OF INTEREST:
  Photography.

NAME(S) OF PROGRAMS:
  ● **The Photographers' Fund**
  ● **Woodstock A-I-R**
  ● **WPW Interns**

TYPE:
  Project/program grants; Residencies;
  Work-study programs. Photography
  Workshops. Photographers' Fund awards
  fellowships to regional photographers of
  vision and talent, selected by portfolio review
  by a panel of noted national artists.

  Woodstock A-I-R is a residency program for
  artists of color working in the photographic
  arts.

YEAR PROGRAM STARTED: 1980

PURPOSE:
  To support artists working in photography
  and related media and engaging their
  audiences through opportunities in which
  creation, discovery and education are made
  possible.

LEGAL BASIS:
  Not-for-profit arts and educational
  organization.

ELIGIBILITY:
  Fellowship applicants must live and work in
  upstate New York.

FINANCIAL DATA:
  Amount of support per award:
  Photographers' Fund: $2,500; Woodstock
  A-I-R: Varies; WPW Interns: $6,000 in-kind
  tuition.

COOPERATIVE FUNDING PROGRAMS: The Center
  receives funds from the National Endowment
  for the Arts and the New York State Council
  on the Arts and has received grants from
  IBM and the New York Council for the
  Humanities, The Avery Foundation, Eastman
  Kodak, Canon, U.S.A. and Andy Warhol
  Foundation.

NUMBER OF AWARDS: Photographers' Fund: 1
  fellowship; Woodstock A-I-R: 8; WPW
  Interns: 4.

APPLICATION INFORMATION:
  Photographers must submit the following:
  (1) portfolio of 10 prints (print portfolios
  strongly encouraged over slide or digital file
  submissions);
  (2) image list detailing titles, medium, year
  and;
  (3) artist statement and bio.

  Submissions cannot be accepted via e-mail.

PUBLICATIONS:
  Photography Quarterly, magazine.

IRS IDENTIFICATION NUMBER: 14-1592639

OFFICERS:
  Ariel Shanberg, Executive Director

ADDRESS INQUIRIES TO:
Ariel Shanberg, Executive Director
(See address above.)

DALLAS MUSEUM OF ART [580]

1717 North Harwood
Dallas, TX 75201
(214) 922-1334
Fax: (214) 720-0862

E-MAIL ADDRESS:
cwylie@dallasmuseumofart.org

WEB SITE ADDRESS:
www.dallasmuseumofart.org

FOUNDED: 1903

AREAS OF INTEREST:
Art. Collections include Pre-Columbian,
Asian and African, abstract expressionist,
17th to 20th century European paintings and
sculpture, 18th to 20th century American
paintings and sculpture, and decorative arts.

NAME(S) OF PROGRAMS:
● **Clare Hart DeGolyer Memorial Fund**

TYPE:
Awards/prizes.

YEAR PROGRAM STARTED: 1980

PURPOSE:
To support younger, emerging visual artists
who reside in the southwestern part of the
U.S.

LEGAL BASIS:
Nonprofit, tax-exempt arts organization.

ELIGIBILITY:
Applicants must be between 15 and 25 years
of age, have lived in the southwestern part of
the U.S. for the past four years and currently
reside there.

Grants are not available for college or art
school tuition.

GEOGRAPHIC RESTRICTIONS:
Arizona, Colorado, New Mexico, Oklahoma
and Texas.

FINANCIAL DATA:
Amount of support per award: Awards
generally shall not exceed $1,500.

NUMBER OF APPLICANTS MOST RECENT YEAR:
25.

APPLICATION INFORMATION:
Applications can be downloaded online.
Deadline: March 18. Announcement in
mid-May.

PUBLICATIONS:
Bimonthly *DMAgenda*; permanent collection
and exhibition catalogues.

ADDRESS INQUIRIES TO:
Charles Wylie, Awards to Artists
(See address above.)

DALLAS MUSEUM OF ART [581]

1717 North Harwood
Dallas, TX 75201
(214) 922-1334
Fax: (214) 720-0862

E-MAIL ADDRESS:
cwylie@dallasmuseumofart.org

WEB SITE ADDRESS:
www.dallasmuseumofart.org

FOUNDED: 1903

AREAS OF INTEREST:
Art. Collections include contemporary art,
Pre-Columbian, Asian, African, American
and European painting and sculpture,
decorative arts and textiles.

NAME(S) OF PROGRAMS:
● **Arch and Anne Giles Kimbrough Fund**

TYPE:
Awards/prizes. Direct grants to artists.

YEAR PROGRAM STARTED: 1980

PURPOSE:
To support younger, emerging visual artists in
Texas.

LEGAL BASIS:
Nonprofit, tax-exempt arts organization.

ELIGIBILITY:
Applicants must be under 30 years of age,
have lived in Texas for the past three years
and currently reside there.

Funds are not available for college or art
school tuition.

GEOGRAPHIC RESTRICTIONS:
Texas.

FINANCIAL DATA:
Amount of support per award: Awards
generally shall not exceed $3,500.

NUMBER OF APPLICANTS MOST RECENT YEAR:
35.

APPLICATION INFORMATION:
Applications can be downloaded online.
Deadline: March 18. Announcement in
mid-May.

PUBLICATIONS:
Bimonthly *DMAgenda*; permanent collection
and exhibition catalogues.

ADDRESS INQUIRIES TO:
Charles Wylie, Awards to Artists
(See address above.)

DALLAS MUSEUM OF ART [582]

1717 North Harwood
Dallas, TX 75201
(214) 922-1334
Fax: (214) 720-0862

E-MAIL ADDRESS:
cwylie@dallasmuseumofart.org

WEB SITE ADDRESS:
www.dallasmuseumofart.org

FOUNDED: 1903

AREAS OF INTEREST:
Art. Collections include contemporary art,
Pre-Columbian, Asian, African, American
and European painting and sculpture,
decorative arts and textiles.

NAME(S) OF PROGRAMS:
● **Otis and Velma Davis Dozier Travel
Grant**

TYPE:
Awards/prizes; Travel grants.

YEAR PROGRAM STARTED: 1990

PURPOSE:
To recognize exceptional talent in
professional artists who wish to expand their
artistic horizons through domestic or foreign
travel.

LEGAL BASIS:
Nonprofit, tax-exempt arts organization.

ELIGIBILITY:
Artists eligible for the grant must be
practicing professionals, be 30 years of age
or older, have lived in Texas for the past
three years and be currently living in Texas.
Financial need will be given consideration
but will not be the determining factor in
making the awards.

GEOGRAPHIC RESTRICTIONS:
Texas.

FINANCIAL DATA:
Amount of support per award: Varies.
Total amount of support: Generally, the total
amount dispersed does not exceed $6,000.

NUMBER OF APPLICANTS MOST RECENT YEAR:
52.

APPLICATION INFORMATION:
Applications can be downloaded online.
Deadline: March 18. Announcement in
mid-May.

PUBLICATIONS:
Bimonthly *DMAgenda*; permanent collection
and exhibition catalogues.

ADDRESS INQUIRIES TO:
Charles Wylie, Awards to Artists
(See address above.)

FINE ARTS WORK CENTER IN
PROVINCETOWN   [583]

24 Pearl Street
Provincetown, MA 02657
(508) 487-9960
Fax: (508) 487-8873

E-MAIL ADDRESS:
general@fawc.org

WEB SITE ADDRESS:
www.fawc.org

FOUNDED: 1968

AREAS OF INTEREST:
Visual arts and creative writing.

NAME(S) OF PROGRAMS:
● **Visual Arts Fellowship**
● **Writing Fellowship**

TYPE:
Fellowships; Residencies. The Fine Arts
Work Center offers seven-month Fellowships
(October 1-May 1) to selected writers and
visual artists. Applicants must be in the
emerging phase of their careers and must
demonstrate significant talent and
commitment. Fellows are provided with
apartments, studios, and a monthly stipend,
and have the support of a resident staff. The
Fine Arts Work Center also offers a Summer
Workshop Program of courses in writing and
the arts, and other arts-related programming.

YEAR PROGRAM STARTED: 1968

PURPOSE:
To offer opportunities to emerging artists and
writers.

LEGAL BASIS:
Nonprofit corporation.

ELIGIBILITY:
Applicants must be individuals (visual artists
and creative writers) who have spent time
working on their own and have created a
considerable body of work which can be
presented in the form of slides or manuscript.

FINANCIAL DATA:
Amount of support per award: Each Fellow
receives a monthly stipend of $750 and is
provided with an apartment and a studio in
Provincetown, MA.

Each Residency includes a stipend of $750
per month plus private living and/or working
studio in Provincetown, MA.

Total amount of support: $5,250, plus housing and work space.

NUMBER OF APPLICANTS MOST RECENT YEAR: 1,000.

NUMBER OF AWARDS: 20.

APPLICATION INFORMATION:
Forms and application information may be requested from the above address by sending a self-addressed, stamped envelope. Applications can also be downloaded at the web site. Application fee is $45.
Duration: Seven months. October 1 to May 1.
Deadline: Writers: December 1. Visual Arts: February 1. Announcement by May 15.

PUBLICATIONS:
Shankpainter, online literary magazine.

OFFICERS OF THE TRUSTEES:
Hatty Walker Fitts, Co-Chairperson
Lynne Kortenhaus, Co-Chairperson
Marty Davis, President
Barbara Kapp, Vice President

ADDRESS INQUIRIES TO:
Coordinator, Visual Arts or
Coordinator, Writing
(See address above.)

*SPECIAL STIPULATIONS:
Fellowships are reserved for emerging writers and visual artists.

J. PAUL GETTY TRUST, GETTY FOUNDATION [584]

1200 Getty Center Drive
Suite 800
Los Angeles, CA 90049-1685
(310) 440-7320
Fax: (310) 440-7703

E-MAIL ADDRESS:
foundation@getty.edu

WEB SITE ADDRESS:
www.getty.edu/grants

FOUNDED: 1984

AREAS OF INTEREST:
Strengthening art history as a global discipline, promoting the interdisciplinary practice of conservation, increasing access to museums and archival collections, and developing current and future professionals and leaders.

TYPE:
Challenge/matching grants; Conferences/seminars; Internships; Matching gifts; Project/program grants; Training grants.

YEAR PROGRAM STARTED: 1984

PURPOSE:
To advance the understanding and preservation of the visual arts locally and throughout the world.

LEGAL BASIS:
The Getty Foundation is part of the J. Paul Getty Trust, a private operating foundation.

ELIGIBILITY:
Requirements vary according to grant category. Individuals at the undergraduate and graduate level may be eligible to apply for internships. Eligibility for all other grant categories is limited to nonprofit organizations.

Generally, grants are not made for operating or endowment purposes, for construction or maintenance of buildings or for acquisition of works of art.

FINANCIAL DATA:
Amount of support per award: $1,000 to $400,000.
Total amount of support: $12,900,000 for fiscal year 2009.
Matching fund requirements: In certain categories.

NUMBER OF APPLICANTS MOST RECENT YEAR: 1,000.

NUMBER OF AWARDS: 200 for fiscal year 2009.

REPRESENTATIVE AWARDS:
$225,000 to Museum of Contemporary Art San Diego, La Jolla, CA, for the exhibition and publication *Phenomenal: California Light and Space*; $152,000 to International Council of African Museums, Nairobi, Kenya, for the implementation of a new strategic plan; $150,000 to New Europe Foundation, Bucharest, Romania, for the second phase of Research Seminars at the New Europe College; $2,200,000 to Claremont Graduate University, CA, for the Getty Leadership Institute.

APPLICATION INFORMATION:
Funding priorities and application information are available on the Foundation web site.
Duration: One to three years, depending upon the grant category.
Deadline: November 1. Internships: Varies.

PUBLICATIONS:
Annual report of J. Paul Getty Trust; *L.A. Art Online.*

IRS IDENTIFICATION NUMBER: 95-1790021

OFFICERS:
Deborah Marrow, Interim President and Chief Executive Officer
Joan Weinstein, Interim Director, The Getty Foundation
Rebecca Martin, Associate Director
Nancy Micklewright, Senior Program Officer
Angie Kim, Program Officer
Antoine Wilmering, Program Officer
Phillip M. Nowlen, Head, Leadership Institute

TRUSTEES:
Mark S. Siegel, Chairperson
Neil Rudenstine, Vice Chairperson
Francis Daly Fergusson
Maria D. Hummer-Tuttle
Joanne C. Kozberg
Paul LeClerc
David Lee
Luis G. Nogales
Stewart A. Resnick
William E.B. Siart
Ronald P. Spogli
Peter Taylor
Jay S. Wintrob

ADDRESS INQUIRIES TO:
The Getty Foundation
(See address above.)

ADOLPH AND ESTHER GOTTLIEB FOUNDATION, INC. [585]

380 West Broadway
New York, NY 10012-5115
(212) 226-0581
Fax: (212) 226-0584

E-MAIL ADDRESS:
sross@gottliebfoundation.org

WEB SITE ADDRESS:
www.gottliebfoundation.org

FOUNDED: 1976

AREAS OF INTEREST:
Visual artists.

NAME(S) OF PROGRAMS:
● **Emergency Assistance Program**
● **Individual Support Program**

TYPE:
Grants-in-aid. Emergency Assistance Program provides cash award to mature creative painters, sculptors and printmakers who are experiencing financial hardship resulting from a current or recent emergency.

Individual Support Program was designed to encourage those artists who have dedicated their lives to developing their art, regardless of their level of commercial success.

YEAR PROGRAM STARTED: 1984

PURPOSE:
To provide interim financial assistance to qualified artists during times of emergencies (such as fire, flood, medical or other unexpected, catastrophic events), or to provide financial assistance as an encouragement to artists who have dedicated their lives to developing their art.

LEGAL BASIS:
Nonprofit corporation.

ELIGIBILITY:
Emergency Assistance Program: Applicant must be able to demonstrate a minimum involvement of 10 years in a mature phase of his or her work as a creative painter, sculptor or printmaker and his or her need must result from current or recent emergency beyond the artist's usual circumstances (medical, fire, flood, etc.). This Program does not consider requests for dental work, chronic situations, capital improvements, or projects of any kind; nor can it consider situations resulting from general indebtedness or lack of employment.

Individual Support Program: Applicant will be able to demonstrate work in a mature phase of his or her art for at least 20 years. Eligibility is also determined by applicant's current financial need. The Foundation does not provide funding for organizations, projects of any type, educational institutions, students, graphic artists, or those working in crafts. The disciplines of photography, film, video or related forms are not eligible unless the work directly involves, or can be interpreted as, painting, printmaking or sculpture.

FINANCIAL DATA:
Amount of support per award: Emergency Assistance Program: Maximum $10,000; typical amount is $4,000. Individual Support Program: $25,000.

Total amount of support: $300,000 for the year 2010.

NUMBER OF AWARDS: Emergency Assistance Grants: Varies; Individual Support Grants: 12.

APPLICATION INFORMATION:
Emergency Assistance Program: Application forms are available from the Foundation throughout the year and may be requested by telephone or in writing.

Individual Support Program: Application forms are available by mail in early September. Only written requests for application forms will be honored.

Deadline: Emergency Assistance Program: Available throughout the year, as budget permits. Individual Support Program: December 15.

PUBLICATIONS:
Information brochure.

BOARD OF DIRECTORS:
Sanford Hirsch, Executive Director
Lynda Benglis
Charlotta Kotik
Robert Mangold

ADDRESS INQUIRIES TO:
Sheila Ross, Grants Manager
(See address above.)

*SPECIAL STIPULATIONS:
The Emergency Assistance Program is to assist individuals in emergency situations only.

THE ELIZABETH GREENSHIELDS FOUNDATION   [586]

1814 Sherbrooke Street West, Suite 1
Montreal QC H3H 1E4 Canada
(514) 937-9225

E-MAIL ADDRESS:
greenshields@bellnet.ca

WEB SITE ADDRESS:
www.elizabethgreenshieldsfoundation.org

FOUNDED: 1955

AREAS OF INTEREST:
Art including painting, drawing, printmaking and sculpture.

NAME(S) OF PROGRAMS:
• **The Elizabeth Greenshields Foundation Grants**

TYPE:
Awards/prizes.

YEAR PROGRAM STARTED: 1955

PURPOSE:
To promote an appreciation of traditional expression in painting, drawing, sculpture and printmaking by aiding worthy art students, artists or sculptors who need further training or other assistance during their formative years.

LEGAL BASIS:
Charitable foundation.

ELIGIBILITY:
Awards are limited to candidates in the early stages of their careers who are working in a representational style in painting, drawing, sculpture and printmaking. Nonobjective art is precluded by the Foundation's charter.

To be eligible for a grant, candidates must:
(1) have already started or completed training in an established school of art and/or;
(2) demonstrate, through past work and future plans, a commitment to making art a lifetime career.
The Foundation will not accept applications from commercial artists, photographers, video artists, filmmakers, craft-makers or any artist whose work falls primarily into these categories.

FINANCIAL DATA:
Funds may be used for any art-related purpose: study, travel, studio rental, purchase of materials, etc. Grants are made directly to the beneficiaries, and not through other organizations.

Amount of support per award: Normally, $12,500 (CAN). The Foundation reserves the right to award grants in other amounts.

APPLICATION INFORMATION:
Applications are available directly from the Foundation upon request. Grants are awarded to applicants of all nationalities and are made directly to the beneficiaries, not through other organizations. Grantees may reapply for a second grant one year after the first grant was awarded. Those applicants who are not awarded a grant may reapply two years after the last application was turned down.

Application instructions:
(1) return Foundation application form in a clear, complete and articulate manner, along with reproductions of six recent works (one image per work) - on CD only -preferably completed within the past two years but definitely no longer than three years ago (do not add any additional documents);
(2) sculptors may send two images of six different works for a maximum of 12 images;
(3) images should be submitted in the best possible resolution (minimum 72 DPI, preferably 140 DPI or higher); images should be sized to fill the screen at a resolution of 1024 pixels wide by 768 pixels high;
(4) any digital treatment or manipulation of the initial picture may invalidate the entire application and;
(5) digital art images should not be presented under separate cover.

No Internet submissions are accepted. Submitted CD will not be returned. Slides are no longer accepted.

All completed applications are duly acknowledged and judged by a Selection Committee. Response time varies from one to six months. The decision of the trustees is final and not subject to review or appeal.

Duration: Award winners may reapply for another grant one year after a grant was awarded. Applicants who were declined a grant may reapply two years from the last decision.

Deadline: The Foundation welcomes applications throughout the year.

PUBLICATIONS:
Application guidelines.

ADDRESS INQUIRIES TO:
Micheline Leduc, Administrator
(See address above.)

*SPECIAL STIPULATIONS:
The Foundation welcomes applications throughout the year.

The Foundation is not a school nor a gallery and does not conduct classes or organize exhibitions.

U.S. citizens sending applications should not enclose a self-addressed, stamped envelope because U.S. postage is not valid in Canada.

When requesting an application form through e-mail, please provide a mailing address.

SAMUEL H. KRESS FOUNDATION   [587]

174 East 80th Street
New York, NY 10075
(212) 861-4993
Fax: (212) 628-3146

E-MAIL ADDRESS:
wyman.meers@kressfoundation.org

WEB SITE ADDRESS:
www.kressfoundation.org

FOUNDED: 1929

AREAS OF INTEREST:
Art history and art conservation.

NAME(S) OF PROGRAMS:
• **Fellowships in Art Conservation**
• **Interpretive Fellowships**
• **Research Fellowships in Art History**

TYPE:
Fellowships; Research grants; Travel grants. Program assistance is provided through Fellowship programs for predoctoral research in art history, advanced training and research in conservation of works of art, development of scholarly resources in museums and universities in support of art history and conservation, and restoration of monuments in Europe.

YEAR PROGRAM STARTED: 1963

PURPOSE:
To encourage the preservation and history of art, especially European art before 1800.

LEGAL BASIS:
Private foundation.

ELIGIBILITY:
Qualified institutions and organizations with appropriate interests are eligible to apply. The Foundation does not consider grants for living artists, films, art history programs below the predoctoral level or the purchase of works of art.

Research Fellowships in Art History provide travel grants to enable predoctoral candidates in the history of art to pursue essential research. They are available annually through a competitive program administered by the Foundation. Applicants must anticipate completion of all requirements for the Ph.D. degree except the dissertation at the time the grant will be received.

Fellowships in Art Conservation provide advanced students in the conservation of works of art the opportunity to compete for funds to support professional studies or apprenticeship. Applicants must have completed a recognized training program and application must be from potential host institution. Fellowships are to be based at U.S. institutions or undertaken by an American if the organization is abroad.

FINANCIAL DATA:
Total amount of support: Approximately $3,900,000 for fiscal year 2011.

NUMBER OF APPLICANTS MOST RECENT YEAR:
Approximately 600.

NUMBER OF AWARDS: Approximately 300.

APPLICATION INFORMATION:
Prospective applicants should, as a first step, submit a brief letter outlining the scope of the proposed project and a budget describing the major anticipated expenses.

Duration: Varies.

Deadline: November 30 for Art History, March 1 for Art Conservation and April 1 for Interpretive Fellowships.

PUBLICATIONS:
Annual report (online).

IRS IDENTIFICATION NUMBER: 13-1624176

STAFF:
Wyman Meers, Program Administrator

OFFICERS AND TRUSTEES:
Frederick W. Beinecke, Chairman

David Rumsey, Vice Chairman
Max Marmor, President
Cheryl Hurley
Barbara A. Shailor

ADDRESS INQUIRIES TO:
Wyman Meers, Program Administrator
(See address above.)

*SPECIAL STIPULATIONS:
No applications accepted via fax or e-mail.

LIGHT WORK   [588]
316 Waverly Avenue
Syracuse, NY 13244
(315) 443-1300
Fax: (315) 443-9516

E-MAIL ADDRESS:
info@lightwork.org

WEB SITE ADDRESS:
www.lightwork.org

FOUNDED: 1972

AREAS OF INTEREST:
Photography.

CONSULTING OR VOLUNTEER SERVICES:
All aspects of visual arts and programs for
artists.

NAME(S) OF PROGRAMS:
● **Light Work Artist-in-Residence
Program**

TYPE:
Project/program grants; Residencies; Visiting
scholars. Artist-in-Residence, exhibitions,
publications, sponsored projects, lectures and
regrants.

YEAR PROGRAM STARTED: 1973

PURPOSE:
To support artists in photography.

LEGAL BASIS:
Not-for-profit organization.

ELIGIBILITY:
Applicants must be working in photography
or related visual arts including video,
installation and electronic media. Students
are ineligible to apply.

FINANCIAL DATA:
Amount of support per award: $4,000.
Total amount of support: $75,000.

COOPERATIVE FUNDING PROGRAMS: Yes.

NUMBER OF APPLICANTS MOST RECENT YEAR:
300 to 500.

NUMBER OF AWARDS: 12 to 15.

APPLICATION INFORMATION:
No application forms required. Applicants
should send a letter of intent, describing in
general terms the project or type of work
they would like to accomplish while in
residence. In addition, they should submit 20
slides, prints or CD of their work, a resume,
and a short statement about their work. They
must include a self-addressed, stamped
envelope for the return of their materials.

Contact Light Work at the address above for
further information.
Duration: One month.

PUBLICATIONS:
Contact Sheet.

STAFF:
Jeffrey Hoone, Executive Director

ADDRESS INQUIRIES TO:
Jeffrey Hoone, Executive Director
(See address above.)

*SPECIAL STIPULATIONS:
Students are not eligible.

THE ROBERTO LONGHI
FOUNDATION FOR THE STUDY
OF THE HISTORY OF ART   [589]
Via Benedetto Fortini, 30
Florence 50125 Italy
39 055 65 80 794
Fax: 39 055 65 80 794

E-MAIL ADDRESS:
longhi@fondazionelonghi.it

WEB SITE ADDRESS:
www.fondazionelonghi.it/

FOUNDED: 1971

AREAS OF INTEREST:
Italian painting from the 13th to the 18th
centuries.

NAME(S) OF PROGRAMS:
● **Art History Fellowships in Florence**

TYPE:
Fellowships. Designed for those who want to
seriously dedicate themselves to research in
the history of art. Fellowship holders may
make use of the study materials available in
the Institute. They must frequent the Institute
and collaborate on a specific group research
project selected by the Scientific Committee.
In particular, successful candidates must give
the assurance that they can dedicate their full
time to the research for which the fellowship
is assigned. They must live in Florence for
the duration of the fellowship, except for
travel required for their research. They may
not exceed the periods of vacation fixed by
the Institute. They are required to attend
seminars, lectures and other activities
arranged by the Institute. In addition, Fellows
must submit a written report at the end of
their stay in Florence, relating the findings of
their individual research undertaken at the
Longhi Foundation. The nonobservance of
the above conditions will be considered
sufficient grounds for the cancellation of a
fellowship.

PURPOSE:
To promote and further the study of art
history by keeping Roberto Longhi's cultural
legacy and methods alive.

LEGAL BASIS:
Private foundation.

ELIGIBILITY:
Open to Italian citizens who possess a degree
from an Italian university with a thesis in the
history of art, and to non-Italian citizens who
have fulfilled the preliminary requirements
for a doctoral degree in the history of art at
an accredited university or an institution of
equal standing. Students who have reached
their 32nd birthday before the application
deadline are not eligible.

FINANCIAL DATA:
Amount of support per award: EUR 5,400
(paid in monthly installments over a period
of nine months).

APPLICATION INFORMATION:
Applications should be addressed to the
Secretariat of the Foundation at the address
above and should contain the candidate's
biographical data (place and date of birth,
domicile, citizenship), a transcript of the
candidate's undergraduate and graduate
records, a copy of the degree thesis (if
available) and other original works, published
or unpublished, a "curriculum studiorum,"

also indicating the knowledge of foreign
languages spoken and written, letters of
reference from at least two persons of
academic standing who are acquainted with
the candidate's work, the subject of the
research that the candidate is interested in
pursuing within the range of the history of
art and two passport photographs.

Recipients of fellowships are asked to
communicate within 15 days of notification
their acceptance and willingness to comply
with the conditions and rules as stated.
Duration: Nine months beginning in October.
Deadline: Applications must arrive by May
15.

PUBLICATIONS:
Proporzioni, art review.

OFFICERS:
Mina Gregori, Chairman and President

MARYLAND INSTITUTE
COLLEGE OF ART   [590]
Office of Graduate Admission
1300 West Mount Royal Avenue
Baltimore, MD 21217
(410) 225-2256
Fax: (410) 225-5275

E-MAIL ADDRESS:
graduate@mica.edu

WEB SITE ADDRESS:
www.mica.edu

FOUNDED: 1823

AREAS OF INTEREST:
Fine arts, design and art education.

NAME(S) OF PROGRAMS:
● **Art Education (Low-residency On-line
MA)**
● **Hoffberger School of Painting (MFA)**
● **MA Social Design**
● **Master of Arts in Community Arts**
● **Master of Arts in Teaching**
● **MBS Art and Business**
● **MFA Community Arts**
● **MFA Curatorial Practice**
● **MFA Illustration Practice**
● **MFA in Graphic Design**
● **Mt. Royal School of Art (MFA)**
● **Photographic and Electronic Media
(MFA)**
● **Post-Baccalaureate Program**
● **Rinehart School of Sculpture (MFA)**
● **Studio Art (Low-residency MFA)**

TYPE:
Assistantships; Awards/prizes;
Challenge/matching grants; Fellowships;
Scholarships; Travel grants; Visiting scholars.

YEAR PROGRAM STARTED: 1896

LEGAL BASIS:
Nonprofit institution.

ELIGIBILITY:
For M.F.A. Summer programs: B.F.A. or
B.A. degree with at least 48 studio credits is
required plus 12 credits in art history. For
M.F.A. Fall programs: must have a
Bachelor's degree.

FINANCIAL DATA:
Amount of support per award: M.I.C.A.
scholarship awards for students in all
graduate programs based on merit, up to half
of tuition.

Total amount of support: Varies.

APPLICATION INFORMATION:
Submit completed application form, application fee of $60, three letters of recommendation, portfolio of 18 to 20 pieces of most recent work and college transcripts. Label each. CD-ROMs and DVDs accepted.

Duration: Two years. Renewable upon application for the second year.

Deadline: January 15. Announcement April 1.

ADDRESS INQUIRIES TO:
Scott G. Kelly
Associate Dean of Graduate Admission
(See address above.)

THE PAUL MELLON CENTRE FOR STUDIES IN BRITISH ART

16 Bedford Square
London WC1B 3JA England
44 (0) 20 7580 0311
Fax: 44 (0) 20 7636 6730

E-MAIL ADDRESS:
info@paul-mellon-centre.ac.uk

WEB SITE ADDRESS:
www.paul-mellon-centre.ac.uk

TYPE:
Conferences/seminars; Fellowships; Project/program grants; Research grants. Educational Programme Grants for lectures, symposia, seminars or conferences on British art and architecture.

The Junior Fellowship is to pursue ongoing doctoral research at an American or British university.

The Paul Mellon Centre Rome Fellowship offers fellowships to scholars working on Grand Tour subjects or in the field of Anglo-Italian cultural and artistic relations.

The Postdoctoral Fellowship works to transform doctoral research into publishable form such as a book, series of articles, or exhibition catalogues.

Research Support Grants are for expenses in pursuit of research.

The Senior Fellowship supports an established scholar in the field of British art and architectural history to complete a manuscript or book for immediate publication.

See entry 447 for full listing.

THE METROPOLITAN MUSEUM OF ART   [591]

1000 Fifth Avenue
New York, NY 10028-0198
(212) 570-3710
Fax: (212) 570-3782

E-MAIL ADDRESS:
mmainterns@metmuseum.org

WEB SITE ADDRESS:
www.metmuseum.org

FOUNDED: 1870

AREAS OF INTEREST:
Internships in art museums.

TYPE:
Internships. Internships for graduate and undergraduate students.

YEAR PROGRAM STARTED: 1972

PURPOSE:
To provide pre-career training and experience for students and graduates in art museums.

ELIGIBILITY:
Most projects require strong preparation in the history of art. Applicants of diverse backgrounds are encouraged to apply.

FINANCIAL DATA:
Amount of support per award: Varies by program; up to $25,000 (the latter with additional stipend for research and educational travel).

NUMBER OF AWARDS: 42 with stipend.

APPLICATION INFORMATION:
Applicants must submit:
(1) internship application form (available online);
(2) full resume of education and employment;
(3) two academic recommendations;
(4) official transcripts;
(5) a separate list of art history or other relevant courses taken, as well as knowledge of foreign languages and;
(6) an essay of not more than 500 words describing the applicant's career goals, interest in museum work, and the reasons for applying to the Internship Program.

After an initial review of the applications, a small number of students will be invited for a personal interview at the Museum.

Duration: Up to 12 months.

Deadline: Generally, early January.

ADDRESS INQUIRIES TO:
Internship Programs
(except for The Cloisters)
The Metropolitan Museum of Art
(See address, phone and e-mail above.)

For The Cloisters:
The Cloisters Summer Internship Program
The Cloisters
Fort Tryon Park
New York, NY 10040
e-mail: cloistersinterns@metmuseum.org
Tel: (212) 650-2280

*PLEASE NOTE:
Final notification for all candidates will be mailed by late March or early April.

THE METROPOLITAN MUSEUM OF ART   [592]

1000 Fifth Avenue
New York, NY 10028-0198
(212) 650-2763
Fax: (212) 396-5168

E-MAIL ADDRESS:
education.grants@metmuseum.org

WEB SITE ADDRESS:
www.metmuseum.org

FOUNDED: 1870

AREAS OF INTEREST:
Museum conservation work.

NAME(S) OF PROGRAMS:
- **The Sherman Fairchild Foundation Fellowships**

TYPE:
Fellowships. Fellowships are awarded annually and make possible study and training in the following Museum conservation departments: Paintings Conservation, Objects Conservation (including sculpture, metalwork, glass, ceramics, furniture and archaeological objects), Musical Instruments, Arms and Armor, Paper Conservation, Textile Conservation, The Costume Institute Conservation.

The Museum offers junior-level and senior-level fellowships in conservation and scientific research. Junior fellowships are intended for those who have recently completed graduate-level training. Senior fellowships are intended for well-established professionals with advanced training in the field and a proven publication record.

All fellowships must take place between September 1 and the following August 31.

PURPOSE:
To make possible study and training in conservation departments of the Museum.

ELIGIBILITY:
Qualified candidates from the U.S. and abroad who have already reached an advanced level of training or experience.

FINANCIAL DATA:
Health care benefits are included.

Amount of support per award: $30,000 plus up to $5,000 for travel and miscellaneous expenses for Junior Conservation Fellow; $40,000 plus up to $5,000 for travel and miscellaneous expenses for Senior Conservation Fellow.

Total amount of support: Varies.

APPLICATION INFORMATION:
Electronically submitted applications and letters of recommendation are not accepted.

There are no application forms. Applicants need not specify the name of a particular fellowship. Fellowship applications must be submitted in English. Three letters of recommendation are required, none of which may be from current Metropolitan Museum of Art staff. The submission in English of the required letters of recommendation is encouraged. There are different application requirements for junior- and senior-level conservators/scientific researchers. Contact the Museum for full details.

Completed applications must be submitted to: Attn: Marcie Karp; Conservation and Scientific Research Fellowship Program; The Metropolitan Museum of Art; at the address above.

Duration: Up to one year.

Deadline: First Friday in December.

ADDRESS INQUIRIES TO:
Marcie Karp
Managing Museum Educator
for Academic Programs
The Metropolitan Museum of Art
(See e-mail address above.)

THE METROPOLITAN MUSEUM OF ART   [593]

1000 Fifth Avenue
New York, NY 10028-0198
(212) 650-2763
(212) 396-5168
Fax: (212) 570-3972

E-MAIL ADDRESS:
education.grants@metmuseum.org

WEB SITE ADDRESS:
www.metmuseum.org

NAME(S) OF PROGRAMS:
- **Andrew W. Mellon Fellowships**

TYPE:
Fellowships; Visiting scholars. Awarded to promising young scholars with commendable research projects related to the Metropolitan

Museum's collections and to distinguished visiting scholars from the U.S. and abroad who can serve as teachers and advisors making their expertise available to catalogue and refine the collections. Fellows are expected to spend most of their tenure at the Metropolitan Museum.

YEAR PROGRAM STARTED: 1974

PURPOSE:
To promote research in the fine arts.

ELIGIBILITY:
Applicants should have received the Doctorate or have completed substantial work toward it.

FINANCIAL DATA:
Amount of support per award: $40,000 stipend for senior fellows for one year, $30,000 for predoctoral fellows, and up to an additional $5,000 for travel and miscellaneous expenses.

APPLICATION INFORMATION:
Electronically submitted applications and letters of recommendation are not accepted.

There are no application forms. Applicants need not specify the name of a particular fellowship. Fellowship applications must be submitted in English. Three letters of recommendation are required, none of which may be from current Metropolitan Museum of Art staff. The submission in English of the required letters of recommendation is encouraged. A typed application in triplicate must include:
(1) name, home and present address, telephone number and e-mail address;
(2) full resume of education and employment;
(3) a two-part statement, not to exceed 1,000 words, describing what the applicant wishes to accomplish in the fellowship period and detailing how the Museum's resources can be utilized to achieve the applicant's objectives;
(4) tentative schedule of work to be accomplished during the fellowship period;
(5) tentative schedule of travel required during the fellowship period;
(6) three letters of recommendation, at least one professional and one academic, sent directly to the Museum and;
(7) a list of other fellowships or grants for which the applicant has applied in the same period.
For predoctoral applicants only: official undergraduate and graduate transcripts (original transcript plus two copies of each).
Duration: Normally, a fellow will be in residence at the Metropolitan for a maximum of one year. Fellowships for senior scholars are also available for as short a term as one month.
Deadline: Application and required letters of recommendation must be received by the first Friday in November. Announcement of awards will be made by late March.

ADDRESS INQUIRIES TO:
Marcie Karp, Managing Museum Educator Academic Programs, Education Department (See address above.)

*SPECIAL STIPULATIONS:
Predoctoral Fellows will generally be expected to assist the hosting curatorial departments up to one-half of their time during the fellowship period with projects that complement their approved scholarly project. They will be expected to participate in a fellows' colloquium in the second half of their fellowship term, in which they will give a 20-minute presentation on their work-in-progress. Senior Fellows will also be invited to participate in these activities.

THE METROPOLITAN MUSEUM OF ART [594]
1000 Fifth Avenue
New York, NY 10028-0198
(212) 650-2763
(212) 396-5168
Fax: (212) 570-3972

E-MAIL ADDRESS:
education.grants@metmuseum.org

WEB SITE ADDRESS:
www.metmuseum.org

AREAS OF INTEREST:
Scholarly research in the fine arts.

NAME(S) OF PROGRAMS:
● **Chester Dale Fellowships**

TYPE:
Fellowships. Awarded for independent scholarly study or research related to the fine arts of the Western world at the Metropolitan Museum.

PURPOSE:
To promote research in the fine arts.

ELIGIBILITY:
Individuals whose fields of study are related to the fine arts of the Western world and who are preferably American citizens under the age of 40.

FINANCIAL DATA:
Fellowships are awarded as available funds permit.
Amount of support per award: $40,000 stipend for senior fellows, $30,000 for predoctoral fellows, and up to an additional $5,000 for travel and miscellaneous expenses.

APPLICATION INFORMATION:
Electronically submitted applications and letters of recommendation are not accepted.

There are no application forms. Applicants need not specify the name of a particular fellowship. Fellowship applications must be submitted in English. Three letters of recommendation are required, none of which may be from current Metropolitan Museum of Art staff. The submission in English of the required letters of recommendation is encouraged. A typed application in triplicate must include:
(1) name, home and present address, telephone number and e-mail address;
(2) full resume of education and employment;
(3) a two-part statement, not to exceed 1,000 words, describing what the applicant wishes to accomplish in the fellowship period and detailing how the Museum's resources can be utilized to achieve the applicant's objectives;
(4) tentative schedule of work to be accomplished during the fellowship period;
(5) tentative schedule of travel required during the fellowship period;
(6) three letters of recommendation, at least one professional and one academic, sent directly to the Museum and;
(7) a list of other fellowships or grants for which the applicant has applied in the same period.
For predoctoral applicants only: official undergraduate and graduate transcripts (original transcript plus two copies of each).
Duration: The grants typically cover periods from three months to one year.

Deadline: Application and required letters of recommendation must be received by the first Friday in November. Announcements of awards will be made by March.

ADDRESS INQUIRIES TO:
Marcie Karp, Managing Museum Educator Academic Programs, Education Department (See address above.)

*SPECIAL STIPULATIONS:
Predoctoral Fellows will generally be expected to assist the hosting curatorial department with projects that complement and are incidental to their approved scholarly project. They will be expected to participate in a fellows' colloquium in the second half of their fellowship term, in which they will give a 20-minute presentation on their work-in-progress. Senior Fellows will also be invited to participate in these activities.

THE METROPOLITAN MUSEUM OF ART [595]
1000 Fifth Avenue
New York, NY 10028-0198
(212) 650-2763
(212) 650-5168
Fax: (212) 570-3972

E-MAIL ADDRESS:
education.grants@metmuseum.org

WEB SITE ADDRESS:
www.metmuseum.org

NAME(S) OF PROGRAMS:
● **J. Clawson Mills Scholarships**

TYPE:
Fellowships. Awarded to scholars interested in pursuing research projects at the Metropolitan Museum or abroad in any branch of the fine arts related to the Museum's collections.

PURPOSE:
To promote research in the fine arts.

ELIGIBILITY:
In general, these grants are reserved for mature scholars of demonstrated ability.

FINANCIAL DATA:
Scholarships are awarded as available funds permit.
Amount of support per award: $40,000 stipend for one year for senior fellows and $30,000 for predoctoral fellows, and up to an additional $5,000 for travel and miscellaneous expenses.

APPLICATION INFORMATION:
Electronically submitted applications and letters of recommendation are not accepted.

There are no application forms. Applicants need not specify the name of a particular fellowship. Fellowship applications must be submitted in English. Three letters of recommendation are required, none of which may be from current Metropolitan Museum of Art staff. The submission in English of the required letters of recommendation is encouraged. A typed application in triplicate must include:
(1) name, home and present address and telephone number;
(2) full resume of education and employment;
(3) a two-part statement, not to exceed 1,000 words, describing what the applicant wishes to accomplish in the fellowship period and detailing how the Museum's resources can be utilized to achieve the applicant's objectives;
(4) tentative schedule of work to be

accomplished during the fellowship period;
(5) tentative schedule of travel required during the fellowship period;
(6) three letters of recommendation, at least one professional and one academic, sent directly to the Museum and;
(7) a list of other fellowships or grants for which the applicant has applied in the same period.

For predoctoral applicants only: official undergraduate and graduate transcripts (original transcript plus two copies of each).

Duration: One year.

Deadline: Application and required letters of recommendation must be received by the first Friday in November. Announcement of awards will be made by March 2.

ADDRESS INQUIRIES TO:
Marcie Karp, Managing Museum Educator Academic Programs, Education Department (See address above.)

*SPECIAL STIPULATIONS:
Predoctoral Fellows will generally be expected to assist the hosting curatorial departments up to one-half of their time during the fellowship period with projects that complement their approved scholarly project. They will be asked to give a gallery talk during their fellowship term and will be expected to participate in a fellows' colloquium in the second half of their term, in which they will give a 20-minute presentation on their work-in-progress. Senior Fellows will also be invited to participate in these activities.

THE METROPOLITAN MUSEUM OF ART   [596]
1000 Fifth Avenue
New York, NY 10028-0198
(212) 650-2763
(212) 396-5168
Fax: (212) 570-3972

E-MAIL ADDRESS:
education.grants@metmuseum.org

WEB SITE ADDRESS:
www.metmuseum.org

NAME(S) OF PROGRAMS:
● **The Bothmer Fellowship**

TYPE:
Fellowships. Awarded to an outstanding graduate student who has been admitted to the doctoral program of a university in the U.S., and who has submitted an outline of a thesis dealing with either Greek or Roman art.

YEAR PROGRAM STARTED: 1976

PURPOSE:
To promote research in the fine arts.

ELIGIBILITY:
An applicant must be an outstanding graduate student who has been admitted to the doctoral program of a university in the U.S. and who has submitted an outline of a thesis dealing with either Greek or Roman art. Preference will be given to the applicant who, in the opinion of the Grants Committee, would profit most from utilizing the resources of the Museum's Department of Greek and Roman Art: its collections, library, photographs and other archives with the guidance of its curatorial staff.

FINANCIAL DATA:
Amount of support per award: $30,000 for one year for predoctoral fellows with up to an additional $5,000 for travel and miscellaneous expenses.

APPLICATION INFORMATION:
Electronically submitted applications and letters of recommendation are not accepted.

There are no application forms. Applicants need not specify the name of a particular fellowship. Fellowship applications must be submitted in English. Three letters of recommendation are required, none of which may be from current Metropolitan Museum of Art staff. The submission in English of the required letters of recommendation is encouraged. A typed application in triplicate must include:
(1) name, home and present address, telephone number and e-mail address;
(2) full resume of education and employment;
(3) a two-part statement, not to exceed 1,000 words, describing what the applicant wishes to accomplish in the fellowship period and detailing how the Museum's resources can be utilized to achieve the applicant's objectives;
(4) tentative schedule of work to be accomplished during the fellowship period;
(5) tentative schedule of travel required during the fellowship period;
(6) three letters of recommendation, at least one professional and one academic, sent directly to the Museum and;
(7) a list of other fellowships or grants for which the applicant has applied in the same period.

For predoctoral applicants only: official undergraduate and graduate transcripts (original transcript plus two copies of each).

Duration: One academic year.

Deadline: Application and required letters of recommendation must be received by the first Friday in November. Announcements of awards will be made by late March.

ADDRESS INQUIRIES TO:
Marcie Karp, Managing Museum Educator Academic Programs, Education Department (See address above.)

*SPECIAL STIPULATIONS:
Predoctoral Fellows will generally be expected to assist the hosting curatorial departments up to one-half of their time during the fellowship period with projects that complement their approved scholarly project. They will be expected to participate in a fellows' colloquium in the second half of their term, in which they will give a 20-minute presentation on their work-in-progress.

MUSEUM OF EARLY SOUTHERN DECORATIVE ARTS (MESDA)   [597]
924 South Main Street
Winston-Salem, NC 27101-5335
(336) 721-7360
Fax: (336) 721-7367

E-MAIL ADDRESS:
sgant@oldsalem.org

WEB SITE ADDRESS:
www.mesda.org

FOUNDED: 1965

AREAS OF INTEREST:
Decorative arts of the South before 1860.

NAME(S) OF PROGRAMS:
● **Horton Fellowship**

TYPE:
Fellowships; Research grants.

YEAR PROGRAM STARTED: 1976

PURPOSE:
To combine the study of history and objects in a museum context.

LEGAL BASIS:
Nonprofit.

ELIGIBILITY:
Graduate student status or present employment in museum-related professions required.

FINANCIAL DATA:
Covers partial tuition for three credit hours.
Amount of support per award: $150 to $500.
Total amount of support: $7,550 for the year 2010.

NUMBER OF APPLICANTS MOST RECENT YEAR:
18 for the year 2010.

NUMBER OF AWARDS: 15 for the year 2010.

APPLICATION INFORMATION:
Applicant must submit a completed application form and letters of recommendation.
Duration: Four weeks.
Deadline: April 20. Notification May 1.

IRS IDENTIFICATION NUMBER: 56-0587289

STAFF:
Sally Gant, Director of Education

ADDRESS INQUIRIES TO:
Sally Gant, Director of Education (See address above.)

NAMTA FOUNDATION FOR THE VISUAL ARTS   [598]
15806 Brookway Drive
Suite 300
Huntersville, NC 28078
(704) 892-6244
Fax: (704) 892-6247

E-MAIL ADDRESS:
foundation@namta.org

WEB SITE ADDRESS:
www.namta.org

FOUNDED: 2005

AREAS OF INTEREST:
The fine arts industry.

NAME(S) OF PROGRAMS:
● **NAMTA Foundation Educational Scholarship**
● **NAMTA Foundation Visual Arts Major Scholarship**

TYPE:
Scholarships.

YEAR PROGRAM STARTED: 1983

PURPOSE:
To help students offset secondary education costs.

LEGAL BASIS:
501(c)(3) nonprofit corporation.

APPLICATION INFORMATION:
Contact the Foundation for application procedures.
Deadline: March.

THE NATIONAL ACADEMY MUSEUM [599]

1083 Fifth Avenue
New York, NY 10128
(212) 369-4880
Fax: (212) 360-6795

E-MAIL ADDRESS:
kim@nationalacademy.org

WEB SITE ADDRESS:
www.nationalacademy.org

FOUNDED: 1825

AREAS OF INTEREST:
19th and 20th Century American Art, training and exhibiting American artists and architects, and exhibition of European works of art which influence American artistic heritage.

NAME(S) OF PROGRAMS:
- **Annual Exhibition of The National Academy Museum**

TYPE:
Awards/prizes. Exhibition of art and possible cash awards.

YEAR PROGRAM STARTED: 1825

PURPOSE:
To recognize exceptional works of art in Annual Exhibition.

LEGAL BASIS:
Nonprofit, tax-exempt educational institution.

ELIGIBILITY:
Original works in painting, sculpture, graphics or architecture. Works previously exhibited in the National Academy Museum Galleries are not eligible. Applicants must be nominated by an Academy member.

GEOGRAPHIC RESTRICTIONS:
United States.

FINANCIAL DATA:
Amount of support per award: $500 to $5,000 depending upon specific award.
Total amount of support: Varies.

APPLICATION INFORMATION:
By invitation only.
Duration: One-time cash awards and medals offered at annual juried exhibition.

PUBLICATIONS:
Prospectus.

ADDRESS INQUIRIES TO:
Sei Kim, Artist Membership Manager
(See address above.)

*SPECIAL STIPULATIONS:
Entries by invitation only.

PEW FELLOWSHIPS IN THE ARTS [600]

1608 Walnut Street, 18th Floor
Philadelphia, PA 19103
(267) 350-4920
Fax: (267) 350-4997

E-MAIL ADDRESS:
pfa@pcah.us
mfranklin@pcah.us

WEB SITE ADDRESS:
www.pcah.us/fellowships

FOUNDED: 1991

AREAS OF INTEREST:
Fellowships are awarded for various art forms, including Choreography, Craft Arts, Folk and Traditional Arts, Literature (Fiction, Literary Non-Fiction and Poetry), Media Arts, Music Composition, Painting, Performance Art, Playwriting, Works on Paper and Visual Arts 3-D.

TYPE:
Fellowships. Opportunities for contemporary artists in the Philadelphia five-county area to concentrate on the development and creation of art. Fellowships to support artists at critical junctures in any stage of their career development. Fellows will be expected to participate annually in at least two meetings with other fellowship recipients.

PURPOSE:
To provide financial support directly to artists so that they will have the opportunity to dedicate themselves wholly to the development of their artwork; to provide such support at a critical juncture in an artist's career, when a concentration on artistic development and exploration is most likely to contribute to personal and professional growth.

ELIGIBILITY:
Artists are nominated and invited to apply for the fellowship. Candidates must be residents of Bucks, Chester, Delaware, Montgomery or Philadelphia counties, PA, for two years or longer. Matriculated students, full- or part-time, or immediate family members of a panelist for the year applied or of Pew Fellowships in the Arts' staff are not eligible.

There is no restriction as to citizenship.

GEOGRAPHIC RESTRICTIONS:
Bucks, Chester, Delaware, Montgomery and Philadelphia counties, Pennsylvania.

FINANCIAL DATA:
Fellowship includes stipend. Funds may be used to support costs such as equipment, materials, assistants, training and travel. The specific use of grant funds will be up to the recipient artist.
Amount of support per award: $60,000.
Total amount of support: Up to $720,000 each year.

COOPERATIVE FUNDING PROGRAMS: Program funded by the Pew Charitable Trusts.

NUMBER OF APPLICANTS MOST RECENT YEAR:
Varies.

NUMBER OF AWARDS: Up to 12 each year.

APPLICATION INFORMATION:
Application by nomination only.

The application procedure involves a panel review by artists and arts professionals. The first level of review is discipline-based; the second level of review is interdisciplinary; the final selection of candidates is based on the applicant's accomplishments or promise in his or her discipline, and the degree to which the fellowship will address a critical juncture in the artist's career and/or artistic development.
Duration: Up to two years.
Deadline: Details are available online.

PUBLICATIONS:
Annual catalogue.

STAFF:
Melissa Franklin, Director
Sarah Biemiller, Senior Program Associate

ADDRESS INQUIRIES TO:
Melissa Franklin, Director
E-mail: mfranklin@pcah.us
(See address above.)

THE POLLOCK-KRASNER FOUNDATION, INC. [601]

863 Park Avenue
New York, NY 10075
(212) 517-5400
Fax: (212) 288-2836

E-MAIL ADDRESS:
grants@pkf.org

WEB SITE ADDRESS:
www.pkf.org

FOUNDED: 1985

AREAS OF INTEREST:
Visual arts.

TYPE:
Grants-in-aid. Grants to individual visual artists for personal and professional needs.

YEAR PROGRAM STARTED: 1985

PURPOSE:
To aid internationally working artists who have embarked on professional careers.

LEGAL BASIS:
Private foundation.

ELIGIBILITY:
Grants are made to painters, sculptors and artists who work on paper, including printmakers who have taken up art as a professional career. The Foundation will not accept applications from commercial artists, photographers, video artists, filmmakers, craft-makers or any artist whose work primarily falls into these categories. It does not make grants to students nor fund academic study.

The Foundation does accept requests for emergency assistance for problems of a catastrophic nature; however, no application can proceed without investigation and evaluation. The Foundation does not make grants to pay for past debts, legal fees, the purchase of real estate, moves to other cities or to pay for the costs of installations, commissions or projects ordered by others. With very few exceptions, the Foundation will not fund travel expenses.

FINANCIAL DATA:
Amount of support per award: The size and length of the grant is determined by the individual circumstances of the artist.
Total amount of support: Varies.

APPLICATION INFORMATION:
Artists are required to submit a cover letter, an application, and 10 images of current work. Artists interested in obtaining application forms and information on the application procedure should write to the address above.
Duration: One year.
Deadline: Grants are awarded throughout the year.

PUBLICATIONS:
Biannual report; application guidelines.

OFFICERS:
Charles C. Bergman, Chairman of the Board and Chief Executive Officer
Samuel Sachs, II, President
Kerrie Buitrago, Executive Vice President

STAFF:
Caroline Black, Program Officer
Beth Cochems, Grants Manager

ADDRESS INQUIRIES TO:
Charles C. Bergman, Chairman of the Board and Chief Executive Officer
(See address above.)

ROSWELL ARTIST-IN-RESIDENCE PROGRAM   [602]

P.O. Box One
Roswell, NM 88202
(575) 622-6037
Fax: (575) 623-5603

E-MAIL ADDRESS:
stephen@rair.org

WEB SITE ADDRESS:
www.rair.org

FOUNDED: 1967

AREAS OF INTEREST:
Studio-based, fine-art residencies.

TYPE:
Residencies. Roswell Artist-in-Residence
Program is for artists who work in drawing,
painting, sculpture, photography, printmaking
and other fine art media.

YEAR PROGRAM STARTED: 1967

PURPOSE:
To provide time for artists to focus on their
work, without distractions or interruptions.

ELIGIBILITY:
Not open to all students, except those whose
degrees will be completed before the
beginning of the grant period.

FINANCIAL DATA:
Amount of support per award: $800 per
month, plus housing, studio and utilities and
$100 per dependent.
Matching fund requirements: Artists cover
phone service, food, art materials and
transportation.

NUMBER OF APPLICANTS MOST RECENT YEAR:
180.

NUMBER OF AWARDS: 6 each year.

APPLICATION INFORMATION:
Applicants must complete the current
application form. If requesting application by
mail, please send a self-addressed, stamped
envelope.
Duration: One year.
Deadline: Varies.

IRS IDENTIFICATION NUMBER: 33-0999247

STAFF:
Stephen Fleming, Director
Nancy Fleming, Programs and Publications

ADDRESS INQUIRIES TO:
Roswell Artist-in-Residence Program
(See address above.)

SAN DIEGO ART INSTITUTE   [603]

1439 El Prado
House of Charm, Balboa Park
San Diego, CA 92101
(619) 236-0011
Fax: (619) 236-1974

E-MAIL ADDRESS:
admin@sandiego-art.org

WEB SITE ADDRESS:
www.sandiego-art.org

FOUNDED: 1941

AREAS OF INTEREST:
Visual arts.

NAME(S) OF PROGRAMS:
● **Annual International Juried Award
  Exhibition**

● **Southern California Regional Juried
  Award**
● **Youth Art**

TYPE:
Awards/prizes; Conferences/seminars;
Internships. Monthly juried exhibitions;
monthly youth art exhibitions; awarded
member solo shows; annual international
juried award exhibition; annual city/county
youth art award show; quarterly
informational lecture series; biannual art
tours; newsletter/journal.

YEAR PROGRAM STARTED: 1954

PURPOSE:
To advance the visual arts through exhibition,
outreach and education.

LEGAL BASIS:
Nonprofit organization.

ELIGIBILITY:
For the International Juried Award
Exhibition, the exhibition is open to any
artist (digital entry only). There are no
residency restrictions. Art must be original.

For the Southern California Regional Juried
Award, southern California residency is
required. Art must be hand-carried to Gallery.

FINANCIAL DATA:
Awards include monetary compensation.
Amount of support per award: For the
International Juried Award Exhibition, one
award of $2,000; two awards of $1,000; one
award of $500; two awards of $150; three
awards of $100. For Southern California
Regional Juried Award Exhibition: one award
of $1,000; two awards of $500.
Total amount of support: $7,100.

NUMBER OF AWARDS: 13.

APPLICATION INFORMATION:
For the International Juried Exhibition, up to
two slides of works of art may be submitted
per artist. Work may be two- or
three-dimensional. All media are welcome
except crafts or functional art. For the
Southern California Regional, one art work
per artist, hand-carried to Gallery. Send a
SASE for prospectus. Entry fee required.
Duration: One-time awards.

PUBLICATIONS:
Journal; guidelines.

IRS IDENTIFICATION NUMBER: 95-1816068

ADDRESS INQUIRIES TO:
Kerstin Robers, Executive Administrator
(See address and e-mail above.)

*SPECIAL STIPULATIONS:
All shows are juried by outside juror.

THE SAN FRANCISCO FOUNDATION   [604]

225 Bush Street
Suite 500
San Francisco, CA 94104
(415) 733-8500
Fax: (415) 477-2783

E-MAIL ADDRESS:
tromo@sff.org

WEB SITE ADDRESS:
www.sff.org

FOUNDED: 1948

AREAS OF INTEREST:
Fine arts.

NAME(S) OF PROGRAMS:
● **Cadogan Fine Arts Fellowships**
● **Murphy Fine Arts Fellowships**

TYPE:
Fellowships.

PURPOSE:
To assist San Francisco Bay Area students in
pursuing graduate academic fine arts study at
eight Bay Area institutions.

LEGAL BASIS:
Community foundation.

ELIGIBILITY:
Applicants must be graduate fine arts
students at one of the eight Bay Area
colleges and universities and should ask a
faculty member to nominate them. They must
have completed at least one semester of
graduate study and must have at least two
semesters remaining before graduation.
Artwork submitted must have been
completed within the past two years.

GEOGRAPHIC RESTRICTIONS:
San Francisco Bay Area, California.

FINANCIAL DATA:
Amount of support per award: $3,500 to
underwrite tuition.
Total amount of support: $55,000 to $80,000
per year.

NUMBER OF APPLICANTS MOST RECENT YEAR:
115 for the year 2010.

NUMBER OF AWARDS: 23 for the year 2010.

APPLICATION INFORMATION:
Application information is available online.
Duration: One year.
Deadline: Spring. Announcement in early
June.

ADDRESS INQUIRIES TO:
Arts and Culture Program Fellow
(See address above.)

SCHOOL OF THE MUSEUM OF FINE ARTS, BOSTON   [605]

230 The Fenway
Boston, MA 02115
(617) 369-3656 (Exhibitions Office)
Fax: (617) 369-3856

WEB SITE ADDRESS:
www.smfa.edu

FOUNDED: 1876

AREAS OF INTEREST:
Studio fine arts.

NAME(S) OF PROGRAMS:
● **Traveling Fellowship Award**

TYPE:
Fellowships. Awarded for travel and study
abroad.

YEAR PROGRAM STARTED: 1899

PURPOSE:
To further the professional development of
the artist recipients.

LEGAL BASIS:
A part of the Museum of Fine Arts, a
nonprofit Massachusetts corporation.

ELIGIBILITY:
Applicants must be alumni of the School of
the Museum of Fine Arts and submit a body
of work to the competition jury no later than
the third year following graduation.

FINANCIAL DATA:
Amount of support per award: Up to
$10,000.

Total amount of support: Approximately $75,000 annually.

NUMBER OF APPLICANTS MOST RECENT YEAR: 165.

APPLICATION INFORMATION:
Proposed plan of travel and study, including itinerary, must be submitted with a presentation of art work.
Duration: Varies according to proposal. Normally not more than one year. Nonrenewable.
Deadline: January. Announcement in May.

PUBLICATIONS:
School catalog.

ADDRESS INQUIRIES TO:
Office of Exhibitions
(See address above.)

SISTER KENNY REHABILITATION INSTITUTE [606]
800 East 28th Street
Mail Route 12101
Minneapolis, MN 55407-3799
(612) 863-4872
Fax: (612) 863-8942

E-MAIL ADDRESS:
diana.kommer@allina.com

WEB SITE ADDRESS:
www.allina.com/ahs/ski.nsf

FOUNDED: 1942

AREAS OF INTEREST:
Physical rehabilitation facility, independent living for disabled persons, research and education and promotion of arts for disabled persons.

NAME(S) OF PROGRAMS:
● **Sister Kenny Rehabilitation Institute International Art Show by Artists with Disabilities**

TYPE:
Awards/prizes. Prize money awards and ribbon awards to disabled artists at annual art show.

YEAR PROGRAM STARTED: 1963

PURPOSE:
To provide a forum for creative talents of persons with disabilities; to give disabled artists an outlet to sell their work on a competitive basis; to create awareness and appreciation of talents of disabled artists.

LEGAL BASIS:
501(c)(3).

ELIGIBILITY:
Any artist may enter who has a disability; that is, a physical or mental impairment which substantially limits one or more major life activities (such as caring for oneself, performing manual tasks, walking, seeing, hearing, breathing, learning and working).

FINANCIAL DATA:
Amount of support per award: $75 to $500 for Award Ribbon Purchases totaling $6,000.
Total amount of support: $20,000.

NUMBER OF APPLICANTS MOST RECENT YEAR: 345.

APPLICATION INFORMATION:
Contact Institute for entry form.

PUBLICATIONS:
Application guidelines.

ADDRESS INQUIRIES TO:
Diana Kommer, Show Coordinator
(See address above.)

SKOWHEGAN SCHOOL OF PAINTING AND SCULPTURE [607]
200 Park Avenue South
Suite 1116
New York, NY 10003-1503
(212) 529-0505
Fax: (212) 473-1342

E-MAIL ADDRESS:
mail@skowheganart.org

WEB SITE ADDRESS:
www.skowheganart.org

FOUNDED: 1946

AREAS OF INTEREST:
All visual arts.

TYPE:
Scholarships.

YEAR PROGRAM STARTED: 1946

PURPOSE:
To bring together a gifted and diverse group of individuals who have demonstrated a commitment to art-making and inquiry to create the most stimulating environment possible for a concentrated period of artistic creation, interaction and growth.

LEGAL BASIS:
Not-for-profit educational institution.

ELIGIBILITY:
Based on need. Candidate must be at least 21 years old.

FINANCIAL DATA:
Scholarships cover room, board and tuition.
Amount of support per award: Average $3,757 for the year 2008.
Total amount of support: Approximately $250,000 for the year 2008.

NUMBER OF APPLICANTS MOST RECENT YEAR: 2,005 for the year 2008.

NUMBER OF AWARDS: 65 for the year 2008.

APPLICATION INFORMATION:
Application information is available online.
Duration: Nine-week summer program, mid-June to mid-August.
Deadline: February 1 for all applications. Notification in mid-April.

STAFF:
Linda Earle, Executive Director, Program

ADDRESS INQUIRIES TO:
Sarah Workneh
Executive Director, Program
(See address above.)

W. EUGENE SMITH MEMORIAL FUND [608]
c/o International Center of Photography
1114 Avenue of the Americas
New York, NY 10036
(212) 857-0038
Fax: (212) 768-4688

WEB SITE ADDRESS:
www.smithfund.org

FOUNDED: 1979

AREAS OF INTEREST:
Photography.

NAME(S) OF PROGRAMS:
● **W. Eugene Smith Grant in Humanistic Photography**

TYPE:
Project/program grants.

PURPOSE:
To support a photographer working on a project in the humanistic tradition of W. Eugene Smith, in order to pursue the work.

ELIGIBILITY:
Open to outstanding photographers of any nationality.

FINANCIAL DATA:
Amount of support per award: $30,000 and a possible additional $5,000 fellowship.

APPLICATION INFORMATION:
Applicants should include a written proposal, resume of educational and professional qualifications, and 20 to 40 images. No entry fee is required.
Duration: One year.
Deadline: May 15.

ADDRESS INQUIRIES TO:
Anna Winand, Executive Assistant
(See address above.)

*SPECIAL STIPULATIONS:
Grant recipients agree to give to the W. Eugene Smith Memorial Fund, Inc., as an unrestricted gift, 12 prints of work completed as part of the project proposed, within 18 months of the award and shall become part of the Legacy Collection.

SIR JOHN SOANE MUSEUM FOUNDATION
1040 First Avenue, Suite 311
New York, NY 10022
(212) 223-2012
Fax: (860) 435-8019

E-MAIL ADDRESS:
info@soanefoundation.com

WEB SITE ADDRESS:
www.soanefoundation.com

TYPE:
Fellowships. Designed to help graduate students and scholars pursue research projects related to the work of Sir John Soane's Museum and its collections.

See entry 451 for full listing.

THE JOHN F. AND ANNA LEE STACEY SCHOLARSHIP FUND [609]
c/o National Cowboy and
Western Heritage Museum
1700 N.E. 63rd Street
Oklahoma City, OK 73111
(405) 478-2250
Fax: (405) 478-4714

E-MAIL ADDRESS:
amorand@nationalcowboymuseum.org

WEB SITE ADDRESS:
www.nationalcowboymuseum.org

FOUNDED: 1955

AREAS OF INTEREST:
Drawing and painting in the conservative mode.

TYPE:
Awards/prizes. Cash awards to be used to further the development of young painters in the classical conservative tradition.

YEAR PROGRAM STARTED: 1975

PURPOSE:
To foster a high standard in the study of form, color, drawing, painting, design and technique, as these are expressed in modes showing patent affinity with the classical tradition of western culture.

LEGAL BASIS:
Nonprofit.

ELIGIBILITY:
Open to U.S. citizens between 18 and 35 years of age. Only those should apply who are skilled and devoted to the painting or drawing of classical or conservative tradition of western culture.

GEOGRAPHIC RESTRICTIONS:
United States.

FINANCIAL DATA:
Amount of support per award: $1,000 to $4,000.
Total amount of support: Varies.

NUMBER OF APPLICANTS MOST RECENT YEAR:
More than 125.

NUMBER OF AWARDS: 3 to 5.

APPLICATION INFORMATION:
Guidelines are posted online by November 1 for the following year. All applicants will be required to submit digital images on a disk representing the best examples of their work. 150 dpi with its maximum width or height set to 16 inches is preferred. Not more than 10 images (clearly labeled with name, title, dimensions, medium and date of execution of the work) of their work in the following categories: painting from life, drawing from the figure (nude), composition, landscape and others. Also include a recent photo of yourself, a letter explaining your goals and where you wish to study, and reference letters. On the basis of these images, the Committee will select a number of finalists who will be required to submit original work for a second and final competition. Application forms must accompany all submissions.
Duration: One year.
Deadline: Entries need to be postmarked by February 1 of each year.

PUBLICATIONS:
Guidelines.

STAFF:
Anne Morand, Curator of Art

ADDRESS INQUIRIES TO:
See e-mail address above.

UNIVERSITY OF ILLINOIS AT URBANA-CHAMPAIGN   [610]
College of Fine and Applied Arts
608 East Lorado Taft Drive, Suite 100
Champaign, IL 61820
(217) 333-1661
(217) 333-1660
Fax: (217) 244-8381

E-MAIL ADDRESS:
rewilcox@illinois.edu

WEB SITE ADDRESS:
www.faa.illinois.edu

FOUNDED: 1931

AREAS OF INTEREST:
Art, architecture, dance, landscape architecture, music, theatre, and urban and regional planning.

NAME(S) OF PROGRAMS:
● **Kate Neal Kinley Memorial Fellowship**

TYPE:
Fellowships. Awarded for advanced study in the fine arts in the U.S. or abroad, in an approved educational institution, with an approved private teacher or in independent study.

Three major Fellowships will be awarded:
(1) one in any field of music;
(2) one in architectural design and history, art and design, theatre, dance, or instrumental or vocal music and;
(3) one in art, architecture, dance, landscape architecture, theatre, or urban and regional planning.

YEAR PROGRAM STARTED: 1931

PURPOSE:
To help defray expenses of advanced study of the fine and applied arts in America or abroad.

Provides a meaningful opportunity for students to enhance their professional status, aid their pursuit of an advanced degree, or finance a special project within the field.

ELIGIBILITY:
Open to graduates of the College of Fine and Applied Arts of the University of Illinois at Urbana-Champaign and to graduates of similar institutions of equal educational standing whose principal or major studies have been in the fields of art, architecture, dance, landscape architecture, music, theatre, and urban and regional planning.

Although there is no age limitation for applicants, other factors being equal, preference will be given to applicants who have not reached their 25th birthday.

Fellowships will be awarded upon the basis of unusual promise in the fine arts as attested by:
(1) high attainment in the applicant's major field of study as evidenced by academic marks and quality of work submitted or performed;
(2) high attainment in related cultural fields as evidenced by academic marks;
(3) the character, merit and suitability of the program proposed by the applicant and;
(4) excellence of personality, seriousness of purpose and good moral character.

FINANCIAL DATA:
The fellowships are to be used by the recipients toward defraying the expenses of advanced study in America or abroad.
Amount of support per award: Varies. For major fellowships: approximately $20,000 in any field of music; approximately $20,000 in architectural design and history, art and design, theatre, dance, or instrumental or vocal music; approximately $9,000 in art, architecture, dance, landscape architecture, theatre, or urban and regional planning.

COOPERATIVE FUNDING PROGRAMS: Funded partially by the John Robert Gregg Fund at Community Funds, Inc. and the New York Community Trust.

NUMBER OF AWARDS: 3 major fellowships, plus up to 3 additional fellowships of lesser amounts, depending upon committee recommendations.

APPLICATION INFORMATION:
The application form and guidelines are available online.
Duration: Tenable for one academic year.
Deadline: December 1.

ADDRESS INQUIRIES TO:
Dr. Robert Graves, Dean and Chair
Kate Neal Kinley
Memorial Fellowship Committee
(See address above.)

*SPECIAL STIPULATIONS:
While receiving a stipend from the Kate Neal Kinley Memorial Fellowship, recipients are precluded from holding appointments as instructors, lecturers or faculty, but may hold other remunerative employment with advance approval of the Fellowship Committee.

Each fellowship is for one academic year of study in a program approved by the Committee. The place of study may be in America or abroad, in an approved educational institution, with an approved private teacher, or in independent study. Fellowship recipients must meet all entrance requirements of the proposed educational institution.

UNIVERSITY OF SOUTHERN CALIFORNIA GAYLE GARNER ROSKI SCHOOL OF FINE ARTS   [611]
Watt Hall 104
Los Angeles, CA 90089-0292
(213) 740-9153
Fax: (213) 740-8938

E-MAIL ADDRESS:
finearts@usc.edu

WEB SITE ADDRESS:
roski.usc.edu

FOUNDED: 1883

AREAS OF INTEREST:
Fine arts.

NAME(S) OF PROGRAMS:
● **M.F.A. Teaching Assistantships**

TYPE:
Assistantships; Travel grants. Tuition remission. Awards are for people pursuing M.F.A. degree, for experience in teaching art on a college level.

YEAR PROGRAM STARTED: 1960

PURPOSE:
To educate artists.

LEGAL BASIS:
Private university.

ELIGIBILITY:
Applicants must be accepted into the Roski School of Fine Arts two-year M.F.A. program at University of Southern California.

FINANCIAL DATA:
Teaching Assistantship includes full tuition remission, generous monthly stipend and private studio.
Amount of support per award: Teaching Assistantship: $43,000 per year; Summer Travel Fellowship: Up to $5,000.
Total amount of support: $475,000.

NUMBER OF APPLICANTS MOST RECENT YEAR:
422.

NUMBER OF AWARDS: 12 Teaching Assistantships; 1 Travel Grant.

APPLICATION INFORMATION:
No separate application is required for assistantships. All applicants to the program are considered regardless of national origin. M.F.A. applications are available online.
Duration: One year. Assistantships are renewable.

Deadline: February 1.

ADDRESS INQUIRIES TO:
Penelope Jones
Assistant Dean for Student Affairs
(See address above.)

History

AGRICULTURAL HISTORY SOCIETY [612]
MSU History Department
P.O. Box H
Mississippi State, MS 39762
(662) 268-2247

E-MAIL ADDRESS:
jgiesen@history.msstate.edu

WEB SITE ADDRESS:
www.aghistorysociety.org

AREAS OF INTEREST:
Agricultural and rural history.

NAME(S) OF PROGRAMS:
- **Everett E. Edwards Awards in Agricultural History**
- **Gilbert C. Fite Dissertation Award**
- **Wayne D. Rasmussen Award**
- **Theodore Saloutos Book Award**

TYPE:
Awards/prizes. The Everett E. Edwards Award is presented to the graduate student who submits the best manuscript on any aspect of agricultural history and rural studies during the current calendar year.

The Gilbert C. Fite Dissertation Award will be presented to the author of the best dissertation on any aspect of agricultural history completed during the current calendar year.

The Wayne D. Rasmussen Award is given to the author of the best article on agricultural history published by a journal other than *Agricultural History* during the current calendar year.

The Theodore Saloutos Book Award is presented to the author of a book on any aspect of agricultural history in the U.S. within the current year, broadly interpreted.

PURPOSE:
To promote research and publication in the field of agricultural and rural history.

FINANCIAL DATA:
Amount of support per award: Edwards Award: Honorarium of $200 and publication in *Agricultural History*; Fite Dissertation Award: Honorarium of $300 and a certificate; Rasmussen Award: Honorarium of $200 for the author and certificates for the author and publisher; Saloutos Book Award: $500 to the author.

APPLICATION INFORMATION:
All submissions should be sent to Claire Strom, Editor, *Agricultural History*, at the above address.
Deadline: December 31.

AMERICAN ANTIQUARIAN SOCIETY (AAS)
185 Salisbury Street
Worcester, MA 01609-1634
(508) 755-5221
Fax: (508) 753-3311

E-MAIL ADDRESS:
cmcrell@mwa.org

WEB SITE ADDRESS:
www.americanantiquarian.org

TYPE:
Fellowships. Visiting fellowship for historical research by creative and performing artists, writers, filmmakers and journalists.
See entry 377 for full listing.

AMERICAN ANTIQUARIAN SOCIETY (AAS)
185 Salisbury Street
Worcester, MA 01609-1634
(508) 755-5221
Fax: (508) 754-9069

E-MAIL ADDRESS:
perickson@mwa.org

WEB SITE ADDRESS:
www.americanantiquarian.org

TYPE:
Conferences/seminars; Fellowships. Fellowships provide support for residence at the Society's library for research on any topic supported by the collections. All awards are for research and writing using the library's resources.
See entry 376 for full listing.

AMERICAN CATHOLIC HISTORICAL ASSOCIATION [613]
Department of African & African-American Studies
Fordham University, Dealy Hall, Room 637
441 East Fordham Road
Bronx, NY 10458
(718) 817-3830

E-MAIL ADDRESS:
acha@achahistory.org
randerson13@fordham.edu

WEB SITE ADDRESS:
research.cua.edu/acha

FOUNDED: 1919

AREAS OF INTEREST:
The history of Catholicism from antiquity to the present.

NAME(S) OF PROGRAMS:
- **The Howard R. Marraro Prize**

TYPE:
Awards/prizes. Prize for a book dealing with Italian history or Italian-American history or relations.

YEAR PROGRAM STARTED: 1973

PURPOSE:
To stimulate interest in the history of Catholicism among young scholars.

LEGAL BASIS:
An endowed fund owned by the Association.

ELIGIBILITY:
To be entered in the competition, a work must be of book length, in English, already published and must deal with Italian history or Italian-American history or relations. To be eligible for the prize, an author must be a citizen or resident of the U.S. or Canada. The work must have been published since June 1 of the previous year.

FINANCIAL DATA:
Amount of support per award: $750.

NUMBER OF AWARDS: 1 per annum.

REPRESENTATIVE AWARDS:
Lance Gabriel Lazar, *Working in the Vineyard of the Lord: Jesuit Confraternities in Early Modern Italy*; 2007: Gerald McKevitt, S.J., *Brokers of Culture: Italian Jesuits in the American West, 1848-1919*; 2008: Prof. Carol Lansing, *Passion and Order: Restraint of Grief in the Medieval Italian Communes* (Cornell University Press).

APPLICATION INFORMATION:
Three copies, if possible, of the work to be considered should be sent, together with a brief curriculum vitae and bibliography of the author, to the American Historical Association, 400 A Street, S.E., Washington, DC 20003.
Deadline: August 1.

ADDRESS INQUIRIES TO:
R. Bentley Anderson, S.J.
Executive Secretary-Treasurer
American Catholic Historical Association
(See street address above.)
E-mail: acha@achahistory.org

AMERICAN CATHOLIC HISTORICAL ASSOCIATION
Department of African & African-American Studies
Fordham University, Dealy Hall, Room 637
441 East Fordham Road
Bronx, NY 10458
(718) 817-3830

E-MAIL ADDRESS:
acha@achahistory.org
randerson13@fordham.edu

WEB SITE ADDRESS:
www.achahistory.org

TYPE:
Awards/prizes. A prize awarded annually to the author whose article, dealing with the history of the Catholic Church, is the first of his or her professional career and is judged to be the best of those in that category accepted for publication in any given year by the editors of the *Catholic Historical Review*.
See entry 847 for full listing.

AMERICAN CATHOLIC HISTORICAL ASSOCIATION
Department of African & African-American Studies
Fordham University, Dealy Hall, Room 637
441 East Fordham Road
Bronx, NY 10458
(718) 817-3830

E-MAIL ADDRESS:
acha@achahistory.org
randerson13@fordham.edu

WEB SITE ADDRESS:
www.achahistory.org

TYPE:
Awards/prizes. Award for a published book which, in the opinion of a committee of judges, has made within a 12-month period the most original and significant contribution to the area of the history of the Catholic Church broadly considered.
See entry 848 for full listing.

THE AMERICAN HISTORICAL ASSOCIATION [614]

400 A Street, S.E.
Washington, DC 20003
(202) 544-2422
Fax: (202) 544-8307

E-MAIL ADDRESS:
aha@historians.org

WEB SITE ADDRESS:
www.historians.org

FOUNDED: 1884

AREAS OF INTEREST:
Promotion of historical studies, the collection and preservation of historical manuscripts and the dissemination of historical research.

NAME(S) OF PROGRAMS:
- The Herbert Baxter Adams Prize
- The George Louis Beer Prize
- The Albert J. Beveridge Award
- Albert J. Beveridge Grant
- The Paul Birdsall Prize
- The James Henry Breasted Prize
- The Albert B. Corey Prize in Canadian-American Relations
- The John H. Dunning Prize in United States History
- The John E. Fagg Prize
- The John K. Fairbank Prize in East Asian History
- The Herbert Feis Award
- The Morris D. Forkosch Prize
- The Leo Gershoy Award
- The Clarence H. Haring Prize
- J. Franklin Jameson Award
- The Joan Kelly Memorial Prize in Women's History
- Martin A. Klein Prize
- Michael Kraus Research Grant
- The Waldo G. Leland Prize
- Littleton-Griswold Grant
- The Littleton-Griswold Prize in American Law and Society
- The J. Russell Major Prize
- The Helen and Howard R. Marraro Prize in Italian History
- The George L. Mosse Prize
- The John E. O'Connor Film Award
- The Premio Del Rey Prize
- The James A. Rawley Prize in Atlantic History
- The James Harvey Robinson Prize
- Bernadotte Schmitt Grant
- The Wesley-Logan Prize

TYPE:
Awards/prizes; Fellowships; Research grants. Prizes and awards for distinguished scholarly books written in English on historical subjects as follows:

Herbert Baxter Adams Prize: Awarded annually for a distinguished book by an American author in the field of European history.

Beer Prize: Awarded annually for the best work on European international history since 1895 by a U.S. citizen.

Beveridge Award: Awarded annually since 1927 for the best book in English on the history of the U.S., Canada, or Latin America from 1492 to the present.

Beveridge Grant: Given for research pertaining to the Western Hemisphere.

Birdsall Prize: For the best work in European military and strategic history since 1870. Awarded biennially in even years, since 1986.

Breasted Prize: Awarded annually for an outstanding book in English in any field of history prior to 1000 A.D.

Corey Prize: Awarded biennially in even years since 1967 for a book on the history of Canadian-U.S. relations, or on the history of both countries.

Dunning Prize: For a book on any subject relating to American history. Awarded biennially in odd years.

Fagg Prize: Awarded annually for the best publication in the history of Spain, Portugal, or Latin America.

Fairbank Prize: Awarded annually since 1969 for an outstanding book on the history of China proper, Vietnam, Chinese Central Asia, Mongolia, Manchuria, Korea or Japan since the year 1800.

Feis Award: Awarded annually since 1984 for the best book, article, or policy paper by an historian not affiliated with academia.

Forkosch Prize: Awarded annually since 1993 in recognition of the best book in English in the field of British, British Imperial or British Commonwealth History since 1485.

Gershoy Prize: Awarded annually since 1977 for an outstanding work published in English on any aspect of the fields of 17th and 18th century western European history.

Haring Prize: For a Latin American who, in the opinion of the committee, has published the most outstanding book on Latin American history during the preceding five years. Awarded every five years since 1966. Next award in 2011.

J. Franklin Jameson Award: Given for outstanding achievement in the editing of historical sources.

Kelly Memorial Prize: Awarded annually since 1984 for the best work in women's history and/or feminist theory.

Martin A. Klein Prize: Awarded in the study of African history.

Michael Kraus Research Grant: Awarded for the study of colonial American history.

Leland Prize: Offered every five years since 1981 for the outstanding reference tool in the field of history, i.e., bibliographies, indexes, encyclopedias and other scholarly apparatus. Next award in 2011.

Littleton-Griswold Grant: Awarded in U.S. legal history and law and society.

Littleton-Griswold Prize: Awarded annually since 1985 for the best book in any subject on the history of American law and society.

J. Russell Major Prize: Awarded annually for the best work in English on any aspect of French history.

Marraro Prize: Awarded annually since 1973 for the best work on any epoch of Italian history or Italian-American relations.

George L. Mosse Prize: Awarded annually for an outstanding major work of extraordinary scholarly distinction, creativity, and originality in the intellectual and cultural history of Europe since the Renaissance.

John E. O'Connor Film Award: Seeks to recognize outstanding interpretations of history through the medium of film or video.

Premio del Rey Prize: Awarded biennially, in even years, since 1990 for the best book in English in the field of early Spanish history, 500 to 1516 A.D.

James A. Rawley Prize in Atlantic History: Awarded annually in recognition of outstanding historical writing that explores aspects of integration of Atlantic worlds before the 20th century.

Robinson Prize: Awarded biennially in even years for the teaching aid that has made the most outstanding contribution to the teaching of history in any field. Award encompasses textbooks, source materials, audio-visual and computer-assisted instruction programs/techniques.

Bernadette Schmitt Grant: Given for research of Europe, Asia and Africa.

Wesley-Logan Prize: Established in 1992 by the AHA and the Association for the Study of African-American Life and History. Awarded annually for the outstanding book in African diaspora history.

PURPOSE:
To promote and honor good historical writing.

LEGAL BASIS:
Nonprofit association.

ELIGIBILITY:
Preference will be given to Ph.D. candidates and postgraduates. Applicant must be a member to apply for grants.

FINANCIAL DATA:
Amount of support per award: Varies.

NUMBER OF AWARDS: 1 in each program on the yearly basis detailed above.

PUBLICATIONS:
Annual report; *American Historical Review*; *Perspectives in History*.

OFFICERS:
Anthony Grafton, President
James R. Grossman, Executive Director
Robert A. Schneider, Editor, *American Historical Review*
Randy B. Norell, Controller

*PLEASE NOTE:
The book prizes are not scholarships. They are awards of distinction to authors who have had their works previously published.

Only books of high scholarly and literary merit will be considered.

THE AMERICAN HISTORICAL ASSOCIATION [615]

400 A Street, S.E.
Washington, DC 20003
(202) 544-2422
Fax: (202) 544-8307

E-MAIL ADDRESS:
rtownsend@historians.org

WEB SITE ADDRESS:
www.historians.org

FOUNDED: 1884

AREAS OF INTEREST:
Scholarly research.

NAME(S) OF PROGRAMS:
- The J. Franklin Jameson Fellowship

TYPE:
Fellowships. Award in American history offered annually by the Library of Congress and the American Historical Association to support significant scholarly research in the collections of the Library of Congress by young historians.

YEAR PROGRAM STARTED: 1977

PURPOSE:
The fellowship is offered annually by the Library of Congress and the American Historical Association to support significant scholarly research in the collections of the Library of Congress by scholars at an early stage in their careers in history.

LEGAL BASIS:
Nonprofit association.

ELIGIBILITY:
At the time of application, applicants must hold the Ph.D. degree or equivalent, must have received this degree within the past seven years and must not have published or had accepted for publication a book-length historical work. The fellowship will not be awarded to complete a doctoral dissertation.

The applicant's project in American history must be one for which the general and special collections of the Library of Congress offer unique research support. Applicants should include a statement substantiating this relationship.

Before the conclusion of the fellowship, the Jameson fellow will summarize the results of his or her research at a professional gathering arranged by the American Historical Association and the Library of Congress. Jameson fellows are not required to complete their project during the tenure of the fellowship, nor need they necessarily have published the results as a discrete work.

The American Historical Association encourages nontenured faculty, public historians, independent scholars and two-year faculty to apply.

FINANCIAL DATA:
Amount of support per award: $5,000 stipend.

NUMBER OF APPLICANTS MOST RECENT YEAR: 7 for the year 2009.

NUMBER OF AWARDS: 1 annually.

APPLICATION INFORMATION:
Letter of application should include a vitae, statement concerning the proposed project and its relationship to Library of Congress holdings, tentative schedule for tenure of the fellowship and three letters of recommendation by persons qualified to judge the project and the applicant's fitness to undertake it.
Duration: Two to three months.
Deadline: March 15. Award announced in May.

PUBLICATIONS:
Annual report.

OFFICERS:
Anthony Grafton, President
James R. Grossman, Executive Director
Robert A. Schneider, Editor, *American Historical Review*
Randy B. Norell, Controller

ADDRESS INQUIRIES TO:
J. Franklin Jameson Fellowship
(See address above.)

THE AMERICAN HISTORICAL ASSOCIATION [616]
400 A Street, S.E.
Washington, DC 20003
(202) 544-2422
Fax: (202) 544-8307

E-MAIL ADDRESS:
rtownsend@historians.org

WEB SITE ADDRESS:
www.historians.org

FOUNDED: 1884

AREAS OF INTEREST:
Scholarly research.

NAME(S) OF PROGRAMS:
● **Fellowship in Aerospace History**

TYPE:
Fellowships. The Association annually funds at least one fellow for a period of six months to one year, to undertake a proposed research project related to aerospace history. The Fellowship is supported by the National Aeronautics and Space Administration (NASA).

YEAR PROGRAM STARTED: 1986

PURPOSE:
To provide a fellow with an opportunity to engage in significant and sustained advanced research in all aspects of the history of aerospace from the earliest human interest in flight to the present, including cultural and intellectual history, economic history, history of law and public policy and the history of science, engineering and management.

LEGAL BASIS:
Nonprofit association.

ELIGIBILITY:
Applicants must possess a Doctorate degree in history or in a closely related field or be enrolled as a student, having completed all course work, in a doctoral degree-granting program.

The Fellowship term is for a period of at least six months, but not more than one year. The fellow will be expected to devote the term entirely to the proposed research project. The fellow will have, and is encouraged to take advantage of, the opportunity to use the documentary resources of the National Aeronautics and Space Administration and may also spend the Fellowship in residence at the NASA headquarters or one of the NASA centers.

FINANCIAL DATA:
Amount of support per award: $20,000 stipend for a six- to nine-month fellowship. The stipend is adjustable to the length of the fellowship term.

NUMBER OF APPLICANTS MOST RECENT YEAR: 8 candidates for the year 2009.

NUMBER OF AWARDS: 1 per year.

APPLICATION INFORMATION:
Applicants must complete an application form, available online, and offer a specific and detailed research proposal that will be the basis of the fellow's research during the term. At the term's conclusion, the fellow will be expected to write a report and present a paper or public lecture on the Fellowship experience.
Duration: Six months to one year.
Deadline: March 1. Announcement in May.

PUBLICATIONS:
Annual report.

OFFICERS:
Anthony Grafton, President
James R. Grossman, Executive Director
Robert A. Schneider, Editor, *American Historical Review*
Randy B. Norell, Controller

ADDRESS INQUIRIES TO:
Fellowship in Aerospace History
(See address above.)

*SPECIAL STIPULATIONS:
Funds may not be used to support tuition or fees. A fellow may not hold other major fellowships or grants during the fellowship term, except sabbatical and supplemental grants from their own institutions and small grants from other sources for specific research expenses. Sources of anticipated support must be listed in the application form.

AMERICAN INSTITUTE OF THE HISTORY OF PHARMACY
University of Wisconsin School of Pharmacy
Rennebohm Hall
777 Highland Avenue
Madison, WI 53705-2222
(608) 262-5378

E-MAIL ADDRESS:
gia@aihp.org

WEB SITE ADDRESS:
www.aihp.org

TYPE:
Grants-in-aid; Research grants.

See entry 2699 for full listing.

AMERICAN ITALIAN HISTORICAL ASSOCIATION, INC. [617]
P.O. Box 487
Millbrae, CA 94030
(408) 554-4142
Fax: (408) 554-4837

E-MAIL ADDRESS:
quinnroseanne@deanza.edu

WEB SITE ADDRESS:
www.aihaweb.org

FOUNDED: 1966

AREAS OF INTEREST:
Encouragement of Italian-American studies, collection, preservation, study and popularization of materials that illuminate the Italian-American experience in the U.S. and Canada.

CONSULTING OR VOLUNTEER SERVICES:
Sponsors an annual national conference, resource depositories and maintains an information network.

NAME(S) OF PROGRAMS:
● **AIHA Memorial Scholarships**

TYPE:
Scholarships.

YEAR PROGRAM STARTED: 1970

PURPOSE:
To promote understanding of the Italian experience in America.

LEGAL BASIS:
Nonprofit, tax-exempt organization.

FINANCIAL DATA:
Amount of support per award: $1,000 stipend.
Total amount of support: $1,000.

NUMBER OF AWARDS: 1.

APPLICATION INFORMATION:
Letter of inquiry requested.
Duration: One year.
Deadline: September 15 (postmark).

PUBLICATIONS:
Annual Proceedings.

OFFICERS:
Josephine Hendin, President

ADDRESS INQUIRIES TO:
Dr. Roseanne Giannini Quinn
(See address above.)

THE AMERICAN NUMISMATIC SOCIETY [618]
75 Varick Street, Floor 11
New York, NY 10013-1917
(212) 571-4470
Fax: (212) 571-4479

E-MAIL ADDRESS:
ans@numismatics.org

WEB SITE ADDRESS:
www.numismatics.org

FOUNDED: 1858

AREAS OF INTEREST:
Numismatics, history and archaeology.

NAME(S) OF PROGRAMS:
● **Frances M. Schwartz Fellowship**

TYPE:
Fellowships.

YEAR PROGRAM STARTED: 1994

PURPOSE:
To support work and the study of numismatic and museum methodology at the Society.

ELIGIBILITY:
Applicants must have a B.A. or equivalent.

FINANCIAL DATA:
Amount of support per award: The stipend will vary with the term of tenure (normally the academic year) but will not exceed $5,000.

NUMBER OF AWARDS: 1.

APPLICATION INFORMATION:
Detailed guidelines are available from the Society.
Duration: Up to one year.

ADDRESS INQUIRIES TO:
Board Secretary
(See address above.)

THE AMERICAN NUMISMATIC SOCIETY [619]
75 Varick Street, 11th Floor
New York, NY 10013
(212) 571-4470 ext. 110
Fax: (212) 571-4479

E-MAIL ADDRESS:
isaac@numismatics.org

WEB SITE ADDRESS:
www.numismatics.org

FOUNDED: 1858

AREAS OF INTEREST:
Numismatics (coins and medals), history and archaeology.

NAME(S) OF PROGRAMS:
● **The Donald Groves Fund**

TYPE:
Fellowships.

YEAR PROGRAM STARTED: 1958

PURPOSE:
To promote publication in the field of early American numismatics involving material dating no later than 1800.

LEGAL BASIS:
Nonprofit.

GEOGRAPHIC RESTRICTIONS:
United States.

FINANCIAL DATA:
Groves funding is available for travel and other expenses in association with research as well as for publication costs.
Amount of support per award: Varies.
Total amount of support: Varies.

APPLICATION INFORMATION:
Applications should be addressed to the Secretary of the Society and should include an outline of the proposed research, the method of accomplishing the research, the funding requested and the specific uses to which funding will be put. Applications are reviewed periodically by a committee, which makes its recommendations to the Society's Board of Trustees.
Duration: Varies.

OFFICERS:
Dr. Ute Wartenberg Kagan, Executive Director

ADDRESS INQUIRIES TO:
Dr. Ute Wartenberg Kagan
Executive Director
(See address above.)

BERKSHIRE CONFERENCE OF WOMEN HISTORIANS [620]
263 Windsor Place
Brooklyn, NY 11218
(718) 768-7994

E-MAIL ADDRESS:
smyohn@verizon.net

WEB SITE ADDRESS:
www.berksconference.org

FOUNDED: 1930

AREAS OF INTEREST:
Women's history.

TYPE:
Awards/prizes. One prize awarded annually for the best first book and one for the best article of historical scholarship published by a woman historian in any field of history during the preceding year.

YEAR PROGRAM STARTED: 1972

PURPOSE:
To promote historical scholarship by women.

ELIGIBILITY:
The book or article must have been published in the year preceding the award date.

FINANCIAL DATA:
Amount of support per award: $1,000 for each book prize; $500 for each article prize.
Total amount of support: $1,500.

NUMBER OF APPLICANTS MOST RECENT YEAR: 150.

APPLICATION INFORMATION:
Detailed guidelines are available from Berkshire.
Deadline: January 15. Notification in June.

ADDRESS INQUIRIES TO:
Laura Lovett, Secretary
Department of History
University of Massachusetts
161 Presidents Drive
Amherst, MA 01003

BRANDEIS UNIVERSITY [621]
Graduate Program in History
Department of History
Waltham, MA 02454-9110
(781) 736-2270
Fax: (781) 736-2273

E-MAIL ADDRESS:
historia@brandeis.edu

WEB SITE ADDRESS:
www.brandeis.edu/gsas

FOUNDED: 1968

AREAS OF INTEREST:
History.

NAME(S) OF PROGRAMS:
● **The Irving and Rose Crown Program**
● **Frank Manuel Fellowships**

TYPE:
Awards/prizes; Fellowships; Research grants. Fellowships and supplemental awards available to candidates of exceptional promise and distinction, leading to the degree of Doctor of Philosophy in history. The Program emphasizes the study of social, political and intellectual history. Heavy emphasis is placed on primary research projects. Strong encouragement is given to comparative history and interdisciplinary studies.

YEAR PROGRAM STARTED: 1968

PURPOSE:
To give financial support to those seeking a Doctorate in the philosophy of history.

LEGAL BASIS:
University.

ELIGIBILITY:
Applicant must be admitted to Brandeis Ph.D. program in History.

FINANCIAL DATA:
Fellowships include full tuition expenses. Supplemental Awards are also available to defray the costs of travel, research and job placement.
Amount of support per award:
Approximately $57,566 per year. $20,000 Fellowship and $37,566 tuition.

NUMBER OF APPLICANTS MOST RECENT YEAR: 72.

NUMBER OF AWARDS: 5 for the year 2010-11.

APPLICATION INFORMATION:
A sample of historical writing must accompany application. Forms and catalogues may be obtained from the Dean of the Graduate School of Arts and Sciences.
Duration: Fellowships are renewable for up to five years.
Deadline: January 15.

STAFF:
Judy Brown, Senior Academic Administrator
Joyce Antler
Silvia Arrom
Rudolph Binion
Brian Donahue
David Engerman
David Hackett Fischer
Gregory Freeze
Karen Hansen
Mark Hulliung
Paul Jankowski
Jane Kamensky
William Kapelle
Alice Kelikian
Antony Polonsky
Jonathan Sarna
Govind Sreenivasan

Ibrahim Sundiata
Michael Willrich

ADDRESS INQUIRIES TO:
Chairperson
Graduate Program in History
(See address above.)

JOHN CARTER BROWN LIBRARY [622]

P.O. Box 1894
Providence, RI 02912
(401) 863-2725
Fax: (401) 863-3477

E-MAIL ADDRESS:
jcbl_fellowships@brown.edu

WEB SITE ADDRESS:
www.jcbl.org

FOUNDED: 1846

AREAS OF INTEREST:
Historical studies pertaining to the Age of Exploration, Latin American history before 1830, North American history to approximately 1800, European impressions of America, New World travel, exploration and colonization. Also, Indian language, cartography, West Indies and Caribbean studies, maritime, slave trade, and the Jewish Experience in the colonial Americas, north and south.

NAME(S) OF PROGRAMS:
- **The John Carter Brown Library Research Fellowships**

TYPE:
Fellowships; Research grants.

YEAR PROGRAM STARTED: 1981

PURPOSE:
To promote scholarly research at the library.

LEGAL BASIS:
Independently funded and administered library and research center.

ELIGIBILITY:
Fellowships and grants will be awarded on the basis of the applicant's scholarly qualifications, the merits of the project, and the appropriateness of the inquiry in relation to the holdings of the John Carter Brown Library.

Short-Term Fellowships are open to U.S. and foreign nationals who are engaged in predoctoral or postdoctoral, or independent research. Graduate students must have passed their preliminary or general examinations at the time of application. A few fellowships-without-stipend will be offered each year to highly qualified applicants.

Long-Term Postdoctoral Fellowships, some of which are funded by the National Endowment for the Humanities and by the Andrew W. Mellon Foundation, are available to U.S. citizens or residents in the U.S. for three years immediately preceding the application deadline. Graduate students are not eligible for this type of fellowship.

Recipients of all Fellowships are expected to relocate to Providence and to be in continuous residence at the John Carter Brown Library for the entire term of the award. Those living within commuting distance of the Library (approximately 45 miles distant) are ordinarily not eligible for JCB Fellowships.

FINANCIAL DATA:
Amount of support per award: Short-Term Fellowships: $2,100 per month; Long-Term Fellowships: $4,200 per month.
Total amount of support: Varies.

NUMBER OF AWARDS: Approximately 40 for the year ending June 30, 2012.

APPLICATION INFORMATION:
Application form is available online.
Duration: Short-Term Fellowships: Two to four months; Long-Term Fellowships: Five to 10 months.
Deadline: December 15 (postmarked). Announcements made by April 15.

PUBLICATIONS:
Application guidelines.

STAFF:
Valerie Andrews, Coordinator

ADDRESS INQUIRIES TO:
Edward L. Widmer
Director and Librarian
(See address above.)

CANADIAN INSTITUTE OF UKRAINIAN STUDIES [623]

University of Alberta
430 Pembina Hall
Edmonton AB T6G 2H8 Canada
(780) 492-2972
Fax: (780) 492-4967

E-MAIL ADDRESS:
cius@ualberta.ca

WEB SITE ADDRESS:
www.cius.ca

AREAS OF INTEREST:
Studies in history, literature, language, education, social sciences, library sciences and women's studies.

NAME(S) OF PROGRAMS:
- **The Helen Darcovich Memorial Doctoral Fellowship**
- **Marusia and Michael Dorosh Master's Fellowship**
- **Neporany Doctoral Fellowship**
- **Research Grants**

TYPE:
Fellowships; Research grants; Scholarships.

PURPOSE:
Fellowships: To aid students to complete a thesis on a Ukrainian or Ukrainian and Canadian topic in education, history, law, humanities, social sciences, women's studies or library sciences. Research grants: To aid scholars with research-related costs.

FINANCIAL DATA:
Total amount of support: Over $100,000 for the year 2009.

NUMBER OF APPLICANTS MOST RECENT YEAR:
Over 100.

NUMBER OF AWARDS: Helen Darcovich Memorial Doctoral Fellowship: 3; Marusia and Michael Dorosh Master's Fellowship: 2; Neporany Doctoral Fellowship: 1; Research grants: 46.

APPLICATION INFORMATION:
Applicants should contact the Institute.
Deadline: March 1.

ADDRESS INQUIRIES TO:
Iryna Fedoriw, Administrator
(See address above.)

CENTURYONE FOUNDATION, INC.

235 Bellefontaine Street
Pasadena, CA 91105
(626) 441-2024
(888) 932-7123
Fax: (626) 441-2694

E-MAIL ADDRESS:
foundation@centuryone.org

WEB SITE ADDRESS:
www.centuryone.org

TYPE:
Project/program grants.

See entry 394 for full listing.

COLLEGE OF PHYSICIANS OF PHILADELPHIA [624]

Francis Clark Wood Institute
for the History of Medicine
19 South 22nd Street
Philadelphia, PA 19103-3097
(215) 399-2305
Fax: (215) 561-6477

E-MAIL ADDRESS:
sereda@collegeofphysicians.org

WEB SITE ADDRESS:
www.collegeofphysicians.org

FOUNDED: 1787

AREAS OF INTEREST:
The history of medicine.

NAME(S) OF PROGRAMS:
- **Wood Institute Travel Grants**

TYPE:
Travel grants; Visiting scholars. This program allows scholars to conduct short-term research in the College's Library and/or Mutter Museum.

YEAR PROGRAM STARTED: 1983

PURPOSE:
To encourage the study and appreciation of medicine in the broader historical and social context in response to current health care issues and public and professional interests.

LEGAL BASIS:
501(c)(3) not-for-profit educational institution.

ELIGIBILITY:
Applicants must reside more than 75 miles from Philadelphia to be eligible. Grants are available to scholars and bona fide researchers.

FINANCIAL DATA:
Amount of support per award: Up to $1,000.
Total amount of support: Up to $2,300.

NUMBER OF APPLICANTS MOST RECENT YEAR:
25.

NUMBER OF AWARDS: Varies.

APPLICATION INFORMATION:
Applicants should submit:
(1) one-page statement of the research project and the applicability of the College's resources;
(2) curriculum vitae (not to exceed three pages in length);
(3) budget estimate of travel and lodging needs and;
(4) one letter of reference (to be sent directly from the source to the College).

Electronic applications are strongly encouraged.
Duration: One to four weeks.

PUBLICATIONS:
Program announcement; guidelines.

ADDRESS INQUIRIES TO:
Sofie Sereda
Assistant to the Director
(See address above.)

COLUMBIA UNIVERSITY [625]
517 Butler Library
535 West 114th Street
New York, NY 10027
(212) 854-2247
Fax: (212) 854-4972

E-MAIL ADDRESS:
jneal@columbia.edu

WEB SITE ADDRESS:
www.columbia.
edu/cu/lweb/eguides/amerihist/bancroft.html

FOUNDED: 1754

NAME(S) OF PROGRAMS:
● **Bancroft Prizes**

TYPE:
Awards/prizes. Prizes of equal rank to be
awarded to the authors of distinguished
works in either or both American History,
including biography and diplomacy.

YEAR PROGRAM STARTED: 1948

PURPOSE:
To honor the authors of books of
distinguished merit and distinction, upon the
subject of American history in its broadest
sense.

LEGAL BASIS:
University.

ELIGIBILITY:
Awards are made for books first published in
the previous calendar year. The competition
is open to all persons whether connected with
Columbia University or not, and whether
citizens of the U.S. or any other country.

The word "American" is interpreted to
include all the Americas, North, Central and
South; however, the award is confined to
works originally written in English or of
which there is a published translation in
English. Volumes of papers, letters and
speeches of famous Americans, unless edited
by the author himself, are not eligible.
Autobiography comes within the terms of the
prize, but books reporting on recent personal
experiences of Americans, within a limited
area both in time and geography, are not
considered eligible.

Previous winners are eligible for an award in
a later year.

FINANCIAL DATA:
Amount of support per award: $10,000.
Total amount of support: $20,000 to $30,000
annually.

NUMBER OF APPLICANTS MOST RECENT YEAR:
200.

NUMBER OF AWARDS: 2 to 3.

APPLICATION INFORMATION:
Works submitted in competition may be sent
to the Bancroft Prize Committee at the
address above. It is requested that four copies
be furnished, three for jury members and one
for the Libraries of Columbia University. A
letter should accompany the books so that
acknowledgement may be made.
Deadline: Works may be submitted after
June 1 and before November 1. Page-proof
copy may be submitted after November 1

provided the work will be published after
that date and before December 31 of the year
preceding the award.

ADDRESS INQUIRIES TO:
Bancroft Prize Committee
(See address above.)

THE COORDINATING COUNCIL FOR WOMEN IN HISTORY, INC.
2210 Dorrington Street, No. 202
Houston, TX 77030

E-MAIL ADDRESS:
nupurc@earthlink.net

WEB SITE ADDRESS:
www.theccwh.org

TYPE:
Scholarships. The Catherine Prelinger Award
is given to a scholar, with a Ph.D. or A.B.D.,
whose career has not followed a traditional
academic path through secondary and higher
education and whose work has contributed to
women in the historical profession.

See entry 1142 for full listing.

THE COORDINATING COUNCIL FOR WOMEN IN HISTORY, INC. [626]
Department of History and
Women's Studies Program
Northern Illinois University
Dekalb, IL 60115
(815) 895-2624

E-MAIL ADDRESS:
sdawson1@niu.edu

WEB SITE ADDRESS:
www.theccwh.org

AREAS OF INTEREST:
Women's history.

NAME(S) OF PROGRAMS:
● **Berkshire Conference of Women Historians Graduate Student Fellowship**
● **Nupur Chaudhuri First Article Prize**
● **National History Day Prize in Women's History, Junior Division**
● **Ida B. Wells Graduate Student Fellowship**

TYPE:
Awards/prizes; Fellowships.

PURPOSE:
To support the exploration of the diverse
experiences and histories of all women; to
educate men and women on the status of
women in the historical profession; to
promote research and interpretation in areas
of women's history.

ELIGIBILITY:
Berkshire Conference of Women Historians
Graduate Student Fellowship: Applicant must
be a woman graduate student completing a
dissertation in a history department.

Nupur Chaudhuri First Article Prize is given
to a CCWH member whose first article is
published in a refereed journal.

National History Day Prize in Women's
History, Jr. Division goes to a precollegiate
student participating in the National History
Day competition.

Ida B. Wells Graduate Student Fellowship is
given to an A.B.D. woman graduate student
working on a historical dissertation, not

necessarily in a history department.
Applicants in interdisciplinary areas such as
women's studies or ethnic studies are
particularly welcome.

GEOGRAPHIC RESTRICTIONS:
United States.

FINANCIAL DATA:
Amount of support per award: Berkshire
Conference, Nupur Chaudhuri Prize and
Wells Fellowships: $1,000; National History
Day Prize: Varies.

ADDRESS INQUIRIES TO:
Sandra Trudgen Dawson, Executive Director
execdir@ccwh.org

CUSHWA CENTER FOR THE STUDY OF AMERICAN CATHOLICISM [627]
407 Geddes Hall
University of Notre Dame
Notre Dame, IN 46556
(574) 631-5441
Fax: (574) 631-8471

E-MAIL ADDRESS:
cushwa.1@nd.edu

WEB SITE ADDRESS:
www.nd.edu/~cushwa

NAME(S) OF PROGRAMS:
● **Hibernian Research Award**

TYPE:
The Hibernian Research Award is offered to
further the scholarly study of Irish America
by scholars of any academic discipline
engaged in a research project studying the
Irish experience in the U.S.

PURPOSE:
To promote the scholarly study of the Irish in
the U.S.

ELIGIBILITY:
Awards are made to scholars in any academic
discipline.

FINANCIAL DATA:
Amount of support per award: Maximum
$2,000.

APPLICATION INFORMATION:
Applicants must include the following:
(1) a current curriculum vitae;
(2) a brief 1,000-word description of the
research project;
(3) a proposed budget and;
(4) letters of recommendation from two
people familiar with the applicant's work.
These letters of recommendation should be
sent directly to the Cushwa Center.
Deadline: December 31. Applicants will be
notified in March.

DIRECTORS:
Timothy Matovina

ADDRESS INQUIRIES TO:
Timothy Matovina, Director
(See address above.)

CUSHWA CENTER FOR THE STUDY OF AMERICAN CATHOLICISM [628]
407 Geddes Hall
University of Notre Dame
Notre Dame, IN 46556
(574) 631-5441
Fax: (574) 631-8471

E-MAIL ADDRESS:
cushwa.1@nd.edu

WEB SITE ADDRESS:
www.nd.edu/~cushwa/

FOUNDED: 1980

AREAS OF INTEREST:
Catholicism in the U.S.

NAME(S) OF PROGRAMS:
● **Research Travel Grants**

TYPE:
Travel grants. Research Travel Grants support projects that require substantial use of the collection of the library and/or the archives of the University of Notre Dame and help to defray travel and lodging costs.

YEAR PROGRAM STARTED: 1980

PURPOSE:
To make it possible for scholars to make use of the Notre Dame archives.

LEGAL BASIS:
University.

ELIGIBILITY:
Grants are made to scholars in any academic discipline.

FINANCIAL DATA:
Amount of support per award: Typically, Research Travel Grants are $1,000 or less, unless extenuating circumstances necessitate greater funding. Assistance at finding affordable accommodations is available.

APPLICATION INFORMATION:
Applicant must include the following:
(1) one copy of the application form;
(2) current curriculum vitae;
(3) 1,000-word description of the project you wish to undertake at the center and;
(4) proposed budget estimating lodging and research expenses.
Duration: Varies.
Deadline: December 31. Applicants will be notified in March.

STAFF:
Timothy Matovina, Director
Kathleen Cummings, Associate Director
Paula Brach, Senior Administrative Assistant

ADDRESS INQUIRIES TO:
Timothy Matovina, Director
(See address above.)

SHELBY CULLOM DAVIS CENTER FOR HISTORICAL STUDIES [629]

Princeton University
129 Dickinson Hall
Princeton, NJ 08544-1017
(609) 258-4997
Fax: (609) 258-5326

E-MAIL ADDRESS:
jhoule@princeton.edu

WEB SITE ADDRESS:
www.princeton.edu/dav

FOUNDED: 1968

AREAS OF INTEREST:
Historical research.

TYPE:
Fellowships.

YEAR PROGRAM STARTED: 1969

LEGAL BASIS:
Center is part of a Charitable Educational Institution.

ELIGIBILITY:
Candidates must have a Ph.D. degree.

FINANCIAL DATA:
Fellowship includes salary plus research expenses.
Amount of support per award: Varies.
Total amount of support: Varies.

NUMBER OF APPLICANTS MOST RECENT YEAR:
130.

NUMBER OF AWARDS: 6 to 8 fellows per year. 8 for the year 2010-2011.

APPLICATION INFORMATION:
Contact the Center for application form and guidelines.
Duration: One semester or one academic year. Nonrenewable.
Deadline: December 1. Notification in early March.

EXECUTIVE COMMITTEE:
Daniel T. Rodgers, Director

ADDRESS INQUIRIES TO:
Jennifer Houle, Manager
(See address above.)

THE DIRKSEN CONGRESSIONAL CENTER

2815 Broadway
Pekin, IL 61554
(309) 347-7113
Fax: (309) 347-6432

E-MAIL ADDRESS:
fmackaman@dirksencenter.org

WEB SITE ADDRESS:
www.dirksencongressionalcenter.org

TYPE:
Project/program grants; Research grants; Seed money grants; Travel grants. Financial awards to individuals conducting research about the U.S. Congress and its leaders.

See entry 2121 for full listing.

FOUNDATION FOR JEWISH CULTURE [630]

330 Seventh Avenue, 21st Floor
New York, NY 10001
(212) 629-0500 ext. 212
Fax: (212) 629-0508

E-MAIL ADDRESS:
grants@jewishculture.org

WEB SITE ADDRESS:
www.jewishculture.org/goldberg

AREAS OF INTEREST:
Jewish experience.

NAME(S) OF PROGRAMS:
● **The Samuel Goldberg & Sons Foundation Prize for Jewish Fiction by Emerging Writers**

TYPE:
Awards/prizes.

PURPOSE:
To recognize the author of a new English language work of fiction reflecting the Jewish experience.

ELIGIBILITY:
Author must be a U.S. citizen or permanent resident and need not have been previously published. The author must not have published more than two book-length works. Books must be published between January 1 and December 31 of the previous calendar year. Books of fiction, including collections of short stories, on any aspect of the Jewish

experience will be considered. Poetry, anthologies, and books in translation are not eligible.

GEOGRAPHIC RESTRICTIONS:
United States.

FINANCIAL DATA:
Prize includes a one-week residency at Ledig House International Writers Colony.
Amount of support per award: $2,500.

NUMBER OF APPLICANTS MOST RECENT YEAR:
15.

NUMBER OF AWARDS: 1.

APPLICATION INFORMATION:
Applications must be submitted directly by publishers.

ADDRESS INQUIRIES TO:
Paul Zakrzewski, Program Officer, Literature and Scholarship
(See address above.)

GERMAN HISTORICAL INSTITUTE [631]

1607 New Hampshire Avenue, N.W.
Washington, DC 20009-2562
(202) 387-3355
Fax: (202) 483-3430

E-MAIL ADDRESS:
info@ghi-dc.org

WEB SITE ADDRESS:
www.ghi-dc.org

AREAS OF INTEREST:
German and U.S. history, transatlantic studies and comparative studies in economic, social, cultural and political history.

NAME(S) OF PROGRAMS:
● **Doctoral and Postdoctoral Fellowships**

TYPE:
Fellowships. The Institute awards short-term fellowships to German and American doctoral students as well as postdoctoral scholars/Habilitanden in the fields of German history, the history of German-American relations, and the role of Germany and the U.S. in international relations.

PURPOSE:
To support research programme for doctoral students and postdoctoral scholars in the fields of German history, the history of German-American relations, the role of Germany and the U.S. in international relations and the history of consumption and consumerism.

ELIGIBILITY:
Open to German and U.S. doctoral and postdoctoral students.

FINANCIAL DATA:
Amount of support per award: Monthly stipend for Europeans: EUR 1,700 for doctoral students and EUR 2,950 for postdoctoral scholars. Monthly stipend for Americans: $1,900 for doctoral students and $3,200 for postdoctoral scholars.

NUMBER OF APPLICANTS MOST RECENT YEAR:
85.

APPLICATION INFORMATION:
Applications should include cover letter, curriculum vitae, proof of academic degree (or transcripts), project description (3,000 words), research schedule for the fellowship period, and at least one letter of reference. Although applicants may write in either

English or German, it is recommended that they use the language in which they are most proficient.

Duration: One to six months, but can be extended one or more months.

Deadline: April 15 and October 15 annually.

ADDRESS INQUIRIES TO:
Prof. Dr. Uwe Spiekermann, Deputy Director
(See address above.)

HAGLEY MUSEUM AND LIBRARY   [632]
Center for the History of
Business, Technology and Society
298 Buck Road
Wilmington, DE 19807
(302) 658-2400
Fax: (302) 655-3188

E-MAIL ADDRESS:
clockman@hagley.org

WEB SITE ADDRESS:
www.hagley.org

FOUNDED: 1953

AREAS OF INTEREST:
American business, economic and labor history and the history of technology and science.

NAME(S) OF PROGRAMS:
- **The Henry Belin du Pont Dissertation Fellowship in Business, Technology, and Society**
- **Henry Belin du Pont Fellowships**
- **Hagley Exploratory Research Grant**

TYPE:
Research grants; Travel grants; Visiting scholars. Grants to support short-term research in the imprint, manuscript, pictorial and artifact collections of the Hagley Museum and Library. Holdings include rich manuscript and imprint collections relating to French history, 1760-1820, and to American economic history, 1800-1950, with special emphasis on American business, industrial and technological developments.

The Henry Belin du Pont Dissertation Fellowship in Business, Technology, and Society supports research and writing by candidates for doctoral degrees. Projects should demonstrate superior intellectual quality and make substantial use of Hagley's collections.

Henry Belin du Pont Fellowships support research in the collections of the museum and library.

Hagley Exploratory Research Grant supports a one-week visit by scholars who believe that their project will benefit from Hagley research collections, but need the opportunity to explore them on-site to determine if a Henry Belin du Pont research grant application is warranted.

YEAR PROGRAM STARTED: 1962

PURPOSE:
To encourage and support research in the collections.

LEGAL BASIS:
Nonprofit educational institution.

ELIGIBILITY:
Degree candidates and advanced scholars working in Hagley's areas of collecting and research interest are invited to apply. Applications should include research proposals specifying the collections or

materials to be studied. Residential award, not a scholarship for college or graduate school.

Hagley Exploratory Research Grant: Priority will be given to junior scholars with innovative projects that seek to expand on existing scholarships.

FINANCIAL DATA:
Amount of support per award: Hagley Exploratory Research Grant: Stipend of $400; Henry Belin du Pont Dissertation Fellowship: Up to $6,000; Henry Belin du Pont Fellowships: Average award of $800 for a two-week period.

Total amount of support: Approximately $50,000.

APPLICATION INFORMATION:
Application forms and guidelines are available online.

Duration: Hagley Exploratory Research Grant: One week; Henry Belin du Pont Dissertation Fellowship: Up to four months; Henry Belin du Pont Fellowships: Up to eight weeks.

Deadline: Hagley Exploratory Research Grant and Henry Belin du Pont Fellowships: March 31, June 30 and October 31; The Henry Belin du Pont Dissertation Fellowship in Business, Technology, and Society: November 15.

PUBLICATIONS:
Guides to Collection; application; guidelines.

STAFF:
Philip Scranton, Executive Director
Roger Horowitz, Center Associate Director
Carol Ressler Lockman, Center Coordinator

RESEARCH STAFF:
Lynn Catanese, Head Manuscripts and Archives Department
Max Moeller, Imprints Department
Jon Williams, Pictorial Collections Department

ADDRESS INQUIRIES TO:
Carol Ressler Lockman, Center Coordinator
(See address above.)

THE HISTORIC NEW ORLEANS COLLECTION   [633]
533 Royal Street
New Orleans, LA 70130-2179
(504) 523-4662
Fax: (504) 598-7108

E-MAIL ADDRESS:
wrc@hnoc.org

WEB SITE ADDRESS:
www.hnoc.org

FOUNDED: 1966

AREAS OF INTEREST:
Louisiana history and support of research in the field.

NAME(S) OF PROGRAMS:
- **Kemper and Leila Williams Prize in Louisiana History**

TYPE:
Awards/prizes.

YEAR PROGRAM STARTED: 1975

PURPOSE:
To encourage excellence in the writing and publishing of Louisiana history.

LEGAL BASIS:
Nonprofit foundation.

ELIGIBILITY:
Published books are eligible, but only in the year of their publication or completion.

FINANCIAL DATA:
Amount of support per award: $1,500.
Total amount of support: $1,500.

NUMBER OF APPLICANTS MOST RECENT YEAR:
29.

NUMBER OF AWARDS: 1.

REPRESENTATIVE AWARDS:
2009: Jennifer Spear, *Race, Sex and Social Order in Early New Orleans.*

APPLICATION INFORMATION:
Nomination forms are available on the web site. Four copies of each entry must be submitted.

Deadline: January 16. Announcement in March.

PUBLICATIONS:
Application guidelines.

OFFICERS:
Mrs. William K. Christovich, Chairperson
Fred M. Smith, President
Drew Jardine, Vice President
Hilton Bell
John Kallenborn
E. Alexandra Stafford
John E. Walker

STAFF:
Priscilla Lawrence, Executive Director

ADDRESS INQUIRIES TO:
John Lawrence, Chairman
Williams Prize Committee
(See address above.)

THE HISTORIC NEW ORLEANS COLLECTION   [634]
533 Royal Street
New Orleans, LA 70130-2179
(504) 523-4662
Fax: (504) 598-7108

E-MAIL ADDRESS:
hnocinfo@hnoc.org

WEB SITE ADDRESS:
www.hnoc.org

FOUNDED: 1966

AREAS OF INTEREST:
Louisana history and support of research in the field.

NAME(S) OF PROGRAMS:
- **The Dianne Woest Fellowship in the Arts and Humanities**

TYPE:
Fellowships.

YEAR PROGRAM STARTED: 2005

PURPOSE:
To encourage research using The Historic New Orleans Collection, as well as other research facilities in the greater New Orleans area.

ELIGIBILITY:
Open to doctoral candidates, academic and museum professionals and independent scholars. U.S. citizenship not required, but applicants should be fluent in English.

FINANCIAL DATA:
Amount of support per award: $4,000 per month stipend.

APPLICATION INFORMATION:
For more information, call Dr. Alfred Lemmon at (504) 598-7124 or Dr. Jessica Dorman at (504) 598-7174.

Duration: One to three months.

Deadline: August 1. Announcement September 15. Research to begin on or after January 1.

ADDRESS INQUIRIES TO:
Priscilla Lawrence, Executive Director
(See address above.)

*SPECIAL STIPULATIONS:
Fellows may select their period of residence, but all research must commence and conclude during the specified calendar year.

Fellows will be expected to:
(1) present a public lecture during their term of residence and;
(2) acknowledge the Collection in any published work drawing on fellowship research.

HISTORY OF SCIENCE SOCIETY [635]

440 Geddes Hall
University of Notre Dame
Notre Dame, IN 46556
(574) 631-1194
Fax: (574) 631-1533

E-MAIL ADDRESS:
info@hssonline.org

WEB SITE ADDRESS:
www.hssonline.org

FOUNDED: 1924

AREAS OF INTEREST:
History of science and its cultural influences.

NAME(S) OF PROGRAMS:
- **Derek Price/Rod Webster Prize**

TYPE:
Awards/prizes. Prize for the best scholarly article published in *Isis* during the past three years.

YEAR PROGRAM STARTED: 1979

PURPOSE:
To acknowledge the best scholarly work to appear in *Isis*.

LEGAL BASIS:
Nonprofit 501(c)(3).

ELIGIBILITY:
Applicant must have published an article in *Isis*.

FINANCIAL DATA:
Amount of support per award: $1,000.

NUMBER OF AWARDS: 1 per year.

PUBLICATIONS:
Syllabus samplers, Topical Essays for Teachers, Non-Western Science.

ADDRESS INQUIRIES TO:
Robert J. Malone, Executive Director
(See address above.)

HISTORY OF SCIENCE SOCIETY [636]

440 Geddes Hall
University of Notre Dame
Notre Dame, IN 46556
(574) 631-1194
Fax: (574) 631-1533

E-MAIL ADDRESS:
info@hssonline.org

WEB SITE ADDRESS:
www.hssonline.org

FOUNDED: 1924

AREAS OF INTEREST:
History of science, women in science and science service.

NAME(S) OF PROGRAMS:
- **Watson Davis and Helen Miles Davis Prize**
- **Joseph H. Hazen Education Prize**
- **Suzanne J. Levinson Prize**
- **Pfizer Prize**
- **Nathan Reingold Prize**
- **Margaret W. Rossiter History of Women in Science Prize**
- **Sarton Medal**

TYPE:
Awards/prizes. The Davis Prize honors books in the history of science directed to a wide public and was established through a long-term pledge from Miles and Audrey Davis.

The Joseph H. Hazen Education Prize recognizes excellence in teaching in the history of science.

The Levinson Prize is awarded in even-numbered years to an outstanding book in the life sciences and natural history.

The Pfizer Prize honors the best English-language work related to the history of science published in the preceding three years.

The Nathan Reingold Prize is given for an original essay in the history of science and its cultural influences. Essay must be no more than 8,000 words in length and thoroughly documented.

The Margaret W. Rossiter History of Women in Science Prize honors an outstanding book, or in even-numbered years an article, published in the preceding four years.

The Sarton Medal is given to an outstanding historian of science selected from the international scholarly community.

YEAR PROGRAM STARTED: 1955

PURPOSE:
To recognize and reward distinguished writing in the field of the history of science.

LEGAL BASIS:
Nonprofit.

ELIGIBILITY:
For the Davis Prize, books should be introductory in assuming no previous knowledge of the subject and be directed to audiences of beginning students and general readers. Books should introduce an entire field, a chronological period, a national tradition or the work of a noteworthy individual. Multi-authored or edited books are eligible, whereas unrevised reprints of previously published works are ineligible.

For the History of Women in Science Prize, books may take a biographical, institutional, theoretical or other approach. Include in the topic, "Women in Science," discussions of women's activities in science, analyses of past scientific practices that deal explicitly with gender and investigations regarding women as viewed by scientists. These may relate to medicine, technology and the social sciences as well as the natural sciences.

The Levinson Prize is open to all books in the life sciences and natural history published in the four years prior to the award year.

The Pfizer Prize is open to all books published in English. The quality of the work is the overriding criterion.

The Reingold Prize is open to graduate students at any American or Canadian college. Essays dealing with medical subjects are not accepted, though papers dealing with the relations between medicine and the natural sciences are welcome.

FINANCIAL DATA:
Amount of support per award: Davis, Hazen, Levinson and Rossiter History of Women in Science Awards: $1,000; Reingold Prize: $500 award, $500 in travel expenses; Pfizer Prize: $2,500.

APPLICATION INFORMATION:
Deadline: April 1.

PUBLICATIONS:
Brochure.

OFFICERS:
Paul Farber, President
Lynn K. Nyhart, Vice President
Adam Apt, Treasurer
Marsha Richmond, Secretary
Bernard Lightman, Editor

ADDRESS INQUIRIES TO:
Robert J. Malone, Executive Director
(See address above.)

*PLEASE NOTE:
Society does not give grants, scholarships or fellowships.

HERBERT HOOVER PRESIDENTIAL LIBRARY ASSOCIATION, INC.

302 Parkside Drive
West Branch, IA 52358
(319) 643-5327
Fax: (319) 643-2391

E-MAIL ADDRESS:
info@hooverassociation.org

WEB SITE ADDRESS:
www.hooverassociation.org

TYPE:
Travel grants. Money is only available for travel to the Hoover Presidential Library in West Branch, IA. The program seeks to encourage scholarly use of the holdings of the Herbert Hoover Presidential Library. It is specifically intended to promote the study of subjects of interest and concern to Herbert Hoover, Lou Henry Hoover, their associates and other public figures as reflected in the Library's 150 manuscript collections.

See entry 2125 for full listing.

IEEE [637]

IEEE History Center
Rutgers University
39 Union Street
New Brunswick, NJ 08901-8538
(732) 562-5468
Fax: (732) 932-1193

E-MAIL ADDRESS:
ieee-history@ieee.org

WEB SITE ADDRESS:
www.ieee.org/history_center

FOUNDED: 1884

AREAS OF INTEREST:
History of technology and sociology of technology.

NAME(S) OF PROGRAMS:
- **IEEE Fellowship in Electrical History**
- **Internship in Electrical History**

TYPE:
Fellowships; Internships. Fellowship in Electrical History: Award for one year of full-time doctoral or postdoctoral work in the history of electrical engineering and technology at a college or university of recognized standing.

Internship in Electrical History: Two-month internship for graduate research.

YEAR PROGRAM STARTED: 1980

ELIGIBILITY:
Fellowship in Electrical History: Individuals doing graduate or postgraduate work in the history of electrical technology. Internship in Electrical History: Scholars at the beginning of their career studying the history of electrical technology and computing.

FINANCIAL DATA:
Total amount of support: Fellowship in Electrical History: $17,000 annually; Internship in Electrical History: $3,500.

NUMBER OF APPLICANTS MOST RECENT YEAR: 12.

NUMBER OF AWARDS: Fellowship in Electrical History: 1 annually; Internship in Electrical History: 1 annually.

APPLICATION INFORMATION:
Identification and description of a research project of value is an important part of the application procedure. Further information is available upon request to the Institute.
Duration: Fellowship in Electrical History: One academic year; Internship in Electrical History: Two months.
Deadline: Fellowship in Electrical History: February 1; Internship in Electrical History: March 1.

PUBLICATIONS:
Newsletter.

ADDRESS INQUIRIES TO:
Director, IEEE History Center
(See address above.)

IRISH AMERICAN CULTURAL INSTITUTE

One Lackawanna Place
Morristown, NJ 07960
(973) 605-1991
Fax: (973) 605-8875

E-MAIL ADDRESS:
info@iaci-usa.org

WEB SITE ADDRESS:
www.iaci-usa.org

TYPE:
Awards/prizes; Exchange programs; Fellowships; Research grants. Grants and awards available for authors of books written in Irish, for Irish artists and composers, for graduate research in Irish-American studies and for lecturers dealing with subjects of Irish interest.

See entry 715 for full listing.

ISTITUTO ITALIANO PER GLI STUDI STORICI   [638]

Via Benedetto Croce, 12
80134 Naples Italy
0039-81-5517159
0039-81-5512390
Fax: 0039-81-5514813

E-MAIL ADDRESS:
istituto@iiss.it

WEB SITE ADDRESS:
www.iiss.it

FOUNDED: 1947

AREAS OF INTEREST:
Postgraduate institute for the study of history and philosophy.

NAME(S) OF PROGRAMS:
● **Federico Chabod Scholarship**
● **Adolfo Omodeo Scholarship**

TYPE:
Awards/prizes; Conferences/seminars; Research grants; Scholarships. Awards for historical and philosophical studies at the Istituto Italiano per gli Studi Storici in Naples.

YEAR PROGRAM STARTED: 1987

PURPOSE:
To promote historical studies.

LEGAL BASIS:
Private foundation.

ELIGIBILITY:
Open to non-Italian students who have completed a B.A. degree in Humanities (history, philosophy and arts). Citizenship is unrestricted.

FINANCIAL DATA:
Amount of support per award: Each scholarship is valued at 11,500 EUR per year, including travel, paid in eight monthly installments beginning in November.

NUMBER OF AWARDS: 2.

APPLICATION INFORMATION:
Application must include birth certificate, proof of citizenship, university diploma, scholarly work, curriculum of studies with indication of language skills, program of research proposed, and letter of reference.
Duration: Eight months, from November to June.
Deadline: September 30.

PUBLICATIONS:
Annali Dell' Istituto Italiano Per Gli Studi Storici; series of monographs; series of historical, philosophical and literary texts.

DIRECTORS:
Prof. Natalino Irti, President
Prof. Gennaro Sasso, Director
Dr. Marta Herling, Secretary
Dr. Elli Catello, Librarian
Dr. Stefano Palmieri, Editor of Publications

ADDRESS INQUIRIES TO:
Dr. Marta Herling, General Secretary
(See address above.)

THE LYNDON BAINES JOHNSON FOUNDATION

2313 Red River Street
Austin, TX 78705-5702
(512) 232-2266
Fax: (512) 232-2285

E-MAIL ADDRESS:
johnson.grants@nara.gov

WEB SITE ADDRESS:
www.lbjlib.utexas.edu
www.lbjfoundation.org

TYPE:
Grants-in-aid.

See entry 2129 for full listing.

LIBRARY COMPANY OF PHILADELPHIA   [639]

1314 Locust Street
Philadelphia, PA 19107
(215) 546-3181
Fax: (215) 546-5167

E-MAIL ADDRESS:
jgreen@librarycompany.org

WEB SITE ADDRESS:
www.librarycompany.org

FOUNDED: 1731

AREAS OF INTEREST:
American studies.

NAME(S) OF PROGRAMS:
● **Albert M. Greenfield Foundation Dissertation Fellowships**
● **NEH Postdoctoral Fellowships**
● **Program in African-American History**
● **Program in Early American Economy and Society**
● **Research Fellowships in American History and Culture**

TYPE:
Fellowships. Albert M. Greenfield Foundation Dissertation Fellowship: Supports dissertation research in residence at the Library Company on any subject relevant to its collections.

Program in African-American History: Literary history or the history of the book in America.

Program in Early American Economy and Society: Pre-1860 American economic and business history.

Research Fellowships in American History and Culture: 18th and 19th Century American social and cultural history.

YEAR PROGRAM STARTED: 1988

PURPOSE:
To promote early American historic studies.

ELIGIBILITY:
Both the short-term and long-term Fellowships support both postdoctoral and dissertation research. Both also require that the project proposal demonstrate that the Library Company has a primary source central to the research topic. NEH fellows must be U.S. citizens or residents at least three years.

FINANCIAL DATA:
Amount of support per award: Long-term: $20,000 to $40,000; Short-term: $2,000.
Total amount of support: Approximately $170,000 annually.

NUMBER OF APPLICANTS MOST RECENT YEAR: 200.

NUMBER OF AWARDS: Long-term: 8; Short-term: 30.

APPLICATION INFORMATION:
For the short-term fellowships, applicants must complete the required electronic cover sheet and submit one portable document format (PDF) containing a resume and a two-to four-page description of the proposed research. One letter of recommendation should arrive under separate cover in PDF format as well. E-mail materials to fellowships@librarycompany.org.
Duration: Short-term: One month; Long-term: One semester.
Deadline: Program and Research Fellowships: March 1; Long-term Postdoctoral Fellowships: November 1.

ADDRESS INQUIRIES TO:
Jim Green, Fellowship Office
(See address above.)

JAMES MADISON MEMORIAL FELLOWSHIP FOUNDATION [640]

2000 K Street, N.W.
Suite 303
Washington, DC 20006
(800) 525-6928
Fax: (319) 337-1204

E-MAIL ADDRESS:
madison@act.org

WEB SITE ADDRESS:
www.jamesmadison.gov

FOUNDED: 1986

AREAS OF INTEREST:
The roots, principles, framing and development of the U.S. Constitution.

NAME(S) OF PROGRAMS:
- **James Madison Fellowships**

TYPE:
Fellowships. The Foundation awards fellowships to college seniors and college graduates without teaching experience (Junior Fellows) and to experienced secondary school teachers in grades seven-12 (Senior Fellows) who will normally enroll respectively in full-time and part-time graduate study leading to one of the following Master's degrees: Master's degree in American history or political science, a degree of Master of Arts in Teaching in history or political science, or a related Master's degree in education that permits a concentration in American history, American government or social studies.

YEAR PROGRAM STARTED: 1992

PURPOSE:
To support the graduate study of the roots, principles, framing and development of the U.S. Constitution.

LEGAL BASIS:
Foundation.

ELIGIBILITY:
Each fellowship recipient must take at least 12 semester hours or their equivalent in topics directly related to the framing and history of the U.S. Constitution.

A James Madison Fellow must be a U.S. citizen or U.S. national, qualify for study toward one of the qualifying Master's degrees indicated and agree to teach full-time in a secondary school for no less than one year for each full academic year of study under a fellowship.

A Senior Fellow must be a full-time teacher of American history, American government, or social studies in grades 7 through 12 during the previous year and be under contract or prospective contract to teach full-time as a secondary school teacher of the same subjects for the upcoming academic year.

A Junior Fellow must possess a Bachelor's degree or plan to receive a Bachelor's degree no later than August 31.

GEOGRAPHIC RESTRICTIONS:
United States and its territories.

FINANCIAL DATA:
Amount of support per award: Up to $24,000 for each award.

NUMBER OF APPLICANTS MOST RECENT YEAR:
400.

NUMBER OF AWARDS: 61.

APPLICATION INFORMATION:
Applicant must register online to complete the application process.
Duration: Up to five years for Senior Fellows. Up to two years for Junior Fellows.
Deadline: March 1, annually.

ADDRESS INQUIRIES TO:
James Madison Fellowship Program
2201 North Dodge Street
Iowa City, IA 52243

*SPECIAL STIPULATIONS:
No funding for Ph.D. programs.

JACOB RADER MARCUS CENTER OF THE AMERICAN JEWISH ARCHIVES

3101 Clifton Avenue
Cincinnati, OH 45220-2488
(513) 221-1875
Fax: (513) 221-7812

E-MAIL ADDRESS:
kproffitt@huc.edu

WEB SITE ADDRESS:
www.americanjewisharchives.org

TYPE:
Awards/prizes; Fellowships; Research grants. The Marcus Center's Fellowship Program provides recipients with month-long fellowships for research and writing at The Jacob Rader Marcus Center of the American Jewish Archives. Fellowship stipends will be sufficient to cover transportation and living expenses while in residence. Applicants must be conducting serious research in some area relating to the history of North American Jewry.

See entry 862 for full listing.

THE MASSACHUSETTS HISTORICAL SOCIETY [641]

1154 Boylston Street
Boston, MA 02215
(617) 646-0512
Fax: (617) 859-0074

E-MAIL ADDRESS:
cwright@masshist.org

WEB SITE ADDRESS:
www.masshist.org

FOUNDED: 1791

AREAS OF INTEREST:
Civil War history, Massachusetts, New England, and U.S. history.

NAME(S) OF PROGRAMS:
- **Suzanne and Caleb Loring Research Fellowship**

TYPE:
Fellowships. Fellowship funds research on the Civil War, its origins, and consequences, for projects that use the resources at the Massachusetts Historical Society and the Boston Athenaeum. Research must be conducted for at least four weeks at each of the two participating institutions.

YEAR PROGRAM STARTED: 2008

PURPOSE:
To encourage projects that draw on the Civil War resources of the participating organizations.

ELIGIBILITY:
Open to independent scholars, advanced graduate students and holders of a Ph.D. or equivalent.

FINANCIAL DATA:
Amount of support per award: $4,000.

NUMBER OF APPLICANTS MOST RECENT YEAR:
11.

NUMBER OF AWARDS: 1.

APPLICATION INFORMATION:
Applicants must submit the following materials:
(1) cover letter;
(2) current curriculum vitae;
(3) project proposal, approximately 1,000 words in length, which includes a description of the project, a statement explaining the historiographical significance of the project, and an indication of the specific Massachusetts Historical Society and Boston Athenaeum collections the applicant wishes to consult and;
(4) letter of recommendation from a faculty member familiar with the student's work and with the project being proposed (graduate students only).
Duration: Minimum of 20 days at each of the two institutions, for a total of 40 days.
Deadline: February 15.

ADDRESS INQUIRIES TO:
Katheryn P. Viens, Research Coordinator
(See address above.)

THE MASSACHUSETTS HISTORICAL SOCIETY [642]

1154 Boylston Street
Boston, MA 02215
(617) 646-0512
Fax: (617) 859-0074

E-MAIL ADDRESS:
cwright@masshist.org

WEB SITE ADDRESS:
www.masshist.org

FOUNDED: 1791

AREAS OF INTEREST:
Massachusetts, New England and U.S. history.

NAME(S) OF PROGRAMS:
- **Short-Term Research Fellowship**

TYPE:
Fellowships; Research grants. Research fellowship to use the Society's collection to complete a major project.

YEAR PROGRAM STARTED: 1983

PURPOSE:
To support at least 20 days of research at the Society for a specific project.

ELIGIBILITY:
Must be U.S. citizens or foreign nationals holding appropriate U.S. government status. Open to independent scholars, advanced graduate students, and holders of a Ph.D. or equivalent.

FINANCIAL DATA:
Amount of support per award: Stipend of $1,500 to $2,000.

NUMBER OF APPLICANTS MOST RECENT YEAR:
143.

NUMBER OF AWARDS: 20.

APPLICATION INFORMATION:
Applicants must submit the following materials:
(1) cover letter;
(2) current curriculum vitae;
(3) project proposal, approximately 1,000 words in length, which includes a description of the project, a statement explaining the historiographical significance of the project, and an indication of the specific MHS collections the applicant wishes to consult and;
(4) letter of recommendation from a faculty member familiar with the student's work and with the project being proposed (graduate students only).

Duration: Minimum of 20 days.

Deadline: March 1.

ADDRESS INQUIRIES TO:
Katheryn P. Viens, Research Coordinator
(See address above.)

THE MASSACHUSETTS HISTORICAL SOCIETY   [643]

1154 Boylston Street
Boston, MA 02215
(617) 646-0512
Fax: (617) 859-0074

E-MAIL ADDRESS:
cwright@masshist.org

WEB SITE ADDRESS:
www.masshist.org

FOUNDED: 1791

AREAS OF INTEREST:
Massachusetts, New England and U.S. history.

NAME(S) OF PROGRAMS:
• Long-Term Research Fellowship

TYPE:
Fellowships. Research fellowship to use the Society's collection to complete a major project.

YEAR PROGRAM STARTED: 1983

PURPOSE:
To support six to 12 months of research at the Society for a specific project.

ELIGIBILITY:
Applicants must be U.S. citizens or foreign nationals who have lived in the U.S. for at least three years prior to the application deadline. Applicants must have completed their professional training. Fellowship is not available to graduate students. Awards committee will pay special attention both to the quality of proposed projects and to their relationship to the Society's collections. Preference will be given to candidates who have not held a long-term grant during the preceding three years.

FINANCIAL DATA:
Amount of support per award: Up to $50,400 stipend with up to $500 per month housing allowance. Up to $750 for professional expenses.

NUMBER OF APPLICANTS MOST RECENT YEAR:
40.

NUMBER OF AWARDS: 2 ten-month or 4 four- to five-month.

APPLICATION INFORMATION:
Applicants must submit the following materials:
(1) cover letter;
(2) current curriculum vitae;

(3) project proposal, approximately 1,000 words in length, which includes a description of the project, a statement explaining the historiographical significance of the project, and an indication of the specific MHS collections the applicant wishes to consult;
(4) Certification for Participants form and;
(5) two letters of recommendation.

Duration: Four to 12 months of continuous tenure.

Deadline: January 15.

ADDRESS INQUIRIES TO:
Katheryn P. Viens, Research Coordinator
(See address above.)

THE MASSACHUSETTS HISTORICAL SOCIETY   [644]

1154 Boylston Street
Boston, MA 02215
(617) 646-0512
Fax: (617) 859-0074

E-MAIL ADDRESS:
cwright@masshist.org

WEB SITE ADDRESS:
www.masshist.org

FOUNDED: 1791

AREAS OF INTEREST:
Massachusetts, New England and U.S. history.

NAME(S) OF PROGRAMS:
• New England Regional Fellowship Consortium

TYPE:
Fellowships. Research fellowship to use the resources at a minimum of three different participating institutions.

YEAR PROGRAM STARTED: 1999

PURPOSE:
To encourage projects that draw on the resources of the participating organizations.

ELIGIBILITY:
Open to individuals with a serious need to use the collections and facilities of the participating organizations.

Fellows must work at each of at least three chosen organizations for at least two weeks.

FINANCIAL DATA:
Amount of support per award: Stipend of $5,000 for eight weeks of research at participating institutions.

NUMBER OF APPLICANTS MOST RECENT YEAR:
67.

NUMBER OF AWARDS: 11.

APPLICATION INFORMATION:
Guidelines and fellowship applications are available at www.nerfc.org.

Duration: Minimum of eight weeks.

Deadline: February 1.

ADDRESS INQUIRIES TO:
Katheryn P. Viens, Research Coordinator
(See address above.)

THE MEDIEVAL ACADEMY OF AMERICA   [645]

104 Mount Auburn Street
5th Floor
Cambridge, MA 02138-5019
(617) 491-1622
Fax: (617) 492-3303

E-MAIL ADDRESS:
speculum@medievalacademy.org

WEB SITE ADDRESS:
www.medievalacademy.org

FOUNDED: 1925

AREAS OF INTEREST:
Any aspect of medieval studies, 500 to 1500 A.D.

NAME(S) OF PROGRAMS:
• **Birgit Baldwin Fellowship**
• **John Nicholas Brown Prize**
• **Van Courtlandt Elliott Prize**
• **Haskins Medal**
• **Schallek Fellowship**

TYPE:
Awards/prizes; Fellowships. Cash prizes for publications of material on medieval topics.

Birgit Baldwin Fellowship supports a graduate student studying in a North American university researching and writing a significant dissertation for a Ph.D. on any subject in French medieval history. Research must be in archives and libraries of France.

The Brown Prize is awarded annually to a first book or monograph on a medieval topic.

The Elliott Prize is awarded annually for a first published article in the medieval field, judged by the selection committee to be of outstanding quality.

The Haskins Medal is awarded to the author of a book of outstanding quality and contribution to the field of medieval studies. This prize usually goes to a senior scholar.

Schallek Fellowship supports Ph.D. dissertation research in any relevant discipline dealing with late-Medieval Britain (circa. 1350-1500).

YEAR PROGRAM STARTED: 1940

PURPOSE:
To promote publication on medieval topics.

LEGAL BASIS:
Nonprofit corporation.

GEOGRAPHIC RESTRICTIONS:
North America.

FINANCIAL DATA:
Amount of support per award: Birgit Baldwin Fellowship: $20,000; Brown Prize: $1,000; Elliott Prize: $500; Schallek Fellowship: $30,000.

NUMBER OF APPLICANTS MOST RECENT YEAR:
30.

NUMBER OF AWARDS: 1 each annually.

APPLICATION INFORMATION:
For Brown Prize, candidates must submit three offprints of an article or book and a letter stating that the submission is the author's first published article or book respectively on a medieval topic. The Brown Prize also requires submission of any reviews that have appeared. For the Elliott Prize, candidates must submit a first published article on a medieval topic, bearing a publication date of two years before the prize. Articles must be at least five pages in length and the author's primary residence must be in North America. For the Haskins Medal, submit three copies of the book accompanied by copies of any major reviews that have appeared.

Duration: Fellowships: One year. Baldwin Fellowship is renewable for a second year.

Deadline: November 15. Announcement in April.

EXECUTIVE DIRECTOR:
Paul E. Szarmach

ADDRESS INQUIRIES TO:
Paul E. Szarmach, Executive Director
(See address above.)

MOUNT VERNON HOTEL MUSEUM & GARDEN [646]
421 East 61st Street
New York, NY 10065
(212) 838-6878
Fax: (212) 838-7390

E-MAIL ADDRESS:
m.caton@mvhm.org

WEB SITE ADDRESS:
www.mvhm.org

AREAS OF INTEREST:
American social history, material culture, historic preservation and museum education.

NAME(S) OF PROGRAMS:
● **William Randolph Hearst Foundation Fellowship**

TYPE:
Fellowships. Provides fellowships to graduate or undergraduate students who are interested in American social history, material culture, historic preservation and museum education.

YEAR PROGRAM STARTED: 1984

PURPOSE:
To promote the study of American history.

ELIGIBILITY:
Applicants must currently be enrolled in a college, university or graduate program.

FINANCIAL DATA:
Amount of support per award: $2,750.
Total amount of support: $5,500.

NUMBER OF AWARDS: 2.

APPLICATION INFORMATION:
Students must submit the completed application form, an essay explaining the applicant's interest in the fellowship, and two letters of recommendation.
Duration: Nine weeks in June and July.
Deadline: Second Friday in March.

ADDRESS INQUIRIES TO:
Deborah O'Neill, Director of Education
(See address above.)

NANTUCKET HISTORICAL ASSOCIATION [647]
P.O. Box 1016
Nantucket, MA 02554-1016
(508) 228-1655
Fax: (508) 325-7968

E-MAIL ADDRESS:
library@nha.org

WEB SITE ADDRESS:
www.nha.org/library/verney.html

AREAS OF INTEREST:
History.

NAME(S) OF PROGRAMS:
● **E. Geoffrey and Elizabeth Thayer Verney Fellowship**

TYPE:
Fellowships; Residencies. To pursue historical research pertaining to Nantucket, MA. This is a residency.

The Verney Fellowship encourages research in the collections of the Nantucket Historical Association Research Library. The Association is the principal repository of Nantucket history, with extensive archives, collections of historic properties, and art and artifacts that broadly illustrate Nantucket's past.

YEAR PROGRAM STARTED: 1999

PURPOSE:
To enhance the public's knowledge and understanding of the heritage of Nantucket, MA.

ELIGIBILITY:
Open to graduate students, independent scholars and academics in any field to conduct research in the collections of the Association.

FINANCIAL DATA:
Amount of support per award: $300 per week stipend; housing will be provided. Travel is reimbursed up to $600.

NUMBER OF AWARDS: 1.

REPRESENTATIVE AWARDS:
Verney Fellows: (2010) Elizabeth Watts Pope, "Life of Phebe Folger Coleman;" (2009) David Milne, "Curatorial & Interpretive Study of NHA Properties;" (2008) Bette S. Weidman, "'Sconset-born Charles Frederick Briggs: Early New York Novelist and Editor."

APPLICATION INFORMATION:
Applicants must send a full description of the proposed project, a curriculum vitae, the names of three references, and an estimate of anticipated time and duration of stay. Send application packet to: Ben Simons, Curator and Editor of *Historic Nantucket*, Nantucket Historical Association, at the address above.
Duration: Up to three weeks.
Deadline: January 1.

ADDRESS INQUIRIES TO:
Ben Simons, Curator
(See address above.)

*PLEASE NOTE:
The Verney Fellow resides in the Thomas Macy House, a historic property owned by the Association, for up to a three-week period.

*SPECIAL STIPULATIONS:
NHA Visiting Research Scholars are expected to produce an article suitable for publication in the summer edition of *Historic Nantucket*, the NHA's quarterly journal, and to deliver a public lecture on the subject of their research, as well as a presentation to NHA staff. Projects resulting in the publication of a book, article, conference paper, or other media, are looked upon favorably.

NATIONAL HISTORICAL PUBLICATIONS AND RECORDS COMMISSION [648]
National Archives Building, Room 106
700 Pennsylvania Avenue, N.W.
Washington, DC 20408
(202) 357-5010
Fax: (202) 357-5914

E-MAIL ADDRESS:
nhprc@nara.gov

WEB SITE ADDRESS:
www.archives.gov/nhprc

FOUNDED: 1934

AREAS OF INTEREST:
Archives and historical manuscripts relating to American history.

TYPE:
Project/program grants; Research grants; Technical assistance; Training grants. Grants to support the collection, preservation, digitization, arrangement, description, editing and publishing of documentary source material relating to the history of the U.S., the papers of American leaders and documents treating major subjects and events in American history.

YEAR PROGRAM STARTED: 1964

PURPOSE:
To promote the preservation and use of historical records important for an understanding and appreciation of the history of the U.S.

LEGAL BASIS:
44 U.S.C. 2501-2506.

ELIGIBILITY:
Tribal, state and local government agencies, nonprofit organizations and institutions.

GEOGRAPHIC RESTRICTIONS:
United States and its territories.

FINANCIAL DATA:
Amount of support per award: Average $70,000.
Total amount of support: $7,000,000 for fiscal year 2011.
Matching fund requirements: Generally, 1:1.

NUMBER OF APPLICANTS MOST RECENT YEAR:
250 for fiscal year 2011.

NUMBER OF AWARDS: 111 for fiscal year 2011.

REPRESENTATIVE AWARDS:
$220,000 to the University of Wisconsin-Madison, Madison, WI, for the Documentary History of the Ratification of the Constitution; $95,000 to the Tennessee State Library and Archives, to support a program of regrants to local archives and statewide activities.

APPLICATION INFORMATION:
All applications must be submitted through grants.gov.
Duration: Up to three years, depending on the individual project.
Deadline: Varies by program.

PUBLICATIONS:
Newsletter and special reports.

NATIONAL SOCIETY DAUGHTERS OF THE AMERICAN REVOLUTION [649]
1776 D Street, N.W.
Washington, DC 20006-5303
(202) 879-3292

WEB SITE ADDRESS:
www.dar.org

FOUNDED: 1895

AREAS OF INTEREST:
American history.

NAME(S) OF PROGRAMS:
● **Dr. Aura-Lee A. and James Hobbs Pittenger American History Scholarship**

TYPE:
Scholarships. The American History Scholarship is awarded to graduating high school students in the upper one-fifth of the class or home schooled who will have a

concentrated study of a minimum of 24 credit hours in American History and American Government.

PURPOSE:
To provide ways and means to help students to attain higher education; to perpetuate the memory and spirit of men and women who achieved American independence by acquisition and protection of historical spots and erection of monuments; to carry out injunction of Washington in his farewell address to American people; to maintain institutions of American Freedom; to aid liberty.

LEGAL BASIS:
Incorporated historical society.

ELIGIBILITY:
Scholarships are awarded without regard to race, religion, sex or national origin. All four-year, or more, scholarships must be for consecutive years and are renewable only upon review and approval of annual transcript. Candidates must be U.S. citizens and must attend an accredited college or university in the U.S. No affiliation or relationship to DAR is required for qualification, but candidate must be sponsored by a local DAR Chapter. Awards are judged on the basis of academic excellence, commitment to field of study, as required, and financial need.

GEOGRAPHIC RESTRICTIONS:
United States.

FINANCIAL DATA:
Amount of support per award: $2,000 per year for maximum of $8,000.
Total amount of support: Varies.

NUMBER OF AWARDS: Varies.

APPLICATION INFORMATION:
To obtain a copy of the scholarship application packet, send a self-addressed, stamped #10 business-size envelope to the Office of the Reporter General, DAR Scholarship Committee at the address listed above.

Included with the application packet is the list of DAR State Scholarship Chairmen. All scholarship applicants are required to have a letter of sponsorship from a chapter. Individuals interested in obtaining a letter of sponsorship from a local chapter are encouraged to contact the DAR State Chairman.

Duration: One academic year. Renewable for up to four years upon annual transcript review and approval.
Deadline: February 15.

PUBLICATIONS:
American Spirit, magazine.

ADDRESS INQUIRIES TO:
Office of the Reporter General
DAR Scholarship Committee
(See address above.)

NATIONAL TRUST FOR HISTORIC PRESERVATION [650]

1785 Massachusetts Avenue, N.W.
Washington, DC 20036
(202) 588-6315
Fax: (202) 588-6223

E-MAIL ADDRESS:
grants@nthp.org

WEB SITE ADDRESS:
www.preservationnation.org

FOUNDED: 1949

AREAS OF INTEREST:
A private nonprofit organization chartered by Congress with the responsibility to encourage public participation in the preservation of sites, buildings and objects significant in American history and culture.

NAME(S) OF PROGRAMS:
● **National Trust Preservation Funds (NTPF)**

TYPE:
Challenge/matching grants; Conferences/seminars; Project/program grants; Seed money grants; Technical assistance; Training grants. Education program curricula. Project grants to support consultants with professional expertise in areas such as architecture, law, planning, economics, archeology and graphic design. Conferences that address subjects of particular importance to historic preservation also are funded. In addition, grants are made for curriculum development in preservation education directed at select audiences.

YEAR PROGRAM STARTED: 1979

PURPOSE:
To increase the flow of information and ideas in the field of preservation by helping stimulate public discussion, enabling local groups to gain the technical expertise needed for particular projects, introducing students to preservation concepts and crafts and encouraging participation by the private sector in preservation.

LEGAL BASIS:
Nonprofit corporation.

ELIGIBILITY:
Applicants must be nonprofit incorporated organizations or public agencies. Applicants are eligible for no more than three NTPF grants in any two-year period.

Activities eligible for National Trust Preservation Funds grants include hiring consultants to undertake preservation planning or design projects, obtaining professional advice to strengthen management capabilities, sponsoring preservation conferences, designing and implementing innovative preservation education programs targeted to a specific audience and undertaking other planning activities that will lead to implementation of a specific preservation project.

Grants can be used for professional consultant services, preservation education programs and conferences and rehabilitation feasibility studies. Projects, programs and conferences are not funded retroactively.

Bricks-and-mortar construction projects and the funding of ongoing staff positions are not eligible activities. In addition, historic resource surveys to create inventories or to list resources on local, state or national registers are generally not eligible for funding.

GEOGRAPHIC RESTRICTIONS:
United States and its territories.

FINANCIAL DATA:
Amount of support per award: $500 to $5,000; Average: $1,000 to $2,000.
Total amount of support: $1,498,202 for fiscal year 2010.
Matching fund requirements: Each grantee must match the funds on at least a dollar-for-dollar basis using cash contributions.

NUMBER OF APPLICANTS MOST RECENT YEAR:
464 for fiscal year 2008.

NUMBER OF AWARDS: 299 for fiscal year 2008.

APPLICATION INFORMATION:
Applications must be completed and postmarked on or before the appropriate deadline. Applicants are encouraged to contact their regional office well in advance of the deadline for assistance in preparing their proposals. Incomplete applications will not be considered. All application materials become the property of the National Trust and will not be returned.
Duration: Usually a one-time award.
Deadline: Applicants should contact the National Trust Regional Office serving their state to obtain information regarding application deadlines.

PUBLICATIONS:
Annual report; grant applications and brochures.

STAFF:
Leah Suhrstedt, Grants Coordinator

ADDRESS INQUIRIES TO:
Leah Suhrstedt, Grants Coordinator
National Trust Preservation Funds
(See address above.)

NEW JERSEY HISTORIC TRUST [651]

101 South Broad Street
Trenton, NJ 08608-2401
(609) 984-0473
Fax: (609) 984-7590

E-MAIL ADDRESS:
njht@dca.state.nj.us

WEB SITE ADDRESS:
www.njht.org

FOUNDED: 1967

AREAS OF INTEREST:
Historic preservation.

NAME(S) OF PROGRAMS:
● **Garden State Historic Preservation Trust Fund (GSHPTF)**

TYPE:
Capital grants; Challenge/matching grants. Planning grants. Provides funding for the preservation of historic properties.

Under the GSHPTF, capital preservation grants are awarded at two levels: the first, level I grants, from $5,000 to $150,000; the second, level II grants, are for larger "bricks and mortar" projects and from $150,001 to $750,000. In addition, matching historic site management grants from $5,000 to $50,000.

Activities eligible for Capital Preservation grants include preservation, rehabilitation, restoration, and limited reconstruction and new construction. Activities eligible for Historic Site Management grants include those intended to aid historic property owners and managers to gain a better understanding of preservation needs for a particular site or structure, to enhance long-term planning for the operations and programs of historic sites, and to broaden public awareness and enjoyment of historic sites.

YEAR PROGRAM STARTED: 1989

PURPOSE:
To advance the preservation of the state's historic properties through financial, educational and stewardship programs.

LEGAL BASIS:
Government agency, established by the New Jersey Legislature. Statutory Citation, N.J.S.A. 13:1B-15.111 and NJSCA 13:8C-1 et seg.

ELIGIBILITY:
Applicants must be state, county or municipal governments or nonprofit organizations who either own or operate property that is listed or eligible for listing in the New Jersey or National Register of Historic Places. Proof of ownership or possession and significant control over property through a valid lease must be provided for capital grants.

GEOGRAPHIC RESTRICTIONS:
New Jersey.

FINANCIAL DATA:
Amount of support per award: Level I Grants: $5,000 to $150,000; Level II Grants: $150,001 to $750,000; Matching Grants: $5,000 to $50,000.

Total amount of support: Since 1990, $125,100,000 awarded to 635 projects.

Matching fund requirements: Under the GSHPTF, applicants must provide matching funds. Awards may be made to a maximum of $750,000 and are paid on a reimbursement basis.

COOPERATIVE FUNDING PROGRAMS: Program is funded through a state sales tax set aside.

NUMBER OF APPLICANTS MOST RECENT YEAR:
163 for the year 2008.

NUMBER OF AWARDS: 60 for the year 2008.

REPRESENTATIVE AWARDS:
$50,000 to Wayne Township, Passaic County, to fund roof restoration study and construction documents of multigenerational home dating to 1695; $529,035 to Cranbury Township, Middlesex County, to fund restoration and adoptive use of school for municipal offices and community space; $574,378 to Monmouth County Parks Commission for rehabilitation of early 18th century house for Bayshore Park Visitors' Center.

APPLICATION INFORMATION:
Applicants must submit a Declaration of Intent to Apply prior to submitting an application for funding, thus allowing grant applicants to receive technical assistance from the Trust's preservation specialists prior to the application deadline.
Duration: Varies.

PUBLICATIONS:
Annual report; program announcement; *Economic Impact of Historic Preservation in New Jersey* (1997), funding resources for history.

STAFF:
Dorothy Guzzo, Executive Director

NEW JERSEY HISTORIC TRUST   [652]
101 South Broad Street
Trenton, NJ 08608-2401
(609) 984-0473
Fax: (609) 984-7590

E-MAIL ADDRESS:
njht@dca.state.nj.us

WEB SITE ADDRESS:
www.njht.org

FOUNDED: 1967

AREAS OF INTEREST:
Capital preservation of historic properties.

NAME(S) OF PROGRAMS:
● **Emergency Loans**

TYPE:
Capital grants; Matching gifts; Project/program grants. Loans. Activities which qualify for funding include emergency repair or stabilization, planning or research necessary to preserve an endangered property, limited rehabilitation, restoration or improvement, acquisition of a historic property or the purchase of an option to acquire a historic property.

PURPOSE:
To provide emergency funding for capital preservation projects of historic properties.

LEGAL BASIS:
Government-approved program. Statutory Citation: P.L. 1967, c. 124.

ELIGIBILITY:
Applicants must be nonprofit, tax-exempt organizations or agencies of county or municipal governments. All properties must be listed or eligible for listing in the State and National Registers of Historic Places. For all requests other than acquisition, applicants must demonstrate control of the property through a deed or a valid lease.

GEOGRAPHIC RESTRICTIONS:
New Jersey.

FINANCIAL DATA:
Awards may take the form of matching grants and/or short-term low-interest loans.
Amount of support per award: $1,000 to $10,000.

Total amount of support: Approximately $15,000.

Matching fund requirements: All grants must be matched on a dollar-for-dollar basis. Matching funds for loans are encouraged but not required.

REPRESENTATIVE AWARDS:
$10,000 to Newark Museum for stabilization of skylight in historic Polhemus House.

APPLICATION INFORMATION:
A nonrefundable application fee of $25 must be submitted with each application. Applicants must consult with Trust staff before making application for these funds.
Duration: Varies.

Deadline: Notification two months after submission of complete application.

PUBLICATIONS:
Program announcement.

IRS IDENTIFICATION NUMBER: 21-6000928

ADDRESS INQUIRIES TO:
Carl Nittinger, Fiscal Officer
(See address above.)

*PLEASE NOTE:
Loan program is temporarily suspended while new sources of support are pursued.

NEW JERSEY HISTORICAL COMMISSION   [653]
New Jersey Department of State
225 West State Street, Fourth Floor
Trenton, NJ 08625-0305
(609) 292-6062
Fax: (609) 633-8168

E-MAIL ADDRESS:
sara.cureton@sos.state.nj.us

WEB SITE ADDRESS:
www.newjerseyhistory.org

FOUNDED: 1969

AREAS OF INTEREST:
New Jersey history.

NAME(S) OF PROGRAMS:
● **General Operating Support Grants**

TYPE:
General operating grants. Provide general assistance to historical organizations, museums, historic sites, archives, libraries and similar organizations with collections or programming relating to the history of New Jersey.

YEAR PROGRAM STARTED: 2000

PURPOSE:
To provide operating support for New Jersey history organizations.

LEGAL BASIS:
Agency within the Department of State, State of New Jersey.

ELIGIBILITY:
To be eligible to apply for a General Operating Support Grant, an organization must:
(1) be a not-for-profit corporation or government (municipal or county) agency, commission or other organization;
(2) be based in New Jersey;
(3) be governed by a board responsible for the programs and policies of the organization;
(4) have a clearly stated mission of service to the promotion, preservation, research, interpretation or public presentation of New Jersey history and;
(5) have a two-year track record of providing programs and services to the public that fulfill that mission.

Eligible applicants include a wide variety of organizations, both public and private.

GEOGRAPHIC RESTRICTIONS:
New Jersey.

FINANCIAL DATA:
Amount of support per award: General Operating Support: $5,000 to $10,000 (budgets under $30,000); up to 33% of the nonstate operating income for either the current or next fiscal year (budgets of $30,000 and up).

Total amount of support: $3,000,000 for fiscal year 2009.

Matching fund requirements: Matching fund ratio of 3:1 (grantee: Commission) for organizations with budgets over $30,000.

NUMBER OF APPLICANTS MOST RECENT YEAR:
104 for fiscal year 2009.

NUMBER OF AWARDS: 83 for fiscal year 2009.

REPRESENTATIVE AWARDS:
$53,000 to Friends at the Hermitage; $46,800 to Alice Paul Institute Inc.; $107,000 to Historic Cold Spring Village; $105,000 to Monmouth County Historical Association; $101,000 to Union County Division of Cultural and Heritage Affairs.

APPLICATION INFORMATION:
The Commission offers assistance to applicants in the technical aspects of completing the application. Applicants may call the Grants Director at (609) 943-3306 for information or check the web site.
Duration: Two-year funding cycle. Successful applicants will receive a grant for fiscal year 2012, and a commitment to

support in fiscal year 2013 if funds are available and all reporting obligations are met.

Deadline: Applicants must notify the Commission of their intent to apply for the grant by March 1. Full proposals must be received in the Commission office by April 5.

PUBLICATIONS:
Annual report; application guidelines.

ADMINISTRATION:
Sara R. Cureton, Director, Grants Program

ADDRESS INQUIRIES TO:
Sara R. Cureton
Director, Grants Program
P.O. Box 305
Trenton, NJ 08625-0305

*SPECIAL STIPULATIONS:
All funding is based on state appropriations.

NEW JERSEY HISTORICAL COMMISSION   [654]
New Jersey Department of State
225 West State Street, Fourth Floor
Trenton, NJ 08625-0305
(609) 292-6062
Fax: (609) 633-8168

E-MAIL ADDRESS:
sara.cureton@sos.state.nj.us

WEB SITE ADDRESS:
www.newjerseyhistory.org
www.state.nj.us/state/history/hisidx.html

FOUNDED: 1969

AREAS OF INTEREST:
New Jersey history.

NAME(S) OF PROGRAMS:
● **Alfred E. Driscoll Dissertation Prize**
● **Mildred Barry Garvin Prize**
● **Richard P. McCormick Prize for Scholarly Publication**

TYPE:
Awards/prizes. The Driscoll Dissertation Prize is awarded in even years to the author of an outstanding doctoral dissertation on any topic on New Jersey history.

The Garvin Prize is awarded annually to a New Jersey teacher, guidance counselor or school librarian for outstanding teaching of Black American history or related activity at any grade, K-12.

The McCormick Prize is awarded in odd years for an outstanding scholarly work on any aspect of New Jersey history.

YEAR PROGRAM STARTED: 1981

PURPOSE:
To stimulate the study and public knowledge of the history of New Jersey.

LEGAL BASIS:
Agency within the Department of State, State of New Jersey.

ELIGIBILITY:
Driscoll Prize: Doctoral dissertations in New Jersey history are eligible.

Garvin Prize: Applicant must be a New Jersey teacher, guidance counselor or school librarian.

McCormick Prize: Scholarly books published in the preceding two years are eligible.

FINANCIAL DATA:
Amount of support per award: $1,500.

NUMBER OF AWARDS: Garvin Prize: One per year. Driscoll and McCormick Prizes alternate; each year the Historical Commission may award either one Driscoll Prize or one McCormick Prize.

APPLICATION INFORMATION:
Guidelines and application forms are available on the web site.
Duration: One-time award. Not renewable.
Deadline: Driscoll (2012) and McCormick (2011) Prizes: March 15; Garvin Prize: October 6.

PUBLICATIONS:
Annual report; application guidelines.

ADMINISTRATION:
Sara R. Cureton, Director, Grants and Prizes Program

ADDRESS INQUIRIES TO:
For the Driscoll or Garvin Prize:
Marc Mappen, Executive Director
For the McCormick Prize:
Sara Cureton, Director, Grants Program
(See address above.)

NEW JERSEY HISTORICAL COMMISSION   [655]
New Jersey Department of State
225 West State Street, Fifth Floor
Trenton, NJ 08625-0305
(609) 943-3306
(609) 292-6062
Fax: (609) 633-8168

E-MAIL ADDRESS:
sara.cureton@sos.state.nj.us

WEB SITE ADDRESS:
www.newjerseyhistory.org

FOUNDED: 1967

AREAS OF INTEREST:
New Jersey history.

NAME(S) OF PROGRAMS:
● **Minigrants**
● **Project Grants**

TYPE:
Project/program grants. Minigrants: Support for smaller projects of the type covered by special projects and research, publication and media.

Projects: Funding for expenses of specific projects relating to New Jersey history. Eligible categories include conservation of historical materials (manuscripts, books, costumes, historical visuals), editorial and publication projects, educational initiatives, exhibitions, media (films, radio, videotape, digital media), public programs, and research (including archaeological projects, fellowships, oral history, and national and New Jersey registers of historic places nominations).

YEAR PROGRAM STARTED: 1975

PURPOSE:
To stimulate the study and popularizaton of New Jersey history.

LEGAL BASIS:
Agency within the New Jersey Department of State.

ELIGIBILITY:
Grants are available for both individuals and organizations. There are general standards of eligibility, as well as specific requirements for programs.

FINANCIAL DATA:
Amount of support per award: Minigrants: Up to $3,000; Projects: $3,000 to $20,000.
Total amount of support: $200,000 to $300,000 projected for fiscal year 2010-11.
Matching fund requirements: Organizations only, depending on budget.

NUMBER OF APPLICANTS MOST RECENT YEAR:
73 for fiscal year 2010.

NUMBER OF AWARDS: 29 for fiscal year 2010.

REPRESENTATIVE AWARDS:
$11,600 to fund an exhibition on Rock and Roll in New Jersey; $7,877 to fund a cataloging project at Newark Library.

APPLICATION INFORMATION:
Applicants must submit a Declaration of Intent online prior to submitting an application for either general operating or project support. Minigrant applicants do not need to do so.
Deadline: Varies.

PUBLICATIONS:
Annual report; application guidelines.

ADMINISTRATION:
Sara R. Cureton, Acting Director
Nicole Primiani, Director of Grants Program

ADDRESS INQUIRIES TO:
Nicole Primiani
Director of Grants Program
P.O. Box 305
Trenton, NJ 08625-0305

NEW YORK LANDMARKS CONSERVANCY   [656]
One Whitehall Street, 21st Floor
New York, NY 10004-2127
(212) 995-5260
Fax: (212) 995-5268

E-MAIL ADDRESS:
nylandmarks@nylandmarks.org

WEB SITE ADDRESS:
www.nylandmarks.org

FOUNDED: 1973

AREAS OF INTEREST:
Historic preservation and restoration of buildings.

NAME(S) OF PROGRAMS:
● **City Ventures Fund**
● **EZ (Empowerment Zone) Consulting Grants**
● **Historic Properties Fund**
● **Sacred Sites Program**
● **Technical Services Program**

TYPE:
Project/program grants.

PURPOSE:
To provide financial and technical services to nonprofit housing corporations, community development organizations, social service agencies, homesteading groups, and mutual housing associations.

LEGAL BASIS:
501(c)(3) not-for-profit.

ELIGIBILITY:
Eligible organizations must be IRS 501(c)(3) tax-exempt.

GEOGRAPHIC RESTRICTIONS:
New York.

FINANCIAL DATA:
Amount of support per award: Varies.
Total amount of support: Varies.

REPRESENTATIVE AWARDS:
$20,000 to Pratt Area Community Council, Clinton Hill, Brooklyn, NY, to install a new wood cornice on the front facade; $30,000 to South Bronx Community Management Company, Inc., Mott Haven, Bronx, NY; $25,000 to New Destiny Housing Corporation, Bedford-Stuyvesant, Brooklyn, NY.

APPLICATION INFORMATION:
Prospective applicants should first contact the Conservatory. Applications must include a copy of the IRS tax determination letter.
Deadline: Varies.

IRS IDENTIFICATION NUMBER: 23-7181785

NEW YORK STATE HISTORICAL ASSOCIATION [657]
5798 State Highway 80
Cooperstown, NY 13326
(607) 547-1416
Fax: (607) 547-1404

E-MAIL ADDRESS:
c.miosek@nysha.org

WEB SITE ADDRESS:
www.nysha.org

FOUNDED: 1899

AREAS OF INTEREST:
The history of New York state.

NAME(S) OF PROGRAMS:
● **The Dixon Ryan Fox Manuscript Prize of the New York State Historical Association**

TYPE:
Awards/prizes. Annual cash prize and publication assistance.

YEAR PROGRAM STARTED: 1973

PURPOSE:
To award the best unpublished, book-length monograph dealing with the history of New York state, as judged by an editorial committee.

LEGAL BASIS:
Private nonprofit association.

ELIGIBILITY:
Manuscripts may deal with any aspect of New York state history. Biographies of individuals whose careers illuminate aspects of the history of the state are also eligible, as are manuscripts dealing with such cultural matters as literature and the arts, provided that in such cases the methodology used is historical. Works of fiction are not eligible.

FINANCIAL DATA:
Amount of support per award: $3,000.
Total amount of support: $3,000.

NUMBER OF APPLICANTS MOST RECENT YEAR: 8.

NUMBER OF AWARDS: 1 annually.

APPLICATION INFORMATION:
Manuscripts must be typed, double-spaced, with at least one-inch margins. Please send two copies. Clear, readable photocopies or computer printouts are acceptable.
Duration: One-time award. Nonrenewable.
Deadline: February 1. Announcement by July 30 annually.

PUBLICATIONS:
Application guidelines.

TRUSTEES:
Sherwood Boehlert

Katharine Booth
Stephen M. Duff
Lucy B. Hamilton
Gates Helms Hawn
George L. Howell
Robert J. A. Irwin
Charles Kieler
Suzanne Kingsley
Thomas Morgan
Jeffery Pressman
Thomas O. Putnam
George Snell
Eugene Thaw

ADDRESS INQUIRIES TO:
Caitlin Miosek, Administrative Assistant
Curatorial and Publications
(See address above.)

NEW YORK STATE HISTORICAL ASSOCIATION
Lake Road
Cooperstown, NY 13326
(607) 547-1400
Fax: (607) 547-1404

E-MAIL ADDRESS:
info@nysha.org

WEB SITE ADDRESS:
www.nysha.org

TYPE:
Awards/prizes. Prizes for published catalogues treating collections located or exhibited in New York state.

See entry 523 for full listing.

THE NEWBERRY LIBRARY [658]
Committee on Awards
60 West Walton Street
Chicago, IL 60610-7324
(312) 255-3666
Fax: (312) 255-3680

E-MAIL ADDRESS:
research@newberry.org

WEB SITE ADDRESS:
www.newberry.org/research/felshp/fellowshome.html

FOUNDED: 1887

AREAS OF INTEREST:
The Newberry Library specializes in the humanities of Western Europe, England and the Americas from the late Middle Ages to the early 20th century.

NAME(S) OF PROGRAMS:
● **American Society for Eighteenth-Century Studies Fellowships**

TYPE:
Fellowships. For scholars wishing to use the Newberry's collections to study the period 1660 to 1815.

PURPOSE:
To help provide access to Newberry resources for people who live beyond commuting distance.

LEGAL BASIS:
Private research library.

ELIGIBILITY:
Applicants must have received their Ph.D. or equivalent degree, or be a Ph.D. candidate at dissertation level.

Applicants must be members of the ASECS at the time of award.

FINANCIAL DATA:
Amount of support per award: $1,600 monthly stipend.

NUMBER OF AWARDS: Varies.

APPLICATION INFORMATION:
Application information is available online.
Duration: One month.
Deadline: February 10.

STAFF:
Diane Dillon, Director of Scholarly and Undergraduate Programs

ADDRESS INQUIRIES TO:
Committee on Awards
(See address above.)

OMOHUNDRO INSTITUTE OF EARLY AMERICAN HISTORY AND CULTURE [659]
400 Landrum Drive, Ground Floor
Swem Library
Williamsburg, VA 23185
(757) 221-1118
Fax: (757) 221-1047

E-MAIL ADDRESS:
fjteut@wm.edu

WEB SITE ADDRESS:
oieahc.wm.edu

FOUNDED: 1943

AREAS OF INTEREST:
Manuscripts about any area of early American studies.

NAME(S) OF PROGRAMS:
● **Jamestown Prize**

TYPE:
Awards/prizes. Prize to the author of the best book-length scholarly manuscript pertaining to the early American period. Subject of the manuscript must pertain to America circa 1450 to 1815 or to the related history of the British Isles, Europe, West Africa or the Caribbean. The award also guarantees publication by the Institute in association with the University of North Carolina Press.

YEAR PROGRAM STARTED: 1957

LEGAL BASIS:
Independent, nonprofit research institution.

ELIGIBILITY:
The competition is open only to authors who have not previously published a book. Previous and current holders of Institute postdoctoral fellowships are not eligible.

FINANCIAL DATA:
Amount of support per award: $3,000, plus publication.

NUMBER OF AWARDS: 1 every two years.

APPLICATION INFORMATION:
Potential entrants should write to the Editor of Publications at the Institute for detailed instructions before sending in any work.
Deadline: April 30.

ADDRESS INQUIRIES TO:
Fredrika J. Teute
Editor of Publications
(See address above.)

*SPECIAL STIPULATIONS:
Past holders of Institute postdoctoral fellowships are ineligible.

OMOHUNDRO INSTITUTE OF EARLY AMERICAN HISTORY AND CULTURE   [660]

400 Landrum Drive, Ground Floor
Swem Library
Williamsburg, VA 23185
(757) 221-1110
Fax: (757) 221-1047

E-MAIL ADDRESS:
ieahc1@wm.edu

WEB SITE ADDRESS:
oieahc.wm.edu

FOUNDED: 1943

AREAS OF INTEREST:
Research leading to book publication on any area of early American studies.

NAME(S) OF PROGRAMS:
- **NEH Postdoctoral Fellowship**
- **Omohundro Institute Postdoctoral Research Fellowship**

TYPE:
Fellowships. The Omohundro Institute of Early American History and Culture, located on the campus of The College of William and Mary, annually offers two postdoctoral fellowships. Both are awarded to a promising young scholar in any area of early American studies whose dissertation shows potential for making a significant book-length contribution to scholarship.

YEAR PROGRAM STARTED: 1945

LEGAL BASIS:
Independent, nonprofit research institution.

ELIGIBILITY:
Applicants may not have previously published a book or have a book under contract. Foreign nationals must have been in continuous residence in the U.S. for the three years immediately preceding the date of their application for the fellowship in order to be eligible for NEH funding.

For the NEH Fellowship: Applicants must have met all requirements for the Doctorate before commencing the fellowship.

For the Omohundro Institute Postdoctoral Research Fellowship: Applicants must have met all requirements for the Doctorate at least 12 months prior to the application deadline.

Two-year fellows hold the rank of Assistant Professor at the College of William and Mary and teach two three-hour courses at the College during the term of the fellowship, which leaves them relatively free to devote a major portion of their time for research and writing. Fellows are designated as NEH Fellows and do not teach during the middle 12-month period of the two-year term. There is no teaching requirement for the one-year fellow.

FINANCIAL DATA:
Amount of support per award: NEH Postdoctoral Fellowship: $50,400 per year stipend; Omohundro Institute Postdoctoral Research Fellowship: $55,000 stipend.

COOPERATIVE FUNDING PROGRAMS: The fellowships are supported by the National Endowment for the Humanities and the College of William and Mary.

NUMBER OF APPLICANTS MOST RECENT YEAR:
NEH Postdoctoral Fellowship: 25; Omohundro Institute Postdoctoral Research Fellowship: 9.

NUMBER OF AWARDS: 2 annually.

APPLICATION INFORMATION:
Applicants should write the Director of the Institute for application forms and instructions.
Duration: NEH Postdoctoral Fellowship: Two years; Omohundro Institute Postdoctoral Research Fellowship: One year.
Deadline: November 1 for the term beginning the following July 1.

PUBLICATIONS:
William and Mary Quarterly, scholarly journal; *Uncommon Sense,* newsletter.

STAFF:
Ronald Hoffman, Director

ADDRESS INQUIRIES TO:
Ronald Hoffman, Director
(See address above.)

PHI ALPHA THETA HISTORY HONOR SOCIETY   [661]

University of South Florida, SOC107
4202 East Fowler Avenue
Tampa, FL 33620-8100
(800) 394-8195
(813) 974-8212
Fax: (813) 974-8215

E-MAIL ADDRESS:
info@phialphatheta.org

WEB SITE ADDRESS:
www.phialphatheta.org

FOUNDED: 1921

AREAS OF INTEREST:
History.

NAME(S) OF PROGRAMS:
- **Member's First Book Award**
- **Member's Subsequent Book Award**

TYPE:
Awards/prizes. Awards for the best books published by members of Phi Alpha Theta, one for his or her first book, one for subsequent books (second, third, etc.), published in the field of history.

PURPOSE:
To encourage the publication of distinctive books in history.

LEGAL BASIS:
Nonprofit, 501(c)(3).

ELIGIBILITY:
Books to be judged must be published during the previous calendar year. Awards restricted to society members.

FINANCIAL DATA:
Amount of support per award: $500.
Total amount of support: $1,000.

NUMBER OF APPLICANTS MOST RECENT YEAR:
15 to 20.

NUMBER OF AWARDS: 2 for the year 2009.

APPLICATION INFORMATION:
Six copies of each book and a completed application must be forwarded to the Society.
Deadline: June 30.

OFFICERS:
Dr. Graydon A. Tunstall, Jr., Executive Director

ADDRESS INQUIRIES TO:
Dr. Graydon A. Tunstall, Jr.
Executive Director
(See address above.)

PHI ALPHA THETA HISTORY HONOR SOCIETY   [662]

University of South Florida
4202 East Fowler Avenue, SOC107
Tampa, FL 33620-8100
(800) 394-8195
(813) 974-8212
Fax: (813) 974-8215

E-MAIL ADDRESS:
info@phialphatheta.org

WEB SITE ADDRESS:
www.phialphatheta.org

FOUNDED: 1921

AREAS OF INTEREST:
History.

NAME(S) OF PROGRAMS:
- **Thomas S. Morgan Scholarship**
- **William P. Parrish Scholarship**
- **Phi Alpha Theta Scholarship**
- **John Pine Memorial Award**
- **Graydon A. Tunstall, Jr. Scholarship**
- **A.F. Zimmerman Scholarship**

TYPE:
Awards/prizes; Scholarships. The Thomas S. Morgan, William P. Parrish and A.F. Zimmerman Scholarships are given to student members entering graduate school for the first time for work leading to a Master's degree in history.

The Phi Alpha Theta Scholarship, the John Pine Memorial Award and two additional awards are given to graduate student members for work leading to a Ph.D. in history.

The Graydon A. Tunstall, Jr. Scholarship is given to exceptional junior-year students majoring in Modern European History (1815 to present.)

PURPOSE:
To promote the study of history at the graduate level.

LEGAL BASIS:
Nonprofit, 501(c)(3).

ELIGIBILITY:
Applicants must be initiated members of the Phi Alpha Theta History Honor Society.

For the Phi Alpha Theta Scholarship and the John Pine Memorial Award, students must have passed general examinations and be ready to start dissertations.

For the Graydon A. Tunstall, Jr. Scholarship, students must be entering the senior year in September.

FINANCIAL DATA:
Amount of support per award: Morgan and Parrish Scholarships, Phi Alpha Theta Scholarship, Pine Memorial and Graydon A. Tunstall, Jr. Scholarship: $1,000 each; Zimmerman Award: $1,250. In some years, there may be two additional awards of $750 each for Doctoral Scholarships.
Total amount of support: Varies.

NUMBER OF APPLICANTS MOST RECENT YEAR:
Pine Memorial Award: 90; Scholarship Grants: 120; Zimmerman Award: 80.

NUMBER OF AWARDS: Master's degree: 3; Ph.D. in history: 4; Undergraduate: 1.

APPLICATION INFORMATION:
Applications may be obtained by writing to the Executive Director or downloaded from the Society web site.
Duration: One year.

Deadline: Applications must be received on or before March 1.

OFFICERS:
Dr. Graydon A. Tunstall, Jr., Executive Director

ADDRESS INQUIRIES TO:
Dr. Graydon A. Tunstall, Jr.
Executive Director
(See address above.)

*SPECIAL STIPULATIONS:
Applicants must be members of Phi Alpha Theta.

PHI ALPHA THETA HISTORY HONOR SOCIETY [663]
University of South Florida, SOC107
4202 East Fowler Avenue
Tampa, FL 33620-8100
(800) 394-8195
(813) 974-8212
Fax: (813) 974-8215

E-MAIL ADDRESS:
info@phialphatheta.org

WEB SITE ADDRESS:
www.phialphatheta.org

FOUNDED: 1921

AREAS OF INTEREST:
History.

NAME(S) OF PROGRAMS:
- **The Nels Andrew N. Cleven Founder's Paper Prize Awards**
- **Dr. George P. Hammond Paper Prize**
- **Dr. Lynn W. Turner Paper Prize**

TYPE:
Awards/prizes. The George P. Hammond Prize award is for the best paper by a graduate student member of the Society.

The Dr. Lynn W. Turner Prize is awarded for the best paper by an undergraduate student member of the Society.

The four Founder's Paper Prizes are awarded to two graduate and two undergraduate student members of the Society.

PURPOSE:
To promote historical research.

LEGAL BASIS:
501(c)(3).

ELIGIBILITY:
All students must be initiated members. All manuscripts must carry a letter of recommendation from either the faculty advisor or the chair of the department of history. Papers should not exceed 25 typewritten pages in length.

FINANCIAL DATA:
Amount of support per award: Founder's Awards: $350; Hammond Prize and Turner Award: $500 each.

NUMBER OF APPLICANTS MOST RECENT YEAR:
50.

NUMBER OF AWARDS: 6.

APPLICATION INFORMATION:
Essay should combine original historical research on significant subjects, based on source material and manuscripts if possible, with good English composition and superior style. Papers should not exceed 25 typewritten double-spaced pages in length, excluding bibliography. Entries received that do not comply with these guidelines will be disqualified.

Title page of the paper must include the applicant's name, mailing address, phone number and e-mail address, as well as the college/university and year at which he or she joined Phi Alpha Theta.

Entrants must submit five copies of each manuscript and a letter of recommendation from either the Faculty Advisor or History Department Chair indicating the applicant's chapter affiliation and whether the individual is a graduate or an undergraduate student. Send to:
Dr. Clayton Drees
Department of History
Virginia Wesleyan College
1584 Wesleyan Drive
Norfolk, VA 23502-5599
E-mail: cdrees@vwc.edu.

Deadline: Postmarked on or before June 30.

OFFICERS:
Dr. Graydon A. Tunstall, Jr., Executive Director

ADDRESS INQUIRIES TO:
Dr. Graydon A. Tunstall, Jr.
Executive Director
(See address above.)

PONTIFICAL INSTITUTE OF MEDIAEVAL STUDIES [664]
59 Queen's Park Crescent East
Toronto ON M5S 2C4 Canada
(416) 926-7142
Fax: (416) 926-7292

E-MAIL ADDRESS:
allan.smith@utoronto.ca

WEB SITE ADDRESS:
www.pims.ca

AREAS OF INTEREST:
Medieval studies.

NAME(S) OF PROGRAMS:
- **Council of the Institute Awards**

TYPE:
Fellowships.

ELIGIBILITY:
Open to scholars engaged in medieval studies. Level of study is postdoctoral.

FINANCIAL DATA:
Amount of support per award: Varies depending on funds available.

APPLICATION INFORMATION:
Application must include official confirmation that the Ph.D. has been examined and that its award has been approved by the appropriate authority.
Duration: One year.
Deadline: February 1.

ROCK ISLAND ARSENAL MUSEUM [665]
Rock Island Arsenal Historical Society
R. Maguire Scholarship Committee
Rock Island Arsenal
Rock Island, IL 61299-5000
(309) 782-5021
Fax: (309) 782-3598

E-MAIL ADDRESS:
rimahoch@aol.com

AREAS OF INTEREST:
Postgraduate, Master's or Doctorate studies in history and museum study.

NAME(S) OF PROGRAMS:
- **Richard C. Maguire Scholarship**

TYPE:
Scholarships.

PURPOSE:
To provide financial support to a student working for a Master's or Doctorate degree in the fields of history, archaeology or museum study.

ELIGIBILITY:
Applicants must be U.S. citizens. Grants will be awarded on an objective and nondiscriminatory basis without regard to age, sex, race, religion or affiliation. Level of study is postdoctoral and postgraduate.

GEOGRAPHIC RESTRICTIONS:
United States.

FINANCIAL DATA:
Amount of support per award: $1,000.

APPLICATION INFORMATION:
Write to the Museum for an application form, enclose a self-addressed, stamped envelope.
Duration: One year.
Deadline: May 2.

ADDRESS INQUIRIES TO:
Dick Hochstetler
(See e-mail address above.)

ROCKEFELLER ARCHIVE CENTER [666]
15 Dayton Avenue
Pocantico Hills
Sleepy Hollow, NY 10591
(914) 366-6311
Fax: (914) 366-6395

E-MAIL ADDRESS:
archive@rockarch.org

WEB SITE ADDRESS:
www.rockarch.org

FOUNDED: 1974

AREAS OF INTEREST:
Preservation of and research in the records of The Rockefeller University, the Rockefeller Foundation, the Rockefeller Brothers Fund, the Rockefeller family and associated organizations and individuals which include major concentrations in philanthropy, education, health, science, social science, agriculture, Black history, international relations and the arts.

CONSULTING OR VOLUNTEER SERVICES:
Reports on holdings and their relevance to research topics and provides assistance to visiting scholars.

NAME(S) OF PROGRAMS:
- **Grants-in-Aid for Research at the Rockefeller Archive Center**

TYPE:
Grants-in-aid. Grants-in-Aid to individual scholars to defray costs of travel, living and research expenses while doing research at the Rockefeller Archive Center in the Center's collections.

YEAR PROGRAM STARTED: 1977

PURPOSE:
To foster, promote and support research by serious scholars in the collections located at the Rockefeller Archive Center, which includes the records of the Rockefeller Family, the Rockefeller University, the Rockefeller Foundation and other philanthropies and associated individuals.

LEGAL BASIS:
Nonprofit and educational.

ELIGIBILITY:
Grants will be made on a competitive basis to applicants from any discipline, usually graduate students or postdoctoral scholars, who are engaged in research that requires use of the collections at the Center.

FINANCIAL DATA:
Grants are for receipted, approved expenses. Expenses are reimbursed after the completion of the research visit.
Amount of support per award: Up to $5,000. Varies by applicant's expenses.
Total amount of support: $100,000 for the year 2011.

NUMBER OF APPLICANTS MOST RECENT YEAR:
93 for the year 2011.

NUMBER OF AWARDS: 47 for the year 2011.

APPLICATION INFORMATION:
Two letters supporting the Grant-in-Aid application are required.
Duration: Applications for second and third-year support will be considered, but preference is given to new applicants.
Deadline: November 15. Announcement of awards at the beginning of March.

PUBLICATIONS:
Research Reports OnLine from the Rockefeller Archive Center; guides to manuscripts and photograph collections; surveys of holdings on specific subjects.

OFFICERS AND STAFF:
Jack Meyers, President
James A. Smith, Vice President
Camilla B. Harris, Grants Administrator

ADDRESS INQUIRIES TO:
Camilla B. Harris, Grants Administrator
(See address above.)

SANTA BARBARA MISSION ARCHIVE-LIBRARY   [667]
2201 Laguna Street
Santa Barbara, CA 93105
(805) 682-4713 ext.124
Fax: (805) 682-9323

E-MAIL ADDRESS:
research@sbmal.org

WEB SITE ADDRESS:
www.sbmal.org

FOUNDED: 1786

AREAS OF INTEREST:
California Mission history.

NAME(S) OF PROGRAMS:
● **Geiger Memorial Fellowship**

TYPE:
Fellowships; Residencies.

YEAR PROGRAM STARTED: 1978

PURPOSE:
To support scholarly research related to the American Southwest prior to 1846, with preferential consideration being given to studies relating to Alta and Baja California.

ELIGIBILITY:
Junior scholars who are beginning careers in an academic professional institution or field. Applicants should hold a Ph.D. degree or the equivalent in an appropriate discipline germane to their research interest and proposal. Consideration also will be given to outstanding graduate students in candidacy for the Doctorate.

FINANCIAL DATA:
Amount of support per award: $2,500 stipend.

NUMBER OF AWARDS: 1 annually.

APPLICATION INFORMATION:
Application information is available online.
Duration: One year. Renewable upon reapplication.
Deadline: February 15. Announcement March 1.

ADDRESS INQUIRIES TO:
Chair of the Award Committee or
Dr. Monica Orozco, Director
E-mail: director@sbmal.org
(See address above.)

SOCIETY FOR FRENCH HISTORICAL STUDIES   [668]
551-101 Milton Court
Long Beach, CA 90803-6352
(562) 494-6764

E-MAIL ADDRESS:
lclark2@csulb.edu

WEB SITE ADDRESS:
www.societyforfrenchhistoricalstudies.net

FOUNDED: 1955

AREAS OF INTEREST:
French history.

NAME(S) OF PROGRAMS:
● **The Gilbert Chinard Prize**
● **Marjorie M. and Lancelot L. Farrar Awards**
● **The William Koren, Jr. Prize**
● **The David Pinkney Prize**
● **Research Travel Award**
● **John B. and Theta H. Wolf Travel Fellowship**

TYPE:
Awards/prizes. The Chinard Prize is for a recent book on historical relations between France and the Americas.

Farrar Award is for dissertation research.

The Koren Prize is for a recent article written on French history.

The Pinkney Prize is for a recent book written on French history.

Research Travel Award is for recent recipients of doctorates (awarded jointly with Western Society for French History).

Wolf Travel Fellowship is for research travel pertaining to a dissertation.

PURPOSE:
To further the study of French history in the U.S. and Canada.

ELIGIBILITY:
Gilbert Chinard Prize: Historical studies of any area or period are acceptable.

Marjorie M. and Lancelot L. Farrar Awards: Must be a doctoral student in French history at a North American university.

David Pinkney Prize: Must be a citizen of the U.S. or Canada or an author with a full-time appointment at a U.S. or Canadian college or university. Books on any aspect and period of French history will be considered.

William Koren, Jr. Prize: Must be a North American scholar who published an article on any era of French History in an American, European or Canadian journal.

Research Travel Award: Granted to an outstanding American or Canadian scholar who has received the Doctorate in History in the five-year period prior to the award.

John B. and Theta H. Wolf Travel Fellowship: Must be a doctoral student at a university in the U.S. or Canada.

FINANCIAL DATA:
Amount of support per award: Chinard and Koren Prize: $1,000; Farrar Awards: $2,500 each; Pinkney Prize: $1,500; Wolf Travel Fellowship: $2,000.

NUMBER OF AWARDS: Chinard Prize, Koren Prize, Pinkney Price and Wolf Travel Fellowship: 1; Farrar Awards: 2.

APPLICATION INFORMATION:
Application materials are available upon request.

ADDRESS INQUIRIES TO:
Linda Clark, Executive Director
(See address above.)

SOCIETY FOR HISTORIANS OF AMERICAN FOREIGN RELATIONS   [669]
Department of History
Ohio State University
106 Dulles Hall, 230 West 17th Avenue
Columbus, OH 43210
(614) 292-1951
Fax: (614) 292-2282

E-MAIL ADDRESS:
shafr@osu.edu

WEB SITE ADDRESS:
www.shafr.org

FOUNDED: 1967

AREAS OF INTEREST:
American diplomatic history.

NAME(S) OF PROGRAMS:
● **Samuel Flagg Bemis Fellowship**
● **Lawrence Gelfand-Armin Rappaport Fellowship**
● **Michael J. Hogan Foreign Language Fellowship**
● **The W. Stull Holt Dissertation Fellowship**
● **Oxford University Press Dissertation Prize in International History**

TYPE:
Awards/prizes; Fellowships; Travel grants. Cash awards to help graduate students in history who are specializing in American foreign relations conduct research on a significant dissertation project, preferably using foreign archives.

YEAR PROGRAM STARTED: 1984

PURPOSE:
To aid research by graduate students in American foreign relations.

ELIGIBILITY:
Fellowships are available to graduate students who have completed all degree requirements except dissertation.

FINANCIAL DATA:
Amount of support per award: Samuel Flagg Bemis Fellowship: Up to $2,000; Lawrence Gelfand-Armin Rappaport Fellowship, Michael J. Hogan Foreign Language Fellowship, and The W. Stull Holt Dissertation Fellowship: $4,000 per award; Oxford University Press Dissertation Prize in International History: $1,000.

APPLICATION INFORMATION:
For the Oxford University Press Dissertation Prize, the dissertation must be submitted for consideration by the author or by the author's advisor. Three copies of the dissertation should be submitted, along with a cover letter explaining why the dissertation deserves consideration. For the Fellowships, self-nominations are expected.

Duration: One year.

ADDRESS INQUIRIES TO:
SHAFR Business Office
(See address above.)

*SPECIAL STIPULATIONS:
Membership in SHAFR required for all awards except the Oxford University Press Dissertation Prize.

SOCIETY FOR HISTORIANS OF AMERICAN FOREIGN RELATIONS [670]
Department of History
Ohio State University
106 Dulles Hall, 230 West 17th Avenue
Columbus, OH 43210
(614) 292-1951
Fax: (614) 292-2282

E-MAIL ADDRESS:
shafr@osu.edu

WEB SITE ADDRESS:
www.shafr.org

FOUNDED: 1967

AREAS OF INTEREST:
American diplomatic history.

NAME(S) OF PROGRAMS:
● **Myrna F. Bernath Book Award**
● **Myrna F. Bernath Fellowship**
● **Stuart L. Bernath Book Prize**
● **Stuart L. Bernath Dissertation Grant**
● **Stuart L. Bernath Lecture Prize**
● **Stuart L. Bernath Scholarly Article Prize**

TYPE:
Awards/prizes; Fellowships. Cash prizes for articles and books published on the history of American foreign relations.

ELIGIBILITY:
Myrna F. Bernath Book Award: Nominees should be women who have published distinguished books in U.S. foreign relations, transnational history, international history, peace studies, cultural interchange, and defense or strategic studies. Membership in SHAFR is required.

Myrna F. Bernath Fellowship: Women at U.S. universities, as well as women abroad who wish to do research in the U.S., are welcomed to apply. Preference will be given to graduate students and those within five years of completion of their Ph.Ds.

Stuart L. Bernath Book Prize: Prize is to be awarded for a first book. The book must be a history of international relations. Biographies of statesmen and diplomats are eligible. General surveys, autobiographies, editions of essays and documents, and works that represent social science disciplines other than history are not eligible.

Stuart L. Bernath Dissertation Grant: Applicants must be actively working on dissertations dealing with some aspect of U.S. foreign relations history. Membership in SHAFR is required.

Stuart L. Bernath Lecture Prize: Prize is open to any person under 41 years of age or within 10 years of the receipt of the Ph.D. whose scholarly achievements represent excellence in teaching and research. Nominations may be made by any member of SHAFR or of any other established history, political science, or journalism department or organization.

Stuart L. Bernath Scholarly Article Prize: Author must be under 41 years of age and within 10 years of receiving the Ph.D. at the time of the article's acceptance for publication. The article must be among the first six publications by the author. Previous winners of the Stuart L. Bernath Book Award or the Myra F. Bernath Book award are ineligible.

FINANCIAL DATA:
Amount of support per award: Myrna F. Bernath Book Award and Stuart L. Bernath Book Prize: $2,500 per award; Myrna F. Bernath Fellowship: $5,000; Stuart L. Bernath Dissertation Grant: $4,000; Stuart L. Bernath Lecture Prize and Stuart L. Bernath Scholarly Article Prize: $1,000 per award.

NUMBER OF AWARDS: 1 each annually.

APPLICATION INFORMATION:
Applicants must submit completed works to the prize committees.

PUBLICATIONS:
Diplomatic History.

OFFICER:
Peter L. Hahn, Executive Director

ADDRESS INQUIRIES TO:
SHAFR Business Office
(See address above.)

*SPECIAL STIPULATIONS:
Membership in SHAFR is required.

SOCIETY FOR HISTORIANS OF AMERICAN FOREIGN RELATIONS [671]
Department of History
Ohio State University
106 Dulles Hall, 230 West 17th Avenue
Columbus, OH 43210
(614) 292-1951
Fax: (614) 292-2282

E-MAIL ADDRESS:
shafr@osu.edu

WEB SITE ADDRESS:
www.shafr.org

FOUNDED: 1967

AREAS OF INTEREST:
American diplomatic history.

NAME(S) OF PROGRAMS:
● **Robert H. Ferrell Book Prize**
● **Norman and Laura Graebner Award**
● **Arthur S. Link-Warren F. Kuehl Prize for Documentary Editing**
● **SHAFR Dissertation Completion Fellowships**
● **SHAFR Summer Institute**
● **Betty M. Unterberger Dissertation Prize**
● **William Appleman Williams Junior Faculty Research Grants**

TYPE:
Awards/prizes; Fellowships; Research grants.

PURPOSE:
To aid research by graduate students in American foreign relations.

ELIGIBILITY:
Robert H. Ferrell Book Prize recognizes any book beyond the first monograph by the author. The book must deal with the history of American foreign relations, broadly defined. Biographies of statesmen and diplomats are eligible. General surveys, autobiographies, or editions of essays and documents are not eligible.

Norman and Laura Graebner Award is presented to a distinguished scholar of diplomatic or international affairs. The recipient's career must demonstrate excellence in scholarship, teaching, and/or service to the profession. Although the prize is not restricted to academic historians, the recipient must have distinguished himself or herself through the study of international affairs from a historical perspective.

Arthur S. Link-Warren F. Kuehl Prize for Documentary Editing is awarded for outstanding collections of primary source materials in the fields of international or diplomatic history, especially those distinguished by the inclusion of commentary designed to interpret the documents and set them within their historical context. Published works, as well as electronic collections and audio-visual compilations, are eligible. The prize is not limited to works on American foreign policy, but is open to works on the history of international, multi-archival, and/or American foreign relations, policy, and diplomacy.

SHAFR Dissertation Completion Fellowship: Applicants should be candidates for the Ph.D. in a humanities or social science doctoral program (most likely history), must have been admitted to candidacy, and must be at the writing stage, with all substantial research completed by the time of the award. Applicants should be working on a topic in the field of U.S. foreign relations history or international history, broadly defined. Because successful applicants are expected to finish writing the dissertation during the tenure of the fellowship, they should not engage in teaching opportunities or extensive paid work, except at the discretion of the Fellowship Committee.

Betty M. Unterberger Dissertation Prize is awarded to the author of a dissertation, completed during the previous two calendar years, on any topic in U.S. foreign relations history.

William Appleman Williams Junior Faculty Research Grants are limited to scholars working on their first research monograph.

Membership in SHAFR required for all awards.

FINANCIAL DATA:
Amount of support per award: Robert H. Ferrell Book Prize: $2,500; Norman and Laura Graebner Award: $2,000; Arthur S. Link-Warren F. Kuehl Prize for Documentary Editing and Betty M. Unterberger Dissertation Prize: $1,000; SHAFR Dissertation Completion Fellowships: $20,000; SHAFR Summer Institute: $500; William Appleman Williams Junior Faculty Research Grants: Up to $2,000.

ADDRESS INQUIRIES TO:
SHAFR Business Office
(See address above.)

THE SOCIETY OF AMERICAN HISTORIANS, INC.   [672]
American Historical Association
Columbia University
603 Fayerweather MC 2538
New York, NY 10027
(212) 222-4902
(212) 854-6495

E-MAIL ADDRESS:
amhistsociety@columbia.edu

WEB SITE ADDRESS:
www.sah.columbia.edu

FOUNDED: 1939

AREAS OF INTEREST:
American history and biography.

NAME(S) OF PROGRAMS:
- **James Fenimore Cooper Prize**
- **Allan Nevins Prize**
- **Francis Parkman Prize**

TYPE:
Awards/prizes. James Fenimore Cooper Prize: Biennial award in odd-numbered years for a book of historical fiction on an American subject which makes a significant contribution to historical understanding, portrays authentically the people and events of the historical past, and displays skills in narrative construction and prose style copyrighted in the previous two years.

Allan Nevins Prize: Award for the best written doctoral dissertation on an American subject completed in the previous year.

Francis Parkman Prize: Award for the best nonfiction book in American history published the previous year.

YEAR PROGRAM STARTED: 1960

PURPOSE:
To encourage literary distinction in the writing of history and biography.

LEGAL BASIS:
Nonprofit.

ELIGIBILITY:
Allan Nevins Prize: Eligible doctoral dissertation manuscripts must be submitted by the university at which the doctoral studies were undertaken.

FINANCIAL DATA:
Amount of support per award: $2,000 per prize.

NUMBER OF AWARDS: James Fenimore Cooper Prize: 1 biennially in odd-numbered years; Allan Nevins and Francis Parkman Prizes: 1 each annually.

APPLICATION INFORMATION:
Application information and guidelines are available online.
Deadline: January 31.

OFFICERS:
Walter Isaacson, President
Andie Tucher, Executive Secretary

ADDRESS INQUIRIES TO:
See e-mail address above.

THE SONS OF THE REPUBLIC OF TEXAS   [673]
SRT Office
1717 Eighth Street
Bay City, TX 77414
(979) 245-6644
Fax: (979) 244-3819

E-MAIL ADDRESS:
srttexas@srttexas.org

WEB SITE ADDRESS:
www.srttexas.org

FOUNDED: 1893

AREAS OF INTEREST:
Republic of Texas (1836-1846).

NAME(S) OF PROGRAMS:
- **Summerfield G. Roberts Award**

TYPE:
Awards/prizes. Cash award to the author of a work of creative writing on the Republic of Texas.

PURPOSE:
To encourage literary effort and research about historical events and personalities during the days of the Republic of Texas (1836-1846), and to stimulate interest in this period.

LEGAL BASIS:
Nonprofit organization.

ELIGIBILITY:
The competition is open to all writers everywhere; they need not reside in Texas nor must the publishers be in Texas. Manuscripts may be either fiction or nonfiction, poems, essays, plays, short stories, novels, or biographies.

FINANCIAL DATA:
Amount of support per award: $2,500.
Total amount of support: $2,500 annually.

NUMBER OF AWARDS: 1 annually.

REPRESENTATIVE AWARDS:
2008: *War of One Thousand Deserts*, by Brian DeLay.

APPLICATION INFORMATION:
Manuscripts must be written or published during the calendar year for which the award is given. No entry may be submitted more than one time. There is no word limit on the material submitted for the award. The title page must have the contestant's full name, address and phone number. Five copies of each entry must be mailed to the General Office of The Sons of the Republic of Texas at the address above. No copies will be returned.
Duration: One-time award.
Deadline: Postmarked no later than January 15 of the year following the qualifying year of the award.

THE SONS OF THE REPUBLIC OF TEXAS   [674]
SRT Office
1717 Eighth Street
Bay City, TX 77414
(979) 245-6644
Fax: (979) 244-3819

E-MAIL ADDRESS:
srttexas@srttexas.org

WEB SITE ADDRESS:
www.srttexas.org

FOUNDED: 1893

AREAS OF INTEREST:
Spanish colonial period of Texas history.

NAME(S) OF PROGRAMS:
- **Presidio La Bahia Award**

TYPE:
Awards/prizes. Presidio La Bahia Award is intended to promote suitable preservation of relics, appropriate dissemination of data, and research into Texas heritage, with particular emphasis on the Spanish colonial period.

PURPOSE:
To encourage literary effort and research about historical events and personalities during the days of the Spanish colonial period of Texas history, and to stimulate interest in this period.

ELIGIBILITY:
Open to all persons interested in the Spanish colonial influence on Texas culture.

Research writings have proved in the past to be the most successful type of entry. However, careful consideration will be given to other literary forms, as well as to art, architecture, and archaeological discovery.

FINANCIAL DATA:
Amount of support per award: First place: a minimum of $1,200 for the best published book. At its discretion, the organization may award a second-place book prize. There is a separate category with a prize for the best published paper, article published in a periodical, or project of a nonliterary nature.
Total amount of support: A total of $2,000 is available annually for winning participants in the competition.

APPLICATION INFORMATION:
Applicants must submit four copies of published writings to the office. Galley proofs are not acceptable.
Deadline: Entries are accepted from June 1 to September 30.

SOUTHERN HISTORICAL ASSOCIATION   [675]
Department of History
University of Georgia
Athens, GA 30602
(706) 542-8848
Fax: (706) 542-2455

E-MAIL ADDRESS:
sdendy@uga.edu

WEB SITE ADDRESS:
www.uga.edu/sha

FOUNDED: 1934

AREAS OF INTEREST:
Promotion of interest and research in Southern history, the collection and preservation of the South's historical records and the encouragement of state and local historical societies in the South.

NAME(S) OF PROGRAMS:
- **H.L. Mitchell Award**
- **Frank L. and Harriet C. Owsley Award**
- **James A. Rawley Award**
- **Francis B. Simkins Award**
- **Charles S. Sydnor Award**
- **Bennett H. Wall Award**

TYPE:
Awards/prizes. The Simkins Award is given for the best first book published by an author in the field of Southern history. Awarded in odd-numbered years.

The Owsley and Sydnor Awards are given for a distinguished book in Southern history. The Owsley is awarded in odd years; the Sydnor in even years.

Bennett H. Wall Award is given for a distinguished book published in Southern or economic history. It is awarded in even-numbered years.

H.L. Mitchell Award is given for a distinguished book concerning the history of the southern working class, including but not limited to industrial laborers and/or small farmers and agricultural laborers. Awarded in even-numbered years.

James A. Rawley Award is given for a distinguished book dealing with secession and/or the sectional crisis published over a two-year period. Awarded in odd-numbered years.

YEAR PROGRAM STARTED: 1956

LEGAL BASIS:
Nonprofit, tax-exempt association.

COOPERATIVE FUNDING PROGRAMS: Longwood College financially supports the Simkins Award.

NUMBER OF APPLICANTS MOST RECENT YEAR:
21 for the Mitchell Award.

NUMBER OF AWARDS: 1 of each in odd- or even-numbered years.

APPLICATION INFORMATION:
Copies of the book for consideration should be sent to the selection committee. Names are available from the address or web site above.
Deadline: March 1. Award announced in November.

EXECUTIVE COUNCIL:
Theda Perdue, President
Orville Vernon Burton, Vice President
John C. Inscoe, Secretary and Treasurer
Raymond Arnesault
Robert Billinger, Jr.
John B. Boles, Editor, *Journal of Southern History*
Laura Edwards
Paul Escott
Gary Gallagher
Barbara Ganson
Michele Gillespie
Glenda Gilmore
Jane Landers
Linda Reed

ADDRESS INQUIRIES TO:
Sheree Dendy, Administrative Coordinator
(See address above.)

THE SUMMERLEE FOUNDATION

5556 Caruth Haven Lane
Dallas, TX 75225
(214) 363-9000
Fax: (214) 363-1941

E-MAIL ADDRESS:
info@summerlee.org

WEB SITE ADDRESS:
www.summerlee.org

TYPE:
Project/program grants; Research grants.
See entry 1475 for full listing.

HARRY S. TRUMAN LIBRARY INSTITUTE

500 West U.S. Highway 24
Independence, MO 64050
(816) 268-8248
Fax: (816) 268-8299

E-MAIL ADDRESS:
lisa.sullivan@truman.nara.gov

WEB SITE ADDRESS:
www.trumanlibrary.org

TYPE:
Awards/prizes; Fellowships; Grants-in-aid; Research grants; Travel grants. The Dissertation Year Fellowships are given to encourage historical scholarship of the public career of Harry S. Truman or the Truman era. Support is given annually to one or two graduate students who have completed the dissertation research and are in the writing stage. Preference will be given to projects based on extensive research at the Truman Library. Successful applicants will be expected to deposit one copy of their completed dissertation, or any publication resulting therefrom, with the Truman Library.

Research Grants are intended to enable graduate students as well as postdoctoral scholars to come to the Library for one to three weeks to use its archival facilities.

The Scholar's Award is given every other year, even-numbered years only, to a scholar engaged in a study of either the public career of Harry S. Truman or some aspect of the history of the Truman administration or of the U.S. during that administration. The scholar's work must be based on extensive research at the Truman Library and must be designed to result in the publication of a book-length manuscript. One copy of such book (and/or any other publication resulting from work done under this award) shall be deposited by the author with the Harry S. Truman Library.

The Harry S. Truman Book Award is given in even years for the best book dealing with some aspect of history of the U.S. between April 12, 1945 and January 20, 1953 or with the public career of Harry S. Truman.

See entry 2144 for full listing.

U.S. ARMY CENTER OF MILITARY HISTORY [676]

103 Third Avenue
Fort McNair
Washington, DC 20319-5058
(202) 685-2066
Fax: (202) 685-2077

E-MAIL ADDRESS:
cmhonline@us.army.mil

WEB SITE ADDRESS:
www.army.mil/cmh-pg

FOUNDED: 1942

AREAS OF INTEREST:
History of warfare on land, with special emphasis on the history of the U.S. Army.

NAME(S) OF PROGRAMS:
● **Dissertation Year Fellowships**

TYPE:
The Center offers two Dissertation Fellowships each year and sometimes awards a third fellowship to exceptional dissertations on museum-related topics. The Center will consider dissertations on the history of land warfare; preference is given to topics on the history of the U.S. Army.

YEAR PROGRAM STARTED: 1970

PURPOSE:
To encourage scholarship in military history.

LEGAL BASIS:
Government agency.

ELIGIBILITY:
Applicants must be civilian citizens or nationals of the U.S. that have demonstrated

ability and special aptitude for advanced training and study in military history, be enrolled in a recognized graduate school and have successfully completed by September of the year of the award all requirements for the Ph.D. except the dissertation.

FINANCIAL DATA:
Amount of support per award: Stipend of $10,000.
Total amount of support: Up to $30,000.

NUMBER OF APPLICANTS MOST RECENT YEAR:
22 for the year 2011.

NUMBER OF AWARDS: Up to 3 annually.

REPRESENTATIVE AWARDS:
"Camouflage, Animal Skin, and the Nature of Modern War;" "Chinese Communist Party Strategy and Policy, 1945-1949;" "Union Soldiers' Adaptation to Combat in the Petersburg Campaign."

APPLICATION INFORMATION:
Applicants must submit by mail or fax the following materials:
(1) completed, typed application form;
(2) proposed research plan and reasons for interest in this topic (not to exceed 10 double-spaced, typed pages);
(3) letter from dissertation director confirming dissertation proposal has been accepted by the committee;
(4) letters of recommendation;
(5) a writing sample of approximately 25 double-spaced, typed pages (e.g. seminar paper, published scholarly article, excerpt from M.A. thesis or Ph.D. dissertation) and;
(6) transcripts from all undergraduate and graduate schools attended.
Duration: One year.
Deadline: January 15. Announcement April 1.

ADDRESS INQUIRIES TO:
Brian F. Neumann
CMH Dissertation Fellowship Committee
(See address above.)

U.S. ARMY MILITARY HISTORY INSTITUTE [677]

U.S. Army Heritage and Education Center
U.S. Army War College
950 Soldiers Drive
Carlisle Barracks, PA 17013-5021
(717) 245-3096 (office)
Fax: (717) 245-4370

E-MAIL ADDRESS:
richard.sommers@us.army.mil

WEB SITE ADDRESS:
www.carlisle.army.mil/ahec/USAMHI/grants.cfm

FOUNDED: 1967

AREAS OF INTEREST:
Military history with emphasis on the U.S. Army.

NAME(S) OF PROGRAMS:
● **General and Mrs. Matthew B. Ridgway Research Grant**

TYPE:
Research grants; Travel grants. Research and travel fellowships to cover expenses incurred while conducting individual research in USAMHI holdings. These grants may not be used to cover costs for travel to and research at other institutions.

YEAR PROGRAM STARTED: 1977

PURPOSE:
To stimulate utilization of holdings of the Institute in preparation of scholarly, mature publications in military history (theses, dissertations or books).

LEGAL BASIS:
U.S. Department of the Army.

ELIGIBILITY:
Applicants must be scholars at the graduate, postgraduate, or instructor/professor level; or be other professional scholars or authors; or have comparable qualifications based on experience who are pursuing research topics on significant subjects in the field of military history which are well represented in USAMHI holdings.

Government historians researching for official projects are not eligible. No recipient is eligible for more than one grant.

FINANCIAL DATA:
Up to 200 pages of free photocopying are provided to recipients.
Amount of support per award: Up to $2,500.

NUMBER OF APPLICANTS MOST RECENT YEAR:
25.

NUMBER OF AWARDS: 12 for the year 2011 (4 grants were awarded to professors; 6 to graduate students; 2 to authors).

APPLICATION INFORMATION:
Applications can be downloaded online.
Duration: Until December 31 of the following year; thus, for instance, grants for 2012 run to December of 2013.
Deadline: Postmarked by December 31, 2011, to be considered when review panel meets in January 2012.

ADDRESS INQUIRIES TO:
Senior Historian/Research Grants
(See address above.)

*SPECIAL STIPULATIONS:
Must do research in U.S. Army Military History Institute holdings.

U.S. MARINE CORPS [678]
Marine Corps History Division
3078 Upshur Avenue
Quantico, VA 22134
(703) 432-5058
Fax: (703) 432-5054

E-MAIL ADDRESS:
paul.j.weber1@usmc.mil

WEB SITE ADDRESS:
www.history.usmc.mil

FOUNDED: 1919

AREAS OF INTEREST:
U.S. military and naval history and history-based studies in the social and behavioral sciences with a direct relationship to the USMC.

NAME(S) OF PROGRAMS:
● **Marine Corps Historical Program Research Grants**

TYPE:
Research grants. Grants in areas of tangible benefit to the Marine Corps to support research that will add materially to the sum of knowledge regarding the Marine Corps and will not duplicate official projects.

YEAR PROGRAM STARTED: 1975

PURPOSE:
To promote the scholarly study of the USMC from 1775 to the present.

LEGAL BASIS:
Funds provided by the Marine Corps Heritage Foundation, a nonprofit, educational organization.

ELIGIBILITY:
Graduate students, postdoctoral scholars and others with demonstrated professional competence to pursue research projects.

FINANCIAL DATA:
Grants ordinarily will be paid in two installments. Half on the initiation of the approved project and half on its successful conclusion. There are no restrictions on how the recipients apply these funds.
Amount of support per award: $400 to $3,000.

NUMBER OF APPLICANTS MOST RECENT YEAR:
8.

NUMBER OF AWARDS: 8 for the year 2009.

APPLICATION INFORMATION:
A letter should be submitted prior to formal application if the applicant feels that the project involved is within the scope of the program as outlined in the brochure describing the program. This letter should describe concisely the project and its intended purpose and will serve to initiate a request for formal application if deemed appropriate.
Duration: Varies with type of project.
Deadline: Applications accepted throughout the year. Decisions on applicants are announced as soon as possible.

PUBLICATIONS:
Brochure describing program.

OFFICER:
Paul J. Weber, Deputy Director

ADDRESS INQUIRIES TO:
Paul J. Weber, Deputy Director
Marine Corps History Division
(See address above.)

U.S. MARINE CORPS [679]
Marine Corps History Division
3078 Upshur Avenue
Quantico, VA 22134
(703) 432-5058
Fax: (703) 432-5054

E-MAIL ADDRESS:
paul.j.weber1@usmc.mil

WEB SITE ADDRESS:
www.history.usmc.mil

FOUNDED: 1919

AREAS OF INTEREST:
U.S. military and naval history and history-based studies in the social and behavioral sciences with a direct relationship to the history of the USMC.

NAME(S) OF PROGRAMS:
● **Dissertation Fellowships in Marine Corps History**

TYPE:
Fellowships. Awarded to a qualified graduate student working on a doctoral dissertation pertinent to U.S. Marine Corps history. Topics in U.S. military and naval history and history-based topics in the social and behavioral sciences with a direct relationship to the history of the U.S. Marine Corps will be considered.

YEAR PROGRAM STARTED: 1975

PURPOSE:
To promote the scholarly study of the USMC from 1775 to the present.

LEGAL BASIS:
Funds provided by the Marine Corps Heritage Foundation, a nonprofit, educational organization.

ELIGIBILITY:
Applicants must be enrolled in a recognized graduate school, have completed all requirements for the Ph.D. degree except the dissertation and have a university-approved dissertation topic pertinent to U.S. Marine Corps history.

FINANCIAL DATA:
Stipend will be provided directly to the recipient in two equal payments. The first upon acceptance of the award and the second at the start of the subsequent academic term.
Amount of support per award: $10,000.
Total amount of support: Varies with number of awards.

NUMBER OF APPLICANTS MOST RECENT YEAR:
2.

NUMBER OF AWARDS: 1 for the year 2009.

APPLICATION INFORMATION:
Applications may be obtained from the chairman of the history department of the applicant's institution or from the Coordinator, Grants and Fellowships, at the address above.
Duration: One year. No renewals.
Deadline: May 1.

PUBLICATIONS:
Brochure.

OFFICER:
Paul J. Weber, Deputy Director

ADDRESS INQUIRIES TO:
Paul J. Weber, Deputy Director
Marine Corps History Division
(See address above.)

U.S. MARINE CORPS [680]
Marine Corps History Division
3078 Upshur Avenue
Quantico, VA 22134
(703) 432-5058
Fax: (703) 432-5054

E-MAIL ADDRESS:
paul.j.weber1@usmc.mil

WEB SITE ADDRESS:
www.history.usmc.mil

FOUNDED: 1919

AREAS OF INTEREST:
U.S. military and naval history and history-based studies in the social and behavioral sciences with a direct relationship to the history of the USMC.

NAME(S) OF PROGRAMS:
● **Master's Thesis Fellowships in Marine Corps History**

TYPE:
Fellowships. Awarded to qualified graduate students with university-approved thesis topics pertinent to U.S. Marine Corps history. Topics may be in U.S. military and naval history or in history-based studies in the social and behavioral sciences, with a direct relationship to the history of the U.S. Marine Corps.

YEAR PROGRAM STARTED: 1986

PURPOSE:
To promote the scholarly study of all aspects of Marine Corps activities from 1775 to the present.

LEGAL BASIS:
Funds provided by the Marine Corps Heritage Foundation, a nonprofit, educational organization.

ELIGIBILITY:
Applicants must be actively enrolled in an accredited Master's degree program requiring a Master's thesis and have a university-approved topic pertinent to U.S. Marine Corps history. Applicants must be U.S. citizens or nationals and must not have held or accepted an equivalent fellowship from any other Department of Defense agency.

FINANCIAL DATA:
Stipend will be provided directly to the recipient in two equal payments. The first upon acceptance of the award and the second at the start of the subsequent academic term.
Amount of support per award: $3,500.
Total amount of support: Varies with number of awards.

NUMBER OF APPLICANTS MOST RECENT YEAR:
1.

NUMBER OF AWARDS: 1 for the year 2009.

APPLICATION INFORMATION:
Applications may be obtained from the chairman of the history department of the applicant's institution or from the Coordinator, Grants and Fellowships, at the address above.
Duration: One year. No renewal; however, thesis fellows are eligible to apply for the Marine Corps Historical Program's doctoral dissertation fellowship when qualified.
Deadline: May 1.

PUBLICATIONS:
Brochure.

OFFICER:
Paul J. Weber, Deputy Director

ADDRESS INQUIRIES TO:
Paul J. Weber, Deputy Director
Marine Corps History Division
(See address above.)

UNITED STATES HOLOCAUST MEMORIAL MUSEUM, CENTER FOR ADVANCED HOLOCAUST STUDIES [681]
100 Raoul Wallenberg Place, S.W.
Washington, DC 20024-2126
(202) 314-7829
Fax: (202) 479-9726

E-MAIL ADDRESS:
visitingscholars@ushmm.org

WEB SITE ADDRESS:
www.ushmm.org

FOUNDED: 1993

AREAS OF INTEREST:
Holocaust and genocide studies.

NAME(S) OF PROGRAMS:
● **Visiting Scholar Program**

TYPE:
Fellowships; Visiting scholars. The Center for Advanced Holocaust Studies is an integral part of the United States Holocaust Memorial Museum, which serves as America's national institution for Holocaust education and remembrance. The Center awards fellowships to support significant research and writing about the Holocaust. Awards are granted on a competitive basis. The Center welcomes proposals from scholars in all relevant academic disciplines, including history, political science, literature, Jewish studies, philosophy, religion, psychology, comparative genocide studies, law and others.

Visiting scholars at the Center have access to more than 47,000,000 pages of Holocaust-related archival documentation; the Museum's extensive library; oral history, film, photo, art, artifacts and memoir collections; and Holocaust survivor database. Many of these sources have not been examined by scholars, offering unprecedented opportunities to deepen knowledge about the Holocaust and further advance the field of Holocaust studies. In addition to these resources, the Museum is the American repository of the International Tracing Service's (ITS) digitized records. It was established by the Allies after World War II to help reunite families and determine the fates of victims. The ITS collection contains approximately 50,000,000 pages of material relating to the fates of more than 17,000,000 people who were subject to incarceration, forced labor and displacement.

In addition to pursuing their individual projects, fellows at the Center work side by side with other new and established Holocaust scholars from the U.S. and abroad, enabling them to test their ideas, share their research findings, debate methodological or interpretive approaches, and develop comparative frameworks for their projects. The Center's weekly fellows meetings and senior seminar programs provide unique settings for debate and discussion. Fellows also participate in the Center's broad array of scholarly programs and outreach activities at universities and other academic institutions, both locally and nationally.

YEAR PROGRAM STARTED: 1994

PURPOSE:
To support scholarship and publication in the field of Holocaust studies; to promote the growth of Holocaust studies at American universities; to seek to foster strong relationships between American and international scholars; to organize programs to ensure the ongoing training of future generations of scholars specializing in the Holocaust.

ELIGIBILITY:
Fellowships are awarded to candidates working on their dissertations (ABD), postdoctoral researchers, and senior scholars. Immediate postdoctorals and faculty between appointments will also be considered.

FINANCIAL DATA:
Amount of support per award: Up to $3,500 monthly.
Total amount of support: Varies.

NUMBER OF APPLICANTS MOST RECENT YEAR:
111.

NUMBER OF AWARDS: 27 for the year 2009-10.

APPLICATION INFORMATION:
Application forms can be obtained by contacting Visiting Scholar Programs at the address above.
Duration: Three to nine months. Must be a minimum of three consecutive months.
Deadline: November of each year. Specific deadline information can be obtained from the museum.

PUBLICATIONS:
Program announcement.

ADDRESS INQUIRIES TO:
Traci Rucker, Program Coordinator
(See address above.)

UNIVERSITY OF DELAWARE, DEPARTMENT OF HISTORY [682]
46 West Delaware Avenue
Newark, DE 19716
(302) 831-8226
Fax: (302) 831-1538

E-MAIL ADDRESS:
pato@udel.edu

WEB SITE ADDRESS:
www.udel.edu

AREAS OF INTEREST:
Professional training in historical studies.

NAME(S) OF PROGRAMS:
● **E. Lyman Stewart Fellowship**

TYPE:
Fellowships. Residential program in history.

PURPOSE:
To provide a program of graduate study leading to an M.A. or Ph.D. degree for students who plan careers as museum professionals, historical agency administrators or seek careers in college teaching and public history.

ELIGIBILITY:
Open to nationals of any country.

FINANCIAL DATA:
Amount of support per award: $16,000, plus tuition.

APPLICATION INFORMATION:
Applications must be submitted online using the University of Delaware application form and include transcripts, Graduate Record Examination scores, TOEFL scores (where applicable), plus three letters of recommendation and a writing sample.
Deadline: January 15.

ADDRESS INQUIRIES TO:
Pat Orendorf, Administrative Assistant
(See address above.)

THE UNIVERSITY OF DELAWARE-HAGLEY PROGRAM [683]
Department of History, John Munroe Hall
University of Delaware
Newark, DE 19716
(302) 831-8226
Fax: (302) 831-1538

E-MAIL ADDRESS:
pato@udel.edu

WEB SITE ADDRESS:
www.udel.edu/hagley

FOUNDED: 1954

AREAS OF INTEREST:
Technology, business, consumption, and work in industrial and post-industrial societies.

TYPE:
Fellowships. The University of Delaware, in association with the Hagley Museum, sponsors a premier graduate resident program for the study of technology, business, consumption, and work in industrial and

post-industrial societies leading to a Master of Arts or Ph.D. in History. Students have access to faculty with international reputations in American, European and non-Western history, and benefit from strong interdisciplinary ties to museum studies and material culture programs, as well as the Hagley Museum and Library. Graduates have gone on to distinguished careers in academia, museums and public history.

YEAR PROGRAM STARTED: 1954

PURPOSE:
To prepare students planning careers as college teachers and as professionals in museums and historical agencies.

LEGAL BASIS:
Not-for-profit organization classified by IRS as 501(c)(3) organization.

ELIGIBILITY:
Hagley Fellows come to the University of Delaware with a variety of interests and backgrounds. They share a common desire to engage in a wide-ranging conversation about social and material dimensions of industrialization. Some plan to go on to careers in university teaching while others are interested in public history or museum work. Most, but not all, have a B.A. or an M.A. in history when they are admitted to the history department. Special preparation in a technical field is not a requirement for admission.

FINANCIAL DATA:
Fellows supported by The Hagley Program receive an annual stipend plus full tuition at the University of Delaware and a small research and travel budget.

Amount of support per award: $16,000 stipend plus full tuition and a $600 research and travel budget.

NUMBER OF APPLICANTS MOST RECENT YEAR:
16.

NUMBER OF AWARDS: Number available each year varies, but the program maintains 8 Hagley Fellows.

APPLICATION INFORMATION:
Interested applicants should complete an online application for the UD History Graduate Program. Applicant should clearly indicate on the top of the personal statement that they wish to be considered for the Hagley Program. Top candidates will be brought to the University at the Program's expense for an interview. Candidates who are not selected may still be considered for the general History Graduate Program.

Duration: Nine-month fellowships may be renewed once for those seeking a terminal Master's degree and up to three times for those seeking a Ph.D.

Deadline: January 15.

ADDRESS INQUIRIES TO:
Patricia Orendorf, Administrative Assistant (See address above.)

*SPECIAL STIPULATIONS:
This is a resident graduate program.

WISCONSIN HISTORICAL SOCIETY PRESS   [684]
816 State Street
Madison, WI 53706-1482
(608) 264-6465
Fax: (608) 264-6486

E-MAIL ADDRESS:
whspress@wisconsinhistory.org

WEB SITE ADDRESS:
www.wisconsinhistory.org/whspress

FOUNDED: 1846

AREAS OF INTEREST:
Wisconsin history and culture.

NAME(S) OF PROGRAMS:
● **D.C. Everest Fellowship**
● **Amy Louise Hunter Fellowship**
● **Alice E. Smith Fellowship**

TYPE:
Fellowships; Research grants. Fellowships awarded for research and writing for publication in book form by the society press on Wisconsin history topics.

YEAR PROGRAM STARTED: 2000

PURPOSE:
To promote research and writing on Wisconsin history topics.

LEGAL BASIS:
Agency of the state of Wisconsin.

ELIGIBILITY:
Individuals, not organizations.

FINANCIAL DATA:
Amount of support per award: $1,000 to $2,000.

NUMBER OF AWARDS: 3.

APPLICATION INFORMATION:
Application form available online.
Duration: One-time award.

PUBLICATIONS:
Program announcement.

ADDRESS INQUIRIES TO:
Kathy Borkowski, Editorial Director (See address above.)

YIVO INSTITUTE FOR JEWISH RESEARCH   [685]
15 West 16th Street
New York, NY 10011-6301
(212) 294-6139
Fax: (212) 292-1892

E-MAIL ADDRESS:
pglasser@yivo.cjh.org
yivomail@yivo.cjh.org

WEB SITE ADDRESS:
www.yivo.org

FOUNDED: 1925

AREAS OF INTEREST:
Yiddish, East European and American Jewish history and culture.

NAME(S) OF PROGRAMS:
● **Rose and Isidore Drench Memorial Fellowship**

TYPE:
Fellowships. Dedicated to doctoral or postdoctoral research in American Jewish history, with special consideration given to scholars working on some aspect of the Jewish labor movement.

YEAR PROGRAM STARTED: 1990

PURPOSE:
To further research of American Jewish history, based on resources from the YIVO Library and Archives.

LEGAL BASIS:
Tax-exempt 501(c)(3) organization.

ELIGIBILITY:
Applicants must be working in American Jewish history with special consideration toward the Jewish Labor Movement. The research must be conducted at YIVO in New York City. The holder is also expected to deliver a public lecture.

FINANCIAL DATA:
Amount of support per award: $2,500.

NUMBER OF AWARDS: 1.

APPLICATION INFORMATION:
Application materials should be sent by regular mail, fax or e-mail to:
Chairperson, Fellowship Committee
YIVO Institute for Jewish Research.

Applicants should include the following materials:
(1) curriculum vitae, including all contact information and detailing education, publications, other scholarly activity (papers presented, etc.), teaching and other relevant work experience, knowledge of relevant languages, honors, awards and fellowships, etc.;
(2) research proposal of no more than four pages, including aims for research during the period of fellowship; whether the proposed work is part of a larger project, such as a dissertation, book, etc.; how the resources of YIVO will contribute to the work and;
(3) two letters of support, which discuss the importance of the applicant's work for the relevant field, as well as the applicant's ability to carry out the proposed work.

Applicants may apply for only one fellowship.

Duration: One to three months.

Deadline: December 31 for upcoming calendar year.

PUBLICATIONS:
YIVO-bleter; Yedies fun YIVO.

BOARD OF DIRECTORS:
Bruce Slovin, Chairman
Rosina Abramson
Jack Bendheim
Martin Flumenbaum
Allan Gerson
Fanya Gottesfeld Heller
Michael Karfunkel
Solomon Krystal
Dr. Chava Lapin
Ruth Levine
Leo Melamed
Jonathan Mishkin
Jacob Morowitz
Bernard Nussbaum
Doris Payson
Martin Peretz
Irena Pletka
David Polen
Dr. Arnold Richards
Charles J. Rose
Lawrence Saper
Joseph S. Steinberg
Michael Trock

ADDRESS INQUIRIES TO:
Dr. Paul Glasser
Chairman, Fellowship Committee
(See address above.)

*SPECIAL STIPULATIONS:
The holder is expected to deliver a public lecture.

YIVO INSTITUTE FOR JEWISH RESEARCH [686]

15 West 16th Street
New York, NY 10011-6301
(212) 294-6139
Fax: (212) 292-1892

E-MAIL ADDRESS:
pglasser@yivo.cjh.org
yivomail@yivo.cjh.org

WEB SITE ADDRESS:
www.yivo.org

FOUNDED: 1925

AREAS OF INTEREST:
Yiddish, East European and American Jewish history and culture.

NAME(S) OF PROGRAMS:
- **Professor Bernard Choseed Memorial Fellowship**
- **Aleksander and Alicja Hertz Memorial Fellowship**
- **Vivian Lefsky Hort Memorial Fellowship**
- **Abraham and Rachela Melezin Fellowship**
- **Natalie and Mendel Racolin Memorial Fellowship**
- **Maria Salit-Gitelson Tell Memorial Fellowship**

TYPE:
Awards/prizes; Fellowships; Grants-in-aid; Project/program grants; Research grants; Scholarships. Awarded to train scholars in the field of Eastern European Jewish history and culture, Yiddish language, linguistics, literature, folklore and ethnography.

The Choseed Memorial Fellowship is given to help support original doctoral or postdoctoral research at the YIVO Library and Archives in the field of East European Jewish Studies. The Fellowship is for a period of one to three months of research. The holder of the Fellowship is required to give a public lecture.

The Hertz Memorial Fellowship supports doctoral or postdoctoral research on Polish-Jewish history in the modern period, particularly Jewish-Polish relations and Jewish contributions to Polish literature and culture.

The Hort Memorial Fellowship helps support original doctoral or postdoctoral research in the field of Yiddish literature. The Fellowship is for one to three months of research at the YIVO Library and Archives and a public lecture by the holder.

The Melezin Fellowship supports doctoral or postdoctoral research on Jewish educational networks in Lithuania, with emphasis on prewar Vilna and the Vilna region.

The Racolin Memorial Fellowship supports original doctoral or postdoctoral research in the field of East European Jewish history. The Fellowship is for one to three months of research at the YIVO Library and Archives and a public lecture by the holder.

The Maria Salit-Gitelson Tell Memorial Fellowship helps support original doctoral or postdoctoral research in the field of Lithuanian Jewish history, the city of Vilna in particular. The Fellowship is for one to three months of research at the YIVO Library and Archives and a public lecture by the holder.

YEAR PROGRAM STARTED: 1994

PURPOSE:
To further research in Yiddish Studies, based on resources from the YIVO Library and Archives.

LEGAL BASIS:
Tax-exempt 501(c)(3) organization.

ELIGIBILITY:
Applicants must have Doctorates in Yiddish literature or a closely related field and must conduct the research at YIVO in New York City.

FINANCIAL DATA:
Amount of support per award: Choseed Memorial Fellowship: $7,500; Hertz Memorial, Melezin, Racolin Memorial and Tell Memorial Fellowships: $1,500; Hort Memorial Fellowship: $2,000.

APPLICATION INFORMATION:
Application materials should be sent by regular mail, fax or e-mail to:
Chairperson, Fellowship Committee
YIVO Institute for Jewish Research.

Applicants should include the following materials:
(1) curriculum vitae, including all contact information and detailing education; publications; other scholarly activity (papers presented, etc.); teaching and other relevant work experience; knowledge of relevant languages; honors, awards and fellowships, etc.;
(2) research proposal of no more than four pages, including aims for research during the period of fellowship; whether the proposed work is part of a larger project, such as a dissertation, book, etc.; how the resources of YIVO will contribute to the work and;
(3) two letters of support, which discuss the importance of the applicant's work for the relevant field, as well as the applicant's ability to carry out the proposed work.

Applicants may apply for one fellowship only.

Duration: One to three months.

Deadline: December 31.

PUBLICATIONS:
Yedies fun YIVO; *YIVO-bleter*.

BOARD OF DIRECTORS:
Bruce Slovin, Chairman
Rosina Abramson
Jack Bendheim
Martin Flumenbaum
Allan Gerson
Fanya Gottesfeld Heller
Michael Karfunkel
Solomon Krystal
Dr. Chava Lapin
Ruth Levine
Leo Melamed
Jonathan Mishkin
Jacob Morowitz
Bernard Nussbaum
Doris Payson
Martin Peretz
Irena Pletka
David Polen
Dr. Arnold Richards
Charles J. Rose
Lawrence Saper
Joseph S. Steinberg
Michael Trock

ADDRESS INQUIRIES TO:
Dr. Paul Glasser
Chairman, Fellowship Committee
(See address above.)

YIVO INSTITUTE FOR JEWISH RESEARCH [687]

15 West 16th Street
New York, NY 10011-6301
(212) 294-6139
Fax: (212) 292-1892

E-MAIL ADDRESS:
pglasser@yivo.cjh.org

WEB SITE ADDRESS:
www.yivo.org

FOUNDED: 1925

AREAS OF INTEREST:
Eastern European Jewish studies.

NAME(S) OF PROGRAMS:
- **Vladimir and Pearl Heifetz Memorial Fellowship**
- **Abram and Fannie Gottlieb Immerman and Abraham Nathan and Bertha Daskal Weinstein Memorial Fellowship in Eastern European Jewish Studies**
- **Samuel and Flora Weiss Research Fellowship**

TYPE:
Fellowships. Vladimir and Pearl Heifetz Memorial Fellowship in Eastern European Jewish Music is designed to assist an undergraduate, graduate or postgraduate researcher at the YIVO Archives and Library. The fellowship carries a stipend to defray expenses connected with research in YIVO's music collection.

Abram and Fannie Gottlieb Immerman and Abraham Nathan and Bertha Daskal Weinstein Memorial Fellowship in Eastern European Jewish Studies is designed to support travel for Ph.D. dissertation research in archives and libraries of the Baltic states. Preference is given to research on the Jews of Courland and Latvia.

Samuel and Flora Weiss Research Fellowship supports research on the destruction of Polish Jewry or on Polish-Jewish relations during the Holocaust period. The research should result in a scholarly publication.

PURPOSE:
To advance Eastern European Jewish studies.

FINANCIAL DATA:
Amount of support per award:
Immerman/Weinstein Memorial Fellowship: $2,000; Heifetz Memorial Fellowship: $1,500; Weiss Research Fellowship: $2,500.

APPLICATION INFORMATION:
Applications should include a curriculum vitae, a research proposal (four-page maximum), and two letters of support.

Duration: Varies.

Deadline: December 31.

ADDRESS INQUIRIES TO:
Dr. Paul Glasser
Chairman, Fellowship Committee
(See address above.)

*PLEASE NOTE:
Immerman Fellowship is not offered every year.

*SPECIAL STIPULATIONS:
Applicants may apply for one fellowship only.

YIVO INSTITUTE FOR JEWISH RESEARCH [688]

15 West 16th Street
New York, NY 10011-6301
(212) 294-6139
Fax: (212) 292-1892

E-MAIL ADDRESS:
pglasser@yivo.cjh.org

WEB SITE ADDRESS:
www.yivo.org

FOUNDED: 1925

AREAS OF INTEREST:
Eastern European Jewish studies.

NAME(S) OF PROGRAMS:
- **Dina Abramowicz Emerging Scholar Fellowship**
- **Joseph Kremen Memorial Fellowship**
- **Dora and Mayer Tendler Fellowship**
- **Workmen's Circle/Dr. Emanuel Patt Visiting Professorship**

TYPE:
Fellowships; Visiting scholars. Dina Abramowicz Emerging Scholar Fellowship is intended for postdoctoral research on a topic in Eastern European Jewish studies. The work should lead to a significant scholarly publication and may encompass the revision of a doctoral dissertation. The fellowship carries a stipend for the holder to conduct research at the YIVO Library and Archives for a period of two to three months and to deliver a public lecture.

Joseph Kremen Memorial Fellowship in Eastern European Jewish Music is designed to assist a researcher at the YIVO Archives and Library. This fellowship carries a stipend to defray expenses connected with research in YIVO's music collection.

Dora and Mayer Tendler Fellowship in Jewish Studies is designed to support graduate research in Jewish studies.

Workmen's Circle/Dr. Emanuel Patt Visiting Professorship in Eastern European Jewish Studies is designed to support three months of postdoctoral research at the YIVO Library and Archives and a public lecture by the visiting faculty member.

PURPOSE:
To advance Eastern European Jewish studies.

FINANCIAL DATA:
Amount of support per award: Abramowicz and Tendler Fellowships: $3,000; Kremen Memorial Fellowship: $2,000; Workmen's Circle: $5,000.

APPLICATION INFORMATION:
Applications should include a cover letter indicating one choice of fellowship, a curriculum vitae, a research proposal (four-page maximum), and two letters of support.

Duration: Varies.

Deadline: December 31.

ADDRESS INQUIRIES TO:
Dr. Paul Glasser
Chair, Fellowship Committee
(See address above.)

*SPECIAL STIPULATIONS:
Applicants may apply for one fellowship only.

Languages

THE AMERICAN CLASSICAL LEAGUE [689]
Miami University
422 Wells Mill Drive
Oxford, OH 45056
(513) 529-7741
Fax: (513) 529-7742

E-MAIL ADDRESS:
info@aclclassics.org

WEB SITE ADDRESS:
www.aclclassics.org

FOUNDED: 1919

AREAS OF INTEREST:
Latin and Classical Studies of ancient Rome and Greece.

CONSULTING OR VOLUNTEER SERVICES:
Placement service for teachers of Latin.

NAME(S) OF PROGRAMS:
- **McKinlay Scholarship**

TYPE:
Grants-in-aid; Scholarships.

YEAR PROGRAM STARTED: 1975

PURPOSE:
To assist high school teachers of Latin to further their educational background.

LEGAL BASIS:
Nonprofit.

ELIGIBILITY:
Applicant must be a member of American Classical League for the preceding three years and current year and teaching high school Latin courses.

GEOGRAPHIC RESTRICTIONS:
United States.

FINANCIAL DATA:
Amount of support per award: Varies.
Total amount of support: Varies.

APPLICATION INFORMATION:
Duration: One-time award.
Deadline: January 15. Award announcement March 15.

ADDRESS INQUIRIES TO:
Geri Dutra, Administrative Secretary
(See address above.)

AMERICAN INSTITUTE OF INDIAN STUDIES [690]
1130 East 59th Street
Chicago, IL 60637
(773) 702-8638
Fax: (773) 702-6636

E-MAIL ADDRESS:
aiis@uchicago.edu

WEB SITE ADDRESS:
www.indiastudies.org

FOUNDED: 1961

AREAS OF INTEREST:
Indian studies.

NAME(S) OF PROGRAMS:
- **Advanced Language Program in India**

TYPE:
Fellowships. Awards for graduate studies in India in an Indian language.

YEAR PROGRAM STARTED: 1969

PURPOSE:
To provide advanced language training in India.

LEGAL BASIS:
Cooperative, nonprofit organization of 47 American colleges and universities.

ELIGIBILITY:
Open to graduate students in U.S. colleges and universities who have had a minimum of two years or 240 class hours of classroom instruction in Bengali, Hindi or Tamil and intend to pursue teaching degrees. Applicants for other Indian languages may be considered, but they should contact the AIIS for further information and advice. Applicants must be U.S. citizens.

FINANCIAL DATA:
Grants will be awarded on a competitive basis and will include round-trip airfare to India and a maintenance allowance sufficient to cover living expenses. No funding will be provided for dependents.

APPLICATION INFORMATION:
Application forms are available from the address above. All applications must include a $25 processing fee.
Duration: Nine months.
Deadline: January 31.

OFFICERS:
Frederick Asher, President
Elise Auerbach, Administrator

ADDRESS INQUIRIES TO:
Fellowship Coordinator
(See address above.)

AMERICAN RESEARCH INSTITUTE IN TURKEY, INC.
c/o The University of Pennsylvania Museum
3260 South Street
Philadelphia, PA 19104-6324
(215) 898-3474
Fax: (215) 898-0657

E-MAIL ADDRESS:
leinwand@sas.upenn.edu

WEB SITE ADDRESS:
ccat.sas.upenn.edu/ARIT

TYPE:
Fellowships. Bogazici University Summer Language Program: For summer study in Turkey. Also offer travel, stipend and tuition grants. This intensive program offers the equivalent of one full academic year of study in advanced Turkish language at the college level.

See entry 932 for full listing.

AXE-HOUGHTON FOUNDATION [691]
c/o Foundation Source
55 Walls Drive, 3rd Floor
Fairfield, CT 06824
(800) 839-1754
Fax: (800) 839-1764

WEB SITE ADDRESS:
www.foundationcenter.
org/grantmaker/axehoughton

FOUNDED: 1965

AREAS OF INTEREST:
Improvement of English speech and its uses in the areas of public affairs, education,

theatre, poetry and debate. A portion of available funds may be devoted to speech remediation.

TYPE:
Project/program grants.

YEAR PROGRAM STARTED: 1965

PURPOSE:
To foster and encourage an appreciation of the English language, with emphasis on the spoken language.

LEGAL BASIS:
Tax-exempt eleemosynary foundation.

ELIGIBILITY:
Applicant institutions must have tax-exempt status. No grants to individuals or for operating budgets, general purposes, continuing support, annual campaigns, emergency funds, deficit financing, capital funds, endowment funds, loans, matching gifts, scholarships, fellowships or publications.

Grants are rarely made to organizations outside of the New York City metropolitan area.

GEOGRAPHIC RESTRICTIONS:
Primarily New York City.

FINANCIAL DATA:
Amount of support per award: $2,500 to $7,000; Average: $4,000.

NUMBER OF AWARDS: 80 for the year 2009.

APPLICATION INFORMATION:
Online proposal only. Application form is available at www.fsrequests.com/axe-houghton.
Duration: One year. Renewals generally of no more than three years.
Deadline: Submit proposals between May 1 and September 1. Award announcements are made in late December. Disbursements will be made at the end of February.

PUBLICATIONS:
Program policy statement; application guidelines.

OFFICERS AND TRUSTEES:
Lynn Angelson, President
Robert B. von Mehren, Vice President
Bruce D. Haims, Treasurer
Suzanne Schwartz Davidson, Secretary

ADDRESS INQUIRIES TO:
Lynn Angelson, President
(See address above.)

*PLEASE NOTE:
Communications by mail only.

DUQUESNE UNIVERSITY, DEPARTMENT OF PHILOSOPHY   [692]
Department of Philosophy
Pittsburgh, PA 15282
(412) 396-6500
Fax: (412) 396-5353

E-MAIL ADDRESS:
thompson@duq.edu

WEB SITE ADDRESS:
www.duq.edu/philosophy/graduate/ma.cfm
www.duq.edu/philosophy/graduate/phd.cfm

AREAS OF INTEREST:
The Ph.D. program in the Department of Philosophy at Duquesne University emphasizes continental philosophy, i.e.,

phenomenology and 20th century French and German philosophy, as well as the history of philosophy.

NAME(S) OF PROGRAMS:
● **Duquesne University Graduate Assistantship**

TYPE:
Assistantships; Conferences/seminars; Exchange programs. Philosophy assistantship.

PURPOSE:
To provide a stipend to enable students to obtain a Ph.D. in philosophy.

ELIGIBILITY:
Open to holders of a Bachelor's degree in philosophy, or its equivalent, who have a grade point average of at least 3.7 and an excellent graduate record examination score. Candidates should have knowledge of a second language.

FINANCIAL DATA:
Amount of support per award: Stipend of $17,000 plus all tuition for coursework.

NUMBER OF APPLICANTS MOST RECENT YEAR:
170.

NUMBER OF AWARDS: 17.

APPLICATION INFORMATION:
Applicants must complete an application including a statement of intent and three letters of recommendation, Graduate Record Examination scores and application form and fee, plus test of English as a Foreign Language scores.
Duration: Four years.
Deadline: Ph.D. January 15; M.A. April 15.

ADDRESS INQUIRIES TO:
James Swindal, Chairperson
(See address above.)

INSTITUTE OF INTERNATIONAL EDUCATION   [693]
U.S. Student Programs
809 United Nations Plaza
New York, NY 10017-3580
(212) 984-5330

WEB SITE ADDRESS:
www.us.fulbrightonline.org

FOUNDED: 1919

AREAS OF INTEREST:
Educational, art and cultural exchange programs.

NAME(S) OF PROGRAMS:
● **Padagogischer Austauschdienst Teaching Assistantships**

TYPE:
Assistantships. The Fulbright U.S. Student Program provides an opportunity for young teachers and university students of German to serve as English language teaching assistants in secondary schools in Germany.

YEAR PROGRAM STARTED: 1951

PURPOSE:
To provide English teaching assistantships to foreign language students.

LEGAL BASIS:
Private, not-for-profit agency.

ELIGIBILITY:
Open to students who possess a Bachelor's degree from a U.S. university.

FINANCIAL DATA:
Assistants receive a 10-month maintenance allowance and international travel.

NUMBER OF APPLICANTS MOST RECENT YEAR:
368.

NUMBER OF AWARDS: Approximately 140 for the year 2012-13.

APPLICATION INFORMATION:
Applications and additional information may be obtained from the address above.
Duration: Tenable for one academic year.
Deadline: October.

ADDRESS INQUIRIES TO:
Walter Jackson, Manager
(See address above.)

THE JAPAN FOUNDATION
152 West 57th Street
17th Floor
New York, NY 10019
(212) 489-0299
Fax: (212) 489-0409

E-MAIL ADDRESS:
info@jfny.org

WEB SITE ADDRESS:
www.jfny.org

TYPE:
Conferences/seminars; Development grants; Fellowships; Grants-in-aid; Product donations; Professorships; Project/program grants; Research grants; Training grants; Travel grants.

See entry 901 for full listing.

LUSO-AMERICAN EDUCATION FOUNDATION   [694]
7080 Dolon Way
Suite 200
Dublin, CA 94568
(925) 828-3883
Fax: (925) 828-3883

E-MAIL ADDRESS:
education@luso-american.org

WEB SITE ADDRESS:
www.luso-american.org

FOUNDED: 1963

AREAS OF INTEREST:
Perpetuation of the Portuguese language and culture in the U.S.

NAME(S) OF PROGRAMS:
● **Luso-American Education**

TYPE:
Scholarships.

LEGAL BASIS:
Tax-exempt corporation.

ELIGIBILITY:
Applicants must be under 21 years of age and a graduate of an accredited high school by the summer of the year of the award with a grade point average of at least 3.0 on a 4.0 scale. Must also be one of the following:
(1) of Portuguese descent;
(2) enrolled in Portuguese classes in a four-year college or university or;
(3) a member of an organization whose scholarships are administered by the Luso-American Education Foundation.

GEOGRAPHIC RESTRICTIONS:
California, Connecticut, Idaho, Massachusetts, Nevada, New Jersey, Pennsylvania and Rhode Island.

FINANCIAL DATA:
Amount of support per award: $300 to $4,000.

NUMBER OF APPLICANTS MOST RECENT YEAR: 100.

APPLICATION INFORMATION:
Application form required. SAT scores should be forwarded to the Foundation along with application form, transcript and letters of recommendation.

Duration: Nonrenewable.

Deadline: Must be postmarked by March 1. Announcement prior to June 1.

PUBLICATIONS:
Program announcement.

ADDRESS INQUIRIES TO:
Bela Ferreira-Goncalves
Administrative Director
(See address above.)

LUSO-AMERICAN EDUCATION FOUNDATION   [695]

7080 Donlon Way, Suite 200
Dublin, CA 94568
(925) 828-3883
Fax: (925) 828-3883

E-MAIL ADDRESS:
education@luso-american.org

WEB SITE ADDRESS:
www.luso-american.org

FOUNDED: 1963

AREAS OF INTEREST:
Perpetuation of the Portuguese language and culture in the U.S., Portuguese education and the teaching of Portuguese in California schools and universities.

CONSULTING OR VOLUNTEER SERVICES:
Provides advisory and reference services, assists teachers and school districts in setting up Portuguese language and literature courses, choosing texts, etc., makes referrals to other sources of information, permits on-site use of collection and holds annual Conference on Portuguese-American Education for educators, administrators and community persons. Services are free and available to California residents only.

NAME(S) OF PROGRAMS:
● **Educational Grant Program**

TYPE:
Grants-in-aid; Scholarships. Educational grants in three categories:
(1) Financial Aid - A limited number of grants for the development of Portuguese curriculum and materials for schools;
(2) Grant to participate in the summer program at universities and colleges in California and;
(3) Grant to participate in the summer program at a Portuguese university.

YEAR PROGRAM STARTED: 1970

PURPOSE:
To foster, sponsor and perpetuate in the U.S. as part of its culture the ethnicity and national culture of Portugal brought to America by Portuguese emigrants; to help students and teachers become qualified to teach and promote the Portuguese language and culture at all levels of education.

LEGAL BASIS:
Tax-exempt corporation.

ELIGIBILITY:
For all programs, candidates must be residents of California.

For category 1, all projects will be judged on how relevant they are to the goals and objectives of the Luso-American Education Foundation and the Portuguese Heritage in California.

For category 2, candidates for the grant to participate in the summer program at universities and colleges in California must demonstrate a desire to study the Portuguese language and culture, be of Portuguese descent or be working in a school setting with Portuguese children and be enrolled in an accredited California university or college and will qualify only if these courses are not offered at their school.

For category 3, candidates for the grant to participate in the summer program at a Portuguese university must be a teacher of Portuguese in grades K-12 in an accredited California school, hold a B.A. or higher degree with emphasis in the Portuguese language, culture and literature, have been admitted to a teaching credential program at an accredited California university or college and must demonstrate a desire to teach the Portuguese language and culture, have been admitted to an advanced degree program at an accredited California university or college in which the study of Portuguese is an integral part, direct or indirect, of the program and must demonstrate a desire to teach the Portuguese language and/or culture.

GEOGRAPHIC RESTRICTIONS:
California.

FINANCIAL DATA:
Amount of support per award: Grants vary in amount, depending on the applicant's need and Foundation funds allocated.

Total amount of support: Varies.

APPLICATION INFORMATION:
Call and request application form.

Deadline: Applications are accepted during January and February only. For completed application, postmark by March 1.

PUBLICATIONS:
The Luso-American, annual; *Portuguese Presence in California; Literatura de Expressao Portuguesa Nos Estados Unidos;* bibliographies; annual report.

ADDRESS INQUIRIES TO:
Carmen Odom, Administrative Director
(See address above.)

MODERN LANGUAGE ASSOCIATION OF AMERICA   [696]

26 Broadway, 3rd Floor
New York, NY 10004-1789
(646) 576-5141
Fax: (646) 458-0030

E-MAIL ADDRESS:
awards@mla.org
areiser@mla.org

WEB SITE ADDRESS:
www.mla.org

FOUNDED: 1883

AREAS OF INTEREST:
Literary studies, languages and education.

NAME(S) OF PROGRAMS:
● **Katherine Singer Kovacs Prize**

● **Fenia and Yaakov Leviant Memorial Prize in Yiddish Studies**
● **James Russell Lowell Prize**
● **Howard R. Marraro Prize**
● **MLA Prize for a Distinguished Bibliography**
● **MLA Prize for a First Book**
● **MLA Prize for Independent Scholars**
● **MLA Prize in United States Latina and Latino and Chicana and Chicano Literary and Cultural Studies**
● **Lois Roth Award for a Translation of a Literary Work**
● **Aldo and Jeanne Scaglione Prize for a Translation of a Literary Work**
● **Aldo and Jeanne Scaglione Prize for a Translation of a Scholarly Study of Literature**
● **Aldo and Jeanne Scaglione Prize for Comparative Literary Studies**
● **Aldo and Jeanne Scaglione Prize for French and Francophone Studies**
● **Aldo and Jeanne Scaglione Prize for Italian Studies**
● **Aldo and Jeanne Scaglione Prize for Slavic Studies**
● **Aldo and Jeanne Scaglione Prize for Studies in Germanic Languages and Literatures**
● **Aldo and Jeanne Scaglione Publication Award for a Manuscript in Italian Literary Studies**
● **William Sanders Scarborough Prize**

TYPE:
Awards/prizes. To recognize outstanding scholarly works in the fields of English, French, Italian, Germanic languages and Slavic languages, Yiddish literature and culture, Black American literature and culture, Latino/Latina and Chicana/Chicano literature and culture. Germanic languages include Danish, Dutch, German, Icelandic, Norwegian, Swedish and Yiddish.

PURPOSE:
To recognize outstanding scholarly work.

LEGAL BASIS:
Membership association.

ELIGIBILITY:
For all awards, works of literary history, literary criticism, philology or literary theory are eligible. Except for translation prizes, books that are primarily translations are ineligible. For French, Germanic, Italian, Lowell, First Book and Marraro Prizes, books must be written by a current member of the Association.

FINANCIAL DATA:
Amount of support per award: Varies.

APPLICATION INFORMATION:
Application form is required for submissions to the Prize for Independent Scholars. To enter books into competition for other prizes, no special form or procedure is needed. Four to six copies of each work are required, depending upon the prize. Shipments of books should be preceded or accompanied by letters identifying the works and where necessary, confirming the author's membership in the MLA.

Duration: One-time awards.

Deadline: James Russell Lowell Prize: March 1. Prize for a First Book, Scaglione Prize for a Translation of a Literary Work and Lois Roth Award: April 1. Scaglione Publication Award for a Manuscript in Italian Literary Studies: August 1. All other awards: May 1.

ADDRESS INQUIRIES TO:
Annie Reiser, Coordinator of Book Prizes
(See address above.)

MODERN LANGUAGE ASSOCIATION OF AMERICA [697]

26 Broadway, 3rd Floor
New York, NY 10004-1789
(646) 576-5141
Fax: (646) 458-0030

E-MAIL ADDRESS:
awards@mla.org

WEB SITE ADDRESS:
www.mla.org

FOUNDED: 1883

AREAS OF INTEREST:
Literary studies, languages and education.

NAME(S) OF PROGRAMS:
● **Morton N. Cohen Award**
● **Kenneth W. Mildenberger Prize**
● **Modern Language Association Prize for a Distinguished Scholarly Edition**
● **Modern Language Association Prize for Independent Scholars**
● **Mina P. Shaughnessy Prize**

TYPE:
Awards/prizes.

PURPOSE:
To recognize outstanding scholarly work.

LEGAL BASIS:
Membership association.

ELIGIBILITY:
Authors are not required to be members of the Association.

The Morton N. Cohen Award is presented biennially in odd-numbered years for important collections of letters published in either of the two preceding years. A multivolume edition is eligible if at least one volume was published during that period.

Editors can apply regardless of the fields they and the authors of the letters represent. The winning collection will be one that provides a clear, accurate and readable text, necessary background information, and succinct and eloquent introductory material and annotations. The collection should be in itself a work of literature.

The Kenneth W. Mildenberger Prize is presented for an outstanding publication in the field of teaching foreign languages and literatures.

The Modern Language Association Prize for a Distinguished Scholarly Edition will be given biennially in odd-numbered years to a book published in either of the two preceding years without regard to the field or language either of the editor or of the text presented in the edition. To qualify for the award, an edition should be based on an examination of all available relevant textual sources; the source texts and the edited text's deviations from them should be fully described; the edition should employ editorial principles appropriate to the materials edited, and those principles should be clearly articulated in the volume; the text should be accompanied by appropriate textual and other historical contextual information; the edition should exhibit the highest standards of accuracy in the presentation of its text and apparatus; and the text and apparatus should be presented as accessibly and elegantly as possible.

The Modern Language Association Prize for Independent Scholars is awarded annually for a distinguished scholarly book published in the field of English or another modern language or literature. Authors enrolled in a program leading to an academic degree and authors holding a tenured, tenure-accruing or tenure-track position in a postsecondary institution at the time of publication of the book are not eligible. Tenure is understood to include any comparable provision for job security in a postsecondary educational institution.

The Mina P. Shaughnessy Prize is presented for an outstanding research publication in the field of teaching English language, literature, rhetoric and composition.

FINANCIAL DATA:
Amount of support per award: Varies.
Total amount of support: Varies.

APPLICATION INFORMATION:
Application form is required for submissions to the Prize for Independent Scholars. To enter book into competition for other prizes, no special form or procedure is needed. Shipments of books should be preceded or accompanied by letters identifying the works.
Duration: One-time award.
Deadline: May 1.

ADDRESS INQUIRIES TO:
Annie Reiser, Coordinator of Book Prizes
(See address above.)

NATIONAL SCIENCE FOUNDATION [698]

Linguistics Program
Division of Behavioral and Cognitive Sciences
4201 Wilson Boulevard, Suite 995
Arlington, VA 22230
(703) 292-8046
Fax: (703) 292-9068

E-MAIL ADDRESS:
jmaling@nsf.gov

WEB SITE ADDRESS:
www.nsf.gov

FOUNDED: 1950

NAME(S) OF PROGRAMS:
● **Doctoral Dissertation Research Improvement Grants (DDIG)**
● **Documenting Endangered Languages (DEL)**
● **Linguistics Program**

TYPE:
Research grants. Conferences/workshops. Awards provide support for research into the syntactic, morphological, semantic, phonological and phonetic properties of individual languages and of language in general. Research into the acquisition of language, the psychological processes in the production and perception of language, the biological foundations of language, the social influences on and effects of language and dialect variation, and the formal and mathematical properties of language models are also supported.

YEAR PROGRAM STARTED: 1975

PURPOSE:
To support scientific research and education to strengthen research potential in language sciences.

LEGAL BASIS:
National Science Foundation Act of 1950.

ELIGIBILITY:
Applicants may be colleges and universities on behalf of their staff members, nonprofit, nonacademic research institutions, such as independent museums, observatories, research laboratories, stock centers and similar organizations, private profit organizations and, under special circumstances, unaffiliated U.S. scientists.

GEOGRAPHIC RESTRICTIONS:
United States and its territories.

FINANCIAL DATA:
Support may cover salaries, research assistantships, staff benefits if a direct cost, permanent equipment, travel, publication costs, computer costs and certain other direct and indirect costs.
Amount of support per award: Averages $275,000 over three-year grant period.
Total amount of support: Approximately $6,000,000 for fiscal year 2010; $2,100,000 for DEL.

NUMBER OF APPLICANTS MOST RECENT YEAR:
Approximately 280 for the year 2009; 75 for DEL.

NUMBER OF AWARDS: Approximately 75 (36 dissertation improvements, 30 standard) plus 9 conferences for fiscal year 2010.

APPLICATION INFORMATION:
A proposal should include information about the institution, principal investigator and business administrator, title and description of proposed research, desired effective date of grant, duration of support, facilities, personnel, biographical sketches, current support and pending applications and budget.
Duration: Research grants may be for periods of up to five years. Most grants are for three years.
Deadline: Linguistics Program: Target dates are July 15 for Fall review and January 15 for Spring review. Proposals received too late for one round of review will be reviewed in the following round with a corresponding delay in the availability of funding. Documenting Endangered Languages Program: September 15.

PUBLICATIONS:
NSF grant proposal guide.

STAFF:
Joan Maling, Program Director

ADDRESS INQUIRIES TO:
Joan Maling, Program Director
(See address above.)

*PLEASE NOTE:
Programs within the Division also consider proposals for specialized research facilities and equipment, doctoral dissertation research with special financial needs (not including stipends) and research conferences and workshops relating to the described areas.

PEN AMERICAN CENTER [699]

588 Broadway, Suite 303
New York, NY 10012-5246
(212) 334-1660 ext. 108
Fax: (212) 334-2181

E-MAIL ADDRESS:
awards@pen.org

WEB SITE ADDRESS:
www.pen.org

FOUNDED: 1922

AREAS OF INTEREST:
Intellectual cooperation among men and women of letters in all countries in the interests of literature, the exchange of ideas, freedom of expression and goodwill.

NAME(S) OF PROGRAMS:
● **PEN Translation Prize**

TYPE:
Awards/prizes. Translation prize awarded for a distinguished translation into English from any language published in the U.S. in 2010.

YEAR PROGRAM STARTED: 1962

PURPOSE:
To promote the art of translation; to pay tribute to the profession.

LEGAL BASIS:
Nonprofit organization affiliated with International PEN.

ELIGIBILITY:
Although all eligible books must have been published in the U.S. in 2010, translators may be of any nationality; U.S. residency or citizenship is not required. There are no restrictions on the subject matter of translated works, although eligible titles should be of a literary character; technical, scientific, or bibliographical translations will not be considered.

FINANCIAL DATA:
Amount of support per award: $3,000.
Total amount of support: $3,000 annually.

NUMBER OF APPLICANTS MOST RECENT YEAR:
100.

NUMBER OF AWARDS: 1 each year.

REPRESENTATIVE AWARDS:
Tiina Nunnally, translator of *Kristin Lavransdottir*, by Sigrid Undset.

APPLICATION INFORMATION:
There is no application form. Three copies of book-length literary translations published during the calendar year under consideration may be submitted by publishers, agents, or the translators themselves. Self-published books are not eligible. Early submissions are strongly recommended.
Duration: One year.
Deadline: December 15.

BOARD OF TRUSTEES:
Kwame Anthony Appiah, President

ADDRESS INQUIRIES TO:
PEN Literary Awards
(See address above.)

THE PHI BETA KAPPA SOCIETY
1606 New Hampshire Avenue, N.W.
Washington, DC 20009
(202) 745-3235
Fax: (202) 986-1601

E-MAIL ADDRESS:
awards@pbk.org

WEB SITE ADDRESS:
www.pbk.org

TYPE:
Fellowships. Fellowship for at least six months of study in France. One award given annually.

See entry 984 for full listing.

SOUTH ATLANTIC MODERN LANGUAGE ASSOCIATION   [700]
Georgia State University
Department of English, GCB 923
38 Peachtree Center Avenue
Atlanta, GA 30303
(404) 413-5816
Fax: (404) 413-5830

E-MAIL ADDRESS:
samla@gsu.edu

WEB SITE ADDRESS:
samla.gsu.edu

FOUNDED: 1928

AREAS OF INTEREST:
All humanities.

NAME(S) OF PROGRAMS:
● **Graduate Student Essay Prize**
● **Harper Fund Award**
● **SAMLA Studies Award**
● **SAR Prize**

TYPE:
Awards/prizes; Travel grants. SAMLA Studies Award is for the best scholarly book written by a SAMLA member. Presses and individual members may nominate their recent publications in the year prior to the year of the convention.

YEAR PROGRAM STARTED: 1934

PURPOSE:
To encourage and honor distinguished scholarship in the modern languages and literatures.

LEGAL BASIS:
Nonprofit organization.

ELIGIBILITY:
Open to SAMLA members.

FINANCIAL DATA:
Amount of support per award: Graduate Student Essay Prize: $250; Harper Fund Award: Up to $500; SAMLA Studies Award: $1,000; SAR Prize: $500.
Total amount of support: Varies.

NUMBER OF APPLICANTS MOST RECENT YEAR:
SAMLA Studies Award: 8; SAR Prizes: 25.

NUMBER OF AWARDS: SAMLA Studies Award, SAR Prizes and Graduate Student Essay Prize: 4. Harper Fund Award: Varies.

APPLICATION INFORMATION:
SAMLA Studies Award: Applicants must be SAMLA members who have had a scholarly book published in the preceding year. No bibliographies or editions. Must be written in English. Presses and individuals may nominate their recent publications.
Duration: One-time award. Nonrenewable.
Deadline: May 1.

PUBLICATIONS:
South Atlantic Review, quarterly journal; *SAMLA News*, newsletter.

IRS IDENTIFICATION NUMBER: 62-0800246

OFFICERS:
Nancy Hargrove, President
Charles Moore, First Vice President
Kathleen Blake Yancey, Second Vice President

EXECUTIVE COMMITTEE:
Martha Cook
Tony Grooms
Jay Lutz
Joan E. McRae
Ennio Rao
Matthew Roudane

Robert Sawyer
Freddy L. Thomas

ADDRESS INQUIRIES TO:
Lara Smith-Sitton, Associate Director
(See address above.)

U.S. DEPARTMENT OF EDUCATION   [701]
International and Foreign Language Education (IFLE)
1990 K Street, N.W., Suite 6000
Washington, DC 20006-8521
(202) 502-7631
(202) 502-7700
Fax: (202) 502-7860

E-MAIL ADDRESS:
OPE_NRC-FLAS@ed.gov

WEB SITE ADDRESS:
www.ed.gov/programs/iegpsflasf/index.html

AREAS OF INTEREST:
Foreign language and area studies.

NAME(S) OF PROGRAMS:
● **Foreign Language and Area Studies Fellowships**

TYPE:
Fellowships. The Foreign Language and Area Studies program provides allocations of academic year and summer fellowships to institutions of higher education or consortia of institutions of higher education to assist meritorious undergraduate students and graduate students undergoing training in modern foreign languages and related international studies.

YEAR PROGRAM STARTED: 1959

LEGAL BASIS:
Section 602, Title VI of the Higher Education Act of 1965, as amended.

ELIGIBILITY:
FLAS grants are awarded to institutions for a four-year project period. Institutions conduct competitions to select eligible undergraduate and graduate students to receive fellowships.

GEOGRAPHIC RESTRICTIONS:
United States.

FINANCIAL DATA:
Each fellowship includes an institutional payment and a subsistence allowance.
Amount of support per award: The estimated institutional payment for 2010-2011 academic year fellowship is $18,000 for a graduate student and $10,000 for an undergraduate student. The estimated institutional payment for summer 2011 fellowship is $5,000 for graduate and undergraduate students.

The estimated subsistence allowance for academic year 2010-2011 fellowship is $15,000 for a graduate student and $5,000 for an undergraduate student. The subsistence allowance for summer 2011 fellowship is $2,500 for graduate and undergraduate students.

APPLICATION INFORMATION:
An electronic application form is available at the web site.
Duration: Varies.
Deadline: March.

ADDRESS INQUIRIES TO:
Carla White, Program Specialist
(See address above.)

U.S. DEPARTMENT OF EDUCATION   [702]

International and Foreign Language Education (IFLE)
Advanced Training & Research Group
Room 6084, 6th Floor
1990 K Street, N.W.
Washington, DC 20006-8521
(202) 502-7689
(202) 502-7700 (main office)
Fax: (202) 502-7860

E-MAIL ADDRESS:
ddra@ed.gov

WEB SITE ADDRESS:
www.ed.gov/programs/iegpsddrap/index.html

AREAS OF INTEREST:
Foreign languages.

NAME(S) OF PROGRAMS:
● **Fulbright-Hays Doctoral Dissertation Research Abroad**

TYPE:
Fellowships. Fellowships to support doctoral dissertation research abroad in modern foreign languages and related area studies. For the purpose of these programs, area studies is defined as a program of comprehensive study of the aspects of a society or societies, including the study of their geography, history, culture, economy, politics, international relations and languages. The program is designed to develop research knowledge and capability in world areas not widely included in American curricula. Awards will not be available for projects focusing on Western Europe.

YEAR PROGRAM STARTED: 1964

PURPOSE:
To enable graduate students who plan to teach in the U.S. to undertake doctoral dissertation research in the field of modern foreign languages and area studies; to assist with the development of language and area studies specialists.

LEGAL BASIS:
The Mutual Educational and Cultural Exchange Act of 1961, Public Law 87-256, as amended (commonly known as the Fulbright-Hays Act), Section 102(b)(6).

ELIGIBILITY:
A student is eligible to receive a fellowship if he or she:
(1) is a citizen or national of the U.S. or is a permanent resident of the U.S.;
(2) is a graduate student in good standing at an institution of higher education who, when the fellowship begins, is admitted to candidacy in a doctoral program in modern foreign languages and area studies at that institution;
(3) is planning a teaching career in the U.S. upon graduation and;
(4) possesses adequate skills in the language(s) necessary to carry out the dissertation project.

FINANCIAL DATA:
Travel expenses, including excess baggage to and from the residence of the fellow to the host country of research. Maintenance allowance based on the cost of living in country(ies) of research for the fellow and his or her dependent(s). Project allowance for research-related expenses such as books, affiliation fees, local travel and other incidental expenses. Health and accident insurance premiums. $100 administrative fee to applicant institution.

Amount of support per award: $39,000 average for the year 2010.
Total amount of support: $6,367,176 for the year 2010.

REPRESENTATIVE AWARDS:
$19,303 for "Testing AIDS Treatment Efficacy by a Northern Thai Community;" $28,565 for "Rethinking Community Through Suburban Nepal;" $22,364 for "Culture, Nationalism and Ethnicity in Twentieth Century Lesotho."

APPLICATION INFORMATION:
Official application materials are available from college and university graduate schools concerned with the fellowship program. Prospective applicants must apply electronically through their institutions. The completed materials are then forwarded electronically by the institution to the U.S. Education Department's Application Control Center (ACC) in accordance with instructions published in the *Federal Register*.
Duration: Fellowships provide support for a minimum period of six months and a maximum period of 12 months.
Deadline: Official deadlines to be determined each fall.

ADDRESS INQUIRIES TO:
Amy Wilson, Senior Program Officer
(See address above.)

U.S. DEPARTMENT OF EDUCATION

Higher Education Programs
1990 K Street, N.W., 6th Floor
Washington, DC 20006-8521
(202) 502-7625
(202) 502-7700
Fax: (202) 502-7860

E-MAIL ADDRESS:
michelle.guilfoil@ed.gov

WEB SITE ADDRESS:
www.ed.gov/programs/iegpsgpa/index.html

TYPE:
Project/program grants. Also, study grants and grants for foreign language and area study programs of educational development for projects to be undertaken abroad. Grants are awarded to higher education institutions, nonprofit educational organizations, state department of education and consortium of such institutions, departments, organizations and institutions which, in turn, enable professors, college and elementary and secondary school teachers and advanced students to attend seminars abroad and to travel and study in foreign countries in order to strengthen the institution's programs in foreign languages, area studies and world affairs.

See entry 994 for full listing.

U.S. DEPARTMENT OF EDUCATION

Office of Postsecondary Education
International and Foreign Language Education
1990 K Street, N.W., 6th Floor
Washington, DC 20006-8521
(202) 502-7589
(202) 502-7700
Fax: (202) 502-7859

E-MAIL ADDRESS:
cynthia.dudzinski@ed.gov

WEB SITE ADDRESS:
www.ed.gov/programs/iegpsfra/index.html

TYPE:
Fellowships; Research grants. This program funds fellowships through institutions of higher education (IHEs) to faculty members who propose to conduct research abroad in modern foreign languages and area studies to improve their skill in language and their knowledge of the culture of the people of these countries.

See entry 995 for full listing.

YIVO INSTITUTE FOR JEWISH RESEARCH

15 West 16th Street
New York, NY 10011-6301
(212) 294-6139
Fax: (212) 292-1892

E-MAIL ADDRESS:
pglasser@yivo.cjh.org
yivomail@yivo.cjh.org

WEB SITE ADDRESS:
www.yivo.org

TYPE:
Awards/prizes; Fellowships; Grants-in-aid; Project/program grants; Research grants; Scholarships. Awarded to train scholars in the field of Eastern European Jewish history and culture, Yiddish language, linguistics, literature, folklore and ethnography.

The Choseed Memorial Fellowship is given to help support original doctoral or postdoctoral research at the YIVO Library and Archives in the field of East European Jewish Studies. The Fellowship is for a period of one to three months of research. The holder of the Fellowship is required to give a public lecture.

The Hertz Memorial Fellowship supports doctoral or postdoctoral research on Polish-Jewish history in the modern period, particularly Jewish-Polish relations and Jewish contributions to Polish literature and culture.

The Hort Memorial Fellowship helps support original doctoral or postdoctoral research in the field of Yiddish literature. The Fellowship is for one to three months of research at the YIVO Library and Archives and a public lecture by the holder.

The Melezin Fellowship supports doctoral or postdoctoral research on Jewish educational networks in Lithuania, with emphasis on prewar Vilna and the Vilna region.

The Racolin Memorial Fellowship supports original doctoral or postdoctoral research in the field of East European Jewish history. The Fellowship is for one to three months of research at the YIVO Library and Archives and a public lecture by the holder.

The Maria Salit-Gitelson Tell Memorial Fellowship helps support original doctoral or postdoctoral research in the field of Lithuanian Jewish history, the city of Vilna in particular. The Fellowship is for one to three months of research at the YIVO Library and Archives and a public lecture by the holder.

See entry 686 for full listing.

Literature

ALPHA SIGMA NU [703]

Jesuit Honor Society
Marquette University
707 North 11th Street, No. 330
Milwaukee, WI 53233
(414) 288-7542
Fax: (414) 288-3259

E-MAIL ADDRESS:
info@alphasigmanu.org

WEB SITE ADDRESS:
www.alphasigmanu.org

FOUNDED: 1915

NAME(S) OF PROGRAMS:
- **Alpha Sigma Nu Book Award**

TYPE:
Awards/prizes; Scholarships. Four awards for best published scholarly works each year (humanities, professional studies and sciences) rotate in three-year cycle.

YEAR PROGRAM STARTED: 1979

PURPOSE:
To give recognition to scholarly excellence at Jesuit colleges and universities.

LEGAL BASIS:
Honor society of Jesuit institutions of higher education (nonprofit).

ELIGIBILITY:
Candidates must be full- or part-time faculty or administration or have emeritus status at a Jesuit institution of higher education.

GEOGRAPHIC RESTRICTIONS:
United States, Canada and Korea.

FINANCIAL DATA:
Amount of support per award: $1,000.
Total amount of support: $4,000.

NUMBER OF APPLICANTS MOST RECENT YEAR:
60 to 100.

NUMBER OF AWARDS: 4 annually.

APPLICATION INFORMATION:
Application forms are available from the Association of Jesuit Colleges and Universities, One Dupont Circle, Suite 405, Washington, DC 20036 and from academic vice presidents and deans of the Jesuit institutions of higher education. Applications are also available at the web site above.
Deadline: March 1. Annual announcement October 1.

PUBLICATIONS:
Two newsletters.

IRS IDENTIFICATION NUMBER: 39-1174431

BOARD OF DIRECTORS:
Rebecca Cates, President
Patrick J. Cain, Vice President
Louise Foster, Treasurer
Michele G. Gilfillan, Secretary
Benjamin Fiore, S.J., Board Faculty Adviser
J. Taylor Calderone, Board Alumni Co-Advisor
Anthony Giordano, Board Alumni Co-Advisor
Carolyn Conkling
Frank R. Haig, S.J.
Patrick Lynch, S.J.
Mark Rzepczynsi
Michael Williams, S.J.
Anne Zehrer

ADDRESS INQUIRIES TO:
Kate Gaertner, Executive Director
Alpha Sigma Nu
(See address above.)

AMERICAN ITALIAN HISTORICAL ASSOCIATION, INC.

P.O. Box 487
Millbrae, CA 94030
(408) 554-4142
Fax: (408) 554-4837

E-MAIL ADDRESS:
quinnroseanne@deanza.edu

WEB SITE ADDRESS:
www.aihaweb.org

TYPE:
Scholarships.
See entry 617 for full listing.

AMERICAN SOCIETY OF COMPOSERS, AUTHORS AND PUBLISHERS (ASCAP) [704]

ASCAP Building, 6th Floor
One Lincoln Plaza
New York, NY 10023
(212) 621-6000
(800) 952-7227
Fax: (212) 621-8453

E-MAIL ADDRESS:
info@ascap.com
esansaurus@ascap.com

WEB SITE ADDRESS:
www.ascap.com/deemstaylor

FOUNDED: 1914

AREAS OF INTEREST:
Music, creative and performing arts.

NAME(S) OF PROGRAMS:
- **ASCAP Deems Taylor Awards**

TYPE:
Awards/prizes. The ASCAP Deems Taylor Awards program recognizes books, articles, broadcasts and web sites on the subject of music selected for their excellence.

YEAR PROGRAM STARTED: 1967

PURPOSE:
To encourage, recognize and reward excellence in a field that is vital to the health and growth of America's musical heritage.

LEGAL BASIS:
Membership association.

ELIGIBILITY:
Any written works published anywhere in the U.S. (the 50 states, Puerto Rico or the District of Columbia) in English during the calendar year preceding the award will be eligible. The subject matter may be biographical or critical, reportorial or historical   almost any form of nonfiction prose about music and/or its creators - not an instructional textbook, how-to guide, or a work of fiction.

Paperbacks that were originally published in hardcover are not eligible. Reprints or translations of works that were previously published outside of the U.S. and are now being published in the U.S. for the first time are eligible. Program notes, recording liner notes, and online publications are also eligible.

GEOGRAPHIC RESTRICTIONS:
United States.

FINANCIAL DATA:
Amount of support per award: Several categories of cash prizes, from $250 to

$1,000. Plaques are also presented to the authors and journalists as well as to their respective publishers.

Total amount of support: Varies.

NUMBER OF AWARDS: 15.

APPLICATION INFORMATION:
There is no official entry form or fee; however, all submissions must include a cover letter containing the following information:
(1) title of the book, article, program or liner notes;
(2) copyright date of book or date of publication for the article (or issue date for recording liner notes);
(3) name, address and daytime phone number of all authors of the book or article and;
(4) contact name, address and daytime phone number of the publisher or publication in which the article appeared.

Four copies of each entry are required. Submissions will not be returned. For articles and liner notes, submissions are limited to three entries per author. Those articles that were published as a series of articles on a single, specific topic may be considered as one entry. When submitting one or more articles, be sure that a copy of every article is put into each of four letter-sized file folders. Label each folder with one's full name only. (This is for the competition judges who will review the entries.) Liner notes should be limited to 4,500 words and include four copies of each recording.

Submissions should be addressed to ASCAP Deems Taylor Awards; American Society of Composers, Authors & Publishers at the address listed above.

Duration: Annual award.

Deadline: Materials accepted March 21 through June 1.

DIRECTORS:
Irwin Robinson, Publisher Vice Chairman
Jimmy Webb, Writer Vice Chairman
Paul Williams, President
James M. Kendrick, Treasurer
Martin Bandier
Richard Bellis
Marilyn Bergman
Caroline Bienstock
Bruce Broughton
Barry Coburn
Hal David
John L. Eastman
Roger Faxon
Dan Foliart
Wayland Holyfield
David H. Johnson
Dean Kay
Leeds Levy
Johnny Mandel
Stephen Paulus
David Renzer
Valerie Simpson
Doug Wood

ADDRESS INQUIRIES TO:
Esther SanSaurus
ASCAP-Deems Taylor Awards
Tel: (212) 621-6323
E-mail: esansaurus@ascap.com
(See address above.)

THE AMERICAN-SCANDINAVIAN FOUNDATION [705]

58 Park Avenue
New York, NY 10016
(212) 879-9779
(212) 847-9728
Fax: (212) 249-3444

E-MAIL ADDRESS:
grants@amscan.org

WEB SITE ADDRESS:
www.amscan.org

FOUNDED: 1910

AREAS OF INTEREST:
Translations of poetry, fiction or drama by Danish, Finnish, Icelandic, Norwegian or Swedish authors born after 1800.

NAME(S) OF PROGRAMS:
● **American-Scandinavian Foundation Translation Prize**

TYPE:
Awards/prizes. Prize for translation of fiction (50 double-spaced manuscript pages) or poetry (25 double-spaced manuscript pages).

YEAR PROGRAM STARTED: 1980

PURPOSE:
To encourage English translation of contemporary Scandinavian literature.

LEGAL BASIS:
Nonprofit educational institution qualifying under statutes 501(c)(3), 509(a)(1) and 170(c)(2) of the IRS code.

ELIGIBILITY:
Entry must be work by one author, though not necessarily from a single work. It should be conceived as part of a book manuscript. A table of contents for the proposed book should also be included.

FINANCIAL DATA:
Amount of support per award: First prize: $2,000; Second Prize: $1,000.
Total amount of support: $3,000.

NUMBER OF APPLICANTS MOST RECENT YEAR:
20.

NUMBER OF AWARDS: 2.

APPLICATION INFORMATION:
Request rules for Translation Prize Competition. Applicants should submit one copy of work in original language and four copies of translation, including title page and table of contents. Name, address and phone number of translator and title and author of the manuscript with the original language specified should be on a separate page. Translator must include written permission from author or author's agent for translation to be entered in competition and published in *Scandinavian Review*. Manuscripts accompanied by self-addressed, stamped envelope will be returned.

Duration: One-time award.

Deadline: June 1. Awards announced by November 1.

PUBLICATIONS:
Competition rules.

OFFICER:
Edward P. Gallagher, President

ADDRESS INQUIRIES TO:
Translation Prize Committee
(See address above.)

THE ASSOCIATION OF WRITERS & WRITING PROGRAMS [706]

Mail Stop 1E3
George Mason University
Fairfax, VA 22030
(703) 993-4301
Fax: (703) 993-4302

E-MAIL ADDRESS:
supriya@awpwriter.org

WEB SITE ADDRESS:
www.awpwriter.org

FOUNDED: 1967

AREAS OF INTEREST:
Creative writing; four genres: short fiction, poetry, creative nonfiction and the novel.

CONSULTING OR VOLUNTEER SERVICES:
The office provides information on curricula for courses or programs in creative writing and members of the Board of Directors occasionally visit campuses in order to consult with departments wishing to establish or improve creative writing programs. The office also sponsors the INTRO Journals Project, an annual competition of fiction, nonfiction and poetry by students of creative writing; runs job placement service for members interested in obtaining teaching and writing-oriented positions.

NAME(S) OF PROGRAMS:
● **AWP Award Series in Creative Nonfiction**
● **AWP Award Series in the Novel**
● **Donald Hall Prize in Poetry**
● **Grace Paley Prize in Short Fiction**

TYPE:
Awards/prizes. Annual open competitions for book-length manuscripts: a collection of short stories, a collection of poems, or a work of creative nonfiction of more than 60,000 words. The award in each case is the publication of the winning manuscript by a university press and a cash honorarium from AWP in addition to royalties from the publisher.

YEAR PROGRAM STARTED: 1974

PURPOSE:
To support American writers and creative writing programs in U.S. colleges and universities; to encourage the publication and distribution of good fiction, poetry and other creative writing; to improve the quality of literary education primarily at the college level, as well as at the public school level; to disseminate information useful to writers and students of writing.

LEGAL BASIS:
Nonprofit, tax-exempt corporation.

ELIGIBILITY:
Original works written in English are eligible.

Only book-length manuscripts are eligible (poetry: 48 pages minimum; short story collection and creative nonfiction: 150 to 300 manuscript pages; novel: at least 60,000 words).

The AWP Award Series is open to all authors writing original works in English. No mixed-genre manuscripts can be accepted. Criticism and scholarly monographs are not acceptable for creative nonfiction, which the Award Series defines as factual and literary writing that has the narrative, dramatic, meditative and lyrical elements of novels, plays, poetry, and memoirs.

To avoid conflict of interest and to avoid the appearance of a conflict of interest, former students of a judge (former students who studied with a judge in an academic degree-conferring program or its equivalent) are ineligible to enter the competition in the genre for which their former teacher is serving as judge.

FINANCIAL DATA:
Negotiations regarding book royalties are left to the author and publisher, but AWP has established minimum standards.

Amount of support per award: AWP Award Series: $2,000 each; Donald Hall Prize in Poetry: $5,000, in addition to royalties from the publisher; Grace Paley Prize in Short Fiction: $5,000.

Total amount of support: $14,000.

COOPERATIVE FUNDING PROGRAMS: Donald Hall Prize in Poetry and Grace Paley Prize for Short Fiction are made possible by the generous support of amazon.com.

NUMBER OF APPLICANTS MOST RECENT YEAR:
Short Fiction: 352; Poetry: 881; Novel: 427; Nonfiction: 146.

NUMBER OF AWARDS: 1 winner per genre; 2 finalists per genre.

APPLICATION INFORMATION:
Submit typed, double-spaced manuscript, on good quality paper, 8 1/2 by 11 inches, arranged as the author would prefer to see the book published, to the Associated Writing Programs. (Poetry manuscripts may be single-spaced.) Photocopies or copies from letter-quality printers are acceptable, but dot matrix is not acceptable. Manuscripts should not be bound or in a folder; they must be binder-clipped or rubber-banded together.

Each manuscript must include:
(1) a cover page with the author's name, address, phone number and manuscript title and;
(2) a title page with the manuscript title only. The cover page will be removed so that each submission can be read anonymously. If the author's name appears anywhere except the cover page, the manuscript will be disqualified. Do not send acknowledgement of previous publications or a biographical note.

No manuscripts can be returned. Enclose a stamped, self-addressed envelope for notification of results along with a stamped, self-addressed postcard to acknowledge receipt of manuscript and a $25 entry/reading fee for nonmembers, $10 for AWP members. Send a self-addressed, stamped envelope for guidelines before submitting.

Deadline: Manuscripts are accepted only with postmark dates of January 1 and February 28.

PUBLICATIONS:
Guidelines; *The Writer's Chronicle*, six times per year.

IRS IDENTIFICATION NUMBER: 05-0314999

EXECUTIVE DIRECTOR:
D.W. Fenza

ADDRESS INQUIRIES TO:
Supriya Bhatnagar
Director of Publications
(See address above.)

ASTRAEA LESBIAN FOUNDATION FOR JUSTICE
116 East 16th Street, 7th Floor
New York, NY 10003
(212) 529-8021
Fax: (212) 982-3321

E-MAIL ADDRESS:
grants@astraeafoundation.org

WEB SITE ADDRESS:
www.astraeafoundation.org

TYPE:
Awards/prizes.

See entry 1034 for full listing.

BREAD LOAF WRITERS' CONFERENCE   [707]
Middlebury College
Kirk Alumni Center
Middlebury, VT 05753
(802) 443-5286
Fax: (802) 443-2087

E-MAIL ADDRESS:
blwc@middlebury.edu

WEB SITE ADDRESS:
www.middlebury.edu/blwc

FOUNDED: 1926

AREAS OF INTEREST:
Poetry, fiction and nonfiction.

NAME(S) OF PROGRAMS:
● **Fellowship and Scholarship Program for Writers**

TYPE:
Fellowships; Scholarships; Work-study programs. Fellowships and scholarships pay all or part of conference fees.

YEAR PROGRAM STARTED: 1926

PURPOSE:
To encourage writers at the beginning of their careers.

LEGAL BASIS:
Nonprofit.

ELIGIBILITY:
Fellowship candidates must have had one or two original books published. Privately printed books are not considered.

Candidates for tuition scholarships must have had their work published in recognized literary periodicals, but will not have published in book form.

Working scholarships as waiters and waitresses are available for people who have not had their work published but who show promise as writers.

People under 18 are not eligible.

FINANCIAL DATA:
Fellowships pay all conference fees, tuition, room and board. Tuition scholarships pay full tuition but not room and board. Working scholarships pay part of tuition and room and board; recipients earn the remainder.
Total amount of support: Varies.

NUMBER OF APPLICANTS MOST RECENT YEAR:
1,400.

NUMBER OF AWARDS: 60.

APPLICATION INFORMATION:
Information is available online.
Duration: Usually one-time award.
Deadline: March 1. Announcement in May.

DIRECTORS:
Michael Collier, Director
Jennifer Grotz, Assistant Director

ADDRESS INQUIRIES TO:
Noreen Cargill, Administrative Manager
(See address above.)

THE WITTER BYNNER FOUNDATION FOR POETRY, INC.   [708]
P.O. Box 10169
Santa Fe, NM 87504-0169
(505) 988-3251
Fax: (505) 986-8222

E-MAIL ADDRESS:
bynnerfoundation@aol.com

WEB SITE ADDRESS:
bynnerfoundation.org

FOUNDED: 1972

AREAS OF INTEREST:
Poetry, with special interest in developing the poetry audience, the process of poetry translation, uses of poetry (including but not limited to dramatic, educational, therapeutic, etc.) and the support of individual poets through existing institutional programs.

TYPE:
Awards/prizes; Challenge/matching grants; Conferences/seminars; Fellowships.

YEAR PROGRAM STARTED: 1972

PURPOSE:
To develop the poetic art through grant support to nonprofit organizations and individuals represented by such organizations.

LEGAL BASIS:
Exempt, private foundation.

ELIGIBILITY:
Only applications from nonprofit tax-exempt organizations will be accepted. No grants to individuals. Publication projects, endowment funds, capital improvements, continued support and operating expenses are not generally funded.

GEOGRAPHIC RESTRICTIONS:
United States.

FINANCIAL DATA:
Amount of support per award: $1,000 to $10,000.
Total amount of support: Approximately $53,250 for the year 2009-10.

NUMBER OF APPLICANTS MOST RECENT YEAR:
217 letters of intent for the year 2010.

NUMBER OF AWARDS: 10 programs for the year 2009-10.

REPRESENTATIVE AWARDS:
Library of Congress/Fellowships in Poetry; Santa Fe Art Institute/Translator Residencies; Santa Fe Girls School/Poetry Workshops; Santa Fe Arts Commission/Poetry Works; Academy of Technology and Classics Charter School; Teatro Paraguas; New Mexico Culture Net; Santa Fe Playhouse; Forest Woods Media Productions.

APPLICATION INFORMATION:
Upon request, the Foundation's guidelines, an annual report, and a list of the most recent grants will be provided. Applicants must submit a letter of intent prior to application.
Duration: One-year grants only; may be renewed at the discretion of the Board of Directors.

Deadline: February 15 annually. Announcement in May. Letters of intent accepted from August 1 to December 31 annually.

PUBLICATIONS:
Annual report; application guidelines.

IRS IDENTIFICATION NUMBER: 23-7169999

BOARD OF DIRECTORS:
Lara Morrow, President
Robert Kurth, Vice President
Helen Brandt, Secretary/Treasurer
Dr. Mark McDaniel
Dr. Douglas Schwartz

ADMINISTRATIVE STAFF:
Steven D. Schwartz, Executive Director
Nanci Caldwell, Business Manager

ADDRESS INQUIRIES TO:
Steven D. Schwartz, Executive Director
(See address above.)

*SPECIAL STIPULATIONS:
The Foundation is interested particularly in using its limited funds as a means to help attract additional monies from other sources to advance the art of poetry. Applications to support the development of seed-money proposals in each of the above areas, therefore, are especially encouraged. While the Foundation has traditionally been supportive of the four areas listed above, it may consider the support of other creative and innovative projects in poetry.

CANADA COUNCIL FOR THE ARTS   [709]
350 Albert Street
Ottawa ON K1P 5V8 Canada
(613) 566-4414 ext. 5060
(800) 263-5588 ext. 5060 (CAN only)
Fax: (613) 566-4390
TTY: (613) 565-5194 (hearing-impaired)

E-MAIL ADDRESS:
info@canadacouncil.ca

WEB SITE ADDRESS:
www.canadacouncil.ca/writing

FOUNDED: 1957

AREAS OF INTEREST:
The arts in Canada (dance, media arts, music, theatre, creative writing and publishing, inter-arts and visual arts).

NAME(S) OF PROGRAMS:
● **Writing and Publishing Section Grants**

TYPE:
Development grants; General operating grants; Grants-in-aid; Project/program grants; Residencies; Travel grants. Council grants support the following types of activities:
(1) Grants for Individual Professional Writers: These grants can help one create new work or travel to events important to one's career.
(2) Operating Funding: These grants offer operating support to book and periodical publishers and nonprofit arts service organizations.
(3) Project Funding: Project grants are available to nonprofit arts organizations, magazine and book publishers, artists' collectives or groups to cover some of the costs of specific, time-limited activities.

PURPOSE:
To provide support for the creation, translation, publication and promotion of Canadian literature.

LEGAL BASIS:
Independent agency established by the Parliament of Canada in 1957.

ELIGIBILITY:
Council grants cannot be used to start a business or to buy capital items, such as computers, musical instruments, film and video equipment, or printing presses.

GEOGRAPHIC RESTRICTIONS:
Canada.

FINANCIAL DATA:
Amount of support per award: Varies depending on project.
Total amount of support: Varies.

APPLICATION INFORMATION:
The Council does not send or accept applications by fax or e-mail.
Deadline: Varies.

PUBLICATIONS:
Program information sheets.

ADDRESS INQUIRIES TO:
Christian Mondor, Information Officer (See address above.)

CARNEGIE FUND FOR AUTHORS [710]
One Old Country Road
Carle Place, NY 11514

NAME(S) OF PROGRAMS:
● **Carnegie Fund for Authors**

TYPE:
Grants-in-aid. Emergency grants for authors who are in need.

PURPOSE:
To help authors who have suffered a hardship which in turn caused a financial emergency.

LEGAL BASIS:
Nonprofit organization.

ELIGIBILITY:
Qualified authors are eligible to apply who have suffered a financial emergency as the result of illness or injury to the author, spouse, or dependent child, or some equivalent misfortune. A qualified author with respect to this Fund is one who has had at least one book of reasonable length published commercially and which book has received reader acceptance. A so-called "vanity" book is not acceptable.

GEOGRAPHIC RESTRICTIONS:
Primarily United States.

FINANCIAL DATA:
Amount of support per award: Varies.
Total amount of support: Varies.

APPLICATION INFORMATION:
Application forms may be requested from the address above.
Duration: Generally, one-time award.

TRUSTEES:
Scott Albarella
Barbara Magalnick
William L. Rothenberg

*SPECIAL STIPULATIONS:
This Fund does not make loans, nor does it make grants for any literary projects, however worthwhile.

CAUZ GROUP [711]
P.O. Box 229
Pymble BC N.S.W. 2073 Australia
(61)(2) 9928-1552

E-MAIL ADDRESS:
trustawards@trust.com.au

WEB SITE ADDRESS:
www.trust.com.au

FOUNDED: 1954

AREAS OF INTEREST:
The advancement, improvement and betterment of Australian literature.

NAME(S) OF PROGRAMS:
● **Miles Franklin Literary Award**

TYPE:
Awards/prizes. Annual cash award for a published book on Australian life.

YEAR PROGRAM STARTED: 1957

PURPOSE:
To improve the educational style of authors; to help and give incentive to authors and to provide them with additional monetary support to enable them to improve their literary efforts.

LEGAL BASIS:
Trustees of estate of the late Miles Franklin.

ELIGIBILITY:
No special requirements as regards nationality, age, etc. The book must be published in the year of entry of the award and be of the highest literary merit and must present Australian life in any of its phases. More than one entry may be submitted by each author. Novels or plays written by two or more authors in collaboration are eligible.

Biographies, collections of short stories, young adult/children's books, poetry, farce or musical comedy are not eligible.

FINANCIAL DATA:
There is an entry fee of $75 (AUD).
Amount of support per award: $42,000 (AUD).

NUMBER OF APPLICANTS MOST RECENT YEAR:
50.

NUMBER OF AWARDS: 1 per year.

APPLICATION INFORMATION:
Conditions of entry including copies of proposed entries are to be submitted by the entrant to Cauz Group Limited including completed application form and six copies of novel. All packages containing entries should be clearly marked "Miles Franklin Literary Award Entry."
Duration: Annual.
Deadline: Second Friday in December of preceding year. Announcement of award in May/June.

PUBLICATIONS:
Application guidelines.

ADDRESS INQUIRIES TO:
Kate Brodie
(See address above.)

CHILDREN'S LITERATURE ASSOCIATION [712]
P.O. Box 138
Battle Creek, MI 49016-0138
(269) 965-8180
Fax: (269) 965-3568

E-MAIL ADDRESS:
info@childlitassn.org

WEB SITE ADDRESS:
www.childlitassn.org

FOUNDED: 1973

AREAS OF INTEREST:
All aspects of children's literature scholarship, research and criticism.

NAME(S) OF PROGRAMS:
● **ChLA Beiter Graduate Student Research Grants**
● **ChLA Faculty Research Grants**

TYPE:
Research grants. ChLA Beiter Graduate Student Research Grants: Grants are awarded for proposals of original scholarship with the expectation that the undertaking will lead to publication or a conference presentation and contribute to the field of children's literature criticism.

ChLA Faculty Research Grants: Grants are awarded for proposals dealing with criticism or original scholarship with the expectation that the undertaking will lead to publication and make a significant contribution to the field of children's literature in the area of scholarship or criticism. Proposals that deal with critical or original work in the areas of fantasy or science fiction for children or adolescents will be awarded the Margaret P. Esmonde Memorial Scholarship.

YEAR PROGRAM STARTED: 1978

PURPOSE:
To promote scholarship and criticism in children's literature.

LEGAL BASIS:
International; tax-exempt 501(c)(3), nonprofit scholarly organization.

ELIGIBILITY:
ChLA Beiter Research Grants for Graduate Students: Grant funds are not intended as income to assist in the completion of a graduate degree, but as support for research that may be related to the dissertation or Master's thesis. The grant may be used to purchase supplies and materials (e.g., books, videos, equipment), as research support (photocopying, etc.), or to underwrite travel to special collections or libraries. Winners must either be members of the Children's Literature Association or join the Association before they receive any funds. Students of ChLA Executive Board members or Scholarship Committee members are not eligible to apply.

ChLA Faculty Research Grants: Applications will be evaluated based upon the quality of the proposal and the potential of the project to enhance or advance children's literature studies. Funds may be used for (but are not restricted to) research-related expenses such as travel to special collections or purchasing materials and supplies. The awards may not be used for obtaining advanced degrees, for researching or writing a thesis or dissertation, for textbook writing, or for pedagogical projects. Winners must either be members of the Children's Literature Association or join the Association before they receive any funds. Members of the Executive Board of ChLA and of the Scholarship Committee are not eligible to apply.

FINANCIAL DATA:
ChLA Faculty Research Grants may be used for such expenses as transportation, living expenses or materials and supplies, but not for obtaining advanced degrees.
Amount of support per award: $500 to $1,500.
Total amount of support: Up to $10,000 annually for both grants.

NUMBER OF APPLICANTS MOST RECENT YEAR:
Faculty: 11; Graduate student: 9 for the year
2009.

NUMBER OF AWARDS: Varies.

APPLICATION INFORMATION:
E-mail proposals as an attachment dated
within the application period of January 1 to
February 1. Incomplete or late applications
will not be considered. Subject line should
read: ChLA Faculty Research Grant
Application or ChLA Beiter Graduate
Research Grant Application. Applications
should include name, mailing address, phone,
e-mail address, academic institution,
academic status or institution applicant is
affiliated with (library, publisher, etc.), a
detailed description of the research proposal,
a vita that includes a bibliography of major
publications and scholarly achievements (for
Beiter Grants, just a curriculum vitae), and
two letters of reference (for Beiter Grant
applicants only). One letter must be from
applicant's dissertation or thesis advisor. For
more information, write to the address listed
above.
For a printed copy of guidelines, please send
a self-addressed, stamped envelope.
Duration: Varies. Usually a one-time award
to run the length of the project or course of
study.
Deadline: February 1. Announcement at the
annual conference.

PUBLICATIONS:
Application guidelines.

IRS IDENTIFICATION NUMBER: 38-2005828

OFFICERS:
Dr. Michelle Martin, President

ADDRESS INQUIRIES TO:
ChLA Grants Committee
(See address above.)

*SPECIAL STIPULATIONS:
Winners should acknowledge ChLA in any
publication resulting from the award.

GEORGE WASHINGTON UNIVERSITY-ENGLISH DEPARTMENT   [713]
Rome Hall 760
801 22nd Street, N.W.
Washington, DC 20052
(202) 994-6180
Fax: (202) 994-7915

E-MAIL ADDRESS:
gwald@gwu.edu

WEB SITE ADDRESS:
www.gwu.edu/~english

FOUNDED: 1974

AREAS OF INTEREST:
Creative writing.

NAME(S) OF PROGRAMS:
● **Visiting Lecturer in Creative Writing**

TYPE:
Professorships; Residencies; Visiting
scholars. Grant, sponsored by George
Washington University, for a writer to spend
a year as visiting lecturer teaching two
courses per semester, one for university
students and one for the community.

YEAR PROGRAM STARTED: 1974

PURPOSE:
To encourage and support the creation of
poetry, fiction and drama.

LEGAL BASIS:
Trust fund.

ELIGIBILITY:
The position is open to any published writer
of fiction with some teaching experience and
sympathetic responses to student writers of
all ages and backgrounds.

FINANCIAL DATA:
Amount of support per award:
Approximately $58,000.
Total amount of support: $58,000.

NUMBER OF APPLICANTS MOST RECENT YEAR:
For teacher, 117. For fifteen places in class,
50.

NUMBER OF AWARDS: 1 lecturer position
annually.

APPLICATION INFORMATION:
Application should be made by letter, listing
publications, teaching experience and other
qualifications. Applicants are encouraged to
send a book along with a self-addressed,
stamped envelope.
Duration: Academic year, commencing in
September.
Deadline: Screening of applications begins
on November 15. Announcement usually
around May 30 for the September following.

ADDRESS INQUIRIES TO:
Prof. Gayle Wald, Chairperson
Department of English
(See address above.)

GREAT LAKES COLLEGES ASSOCIATION NEW WRITERS AWARDS   [714]
535 West William Street
Suite 301
Ann Arbor, MI 48103
(734) 661-2350
Fax: (734) 661-2349

E-MAIL ADDRESS:
shackelford@glca.org

WEB SITE ADDRESS:
www.glca.org

FOUNDED: 1962

AREAS OF INTEREST:
Education.

NAME(S) OF PROGRAMS:
● **New Writers Awards**

TYPE:
Awards/prizes. Winners invited to tour up to
13 Great Lakes Colleges. Honorarium and
expenses included. Awards are made for
yearly, first published best book of fiction,
best book of poetry and best book of creative
nonfiction.

YEAR PROGRAM STARTED: 1970

PURPOSE:
To promote new writers, literature and
colleges.

LEGAL BASIS:
Association of colleges and universities in
Michigan, Indiana, Ohio and Pennsylvania.

ELIGIBILITY:
The book must be the first book by the
author. Only publishers may submit; one
book in each category, four copies.

FINANCIAL DATA:
Amount of support per award: At least $500
per college visited.

NUMBER OF APPLICANTS MOST RECENT YEAR:
80.

NUMBER OF AWARDS: 1 each for creative
nonfiction, fiction and poetry.

APPLICATION INFORMATION:
Applicants should send for rules and enclose
self-addressed, stamped envelope or visit the
GLCA web site to download submission
packet.
Deadline: July 25.

ADDRESS INQUIRIES TO:
New Writers Awards
(See address above.)

IRISH AMERICAN CULTURAL INSTITUTE   [715]
One Lackawanna Place
Morristown, NJ 07960
(973) 605-1991
Fax: (973) 605-8875

E-MAIL ADDRESS:
info@iaci-usa.org

WEB SITE ADDRESS:
www.iaci-usa.org

FOUNDED: 1962

AREAS OF INTEREST:
Promotion of better understanding of Ireland
through publications and educational
programs such as the Institute's IRISH WAY
Program for high school students and its Irish
Perceptions Series which brings Irish
lecturers and performers to the U.S. to tour.

NAME(S) OF PROGRAMS:
● **IACI Visiting Fellowship in Irish
Studies at NUI-G**

TYPE:
Awards/prizes; Exchange programs;
Fellowships; Research grants. Grants and
awards available for authors of books written
in Irish, for Irish artists and composers, for
graduate research in Irish-American studies
and for lecturers dealing with subjects of
Irish interest.

YEAR PROGRAM STARTED: 1966

PURPOSE:
To stimulate, develop and disseminate
information pertinent to the Irish culture.

LEGAL BASIS:
Public foundation under IRS code 501(c)(3).

ELIGIBILITY:
Fellowships are open to scholars of all
disciplines relating to Irish studies. Literary
and art awards to residents of Ireland only.

FINANCIAL DATA:
Lecturers receive expenses, honoraria and
services in arranging tours.
Amount of support per award: Fellowship:
$4,000; Research awards: $1,000 to $5,000.
Total amount of support: Research awards:
$7,000 annually.

NUMBER OF APPLICANTS MOST RECENT YEAR:
40.

NUMBER OF AWARDS: 5 to 12.

REPRESENTATIVE AWARDS:
$5,000 to painter Basil Blackshaw; $5,000 to
author Michael Davitt; $5,000 to poet Patrick
Galvin.

APPLICATION INFORMATION:
Projects are generally initiated by the
Institute with pertinent announcements
distributed when necessary. However, brief
descriptive statements of appropriate

proposed projects are welcomed. Such requests should outline the objectives to be accomplished, the proposed means of accomplishment and the type and amount of assistance desired.

Duration: One-time awards.

Deadline: December 31.

PUBLICATIONS:
Eire-Ireland, magazine.

OFFICERS:
Peter Halas, Chairman
Brian Stack, Vice Chairman
Michael Slattery, Treasurer
Edward F. Ginty, Secretary

ADDRESS INQUIRIES TO:
Fellowship Coordinator
(See address above.)

JEWISH BOOK COUNCIL [716]

520 Eighth Avenue, 4th Floor
New York, NY 10018-4393
(212) 201-2920
Fax: (212) 532-4952

E-MAIL ADDRESS:
jbc@jewishbooks.org

WEB SITE ADDRESS:
www.jewishbookcouncil.org

FOUNDED: 1943

AREAS OF INTEREST:
Jewish literature.

NAME(S) OF PROGRAMS:
- **National Jewish Book Award-American Jewish Studies**
- **National Jewish Book Award-Anthologies and Collections**
- **National Jewish Book Award-Biography, Autobiography and Memoir**
- **National Jewish Book Award-Children's and Young Adult Literature**
- **National Jewish Book Award-Contemporary Jewish Life**
- **National Jewish Book Award-Education and Jewish Identity**
- **National Jewish Book Award-Fiction**
- **National Jewish Book Award-History**
- **National Jewish Book Award-Holocaust**
- **National Jewish Book Award-Illustrated Children's Book**
- **National Jewish Book Award-Jewish Family Literature**
- **National Jewish Book Award-Modern Jewish Thought and Experience**
- **National Jewish Book Award-Poetry**
- **National Jewish Book Award-Scholarship**
- **National Jewish Book Award-Sephardic Culture**
- **National Jewish Book Award-Visual Arts**
- **National Jewish Book Award-Women's Studies**
- **National Jewish Book Award-Writing Based on Archival Materials**

TYPE:
Awards/prizes. National Jewish Book Awards:
(1) Award to the author of a nonfiction book about the Jewish experience in North America;
(2) Award to the author of a book of essays, biographies, short stories, or other collected works by more than one author;
(3) Award to the author of a biography, autobiography, personal memoir or family history. The subject need not be a Jewish person or family, but must have significant relevance to the Jewish experience;
(4) Award to the author of a book on a Jewish theme for ages 7-16;
(5) Award to the author of a nonfiction book about current tools and resources of Jewish living within the greater Ashkenazic and Sephardic communities. These include, but are not limited to, cookbooks, holiday how-to books and life-cycle books;
(6) Award to the author of a nonfiction work that focuses on theory, history and/or practice of Jewish education. Textbooks are not eligible;
(7) Award to the author of a novel or short-story collection with Jewish content;
(8) Award to the author of a nonfiction work about the Jewish historical experience. Books focusing primarily on the Holocaust do not belong in this category;
(9) Award to the author of a nonfiction book concerning the Holocaust including autobiographies, memoirs and academic studies;
(10) Award to the author of a picture or illustrated book with Jewish theme for children from infancy to age 10. The award is shared by the author and illustrator;
(11) Award to the author of a Jewish read-aloud book to be shared by adults and children that stimulates the transmission of Jewish values and learning between the generations;
(12) Award to the author of a nonfiction work addressing Sephardic and/or Ashkenazic Jewish thought and experience;
(13) Award to the author of a book of verse consisting primarily of poems of Jewish concern;
(14) Award to the author of a nonfiction selection that makes an original contribution to Jewish learning. This includes, but is not limited to, works on Bible, Rabbinics and Jewish Law;
(15) Award to the author of a book that explores the traditions and practices unique to Sephardic Jews;
(16) Award to the author of a work of one or more visual artists (painters, weavers, sculptors, photographers, etc.) which includes illustrations and images of Jewish content as a dominant component and;
(17) Award to the author of a nonfiction book about women's role in the Jewish experience.

YEAR PROGRAM STARTED: 1949

PURPOSE:
To promote greater awareness of works of Jewish literature and scholarship.

LEGAL BASIS:
Not-for-profit organization.

ELIGIBILITY:
Books published during the current calendar year will be eligible, except anthologies of previously published material or collections of writings by various authors or reprints and revised editions, unless otherwise specified. No manuscripts are accepted.

Books must be published in the English language unless otherwise specified. This includes books translated into English from any other language.

FINANCIAL DATA:
Amount of support per award: Varies.

Total amount of support: Varies.

NUMBER OF APPLICANTS MOST RECENT YEAR:
400.

NUMBER OF AWARDS: 18 to 20 each year.

APPLICATION INFORMATION:
Guidelines and submission forms are available online in June.

Duration: One year.

Deadline: Submissions accepted early summer to late September.

PUBLICATIONS:
Application guidelines.

EXECUTIVE DIRECTOR:
Carolyn Starman Hessel

ADDRESS INQUIRIES TO:
Carolyn Starman Hessel
Executive Director
(See address above.)

JEWISH BOOK COUNCIL [717]

520 Eighth Avenue, 4th Floor
New York, NY 10018
(212) 201-2920
Fax: (212) 532-4952

E-MAIL ADDRESS:
carolynhessel@jewishbooks.org

WEB SITE ADDRESS:
www.jewishbookcouncil.org

AREAS OF INTEREST:
Jewish literature.

NAME(S) OF PROGRAMS:
- **Sami Rohr Prize for Jewish Literature**

TYPE:
Awards/prizes. In celebration of Sami Rohr's 80th birthday, his children and grandchildren instituted the Sami Rohr Prize for Jewish Literature to honor his lifelong love of Jewish writing. The annual award recognizes the unique role of contemporary writers in the transmission and examination of Jewish values, and is intended to encourage and promote outstanding writing of Jewish interest.

In conjunction with this award, the Rohr family has established the Sami Rohr Jewish Literary Institute, a forum devoted to the continuity of Jewish Literature. The Prize and Institute are coordinated and administered under the exclusive auspices of the Jewish Book Council. Winners will be selected by an independent panel of judges.

YEAR PROGRAM STARTED: 2006

PURPOSE:
To reward an emerging writer of Jewish literature whose work has demonstrated a fresh vision and evidence of future potential.

ELIGIBILITY:
Recipients must have written a book of exceptional literary merit that stimulates an interest in themes of Jewish concern. Fiction and nonfiction books will be considered in alternate years. Books published during the current calendar year and previous publishing year are eligible. Books must be published in the English language unless otherwise specified. This includes books translated into English from any other language.

FINANCIAL DATA:
Amount of support per award: $100,000.

APPLICATION INFORMATION:
An author may not submit directly to the Prize, but may submit their title for review in the Jewish Book Council publication *Jewish Book World* so that the Rohr committee can be made aware of their title.

Duration: One year.

STAFF:
Carolyn Starman Hessel, Director

ADDRESS INQUIRIES TO:
Carolyn Starman Hessel, Director
Sami Rohr Prize for Jewish Literature
(See address above.)

ROBERT F. KENNEDY CENTER FOR JUSTICE AND HUMAN RIGHTS [718]
1367 Connecticut Avenue, N.W.
Suite 200
Washington, DC 20036-1859
(202) 463-7575
Fax: (202) 463-6606

E-MAIL ADDRESS:
greggs@rfkcenter.org

WEB SITE ADDRESS:
www.rfkcenter.org

FOUNDED: 1968

NAME(S) OF PROGRAMS:
- **Robert F. Kennedy Book Award**
- **Robert F. Kennedy Journalism Award**

TYPE:
Awards/prizes. Annual prize for the book which most faithfully and forcefully reflects Robert Kennedy's purposes, namely, his concern for the poor and the powerless, his struggle for honest and even-handed justice, his convictions that a decent society must assure all young people a fair chance and his faith that a free democracy can act to remedy disparities of power and opportunity.

YEAR PROGRAM STARTED: 1980

PURPOSE:
To carry forward the mission of Robert F. Kennedy.

LEGAL BASIS:
Tax-exempt public charity.

ELIGIBILITY:
Fiction and nonfiction books published in the U.S. in the previous calendar year are eligible.

FINANCIAL DATA:
Amount of support per award: Grand prize: $2,500.
Total amount of support: Varies.

NUMBER OF APPLICANTS MOST RECENT YEAR: 75.

NUMBER OF AWARDS: Varies.

REPRESENTATIVE AWARDS:
2008: *The Other Walter Reed*, by Dana Priest and Anne Hall; *Going Down Jericho Road*, by Michael Honey.

APPLICATION INFORMATION:
Entries may be made by either individual authors or publishers. There is a handling fee of $50 per entry. Books must be submitted in quadruplicate with an entry form clipped inside the front cover of each book.
Duration: One-time award.

PUBLICATIONS:
Rules for entry.

ADDRESS INQUIRIES TO:
Simone Greggs, Special Events and Programs Manager
(See address above.)

KNIGHTS OF COLUMBUS VATICAN FILM LIBRARY AT ST. LOUIS UNIVERSITY [719]
Pius XII Memorial Library
St. Louis University
3650 Lindell Boulevard
St. Louis, MO 63108-3302
(314) 977-3090
Fax: (314) 977-3108

E-MAIL ADDRESS:
vfl@slu.edu

WEB SITE ADDRESS:
slulink.slu.edu/special/vfl/fllwshp.html

AREAS OF INTEREST:
Classical languages and literature, palaeography, scriptural and patristic studies, history, philosophy and sciences in the Middle Ages and the Renaissance, early Romance literature, history of music, manuscript illumination, mathematics and technology, theology, liturgy, Roman and canon law or political theory.

NAME(S) OF PROGRAMS:
- **Vatican Film Library Mellon Fellowship**

TYPE:
Fellowships; Travel grants.

YEAR PROGRAM STARTED: 1976

PURPOSE:
To assist scholars wishing to conduct research in the manuscript collections in the Vatican Film Library at St. Louis University.

ELIGIBILITY:
Applicants must be at the postdoctoral level or be a graduate student formally admitted to Ph.D. candidacy and working on their dissertation.

FINANCIAL DATA:
Amount of support per award: $2,250 living allowance per month.

APPLICATION INFORMATION:
Applicants must write a brief project description and notify of the manuscripts to be consulted (for availability), include dates of proposed study, a curriculum vitae, as well as a select bibliography on titles related to project.
Duration: Two to eight weeks. Nonrenewable.
Deadline: March 1 for June to August. June 1 for September to December. October 1 for January to May.

STAFF:
Gregory A. Pass, Assistant University Librarian for Special Collections

ADDRESS INQUIRIES TO:
Barbara Channell, Secretary
(See address above.)

LANNAN FOUNDATION [720]
313 Read Street
Santa Fe, NM 87501-2628
(505) 986-8160
Fax: (505) 986-8195

WEB SITE ADDRESS:
www.lannan.org

FOUNDED: 1960

AREAS OF INTEREST:
Literature, including poetry, nonfiction and fiction, visual arts and Native American communities.

NAME(S) OF PROGRAMS:
- **Cultural Freedom Awards**
- **Indigenous Communities Grants**
- **Lannan Literary Awards**
- **Visual Art Grants**

TYPE:
Awards/prizes; Challenge/matching grants; Demonstration grants; Development grants; Fellowships; General operating grants; Project/program grants. The Lannan Literary Awards recognize established writers of fiction, nonfiction and poetry. Awards are given to writers whom the Foundation believes to have made a significant contribution to English-language literature and to writers of distinctive literary merit who demonstrate potential for outstanding future work.

The Prize for Cultural Freedom was established to recognize people whose extraordinary and courageous work celebrates the human right to freedom of imagination, inquiry and expression. As defined by the Foundation, cultural freedom is the right of individuals and communities to define and protect valued and diverse ways of life currently threatened by globalization.

Visual Art Grants fund organizations which support contemporary art.

Indigenous Communities Grants funds a national grant program limited to the urgent needs of rural Native American communities. Funding priority is given to indigenous projects for education, the revival and preservation of languages and cultures, legal rights, environmental protection and economic development which is sustainable and consistent with traditional values.

YEAR PROGRAM STARTED: 1986

PURPOSE:
To recognize writers whose work is of exceptional quality and to stimulate the creation of high-quality, English-language literature.

LEGAL BASIS:
Nonprofit foundation.

ELIGIBILITY:
Lannan Literary Awards and Prize for Cultural Freedom: Candidates for the award are selected by an anonymous nomination process and approved by the Board of Directors.

Grants are given to nonprofit organizations only. The Foundation does not make grants to individuals.

The Foundation does not accept film or video entries.

GEOGRAPHIC RESTRICTIONS:
United States.

FINANCIAL DATA:
Amount of support per award: Varies.
Total amount of support: Varies.

REPRESENTATIVE AWARDS:
Nonprofit organizations which have been funded include the National Poetry Series, which selects five manuscripts through an annual open competition for publication; Poets & Writers' Readings and Workshops programs in California and in the Midwest; The Poetry Center of Chicago; Small Press Distribution.

APPLICATION INFORMATION:
By invitation only. Letters of inquiry are accepted, but the Foundation prefers to be called before proceeding.

Lannan Literary Awards and Prize for Cultural Freedom: Applications and letters of inquiry are not accepted for these programs.

Duration: One year.

PUBLICATIONS:
Press releases; history sheet; program announcements.

ADDRESS INQUIRIES TO:
For the Cultural Freedom Awards and Indigenous Communities Grants:
Laurie Betlach
For the Lannan Literary Awards:
Jo Chapman
For the Visual Art Grants:
Christie Mazuera-Davis
(See address above.)

STEPHEN LEACOCK ASSOCIATION [721]
R.R. 2
4223 Line 12 North
Coldwater ON L0K 1E0 Canada
(705) 835-3218
Fax: (705) 835-5171

E-MAIL ADDRESS:
judith.rapson@gmail.com

WEB SITE ADDRESS:
www.leacock.ca

FOUNDED: 1946

AREAS OF INTEREST:
Writing of humour by Canadians.

NAME(S) OF PROGRAMS:
● **Stephen Leacock Memorial Medal for Humour**

TYPE:
Awards/prizes. Stephen Leacock Memorial Medal for Humour is presented for a book of humour published in the current calendar year and written by a Canadian. A cash prize from the TD Bank Financial Group accompanies this award.

YEAR PROGRAM STARTED: 1947

PURPOSE:
To promote the writing of Canadian humour.

LEGAL BASIS:
Nonprofit charitable organization.

ELIGIBILITY:
Author must be a Canadian citizen or landed immigrant. Books to be published in year current to year award given. Content to be humour.

FINANCIAL DATA:
Amount of support per award: Awardee receives a sterling silver medal plus a $15,000 (CAN) cash prize; four finalists receive $1,500 (CAN) each.

NUMBER OF APPLICANTS MOST RECENT YEAR:
67 for the year 2009.

NUMBER OF AWARDS: 1.

REPRESENTATIVE AWARDS:
2008: Terry Fallis; 2009: Mark Leiren-Young.

APPLICATION INFORMATION:
$100 entry fee for each title. Send 10 copies of each title plus author biography and 8 x 10-inch photo to Stephen Leacock Associates. Work must be published in previous calendar year. Not more than two authors. All authors must be Canadian citizens or landed immigrants. Books are non-returnable.

Deadline: December 31. Short list announced April 1. Winner announced end of April. Presentation of cash prize and medal in early June.

PUBLICATIONS:
Newspacket.

BOARD OF DIRECTORS:
Michael Hill, President
Don Reid, Vice President
Judith Rapson, Chairman, Award Committee

ADDRESS INQUIRIES TO:
Judith Rapson
Chairman, Award Committee
(See address above.)

THE MANDEL JEWISH COMMUNITY CENTER OF CLEVELAND [722]
26001 South Woodland
Beachwood, OH 44122
(216) 831-0700 ext. 1378
Fax: (216) 831-7796

E-MAIL ADDRESS:
dbobrow@mandeljcc.org

WEB SITE ADDRESS:
www.mandeljcc.org

AREAS OF INTEREST:
A wide range of activities that fill social, recreational, cultural and physical development needs for people of all ages.

NAME(S) OF PROGRAMS:
● **Dorothy Silver Playwriting Award Competition**

TYPE:
Awards/prizes. Cash prize and staged reading by JCC, Cleveland, for a new play that provides fresh and significant perspectives on the range of Jewish experience.

YEAR PROGRAM STARTED: 1981

PURPOSE:
To encourage new plays on the Jewish experience.

ELIGIBILITY:
All entries must be original, not previously produced, suitable for full-length presentation and concerned with the Jewish experience.

FINANCIAL DATA:
Amount of support per award: $500 at announcement of award and $500 on the date of the reading.
Total amount of support: $1,000 annually.

NUMBER OF APPLICANTS MOST RECENT YEAR:
75.

NUMBER OF AWARDS: 1 for each calendar year.

REPRESENTATIVE AWARDS:
G dash D, by Laura Jacqmin.

APPLICATION INFORMATION:
All submissions must be accompanied by a self-addressed, stamped envelope in order to be returned. Manuscripts should be submitted to the address above. Plays must be full-length, previously unproduced and provide a fresh perspective on the Jewish experience.
Deadline: December 31. Announcement by end of March.

OFFICERS:
Jeanne Tobin, President
Michael Hyman, Executive Director

ADDRESS INQUIRIES TO:
Playwriting Coordinator
(See address above.)

WILLIAM MORRIS SOCIETY IN THE U.S.
P.O. Box 53263
Washington, DC 20009

E-MAIL ADDRESS:
us@morrissociety.org

WEB SITE ADDRESS:
www.morrissociety.org

TYPE:
Fellowships; Research grants; Scholarships; Travel grants; Visiting scholars; Research contracts. Supports scholarly, creative, and translation projects about William Morris and his designs, writings and other work.

See entry 513 for full listing.

NATIONAL FEDERATION OF STATE POETRY SOCIETIES, INC. [723]
1305 South Alpine Loop
Provo, UT 84606-5300
(801) 607-5118

E-MAIL ADDRESS:
hbq1@live.com

WEB SITE ADDRESS:
www.nfsps.org

AREAS OF INTEREST:
Poetry.

NAME(S) OF PROGRAMS:
● **The Edna Meudt Memorial Award & The Florence Kahn Memorial Award**
● **NFSPS College University Level Poetry Competition Awards**

TYPE:
Awards/prizes.

PURPOSE:
To encourage the study and writing of poetry.

ELIGIBILITY:
All levels of study at an accredited university or college are eligible (freshman through senior).

GEOGRAPHIC RESTRICTIONS:
Canada and United States.

FINANCIAL DATA:
Amount of support per award: $500 plus 75 copies of published manuscript and an additional $300 travel stipend to be represented at the NFSPS convention to those recipients in attendance.

NUMBER OF APPLICANTS MOST RECENT YEAR:
23.

NUMBER OF AWARDS: 2.

APPLICATION INFORMATION:
Applicant must submit an official NFSPS application that has been notarized and a manuscript of 10 original poems (four copies). Manuscript must be titled and have a cover page with name, address, and phone number in the upper left corner and the title of the manuscript in the center of the page. One poem to each page, single-spaced, is permitted and each poem must be titled. Each poem must be no more than 46 lines and have no more than 50 characters per line (including spaces between words and punctuation). No identification on any page other than the cover page. A dedication page, however, may be included.

Send via First Class Mail only. No special deliveries or e-mail submissions.

Deadline: February 1. Three anonymous, highly qualified judges will evaluate, judge and select scholarship winners on or before March 1.

THE NATIONAL POETRY SERIES   [724]

57 Mountain Avenue
Princeton, NJ 08540
(609) 430-0999
Fax: (609) 430-9933

WEB SITE ADDRESS:
www.nationalpoetryseries.org

FOUNDED: 1978

AREAS OF INTEREST:
Poetry.

NAME(S) OF PROGRAMS:
● **National Poetry Series Open Competition**

TYPE:
Awards/prizes.

YEAR PROGRAM STARTED: 1978

PURPOSE:
To publish five books of poetry each year through sponsorship of a contest and arrangement for publication through two trade publishing houses, two small presses and one university press.

LEGAL BASIS:
Nonprofit, private.

ELIGIBILITY:
The National Poetry Series seeks book-length manuscripts of poetry written by American citizens. All manuscripts must be previously unpublished, although some or all of the individual poems may have appeared in periodicals. Translations, chapbooks, small groups of poems and books previously self-published are not eligible. Manuscript length is not limited; however, a length of 48 to 64 pages is suggested.

GEOGRAPHIC RESTRICTIONS:
United States.

FINANCIAL DATA:
Financial arrangements are between author and publisher.
Amount of support per award: $1,000 and book publication.
Total amount of support: $5,000.

NUMBER OF APPLICANTS MOST RECENT YEAR:
1,850.

NUMBER OF AWARDS: 5.

APPLICATION INFORMATION:
Each manuscript must be accompanied by an entrance fee of $30.

Manuscripts must include two cover pages: (1) title of manuscript, author's name, address and telephone number (this should be the only page with author's identification) and;
(2) title of manuscript only.

Manuscripts must be typed on standard white paper, on one side of the page only, paginated (include a table of contents), and bound only by a clip as more permanent bindings are very difficult to handle. Do not include acknowledgments, explanatory statements, resumes, autobiographical statements, photographs, illustrations or artwork. These will not be considered.

Manuscripts cannot be returned.

Please include a self-addressed, stamped postcard if you would like confirmation of receipt of the manuscript. Include a self-addressed, stamped envelope if you would like to be notified of the NPS winners (announced in August).
Duration: One-time award.
Deadline: Postmarked between January 1 and February 16.

PUBLICATIONS:
Guidelines.

STAFF:
Daniel Halpern, Director
Stephanie Stio, Coordinator

ADDRESS INQUIRIES TO:
Coordinator, National Poetry Series
(See address above.)

PEN AMERICAN CENTER   [725]

588 Broadway, Room 303
New York, NY 10012-5246
(212) 334-1660 ext. 117
Fax: (212) 334-2181

E-MAIL ADDRESS:
prisonwriting@pen.org

WEB SITE ADDRESS:
www.pen.org

FOUNDED: 1922

AREAS OF INTEREST:
Writing of literature and poetry.

NAME(S) OF PROGRAMS:
● **PEN Prison Writing Program**

TYPE:
Awards/prizes.

YEAR PROGRAM STARTED: 1973

PURPOSE:
To help incarcerated writers develop their writing talents and to promote writing as a means of rehabilitation.

LEGAL BASIS:
Tax-exempt, nonprofit organization.

ELIGIBILITY:
U.S. federal, state or county prisoners may apply. Only unpublished manuscripts will be considered, except those that have appeared in a prison publication.

GEOGRAPHIC RESTRICTIONS:
United States.

FINANCIAL DATA:
Amount of support per award: Five first prizes at $200 each, five second prizes at $100 each and five third prizes at $50 each.
Total amount of support: $1,750 annually.

NUMBER OF APPLICANTS MOST RECENT YEAR:
1,500.

NUMBER OF AWARDS: 15 annually.

APPLICATION INFORMATION:
Manuscripts must be typewritten (double-spaced) or clearly printed on standard letter-size paper. Also accept alternative submissions. Authors must not submit more than one entry in each category. Name, inmate number and address must appear on each submission.
Duration: One-time award.
Deadline: September 1. Winners announced in March.

PUBLICATIONS:
PEN Handbook for Writers in Prison (lists resources available to inmates and journals interested in prison writing).

STAFF:
Jackson Taylor, Prison Writing Program Director
Tim Small, Prison Writing Mentorship Program Coordinator
Jonathan Dozier-Ezell, Prison Writing Program Coordinator

ADDRESS INQUIRIES TO:
Director
PEN Writing Award for Prisoners
(See address above.)

PEN AMERICAN CENTER   [726]

588 Broadway, Suite 303
New York, NY 10012-5246
(212) 334-1660 ext. 126
Fax: (212) 334-2181

E-MAIL ADDRESS:
pen@pen.org

WEB SITE ADDRESS:
www.pen.org

FOUNDED: 1922

AREAS OF INTEREST:
Literature, free expression and international literary fellowship.

NAME(S) OF PROGRAMS:
● **PEN Writers' Fund**

TYPE:
Grants-in-aid. Emergency fund for professional (published or produced) writers in acute, emergency financial crisis.

YEAR PROGRAM STARTED: 1958

PURPOSE:
To assist professional literary writers in times of short-term financial emergency and also to assist writers and editors with AIDS or HIV; to advance literature, defend free expression and foster international literary fellowship.

LEGAL BASIS:
Nonprofit organization affiliated with International PEN.

ELIGIBILITY:
The fund aims to assist professional (published or produced) writers facing unexpected financial and medical emergencies, and those who are HIV-positive. The fund does not exist for research purposes, for completing projects or to support publications or organizations. Must be a U.S. resident. Self-published writers are not eligible.

GEOGRAPHIC RESTRICTIONS:
United States.

FINANCIAL DATA:
Amount of support per award: Up to $2,000.

APPLICATION INFORMATION:
Applicants should submit a completed application form, published writing samples, documentation of financial emergency and professional resume. Applications are accepted year-round and are reviewed every three months by the Writers' Fund Committee.

Applications are available online.

PUBLICATIONS:
Application; guidelines.

ADDRESS INQUIRIES TO:
Annmarie Granstrand
Writers' Fund Associate
(See address above.)

PEN AMERICAN CENTER [727]
588 Broadway, Suite 303
New York, NY 10012-5246
(212) 334-1660 ext. 108
Fax: (212) 334-2181

E-MAIL ADDRESS:
alena@pen.org

WEB SITE ADDRESS:
www.pen.org

FOUNDED: 1922

AREAS OF INTEREST:
Promoting the professional development of talented fiction writers.

NAME(S) OF PROGRAMS:
● **PEN/Robert W. Bingham Prize**

TYPE:
Awards/prizes. The PEN/Robert W. Bingham Prize is awarded annually and honors an exceptionally talented fiction writer whose debut work - a first novel or collection of short stories published in the prior year - represents distinguished literary achievement and suggests great promise.

YEAR PROGRAM STARTED: 1990

PURPOSE:
To promote the professional careers of exceptionally talented fiction writers.

LEGAL BASIS:
Nonprofit organization affiliated with International PEN.

ELIGIBILITY:
Candidate's first (and only the first) novel or first collection of short fiction must have been published by a U.S. trade publisher between January 1 and December 31 of the prior year. Candidates must be U.S. residents. There are no restrictions on the candidate's age or on the style of his or her work. Self-published books are not eligible.

GEOGRAPHIC RESTRICTIONS:
Applicants must be residents of the United States; American citizenship is not required.

FINANCIAL DATA:
Amount of support per award: Stipend of $25,000.

NUMBER OF AWARDS: 1.

APPLICATION INFORMATION:
Nominations are welcome from writers, editors, literary agents, and members of the literary community. Describe the literary character of the candidate's work, and the degree of promise evident in his or her first book of literary fiction. Send three copies of the candidate's book with nomination.
Deadline: Submissions: October 15 to February 1.

ADDRESS INQUIRIES TO:
Alena Graedon
Manager, Membership and Awards
(See address above.)

PEN AMERICAN CENTER [728]
588 Broadway, Suite 303
New York, NY 10012-5246
(212) 334-1660
Fax: (212) 334-2181

E-MAIL ADDRESS:
awards@pen.org

WEB SITE ADDRESS:
www.pen.org

FOUNDED: 1922

AREAS OF INTEREST:
Fiction.

NAME(S) OF PROGRAMS:
● **PEN Open Book Award**

TYPE:
Awards/prizes. Invites submissions of book-length writings by authors of color, published during the calendar year.

PURPOSE:
To encourage racial and ethnic diversity within the literary and publishing communities.

ELIGIBILITY:
Open to authors of color who have not received wide media coverage. U.S. residency or citizenship is not required. Works of fiction, literary nonfiction, biography/memoir and other works of literary character are strongly preferred.

FINANCIAL DATA:
Amount of support per award: $5,000.

NUMBER OF AWARDS: 1.

APPLICATION INFORMATION:
There is no application form. Publishers and agents may submit five copies of book-length writings by an author of color published during the calendar year under consideration, with an official letter of recommendation. Self-published books are not eligible. Early submissions are strongly recommended.
Deadline: February 3.

PEN AMERICAN CENTER [729]
588 Broadway, Suite 303
New York, NY 10012-5246
(212) 334-1660 ext. 122
Fax: (212) 334-2181

E-MAIL ADDRESS:
awards@pen.org

WEB SITE ADDRESS:
www.pen.org

FOUNDED: 1922

AREAS OF INTEREST:
Poetry.

NAME(S) OF PROGRAMS:
● **PEN/Joyce Osterweil Award for Poetry**

TYPE:
Awards/prizes. Recognizes the high literary character of the published work to date of a new and emerging American poet of any age and the promise of further literary achievement.

PURPOSE:
To recognize the achievements of new and emerging American poets.

ELIGIBILITY:
Poets nominated for the Award have to be selected by a PEN member.

FINANCIAL DATA:
Amount of support per award: $5,000 awarded in odd-numbered years.

APPLICATION INFORMATION:
Letters of nomination are accepted from PEN members only.

PEN AMERICAN CENTER [730]
588 Broadway, Suite 303
New York, NY 10012-5246
(212) 334-1660 ext. 122
Fax: (212) 334-2181

E-MAIL ADDRESS:
awards@pen.org

WEB SITE ADDRESS:
www.pen.org

FOUNDED: 1922

AREAS OF INTEREST:
Children's/young adult fiction.

NAME(S) OF PROGRAMS:
● **PEN/Phyllis Naylor Working Writer Fellowship**

TYPE:
Fellowships. The Fellowship is offered annually to an author of children's or young adult fiction.

PURPOSE:
To recognize the fact that many writers' work is of high literary caliber but has not yet attracted a broad readership.

ELIGIBILITY:
A candidate is a writer of children's or young adult fiction in financial need. Candidates have published at least two novels for children or young adults which have been warmly received by literary critics, but have not generated sufficient income to support the author. The writer's books must be published by a U.S. publisher.

FINANCIAL DATA:
Amount of support per award: $5,000.

APPLICATION INFORMATION:
Writers must be nominated by an editor or a fellow writer. It is strongly recommended that the nominator write a letter of support, describing in some detail how the candidate meets the criteria for the Fellowship. The nominator should provide the following:
(1) a list of the candidate's published work (preferably accompanied by copies of reviews, where possible);
(2) three copies of the outline of the current novel in progress, together with 50 to 75 pages of the text. Picture books are not eligible and;
(3) on a separate paper, a brief description of the candidate's recent earnings and a statement about why monetary support will make a particular difference in the applicant's writing life at this time. If the candidate is married or living with a domestic partner, please include a brief description of total family income and expenses.
Deadline: March 3.

PEN AMERICAN CENTER [731]
588 Broadway, Suite 303
New York, NY 10012-5246
(212) 334-1660 ext. 122
Fax: (212) 334-2181

E-MAIL ADDRESS:
awards@pen.org

WEB SITE ADDRESS:
www.pen.org

FOUNDED: 1922

AREAS OF INTEREST:
Poetry in translation.

NAME(S) OF PROGRAMS:
● **PEN Award for Poetry in Translation**

TYPE:
Awards/prizes. The award recognizes book-length translations of poetry from any language into English published during the current calendar year and is judged by a single translator of poetry appointed by the PEN Translation Committee. The award was

made possible originally by a bequest from the late translator and PEN member Rae Dalven, and has received current support from The Kaplen Foundation. It is conferred every spring in New York.

YEAR PROGRAM STARTED: 1963

PURPOSE:
To recognize book-length translations of poetry from any language into English published during the current calendar year.

ELIGIBILITY:
Although all eligible books must have been published in the U.S., translators may be of any nationality; U.S. residency or citizenship is not required.

Self-published books or books with more than two translators are not eligible.

FINANCIAL DATA:
Amount of support per award: $3,000.

APPLICATION INFORMATION:
Three copies of book-length translations of poetry published during the calendar year under consideration may be submitted by publishers, agents, or the translators themselves. Early submissions are strongly recommended.
Deadline: February 3.

PEN AMERICAN CENTER   [732]
588 Broadway, Suite 303
New York, NY 10012-5246
(212) 334-1660
Fax: (212) 334-2181

E-MAIL ADDRESS:
awards@pen.org

WEB SITE ADDRESS:
www.pen.org

FOUNDED: 1922

AREAS OF INTEREST:
Poetry.

NAME(S) OF PROGRAMS:
● **PEN/Voelcker Award for Poetry**

TYPE:
Awards/prizes. The Award, established by a bequest from Hunce Voelcker, will be presented to an American poet whose distinguished and growing body of work to date represents a notable and accomplished presence in American literature, for whom the promise seen in earlier work has been fulfilled, and who has matured with each successive volume of poetry.

PURPOSE:
To honor an American poet whose distinguished and growing body of work to date represents a notable and accomplished presence in American literature.

ELIGIBILITY:
Candidates must be American residents and can be nominated only by members of PEN. It is understood that all nominations made for the Award supplement internal nominations made by the panel of judges. There are no restrictions whatsoever to the age of the poet or to the style of his or her work.

FINANCIAL DATA:
Amount of support per award: $5,000 awarded in even-numbered years.

APPLICATION INFORMATION:
All letters of nomination (one to two pages is expected) should describe the scope and literary caliber of the candidate's work, and

summarize the candidate's publications. Most importantly, nominations should articulate the degree of accomplishment the nominated poet has attained, and the esteem in which the candidate's work is held within the American literary community.
Deadline: January 14.

PEN NEW ENGLAND   [733]
Lesley University
29 Everett Street
Cambridge, MA 02138
(617) 349-8113

E-MAIL ADDRESS:
pen-ne@lesley.edu

WEB SITE ADDRESS:
www.pen-ne.org

FOUNDED: 1978

AREAS OF INTEREST:
Authors.

NAME(S) OF PROGRAMS:
● **L.L. Winship/PEN New England Award**

TYPE:
Awards/prizes. Three prizes will be awarded annually for best book of fiction, nonfiction, and poetry by New England authors or books with a New England topic or setting.

YEAR PROGRAM STARTED: 1975

PURPOSE:
To honor *The Boston Globe's* late editor, L.L. Winship, who established this award to celebrate New England's best authors and literature.

LEGAL BASIS:
Nonprofit organization.

ELIGIBILITY:
Books of fiction, nonfiction, and poetry by New England authors or with a New England topic or setting.

GEOGRAPHIC RESTRICTIONS:
Residents of New England states.

FINANCIAL DATA:
Amount of support per award: $1,000 in each category.
Total amount of support: $3,000.

NUMBER OF APPLICANTS MOST RECENT YEAR:
Approximately 200.

NUMBER OF AWARDS: 3; 1 for fiction, 1 for nonfiction and 1 for poetry.

APPLICATION INFORMATION:
Submit three copies of eligible books and an entry fee of $35 per title to the L.L. Winship/PEN New England Award, at the address above.
Deadline: Contact PEN for exact date. Announcement in March at an awards ceremony held at the John F. Kennedy Library.

ADDRESS INQUIRIES TO:
See e-mail address above.

*SPECIAL STIPULATIONS:
No self-published books, electronic submissions, or e-books are eligible for consideration.

PEN NEW ENGLAND   [734]
Lesley University
29 Everett Street
Cambridge, MA 02138
(617) 349-8113

E-MAIL ADDRESS:
pen-ne@lesley.edu

WEB SITE ADDRESS:
www.pen-ne.org

NAME(S) OF PROGRAMS:
● **Hemingway Foundation/PEN Award for First Fiction**

TYPE:
Awards/prizes. Award for the first published book-length work of fiction by an American writer published during the current year.

YEAR PROGRAM STARTED: 1976

PURPOSE:
To promote a culture of literature and maintain intellectual cooperation among men and women of letters in all countries in the interests of literature, the exchange of ideas, freedom of expression and to encourage and give recognition to beginning fiction writers.

LEGAL BASIS:
Nonprofit organization affiliated with International PEN.

ELIGIBILITY:
First published book length work of fiction (a novel or book of short stories) by an American citizen or resident, published in the U.S. in 2011, may be submitted by publishers, agents, or the authors themselves. Authors are not disqualified by the previous publication of nonfiction, poetry, drama, or books for children.

GEOGRAPHIC RESTRICTIONS:
United States.

FINANCIAL DATA:
Total amount of support: $10,000.

NUMBER OF APPLICANTS MOST RECENT YEAR:
150.

NUMBER OF AWARDS: 1 annually. 1 winner; 2 finalists, and 2 honorable mentions.

APPLICATION INFORMATION:
Submit four copies of eligible books and an entry fee of $40 per title to the Hemingway Foundation/PEN Award, at the address above.
Duration: One-time award.
Deadline: Contact PEN for exact date.

ADDRESS INQUIRIES TO:
See e-mail address above.

PEN/FAULKNER FOUNDATION   [735]
PEN/Faulkner Foundation
201 East Capitol Street, S.E.
Washington, DC 20003
(202) 898-9063
Fax: (202) 675-0360

E-MAIL ADDRESS:
jneely@penfaulkner.org

WEB SITE ADDRESS:
www.penfaulkner.org

FOUNDED: 1980

AREAS OF INTEREST:
Fiction.

NAME(S) OF PROGRAMS:
● **PEN/Faulkner Award for Fiction**

TYPE:
Awards/prizes. Cash awards for a published winning author and four nominees.

YEAR PROGRAM STARTED: 1981

PURPOSE:
To honor literary excellence.

LEGAL BASIS:
Nonprofit 501(c)(3) organization.

ELIGIBILITY:
Candidates must be American citizens. Books must be published within the calendar year of the award. No self-published books.

GEOGRAPHIC RESTRICTIONS:
United States.

FINANCIAL DATA:
Amount of support per award: $15,000 for the winner. $5,000 to each of four finalists.
Total amount of support: $35,000.

NUMBER OF APPLICANTS MOST RECENT YEAR:
350.

NUMBER OF AWARDS: 5.

APPLICATION INFORMATION:
Candidates should submit four copies of their book.
Deadline: October 31. Announcement by mid-March.

IRS IDENTIFICATION NUMBER: 52-1431622

OFFICERS:
Susan Richards Shreve, Co-Chairman
Robert Stone, Co-Chairman

ADDRESS INQUIRIES TO:
Executive Director
(See address above.)

*PLEASE NOTE:
This is not a grant program, but a prize for published work.

PERIODICAL MARKETERS OF CANADA [736]

175 Bloor Street East, Suite 1007
South Tower
Toronto ON M4W 3R8 Canada
(416) 968-7311
Fax: (416) 968-6218

E-MAIL ADDRESS:
rargyle@periodical.ca

FOUNDED: 1976

AREAS OF INTEREST:
Canadian literacy and literature.

NAME(S) OF PROGRAMS:
● **PMC Canadian Letters Award**

TYPE:
Awards/prizes. Awards are given for writing, publishing, teaching and administration.

In the area of writing, the award may be bestowed on a Canadian or landed immigrant who has demonstrated through the writing of works of fiction or nonfiction, published in books or periodicals, the contribution of the literary arts to the quality of Canadian life.

In the area of publishing, the award may be bestowed on a Canadian who has demonstrated leadership in publishing by fostering the publication of Canadian works of literature, either fiction or nonfiction, through the book or periodical media.

In the area of teaching, the award may be bestowed on a Canadian who has demonstrated achievement in the field of teaching which has contributed to a greater understanding and appreciation by Canadians of the skills, value and importance of literary expression, or has made a significant contribution to literacy education.

In the area of administration, the award may be bestowed on a Canadian who has demonstrated public leadership through

activities which have fostered and encouraged literary expression by Canadians, or which have contributed to an enhanced level of literacy among Canadians.

YEAR PROGRAM STARTED: 1996

PURPOSE:
To recognize an individual who has made an outstanding contribution to literacy and literature in Canada, either through writing, publishing, teaching or administration.

LEGAL BASIS:
Special-interest foundation.

ELIGIBILITY:
Recipients must be Canadian citizens or landed immigrants. The award may be granted for recognition of achievement in either French or the English language.

GEOGRAPHIC RESTRICTIONS:
Canada.

FINANCIAL DATA:
$5,000 donation to a charity of the winner's choice.

APPLICATION INFORMATION:
Duration: Given as deemed deserved, not necessarily annually.

ADDRESS INQUIRIES TO:
Ray Argyle, Executive Director
(See address above.)

THE PHI BETA KAPPA SOCIETY [737]

1606 New Hampshire Avenue, N.W.
Washington, DC 20009
(202) 745-3235
Fax: (202) 986-1601

E-MAIL ADDRESS:
awards@pbk.org

WEB SITE ADDRESS:
www.pbk.org

FOUNDED: 1776

NAME(S) OF PROGRAMS:
● **Ralph Waldo Emerson Award**
● **Christian Gauss Award**
● **Phi Beta Kappa Award in Science**

TYPE:
Awards/prizes. Three book awards given annually to outstanding scholarly books that have been published in the U.S. in the fields of the humanities, the social sciences, the natural sciences and mathematics.

The Ralph Waldo Emerson Book Award is offered annually for scholarly studies that contribute significantly to interpretations of the intellectual and cultural condition of humanity. This award may recognize work in the fields of history, philosophy and religion; these fields are conceived in sufficiently broad terms to permit the inclusion of appropriate work in related fields such as anthropology and the social sciences. Biographies of public figures may be eligible if their critical emphasis is primarily on the intellectual and cultural condition of humanity.

The Christian Gauss Award is offered for books in the field of literary scholarship or criticism. The prize honors the late Christian Gauss, the distinguished Princeton University scholar, teacher, and dean, who also served as president of the Phi Beta Kappa Society. To be eligible, a literary biography must have a predominantly critical emphasis.

Phi Beta Kappa Book Award in Science is offered for outstanding contributions by scientists to the literature of science. The Award's intent is to encourage literate and scholarly interpretations of the physical and biological sciences and mathematics; monographs and compendiums are not eligible. To be eligible, biographies of scientists must have a substantial critical emphasis on their scientific research.

YEAR PROGRAM STARTED: 1950

PURPOSE:
To recognize outstanding printed work in several fields including the social sciences, humanities, natural science and math.

LEGAL BASIS:
National scholarly honorary society.

ELIGIBILITY:
Awards are given for works published in the U.S. during the period April 1 to March 31. Entries must be original publications. Translations and works previously published as a whole are not eligible. Books that contain chapters or sections previously published as articles in periodicals will be considered only if they have very clear, unifying themes and are not random collections. Books that consist entirely of previously published articles are unlikely to qualify.

Entries ordinarily will be the work of a single writer. Exceptions may be made for books written by small teams of scholars working in close collaboration. Books that are collections of chapters by several different authors are not eligible. Entries should not be highly technical in character, nor should they treat subjects of narrowly limited interest. Monographs and reports on research as such are not eligible. In all cases, the subject and style of the entries should be accessible to the general, literate reader.

Authors must be citizens or residents of the U.S. Entries must have been published originally in the U.S. A book may not be entered for more than one of the awards. Publishers may submit no more than one entry for each award.

GEOGRAPHIC RESTRICTIONS:
United States.

FINANCIAL DATA:
Amount of support per award: $10,000 to the winning author.
Total amount of support: $30,000 annually.

NUMBER OF APPLICANTS MOST RECENT YEAR:
30.

NUMBER OF AWARDS: 1 award in each category each year.

APPLICATION INFORMATION:
Inquiries and entries should be addressed to the appropriate award committee at the address above. Entries must be submitted by the publisher.
Duration: No renewal.
Deadline: March 31.

PUBLICATIONS:
Application guidelines.

OFFICERS:
Fred Cate, President
John Churchill, Secretary

ADDRESS INQUIRIES TO:
Lucinda Morales
Director of Society Affairs
(See address above.)

PITT POETRY SERIES [738]

University of Pittsburgh Press
3400 Forbes Avenue
5th Floor, Eureka Building
Pittsburgh, PA 15260
(412) 383-2456
Fax: (412) 383-2466

E-MAIL ADDRESS:
press@pitt.edu

WEB SITE ADDRESS:
www.upress.pitt.edu

FOUNDED: 1967

AREAS OF INTEREST:
Contemporary American poetry.

NAME(S) OF PROGRAMS:
- **Agnes Lynch Starrett Poetry Prize**

TYPE:
Awards/prizes. Cash prize, plus publication in
the Pitt Poetry Series.

YEAR PROGRAM STARTED: 1980

LEGAL BASIS:
University.

ELIGIBILITY:
Starrett Prize awarded annually for a
manuscript in English by a writer who has
not previously published a full-length book
of poetry.

FINANCIAL DATA:
Amount of support per award: $5,000, plus
book publication.
Total amount of support: $5,000.

NUMBER OF APPLICANTS MOST RECENT YEAR:
900.

NUMBER OF AWARDS: 1.

REPRESENTATIVE AWARDS:
Michael McGriff, *Dismantling the Hills.*

APPLICATION INFORMATION:
Send one copy of manuscript on good quality
white paper, with no fewer than 48 and no
more than 100 typescript pages. Clean,
legible photocopies are acceptable. Name,
address, phone number, and e-mail address
should be on the title page. Also include
curriculum vitae. A $25 reading fee per
manuscript is required.
Deadline: Between March 1 and April 30
only. Announcement in the fall.

PUBLICATIONS:
Competition rules.

OFFICERS:
Ed Ochester, Editor, Pitt Poetry Series

ADDRESS INQUIRIES TO:
See e-mail address above.

*SPECIAL STIPULATIONS:
Competition for the Starrett Prize is severe.
Casual submissions are not encouraged.
Publisher cannot provide critiques of
manuscripts.

Manuscripts will not be returned.

THE PLAYWRIGHTS' CENTER [739]

2301 Franklin Avenue East
Minneapolis, MN 55406
(612) 332-7481
Fax: (612) 332-6037

E-MAIL ADDRESS:
info@pwcenter.org

WEB SITE ADDRESS:
www.pwcenter.org

FOUNDED: 1971

AREAS OF INTEREST:
Playwriting.

CONSULTING OR VOLUNTEER SERVICES:
Advice on career development, jobs and
production for playwrights.

NAME(S) OF PROGRAMS:
- **Core Writer Program**
- **Jerome Fellowships**
- **Many Voices Fellowships**
- **McKnight Advancement Grants**
- **McKnight National Residency and Commission**
- **McKnight Theater Artist Fellowships**

TYPE:
Awards/prizes; Conferences/seminars;
Development grants; Fellowships;
Residencies. Core Writer Program confers
additional membership benefits to committed
professional playwrights.

Jerome Fellowships provide grants to
emerging playwrights, who receive access to
Center's developmental services.

Many Voices Fellowships are awarded to
Minnesota playwrights of color.

McKnight Advancement Grants provide
grants to mid-career Minnesota playwrights.

McKnight National Residency and
Commission aids in the creation and
development of new works from nationally
recognized playwrights not residing in
Minnesota.

McKnight Theater Artist Fellowships are
awarded to Minnesota theater artists (other
than playwrights).

YEAR PROGRAM STARTED: 1971

PURPOSE:
To assist playwrights.

LEGAL BASIS:
Tax-exempt and nonprofit.

ELIGIBILITY:
Core Writer Program is open to professional
playwrights in the U.S.

Jerome Fellowships are open to emerging
playwrights in the U.S. (citizens or
permanent residents).

Many Voices Residencies are for
Minnesota-based writers of color.

McKnight Advancement Grants and
McKnight Theater Artist Fellowships are for
Minnesota residents only.

McKnight National Residency and
Commission is for playwrights residing
outside of Minnesota.

Additional criteria vary for each program.

FINANCIAL DATA:
Amount of support per award: Varies.
Total amount of support: Over $250,000.

NUMBER OF APPLICANTS MOST RECENT YEAR:
200 for fellowships. 500 for all programs.

NUMBER OF AWARDS: Jerome Fellowships: 4 for
the year 2011-12; Many Voices Fellowships:
5; McKnight Advancement Grants: 2;
McKnight Residency and Commission: 1;
McKnight Theater Artist Fellowships: 3.

APPLICATION INFORMATION:
Duration: One year.

PUBLICATIONS:
Annual report; newsletter.

IRS IDENTIFICATION NUMBER: 41-6170139

STAFF:
Hayley Finn, Resident Director and Lab
Producer
Jeremy Cohen, Producing Artistic Director

ADDRESS INQUIRIES TO:
Kevin McLaughlin, Fellowships Manager
(See address above.)

*SPECIAL STIPULATIONS:
Playwright must be in residence in Minnesota
for one year for Jerome Fellowship.
Recipients of McKnight Advancement
Grants, McKnight Theater Artist Fellowships,
and Many Voices Fellowships must maintain
residence in Minnesota during program year.

SEVENTEEN MAGAZINE [740]

Annual Fiction Contest
300 West 57th Street
New York, NY 10019-3741
(212) 649-3100
Fax: (646) 280-1064

WEB SITE ADDRESS:
www.seventeen.com

FOUNDED: 1944

AREAS OF INTEREST:
Fiction writing.

NAME(S) OF PROGRAMS:
- **SEVENTEEN'S Annual Fiction Contest**

TYPE:
Awards/prizes. Awards for the best fiction
writing, plus possible publication in
Seventeen Magazine, if space available for
publication.

PURPOSE:
To encourage young writers to develop their
talents.

LEGAL BASIS:
Corporation.

GEOGRAPHIC RESTRICTIONS:
United States.

FINANCIAL DATA:
Amount of support per award: Top prize is
$2,500 and story published in *Seventeen;*
Second prize: $250; Third prize: $100.

APPLICATION INFORMATION:
Duration: One-time award.

SOCIETY OF CHILDREN'S BOOK WRITERS AND ILLUSTRATORS [741]

8271 Beverly Boulevard
Los Angeles, CA 90048
(323) 782-1010
Fax: (323) 782-1892

E-MAIL ADDRESS:
scbwi@scbwi.org

WEB SITE ADDRESS:
www.scbwi.org

FOUNDED: 1968

AREAS OF INTEREST:
Writers, editors and illustrators of children's
books.

NAME(S) OF PROGRAMS:
- **Don Freeman Memorial Grant-in-Aid**
- **Work-In-Progress Grants**

TYPE:
Grants-in-aid; Project/program grants. The
Freeman Memorial Grant-In-Aid has been

established to enable picture-book artists to further their understanding, training and work in any aspect of the picture-book genre.

Work-In-Progress Grants have been established to assist children's book writers to complete a specific project. Grants are given in four categories: General Work-in-Progress Grant; Grant for a Contemporary Novel for Young People; Nonfiction Research Grant; and Grant for a work whose author has never had a book published.

YEAR PROGRAM STARTED: 1974

PURPOSE:
To encourage continuing excellence in the creation of children's literature and to provide assistance and support to those working in the children's book field.

LEGAL BASIS:
Corporation.

ELIGIBILITY:
Both grants are available to full and associate members of the Society of Children's Book Writers. The SCBW Grant Committee reserves the right to withhold the grants for any given year.

FINANCIAL DATA:
Amount of support per award: Freeman Memorial Grant-In-Aid: $1,500, plus a runner-up grant of $500; Work-In-Progress Grants: $1,500 in each category, plus runner-up grants of $500 in each category.
Total amount of support: $7,500 annually.

NUMBER OF APPLICANTS MOST RECENT YEAR:
285.

NUMBER OF AWARDS: 1 Freeman Memorial Grant-In-Aid and 4 Work-In-Progress Grants are awarded each year. Runner-up grants are made in each category.

APPLICATION INFORMATION:
Applications may be obtained by sending a self-addressed, stamped envelope to the address above beginning October 1 of each year. Instructions for mailing the completed applications and written materials will be sent with the application.

Applicants for the Freeman Memorial Grant-In-Aid must enclose either (a) a rough picture-book dummy, the picture-book text in manuscript form and two finished illustrations (one color and one black and white); or (b) ten finished illustrations that would make a suitable portfolio presentation expressly intended for picture books. Specifications will be sent with the application.

Applicants for the Work-In-Progress Grants must enclose three clearly reproduced copies of a synopsis of the work for which the grant will be used and a two- to 10-page writing sample from that work.
Duration: One-time grant.
Deadline: Freeman Memorial Grant-In-Aid: applications accepted between February 1 and May 1. Announcement on June 15. Work-In-Progress Grants: applications accepted between February 1 and May 1. Announcement the following September.

PUBLICATIONS:
Grants brochure.

OFFICERS:
Stephen Mooser, President
Lin Oliver, Executive Director

ADDRESS INQUIRIES TO:
For the Freeman Memorial Grant-In-Aid:
SCBW Don Freeman Grant-In-Aid
(See address above.)

For the Work-In-Progress Grants:
SCBW Grant Committee
(See address above.)

SYRACUSE UNIVERSITY   [742]
Department of English
401 Hall of Languages
Syracuse, NY 13244-1170
(315) 443-2174
Fax: (315) 443-3660

E-MAIL ADDRESS:
tazollo@syr.edu

WEB SITE ADDRESS:
www.syr.edu/english

FOUNDED: 1861

AREAS OF INTEREST:
Creative writing in poetry and fiction.

NAME(S) OF PROGRAMS:
* **Graduate Program in Creative Writing**

TYPE:
Assistantships; Awards/prizes; Fellowships; Scholarships; Travel grants. Fellowships and teaching assistantships in creative writing.

YEAR PROGRAM STARTED: 1963

PURPOSE:
To assist talented writers to pursue graduate degrees at Syracuse University.

ELIGIBILITY:
Applicant must have a B.A. or B.S. degree.

FINANCIAL DATA:
Fellowships and assistantships include remission of tuition costs for graduate study.
Amount of support per award: University Fellowships: $17,220; Cornelia Carhart Award: $16,480 (fiction only); Mead Fellowship: $16,480 (poetry only); Teaching Assistantships: $14,455; Creative Writing Scholarships: $13,040 (fiction and poetry).
Total amount of support: Varies.

NUMBER OF APPLICANTS MOST RECENT YEAR:
338 for the year 2008-09.

APPLICATION INFORMATION:
An applicant must submit a writing sample (poetry or fiction), statement of purpose, teaching statement, official transcripts, and letters of recommendation.
Duration: Three years.
Deadline: January 1 for writing sample; January 9 for complete application.

ADDRESS INQUIRIES TO:
Christopher Kennedy
Director, Creative Writing Program
(See address above.)

TOWSON UNIVERSITY   [743]
College of Liberal Arts
8000 York Road
Towson, MD 21252
(410) 704-2128
Fax: (410) 704-6392

E-MAIL ADDRESS:
cla@towson.edu

WEB SITE ADDRESS:
www.towson.edu/cla

FOUNDED: 1866

NAME(S) OF PROGRAMS:
* **Towson University Prize for Literature**

TYPE:
Awards/prizes. Awarded to Maryland writer of a single book or book-length manuscript of fiction, poetry, drama or imaginative nonfiction.

YEAR PROGRAM STARTED: 1980

PURPOSE:
To honor a published work of fiction, poetry or imaginative nonfiction by a Maryland resident.

LEGAL BASIS:
Special endowment.

ELIGIBILITY:
Applicant must be a Maryland resident for at least three years at the time of the award. Prize is awarded on the basis of literary and aesthetic excellence. Book must have been published in the three years prior to the award.

The winning author must be willing to be present at the awards ceremony and to grant to Towson State University the right to quote from the winning work in any publicity related to the prize.

GEOGRAPHIC RESTRICTIONS:
Maryland.

FINANCIAL DATA:
Amount of support per award: Generally $1,000.
Total amount of support: $1,000.

NUMBER OF APPLICANTS MOST RECENT YEAR:
14.

NUMBER OF AWARDS: 1 annually.

APPLICATION INFORMATION:
Any individual, institution, group or publisher may nominate one or more works for the prize. Submit three copies of the work by certified mail, bound if published or typewritten if manuscript. If manuscript, proof of acceptance by a publisher and proposed date of publication must be provided. A completed nomination form must accompany entry.
Duration: One-time award.
Deadline: June 15 each year. Announcement in December.

ADDRESS INQUIRIES TO:
Dean, College of Liberal Arts, LI 108
Towson University
(See address above.)

THE UNIVERSITY OF IOWA   [744]
Iowa Writers' Workshop
102 Dey House
507 North Clinton Street
Iowa City, IA 52242-1000
(319) 335-0416
Fax: (319) 335-0420

WEB SITE ADDRESS:
www.uiowa.edu/~iww

AREAS OF INTEREST:
Short story collection.

NAME(S) OF PROGRAMS:
* **The Iowa Short Fiction Award**
* **The John Simmons Short Fiction Award**

TYPE:
Awards/prizes. Publication of short story collection/manuscript.

YEAR PROGRAM STARTED: 1969

PURPOSE:
To encourage writing of short stories.

ELIGIBILITY:
Any writer who has not previously published a volume of prose fiction is eligible. Revised manuscripts which have been previously entered may be resubmitted. Writers who have published a volume of poetry are eligible.

The manuscript must be a collection of short stories of at least 150 word-processed, double-spaced pages. Stories previously published in periodicals are eligible.

COOPERATIVE FUNDING PROGRAMS: The awards are provided with cooperation of the Iowa Writers' Workshop and the University of Iowa Press.

NUMBER OF APPLICANTS MOST RECENT YEAR:
Over 500.

NUMBER OF AWARDS: 1 of each annually.

APPLICATION INFORMATION:
No application forms are necessary. Manuscripts should be mailed to: Iowa Short Fiction Award, Iowa Writers' Workshop, at the address listed above. Do not send the only copy of the manuscript. Xeroxed copies are encouraged. Stamped, self-addressed packaging may be included for return of the manuscript, but is not required.
Deadline: Entries should be postmarked between August 1 and September 30. Announcement of the winners will be made early in the following year.

STAFF:
Lan Samantha Chang, Director

ADDRESS INQUIRIES TO:
Lan Samantha Chang, Director
(See address above.)

UNIVERSITY OF MINNESOTA   [745]
Room 113, Andersen Library
222 21st Avenue South
Minneapolis, MN 55455
(612) 624-4576

E-MAIL ADDRESS:
clrc@umn.edu

WEB SITE ADDRESS:
special.lib.umn.edu/clrc/

AREAS OF INTEREST:
Children's book artist development.

NAME(S) OF PROGRAMS:
● **Ezra Jack Keats/Kerlan Collection Memorial Fellowship**

TYPE:
Travel grants. Award to travel to Kerlan Collection, University of Minnesota, plus per diem.

PURPOSE:
To fund the artist development of a talented writer and/or illustrator of children's books.

ELIGIBILITY:
Grants are awarded to individuals based on need. Candidates do not have to be a U.S. citizen or resident.

FINANCIAL DATA:
Recipient will receive transportation cost and a per diem allotment.
Amount of support per award: $1,500.
Total amount of support: $1,500.

NUMBER OF AWARDS: 1.

APPLICATION INFORMATION:
Electronic application acceptable by deadline. Contact the Foundation for an application form.
Duration: Grants are awarded annually and are nonrenewable.
Deadline: January 30 of research year.

ADDRESS INQUIRIES TO:
Ezra Jack Keats/Kerlan Collection Memorial Fellowship Committee
(See address above.)

UNIVERSITY OF NEW MEXICO   [746]
MSC03 2170
One University of New Mexico
Albuquerque, NM 87131-0001
(505) 277-5572
Fax: (505) 277-2950

E-MAIL ADDRESS:
taosconf@unm.edu

WEB SITE ADDRESS:
www.unm.edu/~taosconf

FOUNDED: 1999

AREAS OF INTEREST:
Fiction, nonfiction and poetry workshops.

NAME(S) OF PROGRAMS:
● **Taos Summer Writers' Conference**

TYPE:
Assistantships; Awards/prizes; Conferences/seminars; Fellowships; Scholarships; Work-study programs. The Taos Summer Writers' Conference has a number of scholarships to provide support for talented writers.

The D.H. Lawrence Fellowship is intended for emerging writers with one book in print. It provides tuition remission and the cost of lodging.

The Taos Resident Writer Award provides tuition remission for one workshop to a resident of the Taos area.

The Hispanic Writer Award is open to any New Mexican resident of Hispanic, Latino, or Spanish heritage. The award provides tuition remission for one workshop and the cost of lodging.

The Leo Love Merit Scholarships are available to any potential conference participant. It pays tuition for a weeklong workshop or partial tuition for a master class. Recipient is responsible for her or his transportation and/or lodging costs.

The Native Writer Award is open to any Native American writer who is a resident of New Mexico. It provides tuition remission for one workshop and the cost of lodging.

YEAR PROGRAM STARTED: 1999

PURPOSE:
To help up-and-coming writers hone their skills by continuing to take courses to advance their writing career.

LEGAL BASIS:
University.

ELIGIBILITY:
Qualified individuals involved in the fields listed above are eligible to apply.

FINANCIAL DATA:
Recipients receive tuition remission, lodging, breakfast and lunch. Lodging costs are excluded from the Leo Love Merit Scholarships.

Amount of support per award: Up to $650.
Total amount of support: Varies.

NUMBER OF APPLICANTS MOST RECENT YEAR:
180.

NUMBER OF AWARDS: 6 annually.

APPLICATION INFORMATION:
Duration: 10 to 12 days.
Deadline: April 15 to May 1 as per award.

IRS IDENTIFICATION NUMBER: 85-6000642

STAFF:
Sharon Oard Warner, Director
Eva Lipton-Ormand, Assistant Director

ADDRESS INQUIRIES TO:
Eva Lipton-Ormand, Assistant Director
Taos Summer Writers' Conference
(See address above.)

THE UNIVERSITY OF SOUTHERN MISSISSIPPI   [747]
118 College Drive
Box 5148
Hattiesburg, MS 39406
(601) 266-4349
Fax: (601) 266-6269

E-MAIL ADDRESS:
ellen.ruffin@usm.edu

WEB SITE ADDRESS:
www.lib.usm.edu/~degrum/html/research/re-fellowships.shtml

FOUNDED: 1966

AREAS OF INTEREST:
American and British children's literature.

NAME(S) OF PROGRAMS:
● **Ezra Jack Keats Children's Literature Research Fellowship Program**

TYPE:
Fellowships; Research grants.

PURPOSE:
To support research in children's literature.

FINANCIAL DATA:
Amount of support per award: Varies.
Total amount of support: Varies.

NUMBER OF APPLICANTS MOST RECENT YEAR: 7 for the year 2011.

NUMBER OF AWARDS: 2 for the year 2011.

APPLICATION INFORMATION:
Duration: One year. Grants not renewable.
Deadline: November 30. Announcement in mid-December.

ADDRESS INQUIRIES TO:
Ellen H. Ruffin, Curator
de Grummond Children's Literature Collection
(See address above.)

UNIVERSITY OF VIRGINIA PRESS   [748]
P.O. Box 400318
Charlottesville, VA 22904-4318
(434) 924-3468
Fax: (434) 982-2655

E-MAIL ADDRESS:
arh2h@virginia.edu

WEB SITE ADDRESS:
www.upress.virginia.edu

FOUNDED: 1989

AREAS OF INTEREST:
18th century studies.

NAME(S) OF PROGRAMS:
- **Walker Cowen Memorial Prize**

TYPE:
Awards/prizes.

YEAR PROGRAM STARTED: 1989

LEGAL BASIS:
University.

ELIGIBILITY:
Author of work in 18th century studies (i.e., the "long" 18th century, from the 1690s to 1815) in history (including the history of science), literature, philosophy or the arts. The work may cover Europe, the Americas, or the Atlantic world.

New manuscripts: Any unpublished, book-length (60,000 to 150,000 words) manuscript in English. The author may be of any nationality. Only manuscripts that are not under review (i.e., not being considered for publication at another press) elsewhere will be considered.

Translation candidates: Books published since July 2008 in a European language may be submitted.

Contact the Press for complete details.

FINANCIAL DATA:
Amount of support per award: $5,000, plus publication by The University of Virginia Press.

NUMBER OF APPLICANTS MOST RECENT YEAR:
10.

NUMBER OF AWARDS: 1 annually.

APPLICATION INFORMATION:
Include three copies of applicant's curriculum vitae and a description (one to two typescript pages) of the manuscript's content, scope and intended readership. New manuscripts: Submit three identical copies of the manuscript simultaneously. Translation candidates: Submit one copy of the work in the original language together with copies of any published reviews.

Submissions should be mailed to the address given above, or, if mailing by courier, to the following:
Cowen Award Judges
c/o The University of Virginia Press
210 Sprigg Lane
Charlottesville, VA 22904-4318.
Deadline: November 1 (postmark). Award announcement in the following March.

ADDRESS INQUIRIES TO:
Angie Hogan, Assistant to the Director
(See address above.)

THE WORD WORKS, INC. [749]
P.O. Box 42164
Washington, DC 20015
(301) 581-9439
Fax: (301) 581-9443

E-MAIL ADDRESS:
editor@wordworksbooks.org

WEB SITE ADDRESS:
www.wordworksbooks.org

FOUNDED: 1974

AREAS OF INTEREST:
Poetry and literature.

NAME(S) OF PROGRAMS:
- **The Washington Prize**

TYPE:
Awards/prizes.

YEAR PROGRAM STARTED: 1981

PURPOSE:
To encourage and promote contemporary American poetry.

LEGAL BASIS:
Nonprofit corporation.

ELIGIBILITY:
The Washington Prize is awarded for a volume of original poetry in English by a living American or Canadian writer.

GEOGRAPHIC RESTRICTIONS:
Canada and United States.

FINANCIAL DATA:
Amount of support per award: $1,500 plus book publication.

NUMBER OF AWARDS: 1 each year.

APPLICATION INFORMATION:
Send self-addressed, stamped envelope for contest rules to address above. There is an entry fee of $25 (U.S.) drawn on a U.S. bank only, payable to The Word Works.
Deadline: January 15 to March 1. Decision by August.

IRS IDENTIFICATION NUMBER: 52-1042022

BOARD OF DIRECTORS:
Karren L. Alenier, Chairperson of the Board
Nancy White, President
J.H. Beall
Michael Davis
Margo Stever

ADDRESS INQUIRIES TO:
Nancy White, Executive Director
The Word Works Washington Prize
Adirondack Community College
640 Bay Road
Queensbury, NY 12804

*PLEASE NOTE:
The Washington Prize is for support of poets. It is not an academic scholarship for higher education.

Museums and libraries

ALABAMA LIBRARY ASSOCIATION SCHOLARSHIP LOAN FUND, INC. [750]
Alabama Library Association
9154 East Chase Parkway, Suite 418
Montgomery, AL 36117
(334) 414-0113

E-MAIL ADDRESS:
administrator@allanet.org

WEB SITE ADDRESS:
www.allanet.org

FOUNDED: 1904

AREAS OF INTEREST:
Library science.

NAME(S) OF PROGRAMS:
- **Scholarships in Library Science**

TYPE:
Scholarships. Scholarships for graduate study in library science/library media.

YEAR PROGRAM STARTED: 1945

PURPOSE:
To provide professional training for librarians and prospective librarians.

LEGAL BASIS:
Nonprofit corporation.

ELIGIBILITY:
Residents of Alabama who have been accepted by an accredited institution offering a graduate course in library science are eligible to apply.

GEOGRAPHIC RESTRICTIONS:
Alabama.

FINANCIAL DATA:
Amount of support per award: ALLA Centennial Memorial Scholarship and ALLA Memorial Scholarship: Up to $1,000 per award.
Total amount of support: Up to $2,000.

NUMBER OF AWARDS: 2.

APPLICATION INFORMATION:
Application forms are available online or from the Association Administrator. Three references are required and proof of admission to school.
Duration: One academic year.
Deadline: June 1.

PUBLICATIONS:
Brochure; application guidelines.

OFFICERS:
Mya Jones, President

ADDRESS INQUIRIES TO:
Mya Jones, President
(See address above.)

AMERICAN ASSOCIATION OF LAW LIBRARIES [751]
105 West Adams Street
Suite 3300
Chicago, IL 60603
(312) 939-4764
Fax: (312) 431-1097

E-MAIL ADDRESS:
membership@aall.org

WEB SITE ADDRESS:
www.aallnet.org

FOUNDED: 1906

AREAS OF INTEREST:
Librarianship, law librarianship and law.

NAME(S) OF PROGRAMS:
- **Library Degree for Law School Graduates**
- **Library Degree for Non-Law School Graduates**
- **Library School Graduates Attending Law School**
- **Library School Graduates Seeking a Non-Law Degree**

TYPE:
Scholarships. For study of law or librarianship, with support intended for prospective law librarians.

YEAR PROGRAM STARTED: 1966

PURPOSE:
To assist qualified persons who are interested in becoming professional law librarians.

LEGAL BASIS:
Not-for-profit corporation.

ELIGIBILITY:
Preference is given to AALL members, but scholarships are not restricted to members. Evidence of financial need must be submitted.

GEOGRAPHIC RESTRICTIONS:
United States.

FINANCIAL DATA:
Amount of support per award: $1,000 to $3,000. Amounts vary according to available funds and may be limited at the discretion of the Scholarships Committee.
Total amount of support: Varies.

NUMBER OF APPLICANTS MOST RECENT YEAR: 40.

NUMBER OF AWARDS: Varies.

APPLICATION INFORMATION:
Duration: Varies by scholarship.
Deadline: April 1.

ADDRESS INQUIRIES TO:
Membership Services Coordinator
(See address above.)

AMERICAN ASSOCIATION OF LAW LIBRARIES   [752]

105 West Adams Street
Suite 3300
Chicago, IL 60603
(312) 939-4764
Fax: (312) 431-1097

E-MAIL ADDRESS:
membership@aall.org

WEB SITE ADDRESS:
www.aallnet.org

FOUNDED: 1906

AREAS OF INTEREST:
Librarianship, law librarianship and minorities.

NAME(S) OF PROGRAMS:
● **George A. Strait Minority Stipend Scholarship Endowment**

TYPE:
Scholarships. Stipend for graduate study leading to a degree at an accredited school of library or information science or an accredited law school. Preference will be given to individuals with previous service to, or interest in, law librarianship.

YEAR PROGRAM STARTED: 1966

PURPOSE:
To assist qualified persons who are interested in becoming professional law librarians.

LEGAL BASIS:
Not-for-profit corporation.

ELIGIBILITY:
Application is limited to minority group members defined by current guidelines of the U.S. government. Applicant must be a degree candidate in an ALA-accredited library school or ABA-accredited law school and intend to have a career in law librarianship.

GEOGRAPHIC RESTRICTIONS:
United States.

FINANCIAL DATA:
Amount of support per award: Up to $2,500.
Total amount of support: Varies.

NUMBER OF APPLICANTS MOST RECENT YEAR: 25.

NUMBER OF AWARDS: Varies.

APPLICATION INFORMATION:
Application packet must include:
(1) an official transcript from the school where applicant completed most recent degree;
(2) a letter from the Admissions Officer of the library school, stating the program for which the applicant has been accepted and

the date the courses begin, or, if applicant has already begun pursuing the degree, a transcript showing they are a degree candidate in good standing, or, if the applicant is attending law school, a transcript showing they are a degree candidate in good standing;
(3) three letters of recommendation from persons who have knowledge of the applicant's abilities and who can evaluate and comment upon law library employment experience and;
(4) a personal statement discussing the applicant's interest in law librarianship, reason for applying for this scholarship, career goals as a law librarian, and any other pertinent information.
Duration: One year.
Deadline: April 1.

ADDRESS INQUIRIES TO:
Membership Services Coordinator
(See address above.)

AMERICAN LIBRARY ASSOCIATION (ALA)   [753]

50 East Huron Street
Chicago, IL 60611-2795
(312) 280-3247
(800) 545-2433 ext. 3247
Fax: (312) 280-5014

E-MAIL ADDRESS:
awards@ala.org
cmalden@ala.org

WEB SITE ADDRESS:
www.ala.org/work/awards/index.html

FOUNDED: 1876

AREAS OF INTEREST:
Librarianship.

NAME(S) OF PROGRAMS:
● **ALA Awards**

TYPE:
Awards/prizes; Conferences/seminars; Development grants; Fellowships; Research grants; Scholarships; Seed money grants; Travel grants. Cash and noncash awards for achievement/distinguished service, authors/illustrators/publishers, exhibits, funding, intellectual freedom, literacy, professional development, public relations, publications/articles and special services, as well as scholarships, fellowships and research grants sponsored by ALA and its units.

PURPOSE:
To honor distinguished service and foster professional growth.

FINANCIAL DATA:
Amount of support per award: Awards: $250 to $10,000; Research Grants and Fellowships: $500 to $10,000.
Total amount of support: Varies.

COOPERATIVE FUNDING PROGRAMS: Some grants are sponsored by Baker and Taylor, H.W. Wilson Company and Voice of Youth Advocates.

NUMBER OF AWARDS: More than 150 annually.

REPRESENTATIVE AWARDS:
Academic or Research Librarian of the Year Award for outstanding contribution to academic and research librarianship and library development, $3,000 (donated by Baker & Taylor); The H.W. Wilson Library Staff Development Grant to library organization for a program to further its goals and objectives, $3,500 (donated by The

H.W. Wilson Company); Frances Henne Research Grant to provide seed money to an individual, institution or group for a project to encourage research on library service to young adults, $500 minimum (donated by Voice of Youth Advocates); David H. Clift Scholarship to worthy U.S. or Canadian citizen to begin an M.L.S. degree in an ALA-accredited program, $3,000 (donated by scholarship endowment interest, individual contributions).

APPLICATION INFORMATION:
Duration: Varies.
Deadline: December 1.

ADDRESS INQUIRIES TO:
Cheryl Malden, Program Officer
(See address above.)

AMERICAN LIBRARY ASSOCIATION (ALA)   [754]

50 East Huron Street
Chicago, IL 60611
(800) 545-2433 ext. 4382
Fax: (312) 280-5276

E-MAIL ADDRESS:
aasl@ala.org

WEB SITE ADDRESS:
www.ala.org/aasl

AREAS OF INTEREST:
Libraries and librarianship.

NAME(S) OF PROGRAMS:
● **AASL Collaborative School Library Award**
● **AASL Frances Henne Award**
● **AASL Innovative Reading Grant**
● **AASL National School Library Program of the Year Award**
● **ABC-CLIO Leadership Grant**

TYPE:
Awards/prizes; Scholarships.

PURPOSE:
To honor distinguished service and foster professional growth in the library industry.

ELIGIBILITY:
Frances Henne Award: The applicant must be a full-time student preparing to be a school library specialist at the preschool, elementary or secondary level.

Applicants for awards/grants must be members of the American Association of School Librarians.

FINANCIAL DATA:
Amount of support per award: $1,000 to $10,000.
Total amount of support: Varies.

NUMBER OF APPLICANTS MOST RECENT YEAR: 50.

NUMBER OF AWARDS: Varies.

APPLICATION INFORMATION:
Application forms and information are available through ALA's American Association of School Librarians at the address above.
Deadline: AASL National School Library Program of the Year Award: January 2; AASL Collaborative School Library Award, AASL Frances Henne Award, and ABC-CLIO Leadership Grant: February 1.

EXECUTIVE DIRECTOR:
Julie Walker

ADDRESS INQUIRIES TO:
See e-mail address above.

AMERICAN LIBRARY ASSOCIATION (ALA) [755]

50 East Huron Street
Chicago, IL 60611
(800) 545-2433 ext. 4382
Fax: (312) 280-5276

E-MAIL ADDRESS:
aasl@ala.org

WEB SITE ADDRESS:
www.ala.org/aasl

AREAS OF INTEREST:
Libraries.

NAME(S) OF PROGRAMS:
● **Distinguished Service Award**

TYPE:
Awards/prizes. Baker and Taylor provides funding for this award.

PURPOSE:
To honor distinguished service and foster professional growth in the library field.

ELIGIBILITY:
Nominator must be a member of AASL.

FINANCIAL DATA:
Amount of support per award: $3,000 and a citation.
Total amount of support: $3,000.

NUMBER OF AWARDS: 1.

APPLICATION INFORMATION:
Application form and information is available through the American Association of School Librarians at the address above.
Deadline: February 1.

ADDRESS INQUIRIES TO:
See e-mail address above.

ASSOCIATION FOR LIBRARY AND INFORMATION SCIENCE EDUCATION [756]

65 East Wacker Place, Suite 1900
Chicago, IL 60601-7246
(312) 795-0996
Fax: (312) 419-8950

E-MAIL ADDRESS:
contact@alise.org

WEB SITE ADDRESS:
www.alise.org

FOUNDED: 1915

AREAS OF INTEREST:
Library and information science education.

NAME(S) OF PROGRAMS:
● **ALISE Research Awards**

TYPE:
Awards/prizes; Research grants. Award for an outstanding research proposal in the field of librarianship and information science.

YEAR PROGRAM STARTED: 1976

PURPOSE:
To provide support for research which will help to promote excellence in education for librarianship and information science.

LEGAL BASIS:
Nonprofit 501(c)(3) corporation.

ELIGIBILITY:
Eligibility is determined on the basis of the project's appropriateness to the goals of the ALISE, evidence of an established methodology and a viable research design, likelihood of completion in 12 to 18 months and on the qualifications of the researcher,

who should be an ALISE member. Evidence that other funds are not available for the project should be presented.

The award cannot be used to support a doctoral dissertation. At least one applicant in a group submitting a proposal must be a personal member of the Association as of the deadline date. Staff training, general operating or overhead expenses, and other indirect costs are not funded.

Recipients of the award must present a progress report at the ALISE Annual Conference, submit written quarterly reports to the Executive Director of ALISE, who will pay the grant in periodic installments as the research progresses, submit the results of the funded study to the Association's Journal of Education for Library and Information Science (JELIS) for possible publication prior to submission to other publications, that is, the Journal will have first option on publication, acknowledge the support of ALISE in any publicity or presentation based on the funded study and inform the Executive Director if they receive research funding in addition to that provided by ALISE.

FINANCIAL DATA:
Allowable expenses include salaries for secretarial and research assistance, purchasing, processing and duplicating of print and nonprint materials, mailing, telephone and other communications costs and travel and per diem directly related to the research project.

Expenses normally not allowed include living expenses to supplement the investigator's salary, institutional overhead and other expenses not normally supported by research grants awarded by the U.S. Department of Education.
Amount of support per award: Up to $5,000.
Total amount of support: $5,000 annually.

NUMBER OF AWARDS: Varies.

REPRESENTATIVE AWARDS:
Joan Cherry, Lusanne Freund and Wendy Duff, University of Toronto for "Learning From Our Student: Assessing Student Perceptions of Information Studies Programs and The Information Professions."

APPLICATION INFORMATION:
Proposals should be succinct and precise. No more than 20 double-spaced, typed pages. If necessary, supporting information may be included in an appendix. Proposals must include the following information to be considered in the competition:
(1) abstract of the project in no greater than 200 words;
(2) problem statement and literature review including justification and need for the research;
(3) project objectives;
(4) project description;
(5) research design, methodology and analysis techniques;
(6) detailed budget (including institutional or departmental contributions, if any);
(7) expected benefits and impact from the research;
(8) vita(e) of project investigator(s) and;
(9) ten copies of the proposal and an e-mail/postal return address should be submitted to ALISE, Attn.: ALISE Res Com Awards, c/o Information International Associates, see address above.
Duration: One year.
Deadline: July 15. Announcement the following January.

PUBLICATIONS:
Application guidelines.

IRS IDENTIFICATION NUMBER: 51-0193882

STAFF:
Kathleen Combs, Executive Director

BOARD OF DIRECTORS AND OFFICERS:
Lynne Howarth, President
Melissa Gross, Vice President
Jean Preer, Secretary/Treasurer
Ann Carlson Weeks, Director for Membership Services
Andrew Wertheimer, Director for Special Interest Groups
Louise Spiteri, Director for External Relations

ADDRESS INQUIRIES TO:
ALISE Awards
(See address above.)

*SPECIAL STIPULATIONS:
The Research Grant award cannot be used to support a doctoral dissertation.

ASSOCIATION FOR LIBRARY AND INFORMATION SCIENCE EDUCATION [757]

65 East Wacker Place, Suite 1900
Chicago, IL 60601-7246
(312) 795-0996
Fax: (312) 419-8950

E-MAIL ADDRESS:
contact@alise.org

WEB SITE ADDRESS:
www.alise.org

FOUNDED: 1915

AREAS OF INTEREST:
Library and information science education.

NAME(S) OF PROGRAMS:
● **The Eugene Garfield/ALISE Doctoral Dissertation Competition**
● **Methodology Paper Competition**
● **Bohdan S. Wynar Research Paper Competition**

TYPE:
Awards/prizes. Awards for an outstanding unpublished research paper, methodology paper and for each of two outstanding doctoral dissertations, respectively.

YEAR PROGRAM STARTED: 1977

PURPOSE:
To encourage research in the field of library and information science education and related areas.

LEGAL BASIS:
Nonprofit 501(c)(3) corporation.

ELIGIBILITY:
The Eugene Garfield/ALISE Doctoral Dissertation Competition is open to doctoral students who have recently graduated in any field of study, or who will have completed their dissertations by the deadline. Dissertations must deal with substantive issues related to library and information science, but applicants may be from within or outside LIS programs.

Methodology Paper Competition is open to all types of methodology. Papers must be limited to description and discussion of a research method or a technique associated with a particular research method. Papers must explain the particular method/technique, including methodological implications for library and information science. Examples to illustrate its value can come from LIS-related published studies, proposed studies, and works in progress. Papers that stress findings are not eligible.

Bohdan S. Wynar Research Paper Competition is open to research papers concerning any aspect of library and information science. This competition is not limited to research regarding LIS education. Any research methodology is acceptable.

FINANCIAL DATA:
Amount of support per award: The Eugene Garfield/ALISE Doctoral Dissertation and Methodology Paper Competitions: $500 each; Bohdan S. Wynar Research Paper Competition: $2,500.

NUMBER OF AWARDS: The Eugene Garfield/ALISE Doctoral Dissertation and Bohdan S. Wynar Research Paper Competitions: Up to 2 each; Methodology Paper Competition: 1.

APPLICATION INFORMATION:
Deadline: The Eugene Garfield/ALISE Doctoral Dissertation Competition: June 30; Methodology Paper and Bohdan S. Wynar Research Paper Competitions: July 15.

IRS IDENTIFICATION NUMBER: 51-0193882

STAFF:
Kathleen Combs, Executive Director

BOARD OF DIRECTORS AND OFFICERS:
Lynne Howarth, President
Melissa Gross, Vice President
Jean Preer, Secretary/Treasurer
Louise Spiteri, Director for External Relations
Ann Carlson Weeks, Director for Membership Services
Andrew Wertheimer, Director for Special Interest Groups

ADDRESS INQUIRIES TO:
ALISE Awards
(See address above.)

BETA PHI MU   [758]
Florida State University
Room 101H LSB, 142 Collegiate Loop
Tallahassee, FL 32306-2100
(850) 644-3907
Fax: (850) 644-9763

E-MAIL ADDRESS:
betaphimuinfo@admin.fsu.edu

WEB SITE ADDRESS:
www.beta-phi-mu.org

FOUNDED: 1948

AREAS OF INTEREST:
Library and information studies.

NAME(S) OF PROGRAMS:
● **Eugene Garfield Doctoral Dissertation Fellowship**
● **Harold Lancour Scholarship for Foreign Study**
● **Sarah Rebecca Reed Scholarship**
● **Frank B. Sessa Scholarship for Continuing Education of a Beta Phi Mu Member**
● **Blanche E. Woolls Scholarship for School Media Service**

TYPE:
Fellowships; Scholarships. Eugene Garfield Doctoral Dissertation Fellowship is funded through the generosity of Eugene Garfield, and provides fellowships for up to six students per year. They are awarded to foster

high-quality research in the field and to expedite the movement of new Doctorates into teaching positions.

The Harold Lancour Scholarship is given for foreign study.

The Sarah Rebecca Reed Scholarship is given to a beginning student at the Master's level accepted in an American Library Association-accredited program.

The Frank B. Sessa Scholarship is given for Continuing Education for a Beta Phi Mu member.

The Blanche Woolls Scholarship is given to a beginning student at the Master's level accepted in an American Library Association-accredited program majoring in School Media Services.

PURPOSE:
To assist qualified persons who are interested in completing a course of advanced study in library and information studies.

LEGAL BASIS:
Nonprofit organization.

FINANCIAL DATA:
Amount of support per award: Garfield Doctoral Dissertation Fellowship: $3,000; Lancour Scholarship: $1,750; Reed and Woolls Scholarships: $2,250; Sessa Scholarship: $1,500.
Total amount of support: Up to $25,750.

NUMBER OF APPLICANTS MOST RECENT YEAR: 85.

NUMBER OF AWARDS: 10.

APPLICATION INFORMATION:
Forms are available from the Executive Director.
Duration: One-time award. Nonrenewable.
Deadline: March 15.

PUBLICATIONS:
The Pipeline, online newsletter.

STAFF:
Christie Koontz, Executive Director
John Paul Walters, Program Director

ADDRESS INQUIRIES TO:
Christie Koontz, Executive Director
(See address above.)

GLADYS BROOKS FOUNDATION
1055 Franklin Avenue
Suite 208
Garden City, NY 11530-2903
(516) 746-6103

WEB SITE ADDRESS:
www.gladysbrooksfoundation.org

TYPE:
Awards/prizes; Capital grants; Endowments; Professorships; Scholarships; Technical assistance. Grants to private, not-for-profit publicly supported libraries, educational institutions, hospitals and clinics in the eastern U.S.

See entry 1266 for full listing.

CALIFORNIA LIBRARY ASSOCIATION   [759]
950 Glenn Drive, Suite 150
Folsom, CA 95630
(916) 233-3298
Fax: (916) 932-2209

E-MAIL ADDRESS:
info@cla-net.org

WEB SITE ADDRESS:
www.cla-net.org

FOUNDED: 1896

AREAS OF INTEREST:
Librarianship.

NAME(S) OF PROGRAMS:
● **CLA Scholarship for Minority Students in Memory of Edna Yelland**
● **Reference Service Press Fellowship**

TYPE:
Fellowships; Scholarships. Support for minority library school students. Support for graduate students in reference/information service librarianship.

YEAR PROGRAM STARTED: 1973

PURPOSE:
To help support the educational goals of minority students in the library service field.

LEGAL BASIS:
Nonprofit.

ELIGIBILITY:
Applicant must be accepted by a graduate library school in California, accredited by the American Library Association, be of ethnic origin and show financial need. California residents and U.S. citizens or permanent U.S. residents may apply. For fellowships, applicants must be preparing for a career in reference or information service librarianship. Students pursuing an M.L.S. on a part-time or full-time basis are equally eligible.

GEOGRAPHIC RESTRICTIONS:
California.

FINANCIAL DATA:
Amount of support per award: Generally $2,500 per scholarship; $3,000 for fellowship.
Total amount of support: $7,500 for scholarships; $3,000 for fellowship.

NUMBER OF APPLICANTS MOST RECENT YEAR: 25.

NUMBER OF AWARDS: 3 scholarships and 1 fellowship each year.

APPLICATION INFORMATION:
Application includes academic record, essay and letters of recommendation.
Duration: One-time award.
Deadline: May 31, with announcement in July.

PUBLICATIONS:
The Clarion, biannual magazine.

ADDRESS INQUIRIES TO:
Holly Macriss, Executive Director
(See address above.)

CAMBRIDGE UNIVERSITY LIBRARY   [760]
West Road
Cambridge CB3 9DR England
(01223) 333083
Fax: (01223) 339973

E-MAIL ADDRESS:
sm683@cam.ac.uk

WEB SITE ADDRESS:
www.lib.cam.ac.uk

FOUNDED: 1400

AREAS OF INTEREST:
Bibliographic research.

NAME(S) OF PROGRAMS:
● **The Munby Fellowship in Bibliography**

TYPE:
Fellowships. Graduate fellowships for bibliographical research based on the collections of Cambridge libraries.

YEAR PROGRAM STARTED: 1977

LEGAL BASIS:
University.

ELIGIBILITY:
Open to university graduates of postdoctoral or equivalent level, of any nationality or age. Research must be bibliographical.

FINANCIAL DATA:
Amount of support per award: GBP 25,751 for the year 2011-12.

NUMBER OF APPLICANTS MOST RECENT YEAR: 50.

NUMBER OF AWARDS: 1.

APPLICATION INFORMATION:
Applicants must send a completed cover sheet (available from the Library), curriculum vitae and statement of proposed research.
Duration: One year.

PUBLICATIONS:
Application guidelines.

ADDRESS INQUIRIES TO:
The Deputy Librarian
(See address above.)

CANADIAN LIBRARY ASSOCIATION/ASSOCIATION CANADIENNE DES BIBLIOTHEQUES   [761]
1150 Morrison Drive
Suite 400
Ottawa ON K2H 8S9 Canada
(613) 232-9625 ext. 301
Fax: (613) 563-9895

E-MAIL ADDRESS:
membership@cla.ca

WEB SITE ADDRESS:
www.cla.ca

FOUNDED: 1946

AREAS OF INTEREST:
Development and promotion of excellence in librarianship and library information services.

NAME(S) OF PROGRAMS:
● **Library Research and Development Grants**

TYPE:
Awards/prizes. Grants are awarded annually, when merited, to personal members of the Canadian Library Association, in support of theoretical and applied research in library and information services.

PURPOSE:
To support theoretical and applied research in the field of library and information services; to encourage and support research undertaken by practitioners in the field of library and information services; to promote research in the field of library and information services by and/or about Canadians.

LEGAL BASIS:
Nonprofit organization.

ELIGIBILITY:
Proposals for funding are judged on originality or necessity of research, appropriateness of proposed project to the goals and objectives of the Canadian Library Association, cost-effectiveness of research in terms of the expected influence and

ramifications of the results, timeliness of the research, assurance of project management and control, appropriateness of the proposed research method and design, completeness of application and availability of other funding to researcher.

Preference will be given to submissions from practitioners in the field of library and information services.

FINANCIAL DATA:
Total amount of support: Maximum $1,000 per year.

NUMBER OF AWARDS: 1.

APPLICATION INFORMATION:
Grant applicants should submit their proposal via e-mail as an MS Word document in either French or English to the Chair, Research and Development Grant. Grant applications should be submitted in the form of a letter, four pages or less, containing the following:
(1) title of the research project;
(2) name and address of applicant, mailing address and date of application (this information should be listed on a separate page from the body of the application);
(3) a reasonable description of the research project identifying methodology and design;
(4) duration of the project, including a detailed project timetable;
(5) assessment of the potential utility of research results to the Canadian library community;
(6) a detailed assessment of costs and statement of other grants/awards received and;
(7) an assessment of relevance of the research to the goals and objectives of the Canadian library community.

Applications that do not follow submission guidelines and headers will not be considered.
Deadline: February 28, midnight.

ADDRESS INQUIRIES TO:
Library Research and Development Committee
(See address above.)

CANADIAN LIBRARY ASSOCIATION/ASSOCIATION CANADIENNE DES BIBLIOTHEQUES   [762]
1150 Morrison Drive
Suite 400
Ottawa ON K2H 8S9 Canada
(613) 232-9625
Fax: (613) 563-9895

E-MAIL ADDRESS:
membership@cla.ca

WEB SITE ADDRESS:
www.cla.ca

FOUNDED: 1946

AREAS OF INTEREST:
Development and promotion of excellence in librarianship and library/information services.

CONSULTING OR VOLUNTEER SERVICES:
Continuing education and professional development for library and information personnel.

NAME(S) OF PROGRAMS:
● **CLA Dafoe Scholarship**
● **The H.W. Wilson Scholarship**

TYPE:
Scholarships. Awarded for advanced study in the field of librarianship. Award is tenable at an accredited library school in either Canada or the U.S.

YEAR PROGRAM STARTED: 1969

PURPOSE:
To support programs of study or series of courses either leading to a further library degree or related to library work.

LEGAL BASIS:
Nonprofit organization.

ELIGIBILITY:
Canadian citizens or individuals holding landed immigrant status are eligible to apply. Candidates must be commencing studies for their first professional library degree at an ALA-accredited institution.

FINANCIAL DATA:
Amount of support per award: CLA Dafoe Scholarship: $5,000; H.W. Wilson Scholarship: $2,000.

COOPERATIVE FUNDING PROGRAMS: Programs supported by H.W. Wilson Company and the CLA Scholarship Fund.

NUMBER OF AWARDS: 1 annually.

APPLICATION INFORMATION:
Official application materials are available upon request to the address above.
Duration: The award is tenable for one academic year consisting of two semesters or three quarters.
Deadline: May 1.

ADDRESS INQUIRIES TO:
Scholarships and Awards Committee
(See address above.)

CATHOLIC LIBRARY ASSOCIATION   [763]
205 West Monroe Street
Suite 314
Chicago, IL 60606-5061
(312) 739-1776

E-MAIL ADDRESS:
cla2@cathla.org

WEB SITE ADDRESS:
www.cathla.org

FOUNDED: 1921

AREAS OF INTEREST:
Promotion of Catholic principles by the improvement of library resources and services through cooperation, publication, education and information.

NAME(S) OF PROGRAMS:
● **Junior Library Guild-Sister Sally Daly Grant**

TYPE:
Conferences/seminars.

YEAR PROGRAM STARTED: 2007

PURPOSE:
To allow a member to attend their first national CLA conference.

ELIGIBILITY:
Applicant must be a new member of the Children's Library Services Section of the CLA.

FINANCIAL DATA:
Amount of support per award: $1,500.
Total amount of support: $1,500.

NUMBER OF AWARDS: 1 annually.

APPLICATION INFORMATION:
Duration: One-time award.

ADDRESS INQUIRIES TO:
CLA Scholarship Committee
(See address above.)

CONNECTICUT LIBRARY ASSOCIATION [764]

234 Court Street
Middletown, CT 06457
(860) 346-2444
Fax: (860) 344-9199

E-MAIL ADDRESS:
cla@ctlibrarians.org

WEB SITE ADDRESS:
www.ctlibraryassociation.org

NAME(S) OF PROGRAMS:
● **Connecticut Library Association's Program for Educational Grants**

TYPE:
Grants-in-aid. Grants for personnel at all levels of library work.

YEAR PROGRAM STARTED: 1976

PURPOSE:
To support the educational goals of library science students in Connecticut.

LEGAL BASIS:
Nonprofit organization.

ELIGIBILITY:
Grants are made to CLA members only.

GEOGRAPHIC RESTRICTIONS:
Connecticut.

FINANCIAL DATA:
Amount of support per award: Varies.
Total amount of support: Varies.

NUMBER OF AWARDS: Up to 4 or 5 grants per year.

APPLICATION INFORMATION:
Apply to the Chairperson, Program for Educational Grants, at the address above.
Duration: One year. Not renewable.
Deadline: Reviewed at quarterly meetings.

ADDRESS INQUIRIES TO:
Pamela Najarian, Association Administrator
(See address above.)

*SPECIAL STIPULATIONS:
Only for continuing education, workshops and seminars.

GEORGIA LIBRARY ASSOCIATION [765]

P.O. Box 793
Rex, GA 30273
(678) 466-4325
Fax: (678) 466-4349

E-MAIL ADDRESS:
gordonbaker@clayton.edu

WEB SITE ADDRESS:
gla.georgialibraries.org/scholarship.htm

FOUNDED: 1897

AREAS OF INTEREST:
Library professional development.

NAME(S) OF PROGRAMS:
● **Beard Scholarship**
● **Hubbard Scholarship**

TYPE:
Scholarships. Awards for graduate study of library science.

PURPOSE:
To recruit excellent librarians for Georgia.

LEGAL BASIS:
Professional association.

ELIGIBILITY:
Applicants must be accepted for admission to a Master's program at an ALA-accredited library school and must indicate intention to complete the Master's program within three years. Recipient must work in a library in Georgia for at least one year after graduation from ALA-accredited library school. Beard Scholarship is for candidates who demonstrate leadership potential.

GEOGRAPHIC RESTRICTIONS:
Georgia.

FINANCIAL DATA:
Amount of support per award: Beard Scholarship: $1,000; Hubbard Scholarship: $3,000.
Total amount of support: $4,000 annually.

NUMBER OF AWARDS: 1 each annually.

APPLICATION INFORMATION:
Applicant must submit to the Chair the following:
(1) one official application form (applicant may be considered for both scholarships via one form and other accompanying documentation; do not submit duplicate materials);
(2) proof of admission to an American Library Association-accredited Master's program/library school, i.e., a letter from the dean of the school/program certifying acceptance (photocopy is acceptable);
(3) three letters of reference sent directly from the reference to the Committee Chair and;
(4) official transcripts of all academic work sent directly to the Chair from each college or university attended.
Duration: Beard Scholarship: Up to two semesters; Hubbard Scholarship: Up to four semesters. Both are nonrenewable.
Deadline: Beard and Hubbard Scholarships: May 21.

ADDRESS INQUIRIES TO:
Sarah Trowbridge
GLA Scholarship Committee
Fayette County Public Library
1821 Heritage Park Way
Fayetteville, GA 30214

*SPECIAL STIPULATIONS:
The scholarship winners must agree to work in Georgia for one year following receipt of the Master's degree or agree to pay back a prorated amount of the award plus interest. Repayment must be made within two years.

HARTFORD PUBLIC LIBRARY [766]

500 Main Street
Hartford, CT 06103-3075
(860) 695-6330
Fax: (860) 722-6900

E-MAIL ADDRESS:
mamodeo@hplct.org

WEB SITE ADDRESS:
www.hplct.org

FOUNDED: 1774

NAME(S) OF PROGRAMS:
● **The Caroline M. Hewins Scholarship**

TYPE:
Scholarships. Awarded to candidates for MLS who will work with children.

YEAR PROGRAM STARTED: 1928

PURPOSE:
To assist in graduate Library Science study, leading to a career in library service with children.

ELIGIBILITY:
Students who plan to specialize in library work with children, who have received or are about to receive a four-year undergraduate degree and who have been admitted to or are attending an ALA-accredited library school are eligible. Preference is given to applicants who plan to pursue a career in public library service.

FINANCIAL DATA:
Amount of support per award: Up to $4,000.
Total amount of support: Up to $4,000 annually.

NUMBER OF AWARDS: 1 annually.

APPLICATION INFORMATION:
Additional information and application forms may be requested from the address above.
Deadline: Completed applications must be submitted by May 1.

ADDRESS INQUIRIES TO:
Caroline M. Hewins Scholarship
c/o Youth Services Manager
(See address above.)

HARVARD UKRAINIAN RESEARCH INSTITUTE [767]

34 Kirkland Street
Cambridge, MA 02138
(617) 495-4053
Fax: (617) 495-8097

E-MAIL ADDRESS:
huri@fas.harvard.edu

WEB SITE ADDRESS:
www.huri.harvard.edu

FOUNDED: 1980

AREAS OF INTEREST:
Ukrainian studies.

NAME(S) OF PROGRAMS:
● **Eugene and Daymel Shklar Fellowships in Ukrainian Studies**

TYPE:
Fellowships.

YEAR PROGRAM STARTED: 1980

PURPOSE:
To promote scholarship in history, literature, philology and other disciplines relating to the Ukraine.

LEGAL BASIS:
Nonprofit organization.

ELIGIBILITY:
Individuals who hold a Doctorate in Ukrainian history, literature, linguistics, philology or culture and other fields in the humanities and social sciences and have demonstrated scholarship in Ukrainian studies are eligible to apply.

FINANCIAL DATA:
Amount of support per award: $3,300 per month.
Total amount of support: Average: $13,200.

APPLICATION INFORMATION:
Duration: Four months average.
Deadline: March 11 for following academic year. Announcement after May 1.

ADDRESS INQUIRIES TO:
Harvard Ukrainian Research Institute
(See address above.)

HERITAGE PRESERVATION [768]
1012 14th Street, N.W., Suite 1200
Washington, DC 20005
(202) 233-0800
Fax: (202) 233-0807

E-MAIL ADDRESS:
cap@heritagepreservation.org

WEB SITE ADDRESS:
www.heritagepreservation.org

FOUNDED: 1973

AREAS OF INTEREST:
Conservation assessment of museum
collections.

CONSULTING OR VOLUNTEER SERVICES:
Professional consulting services.

NAME(S) OF PROGRAMS:
● **Conservation Assessment Program**

TYPE:
Technical assistance. Provides funds for an
independent, professional conservation
assessment of a museum's collections and
environmental conditions and, where
appropriate, historic structures. The assessor's
resulting report will identify conservation
priorities to assist the museum in developing
a long-term plan for collections care and
management.

YEAR PROGRAM STARTED: 1990

PURPOSE:
To make collections care and conservation a
fundamental priority of museums and
historical societies.

LEGAL BASIS:
Private and nonprofit.

ELIGIBILITY:
Institutions including museums, zoos,
aquariums, botanical gardens and arboreta are
eligible for assistance. For museums located
in historic structures, CAP will also support
the on-site participation of an architectural
assessor. Zoos and aquariums that do not
have an assessment of the animals' physical
conditions and habitats can use the program
for a general assessment of those collections.

GEOGRAPHIC RESTRICTIONS:
United States.

FINANCIAL DATA:
Amount of support per award: $3,390 to
$7,190, depending on institution and
collections.
Matching fund requirements: Yes.

NUMBER OF APPLICANTS MOST RECENT YEAR:
207 for the 2011 application year.

NUMBER OF AWARDS: 106 participants for the
2010 program year.

APPLICATION INFORMATION:
Applications will be mailed to all institutions
on the CAP mailing list in October. To
receive an application, an institution must be
on the program's mailing list. Interested
organizations are advised to submit their
name to the address above by September 30
of each year. Institutions applying should
submit application materials as soon as
possible as applications are reviewed as they
are received.
Duration: One year.
Deadline: December 1.

PUBLICATIONS:
Sample CAP application with guidelines;
CAP brochure; *Heritage Preservation*,
publications brochure; annual report.

STAFF:
Kristen Laise, Vice President, Collections
Care Programs
Sara Gonzales, Coordinator, Conservation
Assessment Program

ADDRESS INQUIRIES TO:
Conservation Assessment Program
(See address above.)

INDIANA LIBRARY FEDERATION [769]
941 East 86th Street
Suite 260
Indianapolis, IN 46240
(317) 257-2040
Fax: (317) 257-1389

E-MAIL ADDRESS:
askus@ilfonline.org

WEB SITE ADDRESS:
www.ilfonline.org

FOUNDED: 1891

AREAS OF INTEREST:
Librarian education and training.

NAME(S) OF PROGRAMS:
● **The Esther Schlundt Fund**
● **The Sue Marsh Weller Fund**

TYPE:
Scholarships. Awards for graduate study of
library science at ALA-accredited schools.

PURPOSE:
To aid students in financial need who have
strong undergraduate records and who show
unusual ability in the library field either
public or academic.

LEGAL BASIS:
Professional association.

ELIGIBILITY:
Applicants must be legal residents of Indiana
who intend to work in an Indiana library for
at least one year after completing library
education and must be enrolled in an
ALA-accredited graduate program of library
science.

GEOGRAPHIC RESTRICTIONS:
Indiana.

FINANCIAL DATA:
Amount of support per award: Academic
year scholarships provide up to $1,000.
Total amount of support: Varies.

APPLICATION INFORMATION:
Application must be made in writing. Further
information may be requested from the
Federation.
Duration: One-time award.
Deadline: June 30.

ADDRESS INQUIRIES TO:
Susan Akers, Executive Director
(See address above.)

INSTITUTE OF MUSEUM AND LIBRARY SERVICES [770]
1800 M Street, N.W., 9th Floor
Washington, DC 20036
(202) 653-4657
Fax: (202) 653-4600
TTY: (202) 606-8636

E-MAIL ADDRESS:
imlsinfo@imls.gov

WEB SITE ADDRESS:
www.imls.gov

FOUNDED: 1996

AREAS OF INTEREST:
Museums in all disciplines including art,
history, science, as well as aquariums and
zoological parks, botanical gardens,
arboretums, planetariums, nature centers,
natural history and children's museums.

Libraries, including public libraries, archives,
public elementary or secondary school
libraries, academic libraries, and research
libraries (which make publicly available
library services and materials suitable for
scholarly research and not otherwise
available to the public and are not an integral
part of institutions of higher education) and
private libraries (only if determined by the
state in which they are located that they are
libraries for the purposes of the Library
Services and Technology Act). Special
funding categories for state library
administrative agencies, tribal libraries and
organizations providing library services to
Native Hawaiians.

NAME(S) OF PROGRAMS:
● **Museum Assessment Program**
● **National Leadership Grants**
● **Native American Library Services:
Basic Grants**
● **Native Hawaiian Library Services
Grant**

TYPE:
Awards/prizes; Block grants; Demonstration
grants; Fellowships; Formula grants; General
operating grants; Project/program grants;
Research grants; Scholarships; Technical
assistance; Training grants. Museum
Assessment Program (MAP) provides eligible
museums noncompetitive grants of technical
assistance in one of the following three
categories: institutional assessment,
collections management assessment, and a
public dimension assessment.

National Leadership Grants enhance the
quality of library and museum services
nationwide in several categories of funding.
The competitive grants support model
projects that can be widely replicated.

Native American Library Services grants
provide funds for core library operations,
technical assistance, and innovative project
grants for libraries serving Native Americans
and Alaska Native villages.

A Native Hawaiian Library Services Grant is
awarded annually to an organization
providing library services to Native
Hawaiians.

YEAR PROGRAM STARTED: 1977

PURPOSE:
To foster leadership, innovation and lifetime
learning by supporting museums and
libraries.

LEGAL BASIS:
Federal independent agency within the
Executive Branch.

ELIGIBILITY:
All types of museums, large and small, are
eligible for funding. An eligible museum
must be a public or private nonprofit
institution that exists on a permanent basis
for educational or aesthetic purposes.
All types of libraries and archives, except
federal and for-profit libraries, are eligible for

National Leadership Grants. Restricted funding categories exist for state library administrative agencies and for library services to Native Americans and Native Hawaiians.
Funds cannot be used for construction, renovation of facilities, endowment or acquisition of objects. Contact IMLS for program-specific eligibility.

GEOGRAPHIC RESTRICTIONS:
United States, American Samoa, Guam, the Marshall Islands, Micronesia, Northern Mariana Islands, Palau, Puerto Rico or the Virgin Islands.

APPLICATION INFORMATION:
Grant program guidelines and application instructions are available at IMLS web site.

PUBLICATIONS:
Annual report.

INSTITUTE OF MUSEUM AND LIBRARY SERVICES   [771]

1800 M Street, N.W., 9th Floor
Washington, DC 20036
(202) 653-4657
Fax: (202) 653-4600

E-MAIL ADDRESS:
imlsinfo@imls.gov

WEB SITE ADDRESS:
www.imls.gov

FOUNDED: 1996

AREAS OF INTEREST:
Museums in all disciplines including art, history, science, as well as aquariums and zoological parks, botanical gardens, arboretums, planetariums, nature centers, natural history and children's museums.

Libraries, including public libraries, archives, public elementary or secondary school libraries, academic libraries, and research libraries (which make publicly available library services and materials suitable for scholarly research and not otherwise available to the public and are not an integral part of institutions of higher education) and private libraries (only if determined by the state in which they are located that they are libraries for the purposes of the Library Services and Technology Act). Special funding categories for state library administrative agencies, tribal libraries and organizations providing library services to Native Hawaiians.

NAME(S) OF PROGRAMS:
• **American Heritage Preservation Program**
• **Connecting to Collections Grants**

TYPE:
Project/program grants.

PURPOSE:
To foster leadership, innovation and lifetime learning by supporting museums and libraries.

LEGAL BASIS:
Federal independent agency within the Executive Branch.

ELIGIBILITY:
All types of museums, large and small, are eligible for funding. An eligible museum must be a public or private nonprofit institution that exists on a permanent basis for educational or aesthetic purposes. Restricted funding categories exist for state

library administrative agencies and for library services to Native Americans and Native Hawaiians.

Funds cannot be used for construction, renovation of facilities, endowment or acquisition of objects.

GEOGRAPHIC RESTRICTIONS:
United States, American Samoa, Guam, the Marshall Islands, Micronesia, Northern Mariana Islands, Palau, Puerto Rico or the Virgin Islands.

FINANCIAL DATA:
Amount of support per award: Varies per award.

APPLICATION INFORMATION:
Applicants apply online through grants.gov. Applicants who are unable to use the online process should contact an IMLS program officer.
Deadline: American Heritage Preservation Program: September 15; Connecting to Collections Grants: December 15.

ADDRESS INQUIRIES TO:
Mary Estelle Kennelly
Grants Management Officer or
IMLS e-mail address above.

INSTITUTE OF MUSEUM AND LIBRARY SERVICES   [772]

1800 M Street, N.W., 9th Floor
Washington, DC 20036
(202) 653-4657
Fax: (202) 653-4600

E-MAIL ADDRESS:
imlsinfo@imls.gov

WEB SITE ADDRESS:
www.imls.gov

FOUNDED: 1996

AREAS OF INTEREST:
Museums in all disciplines including art, history, science, as well as aquariums and zoological parks, botanical gardens, arboretums, planetariums, nature centers, natural history and children's museums.

Libraries, including public libraries, archives, public elementary or secondary school libraries, academic libraries, and research libraries (which make publicly available library services and materials suitable for scholarly research and not otherwise available to the public and are not an integral part of institutions of higher education) and private libraries (only if determined by the state in which they are located that they are libraries for the purposes of the Library Services and Technology Act). Special funding categories for state library administrative agencies, tribal libraries and organizations providing library services to Native Hawaiians.

NAME(S) OF PROGRAMS:
• **Laura Bush 21st Century Librarian Program**
• **Museum Grants for African American History and Culture**
• **Museums for America**
• **Native American Library Services: Enhancement Grants**
• **Native American/Native Hawaiian Museum Services Program**

TYPE:
Project/program grants. Laura Bush 21st Century Librarian Program: Project types of collections management, community

engagement, conservation, formal education, informal learning, partnerships, professional development/continuing education, research.

Coming Up Taller: Project types of community engagement, informal learning, partnerships, public programs.

Museum Grants for African American History and Culture: Project types of professional development/continuing education.

Museums for America: Project types of collections management, community engagement, demonstration, digital collections/tools, formal education, informal learning, partnerships, professional development/continuing education, public programs, research.

Native American Library Services: Enhancement Grants: Project types of collections management, community engagement, digital collections/tools, informal learning, partnerships, professional development/continuing education, public programs.

Native American/Native Hawaiian Museum Services Program: Project types of collections management, community engagement, conservation, digital collections/tools, formal education, informal learning, partnerships, professional development/continuing education, public programs, research.

Save America's Treasures: Project type of conservation.

21st Century Museum Professionals: Project types of professional development/continuing education.

PURPOSE:
To foster leadership, innovation and lifetime learning by supporting museums and libraries.

LEGAL BASIS:
Federal independent agency within the Executive Branch.

ELIGIBILITY:
All types of museums, large and small, are eligible for funding. An eligible museum must be a public or private nonprofit institution that exists on a permanent basis for educational or aesthetic purposes.

Restricted funding categories exist for state library administrative agencies and for library services to Native Americans and Native Hawaiians.

Funds cannot be used for construction, renovation of facilities, endowment or acquisition of objects. Contact IMLS for program-specific eligibility.

GEOGRAPHIC RESTRICTIONS:
United States and territories.

FINANCIAL DATA:
Amount of support per award: Varies.
Total amount of support: Laura Bush 21st Century Librarian Program: $22,623,984 for the year 2010.

NUMBER OF APPLICANTS MOST RECENT YEAR:
Laura Bush 21st Century Librarian Program: 110.

NUMBER OF AWARDS: Laura Bush 21st Century Librarian Program: 38.

APPLICATION INFORMATION:
Applications must be submitted on IMLS's official application form. Applications can be obtained by contacting the IMLS Program Office.

Duration: Varies per award.

Deadline: Varies.

ADDRESS INQUIRIES TO:
Mary Estelle Kennelly, Grant Specialist or IMLS e-mail address above.

MEDICAL LIBRARY ASSOCIATION [773]

65 East Wacker Place
Suite 1900
Chicago, IL 60601-7298
(312) 419-9094
Fax: (312) 419-8950

E-MAIL ADDRESS:
mlapd2@mlahq.org

WEB SITE ADDRESS:
www.mlanet.org/awards

FOUNDED: 1898

AREAS OF INTEREST:
Health sciences librarianship.

NAME(S) OF PROGRAMS:
* **MLA Scholarship**
* **Thomson Reuters/MLA Doctoral Fellowship**

TYPE:
Fellowships; Scholarships. Awarded for study and doctoral work in health sciences librarianship.

Thomson Reuters/MLA Doctoral Fellowship is awarded biennially. It was established by the Institute for Scientific Information (ISI) and is administered by the MLA.

YEAR PROGRAM STARTED: 1986

PURPOSE:
To support and encourage individuals who are qualified to make a contribution to librarianship.

LEGAL BASIS:
Nonprofit.

ELIGIBILITY:
Citizens or permanent residents of the U.S. or Canada are eligible to apply.

Applicants for the MLA Scholarship must be entering an ALA-accredited graduate library school or, at the time of the granting of the scholarship (February), have completed no more than one-half of the academic requirements of the graduate program. An applicant who is a past recipient of the MLA Scholarship or the MLA Scholarship for Minority Students is ineligible.

For the Thomson Reuters/MLA Doctoral Fellowship, applicants must be graduates of an ALA-accredited library school. They must also have been accepted to candidacy in a Ph.D. program in health sciences librarianship with an emphasis on biomedical and health-related information science. A past recipient of the MLA Doctoral Fellowship is ineligible.

GEOGRAPHIC RESTRICTIONS:
United States and Canada.

FINANCIAL DATA:
Amount of support per award: MLA Scholarship: Up to $5,000; Thomson Reuters/MLA Doctoral Fellowship: Up to $2,000.

NUMBER OF AWARDS: MLA Scholarships: 1 each per year; Thomson Reuters/MLA Doctoral Fellowship: 1 every two years.

APPLICATION INFORMATION:
For the MLA Scholarship, applicant must submit nine copies of the application form, essay, and all related documents plus a single copy of transcripts and three letters of reference.

For the Thomson Reuters/MLA Doctoral Fellowship, applicant must submit the following:
(1) application form and pertinent documentation;
(2) signed statement of terms and conditions;
(3) two letters of reference, submitted by the reference directly to MLA, Professional Development Department;
(4) transcripts of graduate work or proof of enrollment in the graduate program and a list of courses completed and;
(5) name, title, address, phone and e-mail of doctoral advisor.

If mailing, return nine copies of the application and all supporting documents. If submitting by fax or e-mail, only one copy of the application and supporting documentation is required.

All applications and supporting documents must be received by the deadline to be valid.

Duration: One year.

Deadline: December 1.

EXECUTIVE DIRECTOR:
Carla J. Funk

ADDRESS INQUIRIES TO:
Lisa C. Fried, Coordinator
Research and Professional Recognition
(See address above.)

MEDICAL LIBRARY ASSOCIATION [774]

65 East Wacker Place
Suite 1900
Chicago, IL 60601-7298
(312) 419-9094
Fax: (312) 419-8950

E-MAIL ADDRESS:
mlapd2@mlahq.org

WEB SITE ADDRESS:
www.mlanet.org/awards

FOUNDED: 1898

AREAS OF INTEREST:
Health sciences librarianship.

NAME(S) OF PROGRAMS:
* **Award for Excellence and Achievement in Hospital Librarianship**
* **Estelle Brodman Award for Academic Medical Librarian of the Year**
* **Louise Darling Medal for Distinguished Achievement in Collection Development in the Health Sciences**
* **Janet Doe Lectureship**
* **Ida and George Eliot Prize**
* **Murray Gottlieb Prize**
* **Marcia C. Noyes Award**
* **Rittenhouse Award**
* **Frank Bradway Rogers Information Advancement Award**

TYPE:
Awards/prizes; Visiting scholars. Awards to honor service to libraries and librarianship.

The Award for Excellence and Achievement in Hospital Librarianship is given to an MLA-member who has made significant contributions to the profession in the area of hospital librarianship.

The Estelle Brodman Award for Academic Medical Librarian of the Year recognizes an academic medical librarian at the midcareer level who demonstrates significant achievement or the potential for leadership and continuing excellence.

The Louise Darling Medal for Distinguished Achievement in Collection Development in the Health Sciences is given annually for outstanding collection development in the health sciences.

The Janet Doe Lectureship chooses an individual to present the lecture at the MLA's annual meeting. Recipients are chosen for their unique perspective on the history or philosophy of medical librarianship.

The Ida and George Eliot Prize is presented annually for a work published in the preceding calendar year that has been judged most effective in furthering medical librarianship.

The Murray Gottlieb Prize is awarded annually for the best unpublished essay on the history of medicine and allied health science written by a health science librarian.

The Marcia C. Noyes Award is the highest professional distinction of the MLA. It recognizes a career that has resulted in lasting contributions to medical librarianship.

The Rittenhouse Award recognizes an outstanding paper written by a library student or intern.

The Frank Bradway Rogers Information Advancement Award is presented annually to recognize the application of technology to the delivery of health sciences information.

Fellows and Honorary Members are selected for outstanding lifetime contributions to the advancement of the purposes of the MLA and are ordinarily chosen from members at or near the close of an active professional career. Honorary members are nonmembers who have made outstanding contributions to the advancement of the purposes of the Association.

PURPOSE:
To honor those who have rendered distinguished service to libraries and medical librarianship.

LEGAL BASIS:
Nonprofit organization.

ELIGIBILITY:
Applicants must be health science librarians. Essays submitted must be on the history of medicine or the allied sciences and must be unpublished.

FINANCIAL DATA:
Amount of support per award: Award for Achievement and Excellence in Hospital Librarianship, Rittenhouse Award and Rogers Award: $500 each; Janet Doe Lectureship: $250; Eliot Prize: $200; Gottlieb Prize: $100.

COOPERATIVE FUNDING PROGRAMS: The Rittenhouse Award established and sponsored by the Rittenhouse Book Distributors, Philadelphia, PA. The Murray Gottlieb Prize is given by the MLA History of the Health Sciences Section.

NUMBER OF AWARDS: 1 per award each year.

APPLICATION INFORMATION:
Nominations are invited for some awards; for others, qualified individuals may submit papers.

Deadline: November 1.

PUBLICATIONS:
Honors and awards program announcement.

STAFF:
Carla J. Funk, Executive Director

ADDRESS INQUIRIES TO:
Lisa C. Fried, Coordinator
Research and Professional Recognition
(See address above.)

MEDICAL LIBRARY ASSOCIATION

65 East Wacker Place
Suite 1900
Chicago, IL 60601-7298
(312) 419-9094
Fax: (312) 419-8950

E-MAIL ADDRESS:
mlapd2@mlahq.org

WEB SITE ADDRESS:
www.mlanet.org/awards/grants

TYPE:
Fellowships; Travel grants; Work-study
programs. Work-study program for medical
librarians from countries other than the U.S.
or Canada for a time period of at least two
weeks.

See entry 1013 for full listing.

MEDICAL LIBRARY ASSOCIATION

65 East Wacker Place
Suite 1900
Chicago, IL 60601-7298
(312) 419-9094
Fax: (312) 419-8950

E-MAIL ADDRESS:
mlapd2@mlahq.org

WEB SITE ADDRESS:
www.mlanet.org

TYPE:
Awards/prizes; Scholarships. Awarded for
study in health sciences librarianship.

See entry 1062 for full listing.

THE METROPOLITAN MUSEUM OF ART   [775]

1000 Fifth Avenue
New York, NY 10028-0198
(212) 650-2763
Fax: (212) 570-3972

E-MAIL ADDRESS:
education.grants@metmuseum.org

WEB SITE ADDRESS:
www.metmuseum.org

NAME(S) OF PROGRAMS:
● **Theodore Rousseau Fellowships**

TYPE:
Fellowships. Awarded for the training of
students whose goal is to enter museums as
curators of painting, by enabling them to
undertake related study in Europe, made
possible by a bequest from the late
Curator-in-Chief of the Metropolitan Museum
of Art.

PURPOSE:
To develop the skills of connoisseurship by
supporting firsthand examination of paintings
in major European collections, rather than by
supporting library research for the completion
of degree requirements.

ELIGIBILITY:
Applicants should have been enrolled for at
least one year in an advanced degree
program in the field of art history.

FINANCIAL DATA:
Amount of support per award: Stipends vary
in amount. For one year: $30,000 for
predoctoral fellows, and up to an additional
$5,000 for travel and miscellaneous expenses.

REPRESENTATIVE AWARDS:
Kerry Barrett, Institute of Fine Arts, New
York University, to conduct research for her
dissertation project on the oeuvre and life of
Pieter Claesz Soutman.

APPLICATION INFORMATION:
Electronically submitted applications and
letters of recommendation are not accepted.

There are no application forms. Applicants
need not specify the name of a particular
fellowship. Fellowship applications must be
submitted in English. Three letters of
recommendation are required, none of which
may be from current Metropolitan Museum
of Art staff. The submission in English of the
required letters of recommendation is
encouraged. A typed application in triplicate
must include:
(1) name, home and present address,
telephone number and e-mail address;
(2) full resume of education and
employment;
(3) a two-part statement, not to exceed 1,000
words, describing what the applicant wishes
to accomplish in the fellowship period and
detailing how the Museum's resources can be
utilized to achieve the applicant's objectives;
(4) tentative schedule of work to be
accomplished during the fellowship period;
(5) tentative schedule of travel required
during the fellowship period;
(6) three letters of recommendation, at least
one professional and one academic, sent
directly to the Museum and;
(7) a list of other fellowships or grants for
which the applicant has applied in the same
period.
For predoctoral applicants only: official
undergraduate and graduate transcripts
(original transcript plus two copies of each).
Duration: Three to 12 months.
Deadline: Application and required letters of
recommendation must be received by the first
Friday in November. Announcement of
awards will be made by late March.

ADDRESS INQUIRIES TO:
Marcie Karp, Managing Museum Educator
Academic Programs, Education Department
(See address above.)

THE METROPOLITAN MUSEUM OF ART   [776]

1000 Fifth Avenue
New York, NY 10028-0198
(212) 650-2763
Fax: (212) 570-3972

E-MAIL ADDRESS:
education.grants@metmuseum.org

WEB SITE ADDRESS:
www.metmuseum.org

NAME(S) OF PROGRAMS:
● **Andrew W. Mellon Conservation
Fellowship**

TYPE:
Fellowships. The Fellowship is awarded for
training in one or more of the following

Departments of the Metropolitan Museum:
Arms and Armor, Asian Art Conservation,
The Costume Institute, Musical Instruments,
Objects Conservation (including sculpture,
metalwork, glass, ceramics, furniture and
archaeological objects), Paintings
Conservation, Paper Conservation,
Photograph Conservation, Scientific
Research, or Textile Conservation, and made
possible by the Andrew W. Mellon
Foundation.

All fellowship recipients will be expected to
spend the fellowship in residence in the
department with which they are affiliated.

The Museum offers junior-level and
senior-level fellowships in conservation and
scientific research. Junior fellowships are
intended for those who have recently
completed graduate-level training. Senior
fellowships are intended for well-established
professionals with advanced training in the
field and a proven publication record.

All fellowships must take place between
September 1 and the following August 31.

ELIGIBILITY:
Applicants should have reached an advanced
level of experience or training.

FINANCIAL DATA:
Health care benefits are included.

Amount of support per award: Stipend:
$30,000 per year for junior-level conservators
and researchers, $40,000 for senior-level,
plus $5,000 for travel and miscellaneous
expenses.

APPLICATION INFORMATION:
Electronically submitted applications and
letters of recommendation are not accepted.

There are no application forms. Applicants
need not specify the name of a particular
fellowship. Fellowship applications must be
submitted in English. Three letters of
recommendation are required, none of which
may be from current Metropolitan Museum
of Art staff. The submission in English of the
required letters of recommendation is
encouraged. There are different application
requirements for junior- and senior-level
conservators/scientific researchers. Contact
the Museum for full details.

Completed applications must be submitted to:
Attn: Marcie Karp; Conservation and
Scientific Research Fellowship Program; The
Metropolitan Museum of Art; at the address
above.

Duration: Usually one year in duration.
Shorter term fellowships for senior scholars
are also available.

Deadline: Application and required letters of
recommendation must be received by the first
Friday in December.

ADDRESS INQUIRIES TO:
Marcie Karp
Managing Museum Educator
for Academic Programs
The Metropolitan Museum of Art
E-mail: education.grants@metmuseum.org

*SPECIAL STIPULATIONS:
All fellowship recipients will be expected to
spend the fellowship in residence in the
department with which they are affiliated.

MINNESOTA DEPARTMENT OF EDUCATION [777]

State Library Services
1500 Highway 36 West
Roseville, MN 55113
(651) 582-8791
Fax: (651) 582-8752

E-MAIL ADDRESS:
nancy.walton@state.mn.us

WEB SITE ADDRESS:
education.state.mn.us/mde/learning_support

FOUNDED: 1899

AREAS OF INTEREST:
Development of library services, cooperation among all types of libraries, public library ADA compliance, library technology and resource sharing.

CONSULTING OR VOLUNTEER SERVICES:
Consultant assistance provided on library development.

NAME(S) OF PROGRAMS:
- **Library Services and Technology Act Competitive Grants**
- **Multi-Type Library Cooperation Grants**
- **Regional Library Telecommunications Aid**
- **Regional Public Libraries Systems Support**

TYPE:
Block grants; Capital grants; Challenge/matching grants; Development grants; Formula grants; General operating grants; Project/program grants; Seed money grants; Technical assistance; Training grants. Competitive grants that address activities and priorities in the Minnesota Five-Year Plan.

YEAR PROGRAM STARTED: 1957

PURPOSE:
To extend and improve library and information services for the people of Minnesota through public libraries and cooperation among all types of libraries.

LEGAL BASIS:
Government agency.

ELIGIBILITY:
Local public libraries, Minnesota county and regional public library systems, and multicounty, multitype library systems meeting minimum support requirements, academic libraries and school library media centers are eligible to apply. Specific requirements vary by program. Contact the Department for details.

GEOGRAPHIC RESTRICTIONS:
Minnesota.

FINANCIAL DATA:
Amount of support per award: Varies by grant program.
Total amount of support: $17,200,000 for the year 2011.
Matching fund requirements: Varies by program.

NUMBER OF APPLICANTS MOST RECENT YEAR:
Varies by grant program.

NUMBER OF AWARDS: Varies by grant program.

APPLICATION INFORMATION:
Applications available online.
Duration: Varies by grant program.
Deadline: Varies by grant program.

ADDRESS INQUIRIES TO:
Nancy Walton, Acting State Librarian
(See address above.)

NATIONAL HOME LIBRARY FOUNDATION [778]

3804 Williams Lane, Lower Level
Chevy Chase, MD 20815
(301) 986-4854
Fax: (301) 986-4855

E-MAIL ADDRESS:
natlhomelibrary@yahoo.com

WEB SITE ADDRESS:
www.homelibraryfoundation.com

FOUNDED: 1932

AREAS OF INTEREST:
Grants for the purchase of books and other literacy-related materials.

TYPE:
Project/program grants. Grants in support of libraries, books and publications.

PURPOSE:
To assist in the distribution of books and other literacy-related resources to libraries and community groups with limited access to sources of specific areas of information; to assist in support, promotion and development of programs with the goal of combating illiteracy and/or encouraging an interest in reading and the literacy arts among all ages; to encourage development of programs relating primarily to literary or cultural topics that utilize various means of communications.

ELIGIBILITY:
Applicants must be tax-exempt groups with appropriate interests and activities.

GEOGRAPHIC RESTRICTIONS:
United States, with preference to requests from the Maryland, Virginia and Washington, DC, areas.

FINANCIAL DATA:
Amount of support per award: $500 to $5,000.

REPRESENTATIVE AWARDS:
$1,000 to the city of Coffman Cove, AK, to fund fledgling community library; $2,000 to Calvin Coolidge High, DC, to purchase contemporary books for school library; $5,000 to Washington Jesuit Academy, DC, to fund books for the tuition-free middle school for disadvantaged minority students.

APPLICATION INFORMATION:
Application takes the form of a proposal stating the nature of the project and its sponsors, along with a budget and financial statement.
Duration: Grants are usually awarded for one year.
Deadline: Applications may be submitted at any time and are reviewed at thrice-annual board meetings.

IRS IDENTIFICATION NUMBER: 52-6051013

OFFICERS:
Lynda J. Robb, President
Ervin S. Duggan, Secretary and Treasurer

TRUSTEES:
Vandna Wendy Bhagat
Ervin S. Duggan
Michael R. Gardner
Alice B. Popkin
Lynda J. Robb
Ricardo Urbino
Kathleen M. Vance

ADDRESS INQUIRIES TO:
Joan Smith Sahlgren, Executive Director
(See address above.)

NEW HAMPSHIRE LIBRARY ASSOCIATION [779]

Amherst Town Library
14 Main Street
Amherst, NH 03031
(603) 673-2288
Fax: (603) 672-6063

E-MAIL ADDRESS:
sleonardi@amherst.lib.nh.us

WEB SITE ADDRESS:
www.nhlibrarians.org

FOUNDED: 1889

AREAS OF INTEREST:
Library and information science education.

NAME(S) OF PROGRAMS:
- **Rosalie Norris Scholarship**
- **F. Mabel Winchell Loan Fund**

TYPE:
Scholarships. The Norris Scholarship is awarded to New Hampshire residents for graduate library study. The Winchell Loan Fund provides for interest-free loans for New Hampshire residents to attend graduate library schools.

YEAR PROGRAM STARTED: 1949

PURPOSE:
To promote good library service from all types of libraries to all people of the state.

LEGAL BASIS:
Nonprofit.

ELIGIBILITY:
An applicant must be a member of the New Hampshire Library Association and have been accepted into the appropriate program.

GEOGRAPHIC RESTRICTIONS:
New Hampshire.

FINANCIAL DATA:
Amount of support per award: Scholarship grant provides a maximum of $1,000. Loan provides $1,000 (interest-free) to be repaid in five years.
Total amount of support: Norris Scholarship: $3,000; Winchell Loan Fund: $4,000.

NUMBER OF APPLICANTS MOST RECENT YEAR: 5 for the year 2009.

NUMBER OF AWARDS: 5 Norris Scholarships and 2 F. Mabel Winchell Loans for the year 2009.

APPLICATION INFORMATION:
Applications are approved by the New Hampshire Library Association Scholarship Committee.
Duration: One year.
Deadline: April 1 and September 1.

ADDRESS INQUIRIES TO:
Sarah Leonardi, Scholarship Chairperson
(See address above.)

NEW JERSEY LIBRARY ASSOCIATION [780]

P.O. Box 1534
Trenton, NJ 08607
(609) 394-8032
Fax: (609) 394-8164

E-MAIL ADDRESS:
ptumulty@njla.org

WEB SITE ADDRESS:
www.njla.org

FOUNDED: 1890

AREAS OF INTEREST:
Education, training of members and recruitment into the profession.

NAME(S) OF PROGRAMS:
• **Scholarships for Study in Library Service**

TYPE:
Scholarships. Offered to residents of New Jersey for study leading to a degree in library science at a graduate library school with an ALA-accredited degree program.

YEAR PROGRAM STARTED: 1926

PURPOSE:
To give financial support for tuition to worthy candidates, of New Jersey residency, desiring to work toward a graduate degree in library service as a profession.

LEGAL BASIS:
Nonprofit status.

ELIGIBILITY:
Applicants for scholarships must:
(1) be residents of New Jersey at the time of application or have worked in any New Jersey library for at least 12 months on a full-time or part-time basis;
(2) show substantial financial need and;
(3) present worthy scholarship, as shown by official transcript, a written essay describing what the applicant can contribute to librarianship, and two recommendations by people in the field of librarianship if possible.

GEOGRAPHIC RESTRICTIONS:
New Jersey residents.

FINANCIAL DATA:
Scholarships are awarded in the spring for the following school year for full- or part-time study. Funds must be used for tuition only and are sent directly to the college. Any unused monies are refunded to the treasurer of the New Jersey Library Association.
Total amount of support: $13,000 for the year 2011.

NUMBER OF AWARDS: 9 for the year 2011.

APPLICATION INFORMATION:
Request application form from Chairperson of the Scholarship Committee, c/o NJLA, in the fall of the year prior to the award.
Duration: One year. Renewal by reapplication.
Deadline: Approximately February 15.

ADDRESS INQUIRIES TO:
Patricia Tumulty, Executive Director
(See address above.)

NEW YORK STATE HISTORICAL ASSOCIATION [781]
Cooperstown Graduate Program in History Museum Studies
P.O. Box 800, Lake Road
Cooperstown, NY 13326
(607) 547-2586
Fax: (607) 547-8926

E-MAIL ADDRESS:
raddatc@oneonta.edu
sorings@oneonta.edu

WEB SITE ADDRESS:
www.oneonta.edu/academics/cgp

FOUNDED: 1964

AREAS OF INTEREST:
History museum studies.

NAME(S) OF PROGRAMS:
• **The Cooperstown Graduate Program**

TYPE:
Assistantships; Fellowships; Scholarships. Awards for museum studies for Cooperstown Graduate Program students only.

YEAR PROGRAM STARTED: 1964

PURPOSE:
To provide professionally trained individuals for the museum field.

ELIGIBILITY:
Applicants must have a strong academic record, an interest in public service, excellent writing skills and a demonstrated commitment to the field through museum work in either staff or volunteer capacity.

FINANCIAL DATA:
Amount of support per award: $4,000 to $12,000 per year.
Total amount of support: $150,000.

COOPERATIVE FUNDING PROGRAMS:
Co-sponsored with SUNY College at Oneonta.

NUMBER OF APPLICANTS MOST RECENT YEAR:
50 to 80.

NUMBER OF AWARDS: Approximately 15 to 19 awards for students.

APPLICATION INFORMATION:
Applications and further information may be obtained from the Association.
Duration: Tenable in Cooperstown, NY, for 24 months.
Deadline: Applications must be received by January 10. Notification in April.

PUBLICATIONS:
Viewbook.

ADDRESS INQUIRIES TO:
Director, Cooperstown Graduate Program
(See address above.)

NORTH CAROLINA LIBRARY ASSOCIATION [782]
c/o Scholarships Committee
1841 Capital Boulevard
Raleigh, NC 27604
(919) 839-6252
Fax: (919) 839-6253

E-MAIL ADDRESS:
nclaonline@gmail.com

WEB SITE ADDRESS:
www.nclaonline.org

FOUNDED: 1904

AREAS OF INTEREST:
The promotion of libraries and library service in North Carolina.

NAME(S) OF PROGRAMS:
• **Appalachian Scholarship**
• **McLendon Scholarship**
• **The Query-Long Scholarship**

TYPE:
Scholarships. Scholarships and loans to promote the education of qualified librarians.

PURPOSE:
To promote library science education.

LEGAL BASIS:
Professional association.

ELIGIBILITY:
Applicants must have been a legal resident of North Carolina for two years, have a genuine interest in professional library work, demonstrate need of financial assistance, hold an undergraduate degree and be accepted by a library school.

GEOGRAPHIC RESTRICTIONS:
North Carolina.

FINANCIAL DATA:
Amount of support per award: Appalachian and Query-Long Scholarships: $1,000; McLendon Scholarship: $400.

APPLICATION INFORMATION:
Application and three letters of reference.
Duration: One year.
Deadline: May 30. Notification in the summer. Awarded biennially in Conference years.

ADDRESS INQUIRIES TO:
Lisa Williams
Chairperson for Scholarships
North Carolina Library Association
(See address above.)

OHIO EDUCATIONAL LIBRARY MEDIA ASSOCIATION [783]
17 South High Street, Suite 200
Columbus, OH 43215
(614) 221-1900
Fax: (614) 221-1989

E-MAIL ADDRESS:
kate@assnoffices.com

WEB SITE ADDRESS:
www.oelma.org

FOUNDED: 1976

AREAS OF INTEREST:
School libraries and educational technologies.

NAME(S) OF PROGRAMS:
• **Scholarships for Professional Training as School Media Specialists**

TYPE:
Scholarships. Scholarships for those intending a career as school media specialists (librarians).

ELIGIBILITY:
Applicant for a scholarship must be a college junior or senior or a graduate student who plans a career as a media specialist and needs financial assistance.

GEOGRAPHIC RESTRICTIONS:
Ohio.

FINANCIAL DATA:
Amount of support per award: One award of $1,000 and one award of $500.
Total amount of support: $1,500.

NUMBER OF APPLICANTS MOST RECENT YEAR:
5.

NUMBER OF AWARDS: 2.

APPLICATION INFORMATION:
Application forms and requirements are available on request.
Deadline: Deadline for applications and dossiers to be completed and in the hands of the committee is April 15.

OFFICERS:
Sarah Thornberry, President

ADDRESS INQUIRIES TO:
Kate Brunswick, Director of Services
(See address above.)

ROCK ISLAND ARSENAL MUSEUM

Rock Island Arsenal Historical Society
R. Maguire Scholarship Committee
Rock Island Arsenal
Rock Island, IL 61299-5000
(309) 782-5021
Fax: (309) 782-3598

E-MAIL ADDRESS:
rimahoch@aol.com

TYPE:
Scholarships.

See entry 665 for full listing.

STATE LIBRARY AND ARCHIVES OF FLORIDA   [784]

R.A. Gray Building
500 South Bronough Street
Tallahassee, FL 32399-0250
(850) 245-6600
Fax: (850) 245-6282

E-MAIL ADDRESS:
mdeeney@dos.state.fl.us

WEB SITE ADDRESS:
www.fllibraries.org

FOUNDED: 1925

AREAS OF INTEREST:
Public libraries, public elementary school or secondary school libraries, academic libraries, research libraries, private libraries, or library consortium.

CONSULTING OR VOLUNTEER SERVICES:
Consultant advice to public and institution libraries and libraries for the blind and handicapped.

NAME(S) OF PROGRAMS:
• **Library Services and Technology Act**

TYPE:
Project/program grants. Project grants congruent with the state long-range plan.

YEAR PROGRAM STARTED: 1997

PURPOSE:
To stimulate excellence and promote access to learning and information resources in all types of libraries for individuals of all ages; to promote library services that provide all users access to information through state, regional, national, and international electronic networks; to provide linkages among and between libraries; to promote targeted library services to people of diverse geographic, cultural, and socioeconomic backgrounds, to individuals with disabilities and to people with limited functional literacy or information skills.

LEGAL BASIS:
Based on U.S. Library Services and Technology Act (P.L. 104-208, as amended) and Florida Statutes 257.12, 257.191 and 257.192.

ELIGIBILITY:
Applicants must be libraries that provide free library service or institution libraries that are operated or substantially supported by the state.

GEOGRAPHIC RESTRICTIONS:
Florida.

FINANCIAL DATA:
Amount of support per award: Varies.
Total amount of support: $8,769,875 for fiscal year 2009; $8,976,669 for fiscal year 2010.

Matching fund requirements: Matching funds must equal at least one-third of the grant request or award.

NUMBER OF APPLICANTS MOST RECENT YEAR:
37.

NUMBER OF AWARDS: 22.

APPLICATION INFORMATION:
Applicants should supply project proposal.
Duration: One year. Must reapply for each year.
Deadline: Postmarked by March 15.

PUBLICATIONS:
Grant applications and guidelines; long-range plans.

IRS IDENTIFICATION NUMBER: 59-3466865

ADDRESS INQUIRIES TO:
Dorothy Frank, Library Program Administrator
(See address above.)

*PLEASE NOTE:
This program replaced the Library Services and Construction Act.

TEXAS LIBRARY ASSOCIATION   [785]

3355 Bee Cave Road, Suite 401
Austin, TX 78746
(512) 328-1518
(800) 580-2852
Fax: (512) 328-8852

E-MAIL ADDRESS:
tla@txla.org
catherinel@txla.org

WEB SITE ADDRESS:
www.txla.org

FOUNDED: 1902

AREAS OF INTEREST:
Library and information science.

NAME(S) OF PROGRAMS:
• **Walter H. Escue Memorial Scholarship**
• **Garrett Scholarship**
• **Vivian Greenfield Education Award**
• **Ray C. Janeway Scholarship**
• **Jeanette Marquis Memorial M.L.S. Scholarship**
• **TLA Century Scholarship**
• **TLA Spectrum Scholar**
• **Van Dusen/Brady/Tobin Scholarship**

TYPE:
Scholarships. Awards for graduate study leading to a Master's degree in library science.

YEAR PROGRAM STARTED: 1998

PURPOSE:
To help support the educational goals of students who want to get an advanced degree in library science.

LEGAL BASIS:
Professional association.

ELIGIBILITY:
Walter Escue Scholars must be Texas residents concentrating studies in technical services, system administration or library automation.

Garrett Scholars must have concentrated studies in children's, young adult or school librarianship.

Graduate student scholars must be Texas residents, attained at least a "B" average during the last two years of a Baccalaureate

degree program and have been accepted as a graduate student to a Texas ALA-accredited library education program.

Vivian Greenfield Award applicants must reside in Texas and write a goal statement outlining a desired educational endeavor revolving around youth services.

Jeanette Marquis Scholars must be bilingual (Spanish-English), must plan to or already be working in a public or school library that serves Latino patrons.

TLA Spectrum Scholars must be an ALA Spectrum Scholar, be enrolled in an ALA-recognized Master's degree program in library and information studies at a Texas university, agree to work in a Texas library for two years following completion of degree requirements for the Master's program and be a TLA member.

TLA Century Scholars: same requirement as Spectrum.

Van Dusen/Brady/Tobin Scholars must be pursuing graduate studies leading to a career as an elementary school or children's librarian.

Contact the Association for complete details.

GEOGRAPHIC RESTRICTIONS:
Texas.

FINANCIAL DATA:
Amount of support per award: Escue, Garrett and Marquis Scholarships: $1,000; Janeway Scholarship: $2,000, awarded annually; Greenfield Award: $1,500; TLA Spectrum Scholars: $2,000, awarded annually; Van Dusen/Brady/Tobin Scholarship: $1,000, awarded biennially in even-numbered years.
Total amount of support: Varies.

NUMBER OF AWARDS: Varies.

APPLICATION INFORMATION:
Application forms and further information may be requested from Catherine W. Lee, Director of Administration, at the address above.
Duration: One year.
Deadline: Completed applications must be postmarked by January 31 postmark date of year to be awarded.

IRS IDENTIFICATION NUMBER: 74-6014110

ADDRESS INQUIRIES TO:
Catherine W. Lee
Director of Administration
(See address above.)

*SPECIAL STIPULATIONS:
Scholarships and grants are to be awarded to Texas residents only and only to applicants attending an institution of higher learning in Texas with an accredited School of Library Science. ALA Spectrum Scholars must agree to work in a Texas library for two years after receiving MLS degree. ALA Century Scholars must agree to work in a Texas library for two years following completion of MLS program.

UNITED STATES HOLOCAUST MEMORIAL MUSEUM, CENTER FOR ADVANCED HOLOCAUST STUDIES

100 Raoul Wallenberg Place, S.W.
Washington, DC 20024-2126
(202) 314-7829
Fax: (202) 479-9726

E-MAIL ADDRESS:
visitingscholars@ushmm.org

WEB SITE ADDRESS:
www.ushmm.org

TYPE:
Fellowships; Visiting scholars. The Center for
Advanced Holocaust Studies is an integral
part of the United States Holocaust Memorial
Museum, which serves as America's national
institution for Holocaust education and
remembrance. The Center awards fellowships
to support significant research and writing
about the Holocaust. Awards are granted on a
competitive basis. The Center welcomes
proposals from scholars in all relevant
academic disciplines, including history,
political science, literature, Jewish studies,
philosophy, religion, psychology, comparative
genocide studies, law and others.

Visiting scholars at the Center have access to
more than 47,000,000 pages of
Holocaust-related archival documentation; the
Museum's extensive library; oral history,
film, photo, art, artifacts and memoir
collections; and Holocaust survivor database.
Many of these sources have not been
examined by scholars, offering unprecedented
opportunities to deepen knowledge about the
Holocaust and further advance the field of
Holocaust studies. In addition to these
resources, the Museum is the American
repository of the International Tracing
Service's (ITS) digitized records. It was
established by the Allies after World War II
to help reunite families and determine the
fates of victims. The ITS collection contains
approximately 50,000,000 pages of material
relating to the fates of more than 17,000,000
people who were subject to incarceration,
forced labor and displacement.

In addition to pursuing their individual
projects, fellows at the Center work side by
side with other new and established
Holocaust scholars from the U.S. and abroad,
enabling them to test their ideas, share their
research findings, debate methodological or
interpretive approaches, and develop
comparative frameworks for their projects.
The Center's weekly fellows meetings and
senior seminar programs provide unique
settings for debate and discussion. Fellows
also participate in the Center's broad array of
scholarly programs and outreach activities at
universities and other academic institutions,
both locally and nationally.

See entry 681 for full listing.

UNIVERSITY OF ARIZONA SCHOOL OF INFORMATION RESOURCES AND LIBRARY SCIENCE [786]

University of Arizona
1515 East First Street, Room 3
Tucson, AZ 85719
(520) 621-3565
Fax: (520) 621-3279

E-MAIL ADDRESS:
sirls@u.arizona.edu

WEB SITE ADDRESS:
www.sirls.arizona.edu

FOUNDED: 1963

AREAS OF INTEREST:
Promoting new knowledge and practice in
the library and information professions with
research, education, and public service
through degree programs at the Master's,
doctoral, and certificate levels.

TYPE:
Assistantships; Internships; Scholarships.
Graduate assistantships; Research
assistantships. Awarded to qualified students
to attend SIRLS.

YEAR PROGRAM STARTED: 1963

PURPOSE:
To educate students in the area of
information resources and library science.

LEGAL BASIS:
Nonprofit, tax-exempt.

ELIGIBILITY:
Any student receiving financial aid must be
accepted into the SIRLS degree program.
Awards are made to students who meet the
criteria set by the School. (This includes
students participating in the program online.)
The School requires that the student be
enrolled for the required number of hours for
the semester of award. Assistance is awarded
on a semester basis.

A new financial aid form must be completed
each semester that a student wishes to be
considered for aid. To be considered for
financial assistance, an applicant must meet
the deadlines posted. Criteria for financial aid
are: stellar academic performance, financial
status, and other qualifications as defined by
specific scholarships.

GEOGRAPHIC RESTRICTIONS:
Arizona.

FINANCIAL DATA:
Amount of support per award: Varies by
program.
Total amount of support: Varies.

APPLICATION INFORMATION:
Applicant must complete the Financial
Assistance Application section of Library
Science Application for Admission.
Duration: One or two semesters.

THE UNIVERSITY OF DELAWARE-HAGLEY PROGRAM

Department of History, John Munroe Hall
University of Delaware
Newark, DE 19716
(302) 831-8226
Fax: (302) 831-1538

E-MAIL ADDRESS:
pato@udel.edu

WEB SITE ADDRESS:
www.udel.edu/hagley

TYPE:
Fellowships. The University of Delaware, in
association with the Hagley Museum,
sponsors a premier graduate resident program
for the study of technology, business,
consumption, and work in industrial and
post-industrial societies leading to a Master
of Arts or Ph.D. in History. Students have
access to faculty with international
reputations in American, European and
non-Western history, and benefit from strong
interdisciplinary ties to museum studies and
material culture programs, as well as the
Hagley Museum and Library. Graduates have
gone on to distinguished careers in academia,
museums and public history.

See entry 683 for full listing.

UNIVERSITY OF TORONTO [787]

Faculty of Information
140 St. George Street
Toronto ON M5S 3G6 Canada
(416) 978-8589
Fax: (416) 978-5762

E-MAIL ADDRESS:
inquire.ischool@utoronto.ca

WEB SITE ADDRESS:
www.ischool.utoronto.ca

FOUNDED: 1928

AREAS OF INTEREST:
Education.

NAME(S) OF PROGRAMS:
● **Patricia Fleming Visiting Fellowship in Bibliography and Book History**

TYPE:
Fellowships; Research grants; Visiting
scholars.

YEAR PROGRAM STARTED: 1928

PURPOSE:
To encourage outstanding scholars to conduct
research in the field of bibliographical studies
or book history.

LEGAL BASIS:
University.

GEOGRAPHIC RESTRICTIONS:
Canada.

FINANCIAL DATA:
Amount of support per award: $1,000
(CAN).

APPLICATION INFORMATION:
Applicants should submit a resume, two
letters of recommendation, and a one- to
two-page research proposal describing the
project.
Duration: February/March annually.

ADDRESS INQUIRIES TO:
Adriana Rossini, Registrar and
In-Program Placement Officer
Faculty of Information
(See address above.)

Music

ACCADEMIA MUSICALE CHIGIANA [788]

Via di Città, 89
53100 Siena Italy
(0039) 0577-22091
Fax: (0039) 0577-288124; (0039) 0577-220936

E-MAIL ADDRESS:
allievi@chigiana.it
accademia.chigiana@chigiana.it

WEB SITE ADDRESS:
www.chigiana.it

FOUNDED: 1932

AREAS OF INTEREST:
Music.

NAME(S) OF PROGRAMS:
● **Scholarships for Summer Music Courses**

TYPE:
Awards/prizes; Scholarships. Merit
scholarships to those who are registered as
active students at the Academy, which offers
various summer music master courses in
orchestral conducting, composition, voice and
various instruments.

In addition, there are other scholarships financed by public institutions or private donors and are awarded at the discretion of the Accademia Chigiana Direction.

YEAR PROGRAM STARTED: 1932

PURPOSE:
To allow young musicians from all over the world to perfect themselves in the principal instruments, studying with many world famous musicians.

ELIGIBILITY:
Applicants can be students of any nationality. Active students must hold an Italian music diploma or an equivalent foreign certificate (exception made for the courses of guitar and singing) and must pass an entrance examination. Age limits are as follows: Conducting, 30 years for the session dedicated to the classical orchestral repertoire; 40 years for the session dedicated to the modern symphonic repertoire; Voice, 32 years (sopranos and tenors), 34 years (mezzo sopranos, baritones and basses); Instruments, 30 years; Chamber Music, average of 30 years. The Italian government also finances scholarships for attendance of summer master classes at the Accademia Chigiana.

Scholarships offered by the Accademia Musicale Chigiana are awarded on the basis of the results of the entrance examination and student merit.

No scholarship will be granted to students already benefiting from financial help from other institutions or to those who do not take the entrance examination on the established date.

FINANCIAL DATA:
Amount of support per award: Scholarships consist of reimbursement of tuition fees (after detraction of the added value tax) plus a daily grant of EUR 35 gross.
Total amount of support: EUR 60,000 (with funds of the Academy) plus EUR 30,000 (by public institutions or private donors).

NUMBER OF APPLICANTS MOST RECENT YEAR: 507 for the year 2010.

NUMBER OF AWARDS: 83 scholarships financed with funds of the Accademia Chigiana and 38 scholarships by public institutions or private donors for the year 2010.

APPLICATION INFORMATION:
Further information and application forms are available from the address above. For details of requirements and application formalities about scholarships awarded by the Italian government, candidates should write directly to the Italian Culture Institute or to the Italian Embassy in their own country.
Deadline: May 15 for the Orchestral Conducting Course; May 31 for Composition; June 10 for all other courses.

PUBLICATIONS:
Courses booklet (information and application form).

OFFICERS:
Gabriello Mancini, President
Aldo Bennici, Artistic Director
Lauro Mariani, Administrative Director

ADDRESS INQUIRIES TO:
Guido Burchi, Consulente Musicologico
Fondazione Accademia Musicale Chigiana
(See address above.)

ACCADEMIA MUSICALE CHIGIANA [789]
Via di Citta, 89
Siena 53100 Italy
(0039) 0577-22091
Fax: (0039) 0577-288124; (0039) 0577-220936

E-MAIL ADDRESS:
stampa@chigiana.it
accademia.chigiana@chigiana.it

WEB SITE ADDRESS:
www.chigiana.it

FOUNDED: 1932

AREAS OF INTEREST:
Music.

NAME(S) OF PROGRAMS:
● **Alfredo Casella International Composition Contest**

TYPE:
Awards/prizes. International composition contest. The competition is for trio with piano (violin, viola and piano) or string quartet (two violins, viola and cello).

YEAR PROGRAM STARTED: 1983

PURPOSE:
To allow young composers to continue, without difficulty, to refine their promising musical gift.

ELIGIBILITY:
Applicants may be composers of any nationality. The contest is open to candidates who have not yet reached the age of 35 years by the date of October 1. Compositions must be unpublished and never performed in Italy and must be about 18-25 minutes long.

FINANCIAL DATA:
Amount of support per award: 10,000 EUR (gross) prize. In addition, the score will be published by Ricordi.

NUMBER OF AWARDS: At least 1.

APPLICATION INFORMATION:
Compositions must be sent by registered mail or delivered to Accademia Musicale Chigiana, Concorso "Alfredo Casella" at the address above. Compositions must be sent anonymously and identified with a motto. This same motto is to appear on a separate sealed (closed) envelope containing the composer's name, date of birth, address, phone number and identity card showing the date of birth. In the same envelope, the composer must declare that the composition has never been performed or published. Further information is available upon request.
Deadline: Entries must be postmarked no later than October 1. Announcement by December 31.

PUBLICATIONS:
Application guidelines.

OFFICERS:
Gabriello Mancini, President
Aldo Bennici, Artistic Director
Lauro Mariani, Administrative Director

ADDRESS INQUIRIES TO:
Concorso "Alfredo Casella"
Accademia Musicale Chigiana
(See address above.)

*SPECIAL STIPULATIONS:
Manuscript scores of prize-winning works will remain in the possession of the Accademia Musicale Chigiana. Scores which have not been awarded may be requested from the Accademia Musicale Chigiana on or no later than January 31.

Should the prize winner be under exclusive contract to another publisher, it will be his or her responsibility to obtain permission for publication by Ricordi.

AMERICAN ACADEMY OF ARTS AND LETTERS [790]
633 West 155th Street
New York, NY 10032-7599
(212) 368-5900
Fax: (212) 491-4615

E-MAIL ADDRESS:
academy@artsandletters.org

WEB SITE ADDRESS:
www.artsandletters.org

FOUNDED: 1898

NAME(S) OF PROGRAMS:
● **The Richard Rodgers Awards**

TYPE:
Awards/prizes. Completed musical scripts are accepted by the Academy for this annual competition. The award subsidizes staged readings, studio productions or productions in New York City by a not-for-profit theater group of a musical play by composers and writers who are not already established in this field.

YEAR PROGRAM STARTED: 1978

PURPOSE:
To further the art of the musical theater in the U.S.

LEGAL BASIS:
Nonprofit Internal Revenue Code 501(c)(3).

ELIGIBILITY:
Open only to U.S. citizens or permanent residents of any age. While students may enter the competition, it is primarily intended for work at a professional level.

GEOGRAPHIC RESTRICTIONS:
United States.

FINANCIAL DATA:
Award money is given to the not-for-profit theater for production expenses.
Amount of support per award: Varies.

NUMBER OF APPLICANTS MOST RECENT YEAR: 133.

NUMBER OF AWARDS: 1 to 4.

APPLICATION INFORMATION:
The name(s) of the author(s) must be blocked out on each of the items submitted, with the exception of the application form. Write only the title of the work on the script, plot summary and CD. Entries must include the following items:
(1) script with lyrics, preferably with no binders or metal clips. Do not send score, videos or visuals;
(2) half-page synopsis of the action and a list of characters;
(3) CD which must contain at least 45 minutes of music, including a minimum of eight songs, recorded in chronological order. Orchestrations are not necessary; piano and vocals are sufficient. Songs must be in sequence on the CD and each song clearly keyed into the script. Please include a separate track sheet of recorded songs with page numbers indicating where they appear in the script, and specify the total number of minutes recorded. Audio tapes will not be accepted and;
(4) application form signed by all collaborators in a sealed envelope with the title of the work on the outside. Applicants

submitting work which has already been produced must give full information concerning these productions, including programs. A work is not eligible if one of the collaborators is deceased.

If the submitted work (or a portion thereof) is an adaptation of material which is not in the public domain, candidates must submit licenses, permissions, or authorizations necessary to permit the work to be produced in conformity with applicable copyright laws. The music must be original.

Materials will be returned if a self-addressed, stamped mailer is enclosed. Addresses must be valid for at least six months. The Academy will take all due care of materials, but it cannot be held responsible for their safe return.

Deadline: November 1. Notification by March.

PUBLICATIONS:
Application guidelines.

STAFF:
Virginia Dajani, Executive Director
Jane Bolster, Coordinator, Richard Rodgers Awards

ADDRESS INQUIRIES TO:
The Richard Rodgers Awards
(See address or web site above.)

*SPECIAL STIPULATIONS:
Musical submitted may not be entered again, even if revised.

AMERICAN ACCORDION MUSICOLOGICAL SOCIETY   [791]

322 Haddon Avenue
Westmont, NJ 08108
(856) 854-6628

WEB SITE ADDRESS:
www.aamsaccordionfestival.com

FOUNDED: 1968

AREAS OF INTEREST:
Research and symposiums on accordion history in the U.S.

CONSULTING OR VOLUNTEER SERVICES:
Library services, books and music on the accordion, and records, CDs and DVDs for rental.

NAME(S) OF PROGRAMS:
● **Annual Symposium and Festival**

TYPE:
Awards/prizes; Work-study programs. The Annual Symposium and Festival is held the first weekend of April.

YEAR PROGRAM STARTED: 1970

PURPOSE:
To help and stimulate young composers to write for the accordion.

LEGAL BASIS:
Nonprofit professional association.

ELIGIBILITY:
Composer must be acquainted with the various types of accordions.

FINANCIAL DATA:
Amount of support per award: $100 to $500.

NUMBER OF APPLICANTS MOST RECENT YEAR:
31 for the year 2008.

APPLICATION INFORMATION:
Applicants should write for entry forms.

Deadline: June 30.

PUBLICATIONS:
Annual news bulletin on classical/folk accordion; annual booklet of accordion information.

ADDRESS INQUIRIES TO:
Stanley Darrow, Secretary
(See address above.)

THE AMERICAN BANDMASTERS ASSOCIATION   [792]

Westlake High School
4100 Westbank Drive
Austin, TX 78746
(512) 732-9280 ext. 33820
Fax: (512) 347-7324

E-MAIL ADDRESS:
ktaylor@eanes.isd.net

WEB SITE ADDRESS:
www.americanbandmasters.org

FOUNDED: 1929

AREAS OF INTEREST:
Concert band and band music.

NAME(S) OF PROGRAMS:
● **Sousa/Ostwald Award**

TYPE:
Awards/prizes. Prize sponsored by the American Bandmasters Association, involving a cash award and performance of the winning composition. One award is presented in odd years for grades 1-4; one award is presented in even years for grades 5-6.

YEAR PROGRAM STARTED: 1955

PURPOSE:
To enrich the spectrum of concert band activity.

ELIGIBILITY:
Contact the Association for details.

FINANCIAL DATA:
Amount of support per award: Varies.
Total amount of support: Varies.

NUMBER OF APPLICANTS MOST RECENT YEAR:
91.

NUMBER OF AWARDS: 1.

APPLICATION INFORMATION:
Send manuscripts and tapes and direct all inquiries directly to the Chairman of the Contest Committee at the address above.
Deadline: Early November.

PUBLICATIONS:
Journal of Band Research.

IRS IDENTIFICATION NUMBER: 36-6112860

OFFICERS:
Paula A. Crider, President
Scott Taylor, President-Elect
Thomas G. Leslie, Vice President
William J. Moody, Secretary-Treasurer

BOARD OF DIRECTORS:
Thomas V. Fraschillo, Chairman
Terry Austin
Robert L. Grace
Finley R. Hamilton
John R. Locke
John O'Reilly
Harry Pinchin
Johnnie B. Vinson
David Waybright

ADDRESS INQUIRIES TO:
Kerry Taylor, Chairperson
ABA/Ostwald Committee
(See address above.)

AMERICAN CONSERVATORY OF MUSIC   [793]

252 Wildwood Road
Hammond, IN 46324
(219) 931-6000
Fax: (219) 931-6089

E-MAIL ADDRESS:
amerconsmu@aol.com

WEB SITE ADDRESS:
www.americanconservatory.edu

FOUNDED: 1886

AREAS OF INTEREST:
Music performance, conducting, composition, theory and music technology.

NAME(S) OF PROGRAMS:
● **Leo Heim Presidential Scholarships**

TYPE:
Scholarships.

YEAR PROGRAM STARTED: 1984

PURPOSE:
To provide excellent musical instruction for talented students at all levels of ability.

LEGAL BASIS:
Not-for-profit corporation since 1941; partnership, multiple partners.

ELIGIBILITY:
Applicants must be students with strong musical background.

FINANCIAL DATA:
Award to be applied solely towards tuition at the Conservatory.
Amount of support per award: Varies based on merit and need.
Total amount of support: Varies.

APPLICATION INFORMATION:
Applicants should submit a standard application form and audition.
Duration: One year.

IRS IDENTIFICATION NUMBER: 84-1454666

ADDRESS INQUIRIES TO:
Admissions
(See address above.)

AMERICAN MATTHAY ASSOCIATION   [794]

328 West 88th Street
Apartment 8
New York, NY 10024

E-MAIL ADDRESS:
dfspiano@verizon.net

WEB SITE ADDRESS:
www.matthay.org

FOUNDED: 1925

AREAS OF INTEREST:
Piano performance and teaching.

NAME(S) OF PROGRAMS:
● **Clara Wells Scholarships for Piano Study**

TYPE:
Conferences/seminars; Scholarships; Work-study programs. Prize funds for study of piano with member of the Association, emphasizing the performance and teaching principles of Tobias Matthay. The Clara Wells Scholarships are awarded biennially.

The next Clara Wells Auditions will be held in June 2012 at the Festival of the American Matthay Association for Piano. Contact the Association for the specific date and time.

YEAR PROGRAM STARTED: 1970

PURPOSE:
To foster the teaching principles of Tobias Matthay.

LEGAL BASIS:
Nonprofit organization.

ELIGIBILITY:
Entrants to Wells Competition must be age 25 or younger as of July 1, 2012 (for the 2012 Competition) and must have memorized the required repertoire. Entrants must submit CD recordings for the preliminary phases. Finals require live performance.

FINANCIAL DATA:
Funds must be used to study piano with a member of the Association.
Amount of support per award: First prize: $2,000. Second Prize: $1,500.
Total amount of support: Varies.

NUMBER OF APPLICANTS MOST RECENT YEAR: 6 to 10 per year.

NUMBER OF AWARDS: 2.

APPLICATION INFORMATION:
Contact the Association.
Deadline: April 23.

PUBLICATIONS:
The Matthay News.

ADDRESS INQUIRIES TO:
Dan Franklin Smith
Competition Chair
(See address and e-mail above.)

AMERICAN MUSICOLOGICAL SOCIETY [795]

6010 College Station
Brunswick, ME 04011-8451
(207) 798-4243
(877) 679-7648
Fax: (207) 798-4254

E-MAIL ADDRESS:
ams@ams-net.org

WEB SITE ADDRESS:
www.ams-net.org

FOUNDED: 1934

AREAS OF INTEREST:
Research in the various fields of music as a branch of learning and scholarship.

NAME(S) OF PROGRAMS:
- **Howard Mayer Brown Fellowship**
- **Alvin H. Johnson AMS 50 Dissertation Fellowships**

TYPE:
Fellowships; Grants-in-aid. The Publications Committee of the American Musicological Society makes available funds to help individuals with expenses involved in the publication of works of musical scholarship, including books, articles and works in nonprint media.

The Howard Mayer Brown Fellowship is intended to increase the presence of minority scholars and teachers in musicology. The fellowship supports one year of graduate work for a member of a group historically underrepresented in the discipline.

The Alvin H. Johnson AMS Dissertation Fellowships are intended for full-time study. It is expected that the recipient's dissertation be completed within the fellowship year.

YEAR PROGRAM STARTED: 1989

PURPOSE:
To support the advancement of research in various fields of music.

LEGAL BASIS:
Nonprofit organization.

ELIGIBILITY:
For the AMS Fellowship, applicants must be registered for a doctorate at a North American university and have completed all formal degree requirements except the dissertation.

The Howard Mayer Brown Fellowship will be awarded to a student who has completed at least one year of graduate work, and who intends to complete a Ph.D. in the field. Applications are encouraged from African-Americans, Native Americans, Latinos, Asian-Americans and, in Canada, visible minorities. There are no restrictions as to age or sex.

FINANCIAL DATA:
Amount of support per award: $17,000 stipend.

APPLICATION INFORMATION:
Applications must be submitted electronically.
Duration: One year. No individual can receive a subvention more than once in a three-year period.
Deadline: December 15.

IRS IDENTIFICATION NUMBER: 23-1577392

AMERICAN MUSICOLOGICAL SOCIETY [796]

6010 College Station
Brunswick, ME 04011-8451
(207) 798-4243
(877) 679-7648
Fax: (207) 798-4254

E-MAIL ADDRESS:
ams@ams-net.org

WEB SITE ADDRESS:
www.ams-net.org

FOUNDED: 1934

AREAS OF INTEREST:
Scholastic work in musicology published in any country, any language.

NAME(S) OF PROGRAMS:
- **The Philip Brett Award**
- **The Alfred Einstein Award**
- **Noah Greenberg Award**
- **The Otto Kinkeldey Award**
- **Lewis Lockwood Award**
- **Music in American Culture Award**
- **Claude V. Palisca Award**
- **Paul A. Pisk Prize**
- **H. Colin Slim Award**
- **Ruth A. Solie Award**
- **Robert M. Stevenson Award**

TYPE:
Awards/prizes. The Philip Brett Award honors exceptional musicological work in the field of gay, lesbian, bisexual, transgender/transsexual studies completed during the previous two academic years (ending June 30), in any country and in any language. By "work" is meant a published article, book, edition, annotated translation, a

paper read at a conference, teaching materials (course descriptions and syllabi), and other scholarly work accepted by the award committee that best exemplifies the highest qualities of originality, interpretation, theory and communication in this field of study.

The Alfred Einstein Award honors a musicological article of exceptional merit, published during the previous year in any language and in any country, by a scholar in the early stages of his or her career.

The Noah Greenberg Award is intended as a grant-in-aid to stimulate active cooperation between scholars and performers by recognizing and fostering outstanding contributions to historical performing practices. Both scholars and performers may apply, since the Award may subsidize the publication costs of articles, monographs, or editions, as well as public performance, recordings, or other projects.

The Otto Kinkeldey Award will honor each year a musicological book of exceptional merit published during the previous year in any language and in any country by a scholar who is past the early stages of his or her career.

The Lewis Lockwood Award honors each year a musicological book of exceptional merit published during the previous year in any language and in any country by a scholar in the early stages of his or her career who is a member of the AMS or a citizen or permanent resident of Canada or the U.S.

The Music in American Culture Award honors each year a book of exceptional merit that both illuminates some important aspect of the music of the U.S. and places that music in a rich cultural context. Books published in the previous year in any language and in any country are eligible. The author must be a citizen or permanent resident of the U.S. or Canada.

The Claude V. Palisca Award honors each year a scholarly edition or translation in the field of musicology published during the previous year in any language and in any country by a scholar who is a member of the AMS or a citizen or permanent resident of Canada or the U.S., deemed by a committee of scholars to best exemplify the highest qualities of originality, interpretation, logic and clarity of thought, and communication.

The Paul A. Pisk Prize is awarded annually to a graduate music student for a scholarly paper to be presented at the Annual Meeting of the Society.

The H. Colin Slim Award honors each year a musicological article of exceptional merit, published during the previous year in any language and in any country by a scholar who is past the early stages of his or her career and who is a member of the AMS or a citizen or permanent resident of Canada or the U.S.

The Ruth A. Solie Award honors each year a collection of musicological essays of exceptional merit published during the preceding calendar year in any language and in any country and edited by a scholar or scholars who are members of the AMS or citizens or permanent residents of Canada or the U.S.

The Robert M. Stevenson Award recognizes outstanding scholarship in Iberian music. The prize will be awarded annually to a book, monograph, edition, or journal article by a member of the AMS. The publication must be written in English and must have been published during the preceding three calendar years.

Winners of all awards receive a monetary prize, conferred at the Annual Business Meeting and Awards Presentation of the Society by the chair of the committee.

YEAR PROGRAM STARTED: 1967

LEGAL BASIS:
Private.

GEOGRAPHIC RESTRICTIONS:
United States and Canada.

FINANCIAL DATA:
Amount of support per award: Varies.

APPLICATION INFORMATION:
Deadline: Philip Brett Award: July 1; Noah Greenburg Award: August 15; Paul A. Pisk Prize: October 1; All others: May 1.

IRS IDENTIFICATION NUMBER: 23-1577392

AMERICAN SOCIETY OF COMPOSERS, AUTHORS AND PUBLISHERS (ASCAP)

ASCAP Building, 6th Floor
One Lincoln Plaza
New York, NY 10023
(212) 621-6000
(800) 952-7227
Fax: (212) 621-8453

E-MAIL ADDRESS:
info@ascap.com
esansaurus@ascap.com

WEB SITE ADDRESS:
www.ascap.com/deemstaylor

TYPE:
Awards/prizes. The ASCAP Deems Taylor Awards program recognizes books, articles, broadcasts and web sites on the subject of music selected for their excellence.

See entry 704 for full listing.

ARD INTERNATIONAL MUSIC COMPETITION   [797]

Internationaler Musikwettbewerb der ARD
Bayerischer Rundfunk
Rundfunkplatz 1
D-80335 Munich Germany
(089) 5900 2471
Fax: (089) 5900 3573

E-MAIL ADDRESS:
ard.musikwettbewerb@brnet.de

WEB SITE ADDRESS:
www.ard-musikwettbewerb.de

FOUNDED: 1952

AREAS OF INTEREST:
International music competition.

NAME(S) OF PROGRAMS:
● **Music Competition**

TYPE:
Awards/prizes. Cash prizes; Competition for music.

Intended for a selection of young musicians who are interested in following an international career. The standards are, therefore, high and the prizes are awarded only for outstanding performances. Program categories differ each year. For 2012: clarinet, voice and string quartet.

YEAR PROGRAM STARTED: 1952

PURPOSE:
To create gifted musicians and international soloists.

ELIGIBILITY:
Instrumentalists should be born between 1983 and 1995. Singers should be born between 1980 and 1992.

FINANCIAL DATA:
Concert invitations, recordings at German broadcast stations.
Amount of support per award: Soloists: First prize, EUR 10,000; Second prize, EUR 7,500; Third prize, EUR 5,000. Wind Quintet: First prize, EUR 25,000; Second prize, EUR 20,000; Third prize, EUR 15,000. Piano Duo (2011): First prize, EUR 12,000; Second prize, EUR 9,000; Third prize, EUR 6,000. String Quartet (2012): First prize, EUR 24,000; Second prize, EUR 18,000; Third prize, EUR 12,000. Piano Trio (2013): First Prize, EUR 18,000; Second prize, EUR 13,500; Third prize, EUR 9,000.
Total amount of support: EUR 130,000 for the year 2012.

COOPERATIVE FUNDING PROGRAMS: Theodor - Rogler - Foundation, Alice - Rosner - Foundation, and others.

NUMBER OF APPLICANTS MOST RECENT YEAR:
Approximately 400 each year.

NUMBER OF AWARDS: 12.

APPLICATION INFORMATION:
A valid statement of type and duration of study should accompany the entry form. Students must have permission of their current teacher to participate. A list of the applicant's complete repertoire is required. Upon arrival in Munich, each competitor should present a birth certificate or a valid passport at the Competition Office.

Preselections with CD are obligatory for all categories.
Duration: 2012: September 5 to 21; 2013: September 2 to 20.
Deadline: March 31.

PUBLICATIONS:
Annual prospectus with application guidelines and programs.

OFFICERS:
Axel Linstaedt, Artistic Director

ADDRESS INQUIRIES TO:
Competition Office
(See address above.)

THE ASCAP FOUNDATION   [798]

One Lincoln Plaza, 7th Floor
New York, NY 10023
(212) 621-6588
Fax: (212) 621-6504

E-MAIL ADDRESS:
concertmusic@ascap.com

WEB SITE ADDRESS:
www.ascapfoundation.org

FOUNDED: 1975

AREAS OF INTEREST:
Music, music composition and music education.

NAME(S) OF PROGRAMS:
● **The Morton Gould Young Composer Awards**

TYPE:
Awards/prizes.

YEAR PROGRAM STARTED: 1978

PURPOSE:
To encourage talented young American composers.

LEGAL BASIS:
Publicly supported foundation, 501(c)(3) organization.

ELIGIBILITY:
Individuals must have not reached their 30th birthday as of January 1 of the year of application and must be U.S. citizens, permanent residents or enrolled students with student visas.

Previous recipients are eligible to reapply for the award.

GEOGRAPHIC RESTRICTIONS:
United States.

FINANCIAL DATA:
Amount of support per award: $500 to $2,500, at discretion of judges.
Total amount of support: $45,000.

NUMBER OF APPLICANTS MOST RECENT YEAR:
Approximately 700.

NUMBER OF AWARDS: 39 or more.

APPLICATION INFORMATION:
A completed application form must be submitted along with one reproduction of an original manuscript or score, a listing of music studies and compositions to date, and biographical information.
Deadline: March 1.

PUBLICATIONS:
Annual report; contributions policy; application guidelines.

BOARD OF DIRECTORS:
Paul Williams, President
Irwin Z. Robinson, Vice President
Dean Kay, Treasurer
Ginny Mancini, Secretary
Marilyn Bergman
Charles Bernstein
Bruce Broughton
Tita Cahn
Alf Clausen
Hal David
Dan Foliart
Arthur Hamilton
Wayland Holyfield
James M. Kendrick
Robert Kimball
Ed London
Johnny Mandel
James McBride
Jay R. Morgenstern
Mary Rodgers
Stephen Schwartz
Valerie Simpson
Charles Strouse
Doug Wood

ADMINISTRATION:
Karen Sherry, Executive Director
Colleen McDonough, Director
Ginny Mancini, Secretary

ADDRESS INQUIRIES TO:
Frances Richard, Vice President
Concert Music ASCAP
(See address above.)

BRANDON UNIVERSITY   [799]

School of Music
270 18th Street
Brandon MB R7A 6A9 Canada
(204) 727-7388
Fax: (204) 728-6839

E-MAIL ADDRESS:
music@brandonu.ca

WEB SITE ADDRESS:
www.brandonu.ca/music

AREAS OF INTEREST:
Music education, performance and literature (piano, collaborative piano, strings and composition).

TYPE:
Assistantships; Scholarships.

PURPOSE:
To afford graduate students the opportunity to gain professional experience while studying and to provide monetary assistance.

ELIGIBILITY:
Open to candidates with a Bachelor's degree in music or music education with a minimum grade point average of 3.0 during the final year.

FINANCIAL DATA:
Amount of support per award: Up to $7,000 per year.
Total amount of support: $30,000 per year.

NUMBER OF APPLICANTS MOST RECENT YEAR:
11.

NUMBER OF AWARDS: 9.

APPLICATION INFORMATION:
Applications available both online and from the Graduate Music Programmes Office.
Deadline: May 1.

ADDRESS INQUIRIES TO:
Dr. Sheila Scott
Graduate Music Programmes
(See address above.)

CHAMBER MUSIC AMERICA [800]

305 Seventh Avenue
5th Floor
New York, NY 10001
(212) 242-2022 ext. 13
Fax: (212) 242-7955

E-MAIL ADDRESS:
sdadian@chamber-music.org

WEB SITE ADDRESS:
www.chamber-music.org

FOUNDED: 1978

AREAS OF INTEREST:
The promotion of public interest in and appreciation of chamber music and the promotion of cooperation among and advancement of professional American chamber music ensembles and presenters.

CONSULTING OR VOLUNTEER SERVICES:
Technical assistance provided in such areas as fund-raising, marketing and residency design and implementation.

NAME(S) OF PROGRAMS:
● **Residency Partnership Program**

TYPE:
Challenge/matching grants; Project/program grants. Direct grants for ensembles and concert presenters.

YEAR PROGRAM STARTED: 1978

PURPOSE:
To stimulate the establishment of chamber music residencies.

LEGAL BASIS:
Nonprofit arts service organization.

ELIGIBILITY:
Candidates must be an ensemble member or a presenter in good standing of CMA, have a minimum of two years of continuous public performance and operation, and have experience in touring, workshops or other residency-related activities.

GEOGRAPHIC RESTRICTIONS:
United States.

FINANCIAL DATA:
Amount of support per award: $2,500 to $12,000.
Total amount of support: Varies.
Matching fund requirements: CMA funds up to 75% of the requested amount.

NUMBER OF APPLICANTS MOST RECENT YEAR:
64.

APPLICATION INFORMATION:
Telephone consultations with CMA staff are available for organizations with questions about the application process.
Duration: Three days to one year.
Deadline: November 18, 2011.

PUBLICATIONS:
Chamber Music, magazine; *CMA Matters,* newsletter; application guidelines.

ADDRESS INQUIRIES TO:
Susan Dadian, Program Director
CMA Classical/Contemporary or
Jeanette Vuocolo, Program Director
CMA Jazz
(See address above.)

*SPECIAL STIPULATIONS:
Residencies must take place within the U.S.

CHAMBER MUSIC AMERICA [801]

305 Seventh Avenue
5th Floor
New York, NY 10001
(212) 242-2022 ext. 13
Fax: (212) 242-7955

E-MAIL ADDRESS:
sdadian@chamber-music.org

WEB SITE ADDRESS:
www.chamber-music.org

FOUNDED: 1978

AREAS OF INTEREST:
The promotion of public interest in and appreciation of chamber music and the promotion of cooperation among and advancement of professional American chamber music ensembles and presenters.

NAME(S) OF PROGRAMS:
● **Chamber Music America Classical Commissioning Program**

TYPE:
Awards/prizes. Awards to ensembles, presenters and festivals that perform or present chamber music, for the commissioning of new works by American composers.

YEAR PROGRAM STARTED: 1983

PURPOSE:
To stimulate the composition of new works for chamber ensembles.

LEGAL BASIS:
Nonprofit arts service organization.

ELIGIBILITY:
Ensembles and presenters must be organizational members of Chamber Music

America. Ensembles must have performed together publicly for a minimum of two years at the time of application. Presenters must have produced three seasons at the time of application and must present no fewer than 10 professional chamber music concerts.

GEOGRAPHIC RESTRICTIONS:
United States.

FINANCIAL DATA:
Amount of support per award: Up to $20,000 for composer fee, copying allotment of $1,000 and subsidy of $1,000 per musician.
Total amount of support: Varies.

NUMBER OF APPLICANTS MOST RECENT YEAR:
65.

NUMBER OF AWARDS: 10.

APPLICATION INFORMATION:
Guidelines may be obtained in the fall from the address above.
Duration: Applicants may reapply after one cycle.
Deadline: April 6.

PUBLICATIONS:
Guidelines and applications.

ADDRESS INQUIRIES TO:
Susan Dadian, Program Director
CMA Classical/Contemporary
(See address above.)

CHOPIN FOUNDATION OF THE U.S. [802]

1440 79th Street Causeway, Suite 117
Miami, FL 33141
(305) 868-0624
Fax: (305) 865-5150

E-MAIL ADDRESS:
info@chopin.org

WEB SITE ADDRESS:
www.chopin.org

FOUNDED: 1977

AREAS OF INTEREST:
Chopin and the promotion of classical music in the community by the support of young American pianists.

NAME(S) OF PROGRAMS:
● **Scholarship Program for Young Pianists**

TYPE:
Scholarships. Scholarship program supporting young American pianists, 14 to 17 years of age.

YEAR PROGRAM STARTED: 1997

PURPOSE:
To support talented young American musicians in their struggle for career recognition; to make classical music available to the community.

ELIGIBILITY:
Open to any qualified American pianists (citizens or legal residents) not younger than 14 and not older than 17 years of age on the application deadline, whose field of study is music and whose major is piano. If applicant is older than 17 years of age, he or she may only be accepted if currently in this scholarship program.

GEOGRAPHIC RESTRICTIONS:
United States.

FINANCIAL DATA:
Amount of support per award: $1,000.
Total amount of support: $10,000 for the year 2010.

NUMBER OF AWARDS: 10.

APPLICATION INFORMATION:
Submit application along with the following documents:
(1) statement of career goals;
(2) minimum of two references from piano teachers or performers;
(3) video recording of 20 to 30 minutes of Chopin's works. Each piece must be an unedited performance on the DVD media. Recording must be clearly labeled, including applicant's name, address and works performed and;
(4) $25 registration fee.

Duration: One year. Renewable up to four years as long as the recipient continues to study piano, maintains satisfactory progress, and each year submits an audiocassette, CD or DVD recording of unedited performances of Chopin's works for evaluation as per renewal information.

Deadline: April 15.

IRS IDENTIFICATION NUMBER: 59-1778404

ADDRESS INQUIRIES TO:
Jadwiga Gewert, Executive Director
(See address above.)

*SPECIAL STIPULATIONS:
Registration fee of $25 must be included with application.

CIVIC ORCHESTRA OF CHICAGO [803]

220 South Michigan Avenue
Chicago, IL 60604
(312) 294-3422
Fax: (312) 294-3450

E-MAIL ADDRESS:
civic@cso.org

WEB SITE ADDRESS:
www.cso.org/civic

FOUNDED: 1919

AREAS OF INTEREST:
Training young musicians for professional work in the orchestral field at the highest level with an emphasis on artistic excellence, community engagement and advocacy.

NAME(S) OF PROGRAMS:
● **Civic Orchestra Lesson Scholarship Stipends**

TYPE:
Fellowships; Scholarships. Stipends to help defray cost of private study with Chicago Symphony members and additional music training-related costs. Scholarship funds may be used for full-time two-year graduate-level study at a local academic institution.

YEAR PROGRAM STARTED: 1919

PURPOSE:
The development of aesthetic sensitivity and playing technique through personal instruction with skilled pedagogues.

LEGAL BASIS:
The Civic Orchestra is a training orchestra under the auspices of the Chicago Symphony Orchestra, which is incorporated as a nonprofit, tax-exempt organization.

ELIGIBILITY:
Scholarships are available to all Civic Orchestra members.

FINANCIAL DATA:
Amount of support per award: $6,500 average for 30-week season.

Total amount of support: Varies.

NUMBER OF APPLICANTS MOST RECENT YEAR: 604.

NUMBER OF AWARDS: 90 for the 2011-12 season.

APPLICATION INFORMATION:
Application forms can be filled out when auditioning for the Civic Orchestra. Membership application forms are available from the Civic Orchestra office. Auditions are held in February and March.

Duration: September to May or June, 30 weeks. Renewal possible for up to two years.

Deadline: Mid-January.

OFFICERS:
William A. Osborn, Chairperson
Deborah Rutter, President, Chicago Symphony Orchestra

ADDRESS INQUIRIES TO:
Yoojin Hong, Manager
(See address above.)

CLEVELAND INSTITUTE OF MUSIC [804]

11021 East Boulevard
Cleveland, OH 44106
(216) 791-5000 ext. 262
Fax: (216) 791-3063

E-MAIL ADDRESS:
kxg26@case.edu

WEB SITE ADDRESS:
www.cim.edu

FOUNDED: 1920

NAME(S) OF PROGRAMS:
● **Cleveland Institute of Music Scholarships**

TYPE:
Scholarships.

PURPOSE:
To provide talented students with a professional, world-class education in the art of music.

ELIGIBILITY:
Candidates for the Teaching Fellowships should have a Bachelor of Music degree or equivalent and must be proficient in English.

FINANCIAL DATA:
Amount of support per award: Varies.

NUMBER OF APPLICANTS MOST RECENT YEAR: 1,100 for the year 2010-11.

APPLICATION INFORMATION:
Students must apply online.

Deadline: Returning students: March 1. New students: February 15.

ADDRESS INQUIRIES TO:
Kristie Gripp, Director of Financial Aid
(See address above.)

COLUMBIA UNIVERSITY

709 Journalism Building
2950 Broadway
New York, NY 10027
(212) 854-3841
Fax: (212) 854-3342

E-MAIL ADDRESS:
pulitzer@pulitzer.org

WEB SITE ADDRESS:
www.pulitzer.org

TYPE:
Awards/prizes; Fellowships. Awards in journalism, books and music.

Pulitzer Prizes in Journalism are awarded based on material appearing in a text-based U.S. newspaper or news site that publishes at least once a week during the year. Awards given for:
(1) meritorious public service by a newspaper through the use of its journalistic resources which may include editorials, cartoons, photographs, graphics and online material;
(2) local reporting of breaking news;
(3) investigative reporting by an individual or team, presented as a single article or series;
(4) explanatory journalism that illuminates a significant or complex subject, demonstrating mastery of the subject, lucid writing and clear presentation;
(5) local reporting;
(6) reporting on national affairs;
(7) reporting on international affairs, including United Nations correspondence;
(8) feature writing giving prime consideration to high literary quality and originality;
(9) commentary;
(10) criticism;
(11) editorial writing;
(12) cartoon or portfolio of cartoons;
(13) breaking news photography in black and white or color, which may consist of a photograph or photographs, a sequence or an album and;
(14) feature photography in black and white or color with the same stipulations as above.

Prizes in Letters are restricted to works first published in the U.S. during the year in book form and available for purchase by the general public. Awards given for:
(1) fiction by an American author, preferably dealing with American life;
(2) a play by an American author, preferably original in its source and dealing with American life, produced in the U.S. January 1 to December 31;
(3) appropriately documented book on the history of the U.S.;
(4) appropriately documented biography or autobiography by an American author;
(5) volume of original verse by an American author and;
(6) appropriately documented book of nonfiction by an American author that is not eligible for consideration in any other category.

A prize in music is given for distinguished musical composition by an American that has had its first performance in the U.S. during the year.

Four fellowships enable outstanding graduates to travel, report and study abroad. One fellowship is given to an outstanding graduate who wishes to specialize in drama, music, literary, film or television criticism.

See entry 2050 for full listing.

CONCOURS CLARA HASKIL [805]

31, rue du conseil
case postale 234
CH-1800 Vevey Switzerland
41 21 922 67 04
Fax: 41 21 922 67 34

E-MAIL ADDRESS:
info@clara-haskil.ch

WEB SITE ADDRESS:
www.clara-haskil.ch

FOUNDED: 1963

AREAS OF INTEREST:
Piano.

NAME(S) OF PROGRAMS:
- **Clara Haskil International Piano Competition**

TYPE:
Awards/prizes. Biennial piano competition for young musicians of any nationality.

YEAR PROGRAM STARTED: 1963

PURPOSE:
To honor and perpetuate the memory of Clara Haskil and to assist a young pianist.

LEGAL BASIS:
Private, with assistance of Fondation Nestle' pour l'Art and Radio TV Suisse Romande.

ELIGIBILITY:
The competition is open to pianists of either sex, from any country, age 27 years maximum.

FINANCIAL DATA:
In addition to a first prize of CHF 20,000, concert engagements for broadcast and for live performance are included.
Amount of support per award: One award of CHF 20,000. Each finalist receives CHF 3,000.
Total amount of support: CHF 26,000.

NUMBER OF APPLICANTS MOST RECENT YEAR:
About 100.

NUMBER OF AWARDS: 1 every two years.

REPRESENTATIVE AWARDS:
Till Fellner; Steven Osborne; Richard Goode; Michel Dalberto; Christoph Eschenbach.

APPLICATION INFORMATION:
The competitors must apply before April 30, enclosing a completed entry form and nonrefundable entry fee of CHF 200.
Deadline: Mid-May; check online for exact date in competition year.

OFFICERS:
Patrick Peikert, Director
Olivier Verrey, President
Marina Vatchnadze, Assistant to the Director
Michel Dalberto, President of the Jury

ADDRESS INQUIRIES TO:
Patrick Peikert, Director
(See address above.)

CONCOURS OSM STANDARD LIFE [806]

OSM Office
260 de Maisonneuve Boulevard West
2nd Floor
Montreal QC H2X 1Y9 Canada
(514) 840-7413
Fax: (514) 842-0728

E-MAIL ADDRESS:
concoursosm@osm.ca

WEB SITE ADDRESS:
www.osm.ca

FOUNDED: 1937

AREAS OF INTEREST:
Music.

NAME(S) OF PROGRAMS:
- **OSM Standard Life Competition**

TYPE:
Awards/prizes; Scholarships. Prizes include money, a performance with the Orchestre symphonique de Montreal, assistance from the CBC (Espace musique) in preparing a promotional CD with the winner of the Grand Prize, in a CBC studio, a concert with the Newfoundland Symphony Orchestra, a recital at the Northern Arts and Cultural Centre of Yellowknife, three scholarships for a three-week session in Music and Sound at the Banff Centre (Alberta) and three scholarships for a two-week session at the Orford Centre (Quebec) for winners in the following categories: Strings and Harp.

YEAR PROGRAM STARTED: 1937

PURPOSE:
To encourage young Canadian musicians.

LEGAL BASIS:
Symphony orchestra.

ELIGIBILITY:
Open to Canadian citizens or landed immigrants in the following categories: Piano and Strings, up to 25 years of age; Woodwinds and Brass, 16 to 25 years of age (except tuba, 16 to 30 years of age); Percussion, 16 to 30 years of age; Voice, 22 to 30 years of age.

Each year is for a different category.

FINANCIAL DATA:
Amount of support per award: Three first prizes: $10,000. Three second prizes: $5,000. Three third prizes: $2,000. Three prizes for the best interpretation of a Canadian work: $2,000. The Paul Merkelo Scholarship: $2,000.
Total amount of support: More than $100,000 (CAN) in prizes, scholarships and concert opportunities.

NUMBER OF APPLICANTS MOST RECENT YEAR:
85 to 90.

NUMBER OF AWARDS: Approximately 20 annually.

APPLICATION INFORMATION:
Include application form, registration fee, proof of age and of Canadian citizenship and curriculum vitae. Applicants must contact OSM Competition to acquire full details of application process.
Deadline: September 30.

ADDRESS INQUIRIES TO:
Daniele LeBlanc, Coordinator
Concours OSM Standard Life Competition
(See address above.)

*PLEASE NOTE:
Musical program approved by the jury members of the competition.

CONTEMPORARY MUSIC FESTIVAL [807]

Department of Music
Indiana State University
Terre Haute, IN 47809
(812) 237-2743
Fax: (812) 237-3009

E-MAIL ADDRESS:
kfowler1@indstate.edu

WEB SITE ADDRESS:
www.indstate.edu/music/cmf

FOUNDED: 1966

AREAS OF INTEREST:
Contemporary orchestra music.

NAME(S) OF PROGRAMS:
- **Competition for Orchestral Compositions**

TYPE:
Conferences/seminars; Residencies. Performance of new music by the Indianapolis Chamber Orchestra. Winning composers will take part in seminars that are part of the festival and will receive an honorarium to cover expenses.

YEAR PROGRAM STARTED: 1966

PURPOSE:
Performance of new orchestral music.

ELIGIBILITY:
Contestants must be citizens or legal residents of the U.S. Winners of the competition within the last five years are not eligible.

NUMBER OF APPLICANTS MOST RECENT YEAR:
85.

NUMBER OF AWARDS: 1.

APPLICATION INFORMATION:
Standard chamber orchestra scoring or less: two flutes (or piccolos), two oboes (or English horns), two clarinets, two bassoons, two trumpets, two horns, two trombones, no tuba, timpani, two percussionists, keyboard, harp and strings. Condensed scores and scores which include soloists or extra instruments will not be considered. Compositions may not exceed 15 minutes in length. A composer may send one score with a corresponding cassette tape or compact disc recording of the work (MIDI realizations are acceptable). Large, neat, proofread parts must be available upon request. The composer's name may not appear on the submission materials. A sealed envelope containing the composer's name, address, phone number and e-mail address should be attached to the score. A summary of the necessary instrumentation and accurate timing should be included with the entry.
Deadline: May 15.

ADDRESS INQUIRIES TO:
Indianapolis Chamber Orchestra
4603 Clarendon Road, Suite 36
Indianapolis, IN 46208
Tel: (317) 940-9607

AARON COPLAND FUND FOR MUSIC, INC. [808]

254 West 31st Street, 15th Floor
New York, NY 10001
(212) 461-6956
Fax: (212) 810-4567

E-MAIL ADDRESS:
info@coplandfund.org

WEB SITE ADDRESS:
www.coplandfund.org

FOUNDED: 1992

AREAS OF INTEREST:
Music.

NAME(S) OF PROGRAMS:
- **Performing Ensembles Program**
- **Recording Program**
- **Supplemental Program**

TYPE:
General operating grants; Project/program grants. Performing Ensembles Program: To support performing organizations whose artistic excellence encourages and improves public knowledge and appreciation of serious contemporary American music. Organizations whose principal function is to support a specific performing ensemble should apply to this program.

Recording Program: To document and provide wider exposure for the music of contemporary American composers; to develop audiences for contemporary American music through record distribution and other retail markets; to support the release and dissemination of recordings of previously unreleased contemporary American music and the reissuance of recordings that are no longer available.

Supplemental Program: To support nonprofit organizations that have a history of substantial commitment to contemporary American music but whose needs are not addressed by the Fund's programs of support for performing organizations and recording projects, such as presenters and music service organizations.

YEAR PROGRAM STARTED: 1992

PURPOSE:
To encourage and improve public knowledge and appreciation of contemporary American music.

LEGAL BASIS:
Foundation.

ELIGIBILITY:
For the Performing Ensembles Program, applicants must be nonprofit professional performing ensembles with a history of substantial commitment to contemporary American music and with plans to continue that commitment. Ensembles must have been in existence for at least two years at the time of application. Festivals are only eligible to apply for their professional core ensembles. Individuals, student ensembles, presenters without a core ensemble are not eligible. Grants will not be made for the purpose of commissions to composers.

For the Recording Program, applicants must be nonprofit performance ensembles, presenting institutions or nonprofit or commercial recording companies. Performance ensembles and presenting institutions must include a letter of intent from either a nonprofit or commercial recording company. Organizations receiving grants will be eligible for grants in subsequent years only if previously funded recordings have been released or are likely to be released within acceptable timeframes. Grants will not be made for the purpose of commissions to composers.

Supplemental Program: Applications may be submitted by nonprofit organizations that have a history of substantial commitment to contemporary American music but whose needs are not addressed by the Fund's programs of support for performing organizations and recording projects. Organizations must have been in existence for at least two years at the time of application.

FINANCIAL DATA:
Grants for recordings of orchestral works may cover up to 50% of the total project costs, including musicians' recording fees, production, marketing and distribution. *Amount of support per award:* $1,000 to $20,000 for Performing Ensembles; $2,000 to $20,000 for the Recording Program; $1,500 to $20,000 for the Supplemental Program. *Total amount of support:* $1,000,000.

NUMBER OF APPLICANTS MOST RECENT YEAR:
Approximately 513.

NUMBER OF AWARDS: 228 for calendar year 2010.

APPLICATION INFORMATION:
Fund guidelines and application procedures are available online for prospective applicants.
Duration: Varies depending on needs and nature of the request.
Deadline: June 30 for Performing Ensembles. January 17, 2012 for Recording Program. September 30 for Supplemental Program. Notification by November, June and January respectively.

ADDRESS INQUIRIES TO:
Grants Manager
(See address above.)
E-mail: grantsmanager@coplandfund.org.

THE CURTIS INSTITUTE OF MUSIC   [809]
1726 Locust Street
Philadelphia, PA 19103
(215) 717-3117
Fax: (215) 893-7900

E-MAIL ADDRESS:
admissions@curtis.edu

WEB SITE ADDRESS:
www.curtis.edu

FOUNDED: 1924

AREAS OF INTEREST:
Musical performance.

NAME(S) OF PROGRAMS:
- **Bachelor of Music Degree Program**
- **Certificate**
- **Diploma Program**
- **Master of Music in Opera**

TYPE:
Scholarships. The training of young performing musicians, admitted by competitive audition for a tuition-free musical education.

YEAR PROGRAM STARTED: 1924

PURPOSE:
To train exceptionally gifted young musicians for careers as performing artists on the highest professional level.

LEGAL BASIS:
The school is operated under a Charter granted by the Commonwealth of Pennsylvania and is also included in the list of "Colleges and Universities in Pennsylvania approved by the State Council of Education for the Granting of Degrees."
The U.S. Government has duly approved the Curtis Institute of Music as an institution of learning for the attendance of nonimmigrant students, under the Immigration and Nationality Act.

ELIGIBILITY:
All are eligible for the competitive audition, regardless of race, origin or geographic distribution. There are maximum ages for applicants which vary by instrument.
For Bachelor of Music Degree Program and Diploma Program, eligibility requirements consist of a competitive audition, high school diploma or GED, SAT Scores, English achievement scores and TOEFL for foreign students. For Master of Music Degree Programs, eligibility requirements consist of a competitive audition and previous Bachelor's degree.

FINANCIAL DATA:
All students are on a scholarship basis exclusively and pay no tuition fees.

Amount of support per award: Varies depending upon award program.

NUMBER OF APPLICANTS MOST RECENT YEAR:
893 for the year 2009.

NUMBER OF AWARDS: 39 for the year 2009.

APPLICATION INFORMATION:
An application form with requested information completed in detail and transcript of high school, college and other academic records should be submitted to the Admissions Officer.
Duration: One-time award.
Deadline: December 12.

PUBLICATIONS:
The Curtis Institute of Music Catalogue (includes application form).

IRS IDENTIFICATION NUMBER: 23-1585611

ADDRESS INQUIRIES TO:
Christopher Hodges, Admissions Officer
(See address above.)

EASTMAN SCHOOL OF MUSIC OF THE UNIVERSITY OF ROCHESTER   [810]
26 Gibbs Street
Rochester, NY 14604
(585) 274-1560
Fax: (585) 274-1088

E-MAIL ADDRESS:
gdean@esm.rochester.edu

WEB SITE ADDRESS:
www.rochester.edu/eastman

AREAS OF INTEREST:
Music.

NAME(S) OF PROGRAMS:
- **Eastman School of Music Graduate Awards**

TYPE:
Scholarships.

PURPOSE:
To support the School's academic programs.

ELIGIBILITY:
Open to nationals of all countries. Candidates should have the qualifications necessary for admission to the Eastman School of Music. Non-U.S. citizens are usually offered service scholarships in ensemble work at graduate level.

FINANCIAL DATA:
Amount of support per award: Up to $21,000 in stipend and $36,000 in tuition scholarship per year.

NUMBER OF AWARDS: 300.

APPLICATION INFORMATION:
Applicants must complete an application form. In addition, awards require an interview in Rochester or at one of the regional auditions.
Duration: One academic year. Renewable.
Deadline: December 1.

ADDRESS INQUIRIES TO:
Admissions Office
Eastman School of Music
(See address above.)

AVERY FISHER ARTIST PROGRAM   [811]
c/o M.L. Falcone
155 West 68th Street, Suite 1114
New York, NY 10023
(212) 580-4302
Fax: (212) 787-9638

WEB SITE ADDRESS:
www.averyfisherartistprogram.org

FOUNDED: 1974

AREAS OF INTEREST:
Music, specifically classical instrumentalists.

NAME(S) OF PROGRAMS:
● **The Avery Fisher Career Grants**
● **The Avery Fisher Prize**

TYPE:
Awards/prizes; Grants-in-aid. Awards for excellence and help in launching major careers.

YEAR PROGRAM STARTED: 1974

PURPOSE:
To recognize outstanding classical instrumentalists and chamber ensembles.

LEGAL BASIS:
Not-for-profit, tax-exempt.

ELIGIBILITY:
Instrumentalists who are U.S. citizens or permanent residents may be nominated.

FINANCIAL DATA:
Amount of support per award: Avery Fisher Career Grants: $25,000 each; Avery Fisher Prize: $75,000.

NUMBER OF AWARDS: Up to 5 Career Grants per year. Avery Fisher Prize considered every year, but not necessarily awarded.

APPLICATION INFORMATION:
Individual artists may not apply directly. Nominations are made by the Recommendation Board, which is comprised of nationally known instrumentalists, conductors, music educators and presenters. Final selections are made by the Executive Committee. The Program is administered by the Lincoln Center for the Performing Arts, Inc.
Deadline: Varies.

EXECUTIVE COMMITTEE:
Emanuel Ax
David Finckel
Henry Fogel
Anthony Fogg
Pamela Frank
Ara Guzelimian
Wu Han
Nathan Leventhal
Reynold Levy
Yo-Yo Ma
Zarin Mehta
Jane S. Moss
Joseph W. Polisi
Chad Smith
Matias Tarnopolsky

ADDRESS INQUIRIES TO:
Nathan Leventhal, Chairman
(See address above.)

FROMM MUSIC FOUNDATION AT HARVARD [812]
Department of Music
Harvard University
Cambridge, MA 02138
(617) 495-2791
Fax: (617) 496-8081

E-MAIL ADDRESS:
moncrief@fas.harvard.edu

WEB SITE ADDRESS:
www.fas.harvard.edu/~musicdpt/fromm.html

FOUNDED: 1972

AREAS OF INTEREST:
Commissioning and performance of contemporary music.

TYPE:
Residencies; Scholarships. Commission and grant-in-aid.

YEAR PROGRAM STARTED: 1952

PURPOSE:
To bring contemporary music closer to the public by providing support to composers and performers.

LEGAL BASIS:
Private foundation.

ELIGIBILITY:
Composers must be citizens or residents of the U.S. For these purposes, "residents" shall be deemed to include only lawful permanent residents, temporary residents, asylees, refugees and nonimmigrants who have lawfully been admitted to the U.S. for a term of one year or more.

FINANCIAL DATA:
Amount of support per award: $10,000.

NUMBER OF APPLICANTS MOST RECENT YEAR:
150.

NUMBER OF AWARDS: 12.

APPLICATION INFORMATION:
Applicants must contact the Foundation for an application.
Deadline: June 1 for consideration in following fall. Commissions will be awarded in December.

PUBLICATIONS:
Application guidelines.

STAFF:
Jean Moncrieff, Administrator

DIRECTORS:
Anne Shreffler, Chairperson
Joel Sachs
Chinary Ung

ADDRESS INQUIRIES TO:
Jean Moncrieff, Administrator
(See address above.)

*SPECIAL STIPULATIONS:
For those who have previously received a Fromm Commission, there is a 15-year waiting period before you can apply again. The Fromm Commission cannot be applied to projects that have been awarded other commissions.

THE GRAMMY FOUNDATION [813]
3030 Olympic Boulevard
Santa Monica, CA 90404
(310) 392-3030
Fax: (310) 392-2188

E-MAIL ADDRESS:
grant@grammy.com

WEB SITE ADDRESS:
www.grammy.org/grammy-foundation/grants

FOUNDED: 1989

AREAS OF INTEREST:
Music research, archiving and preserving and the medical and occupational well-being of music professionals.

TYPE:
Challenge/matching grants; Project/program grants; Research grants. The GRAMMY Foundation Grant Program funds the following areas:

(1) Scientific Research Projects - Grants to organizations and individuals to support efforts that advance the research and/or broad reaching implementations of original scientific research projects related to the impact of music on the human condition, such as the links between music study and early childhood development, the effects of music therapy and the medical and occupational well-being of music professionals.
(2) Archiving and Preservation Projects - Grants to organizations and individuals to support efforts that advance the archiving and preservation of the music and recorded sound heritage of the Americas. The Archiving and Preservation area has two funding categories: (a) Preservation Implementation and (b) Planning, Assessment and/or Consultation.

YEAR PROGRAM STARTED: 1989

PURPOSE:
To cultivate the understanding, appreciation and advancement of the contribution of recorded music to American culture.

ELIGIBILITY:
Priority is given to music projects of national significance, that achieve a broad reach and whose final results are accessible to the general public.

The GRAMMY Foundation, Inc., will not fund:
(1) chapters, trustees, officers or staff;
(2) organizations that discriminate on the basis of race, sex, religion, national origin, disability or age;
(3) recording projects, demo tapes or live performances designed to promote the career of an individual or group;
(4) faculty and staff salaries unrelated to the project;
(5) performance events;
(6) purchase or repairs of music instruments or equipment;
(7) competitions and related expenses;
(8) work toward academic degrees;
(9) regular ongoing business activities of corporate clients;
(10) organizations or individuals for more than three consecutive years;
(11) organizations not based in the U.S. or;
(12) documentaries, endowments and web sites.

GEOGRAPHIC RESTRICTIONS:
The Americas.

FINANCIAL DATA:
Amount of support per award: $5,000 to $20,000.

NUMBER OF APPLICANTS MOST RECENT YEAR:
137.

NUMBER OF AWARDS: 10.

APPLICATION INFORMATION:
Letters of inquiry are only accepted online. Applicants must use current grant application only and should also include:
(1) evidence of organization's nonprofit status and copy of IRS tax determination letter;
(2) general description, history and accomplishments of the organization;
(3) current resume for individual applicants and organization's key personnel;
(4) two letters of support for the project and;
(5) an itemized budget.

Duration: Six to 24 months.

Deadline: October 1; invitation to submit full proposal sent in November; notification by March 15. Late or incomplete applications will not be reviewed. Guidelines posted after June 1.

*SPECIAL STIPULATIONS:
Projects must be completed and a final report submitted within 12 to 24 months of project start date. A full set of the completed project is due to The GRAMMY Foundation within 90 days of the project completion date. Grantees must formally credit The GRAMMY Foundation in all published materials and announcements.

GUITAR FOUNDATION OF AMERICA   [814]
P.O. Box 171269
Austin, TX 78717
(877) 570-1651
Fax: (877) 570-3409

E-MAIL ADDRESS:
info@guitarfoundation.org

WEB SITE ADDRESS:
www.guitarfoundation.org

FOUNDED: 1973

AREAS OF INTEREST:
Classical guitar.

NAME(S) OF PROGRAMS:
● **International Concert Artists Competition Award**
● **International Youth Solo Competition**

TYPE:
Awards/prizes. International Youth Solo Competition awarded in two divisions: Division I for 15 to 18 years old and Division II for 14 years old and under.

PURPOSE:
To support the serious study of the guitar in its historic and performance aspects; to promote the guitar as an ensemble instrument; to encourage composition and arrangements of ensemble music involving the guitar; to preserve and make available literature on the guitar.

LEGAL BASIS:
501(c)(3).

ELIGIBILITY:
Open to competitors worldwide.

IRS IDENTIFICATION NUMBER: 51-0147668

EXECUTIVE DIRECTOR:
Galen Wixson

INTERNATIONAL MARGUERITE LONG-JACQUES THIBAUD COMPETITION   [815]
32, avenue Matignon
75008 Paris France
33 (1) 42 66 66 80
Fax: 33 (1) 42 66 06 43

E-MAIL ADDRESS:
information@long-thibaud.com

WEB SITE ADDRESS:
www.concours-long-thibaud.org

FOUNDED: 1943

TYPE:
Awards/prizes. International competition for piano and violin every two years.

ELIGIBILITY:
Competition is open to musicians of any nationality, under 30 years of age.

FINANCIAL DATA:
Amount of support per award: First Grand Prize: EUR 30,500 and 30 engagements around the world.
Total amount of support: Awards range up to EUR 87,100 for each competition.

NUMBER OF APPLICANTS MOST RECENT YEAR:
167.

NUMBER OF AWARDS: 6 prizes and special prizes.

APPLICATION INFORMATION:
Deadline: August 1.

PUBLICATIONS:
Brochures.

OFFICERS:
Jean-Philippe Schweitzer, President

ADDRESS INQUIRIES TO:
Secretaire-General
(See address above.)

THE KOSCIUSZKO FOUNDATION, INC.   [816]
15 East 65th Street
New York, NY 10065
(212) 734-2130
Fax: (212) 628-4552

E-MAIL ADDRESS:
info@TheKF.org

WEB SITE ADDRESS:
www.TheKF.org

FOUNDED: 1925

NAME(S) OF PROGRAMS:
● **Chopin Piano Competition**

TYPE:
Awards/prizes.

YEAR PROGRAM STARTED: 1949

PURPOSE:
To encourage gifted young pianists to further their studies and perform the works of Chopin, Szymanowski and other Polish composers.

LEGAL BASIS:
Public foundation.

ELIGIBILITY:
The competition is open to citizens and permanent residents of the U.S. and to international full-time students with valid student visas. Applicants must be between the ages of 16 and 22. It is expected that applicants will have demonstrated exceptional talent and artistic achievement. Contestants may apply to compete in the preliminaries in New York. Each contestant should have a program of at least 60 minutes and is expected to perform complete works from memory.

FINANCIAL DATA:
Amount of support per award: $5,000 first prize; $2,500 second prize; $1,500 third prize. In addition, the first prize winner may be invited to perform in recitals in the U.S. and Poland.
Total amount of support: $9,000.

NUMBER OF APPLICANTS MOST RECENT YEAR:
10.

NUMBER OF AWARDS: 3.

APPLICATION INFORMATION:
Official application materials are available upon request to the Foundation. Send business-size, self-addressed, stamped envelope.

Deadline: March 1.

OFFICERS:
Alex Storozynski, President

ADDRESS INQUIRIES TO:
Chopin Piano Competition
(See address above.)

THE LEEDS INTERNATIONAL PIANOFORTE COMPETITION   [817]
The Piano Competition Office
The University of Leeds
Leeds LS2 9JT England
(44) 0 113 244 6586
Fax: (44) 0 113 234 6106

E-MAIL ADDRESS:
pianocompetition@leeds.ac.uk

WEB SITE ADDRESS:
www.leedspiano.com

FOUNDED: 1961

AREAS OF INTEREST:
Piano.

NAME(S) OF PROGRAMS:
● **Leeds International Pianoforte Competition**

TYPE:
Awards/prizes. Prizes in pianoforte awarded every third year.

YEAR PROGRAM STARTED: 1963

PURPOSE:
To provide a competition for professional pianists.

LEGAL BASIS:
Charity.

ELIGIBILITY:
The Competition is open to professional pianists of all nationalities up to 30 years of age.

GEOGRAPHIC RESTRICTIONS:
Worldwide entries invited.

FINANCIAL DATA:
Amount of support per award: GBP 100 to GBP 18,000.
Total amount of support: Prize money in excess of GBP 70,000.

NUMBER OF APPLICANTS MOST RECENT YEAR:
Almost 200 from 45 countries for the year 2009.

APPLICATION INFORMATION:
Application information and forms are available from the Administrator at the address above. The official application form must be completed in English.
Deadline: The application form, completed in English, with enclosures, must arrive no later than February 1 of the year of the competition.

ADDRESS INQUIRIES TO:
Administrator
(See address above.)

THE LESCHETIZKY ASSOCIATION, INC.   [818]
884 West End Avenue, Suite 105
New York, NY 10025-3517
(212) 222-2733

E-MAIL ADDRESS:
marafw@gmail.com

WEB SITE ADDRESS:
www.leschetizky.org

FOUNDED: 1942

AREAS OF INTEREST:
Organization founded by Theodore
Leschetizky's pupils to honor the memory of
a great and beloved master and to perpetuate
his principles in piano playing, teaching and
composing.

CONSULTING OR VOLUNTEER SERVICES:
Offers teaching and consulting services in
piano playing and piano education.

NAME(S) OF PROGRAMS:
- **Gifted Young Pianists Concerto Competition**

TYPE:
Awards/prizes. Competition for a debut
recital in New York.

YEAR PROGRAM STARTED: 1942

PURPOSE:
To perpetuate Theodore Leschetizky's
principles in playing and teaching.

LEGAL BASIS:
Tax-exempt organization under the IRS code
501(c)(3).

ELIGIBILITY:
Open to pianists ages 13 to 17 who have not
given New York City debut concert before.

FINANCIAL DATA:
Amount of support per award: $300 to
$1,000.
Total amount of support: $9,000.

NUMBER OF APPLICANTS MOST RECENT YEAR:
50.

NUMBER OF AWARDS: 1 to 3.

APPLICATION INFORMATION:
Write to the Competition Chair, Mara
Waldman, at the address listed above.
Information is also available online.
Deadline: Biennial competition in
odd-numbered years. Next competition in
2011. Application entry deadline information
is available online.

PUBLICATIONS:
Annual bulletin.

OFFICERS:
Mara Waldman, Chairperson

ADDRESS INQUIRIES TO:
Mara Waldman, Chairperson
(See address above.)

LIEDERKRANZ FOUNDATION [819]

6 East 87th Street
New York, NY 10128
(212) 534-0880
Fax: (212) 828-5372

E-MAIL ADDRESS:
info@liederkranznycity.org

WEB SITE ADDRESS:
www.liederkranznycity.org

FOUNDED: 1947

AREAS OF INTEREST:
Vocal music.

NAME(S) OF PROGRAMS:
- **Annual Awards for Voice**

TYPE:
Awards/prizes. Musicals, concerts, operettas,
operas, general opera.

Annual Awards for Voice consist of three
divisions: General Opera, Wagner and Art
Song.

YEAR PROGRAM STARTED: 1960

PURPOSE:
To encourage and provide financial assistance
to deserving talents.

LEGAL BASIS:
Tax-exempt, nonprofit.

ELIGIBILITY:
Only singers may apply.

FINANCIAL DATA:
Amount of support per award: $2,000 to
$8,000.
Total amount of support: $52,000.

NUMBER OF APPLICANTS MOST RECENT YEAR:
365.

NUMBER OF AWARDS: 17.

APPLICATION INFORMATION:
Applicants may apply in one division only.
Application forms are available in September.
In order to consider the application complete,
applicants must submit:
(1) a completed application form (do not
include resume, photo or cover letter);
(2) a stamped, self-addressed business (9 1/2
x 4 1/8) envelope with the Liederkranz
address as the return address;
(3) a $50 (non-refundable) application fee
(with the applicant's name clearly indicated
on the check) and;
(4) proof of age (a copy of the applicant's
passport, driver's license or photo ID) with
the date of birth highlighted.

Failure to enclose all four items will void the
application.
Duration: Nonrenewable.
Deadline: November 15. Award
announcement in January.

OFFICERS:
Joseph Pfeifer, President

ADDRESS INQUIRIES TO:
Liederkranz Competition
(See address above.)

MEET THE COMPOSER, INC. [820]

90 John Street, Suite 312
New York, NY 10038
(212) 645-6949
Fax: (212) 645-9669

E-MAIL ADDRESS:
mtc@meetthecomposer.org

WEB SITE ADDRESS:
www.meetthecomposer.org

FOUNDED: 1974

AREAS OF INTEREST:
Living composers and contemporary music of
all kinds.

NAME(S) OF PROGRAMS:
- **Cary New Music Performance Fund**
- **Commissioning Music/USA**
- **MetLife Creative Connections**
- **Music Alive**
- **Van Lier Fellowships**

TYPE:
Awards/prizes; Fellowships; Residencies.

YEAR PROGRAM STARTED: 1974

PURPOSE:
To increase opportunities for composers by
fostering the creation, performances,

dissemination, and appreciation for their
music; to fund the creation of new work; to
support direct contact between composers
and audiences; to create education programs
that deepen the understanding of composers
and their work; to establish innovative
private- and public-sector partnerships that
create new opportunities.

LEGAL BASIS:
Nonprofit corporation.

GEOGRAPHIC RESTRICTIONS:
United States.

FINANCIAL DATA:
Amount of support per award: Varies by
program.
Total amount of support: Average $1,000,000
annually.

NUMBER OF APPLICANTS MOST RECENT YEAR:
500.

NUMBER OF AWARDS: 100.

APPLICATION INFORMATION:
Duration: Varies.
Deadline: Varies.

PUBLICATIONS:
*Commissioning Music: A Basic Guide;
Composer in Residence: Meet The
Composer's Orchestra Residencies Program,
1982-92; An Individual's Guide to
Commissioning Music.*

IRS IDENTIFICATION NUMBER: 13-2928942

OFFICERS AND BOARD OF DIRECTORS:
Frederick Peters, Chairman
Joseph Walker, Secretary and Treasurer
Rae Alexander-Minter
Theodore Chapin
Edward Harsh
Harriet Kaufman
Alan Kornberg
Marya Martin
Gayle Morgan
Frances Richard
David Thomas

ADDRESS INQUIRIES TO:
Program Department
(See address above.)

MUSIC CENTER THE NETHERLANDS [821]

Rokin 111
1012 KN Amsterdam The Netherlands
+31 (20) 3446000
Fax: +31 (20) 6733588

E-MAIL ADDRESS:
info@muziekcentrumnederland.nl
info@mcn.nl

WEB SITE ADDRESS:
www.muziekcentrumnederland.nl
www.mcn.nl

FOUNDED: 2008

AREAS OF INTEREST:
Contemporary music.

NAME(S) OF PROGRAMS:
- **Dutch Chamber Music Meeting**
- **International Competition for Interpreters of Contemporary Music**
- **International Composers Competition**

TYPE:
Awards/prizes. Prizes for successful
international competition.

Music Center the Netherlands (MCN) is the
Dutch promotion and information center for
music and national and international musical

life. MCN resulted from the merger between the Dutch Rock & Pop Institute, Donemus, Gaudeamus, 'De Kamervraag,' plus the combined Dutch jazz organizations. MCN now is a single Dutch organization for all music genres.

YEAR PROGRAM STARTED: 1947

LEGAL BASIS:
Nonprofit foundation.

ELIGIBILITY:
Young musicians up to 30 years of age for Composers Competition and up to 35 years of age for Interpreters Competition are eligible.

FINANCIAL DATA:
Composers Competition: Selected works will be performed in Gaudeamus Music Week in September. One of the selected works will receive a monetary prize.

Amount of support per award: Composers Competition: EUR 4,550. Interpreters Competition: first prize, EUR 4,500; second prize, EUR 2,250; third prize, EUR 1,125; special prize, EUR 2,250.

NUMBER OF APPLICANTS MOST RECENT YEAR:
400 composers; 100 interpreters.

NUMBER OF AWARDS: Composers Competition, 1 prize as a commission to write a new piece. Interpreters Competition, 3 prizes and 1 special prize for a specified instrument.

PUBLICATIONS:
Composers' brochures.

ADDRESS INQUIRIES TO:
The Secretariat
(See address above.)

*PLEASE NOTE:
The Year Program Started date (1947) indicates the start of the program for Gaudeamus, one of the organizations involved in the merger that resulted in the Music Center the Netherlands.

E. NAKAMICHI FOUNDATION   [822]
6789 Quail Hill Parkway
Suite 618
Irvine, CA 92603
(714) 771-9677
Fax: (866) 879-2140

E-MAIL ADDRESS:
yas@enfoundation.com

WEB SITE ADDRESS:
www.enfoundation.com

FOUNDED: 1985

AREAS OF INTEREST:
Music.

TYPE:
Project/program grants. Performance of baroque or early classical music.

YEAR PROGRAM STARTED: 1986

PURPOSE:
To support appreciation of early, baroque, classical and similar music.

LEGAL BASIS:
Private foundation.

ELIGIBILITY:
Eligible organizations must be 501(c)(3) tax-exempt. Individuals and religious organizations are ineligible.

GEOGRAPHIC RESTRICTIONS:
Japan and United States.

FINANCIAL DATA:
Amount of support per award: $3,000 to $20,000.
Total amount of support: Generally $350,000 to $400,000 per year.

NUMBER OF APPLICANTS MOST RECENT YEAR:
100.

NUMBER OF AWARDS: 35.

APPLICATION INFORMATION:
Contact the Foundation for application procedures.
Duration: Single/multiple performances.
Deadline: March 15 and October 15.

IRS IDENTIFICATION NUMBER: 95-3870341

ADDRESS INQUIRIES TO:
Yas Yamazaki, Director
(See address above.)

*PLEASE NOTE:
The Foundation is only accepting grant applications from those organizations that were successfully awarded a grant in the years 2000 to 2008.

NATIONAL ASSOCIATION OF COMPOSERS, USA (NACUSA)   [823]
P.O. Box 49256
Barrington Station
Los Angeles, CA 90049
(818) 274-6048

E-MAIL ADDRESS:
dkessner@csun.edu

WEB SITE ADDRESS:
www.music-usa.org/nacusa

FOUNDED: 1932

AREAS OF INTEREST:
The performance, publication, broadcasting and archiving of new American concert hall music.

NAME(S) OF PROGRAMS:
• **Young Composers' Competition**

TYPE:
Awards/prizes; Conferences/seminars. Cash awards and guaranteed performances.

YEAR PROGRAM STARTED: 1978

PURPOSE:
To recognize and encourage young talent.

LEGAL BASIS:
501(c)(3) nonprofit organization.

ELIGIBILITY:
Open to all NACUSA members between the ages of 18 and 30. Compositions submitted should not exceed 15 minutes in length. Compositions should not require more than five players; an additional person for tape playback will not be counted as a performer. Compositions submitted must not have been previously published nor won any other musical competition.

GEOGRAPHIC RESTRICTIONS:
United States.

FINANCIAL DATA:
Amount of support per award: First prize: $400 and a guaranteed performance at a Los Angeles NACUSA concert; Second prize: $100 and a guaranteed performance at a NACUSA concert.

COOPERATIVE FUNDING PROGRAMS: Contest is supported, in part, by grants from ASCAP and BMI.

NUMBER OF APPLICANTS MOST RECENT YEAR:
63.

NUMBER OF AWARDS: Varies.

APPLICATION INFORMATION:
One copy of the score is to be submitted. Recordings of the entire composition are highly desirable, but not mandatory. Return postage must accompany each score if the composer wishes to maintain possession of the music. Scores will be judged, in part, on clear and legible music copying. Composers may submit up to two compositions. Scores should be submitted anonymously with an envelope attached containing the name of the work, the name of the composer and the composer's address and phone number.
Deadline: October 31.

PUBLICATIONS:
Composer/USA, newsletter.

IRS IDENTIFICATION NUMBER: 51-0166704

ADDRESS INQUIRIES TO:
Dr. David Lefkowitz, Vice President
(See address above.)

NATIONAL FEDERATION OF MUSIC CLUBS   [824]
1646 Smith Valley Road
Greenwood, IN 46142
(317) 882-4003
Fax: (317) 882-4019

E-MAIL ADDRESS:
info@nfmc-music.org

WEB SITE ADDRESS:
www.nfmc-music.org

FOUNDED: 1898

AREAS OF INTEREST:
Vocal and instrumental music, dance and composition.

NAME(S) OF PROGRAMS:
• **NFMC Competitions and Awards**

TYPE:
Awards/prizes. Competitions. Awards for students and adults who show proficiency in the fields of voice, instrumental performance, dance, composition, etc. The Federation provides a wide range of awards.

PURPOSE:
To support performance and promotion of American music.

LEGAL BASIS:
Nonprofit.

ELIGIBILITY:
Competitions cover a wide range of age groups from age 10 through adult. In general, applicants must be native-born or naturalized American citizens and must be members or become members of the National Federation of Music Clubs either by individual or group affiliation before applications are accepted.

GEOGRAPHIC RESTRICTIONS:
United States.

FINANCIAL DATA:
Awards may include performances at NFMC concerts and conventions.
Amount of support per award: $50 to $10,000.

APPLICATION INFORMATION:
Except in a few instances, applicants must become members of the NFMC on or before application either through individual or group affiliation before applications are considered. Application forms and information may be

obtained from the NFMC at the address above. Enclose a self-addressed, stamped envelope. All requests for information must include $2 for material, postage and handling.
Duration: One-time award.

PUBLICATIONS:
Competitions and awards chart; *Junior Keynotes Magazine*; *Music Club Magazine*.

OFFICERS:
Lana Bailey, President
Barbara Hildebrand, Treasurer
Carole Langley, Recording Secretary

STAFF:
Jennifer Griffin, Administrative Manager

ADDRESS INQUIRIES TO:
Jennifer Griffin, Administrative Manager
(See address above.)

NATIONAL FEDERATION OF MUSIC CLUBS   [825]
1646 Smith Valley Road
Greenwood, IN 46142
(317) 882-4003
Fax: (317) 882-4019

E-MAIL ADDRESS:
info@nfmc-music.org

WEB SITE ADDRESS:
www.nfmc-music.org

FOUNDED: 1898

AREAS OF INTEREST:
Vocal and instrumental music and composition.

NAME(S) OF PROGRAMS:
• **Award Program for Summer Music Festivals and Music Centers**

TYPE:
Awards/prizes. Prizes for the performance and promotion of American music at summer music festivals.

PURPOSE:
To support performance and promotion of American music.

LEGAL BASIS:
Nonprofit.

ELIGIBILITY:
Program open to summer music festivals, centers and camps in the U.S. and its territories. In general, applicants must be native-born or naturalized American citizens and must be members or become members of the National Federation of Music Clubs either by individual or group affiliation before applications are accepted.

GEOGRAPHIC RESTRICTIONS:
United States.

FINANCIAL DATA:
Amount of support per award: Average $225 to $3,100.

NUMBER OF AWARDS: 23 summer music centers totaling over 30 awards.

OFFICERS:
Lana Bailey, President
Barbara Hildebrand, Treasurer
Carole Langley, Recording Secretary

STAFF:
Jennifer Griffin, Administrative Manager

ADDRESS INQUIRIES TO:
Jennifer Griffin, Administrative Manager
(See address above.)

NATIONAL FEDERATION OF MUSIC CLUBS   [826]
1646 Smith Valley Road
Greenwood, IN 46142
(317) 882-4003
Fax: (317) 882-4019

E-MAIL ADDRESS:
info@nfmc-music.org

WEB SITE ADDRESS:
www.nfmc-music.org

FOUNDED: 1898

AREAS OF INTEREST:
Dedicated to finding and fostering young musical talent.

NAME(S) OF PROGRAMS:
• **Dorothy Dann Bullock Music Therapy Award**

TYPE:
Grants-in-aid. Financial assistance.

PURPOSE:
To support performance and promotion of American music.

LEGAL BASIS:
Nonprofit.

ELIGIBILITY:
Offered to Music Therapy Majors (college sophomores, juniors or seniors) in accredited schools offering Music Therapy degrees approved by American Music Therapy Association. Applicants must be native-born or naturalized American citizens and must be members or become members of NFMC either by individual or group affiliation before applications are accepted.

GEOGRAPHIC RESTRICTIONS:
United States.

FINANCIAL DATA:
Amount of support per award: $1,250.
Total amount of support: $1,250 annually.

NUMBER OF AWARDS: 1 annually.

APPLICATION INFORMATION:
Deadline: March 1.

OFFICERS:
Lana Bailey, President
Barbara Hildebrand, Treasurer
Carole Langley, Recording Secretary

STAFF:
Jennifer Griffin, Administrative Manager

ADDRESS INQUIRIES TO:
Bullock Music Therapy Award
(See address above.)

NATIONAL OPERA ASSOCIATION, INC.   [827]
2403 Russell Long Boulevard
Canyon, TX 79016
(806) 651-2857
Fax: (806) 651-2958

E-MAIL ADDRESS:
rhansen@noa.org

WEB SITE ADDRESS:
www.noa.org

FOUNDED: 1955

AREAS OF INTEREST:
Opera production, opera composition, promotion of operatic talent, opera education and opera for youth.

CONSULTING OR VOLUNTEER SERVICES:
Distinguished members available for consultation and workshops.

NAME(S) OF PROGRAMS:
• **Biennial Dissertation Competition**
• **Chamber Opera Competition**
• **Collegiate Opera Scenes Competition**
• **Legacy Career Development Grant Program for Racial/Ethnic Minorities**
• **Opera Production Competition**
• **Sacred in Opera**
• **Scholarly Paper Competition**
• **Student and Artist Vocal Auditions**

TYPE:
Awards/prizes. Cash prizes awarded to Artist Division winners and Scholarship Division winners. Also scholarships to AIMS, awarded in both divisions. Productions of winning operas in Chamber Opera Competition will be scheduled for annual convention.

YEAR PROGRAM STARTED: 1977

PURPOSE:
To assist young opera singers in furthering their training for an operatic career and to honor the best of the new chamber operas and the outstanding opera productions by universities and colleges.

LEGAL BASIS:
Nonprofit organization.

ELIGIBILITY:
All applicants must submit an entrance fee depending on category and membership status.

FINANCIAL DATA:
Amount of support per award: $500 to $2,000 for singing competitors.
Total amount of support: $10,000.

NUMBER OF APPLICANTS MOST RECENT YEAR:
150 for vocal competition, 25 for opera production competition and over 100 for chamber opera competition.

NUMBER OF AWARDS: Approximately 10.

APPLICATION INFORMATION:
Duration: Nonrenewable.
Deadline: Varies by contest.

PUBLICATIONS:
Opera Journal; NOA Newsletter.

ADDRESS INQUIRIES TO:
Robert Hansen, Executive Director
(See address above.)

NATIONAL ORCHESTRAL INSTITUTE   [828]
2110 Clarice Smith Performing Arts Center
University of Maryland School of Music
College Park, MD 20742
(301) 405-2317
Fax: (301) 314-9504

E-MAIL ADDRESS:
noi@umd.edu

WEB SITE ADDRESS:
www.noi.umd.edu

FOUNDED: 1988

AREAS OF INTEREST:
Orchestral music.

TYPE:
Residencies; Scholarships; Training grants; Visiting scholars. Advanced orchestral training program offering talented musicians on the threshold of their professional careers a four-week opportunity to study and perform under internationally renowned conductors and principal musicians from leading American orchestras.

YEAR PROGRAM STARTED: 1988

PURPOSE:
To prepare musicians for professional orchestral careers.

LEGAL BASIS:
University.

ELIGIBILITY:
Applicants must be between the ages of 18 and 28 with appropriate orchestral music skill.

FINANCIAL DATA:
Support includes tuition at the Institute and housing.
Amount of support per award: Over $4,000.
Total amount of support: Varies.

NUMBER OF APPLICANTS MOST RECENT YEAR:
650 for the year 2008.

NUMBER OF AWARDS: 90 for the year 2009.

APPLICATION INFORMATION:
Applicants should submit an application, resume and one letter of recommendation. They should also audition at one of the audition centers in cities across the U.S. between January and March.
Duration: May 27 to June 26.
Deadline: Varies by audition location.

PUBLICATIONS:
Program announcement.

ADDRESS INQUIRIES TO:
Richard Scerbo, Managing Director
(See address above.)

THE WALTER W. NAUMBURG FOUNDATION, INC.   [829]

120 Claremont Avenue
New York, NY 10027
(917) 493-4040
Fax: (212) 362-9877

WEB SITE ADDRESS:
www.naumburg.org

FOUNDED: 1925

AREAS OF INTEREST:
Sponsorship of international competitions for violin, cello, piano, voice, chamber music and composition.

TYPE:
Awards/prizes.

ELIGIBILITY:
Requirements differ with various categories of violin, cello, piano, voice, chamber music and composition. This competition is open to musicians and composers of every nationality. The competitors may not be under 17 years of age or more than 31 years of age, and may not have had a birthday before 1981 for the 2012 Violin, Cello and Chamber Music Competitions. Voice applicants may not be under 17 years of age or more than 35 years of age.

FINANCIAL DATA:
Solo Competition: First prize award includes two fully subsidized New York Recitals - Debut in Weill Hall, Carnegie Hall, recital and orchestral performances, in addition to a cash award. Chamber Music Award: Recital with commission work.
Amount of support per award: Solo Competition: $10,000 first prize, $5,000 second prize and $2,500 third prize.

APPLICATION INFORMATION:
Application forms may be obtained by writing to the Foundation at the address

above. Enclose a self-addressed, stamped envelope. Also, a CD recording screening will be held by a panel of judges.
Duration: One-time award.
Deadline: Application forms and a CD of no less than 30 minutes of satisfactory audible quality must be received at the Naumburg office no later than March 1.

BOARD OF DIRECTORS AND OFFICERS:
Robert Mann, President
David Geber, Vice President
Nicholas Mann, Vice President
Marshall Gibson, Treasurer
Lucy Rowan Mann, Secretary and Assistant Treasurer
Elliott Carter
John Corigliano
Bernard H. Gustin
Bonnie Hampton
Claude Mann
Judith Naumburg
Ursula Oppens
Julius Rudel
Robert Sherman
Benita Valente

ADDRESS INQUIRIES TO:
Lucy Rowan Mann, Executive Director
(See address above.)

PERCUSSIVE ARTS SOCIETY   [830]

110 West Washington
Suite A
Indianapolis, IN 46204
(317) 974-4488
Fax: (317) 974-4499

E-MAIL ADDRESS:
percarts@pas.org

WEB SITE ADDRESS:
www.pas.org

FOUNDED: 1961

AREAS OF INTEREST:
Percussive arts, including music education, performance and literature related to percussion instruments.

CONSULTING OR VOLUNTEER SERVICES:
Consulting committees on acoustics, education curricula, literature, etc.

NAME(S) OF PROGRAMS:
● **Annual Composition Contest**
● **Fred Hoey Scholarship**
● **Hudson Music Drumset Scholarship**
● **Internship Program**
● **Larrie Londin Scholarship**
● **PASIC International Scholarship**
● **PASIC Scholarships**
● **Yamaha Terry Gibbs Scholarship**
● **Armand Zildjian Scholarship**
● **Zildjian Family Opportunity Fund**

TYPE:
Awards/prizes; Internships; Project/program grants; Scholarships.

YEAR PROGRAM STARTED: 1961

PURPOSE:
To promote percussion education, research, performance and appreciation.

LEGAL BASIS:
Not-for-profit corporation.

ELIGIBILITY:
Internship: Enrolled music business major in accredited university program.

FINANCIAL DATA:
Amount of support per award: Varies.

NUMBER OF APPLICANTS MOST RECENT YEAR:
135.

NUMBER OF AWARDS: 12.

PUBLICATIONS:
Percussive Notes, magazine; *Percussion News,* newsletter.

IRS IDENTIFICATION NUMBER: 73-1385751

STAFF:
Michael G. Kenyon, Executive Director

ADDRESS INQUIRIES TO:
Michael G. Kenyon, Executive Director
(See address above.)

THE PITTSBURGH NEW MUSIC ENSEMBLE, INC.   [831]

527 Coyne Terrace
Pittsburgh, PA 15207
(412) 889-7231

E-MAIL ADDRESS:
contactpnme@gmail.com

WEB SITE ADDRESS:
www.pnme.org

FOUNDED: 1975

AREAS OF INTEREST:
New music and allied arts.

NAME(S) OF PROGRAMS:
● **Harvey Gaul Music Composition Contest**

TYPE:
Awards/prizes.

YEAR PROGRAM STARTED: 1975

PURPOSE:
To promote new music and support composers.

LEGAL BASIS:
Nonprofit corporation.

ELIGIBILITY:
Contestants must be U.S. citizens.

FINANCIAL DATA:
Amount of support per award: $6,000 commission.

NUMBER OF AWARDS: 1.

APPLICATION INFORMATION:
An entry form is required. An entry fee of $20 must accompany each composition. Contestants should send a score and CD of a representative instrumental work, along with a current biography and contact information. No MIDI realizations.
Deadline: January 1 of odd-numbered years.

PUBLICATIONS:
Application guidelines.

IRS IDENTIFICATION NUMBER: 25-1364030

OFFICERS:
Kevin Noe, Executive Artistic Director

ADDRESS INQUIRIES TO:
Kevin Noe, Executive Artistic Director
(See address above.)

*PLEASE NOTE:
Contest is biennial.

The Ensemble does not award scholarships.

PRESSER FOUNDATION   [832]

385 Lancaster Avenue
Room 205
Haverford, PA 19041
(610) 658-9030

E-MAIL ADDRESS:
mfrank@presserfoundation.org

WEB SITE ADDRESS:
www.presserfoundation.org

FOUNDED: 1916

AREAS OF INTEREST:
Music education at the postsecondary level.

NAME(S) OF PROGRAMS:
- **Presser Undergraduate Scholar Award**

TYPE:
Fellowships; Project/program grants;
Scholarships.

YEAR PROGRAM STARTED: 1916

PURPOSE:
To provide awards to worthy candidates to
pursue a higher level of music education at
the college level.

LEGAL BASIS:
Private foundation.

ELIGIBILITY:
Only college and university music
departments. Institution must have a
minimum of 40 undergraduate music majors.
Awarded to students at end of his/her junior
year or beginning of senior year. Awards are
granted to institutions, not individuals.
Institution shall select its outstanding
candidate for award. Candidate must take at
least one-third course credits in subjects not
related to music.

GEOGRAPHIC RESTRICTIONS:
United States.

FINANCIAL DATA:
Amount of support per award: Cash stipend
of approximately $4,000 payable at the
beginning of the student's senior year.

NUMBER OF AWARDS: 1 per institution.

APPLICATION INFORMATION:
Application form can be downloaded from
the Foundation web site.
Duration: One year. Nonrenewable.
Deadline: September 1.

ADDRESS INQUIRIES TO:
Mariel Frank, Executive Director
(See address above.)

THE QUEEN ELISABETH INTERNATIONAL MUSIC COMPETITION OF BELGIUM   [833]

20, rue aux Laines
B-1000 Brussels Belgium
(32 2) 213 40 50
Fax: (32 2) 514 32 97

E-MAIL ADDRESS:
info@qeimc.be

WEB SITE ADDRESS:
www.qeimc.be

FOUNDED: 1951

AREAS OF INTEREST:
Singing, violin, piano and composition.

TYPE:
Assistantships; Awards/prizes;
Conferences/seminars.

PURPOSE:
To support young artists and thus help to
establish their reputations with both
professionals and the public through an
international competition for music
interpretation.

LEGAL BASIS:
Nonprofit organization.

ELIGIBILITY:
Programs alternate each year. The
competition is reserved for piano in 2010, for
singing in 2011, and for violin in 2012.

In 2011, in the frame of the 2012 violin
competition, the Queen Elisabeth
Competition organizes a contest devoted to
composers.

The competition is open to musicians of all
nationalities. The minimum age for
applicants is 17. Maximum age for the piano
and violin competitions is 27, 30 for singers,
and 40 for composers. Instrumental
competitors play both assigned works and
pieces of their own selection. The
competition is divided into selection rounds
and final round.

FINANCIAL DATA:
Amount of support per award: First place:
EUR 20,000, plus recording and concerts.
Total amount of support: 12 cash prizes and
distinctions are awarded in each category for
a total of over EUR 120,000.

NUMBER OF APPLICANTS MOST RECENT YEAR:
170 pianists for the year 2010.

NUMBER OF AWARDS: 12 for the year 2009.

APPLICATION INFORMATION:
Applications for registration should be
downloaded online and accompanied by the
following:
(1) a copy of birth certificate;
(2) proof of nationality;
(3) two photographs (passport size);
(4) one 9 x 12-inch photograph;
(5) curriculum vitae;
(6) documentation providing proof of his or
her skill (for example, higher diplomas,
repertoire list with works performed in
public, prizes and diplomas received from
other competitions, press reviews, etc.) and;
(7) a DVD recording (image and sound) with
appropriate music programme.
Deadline: January 15 of the year of the
competition.

PUBLICATIONS:
Competition announcement and rules;
master-class leaflets; brochures; list with
results and addresses to contact laureates.

OFFICERS:
Count Jean-Pierre de Launoit, Chairman
Michel-Etienne Van Neste, Secretary General

ADDRESS INQUIRIES TO:
The Secretariat of the Competition
(See address above.)

SAN ANGELO SYMPHONY SOCIETY   [834]

P.O. Box 5922
San Angelo, TX 76902
(325) 658-5877
Fax: (325) 653-1045

E-MAIL ADDRESS:
director@sanangelosymphony.org

WEB SITE ADDRESS:
www.sanangelosymphony.org

FOUNDED: 1949

AREAS OF INTEREST:
Symphonic music and young artist
competition.

NAME(S) OF PROGRAMS:
- **Sorantin Young Artist Award**

TYPE:
Awards/prizes. Cash prizes. Overall winner
performs with the San Angelo Symphony
Orchestra in February as a guest artist.
Competition is divided into two
classifications: piano and strings.

YEAR PROGRAM STARTED: 1959

PURPOSE:
To recognize young artists.

LEGAL BASIS:
Urban orchestra under Internal Revenue Code
501(c)(3).

ELIGIBILITY:
Open to string players and pianists who have
not reached their 28th birthday at the time of
the auditions. All candidates are judged by
the highest artistic standards in regard to
technical proficiency, musicianship, rhythm,
selection of repertoire and stage deportment.
All contestants will perform all repertoire
from memory. No exceptions are made.

FINANCIAL DATA:
Total amount of support: $10,000.

NUMBER OF APPLICANTS MOST RECENT YEAR:
50.

NUMBER OF AWARDS: Varies.

APPLICATION INFORMATION:
Applications must be accompanied by a fee
of $75 in cashier's check or money order, all
of which is nonrefundable. Complete
information is available online.
Duration: One-time award.

PUBLICATIONS:
Flyer (includes application form).

IRS IDENTIFICATION NUMBER: 75-6003857

OFFICERS:
Charlotte Lewis, Executive Director

ADDRESS INQUIRIES TO:
Charlotte Lewis, Executive Director
(See address above.)

SAN FRANCISCO CONSERVATORY OF MUSIC   [835]

50 Oak Street
San Francisco, CA 94102
(415) 503-6214
Fax: (415) 503-6299

E-MAIL ADDRESS:
dbh@sfcm.edu

WEB SITE ADDRESS:
www.sfcm.edu

FOUNDED: 1917

AREAS OF INTEREST:
Music.

NAME(S) OF PROGRAMS:
- **Performance Scholarships in Music for Students in Bachelor and Master of Music Programs**

TYPE:
Assistantships; Scholarships; Work-study
programs. Awards for the study of music at
the Conservatory.

YEAR PROGRAM STARTED: 1917

PURPOSE:
To enable talented, needy students to attend
the Conservatory.

LEGAL BASIS:
Conservatory of Music.

ELIGIBILITY:
U.S. and foreign citizens may apply.
Candidates must have had considerable
experience in musical performance and must
attend the Conservatory on a full-time basis.

FINANCIAL DATA:
Scholarships are to be applied toward tuition
at the Conservatory.
Amount of support per award: $1,000 and
up.
Total amount of support: $5,500,000 for the
year 2010.

NUMBER OF APPLICANTS MOST RECENT YEAR:
950.

NUMBER OF AWARDS: 356.

APPLICATION INFORMATION:
Applicants must submit the San Francisco
Conservatory of Music Application and either
the Free Application for Federal Student Aid
or the International Student Financial Aid
Application and International Student
Certification of Finances.
Duration: Tenable for one year and may be
renewed.
Deadline: February 15.

OFFICER:
Doris Howard, Director of Financial Aid

ADDRESS INQUIRIES TO:
Financial Aid
finaid@sfcm.edu
(See address above.)

SAN FRANCISCO OPERA CENTER [836]

War Memorial Opera House
301 Van Ness Avenue
San Francisco, CA 94102-4509
(415) 565-3277
Fax: (415) 255-6774

E-MAIL ADDRESS:
merolaauditions@sfopera.com

WEB SITE ADDRESS:
www.sfopera.com/auditions

FOUNDED: 1954

AREAS OF INTEREST:
Young professional singers,
pianists/accompanists and stage directors
interested in a sequence of opera
performance and career development
opportunities.

CONSULTING OR VOLUNTEER SERVICES:
Board of Directors of Merola Opera Program
and a full staff of conductors, coaches, stage
directors and instructors in singing, acting,
movement, stage combat, auditioning, career
development and other activities.

NAME(S) OF PROGRAMS:
● **Adler Fellowships**
● **Merola Opera Program**
● **Schwabacher Debut Recitals**

TYPE:
Assistantships; Awards/prizes; Fellowships;
Internships; Technical assistance. Auditions
by application are held in the fall of each
year for the following summer's Merola
Opera Program in various cities throughout
the U.S. Participants will also be considered
for Adler Fellowships (singers/pianists).

YEAR PROGRAM STARTED: 1954

PURPOSE:
To provide professional opera training and
performance opportunities for talented young
opera professionals.

LEGAL BASIS:
Nonprofit.

ELIGIBILITY:
Open to all singers, pianists/accompanists
and stage directors. All voice types are
eligible, between the ages of 20 and 34.

FINANCIAL DATA:
Merola Opera Program participants receive
shared housing accommodations, weekly
allowance and round-trip airfare from place
of residence to San Francisco. Adler
Fellowships are for a salaried 12-month
contract.
Amount of support per award: Contracted
salary varies, plus benefits.
Total amount of support: Varies.

APPLICATION INFORMATION:
Application form is required. Applicant must
indicate on the application six arias he or she
is prepared to sing, at least two of which
must be in a foreign language.
Duration: Merola Opera Program: June to
August. Adler Fellowships: 12-month
contract.
Deadline: Fall of each year.

PUBLICATIONS:
Application guidelines.

OFFICERS:
Sheri Greenawald, Director
Mark Morash, Director of Musical Studies

ADDRESS INQUIRIES TO:
Jo Ann McStravick, Artists' Services
and Audition Administrator
(See address above.)

SIGMA ALPHA IOTA MUSIC FRATERNITY [837]

One Tunnel Road
Asheville, NC 28805-1229
(828) 251-0606
Fax: (828) 251-0644

E-MAIL ADDRESS:
nh@sai-national.org

WEB SITE ADDRESS:
www.sai-national.org

FOUNDED: 1903

AREAS OF INTEREST:
Music, new compositions.

CONSULTING OR VOLUNTEER SERVICES:
Local volunteers in music.

NAME(S) OF PROGRAMS:
● **Inter-American Music Awards**

TYPE:
Awards/prizes. Music composition contest.

YEAR PROGRAM STARTED: 1948

PURPOSE:
To give to the fraternity, and to the public,
compositions of high musical merit; to bring
distinction to winning composers; to offer
royalties and other benefits coincident with
publication of winning music.

LEGAL BASIS:
Nonprofit corporation.

ELIGIBILITY:
Requirements change each triennium;
however, applicants must be residents of
North, Central or South America.

GEOGRAPHIC RESTRICTIONS:
North, Central or South America.

FINANCIAL DATA:
Financial data changes each triennium.
Winning composition is performed at the
Fraternity's national convention.
Amount of support per award: $2,500 prize,
plus winning composition published by a
major music publisher.

NUMBER OF APPLICANTS MOST RECENT YEAR:
50.

NUMBER OF AWARDS: 1.

APPLICATION INFORMATION:
Duration: One-time award.
Deadline: September 1.

PUBLICATIONS:
Brochure.

STAFF:
Ruth E. Sieber Johnson, Executive Director

ADDRESS INQUIRIES TO:
SAI Philanthropies, Inc.
(See address above.)

SYMPHONY OF THE MOUNTAINS [838]

Kingsport Renaissance Center
1200 East Center Street
Kingsport, TN 37660
(423) 392-8423
Fax: (423) 392-8428

E-MAIL ADDRESS:
cornelia@symphonyofthemountains.org

WEB SITE ADDRESS:
www.symphonyofthemountains.org

FOUNDED: 1946

AREAS OF INTEREST:
Symphonic concerts and educational and
social activities.

NAME(S) OF PROGRAMS:
● **Elizabeth Harper Vaughn Concerto Competition**

TYPE:
Awards/prizes. Cash prize and appearance
with the Symphony of the Mountains
Orchestra.

YEAR PROGRAM STARTED: 1969

PURPOSE:
Career advancement and recognition of
excellence in music performance.

LEGAL BASIS:
Not-for-profit corporation.

ELIGIBILITY:
Open to musicians 25 years of age and
under, with recommendation of private
instructor.

FINANCIAL DATA:
Amount of support per award: $500.
Total amount of support: $500.

NUMBER OF APPLICANTS MOST RECENT YEAR:
10.

NUMBER OF AWARDS: 1.

APPLICATION INFORMATION:
Requires recommendation of private
instructor. Also, CD or DVD of performance
(full concerto or other appropriate musical
arrangement with orchestral accompaniment).
Duration: One-time award.
Deadline: October 1.

PUBLICATIONS:
Posters, postcards, programs for subscription
concerts.

IRS IDENTIFICATION NUMBER: 62-0534228

STAFF:
Cornelia Laemmli Orth, Music Director/Chief
Operating Officer

ADDRESS INQUIRIES TO:
Cornelia Laemmli Orth
Music Director/Chief Operating Officer
(See address above.)

THE RICHARD TUCKER MUSIC FOUNDATION, INC. [839]
1790 Broadway
Suite 715
New York, NY 10019-1412
(212) 757-2218
Fax: (212) 757-2347

E-MAIL ADDRESS:
info@richardtucker.org

WEB SITE ADDRESS:
www.richardtucker.org

FOUNDED: 1975

AREAS OF INTEREST:
Financial aid to American opera singers and
opera companies with development programs
for American singers.

NAME(S) OF PROGRAMS:
• **Richard Tucker Award**
• **Richard Tucker Career Grants**
• **Sara Tucker Study Grants**

TYPE:
Awards/prizes.

YEAR PROGRAM STARTED: 1978

PURPOSE:
To help further the careers of young
American singers.

LEGAL BASIS:
Tax-exempt, not-for-profit organization.

ELIGIBILITY:
Applicants must already be performing in
opera. Open to males and females in all
vocal categories. Singers cannot apply; they
must be recommended by a professional in
the field. Applicants must also be
American-born.

GEOGRAPHIC RESTRICTIONS:
United States.

FINANCIAL DATA:
Amount of support per award: Richard
Tucker Award: $30,000; Richard Tucker
Career Grants: $10,000; Sara Tucker Study
Grants: $5,000.
Total amount of support: $95,000 to
$110,000 annually.

NUMBER OF APPLICANTS MOST RECENT YEAR:
100 to 120.

NUMBER OF AWARDS: Richard Tucker Award: 1;
Richard Tucker Career Grants and Sara
Tucker Study Grants: 4 each.

APPLICATION INFORMATION:
Duration: Varies, but most of the awards are
one-time awards.
Deadline: Recommendations are due
December 31.

IRS IDENTIFICATION NUMBER: 23-7431029

BOARD OF DIRECTORS:
Sanford H. Fisher, Chairman
Barry Tucker, President
Sherrill Milnes, Vice President
John A. Petts, Vice President
Samuel Ramey, Vice President

Robert S. Tucker, Vice President
Peter H. Carwell, Executive Director

ADDRESS INQUIRIES TO:
Peter H. Carwell, Executive Director
(See address above.)

*SPECIAL STIPULATIONS:
Singers cannot apply. Recommendations by a
recognized professional only.

THE VIOLIN SOCIETY OF AMERICA [840]
341 North Maitland Avenue
Suite 130
Maitland, FL 32751
(407) 647-8839
Fax: (407) 629-2502

E-MAIL ADDRESS:
phil@crowsegal.com

WEB SITE ADDRESS:
www.vsa.to

FOUNDED: 1973

AREAS OF INTEREST:
Making and restoring stringed instruments
and their bows, the history of stringed
instruments and performers, technique,
performance practice, repertory and the
acoustics of bowed stringed instruments. The
Society also sponsors conventions that
include lectures, demonstrations, symposia
and concerts, biennial international
competitions for new stringed instruments
and their bows, a Music Fair and a periodical
covering all aspects of bowed string
instruments.

NAME(S) OF PROGRAMS:
• **Kaplan-Goodkind Memorial Scholarship Fund**
• **Kun Scholarship Fund**
• **Aram & Rose Nigogosian Fund**

TYPE:
Scholarships. Tuition grants to students of
violin-making and bow-making enrolled in a
full-time violin-making school.

YEAR PROGRAM STARTED: 1982

PURPOSE:
To bring together people from various fields
to exchange ideas and skills and to help
people learn about the making of bows and
stringed instruments.

LEGAL BASIS:
Tax-exempt educational organization.

ELIGIBILITY:
Applicants must be U.S. citizens and
recommended by school faculty.

GEOGRAPHIC RESTRICTIONS:
United States.

FINANCIAL DATA:
Tuition grants are made to the school in
student's name.
Amount of support per award: $500 average.
Total amount of support: Varies.

NUMBER OF AWARDS: 8 to 12 annually.

APPLICATION INFORMATION:
Apply by letter of recommendation from
school to main office of VSA.
Duration: One-time tuition grant.
Deadline: Grants made on a continuing basis.

PUBLICATIONS:
The Journal, newsletter.

OFFICERS:
Rodney Mohr, President

Fan Tau, First Vice President
Laurie Kirr, Second Vice President
Tom King, Treasurer
Jim Zartman, Secretary

ADDRESS INQUIRIES TO:
Phil Pyster, Executive Director
(See address above.)

THE WORLD PIANO COMPETITION, INC. [841]
441 Vine Street
Suite 1030
Cincinnati, OH 45202
(513) 421-5342
Fax: (513) 421-2672

E-MAIL ADDRESS:
wpc@cincinnatiwpc.org

WEB SITE ADDRESS:
www.cincinnatiwpc.org

FOUNDED: 1956

AREAS OF INTEREST:
Musical education and identification of piano
talent worldwide.

CONSULTING OR VOLUNTEER SERVICES:
Development of piano artistry and education
directed by well renowned artists.

NAME(S) OF PROGRAMS:
• **Educational Training & Evaluations**
• **World Piano Competition**

TYPE:
Awards/prizes; Challenge/matching grants;
Development grants; Internships;
Scholarships; Visiting scholars; Work-study
programs. Annual awards.

YEAR PROGRAM STARTED: 1956

PURPOSE:
To develop talent of young piano prodigies
and artists.

LEGAL BASIS:
Nonprofit association.

FINANCIAL DATA:
Amount of support per award: $50 to
$45,000.
Total amount of support: Varies.

APPLICATION INFORMATION:
Student and teacher applications available
upon request.
Duration: One-time awards.
Deadline: Young Artists: January 3; Artists:
March 1.

BOARD OF TRUSTEES:
George H. Musekamp, III, Chairman
Dr. William B. Selnick, Vice Chairman
Leon Fleisher, President
Gloria Ackerman, Founder and Chief
Executive Officer
Andre Watts

ADDRESS INQUIRIES TO:
Gloria Ackerman, Chief Executive Officer
(See address above.)

YOUNG CONCERT ARTISTS, INC. [842]
250 West 57th Street
Suite 1222
New York, NY 10107
(212) 307-6655
Fax: (212) 581-8894

E-MAIL ADDRESS:
yca@yca.org

WEB SITE ADDRESS:
www.yca.org

FOUNDED: 1961

AREAS OF INTEREST:
Young composers, young solo classical musicians (instruments and voice) and string quartets.

CONSULTING OR VOLUNTEER SERVICES:
YCA sponsors the Young Concert Artists Series in New York City at Carnegie's Zankel Hall and Lincoln Center, and in Washington, DC at the Kennedy Center; books concert engagements in the U.S. and abroad; offers career guidance and development; and provides all promotion and publicity materials, at no cost to the artists. YCA membership generally continues until the artists are signed by commercial management. The organization's work is made possible by contributions from corporations, foundations, individuals and government agencies.

NAME(S) OF PROGRAMS:
• **Young Concert Artists International Auditions**

TYPE:
Awards/prizes.

YEAR PROGRAM STARTED: 1961

PURPOSE:
To discover and launch the careers of exceptional young musicians.

LEGAL BASIS:
Nonprofit, tax-exempt.

ELIGIBILITY:
Instrumentalists, 16 to 26 years of age, and singers, 20 to 28 years of age, must perform required repertoire and have letters of recommendation.

NUMBER OF AWARDS: Varies. Winners are selected only against a standard of excellence; any number can win who are selected by the jury.

APPLICATION INFORMATION:
Auditions dates, application form and requirements are available online.
Duration: Each winner signs a multiyear renewable contract with Young Concert Artists, which may be extended by mutual consent.

PUBLICATIONS:
Brochure.

OFFICER:
Susan Wadsworth, Director

ADDRESS INQUIRIES TO:
Susan Wadsworth, Director

Auditions:
Anne Paulini
(See address above.)

YOUNG MUSICIANS FOUNDATION [843]
195 South Beverly Drive
Suite 414
Beverly Hills, CA 90212
(310) 859-7668
Fax: (310) 859-1365

E-MAIL ADDRESS:
info@ymf.org

WEB SITE ADDRESS:
www.ymf.org

FOUNDED: 1955

AREAS OF INTEREST:
Young musicians, ages nine to 25, aspiring to careers in professional classical music.

NAME(S) OF PROGRAMS:
• **YMF Scholarship Program**

TYPE:
Awards/prizes; Internships; Scholarships. Financial assistance for private study and/or tuition at recognized musical institutions. Significant performance opportunity may be offered.

YEAR PROGRAM STARTED: 1955

PURPOSE:
To assist needy, exceptionally gifted students to continue their classical musical education.

LEGAL BASIS:
Nonprofit organization.

ELIGIBILITY:
Instrumentalists nine to 18 years of age and vocalists 12 to 25 years of age.

GEOGRAPHIC RESTRICTIONS:
Southern California.

FINANCIAL DATA:
Amount of support per award: $500 to $2,500.
Total amount of support: Over $18,000.

NUMBER OF APPLICANTS MOST RECENT YEAR:
100.

NUMBER OF AWARDS: 62 for the year 2008-09.

APPLICATION INFORMATION:
A complete application and financial information form must be accompanied by a letter of recommendation from applicant's music teacher. Applicants must audition in person for an adjudicating panel.
Duration: One year. Recipient must reapply for renewal.
Deadline: June; check online for exact date.

IRS IDENTIFICATION NUMBER: 95-2250007

EXECUTIVE OFFICERS:
Jonathan Weedman, Chairman of the Board
G. Beverly Bergmann, Vice Chairperson
Julia Gaskill, Executive Director

ADDRESS INQUIRIES TO:
Camille Couture-Carter, Programs Director
(See address above.)

THE LOREN L. ZACHARY SOCIETY FOR THE PERFORMING ARTS [844]
2250 Gloaming Way
Beverly Hills, CA 90210-1717
(310) 276-2731
Fax: (310) 275-8245

E-MAIL ADDRESS:
peterhubner@earthlink.net

WEB SITE ADDRESS:
www.zacharysociety.org

FOUNDED: 1972

AREAS OF INTEREST:
Performing arts, operatic vocal only.

NAME(S) OF PROGRAMS:
• **Annual Loren L. Zachary National Vocal Competition for Young Opera Singers**

TYPE:
Awards/prizes.

YEAR PROGRAM STARTED: 1973

PURPOSE:
To promote and discover new operatic talent, making it possible for young singers to obtain gainful employment in their profession.

LEGAL BASIS:
Educational, tax-exempt, nonprofit corporation.

ELIGIBILITY:
Open to female singers between the ages of 21 and 33 and male singers between the ages of 21 and 35, who have completed proper operatic training and are prepared to pursue professional stage careers. Awards are available only through participation in the annual vocal competition in New York and Los Angeles.

GEOGRAPHIC RESTRICTIONS:
United States and Canada.

FINANCIAL DATA:
Amount of support per award: A minimum of $1,000 to $2,500 is presented to each finalist. $10,000 to $12,000 Top Award.
Total amount of support: Approximately $50,000 distributed amongst the finalists.

NUMBER OF APPLICANTS MOST RECENT YEAR:
250.

NUMBER OF AWARDS: 10 for the year 2010.

APPLICATION INFORMATION:
Submit a letter requesting audition information and applications in November. Singers must be present in Los Angeles or New York for all phases of the Auditions. Recordings are not acceptable. Requests for applications must be accompanied by a self-addressed, stamped #10-size envelope. No fax or e-mail requests. Applications are also available at the Society's web site in November.
Deadline: January (for New York Auditions) and March (for Los Angeles Auditions); exact date varies each year. Preliminary and Semifinal Auditions are held in New York in February and in Los Angeles in March. Finalists from the New York and the Los Angeles Competitions make up the National Grand Finals Concert with orchestra, at which time the Awards are distributed at the decision of the judges. The Grand Finals Concert is held in May in Los Angeles.

PUBLICATIONS:
Application; guidelines.

IRS IDENTIFICATION NUMBER: 95-2800160

OFFICERS:
Nedra Zachary, President and Founder
Peter Hubner, Vice President
Carl Mengert, Vice President
Allen Stephan, Vice President
David Wilkerson, Vice President
Nedra Zachary, Treasurer
Sharron Levey, Secretary

ADVISORY BOARD:
Licia Albanese
Tito Capobianco
John de Main
Stephen De Maio
Marta Eggerth-Kiepura
Michael Hampe
Ioan Holender
Marilyn Horne
David Hulme
Mrs. George London
Peter Mark
Thea Musgrave
Julius Rudel
William Wiemhoff
Nedra Zachary

ADDRESS INQUIRIES TO:
Mrs. Nedra Zachary, Director of Competition
(See address above.)

Religion and theology

AMERICAN ACADEMY OF RELIGION [845]

825 Houston Mill Road, N.E.
Suite 300
Atlanta, GA 30329
(404) 727-3049
Fax: (404) 727-7959

E-MAIL ADDRESS:
info@aarweb.org

WEB SITE ADDRESS:
www.aarweb.org

FOUNDED: 1909

AREAS OF INTEREST:
Religion and theology.

NAME(S) OF PROGRAMS:
- **Collaborative Research Grants**
- **Individual Research Grants**
- **International Dissertation Research Grant**

TYPE:
Research grants. Collaborative Research Grants and Individual Research Grants provide support for important aspects of research such as travel to archives and libraries, research assistance, field work and released time. However, funds are not provided for dissertation research.

International Dissertation Research Grants support AAR student members whose dissertation research requires them to travel outside of the country in which their school or university is located. Grants are intended to help candidates complete their doctoral degrees by offsetting costs of travel, lodging, and other dissertation research-related expenses.

YEAR PROGRAM STARTED: 1989

PURPOSE:
To promote research and scholarship in the field of religion; to foster excellence in teaching in the field of religion; to support and encourage members' professional development; to develop programming and participation in AAR regional groups; to advance publication and scholarly communication in the field of religion; to contribute to the public understanding of religion; to welcome the various voices in the field of religion and to support and encourage diversity within the AAR; to help to advance and secure the future of the academic study of religion.

LEGAL BASIS:
501(c)(3).

ELIGIBILITY:
Applicants must be current AAR members who have been in good standing for the previous three years and have not received an AAR Research Award in the previous five years.

FINANCIAL DATA:
Amount of support per award: $500 to $5,000.

NUMBER OF APPLICANTS MOST RECENT YEAR:
85 for the year 2010.

NUMBER OF AWARDS: 10 for the year 2010.

APPLICATION INFORMATION:
Individual or Collaborative grant applicants should submit through the Academy's electronic system:
(1) cover page that includes the following: (a) name, (b) institutional affiliation, (c) title of the project, (d) grant type - Individual or Collaborative;
(2) abstract of 50 words or fewer describing the project;
(3) project budget;
(4) two-page focused description of the research project that details its aims and significance and explains how the award would be used. Collaborative project descriptions should include brief descriptions of the scholarly role of each collaborator and a plan to have the research published and;
(5) curriculum vitae of no more than two pages.

International Dissertation Research Grant applicants must submit:
(1) letter of application (no longer than three pages) that describes their research project and how support for on-site research is critical for the completion of their dissertation;
(2) current curriculum vitae;
(3) proposed budget and project timeline and;
(4) letter of support from their dissertation supervisor.

Duration: Research projects may be undertaken any time within that academic year and up to the end of the following calendar year.

Deadline: Individual or Collaborative Grant: August 1; International Dissertation Grant: December 1.

IRS IDENTIFICATION NUMBER: 25-6063005

STAFF:
Jessica Davenport, Associate Director of Member Services

ADDRESS INQUIRIES TO:
Jessica Davenport
Associate Director of Member Services
(See address above.)

*SPECIAL STIPULATIONS:
Applications accepted through the electronic system only.

AMERICAN ACADEMY OF RELIGION [846]

825 Houston Mill Road, N.E.
Suite 300
Atlanta, GA 30329
(404) 727-3049
Fax: (404) 727-7959

E-MAIL ADDRESS:
dminor@aarweb.org

WEB SITE ADDRESS:
www.aarweb.org

FOUNDED: 1909

AREAS OF INTEREST:
To support projects within the regions that promise to benefit the scholarly and professional life of AAR members and the work of the regions.

NAME(S) OF PROGRAMS:
- **Regional Development Grants**

TYPE:
Development grants. Workshops, special programs, training events and other innovative regional projects may be funded through this source.

PURPOSE:
To promote research and scholarship in the field of religion; to foster excellence in teaching in the field of religion; to support and encourage members' professional development; to develop programming and participation in AAR regional groups; to advance publication and scholarly communication in the field of religion; to contribute to the public understanding of religion; to welcome into our conversation the various voices in the field of religion and to support and encourage diversity within the AAR; to help to advance and secure the future of the academic study of religion.

LEGAL BASIS:
501(c)(3).

GEOGRAPHIC RESTRICTIONS:
United States.

FINANCIAL DATA:
Amount of support per award: Maximum $4,000.
Total amount of support: $10,000.

NUMBER OF APPLICANTS MOST RECENT YEAR:
15.

NUMBER OF AWARDS: 4.

APPLICATION INFORMATION:
Applications should include a narrative description of the project, not to exceed two pages, detailing how the project promises to benefit the scholarly and professional life of AAR members and the work of the region. Please include comments on how these projects or activities may be adapted to other regional groups. The application should state the time period covered by the project and provide a detailed budget (office expenses, travel expenses, honoraria, stipend and other expenses).

Deadline: August 1.

IRS IDENTIFICATION NUMBER: 20-5478525

ADDRESS INQUIRIES TO:
Deborah B. Minor
Director of Business and Finance
(See address above.)

AMERICAN CATHOLIC HISTORICAL ASSOCIATION [847]

Department of African & African-American Studies
Fordham University, Dealy Hall, Room 637
441 East Fordham Road
Bronx, NY 10458
(718) 817-3830

E-MAIL ADDRESS:
acha@achahistory.org
randerson13@fordham.edu

WEB SITE ADDRESS:
www.achahistory.org

FOUNDED: 1919

AREAS OF INTEREST:
The history of Catholicism from antiquity to the present.

NAME(S) OF PROGRAMS:
- **The Peter Guilday Prize**

TYPE:
Awards/prizes. A prize awarded annually to the author whose article, dealing with the history of the Catholic Church, is the first of his or her professional career and is judged

to be the best of those in that category accepted for publication in any given year by the editors of the *Catholic Historical Review*.

YEAR PROGRAM STARTED: 1972

PURPOSE:
To stimulate interest in the history of Catholicism among young scholars.

LEGAL BASIS:
Learned society.

ELIGIBILITY:
The article must deal with some aspect of the history of the Catholic Church broadly considered. Anyone who has already published an historical book or an article in a learned journal will not be eligible for competition. Articles based on doctoral dissertations will be welcome, provided they are self-contained studies. Manuscripts must not exceed 30 typewritten pages (footnotes included). The author must be a citizen or permanent resident of the U.S. or Canada.

FINANCIAL DATA:
Amount of support per award: $100.
Total amount of support: $100 per annum.

NUMBER OF APPLICANTS MOST RECENT YEAR:
3.

NUMBER OF AWARDS: 1 per annum.

REPRESENTATIVE AWARDS:
Hui-hung Chen, "The Human Body as a Universe: Understanding Heaven by Visualization and Sensibility in Jesuit Cartography in China," published in the *Catholic Historical Review*, Vol. XCIII, No. 3 (July, 2007), 517-552.

APPLICATION INFORMATION:
Inquiries and manuscripts should be sent to the individual listed below. One copy should also be sent to the editor at the address above.
Deadline: September 1.

ADDRESS INQUIRIES TO:
R. Bentley Anderson, S.J.
Executive Secretary-Treasurer
American Catholic Historical Association
(See street address above.)
E-mail: acha@achahistory.org

AMERICAN CATHOLIC HISTORICAL ASSOCIATION [848]
Department of African & African-American Studies
Fordham University, Dealy Hall, Room 637
441 East Fordham Road
Bronx, NY 10458
(718) 817-3830

E-MAIL ADDRESS:
acha@achahistory.org
randerson13@fordham.edu

WEB SITE ADDRESS:
www.achahistory.org

FOUNDED: 1919

AREAS OF INTEREST:
The history of Catholicism from antiquity to the present.

NAME(S) OF PROGRAMS:
● **The John Gilmary Shea Prize**

TYPE:
Awards/prizes. Award for a published book which, in the opinion of a committee of judges, has made within a 12-month period

the most original and significant contribution to the area of the history of the Catholic Church broadly considered.

YEAR PROGRAM STARTED: 1945

PURPOSE:
To stimulate interest in the history of Catholicism among young scholars.

LEGAL BASIS:
Learned society.

ELIGIBILITY:
Citizens or permanent residents of the U.S. or Canada are eligible to apply. The work submitted must have been published within the 12 months preceding July 1 of each year.

FINANCIAL DATA:
Amount of support per award: $750.
Total amount of support: $750 per annum.

NUMBER OF APPLICANTS MOST RECENT YEAR:
36.

NUMBER OF AWARDS: 1 per annum.

APPLICATION INFORMATION:
No formal application is required. Publishers or authors may enter by sending three copies of the work to be considered to the address above or directly to the judges. Write to the above address for further details.
Deadline: August 1.

ADDRESS INQUIRIES TO:
R. Bentley Anderson, S.J.
Executive Secretary-Treasurer
American Catholic Historical Association
(See street address above.)
E-mail: acha@achahistory.org

THE AMY FOUNDATION [849]
P.O. Box 16091
Lansing, MI 48901
(517) 323-6233
Fax: (517) 321-2572

E-MAIL ADDRESS:
amyfoundtn@aol.com

WEB SITE ADDRESS:
www.amyfound.org

FOUNDED: 1976

AREAS OF INTEREST:
Moral and spiritual renewal in America.

NAME(S) OF PROGRAMS:
● **Amy Writing Awards**

TYPE:
Awards/prizes. Program is designed to recognize creative, skillful writing that presents in a sensitive, thought-provoking manner the biblical position on issues affecting the world today.

PURPOSE:
To present biblical truth reinforced with scripture in secular, non-religious publications.

ELIGIBILITY:
Submitted articles must be published in a secular, non-religious publication and must be reinforced with at least one passage of scripture. Article must have been published between January 1 and December 31 of the current calendar year.

FINANCIAL DATA:
Amount of support per award: First prize: $10,000; second prize: $5,000; third prize: $4,000; fourth prize: $3,000; fifth prize: $2,000; plus 10 prizes of $1,000 each.
Total amount of support: $34,000.

APPLICATION INFORMATION:
Submission of a printed entry must be in the form of the actual full page(s) or tear sheet(s) from the newspaper or magazine containing the publication name and date. Submission of an online entry must be in the form of a printout of the article on the web site of the newspaper or magazine. The web address of the article and the contact information for the online editor must also be submitted.

The total number of qualified entires (both printed and/or online) that may be submitted by a single author is limited to 10.
Deadline: All entries must be postmarked on or before January 31 of the following year.

ADDRESS INQUIRIES TO:
Mary Spagnuolo, Executive Director
(See address above.)

ATLANTIC SCHOOL OF THEOLOGY [850]
660 Francklyn Street
Halifax NS B3H 3B5 Canada
(902) 423-5592
Fax: (902) 492-4048

E-MAIL ADDRESS:
academicoffice@astheology.ns.ca

WEB SITE ADDRESS:
www.astheology.ns.ca

FOUNDED: 1971

AREAS OF INTEREST:
Any subject offered at the Atlantic School of Theology.

NAME(S) OF PROGRAMS:
● **The Evelyn Hilchie Betts Memorial Fellowship**

TYPE:
Fellowships. The Atlantic School of Theology is an ecumenical university committed to excellence in graduate-level theological education and research. The school is also committed to the provision of training for Christian ministries, both lay and ordained, in church and society, primarily in Atlantic Canada.

PURPOSE:
To enable ordained clergy from the developing world to study at the school for one year and thereby to introduce persons from other Christian communities to the church and theological education in Canada and to share their context with the school.

ELIGIBILITY:
Applicants must be nominated by their denomination. Open to ordained clergy (male or female) from developing countries, who are interested in theological education in an ecumenical atmosphere and are able to speak and write in the English language.

Applicants must be interested in living and working in a Christian community and willing to share their work and experience with the Canadian church. Since the Atlantic School of Theology is a postgraduate school, applicants with university training are encouraged to apply.

FINANCIAL DATA:
Amount of support per award: Up to $18,000 for transportation, tuition, room and board.
Total amount of support: $10,000 to $12,000 (CAN).

NUMBER OF AWARDS: 1 annually.

APPLICATION INFORMATION:
Applicants must submit a completed application form along with a letter of support.
Duration: One year.
Deadline: May 1.

ADDRESS INQUIRIES TO:
Academic Office
Atlantic School of Theology
(See address above.)

*SPECIAL STIPULATIONS:
Must return to own country after scholarship year.

THE LOWELL BERRY FOUNDATION

3685 Mount Diablo Boulevard
Suite 269
Lafayette, CA 94549
(925) 284-4427
Fax: (925) 284-4332

E-MAIL ADDRESS:
info@lowellberryfoundation.org

WEB SITE ADDRESS:
www.lowellberryfoundation.org

TYPE:
General operating grants; Project/program grants.

See entry 45 for full listing.

THE CHATLOS FOUNDATION, INC.   [851]

P.O. Box 915048
Longwood, FL 32791-5048
(407) 862-5077

E-MAIL ADDRESS:
info@chatlos.org

WEB SITE ADDRESS:
www.chatlos.org

FOUNDED: 1953

AREAS OF INTEREST:
Bible colleges, seminaries, religion, liberal arts colleges, medical and social concerns.

TYPE:
General operating grants; Project/program grants; Scholarships; Technical assistance; Training grants. Scholarships are not provided directly to individuals but rather to colleges and seminaries which in turn provide monies to the students of their choice.

YEAR PROGRAM STARTED: 1953

LEGAL BASIS:
Private foundation.

ELIGIBILITY:
The Foundation only funds nonprofit organizations which are tax-exempt for U.S. federal income tax purposes around the globe. Less emphasis on grant requests for bricks and mortar, endowments, conference and administrative expenses and multiyear grants. No grants for medical research, individual church congregations, primary/secondary schools, organizations in existence for less than two years, arts organizations or individuals. Contributions cannot be made to organizations which discriminate on the basis of race, color, sex, creed, age or national origin.

FINANCIAL DATA:
Amount of support per award: Bible colleges: $10,000 to $25,000; Religious causes and medical concerns: $5,000 to $25,000; Liberal arts colleges and social concerns: $2,500 to $10,000.

Initially, the Foundation tends to fund requests for amounts around $10,000.
Total amount of support: $2,507,400 for the year 2009.

NUMBER OF AWARDS: 312 for the year 2009.

APPLICATION INFORMATION:
All requests must be submitted in writing and include the following:
(1) cover letter which includes the specific request amount and project description;
(2) complete proposal (kept brief);
(3) one copy of U.S. IRS tax-exempt status letter;
(4) most recent budget for the organization and;
(5) completed Chatlos Foundation application.

All requests are answered by the Foundation in writing.
Duration: Varies, although multiyear grants are rarely considered.
Deadline: Applications accepted throughout the year.

PUBLICATIONS:
Application guideline brochure.

IRS IDENTIFICATION NUMBER: 13-6161425

BOARD OF DIRECTORS:
Kathryn A. Randle, Chairman of the Board
William J. Chatlos, President
Michele C. Roach, Senior Vice President and Secretary
William J. Chatlos, III, Vice President
Cindee Random, Treasurer and Trustee
Janet A. Chatlos, Trustee
Charles O. Morgan, Jr., Trustee
Brianne Ortt, Trustee

ADDRESS INQUIRIES TO:
Grants Administrator
(See address above.)

CHRISTIAN CHURCH (DISCIPLES OF CHRIST)   [852]

Disciples Home Missions
130 East Washington Street
Indianapolis, IN 46204
(888) 346-2631
Fax: (317) 635-4426

E-MAIL ADDRESS:
mail@dhm.disciples.org

WEB SITE ADDRESS:
www.discipleshomemissions.org/scholarships

NAME(S) OF PROGRAMS:
- **African-American Scholarship Fund (Star Supporter)**
- **Disciple Chaplains Scholarship Fund**
- **David Tamotsu Kagiwada Memorial Fund**
- **Edwin G. & Lauretta M. Michael Scholarship for Minister's Wives**
- **James M. Philputt Memorial Loan Fund**
- **Rowley Fund/Ministerial Education Fund**
- **Katherine J. Schutze Memorial Scholarship for Women Seminary Students**

TYPE:
Scholarships. Scholarship funds for Disciples of Christ students preparing for vocational ministry.

PURPOSE:
To help individuals pursue education in the Disciples of Christ.

LEGAL BASIS:
Religious nonprofit organization.

ELIGIBILITY:
The general eligibility requirements are as follows:
(1) the applicant must be a member of the Christian Church (Disciples of Christ);
(2) plan to prepare for a professional ministry;
(3) be a better-than-average student;
(4) provide evidence of financial need;
(5) be enrolled in an accredited graduate school or seminary as a full-time student;
(6) provide a transcript of academic work;
(7) make a renewal application if eligible;
(8) provide references from a regional minister, pastor, lay leaders and/or professors and;
(9) be under care of a regional commission on the ministry or in the process of coming under care.

Additional requirements are as follows:
(1) African-American Scholarship Fund (Star Supporter) is limited to Black or Afro-American ministerial students;
(2) Michael Scholarship is limited to minister's wives;
(3) James M. Philputt Memorial Loan Fund is limited to seminary or graduate students enrolled in one of the following seminaries including Divinity School of the University of Chicago, Union Theological Seminary, Vanderbilt Divinity School or Yale Divinity School;
(4) Disciple Chaplains Scholarship Fund is limited to first-year seminarians;
(5) David Tamotsu Kagiwada Memorial Fund is limited to Asian ministerial students;
(6) Rowley/Ministerial Education Fund has no additional eligibility limitations and;
(7) Schutze Memorial Scholarship for women seminary students.

FINANCIAL DATA:
Funds issued in the form of a scholarship/loan call for a promissory note to be signed by the recipient. Two options of repayment are provided:
(1) a service option in which each year of full-time professional ministry reduces the scholarship/loan by one-third. Three years of service with the Christian Church (Disciples of Christ) will repay the entire scholarship/loan and;
(2) those not entering the ministry in the Christian Church (Disciples of Christ) are expected to repay the scholarship/loan either in one cash payment or on a monthly installment basis of $100 at the rate of six percent annual interest on the principal. These payments would begin three months after leaving school.

Amount of support per award: $1,500 to $2,000.

APPLICATION INFORMATION:
Duration: Varies.

Deadline: Applications: March 15; Reference material: April 15.

ADDRESS INQUIRIES TO:
Scholarships
(See address above.)

COLLEGEVILLE INSTITUTE FOR ECUMENICAL AND CULTURAL RESEARCH   [853]

14027 Fruit Farm Road
Collegeville, MN 56321
(320) 363-3366
Fax: (320) 363-3313

E-MAIL ADDRESS:
staff@collegevilleinstitute.org

WEB SITE ADDRESS:
www.collegevilleinstitute.org

FOUNDED: 1967

AREAS OF INTEREST:
Religion and ecumenism.

NAME(S) OF PROGRAMS:
● **Hoyt Fellowship**
● **Resident Scholars Program**

TYPE:
Residencies. No cash grants. Grant equivalencies are given in the form of living accommodations for Resident Scholars and their families in well-maintained apartments and excellent study facilities, privileges at Saint John's University and dialogue and community experience. The Hoyt Fellowship covers the residency fee, including housing and utilities.

YEAR PROGRAM STARTED: 1967

PURPOSE:
To facilitate constructive thought and research which bear upon Christianity, ecumenically understood, and its relation to the cultures of our world.

LEGAL BASIS:
Incorporated in Minnesota.

ELIGIBILITY:
Criteria include completion of graduate work and submission of a research or writing project proposal acceptable to the admissions committee. Award normally made to research scholars who already have the Doctorate, though persons writing doctoral dissertations can be considered. Oriented by tradition and conviction to Christian faith, the Institute welcomes people from other religions.

FINANCIAL DATA:
No cash grants. Residency fees include housing for self and family, utilities, spacious private study in Saint John's University library and Institute program.

NUMBER OF APPLICANTS MOST RECENT YEAR:
14.

NUMBER OF AWARDS: 11.

APPLICATION INFORMATION:
Applicants must include application form, three letters of recommendation and statement of project.
Duration: September to December semester, January to May semester or full academic year, September to May.
Deadline: November 1; rolling admission after that. Announcement December 1.

PUBLICATIONS:
Bearings, magazine; annual report; application forms and provisions for Resident Scholars; informational brochures.

IRS IDENTIFICATION NUMBER: 41-6059644

STAFF:
Donald B. Ottenhoff, Executive Director

OFFICERS AND BOARD OF DIRECTORS:
Father Kilian McDonnell, O.S.B., President
Gary Reierson, Chairperson

Darrell H. Jodock, Vice Chairperson
Gary T. Alkire, Secretary and Treasurer

ADDRESS INQUIRIES TO:
Donald B. Ottenhoff, Executive Director
(See address above.)

*SPECIAL STIPULATIONS:
Applicant for Hoyt Fellowship must be a North American person of color who is writing a doctoral dissertation.

EPISCOPAL CHURCH FOUNDATION   [854]

815 Second Avenue, Seventh Floor
New York, NY 10017
(212) 697-2858
Fax: (212) 297-0142

E-MAIL ADDRESS:
all@episcopalfoundation.org

WEB SITE ADDRESS:
www.episcopalfoundation.org

AREAS OF INTEREST:
Innovative programs in leadership development, education and philanthropy for the clergy and laity of the Episcopal Church.

NAME(S) OF PROGRAMS:
● **ECF Fellowship Partners Program**

TYPE:
Fellowships. Religious studies. Fellowships under two categories:
(a) Academic Fellowships and;
(b) Transformational Ministries.

PURPOSE:
To support doctoral study for Episcopalians planning teaching careers in theological education in the Episcopal Church in the U.S.

ELIGIBILITY:
Applications from both lay and clergy are welcome.

Fellowship applicants on the academic track must be engaged in or embarking on a course of study at the graduate level, except for first professional degrees (e.g., M.Div., J.D., M.D.). Acceptable courses of study include doctoral- and Master's-level programs, as well as clinical study or training at the post-undergraduate level.

Transformational ministry applicants will be asked to demonstrate how their ministry has the potential to transform community at the grassroots level, and special consideration will be given to programs in locations with limited resources or among underserved communities.

GEOGRAPHIC RESTRICTIONS:
United States.

FINANCIAL DATA:
Amount of support per award: $3,000 to $15,000 per year.
Total amount of support: Approximately $100,000 annually.

NUMBER OF AWARDS: 3.

APPLICATION INFORMATION:
Duration: One year. Fellowship is renewable for two more years.
Deadline: March 15. Notification by May 15.

ADDRESS INQUIRIES TO:
Anne Ditzler, Senior Program Director
(See address above.)

EVANGELICAL LUTHERAN CHURCH IN AMERICA   [855]

Congregation and Synodical Mission Unit
8765 West Higgins Road
Chicago, IL 60631-4101
(773) 380-2874

E-MAIL ADDRESS:
melinda.valverde@elca.org

WEB SITE ADDRESS:
www.elca.org/egp

FOUNDED: 1988

AREAS OF INTEREST:
Theological education.

NAME(S) OF PROGRAMS:
● **Educational Grant Program**

TYPE:
Scholarships. Educational grants for members of the Evangelical Lutheran Church in America in advanced academic theological education degrees with intent to teach in seminary or university.

YEAR PROGRAM STARTED: 1988

PURPOSE:
To provide support to members of the Evangelical Lutheran Church in America in graduate study that would prepare them to teach in a seminary or college department of religion.

LEGAL BASIS:
Nonprofit religious organization.

ELIGIBILITY:
Applicant church members must have been accepted into an accredited graduate institution, Ph.D. and Th.D. programs in theological areas appropriate to seminary teaching and research. Priority is given to women and Asians, Hispanics, Blacks and Native Americans preparing for leadership in the church and applicants with high potential for making substantial contributions to ministry in the Evangelical Lutheran Church in America.

FINANCIAL DATA:
Amount of support per award: $250 to $3,000.

NUMBER OF APPLICANTS MOST RECENT YEAR:
33 for the academic year 2009-10.

NUMBER OF AWARDS: 27 for the academic year 2009-10.

APPLICATION INFORMATION:
Duration: Up to five years. Must reapply each year.
Deadline: April 15.

STAFF:
Jonathan Strandjord, Director for Seminaries

ADDRESS INQUIRIES TO:
Melinda Valverde, Grant Administrator
(See address above.)

GENERAL BOARD OF HIGHER EDUCATION AND MINISTRY, THE UNITED METHODIST CHURCH   [856]

1001 19th Avenue South
Nashville, TN 37212
(615) 340-7409
Fax: (615) 340-7395

E-MAIL ADDRESS:
eoneal@gbhem.org

WEB SITE ADDRESS:
www.gbhem.org

AREAS OF INTEREST:
Religion.

NAME(S) OF PROGRAMS:
● **Georgia Harkness Scholarships**

TYPE:
Awards/prizes; Scholarships. Awards to encourage women over age 35 to prepare for ordained ministry as an Elder in the United Methodist Church as a second career. The scholarship is to be used for study toward the basic seminary degree in an accredited school of theology.

YEAR PROGRAM STARTED: 1975

PURPOSE:
To support and encourage women for ordained ministry as an Elder in the United Methodist Church.

LEGAL BASIS:
Nonprofit organization.

ELIGIBILITY:
An applicant must be a certified candidate for Elder in the United Methodist Church in the year they are applying. Women over age 35 who have received a Bachelor of Arts or equivalent degree and have been accepted in an accredited school of theology and who have affirmed a specific interest in preparation for ordination as an Elder in the United Methodist Church are eligible.

FINANCIAL DATA:
Amount of support per award: $5,000.
Total amount of support: $55,000 annually.

NUMBER OF APPLICANTS MOST RECENT YEAR:
60.

NUMBER OF AWARDS: 11.

APPLICATION INFORMATION:
Applicants must submit one copy of the application and four copies of the reference letter. Application packets may be obtained from any United Methodist or University Senate-approved seminary financial aid office or the Division of Ordained Ministry at the address or e-mail above. Applications may be requested between November 1 and February 15.
Duration: One year.
Deadline: March 1.

ADDRESS INQUIRIES TO:
Rev. Dr. HiRho Park
Director of Continuing Formation for Ministry
(See address or e-mail above.)

GENERAL COMMISSION ON ARCHIVES AND HISTORY OF THE UNITED METHODIST CHURCH   [857]
36 Madison Avenue
Madison, NJ 07940
(973) 408-3189
Fax: (973) 408-3909

E-MAIL ADDRESS:
rwilliams@gcah.org

WEB SITE ADDRESS:
www.gcah.org

FOUNDED: 1968

AREAS OF INTEREST:
History of the United Methodist Church and antecedent bodies.

NAME(S) OF PROGRAMS:
● **John Harrison Ness Memorial Award**

TYPE:
Awards/prizes. Awards to the students of accredited seminaries who submit the best papers on various aspects of United Methodist denominational history. In general, comprehensive subjects on the history of some phase of the denomination will be preferred, but papers on local church or annual conference subjects will be accepted if approved by the professor advising the project.

YEAR PROGRAM STARTED: 1979

PURPOSE:
To stimulate interest in history of the United Methodist Church.

LEGAL BASIS:
Private church-related organization.

ELIGIBILITY:
The paper must have been appraised by the professor of church history under whom the student has been studying and who will submit the paper. The paper must be properly annotated and be a minimum length of 3,000 words. It is desired that the project be undertaken only after the student has had a course in United Methodist history or at least during the enrollment in such.

FINANCIAL DATA:
Amount of support per award: First prize: $500; Second prize: $300.
Total amount of support: $800 annually.

NUMBER OF AWARDS: 2.

APPLICATION INFORMATION:
Three copies of the paper will be submitted for judging, two of which will be retained by the Commission.
Duration: Annual. A recipient may resubmit if he or she is still in seminary.
Deadline: February 1. Announcement approximately three months later.

OFFICERS:
Dr. Robert J. Williams, General Secretary

ADDRESS INQUIRIES TO:
Dr. Robert J. Williams, General Secretary
(See address above.)

THE STEWART HUSTON CHARITABLE TRUST   [858]
50 South First Avenue
Coatesville, PA 19320
(610) 384-2666
Fax: (610) 384-3396

E-MAIL ADDRESS:
admin@stewarthuston.org

WEB SITE ADDRESS:
www.stewarthuston.org

FOUNDED: 1989

AREAS OF INTEREST:
Health and human services, civic affairs and religion.

TYPE:
Capital grants; Challenge/matching grants; General operating grants; Matching gifts; Project/program grants; Seed money grants.

YEAR PROGRAM STARTED: 1989

PURPOSE:
To provide funds, technical assistance and collaboration on behalf of nonprofit organizations engaged exclusively in religious, charitable or educational work; to extend opportunities to deserving needy persons.

LEGAL BASIS:
Private foundation.

ELIGIBILITY:
Applicants must be tax-exempt and address a particular community need. Grants are not awarded for scholarship support to individuals, endowment purposes, purchase of tickets or advertising for benefit purposes, coverage of continuing operating deficits, and document publication costs. Support is not provided to intermediate or pass-through organizations (other than United Way), groups such as fraternal organizations, political campaigns, veterans, labor or local civic groups, volunteer fire companies, and groups engaged in influencing legislation.

According to Stewart Huston's Indenture of Trust, 60% of distributions go to Trinitarian/Evangelical organizations as defined by the Chester County Orphans Court:
The grant applicant must be organized and operated exclusively to further religious and charitable activities carried on by Protestant churches, other than Unitarian churches, and affiliated or related organizations; grant proceeds must be used exclusively for one or both of the following two activities: dissemination of the Christian Gospel by preaching and conducting religious services, offering a Christian education, etc.; and promotion of Christian principles through charity.

The remaining 40% is to be distributed for secular purposes.

GEOGRAPHIC RESTRICTIONS:
Chester County, Pennsylvania and Savannah, Georgia areas.

FINANCIAL DATA:
Amount of support per award: Maximum grant: $30,000; Average: $10,000 to $15,000.
Total amount of support: $715,000 for the year ended December 31, 2008.

NUMBER OF APPLICANTS MOST RECENT YEAR:
156.

NUMBER OF AWARDS: 60.

REPRESENTATIVE AWARDS:
$15,000 to Bridge of Hope, Coatesville, PA, for housing for five mothers and children; United Ministries of Savannah, Savannah, GA, for food, utility and medical assistance for the needy; Good Works, Inc., Coatesville, PA, for operating support; Chester County Women's Services, Coatesville, PA, for operating support.

APPLICATION INFORMATION:
Applications must be submitted online. Applicants are encouraged to call and discuss their project with the staff. The application form should be submitted with a grant proposal and include the following attachments:
(1) IRS tax-exemption letter;
(2) Pennsylvania charitable organizations registration certificate (any organization with gross revenue over $25,000, regardless of location). Churches exempt;
(3) by-laws;
(4) last independent financial audit;
(5) list of the organization's major public and private funding sources;
(6) list of the Board of Directors with their community/professional affiliations;
(7) agency's current operating budget;
(8) most recent Form 990 filed with the IRS;
(9) latest annual report;
(10) list of the public and private sources

being solicited to fund the project;
(11) detailed project budget;
(12) statement that there has been no change in purpose, character or method of operation since the agency's IRS tax ruling was issued and;
(13) a few examples of media reviews about your agency program.

Duration: No multiyear commitments.

Deadline: Secular organizations: March 1 (letter of intent); Trinitarian/Evangelical/religious organizations: March 1 and September 1.

PUBLICATIONS:
Program announcement; guidelines; annual report.

IRS IDENTIFICATION NUMBER: 23-2612599

TRUSTEES:
Alex L. Cann, Sr.
Samuel A. Cann, Esq.
Charles L. Huston, III

ADDRESS INQUIRIES TO:
Scott G. Huston, Executive Director
(See address above.)

IMMANUEL BIBLE FOUNDATION   [859]
1301 South Fell Avenue
Normal, IL 61761
(309) 452-6710
Fax: (309) 862-4121

E-MAIL ADDRESS:
services@ibfoundation.org

WEB SITE ADDRESS:
www.ibfoundation.org

FOUNDED: 1944

AREAS OF INTEREST:
Local charities and youth-serving organizations.

TYPE:
General operating grants. Special needs grants.

YEAR PROGRAM STARTED: 1949

PURPOSE:
To promote the gospel and serve as a resource for the Christian community.

LEGAL BASIS:
Tax-exempt private foundation.

ELIGIBILITY:
Tax-exempt organizations, entirely local to the Foundation's immediate area. Out-of-state applications not accepted. No grants to individuals.

GEOGRAPHIC RESTRICTIONS:
McLean County, Illinois.

FINANCIAL DATA:
Amount of support per award: $500.
Total amount of support: Up to $10,000.

NUMBER OF APPLICANTS MOST RECENT YEAR:
10 for the year 2009.

NUMBER OF AWARDS: 3 for the year 2009.

APPLICATION INFORMATION:
By letter. Must get form and attach appropriate documentation.

Duration: Varies by need.

Deadline: Applications accepted January 1 to February 28. Announcement by June 1.

IRS IDENTIFICATION NUMBER: 37-0688539

ADDRESS INQUIRIES TO:
Doug Faulkner, Executive Director
(See address above.)

*SPECIAL STIPULATIONS:
No grants to individuals.

KOCH FOUNDATION, INC.   [860]
4421 N.W. 39th Avenue
Building 1, Suite 1
Gainesville, FL 32606
(352) 373-7491
Fax: (352) 337-1548

E-MAIL ADDRESS:
staff@thekochfoundation.org

WEB SITE ADDRESS:
www.thekochfoundation.org

FOUNDED: 1979

AREAS OF INTEREST:
Roman Catholic evangelization.

TYPE:
Development grants; Fellowships; Grants-in-aid; Project/program grants; Training grants. Grants are made for direct evangelization programs, preparation of evangelists, resource-poor Catholic schools that are the principal means of evangelization in the community, a Catholic presence in the media, and capital expenditures such as construction and repair of churches or formation centers.

YEAR PROGRAM STARTED: 1979

PURPOSE:
To provide financial support for evangelization efforts to Catholic organizations throughout the world that propagate the Roman Catholic faith.

LEGAL BASIS:
Not-for-profit corporation.

ELIGIBILITY:
U.S. Catholic organizations must be 501(c)(3) and appear in the *Official Catholic Directory*.

FINANCIAL DATA:
Amount of support per award: Varies depending on needs and nature of the request; typical grant $15,000.
Total amount of support: $8,320,653 for fiscal year ended March 31, 2010.

NUMBER OF APPLICANTS MOST RECENT YEAR:
713 for fiscal year 2010.

NUMBER OF AWARDS: 572 for fiscal year 2010.

APPLICATION INFORMATION:
Application forms are available January 1 to May 1. Briefly describe the project when writing for a grant application. All requests must be in English to assure appropriate attention. Faxed requests are not accepted. Completed applications must be returned within 90 days. Applications must include a budget, a statement of the desired impact on evangelization and, if international, the country and diocese where the program will take place and the U.S. fiscal agent who will be responsible for distributing the funds. Applications for a continuing project must be accompanied by a six-month progress report or yearly evaluation.

Duration: Varies.

Deadline: August 31. Announcement in late March.

PUBLICATIONS:
Application guidelines.

IRS IDENTIFICATION NUMBER: 59-1885997

ADDRESS INQUIRIES TO:
Executive Director
(See address above.)

LUTHERAN FOUNDATION OF ST. LOUIS   [861]
8860 Ladue Road
Suite 200
St. Louis, MO 63124
(314) 231-2244
Fax: (314) 727-7688

E-MAIL ADDRESS:
info@lutheranfoundation.org

WEB SITE ADDRESS:
www.lutheranfoundation.org

FOUNDED: 1984

AREAS OF INTEREST:
Christian voluntarism, congregation social service outreach, Lutheran education, prevention and early intervention in children's mental health, and services to prisoners, ex-offenders and their families.

TYPE:
Capital grants; Challenge/matching grants; General operating grants; Project/program grants; Technical assistance.

YEAR PROGRAM STARTED: 1984

PURPOSE:
To provide grant awards in the areas of Christian voluntarism, congregation social service outreach ministry, Lutheran education, prevention and early intervention in children's mental health, and services to prisoners, ex-offenders and their families.

LEGAL BASIS:
Religious foundation.

ELIGIBILITY:
Applicant must be a 501(c)(3), serve the St. Louis metropolitan area, address one or more of the funding focus areas, and complement the Foundation's core values.

GEOGRAPHIC RESTRICTIONS:
Metropolitan St. Louis, Missouri area.

FINANCIAL DATA:
Amount of support per award: Varies.
Total amount of support: $4,280,434 for the year 2010.

NUMBER OF APPLICANTS MOST RECENT YEAR:
95 for the year 2010.

NUMBER OF AWARDS: 68 for the year 2010.

APPLICATION INFORMATION:
Applicant must submit:
(1) organization and contact information;
(2) relationship to The Lutheran Church-Missouri Synod;
(3) statement of community need;
(4) project description: plan to help who? help how? (expected objectives, measurable outcomes, number of people served), difference in lives of those helped?, any collaborating partners?;

(5) evaluation plan (tie to evidence-based, best or promising practices);

(6) project budget and budget narrative justifying expenditures;

(7) copy of most recent audited financial statements;

(8) bids for capital funding requests;

(9) copy of IRS Letter of Determination indicating 501(c)(3) status and;

(10) list of current board members.

Deadline: April 1, August 1 and December 1. Announcement in June, October and February, respectively.

IRS IDENTIFICATION NUMBER: 43-1379359

BOARD OF DIRECTORS:
Karl A. Dunajcik, Chairperson
Robert E. Beumer, Vice Chairperson
Lynn G. Scudieri, Secretary
Jeffrey A. Craig-Meyer
James R. Dankenbring
Robert P. Ensor
Carl J. Fruend
Elizabeth A. Goad
Evelyn Ann Irving, Ph.D.
Bruce Pompe
Rev. Dr. Ronald D. Rall
Catherine Rodgers-Edmonds
Rev. Dr. Scott K. Seidler
Erickson T. Smith, Ph.D.
Paul N. Tice
Ann L. Vazquez

ADDRESS INQUIRIES TO:
Melinda McAliney
Program Officer/Communications Director
(See address above.)

JACOB RADER MARCUS CENTER OF THE AMERICAN JEWISH ARCHIVES [862]

3101 Clifton Avenue
Cincinnati, OH 45220-2488
(513) 221-1875
Fax: (513) 221-7812

E-MAIL ADDRESS:
kproffitt@huc.edu

WEB SITE ADDRESS:
www.americanjewisharchives.org

FOUNDED: 1947

AREAS OF INTEREST:
American and western hemisphere Jewish history.

NAME(S) OF PROGRAMS:
● **The American Jewish Archives Fellowship Program**

TYPE:
Awards/prizes; Fellowships; Research grants. The Marcus Center's Fellowship Program provides recipients with month-long fellowships for research and writing at The Jacob Rader Marcus Center of the American Jewish Archives. Fellowship stipends will be sufficient to cover transportation and living expenses while in residence. Applicants must be conducting serious research in some area relating to the history of North American Jewry.

YEAR PROGRAM STARTED: 1977

PURPOSE:
To collect, preserve and publish the history of the American Jewish experience.

LEGAL BASIS:
A division of the Hebrew Union College, Jewish Institute of Religion; tax-exempt.

ELIGIBILITY:
Doctoral and postdoctoral applicants working in the field are eligible. For the Rabbi Frederic A. Doppelt Memorial Fellowship, preference will be given to candidates from Eastern Europe or those working on a topic related to East European Jewry in the American context.

FINANCIAL DATA:
Grant amount is based upon the individual's research. Fellowship stipends will be sufficient to cover transportation and living expenses while in residence in Cincinnati.

REPRESENTATIVE AWARDS:
Dr. William Pencak, Pennsylvania State University, "Popular and Political Anti-Semitism in Early America;" Dr. Leonard W. Rogoff, Jewish Heritage Foundation of North Carolina, "A Tale of Two Cities: Race, Riots and Religion in North Carolina, 1898;" Dr. David Dalin, Ave Maria University, FL, "American Jewry and the Republican Party before 1932;" Dr. Raphael Medoff, The David Wyman Institute for Holocaust Studies, "American Jewish Efforts to Solve the Dilemma of Arab-Jewish Relations."

APPLICATION INFORMATION:
Fellowship applicants should provide an up-to-date curriculum vitae, a research proposal (no more than five typewritten, double-spaced pages), and two recommendations, preferably from academic colleagues (for Ph.D. students, one of these recommendations should be from the candidate's dissertation advisor). Research must be done for one month on campus through the archives.

Application should not be made to individually named fellowship funds of the Center. Applicants will be considered for all available Center fellowships.

Prior to completion of the Fellowship applications, the Center strongly recommends that applicants familiarize themselves with its collection. The American Jewish Archives web site (www.AmericanJewishArchives.org) contains a list of holdings and a number of finding aids for applicant to peruse. An archivist can be contacted directly for information at the number above (ext. 403).

Duration: One month.

Deadline: March 18. Announcement by April 30.

PUBLICATIONS:
Program description.

STAFF:
Dr. Gary P. Zola, Executive Director
Kevin Proffitt, Director

ADDRESS INQUIRIES TO:
Kevin Proffitt
Director of Fellowship Programs
(See address above.)

VERNE CATT MCDOWELL CORPORATION [863]

P.O. Box 1336
Albany, OR 97321-0440
(541) 967-4235

FOUNDED: 1963

AREAS OF INTEREST:
Graduate theological education.

NAME(S) OF PROGRAMS:
● **Verne Catt McDowell Scholarship**

TYPE:
Scholarships. Financial assistance for men and women attending an approved seminary to become ordained in the Christian Church (Disciples of Christ) denomination and work actively in that church.

YEAR PROGRAM STARTED: 1966

PURPOSE:
To train men and women to become pastors in the Christian Church (Disciples of Christ) Denomination.

LEGAL BASIS:
Private nonprofit corporation.

ELIGIBILITY:
A graduate from an accredited college and/or university who plans to enter an approved seminary of the Christian Church (Disciples of Christ) is eligible to apply. Study must take place in the U.S. Candidates must plan to be ordained in the Christian Church (Disciples of Christ) Denomination and work actively in that church.

GEOGRAPHIC RESTRICTIONS:
Preference given to students from Oregon.

FINANCIAL DATA:
Amount of support per award: Varies. Approximately $300 to $400 per school month.
Total amount of support: Varies.

NUMBER OF APPLICANTS MOST RECENT YEAR: 12.

NUMBER OF AWARDS: 6 per year.

APPLICATION INFORMATION:
Write for application and include eligibility and where information regarding program was found.
Duration: Varies with each student; continues support until completion of seminary.
Deadline: May 1. Awards are usually announced after annual meeting in May.

IRS IDENTIFICATION NUMBER: 93-6022991

OFFICERS:
Neil Reynolds, President
Debbie Burchfiel, Business Manager
Eldon Chowning, Director
Patty Evans, Director
Emily Killin, Director
Ray Lindley, Director
Doug Wirt, Director

ADDRESS INQUIRIES TO:
Debbie Burchfiel, Business Manager
(See address above.)

MEMORIAL FOUNDATION FOR JEWISH CULTURE [864]

50 Broadway, 34th Floor
New York, NY 10004
(212) 425-6606
Fax: (212) 425-6602

E-MAIL ADDRESS:
office@mfjc.org

WEB SITE ADDRESS:
www.mfjc.org

FOUNDED: 1964

AREAS OF INTEREST:
Support for Jewish cultural and educational programs all over the world, in cooperation with universities and established scholarly organizations. Also, annual scholarship and fellowship program.

NAME(S) OF PROGRAMS:
● **International Community Service Scholarship**

- **International Doctoral Scholarship for Studies Specializing in Jewish Fields**
- **International Fellowship in Jewish Studies and Jewish Culture**

TYPE:
Fellowships; Scholarships. Doctoral scholarships, post-rabbinic scholarships, fellowships in Jewish culture, community service scholarships, institutional grants for research and publication, university Jewish studies grants and grants for documentation and commemoration of the Holocaust.

PURPOSE:
To help assure a creative Jewish future throughout the world by encouraging Jewish scholarship, Jewish education and Jewish cultural creativity; to support communities that are struggling to maintain their Jewish identity; to make possible the training of Jewish men and women for professional careers in communal service in Jewishly deprived communities.

LEGAL BASIS:
IRS Section 501(c)(3) charity; not a private foundation.

ELIGIBILITY:
Individual requirements vary according to the scholarship or fellowship.

FINANCIAL DATA:
Amount of support per award: Up to $10,000 per year. Scholarships and fellowships are given to individuals in amounts which vary according to the cost of living in the grantee's country of residence.

APPLICATION INFORMATION:
Further information and application forms for scholarships and fellowships are available on written request to the Foundation at the address above.
Duration: One academic year.
Deadline: October 31 for doctoral scholarships and fellowships. November 30 for community service scholarships.

OFFICERS:
Dr. Jerry Hochbaum, Executive Vice President

ADDRESS INQUIRIES TO:
Dr. Jerry Hochbaum
Executive Vice President
(See address above.)

THE MUSTARD SEED FOUNDATION

7115 Leesburg Pike, Suite 304
Falls Church, VA 22043
(703) 524-5620

E-MAIL ADDRESS:
ljackson@msfdn.org

WEB SITE ADDRESS:
www.harveyfellows.org

TYPE:
Fellowships.
See entry 1670 for full listing.

PONTIFICAL INSTITUTE OF MEDIAEVAL STUDIES

59 Queen's Park Crescent East
Toronto ON M5S 2C4 Canada
(416) 926-7142
Fax: (416) 926-7292

E-MAIL ADDRESS:
allan.smith@utoronto.ca

WEB SITE ADDRESS:
www.pims.ca

TYPE:
Fellowships.
See entry 664 for full listing.

PRESBYTERIAN CHURCH (U.S.A.) [865]

Office of Financial Aid for Studies
100 Witherspoon Street
Louisville, KY 40202-1396
(502) 569-5224
(800) 728-7228 ext. 5224
Fax: (502) 569-8766

E-MAIL ADDRESS:
finaid@pcusa.org

WEB SITE ADDRESS:
www.pcusa.org/financialaid

NAME(S) OF PROGRAMS:
- **Presbyterian Study Grants**

TYPE:
Grants-in-aid.

PURPOSE:
To assist graduate students who are communicant members of the Presbyterian Church (U.S.A.) in their preparation for professional church occupations.

ELIGIBILITY:
Applicants must demonstrate financial need beyond that which they are able to meet through other grants, scholarships, savings and employment, be enrolled on a full-time basis, be in good academic standing, be recommended by the financial aid officer at their theological institution, be studying in a Presbyterian Church (U.S.A.) seminary, and must be studying in one of the two categories listed below:

(1) students preparing for ordination must be full-time M.Div. and must be enrolled as an inquirer with or received as a candidate by a Presbyterian Church (U.S.A.) presbytery for a church occupation or;

(2) students preparing for occupations as a Christian educator must be full-time M.A.C.E. students.

FINANCIAL DATA:
Grants are meant to be supplemental to other assistance a student has sought and is receiving from presbytery, seminary, home church, etc. Grants are not available for summer study, intern year or studying abroad.
Amount of support per award: Up to $4,000 for the academic year, depending upon demonstrated need and availability of funds.
Total amount of support: Varies.

APPLICATION INFORMATION:
Further information and forms are available on the web site.
Duration: One academic year. Renewals possible (annually).
Deadline: Varies.

*SPECIAL STIPULATIONS:
No grants are available for doctoral study.

RASKOB FOUNDATION FOR CATHOLIC ACTIVITIES [866]

10 Montchanin Road
P.O. Box 4019
Wilmington, DE 19807
(302) 655-4440
Fax: (302) 655-3223

WEB SITE ADDRESS:
www.rfca.org

FOUNDED: 1945

AREAS OF INTEREST:
Religion, education, health, social services and missions.

TYPE:
Challenge/matching grants; Conferences/seminars; Demonstration grants; General operating grants; Matching gifts; Project/program grants; Seed money grants; Technical assistance; Training grants.

YEAR PROGRAM STARTED: 1945

PURPOSE:
To engage in such exclusively religious, charitable, literary and educational activities as will aid the Roman Catholic Church and institutions and organizations identified with it.

LEGAL BASIS:
Nonprofit foundation.

ELIGIBILITY:
Applicants must be Catholic organizations with nonprofit status.

FINANCIAL DATA:
Amount of support per award: $15,000 for the year 2010.
Total amount of support: $4,482,749 for the year 2010.
Matching fund requirements: May be required by board of trustees.

NUMBER OF APPLICANTS MOST RECENT YEAR:
1,374 for the year 2010.

NUMBER OF AWARDS: 264 for the year 2010.

APPLICATION INFORMATION:
To be considered for review, organizations within the U.S. must submit an application with the following required documents:
(1) a fully completed application form;
(2) a detailed breakdown of the budget of the project/program;
(3) financial statements of the incorporated Catholic organization that will conduct the proposed project;
(4) a letter from the Ordinary of the Diocese where the project will take place, commenting upon the applicant's request to the Raskob Foundation and;
(5) a narrative (optional).

Any application lacking any of the first three items will not be considered.

For organizations located outside the U.S., financial statements are optional. Any application lacking either of the first two items above will not be considered.

Organizations can apply online at the web site listed above.
Duration: Varies.
Deadline: Applications will only be accepted for the spring from December 8 to February 8 and for the fall from June 8 to August 8. Announcement is 12 to 16 weeks following closing day of deadline.

PUBLICATIONS:
Application guidelines.

IRS IDENTIFICATION NUMBER: 51-0070060

ADDRESS INQUIRIES TO:
Paul A. Zambernardi
Executive Vice President
(See address above.)

DAVID AND SYLVIA STEINER CHARITABLE TRUST [867]

Steiner Equities Group
75 Eisenhower Parkway
Roseland, NJ 07068
(973) 228-5800
Fax: (973) 228-5817

FOUNDED: 1987

AREAS OF INTEREST:
Jewish organizations and higher education.

TYPE:
Project/program grants.

YEAR PROGRAM STARTED: 1987

LEGAL BASIS:
Private foundation.

ELIGIBILITY:
Applicants must be nonprofit entities. Grants are given to religious organizations and for religious education.

GEOGRAPHIC RESTRICTIONS:
New Jersey and New York.

FINANCIAL DATA:
Amount of support per award: Varies.

REPRESENTATIVE AWARDS:
$55,000 to United Jewish Appeal of Metrowest, East Orange, NJ; $20,000 to American Associates of Ben Gurion University of the Negev, New York, NY; $5,000 to National Council of Jewish Women, New York, NY.

APPLICATION INFORMATION:
Applications should be in letter form and must include a statement of purpose, amount requested and a description of the organization.
Duration: One year.

ADDRESS INQUIRIES TO:
Robert Testa, Chief Financial Officer
(See address above.)

SUBCOMMITTEE ON THE HOME MISSIONS [868]

United States Conference of Catholic Bishops
3211 4th Street, N.E.
Washington, DC 20017-1194
(202) 541-3011
(800) 235-8722
Fax: (202) 541-3473

E-MAIL ADDRESS:
homemissions@usccb.org

WEB SITE ADDRESS:
www.usccb.org/hm

FOUNDED: 1924

AREAS OF INTEREST:
Catholic missions in America, including evangelization, catechesis, parish life and personnel training.

TYPE:
General operating grants; Project/program grants; Seed money grants; Training grants. Annual grants to fund home mission activities, such as evangelization through proclamation of the Word, pastoral services, personnel training and the formation of faith communities in the U.S. and its territories. Home mission activities may be centered at the national, regional, diocesan or local level and may address the country as a whole, a particular group of people or a particular place.

YEAR PROGRAM STARTED: 1924

ELIGIBILITY:
Eligible applicants may come from three sources, including (in order of priority) diocesan bishops of home mission dioceses for activities that serve to establish or strengthen the church in their dioceses, heads of national, regional or interdiocesan Catholic organizations for home mission activities that serve the church at a supra-diocesan level and provincials of religious institutes for home mission activities that form part of their apostolate. No funds are available for endowments or loans.

GEOGRAPHIC RESTRICTIONS:
United States and its Caribbean and Pacific territories.

FINANCIAL DATA:
Amount of support per award: Varies depending on needs and nature of the request.
Total amount of support: $8,500,000 for the year 2011.

NUMBER OF APPLICANTS MOST RECENT YEAR:
88 dioceses.

NUMBER OF AWARDS: 390 programs in 88 dioceses for the year 2011.

APPLICATION INFORMATION:
Application materials are available January of each year. Contact office for other requirements.
Duration: Grants are renewable.
Deadline: April 1. Announcement in October. Disbursements are made quarterly January to December.

PUBLICATIONS:
Annual report; guidelines; Neighbors, quarterly newsletter.

OFFICERS:
Most Rev. Michael W. Warfel, Chairman
Dr. David J. Suley, Director

ADDRESS INQUIRIES TO:
Dr. David J. Suley, Director
Tel: (202) 541-5400
E-mail: dsuley@usccb.org
(See address above.)

THRIVENT FINANCIAL FOR LUTHERANS FOUNDATION [869]

4321 North Ballard Road
Appleton, WI 54919-0001
(920) 628-4889
(800) 236-3736
Fax: (920) 628-5165

E-MAIL ADDRESS:
foundation@thrivent.com

WEB SITE ADDRESS:
www.thriventfoundation.com

FOUNDED: 1982

AREAS OF INTEREST:
Leadership development.

TYPE:
Challenge/matching grants; Development grants; Endowments; Project/program grants; Research grants.

YEAR PROGRAM STARTED: 1982

PURPOSE:
To help with projects proposed by Lutheran organizations.

LEGAL BASIS:
Lutheran nonprofit organization.

ELIGIBILITY:
Lutheran 501(c)(3) nonprofit organizations.

GEOGRAPHIC RESTRICTIONS:
Minneapolis Twin Cities area, Minnesota; Appleton, Wisconsin; and other Lutheran communities.

FINANCIAL DATA:
Amount of support per award: Varies.

APPLICATION INFORMATION:
Deadline: Applications accepted throughout the year. Board meets quarterly.

UNITARIAN UNIVERSALIST ASSOCIATION OF CONGREGATIONS [870]

25 Beacon Street
Boston, MA 02108-2800
(617) 742-2100 ext. 303
Fax: (617) 367-3237

E-MAIL ADDRESS:
nlawrence@uua.org

WEB SITE ADDRESS:
www.uua.org

FOUNDED: 1961

AREAS OF INTEREST:
Religious liberalism, philosophy, social change, child and family welfare, and ethics.

NAME(S) OF PROGRAMS:
● Frederic G. Melcher Book Award

TYPE:
Awards/prizes. Award for the book published in the U.S. during the last calendar year which is judged to make the most significant contribution to religious liberal thought.

YEAR PROGRAM STARTED: 1964

PURPOSE:
To encourage writing in liberal religion.

LEGAL BASIS:
Nonprofit association.

ELIGIBILITY:
Books must be published in the U.S. Any serious book-length publication in the tradition of free inquiry is eligible. Any publisher may submit a candidate. Entries are judged on the basis of scholarship, competence, responsibility and devotion to the ideals of religious liberalism which include freedom, reason and tolerance.

GEOGRAPHIC RESTRICTIONS:
United States.

FINANCIAL DATA:
Amount of support per award: $1,000 and a citation.
Total amount of support: $1,000.

NUMBER OF AWARDS: 1.

APPLICATION INFORMATION:
Publishers should contact office for information.
Deadline: December 31.

JUDGES:
Sue Baldauf
Tim Barger
Rev. David Blanchard
Rev. Phyllis O'Connell

ADDRESS INQUIRIES TO:
Nancy Lawrence, Staff Liaison Assistant
(See address above.)

*SPECIAL STIPULATIONS:
Recipient is expected to come to Boston to accept the award and make a public appearance, including a speech. Expenses paid.

UNITED JEWISH APPEAL-FEDERATION OF JEWISH PHILANTHROPIES OF NEW YORK   [871]

130 East 59th Street
New York, NY 10022
(212) 980-1000
(212) 836-1824
Fax: (212) 836-1368

E-MAIL ADDRESS:
snersonj@ujafedny.org

WEB SITE ADDRESS:
www.ujafedny.org

FOUNDED: 1917

AREAS OF INTEREST:
Human services, Jewish identity and education, rescue and resettlement of Jewish communities in distress.

CONSULTING OR VOLUNTEER SERVICES:
Offers numerous opportunities to volunteer. Please call Resource Line: (212) 836-1447.

TYPE:
Capital grants; Challenge/matching grants; Conferences/seminars; Demonstration grants; Development grants; General operating grants; Internships; Project/program grants; Technical assistance; Travel grants.

YEAR PROGRAM STARTED: 1917

PURPOSE:
To care for those in need, strengthen Jewish peoplehood and foster Jewish renaissance in New York, Israel and throughout the world.

LEGAL BASIS:
501(c)(3).

ELIGIBILITY:
No grants to individuals. Applicants must be 501(c)(3) organizations.

GEOGRAPHIC RESTRICTIONS:
New York including the five boroughs, Nassau, Suffolk and Westchester counties.

FINANCIAL DATA:
Amount of support per award: Varies depending upon needs and nature of the request.
Total amount of support: Approximately $150,000,000.

APPLICATION INFORMATION:
Application form required. Organizations must include documentation of IRS nonprofit status with their application.
Duration: One year. Renewal possible.

PUBLICATIONS:
Annual Report to the Community.

ADDRESS INQUIRIES TO:
Jed Snerson
Executive Director of Grants Program
(See address above.)

UNITED METHODIST COMMUNICATIONS

810 12th Avenue South
Nashville, TN 37203-4704
(888) 278-4862
Fax: (615) 742-5777

E-MAIL ADDRESS:
scholarships@umcom.org

WEB SITE ADDRESS:
www.umcom.org/specialinitiatives

TYPE:
Fellowships. Assists one United Methodist student in graduate study at an accredited U.S. college or university who intends to pursue a career in religious journalism.

See entry 2088 for full listing.

THE WABASH CENTER FOR TEACHING AND LEARNING IN THEOLOGY AND RELIGION   [872]

301 West Wabash Avenue
Crawfordsville, IN 47933
(765) 361-6047
Fax: (765) 361-6051

E-MAIL ADDRESS:
wabashcenter@wabash.edu

WEB SITE ADDRESS:
www.wabashcenter.wabash.edu

FOUNDED: 1995

AREAS OF INTEREST:
Teaching religion and theology, higher education pedagogy in theology and religion.

NAME(S) OF PROGRAMS:
- **Creating New Literature on Theological Teaching**
- **Sustaining Enabling Environments in Theological Schools and Religion Departments**
- **Teaching and Learning in Subject Areas**
- **Transition into Careers as Teachers in Theology and Religion**
- **Vocation of Theological Teachers**
- **Workshops on Teaching and Learning**

TYPE:
Conferences/seminars; Fellowships; Project/program grants; Research grants.

YEAR PROGRAM STARTED: 1995

PURPOSE:
To strengthen and enhance the teaching of religion and theology in North American theological schools, colleges and universities.

ELIGIBILITY:
Full-time faculty members in religion departments of colleges and universities in North America and in theological schools accredited by the Association of Theological Schools are eligible to apply for these grants.

GEOGRAPHIC RESTRICTIONS:
United States and Canada.

FINANCIAL DATA:
Amount of support per award: Up to $20,000.

NUMBER OF APPLICANTS MOST RECENT YEAR:
116.

NUMBER OF AWARDS: 93.

APPLICATION INFORMATION:
Grant proposals should consist of an application form, project proposal (including budget) and letter of support. Specific format for grant proposals is explained in detail on the Center's web site.
Deadline: March 1 and October 1 annually.

PUBLICATIONS:
Teaching Theology and Religion, published quarterly by Wiley-Blackwell Publishers.

ADDRESS INQUIRIES TO:
Paul Myhre, Associate Director
(See address above.)

INTERNATIONAL AFFAIRS
AND AREA STUDIES

International affairs and area studies

AMERICAN COUNCIL OF LEARNED SOCIETIES [873]

633 Third Avenue
New York, NY 10017
(212) 697-1505 ext. 130

E-MAIL ADDRESS:
obukhina@acls.org

WEB SITE ADDRESS:
www.acls.org

FOUNDED: 1919

NAME(S) OF PROGRAMS:
- **East European Language Training**
- **East European Studies Program**

TYPE:
Conferences/seminars; Fellowships; Research grants; Travel grants. East European Language Training involves the following East European languages: Albanian, Bosnian-Croatian-Serbian, Bulgarian, Czech, Estonian, Hungarian, Latvian, Lithuanian, Macedonian, Polish, Romanian, Slovak and Slovene.

Postdoctoral grants for research in the social sciences or humanities.

PURPOSE:
To support research intended to advance the development of East European studies.

ELIGIBILITY:
East European Language Training: Applicants must be U.S. citizens.

East European Studies Program:Applicants must be U.S. citizens or permanent residents. Funds are available for postdoctoral research, dissertation research and writing. In awarding these grants, primary considerations are the scholarly merit of the proposal, its importance to the development of East European studies, and the scholarly potential and accomplishments of the applicant.

FINANCIAL DATA:
Amount of support per award: East European Language Training: Individuals - up to $2,500 (for one summer course); institutions - up to $10,000 (for one summer course).

East European Studies Program: postdoctoral grants: up to $25,000 for at least six months of uninterrupted research in lieu of salary; doctoral stipend: up to $18,000 for one year of support for research and writing of dissertation; conference grants: up to $25,000; travel grants: $1,000-$2,500; workshops: up to $12,500.
Total amount of support: Varies.

COOPERATIVE FUNDING PROGRAMS: East European Language Training and East European Studies Program are funded by the U.S. State Department.

NUMBER OF AWARDS: Approximately 34 for East European Language Training and East European Studies Program combined for the year 2009-10.

APPLICATION INFORMATION:
Applications must be submitted online for postdoctoral and doctoral dissertation grants. Applications for travel, conference and language-training grants may be e-mailed.
Deadline: Postdoctoral and doctoral dissertation grants: November; travel, conference and language-training grants: January.

ADDRESS INQUIRIES TO:
Olga Bukhina
Program Coordinator
(See address above.)

AMERICAN INSTITUTE OF PAKISTAN STUDIES [874]

c/o University of Wisconsin Department of Anthropology
5240 Sewell Social Science Building
1180 Observatory Drive
Madison, WI 53706
(608) 262-5696
Fax: (608) 265-4216

E-MAIL ADDRESS:
aips@pakistanstudies-aips.org

WEB SITE ADDRESS:
www.pakistanstudies-aips.org

FOUNDED: 1973

AREAS OF INTEREST:
All fields of humanities and social sciences if engaged in research on Pakistan and relations between Pakistan and other countries.

NAME(S) OF PROGRAMS:
- **AIPS Post Doctoral Fellowship**
- **AIPS Pre-Doctoral Fellowship**

TYPE:
Fellowships; Research grants. Awarded in several categories including predoctoral research, postdoctoral study, library service and professional development.

YEAR PROGRAM STARTED: 1973

PURPOSE:
To promote research on Pakistan.

ELIGIBILITY:
Applicants must be scholars and advanced graduate students who are American citizens and are engaged in research on Pakistan in ancient, medieval and modern times, in all fields of the humanities and social sciences. Research topics comparing aspects of Pakistan with other Muslim countries are especially encouraged.

Graduate student applicants must have fulfilled all residence, language and preliminary examination requirements for the Doctorate and have an approved dissertation topic.

See web site for current restrictions.

FINANCIAL DATA:
The award will provide a maintenance allowance for the scholar and dependents, plus travel and other benefits.
Amount of support per award: Varies.
Total amount of support: $65,000.

NUMBER OF APPLICANTS MOST RECENT YEAR: 15.

NUMBER OF AWARDS: Varies.

APPLICATION INFORMATION:
Predoctoral applications should include a proposal (five pages), curriculum vitae, a transcript, a letter from the dissertation advisor and contact information for two referees. Postdoctoral applications should include a proposal (five pages), curriculum vitae, and contact information for two referees.

A non-refundable processing fee of $30 must be included with the completed application form. Any forms that are incomplete will be returned without refund of the application fee.

Duration: Two to nine months.
Deadline: Varies.

STAFF:
Laura Hammond, Administrative Program Manager

ADDRESS INQUIRIES TO:
Laura Hammond
Administrative Program Manager
(See address above.)

THE KATHRYN AMES FOUNDATION [875]

c/o Pierson & Pierson
305 West Chesapeake Avenue, Suite 308
Towson, MD 21204
(410) 821-3004
Fax: (410) 821-3007

E-MAIL ADDRESS:
info@kathrynames.org

WEB SITE ADDRESS:
www.kathrynames.org

FOUNDED: 1993

AREAS OF INTEREST:
Israel, education, health care, poverty relief and pluralism.

TYPE:
General operating grants; Project/program grants.

YEAR PROGRAM STARTED: 1993

PURPOSE:
To benefit organizations located in Israel which are working for charitable and benevolent purposes.

LEGAL BASIS:
Private foundation.

ELIGIBILITY:
Eligible organizations must be nonprofit and located in Israel.

GEOGRAPHIC RESTRICTIONS:
Israel.

FINANCIAL DATA:
Amount of support per award: $5,000 to $40,000.
Total amount of support: $300,000 for the year 2010.

NUMBER OF AWARDS: 47 for the year 2010.

APPLICATION INFORMATION:
Application form is available online.
Duration: Typically one year.

PUBLICATIONS:
Application guidelines.

ADDRESS INQUIRIES TO:
Lu Pierson, Grants Administrator
(See address above.)

ARCHAEOLOGICAL INSTITUTE OF AMERICA [876]

656 Beacon Street, 6th Floor
Boston, MA 02215
(617) 358-4184
Fax: (617) 353-6550

E-MAIL ADDRESS:
lsparks@aia.bu.edu

WEB SITE ADDRESS:
www.archaeological.org

FOUNDED: 1879

AREAS OF INTEREST:
Archaeological research and publication.

NAME(S) OF PROGRAMS:
- **The Archaeology of Portugal Fellowship**

TYPE:
Fellowships. The Fellowship supports projects pertaining to the archaeology of Portugal. These include, but are not limited to, research projects, colloquia, symposia, publication, research-related travel, or travel to academic meetings for the purpose of presenting papers on the archaeology of Portugal.

PURPOSE:
To promote archaeological studies pertaining to Portugal.

ELIGIBILITY:
Portuguese, American and other international scholars are invited to apply.

FINANCIAL DATA:
Amount of support per award: Award may vary based on the merit of the proposal. Typically $4,000.

Total amount of support: $4,000 to $10,000.

NUMBER OF APPLICANTS MOST RECENT YEAR:
4.

NUMBER OF AWARDS: 1.

APPLICATION INFORMATION:
Duration: One year.

Deadline: November 1. Announcement by February 1.

ADDRESS INQUIRIES TO:
Laurel Nilsen Sparks
Lecture and Fellowship Coordinator
(See address above.)

ASHBURN INSTITUTE INC. [877]
198 Okatie Village Drive
Suite 103, PMB 301
Bluffton, SC 29909
(843) 705-7643
Fax: (843) 705-7643

E-MAIL ADDRESS:
info@ashburninstitute.org

WEB SITE ADDRESS:
www.ashburninstitute.org

FOUNDED: 1940

AREAS OF INTEREST:
International affairs, international federalism, and political science.

NAME(S) OF PROGRAMS:
- **Frank Educational Fund**

TYPE:
Research grants; Scholarships.

YEAR PROGRAM STARTED: 1991

PURPOSE:
To support the study of federalism and international integration at the graduate and postgraduate level.

ELIGIBILITY:
Open to graduate students of good academic standing working on a thesis or dissertation relating to international integration and federalism, doing coursework that places major weight on international integration and federalism or an independent project relating to international integration and federalism. International (foreign institutions) graduate students are eligible, as well as U.S. students.

FINANCIAL DATA:
Amount of support per award: $1,000 to $3,000.

Total amount of support: $40,000.

APPLICATION INFORMATION:
Applicants must complete the FEF Application Form and submit it along with the following materials:
(1) a description of any courses planned to be completed by the applicant during the period of the proposed grant;
(2) a concise, yet complete description of the project relating to international integration and federalism and how this will fit the requirements of the Fund;
(3) a brief writing sample and;
(4) a copy of the applicant's graduate transcripts if currently enrolled in a graduate program (or have it sent separately by the institution, if so, indicate), or a copy of the applicant's undergraduate transcript if enrolled in a graduate program but has not yet started it.

Only complete applications will be considered for a scholarship.

Deadline: April 1 for Fall term awards and October 1 for Spring term awards.

ADDRESS INQUIRIES TO:
Frank Fund Manager
(See address above.)

AUSTRO-AMERICAN ASSOCIATION OF BOSTON [878]
Department of German
106 Central Street
Wellesley, MA 02481
(781) 283-2255
Fax: (781) 283-3652

E-MAIL ADDRESS:
thansen@wellesley.edu

WEB SITE ADDRESS:
www.austria-boston.org

FOUNDED: 1944

AREAS OF INTEREST:
All aspects of Austrian society, especially culture; Austrian-American relations.

TYPE:
Awards/prizes; Research grants; Scholarships. Support for a project relating to Austrian literature, music, art, history or other aspects of the Austrian contribution to culture.

YEAR PROGRAM STARTED: 1976

PURPOSE:
To further interest in Austrian culture and foster Austro-American friendship.

LEGAL BASIS:
Legally organized and established as of July 6, 1970 by the Secretary of the Commonwealth.

ELIGIBILITY:
The project must be related to Austria.

Undergraduate or graduate students, as well as junior faculty, are eligible:
(1) whose project is related to Austria;
(2) who reside or study in New England and;
(3) who are willing to present the results of their project at an event of the Austro-American Association.

GEOGRAPHIC RESTRICTIONS:
New England.

FINANCIAL DATA:
The stipend does not support tuition or other expenses related to a course of study. However, it may be used to travel to Europe or within the U.S., to purchase books and other materials or to facilitate publications.

Amount of support per award: $1,500.
Total amount of support: $1,500.

NUMBER OF APPLICANTS MOST RECENT YEAR:
5.

NUMBER OF AWARDS: 1 per year (when funds are available).

APPLICATION INFORMATION:
Applications should include a curriculum vitae, a detailed description of the proposed project and two letters of recommendation from faculty members well acquainted with the applicant's background and potential. Applicants may be invited to present the results of their project at a meeting of the Association. A personal interview may be required.

Deadline: April 1.

OFFICERS:
Jan Herrmann, Board Chairman
Traude Acker, President
Marta Stasa, Vice President
Hana Sittler, Treasurer
Judy Zohn, Secretary

ADDRESS INQUIRIES TO:
Prof. Thomas Hansen
Chairman, Scholarship Committee
(See address above.)

*PLEASE NOTE:
E-mail correspondence and electronic submission are recommended.

CANADIAN EMBASSY [879]
Academic Relations Office
501 Pennsylvania Avenue, N.W.
Washington, DC 20001
(202) 682-7727
Fax: (202) 682-7791

E-MAIL ADDRESS:
academicrelations@canadianembassy.org

WEB SITE ADDRESS:
www.washington.gc.ca

FOUNDED: 1927

AREAS OF INTEREST:
Social and human sciences, business and economic issues, Canadian values and culture, communications, environment, national and international security, natural resources (energy, fisheries, forestry, etc.) and trade.

NAME(S) OF PROGRAMS:
- **Canadian Studies Research Grant Program**

TYPE:
Research grants; Travel grants. The Research Grant Program assists individual scholars or a group of scholars in writing an article-length manuscript of publishable quality and reporting their findings in a scholarly publication and at scholarly conferences, thus contributing to the development of expertise on Canada in the U.S.

YEAR PROGRAM STARTED: 1993

PURPOSE:
To promote research that contributes to a better knowledge and understanding of Canada, its relationship with the U.S., and its international affairs.

LEGAL BASIS:
Canadian Embassy.

ELIGIBILITY:
Open to faculty members at accredited U.S. four-year colleges and universities, as well as

scholars at American research institutes. Recent Ph.D. recipients who are citizens or permanent residents of the U.S. are also eligible to apply. Applicants must carry out their own research. Applicants are ineligible to receive the same grant in two consecutive years or to receive two individual category Canadian Studies grants in the same grant period.

FINANCIAL DATA:
Grants are provided to help defray only direct costs related to a project, including travel primarily within Canada and within the U.S. as necessary, and research materials. No provision is made for release time stipends, salaries or overhead costs to the institution. Contractual or commissioned research does not qualify for support and grants are not given for work undertaken as part of the applicant's formal program of studies leading to a degree.

Amount of support per award: Up to $15,000 (U.S.). If applicant's project focuses on a priority topic and the applicant obtains matching funding, the award can be up to $20,000 (U.S.).

Total amount of support: Varies.

NUMBER OF AWARDS: 28 for the year 2009.

APPLICATION INFORMATION:
Applicants must complete the online application form and submit other materials.

Deadline: Applications must be sent electronically no later than November 1. Awards are announced normally within 90 days of the application deadline.

PUBLICATIONS:
Guidelines.

ADDRESS INQUIRIES TO:
Academic Relations Office
(See address above.)

CANADIAN EMBASSY [880]

Academic Relations Office
501 Pennsylvania Avenue, N.W.
Washington, DC 20001
(202) 682-7727
Fax: (202) 682-7791

E-MAIL ADDRESS:
academicrelations@canadianembassy.org

WEB SITE ADDRESS:
www.washington.gc.ca

FOUNDED: 1927

AREAS OF INTEREST:
Business and economic issues, Canadian values and culture, communications, environment, national and international security, natural resources (energy, fisheries, forestry, etc.) and trade.

NAME(S) OF PROGRAMS:
● **Doctoral Student Research Award**

TYPE:
Research grants; Travel grants. Offers doctoral students an opportunity to conduct part of their research in Canada.

YEAR PROGRAM STARTED: 1985

PURPOSE:
To promote research that contributes to a better knowledge and understanding of Canada, its relationship with the U.S., and its international affairs.

LEGAL BASIS:
Canadian Embassy.

ELIGIBILITY:
Open to doctoral students at accredited U.S. and Canadian four-year colleges and universities whose dissertations are related in substantial part to the study of Canada and Canada/U.S. relations. Candidates must be citizens or permanent residents of the U.S. and should have completed all doctoral requirements, except the dissertation, when they apply for a grant. Applicants must carry out their own research. Funds are to be provided only for work undertaken as part of the applicant's formal doctoral program of studies and are to be given only to help defray direct costs (travel within Canada, lodging, meals, research support, etc.) resulting from a period of time spent in Canada while doing research.

FINANCIAL DATA:
Amount of support per award: Up to U.S. $10,000.

Total amount of support: Varies.

NUMBER OF AWARDS: 11 for the year 2009.

APPLICATION INFORMATION:
Applicants must complete the online application form and submit other materials.

Deadline: Applications must be sent electronically no later than December 1. Awards are announced normally within 90 days of the application deadline.

PUBLICATIONS:
Guidelines.

ADDRESS INQUIRIES TO:
Academic Relations Office
(See address above.)

CANADIAN EMBASSY [881]

Academic Relations Office
501 Pennsylvania Avenue, N.W.
Washington, DC 20001
(202) 682-7727
Fax: (202) 682-7791

E-MAIL ADDRESS:
academicrelations@canadianembassy.org

WEB SITE ADDRESS:
www.washington.gc.ca

FOUNDED: 1927

AREAS OF INTEREST:
Priority topics include business and economic issues, Canadian values and culture, communications, environment, national and international security, natural resources (energy, fisheries, forestry, etc.) and trade. The use of new Internet technology to enhance existing courses is especially welcomed. Of particular interest are projects that have policy relevance for Canada and Canada-U.S. relations.

NAME(S) OF PROGRAMS:
● **Canadian Studies Faculty Enrichment Program**

TYPE:
Development grants; Research grants; Travel grants. Faculty Enrichment (Course Development) Program provides faculty members with an opportunity to develop or update a course(s) with substantial Canadian content that will be offered as part of their regular teaching load. Submissions from all fields in the social sciences and humanities are welcomed.

YEAR PROGRAM STARTED: 1976

LEGAL BASIS:
Canadian Embassy.

ELIGIBILITY:
Open to faculty members at accredited U.S. four-year colleges and universities. The candidates should be able to demonstrate that they are already teaching or will be authorized to teach a course with a substantial Canadian content (33% or more). Applicants are ineligible to receive the same grant in two consecutive years or to receive two individual category Canadian Studies grants in the same grant period.

FINANCIAL DATA:
Grants are intended to help defray direct costs related to a project, including travel primarily within Canada and within the U.S. as necessary, as well as research and course materials. No provision is made for release time stipends, salaries or overhead costs to the institution.

Amount of support per award: Up to $6,000. Applicant may request an additional $5,000 (U.S.) specifically to support student travel to Canada.

Total amount of support: Varies.

NUMBER OF AWARDS: 11 for the year 2009.

APPLICATION INFORMATION:
Applicants must complete the online application form and submit other materials.

Deadline: December 1. Awards are announced normally within 90 days after application deadline.

PUBLICATIONS:
Guidelines.

ADDRESS INQUIRIES TO:
Academic Relations Office
(See address above.)

CANADIAN EMBASSY [882]

501 Pennsylvania Avenue, N.W.
Washington, DC 20001
(202) 682-7727
Fax: (202) 682-7791

E-MAIL ADDRESS:
academicrelations@canadianembassy.org

WEB SITE ADDRESS:
www.washington.gc.ca

FOUNDED: 1927

AREAS OF INTEREST:
Social sciences, business, environment, humanities, law and fine arts, with a unique relevance to Canada or the bilateral relationship; expansion of Canadian Studies programs.

NAME(S) OF PROGRAMS:
● **Canadian Studies Program Enhancement Grant**

TYPE:
Development grants; Travel grants. Program Enhancement Grant is administered by Foreign Affairs and International Trade Canada, through the Canadian Embassy, Washington, DC, in cooperation with Canadian consulates general throughout the U.S.

YEAR PROGRAM STARTED: 1927

PURPOSE:
To encourage scholarly inquiry and multidisciplinary professional academic activities which will contribute to the development or expansion of a program dedicated to the study of Canada or Canada-U.S. relations at the applying institution.

LEGAL BASIS:
Government agency.

ELIGIBILITY:
Available to U.S. four-year colleges, universities and research institutions that undertake professional academic activities to further the development of a program dedicated to the study of Canada or Canada-U.S. relations at their institution. Institutions must demonstrate their funding support for the program and that they are bringing innovative ideas to the program.

GEOGRAPHIC RESTRICTIONS:
United States.

FINANCIAL DATA:
Grants are provided to help defray only direct costs related to professional activities initiated by the institution. These costs include travel, honoraria, research and promotion materials, printing, web site development, student mobility, linkages and research collaboration with Canadian universities, and faculty and course development. No provision is made for released time stipends, secretarial services or for overhead costs to the institution.
Amount of support per award: Varies.
Total amount of support: Varies.

NUMBER OF AWARDS: Approximately 35 to 40 per year.

APPLICATION INFORMATION:
Applicants must complete the online application form and submit the following materials in a single file:
(1) an abstract, approximately 200 words in length, outlining the key objectives and proposed activities that would be supported by the requested funding;
(2) a concise proposal (four to eight pages, double-spaced) including an overview of the program, a statement identifying the goals and objectives of the program and indicating how that program advances the study of Canada and/or Canada-U.S. relations and broadens student awareness and appreciation of Canada and Canada-U.S.relations, and a schedule of recent and projected activities;
(3) a detailed budget;
(4) a curriculum vitae of the program director or coordinator (not to exceed five pages) and;
(5) a letter from an appropriate university official indicating institutional agreement to the proposed program development (enhancement).
Deadline: June 15. Awards are announced normally within about 90 days of their application deadline.

PUBLICATIONS:
Guidelines.

ADDRESS INQUIRIES TO:
Academic Relations Office
(See address above.)

CANADIAN EMBASSY   [883]
501 Pennsylvania Avenue, N.W.
Washington, DC 20001
(202) 682-7727
Fax: (202) 682-7791

E-MAIL ADDRESS:
academicrelations@canadianembassy.org

WEB SITE ADDRESS:
www.washington.gc.ca

FOUNDED: 1927

AREAS OF INTEREST:
Social sciences, journalism, business, the environment, humanities, law, fine arts and foreign policy, especially Afghanistan with a unique relevance to Canada or the bilateral relationship.

NAME(S) OF PROGRAMS:
● **Canadian Studies Conference Grant Program**

TYPE:
Conferences/seminars. The Canadian Studies Conference Grant Program is designed to assist an institution in holding a conference and publishing the resulting papers and proceedings in a scholarly fashion.

PURPOSE:
To support conferences addressing important and timely issues about Canada, its relationship with the U.S., and its international affairs.

LEGAL BASIS:
Canadian Embassy.

ELIGIBILITY:
Conference Grants are intended for U.S. four-year colleges and universities or research institutions which undertake a conference on a Canadian, U.S./Canadian or North American issue. Grants are for direct costs related to the proposed conference, including travel, honoraria, and possible publishing fees. No provision is made for released time stipends, salaries or for overhead costs to the institutions.

Applicant's project must focus on one of the priority topics and demonstrate matching funds from other sources.

FINANCIAL DATA:
Amount of support per award: Up to $20,000.
Total amount of support: Varies.

APPLICATION INFORMATION:
Applications must be submitted electronically and include the following information in a single file:
(1) an abstract, approximately 200 words in length, that outlines the focus of the conference, its rationale and relevance, the target audience, any partner institutions, conference date and venue, and publication plans;
(2) a concise proposal (four to eight pages, double-spaced) which will identify the key issues to be addressed by the conference and explain the context of the project as well as its relevance for Canada or Canada-U.S. relations, present a complete schedule of activities, including a timetable for the publication of papers or proceedings, and identify expected participants, partner institutions or organizations, if any, and the intended audience;
(3) detailed budget that describes and justifies anticipated expenditures and indicates other funding sources, particularly those from the institution itself (cost sharing from other sources must be documented);
(4) a curriculum vitae (not to exceed five pages each) of the conference coordinator(s) and;
(5) the names and contact information of two scholars from whom the applicants will solicit recommendations. It is the responsibility of the applicant to ensure that letters of recommendation are sent directly by the letter writers to the Embassy e-mail address above no later than the deadline.
Deadline: June 30.

PUBLICATIONS:
Guidelines.

CDS INTERNATIONAL, INC.   [884]
440 Park Avenue South, 2nd Floor
New York, NY 10016
(212) 497-3510
Fax: (212) 497-3535

E-MAIL ADDRESS:
alfa@cdsintl.org

WEB SITE ADDRESS:
www.cdsintl.org/alfa

FOUNDED: 2004

AREAS OF INTEREST:
Culture, business, law, politics, public policy, government, journalism, mass communications, finance and economics.

NAME(S) OF PROGRAMS:
● **Alfa Fellowship Program**

TYPE:
Exchange programs; Fellowships. A high-level professional development exchange program placing qualified American and British citizens in work assignments at leading organizations in Russia in the fields of business, economics, journalism, law and public policy. The program includes language training, seminar programs, and extended professional work experience. Fellows receive stipends, travel, housing and insurance.

YEAR PROGRAM STARTED: 2004

PURPOSE:
To foster a new generation of future American and British leaders with in-depth practical experience in the modern business and public policy environment of the Russian Federation.

ELIGIBILITY:
Open to U.S. and British citizens with a graduate degree, work experience and professional interest or background in above fields. Russian language proficiency preferred, but not required.

Applicants must:
(1) have U.S. or U.K. citizenship;
(2) be 25 to 35 years of age at time of application;
(3) have a graduate degree or equivalent training in business administration, economics, journalism, law, public policy or government and;
(4) have at least two years relevant work experience in their field of expertise.

GEOGRAPHIC RESTRICTIONS:
United States, United Kingdom and Russia.

FINANCIAL DATA:
Monthly stipend, free accommodations in Russia, all in-country program-related travel, round-trip flight to Moscow, and limited international health, accident and liability insurance during the program in Russia.

NUMBER OF AWARDS: 10.

APPLICATION INFORMATION:
Candidates must submit application, online or via mail, with all supporting materials by the deadline.
Duration: 11 months, June to April.
Deadline: December 1, 2011.

ADDRESS INQUIRIES TO:
Melissa Graves, Program Director
(See address above.)

CENTER FOR COMPARATIVE IMMIGRATION STUDIES AT THE UNIVERSITY OF CALIFORNIA-SAN DIEGO

9500 Gilman Drive, MC 0548
La Jolla, CA 92093-0548
(858) 822-4447
Fax: (858) 822-4432

E-MAIL ADDRESS:
ccis@ucsd.edu

WEB SITE ADDRESS:
ccis-ucsd.org

TYPE:
Fellowships.

See entry 1736 for full listing.

CENTER FOR INTERNATIONAL SECURITY AND COOPERATION (CISAC)   [885]

Freeman Spogli Institute for
International Studies
Encina Hall, C223
Stanford University
Stanford, CA 94305-6165
(650) 724-8055
Fax: (650) 723-0089

E-MAIL ADDRESS:
cisacfellowship@stanford.edu

WEB SITE ADDRESS:
cisac.stanford.edu/fellowships

FOUNDED: 1970

AREAS OF INTEREST:
Arms control and international security, with particular interest in U.S.-Russian security relations and East Asian security issues. Also regional security issues, defense restructuring and weapons proliferation and transfer.

NAME(S) OF PROGRAMS:
- **Fellowships in Science, Technology and International Security**
- **Nuclear Security Fellowships**
- **Predoctoral and Postdoctoral Fellowships in International Security**

TYPE:
Fellowships.

PURPOSE:
To train in international security policy areas.

LEGAL BASIS:
University.

ADDRESS INQUIRIES TO:
CISAC Fellowship Program
(See address above.)

CENTER FOR U.S. - MEXICAN STUDIES, UNIVERSITY OF CALIFORNIA, SAN DIEGO   [886]

9500 Gilman Drive, MC 0510
La Jolla, CA 92093-0510
(858) 534-4503
Fax: (858) 534-6447

E-MAIL ADDRESS:
usmex-applications@ucsd.edu

WEB SITE ADDRESS:
www.usmex.ucsd.edu

FOUNDED: 1979

AREAS OF INTEREST:
The study of U.S. and Mexico relations and the study of Mexico within the social sciences and history.

NAME(S) OF PROGRAMS:
- **USMEX Visiting Scholars Program**

TYPE:
Fellowships; Professorships.

YEAR PROGRAM STARTED: 1980

PURPOSE:
To support the write-up of a Ph.D. dissertation or the write-up of a postdoctoral research project.

ELIGIBILITY:
Open to Mexican citizens, advanced graduate students, recent Ph.D. recipients, junior faculty and advanced faculty members from any campus of the University of California system, as well as other institutions.

GEOGRAPHIC RESTRICTIONS:
United States and Mexico.

FINANCIAL DATA:
Amount of support per award: Predoctoral Fellows: $2,500 per month; Visiting Professors: $3,500 per month.
Total amount of support: $200,000.

APPLICATION INFORMATION:
Applications should be submitted online.
Duration: Up to 10 months. Former Visiting Fellows are eligible to apply again after five years.
Deadline: January.

STAFF:
Graciela Platero, Director of External Affairs and Fellowship and Program Officer

ADDRESS INQUIRIES TO:
Greg Mallinger
Events and Programs Coordinator
(See address above.)

COUNCIL FOR EUROPEAN STUDIES AT COLUMBIA UNIVERSITY   [887]

420 West 118th Street, MC 3307
New York, NY 10027
(212) 854-4172
Fax: (212) 854-8808

E-MAIL ADDRESS:
ces@columbia.edu

WEB SITE ADDRESS:
www.ces.columbia.edu

FOUNDED: 1970

AREAS OF INTEREST:
The study of Europe.

NAME(S) OF PROGRAMS:
- **Book Award**
- **Council for European Studies Pre Dissertation Research Fellowships**

TYPE:
Awards/prizes; Fellowships. The CES Book Award honors talented emerging scholars with an award for the best first book on any subject in European studies.

Council for European Studies Pre Dissertation Research Fellowships are intended to fund students' first major research project in Europe.

YEAR PROGRAM STARTED: 1971

ELIGIBILITY:
Book Award: Must be scholar's first book on any subject in European studies. Books may be nominated by the author, a CES member, or by a publisher.

Fellowship: Limited to graduate students currently enrolled in a doctoral program at a university that is a member of the Council for European Studies Academic Consortium. Member universities and additional eligibility requirements can be found online.

FINANCIAL DATA:
Book Award recipient receives a plaque and recognition at the International Conference. Fellowship recipients receive a stipend, travel support for attending and presenting at the CES International Conference of Europeanists, and the opportunity to publish in *Perspectives on Europe.*
Amount of support per award: Fellowships: $4,000 stipend.
Total amount of support: Varies.

APPLICATION INFORMATION:
Deadline: Fellowship: February 15.

COUNCIL FOR INTERNATIONAL EXCHANGE OF SCHOLARS (CIES)   [888]

1400 K Street, N.W.
Suite 650
Washington, DC 20005-2403
(202) 898-0600

E-MAIL ADDRESS:
fulspec@iie.org

WEB SITE ADDRESS:
www.cies.org/specialists

FOUNDED: 1947

AREAS OF INTEREST:
Scholarly exchange.

NAME(S) OF PROGRAMS:
- **Fulbright Specialist Program**

TYPE:
Exchange programs; Project/program grants; Technical assistance; Travel grants; Visiting scholars. The Fulbright Specialist Program is designed to provide short-term academic opportunities for U.S. faculty and professionals. Also supports the research and teaching of scholars from around the world visiting colleges and universities in the U.S. Grant recipients have a chance to participate in a variety of new and exciting activities: collaborate with counterparts in other countries on curriculum and faculty development, assist in institutional planning, deliver a series of lectures or provide other expertise, etc.

YEAR PROGRAM STARTED: 2001

PURPOSE:
To promote mutual understanding and scholarship.

LEGAL BASIS:
Private, nonprofit organization that receives funding from the U.S. State Department.

ELIGIBILITY:
The Fulbright Specialist Program is open to qualified U.S. scholars and professionals in various fields. Applicants will be considered without regard to race, color, religion, sex, age, national origin and/or physical impairment.

Applicants must meet all of the following minimum eligibility requirements (In matching candidates with grant opportunities, preference will be given to candidates with the most relevant professional experience.):
(1) U.S. citizen at the time of application; permanent resident status is not sufficient;

(2) for academics, a Ph.D. or equivalent professional/terminal degree at the time of application plus a minimum of five years of postdoctoral teaching or professional experience in the field in which person is applying;
(3) for professionals and artists outside academe, recognized professional standing and substantial professional accomplishments plus a minimum of five years of professional experience in the field in which person is applying;
(4) disclosure of prior conviction, current indictment or arrest for commission of a felony or misdemeanor (excluding minor traffic violations); prior conviction or current indictment may result in disqualification and;
(5) U.S. residency required at the time of selection for a grant.

FINANCIAL DATA:
Grants awarded will include travel and per diem plus a $200 per day honorarium. Per diem costs, which are in-country costs for lodging, meals and in-country transportation, will be covered by the host institution.

NUMBER OF APPLICANTS MOST RECENT YEAR:
600.

NUMBER OF AWARDS: Approximately 300 to 400 per year.

APPLICATION INFORMATION:
Qualified U.S. scholars and professionals apply throughout the calendar year for candidacy on the Fulbright Specialists Roster. Peer review is conducted six times each year. CIES builds lists of qualified Specialist candidates for each eligible discipline and facilitates matching Specialist candidates with project requests. There is a two-application process for U.S. scholars.

Non-U.S. postsecondary degree-granting academic institutions submit Specialist project requests through the appropriate Fulbright agency in their country. Once approved by the Fulbright Commission or U.S. Embassy, the Specialist project request is forwarded to the U.S. Department of State for final approval.

Duration: Two to six weeks.

ADDRESS INQUIRIES TO:
See e-mail address above.

COUNCIL FOR INTERNATIONAL EXCHANGE OF SCHOLARS (CIES)   [889]
3007 Tilden Street, N.W.
Suite 5L
Washington, DC 20008-3009
(202) 686-6252
Fax: (202) 362-3442

E-MAIL ADDRESS:
aford@iie.org

WEB SITE ADDRESS:
www.iie.org/cies

FOUNDED: 1947

AREAS OF INTEREST:
Humanities or social sciences, or any field that will benefit from an international perspective.

NAME(S) OF PROGRAMS:
● **Fulbright Scholar-in-Residence Program**

TYPE:
Awards/prizes; Exchange programs; Visiting scholars. Grants support a visiting lecturer

from outside the U.S. to teach regular courses or develop new ones, team teach or participate in special seminars or serve as a resource to faculty and students and, through outreach, to the community at large.

PURPOSE:
To initiate or develop international programs at colleges and universities by using a Foreign scholar-in-residence to internationalize the curriculum, set up global studies or area-specific programs or otherwise expand contacts of students and faculty with other cultures and to strengthen or enrich existing international or area studies programs.

LEGAL BASIS:
Public Law 87-256, as amended, The Mutual Educational and Cultural Exchange Act of 1961.

ELIGIBILITY:
U.S. colleges and universities, including community colleges, are invited to submit proposals to obtain a Foreign scholar-in-residence. Preference is given to proposals in the humanities or social sciences, although other fields focusing on international issues will be considered.

GEOGRAPHIC RESTRICTIONS:
United States.

FINANCIAL DATA:
Monthly stipend as well as round-trip international travel, excess baggage allowance, accident and sickness insurance, and allowances for books, professional development and dependents.

Amount of support per award:
Approximately $2,500 to $2,900 per month, depending on the cost of living in the city where the scholar will reside.

Total amount of support: Over $1,000,000 for the year 2009.

Matching fund requirements: Some cost sharing by the host institution is required, either supplementary funding or in-kind support, such as housing.

COOPERATIVE FUNDING PROGRAMS: U.S. Department of State.

NUMBER OF APPLICANTS MOST RECENT YEAR:
46.

NUMBER OF AWARDS: 45 or more.

APPLICATION INFORMATION:
Guidelines are available in March. Interested institutions must submit one original proposal by mail and are also encouraged to send an electronic copy to the e-mail address above.

Duration: One semester to one academic year.

Deadline: October 15.

PUBLICATIONS:
Directory of Visiting Scholars; descriptive brochure; annual report.

STAFF:
Alma Ford, Program Officer
Drew Hellman, Program Associate

ADDRESS INQUIRIES TO:
Alma Ford, Program Officer
(See address above.)

*PLEASE NOTE:
Priority is given to institutions that do not normally have the opportunity to host visiting scholars from other countries. Such institutions would include: small liberal arts colleges, community colleges and all minority-serving institutions.

COUNCIL FOR INTERNATIONAL EXCHANGE OF SCHOLARS (CIES)
3007 Tilden Street, N.W.
Suite 5L
Washington, DC 20008-3009
(202) 686-6232
Fax: (202) 362-3442; (202) 686-6258

E-MAIL ADDRESS:
tjanes@iie.org

WEB SITE ADDRESS:
www.cies.org

TYPE:
Exchange programs; Project/program grants; Travel grants. The annual two-week German Studies Seminar focuses on current German society and culture and examines political, social and economic institutions.

See entry 1737 for full listing.

COUNCIL FOR INTERNATIONAL EXCHANGE OF SCHOLARS (CIES)
1400 K Street, N.W.
Washington, DC 20005
(202) 686-6232
Fax: (202) 362-3442

E-MAIL ADDRESS:
mbettua@iie.org

WEB SITE ADDRESS:
www.cies.org

TYPE:
Awards/prizes. There are approximately 40 distinguished chair awards in 18 countries. Awards available in a wide variety of disciplines.

See entry 1738 for full listing.

COUNCIL ON FOREIGN RELATIONS   [890]
58 East 68th Street
New York, NY 10065
(212) 434-9489
Fax: (212) 434-9870

E-MAIL ADDRESS:
fellowships@cfr.org

WEB SITE ADDRESS:
www.cfr.org/thinktank/fellowships/index.html

FOUNDED: 1921

NAME(S) OF PROGRAMS:
● **International Affairs Fellowship (IAF)**

TYPE:
Fellowships. Awards to enable the grantee to undertake an examination of an important problem in international affairs and to explore the implications of that problem for the interests and policies of the U.S., foreign states or international organizations. Awarded to individuals with outstanding project proposals and provides fellows the opportunity to carry out research, integrating fellows placed in New York or Washington, DC into the intellectual life of CFR.

The distinctive character of the program lies in the contrasting experiences it provides at the juncture of policy research and policy formulation. Academic and other professionals from the private sector spend Fellowship tenures in public service or in a policymaking setting, while government officials have the opportunity to study foreign policy issues in a scholarly atmosphere free from operational pressure.

YEAR PROGRAM STARTED: 1967

PURPOSE:
To bridge the gap between analysis and action in foreign policy by inviting individuals from the academic, business, government, media and religious communities to engage in a variety of policy studies and actively participate in policymaking.

LEGAL BASIS:
Nonprofit.

ELIGIBILITY:
The program is only open to U.S. citizens and permanent residents between the ages of 27 and 35 who are eligible to work in the U.S. CFR does not sponsor for visas. While a Ph.D. is not a requirement, successful candidates generally hold advanced degrees and possess a strong record of work experience and firm grounding in the field of foreign policy. The program does not fund pre- or postdoctoral research, work toward a degree, or the completion of projects for which substantial progress has been made prior to the Fellowship period.

GEOGRAPHIC RESTRICTIONS:
United States.

FINANCIAL DATA:
Each award is determined on the basis of individual need to carry out the particular project.
Amount of support per award: The program awards a stipend of $85,000. Fellows are considered independent contractors rather than employees of CFR, and are not eligible for employment benefits, including health insurance.

NUMBER OF AWARDS: 8-12, annually.

APPLICATION INFORMATION:
Applications are primarily by invitation, on the recommendation of individuals in academic, government, and other institutions. Others who inquire directly and meet preliminary requirements may also be considered.

Application materials will be forwarded to those invited to apply. Following a preliminary review by the selection committee, candidates selected as finalists will be interviewed. The selection committee deems the following criteria of particular importance: scholarly qualifications; achievements and promise; depth and breadth of professional experience; firm grounding in foreign policy and international relations; and a proposal that focuses on solutions to identified problems in U.S. foreign policy. Candidates are encouraged to plan a systematic approach to assessing the major substantive and process issues of their planned research. The proposal will be judged on the proposed work's originality, practicality, potential, likelihood of completion during the Fellowship period, and the contribution it will make to the candidate's individual career development via a sufficiently contrasting experience.

Duration: The Fellowship lasts for 12 months, preferably beginning in September and extending into August. While deferment is typically not granted, requests for only up to one year will be considered on a case-by-case basis and under special circumstances.

Deadline: Nominations: End of September. Applications: Mid-November.

PUBLICATIONS:
Annual report; program brochure and procedural memo.

STAFF:
Janine W. Hill, Director for Fellowship Affairs and Studies Strategic Planning
Victoria Alekhine, Associate Director, Fellowship Affairs

ADDRESS INQUIRIES TO:
(See e-mail address above.)

COUNCIL ON FOREIGN RELATIONS [891]
58 East 68th Street
New York, NY 10065
(212) 434-9489
Fax: (212) 434-9801

E-MAIL ADDRESS:
fellowships@cfr.org

WEB SITE ADDRESS:
www.cfr.org

FOUNDED: 1921

AREAS OF INTEREST:
International relations.

NAME(S) OF PROGRAMS:
● **International Affairs Fellowship in Japan**

TYPE:
Fellowships; Research grants; Visiting scholars. The program provides for fellows to spend between three to 12 months conducting research while affiliated with a cooperating institution in Japan.

YEAR PROGRAM STARTED: 1997

PURPOSE:
To strengthen the U.S.-Japan relationship by expanding American understanding of Japan and enhancing communication between Americans and Japanese on global problems.

ELIGIBILITY:
Open to U.S. citizens between the ages of 27 and 45. The program is intended primarily for those without prior experience in Japan, although the selection committee has made exceptions where it considered that the fellowship would allow an individual to add new dimension to his or her relationship to Japan. While a Ph.D. is not a requirement, successful candidates generally hold advanced degrees and possess a strong record of work experience. The program does not fund pre-or postdoctoral research, work toward a degree, or the completion of projects for which substantial progress has been made prior to the fellowship period. Knowledge of the Japanese language is not a requirement.

GEOGRAPHIC RESTRICTIONS:
United States.

FINANCIAL DATA:
Stipend covers living and necessary research expenses in Japan.

COOPERATIVE FUNDING PROGRAMS: Hitachi, Ltd.

NUMBER OF AWARDS: Approximately 3 annually.

APPLICATION INFORMATION:
Applications will be primarily by invitation, on recommendation of individuals in academic, government and other institutions

who have occasion to know candidates particularly well-suited for the fellowship. Others who inquire directly and meet preliminary requirements may also be invited to apply.

Duration: Three to 12 months.

Deadline: Late September for nominations. Late October for applications.

STAFF:
L. Camille Massey, Vice President, Membership, Fellowship and Corporate Affairs

ADDRESS INQUIRIES TO:
L. Camille Massey, Vice President Membership, Fellowship and Corporate Affairs
(See address above.)

J.W. DAFOE FOUNDATION [892]
Department of Political Studies
University of Manitoba
University College, Room 351
Winnipeg MB R3T 2M8 Canada
(204) 474-6606
Fax: (204) 474-7645

E-MAIL ADDRESS:
ferguss@cc.umanitoba.ca

AREAS OF INTEREST:
International relations, economics, history and political science.

TYPE:
Awards/prizes; Conferences/seminars; Fellowships; Project/program grants; Research grants. Fellowships for graduate study in international relations, economics, history or political studies.

PURPOSE:
To support graduate study in international relations, economics, history and political science.

LEGAL BASIS:
University association.

ELIGIBILITY:
Master's candidates only in appropriate fields are eligible to apply.

GEOGRAPHIC RESTRICTIONS:
Canada.

FINANCIAL DATA:
Amount of support per award: $17,000 (CAN).
Total amount of support: $17,000 (CAN).

NUMBER OF AWARDS: 1 per year.

APPLICATION INFORMATION:
Application information is available from the Awards Officer, Faculty of Graduate Studies, at the University of Manitoba. Applications are examined annually in May. Requests/proposals to be sent to James Fergusson, Honorary Secretary.

Duration: Fellowships are renewable after one year for a second year of study.

TRUSTEES:
Keith Findlay, Chairperson

*SPECIAL STIPULATIONS:
A submission fee of $50 per entry is required.

THE EAST-WEST CENTER [893]
1601 East West Road
Honolulu, HI 96848-1601
(808) 944-7735
Fax: (808) 944-7730 (Award Service Center)

E-MAIL ADDRESS:
scholarships@eastwestcenter.org

WEB SITE ADDRESS:
www.eastwestcenter.org/studentprograms

FOUNDED: 1960

AREAS OF INTEREST:
Economics; environmental change,
vulnerability and governance; population and
health; politics, governance and security, at a
local, national and/or regional level in the
Asia Pacific region.

NAME(S) OF PROGRAMS:
● **East-West Center Graduate Degree
Fellowship**

TYPE:
Fellowships; Scholarships; Travel grants.

YEAR PROGRAM STARTED: 1960

PURPOSE:
To strengthen relations and understanding
among the peoples and nations of Asia, the
Pacific and the U.S.; to serve as a vigorous
hub for cooperative research, education and
dialogue on critical issues of common
concern to the Asia Pacific region and the
U.S.

LEGAL BASIS:
Public, nonprofit educational corporation
established in Hawaii in 1960 by the U.S.
Congress.

ELIGIBILITY:
Candidates must have obtained a four-year
Bachelor's degree or its equivalent, must be a
citizen or permanent resident of the U.S. or a
country in Asia or the Pacific, and must
come to the Center on the exchange visitor
(J-1) visa.

Priority in the student selection progress is
given to applicants seeking degrees in fields
of study related to research themes at the
East-West Center.

GEOGRAPHIC RESTRICTIONS:
Hawaii.

FINANCIAL DATA:
Award may include housing, stipend, tuition,
health insurance when relevant and
transportation and other academic expenses
as approved. Costs may be shared by
collaborating institutions.

Amount of support per award: Varies.

Total amount of support: Varies.

Matching fund requirements: Cost-sharing on
any Center award is actively sought.

COOPERATIVE FUNDING PROGRAMS: Funding for
the Center comes from the U.S. government,
with additional support provided by private
agencies, individuals, foundations,
corporations, and the governments of the
region.

NUMBER OF APPLICANTS MOST RECENT YEAR:
Over 375.

NUMBER OF AWARDS: 33.

APPLICATION INFORMATION:
Applications are available online.

Duration: Initially 12 months with possible
renewal up to two years for Master's Degree
and four years for doctoral studies.

Deadline: November 1 deadline for
forwarding to the Award Services Office.

ADDRESS INQUIRIES TO:
Award Services Office
(See address above.)

*SPECIAL STIPULATIONS:
Study must be at the University of Hawaii at
Manoa.

THE EAST-WEST CENTER   [894]
1601 East West Road
Honolulu, HI 96848-1601
(808) 944-7744
Fax: (808) 944-7070 (Attn: APLP)

E-MAIL ADDRESS:
aplp@eastwestcenter.org

WEB SITE ADDRESS:
www.eastwestcenter.org/aplp

FOUNDED: 1960

AREAS OF INTEREST:
Issues related to the Asia Pacific region.

NAME(S) OF PROGRAMS:
● **Asia Pacific Leadership Program
Fellowship**

TYPE:
Fellowships.

YEAR PROGRAM STARTED: 2001

PURPOSE:
To create a network of action focused on
building a peaceful, prosperous and just Asia
Pacific community.

LEGAL BASIS:
Public, nonprofit educational corporation.

ELIGIBILITY:
Candidates must have a four-year Bachelor's
degree or its equivalent from an accredited
U.S. college or university or from a
recognized institution of higher learning
abroad.

Priority in the student selection process is
given to candidates with professional work
experience:
(1) international experience and aptitude,
including overseas residence, language skills,
intercultural and diversity exposure;
(2) leadership track record in professional,
public and/or personal realms;
(3) volunteer and community service
experience;
(4) Asia Pacific engagement and evidence of
interest in the region, as well as commitment
to its future prosperity; this might include
classes taken at university, time spent in the
region, languages spoken, membership and
fellowships, specific projects, field studies
and areas of research interest and;
(5) experience working collaboratively in
small teams or in large groups.

GEOGRAPHIC RESTRICTIONS:
Hawaii.

FINANCIAL DATA:
Award may include program fees, living
expenses, field study costs, and other
academic expenses.

Amount of support per award: Varies.

Total amount of support: Varies.

NUMBER OF AWARDS: 39.

APPLICATION INFORMATION:
Application form is available online.

Duration: Mid-August to mid-May.

Deadline: December 1.

PUBLICATIONS:
Annual report.

ADDRESS INQUIRIES TO:
Award Services Office
(See address above.)

THE EISENHOWER
INSTITUTE   [895]
818 Connecticut Avenue, N.W.
Suite 800
Washington, DC 20006
(202) 628-4444
Fax: (202) 628-4445

E-MAIL ADDRESS:
ei@eisenhowerinstitute.org

WEB SITE ADDRESS:
www.eisenhowerinstitute.org

FOUNDED: 1983

AREAS OF INTEREST:
World affairs.

NAME(S) OF PROGRAMS:
● **Eisenhower Institute Scholarship
Programs**

TYPE:
Conferences/seminars; Endowments;
Fellowships; Internships; Scholarships.

PURPOSE:
To promote sound and forward-looking
policies that lay the intellectual and civic
groundwork for the next generation of
opinion-leaders, policy-shapers and public
servants.

ELIGIBILITY:
Open to American high school,
undergraduate, and graduate students.

FINANCIAL DATA:
Amount of support per award: Scholarships
and fellowships: $4,000 to $10,000.

APPLICATION INFORMATION:
Application procedures are available online.

IRS IDENTIFICATION NUMBER: 52-1306218

ADDRESS INQUIRIES TO:
Rick Farwell, Program Coordinator
(See address above.)

EURASIA FOUNDATION
1350 Connecticut Avenue, N.W.
Suite 1000
Washington, DC 20036-1206
(202) 234-7370
Fax: (202) 234-7377

E-MAIL ADDRESS:
eurasia@eurasia.org

WEB SITE ADDRESS:
www.eurasia.org

TYPE:
Conferences/seminars; Development grants;
General operating grants; Project/program
grants; Seed money grants.

See entry 1348 for full listing.

GRADUATE INSTITUTE OF
INTERNATIONAL AND
DEVELOPMENT STUDIES   [896]
Case Postale 136
1211 Geneva 21 Switzerland
41 22 908 57 20
Fax: 41 22 908 57 10

E-MAIL ADDRESS:
scholarships@graduateinstitute.ch

WEB SITE ADDRESS:
graduateinstitute.ch

FOUNDED: 1927

AREAS OF INTEREST:
International history and politics, international economics, international law and political science.

NAME(S) OF PROGRAMS:
- **Financial Aid for Study at The Graduate Institute of International Studies**

TYPE:
Scholarships. Financial aid in advanced study in international relations including intensive research and study towards the Master's degree and the Ph.D. Tenable at the Institute.

PURPOSE:
To support the scientific study of contemporary international relations and the pursuit of advanced studies based on personal work and research.

LEGAL BASIS:
Foundation.

ELIGIBILITY:
Persons who can give evidence of a sound knowledge of the French language and of sufficient prior study in political science, international economics, international law or modern history, by the presentation of a college or university degree, may apply.

Each year, financial assistance is awarded by the Institute in the form of scholarships covering the minimum needs of students. They are allocated on the basis of applicants' academic performance and financial needs.

FINANCIAL DATA:
50 awards are offered yearly with a value of CHF 1,500 per month. Scholars are exempted from Institute fees, but not from the obligatory fees of the University of Geneva which confers the Doctorate.
Amount of support per award: CHF 18,000 per year.
Total amount of support: Approximately CHF 750,000 per year.

APPLICATION INFORMATION:
Applications are available upon request.
Duration: One year. One possible renewal.
Deadline: January 15.

PUBLICATIONS:
Annual report.

ADDRESS INQUIRIES TO:
Secretariat General
(See address above.)

INSTITUTE OF CURRENT WORLD AFFAIRS [897]

4545 42nd Street, N.W.
Suite 311
Washington, DC 20016
(202) 364-4068
Fax: (202) 364-0498

E-MAIL ADDRESS:
icwa@icwa.org

WEB SITE ADDRESS:
www.icwa.org

FOUNDED: 1925

AREAS OF INTEREST:
Current world affairs.

TYPE:
Fellowships. Fellowships are not scholarships, and are not awarded to support work toward academic degrees or for collaborative research projects, or to write books.

PURPOSE:
To provide talented and promising individuals with an opportunity to develop a deep understanding of an issue, country or region outside the U.S. and to share that understanding with a wider public.

ELIGIBILITY:
Fellowships are for self-designed independent study only. Applicants must have a good command of written and spoken English and be women and men under 36 years of age who demonstrate initiative, integrity, outstanding character, good communications skills, seriousness of purpose and enthusiasm for their chosen fields.

FINANCIAL DATA:
Amount of support per award: Varies.

NUMBER OF AWARDS: 2.

APPLICATION INFORMATION:
Applicants should write an initial letter of interest to the Executive Director explaining the personal background and professional experience that would qualify them for the fellowship they have in mind. They should describe the activities they would like to carry out during two years overseas and enclose a resume or curriculum vitae. Select candidates will be invited to submit a more detailed application.

Initial letter should be by e-mail, although fax or regular mail will be accepted. Further information may be obtained from the Institute's web site.
Duration: Minimum period of two years.
Deadline: February 1 and August 1.

ADDRESS INQUIRIES TO:
Steven Butler, Executive Director
(See address above.)

INTERNATIONAL DEVELOPMENT RESEARCH CENTRE (IDRC) [898]

150 Kent Street
Mailroom Suite 990
Ottawa ON K1P 0B2 Canada
(613) 236-6163 ext. 2098
Fax: (613) 236-4026

E-MAIL ADDRESS:
cta@idrc.ca

WEB SITE ADDRESS:
www.idrc.ca/awards

FOUNDED: 1970

AREAS OF INTEREST:
International development.

NAME(S) OF PROGRAMS:
- **Canadian Window on International Development Awards**

TYPE:
Awards/prizes. The Centre offers one award for doctoral research that explores the relationship between Canadian aid, trade, immigration and diplomatic policy, and international development and the alleviation of global poverty. A second award will be granted for doctoral or Master's research into a problem that is common to First Nations or Inuit communities in Canada and a developing region of the world.

PURPOSE:
To explore international development from a Canadian point of view.

ELIGIBILITY:
Applicants must:
(1) hold Canadian citizenship (or permanent residency status in Canada) and citizenship of a developing country;
(2) be registered at a Canadian university;
(3) be conducting the proposed research for a Master's or doctoral dissertation and have completed course work and;
(4) passed comprehensive examinations by the time of the award tenure; Master's-level students will be eligible to apply for the award pertaining to research into the First Nations or Inuit communities and a developing country.

FINANCIAL DATA:
Total amount of support: Up to $20,000 (CAN).

NUMBER OF APPLICANTS MOST RECENT YEAR:
Varies.

NUMBER OF AWARDS: 2 to 3 per year.

APPLICATION INFORMATION:
Duration: Up to 12 months.
Deadline: April 1.

ADDRESS INQUIRIES TO:
Fellowships and Awards
(See address above.)

THE INTERNATIONAL FOUNDATION, INC. [899]

1700 Route 23 North
Suite 300
Wayne, NJ 07470
(973) 406-3970
Fax: (973) 406-3969

E-MAIL ADDRESS:
kgaiser@ccsbcpa.com

WEB SITE ADDRESS:
intlfoundation.org

FOUNDED: 1948

AREAS OF INTEREST:
Agriculture, health, education, social development, the environment and community development.

TYPE:
Development grants; Matching gifts; Project/program grants; Seed money grants; Technical assistance; Training grants.

YEAR PROGRAM STARTED: 1948

PURPOSE:
To help people of the developing world in their endeavors to solve some of their problems; to attain a better standard of living and to obtain a reasonable degree of self-sufficiency.

LEGAL BASIS:
Private foundation.

ELIGIBILITY:
The Foundation funds only projects of U.S.-based, IRS-certified philanthropies.

GEOGRAPHIC RESTRICTIONS:
United States.

FINANCIAL DATA:
Amount of support per award:
Approximately $5,000 to $25,000.
Total amount of support: $800,000 for the year 2010.

NUMBER OF AWARDS: Approximately 100.

APPLICATION INFORMATION:
Applications are to be submitted on the Foundation's web site. Proposals must include a statement from IRS of not-for-profit status, a brief overview of the proposal,

amount of funds requested from The
Foundation, a brief background of
organization applying, a statement of the
problem addressed by project, objectives of
the project, plan of operation/method of
achieving objectives, beneficiaries of the
project, methods of project evaluation and
report, project budget, sources of other
funding applied for or received and date.

All appropriate communications will be
answered.

Duration: One year. Renewal possible upon
receipt of final report on grant.

Deadline: The Board of Trustees begins
considering applications for a given year in
January, but approval may be granted at any
of the quarterly meetings of the Foundation.
Funding is not available until December.

PUBLICATIONS:
Brochure, includes application guidelines.

IRS IDENTIFICATION NUMBER: 13-1962255

OFFICERS:
Frank H. Madden, President
David S. Bate, Vice President
John D. Carrico, Secretary and Treasurer
Dr. Edward A. Holmes, Grants Chairman

BOARD OF TRUSTEES:
David S. Bate
John D. Carrico
Gary Dicovitsky
Dr. Edward A. Holmes
Frank H. Madden
Dr. William McCormick
Douglas Walker

ADDRESS INQUIRIES TO:
Dr. Edward A. Holmes, Grants Chairman
(See address above.)

IRISH AMERICAN CULTURAL INSTITUTE [900]
One Lackawanna Place
Morristown, NJ 07960
(973) 605-1991
Fax: (973) 605-8875

E-MAIL ADDRESS:
info@iaci-usa.org

WEB SITE ADDRESS:
www.iaci-usa.org

FOUNDED: 1962

AREAS OF INTEREST:
Ireland and Irish affairs.

NAME(S) OF PROGRAMS:
● **IACI/NUI-G**

TYPE:
Fellowships; Research grants; Research
contracts.

YEAR PROGRAM STARTED: 1992

PURPOSE:
To stimulate, develop and disseminate
information pertinent to the Irish culture.

LEGAL BASIS:
Public foundation under IRS Code 501(c)(3).

ELIGIBILITY:
Projects from all disciplines, regardless of
historic period or geographic focus, can be
considered for these grants. All projects must
deal with significant research matters, relate
to any aspect of Irish studies and be directed
by competent scholars.

The Fellowship is tenable at NUI-G to
scholars normally residents in the U.S. who
wish to spend a semester (not less than four
months) at NUI-G, and whose work relates
to any aspect of Irish studies.

FINANCIAL DATA:
Amount of support per award: Fellowship
stipend $4,000; Research fund support varies
depending on the project.

NUMBER OF APPLICANTS MOST RECENT YEAR:
Varies.

NUMBER OF AWARDS: Fellowship: 1.

APPLICATION INFORMATION:
Application requirements and guidelines are
available online.

Duration: Varies.

Deadline: December 31. Fellowship
announced in February.

OFFICERS:
Peter Halas, Chairman
Brian Stack, Vice Chairman
Michael Farrell, Treasurer
Edward F. Ginty, Secretary

THE JAPAN FOUNDATION [901]
152 West 57th Street
17th Floor
New York, NY 10019
(212) 489-0299
Fax: (212) 489-0409

E-MAIL ADDRESS:
info@jfny.org

WEB SITE ADDRESS:
www.jfny.org

FOUNDED: 1972

AREAS OF INTEREST:
Cultural exchange and Japanese studies.

NAME(S) OF PROGRAMS:
● **Doctoral Fellowship**
● **Institutional Project Support Program for Japanese Studies**
● **JFNY Grant for Japanese Studies**
● **JFNY Grant Program - Arts and Culture**
● **Performing Arts Japan Program**
● **Research Fellowship**
● **Short-Term Research Fellowship**
● **Support Program for Film and TV Production on Japan**
● **Support Program for Translation and Publication on Japan**

TYPE:
Conferences/seminars; Development grants;
Fellowships; Grants-in-aid; Product
donations; Professorships; Project/program
grants; Research grants; Training grants;
Travel grants.

YEAR PROGRAM STARTED: 1973

PURPOSE:
To conduct international cultural exchange; to
assist Japanese studies programs in the U.S.

LEGAL BASIS:
Independent administrative institution.

FINANCIAL DATA:
For Fellowships, the Foundation will provide
a round-trip, economy class airfare to and
from Japan. The stipend is determined in
accordance with the grantee's professional
status. A dependent allowance will be
provided in some cases to Fellows whose
dependents (spouse and children) reside in
Japan continuously for more than six months.

Amount of support per award: Varies
according to program.

APPLICATION INFORMATION:
Program announcements and application
forms are available at the web site.
Applications from the Western states of
Alaska, Arizona, California, Colorado,
Hawaii, Idaho, Montana, Nevada, New
Mexico, Oregon, Utah, Washington and
Wyoming should be sent to the Japan
Foundation, Los Angeles Office, 333 South
Grand Avenue, Suite 2250, Los Angeles, CA
90071, Tel: (213) 621-2267, Fax: (213)
621-2590. Applications from all other states
should be sent directly to the Japan
Foundation New York Office at the address
above.

Duration: Varies.

Deadline: Varies.

PUBLICATIONS:
Annual report.

IRS IDENTIFICATION NUMBER: 13-2974222

STAFF:
Kazuaki Kubo, Director General
Tatsuaki Kobayashi, Deputy Director General
Mitsuhiro Inada, Program Director, Japanese Studies
Yukihiro Ohira, Program Director, Arts and Culture
Tomomi Tanikawa, Program Associate, Japanese Studies
Kanako Shirasaki, Program Associate, Arts and Culture

ADDRESS INQUIRIES TO:
See e-mail address above.

JAPAN-U.S. FRIENDSHIP COMMISSION [902]
1201 15th Street, N.W.
Suite 330
Washington, DC 20005
(202) 653-9800
Fax: (202) 653-9802

E-MAIL ADDRESS:
jusfc@jusfc.gov

WEB SITE ADDRESS:
www.jusfc.gov

FOUNDED: 1976

AREAS OF INTEREST:
Cultural and educational activities between
Japan and the U.S., including language and
area studies, economic relations, media and
public education.

TYPE:
Project/program grants. Programs of
institutional support. Grants for projects of
research, training and exchange with Japan.

YEAR PROGRAM STARTED: 1977

PURPOSE:
To enhance reciprocal people-to-people
understanding and friendship between the
U.S. and Japan.

LEGAL BASIS:
Independent agency of the U.S. government.

ELIGIBILITY:
Grants are offered to cultural and educational
institutions in the U.S. and Japan.

GEOGRAPHIC RESTRICTIONS:
United States and Japan.

FINANCIAL DATA:
U.S. government trust fund of $43,000,000.

Amount of support per award: Varies.

Total amount of support: Varies.

COOPERATIVE FUNDING PROGRAMS: NEA.

NUMBER OF APPLICANTS MOST RECENT YEAR:
Approximately 100.

NUMBER OF AWARDS: Approximately 30
annually.

APPLICATION INFORMATION:
Application forms are available upon request.
Duration: One year.
Deadline: August 1. Notification in October.

PUBLICATIONS:
Biennial report; program
information/guidelines; application form.

OFFICERS:
Thierry Porte, Chairman
Michael Green, Vice Chairman
Willard G. Clark
Robert Feldman
Ellen Hammond
Velina Hasu Houston
Rocco Landsman
James Leach
Rep. James McDermott
Hon. Lisa Murkowski
Rep. Thomas Petri
Dr. Susan Pharr
Amelia Porges
Sen. John D. Rockefeller, IV

ADDRESS INQUIRIES TO:
Eric J. Gangloff, Executive Director
(See address above.)

*SPECIAL STIPULATIONS:
Institution grants only.

THE MONGOLIA SOCIETY, INC. [903]

Indiana University
322 Goodbody Hall
1011 East Third Street
Bloomington, IN 47405-7005
(812) 855-4078
Fax: (812) 855-4078

E-MAIL ADDRESS:
monsoc@indiana.edu

WEB SITE ADDRESS:
www.mongoliasociety.org

FOUNDED: 1961

AREAS OF INTEREST:
Promoting and furthering the study of
Mongolia and its history, language and
culture.

NAME(S) OF PROGRAMS:
● **Dr. Gombojab Hangin Memorial
Scholarship**

TYPE:
Internships; Scholarships; Work-study
programs. Given to a student of Mongolian
heritage to pursue studies in the U.S.

YEAR PROGRAM STARTED: 1965

PURPOSE:
To advance the knowledge of and promote an
interest in all aspects of historical and
contemporary Mongolia.

LEGAL BASIS:
Private, nonprofit and nonpolitical
organization.

ELIGIBILITY:
An applicant must be of Mongolian heritage
(defined as an individual of Mongolian ethnic
origins who has permanent residency in
Mongolia, the People's Republic of China or

the former Soviet Union) to pursue studies in
the U.S. Must state you are Mongolian on
your passport or I.D. papers.

The award does not include transportation
from the recipient's country to the U.S., nor
board and lodging at the university where the
recipient will study. The recipient will
receive the scholarship monies in one lump
sum after enrollment in the scholarship
holder's institution in the U.S.

FINANCIAL DATA:
Amount of support per award: $1,000 to
$1,500.

NUMBER OF APPLICANTS MOST RECENT YEAR:
19.

NUMBER OF AWARDS: 1.

APPLICATION INFORMATION:
Application forms are available from the
Hangin Scholarship Committee at the address
above. The award will be made through
competitive application.

Each applicant must individually request the
application in English and return the
application written in English, accompanied
with a photocopy of his or her I.D. card (and
passport), complete with photograph and a
curriculum vitae. If applicant has letters of
recommendation, these should be enclosed
with his or her application.
Duration: Support is generally for one
academic year.
Deadline: January 1. Announcement May 1.

OFFICERS:
Dr. Alicia J. Campi, President
Prof. Christopher Atwood, Vice President and
Treasurer
Susan K. Drost, Executive Director

ADDRESS INQUIRIES TO:
Hangin Scholarship Committee
(See address above.)

*SPECIAL STIPULATIONS:
Upon conclusion of the award year, the
recipient must write a report of his or her
activities which resulted from the scholarship.

A.J. MUSTE MEMORIAL INSTITUTE

339 Lafayette Street
New York, NY 10012
(212) 533-4335
Fax: (212) 228-6193

E-MAIL ADDRESS:
info@ajmuste.org

WEB SITE ADDRESS:
www.ajmuste.org

TYPE:
Grants-in-aid. The Institute's regular grant
fund annually funds international, national
and local projects in the U.S. and around the
world. It gives priority to those with small
budgets and little chance of funding from
more traditional sources. The Institute does
not provide academic scholarships.

See entry 1600 for full listing.

THE NATIONAL COUNCIL FOR EURASIAN AND EAST EUROPEAN RESEARCH [904]

University of Washington
Box 353650
Seattle, WA 98195
(206) 829-2445
Fax: (206) 221-0885

E-MAIL ADDRESS:
info@nceeer.org

WEB SITE ADDRESS:
www.nceeer.org

FOUNDED: 1978

AREAS OF INTEREST:
The program is limited to research designed
to contribute to knowledge of current
developments and analysis of their
significance in Eastern Europe and the
successor states of the former Soviet Union.

TYPE:
Research grants; Research contracts.
Institutional grants and research contracts and
policy research scholarships and related
activities, such as meetings and conferences,
research-specific training, contact among
scholars and specialists in government and
private enterprise, development of databanks
and other reference aids and dissemination of
research data, methodology and findings,
both in scholarly forms and through public
media.

YEAR PROGRAM STARTED: 1978

PURPOSE:
To encourage and sustain high-quality
research on Eastern Europe, the former
Soviet Union and its successor states, in the
social sciences (including geography,
demography and environmental studies) and
history.

LEGAL BASIS:
Incorporated, nonprofit, autonomous
academic body.

ELIGIBILITY:
Limited to scholars at the postdoctoral level
for academic participants and to an
equivalent degree of maturity and
professional employment for those from other
fields. Applicant must be a U.S. citizen.
Applications must be submitted to the
Council by U.S. nonprofit institutions in the
form of grant or contract proposals.

GEOGRAPHIC RESTRICTIONS:
United States.

FINANCIAL DATA:
Amount of support per award: Varies;
normally not more than $70,000 for any
individual project.

Total amount of support: Approximately
$1,500,000 for the year 2010.

Matching fund requirements: Cost sharing at
a minimum of 20% from non-federal funds is
mandatory.

COOPERATIVE FUNDING PROGRAMS: NEH
Collaborative Research Fellowship; Carnegie
Research Fellowship Program.

APPLICATION INFORMATION:
Application guidelines, compliance with
which is required, should be obtained from
the Council, at the address above. Required
documentation includes:
(1) identification form;
(2) one-page summary;
(3) detailed description of project;
(4) curriculum vitae and bibliographies for
principal personnel;
(5) description of proposed written or other
products and dissemination methods;
(6) budget and;
(7) letters of recommendation.
Duration: Varies.
Deadline: Spring of each year.

PUBLICATIONS:
  Guidelines.

OFFICERS:
  Bob Huber, President
  Dana Ponte, Senior Program Officer

BOARD OF DIRECTORS:
  Maria Carlson, Chairperson
  Ted Hopf, Vice Chairperson
  Valerie Bunce
  Ted Gerber
  Bruce Grant
  Bob Huber
  Nancy Kollmann
  Martha Lampland
  Susan Linz
  Mieke Meurs
  Douglas Northrup
  Joanna Regulska
  Edward Schatz
  Lewis Siegelbaum

ADDRESS INQUIRIES TO:
  Bob Huber, President
  (See address above.)

NUCLEAR AGE PEACE FOUNDATION [905]

PMB 121
1187 Coast Village Road, Suite 1
Santa Barbara, CA 93108
(805) 965-3443
Fax: (805) 568-0466

E-MAIL ADDRESS:
  wagingpeace@napf.org

WEB SITE ADDRESS:
  www.wagingpeace.org

FOUNDED: 1982

AREAS OF INTEREST:
  Achieving a nuclear weapon-free world,
  international law, international relations,
  liberty, justice, human dignity, human rights,
  nonviolence, responsible use of technology,
  peace education, and youth empowerment.

NAME(S) OF PROGRAMS:
  ● **Barbara Mandigo Kelly Peace Poetry
    Awards**

TYPE:
  Awards/prizes; Internships. An annual series
  of awards to encourage poets to explore and
  illuminate positive visions of peace and the
  human spirit.

PURPOSE:
  To play an important role in making the
  twenty-first century a time of peace and
  justice, and a time in which the rights of all
  individuals to peace, security and a healthy
  environment will be realized.

FINANCIAL DATA:
  Amount of support per award: Adults:
  $1,000; Youth (13-18): $200; Youth (12 and
  under): $200.
  Total amount of support: $1,400.

APPLICATION INFORMATION:
  Deadline: Postmarked by July 1.

ADDRESS INQUIRIES TO:
  Carol Warner, Awards Coordinator
  (See address above.)

ORGANIZATION OF AMERICAN STATES [906]

1889 F Street, N.W.
Sixth Floor
Washington, DC 20006
(202) 458-6166
Fax: (202) 458-3897

E-MAIL ADDRESS:
  scholarships@oas.org

WEB SITE ADDRESS:
  www.educoas.org

FOUNDED: 1890

AREAS OF INTEREST:
  To promote the economic, social, scientific
  and cultural development of the Member
  States in order to achieve a stronger bond
  and better understanding among the peoples
  of the Americas through the advanced
  training of its citizens in the priority areas
  requested by the countries.

NAME(S) OF PROGRAMS:
  ● **Academic Studies**
  ● **Professional Development**

TYPE:
  Fellowships; Scholarships; Technical
  assistance. Awarded for graduate academic
  studies and/or research, and last two years of
  undergraduate studies for students in the
  English-speaking Caribbean, for training in
  areas contributing to the economic, social,
  technical and cultural development of OAS
  member countries.

YEAR PROGRAM STARTED: 1958

PURPOSE:
  Program of Scholarships and Training: to
  assist the member states with their domestic
  efforts in pursuit of integral development
  goals by supporting human resource
  development in the priority areas established
  by the member countries.

ELIGIBILITY:
  Candidates must be citizens or permanent
  residents of an OAS member country, with a
  university degree in the case of academic
  studies, or who have demonstrated ability to
  pursue advanced training in the field chosen
  for professional development courses.
  Scholarships are for graduate or
  undergraduate studies, research, or
  professional training in any field, with the
  exception of the medical sciences and related
  areas and introductory language studies.
  Candidates must know the language of the
  study country. Studies must be undertaken at
  an institution in a member country of the
  OAS, with the exception of the country of
  which the candidate is a citizen or permanent
  resident.

  Graduate scholarships are offered for study
  towards a Master's or Doctorate degree. They
  may also be used for research, if required by
  a specific academic program. Scholarships
  are awarded for an initial period of one
  academic year and may be extended
  subsequently for up to one additional year.
  Under the self-placed modality, candidates
  apply directly for admission to the
  universities or educational institutions of their
  choice and apply separately to the OAS for
  scholarships to assist in financing those
  studies. In the OAS-placed modality,
  candidates apply to the OAS only for a
  scholarship and the OAS seeks admission for
  those candidates selected for scholarships to
  recognized and reputable universities or
  educational institutions determined by the
  OAS, taking into consideration the preferred
  countries and the intended fields and levels
  of study stated by the candidates in their
  applications to the fullest extent practicable.
  Undergraduate scholarships are available only
  to citizens of the English-speaking Caribbean
  member countries for the last two years of
  study for an undergraduate degree.

A fellowship may include, depending upon
the circumstances of each fellow: a
round-trip ticket, tuition fees, study materials,
health insurance, and partial subsistence
allowance (which varies from country to
country). No fellowships will be awarded
retroactively, and no benefits will be provided
to the family of the fellowship holder.

GEOGRAPHIC RESTRICTIONS:
  In any of the active member countries of the
  Organization of American States (Antigua
  and Barbuda, Argentina, Bahamas, Barbados,
  Belize, Bolivia, Brazil, Canada, Chile,
  Colombia, Costa Rica, Dominica, Dominican
  Republic, Ecuador, El Salvador, Grenada,
  Guatemala, Guyana, Haiti, Jamaica, Mexico,
  Nicaragua, Panama, Paraguay, Peru, Saint
  Kitts and Nevis, Saint Lucia, Saint Vincent
  and the Grenadines, Suriname, Trinidad and
  Tobago, United States, Uruguay and
  Venezuela) with the exception of the country
  of which the candidate is a citizen or
  permanent resident.

FINANCIAL DATA:
  Amount of support per award: Not to exceed
  U.S. $30,000.
  Matching fund requirements: Students are
  responsible for covering a portion of their
  subsistence costs.

NUMBER OF APPLICANTS MOST RECENT YEAR:
  5,000.

NUMBER OF AWARDS: 215 for the year 2009-10.

APPLICATION INFORMATION:
  Application materials are available at the web
  site. Except for applicants in the U.S.,
  applications must be presented to the
  National Liaison Offices (ONEs) of the
  applicant's country of origin or permanent
  residence. The ONE is the official channel
  identified by each government for submission
  of applications for OAS scholarships. U.S.
  citizens can send applications directly to the
  Organization's mailing address.
  Duration: Fellowships are tenable for not
  less than one year nor more than two years.
  Deadline: Deadline for presentation of
  applications to the National Liaison Office
  (ONE) differs from country to country and
  should therefore be confirmed with the ONE
  in the applicant's country of origin or
  permanent residence.

OFFICERS:
  Marie Levens, Director

ADDRESS INQUIRIES TO:
  Department of Human Development,
  Education and Culture
  (See address above.)

*SPECIAL STIPULATIONS:
  For countries other than the U.S., the
  fellowship form must be presented to the
  General Secretariat of the OAS in
  Washington, DC, through the official
  channels established by each government.

HERBERT SCOVILLE, JR., PEACE FELLOWSHIP PROGRAM [907]

322 Fourth Street, N.E.
Washington, DC 20002
(202) 446-1565

E-MAIL ADDRESS:
  info@scoville.org

WEB SITE ADDRESS:
www.scoville.org

FOUNDED: 1987

AREAS OF INTEREST:
Arms control research and/or action activities for disarmament, international security, nuclear and conventional arms control and peace organizations.

TYPE:
Fellowships. Grants to college graduates to work in Washington, DC in the program's areas of interest.

YEAR PROGRAM STARTED: 1987

PURPOSE:
To provide an opportunity for college graduates to gain practical knowledge and experience by contributing to the efforts of nonprofit, public-interest organizations working on peace and security issues.

LEGAL BASIS:
Nonprofit program.

ELIGIBILITY:
Prospective Fellows are expected to demonstrate excellent academic accomplishments and a strong interest in issues of peace and security. Graduate study, a college major, course work, or substantial independent reading that reflects the substantive focus of the Fellowship is also a plus. Prior experience with public-interest activism or advocacy is highly desirable. It is preferred, but not required, that such activities be focused on peace and security issues.

Candidates are required to have completed a Baccalaureate degree by the time the Fellowship commences. Preference is given to U.S. citizens, although a Fellowship to a foreign national residing in the U.S. is awarded periodically based on availability of funding. The Scoville Fellowship is not intended for students or scholars interested in pursuing independent research in Washington, DC.

Preference will be given to individuals who have not had substantial prior public-interest or government experience in the Washington, DC area.

FINANCIAL DATA:
Amount of support per award: $2,400 per month, plus $500 in travel expenses to the Washington, DC area and health insurance.
Total amount of support: Varies.

NUMBER OF APPLICANTS MOST RECENT YEAR:
100 to 120.

NUMBER OF AWARDS: 6 to 8 per year.

APPLICATION INFORMATION:
There is no application form. Complete applications must contain the following items:
(1) coversheet that includes the candidate's name, semester for which they are applying, phone number and e-mail address;
(2) signed letter from the candidate indicating his or her desire to apply and providing addresses and telephone numbers of the two people who will be writing the candidate's reference letters;
(3) a full curriculum vitae;
(4) a personal essay discussing the candidate's qualifications, interests, Fellowship objectives and career goals;
(5) a policy/opinion essay, no more than 1,000 words and titled, relevant to the field of peace and security taking a position on a contemporary, contentious issue, such as Ballistic Missile Defense, Comprehensive Test Ban, the role of U.S. troops as part of United Nations Peacekeeping operations, significance of environmental factors as sources of conflict, etc.;
(6) official transcripts detailing the candidate's entire college academic record including undergraduate, graduate and foreign study and;
(7) two letters of reference.

All application materials must be submitted by e-mail to apply@scoville.org.
Duration: Six to nine months.
Deadline: Spring Fellowship: October 1; Fall Fellowship: January 13.

PUBLICATIONS:
Application guidelines; organization description.

ADDRESS INQUIRIES TO:
Paul Revsine, Program Director
(See address above.)

SOCIAL SCIENCE RESEARCH COUNCIL [908]
One Pierrepont Plaza
15th Floor
Brooklyn, NY 11201
(212) 377-2700
Fax: (212) 377-2727

E-MAIL ADDRESS:
japan@ssrc.org

WEB SITE ADDRESS:
www.ssrc.org/fellowships/jsps-fellowship

FOUNDED: 1923

AREAS OF INTEREST:
Social sciences and humanities.

NAME(S) OF PROGRAMS:
- **SSRC/JSPS Long-Term Fellowship**
- **SSRC/JSPS Short-Term Fellowship**

TYPE:
Fellowships; Research grants. The Japan Society for the Promotion of Science (JSPS) Postdoctoral Fellowship for Foreign Researchers provides promising and highly qualified recent Ph.Ds. and ABDs with funding to conduct research in Japan. JSPS guidelines target the applicant who wishes to conduct cooperative research under the leadership of a host researcher, thereby advancing the Fellow's own research and at the same time stimulating Japanese academic circles through close collaboration with young Japanese researchers.

YEAR PROGRAM STARTED: 1967

PURPOSE:
To stimulate Japanese academic circles through close collaboration with young foreign researchers.

LEGAL BASIS:
Not-for-profit organization.

ELIGIBILITY:
Applicants must be U.S. citizens or permanent residents at the time of application. Citizens of other countries are eligible for short-term fellowships if they have completed a Master's or Ph.D. course at an institution of higher education in the U.S. and, upon completing the course, have for at least three continuous years conducted high-level research at a university in the U.S. Japanese citizens are not eligible for a long-term fellowship. Japanese citizens who are permanent residents are eligible to apply for the short-term fellowship.

Applicants for long-term fellowships must submit a copy of a Ph.D. diploma from a university outside Japan dated no more than six years prior to April 1, 2012.

Applicants for short-term fellowships must submit a copy of a Ph.D. diploma from a university outside Japan dated no more than six years prior to April 1, 2012 or a letter from their institution stating that the applicant is a Ph.D. candidate within two years of receiving a Ph.D.

Scholars who have previously received funding from JSPS for 12 months or longer are not eligible to apply for JSPS fellowships.

FINANCIAL DATA:
Grants are to be used for maintenance, travel and research expenses.
Amount of support per award: Varies based on length of research term and doctoral status.
Total amount of support: Varies.

NUMBER OF APPLICANTS MOST RECENT YEAR:
Long-Term and Short-Term Fellowships: 47.

NUMBER OF AWARDS: Long-Term and Short-Term Fellowships: Up to 20 (10 in each category).

APPLICATION INFORMATION:
Duration: Long-Term Fellowships: 12 to 24 months; Short-Term Fellowships: One to 12 months.
Deadline: December 1, annually.

PUBLICATIONS:
Annual report; *Items*, newsletter; *Fellowships and Grants for Training and Research*, brochure.

STAFF:
Nicole Restrick, Japan Program Coordinator
Fernando Rojas, Fellowship Assistant

ADDRESS INQUIRIES TO:
Japan Program
Social Science Research Council
(See address above.)

SOCIAL SCIENCE RESEARCH COUNCIL [909]
One Pierrepont Plaza
15th Floor
Brooklyn, NY 11201
(212) 377-2700
Fax: (212) 377-2727

E-MAIL ADDRESS:
idrf@ssrc.org

WEB SITE ADDRESS:
www.ssrc.org/programs/idrf

FOUNDED: 1923

AREAS OF INTEREST:
Fellowships in social sciences and humanities.

NAME(S) OF PROGRAMS:
- **International Dissertation Research Fellowship Program (IDRF)**

TYPE:
Awards/prizes; Fellowships. Support to graduate students in the humanities and social sciences who are enrolled in doctoral programs in the U.S. and conducting dissertation research outside of the U.S.

YEAR PROGRAM STARTED: 1997

PURPOSE:
To support the advancement of social science and humanistic research.

LEGAL BASIS:
Not-for-profit corporation.

ELIGIBILITY:
Applicants must be enrolled in a full-time doctoral program at a U.S. university.

FINANCIAL DATA:
Amount of support per award: Average $18,750.

NUMBER OF APPLICANTS MOST RECENT YEAR:
More than 1,100.

NUMBER OF AWARDS: 75.

APPLICATION INFORMATION:
Duration: Nine to 12 months.
Deadline: November 3, annually.

ADDRESS INQUIRIES TO:
See e-mail address above.

SOCIAL SCIENCE RESEARCH COUNCIL [910]

One Pierrepont Plaza
15th Floor
Brooklyn, NY 11201
(212) 377-2700
Fax: (212) 377-2727

E-MAIL ADDRESS:
abe@ssrc.org

WEB SITE ADDRESS:
www.ssrc.org/fellowships/abe-fellowship

FOUNDED: 1923

AREAS OF INTEREST:
Issues of global concern.

NAME(S) OF PROGRAMS:
• **Abe Fellowship Program**

TYPE:
Fellowships; Research grants. The program encourages international multidisciplinary research on topics of pressing global concern and fosters the development of a new generation of researchers interested in policy-relevant topics of long-range importance and willing to become key members of a bilateral and global research network built around such topics.

The Abe Fellowship Program administers an annual fellowship competition that provides scholars and nonacademic research professionals in the social sciences and related disciplines with support for research projects addressing one or more of three themes: (1) traditional and nontraditional approaches to security and diplomacy; (2) global and regional economic issues and; (3) the role of civil society.

YEAR PROGRAM STARTED: 1991

PURPOSE:
To encourage international multidisciplinary research on topics of pressing global concern.

ELIGIBILITY:
Competition is open to citizens of the U.S. and Japan as well as to nationals of other countries who can demonstrate strong and serious long-term affiliations with research communities in Japan or the U.S. Applicants must hold the Ph.D. or the terminal degree in their field, or have attained an equivalent level of professional experience. Applications from researchers in professions other than academia are encouraged. Previous language training is not a prerequisite for this

Fellowship. However, if the research project requires language ability, the applicant should provide evidence of adequate proficiency to complete the project. Projects proposing to address key policy issues or seeking to develop a concrete policy proposal must reflect nonpartisan positions.

GEOGRAPHIC RESTRICTIONS:
Japan and United States.

FINANCIAL DATA:
Awards may be used for maintenance, travel and research expenses.
Amount of support per award: Varies.
Total amount of support: Varies.

NUMBER OF AWARDS: 12 to 15.

APPLICATION INFORMATION:
Applications must be submitted online at applications.ssrc.org.
Duration: Three to 12 months of full-time support over a 24-month period. Fellowship tenure must begin between April 1 and December 31 of a given year.
Deadline: Applications are available by early summer. Receipt of applications: September 1.

STAFF:
Nicole Restrick, Assistant Director
Fernando Rojas, Fellowships Assistant

ADDRESS INQUIRIES TO:
Abe Fellowship Program
Social Science Research Council
(See address above.)

SOCIETY FOR FRENCH HISTORICAL STUDIES

551-101 Milton Court
Long Beach, CA 90803-6352
(562) 494-6764

E-MAIL ADDRESS:
lclark2@csulb.edu

WEB SITE ADDRESS:
www.societyforfrenchhistoricalstudies.net

TYPE:
Awards/prizes. The Chinard Prize is for a recent book on historical relations between France and the Americas.

Farrar Award is for dissertation research.

The Koren Prize is for a recent article written on French history.

The Pinkney Prize is for a recent book written on French history.

Research Travel Award is for recent recipients of doctorates (awarded jointly with Western Society for French History).

Wolf Travel Fellowship is for research travel pertaining to a dissertation.

See entry 668 for full listing.

SWEDISH WOMEN'S EDUCATIONAL ASSOCIATION INC. [911]

552 South El Camino Real
Encinitas, CA 92024
(760) 942-1100

E-MAIL ADDRESS:
office@swea.org

WEB SITE ADDRESS:
www.swea.org

AREAS OF INTEREST:
Sweden's culture, history and language.

NAME(S) OF PROGRAMS:
• **SWEA Scholarship in Literature, Language and Area Studies**

TYPE:
Scholarships. The scholarship funds may be used to study in Sweden. Previous trips to Sweden, or lack thereof, are of no consideration. Willingness to travel to Sweden for dissertation work is a plus, but not a requirement.

PURPOSE:
To promote and preserve the Swedish language, cultures and traditions.

ELIGIBILITY:
The applicant must:
(1) be a well-merited doctoral candidate, studying at a non-Swedish university and reside permanently outside of Sweden;
(2) have filed a dissertation topic and;
(3) have a good knowledge of the Swedish language (written and spoken).

FINANCIAL DATA:
Amount of support per award: $10,000.
Total amount of support: $10,000.

NUMBER OF AWARDS: 1.

APPLICATION INFORMATION:
The applicant must submit an application, curriculum vitae, a detailed description of the dissertation project, a statement explaining how the scholarship money will be used, a presentation of himself or herself in Swedish, and three letters of recommendation. Applications are available online.
Duration: One year. Recipients may reapply.
Deadline: November 1.

ADDRESS INQUIRIES TO:
Administrator
(See address above.)

*SPECIAL STIPULATIONS:
There is no discrimination on the basis of gender, race, color, age, religion or nationality.

THE TINKER FOUNDATION INC. [912]

55 East 59th Street
New York, NY 10022
(212) 421-6858
Fax: (212) 223-3326

E-MAIL ADDRESS:
tinker@tinker.org

WEB SITE ADDRESS:
foundationcenter.org/grantmaker/tinker

FOUNDED: 1959

AREAS OF INTEREST:
The Spanish- and Portuguese-speaking countries of the Western Hemisphere for projects addressing (1) Democratic Governance with Growth and Security, (2) Sustainable Resource Management, (3) Education, (4) U.S. Policy toward Latin America, and (5) Antarctica.

NAME(S) OF PROGRAMS:
• **Tinker Field Research Grants**

TYPE:
Travel grants. Travel grants are to be used to support brief periods of individual research in Latin America by graduate students. There are also Institutional Grants for charitable organizations.

YEAR PROGRAM STARTED: 1979

PURPOSE:
To enable emerging scholars to work in the Spanish- and Portuguese-speaking countries of Latin America, thus enabling them to acquire a comprehensive knowledge of language, cultures and terrain, and to gather research data and develop contacts with scholars and institutions in their respective fields.

Institutional Grants: to support research and policy-building by civil society organizations within the five focus areas described in the "Areas of Interest" field.

LEGAL BASIS:
Private foundation.

ELIGIBILITY:
Open to all recognized Centers or Institutes of Ibero-American or Latin American Studies with graduate doctoral programs at accredited U.S. universities. Field Research Grants, awarded to individuals by the appropriate university institutes/centers, are to reflect the Foundation's broad areas of interest.

The Foundation's selection criteria include the quality of the overall graduate program in Ibero-American studies, the immediate benefits to the Ibero-American studies program that will result from the availability of Field Research Grants at the university and the level of general university support for Ibero-American studies as demonstrated by past commitments and future projects.

Institutional Grants: Open to any 501(c)(3) (or equivalent foreign) organization doing work in Latin America.

GEOGRAPHIC RESTRICTIONS:
Latin America. Puerto Rico is not included.

FINANCIAL DATA:
Amount of support per award: $10,000 and $15,000. Institutional Grants: $50,000 to $150,000 up to three years.
Total amount of support: Up to $75,000 in new grants annually.
Matching fund requirements: Field Research Grant applicants are required to match the award by a minimum of $10,000 or $15,000.

COOPERATIVE FUNDING PROGRAMS: Cornell University; New York University; University of California, Davis; University of Connecticut; University of North Carolina, Chapel Hill.

NUMBER OF APPLICANTS MOST RECENT YEAR:
8.

NUMBER OF AWARDS: Up to 6 new annually.

APPLICATION INFORMATION:
Duration: Maximum of three years.
Deadline: March 1 and September 15 of each year. Announcement by January 1 of the following year.

PUBLICATIONS:
Annual report; application guidelines.

STAFF:
Margaret J. Cushing, Senior Program Officer
Kirsten Cowal, Program Officer
Jessica Tomb, Director of Administration and Finance
Karen Nassi, Grants and Technology Associate

DIRECTORS AND OFFICERS:
Renate Rennie, Chairman and President
Kathleen Waldron, Treasurer
Richard de J. Osborne, Secretary
John H. Coatsworth
Sally Grooms Cowal

Arturo C. Porzecanski
Luis Rubio
Susan Segal
Alan Stoga

ADDRESS INQUIRIES TO:
Renate Rennie, Chairman and President
(See address above.)

U.S. DEPARTMENT OF EDUCATION
International and Foreign Language Education (IFLE)
1990 K Street, N.W., Suite 6000
Washington, DC 20006-8521
(202) 502-7631
(202) 502-7700
Fax: (202) 502-7860

E-MAIL ADDRESS:
OPE_NRC-FLAS@ed.gov

WEB SITE ADDRESS:
www.ed.gov/programs/iegpsflasf/index.html

TYPE:
Fellowships. The Foreign Language and Area Studies program provides allocations of academic year and summer fellowships to institutions of higher education or consortia of institutions of higher education to assist meritorious undergraduate students and graduate students undergoing training in modern foreign languages and related international studies.

See entry 701 for full listing.

U.S. DEPARTMENT OF EDUCATION
International and Foreign Language Education (IFLE)
Advanced Training & Research Group
Room 6084, 6th Floor
1990 K Street, N.W.
Washington, DC 20006-8521
(202) 502-7689
(202) 502-7700 (main office)
Fax: (202) 502-7860

E-MAIL ADDRESS:
ddra@ed.gov

WEB SITE ADDRESS:
www.ed.gov/programs/iegpsddrap/index.html

TYPE:
Fellowships. Fellowships to support doctoral dissertation research abroad in modern foreign languages and related area studies. For the purpose of these programs, area studies is defined as a program of comprehensive study of the aspects of a society or societies, including the study of their geography, history, culture, economy, politics, international relations and languages. The program is designed to develop research knowledge and capability in world areas not widely included in American curricula. Awards will not be available for projects focusing on Western Europe.

See entry 702 for full listing.

U.S. INSTITUTE OF PEACE [913]
2301 Constitution Avenue, N.W.
Washington, DC 20037
(202) 429-3842
Fax: (202) 833-1018

E-MAIL ADDRESS:
grants@usip.org

WEB SITE ADDRESS:
www.usip.org/grants-fellowships

FOUNDED: 1984

AREAS OF INTEREST:
International peace and conflict management and related fields. Topic areas of interest include, but are not restricted to, international conflict resolution, diplomacy, negotiation theory, functionalism and "track two" diplomacy, methods of third-party dispute settlement, international law, international organizations and collective security, deterrence and balance of power, arms control, psychological theories about international conflict, the role of nonviolence and nonviolent sanctions, moral and ethical thought about conflict and conflict resolution and theories about relationships among political institutions, human rights and conflict.

NAME(S) OF PROGRAMS:
● **U.S. Institute of Peace Grant Program**

TYPE:
Conferences/seminars; Project/program grants; Research grants; Research contracts. Support for research, education and training and the dissemination of information on international peace and conflict resolution.

In the Annual Grant Competition, grants are provided for any topics that fall within the Institute's broad mandate.

In the Priority Grant Competition, grants are awarded for special priority topics identified in advance by the Institute. Funding is available for projects relating to Afghanistan, Iran, Iraq, Pakistan, Sudan, and communication for peacebuilding.

YEAR PROGRAM STARTED: 1986

PURPOSE:
To carry out basic and applied research on the causes of war and other international conflicts; to develop curricula and texts for high school through postgraduate study and to conduct teacher-training institutes, workshops and seminars; to conduct training, symposia and continuing education programs for practitioners, policymakers, policy implementers and the public; to undertake public information efforts; to increase the store of information on international peace and conflict resolution.

LEGAL BASIS:
Independent, nonpartisan federal institution created and funded by the U.S. Congress.

ELIGIBILITY:
Grant applicants must be nonprofit organizations, official public institutions and individuals, both U.S. and foreign nationals, including the following: institutions of postsecondary, community and secondary education, public and private education, training or research institutions and libraries and public departments and agencies (including state and territorial departments of education and commerce).

Individuals requesting support for degree work are not eligible.

FINANCIAL DATA:
Amount of support per award: The amount of any grant is based on the proposed budget and on negotiations with successful applicants. Average $65,000.
Total amount of support: $5,227,038 for fiscal year 2010.

NUMBER OF APPLICANTS MOST RECENT YEAR:
460 for the year 2010.

NUMBER OF AWARDS: 55 for the year 2010.

APPLICATION INFORMATION:
Duration: One to two years.
Deadline: Annual Grant Competition:
October 1, with notification on March 31.
Priority Grant Competition applications are
accepted on an ongoing basis, or as
advertised on the Institute's web site.

PUBLICATIONS:
Program announcement.

ADDRESS INQUIRIES TO:
The Grant Program
United States Institute of Peace
(See address above.)

*SPECIAL STIPULATIONS:
The Institute does not support funding for
degree work.

U.S. INSTITUTE OF PEACE   [914]
2301 Constitution Avenue, N.W.
Washington, DC 20037
(202) 457-1700
Fax: (202) 429-6063

E-MAIL ADDRESS:
essaycontest@usip.org

WEB SITE ADDRESS:
www.usip.org/npec

FOUNDED: 1984

AREAS OF INTEREST:
International affairs, peace, conflict
resolution, history, writing and research.

NAME(S) OF PROGRAMS:
● **National Peace Essay Contest**

TYPE:
Awards/prizes; Scholarships. Contest for high
school students.

YEAR PROGRAM STARTED: 1987

PURPOSE:
To have students research and write about
issues dealing with international conflict
resolution and peacemaking.

LEGAL BASIS:
Independent, nonpartisan institution created
by the U.S. Congress.

ELIGIBILITY:
Open to students in grades nine-12 from
public and private high schools as well as
home schools throughout the country, U.S.
territories and overseas schools. Those
students in overseas schools must have U.S.
citizenship.

FINANCIAL DATA:
First-place winners receive expense-paid trip
to Washington, DC, for the awards program.
Both state and national high school winners
receive college scholarships.
Amount of support per award: State level:
First place, $1,000; second and third places
receive awards of honorable mention.
National level (including state amounts): First
place, $10,000; second place, $5,000; third
place, $2,500.
Total amount of support: Varies.

NUMBER OF APPLICANTS MOST RECENT YEAR:
Approximately 1,000.

NUMBER OF AWARDS: Varies.

APPLICATION INFORMATION:
Essay Contest kits are available in the spring
from the address above, by e-mail and
online. Applicants should request contest
guidelines by December 15.

Duration: One-time award.
Deadline: February 1. State awards are
announced the following May. National
awards are announced in June.

PUBLICATIONS:
Program guidelines; study guide on contest
topic also available.

ADDRESS INQUIRIES TO:
National Peace Essay Contest
(See address above.)

U.S. INSTITUTE OF PEACE   [915]
Jennings Randolph Fellowship
Programs for International Peace
2301 Constitution Avenue, N.W.
Washington, DC 20037-2900
(202) 429-3853
Fax: (202) 429-6063

E-MAIL ADDRESS:
jrprogram@usip.org

WEB SITE ADDRESS:
www.usip.org

FOUNDED: 1984

AREAS OF INTEREST:
Preventive diplomacy, ethnic and regional
conflicts, peacekeeping and peace operations,
peace settlements, post-conflict reconstruction
and reconciliation, democratization and the
rule of law, cross-cultural negotiations, U.S.
foreign policy in the 21st century and related
fields.

NAME(S) OF PROGRAMS:
● **Jennings Randolph Fellowship
   Programs for International Peace**

TYPE:
Fellowships; Residencies. The U.S. Institute
of Peace is an independent, nonpartisan
institution created by Congress to strengthen
the nation's capacity to promote the peaceful
resolution of international conflict. The
Institute funds projects related to preventive,
ethnic and regional conflicts, peacekeeping
and peace operations, peace settlements,
post-conflict reconstruction and
reconciliation, democratization and the rule
of law, cross-cultural negotiations, U.S.
foreign policy in the 21st century, and related
topics.

Under the Jennings Randolph Fellowship
Programs for International Peace, Senior
Fellowships and Peace Scholar Dissertation
Fellowships are awarded on a competitive
basis.

Senior Fellowships are awarded annually to
scholars and practitioners from a variety of
professions, including college and university
faculty, journalists, diplomats, writers,
educators, military officers, international
negotiators and lawyers. Fellows reside at the
Institute for a period of up to 10 months to
conduct research on their projects, consult
with staff and contribute to the ongoing work
of the Institute.

Peace Scholar program supports doctoral
dissertations that explore the sources and
nature of international conflict, and strategies
to prevent or end conflict and to sustain
peace. Peace Scholars work at their
university or appropriate field research sites.

YEAR PROGRAM STARTED: 1987

PURPOSE:
To enable outstanding scholars, practitioners
and doctoral students to focus their efforts on
critical problems of international peace and
conflict.

Fellows undertake research and education
projects that will increase knowledge and
spread awareness among the public and
policymakers and the public about topics
concerning the sources and nature of
international conflict and the full range of
ways to end or prevent conflict and to sustain
peace.

LEGAL BASIS:
Independent, nonpartisan and educational
institution created by the U.S. Congress.

ELIGIBILITY:
Senior Fellowships: The competition is open
to citizens of all nations. Women and
members of minorities are especially
encouraged to apply. Projects that
demonstrate relevance to current policy
debates will be highly competitive.

Peace Scholar Dissertation Fellowships:
Citizens of all countries are eligible, but must
be enrolled in an accredited college or
university in the U.S. Applicants must have
completed all requirements for the degree
except the dissertation by the commencement
of the award (September 1). Priority will be
given to projects that contribute knowledge
relevant to the formulation of policy on
international peace and conflict issues.

FINANCIAL DATA:
Senior Fellows receive a stipend, an office,
and a part-time research assistant.
Amount of support per award: Senior
Fellows can receive up to $100,000 each for
a 10-month period. Peace Scholar
Dissertation Fellows receive a $20,000 flat
stipend, which may be used to support
writing or field research.
Total amount of support: Varies each year.

NUMBER OF APPLICANTS MOST RECENT YEAR:
Approximately 125 for Senior Fellowships
and 200 for Peace Scholar Awards.

NUMBER OF AWARDS: Approximately 10 Senior
Fellowships and 10 Peace Scholar Awards
per year.

APPLICATION INFORMATION:
For application forms for either the Senior
Fellowships or the Peace Scholar Dissertation
Fellowships, please visit the Institute's web
site (www.usip.org/grants-fellowships) or
contact the Jennings Randolph Fellowship
Programs at the address above.
Duration: Senior Fellowships are 10 months;
Peace Scholar Dissertation Fellowships are
10 months.
Deadline: All application materials for the
Jennings Randolph Senior Fellowships must
arrive by September 8. All application
materials for the Peace Scholar Fellows must
arrive by January 5.

PUBLICATIONS:
Program Description with guidelines;
application form; brochure.

OFFICERS:
Chantal de Jonge Oudraat, Ph.D., Associate
Vice President
Elizabeth Cole, Ph.D., Program Officer

ADDRESS INQUIRIES TO:
Jennings Randolph Fellowship
Programs for International Peace
(See address above.)

*PLEASE NOTE:
Research on conflict within the U.S. may not
be supported under the terms of the
Institute's mandate.

UNITED STATES-JAPAN FOUNDATION [916]

145 East 32nd Street
12th Floor
New York, NY 10016
(212) 481-8753
(212) 481-8757
Fax: (212) 481-8762

E-MAIL ADDRESS:
info@us-jf.org

WEB SITE ADDRESS:
www.us-jf.org

FOUNDED: 1980

AREAS OF INTEREST:
Precollege education and policy studies, communication and public opinion.

TYPE:
Awards/prizes; Fellowships; Project/program grants; Research grants.
In the area of Precollege Education, the Foundation supports the improvement and enhancement of instruction of Japan in the U.S. and on the U.S. in Japan in secondary and elementary schools through programs which foster the creative use of the Internet in education, teacher training, professional development, intensive study tours, and curriculum design. The Foundation also supports the improvement of Japanese language instruction.

In the area of Policy Studies, the Foundation supports joint policy research and has established several nongovernmental channels for ongoing discussions between small groups of prominent experts. Policy projects have been active in such fields as trade and international finance, the environment, multilateral crisis management, and northeast Asian security.

The Foundation will consider communication/public opinion projects that not only raise awareness about Japan in the U.S. and of the U.S. in Japan, but also deal with concrete issues that affect the bilateral relationship. Using creative approaches, these programs should reach broad audiences to stimulate balanced, in-depth and quality media coverage of issues that are central to U.S.-Japan relations.
Projects that link civil society organizations in the two countries are also supported.

YEAR PROGRAM STARTED: 1980

PURPOSE:
To promote stronger ties between Americans and Japanese through education, communication, policy studies and similar activities that foster greater mutual knowledge and understanding regarding each other and issues of common concern.

LEGAL BASIS:
Not-for-profit private foundation.

ELIGIBILITY:
Certain types of programs fall outside the Foundation's current interests. These include undergraduate education, cultural performances or exhibitions, sports exchanges, publication subsidies, scientific research and research conferences. As a rule, grants cannot be made to individuals applying on their own behalf for independent study, research, travel or participation in meetings; grants also cannot be made to for-profit organizations.

Because the Foundation is interested primarily in supporting program activities, it does not award grants as contributions to capital campaigns, endowment funds or deficit operations. In addition, it does not award grants for the construction or maintenance of buildings or other physical premises or for the purchase of equipment.

The Foundation does not administer programs which it supports. Foundation grants may not be used to influence legislation or election to public office.

GEOGRAPHIC RESTRICTIONS:
United States or Japan.

FINANCIAL DATA:
Amount of support per award: $10,000 to $100,000.

Total amount of support: Approximately $2,000,000 annually.

NUMBER OF APPLICANTS MOST RECENT YEAR:
150 to 200.

NUMBER OF AWARDS: Approximately 40.

REPRESENTATIVE AWARDS:
Pre-College Education: $7,500 to Lincoln Memorial University, Harrogate, TN, to enable students from Kanto International Senior High School in Tokyo, Japan to visit primary and secondary schools in Tennessee; Policy Studies: $75,103 to Pacific Forum CSIS, Honolulu, HI, to support the second year of a three-year focused policy dialogue on U.S.-Japan-China relations that will draw attention to the long-term strategic goals of the three countries, and how current policy positions and pronouncements on all three sides impact the realization of those goals; Communications/Public Opinion: $110,000 to Japan Society, New York, NY, to support the 11th year of an intensive fellowship program for American media professionals, allowing them to reside, study and work for six weeks in Japan, focused on research topic of their choice.

APPLICATION INFORMATION:
Applicants should submit a preproposal letter of inquiry, including a brief description of the proposed project and its objectives, any necessary background information on the project and applicant, and a brief budget estimate. If there is interest, the applicant will be invited to prepare a full proposal.
Duration: 12 months. Annual renewal possible.
Deadline: Preproposals are accepted on a rolling basis.

ADDRESS INQUIRIES TO:
David Janes
Director of Foundation Grants
(See address above.)

WORLD SECURITY INSTITUTE [917]

1779 Massachusetts Avenue, N.W.
Suite 615
Washington, DC 20036-2109
(202) 332-0600
Fax: (202) 462-4559

E-MAIL ADDRESS:
internships@cdi.org

WEB SITE ADDRESS:
www.cdi.org
www.worldsecurityinstitute.org

AREAS OF INTEREST:
International law and nuclear disarmament.

TYPE:
Internships. Internships are available within the Center for Defense Information and the WSI Communications/Development Department.

PURPOSE:
To support the development, production and marketing of impartial news and information to a global audience; to provide a unique news and research-based approach to communications, policy development and cooperation focusing on the social, economic, environmental, political and military components of international security and interdependence.

LEGAL BASIS:
Not-for-profit organization.

ELIGIBILITY:
Paid internships are for U.S. nationals or persons that can work legally in the U.S.

FINANCIAL DATA:
Amount of support per award: $1,500 per month.

NUMBER OF APPLICANTS MOST RECENT YEAR:
Approximately 500 for the year 2010.

NUMBER OF AWARDS: 3.

APPLICATION INFORMATION:
A complete application includes:
(1) e-mail address;
(2) resume;
(3) cover letter;
(4) three- to five-page writing sample;
(5) transcripts of all university-level courses and grades;
(6) two letters of recommendation and;
(7) your country of citizenship and, if not the U.S., the availability of appropriate work authorization.

Submit applications to Ron Hinrichs, Internship Coordinator, at the address listed above.
Duration: January to May, June to August or September to December.
Deadline: July 1 for Fall, November 1 for Spring, and April 1 for Summer.

ADDRESS INQUIRIES TO:
internships@cdi.org.

*PLEASE NOTE:
No phone calls.

International studies and research abroad

AFS INTERCULTURAL PROGRAMS/USA   [918]
One Whitehall Street, Second Floor
New York, NY 10004
(800) 876-2377
(212) 479-1158
Fax: (212) 299-9090

E-MAIL ADDRESS:
afsinfo@afs.org

WEB SITE ADDRESS:
www.afsusa.org

FOUNDED: 1947

AREAS OF INTEREST:
International exchange of high school students and secondary teachers who live with host families and attend local schools. Participants go to and from 55 countries, including the former Soviet Union and Eastern Europe.

CONSULTING OR VOLUNTEER SERVICES:
More than 100,000 volunteers around the world.

NAME(S) OF PROGRAMS:
- **AFS Cultural Studies Program**
- **AFS Faces of America Diversity Initiative**
- **AFS Gap Year Program**
- **AFS Language Studies Program**
- **AFS Semester Program**
- **AFS Summer Home Stay Program**
- **AFS Volunteer Development Program**
- **AFS Year Program**

TYPE:
Exchange programs; Scholarships; Visiting scholars. Assistance for summer and school year programs. Exchanges are for high school students and secondary school teachers, community service programs, and ages 18 and above.

YEAR PROGRAM STARTED: 1947

PURPOSE:
To provide cross-cultural learning experiences for young people in another environment.

LEGAL BASIS:
Incorporated under the Not-for-Profit Corporation Laws of the state of New York. Exempt from New York state, New York City and federal taxes.

ELIGIBILITY:
Age, health, academic background, motivation and personality are considered.

FINANCIAL DATA:
Amount of support per award: Dependent upon need.
Total amount of support: Approximately $3,000,000.

NUMBER OF AWARDS: 40% of all participants receive financial aid. AFS deals with 4,400 students each year.

APPLICATION INFORMATION:
Candidate must submit health record, school record, applicant essay, screening group recommendation, interview forms and parental essay.

Duration: Four to six weeks to one year. Nonrenewable.
Deadline: Dependent on program.

PUBLICATIONS:
Annual report; application forms; AFS program catalog; *Partnerships*, newsletter.

IRS IDENTIFICATION NUMBER: 39-1711417

ADDRESS INQUIRIES TO:
Student Services
506 S.W. 6th Avenue, 2nd Floor
Portland, OR 97204

ALBRIGHT INSTITUTE OF ARCHAEOLOGICAL RESEARCH (AIAR)   [919]
Department of Art and Art History
Providence College
Providence, RI 02918
(401) 865-1789
Fax: (401) 865-2410

E-MAIL ADDRESS:
jbranham@providence.edu

WEB SITE ADDRESS:
www.aiar.org

FOUNDED: 1900

AREAS OF INTEREST:
Fellowships are open to those in Near Eastern studies from prehistory through the early Islamic period, including the fields of anthropology, archaeology, art history, Bible, epigraphy, historical geography, history, language, literature, philology and religion, and related disciplines.

NAME(S) OF PROGRAMS:
- **Fellowships at the Albright Institute of Archaeological Research in Jerusalem**

TYPE:
Fellowships; Professorships; Scholarships; Travel grants; Visiting scholars. The ACLS Recent Doctoral Recipients Fellowship is available to awardees and alternates of the Mellon/ACLS Dissertation Completion Fellowships the prior year. For application and more information: www.acls.org.

The Annual Professorship is to postdoctoral scholars, who are U.S. citizens.

The George A. Barton Fellowship is awarded for two months and is open to all doctoral students or recent Ph.D. recipients.

The Council of American Overseas Research Centers (CAORC) Multi-Country Research Fellowships are open to U.S. doctoral candidates and scholars who have already earned their Ph.D. in fields in the humanities, social sciences, or allied natural sciences and wish to conduct research of regional or transregional significance. Fellowships require scholars to conduct research in more than one country, at least one of which hosts a participating American overseas research center. (Apply at www.caorc.org/programs/index.html.)

Educational and Cultural Affairs Fellowships (ECA): (1) Junior Research Fellowships consist of two fellowships of nine months each; these fellowships are open to doctoral students and recent Ph.D. recipients who are U.S. citizens and; (2) Associate Fellowships consist of 13 administrative fee awards for senior and junior fellows (one or two semesters).

Ernest S. Frerichs Fellow and Program Coordinator is for nine months and is open to doctoral and postdoctoral scholars of all

nationalities. Recipient is expected to assist the Albright's Director in planning and implementing the Ernest S. Frerichs Program for Albright Fellows, which requires a working knowledge of living and traveling in Israel.

Glassman Holland Research Fellowship is open to all European postdoctoral researchers who are permanently resident in Europe.

Samuel H. Kress Fellowship is for two years for a doctoral dissertation research fellowship for students specializing in architecture, art history, archaeology and classical studies. Applicants must be U.S. citizens or students matriculating at U.S. universities, and must apply directly to the Kress Foundation: www.kressfoundation.org.

Carol and Eric Meyers Doctoral Dissertation Fellowship is for two months. For doctoral students whose research involves the study of archaeology and society in the biblical or early postbiblical periods. Topics dealing with society at the household level are encouraged.

National Endowment for the Humanities (NEH) Fellowships are awarded for up to 12 months. Open to postdoctoral scholars who are U.S. citizens or alien residents in the U.S. for at least three years.

The Noble Group Fellowships are open to Chinese citizens who are doctoral students and postdoctoral candidates and are either studying or in residence in China or doing research at institutions in other countries.

YEAR PROGRAM STARTED: 1940

PURPOSE:
To help scholars undertake high-quality research and field projects in the Near East; to encourage interdisciplinary study and communication among scholars.

LEGAL BASIS:
Nonprofit, archaeological research corporation.

ELIGIBILITY:
Fellowships are open to those in Near Eastern studies from prehistoric through the early Islamic period, including the fields of archaeology, anthropology, art history, Bible, epigraphy, gender studies, historical geography, history, language, literature, philology and religion and related disciplines. The research period should be continuous, without frequent trips outside the country. Residence at the Albright is required. The option to accommodate dependents is subject to space available at the Albright.

FINANCIAL DATA:
Amount of support per award: Varies.
Total amount of support: $325,000 in fellowships and awards.

COOPERATIVE FUNDING PROGRAMS: With various organizations and foundations, such as the NEH.

NUMBER OF AWARDS: 60 for all programs: 28 in fellowships and awards from the Institute; 32 Associate Fellows receive funding from other sources.

APPLICATION INFORMATION:
All eligible persons are encouraged to apply for as many awards as they wish, but each awardee can hold only one AIAR award at a time. Persons who have received an award in one year can reapply for the same or other awards the following year, but new applicants will be given priority.

Duration: Yearly with possible renewals.

Deadline: October 1 and March 15.

PUBLICATIONS:
Applications.

ADDRESS INQUIRIES TO:
Dr. Joan R. Branham, Chair
Albright Fellowship Committee
(See address above.)

THE AMERICAN ACADEMY IN BERLIN [920]
Am Sandwerder 17-19
D-14109 Berlin Germany
+49 30 804 83 106
Fax: +49 30 804 83 111

E-MAIL ADDRESS:
applications@americanacademy.de

WEB SITE ADDRESS:
www.americanacademy.de

AREAS OF INTEREST:
History, political science, literature,
economics, German studies, art history,
musicology, anthropology, law, linguistics,
writing, composing, and visual arts.

NAME(S) OF PROGRAMS:
• **Berlin Prize Fellowship**

TYPE:
Fellowships; Residencies. Academic semester
fellowship in Berlin with residence at the
Hans Arnhold Center.

YEAR PROGRAM STARTED: 1998

PURPOSE:
To further scholarly professional
development.

ELIGIBILITY:
Must be either a U.S. citizen or permanent
resident, and have completed their Doctorate
or equivalent professional degree. Open to
scholars, artists, and professionals who wish
to engage in independent study in Berlin for
an academic semester or, in very rare cases,
for an entire academic year. Candidates need
not work on German topics, but their project
descriptions should explain how a residency
in Berlin will contribute to further
professional development.

FINANCIAL DATA:
Amount of support per award: Stipend of
$5,000 per month, round-trip airfare, and an
apartment and partial board at the Hans
Arnhold Center.

Total amount of support: $5,000 per month.

NUMBER OF APPLICANTS MOST RECENT YEAR:
300-400.

NUMBER OF AWARDS: Approximately 24 (12
each semester) annually.

APPLICATION INFORMATION:
Applications must be sent to the Berlin
office.

Duration: One academic semester.

Deadline: Early October.

STAFF:
Alissa Burmeister, Manager of Fellows
Selection

ADDRESS INQUIRIES TO:
Alissa Burmeister
Manager of Fellows Selection
(See address above.)

AMERICAN ACADEMY IN ROME
7 East 60th Street
New York, NY 10022-1001
(212) 751-7200
Fax: (212) 751-7220

E-MAIL ADDRESS:
info@aarome.org

WEB SITE ADDRESS:
www.aarome.org

TYPE:
Awards/prizes; Fellowships; Residencies.
Fellowships for independent work in
architecture, landscape architecture, design,
musical composition, visual arts, historic
preservation/conservation, ancient studies,
medieval studies, renaissance and early
modern studies, and modern Italian studies.
Supported projects must be conducted at
American Academy in Rome facilities.

See entry 375 for full listing.

AMERICAN ACADEMY IN ROME
7 East 60th Street
New York, NY 10022
(212) 751-7200
Fax: (212) 751-7220

E-MAIL ADDRESS:
info@aarome.org

WEB SITE ADDRESS:
www.aarome.org

TYPE:
Awards/prizes; Fellowships; Residencies.
Provides a residential year at the American
Academy in Rome for an American
landscape architect for advanced study, travel
and association with other fellows in the arts
and humanities.

See entry 2305 for full listing.

AMERICAN CENTER OF ORIENTAL RESEARCH [921]
656 Beacon Street
5th Floor
Boston, MA 02215-2010
(617) 353-6571
Fax: (617) 353-6575

E-MAIL ADDRESS:
acor@bu.edu

WEB SITE ADDRESS:
www.bu.edu/acor

FOUNDED: 1968

AREAS OF INTEREST:
The study of humanistic disciplines, such as
art and architecture, literature, philology,
prehistory and topography, relating in
particular to the Middle East from prehistoric
times to the modern era. Projects involving
Islamic studies are especially encouraged.

The American Center of Oriental Research in
Amman, Jordan serves as a center of
operations for scholars of all nationalities
wishing to conduct research in Jordan.

NAME(S) OF PROGRAMS:
• **ACOR-CAORC Fellowship**
• **ACOR-CAORC Postgraduate Fellowships**
• **Pierre and Patricia Bikai Fellowship**
• **Bert and Sally de Vries Fellowship**
• **Jennifer C. Groot Fellowships in the Archaeology of Jordan**
• **Harrell Family Fellowship**
• **MacDonald/Sampson Fellowship**
• **National Endowment for the Humanities (NEH) Fellowship**

TYPE:
Fellowships; Research grants; Visiting
scholars. ACOR-CAORC Fellowships are
for M.A. and doctoral students. Fields of
study include all areas of the humanities and
the natural and social sciences. Topics should
contribute to scholarship in Near Eastern
studies.

ACOR-CAORC Postgraduate Fellowships are
for postdoctoral scholars and scholars with a
terminal degree in their field, pursuing
research or publication projects in the natural
and social sciences, humanities, and
associated disciplines relating to the Near
East.

Pierre and Patricia Bikai Fellowship is for a
residency at ACOR and is open to enrolled
graduate students of any nationality
participating in an archaeological project or
conducting archaeological work in Jordan.

Bert and Sally de Vries Fellowship supports
a student for participation on an
archaeological project or research in Jordan.

The Jennifer C. Groot Fellowships support
beginners in archaeological fieldwork who
have been accepted as team members on
archaeological projects with ASOR/CAP
affiliation in Jordan.

Harrell Family Fellowship supports a
graduate student for participation on an
archaeological project or research in Jordan.

MacDonald/Sampson Fellowship is for a
residency at ACOR for research in the fields
of Ancient Near Eastern languages and
history, archaeology, Bible studies, or
comparative religion, or a travel grant to
assist with participation in an archaeological
field project in Jordan.

The National Endowment for the Humanities
(NEH) Fellowship is for scholars who have a
Ph.D. or have completed their professional
training. Fields of research include: modern
and classical languages, linguistics, literature,
history, jurisprudence, philosophy,
archaeology, comparative religion, ethics, and
the history, criticism and theory of the arts.

YEAR PROGRAM STARTED: 1968

PURPOSE:
To help scholars undertake high-quality
research and field projects in the Middle
East; to encourage interdisciplinary study and
communication among scholars.

LEGAL BASIS:
Nonprofit, archaeological research
corporation.

ELIGIBILITY:
Most fellowships are restricted to U.S. or
Canadian citizens.

CAORC, NEH, MacDonald/Sampson and
Bikai Fellows will reside at the ACOR
facility in Amman while conducting their
research. Recipients are expected to
participate actively in the formal and
informal activities of the Center.

FINANCIAL DATA:
Amount of support per award:
ACOR-CAORC Fellowships: $20,200
maximum; ACOR-CAORC Postgraduate
Fellowships: $29,400 maximum; Pierre and
Patricia Bikai Fellowship: $600 monthly
stipend; Bert and Sally de Vries Fellowship:

$1,200; Groot Fellowships: $1,800; Harrell
Family Fellowship: $1,800;
MacDonald/Sampson Fellowship: Room and
board at ACOR and a stipend of $600;
National Endowment for the Humanities
(NEH) Fellowship: $27,800 maximum for up
to 6 months.

Total amount of support: Approximately
$288,000 for the year 2009-10.

COOPERATIVE FUNDING PROGRAMS: With
various organizations and foundations, such
as the NEH.

NUMBER OF APPLICANTS MOST RECENT YEAR:
45 for all programs.

NUMBER OF AWARDS: Bert and Sally de Vries,
Harrell Family, MacDonald/Sampson and
NEH Fellowships: 1 each; Bikai Fellowship:
1 or more; ACOR-CAORC Postgraduate and
Groot Fellowships: 2 or more;
ACOR-CAORC Fellowships: 3 or more.

APPLICATION INFORMATION:
Prospective applicants are encouraged to
consult with the ACOR Administrative
Director about application procedures, the
competitiveness of their applications, or any
other questions they might have about the
awards program.

All eligible persons are encouraged to apply
for as many awards as they wish, but each
awardee can hold only one ACOR award at a
time. Persons who have received an award in
one year can reapply for the same or other
awards the following year, but new applicants
will be given priority.

Duration: ACOR-CAORC Fellowships: Two
to six months; Bikai Fellowship: One to two
months; National Endowment for the
Humanities (NEH): Four to six months.

Deadline: February 1.

PUBLICATIONS:
Program announcements.

IRS IDENTIFICATION NUMBER: 23-7084091

ADDRESS INQUIRIES TO:
ACOR Fellowship Committee
(See address above.)

AMERICAN FRIENDS OF THE ALEXANDER VON HUMBOLDT FOUNDATION [922]

1012 14th Street, N.W.
Suite 1015
Washington, DC 20005
(202) 783-1907
Fax: (202) 783-1908

E-MAIL ADDRESS:
info@americanfriends-of-avh.org

WEB SITE ADDRESS:
www.humboldt-foundation.de
americanfriends-of-avh.org

FOUNDED: 1953

AREAS OF INTEREST:
Postgraduate research in Germany.

NAME(S) OF PROGRAMS:
● **Humboldt Research Fellowship for Experienced Researchers**

TYPE:
Fellowships. This program allows a
researcher to carry out a long-term research
project (six to 18 months) at a research
institution in Germany which the applicant
has selected in cooperation with an academic
host.

PURPOSE:
To support highly qualified scholars and
scientists of all nationalities and disciplines
so that they may carry out a long-term
research project.

ELIGIBILITY:
Open to scientists and scholars from outside
Germany with above average qualifications,
who:
(1) have completed their Doctorate less than
12 years ago;
(2) already have his or her own research
profile and;
(3) are working at least at the level of
Assistant Professor or Junior Research Group
Leader or have a record of several years of
independent academic work.

Fellowships are awarded on the basis of
academic achievement, the quality and
feasibility of the proposed research and the
candidate's publications.

FINANCIAL DATA:
In addition to a monthly stipend, special
allowances are available for accompanying
family members, travel expenses, and
German language instruction.
Amount of support per award: EUR 2,450
monthly stipend.

NUMBER OF AWARDS: Approximately 600.

APPLICATION INFORMATION:
Those interested must use application
documents which can be downloaded from
www.humboldt-foundation.de.
Duration: Six to 18 months. Fellowships may
be divided into a maximum of three visits of
at least three months each.
Deadline: Applications may be submitted at
any time to the Humboldt Foundation in
Bonn, Germany. The review process takes
several months, and the selection committee
meets three times a year to review
applications.

ADDRESS INQUIRIES TO:
Program Coordination
(See address above.) or

Alexander von Humboldt Stiftung
Jean-Paul-Strasse 12
D-53173 Bonn
Germany
Tel: 49 (0228) 833-0
Fax: 49 (0228) 833-199
E-mail: info@avh.de

AMERICAN FRIENDS OF THE ALEXANDER VON HUMBOLDT FOUNDATION [923]

1012-14th St., N.W., Suite 300
Washington, DC 20005
(202) 783-1907
Fax: (202) 783-1908

E-MAIL ADDRESS:
info@americanfriends-of-avh.org

WEB SITE ADDRESS:
www.humboldt-foundation.de
www.americanfriends-of-avh.org

FOUNDED: 1953

AREAS OF INTEREST:
Intercultural exchange.

NAME(S) OF PROGRAMS:
● **German Chancellor Fellowship**

TYPE:
Exchange programs; Fellowships. Fellowship
for one-year stay in Germany for professional

development, study or research. Applicants
design individual projects specific to
Germany and decide at which institutions to
pursue them.

YEAR PROGRAM STARTED: 1990

PURPOSE:
To strengthen ties between Germany and the
U.S. through fellowship recipient's profession
or studies.

ELIGIBILITY:
Intended for career-oriented individuals from
any profession or field of study who show
outstanding potential for U.S. leadership.
Selected fellows represent the private, public,
not-for-profit, cultural and academic sectors.
U.S. citizenship is required.

GEOGRAPHIC RESTRICTIONS:
United States.

FINANCIAL DATA:
Stipend covers housing and living expenses.
In addition, the Fellowship also covers travel
expenses to and from Germany and the costs
of a German language course, introductory
seminar, study tour, and final meeting in
Bonn.
Amount of support per award: Monthly
stipend of EUR 2,150 to 2,750.

NUMBER OF AWARDS: 10 annually.

APPLICATION INFORMATION:
Applications must be submitted to the
Foundation's Bonn, Germany office.
Duration: One year.
Deadline: October 15. Fellowship period
begins the following year on September 1.

ADDRESS INQUIRIES TO:
Margot Pfefferly, Senior Program Director
(See address above.)

*SPECIAL STIPULATIONS:
Prior to submitting an application, applicants
are expected to have established contact with
a mentor in Germany who agrees to provide
professional and/or scholarly assistance
throughout the program year.

AMERICAN INSTITUTE FOR SRI LANKAN STUDIES (AISLS) [924]

155 Pine Street
Belmont, MA 02478

E-MAIL ADDRESS:
rogersjohnd@aol.com

WEB SITE ADDRESS:
www.aisls.org

FOUNDED: 1996

AREAS OF INTEREST:
The promotion of scholarly excellence in Sri
Lankan studies.

NAME(S) OF PROGRAMS:
● **AISLS Fellowship Program**

TYPE:
Fellowships. Program supports research in
Sri Lanka by U.S. citizens who already hold
a Ph.D. or the equivalent at the time they
begin their fellowship tenure.

PURPOSE:
To foster excellence in American research
and teaching on Sri Lanka; to promote the
exchange of scholars and scholarly
information between the U.S. and Sri Lanka.

ELIGIBILITY:
Applicants must hold U.S. citizenship and a
Ph.D. or equivalent academic degree, or show
that they will hold such a degree before

taking up the fellowship. Scholars at all ranks are eligible. Applicants must plan to spend at least two months in Sri Lanka and complete the fellowship within the time frame listed under eligibility guidelines. Projects in all fields in the social sciences and humanities are eligible.

GEOGRAPHIC RESTRICTIONS:
United States.

FINANCIAL DATA:
Fellowship includes reimbursement up to $2,000 for round-trip airfare between the U.S. and Colombo via U.S. carriers, and a limited budget for research expenses, to be negotiated.

Amount of support per award: Stipend of $3,000 per month.

APPLICATION INFORMATION:
The completed application should contain the following items:
(1) AISLS Fellowship Application Cover Sheet;
(2) curriculum vitae, not to exceed three pages;
(3) description of the proposed study, not to exceed three single-spaced pages. This is the most important part of the application. It should cover the questions to be addressed by the project, the approach to be taken, work done to date, work to be accomplished during the fellowship period, the applicant's competence to carry out the project, how the project addresses the criteria of the competition, and a statement of other support received or being sought for the project and;
(4) one-page bibliography, including a selected list of publications by other scholars or primary sources that have been or will be used in the project.

Submissions by fax or e-mail will not be accepted.

Duration: Two to nine months.

Deadline: First week in December.

ADDRESS INQUIRIES TO:
John Rogers, Chairperson
AISLS Selection Committee
(See address above.)

AMERICAN INSTITUTE FOR SRI LANKAN STUDIES (AISLS) [925]
155 Pine Street
Belmont, MA 02478

E-MAIL ADDRESS:
rogersjohnd@aol.com

WEB SITE ADDRESS:
www.aisls.org

FOUNDED: 1996

AREAS OF INTEREST:
The promotion of scholarly excellence in Sri Lankan studies.

NAME(S) OF PROGRAMS:
● **AISLS Dissertation Planning Grant**

TYPE:
Research grants. Grant to assist graduate students intending to do dissertation research in Sri Lanka.

YEAR PROGRAM STARTED: 2006

PURPOSE:
To enable graduate students to make a pre-dissertation visit to Sri Lanka to investigate the feasibility of their topic, to sharpen their research design, or to make other practical arrangements for future research.

ELIGIBILITY:
Applicants must be enrolled in a Ph.D. program (or equivalent) in a U.S. university. There are no citizenship requirements. Applicants should have completed most of their graduate coursework by the time they take up their grant. The grant is especially intended for students who are in the process of completing their dissertation proposals and preparing applications for funds to support their dissertation research, but other purposes may be proposed. Applicants should plan to spend at least six weeks in Sri Lanka. Applicants whose research will also require spending time in libraries or archives in a third country may request funds for up to two weeks beyond the time spent in Sri Lanka.

GEOGRAPHIC RESTRICTIONS:
United States.

FINANCIAL DATA:
Grant includes reimbursement up to $2,000 for round-trip airfare between U.S. and Colombo, and reimbursement for any visa fees paid to the Sri Lankan government.

Amount of support per award: Per diem of $350 per week.

APPLICATION INFORMATION:
The completed application should contain the following items:
(1) AISLS Dissertation Planning Grant Application Cover Sheet;
(2) curriculum vitae, not to exceed two pages, which should include the name and e-mail address of the applicant's dissertation supervisor;
(3) copy of the applicant's graduate transcript. An unofficial copy is acceptable;
(4) project narrative, not to exceed two single-spaced pages. This is the most important part of the application and should contain a summary of the proposed dissertation project, or, if the purpose of the planning grant is to define a dissertation project, a summary of the more general questions the applicant hopes to address in his or her dissertation, a description of what the applicant intends to do during the grant period, and the applicant's competence to carry out his or her proposed project, including language training;
(5) one-page project bibliography, including a selected list of publications by other scholars or primary sources that have been or will be used in the project and;
(6) a confidential letter of recommendation from the applicant's dissertation supervisor. This letter should cover the applicant's academic record and be specific about the applicant's progress to date within the graduate program concerned. This letter should be sent directly to John Rogers at the address listed above.

Submissions by fax or e-mail will not be accepted.

Duration: Six to eight weeks.

Deadline: First week in December. Early submission is encouraged.

ADDRESS INQUIRIES TO:
John Rogers, Chairperson
AISLS Selection Committee
(See address above.)

AMERICAN INSTITUTE FOR YEMENI STUDIES [926]
P.O. Box 311
Ardmore, PA 19003-0311
(610) 896-5412
Fax: (610) 896-9049

E-MAIL ADDRESS:
aiys@aiys.org

WEB SITE ADDRESS:
www.aiys.org

FOUNDED: 1977

AREAS OF INTEREST:
Study and research in or about Yemen.

NAME(S) OF PROGRAMS:
● **General Fellowship Program**

TYPE:
Fellowships. Fellowship program for graduate and postgraduate scholars for Arabic language study, feasibility studies or research projects in Yemen.

PURPOSE:
To foster research in and about Yemen; to utilize American academic talent to strengthen Yemeni scholarship; to promote U.S.-Yemeni understanding.

ELIGIBILITY:
Limited to U.S. citizens who are enrolled as full-time graduate students in recognized degree programs or who are postgraduate researchers. Awards are made on the basis of merit. Collaborative or group projects are eligible for funding. It is permissible to combine Arabic language study with a research or feasibility project.

FINANCIAL DATA:
Amount of support per award: Up to $10,000.

NUMBER OF AWARDS: Approximately 10.

APPLICATION INFORMATION:
There is a $25 processing fee for applications to the U.S. fellowship program. The fee is waived for applicants who are individual AIYS members.

All applicants must submit the original, plus five copies, of each of the following:
(1) completed application form;
(2) curriculum vitae and;
(3) application narrative consisting of a short statement explaining their interest in Yemen and their background in Arabic language (for applicants of Arabic language training grants) or a project description, four to six double-spaced pages, plus a proposed budget and schedule (for all other applicants).

Three letters of recommendation, preferably on institutional stationery, must be sent directly to AIYS postmarked by the deadline. Predoctoral applicants must have both undergraduate and graduate transcripts sent; recent Ph.D. recipients are encouraged to provide a graduate transcript.

Duration: Two months minimum.

Deadline: December 31.

ADDRESS INQUIRIES TO:
Dr. Maria deJ. Ellis, Executive Director
(See address above.)

*SPECIAL STIPULATIONS:
If applicant is not an individual AIYS member, a $25 processing fee for application will apply. Named fellows must become AIYS members before starting their fellowship tenure.

AMERICAN INSTITUTE OF BANGLADESH STUDIES [927]

c/o Feminist, Gender & Sexuality Studies
391 Uris Hall, Cornell University
Ithaca, NY 14850
(607) 255-6480
Fax: (607) 255-2195

E-MAIL ADDRESS:
rf12@cornell.edu

WEB SITE ADDRESS:
www.aibs.net

FOUNDED: 1989

AREAS OF INTEREST:
Bangladesh culture and society.

NAME(S) OF PROGRAMS:
- **Junior Fellowship**
- **Pre-Dissertation Fellowships**
- **Seminar, Workshop and Conference Support**
- **Senior Fellowship**
- **Undergraduate Research Initiative**

TYPE:
Conferences/seminars; Fellowships. Junior Fellowship is for those who are in the ABD phase of their Ph.D. program. Applicants must be prepared to commence field research at the start of the fellowship period.

Pre-Dissertation Fellowships are short-term grants offered to graduate students pursuing studies of Bangladesh. The grant provides a stay of between two and four months in Bangladesh that may be used for language study, resource assessment, or network building to aid the completion of a competitive dissertation proposal.

The Senior Fellowship is for those who have a Ph.D. They may already have research experience in Bangladesh or may be interested in developing a research area on Bangladesh.

YEAR PROGRAM STARTED: 1989

PURPOSE:
To improve the scholarly understanding of Bangladesh culture and society in the U.S. and to promote educational exchange between the U.S. and Bangladesh.

ELIGIBILITY:
Applicants must be U.S. citizens or permanent residents and have their Ph.D.

Pre-Dissertation Fellowship: At the time of application, students must have completed at least one year of graduate study in a recognized Ph.D.-granting institution in either the social sciences or the humanities.

GEOGRAPHIC RESTRICTIONS:
United States.

FINANCIAL DATA:
Amount of support per award: Junior Fellowship: $800; Senior Fellowship: $1,000 plus research and dependents'allowances per month in non-convertible Bangladesh Taka. Round-trip air transportation will be provided via the most direct route and using the Bangladesh carrier whenever possible.

APPLICATION INFORMATION:
Application forms are available online.

For conference support, applicants must submit:
(1) completed application form;
(2) conference travel proposal (not to exceed three pages);
(3) e-mail or other PDF evidence of paper having been accepted;
(4) budget (include all travel costs, hotel costs, and conference registration);
(5) current curriculum vitae and;
(6) (for students) one letter of support from a faculty mentor, to be sent separately.

Duration: Junior Fellowship: Six to 10 months; Pre-Dissertation Fellowship: Two to four months; Senior Fellowship: Four to 12 months.

Deadline: February 1.

ADDRESS INQUIRIES TO:
Professor Shelley Feldman, President
(See address above.)

AMERICAN INSTITUTE OF INDIAN STUDIES [928]

1130 East 59th Street
Chicago, IL 60637
(773) 702-8638
Fax: (773) 702-6636

E-MAIL ADDRESS:
aiis@uchicago.edu

WEB SITE ADDRESS:
www.indiastudies.org

FOUNDED: 1961

AREAS OF INTEREST:
Indian studies.

NAME(S) OF PROGRAMS:
- **AIIS Fellowships**

TYPE:
Fellowships; Research grants. Senior (postdoctoral) Research Fellowships are awarded to academic specialists in Indian studies who possess the Ph.D. or equivalent. While in India, each Senior Research Fellow will be formally affiliated with an Indian university.

Fellowships for Senior Scholarly Development are awarded to established scholars who have not previously specialized in Indian studies and to established professionals who have not previously worked or studied in India. Proposals in this category should have a substantial research or project component and the anticipated results should be clearly defined. While in India, each Fellow will be formally affiliated with an Indian university.

Junior (dissertation) Fellowships are awarded to graduate students from all academic disciplines whose dissertation research requires study in India. Junior Fellows will have formal affiliation with Indian universities and Indian research supervisors.

Senior Performing Arts Fellowships are awarded to accomplished practitioners of the performing arts of India who demonstrate that studying in India will enhance their skills, develop their capabilities to teach or perform in the U.S., enhance American involvement with India's artistic traditions and strengthen their links with peers in India.

YEAR PROGRAM STARTED: 1962

PURPOSE:
To support the advancement of knowledge and understanding of India, its people and culture, primarily through research conducted in India by American scholars.

LEGAL BASIS:
Cooperative, nonprofit organization of 47 American colleges and universities.

ELIGIBILITY:
U.S. citizens are eligible for AIIS grants, as are foreign nationals enrolled or teaching full-time at American colleges or universities. U.S. and Indian government employees are ineligible for AIIS grants. Eligible applicants who are unaffiliated or who are from nonmember institutions are encouraged to apply.

FINANCIAL DATA:
Fellowships include a maintenance allowance and international travel. Fellowships for four months or less have significant travel restrictions. Fellowships for six months or more may include limited dependent coverage if funds are available. Award funds are generally made available in foreign currency only. An administrative overhead charge will be assessed to each AIIS Fellowship; this is not an application fee and is incurred only when a fellowship is awarded.

COOPERATIVE FUNDING PROGRAMS: Fellowship programs of the AIIS have been supported by foreign currency funds received from the Smithsonian Institution and the National Science Foundation. Funding was also provided by the U.S. Information Agency and the AIIS member institutions. Additionally, the Institute receives a continuing grant from the National Endowment for the Humanities (NEH).

NUMBER OF AWARDS: Determined by the amount of support received by AIIS.

APPLICATION INFORMATION:
Application materials are available upon request from the address above.

Duration: Up to nine months for Senior Research Fellowships, Fellowships for Senior Scholarly Development and Senior Performing Arts Fellowships; up to 11 months for Junior Fellowships.

Deadline: July 1. Awards are announced the following spring or summer. Awards begin in July of the following year.

OFFICERS:
Frederick Asher, President
Elise Auerbach, Administrator

ADDRESS INQUIRIES TO:
Elise Auerbach, Administrator
(See address above.)

*PLEASE NOTE:
A limited number of Senior Fellows will be selected to receive $1,000 per month of their fellowship award in U.S. dollars (with the remainder of their award still being in Indian rupees) due to a grant from the National Endowment for the Humanities. Awards will be assigned to those scholars who appear most likely to carry out "distinguished work in the humanities" in India.

*SPECIAL STIPULATIONS:
All AIIS-sponsored research projects and programs must receive the approval of the Indian government.

AMERICAN INSTITUTE OF INDIAN STUDIES

1130 East 59th Street
Chicago, IL 60637
(773) 702-8638
Fax: (773) 702-6636

E-MAIL ADDRESS:
aiis@uchicago.edu

WEB SITE ADDRESS:
www.indiastudies.org

TYPE:
Fellowships. Awards for graduate studies in India in an Indian language.

See entry 690 for full listing.

THE AMERICAN JEWISH JOINT DISTRIBUTION COMMITTEE [929]
711 Third Avenue
New York, NY 10017-4104
(212) 687-6200
Fax: (212) 370-5467

E-MAIL ADDRESS:
globalservice@jdc.org

WEB SITE ADDRESS:
www.jdc.org/ralph

AREAS OF INTEREST:
International Jewish communal service.

NAME(S) OF PROGRAMS:
● **The Ralph I. Goldman Fellowship**

TYPE:
Fellowships. Offers work-study fellowship in overseas locations where JDC is active.

YEAR PROGRAM STARTED: 1987

PURPOSE:
To provide young Jewish leaders with an insider's perspective on JDC's global programs, while also giving them the opportunity to participate in the life of international Jewish communities.

ELIGIBILITY:
Candidates should have the following credentials:
(1) Master's degree or equivalent and proven academic excellence;
(2) some work experience in the candidate's chosen career;
(3) demonstrated exceptional leadership skills;
(4) strong interest in international Jewish communal affairs and social welfare;
(5) knowledge of foreign language(s) is a plus, but not a requirement and;
(6) formal and/or informal Jewish education.

FINANCIAL DATA:
Amount of support per award: $35,000 stipend plus international travel expenses.

NUMBER OF AWARDS: 1 annually.

APPLICATION INFORMATION:
Candidates should submit a Letter of Intent including:
(1) details of educational and work experience;
(2) plans for the future;
(3) reasons for interest in the fellowship and;
(4) examples of leadership qualities.

Based on the letter, the JDC will send an application.
Duration: One year, beginning in September.
Deadline: Letter of Intent: December 30. Application: January 15.

AMERICAN RESEARCH CENTER IN EGYPT, INC. [930]
8700 Crownhill Boulevard, Suite 507
San Antonio, TX 78209
(210) 821-7000
Fax: (210) 821-7007

E-MAIL ADDRESS:
info@arce.org
fellows@arce.org

WEB SITE ADDRESS:
www.arce.org

FOUNDED: 1948

AREAS OF INTEREST:
Research on Egypt and in Egypt on all phases of Egyptian civilization and culture from earliest times to the present.

NAME(S) OF PROGRAMS:
● **Fellowships for Research in Egypt**

TYPE:
Awards/prizes; Fellowships; Research grants. Fellowships awarded to all but dissertation (ABD) stage doctoral students and postdoctoral scholars. Topics for research fellowship encompass the humanities, social sciences and art and archaeology and cover periods from ancient times to the present.

YEAR PROGRAM STARTED: 1974

PURPOSE:
To obtain a fresh and more profound knowledge of Egypt and the Near East through scholarly research; to train American specialists in Near Eastern Studies in academic disciplines which require familiarity with Egypt; to disseminate knowledge of Egypt and thus understanding of the whole Near East and promote American-Egyptian cultural relations.

LEGAL BASIS:
Nonprofit organization.

ELIGIBILITY:
Criteria for selections rest on the Committee's judgment of the applicant's intellectual capacity and maturity, fitness for field work in Egypt, the significance and relevance of the proposed topic and its potential contribution to scholarly research in Egypt. No special consideration is given to applicants from member institutions and candidates need not be members of the ARCE. Awards are open to all qualified candidates without regard to sex, race and religion. All applicants, pre- and postdoctoral, must be U.S. citizens due to funding guidelines. Under certain circumstances, non-U.S. nationality results in funding problems; therefore, it is advisable to contact the U.S. office for further clarification.

GEOGRAPHIC RESTRICTIONS:
Egypt.

FINANCIAL DATA:
Monthly per diem plus round-trip airfare between the U.S. and Cairo. Fellows may receive stipends only for the period of time during which they are present in Egypt. A small dependent allowance for accompanying family members is available.
Amount of support per award:
Approximately $2,200 per month for single predoctoral scholars to approximately $4,000 per month for senior postdoctoral scholars accompanied by two or more family members, depending on the funding source.
Total amount of support: Varies.

NUMBER OF APPLICANTS MOST RECENT YEAR:
24 for the year 2007-08.

NUMBER OF AWARDS: 11.

APPLICATION INFORMATION:
Electronic submission is preferred. Original letters of recommendation and transcripts, if applicable, may also be scanned and sent electronically.

All applicants must submit three letters of recommendation. Predoctoral applicants must submit a fourth recommendation attesting to their capacity in ancient or modern languages as related to their proposed research.
Duration: Three to 12 months.
Deadline: January.

PUBLICATIONS:
Annual report; application guidelines; journal; bulletin.

IRS IDENTIFICATION NUMBER: 04-2319500

GOVERNING BOARD:
Emily Teeter, President
Sameh Iskander, Vice President
Janet Irwine, Treasurer

ADDRESS INQUIRIES TO:
Djodi Deutsch, Academic Programs Coordinator
E-mail: fellows@arce.org

AMERICAN RESEARCH INSTITUTE IN TURKEY, INC. [931]
c/o The University of Pennsylvania Museum
3260 South Street
Philadelphia, PA 19104-6324
(215) 898-3474
Fax: (215) 898-0657

E-MAIL ADDRESS:
leinwand@sas.upenn.edu

WEB SITE ADDRESS:
ccat.sas.upenn.edu/ARIT

FOUNDED: 1964

AREAS OF INTEREST:
Research and study in Turkey, including all fields of the humanities and social sciences.

NAME(S) OF PROGRAMS:
● **ARIT Fellowship Program**

TYPE:
Fellowships. ARIT offers a number of fellowships for research in Turkey in humanities and social sciences. Grant for tenures of up to one year will be considered; some preference is given to projects of shorter duration. ARIT operates hostel, research and study facilities for researchers in Turkey at its branch centers in Istanbul and Ankara.

YEAR PROGRAM STARTED: 1964

PURPOSE:
To support research in humanities and social sciences in Turkey.

LEGAL BASIS:
Funded in part by grants from U.S. Department of State.

ELIGIBILITY:
Scholars and advanced graduate students engaged in research on ancient, medieval or modern times in Turkey, in any field of the humanities and social sciences, are eligible. Student applicants must have fulfilled all preliminary requirements for the Doctorate except the dissertation by June of the program year, and before beginning any ARIT-sponsored research. Non-U.S. applicants are expected to maintain an affiliation with an educational institution in the U.S. or Canada. For questions of eligibility and procedures, please check with the ARIT office in Philadelphia.

FINANCIAL DATA:
Awards cover international travel to and from Turkey and provide a stipend based on Turkish living standards and the fellow's academic status.

Amount of support per award: $4,000 to $16,000, depending on length of stay in Turkey.

Total amount of support: Varies.

COOPERATIVE FUNDING PROGRAMS: The Fellowship program is supported in part by grants from the U.S. Department of State, Bureau of Educational and Cultural Affairs.

NUMBER OF APPLICANTS MOST RECENT YEAR: 93 for the year 2010-11.

NUMBER OF AWARDS: 13 for the year 2009-10.

APPLICATION INFORMATION:
Turkish law requires foreign scholars to obtain formal permission for any research to be carried out at institutions in Turkey. ARIT fellowship applicants are responsible for obtaining the research permission and visa. In general, researchers should seek permission to carry out research from the director(s) of the institution(s) where they intend to work; this includes researchers who wish to work in libraries housed in Turkish museums.

Researchers who wish to work with collections housed in the Turkish archaeological museums, however, should make their applications through the Ministry of Culture and Tourism, General Directorate for Cultural Heritage and Museums. In addition, if the material they wish to work with is part of an excavation, researchers must submit with their application a letter signed by the excavation director giving permission to carry out the research. The new application regulations and format for researchers are posted on the ARIT web site (ccat.sas.upenn.edu/ARIT/Research Permit.htm). Most foreign scholars may enter Turkey on a tourist visa and apply for a research visa from within Turkey, or they may choose to procure a research visa from the Turkish embassy in advance of their arrival. ARIT reserves the right to withhold payment of fellowship stipends if appropriate research permission is not obtained.

Please include letters of reference with your application. Student applicants must provide a copy of their graduate transcript.

Duration: Stipends are provided for a period determined by each Fellow's research requirements, but not exceeding 12 months. Preference will be given to projects of shorter duration.

Deadline: Applications and three letters of recommendation must be received by November 1 to ARIT, c/o University of Pennsylvania Museum.

OFFICERS:
A. Kevin Reinhart, President
Nick Cahill, Vice President
Maria de Jong Ellis, Treasurer
Linda Darling, Secretary

ADDRESS INQUIRIES TO:
Nancy Leinwand
(See telephone and e-mail above.)

AMERICAN RESEARCH INSTITUTE IN TURKEY, INC.   [932]
c/o The University of Pennsylvania Museum
3260 South Street
Philadelphia, PA 19104-6324
(215) 898-3474
Fax: (215) 898-0657

E-MAIL ADDRESS:
leinwand@sas.upenn.edu

WEB SITE ADDRESS:
ccat.sas.upenn.edu/ARIT

FOUNDED: 1964

AREAS OF INTEREST:
Turkey.

NAME(S) OF PROGRAMS:
● **Bogazici University Summer Language Program for Intensive Advanced Turkish Language Study**

TYPE:
Fellowships. Bogazici University Summer Language Program: For summer study in Turkey. Also offer travel, stipend and tuition grants. This intensive program offers the equivalent of one full academic year of study in advanced Turkish language at the college level.

YEAR PROGRAM STARTED: 1981

PURPOSE:
To support the study of advanced Turkish language.

LEGAL BASIS:
Consortium of universities. Funding from the U.S. Department of Education.

ELIGIBILITY:
Full-time students and scholars affiliated at academic institutions are eligible to apply. To be a fellowship applicant, one must:
(1) be a citizen, national or permanent resident of the U.S.;
(2) be enrolled in an undergraduate- or graduate-level academic program, or be faculty;
(3) have a minimum B average in one's studies, if still a student and;
(4) perform at the high-intermediate level on a proficiency-based admissions examination.

FINANCIAL DATA:
Fellowships cover round-trip airfare to Istanbul, application and tuition fees, and a maintenance stipend.

COOPERATIVE FUNDING PROGRAMS: Funded by U.S. Department of Education, Fulbright-Hays Group Projects Abroad Program.

NUMBER OF APPLICANTS MOST RECENT YEAR: Approximately 50.

NUMBER OF AWARDS: Approximately 15.

APPLICATION INFORMATION:
Duration: Approximately eight weeks (late June through early August).
Deadline: February 1.

OFFICERS:
A. Kevin Reinhart, President
Nick Cahill, Vice President
Maria de Jong Ellis, Treasurer
Linda Darling, Secretary

ADDRESS INQUIRIES TO:
Dr. Erika H. Gilson, Director
Princeton University
Department of Near Eastern Studies
110 Jones Hall
Princeton, NJ 08544
E-mail: ehgilson@princeton.edu or

Nancy Leinwand
American Research Institute in Turkey
University of Pennsylvania Museum
3260 South Street
Philadelphia, PA 19104-6324
(See e-mail and web site above.)

AMERICAN RESEARCH INSTITUTE IN TURKEY, INC.   [933]
c/o The University of Pennsylvania Museum
3260 South Street
Philadelphia, PA 19104-6324
(215) 898-3474
Fax: (215) 898-0657

E-MAIL ADDRESS:
leinwand@sas.upenn.edu

WEB SITE ADDRESS:
ccat.sas.upenn.edu/ARIT/

FOUNDED: 1964

AREAS OF INTEREST:
Turkey with all periods in the general range of the humanities and including humanistically oriented aspects of the social sciences, prehistory, history, art, archaeology, literature and linguistics, as well as interdisciplinary aspects of cultural history.

NAME(S) OF PROGRAMS:
● **NEH Fellowships for Research in Turkey**

TYPE:
Fellowships. These advanced fellowships are made possible by support from the National Endowment for the Humanities. The fields of study cover all periods of history in the general range of the humanities and include humanistically oriented aspects of the social sciences, prehistory, history, art, archaeology, literature and linguistics, as well as interdisciplinary aspects of cultural history.

YEAR PROGRAM STARTED: 1991

PURPOSE:
To support long-term postdoctoral research in Turkey in the humanities.

LEGAL BASIS:
Consortium of universities. Funding from the National Endowment for the Humanities.

ELIGIBILITY:
Scholars who have completed their formal academic training and plan to carry out research in Turkey may apply. Applicants may be U.S. citizens or three-year residents of the U.S. Please consult ARIT headquarters on questions of eligibility. Advanced scholars may also apply for ARIT Fellowships in the Humanities and Social Sciences.

FINANCIAL DATA:
Amount of support per award: $16,800 to $50,400 stipend, depending on individual proposals.
Total amount of support: $75,600.

NUMBER OF APPLICANTS MOST RECENT YEAR: 16.

NUMBER OF AWARDS: 2 or 3 advanced fellowships for the 2010-11 academic year.

APPLICATION INFORMATION:
Turkish law requires foreign scholars to obtain formal permission to carry out research at institutions in Turkey. ARIT fellowship applicants are responsible for obtaining the research permission and visa. In general, researchers should seek permission to carry out research from the

director(s) of the institution(s) where they intend to work; this includes researchers who wish to work in libraries housed in Turkish museums.

Researchers who wish to work with collections housed in the Turkish archaeological museums, however, should make their applications through the Ministry of Culture and Tourism, General Directorate for Cultural Heritage and Museums. In addition, if the material they wish to work with is part of an excavation, researchers must submit a letter with their application signed by the excavation director giving permission to carry out the research. The new application regulations and format for researchers are posted on the ARIT web site (ccat.sas.upenn.edu/ARIT/Research Permit.htm). Most foreign scholars may enter Turkey on a tourist visa and apply for a research visa from within Turkey, or they may choose to procure a research visa from the Turkish embassy in advance of their arrival. ARIT reserves the right to withhold payment of fellowship stipends if appropriate research permission is not obtained.

Duration: Four to 12 continuous months.

Deadline: Applications and three letters of recommendation must be received by ARIT by November 1 for the following academic year. Applicants will be notified by the end of January of the following year.

PUBLICATIONS:
Program announcement.

OFFICERS:
A. Kevin Reinhart, President
Nick Cahill, Vice President
Maria de Jong Ellis, Treasurer
Linda Darling, Secretary

ADDRESS INQUIRIES TO:
Nancy Leinwand
(See telephone number above.)

THE AMERICAN SCHOOL OF CLASSICAL STUDIES AT ATHENS [934]

6-8 Charlton Street
Princeton, NJ 08540-5232
(609) 683-0800
Fax: (609) 924-0578

E-MAIL ADDRESS:
application@ascsa.org; ascsa@ascsa.org

WEB SITE ADDRESS:
www.ascsa.edu.gr

FOUNDED: 1881

AREAS OF INTEREST:
Classical studies.

NAME(S) OF PROGRAMS:
- **National Endowment for the Humanities Fellowships**

TYPE:
Fellowships. Fellowships for postdoctoral scholars and professionals in the humanities.

YEAR PROGRAM STARTED: 1881

LEGAL BASIS:
Graduate research and teaching center.

ELIGIBILITY:
Applicants must be U.S. citizens or foreign nationals who have been U.S. residents for three years prior to application deadline. Applicants must hold their Ph.D. or equivalent terminal degree.

FINANCIAL DATA:
Amount of support per award: Stipend up to $42,000.

NUMBER OF AWARDS: 2.

APPLICATION INFORMATION:
Correspondence about fellowships and admission to membership in the school for the regular session should be directed to the address above. Applicants must submit an online application form, letters of reference and successfully pass an examination.

Duration: Four to 10 months during academic year, September 1 to June 1.

Deadline: December 1.

STAFF:
Jack Davis, Director

ADDRESS INQUIRIES TO:
Chairperson
Committee on Admissions and Fellowships
(See address above.)

THE AMERICAN SCHOOL OF CLASSICAL STUDIES AT ATHENS [935]

6-8 Charlton Street
Princeton, NJ 08540-5232
(609) 683-0800
Fax: (609) 924-0578

E-MAIL ADDRESS:
application@ascsa.org; ascsa@ascsa.org

WEB SITE ADDRESS:
www.ascsa.edu.gr

FOUNDED: 1881

AREAS OF INTEREST:
Classical studies, archaeology, art history, post-classical, Byzantine and post-Byzantine, Late Antiquity and Modern Greek Studies.

NAME(S) OF PROGRAMS:
- **M. Alison Frantz Fellowship in Post-Classical Studies at the Gennadius Library**
- **The Jacob Hirsch Fellowship in Archaeology**

TYPE:
Fellowships. The M. Alison Frantz Fellowship and The Jacob Hirsch Fellowship are part of the Student Associate Program, which is open to advanced graduate students in the same fields as the Regular Academic Program (classical studies and ancient Mediterranean studies and related fields such as history of art, anthropology, prehistory, studies in postclassical Greece, etc.), who plan to pursue independent research projects and who do not wish to commit to the full Regular Academic Program.

The Jacob Hirsch Fellowship is also open to students from Israel.

YEAR PROGRAM STARTED: 1963

PURPOSE:
To provide financial assistance to advanced graduate students who plan to pursue independent research projects and who do not wish to commit to the American School's full Regular Academic Program.

LEGAL BASIS:
Graduate educational institution (non-degree granting).

ELIGIBILITY:
Frantz Fellowship: Awarded to Ph.D. candidates at a U.S. or Canadian institution or college or a recent Ph.D. from a U.S. or Canadian institution. Applicants must demonstrate their need to work in the Gennadius Library. Fields of study include late antiquity, Byzantine or modern Greek studies.

Hirsch Fellowship: Awarded to a Ph.D. candidate from a U.S. or Israeli university or college writing a dissertation, or a recent Ph.D. revising a dissertation for publication, for projects carried out in Greece.

FINANCIAL DATA:
In addition to stipend, room and board is provided at the American School of Classical Studies in Athens.

Amount of support per award: Frantz and Hirsch Fellowships: Stipend of $11,500, plus room, board and waiver of School fees.

NUMBER OF APPLICANTS MOST RECENT YEAR: 17.

NUMBER OF AWARDS: 1 of each annually.

APPLICATION INFORMATION:
Frantz Fellowship: Applicants must submit a full curriculum vitae, a project description showing the need for using the Gennadius Library and three supporting letters from qualified scholars. Send application to Chairperson, Gennadius Library Committee.

Hirsch Fellowship: Online application for admission to the American School should be made in conjunction with application for the Hirsch Fellowship. Transcripts of record, three letters of recommendation and a detailed description of the project to be pursued in Greece should be submitted to Chair, Committee on Admissions and Fellowships.

Duration: One academic year (September to June).

Deadline: January 15 (postmark). Announcement by March 15.

STAFF:
Jack Davis, Director
Irene Romano, Administrative Director

ADDRESS INQUIRIES TO:
Frantz Fellowship:
Chair,
Committee on Libraries and Archives
(See address above.)

Hirsch Fellowship:
Chair,
Committee on Admissions and Fellowships
(See address above.)

*SPECIAL STIPULATIONS:
Frantz Fellowship: Recipient must maintain residence in Athens and work at the Gennadius Library during the full term of the Fellowship.

THE AMERICAN SCHOOL OF CLASSICAL STUDIES AT ATHENS [936]

6-8 Charlton Street
Princeton, NJ 08540-5232
(609) 683-0800
Fax: (609) 924-0578

E-MAIL ADDRESS:
application@ascsa.org; ascsa@ascsa.org

WEB SITE ADDRESS:
www.ascsa.edu.gr

FOUNDED: 1881

AREAS OF INTEREST:
Classical studies, history of art, history of architecture, pottery, Mycenaean archaeology, Athenian architecture and archaeology.

NAME(S) OF PROGRAMS:
- **Advanced Fellowships**

TYPE:
Fellowships. Several Fellowships awarded by the School for the full academic year: the Samuel H. Kress Fellowship in art and architecture of antiquity; the Gorham Phillips Stevens Fellowship in the history of architecture; the Ione Mylonas Shear Fellowship in Mycenaean archaeology or Athenian architecture and/or archaeology; the Homer A. and Dorothy B. Thompson Fellowship in the study of pottery. Additionally, three Fellowships are unrestricted as to field: the Edward Capps, the Doreen Canaday Spitzer, and the Eugene Vanderpool Fellowships.

PURPOSE:
To support work on a specific project by students who wish to study at the School for a year.

ELIGIBILITY:
Students who have completed the Regular Program or one year as a Student Associate Member at the ASCSA and plan to return to the School to pursue independent research, usually for the Ph.D. dissertation, may apply. Given only if candidates meet a standard acceptable to the Director and the Committee.

GEOGRAPHIC RESTRICTIONS:
United States and Canada.

FINANCIAL DATA:
Amount of support per award: Stipend of $11,500, plus room, board and waiver of school fees.

NUMBER OF APPLICANTS MOST RECENT YEAR:
17.

NUMBER OF AWARDS: 7.

APPLICATION INFORMATION:
Submit application form, curriculum vitae, transcripts, letters of recommendation and a detailed statement of the project to be pursued in Greece.
Duration: One year.
Deadline: February 19.

STAFF:
Jack Davis, Director

ADDRESS INQUIRIES TO:
Committee Chair
(See address above.)

THE AMERICAN SCHOOL OF CLASSICAL STUDIES AT ATHENS [937]

6-8 Charlton Street
Princeton, NJ 08540-5232
(609) 683-0800
Fax: (609) 924-0578

E-MAIL ADDRESS:
application@ascsa.org; ascsa@ascsa.org

WEB SITE ADDRESS:
www.ascsa.edu.gr

FOUNDED: 1881

AREAS OF INTEREST:
Ancient Greek law.

NAME(S) OF PROGRAMS:
- **The Harry Bikakis Fellowship**

TYPE:
Fellowships. Research fellowship awarded periodically, but not more frequently than once a year.

PURPOSE:
To promote research.

ELIGIBILITY:
Graduate students attending a North American institution whose research subject is ancient Greek law, and who need to work at ASCSA libraries, or Greek graduate students working on a School excavation.

GEOGRAPHIC RESTRICTIONS:
North America.

FINANCIAL DATA:
Amount of support per award: $1,875.

APPLICATION INFORMATION:
Submit Associate Member application, including an outline of the proposed project, and one letter of reference online on the ASCSA web site.
Deadline: January 15.

STAFF:
Jack Davis, Director

ADDRESS INQUIRIES TO:
Committee Chair
(See address above.)

THE AMERICAN SCHOOL OF CLASSICAL STUDIES AT ATHENS [938]

6-8 Charlton Street
Princeton, NJ 08540-5232
(609) 683-0800
Fax: (609) 924-0578

E-MAIL ADDRESS:
application@ascsa.org; ascsa@ascsa.org

WEB SITE ADDRESS:
www.ascsa.edu.gr

FOUNDED: 1881

AREAS OF INTEREST:
Greco-Roman, humanities and classical antiquities.

NAME(S) OF PROGRAMS:
- **Oscar Broneer Traveling Fellowship**

TYPE:
Fellowships. Traveling fellowship awarded annually and held in Athens and Rome in alternate years. Fellows will use either the American Academy in Rome or the American School of Classical Studies at Athens as a base.

PURPOSE:
To pursue work through trips to sites, museums or repositories of materials of interest to the Fellow's studies.

ELIGIBILITY:
Ph.D. candidates must have an approved dissertation proposal or, if they already hold the Ph.D., they should be at the beginning of their teaching career and without tenure.

FINANCIAL DATA:
Amount of support per award: Up to $30,000 to cover all expenses including housing at the host institution, travel and living expenses.

NUMBER OF APPLICANTS MOST RECENT YEAR:
2.

NUMBER OF AWARDS: 1.

APPLICATION INFORMATION:
Send applications to ASCSA and AAR.
Duration: Three to six months.
Deadline: January 31.

STAFF:
Jack Davis, Director

ADDRESS INQUIRIES TO:
Committee Chair
(See address above.)

*SPECIAL STIPULATIONS:
Individuals who have spent a year as a Regular Member of The American School at Athens and are planning to travel in or near to Italy are eligible for a Fellowship based at the Academy in Rome.

THE AMERICAN SCHOOL OF CLASSICAL STUDIES AT ATHENS [939]

6-8 Charlton Street
Princeton, NJ 08540-5232
(609) 683-0800
Fax: (609) 924-0578

E-MAIL ADDRESS:
application@ascsa.org; ascsa@ascsa.org

WEB SITE ADDRESS:
www.ascsa.edu.gr

FOUNDED: 1881

AREAS OF INTEREST:
Gennadeion collections.

NAME(S) OF PROGRAMS:
- **Cotsen Traveling Fellowship for Research in Greece**

TYPE:
Fellowships. Short-term travel-to-collection award.

PURPOSE:
To assist students and scholars in the pursuit of research topics requiring the use of Gennadeion collections.

ELIGIBILITY:
Senior scholars and graduate students. Requires residency in Athens of at least one month during the academic year and recipient to take part in the life of the Library and of the School in addition to pursuing research.

FINANCIAL DATA:
Amount of support per award: $2,000 towards cost of travel, school fees and living expenses while in Athens.

NUMBER OF APPLICANTS MOST RECENT YEAR:
7.

NUMBER OF AWARDS: 1.

APPLICATION INFORMATION:
Application is available online and should include the following:
(1) curriculum vitae;
(2) letter (up to three pages) describing the project, proposed dates, budget, and explanation of the relation of the Gennadius Library's collection to the research project and;
(3) two letters of recommendation.
Deadline: January 15.

STAFF:
Dr. Maria Georgopoulou, Director, Gennadius Library

ADDRESS INQUIRIES TO:
Committee Chair, Libraries and Archives
(See address above.)

THE AMERICAN SCHOOL OF CLASSICAL STUDIES AT ATHENS [940]

6-8 Charlton Street
Princeton, NJ 08540-5232
(609) 683-0800
Fax: (609) 924-0578

E-MAIL ADDRESS:
application@ascsa.org; ascsa@ascsa.org

WEB SITE ADDRESS:
www.ascsa.edu.gr

FOUNDED: 1881

AREAS OF INTEREST:
Medieval Greek language and philology.

NAME(S) OF PROGRAMS:
● **Medieval Greek Summer Session at the Gennadius Library**

TYPE:
Scholarships. Four-week program in intermediate-level Medieval Greek language and philology at the Gennadius Library, with site and museum trips. Seminar given every other year. Next seminar to be held in 2013.

YEAR PROGRAM STARTED: 2005

PURPOSE:
To promote the study of Medieval Greek language and philology.

ELIGIBILITY:
Graduate students and professors in Byzantine studies from a university or graduate center, worldwide.

GEOGRAPHIC RESTRICTIONS:
North America.

FINANCIAL DATA:
The fee of $3,000 includes tuition, travel within Greece, lodging but no meals. Scholarships available (pending funding).

NUMBER OF APPLICANTS MOST RECENT YEAR:
15.

NUMBER OF AWARDS: Possibly 1 scholarship.

APPLICATION INFORMATION:
Duration: One full month.
Deadline: January 15, 2013.

STAFF:
Dr. Maria Georgopoulou, Director, Gennadius Library

ADDRESS INQUIRIES TO:
Committee Chair, Libraries and Archives
(See address above.)

THE AMERICAN SCHOOL OF CLASSICAL STUDIES AT ATHENS [941]

6-8 Charlton Street
Princeton, NJ 08540-5232
(609) 683-0800
Fax: (609) 924-0578

E-MAIL ADDRESS:
application@ascsa.org; ascsa@ascsa.org

WEB SITE ADDRESS:
www.ascsa.edu.gr

FOUNDED: 1881

AREAS OF INTEREST:
Skeletal, faunal, geoarchaeological, environmental studies and archaeological science.

NAME(S) OF PROGRAMS:
● **Wiener Laboratory Fellowships**
● **Wiener Laboratory Post-Doctoral Research Fellowship**
● **Wiener Laboratory Research Associateships**
● **Wiener Laboratory Travel Grants**

TYPE:
Fellowships; Research grants; Travel grants. Fellowships for projects in skeletal, faunal, geoarchaeological or environmental studies.

Post-Doctoral Research Fellowship is for a two-year project at the Wiener Laboratory.

Research Associateships for well-defined research projects.

Travel Grants for projects in archaeological science in Greece.

PURPOSE:
To promote laboratory research pertinent to the American School of Classical Studies at Athens.

ELIGIBILITY:
Fellowships: Graduate students or postdoctoral scholars working on well-defined projects in skeletal, faunal, geoarchaeological or environmental studies.

Post-Doctoral Research Fellowship: A recent postdoctoral scholar working on a well-defined project at the Wiener Laboratory. The project utilizes the resources of the Wiener Laboratory and enhances the teaching mission of the School.

Research Associateships: For well-defined research projects at the Laboratory.

Travel Grants: Graduate students or postdoctoral scholars from North American institutions working on projects in archaeological science in Greece.

FINANCIAL DATA:
Amount of support per award: Fellowships: Stipend of $15,500 to $27,000; Post-Doctoral Research Fellowship: Stipend of $35,000 with additional perquisites; Research Associateships: Up to $7,000; Travel Grants: $2,000.

NUMBER OF APPLICANTS MOST RECENT YEAR:
25.

NUMBER OF AWARDS: Fellowships: 2 to 4 annually; Associateships: 4 to 6; Travel Grant: 1.

APPLICATION INFORMATION:
Applicants for the Fellowships and Research Associateships must submit the following:
(1) cover letter (Fellowship) or application (Research Associateship) naming the applicant and title of the project;
(2) project description, no more than 2,500 words, describing the purpose, nature and methodology of the research project;
(3) copies of permits or letters from relevant authorities to study proposed materials, and copies of permission(s) from relevant excavation or project directors to study the proposed materials;
(4) budget (itemize in as much detail as possible);
(5) curriculum vitae and;
(6) two letters of recommendation.

Applicants seeking the Travel Grant must submit application, curriculum vitae, statement of the project to be pursued (up to 2,000 words), and budget.

Deadline: Fellowships and Post-Doctoral Research Fellowships: January 15.

ADDRESS INQUIRIES TO:
Committee Chair, Wiener Laboratory
(See address above.)

*PLEASE NOTE:
Wiener Laboratory Travel Grants and Wiener Laboratory Research Associateships are suspended for 2011.

AMERICAN SCHOOLS OF ORIENTAL RESEARCH (ASOR) [942]

656 Beacon Street, Fifth Floor
Boston, MA 02215
(617) 353-6570
Fax: (617) 353-6575

E-MAIL ADDRESS:
asor@bu.edu

WEB SITE ADDRESS:
www.asor.org

FOUNDED: 1900

AREAS OF INTEREST:
The study of humanistic disciplines, such as anthropology, archaeology, Biblical studies, epigraphy, history, history of art and architecture, literature, philology, prehistory and topography, relating in particular to the Middle East from prehistoric times to the modern era.

NAME(S) OF PROGRAMS:
● **Heritage Fellowships**
● **Mesopotamian Fellowship**
● **Platt Fellowships**

TYPE:
Conferences/seminars; Fellowships; Research grants; Scholarships; Travel grants.

YEAR PROGRAM STARTED: 1940

PURPOSE:
To encourage scholars to undertake study and research about ancient Mesopotamia.

LEGAL BASIS:
Nonprofit, archaeological research corporation.

ELIGIBILITY:
The Fellowship is open to qualified students and scholars from any country. Applicants must be or become individual professional members of ASOR, or must be affiliated with an institution that is a member of the ASOR corporation.

FINANCIAL DATA:
Amount of support per award: $9,000.
Total amount of support: $9,000.

NUMBER OF APPLICANTS MOST RECENT YEAR:
Varies.

NUMBER OF AWARDS: Varies.

APPLICATION INFORMATION:
All eligible persons are encouraged to apply for as many fellowships and professorships as they wish, but a person can hold only one award at a time. Persons who have received an award in one year can reapply for the same or other awards the following year, but new applicants will have priority.

PUBLICATIONS:
Application forms.

STAFF:
Andrew Vaughn, Executive Director

ADDRESS INQUIRIES TO:
Office Coordinator
(See address above.)

*SPECIAL STIPULATIONS:
Applicants must be or become members of ASOR or attend an ASOR-affiliated institution.

THE AMERICAN SWEDISH INSTITUTE [943]

2600 Park Avenue
Minneapolis, MN 55407
(612) 871-4907
Fax: (612) 871-8682

E-MAIL ADDRESS:
info@americanswedishinst.org

WEB SITE ADDRESS:
www.americanswedishinst.org

AREAS OF INTEREST:
Swedish culture.

NAME(S) OF PROGRAMS:
- **Lilly Lorenzen Scholarship**

TYPE:
Scholarships; Travel grants.

PURPOSE:
To foster and preserve Swedish culture in
America.

ELIGIBILITY:
Must be a Minnesota resident or a student
attending a Minnesota school with working
knowledge of the Swedish language that
presents a creditable plan of study for the
next academic year.

FINANCIAL DATA:
Amount of support per award: $1,000 for the
year 2011.
Total amount of support: $1,000 for the year
2011.

APPLICATION INFORMATION:
Submit application form and college
transcript. If transcript is not available,
include a statement of professional and
community achievement. Contact the Institute
at the address above for an application.
Duration: One-time award.
Deadline: May 1.

ADDRESS INQUIRIES TO:
Karin Krull, Adult Programs Coordinator
(See address above.)

THE AMERICAN SWEDISH INSTITUTE   [944]
2600 Park Avenue
Minneapolis, MN 55407
(612) 871-4907
Fax: (612) 871-8682

E-MAIL ADDRESS:
info@americanswedishinst.org

WEB SITE ADDRESS:
www.americanswedishinst.org

AREAS OF INTEREST:
Swedish culture.

NAME(S) OF PROGRAMS:
- **The Malmberg Scholarship Program**

TYPE:
Scholarships; Travel grants. The Malmberg
Scholarship is awarded for up to one
academic year of study in Sweden.

PURPOSE:
To support intellectual connections between
the U.S. and Sweden by providing grants to
students and scholars.

ELIGIBILITY:
Enrolled undergraduate and graduate students
and qualified scholars are eligible. The
recipient must be a U.S. resident.

FINANCIAL DATA:
Amount of support per award: Up to
$10,000.

NUMBER OF APPLICANTS MOST RECENT YEAR:
12.

NUMBER OF AWARDS: 1.

APPLICATION INFORMATION:
For application forms visit:
www.americanswedishinst.org/
scholarship.htm.
Deadline: Applications: November 15.

ADDRESS INQUIRIES TO:
Karin Krull
Adult Programs Coordinator
(See address above.)

THE AMERICAN-SCANDINAVIAN FOUNDATION   [945]
58 Park Avenue
New York, NY 10016
(212) 879-9779
Fax: (212) 249-3444

E-MAIL ADDRESS:
grants@amscan.org

WEB SITE ADDRESS:
www.amscan.org

FOUNDED: 1910

AREAS OF INTEREST:
Advanced study in Scandinavia.

NAME(S) OF PROGRAMS:
- **ASF Awards for Study in Scandinavia**

TYPE:
Fellowships; Research grants. Short-term
project grants and long-term fellowships for
advanced study in a field which may be
pursued with particular merit in one of the
Scandinavian countries (Denmark, Finland,
Iceland, Norway or Sweden).

Fellowships are intended to support a
year-long stay. Priority is given to candidates
at the graduate level for dissertation-related
study or research.

Grants are considered especially suitable for
graduate and postgraduate scholars,
professionals and candidates in the arts to
carry out research or study visits of one to
three months' duration.

YEAR PROGRAM STARTED: 1911

PURPOSE:
To advance cultural and intellectual
understanding between the U.S. and
Scandinavia, primarily through exchange
programs, cultural programs and publications.

LEGAL BASIS:
Nonprofit educational institution qualifying
under statutes 501(c)(3), 509(a)(1) and
170(c)(2) of the IRS code.

ELIGIBILITY:
Applicants must have a well-defined research
or study project that makes a stay in
Scandinavia essential. Applicants must be
U.S. citizens or permanent residents who will
have completed their undergraduate education
by the start of their project in Scandinavia.
Team projects are eligible, but each member
must apply as an individual, submitting a
separate, fully documented application. First
priority will be given to applicants who have
not previously received an ASF award. Only
in exceptional cases will a third award be
considered. Knowledge of the language of
the country in which the applicant wishes to
study is encouraged, but not necessary. For
projects that require a command of one or
more Scandinavian (or other) languages,
candidates should defer application until they
have the necessary proficiency. Evidence of a
confirmed invitation or affiliation is an
important factor in award consideration.

ASF does not fund the following:
(1) travel for attendance at professional
meetings, conferences, seminars or
conventions;
(2) performances or exhibitions;
(3) publication costs;
(4) equipment purchases, including personal
computers and software;
(5) research assistants;
(6) institutional overhead costs;
(7) foregone salary;
(8) supplementation of substantial sabbatical
support;
(9) support for dependents;
(10) repayment of loans or other personal
obligations;
(11) acquisition of language skills;
(12) study in programs especially designed
for English-speaking students, or at
English-language institutions;
(13) beginning studies in any subject or;
(14) retroactive program support.

Projects must be undertaken in Denmark,
Finland, Iceland, Norway or Sweden.

GEOGRAPHIC RESTRICTIONS:
Scandinavia.

FINANCIAL DATA:
The awards support project-related costs,
including maintenance, transatlantic
round-trip travel, in-country travel, tuition
and fees (where applicable) and materials
expenditures (e.g., books, photocopying, art
supplies).
Amount of support per award: Grants
normally of $5,000, especially suited for
short visits of one to three months and
fellowships of up to $23,000, intended for a
full academic year of study or research.
Total amount of support: Varies annually.
Over $300,000 is available for the 2012-13
competition.

NUMBER OF APPLICANTS MOST RECENT YEAR:
132.

NUMBER OF AWARDS: Varies each year
according to total funds available. Awards
were made to 25 Americans in the 2010-11
competition.

APPLICATION INFORMATION:
Only applications on current official ASF
forms will be considered. Incomplete
applications cannot be processed.
Unsuccessful applications will be discarded.

Applicants for Awards for Study in
Scandinavia are urged to arrange their
academic or professional affiliations as far in
advance as possible. Applicants must secure
these placements or affiliations on their own;
the ASF cannot assist in establishing
contacts. The ASF requires confirmation of
invitation or affiliation from the institution or
individuals detailed in the proposal. Since
July and August are traditionally holiday
months in Scandinavia, many people may not
be available for consultation. Applicants are
cautioned to plan their projects accordingly.
Applicants are expected to devote full-time to
their proposed study or research, and must
justify the length of time needed to complete
their project. Awards are based on the
application submitted; subsequent changes in
the proposal are discouraged and may not be
considered.
Duration: Grants: One to three months.
Fellowships: One academic year.
Deadline: Awards for Study in Scandinavia:
November 1 for receipt of fully documented
applications. Awards announced by the
following March 15.

PUBLICATIONS:
Annual report; fellowship and grant application guidelines; *Scandinavian Review*; *Scan*, newsletter; *Study in Scandinavia*, guide.

ADMINISTRATION:
Edward P. Gallagher, President
Lynn Carter, Executive Vice President
Valeria Hymas, Director of Grants/Fellowships

ADDRESS INQUIRIES TO:
Exchange Division
(See address above.)

ASIAN CULTURAL COUNCIL   [946]
6 West 48th Street, 12th Floor
New York, NY 10036-1802
(212) 843-0403
Fax: (212) 843-0343

E-MAIL ADDRESS:
acc@accny.org

WEB SITE ADDRESS:
www.asianculturalcouncil.org

FOUNDED: 1980

AREAS OF INTEREST:
Cultural exchange between Asia and the U.S. in the performing and visual arts.

NAME(S) OF PROGRAMS:
● **Asian Cultural Council Fellowships**

TYPE:
Exchange programs; Fellowships. Grants are awarded to individuals for research and creative projects across a wide spectrum of the performing and visual arts, and across both traditional and contemporary concentrations. Some grants are also made to educational and cultural organizations engaged in projects of special significance to Asian-American exchange. The ACC is both a grantmaking and grant-seeking organization, raising funding from corporate, foundation and individual donors in both the U.S. and Asia.

YEAR PROGRAM STARTED: 1963

PURPOSE:
To support cultural exchange between the U.S. and Asia and within the countries of Asia.

ELIGIBILITY:
Applicants from Asia must live and work in their home countries and be committed to pursuing professional careers there. The same is true of American applicants. Priority is generally given to individuals with little or no previous opportunity for study and research in the country for which travel assistance is being sought from the ACC.

GEOGRAPHIC RESTRICTIONS:
United States and Asia.

FINANCIAL DATA:
Amount of support per award: $1,000 to $30,000.

NUMBER OF AWARDS: 150.

APPLICATION INFORMATION:
Applicant must complete an inquiry form online. If project meets ACC's requirements, an application is then e-mailed.
Duration: Generally, one to 12 months.
Deadline: Applications must be returned by 5 P.M. (EST) on December 1, 2011.

ADDRESS INQUIRIES TO:
Jennifer P. Goodale, Executive Director
(See address above.)

AUSTRIAN CULTURAL FORUM   [947]
11 East 52nd Street
New York, NY 10022
(212) 319-5300
Fax: (212) 644-8660

E-MAIL ADDRESS:
desk@acfny.org

WEB SITE ADDRESS:
www.acfny.org

TYPE:
Research grants; Scholarships. The Forum serves as a contact point for correspondence about grants.

PURPOSE:
To enable students to carry out research or study projects on contemporary Austrian topics.

LEGAL BASIS:
Agency of the Republic of Austria.

ADDRESS INQUIRIES TO:
Hannah Liko, Deputy Director
(See address above.)

BELGIAN AMERICAN EDUCATIONAL FOUNDATION, INC.   [948]
195 Church Street
New Haven, CT 06510
(203) 777-5765
Fax: (203) 777-5765

E-MAIL ADDRESS:
emile.boulpaep@yale.edu
mail@baef.be

WEB SITE ADDRESS:
www.baef.us
www.baef.be

FOUNDED: 1920

AREAS OF INTEREST:
Educational exchange between the U.S. and Belgium.

NAME(S) OF PROGRAMS:
● **B.A.E.F. Fellowships for Study in Belgium**

TYPE:
Fellowships. Predoctoral and postdoctoral fellowships for advanced study in most fields of knowledge with supported work to be undertaken at a Belgian university. Fellowships for Belgian students are also available.

YEAR PROGRAM STARTED: 1920

PURPOSE:
To allow American candidates to pursue independent study and research in Belgium on projects for which Belgium provides special advantages.

LEGAL BASIS:
Public foundation.

ELIGIBILITY:
The applicant must be a citizen or permanent resident of the U.S. and either have a Master's degree or equivalent degree, or be working towards a Ph.D. or equivalent degree. Candidates under 30 years of age and with a speaking and reading knowledge of Dutch, French or German are preferred.

FINANCIAL DATA:
Fellowships carry a fixed stipend for living expenses, travel and tuition, if any. This stipend is judged adequate for a single person, but additional funds must be provided from other sources if the fellow is to be accompanied by spouse or by spouse and family. Health insurance coverage is also provided.
Amount of support per award: $24,000 for 12 months.
Total amount of support: $3,000,000 for the academic year 2010-11.

NUMBER OF APPLICANTS MOST RECENT YEAR:
30 U.S. applicants per academic year.

NUMBER OF AWARDS: 8 awards to American students per academic year.

APPLICATION INFORMATION:
Applicant shall furnish a completed application form with all its appropriate attachments. Application blanks are available on www.baef.us.
Duration: 12 months preferred; no less than six months.
Deadline: October 31, for the following academic year. Fellowship starting as early as July 1 of that following year.

DIRECTORS:
Dr. Emile L. Boulpaep, President and Chairman
William S. Moody, Vice President
Olivier Trouveroy, Treasurer
L. Gilles Sion, Secretary
Maryan Ainsworth
Marcel Crochet
Jacques de Groote
Diego du Monceau
Susan Friberg
John H.F. Haskell, Jr.
Margaret Hoover
Andre Jacques
Daniel Janssen
Dirk Wauters
Jacques Willems

ADDRESS INQUIRIES TO:
Dr. Emile L. Boulpaep, President
(See address above.)

THE BRITISH INSTITUTE IN EASTERN AFRICA   [949]
Laikipia Road,
Kileleshwa
Nairobi Kenya
(254) (0)20 43 43190/43 43330
Fax: (254) (0)20 43 43365

E-MAIL ADDRESS:
office@biea.ac.uk

WEB SITE ADDRESS:
www.biea.ac.uk/

FOUNDED: 1960

AREAS OF INTEREST:
Any field of the humanities and social sciences in Eastern Africa. Publishes annual journal *Azania* and series of memoirs on substantial research projects in Eastern Africa.

NAME(S) OF PROGRAMS:
● **Minor Research Grant Program**
● **Research Institute**

TYPE:
Research grants; Seed money grants. Ad hoc grants are made for research in the field of pre-colonial history and archaeology in Eastern Africa.

YEAR PROGRAM STARTED: 1960

PURPOSE:
To facilitate original research in Eastern African countries.

LEGAL BASIS:
Self-governing institute with Governing Council in London, sponsored by the British Academy.

ELIGIBILITY:
Applicants should have a B.A. or equivalent degree and graduate or undergraduate training in African studies, archaeology or social anthropology, with ability to undertake independent research. Priority is given to researchers based in the U.K. or Eastern Africa.

GEOGRAPHIC RESTRICTIONS:
Eastern Africa countries.

FINANCIAL DATA:
Size of support dependent on Institute's discretion. Funding does not include institutional overheads, stipendiary element or publication costs.
Amount of support per award: GBP 250 to 1,000.

NUMBER OF APPLICANTS MOST RECENT YEAR:
30.

NUMBER OF AWARDS: 11.

APPLICATION INFORMATION:
Application available from Nairobi office.
Duration: Research must commence within six months of award.
Deadline: April 30 and October 31.

PUBLICATIONS:
AZANIA, annual BIEA journal; annual reports; BIEA memoirs; *Journal of Eastern African Studies.*

STAFF:
David Anderson, Director
Matthew Davies, Ph.D., Assistant Director

ADDRESS INQUIRIES TO:
David Anderson, Director
The British Institute in Eastern Africa
P.O. Box 30710 GPO
00100-Nairobi
Kenya

BRUCEBO FINE ART SCHOLARSHIP FOUNDATION
Department of Geography
McGill University
805 Sherbrooke West
Montreal QC H3A 2K6 Canada
(450) 672-6096
Fax: (514) 398-7437

E-MAIL ADDRESS:
jan.lundgren@mcgill.ca

TYPE:
Scholarships; Travel grants. Grant principally in the fields of fine arts, visual art and design. Grant is either for stay at the Brucebo Studio on the Island of Hanseatic Gotland, Sweden, in the Baltic Sea, for three months during the summer annually, or for undertaking a European Fine Art Travel-Study journey during a period of the fall term, or the following winter/spring term.

See entry 578 for full listing.

CANADIAN BUREAU FOR INTERNATIONAL EDUCATION (CBIE)   [950]
220 Laurier Avenue West, Suite 1550
Ottawa ON K1P 5Z9 Canada
(613) 237-4820
Fax: (613) 237-1073

E-MAIL ADDRESS:
scholarships-bourses@cbie.ca

WEB SITE ADDRESS:
www.scholarships.gc.ca

FOUNDED: 1981

AREAS OF INTEREST:
All disciplines at the Master's, doctoral or postdoctoral levels.

NAME(S) OF PROGRAMS:
● **Foreign Government Awards**

TYPE:
Scholarships. Scholarships for study or research.

PURPOSE:
To provide opportunities for Canadians to pursue studies or research at institutions of higher education abroad.

ELIGIBILITY:
Candidates must be Canadian citizens by the competition deadline and must have obtained the equivalent of a Canadian Bachelor's degree from a recognized university. Studies must take place in France, Korea, Mexico, Russia or Switzerland.
Visit www.scholarships-bourses.gc.ca for more information.

FINANCIAL DATA:
Funding includes tuition and monthly living allowances, with additional benefits provided by varying countries.
Amount of support per award: Varies by geographical location.

NUMBER OF APPLICANTS MOST RECENT YEAR:
40.

NUMBER OF AWARDS: 2 to 15 per year, depending on geographical location.

APPLICATION INFORMATION:
Further information and application forms are available on the web site above.
Duration: One academic year, beginning in September. Renewals possible.

ADDRESS INQUIRIES TO:
Program Coordinator
International Scholarship Programs
(See address above.)

*SPECIAL STIPULATIONS:
Candidates may not hold other awards concurrently.

CANADIAN BUREAU FOR INTERNATIONAL EDUCATION (CBIE)   [951]
220 Laurier West, Suite 1550
Ottawa ON K1P 5Z9 Canada
(613) 237-4820
Fax: (613) 237-1073

E-MAIL ADDRESS:
scholarships-bourses@cbie.ca

WEB SITE ADDRESS:
www.scholarships.gc.ca

AREAS OF INTEREST:
Higher education.

NAME(S) OF PROGRAMS:
● **Commonwealth Scholarship Plan**

TYPE:
Scholarships. Under the Commonwealth Scholarship and Fellowship Plan, scholarships are available for Canadians to pursue studies and/or research at higher education institutions in the Commonwealth.

PURPOSE:
To provide opportunities for candidates to pursue studies and/or research at higher education institutions in the Commonwealth.

ELIGIBILITY:
Candidates must be Canadian citizens by the competition deadline and must have obtained the equivalent of a Canadian Bachelor's degree from a recognized university. Studies must take place in India, New Zealand or the U.K.

FINANCIAL DATA:
Funding includes tuition and monthly living allowances, with additional benefits provided by varying countries.
Amount of support per award: Varies by geographical location.

NUMBER OF APPLICANTS MOST RECENT YEAR:
150.

NUMBER OF AWARDS: 1 to 3.

APPLICATION INFORMATION:
Further information and application forms are available on the web site above.
Duration: Up to three years.

ADDRESS INQUIRIES TO:
Program Coordinator
International Scholarship Programs
(See address above.)

CANADIAN INSTITUTE IN GREECE/L'INSTITUT CANADIEN EN GRECE
330 Albert Street
Waterloo ON N2L 3T8 Canada
(519) 886-4428

E-MAIL ADDRESS:
gschaus@wlu.ca

WEB SITE ADDRESS:
www.cig-icg.gr

TYPE:
Conferences/seminars; Endowments; Fellowships; Internships. Intended to support the graduate work of a person who needs to study in Greece.

See entry 386 for full listing.

THE CANADIAN-SCANDINAVIAN FOUNDATION   [952]
P.O. Box 135
Succursale B
Montreal QC H3B 3J5 Canada

E-MAIL ADDRESS:
csf-fcs@hotmail.com

WEB SITE ADDRESS:
www.canada-scandinavia.ca

FOUNDED: 1950

NAME(S) OF PROGRAMS:
● **CSF Bursary**

TYPE:
Travel grants. CSF Bursary are intended to help defray expenses incurred during a study/research visit to Scandinavian destinations.

YEAR PROGRAM STARTED: 1950

PURPOSE:
To provide assistance and support to qualified and talented young Canadians of university age planning a study sejour or a research visit with a clear Nordic-related project to one or more of the Nordic countries.

LEGAL BASIS:
National, nonprofit organization.

ELIGIBILITY:
Because of the limited funding of the CSF Bursary, the successful candidate must have additional means at his or her disposal for carrying out the intended study/research enterprise.

GEOGRAPHIC RESTRICTIONS:
Canadian.

FINANCIAL DATA:
Amount of support per award: $500 to $1,000 (CAN).
Total amount of support: $13,500 (CAN) for the year 2008-09.

NUMBER OF APPLICANTS MOST RECENT YEAR:
28 for the year 2010.

NUMBER OF AWARDS: 9 for the year 2009-10.

BOARD OF DIRECTORS:
Dr. Derek Yaple-Schobert, Chairperson

BOARD OF TRUSTEES:
Dr. Robert Duguay
Prof. Susan Gold Smith
Dr. Hans Moller

CDS INTERNATIONAL, INC. [953]
440 Park Avenue South, 2nd Floor
New York, NY 10016
(212) 497-3500
Fax: (212) 497-3586

E-MAIL ADDRESS:
bosch@cdsintl.org

WEB SITE ADDRESS:
www.cdsintl.org/bosch

FOUNDED: 1968

AREAS OF INTEREST:
International business, law, economics, public affairs, public policy, journalism, mass communication and political science.

NAME(S) OF PROGRAMS:
● **The Robert Bosch Foundation Fellowship Program**

TYPE:
Exchange programs; Fellowships. Graduate fellowships for extended career training opportunities in Germany.

YEAR PROGRAM STARTED: 1984

PURPOSE:
To provide international professional experience through high-level internships within German industry, business, government and media.

LEGAL BASIS:
Program funded by Robert Bosch Stiftung, a private German foundation.

ELIGIBILITY:
Open to Americans with a graduate degree, work experience and professional interest or background in the fields above. U.S. citizenship is required. No German required to apply.

GEOGRAPHIC RESTRICTIONS:
Germany.

FINANCIAL DATA:
Includes transatlantic flights, language training, three European seminars, travel, health, accident and liability insurance, etc.
Amount of support per award: EUR 2,000 per month.

NUMBER OF APPLICANTS MOST RECENT YEAR:
440.

NUMBER OF AWARDS: 20 for the 2010-11 academic year.

APPLICATION INFORMATION:
Candidates must submit an application form, personal statement, transcripts, letters of recommendation and resume.
Duration: Nine to 12 months.
Deadline: October 15, 2010.

PUBLICATIONS:
General information and applications.

STAFF:
Nicole Sisco, Program Officer
Susana Lee, Assistant Program Officer

ADDRESS INQUIRIES TO:
Nicole Sisco, Program Officer
(See address above.)

CDS INTERNATIONAL, INC. [954]
440 Park Avenue South, Second Floor
New York, NY 10016
(212) 497-3522
Fax: (212) 497-3535

E-MAIL ADDRESS:
wisp@cdsintl.org

WEB SITE ADDRESS:
www.wispgermany.org

FOUNDED: 1968

AREAS OF INTEREST:
Culture, business, technical and engineering.

NAME(S) OF PROGRAMS:
● **Baden-Wuerttemberg-STIPENDIUM Work Immersion Study Program (WISP)**

TYPE:
Fellowships; Internships; Scholarships. Language Instruction. CDS International partners with the Baden-Wuerttemberg Stiftung and the American Association of Teachers of German (AATG) to offer the "Work Immersion Study Program" (WISP) exclusively to students at community colleges. WISP is a three-month work/study immersion program in Germany that includes a one-month intensive German language course and a two-month internship in the state of Baden-Wuerttemberg.

YEAR PROGRAM STARTED: 2001

PURPOSE:
To provide community college students with the unique opportunity to gain practical work experience in their career field, improve their German language skills and experience German culture firsthand.

ELIGIBILITY:
Candidate must:
(1) be a U.S. citizen or permanent resident;
(2) be a minimum age of 18, maximum age of 27;
(3) have at least one semester of German instruction completed upon departure to Germany;
(4) have at least one year of study at a community college in a field related to

business or in a technical field;
(5) have practical experience in the desired field and;
(6) be enrolled in an Associates degree program at time of application.

FINANCIAL DATA:
Scholarship includes transatlantic round-trip flight from New York City to Germany, free housing, monthly stipend, one-month intensive language course, and health and accident insurance while abroad.

NUMBER OF APPLICANTS MOST RECENT YEAR:
49.

NUMBER OF AWARDS: Up to 10.

APPLICATION INFORMATION:
Electronic submission of the application is preferred. All supporting materials must be sent to CDS by the deadline. Upon acceptance to the program, a $300 program fee must be paid.
Duration: Three months, summer.
Deadline: December 1.

PUBLICATIONS:
General information and applications.

ADDRESS INQUIRIES TO:
Will Maier, Program Manager, WISP
(See address above.)

***SPECIAL STIPULATIONS:**
This program is exclusively for community college students.

CDS INTERNATIONAL, INC. [955]
440 Park Avenue South, Second Floor
New York, NY 10016
(212) 497-3500
Fax: (212) 497-3535

E-MAIL ADDRESS:
cbyx@cdsintl.org

WEB SITE ADDRESS:
www.cbyx.info

FOUNDED: 1968

AREAS OF INTEREST:
All areas of culture, business, technical, and engineering.

NAME(S) OF PROGRAMS:
● **Congress-Bundestag Youth Exchange for Young Professionals**

TYPE:
Exchange programs; Fellowships; Internships; Scholarships; Work-study programs. Scholarship program with a strong focus on cultural exchange. One-year scholarship for work/study program to Germany including German language training, academic semester in Germany and internship component.

YEAR PROGRAM STARTED: 1983

PURPOSE:
To give participants understanding for everyday life, education and professional training in Germany.

ELIGIBILITY:
Requirements include:
(1) U.S. citizenship or permanent residency;
(2) 18 to 24 years of age at start of program;
(3) at least high school diploma or equivalent and;
(4) clear career goals, a solid academic background, and relevant work experience or internships in field strongly preferred.

No German language proficiency requirements.

FINANCIAL DATA:
Funding provided for international airfare, language training and study costs, living expenses during study phases, all seminars, and sickness and accident insurance while abroad.

COOPERATIVE FUNDING PROGRAMS: Funded in U.S. by the Bureau of Educational and Cultural Affairs of the Department of State and through the Administration of the Bundestag in Germany.

NUMBER OF APPLICANTS MOST RECENT YEAR: 630.

NUMBER OF AWARDS: 75.

APPLICATION INFORMATION:
Electronic submission of the application is preferred.
Duration: One year (July to July).
Deadline: December 1 for the following program year.

ADDRESS INQUIRIES TO:
Congress-Bundestag Youth Exchange for Young Professionals
(See address above.)

*SPECIAL STIPULATIONS:
Must be U.S. citizens or permanent residents, 18 to 24 years of age at the start of the program. Previous recipients of Congress-Bundestag scholarships are not eligible for this program.

CENTER FOR ADVANCED JUDAIC STUDIES   [956]
420 Walnut Street
Philadelphia, PA 19106
(215) 238-1290
Fax: (215) 238-1540

E-MAIL ADDRESS:
allenshe@sas.upenn.edu

WEB SITE ADDRESS:
www.cajs.upenn.edu

AREAS OF INTEREST:
Advanced research in Judaic and related studies.

NAME(S) OF PROGRAMS:
● **Judaic and Related Studies Postdoctoral Fellowships**

TYPE:
Fellowships.

PURPOSE:
To support education in Judaic and related studies.

ELIGIBILITY:
Individuals are eligible to apply.

FINANCIAL DATA:
Amount of support per award: Up to $45,000.

APPLICATION INFORMATION:
Duration: One year. Grants are not renewable.
Deadline: November 10.

ADDRESS INQUIRIES TO:
Sheila Allen
Fellowship Program Administrator
(See address above.)

CENTRE FOR INTERNATIONAL MOBILITY (CIMO)   [957]
Hakaniemenranta 6, Fifth Floor
FI-00531 Helsinki Finland
(358) 207 868 500
Fax: (358) 207 868 601

E-MAIL ADDRESS:
cimoinfo@cimo.fi

WEB SITE ADDRESS:
www.studyinfinland.fi
www.cimo.fi

FOUNDED: 1991

AREAS OF INTEREST:
International scholarships.

NAME(S) OF PROGRAMS:
● **CIMO Fellowships (Fellowships for Young Researchers)**
● **Finnish Government Scholarship Pool**
● **Scholarships for Finnish Studies and Research**

TYPE:
Fellowships; Research grants; Scholarships. The Finnish Government Scholarships are intended for postgraduate (after Master's-level degree) academic studies and research for three to nine months in a Finnish university. Scholarships are based mainly on bilateral cultural agreements or similar arrangements between Finland and the following countries: Australia, Austria, Belgium, Bulgaria, China, Cuba, Czech Republic, Egypt, France, Germany, Greece, Hungary, Iceland, India, Ireland, Israel, Italy, Japan, Luxembourg, Mexico, Mongolia, Namibia, the Netherlands, Poland, Portugal, Republic of Korea, Romania, Slovakia, Spain, Switzerland, Turkey and Ukraine.

The CIMO Fellowships are intended for postgraduate (after Master's-level degree) but not postdoctorate university-level studies in a Finnish university.

The Scholarships for Finnish Studies and Research are divided into two subprogrammes:
(a) The Scholarships for Post-Master's Studies and Research at a Finnish University are granted to nationals of all countries for postgraduate studies and research in Finnish language and literature, Finno-Ugric linguistics, ethnology and folklore.
(b) Short-Term Scholarships for Post-graduates and Researchers of Finnish language and culture are awarded to foreign post-Master's level students and researchers for short-term visits to archives, seminars, interviews or meetings with a tutor. Attendance at a conference must also include other kinds of work related to the applicant's research. Preference is given to applicants who are working on their Master's thesis.

LEGAL BASIS:
Finnish Government Scholarship Pool.

ELIGIBILITY:
For the Finnish Government Scholarships, applicants should have at least a Master-level degree.

For CIMO Fellowships, applicants should have at least a Master's degree (but not postdoctorate). It is open to nationals of any country.

For the Scholarships for Postgraduate Studies and Research (in Finnish language), applicants should have at least a Master's degree. It is open to nationals of all countries.

Short-Term Scholarships for Post-graduates and Researchers of Finnish language and culture are open to nationals of all countries.

GEOGRAPHIC RESTRICTIONS:
Finland.

FINANCIAL DATA:
Finnish Government Scholarships, CIMO Fellowships and Scholarships for Finnish Studies and Research: Expenses due to international travel to and from Finland are not covered.
Amount of support per award: Finnish Government Scholarships: EUR 1,200 per month; CIMO Fellowships (Fellowships for Young Researchers and University Teaching Staff): EUR 900 to 1,200 per month; Scholarships for Post-Master's Studies and Research: EUR 1,200 per month; Short-Term Scholarships for Post-graduates and Researchers: EUR 300 per week.

COOPERATIVE FUNDING PROGRAMS: Finnish Fulbright Center.

APPLICATION INFORMATION:
Finnish Government Scholarships: Applications should be made to the appropriate authority in the applicant's country and students can contact the CIMO in Finland for further information. It is necessary that applicants establish contact with the receiving institution prior to application.

CIMO Fellowships (Fellowships for Young Researchers): The grant is applied for by the Finnish receiving university department.

Short-Term Scholarships for Post-graduates and Researchers: Applications should be made, preferably in Finnish, on CIMO's application forms, which are available at Finnish embassies and consulates abroad and at CIMO's web site. Applications should be sent to CIMO.

Scholarships for Post-Master's Studies and Research, the grant is applied for by the Finnish receiving university.

Duration: Finnish Government Scholarships: Three to nine months; CIMO Fellowships (Fellowships for Young Researchers): Three to 12 months; Scholarships for Post-Master's Studies and Research: Three to 12 months; Short-Term Scholarships for Post-graduates and Researchers: one to four weeks.

Deadline: Finnish Government Scholarships: Consult the organization; CIMO Fellowships (Fellowships for Young Researchers) and Scholarships for Post-Master's Finnish Studies and Research: Year-round; Short-Term Scholarships for Post-graduates and Researchers: at least five months before the intended scholarship period.

WINSTON CHURCHILL FOUNDATION OF THE U.S. [958]
600 Madison Avenue, 16th Floor
New York, NY 10022-1737
(212) 752-3200
Fax: (212) 246-8330

E-MAIL ADDRESS:
info@winstonchurchillfoundation.org

WEB SITE ADDRESS:
www.winstonchurchillfoundation.org

FOUNDED: 1959

AREAS OF INTEREST:
Science, math and engineering.

NAME(S) OF PROGRAMS:
● **Churchill Scholarship**

TYPE:
Scholarships. Scholarship for one year of graduate work at Cambridge University.

YEAR PROGRAM STARTED: 1963

PURPOSE:
To encourage Anglo-American cooperation and American scientific and technological talent.

LEGAL BASIS:
Public charity.

ELIGIBILITY:
Candidate must be a citizen of the U.S., between 19 and 26 years of age, have a Bachelor's degree from an accredited U.S. college or university and be enrolled at one of 103 participating American institutions.

FINANCIAL DATA:
Amount of support per award: Tuition and fees, plus GBP 10,000 to GBP 12,000, depending on course of study, plus $1,000 travel grant. Total individual package is approximately $45,000 to $50,000.
Total amount of support: Approximately $650,000 in total grants for the year 2010.

NUMBER OF APPLICANTS MOST RECENT YEAR:
100.

NUMBER OF AWARDS: 14 for the year 2009.

APPLICATION INFORMATION:
Application forms are available from Foundation representatives at participating institutions.
Duration: One year.
Deadline: Early November.

OFFICERS:
John L. Loeb, Jr., Chairman
Patrick A. Gerschel, President
Peter Patrikis, Executive Director
David D. Burrows, Treasurer
James A. Fitzpatrick, Jr., Secretary

ADDRESS INQUIRIES TO:
Peter Patrikis, Executive Director
(See address above.)

CORPUS CHRISTI COLLEGE [959]
Trumpington Street
Cambridge, CB2 IRH England
44 (0)1223 338038
Fax: 44 (0)1223 765589

E-MAIL ADDRESS:
graduate-tutor@corpus.cam.ac.uk

WEB SITE ADDRESS:
www.corpus.cam.ac.uk

FOUNDED: 1352

AREAS OF INTEREST:
All subjects of postgraduate research at the University of Cambridge.

NAME(S) OF PROGRAMS:
● **Postgraduate Research at the University of Cambridge**

TYPE:
Scholarships.

PURPOSE:
To enable the candidate to pursue, as a member of the college, research in any subject leading to a research degree of Cambridge University.

LEGAL BASIS:
University College.

ELIGIBILITY:
Applicants must have a first degree from a recognized university and name Corpus Christi College as their college of first

preference on GAF. Candidates must become registered as University of Cambridge graduate students.

FINANCIAL DATA:
Amount of support per award: Up to GBP 13,000.
Matching fund requirements: It is a requirement that individuals who are eligible apply to other funding bodies, e.g. Cambridge Trusts.

NUMBER OF APPLICANTS MOST RECENT YEAR:
300.

NUMBER OF AWARDS: 8 for the year 2007-08.

APPLICATION INFORMATION:
Application forms for graduate study are available from the Board of Graduate Studies, 4 Mill Lane, Cambridge CB2 1YP, England, or online at www.admin.cam.ac.uk/univ/gsprospectus.
Duration: Up to three years.
Deadline: November 15.

ADDRESS INQUIRIES TO:
Tutor for Advanced Students
(See e-mail address above.)

COUNCIL FOR INTERNATIONAL EXCHANGE OF SCHOLARS (CIES) [960]
3007 Tilden Street, N.W., Suite 5L
Washington, DC 20008-3009
(202) 686-4000
Fax: (202) 362-3442

E-MAIL ADDRESS:
scholars@iie.org

WEB SITE ADDRESS:
www.iie.org/cies

FOUNDED: 1947

AREAS OF INTEREST:
Fulbright Scholar grants to more than 125 countries for teaching, research or a combination of both.

NAME(S) OF PROGRAMS:
● **Fulbright Scholar Program**

TYPE:
Awards/prizes. Awards to university faculty and professionals outside academe for teaching and/or advanced research worldwide. Awards are available in 45 disciplines from agriculture to urban planning.

YEAR PROGRAM STARTED: 1947

PURPOSE:
To promote mutual understanding and scholarship.

LEGAL BASIS:
Private, nonprofit organization that receives funding from the U.S. State Department.

ELIGIBILITY:
Applicant must be a U.S. citizen at the time of application and hold a Ph.D or equivalent professional/terminal degree. Recognized professional standing for artists and professionals outside of academe is required.

FINANCIAL DATA:
Amount of support per award: Award benefits vary by country. Usually a base stipend, in-country maintenance and travel.
Total amount of support: Varies.

NUMBER OF APPLICANTS MOST RECENT YEAR:
Approximately 3,000.

NUMBER OF AWARDS: Approximately 800.

APPLICATION INFORMATION:
Application forms and detailed awards information are available February 1 from the Council. Applications will be screened by CIES peer review committees. Recommendations will be made by the binational Fulbright Commissions or U.S. Information Service posts overseas, with final selection by the J. William Fulbright Foreign Scholarship Board.
Duration: Two to 12 months.
Deadline: August 2 for teaching and research grants; November 1 and February 1 for international educator seminars. Rolling deadline for the short-term Fulbright Specialist Program.

PUBLICATIONS:
Annual awards; catalog; descriptive brochure; annual report.

COUNCIL FOR INTERNATIONAL EXCHANGE OF SCHOLARS (CIES) [961]
3007 Tilden Street, N.W.
Suite 5L
Washington, DC 20008-3009
(202) 686-4013
Fax: (202) 362-3442

E-MAIL ADDRESS:
scholars@iie.org

WEB SITE ADDRESS:
www.iie.org/cies

AREAS OF INTEREST:
Academic/professional field in Middle East and North Africa.

NAME(S) OF PROGRAMS:
● **Middle East, North Africa and Regional Research Programs and Country Grants**

TYPE:
Fellowships; Research grants; Scholarships.

ELIGIBILITY:
Applicants must be U.S. citizens with a Ph.D. or equivalent professional/terminal degree at the time of application.

GEOGRAPHIC RESTRICTIONS:
Middle East and North Africa.

FINANCIAL DATA:
Awards include travel, stipend, and monthly payments.
Amount of support per award: Varies.

NUMBER OF AWARDS: U.S. Scholars Grantees: 51 lecturing and 19 research.

APPLICATION INFORMATION:
Applicants must use the Council's application form, which is available online.
Duration: Three to 10 months of research, lecturing one or two semesters.
Deadline: August 1.

ADDRESS INQUIRIES TO:
Danielle Antonio, Senior Program Officer
MiddleEast/North Africa
(See address above.)

COUNCIL OF AMERICAN OVERSEAS RESEARCH CENTERS (CAORC) [962]
P.O. Box 37012
MRC 178
Washington, DC 20013-7012
(202) 633-1599
Fax: (202) 786-2430

E-MAIL ADDRESS:
fellowships@caorc.org

WEB SITE ADDRESS:
www.caorc.org

FOUNDED: 1981

AREAS OF INTEREST:
Promoting the work of American overseas
research centers.

NAME(S) OF PROGRAMS:
- **Multi-Country Research Fellowship
  Program**

TYPE:
Fellowships; Research grants. Requires
scholars to conduct research in more than
one country, at least one of which hosts a
participating American overseas research
center.

PURPOSE:
To advance higher learning and scholarly
research by providing a forum for
communication and cooperation among
American overseas advanced research
centers; to provide general and continuing
publicity about the importance and
contributions of the centers; to exchange
operational and administrative information
among the centers; to exchange scholarly and
research information among the centers; to
encourage joint research projects.

LEGAL BASIS:
501(c)(3) organization.

ELIGIBILITY:
Program is open to U.S. Master's students,
doctoral candidates and scholars who have
already earned their Ph.D. in fields in the
humanities, social sciences, or allied natural
sciences and wish to conduct research of
regional or trans-regional significance. Must
be U.S. citizen or permanent resident.

U.S. State Department travel restrictions
apply.

FINANCIAL DATA:
Amount of support per award: Up to
$10,000.
Total amount of support: Master's: $8,000;
Doctoral and postdoctoral fellows: $12,000.

NUMBER OF APPLICANTS MOST RECENT YEAR:
130.

NUMBER OF AWARDS: Master's: 4;
Ph.D./Postdoctoral: 10.

APPLICATION INFORMATION:
A complete application consists of:
(1) application form;
(2) project description (1,500 words or less)
describing the nature of the proposal and
competence to carry out the required
research;
(3) project bibliography/literature review (one
page maximum);
(4) two signed letters of recommendation;
(5) curriculum vitae (three pages maximum)
and;
(6) graduate transcripts (Master's and Ph.D.
candidates only).

Applicants are urged to review the
Application Instructions before submitting the
application.
Duration: Master's: Minimum of 60 days;
Ph.D./Postdoctoral: Minimum of 90 days.
Deadline: Mid-January.

ADDRESS INQUIRIES TO:
Monica Clark, Program Manager
(See address above.)

*SPECIAL STIPULATIONS:
Fellows must complete their research within
a specific time.

CYPRUS AMERICAN
ARCHAEOLOGICAL RESEARCH
INSTITUTE   [963]
656 Beacon Street, 5th Floor
Boston, MA 02215
(617) 353-6571
Fax: (617) 353-6575

E-MAIL ADDRESS:
caari@bu.edu

WEB SITE ADDRESS:
www.caari.org

FOUNDED: 1900

AREAS OF INTEREST:
The study of humanistic disciplines, such as
anthropology, archaeology, Biblical studies,
epigraphy, history, history of art and
architecture, literature, philology, prehistory
and topography, relating in particular to the
Middle East from prehistoric times to the
modern era.

Cyprus American Archaeological Research
Institute is the only residential archaeological
institute on the island of Cyprus and serves
as a center for the dissemination of
information about the archaeology of Cyprus.

NAME(S) OF PROGRAMS:
- **The Anita Cecil O'Donovan Fellowship**
- **The Danielle Parks Memorial
  Fellowship**
- **The Helena Wylde Swiny and Stuart
  Swiny Fellowship**

TYPE:
Fellowships; Research grants; Residencies;
Travel grants. There are a large variety of
fellowships available through the Near
Eastern Fellowship Program for the
American Schools of Oriental Research and
affiliated overseas research centers. Besides
The Cyprus American Archaeological
Research Institute in Nicosia, Cyprus
(CAARI), there are also The American
Center of Oriental Research in Amman,
Jordan (ACOR) and the W.F. Albright
Institute of Archaeological Research in
Jerusalem, Israel (AIAR). Contact the
American Schools of Oriental Research for
full details.

The Anita Cecil O'Donovan Fellowship is an
award to a graduate student of any
nationality, enrolled in a graduate program in
any nation, to pursue research on a project
relevant to the archaeology and/or culture of
Cyprus.

The Danielle Parks Memorial Fellowship is
for a graduate student of any nationality who
needs to work in Cyprus to further his or her
research on a subject of relevance to Cypriot
archaeology and culture.

The Helena Wylde Swiny and Stuart Swiny
Fellowship is a grant to a graduate student of
any nationality in a U.S. or Canadian
university or college to pursue a research
project relevant to an ongoing field project in
Cyprus or that requires work on Cyprus
itself.

YEAR PROGRAM STARTED: 1940

PURPOSE:
To help scholars undertake high-quality
research and field projects in the Middle East
and to encourage interdisciplinary study and
communication among scholars.

LEGAL BASIS:
Nonprofit, archaeological research
corporation.

ELIGIBILITY:
All ASOR awards are open to qualified
students and scholars from any country.
Applicants must be affiliated with an
institution that is a member of the ASOR
corporation or must be an individual
professional member. Prime consideration is
given to applicants whose projects are
affiliated with ASOR.

ASOR does not conduct the competition nor
take part in the selection process for the
Fulbright Fellowships, but encourages
qualified scholars to apply for these awards.

FINANCIAL DATA:
The Anita Cecil O'Donovan Fellowship and
The Helena Wylde Swiny and Stuart Swiny
Fellowship will be used to fund research time
in residence at CAARI and to help defray
costs of travel.

The Danielle Parks Memorial Fellowship
covers travel to and living expenses in
Cyprus.
Amount of support per award: $1,000 each.
Total amount of support: $3,000.

NUMBER OF APPLICANTS MOST RECENT YEAR:
11.

NUMBER OF AWARDS: 1 each.

APPLICATION INFORMATION:
Application form is available on the Institute
web site. All eligible persons are encouraged
to apply for as many fellowships and
professorships as they wish, but a person can
hold only one award at a time. Persons who
have received an award in one year can
reapply for the same or other awards the
following year, but new applicants will have
priority.
Duration: One-time awards.
Deadline: February 1.

STAFF:
Donald Keller, Administrator

ADDRESS INQUIRIES TO:
Fellowship Committee
(See address above.)

*SPECIAL STIPULATIONS:
For the O'Donovan, Parks and Swiny
Fellowships, residence at CAARI is
mandatory.

For the Danielle Parks Memorial Fellowship,
the fellow is expected during his or her stay
to give a presentation at CAARI on a subject
related to his or her research. The fellow will
periodically keep the Director of CAARI
apprised of his or her research activities and
will acknowledge CAARI and the Danielle
Parks Memorial Fellowship in any
publication that emerges from the research
carried during the Fellowship.

THE LADY DAVIS FELLOWSHIP
TRUST   [964]
Hebrew University
Givat Ram
Jerusalem 91904 Israel
972-2-651-2306 (voice mail)
972-2-658-4723
Fax: 972-2-566-3848

E-MAIL ADDRESS:
ldft@vms.huji.ac.il

WEB SITE ADDRESS:
ldft.huji.ac.il

FOUNDED: 1973

NAME(S) OF PROGRAMS:
- **Doctoral Students Fellowship**
- **Post-doctoral Researchers Fellowship**
- **Visiting Professorships Fellowship**

TYPE:
Fellowships.

YEAR PROGRAM STARTED: 1973

LEGAL BASIS:
University association.

APPLICATION INFORMATION:
Prospective candidates must establish contact with the relevant department at the Hebrew University, and ensure that there is a faculty member willing to sponsor the application.

Duration: Postdoctoral researchers and doctoral students may request an extension of a year to their fellowships. Deadlines are the same as for initial application. There is no need to submit all the information again. A letter from the researcher/student explaining the request for the extension together with a supporting letter from the scholar is sufficient.

Visiting professorships and associate professorships last from three to nine months during the academic year.

Deadline: Hebrew University: Visiting professorships, November 30; Post-doctoral Researchers, December 31.

*PLEASE NOTE:
Doctoral Students Fellowship suspended for the 2010-11 academic year.

*SPECIAL STIPULATIONS:
Fellowships may not be deferred from one year to the next.

Fellows who have won another concurrent fellowship must disclose this to the Trust, whereupon the amount of the award will be reviewed.

A Fellow is expected to take up the Fellowship within the period of the academic year for which he has applied (in other words, between October 1 and September 30 in the following year). Attempts are made to be as elastic as possible should a Fellow expect to arrive before or after October 1.

FLANDERS HOUSE [965]

620 Eighth Avenue, 44th Floor
New York, NY 10018
(212) 584-2200 ext. 2004
Fax: (212) 575-3606

E-MAIL ADDRESS:
info@flandershouse.org

WEB SITE ADDRESS:
www.flandershouse.org

AREAS OF INTEREST:
Belgium.

NAME(S) OF PROGRAMS:
- **Fellowship of the Flanders House**

TYPE:
Fellowships. Granted for study or research at universities, conservatories of music, or art academies recognized by the Flemish Community and encompasses the studies of art, music, humanities, social and political sciences, law, economics, sciences and medicine.

PURPOSE:
To assist American college students who wish to continue their postgraduate education in Flanders, Belgium.

ELIGIBILITY:
Open to U.S. citizens (in case of dual citizenship, please include proof) of no more than 35 years of age at the time of application deadline, who hold a Bachelor's or Master's degree, and who have no other Belgian sources of income.

FINANCIAL DATA:
Includes a monthly stipend, tuition fees at a Flemish institution, health insurance and public liability insurance in accordance with Belgian law. There is no reimbursement of travel expenses.

Amount of support per award: Monthly stipend approximately EUR 770; tuition fees maximum EUR 540. The amount of the stipend is subject to change without notice.

NUMBER OF AWARDS: 5.

APPLICATION INFORMATION:
Duration: 10 months.
Deadline: January 31. Notification by July.

ADDRESS INQUIRIES TO:
Nicolas Polet, Policy Officer
(See address above.)

*PLEASE NOTE:
The academic year, for most institutes of higher learning in Flanders, starts at the end of September.

THE GARDEN CLUB OF AMERICA

14 East 60th Street
New York, NY 10022
(212) 753-8287
Fax: (212) 753-0134

E-MAIL ADDRESS:
scholarships@gcamerica.org

WEB SITE ADDRESS:
www.gcamerica.org

TYPE:
Exchange programs; Fellowships. A graduate academic year in the U.S. for a British student and a work-study program for an American at universities and botanical gardens in the U.K. in fields related to horticulture, botany and landscape design.

See entry 2320 for full listing.

THE GARDEN CLUB OF AMERICA

14 East 60th Street
New York, NY 10022
(212) 753-8287
Fax: (212) 753-0134

E-MAIL ADDRESS:
scholarships@gcamerica.org

WEB SITE ADDRESS:
www.gcamerica.org

TYPE:
Research grants. Anne S. Chatham Fellowship in Medicinal Botany: Grant to enable study in medicinal botany.

GCA Awards in Tropical Botany: Grants to enable field study in tropical botany.

Frances M. Peacock Scholarship for Native Bird Habitat: Financial assistance to college seniors and graduate students to study

habitat-related issues that will benefit threatened or endangered bird species and lend useful information for land management decisions.

See entry 2321 for full listing.

GERMAN ACADEMIC EXCHANGE SERVICE [966]

871 United Nations Plaza
New York, NY 10017
(212) 758-3223
Fax: (212) 755-5780

E-MAIL ADDRESS:
daadny@daad.org

WEB SITE ADDRESS:
www.daad.org

FOUNDED: 1925

AREAS OF INTEREST:
International exchanges in education, research in higher education, and academic teaching staff; scholarships to German and foreign students.

CONSULTING OR VOLUNTEER SERVICES:
DAAD serves on a consultancy service in the field of international academic mobility.

NAME(S) OF PROGRAMS:
- **DAAD Scholarship Programs for Study and Research in Germany**

TYPE:
Awards/prizes; Conferences/seminars; Exchange programs; Fellowships; Internships; Professorships; Project/program grants; Research grants; Scholarships; Visiting scholars. The German Academic Exchange Service is the New York office of the Deutscher Akademischer Austausch Dienst (DAAD), a German organization with its head office in Bonn. DAAD offers a wide range of opportunities to students, scholars and higher education institutions of the U.S. and Canada, from undergraduate students to faculty, for study and research in Germany.

YEAR PROGRAM STARTED: 1971

PURPOSE:
To provide information on study and research opportunities in higher education at home and abroad; to promote international higher education and research through scholarships; to recruit and place German academic teaching staff from all disciplines at foreign institutions of higher education; to maintain a network of former scholarship holders abroad.

LEGAL BASIS:
Registered association under private law.

ELIGIBILITY:
DAAD grants are available to faculty and students in the U.S. and Canada to participate in a wide variety of academic activities.

GEOGRAPHIC RESTRICTIONS:
United States and Canada.

FINANCIAL DATA:
Amount of support per award: Varies.
Total amount of support: Varies.

APPLICATION INFORMATION:
Duration: Varies.
Deadline: Varies.

PUBLICATIONS:
Grants for Study and Research in Germany.

ADDRESS INQUIRIES TO:
Jane Fu, Information Officer
(See address above.)

GERMAN HISTORICAL INSTITUTE

1607 New Hampshire Avenue, N.W.
Washington, DC 20009-2562
(202) 387-3355
Fax: (202) 483-3430

E-MAIL ADDRESS:
info@ghi-dc.org

WEB SITE ADDRESS:
www.ghi-dc.org

TYPE:
Fellowships. The Institute awards short-term fellowships to German and American doctoral students as well as postdoctoral scholars/Habilitanden in the fields of German history, the history of German-American relations, and the role of Germany and the U.S. in international relations.

See entry 631 for full listing.

THE HAGUE ACADEMY OF INTERNATIONAL LAW

Peace Palace
Carnegieplein 2
2517 KJ The Hague The Netherlands
(31-70) 302-4242
Fax: (31-70) 302-4153

E-MAIL ADDRESS:
registration@hagueacademy.nl

WEB SITE ADDRESS:
www.hagueacademy.nl

TYPE:
Project/program grants. Study programs. Residential scholarships for doctoral candidates from developing countries whose thesis, in private international law or public international law, is in an advanced stage of preparation, who reside in their home country and who do not have access to scientific sources.

See entry 2104 for full listing.

THE HAGUE ACADEMY OF INTERNATIONAL LAW

Peace Palace
Carnegieplein 2
2517 KJ The Hague The Netherlands
(31-70) 302-4242
Fax: (31-70) 302-4153

E-MAIL ADDRESS:
registration@hagueacademy.nl

WEB SITE ADDRESS:
www.hagueacademy.nl

TYPE:
Project/program grants; Scholarships. Study programs. A limited number of scholarships are given to cover tuition and living expenses while studying at the three-week summer session of the Hague Academy of International Law. Because of the limited number, granting of scholarships to attendees from every country is not possible.

See entry 2105 for full listing.

HEINRICH HERTZ-STIFTUNG [967]

Ministry of Innovation, Science and
Research des Landes Nordrhein-Westfalen
Heinrich Hertz-Stiftung
Voelklinger Strasse 49
40221 Duesseldorf Germany
(0211) 896 4266
Fax: (0211) 896 4407

E-MAIL ADDRESS:
rosemarie.hillebrand@miwf.nrw.de
heinrich-hertz-stiftung@miwf.nrw.de

WEB SITE ADDRESS:
www.heinrich-hertz-stiftung.de

FOUNDED: 1961

AREAS OF INTEREST:
International exchange of scientists.

TYPE:
Exchange programs; Scholarships. Scholarships to promote the sciences through the exchange of university teachers and young scientists (without special restrictions).

YEAR PROGRAM STARTED: 1962

PURPOSE:
To promote sciences.

LEGAL BASIS:
Public foundation.

ELIGIBILITY:
University teachers and young scientists are eligible. Non-German citizens should have a working knowledge of German and German citizens a working knowledge of the language of the host country.

GEOGRAPHIC RESTRICTIONS:
Land Nordrhine-Westphalia.

FINANCIAL DATA:
Amount of support per award: Award values are dependent upon individual needs.
Total amount of support: Varies.

NUMBER OF AWARDS: 21 for the year 2010.

APPLICATION INFORMATION:
Applications should be submitted only by third persons. A curriculum vitae, examination record, two references and a full description of the planned project with a timetable are to be included. Further information may be obtained on request.
Duration: Dependent upon individual needs. Two years maximum.
Deadline: Three months before the date of the board of trustees of the Heinrich Hertz-Stiftung.

PUBLICATIONS:
Hinweise auf die Antragstellung; *Die Heinrich Hertz-Stiftung*, booklet; Heinrich Hertz-Stiftung, folder; *Festakt anlasslich der 100*; *Kuratoriumssitzung, documentation*, booklet.

ADDRESS INQUIRIES TO:
Ministry of Innovation, Science and Research des Landes Nordrhein-Westfalen Heinrich Hertz-Stiftung
E-mail: heinrich-hertz-stiftung@miwf.nrw.de

INSTITUTE FOR THE INTERNATIONAL EDUCATION OF STUDENTS (IES)

33 North LaSalle Street
15th Floor
Chicago, IL 60602
(312) 944-1750
(800) 995-2300
Fax: (312) 944-1448

E-MAIL ADDRESS:
info@IESabroad.org

WEB SITE ADDRESS:
www.IESabroad.org

TYPE:
Scholarships. IES Merit-Based Scholarships supplement U.S. college and university

awards for undergraduates studying with IES in Argentina, Australia, Austria, Chile, China, Ecuador, England, France, Germany, India, Ireland, Italy, Japan, Morocco, the Netherlands, New Zealand, South Africa and Spain. Merit-Based Scholarships are available for proven strength and interest in cross-cultural and comparative studies, fine arts, foreign language, high achievement, IES Asia programs, IES South American programs, international business, international relations, leadership, science and urban issues. Diversity Scholarships are also available as are scholarships for students who attend historically Black colleges/universities.

Need-based grants available to students with demonstrated financial need.

All IES Abroad aid is available only to students from schools within the IES Abroad Consortium and who attend an IES Abroad program.

See entry 1819 for full listing.

INSTITUTE OF INTERNATIONAL EDUCATION [968]

U.S. Department of State Fulbright U.S. Student Program
U.S. Student Programs Division
809 United Nations Plaza
New York, NY 10017-3580
(212) 984-5330

WEB SITE ADDRESS:
www.us.fulbrightonline.org

FOUNDED: 1919

AREAS OF INTEREST:
International educational and cultural exchange on all levels.

NAME(S) OF PROGRAMS:
- **U.S. Department of State Fulbright U.S. Student Program**

TYPE:
Exchange programs; Scholarships. Grants for graduate study, research or English Teaching Assistantships abroad.

YEAR PROGRAM STARTED: 1946

PURPOSE:
To give U.S. students the opportunity to live and study in a foreign country for one academic year and to increase mutual understanding between the people of the U.S. and other countries through the exchange of persons, knowledge and skills.

LEGAL BASIS:
Nonprofit, as described under Internal Revenue Code 501(c)(3).

ELIGIBILITY:
Candidates must possess U.S. citizenship, a B.A. degree by the beginning date of the grant, language proficiency sufficient to carry out the project overseas and good health. Preference in selecting candidates is for those who have had the majority of high school and undergraduate college education at educational institutions in the U.S. Candidates may not hold a doctoral degree at the time of application.

FINANCIAL DATA:
Fulbright Grants provide round-trip transportation, language or orientation course (where appropriate), tuition, books, maintenance for one academic year in only one country and health and accident

insurance. The maintenance allowance is based on living costs in the host country and is sufficient to meet normal expenses of a single person.

COOPERATIVE FUNDING PROGRAMS: Funds from other scholarships, fellowships or grants in dollars or foreign currency received concurrently with a Fulbright Grant will be deducted if they duplicate the Fulbright benefits. No deduction is made if other grants are for assistance in meeting family expenses of grantees or other expenses not covered by the grant.

NUMBER OF APPLICANTS MOST RECENT YEAR: 9,397.

NUMBER OF AWARDS: Approximately 1,600 for the year 2012-13.

APPLICATION INFORMATION:
Enrolled students should contact the Fulbright Program Adviser on their campus. Candidates who are not enrolled in an educational institution should contact IIE, U.S. Student Programs Division, at the address above to obtain application material.

Duration: One academic year.

Deadline: Enrolled students should submit their applications to their campus Fulbright Program Advisers by the dates set by them. At-large candidates must submit their applications to the IIE office in October.

INTERNATIONAL DEVELOPMENT RESEARCH CENTRE (IDRC) [969]

150 Kent Street
Mailroom Suite 990
Ottawa ON K1P 0B2 Canada
(613) 236-6163 ext. 2098
Fax: (613) 236-4026

E-MAIL ADDRESS:
cta@idrc.ca

WEB SITE ADDRESS:
www.idrc.ca/awards

FOUNDED: 1970

AREAS OF INTEREST:
Agriculture, forestry and biology.

NAME(S) OF PROGRAMS:
● **The Bentley Cropping Systems Fellowship**

TYPE:
Endowments. Fellowship provides assistance to Canadian students or researchers and developing country nationals with a university degree in agriculture, forestry or biology who wish to undertake postgraduate, applied on-farm research in a developing country with cooperating farmers.

PURPOSE:
To promote applied, on-farm research in a developing country with cooperating farmers.

ELIGIBILITY:
Applicants must be citizens, permanent residents of Canada, or citizens of a developing country who are registered in a Canadian university or in a recognized university in a developing country in agriculture, forestry or biology for a Master's or Ph.D. degree.

Program can involve research in any developing region of the world, excluding Burma, Central Asia, Cuba, Eastern Europe, Iran and Iraq.

FINANCIAL DATA:
Amount of support per award: $30,000 (CAN) per year.

NUMBER OF APPLICANTS MOST RECENT YEAR: Varies.

NUMBER OF AWARDS: 1 biennially.

APPLICATION INFORMATION:
Duration: 18 to 24 months. Renewable upon reapplication.

Deadline: October 1 in even-numbered years.

ADDRESS INQUIRIES TO:
Fellowships and Awards
(See address above.)

INTERNATIONAL DEVELOPMENT RESEARCH CENTRE (IDRC)

150 Kent Street
Mailroom Suite 990
Ottawa ON K1P 0B2 Canada
(613) 236-6163 ext. 2098
Fax: (613) 236-4026

E-MAIL ADDRESS:
cta@idrc.ca

WEB SITE ADDRESS:
www.idrc.ca/awards

TYPE:
Awards/prizes. The Internship award program provides exposure to research for international development through a program of training in research management and grant administration under the guidance of Centre program staff. The intern will undertake a program of research on the topic submitted when competing for the internship and will be trained in the techniques of research management through hands-on experience with the Centre's policies and practices for grant administration under the mentorship of a program officer.

See entry 1388 for full listing.

INTERNATIONAL FEDERATION OF UNIVERSITY WOMEN

10, rue du Lac
CH 1207 Geneva Switzerland
(4122) 731 23 80
Fax: (4122) 738 04 40

E-MAIL ADDRESS:
fellowships@ifuw.org

WEB SITE ADDRESS:
www.ifuw.org

TYPE:
Fellowships; Research grants; Training grants. IFUW fellowships and grants are awarded biennially to encourage and enable women graduates to undertake original research or obtain further training in the humanities, social sciences and natural sciences.

See entry 1149 for full listing.

INTERNATIONAL RESEARCH & EXCHANGES BOARD (IREX) [970]

2121 K Street, N.W.
Suite 700
Washington, DC 20037
(202) 628-8188
Fax: (202) 628-8189

E-MAIL ADDRESS:
irex@irex.org

WEB SITE ADDRESS:
www.irex.org

FOUNDED: 1968

AREAS OF INTEREST:
Academic research exchanges and professional training programs in Europe, Eurasia, the Middle East and North Africa, and Asia.

NAME(S) OF PROGRAMS:
● **ECA Alumni Small Grants Program**
● **Eurasia/South Asia Teaching Excellence and Achievement Program (TEA)**
● **Eurasian Undergraduate Exchange Program (UGRAD)**
● **Individual Advanced Research Opportunities (IARO)**
● **International Educators Program (IEP)**
● **Edmund S. Muskie Graduate Fellowship Program**
● **Regional Policy Symposium**
● **Short-Term Travel Grants**

TYPE:
Conferences/seminars; Exchange programs; Fellowships; Project/program grants; Research grants; Training grants; Travel grants; Visiting scholars. IARO: Grants to Master's, predoctoral and postdoctoral U.S. scholars for research at institutions in Europe and Eurasia.

IEP: Grants to secondary teachers from the Near East, South Asia and Southeast Asia to the U.S. to further develop expertise in their subject areas, enhance their teaching skills, and increase their knowledge about the U.S.

Muskie: Grants to graduate students and professionals from Armenia, Azerbaijan, Belarus, Georgia, Kazakhstan, Kyrgyzstan, Moldova, Russia, Tajikistan, Turkmenistan, Ukraine and Uzbekistan for one-year non-degree, one-year degree or two-year degree study in the U.S. in business administration, economics, education, environmental management, international affairs, journalism and mass communication, law, library and information science, public administration, public health and public policy.

Short-term Travel Grants (two to eight weeks) to U.S. researchers for scholarly projects focusing on Eurasia and Europe.

Small Grants: Grants to NIS alumni of ECA-sponsored programs for professional development activities.

Regional Policy Symposium: A symposium for senior and junior scholars to meet and discuss a variety of political, economic, historical and cultural topics. Each year focuses on a new region.

TEA: Grants to secondary-school teachers from Eurasia and South Asia with unique opportunities to develop expertise in their subject areas, enhance their teaching skills, and increase their knowledge about the U.S.

UGRAD: Fellowships for first, second and third-year undergraduate students from Eurasia to study at a U.S. undergraduate institution for one year.

YEAR PROGRAM STARTED: 1968

PURPOSE:
To promote advanced field research and professional training programs between the U.S. and the countries of Europe, Eurasia, Asia and the Middle East and North Africa.

LEGAL BASIS:
Nonprofit organization.

GEOGRAPHIC RESTRICTIONS:
United States, Europe, Eurasia, the Middle East, Asia and North Africa.

FINANCIAL DATA:
Amount of support per award: Varies per program.

APPLICATION INFORMATION:
Application information is available upon request.

PUBLICATIONS:
Policy papers, application materials.

ADDRESS INQUIRIES TO:
Program Coordinator
(See address above.)

ISTITUTO ITALIANO PER GLI STUDI STORICI

Via Benedetto Croce, 12
80134 Naples Italy
0039-81-5517159
0039-81-5512390
Fax: 0039-81-5514813

E-MAIL ADDRESS:
istituto@iiss.it

WEB SITE ADDRESS:
www.iiss.it

TYPE:
Awards/prizes; Conferences/seminars; Research grants; Scholarships. Awards for historical and philosophical studies at the Istituto Italiano per gli Studi Storici in Naples.

See entry 638 for full listing.

JAPAN INFORMATION CENTER   [971]

Consulate General of Japan
299 Park Avenue, 18th Floor
New York, NY 10171-0025
(212) 418-4452
Fax: (212) 371-1294

E-MAIL ADDRESS:
scholarship@ny.mofa.go.jp

WEB SITE ADDRESS:
www.ny.us.emb-japan.go.jp

FOUNDED: 1955

AREAS OF INTEREST:
Japanese language and cultural studies.

NAME(S) OF PROGRAMS:
● **Japanese Government (Monbukagakusho) Scholarships for Japanese Studies**

TYPE:
Scholarships. Undergraduate scholarships awarded to foreign students who wish to pursue Japanese language and cultural studies in Japan. The program offers students an intensive course of Japanese language and introduction to Japanese studies in various aspects.

YEAR PROGRAM STARTED: 1955

PURPOSE:
To provide funding for non-Japanese students who want to pursue a course of Japanese and cultural studies in Japan.

LEGAL BASIS:
Japanese government agency.

ELIGIBILITY:
Applicants must:
(1) be nationals of the country to which the scholarships are offered;
(2) be at least 17 years and less than 22 years of age as of April 1 of the year of application;
(3) be regular students who follow an undergraduate course at a university in their own country or a third country and who are mainly third-year students or above in that course;
(4) be specializing in a field concerning Japanese language or Japanese culture at their university;
(5) have good knowledge of the Japanese language and;
(6) be in good health.

Applicants must have a background in Japanese studies to qualify. A written Japanese examination will be given to selected applicants before being considered by the government offices in Japan.

FINANCIAL DATA:
Amount of support per award: JPY 123,000 per month (subject to change), plus tuition, fees and round-trip transportation costs.

Total amount of support: Varies.

APPLICATION INFORMATION:
Applicants should contact the appropriate Japanese consulate. Consulates General are located in Anchorage, Atlanta, Boston, Chicago, Denver, Detroit, Guam, Honolulu, Houston, Los Angeles, Miami, Nashville, New York City, Portland, San Francisco, Seattle and Washington, DC.

Duration: One academic year.

Deadline: Early August.

PUBLICATIONS:
Application guidelines.

ADDRESS INQUIRIES TO:
MEXT Scholarship Office
(See address above.)

*PLEASE NOTE:
Placement of grantees to universities will be decided by Monbukagakusho after consultation with the universities concerned.

JAPAN INFORMATION CENTER   [972]

Consulate General of Japan
299 Park Avenue, 18th Floor
New York, NY 10171-0025
(212) 371-8222
Fax: (212) 371-1294

E-MAIL ADDRESS:
scholarship@ny.mofa.go.jp

WEB SITE ADDRESS:
www.ny.us.emb-japan.go.jp

FOUNDED: 1955

AREAS OF INTEREST:
Humanities and social sciences: literature, history, aesthetics, law, politics, economics, commerce, pedagogy, psychology, sociology, music, fine arts, natural sciences, pure science, engineering, agriculture, fisheries, pharmacology, medicine, dentistry and home economics.

NAME(S) OF PROGRAMS:
● **Japanese Government (Monbukagakusho) Scholarships for Research Students**

TYPE:
Scholarships. Graduate scholarships awarded to foreign students who wish to study at Japanese universities as nondegree research students.

PURPOSE:
To help students wishing to pursue Japan-related studies.

LEGAL BASIS:
Japanese government agency.

ELIGIBILITY:
Applicants must be nationals of the country to which the scholarships are offered, must be under 35 years of age as of April 1 of the year of the award, must be university or college graduates, must be willing to study the Japanese language and to receive instruction in that language and must be in good health. The study area must be in the same field as the applicant has studied (or is now studying) or a related one.

FINANCIAL DATA:
Amount of support per award: JPY 150,000 per month.

APPLICATION INFORMATION:
Applicants should contact the appropriate Japanese consulate. Consulates General are located in Anchorage, Atlanta, Boston, Chicago, Hagatna (Guam), Honolulu, Houston, Los Angeles, Miami, Nashville, New York City, Portland, San Francisco and Seattle.

Duration: Up to two years, with possibility of extension.

PUBLICATIONS:
Application guidelines.

ADDRESS INQUIRIES TO:
Noriko Furuhata
Educational Program Coordinator
Monbukagakusho Scholarship for Research Students
(See address above.)

*PLEASE NOTE:
Field of study must be one of those available at the Japanese universities and practical training given by factories or companies is excluded.

MACKENZIE KING SCHOLARSHIP TRUST

c/o J. Blom, Faculty of Law
1822 East Mall, University of British Columbia
Vancouver BC V6T 1Z1 Canada
(604) 822-4564
Fax: (604) 822-8108

E-MAIL ADDRESS:
mkingscholarships@law.ubc.ca

WEB SITE ADDRESS:
www.mkingscholarships.ca

TYPE:
Scholarships. For graduate study, either in the U.S. or the U.K., in the field of international or industrial relations (including the international or industrial aspects of law, history, politics or economics).

See entry 1825 for full listing.

THE KOSCIUSZKO FOUNDATION, INC.   [973]

15 East 65th Street
New York, NY 10065
(212) 734-2130 ext. 210.

E-MAIL ADDRESS:
addy@thekf.org

WEB SITE ADDRESS:
www.thekf.org

FOUNDED: 1925

AREAS OF INTEREST:
Strengthening of cultural and educational bonds between the U.S. and Poland through an exchange program to Poland for the purpose of Polish language, culture and history studies.

NAME(S) OF PROGRAMS:
- **The Kosciuszko Foundation Year Abroad Program**

TYPE:
Scholarships. The Year Abroad Program at the Center for Polish Language and Culture in the World, Jagiellonian University (Krakow) offers American students the opportunity to study Polish language, history, literature, and culture for one academic year or one semester. This program allows students to spend their undergraduate junior or senior year in Poland. Undergraduate credit may be transferred.

PURPOSE:
To enable American students to pursue an undergraduate course of Polish language, literature, history and culture at the Center for Polish Language and Culture, Jagiellonian University, Krakow.

LEGAL BASIS:
501(c)(3) not-for-profit organization.

ELIGIBILITY:
U.S. citizens enrolled at a U.S. college or university who will be entering their junior or senior year can apply. Graduate students, with the exception of those at the dissertation level, can also apply. Minimum grade point average of 3.0 is required.

Polish citizens are not eligible.

FINANCIAL DATA:
Scholarship offers a tuition waiver, housing and a monthly stipend paid in zloty towards living expenses. Recipients also receive $150 per month from the Foundation for living expenses. Transportation to and from Poland is not included.

Amount of support per award: $675 per semester plus additional funding from the Polish Ministry.

Total amount of support: $10,800 in year-abroad scholarships awarded towards academic year 2009-10.

NUMBER OF APPLICANTS MOST RECENT YEAR:
11.

NUMBER OF AWARDS: 9.

APPLICATION INFORMATION:
Applications are available on the web site from October to December 31. When requesting information and/or forms, please specify "Year Abroad Program" in the subject line of your e-mail. Applications and supporting materials must be accompanied by a nonrefundable $50 application fee. The Foundation does not accept faxed applications.

Duration: One semester or one academic year.

Deadline: January 5. Notification in June. Funding is for the following academic year.

PUBLICATIONS:
Guidelines; *KF Newsletter*; annual report.

IRS IDENTIFICATION NUMBER: 13-1628179

ADDRESS INQUIRIES TO:
Year Abroad Program
(See address above.)

THE KOSCIUSZKO FOUNDATION, INC. [974]
15 East 65th Street
New York, NY 10065
(212) 734-2130 ext. 210

E-MAIL ADDRESS:
addy@thekf.org

WEB SITE ADDRESS:
www.thekf.org

FOUNDED: 1925

AREAS OF INTEREST:
Strengthening of cultural and educational bonds between the U.S. and Poland through this exchange program for graduate-level students and scholars who wish to conduct research programs in Poland.

NAME(S) OF PROGRAMS:
- **The Kosciuszko Foundation Graduate Studies and Research in Poland**

TYPE:
Exchange programs; Research grants; Scholarships. This program enables American students and scholars to pursue a course of graduate or postgraduate study and research in Poland. It is also open to university faculty who wish to spend a sabbatical conducting research in Poland.

Research may be conducted during the Polish academic year, October through June only. No funding during the summer months of July, August and September.

YEAR PROGRAM STARTED: 1925

PURPOSE:
To assist Americans in continuing their graduate and postgraduate studies and research at institutions of higher learning in Poland.

LEGAL BASIS:
501(c)(3) not-for-profit organization.

ELIGIBILITY:
U.S. citizens with strong Polish language skills who wish to conduct research in Poland can apply. Funds can only be used at institutions of higher learning in Poland which fall under the jurisdiction of the Polish Ministry of Education and Science.

Polish citizens are not eligible.

FINANCIAL DATA:
Scholarship does not cover tuition costs. Participants receive housing and a monthly stipend towards living expenses. No provisions are made for dependents. Transportation to and from Poland is at the expense of the participant.

Amount of support per award: $250 per month of approved study/research.

Total amount of support: $1,000 for the academic year 2009-10.

NUMBER OF APPLICANTS MOST RECENT YEAR:
4.

NUMBER OF AWARDS: 1 for the academic year 2009-10.

APPLICATION INFORMATION:
Official application materials are available upon request to the Foundation at the address above. Please specify "Graduate Study and Research in Poland" when requesting application materials and/or information. Applications are available online at the Foundation's web site from October through December 31. Nonrefundable application fee of $50 is required.

Applicants must submit a letter of invitation from the host university's International Student Office specifying terms of the research including start and end dates of the research project, whether dormitory housing will be provided to the candidate, and provisions for access to university libraries, archives, and/or equipment as needed. A letter from the professor or department chairperson with whom research is to be conducted indicating the feasibility of the research proposal, agreement to act as the candidate's Academic Advisor and provision for letters of introduction as may be necessary for the research proposal. The host institution must fall under jurisdiction of the Polish Ministry of Education and Science in order to be considered.

The Foundation does not accept faxed applications.

Duration: Maximum of nine months. Research may be conducted from October to June. No funding from July through September.

Deadline: January 5. Notification in June/July. Funding is for the following academic year.

PUBLICATIONS:
KF Newsletter; annual report.

IRS IDENTIFICATION NUMBER: 13-1628179

ADDRESS INQUIRIES TO:
Studies and Research in Poland
(See address above.)

THE KOSCIUSZKO FOUNDATION, INC. [975]
15 East 65th Street
New York, NY 10065
(212) 734-2130 ext. 210

E-MAIL ADDRESS:
addy@thekf.org

WEB SITE ADDRESS:
www.thekf.org

FOUNDED: 1925

AREAS OF INTEREST:
Strengthening of cultural and educational bonds between the U.S. and Poland through an exchange program to Poland for the purpose of Polish language, culture and history studies.

NAME(S) OF PROGRAMS:
- **Summer Study Abroad Programs**

TYPE:
Exchange programs; Scholarships. Summer programs. The Summer Study Abroad Programs offer a variety of courses from July through mid-August at the Jagiellonian University in Krakow and at the John Paul II Catholic University of Lublin, Poland. Polish language, culture, history, art and many other subjects are available. The Foundation sponsors this program mainly for paying students; however, some scholarship awards are available for the program at Jagiellonian University in Krakow.

YEAR PROGRAM STARTED: 1970

PURPOSE:
To enable American students to pursue a short-term course of Polish language, culture, history and art studies abroad.

LEGAL BASIS:
501(c)(3) not-for-profit organization.

ELIGIBILITY:
The Summer Study Abroad Programs are open to U.S. undergraduate and graduate students as well as graduating high school students who will be 18 years of age by the first day of the program.

GEOGRAPHIC RESTRICTIONS:
United States.

FINANCIAL DATA:
Program fee includes tuition, cultural events and sightseeing trips, a language placement test, shared dormitory room, three meals a day and assistance from Polish university students. The scholarships which are available cover program fees for three-week programs at the Jagiellonian University in Krakow.
Amount of support per award:
Approximately $2,300.
Total amount of support: $39,780 was awarded towards 2010 Summer Studies in Krakow.

NUMBER OF APPLICANTS MOST RECENT YEAR:
100.

NUMBER OF AWARDS: 17 for the year 2010.

APPLICATION INFORMATION:
Official application materials and other pertinent information are available online. Application is available from January to May. When requesting forms and additional information via e-mail, please indicate "Summer Study Abroad Programs" in the subject line.
Duration: Two to eight weeks.
Deadline: April 18 for scholarship applicants. May 13 for students who wish to pay their own way.

PUBLICATIONS:
KF Newsletter; annual report.

IRS IDENTIFICATION NUMBER: 13-1628179

ADDRESS INQUIRIES TO:
Addy Tymczyszyn, Coordinator
Summer Study Abroad Programs
(See address above.)

*PLEASE NOTE:
Students submit scholarship applications to the Foundation's chapters. Pay-to-go applicants must submit application materials to Kosciuszko Foundation's headquarters in New York City.

*SPECIAL STIPULATIONS:
Students who receive scholarships are required to submit a report upon completion of the program.

THE KOSCIUSZKO FOUNDATION, INC. [976]
15 East 65th Street
New York, NY 10065
(212) 734-2130
Fax: (212) 628-4552

E-MAIL ADDRESS:
cbkuskowski@thekf.org

WEB SITE ADDRESS:
www.thekf.org

FOUNDED: 1925

AREAS OF INTEREST:
Educational and cultural exchange program in Poland.

NAME(S) OF PROGRAMS:
● **Teaching English in Poland**

TYPE:
Summer educational and cultural exchange program for American teachers and teaching assistants in Poland.

YEAR PROGRAM STARTED: 1991

PURPOSE:
To provide Polish students with English language experiences within an American cultural context; to familiarize Polish students with various aspects of American life and culture; to introduce American teachers and teaching assistants to Polish culture, history, traditions and people of Poland so that their knowledge and impressions will be shared.

ELIGIBILITY:
Experienced teachers/administrators certified in the U.S., educators with private/parochial school or other verifiable teaching experience, college/university faculty, and those engaged in student services (school nurse, social worker, guidance counselor, school psychologist, etc.) are eligible for participation. Group flight arrangements will be made by the Foundation. Participants are expected to travel to Poland with the group.

GEOGRAPHIC RESTRICTIONS:
United States.

FINANCIAL DATA:
Amount of support per award: Varies.

APPLICATION INFORMATION:
Faxed applications are not acceptable.
Duration: Approximately one month. May reapply by letter requesting reactivation of application.
Deadline: March 1.

ADDRESS INQUIRIES TO:
Christine Kuskowski, Director
(See address above.)

THE ROBERTO LONGHI FOUNDATION FOR THE STUDY OF THE HISTORY OF ART
Via Benedetto Fortini, 30
Florence 50125 Italy
39 055 65 80 794
Fax: 39 055 65 80 794

E-MAIL ADDRESS:
longhi@fondazionelonghi.it

WEB SITE ADDRESS:
www.fondazionelonghi.it/

TYPE:
Fellowships. Designed for those who want to seriously dedicate themselves to research in the history of art. Fellowship holders may make use of the study materials available in the Institute. They must frequent the Institute and collaborate on a specific group research project selected by the Scientific Committee. In particular, successful candidates must give the assurance that they can dedicate their full time to the research for which the fellowship is assigned. They must live in Florence for the duration of the fellowship, except for travel required for their research. They may not exceed the periods of vacation fixed by the Institute. They are required to attend seminars, lectures and other activities arranged by the Institute. In addition, Fellows must submit a written report at the end of their stay in Florence, relating the findings of their individual research undertaken at the Longhi Foundation. The nonobservance of

the above conditions will be considered sufficient grounds for the cancellation of a fellowship.
See entry 589 for full listing.

MARSHALL AID COMMEMORATION COMMISSION [977]
ACU
Woburn House
20-24 Tavistock Square
London WC1H 9HF England
020 7380 6700
Fax: 0207 3872655

E-MAIL ADDRESS:
macc@acu.ac.uk

WEB SITE ADDRESS:
www.marshallscholarship.org

FOUNDED: 1953

NAME(S) OF PROGRAMS:
● **Marshall Scholarships**

TYPE:
Scholarships. Tenable at any university in the U.K. in any subject leading to the award of a British university degree, which recipients are required to take.

Marshall Scholarships finance young Americans of high ability to study for a degree in the U.K. in a system of higher education recognized for its excellence. These grants have been established to express British gratitude for the European Recovery Program (the Marshall Plan) instituted by General of the Army George C. Marshall.

YEAR PROGRAM STARTED: 1954

PURPOSE:
To enable citizens of the U.S., both men and women, who are graduates of U.S. colleges and universities, to study for a degree from a university in the U.K. for a period of at least one academic year.

LEGAL BASIS:
Programme established by British Parliamentary Act.

ELIGIBILITY:
Graduates of a degree-granting college or university who have graduated from their undergraduate college or university no more than three years before the year the award will be taken up are eligible (e.g., for awards tenable from October 2012, candidates must have graduated after April 2009). Candidates must be American citizens at the time of application and must have obtained a grade point average of not less than 3.7 (or A-). (Exceptions will be considered only on the specific recommendation of the sponsoring college.)

FINANCIAL DATA:
Scholarships include a personal allowance, tuition fees, grants for books, travel, thesis and fares to and from Britain.
Amount of support per award: Currently GBP 844 per month (GBP 1,044 for those studying at Central London institutions) for 12 or 22 months, plus book grants and fares to/from the U.K., plus payment of university tuition fees to GBP 25,000 per year.
Total amount of support: GBP 2,200,000 for the year ended March 31, 2011.

NUMBER OF APPLICANTS MOST RECENT YEAR:
Approximately 800.

NUMBER OF AWARDS: Up to 40 awards annually.

APPLICATION INFORMATION:
Application should be made to a British Consulate-General (in Atlanta, Boston, Chicago, Houston, Los Angeles, New York and San Francisco) or to the British Embassy in Washington.

Duration: One to two years. May be extended for a third year.

Deadline: Early October of the year preceding the award.

OFFICERS:
John Kirkland, Executive Secretary
Mary C. Denyer, Assistant Secretary

COMMISSION MEMBERS:
Dr. Frances Dow, Chairperson
Prof. Bob Deacon
Richard Dendy
Diane Flynn
John Hughes
Ruth Kosmin
Carol Madison-Graham
Simon Morris
Eric Thomas
Nigel Thrift

ADDRESS INQUIRIES TO:
Marshall Aid Commemoration Commission (See address above.) or
Nearest British Consulate General or British Council, U.S.A.
(See web site above for addresses.)

THE MATSUMAE INTERNATIONAL FOUNDATION [978]

4-14-46, Kamiogi, Suginami-ku
Tokyo 167-0043 Japan
+81-3-3301-7600
Fax: +81-3-3301-7601

E-MAIL ADDRESS:
contact2mif@mist.dti.ne.jp

WEB SITE ADDRESS:
www.mars.dti.ne.jp/~mif

FOUNDED: 1979

AREAS OF INTEREST:
First priority: Natural sciences, engineering and medicine.

NAME(S) OF PROGRAMS:
● **Fellowship Program**

TYPE:
Fellowships; Research grants.

YEAR PROGRAM STARTED: 1980

PURPOSE:
To provide opportunity to foreign scientists to conduct research at Japanese institutions.

LEGAL BASIS:
Private foundation.

ELIGIBILITY:
Citizenship is unrestricted. Those of non-Japanese nationality who meet all of the following general eligibility requirements are invited to submit the required application documents:
(1) Applicants must hold a Ph.D. degree, or be recognized by the Foundation as possessing equivalent academic qualifications;
(2) Applicants must be under 49 years of age at the time of application;
(3) Applicants must have sufficient conversational ability in English or Japanese to prevent insurmountable difficulties during their research activities in Japan;
(4) Applicants should not have been in Japan

previously; application must be submitted from the applicant's home country; under no circumstances will an application be accepted from a person already in Japan;
(5) Applicants should have firm positions and professions in their home nations and should return to their countries on completion of their fellowship stay by the Foundation and;
(6) Applicants must be of sound health and not physically handicapped in any way which would prevent them from carrying out research in Japan.

Fields of study such as natural science, engineering and medicine are given first priority.

FINANCIAL DATA:
Awards include stipend, lump sum on arrival, round-trip travel and insurance.

Amount of support per award: Monthly stipend is JPY 240,000. Personal accident insurance with death benefit and medical treatment and sickness insurance with death benefit and medical treatment are also provided. Lump sum on arrival of JPY 100,000 is provided to assist with the cost of lodging, local travel expenses, etc. An economy-class round-trip air ticket is provided between the international airport nearest the Fellow's home residence and Tokyo via the most direct routing. Contact the Foundation for complete details.

NUMBER OF APPLICANTS MOST RECENT YEAR:
135 for the year 2011.

NUMBER OF AWARDS: 20 for the year 2010. For the April 2010 through March 2011 grant period, about 20 fellowships: three to six months.

APPLICATION INFORMATION:
Application form required. Applicants should obtain the current issue of the Fellowship Announcement from the Foundation. The Foundation cannot entertain requests for waivers of the eligibility requirements and other conditions, listed in the Fellowship Announcement, and will not respond to such requests. Applicants cannot submit applications from inside Japan; applications must be submitted from the applicant's home country. The Foundation never receives applications by fax or e-mail.

All documents must be typewritten in English. Applicants must include a photograph (taken within the last three months) along with the completed application form (signed and dated); a description of the research project; complete list of publications; reprint(s) of what the applicant considers to be his or her most important publication(s); a personal history (curriculum vitae); a letter of recommendation from the applicant's employer and/or supervisor testifying to academic ability and achievements and confirming the availability of study leave covering the grant period; a certified copy of the applicant's academic certificates (Ph.D., Master's, Bachelor's) issued by the university concerned (these documents should be in English); a letter with signature from the host scientist confirming the period of stay, the research project and the availability of research facilities/materials, and the arrangement of lodging accommodation under the Foundation Fellowship Program.

Contact the Foundation for complete details.

Duration: Three to six months; extension of the granted period is not allowed.

Deadline: Applications must be received by August 31 for the following year's fellowship.

PUBLICATIONS:
Program announcement.

ADDRESS INQUIRIES TO:
Fellowship Program
(See address above.)

MICHIGAN STATE UNIVERSITY [979]

Office of Study Abroad
109 International Center
East Lansing, MI 48824-1035
(517) 353-8920
Fax: (517) 432-2082

E-MAIL ADDRESS:
osapa@isp.msu.edu

WEB SITE ADDRESS:
www.studyabroad.msu.edu

NAME(S) OF PROGRAMS:
● **MSU Study Abroad Scholarships**

TYPE:
Scholarships. Academic study abroad scholarships for college-level credit. The program includes over 270 overseas study programs in more than 60 countries in a wide variety of academic fields.

PURPOSE:
To assist Michigan State University students who will benefit from study abroad.

LEGAL BASIS:
University.

ELIGIBILITY:
Applicants must be MSU students. Participation in study abroad program is:
(1) based on financial need, must have a FAFSA application on file with MSU office of financial aid and have a minimum 2.5 grade point average;
(2) based on academic performance and must have a minimum 3.5 grade point average. Also, must submit an essay explaining how study abroad would enhance the student's education.

FINANCIAL DATA:
Amount of support per award: $500 to $2,000 available per student.

Total amount of support: Approximately $400,000 annually.

NUMBER OF APPLICANTS MOST RECENT YEAR:
1,200.

APPLICATION INFORMATION:
Duration: Varies.

Deadline: October 15 and March 1.

STAFF:
Lynn Aguado, Study Abroad Program Coordinator

ADDRESS INQUIRIES TO:
Lynn Aguado
Study Abroad Program Coordinator
(See address above.)

THE NANSEN FUND, INC. [980]

5219 Pine Arbor Drive
Houston, TX 77066-2548
(281) 682-4327
Fax: (281) 587-9284

E-MAIL ADDRESS:
anne-brith@nacchouston.org

WEB SITE ADDRESS:
www.noram.no

FOUNDED: 1979

AREAS OF INTEREST:
International educational exchange, international relations, classics, political science and Norwegian culture.

NAME(S) OF PROGRAMS:
● **John Dana Archbold Fellowships**

TYPE:
Fellowships; Scholarships; Travel grants. Stipends for subsistence and quarters. One-year graduate fellowships for study at the University of Oslo in Norway, offered in even-numbered years; in odd-numbered years offered to Norwegians for study in the U.S.

YEAR PROGRAM STARTED: 1981

PURPOSE:
To promote better understanding among peoples for peace among nations and to support educational exchange between the U.S. and Norway.

LEGAL BASIS:
509(a)(2) organization.

ELIGIBILITY:
Fellowships are open to Norwegians and Americans for a year of graduate, postdoctoral or professional study and research. Eligibility is limited to persons 20 to 35 years old, in good health, of good character, and citizens of the U.S. or Norway. Qualified applicants must show evidence of real ability in their chosen field, indicate seriousness of purpose, and have a record of social adaptability. Undergraduate applicants must have a B.A. or B.S. degree (or equivalent) before their departure date. Americans go to Norway in even-numbered years and Norwegians to the U.S. in odd-numbered years.

GEOGRAPHIC RESTRICTIONS:
Norway and United States.

FINANCIAL DATA:
Individual grants vary, depending upon projected costs of tuition, maintenance and travel. The maintenance stipend is sufficient to meet basic expenses for a single person. Some travel allowance.
Amount of support per award: Up to $10,000, depending on projected costs of tuition, maintenance, travel and rate of exchange.
Total amount of support: Up to $10,000.

COOPERATIVE FUNDING PROGRAMS: The University of Oslo charges no tuition to fellows.

NUMBER OF APPLICANTS MOST RECENT YEAR:
Average 6.

NUMBER OF AWARDS: 1 annually.

REPRESENTATIVE AWARDS:
Biochemistry; Law of the Sea; International Relations.

APPLICATION INFORMATION:
Application forms are available from the address above until December 1 of the year preceding the award period. Completed applications require a statement of the proposed study, curriculum vitae, three academic references, foreign language report and transcripts, international relations, classics, political science and Norwegian culture.
Duration: One year, including Oslo International Summer School.
Deadline: February 1. Announcement by March 1.

PUBLICATIONS:
Program description.

IRS IDENTIFICATION NUMBER: 74-6043421

OFFICERS AND DIRECTORS:
Anne-Brith Berge

ADDRESS INQUIRIES TO:
For further information about the University of Oslo, contact:
Ms. Torild Homstad
The University of Oslo International Summer School
North American Branch Office
St. Olaf College
1520 St. Olaf Avenue
Northfield, MN 55057
Tel: (507) 786-3269 or (800) 639-0058
Fax: (507) 786-3732
E-mail: iss@stolaf.edu
Web site: www.uio.no/iss/

*SPECIAL STIPULATIONS:
Successful applicant(s) will be recommended to the University of Oslo by the Nansen Fund, but he or she must make application to, and be accepted by, the University as a graduate student in a particular department. The University of Oslo International Summer School offers orientation and Norwegian language courses for six weeks before the start of the regular academic year. For Americans, tuition is paid. Attendance is required.

NATIONAL SECURITY EDUCATION PROGRAM   [981]
Boren Scholarships
Institute of International Education
1400 K Street, N.W., Sixth Floor
Washington, DC 20005-2403
(800) 618-6737
Fax: (202) 326-7672

E-MAIL ADDRESS:
boren@iie.org

WEB SITE ADDRESS:
www.borenawards.org

FOUNDED: 1991

AREAS OF INTEREST:
Languages and cultures of world regions that are critical to U.S. interests and underrepresented in study abroad, including Africa, Asia, Central and Eastern Europe, Eurasia, Latin America, and the Middle East.

NAME(S) OF PROGRAMS:
● **Boren Scholarships**

TYPE:
Scholarships. Boren Scholarships provide funding for U.S. undergraduate students to study abroad in areas of the world that are critical to U.S. interests and underrepresented in study abroad.

PURPOSE:
To provide American undergraduates with the resources and encouragement they need to acquire language skills and cultural experiences in areas of the world critical to the future security of our nation. In exchange for funding, recipients commit to working in the federal government for a minimum of one year after graduation.

ELIGIBILITY:
Must be a U.S. citizen at the time of application. Open to high school graduates, or those who have earned a GED, and are matriculated as a freshman, sophomore, junior, or senior in a U.S. postsecondary

institution, including universities, colleges, and community colleges accredited by an accrediting body recognized by the U.S. Department of Education. Application must be to engage in a study abroad experience in a country outside of Western Europe, Canada, Australia, or New Zealand that meets home institution standards. Applicant must plan to use the scholarship for study abroad and the study abroad program end prior to graduation.

GEOGRAPHIC RESTRICTIONS:
United States citizens applying to study abroad in Africa, Asia, Central and Eastern Europe, Eurasia, Latin America, and the Middle East.

FINANCIAL DATA:
Amount of support per award: Summer: Up to $8,000; Semester: Up to $10,000; Full academic year: Up to $20,000.

APPLICATION INFORMATION:
Complete details and application information can be found on the Boren Awards web site.
Duration: Summer (minimum eight weeks), fall or spring semester, and full academic year.
Deadline: National Application: early February.

ADDRESS INQUIRIES TO:
See e-mail address or phone number above.

*SPECIAL STIPULATIONS:
In exchange for funding, recipients agree to the National Security Education Program (NSEP) Service Requirement. The NSEP Service Requirement stipulates that an award recipient work for a minimum of one year in the federal government in a position with national security responsibilities. The Departments of Defense, Homeland Security, State, or any element of the Intelligence Community are priority agencies.

NATIONAL SECURITY EDUCATION PROGRAM   [982]
Boren Fellowships
Institute of International Education
1400 K Street, N.W., Sixth Floor
Washington, DC 20005-2403
(800) 618-6737
Fax: (202) 326-7672

E-MAIL ADDRESS:
boren@iie.org

WEB SITE ADDRESS:
www.borenawards.org

FOUNDED: 1991

AREAS OF INTEREST:
Boren Fellowships support study and research in areas of the world that are critical to U.S. interests, including Africa, Asia, Central and Eastern Europe, Eurasia, Latin America, and the Middle East.

NAME(S) OF PROGRAMS:
● **Boren Fellowships**

TYPE:
Fellowships. Fellowship for U.S. graduate students provides support for overseas or domestic study, or a combination of both.

PURPOSE:
To encourage U.S. graduate students to add an important international and language component to their graduate education through specialization in area study, language study, or increased language proficiency; to support study and research in areas of the

world that are critical to U.S. interests, including Africa, Asia, Central and Eastern Europe, Eurasia, Latin America, and the Middle East.

ELIGIBILITY:
Must be a U.S. citizen at the time of application. Applicants must be either enrolled in or applying to a graduate degree program at an accredited U.S. college or university located within the U.S. To receive the award, applicant must provide evidence of admission and enrollment in such a program. Boren Fellows must remain enrolled in their graduate programs for the duration of the fellowship. Applicants are strongly encouraged, where feasible, to study in the country or region relevant to their field of study. Although study outside the U.S. is not required, successful applicants generally include a significant overseas component.

GEOGRAPHIC RESTRICTIONS:
United States citizens applying to study abroad in Africa, Asia, Central and Eastern Europe, Eurasia, Latin America, and the Middle East.

FINANCIAL DATA:
Amount of support per award: Up to $30,000 for a combination of domestic and overseas study; up to $24,000 for overseas study; up to $12,000 for domestic study.

APPLICATION INFORMATION:
Complete details and application information can be found online.

Duration: Up to two years.

Deadline: End of January.

ADDRESS INQUIRIES TO:
See e-mail address or phone number above.

*SPECIAL STIPULATIONS:
In exchange for funding, recipients agree to the National Security Education Program (NSEP) Service Requirement. The NSEP Service Requirement stipulates that an award recipient work for a minimum of one year in the federal government in a position with national security responsibilities. The Departments of Defense, Homeland Security, State, or any element of the Intelligence Community are priority agencies.

NATIONAL SECURITY EDUCATION PROGRAM [983]

The Language Flagship
Institute of International Education
1400 K Street, N.W., Sixth Floor
Washington, DC 20005-2403
(800) 618-6737
Fax: (202) 326-7672

E-MAIL ADDRESS:
flagship@iie.org

WEB SITE ADDRESS:
www.borenawards.org/the_language_flagship

FOUNDED: 1991

AREAS OF INTEREST:
Graduate language fellowships in Arabic, Korean, Chinese or Persian.

NAME(S) OF PROGRAMS:
● **Language Flagship Fellowships**

TYPE:
Fellowships. Domestic/overseas fellowships for qualified American students interested in receiving full financial support to participate in one of The Language Flagship programs.

The Language Flagship offers a limited number of fellowships to qualified American students interested in receiving financial support to participate in one of the graduate Flagship Programs in Arabic, Korean, Chinese or Persian.

Graduate Flagship Programs have a duration of approximately two years. The first year involves intensive language study at a domestic Flagship Institution. The second year is spent in an immersion program overseas, which is designed and managed by domestic Flagship Institutions. All Flagship Fellows who participate in the domestic component are expected to continue to the overseas component and complete the program in its entirety. Provided program requirements are met, the two-year program culminates in a Master's degree.

PURPOSE:
To address the urgent and growing need for Americans with professional levels of competency in languages critical to national security and to provide funding for select U.S. citizens who are highly motivated to work for the federal government in an area related to U.S. national security.

ELIGIBILITY:
Applicants must meet the following requirements:
(1) U.S. citizenship at the time of application;
(2) minimum proficiency of Advanced Low (as defined by ACTFL) or level 2 (as defined by ILR in the appropriate foreign language);
(3) minimum proficiency of Superior (as defined by ACTFL) or level 3 (as defined by ILR in all modalities of English);
(4) completed undergraduate degree by the time the Flagship Program and Fellowship funding period begins;
(5) enrollment in a Master's degree-granting Flagship Program for the duration of the Flagship Fellowship funding period and;
(6) not employed by the U.S. government.

Past recipients of Boren Scholarships or Fellowships are eligible and are encouraged to apply for The Language Flagship Fellowships.

GEOGRAPHIC RESTRICTIONS:
Limited to United States citizens participating in The Language Flagship Programs in Arabic, Korean, Chinese or Persian.

FINANCIAL DATA:
Tuition, stipend for living expenses, support for travel costs and health insurance coverage.

APPLICATION INFORMATION:
Details and application information can be found online at the web site address above.

Duration: Approximately two years.

Deadline: Mid-January.

ADDRESS INQUIRIES TO:
See e-mail address or phone number above.

*SPECIAL STIPULATIONS:
In exchange for funding, recipients agree to the National Security Education Program (NSEP) Service Requirement. The NSEP Service Requirement stipulates that an award recipient work for a minimum of one year in the federal government in a position with national security responsibilities. The Departments of Defense, Homeland Security, State, or any element of the Intelligence Community are priority agencies.

THE PHI BETA KAPPA SOCIETY [984]

1606 New Hampshire Avenue, N.W.
Washington, DC 20009
(202) 745-3235
Fax: (202) 986-1601

E-MAIL ADDRESS:
awards@pbk.org

WEB SITE ADDRESS:
www.pbk.org

AREAS OF INTEREST:
French language, literature and culture.

NAME(S) OF PROGRAMS:
● **The Walter J. Jensen Fellowship for French Language, Literature and Culture**

TYPE:
Fellowships. Fellowship for at least six months of study in France. One award given annually.

YEAR PROGRAM STARTED: 2001

PURPOSE:
To help educators and researchers improve education in standard French language, literature and culture, and in the study of standard French in the U.S.

ELIGIBILITY:
Candidates must be U.S. citizens under 40 years of age who can demonstrate their career does or will involve active use of the French language. They must have earned a Baccalaureate degree from an accredited four-year institution, and have a 3.0 minimum grade point average in French language and literature as a major. They must demonstrate superior competence in French, according to the standards established by the American Association of Teachers of French. Preference may be given to members of Phi Beta Kappa and educators at the secondary school level or above.

GEOGRAPHIC RESTRICTIONS:
United States.

FINANCIAL DATA:
Includes single round-trip, economy class ticket for travel to France.

Amount of support per award: Minimum $10,000 stipend.

NUMBER OF AWARDS: Minimum 1 annually.

APPLICATION INFORMATION:
The application booklet contains:
(1) the Application for the Walter J. Jensen Fellowship;
(2) two Transcript Request forms and;
(3) the Letter of Recommendation Form.

Applicant must submit three complete sets of documents. The Letter of Recommendation and Transcript Request forms may be duplicated. Please indicate the Fellowship name on all correspondence.

Applicant should send the application, official transcripts, and confidential letters of recommendation (in sealed envelopes) to the Walter J. Jensen Fellowship Committee in care of the Phi Beta Kappa Society.

Duration: At least six months.

Deadline: October 1.

ADDRESS INQUIRIES TO:
Lucinda Morales
Director of Society Affairs
(See address above.)

THE ROTARY FOUNDATION OF ROTARY INTERNATIONAL [985]

One Rotary Center
1560 Sherman Avenue
Evanston, IL 60201-3698
(866) 976-8279
Fax: (847) 556-2141

E-MAIL ADDRESS:
rotarypeacecenter@rotary.org

WEB SITE ADDRESS:
www.rotary.org

FOUNDED: 2002

AREAS OF INTEREST:
Higher education and study abroad.

NAME(S) OF PROGRAMS:
● **Rotary Peace Fellowships**

TYPE:
Fellowships. The Rotary Centers for International Studies in Peace and Conflict Resolution offer individuals committed to peace and cooperation the opportunity to pursue a one- to two-year Master's-level degree or a three-month professional certificate in international studies, peace studies and conflict resolution at one of the seven Rotary Peace Centers. The university partners are: Duke University and the University of North Carolina at Chapel Hill (North Carolina, U.S.A.); International Christian University (Tokyo, Japan); Universidad del Salvador (Buenos Aires, Argentina); University of Bradford (West Yorkshire, England); University of Queensland (Brisbane, Queensland, Australia); and Chulalongkorn University (Bangkok, Thailand).

YEAR PROGRAM STARTED: 2002

PURPOSE:
To further peace and international understanding.

LEGAL BASIS:
Incorporated not-for-profit foundation.

ELIGIBILITY:
Applicants must have:
(1) the academic background, training and work experience required for a Master's-level program at the partner universities;
(2) proficiency in more than one language (even if they propose to study in a country where their native language is spoken);
(3) excellent leadership skills;
(4) a demonstrated commitment to peace and international understanding through their personal and community service activities and/or academic and professional achievements and;
(5) endorsement of their local rotary district office.

Persons with disabilities and members of Rotaract clubs are eligible and encouraged to apply.

FINANCIAL DATA:
Fellowship will include funding for tuition and required fees, room and board, transportation, contingency expenses and other funding.
Amount of support per award: Master's Program: Average $60,000; Professional Development Certificate: Average $10,000.
Total amount of support: Varies.

NUMBER OF AWARDS: Approximately 100 each year.

APPLICATION INFORMATION:
All Rotary districts around the world are invited to nominate an unlimited number of candidates for the world-competitive selection each year. Applications generally need to be completed approximately 18 months in advance of the planned study period. Applications are available from the Rotary web site (above) or from local Rotary clubs. Interested applicants must contact a local Rotary club to ask about local application deadlines. Club deadlines may be as early as January or as late as June of the year prior to the study period.
Duration: Master's Program: One to two years; Professional Development Certificate: Three months.
Deadline: July 1.

PUBLICATIONS:
Application; brochure.

ADDRESS INQUIRIES TO:
Local Rotary Club or Contact Center (See e-mail address above.)

THE ROTARY FOUNDATION OF ROTARY INTERNATIONAL [986]

One Rotary Center
1560 Sherman Avenue
Evanston, IL 60201
(866) 976-8279
Fax: (847) 556-2144

E-MAIL ADDRESS:
contact.center@rotary.org

WEB SITE ADDRESS:
www.rotary.
org/en/studentsandyouth/educationalprograms

FOUNDED: 1947

AREAS OF INTEREST:
Higher education and study abroad.

NAME(S) OF PROGRAMS:
● **Ambassadorial Scholarships**

TYPE:
Awards/prizes; Scholarships. International education program for ambassadors of goodwill that awards one academic year of study abroad.

YEAR PROGRAM STARTED: 1947

PURPOSE:
To further international understanding and friendly relations among people of different countries.

LEGAL BASIS:
Incorporated not-for-profit foundation.

ELIGIBILITY:
Applicants must have completed at least two years of university or college course work or equivalent professional experience prior to beginning scholarship studies. All applicants must be citizens of a country in which there is a Rotary club, and must initially apply through a local Rotary club in their legal or permanent residence (or place of full-time study or employment). There are no age restrictions. Persons with disabilities and members of Rotaract clubs are eligible and encouraged to apply. Spouses or descendants of Rotarians may not apply. Scholarship cannot be used to study in an area of a country where the candidate has previously lived for more than 12 months. (The scholarships are not appropriate for foreign students seeking funding to continue studies at a given university.) The scholarship may not be used in conjunction with a study abroad program based in another country.

Although applicants are asked to list their preferred study locations, the Foundation Trustees reserve the right to make assignments to any suitable institution to ensure the widest possible geographical distribution of scholars. Candidates must be flexible in their study institution assignments.

FINANCIAL DATA:
Amount of support per award: $26,000.

NUMBER OF AWARDS: Approximately 600 annually.

APPLICATION INFORMATION:
The availability of Ambassadorial Scholarships is determined by each Rotary district and varies from year to year. Applicants must contact a local Rotary club to:
(1) determine if funding is available;
(2) inquire about local application deadlines and;
(3) obtain application materials.

Applications may also be obtained from www.rotary.org if the applicant has confirmed scholarship availability with the local Rotary club.
Duration: One regular academic year (usually nine months).
Deadline: Varies by Rotary club.

PUBLICATIONS:
Brochure/application.

ADDRESS INQUIRIES TO:
See e-mail address above.

THE ROYAL SOCIETY OF EDINBURGH [987]

22-26 George Street
Edinburgh EH2 2PQ Scotland
44 (0)131 240 5000
Fax: 44 (0)131 240 5024

E-MAIL ADDRESS:
resfells@royalsoced.org.uk

WEB SITE ADDRESS:
www.royalsoced.org.uk

FOUNDED: 1783

AREAS OF INTEREST:
Science, technology, industry and commerce.

NAME(S) OF PROGRAMS:
● **Royal Society of Edinburgh Scottish Government Personal Research Fellowships**

TYPE:
Fellowships. Postdoctoral fellowships for research in any discipline, in any Scottish higher education institution.

YEAR PROGRAM STARTED: 1983

PURPOSE:
To enhance the transfer of ideas and technology from the research community to wealth creation and improvement of the quality of life in Scotland.

ELIGIBILITY:
Applicants must possess a Doctorate, or equivalent higher education qualification, and should have two to six years of relevant postdoctoral academic research experience at the time of the application closing date of March 29. Only applicants who meet these criteria by the date of application will be considered. Applicants must show that they. have an outstanding capacity for innovative research with a strong publication record relevant to their proposed field of study.

Preference will be given to those not holding a permanent position in an academic or research institution.

FINANCIAL DATA:
Amount of support per award: Up to EUR 6,000 per annum.

COOPERATIVE FUNDING PROGRAMS: Fellowships are made with the support of the Scottish government.

NUMBER OF APPLICANTS MOST RECENT YEAR: 60.

NUMBER OF AWARDS: 6.

APPLICATION INFORMATION:
Application form and guidelines available from the Research Fellowships secretary. Also consult the web site: www.royalsoced.org.uk/research_fellowships/seelld.htm.
Duration: Up to five years.
Deadline: March.

OFFICERS:
Lord Wilson, President
Edward Cunningham, Treasurer

ADDRESS INQUIRIES TO:
Anne Fraser, Research Awards Manager
(See address above.)

ST. ANDREW'S SOCIETY OF THE STATE OF NEW YORK [988]

150 East 55th Street, 3rd Floor
New York, NY 10022
(212) 223-4248
Fax: (212) 233-0748

E-MAIL ADDRESS:
office@standrewsny.org

WEB SITE ADDRESS:
www.standrewsny.org

FOUNDED: 1756

AREAS OF INTEREST:
Charitable support of needy persons of Scottish descent and scholarship program.

NAME(S) OF PROGRAMS:
● **Scholarship Program for Graduate Study in Scotland**

TYPE:
Scholarships. Scholarships for American students of Scottish descent for one year of graduate study in any Scottish university.

YEAR PROGRAM STARTED: 1956

PURPOSE:
To promote cultural interchange and goodwill between Scotland and the U.S.

LEGAL BASIS:
Tax-exempt charitable organization.

ELIGIBILITY:
An applicant must have a Bachelor's degree, exhibit financial need, possess an outstanding scholastic and activity record and provide evidence of Scottish descent.

GEOGRAPHIC RESTRICTIONS:
New York, New Jersey, Pennsylvania and the New England states. Must be within a 250-mile radius of New York state.

FINANCIAL DATA:
Award is to be used initially against tuition, then board, room, transportation and other expenses.
Amount of support per award: Up to $30,000.
Total amount of support: Varies each year.

NUMBER OF APPLICANTS MOST RECENT YEAR: 100.

NUMBER OF AWARDS: 2 per year (for U.S. applicants).

APPLICATION INFORMATION:
The applicant must contact Saint Andrew's Society in writing with a request for an application. When the application is completed, it should be submitted to the college/university from/at which the student graduated or is due to graduate. Each college or university is invited to send only one candidate forward to the Saint Andrew's Society Selection Committee. Referral must be by president of the institution the applicant is attending.
Duration: One year. Nonrenewable.
Deadline: December 15. Announcement in early March.

PUBLICATIONS:
Quarterly newsletter.

IRS IDENTIFICATION NUMBER: 13-5602329

OFFICERS:
Robert W. Ker, III, President
Derek Anderson, Treasurer
Heath McLendon, Chairman, Finance Committee

ADDRESS INQUIRIES TO:
Brigid Tucker, Administrative Director
(See address above.)

*SPECIAL STIPULATIONS:
Candidates must be from northeastern U.S. and of Scottish descent, and must be U.S. citizens.

SCAC (FRENCH CULTURAL AND EDUCATIONAL OFFICE) [989]

4101 Reservoir Road, N.W.
Washington, DC 20007
(202) 944-6000
Fax: (202) 944-6268

WEB SITE ADDRESS:
frenchculture.org

FOUNDED: 1980

NAME(S) OF PROGRAMS:
● **Allons en France**
● **Chateaubriand Fellowships Program**
● **Green Connection**
● **The Partner University Fund (PUF)**
● **Rencontres Internationales de Jeunes (RIJ)**
● **Teacher Training in France**
● **Teaching Assistant Program in France**
● **Jules Verne Program**

TYPE:
Assistantships; Exchange programs; Fellowships; Grants-in-aid; Project/program grants; Research grants; Training grants; Travel grants. Allons en France: Participants will travel to France, immerse themselves in the French language and culture, and take part in a unique summer program. Assistantships in France: Offers a short-term teaching assistant post in a French school.

Chateaubriand Fellowships Program: A grant offered by the embassy of France in the U.S., every year it allows doctoral students enrolled in American universities to conduct research in France for up to nine months.

Green Connection: American high school students will participate each year in an educational and scientific trip to France,

organized around the theme of ecology. Participants will be selected through a national competition for which candidates will submit proposals for local or personal projects in the field of environmental protection.

The Partner University Fund (PUF): Grants provided by this Fund support research and graduate education partnerships between French and American universities with emphasis placed on novel, innovative and interdisciplinary projects when relevant.

Rencontres Internationales de Jeunes (RIJ) (Youth International Meetings): Participants in this program will travel to France, immerse themselves in the French language and culture, and take part in a unique summer program.

Teacher Training in France: Each year the Cultural Services Department of the French Embassy offers a number of two-week grants to qualified primary and secondary school teachers of French who would like to enhance their knowledge of French culture and improve their language and teaching skills.

Teaching Assistant Program in France: The French Ministry of Education and the Cultural Services Department of the French Embassy in Washington, DC offer approximately 1,500 teaching assistantships each year for American citizens and permanent residents of the U.S. to teach English in French schools. Assistants may work in primary schools or secondary schools. Jules Verne Program: Allows fully trained and certified elementary and secondary school teachers from France and the U.S. to live and teach outside their country for a full school year, immersing themselves in the culture, language and civilization of the host country.

YEAR PROGRAM STARTED: 1980

PURPOSE:
To promote the exchange of ideas between France and the U.S.

LEGAL BASIS:
Embassy.

ELIGIBILITY:
Details are available online.

GEOGRAPHIC RESTRICTIONS:
Details are available online.

FINANCIAL DATA:
Allons en France: The travel grant covers airfare to and from France, and program expenses for participants including housing, meals, transportation, activities and insurance while in France. Assistantships in France: EUR 780 monthly for six to nine months. Chateaubriand Fellowships Program: 1,400 EUR/month, a round-trip ticket to France and health insurance. Green Connection: The travel grant covers round-trip airfare to France and program expenses for participants including housing, meals, transportation, activities and insurance while in France. The Partner University Fund (PUF): Up to $80,000 (U.S.) per year per project (up to 30% of the total cost of the project). Rencontres Internationales de Jeunes (RIJ): The travel grant covers airfare to and from France, and program expenses for participants including housing, meals, transportation, activities and insurance while in France. Teacher Training in France: Program includes tuition and training fees for two weeks, a round-trip train ticket from

Paris to the destination city; program participants receive a grant of 397.50 EUR for two weeks covering a portion of their accommodation and food expenses; round-trip airfare is not included. Teaching Assistant Program in France: 964.88 EUR per month gross/~780 EUR per month net. Jules Verne Program: The French teacher's full salary is provided by the French Ministry of Education. The American school district is responsible for providing the American teacher's full salary.

NUMBER OF APPLICANTS MOST RECENT YEAR:
Chateaubriand Fellowships Program: 110. The Partner University Fund (PUF): 78. Teaching Assistant Program in France: 2,100.

NUMBER OF AWARDS: Allons en France: 3 in 2011. Chateaubriand Fellowships Program: 15. Green Connection: 10 in 2011. The Partner University Fund (PUF): 11 grantees for the period 2010-13. Rencontres Internationales de Jeunes (RIJ): 3 in 2011. Teacher Training in France: 40 in 2011. Teaching Assistant Program in France: 1,450. Jules Verne Program: 17 French teachers in 2009-10.

APPLICATION INFORMATION:
Details are available online.
Duration: Allons en France: 10 days. Chateaubriand Fellowships Program: nine months. Green Connection: Approximately 10 days. The Partner University Fund (PUF): Three years, with an annual review. Rencontres Internationales de Jeunes (RIJ): nine to 15 days. Teacher Training in France: Two weeks. Teaching Assistant Program in France: One school year (October 1-April 30). Jules Verne Program: One school year, maximum of two years in a row.
Deadline: Details are available online.

ADDRESS INQUIRIES TO:
Allons en France, Rencontres Internationales de Jeunes (RIJ), Teacher Training in France and Jules Verne Program:
E-mail:
scule.washington-amba@diplomatie.gouv.fr.
The Partner University Fund (PUF):
puf@ambafrance-us.org. Teaching Assistant Program in France: assistant.washington-amba@diplomatie.gouv.fr.

SCUOLA NORMALE SUPERIORE   [990]

Area Didattica
Palazzo del Castelletto in Pisa
via del Castelletto n. 11
Pisa, 56100 Italy
(39050) 509236
Fax: (39050) 563513

E-MAIL ADDRESS:
g.dalterio@sns.it
m.landucci@sns.it
a.vettori@sns.it

WEB SITE ADDRESS:
www.sns.it

FOUNDED: 1813

AREAS OF INTEREST:
Classical philology, linguistics and history, modern philology and linguistics, history, art history, philosophy, mathematics and physics and their applications in chemistry and biology.

NAME(S) OF PROGRAMS:
● **Graduate School Scholarships for Study in Italy**

TYPE:
Scholarships. Scholarships for study at the Scuola Normale Superiore, Pisa, Italy, for postgraduate study in the disciplinary areas of the humanities and of mathematics, physics and natural sciences listed above.

PURPOSE:
Research and study leading to Diploma di Perfezionamento (Ph.D.); three years of scholarship. Research and study for a one-year scholarship.

LEGAL BASIS:
State-owned university.

ELIGIBILITY:
Citizens of all countries who have an M.A. degree and know Italian may apply. Students over 30 at the time of application cannot be admitted to the graduate courses. Applicants may not be receiving other forms of assistance.

FINANCIAL DATA:
Amount of support per award:
Perfezionamento (Ph.D.): Study grant of EUR 13,000 per year. One-year scholarship: Study grant of EUR 9,200 per year.

NUMBER OF APPLICANTS MOST RECENT YEAR: 8 for both sciences and humanities.

APPLICATION INFORMATION:
Information is available online. The new announcement appears around May-June each year.
Duration: Up to three years, fellowship may be extended for an additional year for justified academic and/or scientific reasons if possible within the budget.
Deadline: Faculty of Sciences: March 20 for spring session, September 20 for autumn session; Faculty of Arts: August 1.

ADDRESS INQUIRIES TO:
Dott. Mario Landucci
Tel: (39050) 509237

SHASTRI INDO-CANADIAN INSTITUTE (SICI)   [991]

Room 1402, Education Tower
2500 University Drive, N.W.
Calgary AB T2N 1N4 Canada
(403) 220-7467
Fax: (403) 289-0100

E-MAIL ADDRESS:
sici@ucalgary.ca
maldeen@ucalgary.ca

WEB SITE ADDRESS:
www.sici.org

AREAS OF INTEREST:
Understanding of India in Canada.

NAME(S) OF PROGRAMS:
● **India Studies Fellowship Competition**

TYPE:
Fellowships. India Studies Fellowship Competition is intended to support candidates wishing to undertake research or training in India. The focus of study is subjects relating to India in the social sciences and humanities, including education, law, management, the arts, science, and technology.

YEAR PROGRAM STARTED: 1968

PURPOSE:
To promote understanding between Canada and India, mainly through facilitating academic activities.

ELIGIBILITY:
Applicants must be Canadian citizens or permanent residents.

FINANCIAL DATA:
Amount of support per award: $9,000.

COOPERATIVE FUNDING PROGRAMS: Department of Education, Ministry of Human Resources, Government of India.

NUMBER OF APPLICANTS MOST RECENT YEAR: 63 for the year 2009-10.

NUMBER OF AWARDS: 32 for the year 2009-10.

APPLICATION INFORMATION:
Duration: Three months to one year.
Deadline: June 30.

ADDRESS INQUIRIES TO:
Programme Officer
(See address above.)

SOMMERHOCHSCHULE-UNIVERSITY OF VIENNA   [992]

Alser Strasse 4/Hof 1/Tuer 1.16
1090 Vienna Austria
43-1-4277-24131
Fax: 43-1-4277-9241

E-MAIL ADDRESS:
Sommerhochschule@univie.ac.at

WEB SITE ADDRESS:
shs.univie.ac.at/shs

FOUNDED: 1949

AREAS OF INTEREST:
European Studies (with focus on the political, legal, historical, economic and socio-cultural aspects) taught in English; German Language Courses (four levels).

NAME(S) OF PROGRAMS:
● **International Summer Program (Summer Campus Strobl/St. Wolfgang/Austria)**

TYPE:
Scholarships. The European Studies courses focus on the political, economic and legal, but also historical and cultural, aspects of Europe and the EU. The German language courses are offered at four different levels of proficiency (beginners to advanced).

YEAR PROGRAM STARTED: 1949

PURPOSE:
To contribute to an increased understanding of the EU and its possible future shape and to create an environment which encourages intercultural and social exchange and favors mutual understanding among participants.

LEGAL BASIS:
A subcompany of the University of Vienna; nonprofit status; state supported.

ELIGIBILITY:
Applicants have to be at least 18 years old and must have completed at least two years of studies at college or university level in their countries of residence or have an educational background equivalent to one year at a European university before the beginning of the program.

FINANCIAL DATA:
A limited number of partial scholarships are available for the European Studies section of the program. The scholarships are awarded on the basis of academic excellence and financial need.
Amount of support per award: EUR 300 to 2,400.

Total amount of support: EUR 40,000 expected for the year 2011.

NUMBER OF APPLICANTS MOST RECENT YEAR: 80 to 100.

NUMBER OF AWARDS: Varies based on the size of the scholarships.

APPLICATION INFORMATION:
Applicants have to submit the following documents:
(1) completed application form;
(2) transcript of grades;
(3) two letters of recommendation (academic or professional);
(4) official proof of proficiency in English;
(5) statement of purpose (one page maximum);
(6) two passport-size photos taken within the past year and;
(7) application for financial assistance.

All documents have to be submitted either in original or as a certified copy and have to be translated into English or German.

Application material must be sent to the office of the Sommerhochschule (faxed or e-mailed applications cannot be accepted).

Duration: Four weeks, middle of July to middle of August, every year.

Deadline: February 28 for scholarship applications; April 30 for regular applications.

PUBLICATIONS:
Annual brochures and leaflets for the International Summer Program of the Sommerhochschule.

OFFICERS:
Dr. Franz-Stefan Meissel, Director
Nina Gruber, Program Coordinator

ADDRESS INQUIRIES TO:
Nina Gruber, Program Coordinator
(See address above.)

SWEDISH INSTITUTE [993]

Slottsbacken 10, Box 7434
Stockholm 103 91 Sweden
+46 8-453 78 00
Fax: +46 8-20 72 48

E-MAIL ADDRESS:
si@si.se

WEB SITE ADDRESS:
www.si.se

FOUNDED: 1976

AREAS OF INTEREST:
Politics, public administration, working life, human environment, mass media, business and industry, education, research and culture.

NAME(S) OF PROGRAMS:
● **Bicentennial Swedish-American Exchange Fund**

TYPE:
Exchange programs; Travel grants; Visiting scholars. The Swedish Bicentennial Fund for the exchange of qualified persons from the United States and Sweden was established by an Act of the Swedish Parliament in 1976 as a tribute to the United States Bicentennial. The Fund began operations in 1978 with grants to Americans and Swedes working within the fields to which the Fund gives priority, i.e., politics, public administration, working life, human environment, mass media, business and industry, education and culture. The purpose of the Fund is to provide opportunity for those in a position to

influence public opinion and contribute to the development of their society to make a two- to four-week intensive research trip to Sweden.

YEAR PROGRAM STARTED: 1978

PURPOSE:
To provide opportunity for those in a position to influence public opinion and contribute to the development of their society to make a two- to four-week intensive research trip to Sweden.

ELIGIBILITY:
Applicants for grants to Sweden must be U.S. citizens or permanent residents. They must supply a full, realistic project description, which indicates follow-up and a plan for disseminating research results. Persons who have made recurrent visits to or resided in Sweden will be considered only in exceptional cases. The grant may not be used to finance participation in conferences or regular ongoing vocational or academic courses. If co-applicants on the same project are selected, the grant will be divided between them.

GEOGRAPHIC RESTRICTIONS:
United States and Sweden.

FINANCIAL DATA:
Grants cover partial per diem and round-trip travel between the U.S. and Sweden. Monies can be received in U.S. dollars or Swedish crowns. The grant cannot be used to finance participation in conferences or ongoing vocational or academic studies.
Amount of support per award: SEK 30,000.

APPLICATION INFORMATION:
Guidelines and application is available on the web site.
Duration: Two to four-week research visit. No renewals.
Deadline: November 15.

PUBLICATIONS:
Application guidelines; application form.

STAFF:
Niklas Arnegren, Director of Cultural Affairs and Public Programs
Melinda Martino, Director of Public Affairs and Communications

ADDRESS INQUIRIES TO:
See e-mail or mailing addresses above.

*SPECIAL STIPULATIONS:
Research trips must take place between March 1 of the year following application and December 31. Six months after the completed research trip, a report must be submitted to the Swedish Information Service providing a review of the project, a report of how objectives were met and clear indication of how results of the study will be disseminated.

U.S. DEPARTMENT OF EDUCATION [994]

Higher Education Programs
1990 K Street, N.W., 6th Floor
Washington, DC 20006-8521
(202) 502-7625
(202) 502-7700
Fax: (202) 502-7860

E-MAIL ADDRESS:
michelle.guilfoil@ed.gov

WEB SITE ADDRESS:
www.ed.gov/programs/iegpsgpa/index.html

FOUNDED: 1967

AREAS OF INTEREST:
Foreign languages and area studies.

NAME(S) OF PROGRAMS:
● **Fulbright-Hays Group Projects Abroad Program**

TYPE:
Project/program grants. Also, study grants and grants for foreign language and area study programs of educational development for projects to be undertaken abroad. Grants are awarded to higher education institutions, nonprofit educational organizations, state department of education and consortium of such institutions, departments, organizations and institutions which, in turn, enable professors, college and elementary and secondary school teachers and advanced students to attend seminars abroad and to travel and study in foreign countries in order to strengthen the institution's programs in foreign languages, area studies and world affairs.

YEAR PROGRAM STARTED: 1967

PURPOSE:
To contribute to the development and improvement of the study of foreign languages and area studies in the U.S. by providing opportunities for faculty, teachers, upperclassmen and/or graduate students to travel to foreign countries in group projects for research, training and curriculum development.

LEGAL BASIS:
The Mutual Educational and Cultural Exchange Act of 1961, Public Law 87-256 (Fulbright Hays Act), Section 102(b)(6).

ELIGIBILITY:
Under the program, grants are awarded to institutions of higher education, state departments of education, private nonprofit educational organizations and consortiums of such institutions, departments and organizations to conduct overseas group projects in research, training and curriculum development, by groups of individuals engaged in a common endeavor.

A participant must be a citizen, national or permanent resident of the U.S. and either a faculty member in modern foreign languages or area studies, an experienced educator responsible for planning, conducting or supervising programs in modern foreign languages or area studies at the elementary, secondary or postsecondary levels, a graduate student or upperclassman who plans a teaching career in modern foreign languages or area studies.

The grant does not provide funds for project-related expenses within the U.S. Funds may be used only for a maintenance stipend based on 50% of the amount established in the U.S. Department of State publication, *Maximum Travel Per Diem Allowances for Foreign Areas*, round-trip international travel, a local travel allowance for necessary project-related transportation within the country of study, exclusive of the purchase of transportation equipment, the purchase of project-related artifacts, books and other teaching materials in the country of study, rent for instructional facilities in the country of study, and clerical and professional services performed by resident instructional personnel in the country of study.

FINANCIAL DATA:
Amount of support per award: $50,000 to $375,000.

Total amount of support: $4,613,000 in U.S. funds for fiscal year 2008.

APPLICATION INFORMATION:
Duration: Four weeks to one year. No renewal.

Deadline: Fall.

ADDRESS INQUIRIES TO:
Michelle Guilfoil, Senior Program Officer
(See address above.)

U.S. DEPARTMENT OF EDUCATION   [995]

Office of Postsecondary Education
International and Foreign Language Education
1990 K Street, N.W., 6th Floor
Washington, DC 20006-8521
(202) 502-7589
(202) 502-7700
Fax: (202) 502-7859

E-MAIL ADDRESS:
cynthia.dudzinski@ed.gov

WEB SITE ADDRESS:
www.ed.gov/programs/iegpsfra/index.html

NAME(S) OF PROGRAMS:
- **Fulbright-Hays Faculty Research Abroad Program**

TYPE:
Fellowships; Research grants. This program funds fellowships through institutions of higher education (IHEs) to faculty members who propose to conduct research abroad in modern foreign languages and area studies to improve their skill in language and their knowledge of the culture of the people of these countries.

YEAR PROGRAM STARTED: 1964

PURPOSE:
To strengthen college and university programs of international studies by helping key faculty members remain current in their specialties and by assisting institutions in updating curriculums and improving teaching methods and materials.

LEGAL BASIS:
U.S. Government agency.

ELIGIBILITY:
Faculty members must apply through their employing institution. A candidate must be a U.S. citizen, national or permanent resident, an educator experienced in foreign languages and/or area studies, must have engaged in teaching during the two years preceding the date of award and possess adequate skills in the language of the country or in a language germane to the project or region.

GEOGRAPHIC RESTRICTIONS:
United States.

FINANCIAL DATA:
Amount of support per award: $20,000 to $115,000.

Total amount of support: Approximately $1,500,000 for the year 2010.

NUMBER OF APPLICANTS MOST RECENT YEAR:
65 to 70.

NUMBER OF AWARDS: 20 to 24.

APPLICATION INFORMATION:
Applications must be submitted electronically using e-grants.ed.gov.

Duration: Three to 12 months.

Deadline: Late October of the year preceding the year of study.

PUBLICATIONS:
Guidelines.

ADDRESS INQUIRIES TO:
Cynthia Dudzinski, Program Officer
(See address above.)

UNIVERSITY OF BRISTOL   [996]

Senate House
Tyndall Avenue
Bristol BS8 1TH England
44 (0) 117 928 9000
Fax: 44 (0) 117 925 1424

E-MAIL ADDRESS:
student-funding@bris.ac.uk

WEB SITE ADDRESS:
www.bris.ac.uk

FOUNDED: 1909

AREAS OF INTEREST:
Faculties of arts, engineering, medical and veterinary sciences, medicine and dentistry, science, social sciences and law.

NAME(S) OF PROGRAMS:
- **Postgraduate Research Scholarships**

TYPE:
Scholarships. Postgraduate research scholarships for study toward the Ph.D. degree in one of the departments of the University of Bristol.

YEAR PROGRAM STARTED: 1989

PURPOSE:
To attract excellent research students.

LEGAL BASIS:
University.

ELIGIBILITY:
Scholarships are available for the U.K., Europe and overseas students.

FINANCIAL DATA:
Amount of support per award: 27.

APPLICATION INFORMATION:
Information available from the Student Funding Office at the University of Bristol or is also available online.

Duration: Up to three years, subject to satisfactory academic progress.

Deadline: February and March; complete details available online.

PUBLICATIONS:
Annual report; research prospectus.

STAFF:
J. Fitzwalter, Student Funding Manager

ADDRESS INQUIRIES TO:
Student Funding Office
(See address above.)

UNIVERSITY OF ILLINOIS AT URBANA-CHAMPAIGN

College of Fine and Applied Arts
608 East Lorado Taft Drive, Suite 100
Champaign, IL 61820
(217) 333-1661
(217) 333-1660
Fax: (217) 244-8381

E-MAIL ADDRESS:
rewilcox@illinois.edu

WEB SITE ADDRESS:
www.faa.illinois.edu

TYPE:
Fellowships. Awarded for advanced study in the fine arts in the U.S. or abroad, in an approved educational institution, with an approved private teacher or in independent study.

Three major Fellowships will be awarded:
(1) one in any field of music;
(2) one in architectural design and history, art and design, theatre, dance, or instrumental or vocal music and;
(3) one in art, architecture, dance, landscape architecture, theatre, or urban and regional planning.

See entry 610 for full listing.

UNIVERSITY OF LEEDS   [997]

Postgraduate Scholarships Office
Level 9, Marjorie & Arnold Ziff Building
University of Leeds
Leeds LS2 9JT England
44 (0) 113 343 4007
44 (0) 113 343 4077
Fax: 44 (0) 113 343 3941

E-MAIL ADDRESS:
pg_scholarships@leeds.ac.uk

WEB SITE ADDRESS:
scholarships.leeds.ac.uk

AREAS OF INTEREST:
Education abroad.

NAME(S) OF PROGRAMS:
- **Tetley and Lupton Scholarships for International Students**

TYPE:
Scholarships. Awarded for Master's degree study. Tenable at University of Leeds.

YEAR PROGRAM STARTED: 1982

PURPOSE:
To help defray the cost of education for international students.

LEGAL BASIS:
University.

ELIGIBILITY:
Open to international students who are applying to begin courses leading to a postgraduate degree at the University of Leeds. Scholarships will be awarded only to students who are liable to pay the tuition fees at the full-cost rate for international students, accepted for admission as a full-time student for a Master's degree at the University of Leeds, but not holding another award which covers the payment of tuition fees in full. Applicants must be of high academic standard.

FINANCIAL DATA:
Scholarships are to be credited toward academic fees.

Amount of support per award: GBP 4,000 to 5,200 per year.

NUMBER OF AWARDS: Up to 9 new scholarships annually.

APPLICATION INFORMATION:
Duration: One academic year. May be held concurrently with other awards, except those providing full payment of fees.

Deadline: March 1.

PUBLICATIONS:
Brochure.

STAFF:
J.Y. Findlay, Senior Assistant Registrar, Research Student Administration

ADDRESS INQUIRIES TO:
Postgraduate Scholarships Office
(See address above.)

THE UNIVERSITY OF MANCHESTER [998]

Research Office, 2nd Floor
Christie Building
Manchester M13 9PL England
44 (0) 161 275 2434
Fax: 44 (0) 161 275 2445

E-MAIL ADDRESS:
sara.ashworth@manchester.ac.uk

WEB SITE ADDRESS:
www.manchester.ac.uk

FOUNDED: 1824

AREAS OF INTEREST:
Arts, economic, social and legal studies,
education, science, engineering, medicine and
biological sciences.

NAME(S) OF PROGRAMS:
● **British Marshall Scholarships**
● **Fulbright - University of Manchester Scholarship**
● **North American Foundation Awards**

TYPE:
Assistantships; Awards/prizes; Block grants;
Conferences/seminars; Endowments;
Exchange programs; Fellowships; Research
grants; Scholarships; Training grants; Travel
grants; Visiting scholars. Research
studentships for postgraduate-taught and
research programmes in the fields above.
North American Foundation Awards are for
postgraduate study at the University of
Manchester (NAFUM).
The University of Manchester is also a
recognized institution for the purpose of U.S.
federal loans and Canadian student loans.

FINANCIAL DATA:
Studentships include payment of fees at U.K.
level and/or maintenance allowance.
Amount of support per award: Varies.

ADDRESS INQUIRIES TO:
Student Services Centre
ssc@manchester.ac.uk

UNIVERSITY OF OSLO INTERNATIONAL SUMMER SCHOOL [999]

Oslo International Summer School
c/o St. Olaf College
1520 St. Olaf Avenue
Northfield, MN 55057-1098
(507) 786-3269
(800) 639-0058
Fax: (507) 786-3789

E-MAIL ADDRESS:
iss@stolaf.edu

WEB SITE ADDRESS:
www.summerschool.uio.no

FOUNDED: 1947

AREAS OF INTEREST:
The International Summer School offers
undergraduate and graduate courses in the
following areas:
General course offerings - Norwegian
language, Norwegian art history, Nordic
literature, history, political science, culture
and society, international relations and gender
equality in Nordic countries;
Graduate courses - special education, peace
research, international development, media

and communications, international
community health, energy and sustainable
development, and human rights.

TYPE:
Scholarships.

YEAR PROGRAM STARTED: 1947

PURPOSE:
To offer academic instruction to a gathering
of many nationalities in the hope of a modest
but concrete increase in understanding and
goodwill among nations.

LEGAL BASIS:
Part of the University of Oslo.

ELIGIBILITY:
Scholarships awarded only to students
accepted into the Oslo International Summer
School program. Scholarship applicants must
meet the entrance requirements of the
International Summer School and must
present evidence of attending or having
attended a recognized university and have a
good academic record. One year or more of
college or university is required. In addition,
seriousness of academic purpose and personal
qualities likely to make the applicant a good
representative of his or her country.

FINANCIAL DATA:
Amount of support per award: Varies.
Total amount of support: Varies.

NUMBER OF AWARDS: Varies.

APPLICATION INFORMATION:
A financial aid application form and the
application for admission to the International
Summer School and the supporting letters of
recommendation are used by the Financial
Aid Committee to choose financial aid
recipients.
Duration: Six weeks during the summer,
from late June to early August. No renewal
possibilities.
Deadline: Papers are due by February 1.
Results are announced the first week in
April.

PUBLICATIONS:
ISS catalog.

ADMINISTRATION:
Einar Vannebo, Director, International
Summer School Norwegian Office
Torild Homstad, Administrator, North
American Admissions Office

ADDRESS INQUIRIES TO:
Non-North American students should request
information from:
International Summer School
Postbox 1082
N-0317 Oslo, Norway
Tel: (011) 47 2285-6385
Fax: (011) 47 2285-4199

All other applicants can use the North
American address above.

THE UNIVERSITY OF QUEENSLAND [1000]

Ground Floor, Cumbrae-Stewart Building (72)
Research Road
St. Lucia, Brisbane 4072 Australia
61 7 336 53560
Fax: 61 7 336 54455

E-MAIL ADDRESS:
oper@research.uq.edu.au

WEB SITE ADDRESS:
www.uq.edu.au/research/rrtd

FOUNDED: 1910

AREAS OF INTEREST:
Arts, biological sciences, chemical sciences,
health sciences, humanities, physical sciences
and engineering, social sciences, business,
economics and law, natural resources,
agriculture and veterinary science.

NAME(S) OF PROGRAMS:
● **Postdoctoral Research Fellowships at The University of Queensland**

TYPE:
Fellowships. Awarded to early career
researchers of exceptional calibre wishing to
conduct full-time research at the University
in any of its disciplines.

YEAR PROGRAM STARTED: 1968

PURPOSE:
To facilitate postdoctoral research at The
University of Queensland.

LEGAL BASIS:
University incorporated by statute.

ELIGIBILITY:
An applicant must not have had more than
five years' full-time professional experience
or equivalent part-time experience since the
award of a doctoral degree as of June 30 of
the application year. Priority will be given to
applicants in the early stage of their
postdoctoral careers. Prospective Ph.D.
awardees may also apply. For full details,
contact the University.

FINANCIAL DATA:
Maintenance funds of $10,000 (AUD) in the
first year of the Fellowship, and $5,000
(AUD) in each of the two subsequent years
will be made available to the Fellow to
support research costs.
Amount of support per award: $61,711
(AUD)-$68,768 (AUD).

APPLICATION INFORMATION:
The application form and guidelines are
available on the University of Queensland's
web site. Prior to applying, it is imperative
that prospective applicants contact/write to
the Head of the appropriate
school/department or centre to obtain more
details of their research interests, and to
ascertain whether the school is prepared to
support a candidate's application.
Duration: Three years, to be completed by
December 31.
Deadline: View online for current deadline.

PUBLICATIONS:
Annual report; application guidelines.

ADDRESS INQUIRIES TO:
The University of Queensland
Research and Research Training Division
Cumbrae-Stewart (Building 72)
Brisbane, 4072
Australia

THE UNIVERSITY OF SYDNEY [1001]

Scholarships Office
Level 5, Jane Foss Russell Building G02
The University of Sydney N.S.W. 2006
Australia
(02) 8627 8112
Fax: (02) 8627 8145

E-MAIL ADDRESS:
research.training@sydney.edu.au

WEB SITE ADDRESS:
www.sydney.edu.au/scholarships/research

FOUNDED: 1850

NAME(S) OF PROGRAMS:
- **Australian Postgraduate Awards (APA)**
- **International Postgraduate Research Scholarships (IPRS)**

TYPE:
Scholarships. Awarded for research leading to a higher degree. Tenable at the University of Sydney.

LEGAL BASIS:
University.

ELIGIBILITY:
The scholarships are awarded on academic merit and research ability to qualified candidates. Open to qualified foreign graduates from any country eligible to commence a higher degree by research. Australian and New Zealand citizens or permanent residents are not eligible.

FINANCIAL DATA:
Amount of support per award: APA: $22,860 (AUD) per annum for the year 2011; IPRS: Tuition fees.

NUMBER OF AWARDS: 33 for the year 2011.

APPLICATION INFORMATION:
Contact the International Office at the University of Sydney between May and July.
Duration: IPRS: Two years for a Master's research degree and three years for a Ph.D.
Deadline: July 31 for semester one commencement and December 31 for semester two commencement.

ADDRESS INQUIRIES TO:
International Office
Level 4, Jane Foss Russell Building G02
The University of Sydney
N.S.W. 2006 Australia
Tel: (02) 8627 8300
Fax: (02) 8627 8387
E-mail: infoschol@io.usyd.edu.au
Web site:
www.sydney.edu.au/internationaloffice

UNIVERSITY OF VIRGINIA [1002]
120 Vincennes Road
Charlottesville, VA 22911
(434) 924-3192
Fax: (434) 924-3359

E-MAIL ADDRESS:
al4u@virginia.edu

FOUNDED: 1976

AREAS OF INTEREST:
International law and politics, international economics, international institutions and international development.

NAME(S) OF PROGRAMS:
- **Gallatin Fellowships**

TYPE:
Exchange programs; Fellowships; Project/program grants.

YEAR PROGRAM STARTED: 1976

PURPOSE:
To foster international understanding through education and exchange in the field of international studies.

LEGAL BASIS:
University.

ELIGIBILITY:
Ph.D. students in international affairs at the dissertation stage of their work. Applicants must be U.S. citizens or permanent residents.

Intended for students who plan to study at the Graduate Institute of International Studies, Geneva, Switzerland.

GEOGRAPHIC RESTRICTIONS:
United States.

FINANCIAL DATA:
Amount of support per award: $26,000 plus airfare.
Total amount of support: $50,000 to $55,000.

NUMBER OF APPLICANTS MOST RECENT YEAR:
3.

NUMBER OF AWARDS: 1 or more annually.

REPRESENTATIVE AWARDS:
Carol V. Evans, Ph.D. candidate at the London School of Economics and Political Science, received a short-term grant to conduct research on "Defense Industrialization in Newly Industrialized Countries;" Kurt D. Will, Ph.D. candidate at the James F. Byrnes Center for International Studies, University of South Carolina, received a nine-month Gallatin Fellowship to study at the Geneva Institute, on "The World Health Organization and the Transnational AIDS Network;" David Blair, Ph.D. candidate at the Geneva Institute for doctoral research on "The Role of the OECD (Organization for Economic Cooperation & Development) in International Trade Relations;" Yan Lan, Ph.D. candidate at the Geneva Institute, where she finished a dissertation on "Procedural Issues in International Arbitration."

APPLICATION INFORMATION:
Applicants should submit the following in six typewritten copies:
(1) personal data form;
(2) academic record to include a chronological list of all educational institutions attended above high school level, naming institutions, fields of study, years of study and degree, a transcript of graduate work completed, listing courses and grades, a list of published works, articles or topics of research papers undertaken during graduate study including a copy of a published work or research paper, a list of academic distinctions, fellowships, etc., including those currently held or applied for;
(3) international experience, which should consist of a list of the countries, other than the U.S., in which applicant has lived or traveled, with the dates, duration and purpose of these stays (business, education and/or pleasure) indicated and a description, of not more than 300 words, of any aspect of these experiences, or others, which is believed to have contributed notably to applicant's academic career or to their proposed professional interests, including language training;
(4) proficiency in foreign language, in which the applicant should list those foreign languages of which he or she has a speaking, reading and writing knowledge, indicating under each of these headings if knowledge is elementary, medium or advanced and provide among the references an individual who can be consulted on applicant's language competence;
(5) study program, which should consist of an essay of up to 1,500 words describing applicant's research program, showing how the Institute's curriculum of research, seminars, etc., as well as institutions located in Geneva, will contribute to it. Candidates are advised to study the Institute's catalogue in formulating their programs;

(6) career intentions, in which the applicant should briefly describe his or her professional objectives and how he or she sees their current studies and those proposed at the Institute contributing to them. Any professional work which applicant may have already undertaken in the international field should be described, including teaching assistantships, participation in research programs, publications and awards and;
(7) references, which should consist of the above information further supplemented by letters from four individuals who are familiar with the applicant's proposed research program, including thesis supervisor. If possible, one should be able to judge applicant's competence in the French language. These letters of reference should be sent directly to the address above when completed application is submitted. These letters should include the office addresses and telephone numbers of those sending them.
Duration: One academic year. Shorter term grants are also available.
Deadline: March 1.

PUBLICATIONS:
Application guidelines.

STAFF:
Allen C. Lynch, Supervisor, Gallatin Fellowship Program

ADDRESS INQUIRIES TO:
Allen C. Lynch, Supervisor
Gallatin Fellowship Program
(See address above.)

*SPECIAL STIPULATIONS:
Applicant must be engaged in the dissertation phase of Ph.D. work in international affairs.

VILLA I TATTI: THE HARVARD UNIVERSITY CENTER FOR ITALIAN RENAISSANCE STUDIES [1003]
Via di Vincigliata, 26
50135 Florence Italy
(39 055) 603 251
(39 055) 608 909
Fax: (39 055) 603 383

E-MAIL ADDRESS:
info@itatti.it

WEB SITE ADDRESS:
www.itatti.it

FOUNDED: 1961

AREAS OF INTEREST:
All aspects of the Italian Renaissance: fine arts, literature, music, science, philosophy, religion and political, intellectual, economic and social history.

CONSULTING OR VOLUNTEER SERVICES:
Library, photographic collection and archive.

NAME(S) OF PROGRAMS:
- **Fellowships for Independent Study on the Italian Renaissance**
- **Outreach Visiting Fellowship**
- **Craig Hugh Smyth Visiting Fellowships**

TYPE:
Fellowships. Stipendiary and non-stipendiary fellowships for the academic year July 1 through June 30 in residence in Florence for study on any aspect of the Italian Renaissance. There are a limited number of short-term Outreach Visiting Fellowships designed to reach out to Italian Renaissance scholars from areas that have been underrepresented at Villa I Tatti, especially

those from Asia, Latin America, the Iberian Peninsula and the Mediterranean basin (except Italy).There are also a limited number of short-term Craig Hugh Smyth Visiting Fellowships mainly for museum and library professionals, but academic administrators and conservators are welcome to apply, and mothers engaged in some aspect of Italian Renaissance studies.

YEAR PROGRAM STARTED: 1961

PURPOSE:
To promote advanced interdisciplinary study in Renaissance fields.

LEGAL BASIS:
Part of Harvard University.

ELIGIBILITY:
I Tatti Fellowship applicants must be scholars of any nationality, postdoctoral and in the earlier stages of their careers, and must be free to devote full-time to study.

FINANCIAL DATA:
Stipends will be given in accord with the individual needs of the approved applicants and the availability of funds.

Amount of support per award: For a yearlong fellowship, the maximum stipend is $50,000.

Total amount of support: $1,000,200 for the year 2010-11.

COOPERATIVE FUNDING PROGRAMS: Deborah Loeb Brice Fellowship, Committee to Rescue Italian Art, Francesco E. de Dombrowski Bequest, Florence Gould Foundation, Hanna Kiel Fellowship, Melville J. Kahn Fellowship Fund, Samuel H. Kress Foundation, Robert Lehman Fellowship, Jean Francois Malle Fellowship Fund, Andrew W. Mellon Foundation, Ahmanson Foundation, Lila Wallace - Reader's Digest Endowment Fund.

NUMBER OF APPLICANTS MOST RECENT YEAR: 93 for the year 2011-12.

NUMBER OF AWARDS: 15 for the 2011-12 academic year.

APPLICATION INFORMATION:
Application forms are available online. Applications by fax are not accepted.

Duration: July 1 to June 30.

Deadline: I Tatti Fellowships: To be received by October 15. Announcement by early spring.

Outreach Visiting Fellowships and Craig Hugh Smyth Visiting Fellowships: To be received by April 15. Announcement by early spring.

IRS IDENTIFICATION NUMBER: 04-2103580

ADVISORY COMMITTEE:
Lino Pertile, Director and Chairman
Lina Bolzoni
Giuseppe Gerbino
James Hankins
Machtelt Israels
Thomas Kelly
Kate Lowe
John Najemy
Katharine Park
Alina Payne
Carl Strehlke
Jane Tylus

ADDRESS INQUIRIES TO:
Lino Pertile, Director
(See address above.)

THOMAS J. WATSON FELLOWSHIP PROGRAM
11 Park Place, Suite 1503
New York, NY 10017
(212) 245-8859
Fax: (212) 245-8860

E-MAIL ADDRESS:
tjw@watsonfellowship.org

WEB SITE ADDRESS:
watsonfellowship.org

TYPE:
Fellowships. The Foundation provides Fellows an opportunity for a focused and disciplined "Wanderjahr" of their own devising or design-time in which to explore with thoroughness a particular interest, test their aspirations and abilities, view their lives and American society in greater perspective and concomitantly, to develop a more informed sense of international concern. The Fellowship experience is intended to provide Fellows an opportunity to immerse themselves in cultures other than their own for an entire year. The candidate's proposed project should involve investigation into an area of demonstrated concern and personal interest.

See entry 1764 for full listing.

WEIZMANN INSTITUTE OF SCIENCE   [1004]
Feinberg Graduate School of the Weizmann Institute of Science
P.O. Box 26
Rehovot 76100 Israel
(972-8) 9343843
(972-8) 9342924
Fax: (972-8) 9344114

E-MAIL ADDRESS:
postdoc@weizmann.ac.il

WEB SITE ADDRESS:
www.fgs.org.il

FOUNDED: 1934

AREAS OF INTEREST:
Life sciences, chemistry, physics, mathematics and computer science.

NAME(S) OF PROGRAMS:
● **Postdoctoral Fellowships Program at the Weizmann Institute of Science**

TYPE:
Fellowships. The Feinberg Graduate School of the Weizmann Institute of Science offers a limited number of postdoctoral fellowships in all areas of research in which the Weizmann Institute is engaged. The fellowships are offered in various fields of biology, chemistry, physics, biochemistry-biophysics, mathematics and computer science.

YEAR PROGRAM STARTED: 1976

PURPOSE:
Postdoctoral training at the Weizmann Institute of Science.

LEGAL BASIS:
Research institute.

ELIGIBILITY:
Postdoctoral fellowship applicants must have received a Ph.D. or equivalent degree within four years of the submission deadline. Candidates may be citizens of any country.

FINANCIAL DATA:
The annual stipend is adjusted periodically in accordance with living costs. Also offered is

a small relocation allowance and a one-way economy class airfare (round-trip airfare in case the fellowship is extended to two years).

Amount of support per award:
Approximately $28,000 per year.

APPLICATION INFORMATION:
Application forms and additional information may be obtained from the Feinberg Graduate School, Weizmann Institute of Science and from the web site.

Duration: 12 months. Possible renewal for a second and third year.

Deadline: Applications may be submitted year-round.

OFFICERS:
Prof. Daniel Zajfman, President
Prof. Elior Peles, Head, Postdoctoral Program

ADDRESS INQUIRIES TO:
Feinberg Graduate School
(See address above.)

YOUTH FOR UNDERSTANDING USA   [1005]
6400 Goldsboro Road
Suite 100
Bethesda, MD 20817
(240) 235-2100
(800) 833-6243
(866) 493-8872
Fax: (240) 235-2188

E-MAIL ADDRESS:
admissions@yfu.org

WEB SITE ADDRESS:
www.yfu-usa.org

FOUNDED: 2002

AREAS OF INTEREST:
The exchange of U.S. and international high school students in over 60 countries.

CONSULTING OR VOLUNTEER SERVICES:
Intercultural education and training and research.

NAME(S) OF PROGRAMS:
● **Americans Overseas Summer, Semester and Year Programs**
● **Congress-Bundestag Youth Exchange Program**
● **Corporate Scholarship Program**
● **Finland-U.S. Senate Youth Exchange Program**
● **International Semester and Year Programs**
● **Japan-U.S. Senate Youth Exchange Program**

TYPE:
Exchange programs; Grants-in-aid; Scholarships; Travel grants. Students on summer semester and year programs live with volunteer host families overseas. Students on semester and academic year programs also attend school. International students live and study at U.S. high schools or community colleges. Competitive, full and partial scholarships for Corporate, Finland-U.S. Senate, Japan-U.S. Senate Programs and Japan-America Friendship Scholars Program.

YEAR PROGRAM STARTED: 2002

PURPOSE:
To prepare young people for their responsibilities and opportunities in a changing, interdependent world.

LEGAL BASIS:
Tax-exempt, 501(c)(3) international educational organization.

ELIGIBILITY:
Applicants must be U.S. or international high school students between the ages of 15 and 18. Full scholarships for special programs are awarded through merit competition. Partial scholarships (10 to 25%) are awarded on the basis of need.

FINANCIAL DATA:
Amount of support per award: From $500 to full support.

COOPERATIVE FUNDING PROGRAMS: Funding sources for scholarships include a multitude of governments, corporations, foundations and individuals.

NUMBER OF AWARDS: Approximately 2,500.

APPLICATION INFORMATION:
Applicants for programs involving full scholarships must complete special application materials. For corporate programs, applicants must meet special eligibility requirements. Applicants for partial scholarships must complete financial aid forms.
Duration: Scholarships awarded for the program period.
Deadline: Between September and March, depending on program. Announcement between February and April.

IRS IDENTIFICATION NUMBER: 02-0557010

OFFICERS:
Michael Finnell, President and Chief Executive Officer
Margie Ott, Director of Programs and Contracts

BOARD OF TRUSTEES:
Ulrich Zahllen, Chairman
David Bachner
Michael Finnell
William Schupp

ADDRESS INQUIRIES TO:
Neil Routman, Communications and Development Specialist
(See address and toll-free telephone number above.)

Programs for foreign scholars

AMERICA-ISRAEL CULTURAL FOUNDATION   [1006]
20 East 46th Street, 15th Floor
New York, NY 10017
(212) 557-1600
Fax: (212) 557-1611

E-MAIL ADDRESS:
info@aicf.org

WEB SITE ADDRESS:
www.aicf.org

FOUNDED: 1939

AREAS OF INTEREST:
Music, dance, theater, visual arts, film and television.

NAME(S) OF PROGRAMS:
● **Scholarship Program for Israelis**

TYPE:
Awards/prizes; Endowments; Fellowships; Project/program grants; Scholarships. For study in the arts of music, painting and

sculpture, dance and drama, film and television, to be pursued either in Israel or in other countries.

YEAR PROGRAM STARTED: 1952

PURPOSE:
To further Israeli talent in the fields of music, visual arts, dance and drama, film and television.

ELIGIBILITY:
Only Israeli nationals that live and study in Israel are eligible to apply for domestic scholarships. Israeli nationals studying abroad are able to apply for scholarships to any international location of study.

FINANCIAL DATA:
Amount of support per award: $600 to $10,000.
Total amount of support: $2,000,000 per year.

NUMBER OF APPLICANTS MOST RECENT YEAR: Approximately 2,500.

NUMBER OF AWARDS: Approximately 1,100.

APPLICATION INFORMATION:
Application materials are available upon request to America-Israel Cultural Foundation, 8 Shaul Hamelech Boulevard, Tel Aviv 64733, Israel.
Duration: Grants are awarded for one to two years of study. Teachers of the arts may also apply for up to six-month fellowships.

IRS IDENTIFICATION NUMBER: 13-1664048

ADDRESS INQUIRIES TO:
Scholarships: Orit Naor
Executive Director
8 Shaul Hamelech Boulevard, Tel Aviv 64733, Israel

AMERICAN ASSOCIATION OF FAMILY AND CONSUMER SCIENCES (AAFCS)   [1007]
400 North Columbus Street
Suite 202
Alexandria, VA 22314-2752
(703) 706-4600
(800) 424-8080
Fax: (703) 706-4663

E-MAIL ADDRESS:
staff@aafcs.org

WEB SITE ADDRESS:
www.aafcs.org/programs/index.html

FOUNDED: 1909

AREAS OF INTEREST:
Family and consumer sciences.

NAME(S) OF PROGRAMS:
● **National and International Fellowships**

TYPE:
Fellowships. AAFCS awards fellowships to individuals who have exhibited the potential to make contributions to the family and consumer sciences profession.

YEAR PROGRAM STARTED: 1962

PURPOSE:
To support graduate study in the field of family and consumer sciences.

LEGAL BASIS:
501(c)(3) nonprofit charity.

FINANCIAL DATA:
Amount of support per award: $3,500 to $5,000 for each fellowship, plus up to $1,000 of support.

Total amount of support: Varies.

NUMBER OF APPLICANTS MOST RECENT YEAR:
28 for the year 2010.

NUMBER OF AWARDS: Up to 10 annually.

APPLICATION INFORMATION:
Duration: One academic year.
Deadline: Early January.

PUBLICATIONS:
Brochure.

ADDRESS INQUIRIES TO:
Award Programs
(See address above.)

AMERICAN ASSOCIATION OF UNIVERSITY WOMEN EDUCATIONAL FOUNDATION   [1008]
101 ACT Drive
Iowa City, IA 52243
(319) 337-1716

E-MAIL ADDRESS:
aauw@act.org

WEB SITE ADDRESS:
www.aauw.org

FOUNDED: 1958

AREAS OF INTEREST:
Advancement of educational and professional opportunities for women in the U.S. and around the globe.

NAME(S) OF PROGRAMS:
● **AAUW Educational Foundation International Fellowships**

TYPE:
Fellowships. Awards for women who are not citizens or permanent residents of the U.S. for full-time graduate or postgraduate study or research in the U.S.

A limited number of project grants are available to successful applicants who wish to implement a community-based project in the year immediately following the fellowship. Eligible project proposals must demonstrate that they will be implemented in the applicant's home country and will have a direct impact on women and girls. Only applicants who are selected to receive an International Fellowship will be considered for project grant funding.

YEAR PROGRAM STARTED: 1917

PURPOSE:
To provide advanced study and training for non-American women (i.e., women who are not U.S. citizens or permanent residents) of outstanding academic ability who may be expected to give effective leadership in their homelands.

ELIGIBILITY:
Women from countries other than the U.S. who hold the equivalent of an American Bachelor's degree at the time of application and have scored a minimum of 550 (paper-based), 213 (computer-based) or 79 (Internet-based) on the TOEFL within the past two years. Strong preference is given to women whose credentials demonstrate prior commitment to improving the lives of other women and girls through civic, community or professional work, whose study or research proposals show a continued interest in the advancement of women.

Upon completion of study, fellowship recipients are expected to return to their home countries to pursue professional careers. Preference is given to applicants who can verify that they have definite positions to which they will return.

Applicants are judged on their professional potential and on the importance of their projects in relation to their country of origin. Previous and current recipients of AAUW fellowships are not eligible to apply.

FINANCIAL DATA:
Amount of support per award: $18,000 to $30,000 for fellowships.
Total amount of support: Approximately $716,000 for the year 2009-10.

NUMBER OF APPLICANTS MOST RECENT YEAR: 1,049.

NUMBER OF AWARDS: 30 to 50 annually.

APPLICATION INFORMATION:
Guidelines are posted on the web site. Applications become available August 1 and must be submitted online.
Duration: Fellowships are awarded for one academic year, beginning July 1.
Deadline: December 1.

ADDRESS INQUIRIES TO:
Todd Beckman, Specialist
(See address above.)

*SPECIAL STIPULATIONS:
Applicants must be accepted to or have applied to an accredited institution of study.

THE AMERICAN SOCIETY OF MECHANICAL ENGINEERS AUXILIARY, INC.

3 Park Avenue, MS-RB
New York, NY 10016-5990
(212) 591-7650
Fax: (212) 591-7739

E-MAIL ADDRESS:
bigleyr@asme.org

WEB SITE ADDRESS:
www.asme.org/about-asme/scholarship-and-loans/the-asme-auxiliary,-inc-

TYPE:
Scholarships. Student loans. ASME Auxiliary FIRST Clarke Scholarship is for incoming freshman enrolling in a mechanical engineering program.

Baldwin, Cartwright, Farny, Kezios and Scharp Scholarships are for undergraduate students in mechanical engineering.

Parsons and Rothermel Scholarships are for graduate students with a degree in mechanical engineering, to be used to pursue a Master's degree in mechanical engineering.

Rice-Cullimore Scholarship is for foreign students at the graduate level.

Student Loan Fund is for juniors, seniors or graduate students enrolled as degree candidates in good standing.

See entry 2818 for full listing.

BELGIAN AMERICAN EDUCATIONAL FOUNDATION, INC.

195 Church Street
New Haven, CT 06510
(203) 777-5765
Fax: (203) 777-5765

E-MAIL ADDRESS:
emile.boulpaep@yale.edu
mail@baef.be

WEB SITE ADDRESS:
www.baef.us
www.baef.be

TYPE:
Fellowships. Predoctoral and postdoctoral fellowships for advanced study in most fields of knowledge with supported work to be undertaken at a Belgian university. Fellowships for Belgian students are also available.

See entry 948 for full listing.

THE ENGLISH-SPEAKING UNION   [1009]

Dartmouth House
37 Charles Street
London W1J 5ED England
44 (0) 20 7529 1550
Fax: 44 (0) 20 7495 6108

E-MAIL ADDRESS:
education@esu.org

WEB SITE ADDRESS:
www.esu.org

FOUNDED: 1918

AREAS OF INTEREST:
Education.

NAME(S) OF PROGRAMS:
- **The British Morehead-Cain Scholarship to the University of North Carolina at Chapel Hill**
- **The Chautauqua Institution Scholarships**
- **The Lindemann Trust Fellowships**
- **Walter Hines Page Scholarships**

TYPE:
Exchange programs; Fellowships; Scholarships; Travel grants. The Chautauqua Institution Scholarships are open to all qualified teachers. The award covers the cost of attendance at the Institution and includes lectures, classes, board, lodging, and entertainment for up to six weeks' stay.

The Lindemann Trust Fellowships are awarded for research in the U.S. to graduates of exceptional promise in both the pure and applied physical sciences, who have shown capacity for achieving original research.

The British Morehead-Cain Scholarship is open to all secondary schools in the United Kingdom. All nominees should show evidence of outstanding achievement in four criteria: leadership, scholarship, moral force of character and physical vigor.

Walter Hines Page Scholarships are awarded to teachers and educators from the U.K. and are intended to promote the exchange of educational ideas between Britain and America. Scholars travel to the United States to study a specific aspect of American education which interests them and which is relevant to their own professional responsibilities.

YEAR PROGRAM STARTED: 1923

PURPOSE:
To enable teachers and students in Great Britain to observe teaching methods in the U.S. The same applies for U.S. and Canadian students spending time in the U.K.

LEGAL BASIS:
Educational charity.

ELIGIBILITY:
U.K. citizens. Secondary School Exchange Scholarships: U.K., U.S. and Canadian citizens.

GEOGRAPHIC RESTRICTIONS:
Canada, United Kingdom and United States.

FINANCIAL DATA:
Amount of support per award: Varies.
Total amount of support: Varies.

COOPERATIVE FUNDING PROGRAMS: Sponsored by the English-Speaking Union and various teaching unions.

NUMBER OF AWARDS: Chautauqua Institution Scholarships: 2; Lindemann Trust Fellowships and Walter Hines Page Scholarships: Varies; Morehead-Cain Scholarship: Up to 4.

APPLICATION INFORMATION:
Applications must be made to the address above.
Duration: Chautauqua Institution Scholarships: Two to six weeks; Lindemann Trust Fellowships: One year; Morehead-Cain: Full four-year scholarship; Walter Hines Page Scholarships: One academic year.
Deadline: Varies.

PUBLICATIONS:
Annual report; *Concord*, newsletter.

ADDRESS INQUIRIES TO:
Katherine Plummer
Head of Education Programmes
(See address above.)

INTERNATIONAL ROAD FEDERATION   [1010]

500 Montgomery Street, Suite 525
Alexandria, VA 22314
(703) 535-1001
Fax: (703) 535-1007

E-MAIL ADDRESS:
kmejasich@irfnews.org
info@irfnews.org

WEB SITE ADDRESS:
www.irfnews.org

FOUNDED: 1948

AREAS OF INTEREST:
Highway engineering and management.

NAME(S) OF PROGRAMS:
- **IRF Fellowship Program**

TYPE:
Fellowships; Scholarships. Annual awards for graduate study in highway and traffic engineering for graduate engineers.

YEAR PROGRAM STARTED: 1949

PURPOSE:
To train personnel in the field of highways and highway transport.

LEGAL BASIS:
Corporate foundation.

ELIGIBILITY:
Open to non-U.S. graduate students. Qualified civil engineers must return to home country following completion of program.

FINANCIAL DATA:
Amount of support per award: $2,500 to $15,000 to defray partially one year of graduate study.
Total amount of support: Approximately $78,000 for the year 2010-11.
Matching fund requirements: Home country donors must make up differential.

NUMBER OF APPLICANTS MOST RECENT YEAR: 50 for the year 2009.

NUMBER OF AWARDS: 5 to 10.

APPLICATION INFORMATION:
Application must be made to the national road association or ministry in one's home country.
Duration: One year.
Deadline: October 31.

PUBLICATIONS:
Annual Report; *Directory of Students.*

IRS IDENTIFICATION NUMBER: 52-0793883

STAFF:
C. Patrick Sankey, Director General and Chief Executive Officer
Kathy Mejasich, Vice President, Marketing and Organizational Investment

ADDRESS INQUIRIES TO:
Kathy Mejasich, Vice President
Marketing and Organizational Investment
(See address above.)

THE KENNEDY MEMORIAL TRUST   [1011]
3 Birdcage Walk
Westminster
London SW1H 9JJ England
(020) 7222 1151
Fax: (020) 7222 7189

WEB SITE ADDRESS:
www.kennedytrust.org.uk

FOUNDED: 1966

NAME(S) OF PROGRAMS:
● **Kennedy Scholarships**

TYPE:
Scholarships. Awarded for postgraduate work for one year at Harvard or the Massachusetts Institute of Technology. Field of study is unrestricted.

YEAR PROGRAM STARTED: 1966

LEGAL BASIS:
Private.

ELIGIBILITY:
British citizens ordinarily resident in the U.K. who have graduated not earlier than 2009 from a U.K. university or are currently studying for a first or higher degree and have spent two of the last five years at such an institution and will have graduated in the academic year 2011-12. Applications from otherwise qualified persons who are already in the U.S. cannot be considered.

Awards are tenable either at Harvard University or the Massachusetts Institute of Technology. Kennedy Scholars are not required to study for a degree in the U.S., but are free to do so if they are eligible and able to complete the necessary requirements.

FINANCIAL DATA:
Stipend, plus transatlantic transportation, full tuition and university health insurance fees for the year.
Amount of support per award: Minimum $23,000 stipend.

NUMBER OF APPLICANTS MOST RECENT YEAR: 297.

NUMBER OF AWARDS: 6 for the year 2011.

APPLICATION INFORMATION:
Applications must be submitted online via the Trust's web site.
Duration: One year.
Deadline: Early November.

OFFICERS AND TRUSTEES:
Tony Badger, Chairman
Annie Thomas, Secretary
Daniel Alexander, QC
Dr. Peter Englander
J.J. Grimond
Prof. Kay-Tee Khaw
Prof. Richard Lester
Prof. Susan Manning
Prof. Anthony Saich
Dr. Martin Weale

ADDRESS INQUIRIES TO:
Secretary
(See address above.)

LASPAU: ACADEMIC AND PROFESSIONAL PROGRAMS FOR THE AMERICAS   [1012]
25 Mount Auburn Street
Suite 300
Cambridge, MA 02138-6095
(617) 495-5255
Fax: (617) 495-8990

E-MAIL ADDRESS:
laspau-webmaster@calists.harvard.edu

WEB SITE ADDRESS:
www.laspau.harvard.edu

FOUNDED: 1964

AREAS OF INTEREST:
Designing and administering academic and professional exchange programs in Latin America, the Caribbean, Canada and the U.S.

CONSULTING OR VOLUNTEER SERVICES:
Specialized educational consulting services are offered by LASPAU.

TYPE:
Conferences/seminars; Exchange programs; Fellowships; Project/program grants; Scholarships; Technical assistance; Training grants; Travel grants. LASPAU administers school programs, institutional development programs through executive training, and graduate admission tests. LASPAU is involved in these exchange areas: professional/business, students/educators and training.

YEAR PROGRAM STARTED: 1964

PURPOSE:
LASPAU's efforts are guided by the vision of social and economic development in Latin America and the Caribbean, achieved through long-term investment in education. We see the ability of a society to empower its citizens through education and professional development as a necessity in today's global context. A central tenet of our vision is that high quality academic preparation and training in the Americas should be available throughout society and not a reserve of privileged elites. LASPAU therefore gives special priority to regional, socio-economic and ethnic diversity in order to broaden opportunities for underserved populations.

LEGAL BASIS:
Nonprofit corporation.

ELIGIBILITY:
In most cases, individuals wishing to apply for an award must be nominated through the program sponsor by a participating Latin American, Caribbean or other institution. (Similarly, all scholarship and loan recipients agree to return promptly to their home institutions.) Independent applications are

accepted only for certain programs; details are available at the Programs section on the web site.

GEOGRAPHIC RESTRICTIONS:
Latin America and the Caribbean.

FINANCIAL DATA:
LASPAU provides grantees and their sponsors with comprehensive financial services, disbursement of scholarship grants and regular reports to sponsoring agencies.
Amount of support per award: Varies.
Total amount of support: Approximately $15,000,000.

APPLICATION INFORMATION:
Application procedures vary by program. Please check the Programs section on the web site for details.

PUBLICATIONS:
eNewsletter, annual report; *Informativo*, newsletter; brochures; grantee guides.

OFFICERS:
Ambassador Peter DeShazo, Executive Director
Rodrigo DelaTorre, Associate Director for Finance
Craig Hastings, Associate Director for Programs

TRUSTEES:
Gustavo Herrero, Chairperson
John F. Coburn, Vice Chairperson
Cristian Shea, Vice Chairperson
John Knutson, Treasurer
Hilda Catalina Cruz Solis
Everett Eggington
William Fulbright Foote
Merilee S. Grindle
James Honan
Tara Kenney
Felipe Medina
Aldo Musacchio
Fernando Reimers
Francisco Sananez
Diana Sorenson
Ned D. Strong
Eugenia Wilds

ADDRESS INQUIRIES TO:
Ambassador Peter DeShazo, Executive Director
(See address above.)

MEDICAL LIBRARY ASSOCIATION   [1013]
65 East Wacker Place
Suite 1900
Chicago, IL 60601-7298
(312) 419-9094
Fax: (312) 419-8950

E-MAIL ADDRESS:
mlapd2@mlahq.org

WEB SITE ADDRESS:
www.mlanet.org/awards/grants

FOUNDED: 1898

AREAS OF INTEREST:
Health sciences librarianship.

NAME(S) OF PROGRAMS:
● **Cunningham Memorial International Fellowship**

TYPE:
Fellowships; Travel grants; Work-study programs. Work-study program for medical librarians from countries other than the U.S. or Canada for a time period of at least two weeks.

YEAR PROGRAM STARTED: 1971

PURPOSE:
To educate and train medical librarians from countries outside the continental U.S. and Canada in areas where improved medical library service is essential to the health and welfare of the people through the education of physicians and scientists.

LEGAL BASIS:
Nonprofit.

ELIGIBILITY:
Candidate must be working in a medical library or be preparing to work in one in his country and must have an undergraduate and library degree. Candidate must have a statement from a responsible official of the institution where he is working or plans to work that he will be guaranteed a position in a medical library when he returns to his country, he must pass the TOEFL exam to demonstrate competence in English and he must present three letters of recommendation and a health certificate.

FINANCIAL DATA:
Travel to and from the U.S. or Canada must be financed by the candidate.
Amount of support per award: $3,600 including eligible expenses for the program.
Matching fund requirements: Candidate may need additional resources during the period of his fellowship.

NUMBER OF AWARDS: 2 per year.

APPLICATION INFORMATION:
Applicant must submit seven complete sets of the application form, including the following:
(1) three letters of reference, in English, from responsible persons who are familiar with the applicant's qualifications;
(2) a signed statement, in English, from a responsible official of the institution where he or she is working or plans to work, guaranteeing a position in a health sciences library upon his or her return;
(3) a TOEFL score of 500 or greater, except for applicants whose native language is English or whose language of instruction at the university level was English;
(4) seven copies of an audio or videotape, as well as a typed transcript of the tape, responding to the questions on the application;
(5) a project overview in accordance to the guidelines described in the "Project Goals" and;
(6) a certificate of good physical health, written in English, from a licensed physician.
Duration: At least two weeks.
Deadline: December 1. Announcement in March.

STAFF:
Carla J. Funk, Executive Director

ADDRESS INQUIRIES TO:
Lisa C. Fried
Research and Professional Recognition
(See address above.)

NATIONAL INSTITUTES OF HEALTH
Division of International Services
9000 Rockville Pike, MSC-2028
Bethesda, MD 20892-2028
(301) 496-6166
Fax: (301) 496-0847

E-MAIL ADDRESS:
dis@mail.nih.gov

WEB SITE ADDRESS:
www.training.nih.gov
dis.ors.od.nih.gov

TYPE:
Fellowships; Visiting scholars. Visiting foreign scholars.

See entry 1554 for full listing.

ORGANIZATION OF AMERICAN STATES [1014]
Department of Human Development
1889 F Street, N.W., Sixth Floor
Washington, DC 20006
(202) 458-6208
Fax: (202) 458-3897

E-MAIL ADDRESS:
rowefund@oas.org

WEB SITE ADDRESS:
www.oas.org/en/rowefund

AREAS OF INTEREST:
Education.

NAME(S) OF PROGRAMS:
● **The Leo S. Rowe Pan American Fund**

TYPE:
Assistantships; Awards/prizes; Visiting scholars. Loan program. The Leo S. Rowe Pan American Fund awards interest-free student loans to citizens from Latin America and the Caribbean countries, to help them finance their higher studies or research in accredited universities across the U.S.

YEAR PROGRAM STARTED: 1948

PURPOSE:
To provide a loan program to qualified citizens from Latin America and the Caribbean countries to help them finance their higher education or research at accredited institutions in the U.S. by awarding interest-free loans.

ELIGIBILITY:
Rowe Fund loans are granted to individuals for graduate, postgraduate and the last two years of undergraduate studies. Additionally, professionals or university faculty who are currently pursuing, or wish to pursue, advanced training, research or technical certificates at accredited institutions in the U.S. are also eligible. This includes semester-abroad programs and professional development courses, with the exception of English-as-a-Second-Language courses.

Candidates must:
(1) be nationals of a Latin American or Caribbean member state of the OAS (U.S. and Canadian citizens are not eligible);
(2) have an international student visa (F, J or M) allowing them to study full-time in the U.S.;
(3) be accepted as a full-time student in an accredited institution of higher learning in the U.S.;
(4) have adequate academic records;
(5) be able to demonstrate other sources of financing (such as savings, employment, fellowship, funds supplied by the university or relatives, etc.) to cover the greater portion of their academic expenses;
(6) ensure that loans are underwritten by a guarantor (citizen or permanent resident of the U.S.) and;
(7) promise that upon completion of his or her studies, he or she will repay the loan in full and return to his or her country; (if OPT is granted, the return date can be extended up to a year upon completion of studies).

GEOGRAPHIC RESTRICTIONS:
Only for citizens of Latin America and Caribbean Organization of American States member states.

FINANCIAL DATA:
Loans can be used to cover a portion of the tuition and other university fees; essential books and supplies; room and board; local transportation; and/or emergencies not covered by their principal source of funding. No application or processing fees. Funding is sent directly to the student after approval.
Amount of support per award: Loan amount: up to U.S. $7,500 per academic period. Loan recipients may apply for additional loans for subsequent academic periods, providing the total amount of loans granted does not exceed U.S. $15,000 over the course of the studies for which the loan is granted.
Matching fund requirements: The prospective applicant must demonstrate other sources of financing (such as savings, employment, a fellowship, funds supplied by the university or relatives, etc.), to cover the greater part of their academic expenses.

APPLICATION INFORMATION:
Loan Applications are usually submitted directly from students to the Rowe Fund Secretariat and are accepted and reviewed year-round at any time during the studies in the U.S. by the Rowe Fund Committee. Eligible candidates may download the application forms from the web site address above, or may send an e-mail requesting the application forms at the e-mail address above.
Duration: Two years maximum.

ADDRESS INQUIRIES TO:
Leo S. Rowe Pan American Fund
(See address above.)

*SPECIAL STIPULATIONS:
Repayment is deferred while the loan recipient is in school. Loans must be repaid within 50 months of completion of the degree.

These loans are made with the understanding that, upon completing those studies, loan recipients commit to repay the loan in full and return to their home countries to apply their knowledge and training as well as continue fostering friendship and communication among the peoples of the Americas.

ORGANIZATION OF AMERICAN STATES
1889 F Street, N.W.
Sixth Floor
Washington, DC 20006
(202) 458-6166
Fax: (202) 458-3897

E-MAIL ADDRESS:
scholarships@oas.org

WEB SITE ADDRESS:
www.educoas.org

TYPE:
Fellowships; Scholarships; Technical assistance. Awarded for graduate academic studies and/or research, and last two years of undergraduate studies for students in the English-speaking Caribbean, for training in areas contributing to the economic, social, technical and cultural development of OAS member countries.

See entry 906 for full listing.

P.E.O. SISTERHOOD   [1015]

P.E.O. Executive Office
3700 Grand Avenue
Des Moines, IA 50312
(515) 255-3153
Fax: (515) 255-3820

E-MAIL ADDRESS:
ips@peodsm.org

WEB SITE ADDRESS:
www.peointernational.org

FOUNDED: 1869

NAME(S) OF PROGRAMS:
• **P.E.O. International Peace Scholarships**

TYPE:
Grants-in-aid; Scholarships. Awards for
selected women from countries other than the
U.S. and Canada to pursue graduate study in
the U.S. or Canada. Support is available for
advanced study in any field except for
research. No new applications at the
dissertation level.

YEAR PROGRAM STARTED: 1949

PURPOSE:
To promote world peace and understanding
through scholarship aid to selected women
from other countries to further their
education in the U.S. and Canada.

LEGAL BASIS:
Nonprofit organization.

ELIGIBILITY:
Prerequisites for applicants:
(1) Applicant must be qualified for admission
to full-time graduate study, working toward a
graduate degree in the college or university
she will attend.
(2) A copy of the applicant's confirmation of
admission must be received by the IPS office
by April 1 in order to complete the
application. This notice must specify the
graduate degree program. No consideration
will be given to applicants lacking evidence
of admission.
(3) Prerequisites 1 and 2 do not apply to the
applicant who enrolls at Cottey College
(Nevada, MO), which is owned and operated
by the P.E.O. Sisterhood. The applicant shall
present evidence of admission to Cottey.

Applicants must secure a non-academic
advisor as sponsor who is a citizen and
resident of the U.S. or Canada. Applicant
must submit a witnessed statement certifying
that upon completion of her degree program,
she will return to her own country to pursue
her professional career.

Criteria for ineligibility:
(1) A student holding citizenship or
permanent residency in the U.S. or Canada is
ineligible.
(2) Scholarships are not given for research,
internships or for practical training if not
combined with coursework.
(3) Scholarships are not awarded for travel.
(4) In order to qualify for her first
scholarship, an applicant must have a full
year of coursework remaining and be
enrolled and on campus for the entire school
year.
(5) Doctoral students who have completed
coursework and are working on dissertations
only are not eligible as first-time applicants.
(6) Doctoral students in medicine or dentistry
will be considered only in the final two years
of study.

FINANCIAL DATA:
Scholarships to students studying in Canadian
universities will be paid in Canadian dollars.

Amount of support per award: $10,000
maximum per year. Varies according to need.

NUMBER OF APPLICANTS MOST RECENT YEAR:
431.

NUMBER OF AWARDS: 193 for the year 2010-11.

APPLICATION INFORMATION:
In order to be considered for an IPS
Scholarship, a student must submit an
eligibility form electronically through the
P.E.O. International web site. Paper forms
sent to the P.E.O. International office will no
longer be accepted. The online form is
available on August 1 for the student to enter
and save eligibility information - a form
cannot be submitted to P.E.O. International
until August 15.
Duration: Initial support is for a period not
to exceed one year (two semesters and one
summer session or the equivalent), with one
renewal possible. Not to exceed a total of
two years. A first-time applicant must have a
full year of course work remaining and be
enrolled and on campus for the entire school
year.
Deadline: Deadline to establish eligibility:
December 15. Receipt of application
materials (postmark): January 31. Final date
for receipt of confirmation of admission from
university and verification of other income,
scholarships, etc.: April 1. Notification of
scholarships: May 1. Final date for student
acceptance of scholarships: June 1.

No eligibility information will be accepted
before August 15 or after December 15.

PUBLICATIONS:
Information sheet.

ADDRESS INQUIRIES TO:
Carolyn Larson, Project Supervisor
(See address above.)

*PLEASE NOTE:
Scholarships to students studying in Canadian
universities will be paid in Canadian dollars.

*SPECIAL STIPULATIONS:
At time of application, grant recipient must
sign a witnessed statement (to be included in
application material) that she will return to
her home country upon completion of the
supported educational program. This
statement must be signed by both applicant
and witness. Applicant must have her
round-trip or return travel expense guaranteed
at the time of application. Student will be
required to repay grant if she does not return
to her homeland upon completion of her
terminal degree program.

THE UNIVERSITY OF
SYDNEY   [1016]

Scholarships Office
Level 5, Jane Foss Russell Building G02
The University of Sydney N.S.W. 2006
Australia
(02) 8627 8112
Fax: (02) 8627 8145

E-MAIL ADDRESS:
research.training@sydney.edu.au

WEB SITE ADDRESS:
www.sydney.edu.au/scholarships/research

FOUNDED: 1850

NAME(S) OF PROGRAMS:
• **Walter Mersh Strong Scholarship**

TYPE:
Scholarships. Scholarship awarded for studies
at postgraduate level. Tenable at the

University of Sydney. The scholarship will
rotate among the three program areas:
commerce/economics/transport management,
engineering studies, or public health.

PURPOSE:
To provide opportunities for graduate
students from Papua New Guinea to attend
the University of Sydney to undertake a
Master by coursework program in
commerce/economics/transport management,
engineering studies or public health.

LEGAL BASIS:
University.

ELIGIBILITY:
Open to graduates from Papua New Guinea
who qualify for admission to the University
of Sydney.

GEOGRAPHIC RESTRICTIONS:
Papua New Guinea.

FINANCIAL DATA:
Amount of support per award: Tuition fees
and living allowance of $25,000 (AUD) per
annum for the year 2011.

NUMBER OF AWARDS: Offered as vacancies
occur.

APPLICATION INFORMATION:
Duration: Normal duration of the Master by
coursework program.
Deadline: As advertised, when funds are
available.

ADDRESS INQUIRIES TO:
The International Office
Level 4, Jane Foss Russell Building G02
The University of Sydney
N.S.W. 2006 Australia
Tel: (02) 8627 8302
Fax: (02) 8627 8387
E-mail: io.studentadvisers@sydney.edu.au

WENNER-GREN FOUNDATION
FOR ANTHROPOLOGICAL
RESEARCH, INC.

470 Park Avenue South, 8th Floor
New York, NY 10016-6819
(212) 683-5000
Fax: (212) 683-9151

E-MAIL ADDRESS:
internationalprograms@wennergren.org

WEB SITE ADDRESS:
www.wennergren.org

TYPE:
Fellowships; Scholarships; Training grants.
Wadsworth International Fellowship is for
scholars and advanced students from
developing countries who need to leave their
country in order to obtain advanced training
in anthropology and its related subdisciplines.
The proposed course of study must enhance
their skills or expand their area of expertise.

The program offers a Predoctoral Fellowship
for study leading to a Ph.D.

See entry 2154 for full listing.

Technical assistance and
cooperative research

CRDF GLOBAL

1530 Wilson Boulevard, Third Floor
Arlington, VA 22209
(703) 526-9720
Fax: (703) 526-9721

E-MAIL ADDRESS:
cgp@crdf.org

WEB SITE ADDRESS:
www.crdf.org

TYPE:
Block grants; Challenge/matching grants;
Conferences/seminars; Development grants;
Exchange programs; Fellowships;
Grants-in-aid; Product donations;
Project/program grants; Research grants;
Technical assistance; Training grants. Centers
& Institution Building programs build
sustainable institutions patterned on
successful international analogs that enable
international scientists to develop national
and global science and technology advances.

Cooperative Grants Program provides up to
two years of support for joint U.S. and
international research teams in all areas of
basic and applied research in the natural
sciences.

Industry Programs enable American
companies and international scientists,
engineers, and organizations to explore new
commercial research partnerships, and move
the product of their collaborations to the
market through a progressive series of grants
programs.

Nonproliferation Initiatives (NPI) program
develops and implements innovative ways to
encourage the participation of former
weapons of mass destruction (WMD)
scientists in Foundation grant programs.

See entry 2015 for full listing.

JOHN E. FOGARTY INTERNATIONAL CENTER

Division of International Training and Research
Building 31, B2C39
31 Center Drive, MSC 2220
Bethesda, MD 20892-2220
(301) 496-1653
Fax: (301) 402-0779

WEB SITE ADDRESS:
www.fic.nih.gov

TYPE:
Research grants. A small grants program to
support biomedical, behavioral and social
sciences health research.

See entry 2282 for full listing.

NATIONAL INSTITUTES OF HEALTH [1017]

Division of International Relations
Fogarty International Center
Building 31, Room B2C11
31 Center Drive, MSC 2220
Bethesda, MD 20892-2220
(301) 496-4784
(301) 496-1653
Fax: (301) 480-3414

E-MAIL ADDRESS:
chungt@mail.nih.gov
mili.ferreira@nih.gov
ficjspsextramural@mail.nih.gov

WEB SITE ADDRESS:
www.fic.nih.gov/programs

AREAS OF INTEREST:
Biomedical and behavioral sciences.

NAME(S) OF PROGRAMS:
● **Japan Society for the Promotion of Science Postdoctoral Research Fellowships (Extramural)**

TYPE:
Fellowships. A limited number of
postdoctoral research fellowships are
provided by the Japan Science and
Technology Agency (JSTA) to U.S. scientists
to conduct research in Japan. Types of
activity supported include collaboration in
basic or clinical research and familiarization
with or utilization of special techniques and
equipment not otherwise available to the
applicant.

YEAR PROGRAM STARTED: 1987

PURPOSE:
To provide a research experience in the
biomedical, clinical and behavioral sciences
in Japanese laboratories.

LEGAL BASIS:
Government agency.

ELIGIBILITY:
Applicants for the program must be U.S.
citizens or permanent U.S. residents, hold a
Doctorate in one of the clinical, behavioral or
biomedical sciences and make prior
arrangements with the appropriate Japanese
host researcher as to the research plan.

The program does not provide support for
activities that have as their principal purpose
brief observational visits, attendance at
scientific meetings or independent study.

FINANCIAL DATA:
Total amount of support: $5,460 monthly for
the year 2009.

NUMBER OF AWARDS: Up to 10 short-term, 5
long-term.

APPLICATION INFORMATION:
Duration: Short-term: Under 11 months;
Long-term: 12 to 24 months.
Deadline: May 31.

ADDRESS INQUIRIES TO:
Tina Chung, M.P.H., Program Officer
(See address above.)

NORTH ATLANTIC TREATY ORGANIZATION [1018]

Public Diplomacy Division
NATO HQ, Boulevard Leopold III
B-1110 Brussels Belgium
32 2 707 4111
Fax: 32 2 707 4232

E-MAIL ADDRESS:
science@hq.nato.int

WEB SITE ADDRESS:
www.nato.int/science

FOUNDED: 1958

AREAS OF INTEREST:
International scientific cooperation.

NAME(S) OF PROGRAMS:
● **Science for Peace and Security Programme**

TYPE:
Research grants. Collaborative research
grants; Expert workshop grants; Training
courses; Tutorial research grants.

Offers grants to scientists in NATO, Partner
and Mediterranean Dialogue countries to
collaborate on priority research topics, which
include NATO priorities and additional
Partner country priorities. Grants are also
offered to assist the academic community in
Partner countries to set up computer
networking infrastructure and to optimize
their use of electronic communication.

In addition to activities funded by the NATO
international budget, the Science for Peace
and Security Programme also engages in
activities funded directly by one or more
nations. These consist of pilot studies,
short-term projects and topical workshops
which are aligned with NATO's Strategic
Objectives and are in areas of priority to
NATO, Partner or Mediterranean Dialogue
countries. Any NATO or Partner country can
initiate a new proposal. The initiating nation
seeks the participation of other NATO and
Partner nations and this participation is
always voluntary. Support Grant Programme
is open to experts from both NATO countries
and those Partner countries eligible for
support.

YEAR PROGRAM STARTED: 1960

PURPOSE:
To stimulate collaboration between
laboratories in different countries and thus
enhance the effectiveness of research.

GEOGRAPHIC RESTRICTIONS:
NATO countries: Albania, Belgium, Bulgaria,
Canada, Croatia, Czech Republic, Denmark,
Estonia, France, Germany, Greece, Hungary,
Iceland, Italy, Latvia, Lithuania, Luxembourg,
Netherlands, Norway, Poland, Portugal,
Romania, Slovak Republic, Slovenia, Spain,
Turkey, United Kingdom and United States.

Partner countries eligible for support:
Armenia, Austria, Azerbaijan, Belarus,
Bosnia, Finland, Georgia, Herzegovina,
Ireland, Kazakhstan, Kyrgyz Republic, the
former Yugoslav Republic of Macedonia,
Malta, Moldova, Montenegro, Russia, Serbia,
Sweden, Switzerland, Tajikistan,
Turkmenistan, Ukraine and Uzbekistan.

Mediterranean Dialogue Countries: Algeria,
Egypt, Israel, Jordan, Mauritania, Morocco
and Tunisia.

FINANCIAL DATA:
Assistance is provided for scientists to
participate in workshops, tutorials, training
courses, collaborative research grants,
project-related costs and travel costs.
Amount of support per award: EUR 5,000 to
EUR 50,000 depending on the type of
support mechanism.

APPLICATION INFORMATION:
Applications should be presented on the
official application forms that can be
downloaded from the Science for Peace and
Security web site.
Duration: Up to three years.

PUBLICATIONS:
Results of workshops are published in the
NATO Science Series.

ADDRESS INQUIRIES TO:
See e-mail address above.

SEMICONDUCTOR RESEARCH CORPORATION

1101 Slater Road
Brighton Hall, Suite 120
Durham, NC 27703
(919) 941-9418
Fax: (919) 941-9450

E-MAIL ADDRESS:
steve.hillenius@src.org

WEB SITE ADDRESS:
www.src.org

TYPE:
Assistantships; Awards/prizes;
Conferences/seminars; Demonstration grants;
Fellowships; Research grants; Scholarships;
Research contracts. Primarily research
contracts. Also student design contests.
See entry 2779 for full listing.

U.S.-ISRAEL BINATIONAL SCIENCE FOUNDATION (BSF) [1019]
P.O. Box 45086 (Hamarpeh Street, No. 8)
Har Hotzvim
Jerusalem 91450 Israel
972-2-5828239
Fax: 972-2-5828306

E-MAIL ADDRESS:
bsf@bsf.org.il

WEB SITE ADDRESS:
www.bsf.org.il

FOUNDED: 1972

AREAS OF INTEREST:
Science.

TYPE:
Research grants. Workshops.

Promotes cooperation between the countries
in research concerned with science and
technology for peaceful purposes through
grants to cooperative research projects.
Grants are for bilateral, cooperative research
between U.S. and Israeli scientists for
research conducted in either country.

YEAR PROGRAM STARTED: 1974

PURPOSE:
To strengthen U.S.-Israel science cooperation.

LEGAL BASIS:
Established by government-to-government
agreement.

ELIGIBILITY:
Any scientist on the staff of a U.S. or Israel
nonprofit research institution may apply by
submitting a cooperative research proposal.

Eligible research areas are health sciences,
life sciences, physics, chemistry,
mathematical sciences, atmospheric and earth
sciences, oceanography and limnology,
materials research, environmental research,
energy research, biomedical engineering,
economics, sociology, social and
developmental psychology.

Submission of grant applications is on a
split-program basis; namely, eligibility is
limited, in alternate years, to either health
and life sciences or to exact, natural and
social sciences.

GEOGRAPHIC RESTRICTIONS:
Territories occupied by Israel in 1967 are
excluded.

FINANCIAL DATA:
Awards are made to cover the direct cost of
executing the approved research, i.e., salaries
for research assistants, supplies, travel, etc.
Salaries of principal investigators are not
included.
Amount of support per award: Up to
$230,000. Average $40,000 per year.
Total amount of support: Approximately
$15,000,000.

NUMBER OF APPLICANTS MOST RECENT YEAR:
500.

NUMBER OF AWARDS: 148 for the year 2009.

APPLICATION INFORMATION:
Proposals are unsolicited and should be
submitted jointly by the collaborating
scientists via the prospective grantee
institution where the research will be
performed.
Duration: Up to four years.
Deadline: The completed application form
must reach the BSF by November 15 for a
grant to be awarded in the following year.
Awards are made annually and are
announced in July.

OFFICERS:
Dr. Yair Rotstein, Director
Dr. Rachel Haring, Assistant Director

ADDRESS INQUIRIES TO:
Dr. Yair Rotstein, Director
(See address above.)

*PLEASE NOTE:
The programs described above are programs
of the U.S.-Israel Binational Science
Foundation and should not be confused with
National Science Foundation programs.

UC DISCOVERY GRANT PROGRAM (INDUSTRY-UNIVERSITY COOPERATIVE RESEARCH) [1020]
University of California, Office of the President
300 Lakeside Drive, 6th Floor
Oakland, CA 94612
(510) 987-9386

WEB SITE ADDRESS:
www.ucop.edu/ucdiscovery

AREAS OF INTEREST:
Biotechnology, health and information
technology for life sciences; communications,
networking, digital media and Internet
enabled services; electronics design,
manufacturing and new materials; energy,
environment and clean technology;
microelectronics and computing innovations;
nanotechnology.

NAME(S) OF PROGRAMS:
● **UC Discovery Grant**

TYPE:
Challenge/matching grants. UC Discovery
Grants form a three-way partnership between
the University of California, industry
sponsors, and the state of California.

PURPOSE:
To strengthen and expand California's
economy through jointly sponsored
industry-university research partnerships.

ELIGIBILITY:
Any researcher with Principal Investigator
(PI) status at the University of California is
eligible to apply. Applicants with a waiver of
UC PI status must submit, with the proposal,
documentation of the approved waiver
authorized by the appropriate campus official.
Lawrence Berkeley Laboratory researchers
who hold PI status at a University of
California campus may submit proposals
through that campus.

GEOGRAPHIC RESTRICTIONS:
California.

FINANCIAL DATA:
Amount of support per award: Typically
$25,000 to $2,000,000 per year.

Matching fund requirements: Industry
Sponsor(s) will share the direct costs of the
project with the University of California and
contribute applicable indirect costs.

APPLICATION INFORMATION:
There is a three-step application process.
Applicants must first submit a Letter of
Intent. Once the Letter of Intent is approved,
applicants will be granted access to the full
application materials through
proposalCENTRAL. An Industry Sponsor
Letter of Intent to fund the proposed project
through a matching gift or grant must be
submitted with the proposal, confirming the
amount of the company's financial
contribution and a commitment to negotiate a
research agreement, when required, consistent
with the terms set forth in the Request for
Proposals. In cases of more than one industry
sponsor, each sponsor must submit a letter.

SPECIAL POPULATIONS

Special Populations

THE ABLE TRUST [1021]

3320 Thomasville Road
Suite 200
Tallahassee, FL 32308
(888) 838-2253
(850) 224-4493
Fax: (850) 224-4496

E-MAIL ADDRESS:
info@abletrust.org

WEB SITE ADDRESS:
www.abletrust.org

FOUNDED: 1991

AREAS OF INTEREST:
Disabilities and handicapped persons.

NAME(S) OF PROGRAMS:
- **Agency Grant Program**
- **Emergency and Supplemental Grant Program**
- **Special Projects Program**

TYPE:
Project/program grants. The Agency Grant Program funds innovative employment programs from agencies in Florida.

The Special Projects Program solicits proposals which focus on underserved areas in Florida and provide innovative approaches on service delivery or new concept. These special projects often are pilot or demonstration projects.

YEAR PROGRAM STARTED: 1990

PURPOSE:
To provide Floridians with disabilities fair employment opportunities through fund-raising grant programs, public awareness and education.

LEGAL BASIS:
501(c)(3) public-private partnership foundation.

ELIGIBILITY:
Proposals will be accepted from Florida-based nonprofit agencies serving disabled Florida citizens and to individual Florida citizens with documented disabilities. Each agency or individual recipient may have only one active grant in any one year time period.

GEOGRAPHIC RESTRICTIONS:
Florida.

FINANCIAL DATA:
Amount of support per award: Average award is $40,000 for agencies (low $11,000; high $75,000).
Total amount of support: $21,000,000.

NUMBER OF APPLICANTS MOST RECENT YEAR:
150.

NUMBER OF AWARDS: 74.

PUBLICATIONS:
Information booklet; guidelines.

IRS IDENTIFICATION NUMBER: 59-3052307

STAFF:
Dr. Susanne Homant, President and Chief Executive Officer
Guenevere Crum, Senior Vice President
Sally Ash, Assistant Director, Disability Mentoring Day and High School/High Tech Programs
Ray Ford, Assistant Director of Communications and Events
Leona Boutwell, Financial Manager

BOARD OF DIRECTORS:
Richard L. Cole, Jr., Esq., Chairperson
Barbara Gill MacArthur, R.N., M.N., Vice Chairperson
Jason E. Havens, Esq., Treasurer
Bridget R. Pallango, M.B.A., Secretary
Jeannie Amendola
Marcy Pinkney Benton, M.B.A.
Robert A. Butterworth, Esq.
James Raymond Harding, II, Ed.D.
Anne Marie Taglienti, M.A.

ADDRESS INQUIRIES TO:
Dr. Susanne Homant
President and Chief Executive Officer
(See address above.)

THE ACTUARIAL FOUNDATION

475 North Martingale Road
Suite 600
Schaumburg, IL 60173-2226
(847) 706-3500
Fax: (847) 706-3599

E-MAIL ADDRESS:
Scholarships@ActFnd.org

WEB SITE ADDRESS:
www.actuarialfoundation.org

TYPE:
Scholarships. The scholarship promotes diversity through an annual scholarship program for Black/African American, Hispanic and Native North American students recognizing and encouraging academic achievements by awarding scholarships to full-time undergraduate and graduate students pursuing a degree that may lead to a career in the actuarial profession.

See entry 2222 for full listing.

ALZHEIMER'S DRUG DISCOVERY FOUNDATION

57 West 57th Street
Suite 904
New York, NY 10019
(212) 901-8000
Fax: (212) 901-8010

E-MAIL ADDRESS:
hfillit@alzdiscovery.org

WEB SITE ADDRESS:
www.alzdiscovery.org

TYPE:
Awards/prizes; Conferences/seminars; Research grants.

See entry 2360 for full listing.

THE AMERICAN ACADEMY OF ESTHETIC DENTISTRY

303 West Madison Street
Suite 2650
Chicago, IL 60606
(312) 981-6770
Fax: (312) 265-2908

E-MAIL ADDRESS:
info@estheticacademy.org

WEB SITE ADDRESS:
www.estheticacademy.org

TYPE:
Research grants.

See entry 2498 for full listing.

AMERICAN ASSOCIATION OF LAW LIBRARIES

105 West Adams Street
Suite 3300
Chicago, IL 60603
(312) 939-4764
Fax: (312) 431-1097

E-MAIL ADDRESS:
membership@aall.org

WEB SITE ADDRESS:
www.aallnet.org

TYPE:
Scholarships. Stipend for graduate study leading to a degree at an accredited school of library or information science or an accredited law school. Preference will be given to individuals with previous service to, or interest in, law librarianship.

See entry 752 for full listing.

AMERICAN BAR FOUNDATION [1022]

750 North Lake Shore Drive
Fourth Floor
Chicago, IL 60611
(312) 988-6515
Fax: (312) 988-6579

E-MAIL ADDRESS:
fellowships@abfn.org

WEB SITE ADDRESS:
www.americanbarfoundation.org

FOUNDED: 1952

AREAS OF INTEREST:
Law and social science.

NAME(S) OF PROGRAMS:
- **Summer Research Diversity Fellowships in Law and Social Science for Undergraduate Students**

TYPE:
Fellowships; Internships.

YEAR PROGRAM STARTED: 1988

PURPOSE:
To interest undergraduate students from diverse backgrounds in pursuing graduate study in the social sciences; to introduce students to the rewards and demands of a research-oriented career in the field of law and social science.

LEGAL BASIS:
Private foundation.

ELIGIBILITY:
Must be a U.S. citizen or permanent resident. The program is open, but not limited to, persons who are African-American, Hispanic/Latino, Native American, or Puerto Rican. Applicants must be sophomores or juniors in college with a grade point average of at least 3.0 on a scale of 4.0 and must be moving toward an academic major in one of the social science or humanities disciplines.

GEOGRAPHIC RESTRICTIONS:
United States.

FINANCIAL DATA:
Amount of support per award: $3,600.
Total amount of support: $14,400.

NUMBER OF AWARDS: 4 each year.

APPLICATION INFORMATION:
Application form is available online.
Duration: Eight weeks during the summer.
Deadline: Usually February or March.

PUBLICATIONS:
Annual report, application guidelines and forms.

ADDRESS INQUIRIES TO:
Tim Watson, Development Associate
(See address above.)

AMERICAN COUNCIL OF THE BLIND

2200 Wilson Boulevard, Suite 650
Arlington, VA 22201
(202) 467-5081
(800) 424-8666
Fax: (703) 465-5085

E-MAIL ADDRESS:
info@acb.org

WEB SITE ADDRESS:
www.acb.org

TYPE:
Assistantships; Awards/prizes; Internships; Scholarships. Scholarships for outstanding blind students enrolled in academic, vocational, technical or professional training programs beyond the high school level.

See entry 1770 for full listing.

AMERICAN FOUNDATION FOR THE BLIND, INC.   [1023]

2 Penn Plaza
Suite 1102
New York, NY 10121
(212) 502-7600
(800) 232-5463
Fax: (888) 545-8331
TDD: (212) 502-7662

E-MAIL ADDRESS:
afbinfo@afb.net

WEB SITE ADDRESS:
www.afb.org/scholarships.asp

FOUNDED: 1921

AREAS OF INTEREST:
Blindness, education, vocational and social services, public education, consultation and publications related to blindness and visual impairment.

NAME(S) OF PROGRAMS:
- **Gladys C. Anderson Memorial Scholarship**
- **The Karen D. Carsel Memorial Scholarship**
- **The Delta Gamma Foundation Florence Margaret Harvey Memorial Scholarship**
- **The Rudolph Dillman Memorial Scholarship**
- **The R.L. Gillette Scholarship**
- **The Paul and Ellen Ruckes Scholarship**
- **The Ferdinand Torres Scholarship**

TYPE:
Scholarships. Undergraduate and graduate scholarships for students who are legally blind.

The Gladys C. Anderson Memorial Scholarship is offered to a female undergraduate or graduate student studying classical or religious music.

The Karen D. Carsel Memorial Scholarship provides a grant to a full-time graduate student who is legally blind and who presents evidence of economic need.

The Delta Gamma Foundation Florence Margaret Harvey Memorial Scholarship is offered to an undergraduate or graduate

student who is legally blind, has exhibited academic excellence, and is studying in the field of rehabilitation and/or education of persons who are visually impaired or blind.

The Rudolph Dillman Memorial Scholarship provides four grants to undergraduate or graduate students who are legally blind and studying in the field of rehabilitation and/or education of persons who are blind or visually impaired.

The R. L. Gillette Scholarship offers two scholarships to women who are legally blind and are enrolled in a four-year undergraduate degree program in literature or music.

The Paul and Ellen Ruckes Scholarship is offered to an undergraduate or graduate student who is legally blind and studying engineering, computer, physical or life sciences.

The Ferdinand Torres Scholarship is offered to a full-time undergraduate or graduate student who is legally blind and who presents evidence of economic need.

LEGAL BASIS:
Not-for-profit corporation.

ELIGIBILITY:
Applicants must be U.S. citizens or residents who are, by definition, legally blind. Other criteria vary depending on the specific scholarship.

For the Ferdinand Torres Scholarship, the applicant must reside in the U.S. but need not be a citizen. Preference will be given to applicants residing in the New York City metropolitan area and new immigrants to the U.S.

FINANCIAL DATA:
Amount of support per award: Gladys C. Anderson Memorial, Delta Gamma Foundation Florence Margaret Harvey Memorial, R. L. Gillette, and Paul and Ellen Ruckes Scholarships: $1,000 each; Karen D. Carsel Memorial Scholarship: $500; Rudolph Dillman Memorial Scholarship: $2,500; Ferdinand Torres Scholarship: $3,500.
Total amount of support: $19,000.

NUMBER OF AWARDS: 7 scholarships with 11 total awards.

APPLICATION INFORMATION:
Applications must be submitted online. No paper applications will be accepted.

In general, applicants must submit a completed scholarship application form, evidence of legal blindness (or official letter from a state or private agency for the blind), certified transcripts, proof of acceptance in a postsecondary school, proof of U.S. citizenship, two letters of reference and typewritten statement of educational and personal goals, the field of study applicant is pursuing and why he or she has chosen it, the applicant's work experience, extracurricular activities and how the award will be used.
Duration: One academic year.
Deadline: Usually April 30, but can vary.

OFFICERS:
Carl R. Augusto, President and Chief Executive Officer

ADDRESS INQUIRIES TO:
Tara Annis, Information Center
100 Fifth Avenue, Suite 350
Huntington, WV 25701

AMERICAN GEOLOGICAL INSTITUTE

4220 King Street
Alexandria, VA 22302-1502
(703) 379-2480 ext. 227
Fax: (703) 379-7563

E-MAIL ADDRESS:
cmm@agiweb.org
mpp@agiweb.org

WEB SITE ADDRESS:
www.agiweb.org/mpp

TYPE:
Scholarships. Awards to expand the role of underrepresented minorities in the earth sciences.

See entry 2203 for full listing.

THE AMERICAN HELLENIC EDUCATIONAL PROGRESSIVE ASSOCIATION   [1024]

1909 Q Street, N.W.
Suite 500
Washington, DC 20009
(202) 232-6300
Fax: (202) 232-2140

E-MAIL ADDRESS:
ahepa@ahepa.org

WEB SITE ADDRESS:
www.ahepa.org

FOUNDED: 1922

AREAS OF INTEREST:
Culture, history, and issues relating to Greece and Cyprus.

TYPE:
Scholarships.

PURPOSE:
To promote, encourage, induce and advance education at the college, university and graduate school level.

ELIGIBILITY:
Applicants must be of Hellenic heritage, although their ancestry does not have to be 100% Greek. The applicant must be a member in good standing of AHEPA or affiliated organizations, demonstrate financial need and have no criminal record.

FINANCIAL DATA:
Amount of support per award: $500 to $2,000.
Total amount of support: $100,000 for the year 2009.

NUMBER OF AWARDS: 77.

APPLICATION INFORMATION:
Contact the Organization for application procedures.
Duration: One year. Renewal possible.
Deadline: March 31.

ADDRESS INQUIRIES TO:
Basil Mossaidis, Executive Director
(See address above.)

THE AMERICAN INSTITUTE OF ARCHITECTS

1735 New York Avenue, N.W.
Washington, DC 20006-5292
(202) 626-7529
Fax: (202) 626-7399

E-MAIL ADDRESS:
scholarships@aia.org

WEB SITE ADDRESS:
www.aia.org

TYPE:
Scholarships. Awards to provide an opportunity for financially disadvantaged and/or minority groups to pursue a professional degree in architecture.

See entry 439 for full listing.

AMERICAN INSTITUTE OF CHEMICAL ENGINEERS (AICHE)

3 Park Avenue, 19th Floor
New York, NY 10016
(203) 702-7660
Fax: (203) 775-5177

E-MAIL ADDRESS:
awards@aiche.org

WEB SITE ADDRESS:
www.aiche.org

TYPE:
Scholarships.

See entry 2803 for full listing.

AMERICAN PLANNING ASSOCIATION   [1025]

205 North Michigan Avenue
Suite 1200
Chicago, IL 60601
(312) 786-6722
Fax: (312) 786-6727

E-MAIL ADDRESS:
kblank@planning.org

WEB SITE ADDRESS:
www.planning.org

FOUNDED: 1909

AREAS OF INTEREST:
Urban and regional planning and the promotion of the art and science of planning.

NAME(S) OF PROGRAMS:
- **Judith McManus Fellowship**

TYPE:
Fellowships; Scholarships.

YEAR PROGRAM STARTED: 1970

PURPOSE:
To celebrate planning by providing partial funding for all women and minority (African American, Hispanic American or Native American) students.

LEGAL BASIS:
Private, nonprofit educational association.

ELIGIBILITY:
Applicants must be citizens of the U.S. and enrolled or accepted for enrollment in a planning program accredited by the Planning Accreditation Board (PAB). Applicants must document the need for financial assistance.

GEOGRAPHIC RESTRICTIONS:
United States.

FINANCIAL DATA:
Fellowship provides partial funding for tuition and living expenses. One-year student membership in the American Planning Association. Scholarship provides partial tuition funding.
Amount of support per award: Judith McManus Fellowship: $1,500 to $4,000.

NUMBER OF APPLICANTS MOST RECENT YEAR:
70.

NUMBER OF AWARDS: Varies.

APPLICATION INFORMATION:
Duration: One academic year.
Deadline: April 30.

PUBLICATIONS:
Program announcement.

ADDRESS INQUIRIES TO:
Kriss Blank, Leadership Affairs Associate
(See address above.)

AMERICAN POLITICAL SCIENCE ASSOCIATION

1527 New Hampshire Avenue, N.W.
Washington, DC 20036
(202) 483-2512
Fax: (202) 483-2657

E-MAIL ADDRESS:
minority@apsanet.org

WEB SITE ADDRESS:
www.apsanet.org

TYPE:
Fellowships; Grants-in-aid; Scholarships. Awards to aid prospective African American, Asian Pacific, Latino/Latina and Native American political science students beginning the doctoral study of political science.

See entry 2114 for full listing.

AMERICAN PSYCHOLOGICAL ASSOCIATION

Minority Fellowship Program/APA
750 First Street, N.E.
Washington, DC 20002-4242
(202) 336-6127
Fax: (202) 336-6012

E-MAIL ADDRESS:
mfp@apa.org

WEB SITE ADDRESS:
www.apa.org/mfp

TYPE:
Fellowships. Fellowship is geared to those pursuing careers as practitioners and as researchers specializing in the delivery of mental health services to ethnic minority populations. Students specializing in clinical, school and counseling psychology are encouraged to apply.

See entry 2727 for full listing.

AMERICAN PSYCHOLOGICAL ASSOCIATION   [1026]

Minority Fellowship Program/APA
750 First Street, N.E.
Washington, DC 20002-4242
(202) 336-6127
Fax: (202) 336-6012

E-MAIL ADDRESS:
mfp@apa.org

WEB SITE ADDRESS:
www.apa.org/pi/mfp

FOUNDED: 1892

AREAS OF INTEREST:
Mental health and substance abuse services.

NAME(S) OF PROGRAMS:
- **Mental Health and Substance Abuse Services Fellowship**

TYPE:
Fellowships. Geared to those pursuing careers in substance abuse treatment and prevention as practitioners and as researchers specializing in the delivery of mental health services to ethnic minority populations.

PURPOSE:
To increase the knowledge of issues related to ethnic minority mental health and to improve the quality of mental health treatment delivered to ethnic minority populations by providing financial support and professional guidance to individuals pursuing doctoral degrees in psychology.

LEGAL BASIS:
Nonprofit.

ELIGIBILITY:
Applicants must be citizens or permanent residents of the U.S. and must be a member of an underrepresented ethnic minority group including, but not limited to, African American, Alaskan Native, Asian American, Latino/Hispanic, Native American and Pacific Islander.

FINANCIAL DATA:
Amount of support per award: Varies.
Total amount of support: Varies.

NUMBER OF AWARDS: 5 to 10.

APPLICATION INFORMATION:
Duration: One academic year.
Deadline: January 15. Announcement by April.

ADDRESS INQUIRIES TO:
Andrew Austin-Daley, Director
Minority Fellowship Program/APA
(See address above.)

*SPECIAL STIPULATIONS:
Applicants may apply for only one Fellowship at a time.

AMERICAN SOCIETY FOR MICROBIOLOGY

Education Department
1752 N Street, N.W.
Washington, DC 20036
(202) 942-9295
(202) 942-9283
Fax: (202) 942-9329

E-MAIL ADDRESS:
fellowships@asmusa.org

WEB SITE ADDRESS:
www.asm.org/education

TYPE:
Fellowships. ASM/CDC Postdoctoral Research Fellowship Program: The American Society for Microbiology and Centers for Disease Control and Prevention (ASM/CDC) Postdoctoral Research Fellowship Program is a comprehensive training program which provides opportunities to participate in interdisciplinary training on global public health issues. Fellows will perform research at one of the Centers for Disease Control and Prevention (CDC) locations.

Undergraduate Research Fellowship: This fellowship encourages students to pursue careers or advanced degrees in the microbiological sciences by providing an opportunity to participate in a research project at their institution and gain experience in presenting their results. The fellowship allows students to conduct research in the summer with an ASM member faculty mentor and present the results at the ASM General Meeting the following year.

See entry 2272 for full listing.

AMERICAN SOCIETY FOR MICROBIOLOGY

Education Department
1752 N Street, N.W.
Washington, DC 20036
(202) 942-9283
Fax: (202) 942-9329

E-MAIL ADDRESS:
fellowships-careerinformation@asmusa.org
fellowships@asmusa.org

WEB SITE ADDRESS:
www.asm.org/students

TYPE:
Fellowships. Graduate fellowships. This
fellowship encourages underrepresented and
historically excluded graduate students to
conduct research in the microbiological
sciences.

See entry 2273 for full listing.

AMERICAN SOCIOLOGICAL ASSOCIATION [1027]

1430 K Street, N.W.
Suite 600
Washington, DC 20005
(202) 383-9005 ext. 321
TDD: (202) 638-0981
Fax: (202) 638-0882

E-MAIL ADDRESS:
minority.affairs@asanet.org

WEB SITE ADDRESS:
www.asanet.org

FOUNDED: 1905

AREAS OF INTEREST:
All areas of sociology.

NAME(S) OF PROGRAMS:
● **Minority Fellowship Program**

TYPE:
Fellowships. Predoctoral training fellowships
for minority-group members studying
sociology.

YEAR PROGRAM STARTED: 1974

PURPOSE:
To provide predoctoral students with financial
support, academic and research training, and
mentoring, in coordination with university
graduate programs, in order to increase the
talent pool of minority sociologists in the
U.S.

LEGAL BASIS:
Nonprofit professional association.

ELIGIBILITY:
Applicants must be citizens, non-citizen
nationals of the U.S. or have been lawfully
admitted to the U.S. for permanent residence
and have in their possession an Alien
Registration Card, and they must be accepted
and/or enrolled in a full-time sociology
doctoral program in the U.S. at the time of
appointment.

In addition, applicants must be members of
an underrepresented racial and ethnic group,
including African Americans, Latinos (e.g.,
Chicano, Cuban, Puerto Rican), American
Indians or Alaskan Natives and Asians (e.g.,
Chinese, Japanese, Korean, Southeast Asian)
or Pacific Islanders (e.g., Hawaiian,
Guamanian, Samoan, Filipino) and who are
college or university seniors and/or students
in Master's-only programs who have been
accepted or are applying to doctoral
programs and have strong interests in
sociology. If, however, an applicant is

selected for an award, but not enrolled in an
appropriate doctoral program by the time the
funding year begins, the applicant will not be
eligible to receive the award.

GEOGRAPHIC RESTRICTIONS:
United States.

FINANCIAL DATA:
Award includes stipend and some tuition
assistance.
Amount of support per award: $18,000 for
ASA-funded students.

NUMBER OF APPLICANTS MOST RECENT YEAR:
60.

NUMBER OF AWARDS: Up to 6 annually.

APPLICATION INFORMATION:
Applicants must submit completed
application forms, transcripts, letters of
recommendation and goal statement.
Selection is based upon evidence of
scholarship, writing ability, research
potential, financial need and racial and ethnic
minority identification.
Duration: Fellowships are tenable for one
calendar year, with possibility for renewal.
Deadline: January 31. Announcement by
April 30.

STAFF:
Jean H. Shin, Program Director
Beth Moran, Program Assistant

ADDRESS INQUIRIES TO:
Beth Moran, Program Assistant
(See address above.)

ARMENIAN GENERAL BENEVOLENT UNION

55 East 59th Street
New York, NY 10022-1112
(212) 319-6383
Fax: (212) 319-6507

E-MAIL ADDRESS:
scholarship@agbu.org

WEB SITE ADDRESS:
www.agbu.org

TYPE:
Fellowships; Scholarships.

See entry 1781 for full listing.

ARMENIAN RELIEF SOCIETY OF THE EASTERN U.S. [1028]

80 Bigelow Avenue
Suite 200
Watertown, MA 02472
(617) 926-3801
Fax: (617) 924-7238

E-MAIL ADDRESS:
arseastus@aol.com

WEB SITE ADDRESS:
www.arseastusa.org

FOUNDED: 1910

NAME(S) OF PROGRAMS:
● **A.R.S. Lazarian Graduate Scholarship**
● **A.R.S. Undergraduate Scholarship**

TYPE:
Awards/prizes; Scholarships. Scholarships to
assist students of Armenian ancestry in their
higher education studies.

PURPOSE:
To aid Armenian students residing in the
U.S.

LEGAL BASIS:
Nonprofit organization.

ELIGIBILITY:
Undergraduate or graduate student of
Armenian ancestry attending a four-year
college or university.

For the Undergraduate Scholarship, the
applicant must:
(1) be an undergraduate student attending an
accredited four-year college or university in
the U.S. and;
(2) be a full-time matriculated student having
completed at least one college semester and
who is presently enrolled.
These Undergraduate Scholarships are
awarded on the basis of financial need, merit
and involvement in the Armenian community.

The Lazarian Graduate Scholarships are open
to students who intend to pursue their studies
at the Master's or Doctorate level in the
fields of law, history, political science,
international relations, journalism,
government, economics, business
administration, medicine and public service.
Selection is based on scholastic
qualifications, financial need and involvement
in the Armenian community.

FINANCIAL DATA:
Amount of support per award: Varies,
according to donations.

NUMBER OF APPLICANTS MOST RECENT YEAR:
250.

APPLICATION INFORMATION:
To receive an application, send a
self-addressed, stamped envelope to the ARS
office, and state undergraduate or graduate
status. Scholarships are awarded based on
merit, need and involvement in the Armenian
community.

For Undergraduate Scholarships, the
following information must accompany the
application:
(1) financial aid forms filed with a testing
service or school's financial aid office or a
copy of a recent income tax return of the
applicant's parents;
(2) a recent official transcript of college
grades with a raised seal (no faxes or copies
will be accepted) and;
(3) three letters of recommendation from a
college professor or advisor, affiliate(s) of
Armenian organization(s) of which the
student is a member, and a personal
acquaintance other than a relative.

For the Lazarian Graduate Scholarship:
(1) applicants must be currently enrolled in a
graduate program or provide proof of
acceptance and entrance into a program
within the coming six months;
(2) applicants must provide official, sealed
transcripts as requested (unofficial, unsealed
transcripts will not be accepted);
(3) applications and all required documents
must be postmarked by April 1 to be
considered;
(4) applicants will not be considered for a
scholarship if they have already received it
twice;
(5) applicants must provide a copy of the
most recent income tax return and tuition bill
to be considered for a scholarship;
(6) applications will not be considered
without the required three recommendations
(if from an institution/organization, it should
be on official letterhead) and;
(7) incomplete applications will not be
considered under any circumstance.
Deadline: April 1.

STAFF:
Vart Chiloyan, Executive Secretary

ADDRESS INQUIRIES TO:
Scholarship Committee
(See address above.)

ASSOCIATION OF UNIVERSITIES AND COLLEGES OF CANADA [1029]

350 Albert Street, Suite 600
Ottawa ON K1R 1B1 Canada
(613) 563-1236
Fax: (613) 563-9745

E-MAIL ADDRESS:
awards@aucc.ca

WEB SITE ADDRESS:
www.aucc.ca

FOUNDED: 1911

AREAS OF INTEREST:
Financial aid for disabled students.

NAME(S) OF PROGRAMS:
● **Mattinson Endowment Fund Scholarship for Disabled Students**

TYPE:
Scholarships.

PURPOSE:
To encourage Canadian students with permanent disabilities to pursue university studies with the ultimate objective of obtaining a first university degree.

LEGAL BASIS:
Nonprofit association.

ELIGIBILITY:
All candidates must be Canadian citizens or permanent residents who have lived in Canada for at least two years and be diagnosed with a documented permanent disability that is the primary disability for which they are applying.

All disciplines are eligible.

GEOGRAPHIC RESTRICTIONS:
Canada.

FINANCIAL DATA:
Amount of support per award: $2,500.
Total amount of support: Varies.

NUMBER OF AWARDS: Varies.

APPLICATION INFORMATION:
Duration: One year. Renewable upon reapplication.

PUBLICATIONS:
Program announcement.

ADDRESS INQUIRIES TO:
Jeannette Kerr, Program Officer or
Christine Paramanoss, Program Officer
(See address above.)

*SPECIAL STIPULATIONS:
The recipients must enter/attend their educational institution on a full-time basis in the year of application and complete each academic term. Requests for deferment in all programs will be considered only in unusual circumstances.

ASSOCIATION OF UNIVERSITIES AND COLLEGES OF CANADA [1030]

350 Albert Street, Suite 600
Ottawa ON K1R 1B1 Canada
(613) 563-1236
Fax: (613) 563-9745

E-MAIL ADDRESS:
awards@aucc.ca

WEB SITE ADDRESS:
www.aucc.ca

FOUNDED: 1911

AREAS OF INTEREST:
Financial aid for disabled students.

NAME(S) OF PROGRAMS:
● **AUCC Scholarship Program for Students with Disabilities**

TYPE:
Scholarships.

PURPOSE:
To encourage Canadian students with permanent disabilities to pursue university studies with the ultimate objective of obtaining a first university degree.

ELIGIBILITY:
Students must be Canadian citizens or permanent residents who have lived in Canada for a minimum of two years and be diagnosed with a documented permanent disability that is the primary disability for which they are applying.

FINANCIAL DATA:
Amount of support per award: $2,500 (CAN).

NUMBER OF AWARDS: Up to 5.

APPLICATION INFORMATION:
Application package must contain:
(1) the completed application form;
(2) an official transcript of the last three semesters of available marks;
(3) a description of extracurricular activities or volunteer/community involvement;
(4) two letters of reference;
(5) a 1,000-word essay and;
(6) proof of disability (medical certificate, documentation showing receipt of federal and/or provincial disability assistance, or a letter confirming the permanent disability from an official from a college or university centre for students with disabilities signed and on a letterhead).

Further information and application forms should be requested directly from the AUCC at the address above.
Duration: One academic year. Previous scholarship holders may reapply in subsequent years.
Deadline: June 30.

ADDRESS INQUIRIES TO:
AUCC Scholarship Program for Students with Disabilities
(See address above.)

ASTRAEA LESBIAN FOUNDATION FOR JUSTICE [1031]

116 East 16th Street, 7th Floor
New York, NY 10003
(212) 529-8021
Fax: (212) 982-3321

E-MAIL ADDRESS:
grants@astraeafoundation.org

WEB SITE ADDRESS:
www.astraeafoundation.org

FOUNDED: 1977

AREAS OF INTEREST:
Social, racial, and economic justice for lesbian, gay, bisexual, transgender, and intersex (LGBTI) peoples in the global south and east.

NAME(S) OF PROGRAMS:
● **International Fund for Sexual Minorities**

TYPE:
General operating grants; Grants-in-aid; Project/program grants.

PURPOSE:
To provide critically needed financial support to lesbian-led, LGBTI and progressive organizations striving to eliminate oppression based on race, age, sex, religion, sexual orientation, gender identity, economic exploitation, physical and mental ability, anti-semitism, and other such factors.

ELIGIBILITY:
Must be charitable nongovernmental organizations and meet the criteria used in determining 501(c)(3) status in the U.S. Those eligible to apply are:
(1) groups led by and/or for LGBTI communities;
(2) groups doing work towards social change on issues affecting LGBTI people;
(3) nongovernmental, not-for-profit groups with organizational budgets of $500,000 USD or less and;
(4) groups active for at least one year at the time of proposal.

Organizations applying must not have a budget of over $500,000 USD.

FINANCIAL DATA:
Amount of support per award: $5,000 to $10,000.

APPLICATION INFORMATION:
Organizations must submit letter of interest.
Duration: One year. Must reapply.
Deadline: Letter of interest accepted throughout the year.

ADDRESS INQUIRIES TO:
Namita Chad, Grants Manager
(See address above.)

ASTRAEA LESBIAN FOUNDATION FOR JUSTICE [1032]

116 East 16th Street, 7th Floor
New York, NY 10003
(212) 529-8021
Fax: (212) 982-3321

E-MAIL ADDRESS:
grants@astraeafoundation.org

WEB SITE ADDRESS:
www.astraeafoundation.org

FOUNDED: 1977

AREAS OF INTEREST:
Social change organizations and projects (including film, video, media and cultural projects) that directly address the depth and complexity of critical issues in LGBTI communities.

NAME(S) OF PROGRAMS:
● **U.S. General Fund**

TYPE:
General operating grants; Grants-in-aid; Project/program grants.

PURPOSE:
To provide critically needed financial support to lesbian-led, LGBTI and progressive organizations striving to eliminate oppression based on race, age, sex, religion, sexual

orientation, gender identity, economic exploitation, physical and mental ability, anti-semitism, and other such factors.

ELIGIBILITY:
501(c)(3) organizations. No grants to individuals.

GEOGRAPHIC RESTRICTIONS:
United States and its territories.

FINANCIAL DATA:
Amount of support per award: $5,000 to $10,000.

APPLICATION INFORMATION:
Organizations must be invited to apply. Faxed proposals are not accepted. IRS letter certifying organization's or fiscal sponsor's nonprofit tax-exempt status is required.
Duration: One year. Must reapply.

ADDRESS INQUIRIES TO:
Namita Chad, Grants Manager
(See address above.)

ASTRAEA LESBIAN FOUNDATION FOR JUSTICE [1033]
116 East 16th Street, 7th Floor
New York, NY 10003
(212) 529-8021
Fax: (212) 982-3321

E-MAIL ADDRESS:
grants@astraeafoundation.org

WEB SITE ADDRESS:
www.astraeafoundation.org

FOUNDED: 1977

AREAS OF INTEREST:
Visual art promoting lesbian visibility and social justice.

NAME(S) OF PROGRAMS:
● **Astraea Visual Arts Fund**

TYPE:
Awards/prizes.

PURPOSE:
To recognize the work of contemporary lesbian artists by providing support to those who show artistic merit and whose art and perspective reflect a commitment to Astraea's mission and efforts to promote lesbian visibility and social justice.

ELIGIBILITY:
Must be a lesbian-identified visual artist, a U.S. resident, and submit digital slides of current original works of art produced within the last three years in the following categories only: sculpture, painting in any medium, print, drawing, work on paper, mixed media. Art with an audio component is judged on visual content alone.

GEOGRAPHIC RESTRICTIONS:
United States.

FINANCIAL DATA:
Amount of support per award: $2,500.

NUMBER OF AWARDS: 3.

ADDRESS INQUIRIES TO:
Namita Chad, Grants Manager
(See address above.)

ASTRAEA LESBIAN FOUNDATION FOR JUSTICE [1034]
116 East 16th Street, 7th Floor
New York, NY 10003
(212) 529-8021
Fax: (212) 982-3321

E-MAIL ADDRESS:
grants@astraeafoundation.org

WEB SITE ADDRESS:
www.astraeafoundation.org

FOUNDED: 1977

AREAS OF INTEREST:
Poetry or fiction, including some lesbian content.

NAME(S) OF PROGRAMS:
● **Lesbian Writers Fund**

TYPE:
Awards/prizes.

YEAR PROGRAM STARTED: 1990

PURPOSE:
To support the work of emerging lesbian writers; to acknowledge the contributions of established lesbian writers to our movement and culture.

ELIGIBILITY:
Must be a lesbian-identified writer of poetry and/or fiction residing in the U.S.

GEOGRAPHIC RESTRICTIONS:
United States.

FINANCIAL DATA:
Amount of support per award: $10,000 for awardee; $1,500 for runners-up; $100 for honorable mention.

ADDRESS INQUIRIES TO:
Namita Chad, Grants Manager
(See address above.)

ALEXANDER GRAHAM BELL ASSOCIATION FOR THE DEAF AND HARD OF HEARING [1035]
3417 Volta Place, N.W.
Washington, DC 20007
(202) 337-5220
Fax: (202) 337-8314

E-MAIL ADDRESS:
financialaid@agbell.org

WEB SITE ADDRESS:
www.agbell.org

FOUNDED: 1890

AREAS OF INTEREST:
All areas of study.

NAME(S) OF PROGRAMS:
● **Alexander Graham Bell College Scholarship Awards**

TYPE:
Scholarships.

YEAR PROGRAM STARTED: 1967

PURPOSE:
To assist students with pre-lingual hearing loss to attend mainstream colleges.

ELIGIBILITY:
Based on age of diagnosis, degree of hearing loss and grade point average.

FINANCIAL DATA:
Amount of support per award: $1,000 to $10,000.
Total amount of support: Varies.

NUMBER OF APPLICANTS MOST RECENT YEAR: 173.

NUMBER OF AWARDS: 18.

APPLICATION INFORMATION:
Applicants must download the application or request via e-mail. Photocopies are not accepted.

Duration: One year; nonrenewable.
Deadline: March.

ADDRESS INQUIRIES TO:
College Scholarships
(See address and e-mail above.)
E-mail preferred.

BEN & JERRY'S FOUNDATION [1036]
30 Community Drive
South Burlington, VT 05403-6828
(802) 846-1500
Fax: (802) 846-1610

WEB SITE ADDRESS:
www.benandjerrysfoundation.org

FOUNDED: 1985

AREAS OF INTEREST:
Economic, environmental and social justice.

TYPE:
General operating grants; Project/program grants. Grants to nonprofit organizations which facilitate progressive social change by addressing the underlying conditions of societal and/or environmental problems.

YEAR PROGRAM STARTED: 1986

PURPOSE:
To support and encourage organizations that facilitate progressive social change by addressing the underlying conditions of societal and environmental problems.

LEGAL BASIS:
Private foundation.

ELIGIBILITY:
The Foundation generally funds organizations with budgets less than $500,000. Applicant must be a nonprofit 501(c)(3) organization or have a sponsoring agent that has this status. No grants to support basic services. Applicants need to demonstrate that their projects will lead to societal, institutional or environmental change, help ameliorate an unjust or destructive situation by empowering constituents and address the root causes of social and/or environmental problems.

No funding for discretionary or emergency requests, colleges or universities, individuals or scholarships, research projects, religious projects, state agencies, international or foreign programs or direct service programs.

GEOGRAPHIC RESTRICTIONS:
United States and its territories.

FINANCIAL DATA:
Amount of support per award: $500 to $15,000.
Total amount of support: $1,500,000 for the year 2009.

REPRESENTATIVE AWARDS:
$10,000 to Ohio Valley Environmental Coalition, to continue funding to support their work organizing broad-based opposition to mountaintop removal/valley fill coal mining practices as well as unsafe coal waste ponds; $10,000 to Little Village Environmental Justice Organization, to continue funding for the People United for Dignity, Democracy and Justice project.

APPLICATION INFORMATION:
Duration: One year. Must reapply.

PUBLICATIONS:
Annual report; application guidelines; grant recipients list.

IRS IDENTIFICATION NUMBER: 03-0300865

STAFF:
Lisa Pendolino, Managing Director
Rebecca Golden, Director of Programs

JACOB AND HILDA BLAUSTEIN FOUNDATION [1037]

10 East Baltimore Street
Suite 1111
Baltimore, MD 21202
(410) 347-7201

E-MAIL ADDRESS:
info@blaufund.org

WEB SITE ADDRESS:
www.blaufund.org

FOUNDED: 1957

AREAS OF INTEREST:
Jewish life and Israel, education, human rights, health and mental health.

TYPE:
General operating grants; Matching gifts; Project/program grants.

ELIGIBILITY:
Grants are made to organizations that have tax-exempt status under Section 501(c)(3) of the Internal Revenue Code. No grants are made to individuals.

GEOGRAPHIC RESTRICTIONS:
United States (primarily in Baltimore, Maryland) and Israel.

FINANCIAL DATA:
Total amount of support: $6,900,000 for the year 2011.

APPLICATION INFORMATION:
Send a letter of inquiry outlining the organization's goal and purposes, and the intended use and amount of the grant requested.
Duration: One to five years.

ADDRESS INQUIRIES TO:
Michael Hirschhorn, President
(See address above.)

CALIFORNIA LIBRARY ASSOCIATION

950 Glenn Drive, Suite 150
Folsom, CA 95630
(916) 233-3298
Fax: (916) 932-2209

E-MAIL ADDRESS:
info@cla-net.org

WEB SITE ADDRESS:
www.cla-net.org

TYPE:
Fellowships; Scholarships. Support for minority library school students. Support for graduate students in reference/information service librarianship.
See entry 759 for full listing.

THE CENTER FOR LESBIAN AND GAY STUDIES [1038]

The Graduate Center
365 5th Avenue, Room 7115
New York, NY 10016
(212) 817-1955
Fax: (212) 817-1567

E-MAIL ADDRESS:
clagsmembership@gc.cuny.edu

WEB SITE ADDRESS:
www.clags.org

FOUNDED: 1991

AREAS OF INTEREST:
Gay, lesbian, bisexual, queer or transgender issues.

NAME(S) OF PROGRAMS:
- **The Joan Heller-Diane Bernard Fellowship in Lesbian and Gay Studies**

TYPE:
Fellowships. Supports research into the impact of lesbians and/or gay men on U.S. society and culture.

PURPOSE:
To foster research and scholarship about lesbian and gay lives and social institutions, as well as homophobia and oppression.

ELIGIBILITY:
Open to researchers in the U.S., both inside and outside the academy, and is adjudicated by the Joan Heller-Diane Bernard Fellowship committee in conjunction with the Center. The winner may be asked to participate in the Center's colloquium series the following academic year to present her/his research project. Scholars conducting research on lesbians are especially encouraged to apply.

GEOGRAPHIC RESTRICTIONS:
United States.

FINANCIAL DATA:
Amount of support per award: $1,250 to $5,000.
Total amount of support: $12,500.

NUMBER OF AWARDS: 4 (2 for $1,250; 2 for $5,000).

APPLICATION INFORMATION:
Duration: One year. Nonrenewable.
Deadline: November.

PUBLICATIONS:
CLAGS News.

ADDRESS INQUIRIES TO:
Fellowships Coordinator
(See address above.)

THE CENTER FOR LESBIAN AND GAY STUDIES [1039]

The Graduate Center/CUNY
365 Fifth Avenue, Room 7115
New York, NY 10016
(212) 817-1958
Fax: (212) 817-1567

E-MAIL ADDRESS:
claggsfellowships@gmail.com

WEB SITE ADDRESS:
www.clags.org

AREAS OF INTEREST:
Scholarly research on the lesbian, gay, bisexual, transgender, and queer experience.

NAME(S) OF PROGRAMS:
- **The Martin Duberman Fellowship**

TYPE:
Awards/prizes; Fellowships.

PURPOSE:
To promote the study of historical, cultural, and political issues of vital concern to lesbian, gay, bisexual, and transgendered individuals.

ELIGIBILITY:
Senior scholars (tenured university professors or advanced independent scholars) from any country doing scholarly research on the lesbian, gay, transgender, bisexual, or queer (LGTBQ) experience. University affiliation is not necessary, but the applicant must be able to show a prior contribution to the field of LGTBQ studies.

FINANCIAL DATA:
Amount of support per award: $7,500.
Total amount of support: $7,500 annually.

NUMBER OF AWARDS: 1.

APPLICATION INFORMATION:
Electronic submission by e-mail is preferred by CLAGS. Guidelines and application form is available at the web site.
Deadline: November.

PUBLICATIONS:
CLAGS News.

ADDRESS INQUIRIES TO:
Lolan Seville, Fellowships and Awards
(See address above.)

CHINESE AMERICAN CITIZENS ALLIANCE FOUNDATION [1040]

763 Yale Street
Los Angeles, CA 90012
(213) 628-6368

E-MAIL ADDRESS:
cacafoundation@gmail.com

WEB SITE ADDRESS:
www.cacafoundation.org

FOUNDED: 1971

NAME(S) OF PROGRAMS:
- **CACA Foundation Scholarships**

TYPE:
Scholarships. For college students of Chinese descent attending a college or university in California.

YEAR PROGRAM STARTED: 1971

PURPOSE:
To award academic scholarships to worthy college students of Chinese descent to further their higher education and to achieve their career goals.

ELIGIBILITY:
Open to undergraduate students of Chinese descent who will be a junior in the fall, attending a California college or university.

GEOGRAPHIC RESTRICTIONS:
California.

FINANCIAL DATA:
Amount of support per award: $1,000.
Total amount of support: $8,000 for the year 2010.

NUMBER OF AWARDS: 8 for the year 2010.

APPLICATION INFORMATION:
Applicants must be available for an in-person interview in Los Angeles.
Duration: One year. No renewals.
Deadline: June 17.

ADDRESS INQUIRIES TO:
Alliance Scholarship Committee
(See address above.)

CHINESE AMERICAN CITIZENS ALLIANCE FOUNDATION [1041]

Los Angeles Lodge
415 Bamboo Lane
Los Angeles, CA 90012
(213) 628-8015

WEB SITE ADDRESS:
www.cacala.org

FOUNDED: 1971

NAME(S) OF PROGRAMS:
- **751 Yale Legacy Fund Award**

TYPE:
Scholarships. Scholarship for high school seniors of Chinese descent planning to attend a junior/community college in California.

YEAR PROGRAM STARTED: 2005

PURPOSE:
To help further the higher education of students of Chinese descent and help to achieve their career goals.

ELIGIBILITY:
Open to high school seniors of Chinese descent planning to attend a junior/community college in California.

GEOGRAPHIC RESTRICTIONS:
California.

FINANCIAL DATA:
Amount of support per award: $500.
Total amount of support: $1,000 for the year 2011.

NUMBER OF AWARDS: 2 for the year 2011.

APPLICATION INFORMATION:
Duration: One year. No renewals.

ADDRESS INQUIRIES TO:
Los Angeles Lodge Scholarship Committee (See address above.)

CINTAS FOUNDATION
c/o Morrison, Brown, Argiz & Farra LLP
1001 Brickell Bay Drive
Miami, FL 33131
(305) 373-5500 ext. 2202
Fax: (305) 373-0056

E-MAIL ADDRESS:
fgonzalez@mbafcpa.com

WEB SITE ADDRESS:
www.cintasfoundation.org

TYPE:
Fellowships. Awarded to persons of Cuban citizenship or lineage residing outside Cuba for achievement of a creative nature in architecture, painting, sculpture, printmaking, music composition and literature.

See entry 470 for full listing.

CONSORTIUM FOR GRADUATE STUDY IN MANAGEMENT
5585 Pershing Avenue
Suite 240
St. Louis, MO 63112
(314) 877-5500
Fax: (314) 877-5505

E-MAIL ADDRESS:
frontdesk@cgsm.org

WEB SITE ADDRESS:
www.cgsm.org

TYPE:
Fellowships. Graduate fellowships for minority students interested in management careers in business.

See entry 2014 for full listing.

COUNCIL ON SOCIAL WORK EDUCATION   [1042]
1701 Duke Street, Suite 200
Alexandria, VA 22314-3457
(703) 683-8080
Fax: (703) 683-8099

E-MAIL ADDRESS:
gmeeks@cswe.org

WEB SITE ADDRESS:
www.cswe.org/mfp

FOUNDED: 1952

AREAS OF INTEREST:
Improvement of social services and mental health.

NAME(S) OF PROGRAMS:
- **The Mental Health and Substance Abuse Fellowship Program**

TYPE:
Fellowships. Awards for minority doctoral level studies in social work, specializing in mental health and substance abuse-related education, research, policy and leadership.

YEAR PROGRAM STARTED: 1974

PURPOSE:
To equip ethnic minority individuals for the provision of leadership, teaching, consultation, training, policy development and administration in mental health and/or substance abuse programs and to enhance the development and dissemination of knowledge requisite for the provision of relevant clinical and social services to ethnic minority individuals and communities.

LEGAL BASIS:
Nonprofit organization.

ELIGIBILITY:
Applicants must be American citizens or non-citizen nationals of the U.S. or have permanent residence status, including but not limited to persons who are American Indian/Alaskan Native, Asian/Pacific Islander (e.g., Chinese, East Indian and other South Asians, Filipino, Hawaiian, Japanese, Korean, Samoan), Black and Hispanic (e.g., Mexican/Chicano, Cuban, Central or South American).

The Fellowship is open to students with a Master's degree in social work who will begin full-time study leading to a doctoral degree in social work or who are currently enrolled as full-time students in a doctoral social work program. Applicants should demonstrate potential for assuming leadership roles, potential for success in doctoral studies and commitment to a career in providing mental health and/or substance abuse services to ethnic/racial/social/cultural minority clients and communities.

FINANCIAL DATA:
Fellowship awards include a monthly stipend for one year to help meet living expenses.
Amount of support per award: Up to $3,000.
Total amount of support: Varies.

COOPERATIVE FUNDING PROGRAMS: Funded by the Substance Abuse and Mental Health Services Administration (SAMHSA), Department of Health and Human Services.

NUMBER OF AWARDS: Up to 25.

APPLICATION INFORMATION:
Duration: Three years maximum. Renewable each year subject to availability of funds.
Deadline: Announcement by mid-Summer.

ADDRESS INQUIRIES TO:
CSWE Minority Fellowship Programs (See address above.)

DARTMOUTH COLLEGE   [1043]
Office of Graduate Studies
Chavez/Eastman/Marshall
Dissertation Fellowship Committee
6062 Wentworth Hall, Room 304
Hanover, NH 03755-3526
(603) 646-6578
Fax: (603) 646-8762

E-MAIL ADDRESS:
jane.b.seibel@dartmouth.edu

WEB SITE ADDRESS:
www.dartmouth.
edu/~gradstdy/funding/fellowships

FOUNDED: 1769

AREAS OF INTEREST:
Fellowships for underrepresented minority scholars (including African-American, Latina/o and Native American scholars) and other graduate scholars with a demonstrated commitment and ability to advance educational diversity.

NAME(S) OF PROGRAMS:
- **Chavez/Eastman/Marshall Dissertation Fellowships**

TYPE:
Exchange programs; Fellowships.

YEAR PROGRAM STARTED: 1991

PURPOSE:
To increase the number of underrepresented minority faculty in American higher education by supporting African-American, Latina/o, Native American and other scholars with a demonstrated commitment to the advancement of educational diversity.

LEGAL BASIS:
University.

ELIGIBILITY:
Applicants will be chosen on the basis of academic achievement and promise, membership in a racial or ethnic group that is currently underrepresented among faculty in the applicant's academic field, demonstrated commitment to increasing opportunities for underrepresented minorities and increasing cross-racial understanding, and potential for serving as an advocate and mentor for minority undergraduate and graduate students.

GEOGRAPHIC RESTRICTIONS:
United States and Canada.

FINANCIAL DATA:
Fellowship provides stipend, office space, library privileges, research assistance and housing or allowance.
Amount of support per award: $25,000 stipend and $2,500 research assistance.
Total amount of support: $82,500 annually.

NUMBER OF AWARDS: 3.

APPLICATION INFORMATION:
Application form required. Contact the Office of Graduate Studies. Supporting documentation includes abstract of dissertation prospectus, statement of academic career plan, curriculum vitae, transcripts and three letters of reference.
Duration: One academic year.
Deadline: February 1. Announcement April 1.

PUBLICATIONS:
Program announcement.

ADDRESS INQUIRIES TO:
Gary Hutchins, Assistant Dean of Graduate Studies
(See address above.)

*SPECIAL STIPULATIONS:
Fellows are expected to complete the dissertation during the tenure of the Fellowship and may have the opportunity to participate in teaching, either as a primary instructor or as part of a team.

DAUGHTERS OF ITALY LODGE #2825

14 South Jupiter Avenue
Clearwater, FL 33755
(727) 447-6890

E-MAIL ADDRESS:
vincenzad@verizon.net

WEB SITE ADDRESS:
www.daughtersofitaly.com

TYPE:
Scholarships. Open to full-time students at a Florida-accredited junior college, college or university or students graduating from high school.

Filomena Genovese Meo Scholarship is open to female students. Scholarships are awarded on the basis of eligibility, scholastic achievement, financial need and participation in school and community programs.

See entry 1797 for full listing.

DAUGHTERS OF PENELOPE FOUNDATION, INC. [1044]

1909 Q Street, N.W., Suite 500
Washington, DC 20009
(202) 234-9741
(202) 232-6300
Fax: (202) 483-6983

E-MAIL ADDRESS:
president@dopfoundationinc.com

WEB SITE ADDRESS:
www.dopfoundationinc.com

FOUNDED: 1983

AREAS OF INTEREST:
Philanthropic, educational and cultural activities pertaining to Greek culture.

NAME(S) OF PROGRAMS:
● **Daughters of Penelope National Scholarship Awards**

TYPE:
Scholarships. Academic and Financial Need.

YEAR PROGRAM STARTED: 1984

PURPOSE:
To promote the social, ethical and intellectual interests of members; to perpetuate the study of American ideals and to encourage Hellenic study; to cultivate citizenship and patriotism.

ELIGIBILITY:
Applicant must be a woman and have a current member of their immediate family or legal guardian (court-appointed) in the Daughters of Penelope or the Order of Ahepa, in good standing for a minimum of two years, or be a member in good standing for two years in the Daughters of Penelope or the Maids of Athena.

FINANCIAL DATA:
Amount of support per award: $1,000 to $1,500 depending on scholarship.

NUMBER OF APPLICANTS MOST RECENT YEAR:
Varies.

NUMBER OF AWARDS: Varies.

APPLICATION INFORMATION:
Contact the Foundation for application procedures.
Duration: One year.
Deadline: Varies.

THE BARON DE HIRSCH FUND [1045]

130 East 59th Street, 10th Floor
New York, NY 10022
(212) 836-1305
Fax: (212) 836-1172

E-MAIL ADDRESS:
baumblatts@ujafed.ny.org

FOUNDED: 1891

AREAS OF INTEREST:
Jewish immigrant resettlement, education and employment training.

TYPE:
Project/program grants.

PURPOSE:
To help Jewish immigrants resettle in the U.S. or Israel.

LEGAL BASIS:
Private foundation.

ELIGIBILITY:
Qualifying organizations must be nonprofit. Grants are not given to individuals.

GEOGRAPHIC RESTRICTIONS:
New York City and Israel.

FINANCIAL DATA:
Amount of support per award: $10,000 to $50,000.
Total amount of support: Varies.

REPRESENTATIVE AWARDS:
U.S. grant: $25,000 to Jewish Child Care Association of New York; Israel grant: $30,000 to the Gevanim Center for Community Diversity.

APPLICATION INFORMATION:
Interested applicants should first call the Fund.
Duration: One year.

ADDRESS INQUIRIES TO:
Stan Baumblatt, Secretary and Treasurer (See e-mail address above.)

EDUCATIONAL TESTING SERVICE

660 Rosedale Road, MS 19-T
Princeton, NJ 08541
(609) 734-5543
Fax: (609) 734-5010

E-MAIL ADDRESS:
internfellowships@ets.org

WEB SITE ADDRESS:
www.ets.org

TYPE:
Fellowships.

See entry 1644 for full listing.

EDUCATIONAL TESTING SERVICE

660 Rosedale Road, MS 19-T
Princeton, NJ 08541
(609) 734-5543
Fax: (609) 734-5010

E-MAIL ADDRESS:
internfellowships@ets.org

WEB SITE ADDRESS:
www.ets.org/research/fellowships.html

TYPE:
Internships. Interns in this eight- or 12-week program participate in research under the guidance of a senior ETS staff member in one of the areas of interest listed above. Interns also participate in seminars and workshops on a variety of topics.

See entry 1643 for full listing.

LOIS & RICHARD ENGLAND FAMILY FOUNDATION

P.O. Box 34-1077
Bethesda, MD 20827
(301) 657-7737
Fax: (301) 657-7738

E-MAIL ADDRESS:
englandfamilyfdn@verizon.net

WEB SITE ADDRESS:
fdncenter.org/grantmaker/england

TYPE:
Capital grants; Challenge/matching grants; Development grants; General operating grants; Matching gifts; Project/program grants; Seed money grants; Technical assistance; Training grants.

See entry 1190 for full listing.

THE ENTOMOLOGICAL FOUNDATION

9332 Annapolis Road
Suite 210
Lanham, MD 20706
(301) 459-9082
Fax: (301) 459-9084

E-MAIL ADDRESS:
melodie@entfdn.org

WEB SITE ADDRESS:
www.entfdn.org

TYPE:
Fellowships. Awarded annually to assist needy students at the graduate or undergraduate level of their education. The need may be based on physical limitations or economic, minority, or environmental conditions.

See entry 2278 for full listing.

EVANGELICAL LUTHERAN CHURCH IN AMERICA

Congregation and Synodical Mission Unit
8765 West Higgins Road
Chicago, IL 60631-4101
(773) 380-2874

E-MAIL ADDRESS:
melinda.valverde@elca.org

WEB SITE ADDRESS:
www.elca.org/egp

TYPE:
Scholarships. Educational grants for members of the Evangelical Lutheran Church in America in advanced academic theological education degrees with intent to teach in seminary or university.

See entry 855 for full listing.

FALK FOUNDATION   [1046]

3315 Grant Building
330 Grant Street
Pittsburgh, PA 15219
(412) 261-2485
Fax: (412) 471-7739

E-MAIL ADDRESS:
kerryo@falkfund.org

WEB SITE ADDRESS:
www.falkfund.org

FOUNDED: 1960

AREAS OF INTEREST:
Education, health care, workforce
development, housing, and criminal justice.

TYPE:
Challenge/matching grants;
Conferences/seminars; Demonstration grants;
Project/program grants; Seed money grants;
Technical assistance; Training grants; Travel
grants.

YEAR PROGRAM STARTED: 1961

PURPOSE:
To address disparities and inequities based on
race, gender or sexual orientation.

ELIGIBILITY:
Qualified institutions and organizations with
appropriate interests are eligible to apply.

FINANCIAL DATA:
Amount of support per award: Grants vary in
amount, depending upon the needs and
nature of the request.
Total amount of support: $766,516 in
payment of grants for the year 2009-10.

NUMBER OF APPLICANTS MOST RECENT YEAR:
Approximately 75.

NUMBER OF AWARDS: 48 for the year 2009-10.

REPRESENTATIVE AWARDS:
$525,000 to Chatham University, Pittsburgh,
PA, for support of the Sigo Falk Chair in
Social Justice and Sustainability; $70,000 to
Demos, New York, NY, for enforcement of
the National Voter Registration Act in
Pennsylvania; $42,800 to Fair Housing
Partnership of Greater Pittsburgh, Pittsburgh,
PA, for testing for discrimination in mortgage
lending.

APPLICATION INFORMATION:
Duration: One year.
Deadline: March 1 and October 1.

IRS IDENTIFICATION NUMBER: 25-1099658

OFFICERS AND TRUSTEES:
Sigo Falk, Chairman
Kerry J. O'Donnell, President
Andrew D. Falk, Treasurer
Estelle F. Comay, Secretary
Michele R. Cooper, Trustee
William S. Lipscomb, Trustee
Angela M. Reynolds, Trustee
Eric W. Springer, Trustee

ADDRESS INQUIRIES TO:
Kerry J. O'Donnell, President
(See address above.)

FEDERAL HIGHWAY ADMINISTRATION

National Highway Institute
1310 North Courthouse Road, Suite 300
Arlington, VA 22201
(703) 235-0500
Fax: (703) 235-0593

E-MAIL ADDRESS:
hcnry.murdaugh@dot.gov

WEB SITE ADDRESS:
www.nhi.fhwa.dot.gov

TYPE:
Fellowships; Internships; Research grants;
Technical assistance. Dwight David
Eisenhower Transportation Fellowship
Program's objectives are to attract the
nation's brightest minds to the field of
transportation, to enhance the careers of
transportation professionals by encouraging
them to seek advanced degrees, and to retain
top talent in the transportation industry of the
U.S. This Program encompasses all areas of
transportation. The Program has seven award
categories:
(1) Eisenhower Graduate (GRAD)
Fellowships enable students to pursue
master's degrees or doctorates in
transportation-related fields at the university
of their choice;
(2) Eisenhower Grants for Research (GRF)
Fellowships acquaint undergraduate and
graduate students with transportation
research, development and technology
transfer activities at the U.S. Department of
Transportation facilities;
(3) Eisenhower Historically Black Colleges
and Universities (HBCU) Fellowships
provide HBCU students with additional
opportunities to enter careers in
transportation. The Fellowships also serve as
a feeder for other Eisenhower fellowships;
(4) Eisenhower Hispanic Serving Institutions
(HSI) Fellowships provide HSI students with
additional opportunities to enter careers in
transportation. The Fellowships also serve as
a feeder for other Eisenhower fellowships;
(5) Eisenhower Tribal College Fellowships
(TC) identify transportation-related activities
and provide student fellowship opportunities
at tribal colleges. The Fellowships also serve
as a feeder for other Eisenhower fellowships;
(6) Eisenhower Intern Fellowships (EIF) and;
(7) Eisenhower People with Disabilities
(PWD) Fellowships.

See entry 2770 for full listing.

FOUNDATION FOR SCIENCE AND DISABILITY   [1047]

503 N.W. 89th Street
Gainesville, FL 32607
(352) 374-5774
Fax: (352) 374-5781

E-MAIL ADDRESS:
rmankin@nersp.nerdc.ufl.edu

WEB SITE ADDRESS:
stemd.org

FOUNDED: 1978

AREAS OF INTEREST:
Science, mathematics, medicine, engineering
and computer science.

TYPE:
Grants-in-aid; Research grants.

YEAR PROGRAM STARTED: 1978

PURPOSE:
To assist disabled students who are interested
in obtaining a graduate degree in one of the
above fields.

LEGAL BASIS:
Affiliate of American Association for
Advancement of Science.

ELIGIBILITY:
Open to college seniors and graduate students
who have some physical or sensory disability
and who have been accepted to graduate or

professional school. Selection is based on
sincerity of purpose and scholarship and/or
research ability.

FINANCIAL DATA:
Funds may be used for an assistive device or
instrument, or as financial support to work
with a professor on an individual research
project, or for some other special need.
Amount of support per award: $1,000.

NUMBER OF APPLICANTS MOST RECENT YEAR:
8.

NUMBER OF AWARDS: Varies, depending on
funds available.

APPLICATION INFORMATION:
Application forms are available from Dr.
Richard Mankin, Chairperson, Science
Student Grant Committee, at the address
above or by e-mail. Applicants should submit
a copy of college transcript, two letters of
recommendation, 250-word summary of
educational goals including what the funds
will be used for, if awarded, and a copy of a
U.S. birth or naturalization certificate.
Deadline: December 1.

ADDRESS INQUIRIES TO:
Dr. Richard Mankin, Chairperson
Science Student Grant Committee
(See address above.)

*SPECIAL STIPULATIONS:
For college seniors with a disability who
have been accepted to graduate or
professional school, or graduate students
working toward a higher degree.

THE FOUNDATION OF THE AMERICAN COLLEGE OF HEALTHCARE EXECUTIVES

One North Franklin Street
Suite 1700
Chicago, IL 60606-3529
(312) 424-9400
Fax: (312) 424-9405

E-MAIL ADDRESS:
contact@ache.org

WEB SITE ADDRESS:
www.ache.org

TYPE:
Scholarships. Offered annually, the Albert W.
Dent and the Foster G. McGaw Graduate
Student Scholarships are designated for
students enrolled in their final year of
classroom work in a health care management
graduate program.

Albert W. Dent Graduate Student Scholarship
is only available to minority students.

See entry 1528 for full listing.

4A'S   [1048]

405 Lexington Avenue, 18th Floor
New York, NY 10174-1801
(800) 676-9333
Fax: (212) 867-8329

E-MAIL ADDRESS:
maip@aaaa.org

WEB SITE ADDRESS:
www.adunity.aaaa.org

FOUNDED: 1917

AREAS OF INTEREST:
Advertising.

NAME(S) OF PROGRAMS:
- **Multicultural Advertising Intern Program**

TYPE:
Internships.

YEAR PROGRAM STARTED: 1973

PURPOSE:
To assist minority students in attaining skills and knowledge necessary for careers in advertising and to assist advertising agencies in recruiting minorities for the professional level.

LEGAL BASIS:
Nonprofit organization.

ELIGIBILITY:
Open to any Black, Asian, Hispanic, Native American, multiracial or multiethnic student. Students must be currently enrolled in an undergraduate or graduate program and have completed at least their junior year by the time of the internship. Applicants must have a grade point average minimum of 3.0 on a scale of 4.0 and must be citizens or permanent residents of the U.S.

Students have the opportunity to work in one of the basic career areas of advertising including account management, media, research and creative (art direction or copywriting), broadcast and print production, traffic, strategic and account planning.

GEOGRAPHIC RESTRICTIONS:
United States.

FINANCIAL DATA:
Students who do not live in the metropolitan area of their host agency are housed in 4A's-arranged housing. MAIP interns requesting travel/housing assistance will be responsible for paying $1,000 to the 4A's toward summer housing and transportation cost, payable in two installments during the internship period.
Amount of support per award: $10 per hour.
Total amount of support: Varies.

NUMBER OF APPLICANTS MOST RECENT YEAR:
500.

NUMBER OF AWARDS: 100 to 150.

APPLICATION INFORMATION:
Candidates must submit an application, resume, letters of recommendation, school transcripts and supporting materials (such as artwork). Semi-finalists are interviewed before final selections are made.
Duration: 10 weeks during the summer.
Deadline: End of November.

ADDRESS INQUIRIES TO:
Michelle Castillo
Manager of Diversity Programs
(See address above.)

FUNDING EXCHANGE [1049]
666 Broadway
Suite 500
New York, NY 10012
(212) 529-5300

E-MAIL ADDRESS:
information@fex.org

WEB SITE ADDRESS:
www.fex.org

AREAS OF INTEREST:
Lesbians, gay men, bisexuals and transgender issues, communities of color, and various social justice issues.

NAME(S) OF PROGRAMS:
- **Out Fund**
- **Saguaro Fund**

TYPE:
General operating grants; Project/program grants; Seed money grants. Out Fund supports lesbian/gay/bisexual/transgender issues. Saguaro Fund supports communities of color.

PURPOSE:
To support radical organizing projects working to build community among lesbians, gay men, bisexuals and transgender people; to provide support for communities of color; to give assistance to various social justice issues.

ELIGIBILITY:
Lesbian/gay/bisexual/transgender: Grants are made to tax-exempt organizations or to organizations whose fiscal sponsor has a tax-exempt status under Section 501(c)(3) of the Internal Revenue Code. No grants are made to individuals or governmental agencies. Nonsectarian religious programs may apply.

Priority is given to those organizing projects that reflect a vision for progressive social change, that demonstrate a capacity for addressing race, class, gender and sexuality as interrelated constructs in systems of oppression, and that address the politics of sexuality and gender and work to develop long-lasting coalitions.

Communities of color and various social justice issues: Grants are made to organizations that have tax-exempt status under Section 501(c)(3) of the Internal Revenue Code. No grants are made to individuals or governmental agencies.

GEOGRAPHIC RESTRICTIONS:
United States and its territories.

FINANCIAL DATA:
Amount of support per award:
Lesbian/gay/bisexual/transgender and communities of color: $5,000 to $15,000. In rare cases, maximum grants of $20,000.

APPLICATION INFORMATION:
Contact the Organization for application procedures.
Duration: One year.
Deadline: March 1.

THE GAMBLE FOUNDATION
1660 Bush Street, Suite 300
San Francisco, CA 94109
(415) 561-6540
Fax: (415) 561-6477

WEB SITE ADDRESS:
www.pfs-llc.net/gamble/gamble.html

TYPE:
Project/program grants.

See entry 1651 for full listing.

THE GAY & LESBIAN FUND FOR COLORADO, A PROGRAM OF THE GILL FOUNDATION [1050]
315 East Costilla Street
Colorado Springs, CO 80903-2105
(719) 473-4455
(800) 964-5643
Fax: (719) 473-2254

E-MAIL ADDRESS:
info@gayandlesbianfund.org

WEB SITE ADDRESS:
www.gayandlesbianfund.org

FOUNDED: 1996

AREAS OF INTEREST:
Arts and culture, healthy families, civic leadership and public broadcasting.

NAME(S) OF PROGRAMS:
- **Gay & Lesbian Fund for Colorado**

TYPE:
Challenge/matching grants; General operating grants. Event sponsorship.

YEAR PROGRAM STARTED: 1996

PURPOSE:
To support nonprofit organizations in Colorado that are working to advance equality for all people; to highlight the contributions of gay, lesbian, bisexual and transgender people.

ELIGIBILITY:
Applicants must meet one or more of the following objectives:
(1) 501(c)(3) public charity status;
(2) board approved organizational nondiscrimination policy including sexual orientation and gender expression;
(3) match a program area or;
(4) be working to advance equality.

GEOGRAPHIC RESTRICTIONS:
Colorado.

FINANCIAL DATA:
Total amount of support: Over $22,000,000.

APPLICATION INFORMATION:
Up-to-date funding guidelines are available online.

IRS IDENTIFICATION NUMBER: 84-1264186

ADDRESS INQUIRIES TO:
See e-mail address above.

*SPECIAL STIPULATIONS:
Proposals must include organization nondiscrimination policies which include sexual orientation and gender expression.

GILL FOUNDATION [1051]
2215 Market Street
Denver, CO 80205
(303) 292-4455
Fax: (303) 292-2155

E-MAIL ADDRESS:
grantsmanager@gillfoundation.org

WEB SITE ADDRESS:
www.gillfoundation.org

FOUNDED: 1994

AREAS OF INTEREST:
Lesbian, gay, bisexual, and transgender (LGBT).

NAME(S) OF PROGRAMS:
- **Gill Foundation General Fund**

TYPE:
Challenge/matching grants; General operating grants; Project/program grants.

YEAR PROGRAM STARTED: 1994

PURPOSE:
To secure equal opportunity for all people, regardless of sexual orientation or gender expression.

ELIGIBILITY:
Grants are by invitation only. Unsolicited grant requests will not be accepted. 501(c)(3) organizations with a copy of an official

nondiscrimination policy for your organization including sexual orientation and gender expression.

FINANCIAL DATA:
Total amount of support: $10,000,000.

APPLICATION INFORMATION:
Duration: One year.

PUBLICATIONS:
Annual report.

IRS IDENTIFICATION NUMBER: 84-1264186

ADDRESS INQUIRIES TO:
Grants Department
(See address above.)

GOVERNMENT EMPLOYEES INSURANCE COMPANY (GEICO)   [1052]
One GEICO Plaza, Room 4T
Washington, DC 20076-0001
(301) 986-3438
Fax: (301) 986-2888

E-MAIL ADDRESS:
federal@geico.com

WEB SITE ADDRESS:
www.geico.com

FOUNDED: 1936

AREAS OF INTEREST:
Substance abuse prevention/treatment, fire prevention and safety, physical rehabilitation, traffic safety and accident prevention.

NAME(S) OF PROGRAMS:
● **GEICO Public Service Awards**

TYPE:
Awards/prizes. Cash awards and recognition to five federal employees, including one award to a young federal employee (between the ages of 21 and 30), and one retired civilian federal employee on a federal retiree annuity. Awards are for outstanding achievement in one of the following areas including substance abuse prevention/treatment, fire prevention and safety, physical rehabilitation, traffic safety and accident prevention.

YEAR PROGRAM STARTED: 1980

PURPOSE:
To provide recognition for outstanding achievements that benefit the quality of life in the U.S.

LEGAL BASIS:
Corporation.

ELIGIBILITY:
All career civil service employees are eligible. For special retiree award, only retired civilian federal employees on a federal retiree annuity may be nominated.

GEOGRAPHIC RESTRICTIONS:
United States.

FINANCIAL DATA:
Awards include trip to Washington, DC, for winner and guest.
Amount of support per award: $2,500 cash award.
Total amount of support: $15,000 total annual support.

NUMBER OF APPLICANTS MOST RECENT YEAR:
Approximately 100.

NUMBER OF AWARDS: 6 annually.

APPLICATION INFORMATION:
Established nomination and selection procedures allow each federal department,

independent agency and office in the Executive Branch to identify employees who have provided outstanding service to the public or otherwise contributed noteworthy achievements in the fields recognized by the GEICO Awards.
Deadline: December 31. Announcements: July 1.

ADDRESS INQUIRIES TO:
Samantha Abrams
Federal Program Administrator/Program Coordinator
(See address above.)

*SPECIAL STIPULATIONS:
Nominees must be full-time or retired federal employees.

GRADUATE EDUCATION OPPORTUNITY PROGRAM   [1053]
Michigan State University
The Graduate School, 116 Linton Hall
East Lansing, MI 48824-1044
(517) 353-3262
Fax: (517) 353-3355

WEB SITE ADDRESS:
www.grad.msu.edu

FOUNDED: 1855

AREAS OF INTEREST:
Higher education.

NAME(S) OF PROGRAMS:
● **Academic Achievement Graduate Assistantships**
● **Education Opportunity Program**
● **University Distinguished Fellowships**
● **University Enrichment Fellowships**

TYPE:
Assistantships; Fellowships.

YEAR PROGRAM STARTED: 1970

PURPOSE:
To increase participation by all U.S. students in graduate programs leading to advanced degrees in fields that do not yet reflect the inclusive diversity of the U.S. population; to enhance their retention and degree completion.

LEGAL BASIS:
University.

ELIGIBILITY:
Candidates are considered for the Academic Achievement Graduate Assistantship if nominated by the academic unit of the graduate program. Candidates for the Education Opportunity Fellowship may apply directly upon admission into a graduate program.

Candidate must be admitted to or enrolled in a graduate/professional degree-granting program at Michigan State University. Some programs require a student to demonstrate financial need. To be considered for financial support under the Graduate Education Opportunity Programs (GEOP), all recipients must be able to prove U.S. citizenship or permanent residency. Funding based on financial need.

University Distinguished Fellowship and University Enrichment Fellowship are merit-based recruitment fellowships.

GEOGRAPHIC RESTRICTIONS:
United States.

FINANCIAL DATA:
Amount of support per award: Academic Achievement Graduate Assistantship (AAGA): Level I, half-time, $11,988 to $20,790, plus nine credits (Fall/Spring), including health care; Education Opportunity Program (EOP): $1,500 per semester plus $400 per dependent for each semester; University Distinguished Fellowships (UDF) and University Enrichment Fellowships (UEF): $24,000, plus six to 10 credits (Fall/Spring) or three to five credits (Summer), including health care.
Total amount of support: Education Opportunity Program: $250,000.

APPLICATION INFORMATION:
Duration: Up to five years.
Deadline: Academic Achievement Graduate Assistantship and University Distinguished and Enrichment Fellowships: December 31. Education Opportunity Program: Spring;

ADDRESS INQUIRIES TO:
Karen Klomparens
Dean of the Graduate School
Associate Provost for Graduate Education
(See address above.)

*SPECIAL STIPULATIONS:
Students must be enrolled in a graduate/professional program at Michigan State University.

GSBA SCHOLARSHIP FUND   [1054]
400 East Pine Street, Suite 322
Seattle, WA 98122
(206) 363-9188
Fax: (206) 568-3123

E-MAIL ADDRESS:
jessicaw@thegsba.org

WEB SITE ADDRESS:
www.thegsba.org

FOUNDED: 1981

AREAS OF INTEREST:
Leadership and service in the gay and lesbian community.

NAME(S) OF PROGRAMS:
● **GSBA Scholarships**

TYPE:
Awards/prizes; Scholarships. Scholarships are intended for undergraduate college, creative study, vocational training and postsecondary education.

YEAR PROGRAM STARTED: 1991

PURPOSE:
To enhance self-esteem, recognize diversity, support leadership development and promote sensitivity to human rights.

LEGAL BASIS:
Business association.

ELIGIBILITY:
Applicants must demonstrate academic ability, significant need, a commitment to diversity and potential leadership in the lesbian, gay, bisexual & transgender community, and must be a resident of Washington State.

Scholarships are available for:
(1) gay, lesbian, bisexual, transgender and allied students;
(2) LGBTQA students of color;
(3) students raised by lesbian or gay parents and;
(4) potential leaders in the sexual minority community.

GEOGRAPHIC RESTRICTIONS:
Washington State.

FINANCIAL DATA:
Amount of support per award: $2,500 to $10,000.
Total amount of support: $135,000.

NUMBER OF APPLICANTS MOST RECENT YEAR:
400.

NUMBER OF AWARDS: 35 for the year 2010.

APPLICATION INFORMATION:
Applicants must submit the online application form, letters of recommendation, transcript and an essay.
Duration: One-time award; can reapply as long as an undergraduate student.
Deadline: January 31.

PUBLICATIONS:
Guide/Directory, business listing and resources; *Perspective*, monthly newsletter.

IRS IDENTIFICATION NUMBER: 94-3138514

STAFF:
Louise Chernin, Executive Director
April Thanos, Program Manager
Jerome Bader, Sales/Marketing
Rachel Chernin, Operations Manager
Joshua Rumley, Office and Events Coordinator
Jessica Swetin, Membership Services Coordinator
Jessica Wootten, Development Associate and Scholarship Manager

BOARD OF DIRECTORS:
Roen Ako
Allan Aquila
Bob Blackburn
Kevin Bohnert
Rachael Brister
Amy Burdick
Teri Burnett
Gary Collins
Martha Davis
Glenda Downs
Lori Dugdale
Mitch Evans
Louis Haselett
Frank Huguenin
Kristine Messick
Joe Mirabella
Rene Neidhart
Martha Norberg
Victoria Odell
Nikki Plaid
Mark Rosen
Kurt Sarchet
Mona Smith
Michael Staeb
Kirsten Weiss
John Wong

ADDRESS INQUIRIES TO:
Jessica Wootten
Development Associate
and Scholarship Manager
(See address above.)

THE DONALD D. HAMMILL FOUNDATION   [1055]
8700 Shoal Creek Boulevard
Austin, TX 78757-6897
Fax: (512) 451-1888

E-MAIL ADDRESS:
jvoress@hammillfoundation.org

WEB SITE ADDRESS:
www.hammillfoundation.org

FOUNDED: 1987

AREAS OF INTEREST:
Financially disadvantaged, disabled people, chronically ill and aged.

NAME(S) OF PROGRAMS:
- **Organizational Grants**

TYPE:
General operating grants; Project/program grants. Fund nonprofit organizations that provide direct services to meet basic needs of clients in the Austin community.

YEAR PROGRAM STARTED: 1987

PURPOSE:
To improve the quality of life for people who have disabilities or who are financially disadvantaged, including those who are indigent, chronically ill, and aged.

LEGAL BASIS:
Private foundation.

GEOGRAPHIC RESTRICTIONS:
Austin, Texas.

FINANCIAL DATA:
Amount of support per award: Up to $10,000.
Total amount of support: $257,853 for the year 2009.

NUMBER OF APPLICANTS MOST RECENT YEAR:
Approximately 45 for the year 2009.

NUMBER OF AWARDS: 38 for the year 2009.

REPRESENTATIVE AWARDS:
$5,000 to Arc of Texas; $10,000 to Capital Area Food Bank; $6,838 to Gray Panthers of Austin.

APPLICATION INFORMATION:
Guidelines available at the web site.
Deadline: March 15.

PUBLICATIONS:
Application guidelines.

IRS IDENTIFICATION NUMBER: 74-2499947

OFFICERS:
Donald D. Hammill, Ed.D., President
Stephen C. Larsen, Ed.D., Vice President
Judith K. Voress, Ph.D., Executive Director
Cindy Thigpen, Treasurer
Nils Pearson, Ph.D., Secretary

BOARD OF TRUSTEES:
Donald D. Hammill, Ed.D.
Stephen C. Larsen, Ed.D.
Phyllis L. Newcomer, Ed.D.
Jim Patton, Ed.D.
Nils Pearson, Ph.D.
Judith K. Voress, Ph.D.

ADDRESS INQUIRIES TO:
Judith K. Voress, Ph.D., Executive Director
(See address above.)

*SPECIAL STIPULATIONS:
Programs are only funded locally in Austin, Texas. The Foundation does not fund directly to individuals.

HEBREW IMMIGRANT AID SOCIETY (HIAS)   [1056]
333 Seventh Avenue, 16th Floor
New York, NY 10001-5004
(212) 613-1358
Fax: (212) 967-4483

E-MAIL ADDRESS:
scholarship@hias.org

WEB SITE ADDRESS:
www.hias.org/scholarships

FOUNDED: 1880

AREAS OF INTEREST:
Worldwide Jewish migration agency.

CONSULTING OR VOLUNTEER SERVICES:
All services in the U.S. and abroad relevant to rescue, migration and initial resettlement of Jewish refugees. State of Israel excepted.

NAME(S) OF PROGRAMS:
- **HIAS U.S. Scholarship Competition**

TYPE:
Awards/prizes; Scholarships. Cash awards made annually to refugees assisted by HIAS in recognition of their academic excellence, financial need and community service.

YEAR PROGRAM STARTED: 1974

PURPOSE:
To support students pursuing a postsecondary education at a college, graduate school or technical school.

LEGAL BASIS:
Incorporated in New York state.

ELIGIBILITY:
Available only to refugees who were assisted by HIAS to immigrate to the U.S. and are pursuing postsecondary education. Applicants must demonstrate at least one year's attendance in an American high school or college. There are no restrictions on age or sex.

GEOGRAPHIC RESTRICTIONS:
United States.

FINANCIAL DATA:
Amount of support per award: Average: $4,000.
Total amount of support: Approximately $250,000.

APPLICATION INFORMATION:
Duration: One-time grant. Past recipients may reapply.
Deadline: February or March.

ADDRESS INQUIRIES TO:
HIAS Scholarship Department
(See address above.)

WILLIAM G. AND MYRTLE E. HESS CHARITABLE TRUST   [1057]
c/o JPMorgan Chase Bank, NA
1116 West Long Lake
Bloomfield Hills, MI 48302
(248) 645-7308
Fax: (248) 645-5742

E-MAIL ADDRESS:
nayda.schwartz@jpmorgan.com

WEB SITE ADDRESS:
www.jpmorgan.com/onlinegrants

FOUNDED: 1985

AREAS OF INTEREST:
Catholic charitable organizations located in Oakland County, MI; Catholic charitable, educational and scientific objectives.

TYPE:
Capital grants; Development grants; Endowments; General operating grants; Project/program grants.

YEAR PROGRAM STARTED: 1985

PURPOSE:
To provide funds in perpetuity for charitable purposes.

LEGAL BASIS:
Private foundation.

ELIGIBILITY:
Limited to Catholic organizations with charitable, educational and scientific objectives. Particular preference being given to such objectives within the confines of Waterford and White Lake Townships.

GEOGRAPHIC RESTRICTIONS:
Oakland County, Michigan.

FINANCIAL DATA:
Amount of support per award: $2,500 to $25,000.

NUMBER OF APPLICANTS MOST RECENT YEAR:
28.

NUMBER OF AWARDS: 26.

APPLICATION INFORMATION:
Only online applications are accepted.
Duration: One year. Renewals possible.
Deadline: April 30.

ADDRESS INQUIRIES TO:
Bonnie S. Kopp
(See address above.)

THE HIGHER EDUCATION STUDENT ASSISTANCE AUTHORITY
P.O. Box 540
Trenton, NJ 08625
(609) 588-3266
(800) 792-8670
Fax: (609) 588-2390

WEB SITE ADDRESS:
www.hesaa.org

TYPE:
Grants-in-aid. The Higher Education Student Assistance Authority (HESAA) is a New Jersey authority that provides students and families with the financial and informational resources for students to pursue their education beyond high school. With roots dating back to 1959, HESAA's singular focus has always been to benefit the students it serves. HESAA provides state supplemental loans, grants and scholarships. HESAA also administers the state's college savings plan.

Educational Opportunity Fund Grants (EOF) provide financial aid to eligible students from educationally and economically disadvantaged backgrounds at participating in-state institutions.

See entry 1809 for full listing.

HISPANIC COLLEGE FUND
1300 L Street, N.W.
Suite 975
Washington, DC 20005
(202) 296-5400
(800) 644-4223
Fax: (202) 296-3774

E-MAIL ADDRESS:
hcf-info@hispanicfund.org

WEB SITE ADDRESS:
www.hispanicfund.org

TYPE:
Scholarships. Merit and need-based scholarships to Latino students.

See entry 1813 for full listing.

IMMUNE DEFICIENCY FOUNDATION   [1058]
40 West Chesapeake Avenue
Suite 308
Towson, MD 21204
(800) 296-4433
Fax: (410) 321-9165

E-MAIL ADDRESS:
dgill@primaryimmune.org

WEB SITE ADDRESS:
www.primaryimmune.org

FOUNDED: 1980

AREAS OF INTEREST:
Immunodeficiency diseases.

TYPE:
Scholarships.

YEAR PROGRAM STARTED: 1986

ELIGIBILITY:
Open to those with diagnosis of primary immunodeficiency that are attending undergraduate college. Must be resident of the U.S.

GEOGRAPHIC RESTRICTIONS:
United States.

FINANCIAL DATA:
Amount of support per award: $500 to $1,000.

NUMBER OF AWARDS: 60.

APPLICATION INFORMATION:
Contact the Foundation for application procedures.
Duration: Renewable yearly based on financial need and academic participation.
Deadline: March 31.

ADDRESS INQUIRIES TO:
Diana Gill
Director of Program Services
(See address above.)

INSTITUTE OF INDUSTRIAL ENGINEERS (IIE)
3577 Parkway Lane, Suite 200
Norcross, GA 30092
(770) 449-0461
Fax: (770) 441-3295

E-MAIL ADDRESS:
bcameron@iienet.org

WEB SITE ADDRESS:
www.iienet.org

TYPE:
Fellowships; Scholarships. The Institute supports the advancement of engineering education and research through scholarships and fellowships to recognize and support these types of endeavors.

See entry 2823 for full listing.

THE JAPANESE AMERICAN CITIZENS LEAGUE (JACL)
New York JACL
75 Grove Street
Bloomfield, NJ 07003
(973) 680-1441

E-MAIL ADDRESS:
lckimura@att.net

WEB SITE ADDRESS:
www.jacl.org

TYPE:
Awards/prizes. Biennial playwright award.
See entry 568 for full listing.

JEWISH COMMUNITY FOUNDATION OF LOS ANGELES
6505 Wilshire Boulevard
Suite 1200
Los Angeles, CA 90048
(323) 761-8700
Fax: (323) 761-8666

E-MAIL ADDRESS:
grants@jewishfoundationla.org

WEB SITE ADDRESS:
www.jewishfoundationla.org

TYPE:
Awards/prizes; Capital grants; Project/program grants; Seed money grants.

See entry 1391 for full listing.

THE JOSEPH P. KENNEDY, JR. FOUNDATION   [1059]
1133 19th Street, N.W.
12th Floor
Washington, DC 20036-3604
(202) 393-1250
Fax: (202) 824-0351

E-MAIL ADDRESS:
eidelman@jpkf.org

WEB SITE ADDRESS:
www.jpkf.org

FOUNDED: 1946

AREAS OF INTEREST:
Programs and services that benefit persons with mental retardation and their families.

CONSULTING OR VOLUNTEER SERVICES:
Consultation to schools, school systems and community programs.

NAME(S) OF PROGRAMS:
- **Public Policy Fellowships in the Field of Mental Retardation**
- **Research and Development Grants in the Field of Mental Retardation**

TYPE:
Demonstration grants; Fellowships; Project/program grants; Research grants; Seed money grants; Technical assistance; Training grants. The Grants program provides support for research into the causes and amelioration of mental retardation and for unique and innovative programs for the mentally retarded. The Foundation is interested in providing seed money for model programs that will serve as agents of change in education, treatment, health and well-being of individuals with mental retardation.

Public Policy Fellowships in the Field of Mental Retardation is a program that supports one or two future national leaders in the field of mental retardation for one-year work experiences in Washington, DC.

PURPOSE:
To support innovative programs related to services and supports for persons with mental retardation and their families.

LEGAL BASIS:
Tax-exempt private foundation.

ELIGIBILITY:
The Foundation makes grants only to tax-exempt organizations, not individuals. It

does not fund capital costs or costs of equipment for projects, nor provide support for services or general operating expenses for agencies and programs.

The Foundation only funds innovative projects which are not supported elsewhere by public funds and is most interested in providing seed money for projects that can be replicated elsewhere and that will have regional and national influence on policy.

FINANCIAL DATA:
Distributable income approximately $2,400,000 per year. Ongoing projects use great bulk of this income; hence, ability to take on new financial obligations is strictly limited.

Amount of support per award: $15,000 to $60,000 for up to three years.

NUMBER OF APPLICANTS MOST RECENT YEAR:
100.

NUMBER OF AWARDS: 6 to 12.

APPLICATION INFORMATION:
Applications should be directed to the Foundation in the form of a concept letter of intent that includes a brief description of the proposed project, a budget, qualifications of personnel involved and specific goals of the project. If the proposal is considered eligible for possible funding, the Foundation will subsequently request a full proposal. The Foundation does not consider unsolicited proposals.

Duration: One to three years.

Deadline: November 1.

PUBLICATIONS:
Application guidelines.

ADDRESS INQUIRIES TO:
Steve Eidelman, Executive Director
(See address above.)

*SPECIAL STIPULATIONS:
Funding is restricted to programs benefitting persons with mental retardation and their families. Funding is awarded to organizations, not individuals.

MARCUS AND THERESA LEVIE EDUCATION FUND

Jewish Vocational Service
216 West Jackson Boulevard, Suite 700
Chicago, IL 60606-6921
(312) 673-3444
Fax: (312) 553-5544
TTY: (312) 444-2877

E-MAIL ADDRESS:
jvsscholarship@jvschicago.org

WEB SITE ADDRESS:
www.jvschicago.org

TYPE:
Awards/prizes; Scholarships. Awards to individuals for the academic year.

See entry 1831 for full listing.

THE LUCIUS N. LITTAUER FOUNDATION, INC. [1060]

60 East 42nd Street, Suite 4600
New York, NY 10165
(212) 697-2677

FOUNDED: 1929

AREAS OF INTEREST:
Scholarly research and publications in Jewish Studies, public service, New York City parks, etc.

TYPE:
Challenge/matching grants; Conferences/seminars; Endowments; Matching gifts; Project/program grants; Research grants; Travel grants. Judaica Book Funds. Publication subventions.

YEAR PROGRAM STARTED: 1929

PURPOSE:
To help support researchers working in the area of Jewish history and related studies.

LEGAL BASIS:
Independent foundation.

ELIGIBILITY:
Funds are awarded to nonprofit institutions. No grants to individuals.

FINANCIAL DATA:
Amount of support per award: $3,000 to $5,000 average.

Total amount of support: $1,860,495 for the year 2009.

NUMBER OF AWARDS: 221 grant awards for the year 2008.

APPLICATION INFORMATION:
Application includes a full description of project, budget request, curriculum vitae, timetable for competition, institution which will administer grant without deductions and contact person.

Duration: Varies. Renewal possible.

PUBLICATIONS:
Guidelines.

IRS IDENTIFICATION NUMBER: 13-1688027

TRUSTEES:
William Lee Frost, President
Peter J. Soloman, Vice President
Noah Perlman, Treasurer and Secretary
Charles Berlin
Berthald Bilski
Mark A. Bilski
Robert D. Frost
George Harris
Henry A. Lowet
Geula R. Solomon

STAFF:
William Lee Frost, President

ADDRESS INQUIRIES TO:
William Lee Frost, President
(See address above.)

LUSO-AMERICAN EDUCATION FOUNDATION

7080 Dolon Way
Suite 200
Dublin, CA 94568
(925) 828-3883
Fax: (925) 828-3883

E-MAIL ADDRESS:
education@luso-american.org

WEB SITE ADDRESS:
www.luso-american.org

TYPE:
Scholarships.

See entry 694 for full listing.

MARINE BIOLOGICAL LABORATORY

Education Office
7 MBL Street
Woods Hole, MA 02543
(508) 289-7173
Fax: (508) 289-7934

E-MAIL ADDRESS:
fellows@mbl.edu

WEB SITE ADDRESS:
www.mbl.edu

TYPE:
Research grants.

See entry 2289 for full listing.

THURGOOD MARSHALL COLLEGE FUND/AMERICAN INTELLECTUAL PROPERTY LAW EDUCATION FOUNDATION

80 Maiden Lane, Suite 2204
New York, NY 10038
(212) 573-8888
Fax: (212) 573-8497

E-MAIL ADDRESS:
tamekia.jackson@tmcfund.org

WEB SITE ADDRESS:
www.thurgoodmarshallfund.org
www.aiplef.org

TYPE:
Scholarships. Program for underrepresented minority students who intend to enter the intellectual property law field, to attend law school.

See entry 2108 for full listing.

MAURICE J. MASSERINI CHARITABLE TRUST [1061]

c/o Wells Fargo Private Bank
4475 Executive Drive, Suite 100
San Diego, CA 92121
(858) 597-4328
Fax: (858) 597-4360

E-MAIL ADDRESS:
dschmutz@wellsfargo.com

WEB SITE ADDRESS:
www.grantsrequests.com

AREAS OF INTEREST:
Underprivileged children and the elderly.

TYPE:
Project/program grants.

ELIGIBILITY:
Eligible organizations must be IRS 501(c)(3) tax-exempt and be located in San Diego County, CA. Start-up organizations or salaries are generally not supported.

GEOGRAPHIC RESTRICTIONS:
San Diego County, California.

FINANCIAL DATA:
Amount of support per award: Generally $5,000 to $25,000.

NUMBER OF APPLICANTS MOST RECENT YEAR:
200.

NUMBER OF AWARDS: More than 60 per year.

APPLICATION INFORMATION:
Applications are submitted through an online application process.

Duration: One year. Renewable by reapplication.

Deadline: April 30, August 31 and December 31.

ADDRESS INQUIRIES TO:
M. David Schmutz, Senior Vice President and Wealth Advisor
(See address above.)

MEDICAL LIBRARY ASSOCIATION [1062]

65 East Wacker Place
Suite 1900
Chicago, IL 60601-7298
(312) 419-9094
Fax: (312) 419-8950

E-MAIL ADDRESS:
mlapd2@mlahq.org

WEB SITE ADDRESS:
www.mlanet.org

FOUNDED: 1898

AREAS OF INTEREST:
Health sciences librarianship.

NAME(S) OF PROGRAMS:
● **MLA Scholarship for Minority Students**

TYPE:
Awards/prizes; Scholarships. Awarded for study in health sciences librarianship.

YEAR PROGRAM STARTED: 1964

PURPOSE:
To contribute to the support of minority individuals who are qualified to make a contribution to health sciences librarianship.

LEGAL BASIS:
Nonprofit.

ELIGIBILITY:
Applicant must be:
(1) a member of a minority group. A minority group is defined as African-American, Asian, Hispanic, Native American or Pacific Islander;
(2) entering an ALA-accredited graduate library school or must have completed no more than half of his or her graduate program at the time the award is made and;
(3) a citizen of or have permanent residence status in the U.S. or Canada.

A past recipient of the MLA Scholarship for Minority Students is ineligible.

FINANCIAL DATA:
Amount of support per award: Up to $5,000.

NUMBER OF AWARDS: 1 per year.

APPLICATION INFORMATION:
Applicant must submit, via postal mail, the following:
(1) nine copies of the completed application;
(2) two to three letters of reference from persons not related to the applicant who are knowledgeable about the applicant's character, education and abilities;
(3) official transcript from each college or university attended, sent directly from the respective institution that grants either Baccalaureate degree or library study degree and;
(4) statement of career objectives.
Duration: One year.
Deadline: December 1.

EXECUTIVE DIRECTOR:
Carla J. Funk

ADDRESS INQUIRIES TO:
Lisa C. Fried, Coordinator
Research and Professional Recognition
(See address above.)

MITSUBISHI ELECTRIC AMERICA FOUNDATION

1560 Wilson Boulevard
Suite 1150
Arlington, VA 22209
(703) 276-8240
Fax: (703) 276-8260

E-MAIL ADDRESS:
mea.foundation@meus.mea.com

WEB SITE ADDRESS:
www.meaf.org

TYPE:
Demonstration grants; General operating grants; Internships; Matching gifts; Project/program grants; Seed money grants; Technical assistance; Training grants. Grants are offered to make a better world for all by helping young people with disabilities to maximize their potential and participation in society.

See entry 1717 for full listing.

NATIONAL ACTION COUNCIL FOR MINORITIES IN ENGINEERING, INC. (NACME) [1063]

440 Hamilton Avenue
Suite 302
White Plains, NY 10601-1813
(914) 539-4010
Fax: (914) 539-4032

E-MAIL ADDRESS:
scholars@nacme.org

WEB SITE ADDRESS:
www.nacme.org

FOUNDED: 1974

CONSULTING OR VOLUNTEER SERVICES:
NACME communicates and cooperates with the precollege, college and industry communities that are involved in the minority engineering effort.

TYPE:
Block grants; Endowments; Fellowships; Scholarships. NACME encourages students to consider engineering as a career and to pursue the requisite preparation in mathematics and science. It motivates high school students and channels them to engineering schools and provides scholarship support and leadership development seminars to its university scholars. The retention of minority students in engineering is a priority issue for NACME.

YEAR PROGRAM STARTED: 1975

PURPOSE:
To significantly increase the number of historically underrepresented minorities (African American, Mexican American, Puerto Rican and American Indian) who earn Bachelor's degrees in engineering.

LEGAL BASIS:
Nonprofit organization incorporated in New York.

ELIGIBILITY:
Participating schools nominate students to apply. The student must be a U.S. citizen or permanent resident and must also be a member of one of the four groups historically underrepresented in engineering.

GEOGRAPHIC RESTRICTIONS:
United States.

FINANCIAL DATA:
Amount of support per award: Up to $2,500 per student per year.
Total amount of support: Approximately $1,300,000.

NUMBER OF AWARDS: Approximately 1,000 annually.

APPLICATION INFORMATION:
Duration: Students selected by participating schools for NACME awards will be funded until graduation or a maximum of five years, assuming they maintain their eligibility.
Deadline: Varies.

BOARD OF DIRECTORS:
Dr. Irving Pressley McPhail, President and Chief Executive Officer, NACME, Inc.
Eileen Campbell, Chairperson
Mary Adamo
Rod C. Adkins
Mark W. Albers
Dr. James H. Ammons
Michael J. Barber
John E. Bethancourt
Erwin W. Bieber
Mark R. Bly
Curtis Brunson
Gary M. Budzinski
Arthur P. Burson
Howard D. Elias
Felicia J. Fields
William P. Gipson
William Hoffmann
Jerry M. Hultin
Dr. Alexis C. Livanos
John Lucas
Michele Macauda
John A. MacDonald
Michael L. Marsh
Willie C. Martin
Marilyn Nagel
Diana Natalicio
Anthony Neal-Graves
Douglas M. Owen
Joseph A. Patti
Ramanath I. Ramakrishman
Mark E. Russell
Terry R. Seamons
Randy Stashick
Brigitta Tadmor
Don W. Taylor
John J. Tracy
James C. Vardell, III
Charles M. Vest
Gregory G. Weaver
Michael R. Wilson
John K. Woodworth

ADDRESS INQUIRIES TO:
Melonia Simpson, Program Manager
(See address above.)

*SPECIAL STIPULATIONS:
Grants are given directly to universities. Individuals cannot apply.

NATIONAL ASSOCIATION OF HISPANIC JOURNALISTS [1064]

National Press Building
529 14th Street, N.W., Suite 1000
Washington, DC 20045-2001
(202) 662-7145
Fax: (202) 662-7144

E-MAIL ADDRESS:
iroman@nahj.org

WEB SITE ADDRESS:
www.nahj.org

AREAS OF INTEREST:
English or Spanish language print, photo, broadcast or online journalism.

NAME(S) OF PROGRAMS:
● **Ford Motor Scholarship**
● **Gannett Foundation Scholarship**
● **NAHJ General Scholarships (Ruben Salazar Fund)**
● **Soledad O'Brien Scholarship**

- **Geraldo Rivera Scholarship**
- **Michael and Maggie Rodriguez Scholarship**
- **Maria Elena Salinas Scholarship**

TYPE:
Awards/prizes; Internships; Scholarships.

YEAR PROGRAM STARTED: 1986

PURPOSE:
To encourage the study and practice of journalism and mass communications by Hispanics.

ELIGIBILITY:
Open to high school seniors, college undergraduates and first-year graduate students pursuing careers in print, photo, broadcast or online journalism.

Gannett Foundation Scholarship applicant must be Florida International University student.

GEOGRAPHIC RESTRICTIONS:
United States and Puerto Rico.

FINANCIAL DATA:
Amount of support per award: Ford Motor Scholarship: Up to $3,000; NAHJ General Scholarships: $1,000 to $2,000; Gannett Foundation Scholarship, Soledad O'Brien Scholarship, Geraldo Rivera Scholarship, Michael and Maggie Rodriguez Scholarship and Maria Elena Salinas Scholarship: $5,000 per award.

NUMBER OF APPLICANTS MOST RECENT YEAR:
Approximately 230.

NUMBER OF AWARDS: 50 scholarships.

APPLICATION INFORMATION:
Scholarship applications are available online in January of each year.
Duration: One to three years.
Deadline: March.

IRS IDENTIFICATION NUMBER: 95-3927141

ADDRESS INQUIRIES TO:
Scholarships Department
(See address above.)

NATIONAL CENTER ON MINORITY HEALTH AND HEALTH DISPARITIES [1065]
6707 Democracy Boulevard, Suite 800
MSC 5465
Bethesda, MD 20892-5465
(301) 402-1366
Fax: (301) 480-4049

E-MAIL ADDRESS:
ncmhdinfo@od.nih.gov

WEB SITE ADDRESS:
www.ncmhd.nih.gov

AREAS OF INTEREST:
Minority opportunities in biomedical and behavioral science.

NAME(S) OF PROGRAMS:
- **Minority Health and Health Disparities International Research Training Grant (MIRT)**

TYPE:
Research grants; Training grants. Awards to U.S. colleges and universities to encourage students to pursue careers and degrees in the biological sciences by broadening their undergraduate and graduate education through international experiences.

Award provides support for undergraduates to undertake research and course work for 10 to 12 weeks during the summer or one semester during the academic year.

YEAR PROGRAM STARTED: 1993

PURPOSE:
To provide research training opportunities for minority undergraduate students, minority graduate students and minority faculty members in biomedical and behavioral research; to support faculty members to conduct independent research abroad and to serve as mentors to students abroad.

ELIGIBILITY:
Minority participants must be from underrepresented minority groups including African Americans, Native Americans, Hispanic Americans, Alaskan Natives and Pacific Islanders.

Applicants must be undergraduate students pursuing life science curricula, students pursuing doctoral degrees in the biomedical or behavioral sciences and/or faculty members in the biomedical and behavioral sciences.

GEOGRAPHIC RESTRICTIONS:
United States and its territories.

FINANCIAL DATA:
Amount of support per award: Up to $225,000.
Total amount of support: Approximately $5,000,000.

NUMBER OF AWARDS: Up to 24.

APPLICATION INFORMATION:
Duration: Up to four years.
Deadline: Varies.

PUBLICATIONS:
Program announcement; guidelines.

ADDRESS INQUIRIES TO:
Nathaniel Stinson, Ph.D., Program Officer
Division of Research and Training Activities
(See address above.)

NATIONAL FEDERATION OF THE BLIND [1066]
200 East Wells Street
Baltimore, MD 21230
(410) 659-9314 ext. 2415

E-MAIL ADDRESS:
scholarships@nfb.org

WEB SITE ADDRESS:
www.nfb.org/scholarships

FOUNDED: 1940

AREAS OF INTEREST:
Improving the quality of life for blind persons by creating opportunity and combating discrimination.

CONSULTING OR VOLUNTEER SERVICES:
Major programs in scholarships, promoting employment for the blind, civil rights litigation, helping parents of blind children, public education, etc.

NAME(S) OF PROGRAMS:
- **National Federation of the Blind Scholarship Program**

TYPE:
Conferences/seminars; Scholarships. Awarded on the basis of academic excellence and service to the community. Provides a one-time grant plus a continuing program of mentors and seminars for blind college students.

PURPOSE:
To create opportunities for all blind persons.

LEGAL BASIS:
Nonprofit, tax-deductible, nationwide membership organization of the blind.

ELIGIBILITY:
Applicants must be legally blind and pursuing or planning to pursue a full-time postsecondary course of study in the upcoming fall semester in the U.S. One scholarship, however, may be given to a full-time employee also attending school part-time. In addition, some scholarships have been further restricted by the donor. Recipients of Federation scholarships need not be members of the National Federation of the Blind.

GEOGRAPHIC RESTRICTIONS:
United States and Puerto Rico.

FINANCIAL DATA:
Amount of support per award: $3,000 to $12,000; other gifts vary in value.

NUMBER OF APPLICANTS MOST RECENT YEAR:
470.

NUMBER OF AWARDS: 30 (1 $12,000 scholarship, 1 $10,000 scholarship, 2 $7,000 scholarships, 4 $5,000 scholarships and 22 $3,000 scholarships).

APPLICATION INFORMATION:
Applicants should submit a completed application plus personal letter of goals and aspirations, two letters of recommendation, current transcript from institution now attending and transcripts from all other postsecondary institutions attended (if none, send high school transcript) and letter from state president of the National Federation of the Blind or a designee. Address of Federation president in your state furnished upon request. High school seniors applying must submit Score Reports.
Duration: One year. Renewals possible upon reapplication.
Deadline: Scholarship applications are accepted from November 1 of previous year to March 31 of the year in which the scholarship is to be awarded. Notification early May.

ADDRESS INQUIRIES TO:
Scholarship Committee
(See address above.)

*SPECIAL STIPULATIONS:
Applicants must be legally blind in both eyes.

THE NATIONAL GEM CONSORTIUM [1067]
1430 Duke Street
Alexandria, VA 22314
(703) 562-3646
Fax: (202) 207-2518

E-MAIL ADDRESS:
info@gemfellowship.org

WEB SITE ADDRESS:
www.gemfellowship.org

FOUNDED: 1976

AREAS OF INTEREST:
Engineering at the Master's and Doctorate levels and science at the Doctorate level.

CONSULTING OR VOLUNTEER SERVICES:
Mentor/protege training, graduate study preparedness training, success training, programs and publications designed to promote graduate education in engineering and science.

NAME(S) OF PROGRAMS:
- The GEM M.S. Engineering Fellowship
- The GEM Ph.D. Engineering Fellowship
- The GEM Ph.D. Science Fellowship
- Grad Lab
- Graduate and Faculty Development Program

TYPE:
Conferences/seminars; Fellowships; Internships; Matching gifts. All-expense fellowship for graduate study (tuition and stipend) and paid summer work experience in a scientific or engineering environment.

YEAR PROGRAM STARTED: 1976

PURPOSE:
To increase the number of minorities with graduate degrees in engineering and science.

LEGAL BASIS:
Incorporated in the State of Indiana; 501(c)(3) tax-exempt.

ELIGIBILITY:
Must be a U.S. citizen or permanent resident and an American Indian, Black American, Mexican American, Puerto Rican, or other Hispanic American with a minimum junior year status.

FINANCIAL DATA:
Amount of support per award: Master's-level study in engineering: tuition and fees, plus a $10,000 stipend; Doctorate-level studies in engineering or science: tuition and fees, plus a $14,000 stipend. Master's-level students also are assigned to a paid summer internship.
Total amount of support: Varies.

NUMBER OF APPLICANTS MOST RECENT YEAR: 800.

NUMBER OF AWARDS: 160 for the year 2010.

APPLICATION INFORMATION:
Three letters of recommendation, GRE scores, and transcript of all college work.
Duration: Average three semesters or four quarters for Master's; five years renewable for Doctorate.
Deadline: November 15. Announcement March 15.

PUBLICATIONS:
Annual report; application brochure; *Graduate Financial Resources in Engineering and Science for Minority Students*; *Making the Grade in Graduate School: Survival Strategy 101*; *Successfully Negotiating the Graduate School Process: A Guide for Minority Students*; Minority Student Graduate School Information Kit; *Your Internship Is as Good as You Make It: A Practical Guide to Student Internships*; *Transitioning New Hires Into the Workplace: The Strategy of Mentoring*.

OFFICERS:
Alfred Grasso, President

ADDRESS INQUIRIES TO:
Valerie Washington, Coordinator of Information
(See address above.)

NATIONAL INSTITUTE OF GENERAL MEDICAL SCIENCES
National Institutes of Health
45 Center Drive, MSC 6200
Bethesda, MD 20892-6200
(301) 496-7301
Fax: (301) 402-0224

E-MAIL ADDRESS:
info@nigms.nih.gov

WEB SITE ADDRESS:
www.nigms.nih.gov

TYPE:
Conferences/seminars; Development grants; Fellowships; Internships; Project/program grants; Research grants; Technical assistance; Training grants; Travel grants; Visiting scholars; Research contracts. Grants to support research on the structure and function of cells and cell organelles. Research to gain knowledge that will lead to the prevention, therapy and control of genetic diseases, as well as research to increase knowledge of drug action in order to increase safety of administration and diminish toxicity. Grants also given for research in biophysics and the physiological sciences and in certain clinical areas, particularly anesthesiology and trauma and burns. All of the research programs also support research training.

In addition, the Institute has special research and research training programs designed to increase the numbers and capabilities of minority scientists engaged in biomedical research.

See entry 2442 for full listing.

NATIONAL INSTITUTE OF GENERAL MEDICAL SCIENCES
Division of Minority Opportunities in Research
45 Center Drive, Room 2AS-37
MSC 6200
Bethesda, MD 20892-6200
(301) 594-3900
Fax: (301) 480-2753

E-MAIL ADDRESS:
zlotnikh@nigms.nih.gov

WEB SITE ADDRESS:
www.nigms.nih.gov

TYPE:
Development grants; Research grants; Technical assistance. Grants to assist eligible institutions to strengthen the institutions' biomedical research capabilities and provide opportunities to students to engage in biomedical or behavioral research and other activities in preparation for Ph.D. training in these areas.

See entry 2443 for full listing.

THE NATIONAL ITALIAN AMERICAN FOUNDATION
1860 19th Street, N.W.
Washington, DC 20009-5501
(202) 939-3118
Fax: (202) 483-2618

E-MAIL ADDRESS:
scholarships@niaf.org

WEB SITE ADDRESS:
www.niaf.org/scholarships

TYPE:
Scholarships. The National Italian American Foundation (NIAF) will award scholarships and grants to outstanding students for use during the following academic year. The awards will be made on the basis of academic merit and divided between two groups of students.

See entry 1843 for full listing.

NATIONAL LESBIAN & GAY JOURNALISTS ASSOCIATION   [1068]
2120 L Street, N.W.
Suite 850
Washington, DC 20037
(202) 588-9888

E-MAIL ADDRESS:
info@nlgja.org

WEB SITE ADDRESS:
www.nlgja.org

FOUNDED: 1990

AREAS OF INTEREST:
Journalism.

NAME(S) OF PROGRAMS:
- Journalist of the Year Award
- The LGBT Excellence in Journalism Awards
- Sarah Pettit Memorial Award for Excellence in LGBT Media

TYPE:
Awards/prizes.

YEAR PROGRAM STARTED: 1990

PURPOSE:
To work within the journalism industry to foster fair and accurate coverage of the lesbian, gay, bisexual and transgender community; to oppose workplace bias against all minorities and provide professional development for its members.

FINANCIAL DATA:
Total amount of support: Approximately $25,000 to $30,000 for the year 2010.

NUMBER OF AWARDS: 12.

APPLICATION INFORMATION:
Deadline: End of April.

ADDRESS INQUIRIES TO:
Bach Polakowski
E-mail: bach@nlgja.org

NATIONAL MEDICAL FELLOWSHIPS, INC.
347 Fifth Avenue, Suite 510
New York, NY 10016
(212) 483-8880
Fax: (212) 483-8897

E-MAIL ADDRESS:
nmf1@nmfonline.org

WEB SITE ADDRESS:
www.nmfonline.org

TYPE:
Awards/prizes; Fellowships; Scholarships. In addition to its general scholarship program, NMF administers a number of special award and fellowship programs that recognize and encourage extraordinary accomplishments.

The General Scholarship Program offers need-based awards to students enrolled in the first or second year of medical school.

The Metropolitan Life Foundation Awards for Academic Excellence in Medicine are awarded to students who reside or attend school in designated cities and who demonstrate academic achievement, leadership, and financial need.

The National Medical Association Special Award Programs sponsor annual prizes that recognize achievement among African-American students.

NMF/GE Medical Scholar Program is an international program for 12 fourth-year minority students who demonstrate academic achievement and leadership, and who are selected for a medical elective in West Africa for a two-month period.

The Aura E. Severinghaus Award is presented to a senior of outstanding academic excellence and leadership attending the College of Physicians and Surgeons of Columbia University.

See entry 2449 for full listing.

NATIONAL RESEARCH COUNCIL OF THE NATIONAL ACADEMIES   [1069]

The Fellowship Office-KECK576
500 Fifth Street, N.W.
Washington, DC 20001
(202) 334-2872
Fax: (202) 334-3419

E-MAIL ADDRESS:
infofell@nas.edu

WEB SITE ADDRESS:
www.national-academies.org/fellowships

AREAS OF INTEREST:
Behavioral and social sciences, humanities, engineering, mathematics, physical sciences, biological sciences, (postdoctoral) education and interdisciplinary programs comprised of two or more eligible disciplines.

NAME(S) OF PROGRAMS:
- **Ford Foundation Dissertation Fellowships for Minorities**
- **Ford Foundation Postdoctoral Fellowships for Minorities**
- **Ford Foundation Predoctoral Fellowships for Minorities**

TYPE:
Fellowships. Awards for study in research-based doctoral programs leading to the Ph.D. or Sc.D. degrees, as well as postdoctoral studies.

YEAR PROGRAM STARTED: 1986

PURPOSE:
To increase the presence of underrepresented minorities on the nation's college and university faculties and to encourage students to achieve their full potential as scholars who will inspire others to follow an academic career in teaching and research.

LEGAL BASIS:
Private foundation.

ELIGIBILITY:
Applicants to these Ford Foundation Fellowships must be citizens or nationals of the U.S. at the time of application and must be members of the following minority groups: Alaskan Natives (Eskimo or Aleut), Native American Indians, Black/African Americans, Mexican Americans/Chicanos, Native Pacific Islanders (Polynesian or Micronesian) and Filipino Americans, and Puerto Ricans.

Predoctoral Fellowships are intended for students who plan to work toward the Ph.D. or Sc.D. degree in selected academic disciplines that lead to careers in teaching and research at the college or university level, and who are at or near the beginning of their graduate study or Sc.D. program. They may be college seniors, or individuals who have completed undergraduate study, or who have completed some graduate study, or who have already enrolled in a Ph.D. or Sc.D. program.

Dissertation Fellowships are intended for Ph.D. or Sc.D. degree candidates who have finished all required course work and examinations except for the writing and defense of the dissertation. Fellowship support is intended for the final year of dissertation writing.

Predoctoral and Dissertation Fellowships for Minorities: Persons holding a doctoral degree earned at any time and in any field are not eligible to apply. Applicants must be Ph.D. or Sc.D. degree candidates studying one of the fields in the behavioral sciences, humanities, social sciences, life sciences, chemistry, earth sciences, physics and astronomy, engineering, mathematics, or computer science. They must aspire to a teaching and research career. Awards are not made for work leading to degrees in such areas as business administration and management, health sciences, public health, home economics, library science, speech pathology and audiology, personnel and guidance, social work, fine arts and performing arts and education.

Postdoctoral Fellowships for Minorities: Intended for fellows to engage in a year of postdoctoral research and scholarship in an environment free from the interference of their normal professional duties. Applicants are required to have earned a Ph.D. or Sc.D. degree from a U.S. educational institution within a specified time period. Only those individuals already engaged in a teaching and research career or those planning such a career are eligible to apply in this program. Previous Foundation postdoctoral fellows may not reapply. Awards will be made in research-based areas of the behavioral and social sciences, humanities, engineering, mathematics, physical sciences, life sciences, education, or for interdisciplinary programs composed of two or more eligible disciplines.

FINANCIAL DATA:
Amount of support per award: Dissertation Fellowships: $21,000 for one year and expenses paid to attend one Conference of Ford Fellows; Predoctoral Fellowships: Annual $20,000 stipend, expenses paid to attend at least one Conference of Ford Fellows and $2,000 institutional award to be accepted in lieu of tuition/fees; Postdoctoral Fellowships: $40,000 stipend plus $1,500 employing institution allowance and expenses paid to attend one Conference of Ford Fellows.

COOPERATIVE FUNDING PROGRAMS: Program funded by the Ford Foundation.

NUMBER OF AWARDS: Approximately 60 Predoctoral Fellowships, 40 Dissertation Fellowships, and 30 Postdoctoral Fellowships.

APPLICATION INFORMATION:
Complete eligibility guidelines and application materials are available from the Society.

Duration: Predoctoral Fellowships: Up to three years; Dissertation Fellowships: Nine to 12 months; Postdoctoral Fellowships: Nine or 12 months.

PUBLICATIONS:
Program announcement.

NATIONAL SOCIETY OF HISPANIC MBAS (NSHMBA)   [1070]

1303 Walnut Hill Lane, Suite 100
Irving, TX 75038
(214) 596-9338
(877) 467-4622
Fax: (214) 596-9325

E-MAIL ADDRESS:
scholarships@nshmba.org

WEB SITE ADDRESS:
www.nshmba.org

AREAS OF INTEREST:
Business administration.

NAME(S) OF PROGRAMS:
- **NSHMBA Scholarship Program**

TYPE:
Scholarships.

YEAR PROGRAM STARTED: 1989

PURPOSE:
To foster Hispanic leadership through graduate management education and professional development.

ELIGIBILITY:
Applicants must:
(1) be U.S. citizen or legal permanent resident;
(2) be of Hispanic heritage;
(3) have a minimum grade point average of 3.0 on a 4.0 scale from either a Bachelor's degree or Master's degree, or have a minimum grade point average of 2.75 on a 4.0 scale from a Bachelor's degree in combination with two years of full-time work experience;
(4) be a current NSHMBA member and;
(5) be enrolled in a graduate business program in a college or university in the U.S. or Puerto Rico, accredited by the AACSB at the time of award.

GEOGRAPHIC RESTRICTIONS:
United States and Puerto Rico.

FINANCIAL DATA:
Amount of support per award: Up to $10,000 a year.

NUMBER OF APPLICANTS MOST RECENT YEAR:
140 for the year 2010.

NUMBER OF AWARDS: 78 for the year 2009.

APPLICATION INFORMATION:
Interested students must submit an online application, available March 1 to April 30, and mail all supporting documentation to Scholarship Management Services. Application must include:
(1) all undergraduate and graduate official transcripts (grade reports are not acceptable). Online transcripts must display student name, school name, grade and credit hours earned for each course, and the term in which each course was taken;
(2) two letters of recommendation from professors, advisors, or employers addressing current academic achievement, personal qualities, potential for future success and contributions to the community.

Duration: One academic year.

Deadline: April 30.

ADDRESS INQUIRIES TO:
NSHMBA Scholarship Program
Scholarship Management Services - Julie Farlinger
One Scholarship Way
P.O. Box 297
St. Peter, MN 56082
Tel: (507) 931-1682

NATIONAL TAXIDERMISTS ASSOCIATION [1071]

108 Branch Road
Slidell, LA 70461
(985) 641-4682
(866) 662-9054
Fax: (985) 641-9463

E-MAIL ADDRESS:
ntahq@aol.com

WEB SITE ADDRESS:
nationaltaxidermists.com

AREAS OF INTEREST:
Taxidermy and education.

NAME(S) OF PROGRAMS:
● **Charlie Fleming Scholarship**

TYPE:
Scholarships.

PURPOSE:
To promote higher education and taxidermy education.

ELIGIBILITY:
Students must be a member, spouse or dependent of the NTA for three consecutive years.

FINANCIAL DATA:
Amount of support per award: Generally $500.
Total amount of support: Generally $1,000.

APPLICATION INFORMATION:
Contact the Organization for application procedures.
Duration: One year.
Deadline: April 30.

ADDRESS INQUIRIES TO:
Cindy Crain, Membership Management
(See address above.)

PEN AMERICAN CENTER

588 Broadway, Suite 303
New York, NY 10012-5246
(212) 334-1660
Fax: (212) 334-2181

E-MAIL ADDRESS:
awards@pen.org

WEB SITE ADDRESS:
www.pen.org

TYPE:
Awards/prizes. Invites submissions of book-length writings by authors of color, published during the calendar year.

See entry 728 for full listing.

PRIDE FOUNDATION [1072]

1122 East Pike Street
PMB 1001
Seattle, WA 98122-3934
(206) 323-3318
Fax: (206) 323-1017

E-MAIL ADDRESS:
giving@pridefoundation.org

WEB SITE ADDRESS:
www.pridefoundation.org

FOUNDED: 1985

AREAS OF INTEREST:
Advocacy and outreach, arts and recreation, education, HIV/AIDS, lesbian health, youth and family and other health and community services.

TYPE:
Endowments; General operating grants; Project/program grants; Scholarships; Seed money grants.

YEAR PROGRAM STARTED: 1987

PURPOSE:
To strengthen the lesbian, gay, bisexual and transgender community today and build an endowment fund for tomorrow.

ELIGIBILITY:
Projects must support lesbian, gay, bisexual and transgender causes. Organizations applying for funds must have 501(c)(3) nonprofit tax status, or be affiliated with an organization that has 501(c)(3) status that will assume responsibility for administering all funds received and expended. Grants to individuals cannot be considered.

GEOGRAPHIC RESTRICTIONS:
Alaska, Idaho, Montana, Oregon and Washington.

FINANCIAL DATA:
Amount of support per award: Maximum $5,000; some rare special projects exceptions.
Total amount of support: $750,000 projected for the year 2010-11, not including over $6,000,000 in grants designated through a special fund to specific organizations.

NUMBER OF APPLICANTS MOST RECENT YEAR:
250.

NUMBER OF AWARDS: 150 for the year 2010.

REPRESENTATIVE AWARDS:
$5,000 to Bend-It Extravaganza for youth focused arts festival; $8,000 to Montana Two-Spirit Society for general operating support; $5,000 to Human Dignity Coalition for general operating support.

APPLICATION INFORMATION:
Contact the Foundation.
Duration: One year.
Deadline: Varies.

PUBLICATIONS:
Newsletter.

IRS IDENTIFICATION NUMBER: 91-1325007

ADDRESS INQUIRIES TO:
Jeffrey Hedgepeth, Grants Program Director
(See address above.)

THE RETIREMENT RESEARCH FOUNDATION [1073]

8765 West Higgins Road
Suite 430
Chicago, IL 60631-4170
(773) 714-8080
Fax: (773) 714-8089

E-MAIL ADDRESS:
info@rrf.org

WEB SITE ADDRESS:
www.rrf.org

FOUNDED: 1950

AREAS OF INTEREST:
Aging.

NAME(S) OF PROGRAMS:
● **Accessible Faith Program**
● **Core Grants Program**
● **Organizational Capacity Building Initiative**

TYPE:
Challenge/matching grants; Demonstration grants; Development grants; Project/program grants; Research grants; Seed money grants;

Technical assistance; Training grants. For the Core Grants Program, awards are generally limited to projects directed to the stated objective.

Funding of service/service development projects which do not have potential for national or regional impact are limited to the six Midwestern states (Illinois, Indiana, Iowa, Kentucky, Missouri, Wisconsin) and Florida. The Foundation has strong interest in serving the Chicago metropolitan area.

The Accessible Faith Grants Program is designed to assist Chicago-area houses of worship make their facilities more accessible for elder adults and individuals with disabilities.

The Organizational Capacity Building Initiative is designed to strengthen the effectiveness of Chicago-area nonprofit groups serving the elderly. Grants are available to help these organizations make long-term improvements in their management and governance, and by doing so, to sustain and enhance their services to the elderly.

YEAR PROGRAM STARTED: 1979

PURPOSE:
To improve access to and quality of community-based and residential long-term care; to promote economic security for all older persons by strengthening social insurance, pension and personal savings programs and; to support adequate training of and compensation for those working directly with the elderly and their families to assure the highest quality of care. The Foundation is devoted exclusively to improving the quality of life for the nation's older population.

LEGAL BASIS:
Private foundation.

ELIGIBILITY:
To be eligible for support, organizations, congregations and institutions must qualify under the regulations of the IRS.

To achieve its goals, the Foundation supports:
(1) education and training;
(2) advocacy;
(3) direct service;
(4) replications of evidence-based programs, models and practices and;
(5) applied clinical, policy and social science research.

The Foundation is particularly interested in innovative projects that develop and/or demonstrate new approaches to the problems of older Americans and that have the potential for national or regional impact.

The Foundation normally does not provide support for construction of facilities, general operating expenses, computers, endowment or developmental campaigns, scholarships or loans, grants to individuals, projects outside the U.S., conferences, publications and travel unless components of a larger Foundation-funded project, dissertation research or the production of films and videos.

GEOGRAPHIC RESTRICTIONS:
Florida, Illinois, Iowa, Kentucky, Michigan, Missouri and Wisconsin.

FINANCIAL DATA:
Assets of $116,094,527 for the year 2010.
Amount of support per award: $2,500 to $324,999; $30,000 average.
Total amount of support: $9,050,044 for the year 2008.

NUMBER OF APPLICANTS MOST RECENT YEAR:
266 for the year 2010.

NUMBER OF AWARDS: 95 for the year 2010.

REPRESENTATIVE AWARDS:
$50,000 to Pension Rights Center to provide technical support to pension counseling projects across the country; $49,524 to Aurora Family Service, Inc. to refine and incorporate an aging-focused curriculum at The Family Therapy Training Institute, a postgraduate professional school; $32,785 to Women's Institute for a Secure Retirement to train leaders from a national Hispanic organization how to provide basic financial information to older Latinas.

APPLICATION INFORMATION:
The Foundation does not have a standard grant application form. Requests for funds should contain the following information:
(1) a short statement summarizing the project, its significance and the amount of funds requested (two to three pages);
(2) a complete statement of the specific objectives of the proposed project with the accomplishments of the project defined;
(3) explanation of the project's significance including background information on the problem addressed in the proposal, existing knowledge and gaps;
(4) a description of the methods and criteria which will be used to evaluate the project. Research proposals should describe the experimental design, the procedures used to accomplish the objectives, the sequence of the investigation, the kinds of data to be obtained and the means by which data will be analyzed and interpreted. Model projects and service proposals should describe the project design, the target group, the change to be effected, the resources and the method of delivery, the sequence of activities planned to meet the project objectives, the methods and criteria that will be used to evaluate the outcome of the project. Education and training proposals should describe the target group, educational needs to be met, the content, methods, sequence and location of educational experiences and the methods and criteria that will be used to evaluate the educational program;
(5) a detailed timetable and line item budget for the project, which includes grant funds requested from the Retirement Research Foundation as well as other sources of financial support. Where project personnel are engaged in other projects, the percent of time in and compensation from other projects should be identified;
(6) plans for continued support of project;
(7) curriculum vitae not to exceed five pages for project director(s) and key personnel should be included;
(8) the qualifications of the organization to carry out the project including brief history, past accomplishments, financial and annual reports;
(9) a copy of the applicant's tax-exempt status under Section IRS 501(c)(3) of the Internal Revenue Code and IRS determination letter classifying the applicant organization as not being a private foundation under Section 509(a) of the Internal Revenue Code. If this is not available, an explanation should be submitted as to the status of the applicant. A statement that the (501)(c)(3) classification and "not a private foundation" status has not been revoked or modified should be included and;
(10) signature of Chief Executive Officer and Board President.

Duration: 3 years.
Deadline: February 1, May 1 and August 1, with award announcement three to six months after submission date.

TRUSTEES AND OFFICERS:
Nathaniel McParland, M.D., Chairman of the Board
Irene Frye, Executive Director
Downey Varey, Treasurer
Ruth Ann Watkins, Secretary
Marilyn Hennessy
Edward J. Kelly
Richard Kissel
Sister Stella Louise
Marvin Meyerson

ADDRESS INQUIRIES TO:
Irene Frye, Executive Director
(See address above.)

RIGHTEOUS PERSONS FOUNDATION [1074]

2800 28th Street, Suite 105
Santa Monica, CA 90405
(310) 314-8393
Fax: (310) 314-8396

E-MAIL ADDRESS:
tal@tabankinassoc.com

WEB SITE ADDRESS:
www.righteouspersons.org

FOUNDED: 1994

AREAS OF INTEREST:
Primarily Jewish organizations.

TYPE:
General operating grants; Matching gifts; Project/program grants; Seed money grants; Technical assistance.

PURPOSE:
To strengthen Jewish life in America.

LEGAL BASIS:
Nonprofit.

ELIGIBILITY:
Applicants must be tax-exempt organizations. Priority is given to national organizations and projects which create meaningful experiences for Jewish youth, promote Jewish learning, provide leadership training grounded in Jewish tradition, employ the arts and media to explore the relevance of modern Jewish identity, promote tolerance and understanding between Jews and non-Jews, and encourage Jews to participate in the work of social justice.

The Foundation does not make grants to individuals. Also, the Foundation does not support university faculty chairs, individual synagogues or day schools, research, the publication of books or magazines, or organizations or projects based outside of the U.S. In addition, the Foundation generally does not support endowments, capital campaigns, building funds, or social service projects.

GEOGRAPHIC RESTRICTIONS:
United States.

APPLICATION INFORMATION:
Applicants should submit a two-to three-page letter of inquiry including:
(1) a description of the proposed project including the issues the project will address and the target population(s);
(2) a brief description of the organization's mission, activities and history;
(3) the total amount of the organization's operating budget;

(4) the total amount requested from the Foundation;
(5) the name, mailing address and telephone number of a contact person;
(6) a detailed project budget;
(7) a list of the organization's board of directors;
(8) documentation of the organization's 501(c)(3) status;
(9) the total amount requested from the Foundation and;
(10) a list of the organization/project's primary sources of support over the last two years including names of foundations and amounts provided each year.

If there is a fiscal sponsor for the project, include a current copy of the sponsor's tax-exempt letter from the IRS as well as a letter of support from the sponsor acknowledging their responsibilities. Do not send full proposals or video or audio tapes unless otherwise requested. Faxed applications will not be considered.

PUBLICATIONS:
Program announcement; guidelines.

STAFF:
Margery Tabankin, Executive Director
Rachel Levin, Associate Director

BOARD OF DIRECTORS:
Steven Spielberg, Chairman
Gerald Breslauer, President
Bruce Ramer
Michael Rutman

ADDRESS INQUIRIES TO:
Tal Gozani, Senior Program Officer
(See address above.)

JACKIE ROBINSON FOUNDATION [1075]

75 Varick Street, 2nd Floor
New York, NY 10013-1917
(212) 290-8600
Fax: (212) 290-8081

E-MAIL ADDRESS:
general@jackierobinson.org

WEB SITE ADDRESS:
www.jackierobinson.org

FOUNDED: 1973

AREAS OF INTEREST:
Providing college education for academically gifted students of color with financial need.

NAME(S) OF PROGRAMS:
● **Education and Leadership Development Program**

TYPE:
Conferences/seminars; Internships; Scholarships.

PURPOSE:
To award four-year college scholarships to academically gifted students of color with financial need, enabling them to attend the college of their choice.

ELIGIBILITY:
Foundation Scholar applicants must meet all of the following criteria:
(1) have U.S. citizenship;
(2) be a minority student;
(3) be a high school senior enrolling in college in the coming fall;
(4) have an SAT score of 900 or above, an ACT of 21 or above;
(5) have leadership potential and;
(6) be in financial need.

FINANCIAL DATA:
Amount of support per award: Scholarships: Up to $6,000 per year; maximum $24,000.
Total amount of support: $1,700,000 for the year 2008.

APPLICATION INFORMATION:
Scholarship application is available online on October 15
Duration: Four years.
Deadline: March 15. Applicants notified of status June 1.

SANTA FE COMMUNITY FOUNDATION   [1076]
516 Alto Street
Santa Fe, NM 87501
(505) 988-9715
Fax: (505) 988-1829

E-MAIL ADDRESS:
foundation@santafecf.org

WEB SITE ADDRESS:
www.santafecf.org

FOUNDED: 1981

AREAS OF INTEREST:
Arts, education, economic development, environment, health, human services, lesbian, gay, bisexual and transgender community and Native American.

CONSULTING OR VOLUNTEER SERVICES:
Online directories for consultants and for organizations needing volunteers.

TYPE:
General operating grants; Project/program grants; Scholarships. Emergency funds.

YEAR PROGRAM STARTED: 1981

PURPOSE:
Charitable.

LEGAL BASIS:
Community foundation.

ELIGIBILITY:
The Foundation awards grants to nonprofit organizations only. The Foundation does not award grants for religious or political purposes, capital outlay, endowment or to individuals.

GEOGRAPHIC RESTRICTIONS:
Santa Fe and northern New Mexico.

FINANCIAL DATA:
Amount of support per award: $5,000 to $15,000.
Total amount of support: $3,100,000 (including donor-advised funds).

COOPERATIVE FUNDING PROGRAMS: Hispanics in Philanthropy.

NUMBER OF APPLICANTS MOST RECENT YEAR: 204.

NUMBER OF AWARDS: 58.

REPRESENTATIVE AWARDS:
Santa Fe Indian School Spoken Word Program; Esperanza Shelter for Battered Families.

APPLICATION INFORMATION:
Applicants must submit proof of IRS 501(c)(3) status.
Duration: One year.
Deadline: Varies.

PUBLICATIONS:
Newsletters; general purpose brochure; fundholder update; issue guide; *Giving Together* catalogues; guide to giving materials.

IRS IDENTIFICATION NUMBER: 85-0303044

OFFICER:
Brian Byrnes, President and Chief Executive Officer

ADDRESS INQUIRIES TO:
Christa Coggins
Vice President for Community Philanthropy
(See address above.)

ALFRED P. SLOAN FOUNDATION   [1077]
630 Fifth Avenue, Suite 2550
New York, NY 10111
(212) 649-1649
Fax: (212) 757-5117

E-MAIL ADDRESS:
boylan@sloan.org

WEB SITE ADDRESS:
www.sloanphds.org

FOUNDED: 1934

AREAS OF INTEREST:
Multiple special purpose.

NAME(S) OF PROGRAMS:
● **Minority Ph.D. Program**

TYPE:
Fellowships; Scholarships. Offers substantial scholarship support to underrepresented minority (African American, Hispanic American or Native American) students who are U.S. citizens and who are beginning their doctoral work in engineering, natural science and mathematics in selected departments at selected U.S. universities.

YEAR PROGRAM STARTED: 1995

PURPOSE:
To increase the number of Ph.Ds. among underrepresented minorities.

ELIGIBILITY:
African Americans, Hispanic Americans and American Indians/Alaskan Natives. Candidates must first apply for and be accepted at one of the academic departments in their discipline supported by the Foundation. Those accepted qualify as a candidate for a Foundation scholarship.

GEOGRAPHIC RESTRICTIONS:
United States.

FINANCIAL DATA:
Amount of support per award: Varies.
Total amount of support: $3,500,000 per year.
Matching fund requirements: Universities must provide balance of support needed by students.

NUMBER OF AWARDS: Approximately 80 annually.

ADDRESS INQUIRIES TO:
Liz Boylan, Program Director
(See address above.)

ALFRED P. SLOAN FOUNDATION   [1078]
630 Fifth Avenue, Suite 2550
New York, NY 10111
(212) 649-1649
Fax: (212) 757-5117

E-MAIL ADDRESS:
boylan@sloan.org

WEB SITE ADDRESS:
www.sloanphds.org

FOUNDED: 1934

AREAS OF INTEREST:
Multiple special purpose.

NAME(S) OF PROGRAMS:
● **Sloan Indigenous Graduate Partnership**

TYPE:
Fellowships; Scholarships. Offers substantial scholarship support to indigenous students (Native Americans, including American Indians, Native Alaskans and Native Hawaiians) who are beginning their Master's or doctoral work in engineering, natural science and mathematics in selected departments at selected U.S. universities.

YEAR PROGRAM STARTED: 2003

PURPOSE:
To increase the number of Master's and Ph.D. degrees among indigenous people.

ELIGIBILITY:
American Indians/Alaskan Natives/Hawaiian Natives. Candidates must first apply for and be accepted at one of the academic departments in their discipline at a university in the program. Those accepted qualify as a candidate for a Foundation scholarship.

GEOGRAPHIC RESTRICTIONS:
United States.

FINANCIAL DATA:
Amount of support per award: Varies.
Total amount of support: $1,300,000 per year.
Matching fund requirements: Universities must provide balance of support needed by students.

ADDRESS INQUIRIES TO:
Liz Boylan, Program Director
(See address above.)

SONS OF ITALY FOUNDATION   [1079]
219 E Street, N.E.
Washington, DC 20002
(202) 547-2900
Fax: (202) 546-8168

E-MAIL ADDRESS:
scholarships@osia.org

WEB SITE ADDRESS:
www.osia.org

FOUNDED: 1959

AREAS OF INTEREST:
Cultural preservation and advancement for Italian Americans; education.

NAME(S) OF PROGRAMS:
● **National Leadership Grant Competition**

TYPE:
Awards/prizes; Scholarships. The Foundation provides Italian language scholarships, study-abroad scholarships and merit-based higher education scholarships.

YEAR PROGRAM STARTED: 1959

PURPOSE:
To help educate Italian Americans and improve their lives.

LEGAL BASIS:
Public, tax-exempt organization as defined by Section 501(c)(3) and Section 509(a)(1) of the Internal Revenue Code.

ELIGIBILITY:
Open to high school seniors, undergraduate and graduate students. Applicants must be U.S. citizens of Italian heritage.

FINANCIAL DATA:
Amount of support per award: Scholarships: $5,000 to $25,000.
Total amount of support: Varies.

NUMBER OF APPLICANTS MOST RECENT YEAR:
1,000.

NUMBER OF AWARDS: 10 to 12.

APPLICATION INFORMATION:
Duration: One year.
Deadline: Last Friday in February.

PUBLICATIONS:
Annual report; *Grant Priorities, Guidelines and Procedures,* booklet.

STAFF:
Philip R. Piccigallo, Ph.D., National Executive Director

OFFICERS OF THE TRUSTEES:
Vincent Sarno, President
Joseph DiTrapani, Chairman

ADDRESS INQUIRIES TO:
Scholarship Coordinator
(See address above.)

THE SOSLAND FOUNDATION [1080]

4800 Main Street, Suite 100
Kansas City, MO 64112
(816) 756-1000
Fax: (816) 756-0494

E-MAIL ADDRESS:
debbie@sosland.com

WEB SITE ADDRESS:
www.soslandfoundation.org

FOUNDED: 1954

AREAS OF INTEREST:
Jewish organizations, cultural arts, social welfare, education, health and civic concerns.

TYPE:
Capital grants; Development grants; Endowments; General operating grants; Project/program grants.

YEAR PROGRAM STARTED: 1954

PURPOSE:
To carry on a family tradition of helping the community to help themselves; to make sure the community continues to grow and meet the needs of its residents.

LEGAL BASIS:
Family foundation.

ELIGIBILITY:
Grants to 501(c)(3) organizations only. No grants to individuals.

GEOGRAPHIC RESTRICTIONS:
Metropolitan Kansas City area.

FINANCIAL DATA:
Amount of support per award: Varies.
Total amount of support: $3,692,950 for the year 2010.
Matching fund requirements: Family members only.

NUMBER OF AWARDS: 241 for the year 2008.

APPLICATION INFORMATION:
Applicants should send a letter including a description of the project, organization background, budget, list of board and staff and copy of recent tax-exempt ruling.

Duration: One year. Renewal possible.

PUBLICATIONS:
Application guidelines.

IRS IDENTIFICATION NUMBER: 44-6007129

STAFF:
Debbie Sosland-Edelman, Executive Director

BOARD OF DIRECTORS:
Neil N. Sosland, President
Blanche E. Sosland
Charles S. Sosland
Estelle G. Sosland
L. Joshua Sosland
Morton I. Sosland

ADDRESS INQUIRIES TO:
Debbie Sosland-Edelman
Executive Director
(See above address.)

THE SPECIAL HOPE FOUNDATION [1081]

2225 East Bayshore Road
Suite 200
Palo Alto, CA 94303
(650) 644-5376
Fax: (650) 320-1716

E-MAIL ADDRESS:
proposals@specialhope.org

WEB SITE ADDRESS:
www.specialhope.org

FOUNDED: 2002

AREAS OF INTEREST:
Health care access and health care research benefiting the physically, mentally and developmentally disabled.

TYPE:
Challenge/matching grants; Conferences/seminars; General operating grants; Project/program grants; Research grants; Technical assistance.

YEAR PROGRAM STARTED: 2002

PURPOSE:
To provide financial support to organizations that champion the causes of physically, mentally, and developmentally disabled children and adults.

ELIGIBILITY:
Organizations must be nonprofit 501(c)(3). Only grant proposals consistent with the Foundation's mission statement will be eligible for funding. No grants are made to individuals.

GEOGRAPHIC RESTRICTIONS:
United States.

FINANCIAL DATA:
Amount of support per award: $20,000 to $50,000.
Matching fund requirements: By invitation only.

NUMBER OF APPLICANTS MOST RECENT YEAR:
150.

NUMBER OF AWARDS: 30.

APPLICATION INFORMATION:
Pre-application questionnaire must be completed online.
Duration: One to three years.

ADDRESS INQUIRIES TO:
Lynne O'Hara, Executive Director
(See above address.)

THE ROBERT A. TOIGO FOUNDATION

180 Grand Avenue, Suite 900
Oakland, CA 94612
(510) 763-5771
Fax: (510) 763-5778

E-MAIL ADDRESS:
ligia.gomez@toigofoundation.org

WEB SITE ADDRESS:
www.toigofoundation.org

TYPE:
Fellowships.

See entry 2037 for full listing.

U.S. DEPARTMENT OF EDUCATION

Office of English Language Acquisition, Language Enhancement and Academic Achievement
LBJ Education Building, Room 5C-132, MS-6510
400 Maryland Avenue, S.W.
Washington, DC 20202
(202) 401-1402
(202) 401-1436
Fax: (202) 260-5496

E-MAIL ADDRESS:
oela@ed.gov

WEB SITE ADDRESS:
www.ed.gov/offices/oela

TYPE:
Formula grants. Foreign Language Assistance Program - LEA Grants: This program provides grants to establish, improve or expand innovative foreign language programs for elementary and secondary school students.

Foreign Language Assistance Program - SEA Grants: This program provides grants to establish, improve or expand innovative foreign language programs for elementary and secondary school students.

National Professional Development Program: This program provides professional development activities intended to improve instruction for students with limited English proficiency (LEP) and assists education personnel working with such children to meet high professional standards.

Native American and Alaska Native Children in School Program: This program provides grants to eligible entities that support language instruction education projects for limited English proficient (LEP) children from Native American, Alaska Native, native Hawaiian, and Pacific Islander backgrounds. The program is designed to ensure that LEP children master English and meet the same rigorous standards for academic achievement that all children are expected to meet. Funds may support the study of Native American languages.

See entry 1704 for full listing.

UCLA INSTITUTE OF AMERICAN CULTURES (IAC) [1082]

1237 Murphy Hall, Box 951419
Los Angeles, CA 90095-1419
(310) 794-5115
Fax: (310) 825-8099

E-MAIL ADDRESS:
iaccoordinator@gdnet.ucla.edu

WEB SITE ADDRESS:
www.gdnet.ucla.edu/iacweb/iachome.htm

FOUNDED: 1969

AREAS OF INTEREST:
Advancing knowledge, strengthening and integrating interdisciplinary research and enriching instruction on African Americans, American Indians, Asian Americans and Chicanos.

NAME(S) OF PROGRAMS:
• **UCLA IAC Visiting Scholar/Researcher Program in Ethnic Studies**

TYPE:
Fellowships. Deals with arts and humanities, education and teacher training, fine arts, applied arts, law, social sciences, and sciences. The IAC, in cooperation with UCLA's four Ethnic Studies Research Centers (American Indian Studies Center, Asian American Studies Center, Bunche Center for African American Studies Center, and Chicano Studies Research Center) offers awards to visiting scholars to support research on African Americans, American Indians, Asian Americans and Chicanas/os.

PURPOSE:
To enable Ph.D. scholars wishing to work in association with the American Indian Studies Center, the Bunche Center for African American Studies, the Asian American Studies Center, and the Chicano Studies Research Center, in order to conduct research and publish books or manuscripts.

ELIGIBILITY:
Open to U.S. citizens or permanent residents of the U.S. who hold a Ph.D. from an accredited college or university (or, in the case of the arts, a terminal degree) in the appropriate field at the time of appointment. UCLA faculty, staff and currently enrolled students are not eligible to apply.

FINANCIAL DATA:
Amount of support per award: $32,000 to $35,000 stipend, plus health benefits and up to $4,000 in research support. Amount contingent upon rank, experience and date of completion of Ph.D.

NUMBER OF AWARDS: Up to 4.

APPLICATION INFORMATION:
Applicants are encouraged to contact the Studies Research Center of interest prior to applying.
Duration: Up to one year.
Deadline: February 1.

ADDRESS INQUIRIES TO:
Megan Odegaard, Coordinator
(See address above.)

UNITED METHODIST COMMUNICATIONS   [1083]
810 12th Avenue South
Nashville, TN 37203-4704
(888) 278-4862
Fax: (615) 742-5485

E-MAIL ADDRESS:
scholarships@umcom.org

WEB SITE ADDRESS:
www.umcom.org/specialinitiatives

FOUNDED: 1948

AREAS OF INTEREST:
Religious communications.

NAME(S) OF PROGRAMS:
• **The Leonard M. Perryman Communications Scholarship for Ethnic Minority Students**

TYPE:
Fellowships; Scholarships. Award for junior or senior undergraduate study in religion journalism or mass communications. The term *communications* is meant to cover various media as audio-visual, electronic and print journalism.

PURPOSE:
To enable the recipient to continue his or her studies in communication and to promote a level of excellence in communication on the undergraduate level by an ethnic minority student.

ELIGIBILITY:
Applicants must be members of The United Methodist Church and must be racial ethnic minority undergraduate students, junior or senior, who have an intention to pursue a career in religion journalism or mass communications and are enrolled in an accredited U.S. college or university. Candidates must be in their junior or senior year to qualify.

FINANCIAL DATA:
Amount of support per award: $2,500.

Total amount of support: $2,500 per academic year.

NUMBER OF AWARDS: 1.

APPLICATION INFORMATION:
Applicant must submit:
(1) an application form (completed and submitted electronically or printed and mailed);
(2) official transcripts from the current institution of higher education and any others attended. Transcripts should be mailed by the school directly to the address listed in the application packet;
(3) three letters of recommendation, one from the local church pastor or a denominational official, one from the chairperson of the department in which the applicant is majoring as an undergraduate student, and one from an employer or supervisor in a position to evaluate the applicant's communications skills;
(4) an essay (no more than 500 words) about the applicant's commitment to the Christian faith and interest in communications, and how the applicant sees the two intersecting in their life presently and in the future;
(5) three examples of journalistic work (audiovisual, electronic, print). If requested in writing, these materials will be returned after the committee has completed its selection and;
(6) a recent photograph, preferably head and shoulders, suitable for publicity use if awarded the scholarship.

Duration: One academic year.

Deadline: March 15 (postmarked).

PUBLICATIONS:
Application guidelines.

ADDRESS INQUIRIES TO:
Scholarships Coordinator
(See address above.)

UNIVERSITY OF CALIFORNIA   [1084]
President's Postdoctoral Fellowship Program
403 Sproul
Berkeley, CA 94720-5920
(510) 643-6566
Fax: (510) 642-1811

E-MAIL ADDRESS:
kadkinson@berkeley.edu

WEB SITE ADDRESS:
www.ucop.edu/acadadv/ppfp

FOUNDED: 1869

AREAS OF INTEREST:
Education and research.

NAME(S) OF PROGRAMS:
• **University of California President's Postdoctoral Fellowship Program**

TYPE:
Fellowships. Awarded for research conducted under faculty sponsorship on any one of the University of California's 10 campuses.

YEAR PROGRAM STARTED: 1984

PURPOSE:
To encourage outstanding women and minority Ph.D. recipients to pursue academic careers at the University of California; to offer research fellowships to all qualified candidates who are committed to university careers in research, teaching and service that will enhance the diversity of the academic community at the University of California.

LEGAL BASIS:
University.

ELIGIBILITY:
Applicants must be U.S. citizens or permanent residents and must hold or receive a Ph.D. from an accredited university. Applicants should expect to have earned their Ph.D. degree by June 30 of the year for which they are applying.

The program will prefer candidates who have research interests focusing on underserved populations and understanding issues of racial or gender inequalities.

The program also prefers candidates with a record of leadership or significant experience teaching and mentoring students from groups that have been historically underrepresented in higher education.

FINANCIAL DATA:
The award includes salary, health, vision and dental benefits, and up to $4,000 for research-related expenses.

Amount of support per award:
Approximately $45,000 per fellow, depending upon the field and level of experience, plus benefits for self and dependents.

NUMBER OF APPLICANTS MOST RECENT YEAR:
450 for the year 2011-12.

NUMBER OF AWARDS: 15 for the year 2011-12.

APPLICATION INFORMATION:
Application consists of curriculum vitae, research proposal, dissertation abstract, personal statement, writing sample, mentor support letter and thesis advisor letter.

Duration: Initially one academic year beginning July 1. Renewal for a second year will be granted upon demonstration of academic productivity and participation in program events.

Deadline: November 1. Announcement of awardees in the spring.

ADDRESS INQUIRIES TO:
Kimberly M. Adkinson
President's Postdoctoral Fellowship Program
(See address above.)

UNIVERSITY OF CALIFORNIA, LOS ANGELES [1085]

Asian American Studies Center
3230 Campbell Hall
405 Hilgard Avenue, Box 951546
Los Angeles, CA 90095-1546
(310) 825-2974
Fax: (310) 206-9844

E-MAIL ADDRESS:
dkyoo@ucla.edu

WEB SITE ADDRESS:
www.aasc.ucla.edu

FOUNDED: 1969

AREAS OF INTEREST:
Asian American studies, policy research on Asian Americans, and arts and humanities on Asian Americans.

NAME(S) OF PROGRAMS:
● **Ethnic Studies Fellowships**

TYPE:
Awards/prizes; Fellowships; Research grants; Scholarships; Visiting scholars; Work-study programs. Support for postdoctoral fellows and visiting scholars.

YEAR PROGRAM STARTED: 1969

PURPOSE:
To provide funding for studies in the field of Asian American arts, humanities, social sciences and applied research.

LEGAL BASIS:
University.

ELIGIBILITY:
Applicants must have the Ph.D. in place at the time Fellowship is awarded. UCLA faculty members are not eligible for support.

FINANCIAL DATA:
Amount of support per award: $32,000 to $35,000, depending upon rank and experience, for fellows who have recently completed the Ph.D. Senior scholars receive a supplement to the sabbatical salaries provided by their own institutions. Up to $4,000 in research support and health benefits. If applicable, stipend is paid in the form of a reimbursement to home institution.
Total amount of support: Varies.

NUMBER OF APPLICANTS MOST RECENT YEAR:
30.

NUMBER OF AWARDS: 1.

APPLICATION INFORMATION:
Duration: Nine months.
Deadline: January 12.

ADDRESS INQUIRIES TO:
Melany Dela Cruz-Viesca
Assistant Director/IAC Coordinator
Asian American Studies Center
(See address above.)

UNIVERSITY OF SOUTHERN CALIFORNIA

USC Graduate School
3601 Watt Way, GFS 315
Los Angeles, CA 90089-1695
(213) 740-9033
Fax: (213) 740-9048

E-MAIL ADDRESS:
gradsch@usc.edu

WEB SITE ADDRESS:
www.usc.edu/schools/GraduateSchool/

TYPE:
Fellowships. Merit fellowships. Fellowships will be combined with matching funds from individual schools to provide four or more years of funding toward the Ph.D.
See entry 1915 for full listing.

VIRGINIA POLYTECHNIC INSTITUTE AND STATE UNIVERSITY [1086]

MAOP Office
110 Femoyer Hall
Blacksburg, VA 24061
(540) 231-5023
Fax: (540) 231-2618

E-MAIL ADDRESS:
maop@vt.edu

WEB SITE ADDRESS:
www.maop.vt.edu

AREAS OF INTEREST:
Graduate programs particularly in science, math and technology.

NAME(S) OF PROGRAMS:
● **Multicultural Academic Opportunity Graduate Student Scholars Program**

TYPE:
Assistantships; Fellowships; Internships; Scholarships. The program assists with graduate school financing in exchange for assistance to MAOP administration. Graduate students assist with programming implementation such as mentoring to undergraduate students.

YEAR PROGRAM STARTED: 1973

PURPOSE:
To improve professional and educational opportunities for minority students in architecture, planning, public and international affairs, and landscape architecture.

ELIGIBILITY:
GPA average of 3.0 during the last two years of undergraduate school is required along with an essay focusing upon their commitment to academic diversity at Virginia Tech and admission to the Graduate School. Scholars must maintain a 3.0 GPA average to remain qualified for the program.

FINANCIAL DATA:
Amount of support per award: Varies.
Total amount of support: Varies.

APPLICATION INFORMATION:
Duration: One year. Renewable.
Deadline: April 1.

ADDRESS INQUIRIES TO:
Dr. Eric Williams
Director, MAOP Office
(See address above.)

WIDENER MEMORIAL FOUNDATION IN AID OF HANDICAPPED CHILDREN [1087]

4060 Butler Pike
Suite 225
Plymouth Meeting, PA 19462
(610) 825-8900
Fax: (610) 825-8904

FOUNDED: 1912

AREAS OF INTEREST:
Handicapped children and education.

TYPE:
Capital grants; Project/program grants.

PURPOSE:
To benefit orthopedically handicapped children.

LEGAL BASIS:
Special interest foundation.

ELIGIBILITY:
Applicants must be 501(c)(3) organizations that are not classified as private foundations. Organizations must benefit orthopedically handicapped children in some way.

GEOGRAPHIC RESTRICTIONS:
Greater Delaware Valley area (including the city of Philadelphia, Pennsylvania), and Bucks, Burlington, Camden, Chester, Delaware, Gloucester, Montgomery and Philadelphia counties.

FINANCIAL DATA:
Amount of support per award: Varies.
Total amount of support: Approximately $900,000 annually.

APPLICATION INFORMATION:
Applicant should include a letter describing the purpose for which grant would be used, persons who would benefit from the activity for which the grant is requested, in addition to orthopedically handicapped children, and statements showing that the organization is exempt under 501(c)(3) of the Internal Revenue Code and also not classified as a private foundation.
Duration: Varies.
Deadline: Call for specific dates. Trustees usually meet in May and November.

OFFICERS:
Edith R. Dixon, President
Peter M. Mattoon, Esq., Vice President and Trustee
George W. Dixon, Secretary and Treasurer
Bruce L. Castor, Esq., Trustee
Michael Clancy, M.D., Trustee
Mark S. DePillis, Esq., Trustee
Linda Grobman, Ed.D., Trustee
Edith Dixon Miller, Trustee

ADDRESS INQUIRIES TO:
Edith R. Dixon
P.O. Box 178
Lafayette Hill, PA 19444-0178

WISCONSIN HIGHER EDUCATIONAL AIDS BOARD

131 West Wilson Street
Madison, WI 53703
(608) 267-2206
Fax: (608) 267-2808

E-MAIL ADDRESS:
heabmail@wisconsin.gov

WEB SITE ADDRESS:
heab.wi.gov

TYPE:
Grants-in-aid; Scholarships; Loan forgiveness programs. Student financial aid programs in Wisconsin.
See entry 1924 for full listing.

African-American

AFRICAN AMERICAN FUND OF NEW JERSEY [1088]

132 South Harrison Street
East Orange, NJ 07018
(908) 561-0123
Fax: (908) 561-4710

E-MAIL ADDRESS:
aafnj@aol.com

WEB SITE ADDRESS:
www.aafnj.org

FOUNDED: 1980

AREAS OF INTEREST:
Primarily African-American communities in the state of New Jersey.

TYPE:
Conferences/seminars; Demonstration grants; General operating grants; Project/program grants; Seed money grants; Training grants. The African American Fund of New Jersey is a philanthropic organization that funds community-based agencies and programs in and for, but not limited to, African-American communities in the state of New Jersey.

The Fund supports social programs that are important to its donors. Its goal is to provide more extensive educational programs that cater to all age groups. The focus of the grants is to agencies that provide services in the following areas: Early Childhood and Youth Education, Healthcare, Teen Pregnancy Prevention, Substance Abuse, Aid to the Homeless, Adult Literacy, Child Abuse Prevention, AIDS Education, Recreation, Arts and Culture and Leadership Development.

YEAR PROGRAM STARTED: 1980

PURPOSE:
To develop and perpetuate the empowerment of the African-American community through fund-raising and volunteerism for the purpose of Black philanthropy.

LEGAL BASIS:
Private 501(c)(3).

ELIGIBILITY:
Applicants may be any 501(c)(3) nonprofit, tax-exempt organization, agency or community-based organization operating in the state of New Jersey.

GEOGRAPHIC RESTRICTIONS:
New Jersey.

NUMBER OF APPLICANTS MOST RECENT YEAR:
60.

NUMBER OF AWARDS: 20.

APPLICATION INFORMATION:
Request for Proposal (RFP) application required. Forms must be typed and complete. Information and/or technical assistance is available by contacting BUF/NJ State Office in East Orange.
Duration: One year.

PUBLICATIONS:
Annual report.

IRS IDENTIFICATION NUMBER: 22-2349446

OFFICERS:
Sondra Clark, President and Chief Executive Officer

BOARD OF DIRECTORS:
Sondra Clark, President and Chief Executive Officer
Robert T. Pickett, Chairperson
Pia Winslow, Vice Chairperson

Hon. Charles Craig, Treasurer/Secretary
Robert L. Rivers, Secretary
Dr. Alfred Gaymon

ADDRESS INQUIRIES TO:
Lisa Gibbs, Grants Coordinator
(See address above.)

CONGRESSIONAL BLACK CAUCUS FOUNDATION, INC. [1089]

1720 Massachusetts Avenue, N.W.
Washington, DC 20036
(202) 263-2800
Fax: (202) 263-0846

E-MAIL ADDRESS:
info@cbcfinc.org

WEB SITE ADDRESS:
www.cbcfinc.org

FOUNDED: 1976

AREAS OF INTEREST:
Promoting educational and leadership opportunities for African Americans.

NAME(S) OF PROGRAMS:
- **CBC Spouses Cheerios Brand Health Initiative Scholarship**
- **The CBCF Congressional Internship Program**
- **The Congressional Black Caucus Foundation Congressional Fellows Program**
- **Congressional Black Caucus Spouses Education Scholarship Fund**

TYPE:
Fellowships; Internships; Scholarships. The Congressional Black Caucus Foundation Congressional Fellows Program helps participants gain invaluable experience as they assist in the development of legislative and public policy initiatives while working as congressional staff for a year. This program targets early career policy professionals who have completed a professional and/or graduate degree and have demonstrated commitment to improving the lives and services for individuals living in underserved communities. Fellows work on Capitol Hill in the office of a Congressional Black Caucus member.

The Congressional Internship Program provides undergraduate students with an in-depth orientation to Capitol Hill and the legislative process through actual work experience in the offices of Congressional Black Caucus Members. In this way interns prepare to become decision makers in the policymaking process.

The Congressional Black Caucus Spouses Education Scholarship Fund is a national program that awards scholarships to academically talented and highly motivated students who intend to pursue full-time undergraduate, graduate or doctoral degrees.

CBC Spouses Cheerios Brand Health Initiative Scholarship is intended to increase the number of minority students pursuing degrees in the fields of medicine, engineering, technology, nutrition and other health-related professions.

YEAR PROGRAM STARTED: 1983

PURPOSE:
To increase the number of African Americans on congressional committees and subcommittees by providing students the opportunity to participate in all aspects of the legislative process.

LEGAL BASIS:
Nonpartisan, nonprofit foundation.

ELIGIBILITY:
Applicants to the Fellows Program must have completed graduate coursework. Internship Program applicants must be college undergraduates. CBC Spouses Scholarship is for undergraduate or graduate students residing or attending school in district of CBC member. CBC Spouses Cheerios Brand Health Initiative Scholarship is for students pursuing career in a health profession, who must reside or attend school in district represented by CBC member.

FINANCIAL DATA:
Fellows are responsible for their own travel arrangements, expenses and housing accommodations. CBCF provides health and dental insurance coverage during term of fellowship. Interns receive a stipend and housing at a local university.
Amount of support per award: Fellows Program: $40,000 annual stipend; $3,000 for Interns.
Total amount of support: Varies.

APPLICATION INFORMATION:
Submit a completed application with detailed resume, certificate of academic standing and/or faculty certification, a writing sample of up to 10 pages, three letters of recommendation, one of which must be from the dean, department chairperson, faculty or advisor and an official transcript from each school attended.
Duration: All Fellows serve 20 months. Internships occur during the Spring, Fall and Summer.
Deadline: April for Fellows Program. February, May and November for Internship Program. June 1 for the CBC Spouses Scholarships and the CBC Spouses Cheerios Brand Health Initiative Scholarship.

PUBLICATIONS:
Policy review; annual report.

IRS IDENTIFICATION NUMBER: 52-1160561

BOARD OF DIRECTORS:
Donald M. Payne, Chairman
A. Shaunise Washington, Vice Chairman
Virgil Griffin, Treasurer
Kevin Brown, Secretary
Amy Goldson, Counsel

ADDRESS INQUIRIES TO:
Educational Department
(See address above.)

CONGRESSIONAL BLACK CAUCUS FOUNDATION, INC. [1090]

1720 Massachusetts Avenue, N.W.
Washington, DC 20036
(202) 263-2800
Fax: (202) 775-0773

E-MAIL ADDRESS:
info@cbcfinc.org

WEB SITE ADDRESS:
www.cbcfinc.org

FOUNDED: 1976

AREAS OF INTEREST:
Domestic and international research on issues that affect African Americans, fund-raising and development projects, education and information dissemination.

NAME(S) OF PROGRAMS:
- **The Louis Stokes Urban Health Policy Fellowship Program**

TYPE:
Fellowships. This Fellowship is designed around three components: public policy training, educational enrichment and leadership development.

The centerpiece of the public policy training component is a 20-month Congressional office/committee placement. Fellows are assigned to the office of CBC Members who sit on the House Committee on Energy and Commerce for a period of two months at the beginning of the Fellowship year. This initial placement is designed to allow the Fellows to acclimate to the Congressional work environment and obtain a general understanding of the legislative process and minority health policy issues. Following the office placement, Fellows are assigned to the House Committee on Energy and Commerce where they stay for the remainder of the program. Fellows work 40 hours per week on a range of staff assignments, including conducting research and analysis, drafting legislation, and coordinating logistics and public testimony for Congressional hearings. Additionally, Fellows are required to write a public policy research paper, legislative briefing paper, and op-ed article on a matter of mutual interest to themselves and the Member for whom they work.

During the fall and summer recesses, Fellows leave Capitol Hill to conduct site visits at national public and private health-related organizations. The site visits are designed to expose Fellows to the inner workings of the institutions that influence Congress during the policymaking process and/or execute the will of Congress. These site visits will last for one week each.

Fellows also participate in a rigorous educational program centered around monthly seminars on policy and politics. These seminars explore topics such as African Americans'relationship with the two major parties, the history of the CBC, and relevant policy issues. The seminars are supplemented by a series of lectures and briefings by Members of the CBC and other Congressional leaders, federal government officials, and public policy experts.

Participants in the Fellowship must reside in or relocate to the Washington, DC metropolitan area. Fellows receive health and dental insurance and are responsible for all relocation, housing and transportation costs.

YEAR PROGRAM STARTED: 2003

PURPOSE:
To increase the pool of qualified ethnic health policy professionals by targeting the next generation of leaders; to facilitate the collaboration of health organizations and governmental agencies to develop health policy and legislation designed to eliminate health disparities and; to inform the Congressional Black Caucus and the U.S. House of Representatives Health Agenda about issues related to and ways to address health disparities.

ELIGIBILITY:
Applicants for the Fellowship must possess the equivalent of a Master's degree in a health-related field (behavioral science, social sciences, biological sciences and health professions) from an accredited institution and a minimum of a 3.5 grade point average.

It is preferred that applicants have academic training/experience in minority HIV/AIDS issues, the Healthy Peoples 2010 Initiative, health insurance coverage, the health professions training industry, and international experience and/or foreign language fluency.

GEOGRAPHIC RESTRICTIONS:
Washington, District of Columbia.

FINANCIAL DATA:
Amount of support per award: Salary totaling $40,000.

NUMBER OF AWARDS: 1 to 4.

APPLICATION INFORMATION:
All applications must be mailed to The Louis Stokes Urban Health Policy Program, CBCF Leadership Institute for Public Service, at the address above.
Duration: 20 months.
Deadline: March 20 (postmark).

ADDRESS INQUIRIES TO:
The Louis Stokes Urban Health Policy Program
CBCF Leadership Institute for Public Service
(See address above.)

*SPECIAL STIPULATIONS:
Participation in all program components is required.

CONGRESSIONAL BLACK CAUCUS FOUNDATION, INC. [1091]
1720 Massachusetts Avenue, N.W.
Washington, DC 20036
(202) 263-2800
Fax: (202) 775-0773

E-MAIL ADDRESS:
info@cbcfinc.org

WEB SITE ADDRESS:
www.cbcfinc.org

FOUNDED: 1976

NAME(S) OF PROGRAMS:
- **CBCS Performing Arts Scholarship**
- **CBCS Visual Arts Scholarship**

TYPE:
Scholarships. CBCS Performing Arts Scholarship, developed in honor of the late Curtis Mayfield, is intended to ensure that students pursuing a career in the performing arts receive the financial assistance to achieve their goals.

CBCS Visual Arts Scholarship was established for students who are pursuing a career in the visual arts.

PURPOSE:
To encourage education in the performing and visual arts among minority students.

ELIGIBILITY:
Applicants must:
(1) be preparing to pursue an undergraduate degree full-time, or be a current full-time student in good academic standing at an accredited college or university;
(2) have a minimum 2.5 grade point average and;
(3) exhibit leadership ability and participate in community service activities.

The scholarships do not have a residency requirement.

APPLICATION INFORMATION:
Complete applications must be sent directly to CBCF and need to include:

(1) a completed CBC Spouses scholarship application;
(2) personal statement;
(3) official sealed transcript(s) from all institutions attended;
(4) letter of acceptance from intended institution;
(5) two letters of recommendation (one from community involvement experience);
(6) one-page resume listing extracurricular activities, honors, employment, community service and special skills;
(7) recent photograph–cap and gown or professional dress (no group or social photos) and;
(8) for performing arts: a two-minute CD-R or DVD of a recent performance (a visual recording is required to be eligible);
for visual arts: a CD-R of five original pieces or artwork (an art sample must be provided to be eligible). Must be saved in a format that is playable on Windows Media Player.
Deadline: April 30.

ADDRESS INQUIRIES TO:
Educational Department
(See address above.)

FREDERICK DOUGLASS INSTITUTE FOR AFRICAN AND AFRICAN-AMERICAN STUDIES
University of Rochester
302 Morey Hall
Rochester, NY 14627-0440
(585) 275-7235
Fax: (585) 256-2594

E-MAIL ADDRESS:
fdi@mail.rochester.edu

WEB SITE ADDRESS:
www.cc.rochester.edu/college/aas

TYPE:
Awards/prizes; Conferences/seminars; Fellowships.

See entry 1642 for full listing.

FLORIDA DEPARTMENT OF EDUCATION [1092]
Office of Student Financial Assistance
325 West Gaines Street, Suite 1314
Tallahassee, FL 32399-0400
(850) 410-5200
(888) 827-2004
Fax: (850) 487-1809

E-MAIL ADDRESS:
osfa@fldoe.org

WEB SITE ADDRESS:
www.FloridaStudentFinancialAid.org

NAME(S) OF PROGRAMS:
- **Rosewood Family Scholarship Program**

TYPE:
Scholarships. Financial assistance for descendants of the Rosewood family to attend a state university, public community college or public postsecondary vocational-technical school.

PURPOSE:
To encourage and assist minority students to continue on to higher education.

LEGAL BASIS:
Governmental agency.

ELIGIBILITY:
An applicant must:
(1) not owe a repayment or be in default under any state or federal grant, loan or

scholarship program unless satisfactory arrangements to repay have been made;
(2) not have previously received a Bachelor's degree;
(3) enroll full-time in a program of study leading to an undergraduate degree, a certificate or a diploma at an eligible postsecondary institution and;
(4) provide copies of documents of ancestry by April 1.

FINANCIAL DATA:
Awards will be prorated if funds are not sufficient to accommodate all selected recipients.

A student participating in college-preparatory instruction or remedial courses, a student requiring additional time to complete the college-level communication and computation skills testing programs (CLAST), or a student enrolled in a five-year undergraduate degree program are eligible to receive financial aid for a maximum of 10 semesters or 15 quarters.

NUMBER OF AWARDS: Up to 25.

APPLICATION INFORMATION:
Student will submit a fully completed, error-free Initial Student Florida Financial Aid Application. If a Florida resident, complete and submit the Free Application for Student Financial Aid (FAFSA) online in time to be processed by the U.S. Department of Education. If not a Florida resident, complete and submit the FAFSA in time to receive the Student Aid Report (SAR) from the processor and postmark a copy of the SAR to the Office of Student Financial Assistance.

FAFSA applications may be obtained through high school guidance offices, college financial aid offices or at the web site.
Duration: Maximum of eight semesters or 12 quarters or the equivalent or until the receipt of the first Bachelor's degree, whichever occurs first.
Deadline: Initial Student Florida Financial Aid Application: April 1. FAFSA for Florida residents: May 15. FAFSA for non-Florida residents: May 15.

ADDRESS INQUIRIES TO:
State Scholarship and Grant Programs (See address above.)

THE JACK AND JILL OF AMERICA FOUNDATION   [1093]
1930 17th Street, N.W.
Washington, DC 20009-6207
(202) 232-5290
Fax: (202) 232-1747

E-MAIL ADDRESS:
administration@jackandjillfoundation.org

WEB SITE ADDRESS:
www.jackandjillfoundation.org

FOUNDED: 1968

AREAS OF INTEREST:
Cultural, social, educational, civic and recreational activities for children; youth leadership development.

CONSULTING OR VOLUNTEER SERVICES:
Volunteer services.

NAME(S) OF PROGRAMS:
● **Violet D. Greer Proposals**
● **Independent Grant Awards**
● **Jacqueline Robinson Regional Competition Awards**

TYPE:
Challenge/matching grants; Conferences/seminars; Demonstration grants; General operating grants; Grants-in-aid; Internships; Matching gifts; Project/program grants; Seed money grants; Training grants.

YEAR PROGRAM STARTED: 1968

PURPOSE:
To influence the ongoing positive development of children.

LEGAL BASIS:
Public charity.

ELIGIBILITY:
Independent Grant Awards are awarded to nonprofit organizations when their project's thematic emphasis corresponds to the Foundation's focus.

For the Jacqueline Robinson Regional Competition Awards, applications are submitted by adult or teen members of local chapters to their region for programs that benefit youth outside the organization.

GEOGRAPHIC RESTRICTIONS:
United States.

FINANCIAL DATA:
Amount of support per award: $2,000 to $5,000.

Total amount of support: Varies.

NUMBER OF APPLICANTS MOST RECENT YEAR:
40.

NUMBER OF AWARDS: Varies.

APPLICATION INFORMATION:
Applicant should carefully read the Information for Grant Applicants before submitting an application on the designated form. Furthermore, answers on the application coversheet must be given in the space provided; no additional sheets can be attached. Type the application (using at least 10-point type). Applications may not be faxed. All signatures should be signed in blue ink. A complete application consists of an application coversheet along with the following materials:
(1) proposal;
(2) copy of IRS 501(c)(3) letter or documentation of 501(c)(4) status, whichever is applicable;
(3) most recent audited income statement or 990 tax return, if 501(c)(3) organization, or most recent year-end statement of income and expenses, if 501(c)(4) organization and;
(4) brief resume or bio of your Project Director and other relevant supporting material.

Duration: One year.

Deadline: Violet D. Greer and Independent Grant Awards: December 1.

PUBLICATIONS:
Newsletter; annual report; application guidelines.

IRS IDENTIFICATION NUMBER: 51-0224656

STAFF:
Pier A.H. Blake, Executive Director

ADDRESS INQUIRIES TO:
Pier A.H. Blake, Executive Director (See address above.)

THE NAACP LEGAL DEFENSE AND EDUCATIONAL FUND, INC.   [1094]
99 Hudson Street, Suite 1600
New York, NY 10013
(212) 965-2225
Fax: (212) 219-1595

E-MAIL ADDRESS:
scholarships@naacpldf.org
kthompson@naacpldf.org
mcorro@naacpldf.org

WEB SITE ADDRESS:
www.naacpldf.org/scholarships

FOUNDED: 1964

AREAS OF INTEREST:
Financial assistance for African-American undergraduates and for law students with a demonstrable interest in civil rights.

NAME(S) OF PROGRAMS:
● **LDF Herbert Lehman Education Fund Scholarship Program**
● **LDF Earl Warren Legal Training Program**

TYPE:
Awards/prizes; Grants-in-aid; Internships; Scholarships. LDF Herbert Lehman Education Fund Scholarship Program: Scholarships for African-American high school seniors, high school graduates and college freshmen to attend four-year accredited colleges and universities.

LDF Earl Warren Legal Training Program: Scholarships for law students to attend three-year accredited law schools. Law students already enrolled in law school are ineligible to apply.

YEAR PROGRAM STARTED: 1964

PURPOSE:
To encourage students to continue the work of the Legal Defense Fund; to encourage young people to be involved in public service; to increase the presence of African-American students in colleges, universities and law schools in the U.S.

LEGAL BASIS:
501(c)(3) corporation.

ELIGIBILITY:
Both Herbert Lehman and Earl Warren scholarship candidates must have outstanding potential evidenced by their recommendations, high school academic records, test scores and essays. They must understand their educational goals and academic abilities. Candidates should have a clear commitment to working in the public service as exemplified by their community and school involvements. Candidates should have exceptional leadership potential with an ability to work well in diverse settings. There is no citizenship requirement for LDF scholarships.

GEOGRAPHIC RESTRICTIONS:
United States.

FINANCIAL DATA:
Amount of support per award: $3,000-$5,000 per year.

NUMBER OF APPLICANTS MOST RECENT YEAR:
Over 2,000.

NUMBER OF AWARDS: 50-100 each year.

APPLICATION INFORMATION:
Applications will be available for online submission by November 1 of each year. Applicants who do not meet the basic criteria

for eligibility or do not satisfy program requirements for the completion of applications will not be considered.

Duration: Up to four years depending upon availability of funds. Renewable during undergraduate career, if student remains in good standing with their college or university.

Deadline: March 31 for the Lehman Scholarship and April 30 for the Warren Scholarship. Notification normally takes place at the end of July, prior to the fall semester of the student's first academic year.

STAFF:
Karen Thompson, Director of Scholarship Programs
Maruja Corro, Program Assistant

ADDRESS INQUIRIES TO:
Maruja Corro
Program Assistant
(See address above.)

THE NATIONAL ASSOCIATION OF BLACK SOCIAL WORKERS   [1095]

2305 Martin Luther King Jr. Avenue, S.E.
Washington, DC 20020
(202) 678-4570
Fax: (202) 678-4572

E-MAIL ADDRESS:
harambee@nabsw.org
office-manager@nabsw.org

WEB SITE ADDRESS:
www.nabsw.org

FOUNDED: 1968

AREAS OF INTEREST:
Social work and community advocacy.

NAME(S) OF PROGRAMS:
- **Dr. Joyce Beckett Scholarship**
- **Selena Danette Brown Book Scholarship**
- **Guynn Family Book Scholarship**
- **Emma Meloid and Algood Tuition Scholarship (Undergraduate)**
- **Cenie Jomo Williams Tuition Scholarship**

TYPE:
Scholarships.

YEAR PROGRAM STARTED: 1968

PURPOSE:
To promote the welfare, survival and liberation of communities of African ancestry.

LEGAL BASIS:
Nonprofit membership association.

ELIGIBILITY:
Student must be a member of NABSW. For the Emma and Meloid Algood Tuition Scholarship, student must have a 3.0 grade point average on a 4.0 scale. For all other scholarships, students must have a 2.5 grade point average on a 4.0 scale. Student must express research interest in African Americans or those of African ancestry. Student must be enrolled for full-time study at an accredited U.S. social work program for the semester that the award will be granted.

GEOGRAPHIC RESTRICTIONS:
United States.

FINANCIAL DATA:
Amount of support per award: $250 to $2,000.
Total amount of support: Varies.

NUMBER OF APPLICANTS MOST RECENT YEAR:
10.

NUMBER OF AWARDS: Varies.

APPLICATION INFORMATION:
Scholarship applications can be obtained from the National Office.
Duration: One-time award. May reapply for the Emma Meloid and Algood Tuition Scholarship.
Deadline: Third Friday of December.

PUBLICATIONS:
Quarterly newsletters.

IRS IDENTIFICATION NUMBER: 13-2779773

ADDRESS INQUIRIES TO:
Terrence Bradford, National Office Manager
(See address above.)

NATIONAL BLACK NURSES ASSOCIATION, INC.

8630 Fenton Street
Suite 330
Silver Spring, MD 20910
(301) 589-3200
Fax: (301) 589-3223

E-MAIL ADDRESS:
info@nbna.org

WEB SITE ADDRESS:
www.nbna.org

TYPE:
Scholarships.

See entry 2651 for full listing.

NEED   [1096]

Warner Centre
332 Fifth Avenue, 1st Floor
Pittsburgh, PA 15222
(412) 566-2760
Fax: (412) 471-6643

E-MAIL ADDRESS:
atyler@needld.org

WEB SITE ADDRESS:
www.needld.org

FOUNDED: 1963

AREAS OF INTEREST:
Higher education.

CONSULTING OR VOLUNTEER SERVICES:
Counseling for postsecondary education; assistance to students and parents needing help with the completion of financial aid forms.

TYPE:
Scholarships. Supplemental grants for postsecondary education at colleges and business, trade and technical schools.

YEAR PROGRAM STARTED: 1963

PURPOSE:
To help talented, needy students get to a college, business, trade or technical school.

LEGAL BASIS:
Incorporated nonprofit, tax-exempt.

ELIGIBILITY:
Applicant must be African American, with a high school diploma or GED, resident in Allegheny, Armstrong, Beaver, Butler, Fayette, Greene, Lawrence, Washington or Westmoreland counties in Pennsylvania and enrolled in or planning to enroll in a state-approved program.

GEOGRAPHIC RESTRICTIONS:
Allegheny, Armstrong, Beaver, Butler, Fayette, Greene, Lawrence, Washington and Westmoreland counties, Pennsylvania.

FINANCIAL DATA:
Amount of support per award: $1,000 to $3,500.
Total amount of support: $770,000 for the 2008-09 academic year.

NUMBER OF APPLICANTS MOST RECENT YEAR:
1,700 for the year 2008-09.

NUMBER OF AWARDS: 601 for the 2008-09 academic year.

APPLICATION INFORMATION:
Applicant must submit:
(1) NEED application;
(2) high school, college, or school transcript (whichever is most recent) and;
(3) documentation of family income.
Duration: Academic year. May reapply in subsequent years.
Deadline: May 31.

PUBLICATIONS:
Annual report.

OFFICERS:
Ann Hoover, Chairman of the Board

ADDRESS INQUIRIES TO:
Student Services Department
(See address above.)

SACHS FOUNDATION   [1097]

90 South Cascade Avenue
Suite 1410
Colorado Springs, CO 80903
(719) 633-2353
Fax: (719) 633-3663

E-MAIL ADDRESS:
lisa@sachsfoundation.org

WEB SITE ADDRESS:
sachsfoundation.org

FOUNDED: 1931

AREAS OF INTEREST:
Education.

NAME(S) OF PROGRAMS:
- **Financial Aid for Education of Black Residents of Colorado**

TYPE:
Grants-in-aid; Scholarships.

YEAR PROGRAM STARTED: 1931

PURPOSE:
To promote education of Black residents of Colorado.

LEGAL BASIS:
Private foundation.

ELIGIBILITY:
Applicants must be U.S. citizens, Black, residents of the state of Colorado for five or more years and high school seniors with about a 3.5 grade point average or better, on a 4.0 scale, depending on the number of applications. Awardees may attend any accredited college or university.

GEOGRAPHIC RESTRICTIONS:
Colorado.

FINANCIAL DATA:
Amount of support per award: $5,000 maximum per annum for undergraduates; $6,000 for graduate grants.

NUMBER OF APPLICANTS MOST RECENT YEAR:
400.

NUMBER OF AWARDS: Approximately 35 for the year 2010.

APPLICATION INFORMATION:
Application forms are only available online.
Duration: Four years for undergraduate and some graduate degrees, if requirements are met.
Deadline: March 15.

PUBLICATIONS:
Annual report; other printed materials available upon written request.

OFFICERS:
Craig S. Ralston, President
Stuart Dodge, Vice President
Wilton Cogswell, III, Second Vice President
Lisa M. Harris, Secretary/Treasurer

TRUSTEES:
Morris A. Esmiol, Jr.
Thomas James

ADDRESS INQUIRIES TO:
Lisa M. Harris, Secretary/Treasurer
(See address above.)

*SPECIAL STIPULATIONS:
Must be Black Colorado resident for five years.

THE SCHOMBURG CENTER FOR RESEARCH IN BLACK CULTURE
515 Malcolm X Boulevard
New York, NY 10037-1801
(212) 491-2228
Fax: (212) 491-2098

WEB SITE ADDRESS:
www.nypl.org/locations/tid/64/node/131

TYPE:
Fellowships. Awarded to scholars and professionals whose research in the Black experience can benefit from extended access to the Center's collections. Seminars, colloquia, forums, symposia and conferences complement the residency program.

See entry 425 for full listing.

TWENTY-FIRST CENTURY FOUNDATION   [1098]
132 West 112th Street
Lower Level No. 1
New York, NY 10026
(212) 662-3700
Fax: (212) 662-6690

E-MAIL ADDRESS:
info@21cf.org

WEB SITE ADDRESS:
www.21cf.org

FOUNDED: 1971

AREAS OF INTEREST:
Capacity building; community organizing; policy and leadership development; improving education; health and criminal justice outcomes for Black men and boys.

CONSULTING OR VOLUNTEER SERVICES:
Donor education and philanthropic advising.

NAME(S) OF PROGRAMS:
● **Gulf Coast Organizing Advocacy and Leadership Fund (GOAL)**

TYPE:
Challenge/matching grants; General operating grants; Project/program grants; Seed money grants. Donor-advised fund grants.

YEAR PROGRAM STARTED: 1971

PURPOSE:
To lead, innovate and influence giving for Black community change.

LEGAL BASIS:
Public foundation.

ELIGIBILITY:
Applicant organization must have 501(c)(3) status, or identify a 501(c)(3) as a fiscal sponsor. No funds are provided to individuals.

GEOGRAPHIC RESTRICTIONS:
United States.

FINANCIAL DATA:
Total amount of support: $1,804,278 for the year 2008.

COOPERATIVE FUNDING PROGRAMS: New York Black Males Donor Collaborative; Gulf Coast Funders for Equity; Rye Collaborative.

NUMBER OF APPLICANTS MOST RECENT YEAR:
Approximately 200.

NUMBER OF AWARDS: 100 for the year 2008.

REPRESENTATIVE AWARDS:
$70,000 to Grand Boulevard Federation/Chicago; $10,000 to Families and Friends of Incarcerated Children of New Orleans; $5,000 to Black Men and Boys Oakland Collaborative.

APPLICATION INFORMATION:
The Foundation furnishes instructions on request and on its web site.
Duration: Usually one year.
Deadline: First Friday in September.

PUBLICATIONS:
African American Philanthropy: A Legacy of Giving; Time, Talent and Treasure: A Study of Black Philanthropy; Harnessing the Power of Collective Black Giving; Vision News; Community Returns: Investing in Black Men and Boys; After the Deluge: Fighting the Impacts of Katrina and Rita.

IRS IDENTIFICATION NUMBER: 13-3363860

STAFF:
Chandra Y. Anderson, Interim President
Julia Betty, Program Director

BOARD MEMBERS:
Rev. Alfonso Wyatt, Chairman of the Board
Jean Jeremie, Treasurer
Robert C. Andrews, Secretary
Judith Browne-Dianis
Darryl Smith

ADDRESS INQUIRIES TO:
Chandra Y. Anderson, Interim President
(See address above.)

UNITED NEGRO COLLEGE FUND   [1099]
8260 Willow Oaks Corporate Drive
Fairfax, VA 22031-4503
(703) 205-3400
(800) 331-2244
Fax: (703) 205-3550

E-MAIL ADDRESS:
scholarships@uncf.org

WEB SITE ADDRESS:
www.uncf.org

FOUNDED: 1944

TYPE:
Fellowships; Internships; Scholarships; Technical assistance. The Fund, since its founding, has raised money for 39 private, historically Black colleges.

Faculty fellowship programs make it possible for hundreds of instructors to earn doctoral degrees.

Mentoring and internship opportunities are provided for hundreds of UNCF students.

Scholarships are offered to a pool of more than 60,000 talented students attending UNCF colleges and universities. The Fund oversees more than 450 scholarship programs in the following general categories:
(1) geographically based scholarships;
(2) scholarships based on academic major;
(3) scholarships based on merit and need and;
(4) financial aid for graduate study

PURPOSE:
To provide low-cost quality education in an environment that enables students to excel.

FINANCIAL DATA:
Amount of support per award: Scholarships: $500 to $10,000.

APPLICATION INFORMATION:
Contact the Fund for detailed information.

OFFICERS:
Michael L. Lomax, Ph.D, President and Chief Executive Officer

ADDRESS INQUIRIES TO:
Kimberly Hall, Director Program Services
(See address above.)

Native American

AMERICAN INDIAN GRADUATE CENTER   [1100]
4520 Montgomery Boulevard, N.E.
Suite 1-B
Albuquerque, NM 87109-1291
(505) 881-4584
Fax: (505) 884-0427

E-MAIL ADDRESS:
marveline@aigcs.org

WEB SITE ADDRESS:
www.aigcs.org

FOUNDED: 1969

AREAS OF INTEREST:
Graduate level education in any field.

NAME(S) OF PROGRAMS:
● **Fellowships for American Indians or Alaskan Natives**

TYPE:
Fellowships; Grants-in-aid; Scholarships. Grants on an academic year basis. Summer funding available to continuing students only; these are students who are currently in the fellowship program.

YEAR PROGRAM STARTED: 1969

PURPOSE:
To help open doors to graduate education and help tribes obtain the educated professionals they need to become more self-sufficient and exercise their rights to self-determination.

LEGAL BASIS:
IRS status 501(c)(3), tax-exempt, incorporated in New Mexico.

ELIGIBILITY:
An applicant must be an enrolled member of a U.S. federally recognized American Indian tribe or Alaska Native group, or possess one-fourth degree Indian blood from a

federally recognized tribe. Applicant must be pursuing a Master's, Doctorate or professional degree as a full-time graduate student at an accredited graduate school in the U.S. and must be in financial need. They must submit an essay as described in application packet. Applicants must apply for federal financial and campus-based aid at the financial aid office of the university they plan to attend.

GEOGRAPHIC RESTRICTIONS:
United States.

FINANCIAL DATA:
Awards are based on each applicant's unmet financial need as verified by the applicant's college financial aid office. Fellowships are supplementary grants and are only a percentage of a student's total unmet financial need.
Amount of support per award: Varies.
Matching fund requirements: Universities are encouraged to provide assistance.

COOPERATIVE FUNDING PROGRAMS: The organization works with other scholarship agencies to assure that there will be no overfunding of students.

NUMBER OF APPLICANTS MOST RECENT YEAR:
Over 600 for the year 2010.

NUMBER OF AWARDS: Over 400 for the year 2010.

APPLICATION INFORMATION:
Application packets are available from January through May upon request to the address above. All documentation to verify financial status and tribal eligibility are included in application packet. Packets must be sent directly to the applicant. A $15 application fee is required when the application is submitted for new applicants.

AIG does not accept faxed applications.
Duration: One academic year at a time. Students may reapply each year.
Deadline: June 1, including the $15 application fee.

PUBLICATIONS:
Annual report; newsletter; brochure.

IRS IDENTIFICATION NUMBER: 85-0222386

ADDRESS INQUIRIES TO:
Marveline Vallo Gabbard
Program Assistant
(See address above.)

AMERICAN INDIAN SCIENCE AND ENGINEERING SOCIETY (AISES) [1101]
P.O. Box 9828
Albuquerque, NM 87119-9828
(505) 765-1052

E-MAIL ADDRESS:
scholarship@aises.org

WEB SITE ADDRESS:
www.aises.org

FOUNDED: 1977

AREAS OF INTEREST:
American Indian education in the science and engineering fields.

NAME(S) OF PROGRAMS:
● A.T. Anderson Memorial Scholarship

TYPE:
Scholarships. AISES scholarships are intended to partially defray tuition and other educational expenses, thereby increasing access to higher education and improving college retention rates for AISES members.

AISES scholarships are made possible by corporations, government agencies, foundations, and individuals who wish to support the advancement of American Indian/Alaskan Natives. Scholarships are distributed in two disbursements and awarded for one academic year, unless otherwise specified. Recipients cannot receive more than one scholarship in any of the five programs.

Scholarships are also awarded to members of AISES who are American Indian/Alaskan Native college students who meet the eligibility requirements for each scholarship.

YEAR PROGRAM STARTED: 1983

PURPOSE:
To significantly increase the number of American Indian/Alaskan Native scientists and engineers, and develop knowledgeable leaders within native communities; to foster the building of community by bridging science and technology with traditional native values.

LEGAL BASIS:
Private, nonprofit corporation.

ELIGIBILITY:
Applicant must be a current member of AISES and a full-time undergraduate or graduate student at an accredited four-year college/university, or a full-time student at a two-year college enrolled in a program leading to an academic degree, with a 3.0 minimum, cumulative grade point average. Candidate must major in Math, Science, Engineering, Physical Science, Medicine, or Natural Resources. Candidate must be at least one quarter American Indian/Alaskan Native and/or is recognized as a member of a federally recognized tribe.

FINANCIAL DATA:
Amount of support per award: $1,000 undergraduate and $2,000 graduate per year.
Total amount of support: Approximately $97,000 for the year 2010-11.

NUMBER OF AWARDS: 85 for the year 2009-10.

APPLICATION INFORMATION:
Guidelines and application is available on the web site after February 1, or can be requested from the Society.
Duration: One academic year.
Deadline: June 15 (postmark).

PUBLICATIONS:
AISES Scholarship Program brochure.

IRS IDENTIFICATION NUMBER: 73-1023474

STAFF:
Cara Thunder, Program Director

ADDRESS INQUIRIES TO:
Liz Encinias, Program Officer
(See address above.)

AMERICAN INDIAN SCIENCE AND ENGINEERING SOCIETY (AISES) [1102]
P.O. Box 9828
Albuquerque, NM 87119-9828
(505) 765-1052

E-MAIL ADDRESS:
info@aises.org

WEB SITE ADDRESS:
www.aises.org/Programs/
ScholarshipsandInternships/Scholarships

FOUNDED: 1977

AREAS OF INTEREST:
American Indian education in the science, engineering and other related technical fields.

NAME(S) OF PROGRAMS:
● AISES Google Scholarship

TYPE:
Scholarships.

PURPOSE:
To aid in the education of American Indians and Alaskan Natives in the science, engineering fields and other related technical fields.

ELIGIBILITY:
Applicant must:
(1) be a current AISES member;
(2) be a member of an American Indian tribe, Alaska Native or Native Hawaiian or otherwise considered to be an American Indian by the tribe with which affiliation is claimed; or is at least one-fourth American Indian blood; or is at least one-fourth Alaskan Native or considered to be an Alaskan Native by an Alaskan Native group by which affiliation is claimed;
(3) be a full-time undergraduate or graduate student at an accredited four-year college or university, or in the second year at a two-year college leading to a four-year degree and;
(4) be majoring in one of the following disciplines: computer science or computer engineering.
Minimum cumulative grade point average of 3.5.
Proof of tribal enrollment is required.

FINANCIAL DATA:
Amount of support per award: $10,000 (disbursed over award recipient's course of study).
Total amount of support: $90,000 for the year 2009.

APPLICATION INFORMATION:
Deadline: February 15.

ADDRESS INQUIRIES TO:
Liz Encinias, Program Officer
(See address above.)

AMERICAN PHILOSOPHICAL SOCIETY [1103]
104 South Fifth Street
Philadelphia, PA 19106-3387
(215) 440-3429

E-MAIL ADDRESS:
lmusumeci@amphilsoc.org

WEB SITE ADDRESS:
www.amphilsoc.org

FOUNDED: 1743

AREAS OF INTEREST:
Scholarly research.

NAME(S) OF PROGRAMS:
● Phillips Fund Grants for Native American Research

TYPE:
Grants-in-aid; Research grants. Postgraduate grants for research on North American Indian linguistics, ethnohistory and the history of studies of Native Americans in the continental U.S. and Canada. The Committee prefers supporting the work of younger

scholars/graduate students for research on Master's or doctoral dissertations. Grants are for travel costs, tapes and consultants' fees.

YEAR PROGRAM STARTED: 1940

LEGAL BASIS:
Nonprofit learned society.

ELIGIBILITY:
Open to graduate students and postdoctoral candidates.

The grants described above are for research in Native American linguistics and ethnohistory, as well as in the history of studies of Native Americans. There are no ethnic restrictions on applicants. Work must be on groups located north of the U.S.-Mexican border.

The Committee will seldom approve more than two awards to the same person within a five-year period. Grants are not made for projects in archaeology, ethnography, psycholinguistics, or for the preparation of pedagogical materials, general maintenance or purchase of permanent equipment (tape recorders, books, etc.).

FINANCIAL DATA:
The grants are intended for such extra costs as travel, tapes, films, consultants' fees, etc., but not for the purchase of permanent equipment (tape recorders, books, etc.)

Amount of support per award: Awards average $2,300; grants do not exceed $3,500.

Total amount of support: $44,000 for the year 2010.

NUMBER OF APPLICANTS MOST RECENT YEAR:
49 for the year 2010.

NUMBER OF AWARDS: 18 for the year 2010.

APPLICATION INFORMATION:
Application must be submitted electronically through the Society's online portal. Up to two additional pages may be submitted for the project statement.

Two letters of support are required.

The application and both letters of reference must be received by the deadline.
Duration: One year.
Deadline: March 1. Notification by May.

ADDRESS INQUIRIES TO:
Phillips Fund, Native American Research
(See address above.)

ASSOCIATION ON AMERICAN INDIAN AFFAIRS   [1104]
966 Hungerford Drive, Suite 12-B
Rockville, MD 20850
(240) 314-7155
Fax: (240) 314-7159

E-MAIL ADDRESS:
lw.aaia@verizon.net

WEB SITE ADDRESS:
www.indian-affairs.org

FOUNDED: 1922

AREAS OF INTEREST:
Advocates for the well-being of Indian people. Primary focus on cultural preservation, youth/scholarships, health and sovereignty.

NAME(S) OF PROGRAMS:
● **David Risling Emergency Aid Scholarships**

TYPE:
Grants-in-aid; Scholarships. Emergency Aid Scholarships are for full-time graduate and undergraduate students. This program is limited by the availability of scholarship funds.

YEAR PROGRAM STARTED: 1922

PURPOSE:
To promote the welfare of American Indians and Alaska Natives by supporting efforts; to sustain and perpetuate their cultures and languages; to protect their sovereignty, constitutional, legal and human rights and natural resources; to improve their health, education and economic and community development.

ELIGIBILITY:
This scholarship is offered for acute, temporary emergencies (eviction, day care dismissal and utility disconnection) that would prevent the student from attending school.

Tuition, books, computers and expected expenses are not considered emergencies.

GEOGRAPHIC RESTRICTIONS:
Continental United States and Alaska.

FINANCIAL DATA:
Amount of support per award: $100 to $400.

NUMBER OF AWARDS: Varies.

ADDRESS INQUIRIES TO:
Lisa Wyzlic
Director of Scholarship Programs
(See address above.)

ASSOCIATION ON AMERICAN INDIAN AFFAIRS   [1105]
966 Hungerford Drive, Suite 12-B
Rockville, MD 20850
(240) 314-7155
Fax: (240) 314-7159

E-MAIL ADDRESS:
lw.aaia@verizon.net

WEB SITE ADDRESS:
www.indian-affairs.org

FOUNDED: 1922

AREAS OF INTEREST:
Advocates for the well-being of Indian people. Primary focus on cultural preservation, youth/scholarships, health and sovereignty.

NAME(S) OF PROGRAMS:
● **Adolph Van Pelt Scholarships**

TYPE:
Scholarships.

PURPOSE:
To promote the welfare of American Indians and Alaska Natives by supporting efforts to sustain and perpetuate their cultures and languages; to protect their sovereignty, constitutional, legal and human rights and natural resources; to improve their health, education and economic and community development.

LEGAL BASIS:
Charitable nonprofit foundation.

ELIGIBILITY:
Open to undergraduates in any curriculum.

GEOGRAPHIC RESTRICTIONS:
Continental United States and Alaska.

FINANCIAL DATA:
Amount of support per award: $1,500 per year.

NUMBER OF AWARDS: Varies.

APPLICATION INFORMATION:
Students are eligible to apply on a yearly basis. The following items must be submitted:
(1) complete application;
(2) copy of tribal enrollment;
(3) copy of certificate of Indian blood, minimum one-quarter;
(4) student essay;
(5) two letters of recommendation;
(6) minimum of two years transcripts through most recent semester and;
(7) document of class standing.

Incomplete applications will not be considered. Application packages must be mailed. Faxed or e-mailed documents will not be considered.
Duration: One year. Reapplication on a yearly basis.
Deadline: Application packages are accepted April 4 to June 13.

ADDRESS INQUIRIES TO:
Lisa Wyzlic
Director of Scholarship Programs
(See address above.)

ASSOCIATION ON AMERICAN INDIAN AFFAIRS   [1106]
966 Hungerford Drive, Suite 12-B
Rockville, MD 20850
(240) 314-7155
Fax: (240) 314-7159

E-MAIL ADDRESS:
lw.aaia@verizon.net

WEB SITE ADDRESS:
www.indian-affairs.org

FOUNDED: 1922

AREAS OF INTEREST:
Advocates for the well-being of Indian people. Primary focus on cultural preservation, youth/scholarships, health and sovereignty.

NAME(S) OF PROGRAMS:
● **Sequoyah Graduate Scholarships**

TYPE:
Scholarships. Sequoyah Graduate Scholarships are for American Indian and Alaskan Natives who are pursuing graduate degrees in many diverse fields.

PURPOSE:
To promote the welfare of American Indians and Alaska Natives by supporting efforts to sustain and perpetuate their cultures and languages; to protect their sovereignty, constitutional, legal and human rights and natural resources; to improve their health, education and economic and community development.

ELIGIBILITY:
Open to graduate students in any curriculum.

GEOGRAPHIC RESTRICTIONS:
Continental United States and Alaska.

FINANCIAL DATA:
Amount of support per award: $1,500.

NUMBER OF AWARDS: Varies.

APPLICATION INFORMATION:
Students are eligible to apply on a yearly basis. When applying they must submit:
(1) completed application;
(2) copy of tribal enrollment;
(3) copy of certificate of Indian blood (one-fourth minimum);
(4) student essay;

(5) two letters of recommendation and;
(6) minimum of two years' transcripts through most recent semester.

Incomplete application will not be considered.

Faxed or e-mailed documents will not be considered. Application packages must be mailed.

Duration: One academic year. This scholarship does not automatically renew. Students are eligible to apply on a yearly basis.

Deadline: Application packages are accepted April 4 to June 13.

PUBLICATIONS:
Brochure.

ADDRESS INQUIRIES TO:
Lisa Wyzlic
Director of Scholarship Programs
(See address above.)

ASSOCIATION ON AMERICAN INDIAN AFFAIRS [1107]

966 Hungerford Drive, Suite 12-B
Rockville, MD 20850
(240) 314-7155
Fax: (240) 314-7159

E-MAIL ADDRESS:
lw.aaia@verizon.net

WEB SITE ADDRESS:
www.indian-affairs.org

FOUNDED: 1922

AREAS OF INTEREST:
Advocates for the well-being of Indian people. Primary focus on cultural preservation, youth/scholarships, health and sovereignty.

NAME(S) OF PROGRAMS:
● **Displaced Homemaker Scholarships**

TYPE:
Scholarships. Intended for those men and women who would not otherwise be able to complete their educational goals due to family responsibilities.

PURPOSE:
To promote the welfare of American Indians and Alaska Natives by supporting efforts to sustain and perpetuate their cultures and languages; to protect their sovereignty, constitutional, legal and human rights and natural resources; to improve their health, education and economic and community development.

ELIGIBILITY:
Open to displaced homemakers, men and women, 30 years and older.

GEOGRAPHIC RESTRICTIONS:
Continental United States and Alaska.

FINANCIAL DATA:
Amount of support per award: $1,500.

NUMBER OF AWARDS: Varies.

APPLICATION INFORMATION:
Those applying must include:
(1) copy of tribal enrollment;
(2) completed application;
(3) copy of certificate of Indian blood (minimum one-fourth);
(4) student essay;
(5) minimum of two years of transcripts through most recent semester;
(6) two letters of recommendation;

(7) essay of family responsibilities;
(8) monthly budget and;
(9) document of class standing.

Faxed or e-mailed documents cannot be considered. Application packages must be mailed. Incomplete applications will not be considered.

Duration: One year. Reapplication necessary.

Deadline: Application packages are accepted April 4 to June 13.

ADDRESS INQUIRIES TO:
Lisa Wyzlic
Director of Scholarship Programs
(See address above.)

ASSOCIATION ON AMERICAN INDIAN AFFAIRS [1108]

966 Hungerford Drive, Suite 12-B
Rockville, MD 20850
(240) 314-7155
Fax: (240) 314-7159

E-MAIL ADDRESS:
lw.aaia@verizon.net

WEB SITE ADDRESS:
www.indian-affairs.org

FOUNDED: 1922

AREAS OF INTEREST:
Advocates for the well-being of Indian people. Primary focus on cultural preservation, youth/scholarships, health and sovereignty.

NAME(S) OF PROGRAMS:
● **Allogan Slagle Memorial Scholarship**

TYPE:
Scholarships. Offered to American Indian and Alaskan Native graduate and undergraduate students who are members of tribes that are not federally recognized.

PURPOSE:
To promote the welfare of American Indians and Alaska Natives by supporting efforts to sustain and perpetuate their cultures and languages; to protect their sovereignty, constitutional, legal and human rights and natural resources; to improve their health, education and economic and community development.

ELIGIBILITY:
Applicants must be American Indian and Native Alaskan graduate or undergraduate students who are members of tribes that are not federally recognized.

FINANCIAL DATA:
Amount of support per award: $1,500.

NUMBER OF AWARDS: Varies.

APPLICATION INFORMATION:
Students are eligible to apply on a yearly basis. Those applying must include:
(1) copy of tribal enrollment; (2) completed application;
(3) certificate of Indian blood is requested; documents showing lineal descent are acceptable;
(4) student essay;
(5) minimum of two years of transcripts through most recent semester and;
(6) two letters of recommendation.

Incomplete application packages will not be considered.

Faxed or e-mailed documents cannot be considered. Applications must be mailed.

Duration: One year.

Deadline: Application packages are accepted April 4 to June 13.

ADDRESS INQUIRIES TO:
Lisa Wyzlic
Director of Scholarship Programs
(See address above.)

ASSOCIATION ON AMERICAN INDIAN AFFAIRS [1109]

966 Hungerford Drive, Suite 12-B
Rockville, MD 20850
(240) 314-7155
Fax: (240) 314-7159

E-MAIL ADDRESS:
lw.aaia@verizon.net

WEB SITE ADDRESS:
www.indian-affairs.org

FOUNDED: 1922

AREAS OF INTEREST:
Advocates for the well-being of Indian people. Primary focus on cultural preservation, youth/scholarships, health and sovereignty.

NAME(S) OF PROGRAMS:
● **Florence Young Memorial Scholarships**

TYPE:
Scholarships. Offered to American Indian or Alaskan Native graduate students pursuing a Master's in the arts, law or public health.

PURPOSE:
To promote the welfare of American Indians and Alaska Natives by supporting efforts to sustain and perpetuate their cultures and languages; to protect their sovereignty, constitutional, legal and human rights and natural resources; to improve their health, education and economic and community development.

ELIGIBILITY:
Open to graduate students seeking a degree in law, art or public health.

GEOGRAPHIC RESTRICTIONS:
Continental United States and Alaska.

FINANCIAL DATA:
Amount of support per award: $1,500.

NUMBER OF AWARDS: Varies.

APPLICATION INFORMATION:
Students are eligible to apply on a yearly basis. Those applying must include:
(1) completed application;
(2) copy of tribal enrollment;
(3) copy of certificate of Indian blood (minimally one-quarter);
(4) student essay;
(5) minimum of two years of transcripts through most recent semester and;
(6) two letters of recommendation.

Incomplete application packages will not be considered.

Faxed or e-mailed documents cannot be considered. Application packages must be mailed.

Duration: One year.

Deadline: Application packages are accepted April 4 to June 13.

ADDRESS INQUIRIES TO:
Lisa Wyzlic
Director of Scholarship Programs
(See address above.)

ASSOCIATION ON AMERICAN INDIAN AFFAIRS   [1110]

966 Hungerford Drive, Suite 12-B
Rockville, MD 20850
(240) 314-7155
Fax: (240) 314-7159

E-MAIL ADDRESS:
lw.aaia@verizon.net

WEB SITE ADDRESS:
www.indian affairs.org

FOUNDED: 1922

AREAS OF INTEREST:
Advocates for the well-being of Indian people. Primary focus on cultural preservation, youth/scholarships, health and sovereignty.

NAME(S) OF PROGRAMS:
- **Elizabeth and Sherman Asche Memorial Scholarship Fund**

TYPE:
Scholarships. Offered to graduate and undergraduate students pursuing a major in public health and science.

PURPOSE:
To provide financial assistance to graduate and undergraduate students pursuing a major in public health or science.

ELIGIBILITY:
Open to graduate and undergraduate students in public health and science fields.

GEOGRAPHIC RESTRICTIONS:
Continental United States and Alaska.

FINANCIAL DATA:
Amount of support per award: $1,500.

NUMBER OF AWARDS: Varies.

APPLICATION INFORMATION:
Students are eligible to apply on a yearly basis. The following items must be submitted:
(1) complete application;
(2) copy of tribal enrollment;
(3) copy of certificate of Indian blood, minimum one-quarter;
(4) student essay;
(5) two letters of recommendation;
(6) minimum of two years transcripts through most recent semester and;
(7) document of class standing (undergraduates) or number of credits needed to be considered full-time status (graduates).

Application packages must be mailed. Faxed or e-mailed documents will not be accepted.

Incomplete applications will not be considered.

Deadline: Application packages are accepted April 4 to June 13.

ADDRESS INQUIRIES TO:
Lisa Wyzlic
Director of Scholarship Programs
(See address above.)

ASSOCIATION ON AMERICAN INDIAN AFFAIRS   [1111]

966 Hungerford Drive, Suite 12-B
Rockville, MD 20850
(240) 314-7155
Fax: (240) 314-7159

E-MAIL ADDRESS:
lw.aaia@verizon.net

WEB SITE ADDRESS:
www.indian-affairs.org

FOUNDED: 1922

AREAS OF INTEREST:
Advocates for the well-being of Indian people. Primary focus on cultural preservation, youth/scholarships, health and sovereignty.

NAME(S) OF PROGRAMS:
- **Emilie Hesemeyer Memorial Scholarship**

TYPE:
Scholarships.

PURPOSE:
To promote the welfare of American Indians and Alaska Natives by supporting efforts to sustain and perpetuate their cultures and languages; to protect their sovereignty, constitutional, legal and human rights and natural resources; to improve their health, education and economic and community development.

ELIGIBILITY:
Preference is given, but not limited to, students pursuing a major in education.

GEOGRAPHIC RESTRICTIONS:
Continental United States and Alaska.

FINANCIAL DATA:
Amount of support per award: $1,500 per year; $750 disbursement per semester, with subsequent disbursements requiring a copy of the first semester's grades and second semester class schedule. Student progress will be monitored and reported to outside funder. For the 2011-12 school year, scholarships will only be awarded as funding allows. Current recipients will receive funding as previously allocated.

NUMBER OF AWARDS: Varies.

APPLICATION INFORMATION:
Students are eligible to apply on a yearly basis. Those applying must submit:
(1) completed application;
(2) copy of tribal enrollment;
(3) copy of certificate of Indian blood (one-fourth minimum);
(4) student essay;
(5) two letters of recommendation;
(6) minimum of two years transcripts through most recent semester and;
(7) document of class standing.

Incomplete applications will not be considered. Application packages must be mailed. Faxed or e-mailed documents will not be accepted.

Duration: Renewable up to four years toward any single degree pending satisfactory progress.

Deadline: Application packages are accepted April 4 to June 13.

ADDRESS INQUIRIES TO:
Lisa Wyzlic
Director of Scholarship Programs
(See address above.)

*SPECIAL STIPULATIONS:
Recipients' progress will be monitored and reported to outside funding source. Additional information and contact with academic advisor may be required.

BNSF FOUNDATION   [1112]

2650 Lou Menk Drive
Fort Worth, TX 76131-2830
(817) 867-6458
Fax: (817) 352-7925

E-MAIL ADDRESS:
bnsffoundation@bnsf.com

WEB SITE ADDRESS:
www.bnsffoundation.org

NAME(S) OF PROGRAMS:
- **Native American Scholarship Program**

TYPE:
Scholarships. Awarded annually to outstanding Native American high school seniors from funds provided by the Foundation, for up to four years or until undergraduate degree requirements are completed, whichever occurs first. Scholarship winners may attend any accredited college (two-year leading to a four-year degree) or university in the U.S.

LEGAL BASIS:
Corporate foundation.

ELIGIBILITY:
High school seniors having one-fourth or more Indian blood are eligible. Applicants need not be related to Burlington Northern Santa Fe personnel to qualify. Two scholarships are provided exclusively for members of the Navajo Tribe and the other three are available to any Native American high school students residing in Arizona, California, Colorado, Kansas, Minnesota, Montana, New Mexico, North Dakota, Oklahoma, Oregon, South Dakota, and Washington.

Winners are selected on the basis of strong academic performance in high school, with award preference being given to the study of any of the sciences such as medicine, engineering, natural and physical sciences, as well as business, education and health administration.

GEOGRAPHIC RESTRICTIONS:
Arizona, California, Colorado, Kansas, Minnesota, Montana, New Mexico, North Dakota, Oklahoma, Oregon, South Dakota and Washington.

FINANCIAL DATA:
Amount of support per award: $1,000 to $2,500 annually for up to four years or until undergraduate degree requirements are completed, whichever occurs first (but not to exceed five years). Financial need determines the amount awarded.

NUMBER OF AWARDS: 5.

APPLICATION INFORMATION:
The scholarship is administered by the American Indian Science and Engineering Society (AISES) and all winners are selected by the organization. Applications may be obtained by writing American Indian Science and Engineering Society, P.O. Box 9828, Albuquerque, NM 87119-9828. All correspondence and questions should be directed to AISES.

Duration: Up to four years or until undergraduate degree requirements are completed, whichever occurs first, but not to exceed five years.

Deadline: April 1.

ADDRESS INQUIRIES TO:
American Indian Science and Engineering Society
(See address above.)

BUREAU OF INDIAN EDUCATION [1113]

215 Dean A. McGee
Suite 610
Oklahoma City, OK 73102
(405) 605-6001
Fax: (405) 605-6010

E-MAIL ADDRESS:
alicia.henson@bie.edu

WEB SITE ADDRESS:
www.bie.edu

FOUNDED: 1824

AREAS OF INTEREST:
Elementary and secondary education tribal colleges.

NAME(S) OF PROGRAMS:
- **Higher Education Grant Program for American Indians**

TYPE:
Fellowships; Scholarships.

YEAR PROGRAM STARTED: 1949

PURPOSE:
To provide financial aid to eligible Indian students enabling them to attend accredited institutions of higher education.

LEGAL BASIS:
Snyder Act.

ELIGIBILITY:
Applicant must be a member of a tribe eligible for services from the Bureau, enrolled or accepted for enrollment in an accredited college and have financial need as determined by the institution's financial aid office.

FINANCIAL DATA:
The grants are intended to supplement the financial aid package prepared by the educational institution's financial aid officer. The grant meets the unmet need portion of the package.
Amount of support per award: Varies.
Matching fund requirements: Meets the unmet need portion of the institution's financial aid package.

COOPERATIVE FUNDING PROGRAMS: Other donor's funding programs are a part of the financial aid package.

NUMBER OF APPLICANTS MOST RECENT YEAR: 20,000.

NUMBER OF AWARDS: 15,000.

APPLICATION INFORMATION:
Candidates should request an application from a home agency or tribal Higher Education Grant Program (HEGP). Contact the BIA/Tribal census office to obtain a Certificate of Degree of Indian Blood (CDIB) and tribal enrollment and submit with the application. Write to the admissions office of the chosen school for an application. Request a financial aid packet from the school's Financial Aid Officer, who will prepare a financial aid package based on the applicant's need. Then submit all these forms to the appropriate offices well in advance of the deadline.
Duration: One academic year. Must renew annually.

PUBLICATIONS:
Newsletter for prospective college students.

ADDRESS INQUIRIES TO:
Home agency or tribally administered Higher Education Grant Program

CATCHING THE DREAM [1114]

8200 Mountain Road, N.E.
Suite 203
Albuquerque, NM 87110
(505) 262-2351
Fax: (505) 262-0534

E-MAIL ADDRESS:
NScholarsh@aol.com

WEB SITE ADDRESS:
www.catchingthedream.org

FOUNDED: 1986

AREAS OF INTEREST:
Scholarships for Native college students and improvement of Indian schools and postsecondary education for Native American students in the fields of math, engineering, science, business, education and computers.

CONSULTING OR VOLUNTEER SERVICES:
The Fund assists Native American students who need help in locating other sources of funding and provides fund-raising, management training, conferences, and seminars.

NAME(S) OF PROGRAMS:
- **MESBEC (Math, Engineering, Science, Business, Education and Computers) Program**
- **Native American Leadership in Education (NALE) Program**
- **Tribal Business Management (TBM) Program**

TYPE:
Conferences/seminars; Project/program grants; Scholarships; Technical assistance. CTD also works to improve Indian schools through a program of grants and technical assistance. This work has led to the development of 35 Exemplary Programs in Indian education since 1988. The annual Exemplary Institute is a meeting of these Exemplary Programs, where they teach other people how to develop similar programs.

MESBEC Program consists of competitive scholarships for high-potential Native Americans studying in math, engineering, science, business, education and computers.

NALE Program consists of competitive scholarships for high-potential paraprofessional Native Americans who plan to complete their degrees and obtain credentials as teachers, counselors or administrators.

Tribal Business Management (TBM) Program consists of competitive scholarships for native students in all fields of business.

YEAR PROGRAM STARTED: 1986

PURPOSE:
To help tribes prepare young people to work in the fields which are critical for economic, social, business and political development in Indian Country.

LEGAL BASIS:
Nonprofit organization.

ELIGIBILITY:
Applicants must be at least one-quarter blood member of a federally recognized, state recognized or terminated Indian tribe. They must have high potential for the field of study and work for which they are preparing. They must attend an accredited U.S. college or university. They must have clear goals in mind and have done some work toward accomplishing these goals. The goals must be related to the betterment of Indian people or the betterment of an Indian tribe or

community. Progress toward accomplishing a goal may be demonstrated by study, by work, by volunteer work or by other means.

Students with no clear goals are discouraged from applying. Normally, successful applicants will plan to earn a four-year degree or a graduate degree. In a few cases, associate degrees are approved. Applicants must apply for all other sources of funding for which they are eligible, including private scholarship sources, corporate traineeships, federal funds, loans, jobs, grants and so forth.

Students can contact CTD up to three years in advance.

GEOGRAPHIC RESTRICTIONS:
United States.

FINANCIAL DATA:
Amount of support per award: $500 to $5,000.
Total amount of support: $280,000 for fiscal year 2010.

NUMBER OF APPLICANTS MOST RECENT YEAR: 150.

APPLICATION INFORMATION:
Duration: Until completion of degree.
Deadline: March 15 for summer school. September 15 for winter quarter and spring semester. April 15 for fall semester.

PUBLICATIONS:
The National Indian Grant Directory; Preparing Indian Students for College; Exemplary Programs in Indian Education; Reading for College.

IRS IDENTIFICATION NUMBER: 85-0360858

BOARD OF DIRECTORS:
James Lujan, President
Darrell Jeanotte, Vice President
Gloria Hale, Treasurer
Jodie Palmer, Secretary
Dr. Dean Chavers
Ed Harris
Parry Murray
John Tohtsoni, Jr.
Lindsay Wagner

CHEROKEE NATION OF OKLAHOMA [1115]

P.O. Box 948
Tahlequah, OK 74465
(918) 453-5000
(918) 453-5577
Fax: (918) 458-5898

E-MAIL ADDRESS:
reva-crawford@cherokee.org

WEB SITE ADDRESS:
www.cherokee.org

FOUNDED: 1904

AREAS OF INTEREST:
Planning and development (individual and tribal), health, education and welfare.

CONSULTING OR VOLUNTEER SERVICES:
Tribal government administration consultants and volunteers in all interest areas available to eligible tribal members.

NAME(S) OF PROGRAMS:
- **Community Self-Help Grants**
- **Graduate Scholarships**
- **Higher Education Program**

TYPE:
Project/program grants; Scholarships; Technical assistance. Self-help grants. Financial and other support through all programs to eligible tribal members.

YEAR PROGRAM STARTED: 1964

PURPOSE:
To serve its tribes and members in the areas indicated.

LEGAL BASIS:
Federally recognized Indian tribe.

ELIGIBILITY:
Tribal membership is required for majority of services.

GEOGRAPHIC RESTRICTIONS:
Primarily northeast Oklahoma.

FINANCIAL DATA:
Tribe operates $200,000,000 in social and economic programs.
Amount of support per award: Varies.
Total amount of support: Varies.

APPLICATION INFORMATION:
Guidelines and application form is available on the web site.
Duration: Continuous.

ADDRESS INQUIRIES TO:
Reva Crawford
Director of Solutions Development
(See address above.)

FIRST NATIONS DEVELOPMENT INSTITUTE   [1116]
351 Coffman Street
Suite 200
Longmont, CO 80501
(303) 774-7836
Fax: (303) 774-7841

E-MAIL ADDRESS:
info@firstnations.org

WEB SITE ADDRESS:
www.firstnations.org

FOUNDED: 1980

AREAS OF INTEREST:
Native American community development, Native American-owned business, small business development and capacity building.

CONSULTING OR VOLUNTEER SERVICES:
Yes.

NAME(S) OF PROGRAMS:
• **The Eagle Staff Fund**

TYPE:
Capital grants; Conferences/seminars; Development grants; Internships; Project/program grants; Research grants; Seed money grants; Technical assistance; Training grants; Research contracts. Institute has program development type of grants.

YEAR PROGRAM STARTED: 1994

PURPOSE:
To assist native communities to control their assets and to build capacity so that they can direct their economic futures.

LEGAL BASIS:
Nonprofit organization.

ELIGIBILITY:
Eligible organizations include:
(1) tribal or Native government programs, entities, and enterprises;
(2) tribally or community-controlled

development organizations;
(3) tribally or Native-controlled health, education, or other social programs or institutions;
(4) Native arts and crafts associations, co-ops and guilds;
(5) intertribal and regional tribal or Native groups;
(6) Native grassroots efforts and community programs and;
(7) Native non-profit on or near Reservation.

Grants are not made to individuals for for-profit businesses, programs serving exclusively urban Native communities, programs serving Natives but not controlled by a majority of Natives, for-profit Native consulting firms, for-profit Native businesses except those associated with a nonprofit Native enterprise, or religious organizations (except for traditional Native American spiritual programs).

GEOGRAPHIC RESTRICTIONS:
United States and its territories.

FINANCIAL DATA:
Amount of support per award: $500 to $56,000 over three years; Average: $20,673.
Total amount of support: $537,500.

NUMBER OF AWARDS: 26.

APPLICATION INFORMATION:
Only invited proposals are being accepted.
Duration: Up to three years. Renewal possible.

PUBLICATIONS:
Publications list; annual report.

IRS IDENTIFICATION NUMBER: 54-1254491

ADDRESS INQUIRIES TO:
Michael E. Roberts, President
First Nations Development Institute
(See address above.)

INSTITUTE OF AMERICAN INDIAN ARTS (IAIA)   [1117]
83 Avan Nu Po Road
Santa Fe, NM 87508
(505) 424-2331
(800) 804-6422
Fax: (505) 424-4500

E-MAIL ADDRESS:
enrollment@iaia.edu

WEB SITE ADDRESS:
www.iaia.edu

FOUNDED: 1962

AREAS OF INTEREST:
Education of Native American and Alaska Native Corporation students through a four-year program leading to a Bachelor of Fine Arts or Bachelor of Arts degree.

CONSULTING OR VOLUNTEER SERVICES:
Serve as a resource to Indian tribes seeking to develop arts educational programs or tribal museums and cultural centers.

NAME(S) OF PROGRAMS:
• **IAIA Merit Scholarship**
• **IAIA Tuition Scholarship**

TYPE:
Awards/prizes; Scholarships.

YEAR PROGRAM STARTED: 1962

PURPOSE:
To provide a four-year postsecondary education to American Indian and Alaska natives.

LEGAL BASIS:
Congressionally chartered, fully accredited institute.

ELIGIBILITY:
Applicants for scholarships must be members of federally recognized tribes and must be enrolled at IAIA.

IAIA Tuition Scholarship:
(1) need based;
(2) federally recognized Indian tribe or Alaska native and;
(3) full or part-time, degree seeking.

IAIA Merit Scholarship:
(1) academic performance (3.0 or above);
(2) any/all students (non-Indian eligibility) and;
(3) American Indian College Fund is need-based and merit (only Native Americans can apply).

FINANCIAL DATA:
Amount of support per award: IAIA Merit Scholarship: $500 to $1,000; IAIA Tuition Scholarship: $200 to $500.

COOPERATIVE FUNDING PROGRAMS: Federal Pell Grant; Federal College Work-Study; Bureau of Indian Affairs fund programs (home agency): awarded for personal/miscellaneous, books, supplies and transportation.

NUMBER OF APPLICANTS MOST RECENT YEAR:
142.

APPLICATION INFORMATION:
Contact IAIA Financial Aid Manager for information. Submit FAFSA and tax information, as well as tribal enrollment documentation.
Deadline: May 1,

PUBLICATIONS:
Academic catalog; academic brochures; admissions application; financial aid applications.

IRS IDENTIFICATION NUMBER: 85-0365964

OFFICERS:
Dr. Robert Martin, President
Nena Anaya, Director of Admissions, Recruitment and Enrollment
David Rivard, Director of Finance
Roy Melandez, Director of Institutional Advancement
Dr. Ann Filemyr, Academic Dean
Carmen Henan, Dean of Students

ADDRESS INQUIRIES TO:
Manager, Office of Enrollment Management
(See address above.)

*PLEASE NOTE:
Non-Indian and/or foreign students accepted.

NATIONAL SOCIETY DAUGHTERS OF THE AMERICAN REVOLUTION
1776 D Street, N.W.
Washington, DC 20006-5303
(202) 879-3292
Fax: (202) 879-3348

WEB SITE ADDRESS:
www.dar.org

TYPE:
Scholarships. Intended to help Native American college/university and technical school students at the undergraduate or graduate level.

See entry 1845 for full listing.

NATIONAL SOCIETY DAUGHTERS OF THE AMERICAN REVOLUTION
1776 D Street, N.W.
Washington, DC 20006-5303
(202) 879-3292
Fax: (202) 879-3348

WEB SITE ADDRESS:
www.dar.org

TYPE:
Scholarships. Intended to help Native American students enrolled full-time at a two- or four-year college or university.

See entry 1846 for full listing.

NATIVE AMERICAN COMMUNITY BOARD (NACB) [1118]
P.O. Box 572
Lake Andes, SD 57356-0572
(605) 487-7072
Fax: (605) 487-7964

E-MAIL ADDRESS:
charon@charles-mix.com

WEB SITE ADDRESS:
www.nativeshop.org

FOUNDED: 1986

AREAS OF INTEREST:
Civil rights, women's rights, reproductive justice, and a healthy environment.

NAME(S) OF PROGRAMS:
● **College Intern Program**

TYPE:
Internships.

PURPOSE:
To address pertinent issues of health, education, land and water rights, and economic development of Native American people.

ELIGIBILITY:
College juniors, seniors or graduate students interested in Native American rights and health issues. Priority will be given to those wishing to stay long-term (six months or longer).

FINANCIAL DATA:
Amount of support per award: $250 biweekly.
Total amount of support: Varies.

NUMBER OF AWARDS: 8.

APPLICATION INFORMATION:
Contact the NACB for application procedures.
Duration: Three months to one year, with three months being the preferred minimum stay.

ADDRESS INQUIRIES TO:
Charon Asetoyer, Executive Director
(See address above.)

THE NEWBERRY LIBRARY [1119]
Committee on Awards
60 West Walton Street
Chicago, IL 60610-7324
(312) 255-3666
Fax: (312) 255-3680

E-MAIL ADDRESS:
research@newberry.org

WEB SITE ADDRESS:
www.newberry.
org/research/felshp/fellowshome.html

AREAS OF INTEREST:
Native American women, humanities and social sciences.

NAME(S) OF PROGRAMS:
● **Frances C. Allen Fellowships**

TYPE:
Fellowships; Visiting scholars. Allen fellows are expected to spend a significant part of their tenure in residence at Newberry's D'Arcy McNickle Center for American Indian History.

PURPOSE:
To encourage study by Native American women of the humanities and social sciences.

LEGAL BASIS:
Research library.

ELIGIBILITY:
Applicants must be women of Native American heritage. While candidates for this award may be working on any graduate or preprofessional field, the particular goal of the Fellowship is to encourage Native American women in their studies of the humanities and social sciences.

FINANCIAL DATA:
Financial support may include travel expenses.
Amount of support per award: Up to $8,000 of approved expenses.

NUMBER OF APPLICANTS MOST RECENT YEAR:
1.

NUMBER OF AWARDS: Varies.

APPLICATION INFORMATION:
Contact the Committee for application materials. Applicants must submit a budget of travel and research expenses.
Duration: One month to one year.
Deadline: First weekday in March.

STAFF:
Diane Dillon, Director of Scholarly and Undergraduate Programs

ADDRESS INQUIRIES TO:
Committee on Awards
(See address above.)

*SPECIAL STIPULATIONS:
Allen Fellows are expected to spend a significant part of their tenure in residence at the D'Arcy McNickle Center for American Indian History.

NORTH DAKOTA STATE BOARD FOR INDIAN SCHOLARSHIPS [1120]
1815 Schafer Street
Suite 202
Bismarck, ND 58501-1217
(701) 224-2501
Fax: (701) 224-2500

E-MAIL ADDRESS:
rhonda.schauer@ndus.nodak.edu

WEB SITE ADDRESS:
www.ndus.nodak.edu

FOUNDED: 1963

AREAS OF INTEREST:
Native Americans interested in pursuing a higher education degree.

NAME(S) OF PROGRAMS:
● **North Dakota Indian Scholarship Program**

TYPE:
Scholarships. Grants to undergraduate and graduate Indian students in North Dakota colleges.

YEAR PROGRAM STARTED: 1963

PURPOSE:
To provide assistance for Native Americans to attend college.

LEGAL BASIS:
Chapter 15 to 63 of the North Dakota Century Code, as amended.

ELIGIBILITY:
Applicants must be of at least one-fourth degree Indian blood and resident of North Dakota or be an enrolled member of a tribe resident in North Dakota, be accepted by an institution of higher learning in North Dakota, demonstrate financial need and indicate probable and continuing success as a student.

GEOGRAPHIC RESTRICTIONS:
North Dakota.

FINANCIAL DATA:
Amount of support per award: $700 to $2,000 per academic year. Average $700. Annual sum is divided into semester or quarter amounts and payment is dependent upon maintenance of C average.

COOPERATIVE FUNDING PROGRAMS: College financial aid directors work out students' aid packages using BIA, Pell, GI Bill, etc.

NUMBER OF APPLICANTS MOST RECENT YEAR:
389.

NUMBER OF AWARDS: 324.

APPLICATION INFORMATION:
Submit application form, budget form, certificate of Indian blood and residence or tribal enrollment, high school credit record and college transcript if previously enrolled.
Duration: Four years to degree for full-time course of study if C average is maintained and continued need is demonstrated.
Deadline: July 15.

OFFICERS:
Mike Hillman, Vice Chancellor
Scott Davis, Secretary
Cornelius P. Grant, Appointee
Rhonda M. Schauer, Administrator

ADDRESS INQUIRIES TO:
Rhonda M. Schauer, Administrator
(See address above.)

OFFICE OF INDIAN ENERGY AND ECONOMIC DEVELOPMENT [1121]
Division of Workforce Development
MS-SIB-20
1951 Constitution Avenue, N.W.
Washington, DC 20245
(202) 219-0740
Fax: (202) 208-4564

E-MAIL ADDRESS:
lynn.forcia@bia.gov

WEB SITE ADDRESS:
www.doi.gov
www.bia.gov

FOUNDED: 1824

AREAS OF INTEREST:
Vocational training, job placement, education, childcare and related services.

NAME(S) OF PROGRAMS:
- **Indian Employment Assistance**
- **Public Law 102-477**

TYPE:
Project/program grants; Training grants. Vocational training and job placement, advisory services and counseling, education, childcare and youth development programs.

YEAR PROGRAM STARTED: 1956

PURPOSE:
To provide individual grants for adult vocational training and job placement services for Indians.

LEGAL BASIS:
Public Law 67-85, The Snyder Act of November 2, 1921; Public Law 84-959, Indian Adult Vocational Training Act of August 3, 1956; Public Law 102-477.

ELIGIBILITY:
Applicant must be a member of a federally recognized tribe, band or group of Indians, whose residence is on or near an Indian reservation under the jurisdiction of BIA.

GEOGRAPHIC RESTRICTIONS:
United States.

FINANCIAL DATA:
Amount of support per award: $800 to $6,500 per year. $5,000 average.
Total amount of support: Over $100,000,000 disbursed annually.

COOPERATIVE FUNDING PROGRAMS: Indian Education, Training and Employment.

APPLICATION INFORMATION:
Applicants should make application to the nearest Agency or Tribal Employment Assistance. Contact tribal office nearest to place of residence.
Duration: One year. Renewal possible if continuing training.

STAFF:
Lynn Forcia, Chief, Division of Workforce Development
Jody Garrison, Manpower Development Specialist

ADDRESS INQUIRIES TO:
Jody Garrison, Manpower Development Specialist
(See address above.)

RUNNING STRONG FOR AMERICAN INDIAN YOUTH   [1122]

2550 Huntington Avenue
Suite 200
Alexandria, VA 22303-1400
(703) 317-9881
Fax: (703) 317-9690

E-MAIL ADDRESS:
info@indianyouth.org

WEB SITE ADDRESS:
www.indianyouth.org

FOUNDED: 1986

AREAS OF INTEREST:
Native Americans.

TYPE:
Capital grants; Challenge/matching grants; General operating grants; Project/program grants; Seed money grants.

YEAR PROGRAM STARTED: 1986

PURPOSE:
To help American Indian people meet their immediate survival needs - food, water and shelter - while implementing and supporting programs designed to create opportunities for self-sufficiency and self-esteem, particularly for tribal youth.

ELIGIBILITY:
No grants are made to individuals or fund-raising events. Grants made only to programs that support Native Americans.

GEOGRAPHIC RESTRICTIONS:
United States.

FINANCIAL DATA:
Amount of support per award: Up to $5,000 for new applicants.
Total amount of support: Approximately $1,500,000 for fiscal year 2009 (a large majority of which is committed to long-term programs).

NUMBER OF AWARDS: Varies.

APPLICATION INFORMATION:
E-mail or call for grant guidelines.
Duration: Up to five years. Must reapply each year.

PUBLICATIONS:
Annual report; application guidelines.

IRS IDENTIFICATION NUMBER: 54-1594578

ADDRESS INQUIRIES TO:
Lauren Haas Finkelstein
Executive Director
(See address above.)

U.S. DEPARTMENT OF EDUCATION   [1123]

Office of Indian Education
Office of Elementary and Secondary Education
400 Maryland Avenue, S.W.
Washington, DC 20202
(202) 401-0113
(202) 260-1454
Fax: (202) 260-7779

E-MAIL ADDRESS:
bernard.garcia@ed.gov

WEB SITE ADDRESS:
www.ed.gov

NAME(S) OF PROGRAMS:
- **Indian Education-Formula Grants to Local Education Agencies (LEAs)**

TYPE:
Formula grants. Grants to provide financial assistance to LEAs and tribal schools to develop and carry out elementary and secondary school programs specially designed to meet the special educational and culturally related educational needs of Indian children.

LEGAL BASIS:
Public Law 92-318, Title IV, Part A, as amended (25 U.S.C. 2601-2606, 2651).

ELIGIBILITY:
Local educational agencies which have at least 10 Indian children or in which Indians constitute at least 25% of the total enrollment may apply. However, these enrollment requirements do not apply to an LEA in Alaska, California or Oklahoma that serves Indian children or an LEA on, or in proximity to, an Indian reservation. An Indian tribe or an organization controlled or sanctioned by an Indian tribal government and that operates a school for children of that tribe is eligible if that school provides its students an educational program that meets the standards established by the Bureau of Indian Affairs (BIA) or is operated by that tribe or organization under a contract with the BIA.

FINANCIAL DATA:
Amount of support per award: Varies.
Total amount of support: Varies.

APPLICATION INFORMATION:
Application instructions and forms are available upon request.
Duration: 12 to 36 months, with budget periods of one year's duration.

ADDRESS INQUIRIES TO:
Indian Education Programs
(See address above.)

U.S. DEPARTMENT OF HEALTH AND HUMAN SERVICES   [1124]

HHS/ACF/ANA Aerospace Center
901 D Street, S.W., 2nd Floor W.
Washington, DC 20447
(202) 690-7776
(877) 922-9262 (Help Desk)
Fax: (202) 690-8145

E-MAIL ADDRESS:
anacomments@acf.hhs.gov

WEB SITE ADDRESS:
www.acf.hhs.gov

FOUNDED: 1974

AREAS OF INTEREST:
General community programming, training and technical assistance and research, demonstration and evaluation.

NAME(S) OF PROGRAMS:
- **Native American Programs**

TYPE:
Demonstration grants; Development grants; Project/program grants; Research grants; Seed money grants; Technical assistance; Training grants. Financial Assistance grants may be used for such purposes as, but not limited to, Governance Projects, development of codes and ordinances and status clarification activities; Economic Development Projects, to promote business starts for Native-owned businesses and improve Native American housing management; and Social Development Projects, to assume local control of planning and delivering social services in Native American communities, developing local models related to comprehensive planning and delivery of social services and developing or coordinating activities with state-funded projects in decreasing the incidence of child abuse, neglect and fetal alcohol syndrome.

YEAR PROGRAM STARTED: 1973

PURPOSE:
To support projects that improve social and economic conditions of Native Americans within their communities and increase the effectiveness of Indian Tribes and Native American organizations in meeting their economic and social goals.

LEGAL BASIS:
Native American Programs Act of 1974, as amended, Public Law 93-644; Older Americans Act Amendments of 1987, Title V, Public Law 100-175; Indian Reorganization Act Amendments, Section 215, Public Law 100-581; Older Americans Act Amendments of 1992, Title VIII, Public Law 102-375; 42 U.S.C. 2991 et. seq.

ELIGIBILITY:
Governing bodies of Indian tribes, Alaskan Native villages and regional associations established by the Alaska Native Claims Settlement Act, Indian and Alaska Native Organizations in urban or rural nonreservation areas, public and nonprofit agencies serving Native Hawaiians and other Native American Pacific Islanders which include the Native peoples from Guam, American Samoa, Palau or the Commonwealth of the Northern Mariana Islands. The populations served may be located on those islands or in the U.S.

GEOGRAPHIC RESTRICTIONS:
United States.

FINANCIAL DATA:
Amount of support per award: Approximately $125,000 average.

Total amount of support: Approximately $38,500,000 annually.

Matching fund requirements: A matching share of 20% is required unless waived in accordance with criteria which is published in 45 CFR, Part 1336.50. This program has maintenance of effort requirements.

APPLICATION INFORMATION:
Nonprofit organizations which have not previously received ACF program support must submit proof of nonprofit status. The Administration for Native Americans will provide each applicant agency with the appropriate forms for applying for Federal Assistance and instructions for preparation of application for grants from Human Development Services programs.

Applications should be submitted to ACF Division of Grants Management Administration for Children and Families, Mail Stop AERO-6, OPS/ODG, 370 L'Enfant Promenade, S.W., Washington, DC 20447.

Duration: One year with possibility of multiyear funding.

Deadline: Varies.

STAFF:
Lillian Sparks, Deputy Commissioner

ADDRESS INQUIRIES TO:
Administration for Native Americans
(See address above.)

THE MORRIS K. UDALL AND STEWART L. UDALL FOUNDATION [1125]

130 South Scott Avenue
Tucson, AZ 85701
(520) 342-6566
Fax: (520) 901-8570

E-MAIL ADDRESS:
halpern@udall.gov

WEB SITE ADDRESS:
www.udall.gov

FOUNDED: 1992

AREAS OF INTEREST:
Educating young Americans in our nation's heritage, environmental studies, Native American affairs and public policy conflict resolution.

NAME(S) OF PROGRAMS:
● **Congressional Internships**

TYPE:
Internships. Congressional Internships: Native American college students work in congressional offices and the White House to

gain a firsthand understanding of the federal government. They also take field trips and meet with congressional members, agency heads and cabinet secretaries.

YEAR PROGRAM STARTED: 1996

PURPOSE:
To educate a new generation of Americans to preserve and protect their national heritage through studies in the environment, Native American health and tribal policy and effective public policy conflict resolution.

LEGAL BASIS:
The Foundation is an executive branch agency. The President of the U.S. appoints its board of trustees with the advice and consent of the U.S. Senate.

ELIGIBILITY:
Interns will be selected by an independent committee. Applicants must demonstrate a commitment to learning about the federal government. They must be self-motivated and interested in taking advantage of the rich and diverse resources available to them in Washington, DC. Additionally, candidates for the internship program must:
(1) be an enrolled member of a recognized tribe or state-recognized tribe;
(2) be a college junior, senior, graduate student, law student or graduating from a tribal college;
(3) have a minimum 3.0 grade point average or a "B" average and;
(4) have an interest in tribal government and policy.

FINANCIAL DATA:
Interns are provided with airfare to and from Washington, DC, lodging convenient to Capitol Hill, and a daily allowance sufficient for meals, transportation and incidentals.

Amount of support per award: $1,200 educational stipend to be paid at the conclusion of the internship.

NUMBER OF APPLICANTS MOST RECENT YEAR:
50.

NUMBER OF AWARDS: 12.

APPLICATION INFORMATION:
Application packet must be sent to The Morris K. Udall and Stewart L. Udall Foundation, Internship Program, at the address above.

Duration: 10 weeks.

Deadline: January 29.

STAFF:
Chia Halpern, Program Manager

ADDRESS INQUIRIES TO:
Chia Halpern, Program Manager
(See address above.)

UNITED SOUTH AND EASTERN TRIBES, INC. [1126]

711 Stewarts Ferry Pike
Suite 100
Nashville, TN 37214
(615) 872-7900
Fax: (615) 872-7417

E-MAIL ADDRESS:
cleasure@usetinc.org

WEB SITE ADDRESS:
www.usetinc.org

FOUNDED: 1969

AREAS OF INTEREST:
Indian tribes.

TYPE:
Scholarships.

PURPOSE:
To enhance the development of Indian Tribes; to improve the capabilities of Tribal governments; to assist the member Tribes and their governments in dealing effectively with public policy issues and in serving the broad needs of Indian people.

ELIGIBILITY:
Supplemental monies are awarded to USET area Indian students who are enrolled members of USET member tribes.

Must be an Indian student that meets the following criteria:
(1) a demonstrated need for additional funding;
(2) satisfactory scholastic standing and;
(3) current enrollment or acceptance in a postsecondary educational institution.

FINANCIAL DATA:
Amount of support per award: Supplemental scholarships: $500.

Total amount of support: $7,000 for the year 2009.

APPLICATION INFORMATION:
Contact the Organization for application procedures.

Duration: Annual supplemental scholarship. Must reapply for additional term.

Deadline: Postmark or delivery of applications: April 30.

ADDRESS INQUIRIES TO:
USET Scholarship Fund
(See address above.)

UNIVERSITY OF CALIFORNIA, LOS ANGELES [1127]

American Indian Studies Center
UCLA - 3220 Campbell Hall, Box 951548
Los Angeles, CA 90095-1548
(310) 825-7315
Fax: (310) 206-7060

E-MAIL ADDRESS:
rhrosser@aisc.ucla.edu

WEB SITE ADDRESS:
www.gdnet.ucla.edu

FOUNDED: 1970

AREAS OF INTEREST:
American Indian studies and related topics in policy, education, economics, culture and community.

NAME(S) OF PROGRAMS:
● **Institute of American Cultures Grant**

TYPE:
Fellowships; Research grants; Visiting scholars.

YEAR PROGRAM STARTED: 1969

PURPOSE:
Research in Native American Studies.

LEGAL BASIS:
University research organization; nonprofit organization.

ELIGIBILITY:
Applicants must hold the Ph.D. Faculty members at U.C.L.A. are not eligible for support.

FINANCIAL DATA:
Senior scholars receive a supplement to the sabbatical salaries provided by their own institutions. Additional support, including

office space and computer support, may be available for specific research upon application to the center.

Amount of support per award: Institute of American Cultures Grant: $39,000; Visiting Scholars: $27,000 to $32,000, depending upon rank and experience, plus $4,000 in research support and health benefits.

APPLICATION INFORMATION:
Write to the address above for forms.
Duration: Nine to 12 months. Nonrenewable.
Deadline: April 23.

PUBLICATIONS:
American Indian Culture and Research Journal; brochures; books.

IRS IDENTIFICATION NUMBER: 195006143-AI

STAFF:
Angela Riley, Director
Rebecca Rosser, Assistant Director
Pam Grieman, Managing Editor
Ken Wade, Librarian

ADDRESS INQUIRIES TO:
Rebecca Rosser, Assistant Director
(See address above.)

WASHINGTON HIGHER EDUCATION COORDINATING BOARD   [1128]

American Indian Endowed Scholarship
917 Lakeridge Way
Olympia, WA 98504-3430
(360) 753-7843
Fax: (360) 704-6243; (360) 753-7808

E-MAIL ADDRESS:
aies@hecb.wa.gov
annv@hecb.wa.gov

WEB SITE ADDRESS:
www.hecb.wa.gov

AREAS OF INTEREST:
Student financial aid.

NAME(S) OF PROGRAMS:
● **American Indian Endowed Scholarship Program**

TYPE:
Scholarships.

YEAR PROGRAM STARTED: 1993

PURPOSE:
To create an educational opportunity for students with close social and cultural ties to the American Indian community to pursue undergraduate and graduate studies who might not be able otherwise to attend and graduate from higher education institutions in Washington state.

LEGAL BASIS:
Government agency.

ELIGIBILITY:
Applicants must be financially needy residents and students of Washington state with close social and cultural ties to the American Indian community in the state. Must have applied for financial aid via FAFSA. Applicant must commit to return service to the state Native American community. Academic merit is also a consideration.

FINANCIAL DATA:
Amount of support per award: $500 to $2,000.
Total amount of support: Varies.

NUMBER OF APPLICANTS MOST RECENT YEAR:
40 for the year 2011.

NUMBER OF AWARDS: Approximately 14 for the year 2011.

APPLICATION INFORMATION:
Application includes statement of commitment to return service to Washington American Indian communities, statement of close social and cultural ties, three letters of recommendation, completed application and release of information form and transcripts.
Duration: One year. Renewable for a maximum of four additional years.
Deadline: February 1. Announcement will be made by April.

ADDRESS INQUIRIES TO:
Ann M. Voyles, Program Manager
American Indian Endowed Scholarship
P.O. Box 43430
Olympia, WA 98504-3430

Spanish-speaking

BNSF FOUNDATION   [1129]

2650 Lou Menk Drive
Fort Worth, TX 76131-2830
(817) 867-6458
Fax: (817) 352-7925

E-MAIL ADDRESS:
bnsffoundation@bnsf.com

WEB SITE ADDRESS:
www.bnsffoundation.org

NAME(S) OF PROGRAMS:
● **Hispanic American Scholarship Program**

TYPE:
Scholarships. Scholarships awarded to high school graduates of Hispanic origin through the Hispanic College Fund (HCF).

LEGAL BASIS:
Corporate foundation.

ELIGIBILITY:
Scholarships are awarded to high school graduates of Hispanic origin. All applicants must be U.S. citizens or legal residents and have already been accepted or enrolled in a college (two-year leading to a four-year degree) or university. Winners are selected by Hispanic Scholarship Fund (HSF) with scholarships to be awarded in each of the following Burlington Northern Santa Fe-served states: Arizona, California, Colorado, Illinois, Kansas, Missouri, New Mexico and Texas.

GEOGRAPHIC RESTRICTIONS:
Arizona, California, Colorado, Illinois, Kansas, Missouri, New Mexico and Texas.

FINANCIAL DATA:
Each Scholarship stipend is determined by HSF and funds are allocated from an annual $25,000 grant provided by the Foundation.
Amount of support per award: $500 to $2,500.
Total amount of support: $25,000 per academic year.

APPLICATION INFORMATION:
Applications are available from Hispanic College Fund, Inc., 1301 K Street, N.W., Suite 450-A West, Washington, DC 20005.
Deadline: April 1.

ADDRESS INQUIRIES TO:
Hispanic College Fund, Inc.
1301 K Street, N.W.
Suite 450-A West
Washington, DC 20005

FLORIDA DEPARTMENT OF EDUCATION   [1130]

Office of Student Financial Assistance
325 West Gaines Street, Suite 1314
Tallahassee, FL 32399-0400
(888) 827-2004
Fax: (850) 487-1809

E-MAIL ADDRESS:
osfa@fldoe.org

WEB SITE ADDRESS:
www.FloridaStudentFinancialAid.org

NAME(S) OF PROGRAMS:
● **Jose Marti Scholarship Challenge Grant Fund**

TYPE:
Challenge/matching grants; Grants-in-aid. Jose Marti Scholarship Challenge Grant Fund is a need-based merit scholarship that provides financial assistance to eligible students of Hispanic origin who will attend Florida public or eligible private institutions.

YEAR PROGRAM STARTED: 1986

PURPOSE:
To provide financial assistance to Hispanic-American high school seniors and graduate students in Florida.

LEGAL BASIS:
Florida Department of Education in cooperation with U.S. Department of Education.

ELIGIBILITY:
Applicants for undergraduate study must apply during their senior year of high school. Graduate students may apply, but priority for the scholarships is given to graduating high school seniors.

An applicant must:
(1) be a Florida resident and a U.S. citizen or eligible non-citizen;
(2) not owe a repayment or be in default under any state or federal grant, loan or scholarship program unless satisfactory arrangements to repay have been made;
(3) be a person of Spanish culture who was born in or whose natural parent was born in either Mexico or a Hispanic country of the Caribbean, Central America or South America, regardless of race;
(4) have earned, by the end of the seventh semester, a minimum unweighted institutional cumulative grade point average of 3.0 on a 4.0 scale in high school for an undergraduate scholarship or, if a graduate applicant, earned an unweighted institutional cumulative grade point average of 3.0 for undergraduate college-level courses and;
(5) enroll as a degree-seeking student at an eligible postsecondary institution and enroll each academic term for a minimum of 12 credit hours of undergraduate study or nine credit hours of graduate study.

GEOGRAPHIC RESTRICTIONS:
Florida.

FINANCIAL DATA:
An undergraduate student participating in college-preparatory instruction, a student requiring additional time to complete the college-level communication and computation skills testing programs (CLAST), or a student enrolled in a five-year undergraduate degree

program are eligible to receive financial aid for a maximum of 10 semesters or 15 quarters.

Amount of support per award: $2,000 per academic year. Annual award set by Florida statute.

NUMBER OF AWARDS: 46 for the year 2009-10.

APPLICATION INFORMATION:
Applications are available from high school guidance offices, college financial aid offices or the Office of Student Financial Assistance.

Duration: One academic year. Renewable annually for a maximum of eight semesters or 12 quarters (not to exceed six years) of undergraduate study or a maximum of four semesters or six quarters of graduate study.

Deadline: April 1.

PUBLICATIONS:
Financial Aid Sources for Florida Students.

ADDRESS INQUIRIES TO:
State Scholarship and Grant Programs
(See address above.)

HISPANIC NATIONAL BAR FOUNDATION

1900 K Street, N.W.
Suite 100
Washington, DC 20006
(202) 496-7206
Fax: (202) 496-7756

E-MAIL ADDRESS:
mprego@hnbf.org

WEB SITE ADDRESS:
www.hnbf.org

TYPE:
Conferences/seminars; Training grants. Week-long program held by the Foundation in Washington, DC which provides 25 Latino high school students with the opportunity to learn more about the legal profession. The Law Camp offers students the chance to come to the nation's capital and learn more about the college application process, meet influential Latino leaders, and tour national monuments and various government agencies.

See entry 2107 for full listing.

HISPANIC SCHOLARSHIP FUND   [1131]

55 Second Street
Suite 1500
San Francisco, CA 94105
(877) 473-4636
(415) 808-2355
Fax: (415) 808-2301

E-MAIL ADDRESS:
info@hsf.net
gmsinfo@hsf.net

WEB SITE ADDRESS:
www.hsf.net
www.gmsp.org

FOUNDED: 1975

AREAS OF INTEREST:
College scholarships for Hispanic American students.

NAME(S) OF PROGRAMS:
- **Gates Millennium Scholars Program**
- **General College Scholarship Program**

TYPE:
Scholarships. Awarded to Hispanic community college, undergraduate and graduate students.

YEAR PROGRAM STARTED: 1975

PURPOSE:
To strengthen America by generating support for the educational advancement of Hispanics by increasing the rate of Hispanics earning a college degree.

LEGAL BASIS:
Nonprofit 501(c)(3) organization.

ELIGIBILITY:
Gates Millennium Scholars Program: The applicant must:
(1) be African American, American Indian/Alaska Native, Asian Pacific Islander American or Hispanic American;
(2) be a citizen, national or legal permanent resident of the U.S.;
(3) have attained a cumulative high school grade point average of 3.3 on a 4.0 scale (unweighted) or have earned a GED;
(4) be enrolling for the first time at a U.S.-accredited college or university as a full-time, degree-seeking, first-year student in the coming fall;
(5) have demonstrated leadership abilities through participation in community service, extracurricular or other activities;
(6) meet the federal Pell Grant eligibility criteria and;
(7) have completed and submitted all three required forms (Nominee Personal Information Form, Nominator Form and Recommender Form) by the deadline.

General College Scholarship Program: Applicants must meet the following requirements to apply for a scholarship through the Fund:
(1) be of Hispanic heritage;
(2) be a U.S. citizen or legal permanent resident;
(3) have a minimum 3.0 cumulative grade point average (on a 4.0 scale) and;
(4) must apply for federal financial aid using FAFSA.

FINANCIAL DATA:
Amount of support per award: Gates Millennium Scholars Program: $500 and up, depending on unmet need; General College Scholarship Program: $1,000 to $15,000.

Total amount of support: Approximately $28,000,000 for the year 2010.

NUMBER OF AWARDS: 4,650 for the year 2009.

APPLICATION INFORMATION:
Electronic application only; forms available at the web site.

Duration: Students may reapply until they obtain a degree, providing they satisfy full-time enrollment.

Deadline: Gates Millenium Scholars Program: Applications become available August 1, deadline in January; General College Scholarship Program: December 15.

PUBLICATIONS:
Annual report; newsletter.

IRS IDENTIFICATION NUMBER: 52-1051044

BOARD OF DIRECTORS:
Raul R. Romero, Chairman, Executive Committee
James McNamara, Vice Chairperson, Executive Committee
Frank Ros, Treasurer, Executive Committee
Lisa M. Quiroz, Secretary, Executive Committee
Dr. Roger Benjamin, Executive Committee
Frank D. Alvarez
Margarita Flores
Tim Hanlon

Cheech Marin
David E. Roberts
Thomas A. Roupe
Anthony Salcido
Maria Elena Salinas
Jeffrey K. Schomburger
Raul Vazquez

ADDRESS INQUIRIES TO:
Selection Committee
(See address above.)

UCLA CHICANO STUDIES RESEARCH CENTER   [1132]

193 Haines Hall
Box 951544
Los Angeles, CA 90095
(310) 794-9646
Fax: (310) 206-1784

E-MAIL ADDRESS:
csrcinfo@chicano.ucla.edu

WEB SITE ADDRESS:
www.chicano.ucla.edu

FOUNDED: 1969

AREAS OF INTEREST:
Chicano Studies and relevant fields.

NAME(S) OF PROGRAMS:
- **Institute of American Cultures Fellowship Program**

TYPE:
Fellowships; Visiting scholars.

YEAR PROGRAM STARTED: 1976

PURPOSE:
To advance scholarship in the Chicano community in the U.S.

LEGAL BASIS:
University program.

ELIGIBILITY:
Applicants must possess a Ph.D. and a project proposal.

FINANCIAL DATA:
Amount of support per award: $32,000 to $35,000, health insurance, and $4,000 research grant, of which $1,000 can be used for relocation expenses.

Total amount of support: Up to $39,000 annually.

NUMBER OF APPLICANTS MOST RECENT YEAR:
16.

NUMBER OF AWARDS: 1.

APPLICATION INFORMATION:
Application information available upon request.

Duration: One fiscal year, July 1 to June 30.

Deadline: January.

OFFICERS:
Chon Noriega, Director
Belinda Tucker, Chairperson, Executive Committee, Institute of American Cultures

ADDRESS INQUIRIES TO:
Javier Iribarren
Assistant Director/IAC Coordinator
(See address above.)

Women

THE ISABEL ALLENDE FOUNDATION [1133]

116 Caledonia Street
Sausalito, CA 94965
(415) 289-0992
Fax: (415) 289-1154

E-MAIL ADDRESS:
lori@isabelallendefoundation.org

WEB SITE ADDRESS:
www.isabelallendefoundation.org

FOUNDED: 1996

AREAS OF INTEREST:
Women's social and economic justice, empowerment of women and girls, and protection of women and children.

NAME(S) OF PROGRAMS:
• **Esperanza Grants**

TYPE:
Project/program grants. Promotes and preserves the fundamental rights of women and children to be empowered and protected.

PURPOSE:
To promote reproductive self-determination and health care, economic independence and social justice for women and girls, and the protection of women and children.

ELIGIBILITY:
Nonprofit 501(c)(3) grassroots organizations and equivalent international organizations that benefit the San Francisco Bay area and/or Chile are eligible to apply. No grants to individuals. The Foundation does not fund capital campaigns, individual trips or tours, conferences or events, and projects that benefit political, religious, and/or military organizations.

GEOGRAPHIC RESTRICTIONS:
San Francisco Bay area, California and Chile.

FINANCIAL DATA:
Amount of support per award: $1,000 to $5,000.

APPLICATION INFORMATION:
New organization proposals are not being accepted at this time. Current grantees may apply for renewal and will receive instructions from the Foundation on how to apply.
Deadline: January 1, April 1, July 1 and October 1.

ADDRESS INQUIRIES TO:
Lori Barra, Executive Director
(See address above.)

AMERICAN ASSOCIATION OF UNIVERSITY WOMEN EDUCATIONAL FOUNDATION [1134]

301 ACT Drive
Iowa City, IA 52243-4030
(319) 337-1716
(800) 326-2289
Fax: (319) 337-1204

E-MAIL ADDRESS:
aauw@act.org

WEB SITE ADDRESS:
www.aauw.org

FOUNDED: 1888

AREAS OF INTEREST:
Advancement of educational and professional opportunities for women in the U.S.

NAME(S) OF PROGRAMS:
• **Selected Professions Fellowships**

TYPE:
Fellowships. Awarded to women who are U.S. citizens or permanent residents and who intend to pursue a full-time course of study (during the fellowship year) in designated degree programs where women's participation has been traditionally low.

PURPOSE:
To encourage women's participation in fields where they have been traditionally underrepresented.

ELIGIBILITY:
Candidates in all programs except Master's degrees in engineering and medicine are eligible to apply for support for the final year of study only and are expected to receive their degrees at the end of the fellowship year. Women pursuing Master's degrees in engineering programs and women in medical programs may apply for any year of study. Doctoral candidates in engineering must be entering the final stages of dissertation writing.

GEOGRAPHIC RESTRICTIONS:
United States.

FINANCIAL DATA:
Amount of support per award: $5,000 to $18,000.

APPLICATION INFORMATION:
Applications are available August 1.

AMERICAN ASSOCIATION OF UNIVERSITY WOMEN EDUCATIONAL FOUNDATION [1135]

101 ACT Drive
Iowa City, IA 52243
(319) 337-1716

E-MAIL ADDRESS:
aauw@act.org

WEB SITE ADDRESS:
www.aauw.org

FOUNDED: 1958

AREAS OF INTEREST:
Advancement of educational and professional opportunities for women in the U.S. and around the globe.

NAME(S) OF PROGRAMS:
• **American Fellowships**

TYPE:
Fellowships; Visiting scholars. Dissertation, postdoctoral and summer/short-term research publication grants for women, for the support of scholarly research. Open to all fields of study.

YEAR PROGRAM STARTED: 1888

PURPOSE:
To encourage and support American women who show distinction or promise of distinction in their fields of scholarly work and who plan to pursue professional careers in the U.S.

ELIGIBILITY:
Applicants must be citizens of the U.S. There are no restrictions as to place of study or age. Women who will have completed all requirements for the Doctorate, except the writing of the dissertation, by November 15 preceding the fellowship year, July 1 to June 30, or who hold the Ph.D. at the time of application. Applicants are evaluated by

academic professionals on the scholarly excellence of their proposals, experience teaching or mentoring female students. In addition, applicants will be asked to outline their commitment to helping women and girls through community service, service in their profession and/or service in their field of research.

FINANCIAL DATA:
Amount of support per award: Stipend for dissertation is $20,000; Postdoctoral award stipend is $30,000; Summer/Short-term award stipend is $6,000.
Total amount of support: Approximately $1,200,000 for the year 2010-11.

NUMBER OF APPLICANTS MOST RECENT YEAR:
Approximately 1,000.

NUMBER OF AWARDS: 97.

APPLICATION INFORMATION:
Application form is available online.
Duration: Fellowships are tenable for a year of full-time project research beginning July 1.
Deadline: Completed applications must be submitted by November 15.

ADDRESS INQUIRIES TO:
Todd Beckman, Specialist
(See address above.)

AMERICAN ASSOCIATION OF UNIVERSITY WOMEN EDUCATIONAL FOUNDATION [1136]

101 ACT Drive
Iowa City, IA 52243
(319) 337-1716

E-MAIL ADDRESS:
aauw@act.org

WEB SITE ADDRESS:
www.aauw.org

FOUNDED: 1888

AREAS OF INTEREST:
Non-traditional fields.

NAME(S) OF PROGRAMS:
• **Career Development Grants**

TYPE:
Grants-in-aid. Support women currently holding a Bachelor's degree who are preparing to advance their careers, change careers or re-enter the work force.

YEAR PROGRAM STARTED: 1972

PURPOSE:
To assist women who are continuing their self-development through higher education.

ELIGIBILITY:
Funding is provided to women who are preparing to re-enter the work force, change careers or advance their current careers. Candidates must be in the early stages of their programs. Special consideration is given to qualified AAUW members, minority women and applicants who are not pursuing a second Master's or terminal degree. Preference is also given to women pursuing degrees in non-traditional fields.

Grants are open to women who are U.S. citizens or permanent residents, hold a Baccalaureate degree, plan to pursue course work at a fully accredited two- or four-year college or university or at a technical school that is licensed, accredited or approved by the Department of Education and enroll in courses that are prerequisites for professional employment plans and are not in the final year of a degree program at the time of application. Funds are provided for study at professional development institutes.

Funds are not available for the final year of terminal degree professional programs (i.e., MBA, J.D., M.D., etc.). Funds are not provided for doctoral study. Candidates who fulfill eligibility requirements of other fellowship programs offered by the AAUW Educational Foundation will not be considered for funding from this grant and therefore must apply to the appropriate program.

GEOGRAPHIC RESTRICTIONS:
United States.

FINANCIAL DATA:
Funds are provided for tuition, fees, books, transportation (to, from and at school) and dependent care.
Amount of support per award: $2,000 to $12,000.
Total amount of support: Varies.

NUMBER OF APPLICANTS MOST RECENT YEAR:
950 for the year 2009-10.

NUMBER OF AWARDS: 50 for the year 2009-10.

APPLICATION INFORMATION:
Official application materials are available August 1 to December 15. Application and recommendations must be submitted online.
Duration: One academic year, beginning July 1.
Deadline: December 15.

PUBLICATIONS:
Application guidelines.

ADDRESS INQUIRIES TO:
Career Development Academic Grants
P.O. Box 4030
Iowa City, IA 52243-4030

*SPECIAL STIPULATIONS:
Previous and current recipients of an AAUW Educational Foundation Career Development Grant are not eligible to apply.

AMERICAN ASSOCIATION OF UNIVERSITY WOMEN EDUCATIONAL FOUNDATION [1137]

101 ACT Drive
Iowa City, IA 52243
(319) 337-1716

E-MAIL ADDRESS:
aauw@act.org

WEB SITE ADDRESS:
www.aauw.org

FOUNDED: 1888

AREAS OF INTEREST:
Equity and education for women and girls.

NAME(S) OF PROGRAMS:
● **Community Action Grants**

TYPE:
Project/program grants; Seed money grants.

YEAR PROGRAM STARTED: 1972

PURPOSE:
To provide seed money to AAUW branches, AAUW state organizations, community-based nonprofit organizations, and individual women for projects that promote education and equity for women and girls.

ELIGIBILITY:
Project directors must be U.S. citizens or permanent residents. The proposed activity must demonstrate direct community or public impact. Proposals from AAUW branches and AAUW state organizations must be approved and signed by the branch or state president. Men, as leaders of AAUW branches and organizations, are eligible to apply.

Grant projects may not seek to influence new or pending legislation or favor a particular political candidate or party. Nonpartisan study analysis and research must present findings based on facts.

GEOGRAPHIC RESTRICTIONS:
United States and its territories.

FINANCIAL DATA:
Funds are available for such project-related costs as office and mailing expenses, promotional materials, honoraria and transportation costs. Funds cannot cover salaries for project directors.
Amount of support per award: $2,000 to $7,000 for one-year grants; $5,000 to $10,000 for two-year grants.
Total amount of support: Varies.

REPRESENTATIVE AWARDS:
Projects funded in the past include math/science camps for girls, mentoring programs for girls and women, parenting/family education programs, adolescent pregnancy prevention campaigns, and women's history projects.

APPLICATION INFORMATION:
Complete application details are available online August 1 to January 15. All applications must be submitted online.
Deadline: January 15.

PUBLICATIONS:
Application guidelines.

ADDRESS INQUIRIES TO:
Program Officer
P.O. Box 4030
Iowa City, IA 52243-4030

AMERICAN ASSOCIATION OF UNIVERSITY WOMEN EDUCATIONAL FOUNDATION

101 ACT Drive
Iowa City, IA 52243
(319) 337-1716

E-MAIL ADDRESS:
aauw@act.org

WEB SITE ADDRESS:
www.aauw.org

TYPE:
Fellowships. Awards for women who are not citizens or permanent residents of the U.S. for full-time graduate or postgraduate study or research in the U.S.

A limited number of project grants are available to successful applicants who wish to implement a community-based project in the year immediately following the fellowship. Eligible project proposals must demonstrate that they will be implemented in the applicant's home country and will have a direct impact on women and girls. Only applicants who are selected to receive an International Fellowship will be considered for project grant funding.

See entry 1008 for full listing.

AMERICAN NUCLEAR SOCIETY (ANS)

555 North Kensington Avenue
LaGrange Park, IL 60526
(708) 352-6611
Fax: (708) 352-0499

E-MAIL ADDRESS:
outreach@ans.org

WEB SITE ADDRESS:
www.ans.org

TYPE:
Scholarships. Delayed Education for Women Scholarship is designed for women in a nuclear-related field whose formal studies have been delayed or interrupted for at least one year.

Landis Scholarships are administered by the ANS NEED Committee, and are awarded to undergraduate and graduate students who have greater-than-average financial need.

See entry 2804 for full listing.

ASSOCIATION FOR WOMEN IN SCIENCE EDUCATIONAL AWARDS [1138]

1321 Duke Street
Suite 210
Alexandria, VA 22314
(703) 894-4490
Fax: (703) 894-4489

E-MAIL ADDRESS:
awis@awis.org

WEB SITE ADDRESS:
www.awis.org

FOUNDED: 1974

AREAS OF INTEREST:
Science, technology, engineering, mathematics (STEM).

NAME(S) OF PROGRAMS:
● **AWIS Educational Awards**

TYPE:
Awards/prizes. (Graduate and Predoctoral): To recognize and honor women and men who have demonstrated exemplary commitment to the achievement of equity for women in science, technology, engineering and mathematics (STEM).

YEAR PROGRAM STARTED: 1975

PURPOSE:
To support women planning a career in science, technology, engineering and mathematics (STEM).

LEGAL BASIS:
Nonprofit organization.

ELIGIBILITY:
Applicants must be an American citizen, or a foreign national, attending a college/university in the U.S.; must be enrolled in a graduate or doctoral degree program in one of the STEM fields.

GEOGRAPHIC RESTRICTIONS:
United States.

FINANCIAL DATA:
Awards may be used for any aspect of education, including tuition, books, housing, research, expenses, equipment, etc.
Amount of support per award: Varies; up to $1,000.

APPLICATION INFORMATION:
Applications and updated criteria are available online. Applications must be made online; paper applications are not accepted.

Duration: One-time award.

Deadline: End of January. Award notification after June 15.

OFFICERS:
Janet Bandows Koster, Executive Director, AWIS

ADDRESS INQUIRIES TO:
Erin DiMenna, Membership Manager
AWIS Educational Awards
(See address above.)

*SPECIAL STIPULATIONS:
If not U.S. citizen, recipient must be studying in a U.S. institution.

BERKSHIRE CONFERENCE OF WOMEN HISTORIANS

263 Windsor Place
Brooklyn, NY 11218
(718) 768-7994

E-MAIL ADDRESS:
smyohn@verizon.net

WEB SITE ADDRESS:
www.berksconference.org

TYPE:
Awards/prizes. One prize awarded annually for the best first book and one for the best article of historical scholarship published by a woman historian in any field of history during the preceding year.

See entry 620 for full listing.

BOSTON WOMEN'S FUND [1139]

14 Beacon Street
Suite 805
Boston, MA 02108
(617) 725-0035
Fax: (617) 725-0277

E-MAIL ADDRESS:
josefina@bostonwomensfund.org
info@bostonwomensfund.org

WEB SITE ADDRESS:
www.bostonwomensfund.org

FOUNDED: 1984

AREAS OF INTEREST:
Women organized for social and economic change.

TYPE:
Conferences/seminars; General operating grants; Grants-in-aid; Internships; Project/program grants; Seed money grants.

PURPOSE:
To pool funds from individuals; to channel money to support women's and girls' organizations for economic and social justice.

LEGAL BASIS:
Public foundation.

ELIGIBILITY:
Applicants or their fiscal agents must be 501(c)(3) organizations. Also funded are direct service projects which have an organizing component. Groups just getting started are encouraged to apply, particularly those women who are most vulnerable and have the least access to other resources including women of color, low-income women, disabled women, lesbians, girls, older women, transgender people, immigrant

and refugee women. Applicants with organizational budgets of less than $350,000 per year are preferred. No grants to individuals.

GEOGRAPHIC RESTRICTIONS:
Preference given to the Boston metropolitan area, and to selected outlying areas such as Brockton, Lawrence, Lowell and Worcester, Massachusetts.

FINANCIAL DATA:
Amount of support per award: $3,000 to $20,000.

NUMBER OF APPLICANTS MOST RECENT YEAR:
Varies.

NUMBER OF AWARDS: Varies.

APPLICATION INFORMATION:
Download a Letter of Intent form at the web site, complete and submit to the Fund. Selected letters will be invited to submit a proposal.

Duration: One year.

PUBLICATIONS:
Application guidelines; donor contribution information in annual report.

ADDRESS INQUIRIES TO:
Amy Leung, Program Officer
(See address above.)

BROOKHAVEN WOMEN IN SCIENCE [1140]

P.O. Box 183
Upton, NY 11973
(631) 344-2425
Fax: (631) 344-5676

E-MAIL ADDRESS:
bwisawards@bnl.gov

WEB SITE ADDRESS:
www.bnl.gov/bwis/awards.asp

FOUNDED: 1979

AREAS OF INTEREST:
Advancement of women in the natural sciences, engineering or mathematics fields.

NAME(S) OF PROGRAMS:
● **Renate W. Chasman Scholarship for Women**

TYPE:
Awards/prizes; Scholarships. These scholarships are offered to encourage women to resume their formal education in the natural sciences, engineering or mathematics.

YEAR PROGRAM STARTED: 1986

PURPOSE:
To encourage women to resume their formal education in a technical field.

LEGAL BASIS:
Tax-exempt, incorporated under the Educational Laws of New York state.

ELIGIBILITY:
Candidates must be citizens or permanent residents of the U.S. and must be residents of Long Island in New York state (Nassau or Suffolk counties and Boroughs of Brooklyn or Queens). Applicant must be entering the junior or senior undergraduate or first year graduate level at an accredited institution and accepted for credit in natural sciences, engineering or mathematics courses. Applicant must have had an interruption in academic career. For example: illness, marriage, birth of a child, economic reasons (re-entry woman is a mandatory criteria).

Selection is based upon academic and life/career record, letter of reference and a short essay on career goals. Finalists are chosen on merit and career goals.

GEOGRAPHIC RESTRICTIONS:
Nassau and Suffolk counties and boroughs of Brooklyn and Queens, New York.

FINANCIAL DATA:
Amount of support per award: $2,000.

Total amount of support: $2,000 for the year 2010.

NUMBER OF APPLICANTS MOST RECENT YEAR:
Less than 12.

NUMBER OF AWARDS: Generally, 1 per year.

APPLICATION INFORMATION:
Requests for application via mail must include a self-addressed, stamped envelope.

Duration: One year. Nonrenewable.

Deadline: April 1. Announcement in July.

ADDRESS INQUIRIES TO:
Chasman Scholarship, BWIS
(See address above.)

CANADIAN FEDERATION OF UNIVERSITY WOMEN [1141]

251 Bank Street, Suite 305
Ottawa ON K2P 1X3 Canada
(613) 234-8252
Fax: (613) 234-8221

E-MAIL ADDRESS:
fellowships@cfuw.org

WEB SITE ADDRESS:
www.cfuw.org

FOUNDED: 1919

AREAS OF INTEREST:
Graduate education for women.

NAME(S) OF PROGRAMS:
● **Ruth Binnie Fellowship**
● **Canadian Home Economics Association (CHEA) Fellowship**
● **CFUW Memorial Fellowship**
● **CFUW/Bourse Georgette Lemoyne**
● **CFUW/Dr. Marion Elder Grant Fellowship**
● **CFUW/Beverley Jackson Fellowship**
● **CFUW/Elizabeth Massey Award**
● **CFUW/Dr. Margaret McWilliams Pre-Doctoral Fellowship**
● **CFUW/1989 Ecole Polytechnique Commemorative Award**
● **CFUW/Margaret Dale Philp Award**
● **CFUW/Dr. Alice E. Wilson Awards**
● **IFUW/Dr. A. Vibert Douglas International Triennial Fellowship**

TYPE:
Fellowships. The Ruth Binnie Fellowship is for Master's studies with a focus on one or more aspects of the field of home economics. The candidate may be studying abroad.

Canadian Home Economics Association Fellowship candidate must be studying one or more aspects in the field of home economics at the Master's or doctoral level in Canada.

CFUW/Bourse Georgette Lemoyne Fellowship is for graduate study at a Canadian university. The candidate must be studying in French.

The candidate for the CFUW/Dr. Marion Elder Grant Fellowship, funded by CFUW/Wolfville, must be studying full-time at the doctoral level in Canada or abroad. All else being equal, preference will be given to the holder of an Acadia University degree.

CFUW/Beverley Jackson Fellowship, funded by UWC North York, is awarded to a candidate over the age of 35 enrolled in graduate work at an Ontario university.

CFUW/Elizabeth Massey Award is for postgraduate studies in music, painting or sculpture in Canada or abroad.

CFUW/Margaret McWilliams Pre-Doctoral Fellowship candidate must have completed at least one full calendar year as a full-time student in doctoral-level studies and be a full-time student in Canada or abroad at the time of application.

CFUW Memorial Fellowship candidate must be enrolled in a Master's degree program in science, mathematics, or engineering in Canada or abroad.

CFUW/1989 Ecole Polytechnique Commemorative Award is for graduate studies in any field. The candidate must justify the relevance of her work to women.

CFUW/Margaret Dale Philp Award, funded by CFUW/Kitchener-Waterloo, is for graduate studies in the humanities or social sciences, with special consideration given to study in Canadian history. The candidate must reside in Canada.

CFUW/Dr. Alice E. Wilson Award is for graduate studies in any field, with special consideration given to candidates returning to study after at least three years.

IFUW/Dr. A. Vibert Douglas International Fellowship is a biennial fellowship funded by CFUW but administered by International Federation of University Women (IFUW). This fellowship will be offered in academic year 2013-14.

YEAR PROGRAM STARTED: 1921

PURPOSE:
To support the education of women at the postgraduate level in Canada and abroad.

LEGAL BASIS:
Foundation of a nonprofit organization.

ELIGIBILITY:
Candidates must hold at least a Bachelor's degree or equivalent from a recognized university, have been accepted into the proposed program and place of study, and be a Canadian citizen or permanent resident.

GEOGRAPHIC RESTRICTIONS:
Canada.

FINANCIAL DATA:
Amount of support per award: $2,000 to $11,500.
Total amount of support: Approximately $100,000 for the year 2011-12.

NUMBER OF AWARDS: 16 for the year 2011-12.

APPLICATION INFORMATION:
Application form and guidelines are posted in May on the Federation's web site. There is a $60 fee per application.
Duration: One year. Grants not renewable.
Deadline: November 1 (postmark). Announcement May 31.

PUBLICATIONS:
The Communicator; *CFUW Education and Outreach*; *The Chronicle*; *CFUW Charitable Trust*; *CFUW Fellowships and Awards*; *CFUW External Annual Report*; *Action and Advocacy*; *Women in Action*.

ADDRESS INQUIRIES TO:
Betty Dunlop
Fellowships Program Manager
(See address above.)

CHATHAM UNIVERSITY
Woodland Road
Pittsburgh, PA 15232-9987
(412) 365-1825
Fax: (412) 365-1609

E-MAIL ADDRESS:
admission@chatham.edu

WEB SITE ADDRESS:
www.chatham.edu

TYPE:
Awards/prizes; Endowments; Formula grants; General operating grants; Grants-in-aid; Internships; Scholarships. The Chatham University Merit Scholarship Programs include the Presidential, Trustee, Founders, and Dean Scholarship.

See entry 1790 for full listing.

THE COORDINATING COUNCIL FOR WOMEN IN HISTORY, INC.   [1142]
2210 Dorrington Street, No. 202
Houston, TX 77030

E-MAIL ADDRESS:
nupurc@earthlink.net

WEB SITE ADDRESS:
www.theccwh.org

FOUNDED: 1969

AREAS OF INTEREST:
Women's history.

NAME(S) OF PROGRAMS:
● **Catherine Prelinger Award**

TYPE:
Scholarships. The Catherine Prelinger Award is given to a scholar, with a Ph.D. or A.B.D., whose career has not followed a traditional academic path through secondary and higher education and whose work has contributed to women in the historical profession.

YEAR PROGRAM STARTED: 1998

PURPOSE:
To explore the diverse experiences and histories of all women; to honor scholars that have not followed a traditional academic path of uninterrupted and completed secondary, undergraduate, and graduate degrees leading into a tenured faculty position and whose work has contributed to women in the historical profession; to promote research and interpretation in areas of women's history; to recognize or to enhance the ability of the recipient to contribute significantly to women in history, whether in the profession in the present or in the study of women in the past.

ELIGIBILITY:
The applicant:
(1) must be a member in good standing of the Coordinating Council for Women in History;
(2) must hold either A.B.D. status or the Ph.D. at the time of application;
(3) shall be actively engaged in scholarship that is historical in nature, although the degree may be in related fields;
(4) shall have already contributed or shown potential for contributing significantly to women in history, whether in the profession in the present or in the study of women in the past and;
(5) has not followed a traditional academic path of uninterrupted and completed secondary, undergraduate and graduate degrees leading to a tenure-track faculty position.

FINANCIAL DATA:
Amount of support per award: $20,000.

NUMBER OF APPLICANTS MOST RECENT YEAR:
16.

NUMBER OF AWARDS: 1.

APPLICATION INFORMATION:
Contact the organization.
Deadline: September 15.

ADDRESS INQUIRIES TO:
Nupur Chaudhuri
(See e-mail address above.)

*SPECIAL STIPULATIONS:
All recipients will be required to submit a final paper to CCWH on how the award was expended and summarizing the scholarly work completed.

THE COORDINATING COUNCIL FOR WOMEN IN HISTORY, INC.
Department of History and
Women's Studies Program
Northern Illinois University
Dekalb, IL 60115
(815) 895-2624

E-MAIL ADDRESS:
sdawson1@niu.edu

WEB SITE ADDRESS:
www.theccwh.org

TYPE:
Awards/prizes; Fellowships.

See entry 626 for full listing.

DALLAS WOMEN'S FOUNDATION   [1143]
4300 MacArthur Avenue
Suite 255
Dallas, TX 75209
(214) 525-5308
(214) 965-9977
Fax: (214) 526-3633

E-MAIL ADDRESS:
dwf@dallaswomensfoundation.org

WEB SITE ADDRESS:
www.dallaswomensfoundation.org

FOUNDED: 1985

AREAS OF INTEREST:
Economic independence of women and girls.

TYPE:
General operating grants; Project/program grants.

YEAR PROGRAM STARTED: 1985

PURPOSE:
To promote women's philanthropy and raise money to support community programs that help women and girls realize their full potential.

LEGAL BASIS:
Community organization.

ELIGIBILITY:
Applicants must be 501(c)(3) organizations based in Collin, Dallas and Denton counties, TX. The applying program must serve at least 75% women and/or girls.

GEOGRAPHIC RESTRICTIONS:
Collin, Dallas and Denton counties, Texas.

FINANCIAL DATA:
Amount of support per award: Up to $30,000.

Total amount of support: $2,400,000 for fiscal year 2010.

NUMBER OF AWARDS: 117 for the year 2008.

APPLICATION INFORMATION:
The guidelines and application form is available online.
Duration: One year.
Deadline: June.

IRS IDENTIFICATION NUMBER: 75-2048261

STAFF:
Becky R. Sykes, Executive Director
Carol Patrick, Chief Financial and Operating Officer
Pat Alexander, Chief Grants Officer
Mary Valadez, Grants Director
Lesly Annen, Director of Philanthropy
Chayse Hood, Assistant Philanthropy Director
Twyla Allison, Controller

ADDRESS INQUIRIES TO:
Mary Valadez, Grants Director
E-mail:
mvaladez@dallaswomensfoundation.org

DAUGHTERS OF PENELOPE FOUNDATION, INC. [1144]
Supreme Headquarters
1909 Q Street, N.W., Suite 500
Washington, DC 20009
(770) 365-2488
Fax: (202) 483-6983

E-MAIL ADDRESS:
cmondore@mindspring.com

WEB SITE ADDRESS:
www.ahepa.org/dop
www.dopfoundationinc.com

FOUNDED: 1929

AREAS OF INTEREST:
Education, health and philanthropy.

NAME(S) OF PROGRAMS:
- **Joanne V. Hologgitas, Ph.D. Scholarship**
- **Kottis Family Scholarship**
- **Past Grand Presidents' Scholarship**
- **Alexandra Apostolides Sonenfeld Memorial Scholarship**
- **Sonja Stefanadis Graduate Student Scholarship**
- **Mary M. Verges Scholarship**

TYPE:
Scholarships.

PURPOSE:
To support education for women of Greek descent.

LEGAL BASIS:
Affiliated with American Hellenic Educational Progressive Association; tax-exempt.

ELIGIBILITY:
Scholarships are based on financial need or academic merit (or both). Contact the organization for full details.

GEOGRAPHIC RESTRICTIONS:
Canada, Greece and United States.

FINANCIAL DATA:
Amount of support per award: $1,000 each for Kottis Family Award, Mary M. Verges,

Joanne V. Hologgitas and Sonja Stefanadis; $1,500 each for Alexandra Apostolides Sonenfeld and Past Grand President's.

APPLICATION INFORMATION:
Information and guidelines available online.
Deadline: Postmarked by June 1.

PUBLICATIONS:
President's Bulletin, monthly publication.

IRS IDENTIFICATION NUMBER: 23-7134317

ADDRESS INQUIRIES TO:
Connie Mondore
National Scholarship Chairman
7913 Chapel Creek Drive
Denver, NC 28037

*SPECIAL STIPULATIONS:
Scholarship may not be deferred to be used at a later date. These awards are not renewable. Application must be typewritten. All requirements must be met and all questions answered or applicant will be disqualified.

DAUGHTERS OF THE CINCINNATI
20 West 44th Street, Room 508
New York, NY 10036
(212) 991-9945

E-MAIL ADDRESS:
scholarships@daughters1894.org

WEB SITE ADDRESS:
fdncenter.org/grantmaker/cincinnati
www.daughters1894.org

TYPE:
Scholarships. Undergraduate scholarships.

See entry 1798 for full listing.

DREXEL UNIVERSITY COLLEGE OF MEDICINE ARCHIVES AND SPECIAL COLLECTIONS [1145]
2900 West Queen Lane
Philadelphia, PA 19129
(215) 991-8340
Fax: (215) 991-8172

E-MAIL ADDRESS:
archives@drexelmed.edu

WEB SITE ADDRESS:
archives.drexelmed.edu

FOUNDED: 1977

AREAS OF INTEREST:
Medicine as it relates to women in professional practice.

NAME(S) OF PROGRAMS:
- **M. Louise Carpenter Gloeckner M.D. Summer Research Fellowship**

TYPE:
Fellowships. For four to six weeks of research at the Archives and Special Collections on Women in Medicine. Collections house the business and academic records of the Medical College of Pennsylvania, the personal papers of women physicians, records of national and international women's medical organizations, schools, associations, hospitals and a historic photograph collection.

YEAR PROGRAM STARTED: 1985

PURPOSE:
To encourage the use of the institution's archival collections in the study of women in medicine.

LEGAL BASIS:
University.

ELIGIBILITY:
Applicants must be either undergraduate or graduate students, medical students, faculty members or independent researchers. Preference is given to researchers with well-defined projects to be completed in one summer.

FINANCIAL DATA:
Total amount of support: $4,000.

NUMBER OF AWARDS: 1.

APPLICATION INFORMATION:
Guidelines and application form is available on the web site.
Duration: Four to six weeks depending on project.
Deadline: March 1.

PUBLICATIONS:
Program announcement.

STAFF:
Joanne Murray, Historian and Director

ADDRESS INQUIRIES TO:
Joanne Murray, Historian and Director
(See address above.)

THE EDUCATIONAL FOUNDATION FOR WOMEN IN ACCOUNTING
136 South Keowee Street
Dayton, OH 45402-2241
(937) 424-3391
Fax: (937) 222-5794

E-MAIL ADDRESS:
info@efwa.org

WEB SITE ADDRESS:
www.efwa.org

TYPE:
Scholarships. Laurels Fund provides a one-year academic scholarship for women pursuing a Ph.D. in accounting.

Women in Need Scholarship is available to women in their third, fourth or fifth year of academic pursuit who need the financial support to complete their degrees. It is renewable annually upon satisfactory completion of course requirements.

Women in Transition Scholarship is intended for women returning to school as freshmen to earn a Bachelor's degree in accounting. It is renewable annually upon satisfactory completion of course requirements.

See entry 2020 for full listing.

GENERAL BOARD OF HIGHER EDUCATION AND MINISTRY, THE UNITED METHODIST CHURCH
1001 19th Avenue South
Nashville, TN 37212
(615) 340-7409
Fax: (615) 340-7395

E-MAIL ADDRESS:
eoneal@gbhem.org

WEB SITE ADDRESS:
www.gbhem.org

TYPE:
Awards/prizes; Scholarships. Awards to encourage women over age 35 to prepare for ordained ministry as an Elder in the United Methodist Church as a second career. The

scholarship is to be used for study toward the basic seminary degree in an accredited school of theology.

See entry 856 for full listing.

GLOBAL FUND FOR WOMEN [1146]

222 Sutter Street, Suite 500
San Francisco, CA 94108
(415) 248-4800
Fax: (415) 248-4801

E-MAIL ADDRESS:
gfw@globalfundforwomen.org

WEB SITE ADDRESS:
www.globalfundforwomen.org

FOUNDED: 1987

AREAS OF INTEREST:
Female human rights, women's access to communications, economic autonomy of women, and girls' education.

NAME(S) OF PROGRAMS:
● **Assisting Women's Groups Globally**

TYPE:
Conferences/seminars; General operating grants; Seed money grants; Technical assistance; Training grants. The Global Fund for Women is a grantmaking foundation that brings together a worldwide network of women and men to strengthen women's rights around the world. Initiatives include promoting women's economic independence, girls' education, women's rights within religious and cultural tradition, and women's health and safety. The Fund also provides assistance to groups overseas that wish to establish philanthropic organizations designed to benefit women.

YEAR PROGRAM STARTED: 1987

PURPOSE:
To promote a world of equality and social justice; to provide the financial means to enable women to attain this vision.

LEGAL BASIS:
Nonprofit corporation, 501(c)(3) tax-exempt.

ELIGIBILITY:
The Global Fund does not make grants to individuals, groups based and working primarily or solely in the U.S., groups whose main or only purpose is to generate income for its members or the community or groups headed and managed by men and without women in important management functions.

The Global Fund considers support to groups which demonstrate a clear commitment to women's equality and female human rights, are governed and directed primarily by women, have defined plans to strengthen the work of the group over time and may be unlikely to obtain funding from other sources.

FINANCIAL DATA:
Amount of support per award: $1,000 to $30,000.

NUMBER OF AWARDS: 650.

APPLICATION INFORMATION:
Applicants may request and respond to grant request guidelines or send a letter describing the group and including contact information, organizational information and grant request information.
Duration: Varies depending on needs and nature of the request.

PUBLICATIONS:
Annual report; brochure; *Raising Our Voices*, newsletter.

IRS IDENTIFICATION NUMBER: 77-0155782

STAFF:
Deborah Holmes, Vice President of Communications
Dale Needles, Vice President Finance and Administration
Shalina Nataraj, Vice President Programs

ADDRESS INQUIRIES TO:
Deborah Holmes
Vice President of Communications
(See address above.)

THE HAFIF FAMILY FOUNDATION [1147]

Claremont Professional Building
265 West Bonita Avenue
Claremont, CA 91711
(909) 625-7971
Fax: (909) 621-4851

E-MAIL ADDRESS:
hffconcerts@yahoo.com

FOUNDED: 1987

AREAS OF INTEREST:
Drugs, gangs, battered women, poverty and education.

TYPE:
Scholarships.

PURPOSE:
To serve the poorest of the poor.

LEGAL BASIS:
Private foundation.

ELIGIBILITY:
No capital projects; no large staffs; more volunteer work.

GEOGRAPHIC RESTRICTIONS:
Pomona Valley, California.

FINANCIAL DATA:
Amount of support per award: Varies.
Total amount of support: $200,000 for the year 2010.

NUMBER OF AWARDS: Over 100.

APPLICATION INFORMATION:
Contact the Foundation for guidelines.

ADDRESS INQUIRIES TO:
Burnis Simon, Executive Director
(See address above.)

HORIZONS FOUNDATION [1148]

WID HORIZONS
2111 Wilson Boulevard, Suite 400
Arlington, VA 22201
(703) 247-2552
Fax: (703) 527-6945

E-MAIL ADDRESS:
jcasey@ndia.org

WEB SITE ADDRESS:
wid.ndia.org

AREAS OF INTEREST:
Increasing women's participation in national security fields.

NAME(S) OF PROGRAMS:
● **Horizons Foundation Scholarship Program**

TYPE:
Scholarships. The Horizons Foundation Scholarship Program is supported by

accredited colleges and universities. Awards are made on an annual basis. The Foundation selects all scholarship recipients based on criteria it sets. Scholarships are awarded to applicants who require financial assistance, demonstrate strong academic credentials and a commitment to a career in national security.

PURPOSE:
To encourage women to pursue careers related to the national security interests of the U.S.; to provide development opportunities to women who are already working in national security fields.

ELIGIBILITY:
Scholarship Program applicants should be pursuing studies in engineering, computer science, physics, mathematics, business, law, international relations, political science, operations research or economics. Other disciplines will be considered if the applicant can successfully demonstrate relevance to a career in the areas of national security or defense.

Scholarship Program applicants also must meet the following criteria (no exceptions will be considered):
(1) be currently enrolled at an accredited university or college, either full-time or part-time;
(2) undergraduate and graduate students are eligible; undergraduates must have attained at least junior-level status (60 credits);
(3) demonstrate interest in pursuing a career related to national security/national defense;
(4) demonstrate financial need;
(5) have a minimum grade point average of 3.25 and;
(6) be a citizen of the U.S.

Recipients of past awards may apply for future financial assistance.

NUMBER OF AWARDS: 5 for academic year 2007-08.

APPLICATION INFORMATION:
Applications must be completed in full and include only the requested items (essays, recommendations and transcripts). Do not include copies of awards, certificates or photographs. Only students meeting eligibility requirements will be considered.
Deadline: July 1.

INTERNATIONAL FEDERATION OF UNIVERSITY WOMEN [1149]

10, rue du Lac
CH 1207 Geneva Switzerland
(4122) 731 23 80
Fax: (4122) 738 04 40

E-MAIL ADDRESS:
fellowships@ifuw.org

WEB SITE ADDRESS:
www.ifuw.org

FOUNDED: 1919

AREAS OF INTEREST:
Status of women, education and human rights.

CONSULTING OR VOLUNTEER SERVICES:
At the international level, IFUW has working relationships with a number of non-governmental organizations, consultative status with ECOSOC, ILO and UNESCO, as well as periodic cooperation with other UN bodies. At the national level, affiliates in 78 countries work to accomplish IFUW's goals and to address issues of global concern, both

through project work and interaction with their governments and other interested groups.

NAME(S) OF PROGRAMS:
- **British Federation Crosby Hall Fellowship**
- **Winifred Cullis Grants**
- **IFUW Study and Action Programme Fellowship**
- **Dorothy Leet Grants**
- **Ida Smedley MacLean International Fellowship**

TYPE:
Fellowships; Research grants; Training grants. IFUW fellowships and grants are awarded biennially to encourage and enable women graduates to undertake original research or obtain further training in the humanities, social sciences and natural sciences.

YEAR PROGRAM STARTED: 1919

PURPOSE:
To promote understanding and friendship among the university women of the world, irrespective of their race, nationality, religion or political opinions; to encourage international cooperation; to further the development of education; to represent university women in international organizations; to encourage the full application of members' skills to the problems which arise at all levels of public life, whether local, national, regional or worldwide; to encourage their participation in the solving of these problems.

LEGAL BASIS:
International non-governmental organization.

ELIGIBILITY:
Open only to members of the International Federation of University Women. Applicants for fellowships must be well started on the research program to which the application relates. A fellowship will not be awarded for the first year of a Ph.D. program.

Winifred Cullis Grants are open to women graduates who seek to obtain specialized training essential to their research, train in new techniques or carry out independent research, including completion of a piece of research well advanced.

Dorothy Leet Grants are open to women graduates of countries with a comparatively low per capita income and to other women graduates who either wish to work as experts in these countries or whose research is of value to such countries. They are available for obtaining special training essential to research and survey work, training in new techniques in group research and further study and carrying out independent research or surveys, including completion of a project well-advanced at the time of the application. Special consideration will be given to applicants whose research or training will have a multiplier effect in their home country.

In the case of both Winifred Cullis and Dorothy Leet Grants, preference is given for work in a country other than that in which the candidate has received her education or habitually resides.

Applications are welcomed from the humanities, social sciences and natural sciences.

FINANCIAL DATA:
Amount of support per award: Fellowships: CHF 8,000 to 10,000; Grants: CHF 3,000 to 6,000.
Total amount of support: CHF 50,000 to 75,000.

NUMBER OF AWARDS: 16 to 25 fellowships and grants are offered in each competition.

APPLICATION INFORMATION:
Members of one of IFUW's national affiliates must apply through that affiliate, not directly to Geneva. Application forms may be obtained only from this national affiliate and should be returned to it when completed with all supporting documentation. Independent members automatically receive application forms.
Duration: Fellowships are intended to cover at least eight months of work. Grants are awarded for a few months.
Deadline: For the U.S., October 1. Notification by April 1. Varies for other countries, but no later than November 1.

OFFICERS:
Louise Croot, President
Sushil Bhardwaj, Vice President
Marianne Haslegrave, Vice President
Shirley Randall, Vice President
Phyllis Scott, Vice President
Catherine Bell, Treasurer

ADDRESS INQUIRIES TO:
See e-mail address above.

*SPECIAL STIPULATIONS:
Women graduates only.

KENTUCKY FOUNDATION FOR WOMEN   [1150]
1215 Heyburn Building
332 West Broadway
Louisville, KY 40202-2184
(502) 562-0045
Fax: (502) 561-0420

E-MAIL ADDRESS:
kfw@kfw.org

WEB SITE ADDRESS:
www.kfw.org

FOUNDED: 1985

AREAS OF INTEREST:
Arts, social change and feminism.

NAME(S) OF PROGRAMS:
- **Art Meets Activism**
- **Artist Enrichment**
- **Hopscotch House Artist Retreat Center**

TYPE:
Project/program grants; Residencies.

PURPOSE:
To promote positive social change through feminist expression in the arts.

ELIGIBILITY:
Individuals must be doing work focusing exclusively in Kentucky.

GEOGRAPHIC RESTRICTIONS:
Kentucky.

FINANCIAL DATA:
Amount of support per award: $1,000 to $7,500.
Total amount of support: $200,000 annually.

NUMBER OF APPLICANTS MOST RECENT YEAR:
Varies.

NUMBER OF AWARDS: 73.

APPLICATION INFORMATION:
Contact the Foundation for guidelines and application form.
Duration: One year. No renewals.
Deadline: Art Meets Activism: first Friday of March; Artist Enrichment: first Friday of September.

STAFF:
Judith Jennings, Executive Director
Rae Strobel, Grant Programs Administrator

ADDRESS INQUIRIES TO:
Judith Jennings, Executive Director
(See address above.)

THE LEEWAY FOUNDATION   [1151]
1315 Walnut Street
Suite 832
Philadelphia, PA 19107
(215) 545-4078
Fax: (215) 545-4021

E-MAIL ADDRESS:
info@leeway.org

WEB SITE ADDRESS:
www.leeway.org

FOUNDED: 1993

AREAS OF INTEREST:
Women and trans artists and art for social change.

NAME(S) OF PROGRAMS:
- **Art and Change Grant**
- **Leeway Transformation Award**

TYPE:
Project/program grants. Art and Change Grant: Semiannual award for women and trans artists who engage in art and social change work and have financial need.

Leeway Transformation Award: Celebrates women and trans artists who create art and social change and have done so for the past five years or more, demonstrating a commitment to art for social change work.

YEAR PROGRAM STARTED: 1998

PURPOSE:
To support women and trans artists creating change.

ELIGIBILITY:
Women and trans artists residing in the Delaware Valley region.

Art and Change Grant awarded to those artists needing financial assistance to take advantage of an opportunity for art and change. All opportunities must have an impact on the work of the artist and/or a larger community of people, create change, and be in collaboration with or supported by a Change Partner.

Leeway Transformation Award is given to those artists whose work engages in change and has an impact on the artist themself or a larger group, audience or community, represents artistic excellence, and demonstrates continued growth and commitment to art and change. Artist must have performed this type of work for at least five years.

GEOGRAPHIC RESTRICTIONS:
Camden County, New Jersey; Bucks, Chester, Delaware, Montgomery and Philadelphia counties, Pennsylvania.

FINANCIAL DATA:
Amount of support per award: Art and Change Grant: $2,500; Leeway Transformation Award: $15,000.

APPLICATION INFORMATION:
Contact the Foundation for application or download a copy of the current application and guideline procedures from the web site.

STAFF:
Denise Brown, Executive Director

ADDRESS INQUIRIES TO:
Sham-e Ali Al-Jamil, Program Director
(See address above.)

MICHIGAN WOMEN'S FOUNDATION [1152]

333 W. Fort Street
Suite 1920
Detroit, MI 48226
(313) 962-1920
Fax: (313) 962-1926

E-MAIL ADDRESS:
grants@miwf.org

WEB SITE ADDRESS:
www.miwf.org

FOUNDED: 1986

AREAS OF INTEREST:
Needs of women and girls.

NAME(S) OF PROGRAMS:
● Young Women for Change

TYPE:
General operating grants; Project/program grants; Seed money grants. Specific focus changes yearly and is determined by each of seven chapters.

YEAR PROGRAM STARTED: 1986

PURPOSE:
To develop young women through the process of philanthropy and grantmaking into successful, fiscally responsible and socially responsive women.

LEGAL BASIS:
Nonprofit 501(c)(3) organization.

ELIGIBILITY:
Eligible organizations must be IRS 501(c)(3) tax-exempt.

GEOGRAPHIC RESTRICTIONS:
Michigan.

FINANCIAL DATA:
Amount of support per award: $500 to $5,000.
Total amount of support: $78,000 for the year 2009.

NUMBER OF APPLICANTS MOST RECENT YEAR:
68 for the year 2008.

NUMBER OF AWARDS: 35 for the year 2008.

APPLICATION INFORMATION:
Guidelines and application form is available on the web site.
Duration: One year.
Deadline: Mid-February.

PUBLICATIONS:
Trillium, newsletter.

IRS IDENTIFICATION NUMBER: 38-2689979

STAFF:
Carolyn J. Cassin, President and Chief Executive Officer
Lisa Mower Gandelot, Director of Development
Michele L. Watts, Program Director
Kate Spratt, Senior Financial Consultant

ADDRESS INQUIRIES TO:
Lori Kitchen, Program Officer
(See address above.)

MONEY FOR WOMEN/BARBARA DEMING MEMORIAL FUND, INC. [1153]

P.O. Box 309
Wilton, NH 03086

FOUNDED: 1975

AREAS OF INTEREST:
Visual art, fiction, nonfiction and poetry.

NAME(S) OF PROGRAMS:
● Individual Artist Support Grants

TYPE:
Awards/prizes. Small grants awarded biannually to individual feminists in the arts.

PURPOSE:
To support feminists in the arts.

LEGAL BASIS:
Private foundation.

ELIGIBILITY:
Open to individual feminist women in the arts, in visual art, fiction (prose), nonfiction (prose) and poetry whose work addresses women's concerns and/or speaks for peace and justice from a feminist perspective. Applicants must be citizens of the U.S. or Canada. No educational or study scholarships.

GEOGRAPHIC RESTRICTIONS:
United States and Canada.

FINANCIAL DATA:
Amount of support per award: $500 to $1,500.

NUMBER OF APPLICANTS MOST RECENT YEAR:
350.

NUMBER OF AWARDS: 20.

REPRESENTATIVE AWARDS:
Ana-Maurine Lara (poetry), Austin, TX, *Kohnjehr Woman*; Sarah Levine (nonfiction), Cambridge, MA, *What Hands Can Do*; Robin Parks (nonfiction), Bryn Mawr, PA, *Famished*.

APPLICATION INFORMATION:
Send self-addressed, stamped envelope for required application form. A new application is required for each round. Completed applications require an application/processing fee of $20.
Deadline: June 30 for nonfiction and poetry. December 31 for fiction, visual art and mixed genre. Announcement by May and October.

PUBLICATIONS:
Newsletter.

IRS IDENTIFICATION NUMBER: 51-0176956

BOARD OF DIRECTORS:
Maureen Brady
Martha Hughes
Lisa C. Moore
Lisa Weil

ADDRESS INQUIRIES TO:
Susan Pliner, Executive Director
(See address above.)

*PLEASE NOTE:
Applicant will receive no response without a self-addressed, stamped envelope.

MS. FOUNDATION FOR WOMEN [1154]

12 Metro Tech Center
26th Floor
Brooklyn, NY 11201
(212) 742-2300
Fax: (212) 742-1653

E-MAIL ADDRESS:
info@ms.foundation.org

WEB SITE ADDRESS:
www.ms.foundation.org

FOUNDED: 1972

AREAS OF INTEREST:
Economic security, entailing job creation, women's employment issues, workplace rights and child care, and health and safety.

NAME(S) OF PROGRAMS:
● Building Democracy
● Economic Justice
● Ending Violence
● Women's Health

TYPE:
General operating grants; Project/program grants; Technical assistance; Training grants. General support.

YEAR PROGRAM STARTED: 1976

PURPOSE:
To support the efforts of women and girls to govern their own lives and influence the world around them; to champion an equitable society by effecting change in public consciousness, law, philanthropy and social policy through its leadership, expertise and financial support.

LEGAL BASIS:
Public foundation.

ELIGIBILITY:
Within its funding priorities, the Foundation gives priority to:
(1) efforts that engage women and girls in crafting activist solutions to the particular challenges they face in their communities based on gender, race, ethnicity, class, age, disability, sexual orientation and culture and;
(2) national, regional or state level public policy advocacy informed by local organizing work and undertaken by organizations with strong linkages to a grassroots constituency.

Special consideration is given to the organizations that:
(1) are pro-women's empowerment, proactively antiracist and working to dismantle heterosexism, class oppression and discrimination based on disability;
(2) address the particular challenges faced by low-income women and girls;
(3) clearly articulate and respond to issues of gender as related to class and race/ethnicity;
(4) are multi-issue and involved in a form of cross-constituency organizing and coalition work;
(5) encourage intergenerational work that empowers younger as well as older women;
(6) include in leadership positions those who are affected most directly by the issues addressed and;
(7) have limited access to other funding sources.

The Foundation does not fund direct service projects, stand-alone cultural or media projects, publications, individuals, scholarships, religious institutions, conferences, university-based research or government agencies.

GEOGRAPHIC RESTRICTIONS:
United States.

FINANCIAL DATA:
Amount of support per award: $10,000 to $75,000.

Total amount of support: Approximately $4,000,000 in grants and practical training to community-based and national activist women's organizations throughout the U.S. each year.

NUMBER OF APPLICANTS MOST RECENT YEAR:
1,000.

NUMBER OF AWARDS: 100.

APPLICATION INFORMATION:
Duration: Generally one-time grants. Some renewal funding.
Deadline: Varies per program.

PUBLICATIONS:
Annual report; application guidelines; most recent grants list.

BOARD OF DIRECTORS:
Cathy Raphael, Chairperson
Phoebe Eng, Vice Chairperson
Sara E. Melendez, Secretary
Ashley Blanchard
Elizabeth Bremner
Jeannie Diefenderfer
Eve Ellis
Lauren Embrey
Katie Grover, C.S.W.
Don McPherson
Wenda Weekes Moore
Rene Redwood
Kathleen Stephansen
Dorothy Q. Thomas
Verna L. Williams

ADDRESS INQUIRIES TO:
Vice President, Programs
(See address above.)

NATIONAL FEDERATION OF REPUBLICAN WOMEN   [1155]
124 North Alfred Street
Alexandria, VA 22314
(703) 548-9688
Fax: (703) 548-9836

E-MAIL ADDRESS:
mail@nfrw.org

WEB SITE ADDRESS:
www.nfrw.org

FOUNDED: 1938

AREAS OF INTEREST:
The political process.

NAME(S) OF PROGRAMS:
- **Dorothy Kabis Internship**
- **National Pathfinder's Scholarship**
- **Betty Rendel Scholarship**

TYPE:
Internships; Scholarships. Dorothy Kabis Internship includes a six-week internship in Washington, DC, housing, travel and stipend.

National Pathfinder's Scholarships are given to the best nominated candidates.

Betty Rendel Scholarships are given to undergraduate women who are majoring in political science, government or economics.

PURPOSE:
To involve more women in the political process and provide educational opportunities.

ELIGIBILITY:
National Pathfinder's Scholarship is open to young women seeking undergraduate or postgraduate degrees, college sophomores, juniors, seniors and students enrolled in a Master's program. Recent high school graduates and first-year college women are not eligible.

Betty Rendel Scholarship applicants must be undergraduate women who are majoring in political science, government or economics. Open only to women who have successfully completed two years of college work.

GEOGRAPHIC RESTRICTIONS:
United States.

FINANCIAL DATA:
Dorothy Kabis Internship includes a small stipend, housing and airfare.
Amount of support per award: National Pathfinder's Scholarship: $2,500; Betty Rendel Scholarship: $1,000.

NUMBER OF AWARDS: 3 for each program.

APPLICATION INFORMATION:
All grant information, including a printable version of the application, can be found online.
Duration: One-time award.
Deadline: June 1 for the National Pathfinder's Scholarship and Betty Rendel Scholarship. February 20 for Dorothy Kabis Internship.

ADDRESS INQUIRIES TO:
Scholarship Coordinator
(See address above.)

*SPECIAL STIPULATIONS:
Applicants must be U.S. citizens and may only apply to one program in a given year. Winners may not reapply.

NATIVE AMERICAN COMMUNITY BOARD (NACB)
P.O. Box 572
Lake Andes, SD 57356-0572
(605) 487-7072
Fax: (605) 487-7964

E-MAIL ADDRESS:
charon@charles-mix.com

WEB SITE ADDRESS:
www.nativeshop.org

TYPE:
Internships.

See entry 1118 for full listing.

THE NEWBERRY LIBRARY
Committee on Awards
60 West Walton Street
Chicago, IL 60610-7324
(312) 255-3666
Fax: (312) 255-3680

E-MAIL ADDRESS:
research@newberry.org

WEB SITE ADDRESS:
www.newberry.
org/research/felshp/fellowshome.html

TYPE:
Fellowships; Visiting scholars. Allen fellows are expected to spend a significant part of their tenure in residence at Newberry's D'Arcy McNickle Center for American Indian History.

See entry 1119 for full listing.

OPEN MEADOWS FOUNDATION   [1156]
P.O. Box 150-607
Van Brunt Station
Brooklyn, NY 11215
(718) 885-0969

E-MAIL ADDRESS:
openmeadows@igc.org

WEB SITE ADDRESS:
www.openmeadows.org

FOUNDED: 1986

AREAS OF INTEREST:
Projects led by and benefiting women and girls, reflecting community diversity, building community power, and promoting racial, social, economic and environmental justice.

TYPE:
Development grants; Project/program grants; Training grants. International program for women and girls.

PURPOSE:
To fund projects that are led by and benefit women and girls.

ELIGIBILITY:
Applicant organization must be nonprofit 501(c)(3) or have a fiscal sponsor that is tax-exempt 501(c)(3). Small and start-up organizations are strongly encouraged to apply. Proposals not previously funded have priority. Proposals for projects that have limited financial access or have encountered obstacles in their search for funding are eligible to apply. Applicant's organizational budget should not exceed $150,000. Projects must be led by and benefit women and girls. No grants are made to individuals.

FINANCIAL DATA:
Amount of support per award: Up to $2,000.
Total amount of support: $60,000 per year.

NUMBER OF APPLICANTS MOST RECENT YEAR:
500.

NUMBER OF AWARDS: 40 per year.

APPLICATION INFORMATION:
Only mailed applications are accepted. Must include copy of tax-exempt letter from the IRS giving 501(c)(3) status.
Duration: One year. Must reapply.
Deadline: February 15 and August 15.

ADDRESS INQUIRIES TO:
Di Eckerle, Director
(See address above.)

P.E.O. SISTERHOOD
P.E.O. Executive Office
3700 Grand Avenue
Des Moines, IA 50312
(515) 255-3153
Fax: (515) 255-3820

E-MAIL ADDRESS:
ips@peodsm.org

WEB SITE ADDRESS:
www.peointernational.org

TYPE:
Grants-in-aid; Scholarships. Awards for selected women from countries other than the U.S. and Canada to pursue graduate study in the U.S. or Canada. Support is available for advanced study in any field except for research. No new applications at the dissertation level.

See entry 1015 for full listing.

THE PHI BETA KAPPA SOCIETY   [1157]
1606 New Hampshire Avenue, N.W.
Washington, DC 20009
(202) 745-3235
Fax: (202) 986-1601

E-MAIL ADDRESS:
awards@pbk.org

WEB SITE ADDRESS:
www.pbk.org

FOUNDED: 1776

NAME(S) OF PROGRAMS:
● **Mary Isabel Sibley Fellowship**

TYPE:
Awards/prizes; Fellowships; Project/program grants; Research grants; Scholarships; Travel grants. Grant to women scholars made in alternate years for advanced research dealing with Greek language, literature, history or archaeology (odd-numbered years) or with French language or literature (even-numbered years).

YEAR PROGRAM STARTED: 1939

PURPOSE:
To assist women scholars conducting original research.

LEGAL BASIS:
National scholarly honorary society.

ELIGIBILITY:
Unmarried women between 25 and 35 years of age (inclusive) are eligible to apply. They must hold the Doctorate or have fulfilled all requirements for the Doctorate except the dissertation. Applicants must have demonstrated ability to carry on original research and must plan to devote full-time work to research during the fellowship year. Eligibility is not restricted to members of the Society or to U.S. citizens.

FINANCIAL DATA:
The Fellowship carries a $20,000 stipend with one-half of the amount payable after July following announcement of the Fellowship and the balance after another six months have elapsed.
Amount of support per award: $20,000.
Total amount of support: $20,000.

NUMBER OF APPLICANTS MOST RECENT YEAR: 40.

NUMBER OF AWARDS: 1 each year.

APPLICATION INFORMATION:
Official application materials are available upon request to the Awards Coordinator or on the web site. Fellowships are awarded alternately in the fields of Greek language, literature, history or archaeology (odd-numbered years) and French language or literature (even-numbered years). Send brief description of intended research project when requesting an application.
Duration: The Fellowship is tenable for one year.
Deadline: Applications must be filed before January 15 for the Fellowship to be announced by the following May 15.

OFFICERS:
Fred Cate, President
John Churchill, Secretary

ADDRESS INQUIRIES TO:
Mary Isabel Sibley Fellowship Committee (See address above.)

ROCHESTER AREA COMMUNITY FOUNDATION [1158]
500 East Avenue
Rochester, NY 14607-1912
(585) 271-4100
Fax: (585) 271-4292

WEB SITE ADDRESS:
www.racf.org

FOUNDED: 1972

AREAS OF INTEREST:
Women and girls, organizational capacity building, aging, arts, the environment, civic engagement, youth and families, historical preservation and health.

TYPE:
Project/program grants; Scholarships.

PURPOSE:
To support community responsibility and leadership, healthy options for young people and their families, early childhood development and quality of life.

LEGAL BASIS:
Tax-exempt public charity.

GEOGRAPHIC RESTRICTIONS:
Genesee, Livingston, Monroe, Ontario, Orleans and Wayne counties, New York.

FINANCIAL DATA:
$206,000,000 in grants since 1972.
Amount of support per award: Varies.
Total amount of support: $17,219,457 for fiscal year 2009-10.

IRS IDENTIFICATION NUMBER: 23-7250641

ADDRESS INQUIRIES TO:
Grant inquiries to: Mairead Hartmann Program Associate
All other inquiries to: Jennifer Leonard President and Executive Director

SIGMA DELTA EPSILON/GRADUATE WOMEN IN SCIENCE
P.O. Box 240607
St. Paul, MN 55124-0607
(952) 236-9112

E-MAIL ADDRESS:
gwised@mac.com

WEB SITE ADDRESS:
www.gwis.org

TYPE:
Awards/prizes; Fellowships; Travel grants. Leadership Awards are given to Graduate Women in Science officers.

See entry 1960 for full listing.

THE SISTER FUND [1159]
79 Fifth Avenue, 4th Floor
New York, NY 10003
(212) 260-4446
Fax: (212) 260-4633

E-MAIL ADDRESS:
info@sisterfund.org

WEB SITE ADDRESS:
www.sisterfund.org

FOUNDED: 1993

AREAS OF INTEREST:
"Faith and Feminism" initiative and women's religious empowerment.

TYPE:
Challenge/matching grants; Conferences/seminars; General operating grants; Project/program grants; Research grants; Technical assistance. Grants are distributed one-half to local projects in New York City and one-half to national or international projects.

PURPOSE:
To fund programs that foster women's spiritual, political and social empowerment.

LEGAL BASIS:
Private fund.

ELIGIBILITY:
Applicants must be 501(c)(3) tax-exempt organizations. No grants to individuals.

FINANCIAL DATA:
Amount of support per award: $5,000 to $20,000.
Total amount of support: $500,000.

NUMBER OF APPLICANTS MOST RECENT YEAR: 166.

NUMBER OF AWARDS: 58.

REPRESENTATIVE AWARDS:
Faith and Feminism Dialogue Project; The Interchurch Center's "Women in 21st Century Religion" Conference; CODIMUJ; Institute for Women's Policy Research.

APPLICATION INFORMATION:
By invitation only.

PUBLICATIONS:
Special reports; brochures.

OFFICERS:
Helen Lakelly Hunt, President
Harvelle Hendrix, Vice President
Vincent McGee, Secretary

STAFF:
Alexie Torres-Fleming, Executive Director
Brandy Sorro, Grants Administrator

SKILLBUILDERS FUND [1160]
10055 Craig Drive
Overland Park, KS 66212
(913) 403-9532
Fax: (913) 403-9532

E-MAIL ADDRESS:
info@skillbuildersfund.org

WEB SITE ADDRESS:
skillbuildersfund.org

FOUNDED: 1983

AREAS OF INTEREST:
Programs benefiting low-income women and girls.

TYPE:
Project/program grants. Programs that help women and girls with economic self-sufficiency. Matching gifts are for directors only. Scholarships are only given to organizations, not to individuals.

YEAR PROGRAM STARTED: 1984

PURPOSE:
To enhance the capabilities of women and girls of all ages in the Kansas City metropolitan area and to realize their full potential.

LEGAL BASIS:
Private foundation.

ELIGIBILITY:
Organizations must be IRS 501(c)(3) not-for-profit. Funding primarily is directed to 501(c)(3) organizations that specifically benefit women and girls. Individuals, businesses and other for-profit organizations do not qualify.

GEOGRAPHIC RESTRICTIONS:
Kansas City metropolitan area, including Cass, Clay, Jackson, Johnson, Leavenworth, Platte, Ray and Wyandotte counties.

FINANCIAL DATA:
Amount of support per award: $20,000 to
$50,000.
Total amount of support: Varies.
Matching fund requirements: Available only
to directors of the SkillBuilders Fund.

NUMBER OF AWARDS: 3 to 9 annually.

REPRESENTATIVE AWARDS:
TLC for Children and Families; Urban
League of Greater Kansas City; Wildwood
Outdoor Education Center.

APPLICATION INFORMATION:
Information brochures are available at the
address listed above. Applicants must include
a copy of their IRS tax determination letter
with the application.
Duration: One year.
Deadline: March 1. Call to confirm deadline
date.

PUBLICATIONS:
Information brochure with application
procedures.

IRS IDENTIFICATION NUMBER: 48-0984713

ADDRESS INQUIRIES TO:
Stephanie Stollsteimer, Executive Director
(See address above.)

SOCIETY OF DAUGHTERS OF
THE U.S. ARMY
11804 Grey Birch Place
Reston, VA 20191-4223

TYPE:
Scholarships.

See entry 1878 for full listing.

SOCIETY OF WOMEN
ENGINEERS   [1161]
120 South La Salle Street
Suite 1515
Chicago, IL 60603
(312) 596-5223
Fax: (312) 596-5252

E-MAIL ADDRESS:
hq@swe.org

WEB SITE ADDRESS:
www.swe.org

FOUNDED: 1950

AREAS OF INTEREST:
Engineering.

NAME(S) OF PROGRAMS:
● Society of Women Engineers
  Scholarship Program

TYPE:
Awards/prizes; Conferences/seminars;
Scholarships. Support for undergraduate and
graduate engineering studies including
women who have been out of the engineering
job market for a minimum of two years and
who will return to school for an engineering
program.

YEAR PROGRAM STARTED: 1950

PURPOSE:
To encourage women to achieve their utmost
in careers as professional engineers and as
the leaders of tomorrow and to attain high
levels of education.

LEGAL BASIS:
Nonprofit educational organization under IRS
501(c)(3) classification.

ELIGIBILITY:
Scholarships are open only to women
majoring in engineering in a school, college
or university with an accredited engineering
program. Candidate is evaluated on the basis
of scholastic standing in high school and/or
college and extracurricular activity.

Some scholarships require applicant to be a
U.S. citizen.

FINANCIAL DATA:
Scholarship payments are made directly to
academic institutions on the recipient's
behalf.
Amount of support per award: $1,000 to
$10,000.
Total amount of support: $500,000.

NUMBER OF APPLICANTS MOST RECENT YEAR:
Approximately 3,000.

NUMBER OF AWARDS: 170 for the year 2010.

APPLICATION INFORMATION:
Completed application form and letters of
reference are required.
Duration: One year. Possible renewal.
Deadline: May 15 for freshmen. February 15
for sophomore, junior, senior and graduate.
Announcement in late spring and summer,
respectively, for use during the following
academic year.

PUBLICATIONS:
Applications; scholarship program brochure;
SWE magazine.

IRS IDENTIFICATION NUMBER: 13-1947735

ADDRESS INQUIRIES TO:
E-mail: scholarshipapplication@swe.org

WASHINGTON UNIVERSITY
Graduate School of Arts and Sciences
Campus Box 1187
One Brookings Drive
St. Louis, MO 63130
(314) 935-6818
Fax: (314) 935-4887

E-MAIL ADDRESS:
buchanan@wustl.edu

WEB SITE ADDRESS:
olinfellowship.wustl.edu

TYPE:
Fellowships. The Olin Fellowships are open
to candidates for any of the following
graduate and professional schools at
Washington University: architecture, art, arts
and sciences, business, engineering,
medicine, and social work.

See entry 1919 for full listing.

WELLESLEY COLLEGE   [1162]
Center for Work and Service
Green Hall 442, 106 Central Street
Wellesley, MA 02481-8203
(781) 283-2352
Fax: (781) 283-3674

E-MAIL ADDRESS:
cws-fellowships@wellesley.edu

WEB SITE ADDRESS:
www.wellesley.edu/CWS

AREAS OF INTEREST:
Graduate education.

NAME(S) OF PROGRAMS:
● Anne Louise Barrett Fellowship
● Margaret Freeman Bowers Fellowship
● The Eugene L. Cox Fellowship

● Professor Elizabeth F. Fisher
  Fellowship
● Ruth Ingersoll Goldmark Fellowship
● Horton-Hallowell Fellowship
● Peggy Howard Fellowship in
  Economics
● Edna V. Moffett Fellowship
● Alice Freeman Palmer Fellowship
● Kathryn Conway Preyer Fellowship
● Vida Dutton Scudder Fellowship
● Harriet A. Shaw Fellowship
● Mary Elvira Stevens Traveling
  Fellowship
● Sarah Perry Wood Medical Fellowship
● Fanny Bullock Workman Fellowship

TYPE:
Fellowships; Research grants. The Anne
Louise Barrett Fellowship is given preferably
in music and primarily for study or research
in musical theory, composition, or in the
history of music, abroad or in the U.S.

The Margaret Freeman Bowers Fellowship is
given for first year of study in the fields of
social work, law, or policy/public
administration, including M.B.A. candidates
with plans for a career in the field of social
services.

The Eugene L. Cox Fellowship is for
graduate study in medieval or renaissance
history and culture abroad or in the U.S.

The Professor Elizabeth F. Fisher Fellowship
is given for research or further study in
geology or geography, including urban,
environmental or ecological studies.

The Ruth Ingersoll Goldmark Fellowship is
awarded for graduate study in English
literature, English composition or in the
classics.

The Horton-Hallowell Fellowship is awarded
for graduate study in any field, preferably in
the last two years of candidacy for the Ph.D.
degree, or its equivalent, or for private
research of equivalent standard.

The Peggy Howard Fellowship in Economics
is given to provide financial aid for Wellesley
students or alumnae continuing their study of
economics. Administered by the economics
faculty who may name one or two recipients
depending on the income available.

The Edna V. Moffett Fellowship is given to a
young alumna, preferably for a first year of
graduate study in history.

The Alice Freeman Palmer Fellowship is
awarded for study or research abroad or in
the U.S.

The Kathryn Conway Preyer Fellowship is
for advanced study in history.

The Vida Dutton Scudder Fellowship is given
for study in the field of social science,
political science or literature.

The Harriet A. Shaw Fellowship is given for
study or research in music and the allied arts,
in the U.S. or abroad.

Mary Elvira Stevens Traveling Fellowship is
awarded for travel or study outside the U.S.

The Sarah Perry Wood Medical Fellowship is
awarded for the study of medicine at an
accredited medical school approved by the
American Medical Association.

The Fanny Bullock Workman Fellowship is
given for graduate study in any field.

ELIGIBILITY:
Applicants must be graduating seniors of
alumnae of Wellesley College for all of these
fellowships. Awards will be based on merit

and financial need. Awards are usually made to applicants who plan full-time graduate study for the coming year. Preference in all cases, except for the Peggy Howard Fellowship, will be given to applicants who have not held one of these awards.

Alice Freeman Palmer Fellows must be no more than 26 years of age at the time of their appointment and unmarried throughout the whole of their tenure.

Preference for the Harriet A. Shaw Fellowship is given to music candidates; undergraduate work in history of art is required of other candidates.

Candidates for the Mary Elvira Stevens Traveling Fellowship must be at least 25 years of age in the year of application. Any scholarly, artistic, or cultural purpose may be considered.

FINANCIAL DATA:
Amount of support per award: $3,000 to $76,000.
Total amount of support: Varies.

NUMBER OF APPLICANTS MOST RECENT YEAR:
148.

APPLICATION INFORMATION:
Application forms for the Peggy Howard Fellowship may be obtained from the Economics Department at the College.
Deadline: Peggy Howard Fellowship: Early April. Mary Elvira Stevens Fellowship: December 1. All other awards: Early January.

PUBLICATIONS:
Program announcement.

*SPECIAL STIPULATIONS:
These fellowships are for study at institutions other than Wellesley College.

WELLESLEY COLLEGE [1163]
Center for Work and Service
Green Hall 442, 106 Central Street
Wellesley, MA 02481-8203
(781) 283-2352
Fax: (781) 283-3674

E-MAIL ADDRESS:
cws-fellowships@wellesley.edu

WEB SITE ADDRESS:
www.wellesley.edu/CWS

AREAS OF INTEREST:
Graduate study for women.

NAME(S) OF PROGRAMS:
● **Mary McEwen Schimke Scholarship**
● **M.A. Cartland Shackford Medical Fellowship**

TYPE:
Fellowships; Scholarships. Awards are made to female applicants who plan for full-time graduate study for the coming year.

The Mary McEwen Schimke Scholarship is a supplemental award given to afford relief from household and child care expenses while pursuing graduate study.

The M.A. Cartland Shackford Medical Fellowship is given for study of medicine with a view to general practice, not psychiatry.

ELIGIBILITY:
The Mary McEwen Schimke Scholarship is made on the basis of scholarly expectation and identified need. The candidate must be over 30 years of age, have household and childcare responsibilities, and be currently

engaged in graduate study in literature and/or history. Preference is given to American Studies.

FINANCIAL DATA:
Amount of support per award: McEwen Scholarship: Up to $1,500; Shackford Medical Fellowship: Up to $11,000.
Total amount of support: Varies.

APPLICATION INFORMATION:
Duration: One year.
Deadline: Early January.

PUBLICATIONS:
Announcement.

THE WHO (WOMEN HELPING OTHERS) FOUNDATION [1164]
2121 Midway Road
Carrollton, TX 75006
(972) 458-0601
(800) 946-4663
Fax: (972) 341-3080

WEB SITE ADDRESS:
www.whofoundation.org

FOUNDED: 1993

AREAS OF INTEREST:
Women's and children's health, education and social services issues.

TYPE:
Development grants; Product donations; Project/program grants.

YEAR PROGRAM STARTED: 1993

PURPOSE:
To support community-focused charities that serve the overlooked needs of women, children and families.

LEGAL BASIS:
Tax-exempt, nonprofit foundation.

ELIGIBILITY:
Applicants must be non-political charities and organizations that have been incorporated with 501(c)(3) status for a minimum of three years prior to application. No grants to individuals. Prefer requests dealing with projects and programs.

GEOGRAPHIC RESTRICTIONS:
United States and Puerto Rico.

FINANCIAL DATA:
Amount of support per award: Varies depending on needs and nature of the request.
Total amount of support: $4,000,000 since 1993.

NUMBER OF APPLICANTS MOST RECENT YEAR:
Approximately 450 for the year 2010.

NUMBER OF AWARDS: 31 for the year 2010.

APPLICATION INFORMATION:
Application form required. Required attachments include a copy of the organization's most recent audit, board list, budget outline and most recent annual report, if available, and 501(c)(3) document.
Duration: Varies.
Deadline: General grant: Early September.

PUBLICATIONS:
Application; newsletters; cancer booklet for women.

IRS IDENTIFICATION NUMBER: 75-2504646

BOARD OF DIRECTORS:
Lou Sartor, Chairman
Katherine A. Staton, Treasurer

Jasmine Harris, Secretary
Kathy Bailey
Julianne Bosch
Donna Coyne
Linda Honker
David Kihneman
Kenneth Kracmer
Judy Mynett
Martha Rocha
Tracey Wallace

ADDRESS INQUIRIES TO:
Grants Manager
(See address above.)

*PLEASE NOTE:
No phone calls or e-mails please.

WOMEN IN FILM [1165]
6100 Wilshire Boulevard
Suite 710
Los Angeles, CA 90048
(323) 935-2211
Fax: (323) 935-2212

E-MAIL ADDRESS:
foundation@wif.org

WEB SITE ADDRESS:
www.wif.org/foundation

FOUNDED: 1985

AREAS OF INTEREST:
Filmmaking.

NAME(S) OF PROGRAMS:
● **Women in Film Foundation Film Finishing Fund**

TYPE:
Project/program grants. Awards for completion of films or videotapes on subjects that meet the stated guidelines of WIF on an annual basis.

YEAR PROGRAM STARTED: 1985

PURPOSE:
To increase employment and promote equal opportunities for women; to encourage individual creative projects by women; to enhance media images of women; to further the professional development of women; to influence prevailing attitudes and practices regarding and on behalf of women.

LEGAL BASIS:
Nonprofit organization.

ELIGIBILITY:
All independent producers and nonprofit corporations are eligible to submit proposals for completion funding on an existing film or video. Projects in development or pre-production will not be considered. No student projects, graduate or undergraduate, will be considered. Applicants do not need to be members of Women In Film.

FINANCIAL DATA:
Amount of support per award: Up to $15,000 in cash and/or in-kind services.

NUMBER OF APPLICANTS MOST RECENT YEAR:
Over 100.

NUMBER OF AWARDS: 7.

APPLICATION INFORMATION:
Detailed guidelines and application form can be obtained at the Foundation web site.

ADDRESS INQUIRIES TO:
Meg Linker-Estes, Executive Assistant
(See address above.)

*SPECIAL STIPULATIONS:
Projects must be in post-production by the deadline. Filmmakers must submit a rough cut of their films to be considered.

WOMEN'S FOUNDATION OF MINNESOTA [1166]

155 Fifth Avenue South
Suite 500
Minneapolis, MN 55401-2549
(612) 337-5010
Fax: (612) 337-0404

E-MAIL ADDRESS:
contactus@wfmn.org

WEB SITE ADDRESS:
www.wfmn.org

FOUNDED: 1983

AREAS OF INTEREST:
Women and girls in Minnesota.

NAME(S) OF PROGRAMS:
● **Social Change Fund**

TYPE:
Development grants; General operating grants; Project/program grants; Technical assistance. Start-up grants.

YEAR PROGRAM STARTED: 1986

PURPOSE:
To increase financial resources available to programs and organizations by and for women and girls creating change on their own behalf.

LEGAL BASIS:
Public foundation.

ELIGIBILITY:
Must primarily benefit women and girls and be not-for-profit or informal not-for-profit.

GEOGRAPHIC RESTRICTIONS:
Minnesota.

FINANCIAL DATA:
Amount of support per award: Up to $20,000.

Total amount of support: Approximately $1,000,000 total funding in all programs.

NUMBER OF APPLICANTS MOST RECENT YEAR: 200.

NUMBER OF AWARDS: 38.

REPRESENTATIVE AWARDS:
Creating Economic Justice for Women: $6,500 to The Minnesota Project, St. Paul; Assuring Safety and Security for Women: $7,500 to Women of Nations, St. Paul; Guaranteeing Women's Health and Reproductive Rights: $7,500 to Women's Health Center of Duluth; Expanding Women's Political Representation: $6,500 to Sheila Wellstone Institute, St. Paul, for Wellstone Action Fund; Promoting Human Rights for Women: $6,000 to OutFront Minnesota, Minneapolis.

APPLICATION INFORMATION:
Detailed instructions and guidelines are available from the Foundation.
Duration: Three years.
Deadline: Varies.

PUBLICATIONS:
Annual report; equality report; brochure; grant guidelines; research/issue reports.

IRS IDENTIFICATION NUMBER: 41-1635761

ADDRESS INQUIRIES TO:
Charlotte Flowers, Program Officer
(See address above.)

*SPECIAL STIPULATIONS:
Funds only in Minnesota. Does not fund individuals.

WOMEN'S FOUNDATION OF MINNESOTA [1167]

155 Fifth Avenue South
Suite 500
Minneapolis, MN 55401
(612) 337-5010
Fax: (612) 337-0404

E-MAIL ADDRESS:
contactus@wfmn.org

WEB SITE ADDRESS:
www.wfmn.org

FOUNDED: 1983

AREAS OF INTEREST:
Women and girls in Minnesota.

NAME(S) OF PROGRAMS:
● **girlsBEST**

TYPE:
Project/program grants. The girlsBEST program has five program tracks: Academic; Entrepreneurial; Employment Development and High-Paying/High-Skill Careers; Public Education and Advocacy; Sports and Arts.

PURPOSE:
To increase financial resources available to programs and organizations by and for women and girls creating change on their own behalf; to increase future economic success for women and girls.

LEGAL BASIS:
Public foundation.

ELIGIBILITY:
Must primarily benefit women and girls and be not-for-profit or informal not-for-profit.

GEOGRAPHIC RESTRICTIONS:
Minnesota.

FINANCIAL DATA:
Amount of support per award: $10,000 to $15,000.

Total amount of support: Approximately $200,000 for the year 2009.

NUMBER OF APPLICANTS MOST RECENT YEAR: 54.

NUMBER OF AWARDS: 13.

REPRESENTATIVE AWARDS:
Entrepreneurial: $10,000 to Centro, Inc.; Academic: $12,000 to Laura Jeffrey Academy; Public Education and Advocacy: $11,000 to Crisis Center for Teens Against Dating Abuse.

APPLICATION INFORMATION:
Duration: Three years.
Deadline: May 2013.

ADDRESS INQUIRIES TO:
Charlotte Flowers
Senior Program Officer
(See address above.)

*SPECIAL STIPULATIONS:
Funds only in Minnesota. Does not fund individuals.

WOMEN'S RESEARCH AND EDUCATION INSTITUTE (WREI) [1168]

714 G Street, S.E.
Suite 200
Washington, DC 20003
(202) 280-2720
Fax: (202) 293-4507

E-MAIL ADDRESS:
wrei@wrei.org

WEB SITE ADDRESS:
www.wrei.org

FOUNDED: 1977

AREAS OF INTEREST:
Women's public policy issues.

NAME(S) OF PROGRAMS:
● **Congressional Fellowships on Women and Public Policy**

TYPE:
Fellowships.

YEAR PROGRAM STARTED: 1980

PURPOSE:
To encourage more effective participation by women in the formulation of policy options that recognize the needs of all people; to promote activities that encourage the translation of research into policy; to raise awareness that national and international issues concerning women are interdependent; to increase understanding that those issues often defined as women's issues are, in fact, human issues of equal importance to both women and men.

LEGAL BASIS:
501(c)(3) nonprofit organization.

ELIGIBILITY:
Applicants must be currently enrolled in, or have graduated within the last 18 months from, a graduate or professional degree program in the U.S. Preliminary selection is based on academic performance, writing skills, experience with community groups and interest in the analysis of gender differences as they affect federal laws and legislating. Candidates from all academic disciplines are considered. Final selection follows an interview by WREI.

WREI does not assist in student visas for applicants studying at U.S. universities.

FINANCIAL DATA:
Amount of support per award: Monthly stipends of $1,450, plus $1,500 for tuition and $500 health care allowance.

Total amount of support: $11,600 per awardee for academic year 2009.

COOPERATIVE FUNDING PROGRAMS:
Underwritten by Amgen; Eli Lilly; sanofi-aventis; Martha, Emily and Betta Ehrenfeld.

NUMBER OF APPLICANTS MOST RECENT YEAR: Approximately 100.

NUMBER OF AWARDS: Approximately 6 to 10 each year.

APPLICATION INFORMATION:
Applications are available in February. Applicants must submit all academic transcripts, three letters of recommendation, completed application form and an essay.
Duration: January to August. No renewals.
Deadline: May 21. Regional interviews of semi-finalists are held in July and awards made by August 30.

IRS IDENTIFICATION NUMBER: 52-1104895

STAFF:
Susan P. Scanlan, President
Lori Manning, Women in the Military Project Director
Bernice Sandler, Senior Fellow

ADDRESS INQUIRIES TO:
Susan P. Scanlan, President
(See address above.)

***SPECIAL STIPULATIONS:**
Foreign students at international universities are not eligible. Must come to Washington to work full-time in a congressional office from January until July/August.

WOMEN'S SPORTS FOUNDATION   [1169]

Eisenhower Park
1899 Hempstead Turnpike, Suite 400
East Meadow, NY 11554
(516) 542-4700
(800) 227-3988
Fax: (516) 542-4716

E-MAIL ADDRESS:
info@womenssportsfoundation.org

WEB SITE ADDRESS:
www.womenssportsfoundation.org

FOUNDED: 1974

AREAS OF INTEREST:
The Foundation–the leading authority on the participation of women and girls in sports–advocates for equality, educates the public, conducts research and offers grants to promote sports and physical activity for girls and women.

CONSULTING OR VOLUNTEER SERVICES:
Sponsors internship program.

NAME(S) OF PROGRAMS:
- **GoGirlGo! Grant Program**

TYPE:
Project/program grants. Founded by Billie Jean King in 1974, the Women's Sports Foundation builds on her legacy as a champion athlete, advocate of social justice and agent of change. The Foundation strives for gender equity and fights discrimination in sports. Its work shapes public attitude about women's sports and athletes, builds capacities for organizations that get girls active, provides equal opportunities for girls and women, and supports physically and emotionally healthy lifestyles. The Foundation is recognized worldwide for its leadership, vision, strength, expertise and influence.

GoGirlGo! Grant Program works across the country to improve the health of sedentary girls and to keep girls involved in physical activity. The program gets girls moving not through direct service, but by supporting programs and organizations that work with girls.

YEAR PROGRAM STARTED: 1984

PURPOSE:
To provide financial assistance in the training of women as sports leaders, coaches, officials and administrators of girls and women in sports; to advance the lives of girls and women through sports and physical activity.

LEGAL BASIS:
501(c)(3) nonprofit organization.

FINANCIAL DATA:
Amount of support per award: $1,000 to $25,000.
Total amount of support: The Foundation awards between $500,000 and $1,000,000 per year in grants.

NUMBER OF AWARDS: Varies.

APPLICATION INFORMATION:
Contact the Foundation for guidelines.
Duration: One year.

PUBLICATIONS:
Annual report; research reports; educational guides; educational curriculum.

IRS IDENTIFICATION NUMBER: 23-7380557

OFFICERS:
Kathryn Olson, Chief Executive Officer
Jessica Mendoza, President

ADDRESS INQUIRIES TO:
Program Staff
(See address above.)

***SPECIAL STIPULATIONS:**
Applicants must demonstrate accomplishments and potential to be considered.

ZONTA INTERNATIONAL FOUNDATION

1211 West 22nd Street, Suite 900
Oak Brook, IL 60523-3384
(630) 928-1400
Fax: (630) 928-1559

E-MAIL ADDRESS:
programs@zonta.org

WEB SITE ADDRESS:
www.zonta.org

TYPE:
Fellowships. Awarded annually to women for graduate study in aerospace-related sciences and aerospace-related engineering at any university or college offering accredited graduate courses and degrees.
See entry 2188 for full listing.

ZONTA INTERNATIONAL FOUNDATION

1211 West 22nd Street, Suite 900
Oak Brook, IL 60523-3384
(630) 928-1400
Fax: (630) 928-1559

E-MAIL ADDRESS:
programs@zonta.org

WEB SITE ADDRESS:
www.zonta.org

TYPE:
Scholarships. For women of any nationality pursuing degrees in business who demonstrate outstanding potential in the field of business.
See entry 2043 for full listing.

ZONTA INTERNATIONAL FOUNDATION   [1170]

1211 West 22nd Street, Suite 900
Oak Brook, IL 60523-3384
(630) 928-1400
Fax: (630) 928-1559

E-MAIL ADDRESS:
programs@zonta.org

WEB SITE ADDRESS:
www.zonta.org

FOUNDED: 1919

AREAS OF INTEREST:
Encouraging women's involvement in public affairs.

NAME(S) OF PROGRAMS:
- **Young Women in Public Affairs Awards**

TYPE:
Awards/prizes.

PURPOSE:
To encourage young women's involvement and interest in public affairs.

LEGAL BASIS:
Incorporated in the state of Illinois as a nonprofit organization.

ELIGIBILITY:
Preuniversity or precollege women students (ages 16-19) at the time of application are eligible to apply.

FINANCIAL DATA:
Amount of support per award: District award recipients receive $1,000 (U.S.) from the Zonta International Foundation YWPA Fund. Districts may choose to add to this award amount. International award recipients are selected from district recipients and receive $3,000 (U.S.)

NUMBER OF AWARDS: Zonta has given 565 awards to women from 49 countries.

APPLICATION INFORMATION:
The YWPA Awards program operates at the club, district and international levels of Zonta International and is managed by Zonta members. To apply, contact the Zonta Club within the applicant's district/region for deadlines and an address to mail application or e-mail one's name and contact information to the YWPA Coordinator.

ADDRESS INQUIRIES TO:
Ana Ubides, Programs Manager
(See address above.)

URBAN AND REGIONAL AFFAIRS

Children and youth

THE JOHN W. ALDEN TRUST [1171]

c/o Rackemann, Sawyer & Brewster
160 Federal Street, 15th Floor
Boston, MA 02110-1700
(617) 951-1108
Fax: (617) 542-7437

E-MAIL ADDRESS:
smonahan@rackemann.com

WEB SITE ADDRESS:
www.cybergrants.com/alden

AREAS OF INTEREST:
Education and therapy for children who are
blind, retarded, disabled, mentally or
physically ill; medical and scientific research
for the prevention and/or cure of the
conditions.

TYPE:
Capital grants; Challenge/matching grants;
Conferences/seminars; Demonstration grants;
Development grants; Matching gifts;
Project/program grants; Research grants;
Scholarships; Seed money grants; Technical
assistance; Training grants. Grants will
normally be made for specific projects rather
than general operating expenses.

LEGAL BASIS:
Private foundation.

ELIGIBILITY:
Organizations must be IRS 501(c)(3)
tax-exempt and be located in eastern
Massachusetts.

GEOGRAPHIC RESTRICTIONS:
Eastern Massachusetts.

FINANCIAL DATA:
Amount of support per award: $5,000 to
$15,000.
Total amount of support: Approximately
$375,000 for fiscal year 2010.
Matching fund requirements: Determined on
a case-by-case basis.

NUMBER OF AWARDS: 33 grants for the year
2010.

REPRESENTATIVE AWARDS:
Massachusetts General Hospital; New
England Home for Little Wanderers; Cotting
School; Adolescent Consultation Services;
Perkins School for the Blind.

APPLICATION INFORMATION:
All applications must be submitted online.
Deadline: January 5, April 5, July 5 and
October 5; dates may vary.

PUBLICATIONS:
Guidelines.

TRUSTEES:
Kim Igoe-Kasper
Susan T. Monahan, Grants Coordinator
William B. Tyler, Esq.

ADDRESS INQUIRIES TO:
Susan T. Monahan, Grants Coordinator
(See e-mail address above.)

THE ISABEL ALLENDE FOUNDATION

116 Caledonia Street
Sausalito, CA 94965
(415) 289-0992
Fax: (415) 289-1154

E-MAIL ADDRESS:
lori@isabelallendefoundation.org

WEB SITE ADDRESS:
www.isabelallendefoundation.org

TYPE:
Project/program grants. Promotes and
preserves the fundamental rights of women
and children to be empowered and protected.

See entry 1133 for full listing.

AMERICAN ACADEMY OF CHILD AND ADOLESCENT PSYCHIATRY

3615 Wisconsin Avenue, N.W.
Washington, DC 20016-3007
(202) 966-7300 ext. 117
Fax: (202) 969-2891

E-MAIL ADDRESS:
apartner@aacap.org

WEB SITE ADDRESS:
www.aacap.org

TYPE:
Awards/prizes; Conferences/seminars;
Fellowships; Research grants; Travel grants.
The Robinson-Cunningham Award recognizes
a paper on some aspect of child and
adolescent psychiatry started during residency
and completed within three years of
graduation. Preference will be given to
independent work. If the research is done as
part of a collaborative team, the resident or
recently trained child and adolescent
psychiatrist should be the first author or
principal investigator. The selected author
will be invited to attend the AACAP Annual
Meeting. A certificate will be awarded with a
$200 honorarium.

Jeanne Spurlock Research Fellowship in
Substance Abuse and Addiction for Minority
Medical Students Program, supported by the
National Institute on Drug Abuse (NIDA),
includes a $3,500 fellowship for work during
the summer with a child and adolescent
psychiatrist research-mentor, plus five days at
the AACAP Annual Meeting.

See entry 2723 for full listing.

ANDRUS FAMILY FUND

330 Madison Avenue
Suite 30
New York, NY 10017
(212) 687-6975
Fax: (212) 687-6978

E-MAIL ADDRESS:
info@affund.org

WEB SITE ADDRESS:
www.affund.org

TYPE:
Project/program grants; Research grants.

See entry 1246 for full listing.

AON FOUNDATION [1172]

200 East Randolph Street, 6th Floor
Chicago, IL 60601
(312) 381-3551
Fax: (312) 381-6166

E-MAIL ADDRESS:
aon_foundation@aon.com

WEB SITE ADDRESS:
www.aon.com

FOUNDED: 1984

AREAS OF INTEREST:
Education, youth development, culture and
the arts.

NAME(S) OF PROGRAMS:
● **Employee Matching Gifts Program**

TYPE:
Capital grants; Development grants;
Matching gifts; Professorships. The Matching
Gifts Program was established to encourage
employees to contribute to and broadly
support the efforts of qualifying nonprofit
organizations in the areas of higher
education, culture and the arts, health,
community and human services and youth
development. The Foundation will match on
a dollar-for-dollar basis.

LEGAL BASIS:
Corporate foundation.

ELIGIBILITY:
Applicants must be 501(c)(3) organizations.
No grants to individuals.

Matching Gifts Program: Only organizations
and institutions that have been granted a
tax-exempt status by the IRS under Section
501(c)(3) of the Internal Revenue Code, are
located in the U.S., and are open to and
operated for the general public are eligible.
Ineligible organizations include:
(1) any pre-college educational institution
(e.g., day care through high school) or any
extracurricular activity group associated with
these organizations (e.g., PTA, fund drives);
(2) athletic organizations, including athletic
booster clubs of educational institutions;
(3) scholarship funds;
(4) any religious organization or campaign
(e.g., churches, seminaries, religious fund
drives);
(5) organizations which promote a political
party or candidate or engage in any political
lobbying efforts;
(6) any United Way campaign or other
federated drive (e.g., United Funds,
Community Chest) or;
(7) any organization that discriminates in any
way that is inconsistent with national equal
opportunity practices.

Ineligible gifts are payment for tuition or
other student expenses, membership dues,
fees for services, reimbursement of expenses,
purchase of goods, unpaid pledges, bequests,
subscription fees to publications, insurance
premium payments, tickets for sports or
cultural events, real estate or personal gifts,
testamentary gifts, or any gifts made with
funds provided in whole or in part by other
individuals, groups or organizations.

GEOGRAPHIC RESTRICTIONS:
United States.

FINANCIAL DATA:
Amount of support per award: Matching
Gifts Program: Minimum individual
employee contribution is $25; Maximum is
$1,000 per employee per calendar year.
Total amount of support: Varies.

APPLICATION INFORMATION:
Grants by invitation only.
Duration: Varies.

PUBLICATIONS:
Application guidelines.

OFFICER:
Carolyn Barry Frost, Vice President and
Executive Director
Beth Gallagher, Director, Community
Involvement

ADDRESS INQUIRIES TO:
Beth Gallagher
Director, Community Involvement
(See address above.)

BASEBALL TOMORROW
FUND   [1173]
245 Park Avenue
New York, NY 10167
(212) 931-7991
Fax: (212) 949-5405

E-MAIL ADDRESS:
btf@mlb.com

WEB SITE ADDRESS:
www.baseballtomorrowfund.com

FOUNDED: 1999

AREAS OF INTEREST:
Youth baseball and softball.

TYPE:
Capital grants; Challenge/matching grants;
Project/program grants. These grants are
offered to promote and enhance the growth
of baseball and softball in the U.S., Canada
and throughout the world.

YEAR PROGRAM STARTED: 2000

PURPOSE:
To promote and enhance the growth of
baseball in the U.S., Canada and throughout
the world by funding programs, fields,
equipment purchases, designed to encourage
and maintain youth participation in the game.

ELIGIBILITY:
Grants are made to incremental programs
and/or for facilities for youth baseball and
softball. Organizations must be nonprofit or
tax-exempt.

FINANCIAL DATA:
Amount of support per award:
Approximately $50,000 average.
Total amount of support: $2,000,000
annually.
Matching fund requirements: 50% match
required.

NUMBER OF APPLICANTS MOST RECENT YEAR:
500.

NUMBER OF AWARDS: 69.

APPLICATION INFORMATION:
Initially, a Letter of Inquiry (no more than
two pages) on organization letterhead must
be submitted to determine whether the
project meets the basic criteria of the Fund.
If invited to submit a formal grant
application, include only information that
creates a better understanding of the project
and how it corresponds to the Fund's grant
evaluation criteria. Applications will not be
accepted via fax.
Deadline: January 1, April 1, July 1 and
October 1.

ADDRESS INQUIRIES TO:
Executive Director
(See address above.)

ROBERT BOWNE
FOUNDATION   [1174]
6 East 39th Street, 10th Floor
New York, NY 10016
(212) 792-6250
Fax: (212) 279-1155

E-MAIL ADDRESS:
anne.lawrence@bownefoundation.org

WEB SITE ADDRESS:
www.robertbownefoundation.org

FOUNDED: 1968

AREAS OF INTEREST:
Literacy programs for young people in
out-of-school time programs.

TYPE:
Project/program grants; Technical assistance.
Direct service grants to after-school programs
in children and youth literacy.

PURPOSE:
To develop quality programs which offer
literacy education to children and youth in
the out-of-school hours, especially for those
living in economically disadvantaged
neighborhoods.

ELIGIBILITY:
Organizations classified as 501(c)(3) by the
IRS can apply. Individuals and religious
organizations are ineligible.

GEOGRAPHIC RESTRICTIONS:
Five boroughs of New York City.

FINANCIAL DATA:
Amount of support per award: $20,000 to
$30,000.
Total amount of support: $1,358,222 for the
year 2009.

NUMBER OF AWARDS: 55 for the year 2008.

STAFF:
Lena O. Townsend, Executive Director
Anne Lawrence, Program Officer

ADDRESS INQUIRIES TO:
Anne Lawrence, Program Officer
(See address above.)

THE BOY SCOUTS OF
AMERICA, NATIONAL EAGLE
SCOUT ASSOCIATION   [1175]
1325 West Walnut Hill Lane
P.O. Box 152079
Irving, TX 75015-2079
(972) 580-2000

E-MAIL ADDRESS:
nesa@scouting.org

WEB SITE ADDRESS:
www.nesa.org

AREAS OF INTEREST:
Scouting and youth.

NAME(S) OF PROGRAMS:
- **Hall/McElwain Merit Scholarships**

TYPE:
Scholarships.

PURPOSE:
To serve Eagle Scouts and through them, the
entire movement of Scouting.

ELIGIBILITY:
Must be graduating high school seniors or an
undergraduate college student no later than
completion of their junior year. Applicant
must have demonstrated leadership ability in
scouting and a strong record of participation
in activities outside of scouting. May receive
scholarship one time only.

FINANCIAL DATA:
Scholarships are for tuition, room, board and
books.
Amount of support per award: Typically
$1,000.
Total amount of support: $391,000 for the
year 2010.

NUMBER OF AWARDS: Varies, depending on
funds available.

APPLICATION INFORMATION:
Must supply Scout history and participation.
Award is not based on financial need or
grades.
Deadline: Applications must be postmarked
after October 1, but no later than midnight
on the following January 31. Use sufficient
postage.

ADDRESS INQUIRIES TO:
Jeff Laughlin, Manager
(See address above.)

*PLEASE NOTE:
This scholarship is not available to students
attending any of the U.S. military academies.

*SPECIAL STIPULATIONS:
Applicant must fill out new application each
year.

THE BOY SCOUTS OF
AMERICA, NATIONAL EAGLE
SCOUT ASSOCIATION   [1176]
1325 West Walnut Hill Lane
P.O. Box 152079
Irving, TX 75015-2079
(972) 580-2000

E-MAIL ADDRESS:
nesa@scouting.org

WEB SITE ADDRESS:
www.nesa.org

AREAS OF INTEREST:
Scouting and youth.

NAME(S) OF PROGRAMS:
- **Mabel and Lawrence S. Cooke
  Scholarship**
- **National Eagle Scout Scholarship Fund**

TYPE:
Scholarships.

PURPOSE:
To serve Eagle Scouts and through them, the
entire movement of Scouting.

ELIGIBILITY:
For the Mabel and Lawrence S. Cooke
Scholarship Endowment, applicant must
register and maintain status as a full-time
student at a college/university. The
scholarship is not available to students
attending any of the U.S. military academies,
because at these academies, the U.S.
government pays expenses that are covered
by NESA scholarships.

National Eagle Scout Scholarship Fund
applicants must register and maintain status
as a full-time student at a college/university.

FINANCIAL DATA:
Funds are for tuition, room, board, and
books.
Amount of support per award: Mabel and
Lawrence S. Cooke Scholarship: One
scholarship of up to $48,000 (up to $12,000
per year for four years) and four $20,000
scholarships ($5,000 per year for four years)
are given annually.

National Eagle Scout Scholarship Fund varies
each year, depending on the funds available.

NUMBER OF AWARDS: Varies per award.

APPLICATION INFORMATION:
Deadline: Applications must be postmarked
after October 1, but no later than midnight
on the following January 31. Use sufficient
postage.

ADDRESS INQUIRIES TO:
Jeff Laughlin, Manager
(See address above.)

THE LOUIS CALDER FOUNDATION [1177]

175 Elm Street
New Canaan, CT 06840
(203) 966-8925
Fax: (203) 966-5785

E-MAIL ADDRESS:
proposals@calderfdn.org

WEB SITE ADDRESS:
www.louiscalderfdn.org

FOUNDED: 1951

AREAS OF INTEREST:
Education.

TYPE:
Capital grants; Project/program grants.
Curriculum development.

YEAR PROGRAM STARTED: 1951

PURPOSE:
To promote the educational and scholastic development of children and youth by improving academic content at charter and parochial schools and community-based organizations.

LEGAL BASIS:
Private foundation.

ELIGIBILITY:
Nonprofit organizations with populations no greater than 500,000.

GEOGRAPHIC RESTRICTIONS:
Northeast Corridor and as far west as the Mississippi River, including the greater New York metropolitan area.

FINANCIAL DATA:
Amount of support per award: $2,000 to $500,000.
Total amount of support: $6,326,025 for the year 2010.

REPRESENTATIVE AWARDS:
$325,000 to HOPE Christian Schools for development and implementation of a coherent content-based curriculum and for construction of K-8 school; $75,000 to New Leaders for New Schools for expansion; $50,000 to Cathedral Education Cluster for Literacy Initiative.

APPLICATION INFORMATION:
The Foundation does not accept unsolicited proposals. Organizations are welcome to submit a letter of inquiry. A brief background letter describing the organization's plans and efforts should include a concise statement of the purpose of the program proposed for funding. The Foundation has no formal application form and requests that organizations use the Philanthropy New York Common Application Form which can be downloaded from the web site.
Duration: Varies.

PUBLICATIONS:
Annual report.

IRS IDENTIFICATION NUMBER: 13-6015562

TRUSTEES:
Peter D. Calder
Frank E. Shanley

ADDRESS INQUIRIES TO:
Holly Nuechterlein
Grant Program Director
(See address and e-mail above.)

CAMPBELL FOUNDATION, INC. [1178]

705 York Road
Towson, MD 21204
(410) 828-1961
Fax: (410) 821-8814

E-MAIL ADDRESS:
lsperato@stoycpa.com

AREAS OF INTEREST:
Social services, education, arts and cultural programs.

TYPE:
Capital grants; General operating grants; Project/program grants.

PURPOSE:
To provide support for cultural, educational and social services and institutions.

LEGAL BASIS:
Nonprofit foundation.

GEOGRAPHIC RESTRICTIONS:
Maryland, primarily Baltimore.

FINANCIAL DATA:
Amount of support per award: Up to $1,500 general operating grant; $20,000 capital grant.
Total amount of support: Average $150,000 per year.

APPLICATION INFORMATION:
Organizations must submit a written proposal, up to two pages in length.
Duration: One year. Renewal by reapplication.
Deadline: November 15.

ADDRESS INQUIRIES TO:
Virginia T. Campbell, President
(See address above.)

THOMAS AND AGNES CARVEL FOUNDATION [1179]

35 East Grassy Sprain Road
Yonkers, NY 10710
(914) 793-7300
Fax: (914) 793-7381

AREAS OF INTEREST:
Children, youth, health and religion.

TYPE:
General operating grants; Grants-in-aid; Matching gifts; Project/program grants; Research grants.

ELIGIBILITY:
Applicants must be 501(c)(3) tax-exempt organizations. Grants may be given to religious organizations that meet geographic requirements. No grants to individuals.

GEOGRAPHIC RESTRICTIONS:
Connecticut, New Jersey and New York.

FINANCIAL DATA:
Amount of support per award: Varies, depending on needs and nature of the request.
Total amount of support: $1,640,400 for the year 2008.

APPLICATION INFORMATION:
No application form required. Applicants must provide IRS tax-exempt documentation.
Duration: One year. Nonrenewable.

ADDRESS INQUIRIES TO:
William E. Griffin, President
(See address above.)

THE ANNIE E. CASEY FOUNDATION [1180]

701 St. Paul Street
Baltimore, MD 21202
(410) 547-6600
Fax: (410) 547-6624

E-MAIL ADDRESS:
webmail@aecf.org

WEB SITE ADDRESS:
www.aecf.org

FOUNDED: 1948

AREAS OF INTEREST:
Disadvantaged or low-income children and youth, their families and communities.

TYPE:
Awards/prizes; Demonstration grants; Project/program grants; Research grants; Seed money grants; Technical assistance; Training grants; Research contracts.

PURPOSE:
To foster public policies, human-service reforms and community reports that more effectively meet the needs of today's vulnerable children and families; to build better futures for disadvantaged children and their families in the U.S.

LEGAL BASIS:
Private foundation.

ELIGIBILITY:
Applying organizations must be nonprofit classified as 501(c)(3). No grants to individuals. No support to capital projects that are not an integral part of a foundation-sponsored initiative.

GEOGRAPHIC RESTRICTIONS:
United States.

FINANCIAL DATA:
Amount of support per award: Varies.

APPLICATION INFORMATION:
Submit letter of inquiry outlining proposal, the goals of the project, population served, amount of funds requested and brief history of organization.
Duration: One year.

PUBLICATIONS:
Annual report; *AdvoCasey Magazine; Kids Count; CaseyConnects.*

STAFF:
Patrick T. McCarthy, President

ADDRESS INQUIRIES TO:
Grants Department
(See address above.)

CHILDREN'S BRAIN TUMOR FOUNDATION [1181]

274 Madison Avenue
Suite 1004
New York, NY 10016
(212) 448-9494
Fax: (212) 448-1022

E-MAIL ADDRESS:
info@cbtf.org

WEB SITE ADDRESS:
www.cbtf.org

FOUNDED: 1988

AREAS OF INTEREST:
Children with brain and spinal cord tumors.

NAME(S) OF PROGRAMS:
- **Brain Research Tumor Grant**

TYPE:
Research grants. Basic science research grants for pediatric brain and spinal cord tumors.

YEAR PROGRAM STARTED: 1988

PURPOSE:
To improve the treatment, quality of life and the long-term outlook for children with brain and spinal cord tumors through research, support, education, and advocacy to families and survivors.

ELIGIBILITY:
No grants are made to individuals.

GEOGRAPHIC RESTRICTIONS:
United States and Canada.

FINANCIAL DATA:
Amount of support per award: $75,000 per year.
Total amount of support: Up to $150,000, depending on positive review after first year.

NUMBER OF AWARDS: 4.

APPLICATION INFORMATION:
Contact the Foundation for application procedures.
Duration: Up to two years.
Deadline: April.

IRS IDENTIFICATION NUMBER: 13-3512123

ADDRESS INQUIRIES TO:
Joseph Fay, Executive Director
(See address above.)

CHILDREN'S BUREAU   [1182]
Administration on Children, Youth and Families
1250 Maryland Avenue, S.W., Eighth Floor
Washington, DC 20024
(202) 205-8172
Fax: (202) 205-9721

E-MAIL ADDRESS:
jshafer@acf.hhs.gov

WEB SITE ADDRESS:
www.acf.hhs.gov/programs/cb

FOUNDED: 1974

AREAS OF INTEREST:
Prevention, identification, assessment and treatment of child abuse and neglect, sexual abuse, incidence of abuse and neglect.

NAME(S) OF PROGRAMS:
● **Child Abuse Prevention and Treatment Act (CAPTA) Research and Demonstration Grants**

TYPE:
Demonstration grants; Project/program grants; Research grants; Technical assistance; Training grants.

YEAR PROGRAM STARTED: 1974

PURPOSE:
To assist state, local and voluntary agencies and organizations to strengthen their capacities to prevent child abuse and neglect, identify and assess abused and neglected children and provide necessary ameliorative services to them and their families.

LEGAL BASIS:
Public Law 102-295, 45 CFR Subtitle B, part 1340.

ELIGIBILITY:
Grants for demonstration programs or projects and research projects may be made to states, public agencies, community-based organizations or nonprofit private organizations.

FINANCIAL DATA:
Amount of support per award: $300,000.

APPLICATION INFORMATION:
Standard grant application forms provided by the agency must be used. Complete instructions and necessary forms are issued with each announcement or solicitation.
Duration: Normally 36 to 60 months.

*SPECIAL STIPULATIONS:
Financial reports are required semiannually; program progress reports are required semiannually; a final report and an expenditure report are required no later than 90 days after the completion of the project. Audits conducted. Records must be maintained for three years.

COMMONWEAL FOUNDATION, INC.   [1183]
10770 Columbia Pike, Suite 150
Silver Spring, MD 20901
(240) 450-0000
Fax: (240) 450-4115

E-MAIL ADDRESS:
vgentilcore@cweal.org

WEB SITE ADDRESS:
www.cweal.org

FOUNDED: 1968

AREAS OF INTEREST:
Disadvantaged youth.

TYPE:
General operating grants; Project/program grants.

YEAR PROGRAM STARTED: 1968

PURPOSE:
To support educational programs assisting disadvantaged youth.

LEGAL BASIS:
Private foundation.

ELIGIBILITY:
Eligible organizations must be IRS 501(c)(3) tax-exempt.

GEOGRAPHIC RESTRICTIONS:
Baltimore, Maryland; Washington, DC; and northern Virginia.

FINANCIAL DATA:
Amount of support per award: $5,000 to $50,000.
Total amount of support: Approximately $1,100,000 for the year 2010.

NUMBER OF AWARDS: 64 for the year 2008.

APPLICATION INFORMATION:
Applications must include IRS tax determination letter, audited financial reports and most recent 990.
Duration: One year.
Deadline: February 1 and August 1.

ADDRESS INQUIRIES TO:
Jennifer Schauffler, Grants Manager
(See address above.)

ADOLPH COORS FOUNDATION   [1184]
4100 East Mississippi Avenue, Suite 1850
Denver, CO 80246
(303) 388-1636
Fax: (303) 388-1684

E-MAIL ADDRESS:
generalinfo@acoorsfdn.org

WEB SITE ADDRESS:
www.coorsfoundation.org

FOUNDED: 1975

AREAS OF INTEREST:
Primarily youth, job training, and self-sufficiency; also health, education, community and human services, and civic and cultural.

TYPE:
Capital grants; General operating grants; Project/program grants.

PURPOSE:
To build a stronger, healthier society.

ELIGIBILITY:
Organizations must be classified as 501(c)(3) and operate within the U.S. The Foundation does not consider grants to organizations that in policy or practice discriminate on the basis of race, creed or gender. No grants to religious organizations or individuals.

GEOGRAPHIC RESTRICTIONS:
Colorado.

FINANCIAL DATA:
Amount of support per award: Average: $10,000.
Total amount of support: $6,200,000.

APPLICATION INFORMATION:
Applications may only be submitted online.
Duration: One year.
Deadline: March 1, July 1 and November 1.

ADDRESS INQUIRIES TO:
John Jackson, Executive Director
(See address above.)

THE CRAIL-JOHNSON FOUNDATION   [1185]
461 West 6th Street
Suite 300
San Pedro, CA 90731
(310) 519-7413
Fax: (310) 519-7221

E-MAIL ADDRESS:
patc@crail-johnson.org

WEB SITE ADDRESS:
www.crail-johnson.org

FOUNDED: 1987

AREAS OF INTEREST:
Underserved children, youth and families in the areas of health, education and social services.

TYPE:
Capital grants; Challenge/matching grants; Development grants; General operating grants; Matching gifts; Project/program grants; Seed money grants; Technical assistance.

YEAR PROGRAM STARTED: 1987

PURPOSE:
To promote the well-being of children in need through effective application of human and financial resources.

LEGAL BASIS:
Private foundation.

ELIGIBILITY:
Applicants must be tax-exempt 501(c)(3) organizations. No grants to individuals.

GEOGRAPHIC RESTRICTIONS:
Los Angeles, California.

FINANCIAL DATA:
Amount of support per award: $5,000 to $30,000.

Total amount of support: Approximately $850,000 for the year 2010.

NUMBER OF APPLICANTS MOST RECENT YEAR:
75 to 80 grant applicants.

REPRESENTATIVE AWARDS:
$30,000 to Harbor Interface Services; $30,000 to Rainbow Services; $5,000 to Shoes That Fit.

APPLICATION INFORMATION:
Send letter of intent as initial inquiry. Formal proposals will be solicited by the Foundation and will include a copy of IRS tax-exempt letter, project proposal and project budget. Limit three pages; no attachments except 501(c)(3) letter.
Duration: Typically one year.
Deadline: Letters of Intent accepted October to December.

PUBLICATIONS:
Guidelines.

OFFICERS:
Eric C. Johnson, Chairman
Alan C. Johnson, President
John S. Peterson, Secretary
Byung Kim, Chief Financial Officer
Pat McMicheaux, Program Officer

ADDRESS INQUIRIES TO:
Pat McMicheaux, Program Officer
(See address above.)

MICHAEL AND SUSAN DELL FOUNDATION [1186]

P.O. Box 163867
Austin, TX 78716
(512) 600-5586
Fax: (512) 600-5501

E-MAIL ADDRESS:
info@msdf.org

WEB SITE ADDRESS:
www.msdf.org

AREAS OF INTEREST:
Needs of children, health, education, safety, youth development and early childhood care.

TYPE:
Project/program grants. Grants to support and initiate programs that directly serve the needs of children living in urban poverty.

PURPOSE:
To improve outcomes for children, living in urban poverty around the world, in a measurable way.

ELIGIBILITY:
Eligible organizations must be 501(c)(3).

GEOGRAPHIC RESTRICTIONS:
California; Chicago, Illinois; New York, New York; Texas; India and South Africa.

FINANCIAL DATA:
Foundation will not fund more than 25% of a project's budget or more than 10% of an organization's total annual operating expenses.
Amount of support per award: Varies.

APPLICATION INFORMATION:
All grant requests should be submitted via online form.

THE CLEVELAND H. DODGE FOUNDATION, INC. [1187]

420 Lexington Avenue, Suite 2331
New York, NY 10170
(212) 972-2800
Fax: (212) 972-1049

E-MAIL ADDRESS:
chdodgefdn@aol.com

WEB SITE ADDRESS:
www.chdodgefoundation.org

FOUNDED: 1917

AREAS OF INTEREST:
Educational institutions and welfare agencies serving the needs and training of young people. Those agencies which are demonstrating a visible and effective effort toward reversing global overpopulation.

TYPE:
Project/program grants.

YEAR PROGRAM STARTED: 1917

PURPOSE:
To help better mankind by providing funds for education and social welfare organizations.

LEGAL BASIS:
Private foundation.

ELIGIBILITY:
Grants are made to nonprofit, 501(c)(3) organizations in the Foundation's areas of interest. No grants are made to individuals.

GEOGRAPHIC RESTRICTIONS:
United States.

FINANCIAL DATA:
Amount of support per award: Varies.
Total amount of support: Approximately $2,500,000.

NUMBER OF APPLICANTS MOST RECENT YEAR:
150.

NUMBER OF AWARDS: 75.

APPLICATION INFORMATION:
Applicants must provide:
(1) a letter describing the organization and grant request, including budget;
(2) annual report and;
(3) proof of 501(c)(3) status.
Duration: One year. Some renewable.
Deadline: January 15, April 15 and September 15.

ADDRESS INQUIRIES TO:
Phyllis M. Criscuoli, Executive Director
(See address above.)

EAST TENNESSEE FOUNDATION [1188]

625 Market Street
Suite 1400
Knoxville, TN 37902
(865) 524-1223
(877) 524-1223
Fax: (865) 637-6039

E-MAIL ADDRESS:
etf@etf.org

WEB SITE ADDRESS:
www.easttennesseefoundation.org

FOUNDED: 1986

AREAS OF INTEREST:
Arts and culture, youth-at-risk, community development, affordable housing construction, and scholarships.

CONSULTING OR VOLUNTEER SERVICES:
A variety of technical assistance to applicants and grantees.

TYPE:
Project/program grants; Scholarships; Seed money grants; Technical assistance.

LEGAL BASIS:
Community foundation; 501(c)(3) organization.

ELIGIBILITY:
The Foundation does not make grants or loans to individuals.

GEOGRAPHIC RESTRICTIONS:
Campbell, Carter, Greene, Johnson, Monroe, Sullivan and Washington counties, Tennessee.

FINANCIAL DATA:
The Foundation administers 12 affiliate funds. Total Foundation assets of $157,000,000 as of 2010.
Amount of support per award: Funding support generally $500 to $10,000 per year for competitive grants and scholarships; $15,000 to $140,000 in Affordable Housing Trust Fund (AHTF) grants for the year 2010.
Total amount of support: $10,800,000 in grants for the year 2009.

PUBLICATIONS:
Connections, Funding Focus, quarterly newsletter; annual reports; documents; brochures.

IRS IDENTIFICATION NUMBER: 62-0807696

STAFF:
Michael McClamroch, President and Chief Executive Officer
Carolyn Schwenn, Senior Vice President for Finance and Administration
Terry L. Holley, Senior Vice President for Programs and Regional Development
Bob Calloway, Vice President for Advancement
Jackie Lane, Vice President for Communications
Leanna Millard, Financial and Administrative Officer
Jeanette Kelleher, Housing and Financial Officer
Jan Elston, Senior Program Officer
Beth Heller, Program Officer and Scholarships
Dan Foltz-Gray, Coordinator, Coffey Memorial Scholarship Fund
Mary Amber Dunn, Advancement Associate
Precy Sturgeon, Financial Administrator

ADDRESS INQUIRIES TO:
Terry L. Holley, Senior Vice President for Programs and Regional Development
(See address above.)

*PLEASE NOTE:
Organizations located outside of the Foundation's service area are not eligible for funding.

THE EISNER FOUNDATION [1189]

9401 Wilshire Boulevard
Suite 735
Beverly Hills, CA 90212
(310) 228-6808

E-MAIL ADDRESS:
gabriella.stumpf@eisnerfoundation.org

WEB SITE ADDRESS:
www.eisnerfoundation.org

FOUNDED: 1996

AREAS OF INTEREST:
After-school programs, learning differences, K-12 public education, and prevention and treatment of abused children.

TYPE:
Grants-in-aid.

PURPOSE:
To provide financial support to organizations working to create lasting positive changes in the lives of at-risk and disadvantaged seniors and children in the community; to fund programs that will make permanent changes in a child's life and give them tools to enable them to achieve their dreams and become productive adults.

LEGAL BASIS:
501(c)(3) organization.

ELIGIBILITY:
Grants are made to 501(c)(3) nonprofit organizations that serve Los Angeles County, California. Grants are not made to individuals.

GEOGRAPHIC RESTRICTIONS:
Los Angeles County, California.

FINANCIAL DATA:
Assets of approximately $136,000,000 as of December 31, 2009.
Total amount of support: Approximately $7,500,000 per year.

APPLICATION INFORMATION:
Applicants must submit a letter of inquiry (no more than two pages) to the Executive Director via regular mail. If deemed eligible, the applicant will be sent full application and guideline information.

IRS IDENTIFICATION NUMBER: 95-4607191

ADDRESS INQUIRIES TO:
Trent Stamp, Executive Director
(See address above.)

LOIS & RICHARD ENGLAND FAMILY FOUNDATION [1190]
P.O. Box 34-1077
Bethesda, MD 20827
(301) 657-7737
Fax: (301) 657-7738

E-MAIL ADDRESS:
englandfamilyfdn@verizon.net

WEB SITE ADDRESS:
fdncenter.org/grantmaker/england

FOUNDED: 1990

AREAS OF INTEREST:
Human services, education, Jewish life and causes, and afterschool programs in Washington, DC.

TYPE:
Capital grants; Challenge/matching grants; Development grants; General operating grants; Matching gifts; Project/program grants; Seed money grants; Technical assistance; Training grants.

YEAR PROGRAM STARTED: 1994

PURPOSE:
To improve the lives of those in need in the Washington, DC metropolitan area; to strengthen Jewish life and institutions locally, nationally and in Israel.

LEGAL BASIS:
Private family foundation.

ELIGIBILITY:
The Foundation does not accept unsolicited applications but may request letters of inquiry.

GEOGRAPHIC RESTRICTIONS:
Washington, DC and Israel.

FINANCIAL DATA:
Amount of support per award: $15,000 to $50,000; the majority of grants are $15,000 to $25,000.
Total amount of support: $985,000 for the year 2010.

NUMBER OF APPLICANTS MOST RECENT YEAR: 80.

NUMBER OF AWARDS: Approximately 50.

REPRESENTATIVE AWARDS:
Jewish Giving: $15,000 to American Jewish Committee. Washington, DC Giving: $25,000 to Heads Up. Discretionary Grants: $30,000 to Lymphoma Research Foundation.

APPLICATION INFORMATION:
Detailed instructions are available online.
Duration: Annual grants.

BOARD OF DIRECTORS:
Cathy England, Chairperson
Richard England, President
Lois England, Vice President
Rick England, Treasurer
Larry Akman
Nonie Akman
Diana England

ADDRESS INQUIRIES TO:
Monica Smith, Program Assistant
(See address above.)

FOUNDATION FOR CHILD DEVELOPMENT [1191]
295 Madison Avenue, 40th Floor
New York, NY 10017
(212) 867-5777
Fax: (212) 867-5844

E-MAIL ADDRESS:
info@fcd-us.org

WEB SITE ADDRESS:
www.fcd-us.org

FOUNDED: 1900

AREAS OF INTEREST:
Children, particularly the disadvantaged.

NAME(S) OF PROGRAMS:
● **New American Children**
● **PreK-3rd**

TYPE:
Research grants. Research, policy analysis, advocacy, leadership and program development. The Foundation has a special interest in the children of families that are working, but poor, particularly in those families that are struggling to meet their children's basic human needs.

The New American Children initiative aims to stimulate basic and applied research on immigrant children (birth through age 10), particularly those living in low-income families.

PreK-3rd supports the restructuring of Prekindergarten, Kindergarten, and Grades 1-3 into a well-aligned, first level of public education (ages three to eight) in the U.S.

YEAR PROGRAM STARTED: 1900

PURPOSE:
To understand children, particularly the disadvantaged, and to promote their well-being.

LEGAL BASIS:
Independent private foundation.

ELIGIBILITY:
FCD supports research, policy development, advocacy, and communications strategies related to PreK-3rd.

The Foundation does not fund the direct provision of Prekindergarten education, child care or health care, capital campaigns and endowments, or the purchase, construction or renovation of buildings. The Foundation does not make grants for projects outside the U.S.

GEOGRAPHIC RESTRICTIONS:
United States.

FINANCIAL DATA:
Amount of support per award: $1,000 to $440,000 (multiyear).

NUMBER OF APPLICANTS MOST RECENT YEAR:
Approximately 400.

NUMBER OF AWARDS: Average 14 grants per year.

APPLICATION INFORMATION:
FCD does not accept unsolicited proposals.
Duration: One to three years.

PUBLICATIONS:
Annual report; grants list; guidelines; policy briefs (all available online).

BOARD OF DIRECTORS:
P. Lindsay Chase-Landsdale, Chairperson
Ruth Ann Burns, Vice Chairperson
Ruby Takanishi, President
Margaret Beale Spencer, Secretary
Michael I. Cohen

ADDRESS INQUIRIES TO:
Mark Bogosian
Communications and Grants Manager
(See address above.)

FREDDIE MAC FOUNDATION [1192]
8250 Jones Branch Drive
Mail Stop A40
McLean, VA 22102
(703) 918-8888
Fax: (703) 918-8895

E-MAIL ADDRESS: -
freddiemac_foundation@freddiemac.com

WEB SITE ADDRESS:
www.freddiemacfoundation.org

FOUNDED: 1990

AREAS OF INTEREST:
Helping children in foster care move to permanent homes, academic and careers success and stable homes, stable families programs, children and youth must be 18 or below and families served must include children.

CONSULTING OR VOLUNTEER SERVICES:
Volunteers in Active Corporate Volunteer Program.

NAME(S) OF PROGRAMS:
● **J.C. Nalle Community School**
● **Stable Homes, Stable Families**
● **Wednesday's Child**

TYPE:
General operating grants; Project/program grants. Public Awareness and Education.

YEAR PROGRAM STARTED: 1991

PURPOSE:
To open the doors to hope and opportunity for children, youth and their families.

LEGAL BASIS:
Corporate foundation.

ELIGIBILITY:
Applying organization must be operated and organized so that it does not discriminate in the hiring of staff on the basis of race, religion, sex or disabilities. Applicants must be exempt from income taxes under Section 501(c)(3) or 509(a) of the Internal Revenue Code and be defined as a public charity.

GEOGRAPHIC RESTRICTIONS:
Metropolitan Washington, DC area.

FINANCIAL DATA:
Amount of support per award: $5,000 to $50,000, unless approved by board of directors. Requests for grants greater than $50,000 are by invitation only.

APPLICATION INFORMATION:
See the Foundation web site for specific outcomes that must be addressed in an application.
Deadline: March 1 and August 15.

IRS IDENTIFICATION NUMBER: 54-1573760

STAFF:
Ralph F. Boyd, Chairman and Chief Executive Officer
Margaret Meiers, Senior Director and Vice President, Foundation Programs

ADDRESS INQUIRIES TO:
Grants Manager
(See address above.)

H.B. FULLER COMPANY FOUNDATION [1193]
1200 Willow Lake Boulevard
St. Paul, MN 55164
(651) 236-5217
Fax: (651) 236-5056

E-MAIL ADDRESS:
christine.meyer@hbfuller.com

WEB SITE ADDRESS:
www.hbfuller.com

FOUNDED: 1974

AREAS OF INTEREST:
Science, technology, education and math K-12.

TYPE:
Matching gifts; Project/program grants.

PURPOSE:
To support charitable activities of the company.

ELIGIBILITY:
No grants are given to individuals or religious organizations. Eligible organizations must be of 501(c)(3) not-for-profit character.

FINANCIAL DATA:
Amount of support per award: Varies.
Total amount of support: Varies.

APPLICATION INFORMATION:
Application forms are available upon request to the Foundation or can be downloaded from the web site.
Deadline: March 31 and August 31.

ADDRESS INQUIRIES TO:
Christine Meyer, Administrator
(See address above.)

THE GERBER FOUNDATION [1194]
4747 West 48th Street
Suite 153
Fremont, MI 49412
(231) 924-3175
Fax: (231) 924-7906

E-MAIL ADDRESS:
tgf@ncresa.org

WEB SITE ADDRESS:
www.gerberfoundation.org

FOUNDED: 1952

AREAS OF INTEREST:
Enhancing the quality of life of infants and young children in nutrition, care and development.

TYPE:
Research grants. Grants to ensure the continuity of scientific and educational research in infant nutrition and child health. Matching gifts to 501(c)(3) educational, health and human services institutions within the U.S.

YEAR PROGRAM STARTED: 1952

PURPOSE:
To enhance the quality of life of infants and young children.

LEGAL BASIS:
Private foundation.

ELIGIBILITY:
Must be 501(c)(3).

GEOGRAPHIC RESTRICTIONS:
United States.

FINANCIAL DATA:
Amount of support per award: $20,000 to $300,000.
Total amount of support: $2,784,500 for the year 2010.

NUMBER OF APPLICANTS MOST RECENT YEAR:
160 for the year 2010.

NUMBER OF AWARDS: 65 for the year 2010.

APPLICATION INFORMATION:
Applicants should submit a two- to three-page letter of inquiry initially. If accepted, an application form will be provided.
Duration: One-time award with annual review.
Deadline: Letters of inquiry due June 1 and December 1. Grants made in May and November.

PUBLICATIONS:
Guidelines; application.

IRS IDENTIFICATION NUMBER: 38-6068090

OFFICERS:
Barbara J. Ivens, President
Fernando Flores-New, Vice President
Stan VanderRoest, Treasurer
Tracy Baker, Secretary

ADDRESS INQUIRIES TO:
Catherine Obits, Program Manager
(See address above.)

THE GRABLE FOUNDATION [1195]
650 Smithfield Street
Suite 240
Pittsburgh, PA 15222
(412) 471-4550
Fax: (412) 471-2267

E-MAIL ADDRESS:
grable@grable.org

WEB SITE ADDRESS:
www.grable.org

FOUNDED: 1976

AREAS OF INTEREST:
Education, youth, leadership and families.

TYPE:
Project/program grants. This grant is offered to support community efforts that create an environment in which children can achieve and succeed.

YEAR PROGRAM STARTED: 1976

PURPOSE:
To improve educational opportunities so that children can achieve their potential; to strengthen families so they can serve as the core support of children and society; to support community efforts that create an environment in which children can succeed.

LEGAL BASIS:
Private foundation.

ELIGIBILITY:
Organizations must be classified as 501(c)(3) and include copy of IRS letter of determination. Grants are not awarded to individuals. Focus of grant must be southwestern Pennsylvania.

GEOGRAPHIC RESTRICTIONS:
Southwestern Pennsylvania.

FINANCIAL DATA:
Amount of support per award: Varies.
Total amount of support: $9,995,263 for the year 2010.

NUMBER OF APPLICANTS MOST RECENT YEAR:
375 for the year 2010.

NUMBER OF AWARDS: 217 for the year 2010.

REPRESENTATIVE AWARDS:
$50,000 to Carnegie Library of Pittsburgh to support a digital learning librarian for teen services at the library; $100,000 to Carnegie Mellon University to support the development of robotics and computer-based tools to promote interest in computer science and STEM education; $210,000 to Consortium for Public Education to support efforts to build support for public education across western Pennsylvania through public engagement and professional development; $150,000 to The Fred Rogers Company to support an animated children's television series and educational outreach materials that will extend Fred Rogers' values for living and learning to a new generation of children and families; $108,660 to Pittsburgh Public Schools to support an integrated and systematic approach to arts education in the Pittsburgh Public School District.

APPLICATION INFORMATION:
All organizations applying to the Foundation should submit a one- to two-page letter of inquiry describing the project prior to submitting a full proposal.

Proposals must include:
(1) Grable inquiry sheet;
(2) one-page summary of the proposal;
(3) description of the applicant organization;
(4) statement of need for the project;
(5) project description, including a detailed listing of project activities;
(6) anticipated project outcomes and how they will be measured;
(7) project budget, detailing expenses, committed and anticipated revenues, and including a narrative;
(8) organization's current operating budget;
(9) explanation of how the project will be sustained after the grant has ended;
(10) list of board members;
(11) copy of IRS tax-exempt certification;

(12) current audited financial statements and; (13) letters of support when appropriate, e.g., from collaborating organizations.

Duration: Funding for up to three years.

Deadline: Letters of inquiry: January 1, May 1 and September 1 of each year. Full proposals: February 1, June 1 and October 1 of each year.

PUBLICATIONS:
Program announcement; guidelines.

IRS IDENTIFICATION NUMBER: 25-1309888

STAFF:
Gregg S. Behr, Executive Director
Steven E. Burke, Treasurer
Dana M. Lamenza, Financial Administrator
Mary Anne Mistick, Grants Administrator
Kristen Burns, Program Officer
D'Ann Swanson, Program Officer

BOARD OF TRUSTEES:
Charles R. Burke, Jr., Chairman
Jan Nicholson, President
Susan H. Brownlee
Patricia Grable Burke
Steven E. Burke
William H. Isler
Barbara Nicholson McFayden
Marion Grable Nicholson

ADDRESS INQUIRIES TO:
Mary Anne Mistick, Grants Administrator
(See address above.)

THE WILLIAM T. GRANT FOUNDATION   [1196]
570 Lexington Avenue
18th Floor
New York, NY 10022-6837
(212) 752-0071
Fax: (212) 752-1398

E-MAIL ADDRESS:
info@wtgrantfdn.org

WEB SITE ADDRESS:
www.wtgrantfoundation.org

FOUNDED: 1936

AREAS OF INTEREST:
Supporting research to improve the lives of young people in the U.S.

NAME(S) OF PROGRAMS:
- **William T. Grant Distinguished Fellows**
- **William T. Grant Scholars Program**
- **Investigator Initiated Grants**
- **Youth Service Improvement Grants Program**

TYPE:
Fellowships; Project/program grants; Research grants. William T. Grant Distinguished Fellows program gives influential midcareer researchers the opportunity to immerse themselves in practice or policy settings and conversely influential practitioners and policymakers the opportunity to work in research settings.

William T. Grant Scholars Program supports promising early career researchers from diverse disciplines. The award is intended to facilitate the professional development of early career scholars who have demonstrated success in conducting high-quality research and are seeking to further develop their skills and research program.

Investigator Initiated Grants support high-quality research that addresses the Foundation's current research interests: enhancing our understanding of how youth

settings work, how they affect youth development, and how they can be improved; and when, how, and under what conditions research evidence is used in policy and practice that affect youth, and how its use can be improved.

The Youth Service Improvement Grants Program supports activities conducted by community-based organizations in the five boroughs of New York City to improve the quality of services for young people ages 8 to 25.

YEAR PROGRAM STARTED: 1936

PURPOSE:
To help create a society that values young people and enables them to reach their full potential. In pursuit of this goal, the Foundation invests in research and in people and projects that use evidence-based approaches.

LEGAL BASIS:
Private foundation.

ELIGIBILITY:
Organization must have 501(c)(3) status. No grants to individuals.

GEOGRAPHIC RESTRICTIONS:
United States; Youth Service Improvement Grants: New York City.

FINANCIAL DATA:
Amount of support per award: William T. Grant Distinguished Fellows: Up to $175,000, with up to $25,000 to fellowship site(s) to defray hosting costs; William T. Grant Scholars Program: $350,000; Investigator Initiated Grants: $100,000 to $600,000; Youth Service Improvement Grants Program: $25,000.

Total amount of support: Varies.

NUMBER OF AWARDS: William T. Grant Scholars Program: 4 to 6 annually; Youth Service Improvement Grants Program: Varies.

APPLICATION INFORMATION:
Application, requirements and procedures are available online.

Duration: William T. Grant Distinguished Fellows and Youth Service Improvement Grants: Six months to two years; William T. Grant Scholars Program: Five years; Investigator Initiated Grants: Two to three years.

Deadline: Varies.

PUBLICATIONS:
Annual report; guidelines; *William T. Grant Scholars*, brochure.

TRUSTEES:
J. Lawrence Aber
Olivia Golden
Nancy Gonzales
Henry Gooss
Robert Granger
Lisa Hess
Christine James-Brown
Kathleen Hall Jamieson
Bridget Macaskill
Sarah McLanahan
Melvin Oliver
Russell Pennoyer
Andrew Porter

STAFF:
Robert Granger, President
Lawrence Moreland, Senior Vice President, Finance and Administration
Edward Seidman, Senior Vice President, Program
Sharon Brewster, Grants Coordinator

Irene Williams, Grants Coordinator, Scholars Program
Nancy Rivera-Torres, Grants Coordinator, Research
Julie Wong, Coordinator, New Project Development
Vivian Tseng, Senior Program Officer

ADDRESS INQUIRIES TO:
Mary Heglar, Communications Assistant
(See address above.)

ALLEN P. AND JOSEPHINE B. GREEN FOUNDATION
200 West Boulevard
Mexico, MO 65265
(573) 581-5568
Fax: (573) 581-1714

E-MAIL ADDRESS:
carlf@greenfdn.org

WEB SITE ADDRESS:
www.greenfdn.org

TYPE:
Capital grants; Challenge/matching grants; Conferences/seminars; Demonstration grants; Development grants; Endowments; Matching gifts; Project/program grants; Seed money grants; Training grants; Work-study programs.

See entry 1374 for full listing.

HASBRO CHILDREN'S FUND   [1197]
1027 Newport Avenue
Pawtucket, RI 02862
(401) 727-5091
Fax: (401) 721-7275

WEB SITE ADDRESS:
www.hasbro.org

FOUNDED: 2006

AREAS OF INTEREST:
The welfare and development of children.

NAME(S) OF PROGRAMS:
- **Community Grants**

TYPE:
Product donations; Project/program grants. The Fund supports programs which provide terminal and seriously ill children respite and access to play, educational programs for children at risk, and basics for children in need.

YEAR PROGRAM STARTED: 1985

PURPOSE:
To assist children in triumphing over critical life obstacles as well as bringing the joy of play into their lives.

ELIGIBILITY:
U.S.-based 501(c)(3) organizations who deliver programs to children in Springfield, MA; Rhode Island; or Renton/Seattle, WA.

FINANCIAL DATA:
Amount of support per award: Varies.
Total amount of support: Varies.

APPLICATION INFORMATION:
All interested organizations are asked to apply through the Fund's online application system.

CHARLES HAYDEN FOUNDATION [1198]

140 Broadway, 51st Floor
New York, NY 10005
(212) 785-3677
Fax: (212) 785-3689

E-MAIL ADDRESS:
fdn@chf.org

WEB SITE ADDRESS:
www.charleshaydenfoundation.org

FOUNDED: 1937

AREAS OF INTEREST:
Education and youth agencies.

TYPE:
Capital grants; Challenge/matching grants;
Project/program grants. Grant priorities focus
on institutions and programs primarily
serving youth at risk of not reaching their
full potential, especially youth in low-income
communities. Support is provided for youth
development programs, charter schools,
independent and parochial schools, and
informal educational enrichment programs in
institutions such as zoos, museums or
libraries.

YEAR PROGRAM STARTED: 1937

PURPOSE:
To promote the mental, moral and physical
development of children and youth five to 18
years of age in the New York and Boston
metropolitan areas.

LEGAL BASIS:
Private foundation.

ELIGIBILITY:
Grants are restricted to institutions and
organizations in the New York and Boston
metropolitan areas, as defined by the
Foundation. The Foundation focuses on those
grants primarily serving youth, five to 18
years of age, that are most at-risk of not
reaching their full potential, especially youth
in low-income communities. Grants are
available for capital and program support.
Program grants must have clear goals to be
met within specified time frame. Program
support goes mainly for new and expanded
programs. No grants to individuals.

GEOGRAPHIC RESTRICTIONS:
New York and Boston, Massachusetts
metropolitan areas.

FINANCIAL DATA:
Amount of support per award: Average
$50,000.
Total amount of support: $12,948,370 in
grants paid and $12,945,195 in new
authorizations for the fiscal year ended June
30, 2010.

NUMBER OF APPLICANTS MOST RECENT YEAR:
260.

NUMBER OF AWARDS: 151.

APPLICATION INFORMATION:
Applicants are required to use the New York
Area or AGM (Boston Area) Common
Application Forms. All applications should
note number and ages of youth to be served.

Interviews, if required or requested, are not
arranged until the written grant application
has been submitted and the preliminary
review is completed.
Duration: Most grants are for one year.
Grant renewals are sometimes considered.

IRS IDENTIFICATION NUMBER: 13-5562237

OFFICERS:
Dean H. Steeger, Chairman of the Board

Kenneth D. Merin, President and Chief
Executive Officer
Robert Howitt, Treasurer
Robert Andrews, Secretary
Maureen T. Fletcher, Assistant Secretary
Carol Van Atten, Assistant Secretary

BOARD OF TRUSTEES:
Robert Andrews
Robert Howitt
Kristen J. McCormack
Kenneth D. Merin
Dean H. Steeger

ADDRESS INQUIRIES TO:
Kenneth D. Merin
President and Chief Executive Officer
(See address above.)

*SPECIAL STIPULATIONS:
Institutions receiving capital support must
wait two years before seeking additional
assistance.

EDWARD W. HAZEN FOUNDATION [1199]

333 Seventh Avenue, 14th Floor
New York, NY 10001
(212) 889-3034
Fax: (212) 889-3039

E-MAIL ADDRESS:
hazen@hazenfoundation.org

WEB SITE ADDRESS:
www.hazenfoundation.org

FOUNDED: 1925

AREAS OF INTEREST:
Public education and youth organizing,
school reform, community organizations, and
racial justice.

TYPE:
Grants-in-aid; Project/program grants. In the
area of Public Education, current programs
support the strengthening of the connection
between schools and community
organizations, including school reform. The
Foundation is primarily interested in parent
organizing and training initiatives.

In the area of Youth Organizing, there is
support for youth organizing around concrete
social issues or issues of concern to youth.

For both Public Education and Youth
Organizing, community-based projects
directed toward middle and high school-age
minority and low-income youth are given
priority consideration.

There is limited support for Philanthropy and
Special Projects including support for
collaborative projects that encourage the
growth of grantmaking.

PURPOSE:
To increase opportunities for middle and high
school-age minority and low-income youth
by strengthening those community-based
organizations that focus on the needs of the
young and the institutions that most directly
and profoundly influence them.

LEGAL BASIS:
Nonprofit, tax-exempt organization.

ELIGIBILITY:
Grants are made only to federally
tax-exempt, nonprofit organizations. The
Foundation does not consider requests for
endowments or buildings, deficits or
individual scholarships or fellowships. No
support for schools, school districts or public
agencies.

GEOGRAPHIC RESTRICTIONS:
United States.

FINANCIAL DATA:
Amount of support per award: $30,000 to
$35,000.

Total amount of support: $1,700,000 for the
year 2010.

REPRESENTATIVE AWARDS:
People United for a Better Oakland for youth
advocacy and organizing around KIDS
FIRST! Campaign, an initiative that will
generate $5,000,000 annually to pay for
youth programs; Southern Echo toward the
Mississippi Education Working Group, an
emerging coalition of grassroots groups
which seek to impact the formulation of
education policy at the local and state level
and to create a quality public education
system; Northwest Bronx Community and
Clergy toward the Parent Led Campaign for
School Reform, created to unite parents
across schools and district lines, and to get
the School Construction Authority to
complete construction of two new elementary
schools which will alleviate overcrowding at
six other schools.

APPLICATION INFORMATION:
Board does not accept unsolicited requests.
There is a two-step process. Applicants
should first send a two-page letter of inquiry,
highlighting the goals, objectives, approach,
target population, duration and total cost of
the project for which funding is sought.
Additional materials such as video, audio
cassettes, books, etc. and articles should not
be sent unless specifically requested by the
Foundation staff. Grant applications will be
sent if the staff decides the goals of the
project address the Foundation's mission and
program interest. The board has the ultimate
responsibility for setting Foundation policy
and making grants at meetings held twice a
year. Neither a request for a formal
application nor recommendation to the board
guarantees funding.

The Foundation does not accept faxed or
electronic requests.
Duration: One year.

PUBLICATIONS:
Hazen Highlights, newsletter; guidelines.

ADMINISTRATION:
Lori Bezahler, President
Phillip Giles, Program Officer

TRUSTEES AND OFFICERS:
Angela Sanbrano, Chairperson
Beverly Cross, Vice Chairperson
Lori Bezahler, Secretary
Charles Fields
Sonia Jarvis
Michael Lent
David Martinez-Hosang
Rachel Tompkins
Lori Villarosa

ADDRESS INQUIRIES TO:
Lori Bezahler, President
(See address above.)

*PLEASE NOTE:
Prospective applicants should keep in mind
that there must be enough time for the
inquiry letter to be received, reviewed and
the application sent.

THE JACK AND JILL OF AMERICA FOUNDATION

1930 17th Street, N.W.
Washington, DC 20009-6207
(202) 232-5290
Fax: (202) 232-1747

E-MAIL ADDRESS:
administration@jackandjillfoundation.org

WEB SITE ADDRESS:
www.jackandjillfoundation.org

TYPE:
Challenge/matching grants;
Conferences/seminars; Demonstration grants;
General operating grants; Grants-in-aid;
Internships; Matching gifts; Project/program
grants; Seed money grants; Training grants.

See entry 1093 for full listing.

KANSAS HEALTH FOUNDATION

309 East Douglas
Wichita, KS 67202
(316) 262-7676
(800) 373-7681
Fax: (316) 262-2044

E-MAIL ADDRESS:
ghess@khf.org

WEB SITE ADDRESS:
www.kansashealth.org

TYPE:
Project/program grants.

See entry 1542 for full listing.

THE KLINGENSTEIN THIRD GENERATION FOUNDATION

787 Seventh Avenue
6th Floor
New York, NY 10019-6016
(212) 492-6179
Fax: (212) 492-7007

E-MAIL ADDRESS:
sally@ktgf.org

WEB SITE ADDRESS:
www.ktgf.org

TYPE:
Fellowships; Research grants. The
Foundation funds research and other
programs related to childhood and adolescent
ADHD and depression. All funding is
directed towards two research fellowship
programs and the medical student training
program. The Foundation does not accept
general applications for project or research
funding.

See entry 2742 for full listing.

THE AGNES M. LINDSAY TRUST [1200]

660 Chestnut Street
Manchester, NH 03104
(603) 669-1366
(866) 669-1366
Fax: (603) 665-8114

E-MAIL ADDRESS:
admin@lindsaytrust.org

WEB SITE ADDRESS:
www.lindsaytrust.org

FOUNDED: 1939

AREAS OF INTEREST:
Health and welfare, children, and the elderly.

TYPE:
Capital grants; Scholarships. Awards grants
for capital campaigns, capital items and
renovation needs. Also, supports a number of
health and welfare organizations, health
projects, dental projects, special needs
including blind, deaf and learning-disabled,
elderly, children's hospitals, children's
homes, youth organizations, youth and family
services and summer camperships (summer
enrichment programs). In addition, Trust
supports colleges and universities and private
secondary schools through scholarship aid.

PURPOSE:
To support the education of poor and
deserving students from rural communities;
to relieve suffering through child welfare.

ELIGIBILITY:
Eligible organizations must be IRS 501(c)(3)
tax-exempt and be located in the New
England states of Maine, Massachusetts, New
Hampshire and Vermont. The Trust does not
fund in Connecticut or Rhode Island.

The Trust rarely, if ever, approves grants for
general operating funds, nor does it fund
grant requests from public entities,
municipalities, sectarian organizations, or
individuals.

GEOGRAPHIC RESTRICTIONS:
Maine, Massachusetts, New Hampshire and
Vermont.

FINANCIAL DATA:
$23,500,000 in assets for the year ended
2010.
Amount of support per award: $500 to
$5,000.
Total amount of support: Distributed
$808,670 in grants for the year 2010.

NUMBER OF APPLICANTS MOST RECENT YEAR:
647 for the year 2010.

NUMBER OF AWARDS: 295 for the year 2010.

APPLICATION INFORMATION:
Guidelines are available online. Proposals can
be submitted electronically at
proposals@lindsaytrust.org.
Duration: One year.
Deadline: Trustees meet monthly. It generally
takes two months from time of submission of
application to receipt of letter of decision.

IRS IDENTIFICATION NUMBER: 02-6004971

TRUSTEES:
Ernest E. Dion
Alan G. Lampert

ADDRESS INQUIRIES TO:
Susan Bouchard, Administrative Director
(See address above.)

*PLEASE NOTE:
It is highly recommended that applicants
review the information available online prior
to submission of a grant proposal.

*SPECIAL STIPULATIONS:
The Trust does not make grants to operating
funds or to individuals. If your organization
is awarded a grant, the Trust requests that
your organization wait one year before
reapplying.

LOUIS R. LURIE FOUNDATION [1201]

One Embarcadero Center
Suite 4150
San Francisco, CA 94111
(415) 392-2470
Fax: (415) 421-8669

E-MAIL ADDRESS:
nterry@lurie.com

FOUNDED: 1948

AREAS OF INTEREST:
Youth under 18 years of age and their
families.

TYPE:
General operating grants; Project/program
grants. Grants will be made for special
projects, general operating support,
equipment, and program initiatives generated
by the Foundation.

PURPOSE:
To improve the lives of youth and their
families; to heighten skills that develop
self-reliance, compassion, self-esteem, respect
for diversity and a strong desire to give back
to others in the community.

ELIGIBILITY:
Grants are made to organizations that have
tax-exempt status under Section 501(c)(3) of
the Internal Revenue Code. No grants are
made to individuals.

GEOGRAPHIC RESTRICTIONS:
San Francisco, California.

FINANCIAL DATA:
Amount of support per award: $10,000 to
$20,000.

APPLICATION INFORMATION:
The Foundation accepts proposals by
invitation only.

ADDRESS INQUIRIES TO:
Nancy Terry, Foundation Administrator
(See address above.)

THE DR. JOHN T. MACDONALD FOUNDATION, INC. [1202]

1550 Madruga Avenue, Suite 215
Coral Gables, FL 33146
(305) 667-6017
Fax: (305) 667-9135

E-MAIL ADDRESS:
info@jtmacdonaldfdn.org

WEB SITE ADDRESS:
www.jtmacdonaldfdn.org

FOUNDED: 1992

AREAS OF INTEREST:
Health education, prevention and early
detection of disease, children, economically
disadvantaged, and medical rehabilitation.

TYPE:
Capital grants; Challenge/matching grants;
Project/program grants; Seed money grants;
Training grants.

YEAR PROGRAM STARTED: 1992

PURPOSE:
To provide funding for programs and projects
designed to improve, preserve or restore the
health and health care of people in
Miami-Dade County, FL, with priority given
to projects in the Coral Gables community.

LEGAL BASIS:
Private.

ELIGIBILITY:
Tax-exempt organizations that are registered
to solicit funds under Florida law. The
Foundation funds projects for medical and
health-related programs with priority for
children and youth. The Foundation does not
fund national projects, multiyear funding
requests, for-profit organizations, political

candidates or campaigns, religious projects, support for individuals, or other grantmaking foundations.

GEOGRAPHIC RESTRICTIONS:
Miami-Dade County, Florida.

FINANCIAL DATA:
Amount of support per award: $25,000 to $75,000.
Total amount of support: Approximately $1,237,000 per year.

NUMBER OF APPLICANTS MOST RECENT YEAR:
40.

NUMBER OF AWARDS: 13, plus 2 multiyear signature projects developed by the Foundation.

REPRESENTATIVE AWARDS:
Foundation Grants 2010: Camp Boggy Creek to allow 10 seriously ill children from Miami-Dade County to attend the HIV/AIDS 2010 summer camp session; Cancer Support Community Greater Miami to support six diagnosis-specific "support and learn" groups per month attended by cancer patients and primary caregivers, and one support group per week attended by cancer patients only; Coral Gables Woman's Club/May Van Sickle Children's Dental Clinic to be used exclusively for the operation of the dental clinic to provide free primary dental care to disadvantaged children of Miami-Dade County.

Scholarships 2010: Barry University School of Nursing for Dr. Harold Norman Nursing Scholarship.

Multi-year Million+ Signature Programs: Dr. John T. Macdonald Foundation School Health Initiative.

APPLICATION INFORMATION:
All applicants must submit a letter of inquiry. Those selected to apply will submit a grant application using a standard format, including the following sections:
(1) general information about the organization;
(2) a detailed description of the proposed project and project activities;
(3) sources of funding and plans for future funding and;
(4) a line item budget.

The original application plus one copy must be stapled in the top lefthand corner and signed by an authorized representative of the organization.

PUBLICATIONS:
Program announcement; guidelines; application packet.

IRS IDENTIFICATION NUMBER: 59-0818918

ADDRESS INQUIRIES TO:
Kim Greene, Executive Director
(See address above.)

A.L. MAILMAN FAMILY FOUNDATION, INC. [1203]
707 Westchester Avenue
White Plains, NY 10604
(914) 683-8089
Fax: (914) 686-5519

E-MAIL ADDRESS:
info@mailman.org

WEB SITE ADDRESS:
www.mailman.org

FOUNDED: 1980

AREAS OF INTEREST:
Early childhood education.

TYPE:
Project/program grants; Technical assistance; Training grants.

PURPOSE:
To support projects or organizations that promote the well-being of children and families.

LEGAL BASIS:
Nonprofit foundation.

ELIGIBILITY:
The Foundation is not currently accepting unsolicited proposals.

FINANCIAL DATA:
Amount of support per award: Average $25,000.

NUMBER OF APPLICANTS MOST RECENT YEAR:
300.

APPLICATION INFORMATION:
Proposals are submitted upon invitation only.
Duration: Varies.
Deadline: January 15 and June 15 for consideration in April and October, respectively.

PUBLICATIONS:
Guidelines.

ADDRESS INQUIRIES TO:
Luba H. Lynch, Executive Director
(See address above.)

MAURICE J. MASSERINI CHARITABLE TRUST
c/o Wells Fargo Private Bank
4475 Executive Drive, Suite 100
San Diego, CA 92121
(858) 597-4328
Fax: (858) 597-4360

E-MAIL ADDRESS:
dschmutz@wellsfargo.com

WEB SITE ADDRESS:
www.grantsrequests.com

TYPE:
Project/program grants.

See entry 1061 for full listing.

RONALD MCDONALD HOUSE CHARITIES [1204]
One Kroc Drive
Oak Brook, IL 60523
(630) 623-7048
Fax: (630) 623-7488

E-MAIL ADDRESS:
laurel.schumm@us.mcd.com

WEB SITE ADDRESS:
www.rmhc.org

FOUNDED: 1984

AREAS OF INTEREST:
Primarily, the health and well-being of children.

TYPE:
Capital grants; Challenge/matching grants; Grants-in-aid; Project/program grants; Scholarships; Seed money grants. Disaster relief.

YEAR PROGRAM STARTED: 1984

PURPOSE:
To provide comfort and care to children.

LEGAL BASIS:
Nonprofit, 501(c)(3) tax-exempt organization.

ELIGIBILITY:
Not-for-profit tax-exempt organizations. Projects must address real problems that have measurable impact in a definitive manner. Proposed projects must directly benefit children. No grants to individuals, political campaigns, secular religious activities, for salaries, travel or ongoing expenses.

Must be national or international organization. Grant requests from organizations more regional in nature will be referred to the closest local chapter.

FINANCIAL DATA:
Amount of support per award: $25,000 to $100,000.
Total amount of support: Approximately $4,000,000 for the year 2010.

REPRESENTATIVE AWARDS:
$250,000 to Phoenix Children's Hospital; $520,000 to Interplast; $150,000 to America's Second Harvest.

APPLICATION INFORMATION:
Duration: One-year to multiyear funding.
Deadline: Each project submitted is reviewed and evaluated by RMHC's Board of Trustees, which meets three times per year. Announcement is within 30 days following board meetings.

PUBLICATIONS:
Application form; annual report; application guidelines.

BOARD OF TRUSTEES:
Linda Dunham, Chairman of the Board
Marty J. Coyne, Jr., President and Chief Executive Officer
Donald G. Lubin, Vice President
James D. Watkins, Vice President
Michael D. Richard, Treasurer
Adele M. Jamieson, Secretary
Jean L. Zajac, Controller

ADDRESS INQUIRIES TO:
Laurel Schumm, Senior Manager
Special Programs
(See address above.)

*SPECIAL STIPULATIONS:
Applications not accepted by fax.

R.J. MCELROY TRUST [1205]
425 Cedar Street, Suite 312
Waterloo, IA 50701-1351
(319) 287-9102
Fax: (319) 287-9105

E-MAIL ADDRESS:
vangorp@mcelroytrust.org

WEB SITE ADDRESS:
www.mcelroytrust.org

FOUNDED: 1965

AREAS OF INTEREST:
Education, children and youth.

NAME(S) OF PROGRAMS:
● R.J. McElroy Trust Award

TYPE:
Capital grants; Challenge/matching grants; Fellowships; General operating grants; Internships; Professorships; Project/program grants; Scholarships; Seed money grants; Technical assistance; Training grants.

PURPOSE:
To assist nonprofit tax-exempt organizations which provide education services to youth.

LEGAL BASIS:
Private.

ELIGIBILITY:
Applicant must be nonprofit, tax-exempt organizations which provide services to youth. Preference is also given to grants which fund programs rather than capital projects as well as challenge/matching grants. No grants may be made directly to individuals.

GEOGRAPHIC RESTRICTIONS:
Northeast quarter of Iowa.

FINANCIAL DATA:
Amount of support per award: Varies per project.
Total amount of support: $1,685,072 for the year 2008.
Matching fund requirements: Varies.

NUMBER OF APPLICANTS MOST RECENT YEAR:
133.

NUMBER OF AWARDS: 71.

APPLICATION INFORMATION:
An application should include:
(1) general information on the organization;
(2) verification of tax-exempt status;
(3) description of the project with goals and objectives, planned activities, a timetable, population to be served and budget;
(4) copy of the organization's most recent audited financial statement;
(5) the amount requested;
(6) other funding sources and;
(7) plans for ongoing funds.
Duration: One to three years. Renewals possible.
Deadline: March 1, June 1, September 1 and December 1. Announcement by February 1, May 1, August 1 and November 1, respectively.

PUBLICATIONS:
Brochure; guidelines; grants list.

IRS IDENTIFICATION NUMBER: 42-6173496

TRUSTEES:
Raleigh D. Buckmaster
Ross D. Christensen
James B. Waterbury
Rick Young

STAFF:
Stacy Van Gorp, Executive Director

ADDRESS INQUIRIES TO:
Stacy Van Gorp, Executive Director
(See address above.)

*SPECIAL STIPULATIONS:
Contact the Executive Director before applying.

THE MCJ AMELIOR FOUNDATION   [1206]
310 South Street
Morristown, NJ 07960
(973) 540-1946
Fax: (973) 538-8175

AREAS OF INTEREST:
Youths at risk, children, community empowerment and mentoring.

TYPE:
Challenge/matching grants; General operating grants; Project/program grants; Seed money grants; Technical assistance.

LEGAL BASIS:
Private foundation.

ELIGIBILITY:
Applicants must be 501(c)(3) organizations.

GEOGRAPHIC RESTRICTIONS:
Newark, New Jersey.

FINANCIAL DATA:
Amount of support per award: $5,000 to $25,000.

APPLICATION INFORMATION:
The Foundation does not accept unsolicited proposals.
Duration: Varies.

STAFF:
Suzanne Spero, Executive Director
Christine C. Gilfillan, President

ADDRESS INQUIRIES TO:
Suzanne Spero, Executive Director
(See address above.)

MEBANE CHARITABLE FOUNDATION, INC.   [1207]
232 South Main Street
Mocksville, NC 27028
(336) 936-0041
Fax: (336) 936-0038

E-MAIL ADDRESS:
lcolbourne@mebanefoundation.com

WEB SITE ADDRESS:
www.mebanefoundation.com

FOUNDED: 1992

AREAS OF INTEREST:
Children's education.

NAME(S) OF PROGRAMS:
* **The Davie & Yadkin County Program**
* **The Early Childhood Development Program**
* **The Teacher Training and Professional Development Program**

TYPE:
Endowments.

PURPOSE:
To teach children first to read and to further their education at all levels of learning, thereby attempting to break the cycle of poverty.

ELIGIBILITY:
Organizations qualified for exemption under Section 501(c)(3) of the IRS code and not private foundations as defined by Section 509(a).

GEOGRAPHIC RESTRICTIONS:
North Carolina.

FINANCIAL DATA:
Amount of support per award: Varies.
Total amount of support: $1,600,000 for the year 2010.

APPLICATION INFORMATION:
Organization must first complete a phone interview with the President to determine if their proposal is within the objectives and interest of the Foundation.
Duration: Up to multiyear grants.
Deadline: Application must be postmarked by July 1 for fall meeting of the board of directors, or by January 1 for spring meeting.

ADDRESS INQUIRIES TO:
Larry Colbourne, President
(See address above.)

THE MOYER FOUNDATION   [1208]
2426 32nd Avenue West, Suite 200
Seattle, WA 98199
(206) 298-1217
Fax: (206) 298-1207

E-MAIL ADDRESS:
info@moyerfoundation.org

WEB SITE ADDRESS:
www.moyerfoundation.org

FOUNDED: 2000

AREAS OF INTEREST:
Children suffering and enduring severe physical or emotional distress.

TYPE:
Grants-in-aid; Internships; Matching gifts.

YEAR PROGRAM STARTED: 2000

PURPOSE:
To empower children in distress by providing education and support, thereby helping them to live a healthy and inspired life.

LEGAL BASIS:
Public, 501(c)(3) nonprofit organization.

ELIGIBILITY:
501(c)(3) nonprofit organizations. Grants are not made to individuals.

GEOGRAPHIC RESTRICTIONS:
Pacific Northwest.

FINANCIAL DATA:
Total amount of support: $4,000,000 in grants awarded over the past five years.

NUMBER OF APPLICANTS MOST RECENT YEAR:
220.

NUMBER OF AWARDS: 25.

APPLICATION INFORMATION:
Duration: Nonrenewable.
Deadline: September 1 and March 1.

IRS IDENTIFICATION NUMBER: 91-2065051

NATIONAL FOSTER PARENT ASSOCIATION   [1209]
1102 Prairie Ridge Trail
Pflugerville, TX 78660
(512) 706-7513
Fax: (253) 238-4252

E-MAIL ADDRESS:
info@nfpaonline.org

WEB SITE ADDRESS:
www.nfpaonline.org

FOUNDED: 1972

AREAS OF INTEREST:
Foster children.

NAME(S) OF PROGRAMS:
* **NFPA Scholarship**

TYPE:
Scholarships.

PURPOSE:
To support foster youth and children of foster parents that wish to further their education beyond high school, including college or university studies, vocational and job training, and correspondence courses, including the GED.

LEGAL BASIS:
Nonprofit, volunteer organization established in 1972, with tax-exempt status under Section 501(c)(3) of the Internal Revenue Code.

ELIGIBILITY:
Must be a foster youth or an adoptive or birth child of foster parent members who is a college- or university-bound senior or is 17 years of age (either in school or out) in pursuit of vocational/job training/correspondence GED/other educational advancement.

GEOGRAPHIC RESTRICTIONS:
United States and territories.

FINANCIAL DATA:
Amount of support per award: $1,000.
Total amount of support: $5,000.

NUMBER OF APPLICANTS MOST RECENT YEAR:
23.

NUMBER OF AWARDS: 5; 3 to foster children and 2 to adoptive or birth children of foster parents.

APPLICATION INFORMATION:
Complete application, which is available from the Association at the address above. A minimum of two letters of recommendation and a typewritten statement of 300 to 500 words on "Why I want to further my education and why I should be considered for a National Foster Parent Association Scholarship" is also required.
Duration: Possible renewal.
Deadline: Applications must be postmarked on or before March 31.

IRS IDENTIFICATION NUMBER: 06-0894870

ADDRESS INQUIRIES TO:
Irene Clements, President
(See address above.)

NATIONAL JEWISH COMMITTEE ON SCOUTING

1325 West Walnut Hill Lane
Irving, TX 75015
(972) 580-2091
Fax: (972) 580-2535

E-MAIL ADDRESS:
lee.shaw@scouting.org

WEB SITE ADDRESS:
www.jewishscouting.org

TYPE:
Scholarships. Awarded annually.
See entry 1844 for full listing.

OFFICE OF POPULATION AFFAIRS [1210]

Office of Adolescent Pregnancy Programs
The Tower Building at Tower Oaks
1101 Wootton Parkway, Suite 700
Rockville, MD 20852
(240) 453-2828
Fax: (240) 453-2829

E-MAIL ADDRESS:
oapp@hhs.gov

WEB SITE ADDRESS:
opa.osophs.dhhs.gov

FOUNDED: 1979

AREAS OF INTEREST:
Adolescent pregnancy and adolescent health.

NAME(S) OF PROGRAMS:
● **Adolescent Family Life Demonstration Projects Grants**

TYPE:
Demonstration grants. Grants for community-based and community-supported demonstration projects.

YEAR PROGRAM STARTED: 1982

PURPOSE:
To find effective means of preventing adolescent pregnancy and to establish innovative, comprehensive and integrated approaches to the delivery of services to pregnant adolescents, adolescent parents and their children.

LEGAL BASIS:
Government agency.

ELIGIBILITY:
Grants are made to public and private nonprofit organizations and agencies. Two categories of demonstration projects are funded including Care Projects and Prevention Projects. Care Projects provide health, education and social services to pregnant and parenting adolescents. Prevention Projects are aimed primarily at promoting abstinence from sexual activity among unmarried adolescents to prevent pregnancies and STDs. Applications for both types may contain evaluation-intensive components designed to produce better evaluation findings.

Funding is limited to states with high teen birth rates and rural areas.

OAPP encourages the submission of prevention applications which propose innovative abstinence education interventions for adolescents and their parents and increase parent-child communication. OAPP is also interested in care applications which propose effective ways of involving families, of promoting adoption as a positive option, and of stressing school completion and/or job training and preparation.

FINANCIAL DATA:
Amount of support per award: Care Grant: Average $400,000; Prevention Grant: Average $500,000.
Total amount of support: $16,641,361 for fiscal year 2010.
Matching fund requirements: 30% for the first two years; 40% for the third year; 50% for the fourth year; 60% for the fifth year.

NUMBER OF APPLICANTS MOST RECENT YEAR:
Care Grants: 26.

NUMBER OF AWARDS: 26 Care Grants for the year 2010-11.

APPLICATION INFORMATION:
Electronic application form is available at GrantSolutions.gov or Grants.gov.
Duration: Up to five years.
Deadline: Specified by requests for applications.

PUBLICATIONS:
Application guidelines.

ADDRESS INQUIRIES TO:
Office of Adolescent Pregnancy Programs
(See address above.)

ORLANDO MAGIC YOUTH FUND [1211]

8701 Maitland Summit Boulevard
Orlando, FL 32810
(407) 916-2400
Fax: (407) 916-2985

E-MAIL ADDRESS:
omyf@orlandomagic.com

WEB SITE ADDRESS:
www.orlandomagic.com

FOUNDED: 1988

AREAS OF INTEREST:
Literacy, health and wellness, the arts, and children and families at-risk in central Florida.

NAME(S) OF PROGRAMS:
● **Orlando Magic Youth Fund Grant Awards**

TYPE:
Challenge/matching grants. OMYF was founded to raise funds and community awareness to help combat the many physical, emotional and social challenges facing the low-income, at-risk children of central Florida.

In the area of literacy, the Fund supports in- and after-school programs operated by nonprofit agencies for school age students who are at risk of illiteracy, and family literacy programs promoting the role of parents as first teacher to their children.

In the area of health and wellness, the Fund supports programs that focus on nutrition and exercise programs educating youth to live a healthy lifestyle and prevent obesity. Programs that focus on preventing and addressing malnutrition and hunger relief in children and youth are also considered.

In the area of arts, the Fund supports programs and curriculum that expose children and youth to art and culture and provide educational enrichment.

PURPOSE:
To support the betterment of all central Florida youth and those children considered to be at-risk as a result of physical, emotional, economic or environmental disadvantage.

ELIGIBILITY:
Organizations must be classified as 501(c)(3) or 170(c)(3) by the IRS and have a constituency open to all segments of the community with a focus on low income. The Fund does not typically provide funding for general operating expenses, private schools, legal aid societies, political, lobbying or advocacy groups, or capital requests for building and/or major improvements, except those for equipment/supplies that are critical to the delivery of a program or service.

GEOGRAPHIC RESTRICTIONS:
Orange, Osceola and Seminole counties, Florida.

FINANCIAL DATA:
Amount of support per award: $3,000 to $200,000.
Total amount of support: $1,000,000.
Matching fund requirements: The McCormick Foundation contributes $.50 for every dollar that the OMYF generates to supplement contributions in the partners' local communities. In addition to the matching monies, they assist in the administration of the funds and share expenses.

NUMBER OF APPLICANTS MOST RECENT YEAR:
100.

NUMBER OF AWARDS: 25.

APPLICATION INFORMATION:
Duration: One year. May reapply.
Deadline: Varies. Early summer.

ORPHAN FOUNDATION OF AMERICA
21351 Gentry Drive, Suite 130
Sterling, VA 20166
(571) 203-0270
Fax: (571) 203-0273

E-MAIL ADDRESS:
scholarships@orphan.org
office@orphan.org

WEB SITE ADDRESS:
www.orphan.org

TYPE:
Scholarships.

See entry 1692 for full listing.

LUCILE PACKARD FOUNDATION FOR CHILDREN'S HEALTH [1212]
400 Hamilton Avenue, Suite 340
Palo Alto, CA 94301
(650) 497-8365
(650) 736-0676

E-MAIL ADDRESS:
grants@lpfch.org

WEB SITE ADDRESS:
www.lpfch.org/programs/cshcn/process.html

FOUNDED: 1997

AREAS OF INTEREST:
Children's health.

TYPE:
Project/program grants.

YEAR PROGRAM STARTED: 2000

PURPOSE:
To promote the health and well-being of children through statewide and local partnerships.

ELIGIBILITY:
Organizations must be 501(c)(3) nonprofit.

GEOGRAPHIC RESTRICTIONS:
California.

FINANCIAL DATA:
Amount of support per award: Varies.

NUMBER OF APPLICANTS MOST RECENT YEAR:
4.

NUMBER OF AWARDS: Varies.

APPLICATION INFORMATION:
The Foundation is not accepting unsolicited proposals at this time.
Duration: Varies.

ADDRESS INQUIRIES TO:
Jordan Handcox, Grants and Program Coordinator
(See address above.)

PARENTS WITHOUT PARTNERS
1100-H Brandywine Boulevard
Zanesville, OH 43701
(740) 450-1332
Fax: (740) 452-2552

E-MAIL ADDRESS:
pwppn@parentswithoutpartners.org

WEB SITE ADDRESS:
www.parentswithoutpartners.org

TYPE:
Scholarships.

See entry 1694 for full listing.

THE PINKERTON FOUNDATION [1213]
610 Fifth Avenue
Suite 316
New York, NY 10020
(212) 332-3385
Fax: (212) 332-3399

E-MAIL ADDRESS:
pinkfdn@pinkertonfdn.org

WEB SITE ADDRESS:
www.thepinkertonfoundation.org

FOUNDED: 1966

AREAS OF INTEREST:
Economically disadvantaged children, youth and families.

TYPE:
Challenge/matching grants; General operating grants; Internships; Project/program grants. Support for programs that develop individual competencies, instill values and increase opportunities to participate in society.

Support for community-based programs with preference given to projects for children, youth and families that intervene before a pattern of failure has been established.

YEAR PROGRAM STARTED: 1968

LEGAL BASIS:
Not-for-profit corporation organized in the state of Delaware in 1966.

ELIGIBILITY:
Grant applicants must be nonprofit public charitable organizations which are tax-exempt under Section 501(c)(3) of the Internal Revenue Code. The Foundation does not make grants to individuals or give loans or emergency assistance, nor does it support medical research or the direct provision of health care or religious education. It generally does not make grants to support conferences, publications, media or to building renovations or other capital projects, unless they are integrally related to the Foundation's program objectives or are an outgrowth of one of its grantee's programs.

GEOGRAPHIC RESTRICTIONS:
New York, New York.

FINANCIAL DATA:
Amount of support per award: $20,000 to $100,000; average $40,000.
Total amount of support: $7,000,000 to $8,000,000 annually.

NUMBER OF APPLICANTS MOST RECENT YEAR:
300.

NUMBER OF AWARDS: 120 for the year 2010.

APPLICATION INFORMATION:
Applicants should write a brief letter of inquiry, not exceeding two pages, before submitting a formal proposal or applying for a grant. The proposal should describe the grantee organization and the proposed project and its goals and include an estimated budget and the name and qualifications of the person directing the project. For other than direct service projects, the program description should also include the possibilities for practical application of the efforts and findings of the project or program.

The Foundation's program staff will determine whether or not a proposal will be considered. They will request other materials or arrange meetings as appropriate after reviewing the initial letter.
Duration: Usually up to three years.
Deadline: February 1 and September 1.

OFFICERS:
George J. Gillespie, III, Chairman
Richard Smith, President
Daniel Mosley, Treasurer
Joan Colello, Secretary and Executive Director

STAFF:
Christopher J. Bell, Senior Program Officer
Laurie Dien, Senior Program Officer

ADDRESS INQUIRIES TO:
Christopher J. Bell or Laurie Dien
Senior Program Officers
(See address above.)

PIONEER HI-BRED, A DUPONT BUSINESS [1214]
7100 N.W. 62nd Avenue
Johnston, IA 50131
(515) 535-6677
(800) 247-6803 ext. 56867
Fax: (515) 535-4842

E-MAIL ADDRESS:
community.investment@pioneer.com

WEB SITE ADDRESS:
www.pioneer.com

AREAS OF INTEREST:
Agriculture, farm safety and science education.

NAME(S) OF PROGRAMS:
• **Community Investment Program**

TYPE:
Capital grants; Challenge/matching grants; Fellowships; General operating grants; Matching gifts; Research grants; Scholarships. Community outreach programs.

PURPOSE:
To help improve the quality of life in the communities in which customers and employees live and work.

LEGAL BASIS:
Corporation giving program.

ELIGIBILITY:
Must be an IRS tax-exempt 501(c)(3) organization. No grants to individuals or religious organizations that promote a particular doctrine.

FINANCIAL DATA:
Amount of support per award: Varies.
Total amount of support: $5,000,000 for the year 2009.

NUMBER OF AWARDS: Approximately 1,000 per year.

APPLICATION INFORMATION:
Program application form is available on Pioneer web site.
Duration: One year.

ADDRESS INQUIRIES TO:
Michelle Gowdy
Senior Manager Community Investment
(See address above.)

PRITCHETT TRUST [1215]
Marshall & Ilsley Trust Company
417 North Broadway
Pittsburg, KS 66762
(620) 231-2000
Fax: (620) 231-3974

AREAS OF INTEREST:
Children, families and youth.

TYPE:
Project/program grants; Seed money grants.

PURPOSE:
To promote projects that support children, youth and families.

LEGAL BASIS:
Private trust.

ELIGIBILITY:
Grants are made to organizations that have tax-exempt status under Section 501(c)(3) of the Internal Revenue Code. No grants are made to individuals.

GEOGRAPHIC RESTRICTIONS:
Southeast Kansas, with an emphasis on Crawford County.

FINANCIAL DATA:
Amount of support per award: Varies.
Total amount of support: $5,872,000 since inception as of year ended 2009.

APPLICATION INFORMATION:
Applicants must submit a brief letter outlining the purpose of the grant.
Duration: One year. Renewal possible.
Deadline: May 31.

ADDRESS INQUIRIES TO:
Gayle Wood, Trust Officer
(See address above.)

HENRY AND RUTH BLAUSTEIN ROSENBERG FOUNDATION

10 East Baltimore Street, Suite 1111
Baltimore, MD 21202
(410) 347-7201
Fax: (410) 347-7210

E-MAIL ADDRESS:
info@blaufund.org

WEB SITE ADDRESS:
www.blaufund.org

TYPE:
Capital grants; General operating grants; Project/program grants. Programs of benefit to the underserved community in the Baltimore, MD area.

See entry 1451 for full listing.

THE SAIGH FOUNDATION [1216]

7777 Bonhomme Avenue
Suite 2007
St. Louis, MO 63105
(314) 862-3055
Fax: (314) 862-9288

E-MAIL ADDRESS:
joann@thesaighfoundation.org

WEB SITE ADDRESS:
www.thesaighfoundation.org

FOUNDED: 2000

AREAS OF INTEREST:
Children and youth in the field of education and health care in the St. Louis metropolitan area.

TYPE:
Endowments; General operating grants.

PURPOSE:
To enhance the quality of life in St. Louis metropolitan region through support for charitable projects and initiatives which primarily benefit children and youth through education and health care.

LEGAL BASIS:
501(c)(3).

GEOGRAPHIC RESTRICTIONS:
St. Louis, Missouri metropolitan area.

FINANCIAL DATA:
Amount of support per award: Varies.
Total amount of support: Varies.

APPLICATION INFORMATION:
Deadline: January, April, July and October.

STAFF:
JoAnn Hejna, Executive Director
Mary Kemp, Assistant Director

ADDRESS INQUIRIES TO:
JoAnn Hejna, Executive Director
(See address above.)

ST. LOUIS RAMS FOUNDATION [1217]

One Rams Way
St. Louis, MO 63045
(314) 516-8760
Fax: (314) 770-9261; (314) 516-8888

E-MAIL ADDRESS:
myarbrough@rams.nfl.com

WEB SITE ADDRESS:
www.stlouisrams.com

FOUNDED: 1997

AREAS OF INTEREST:
Health, fitness and character education.

TYPE:
General operating grants; Project/program grants.

YEAR PROGRAM STARTED: 1997

PURPOSE:
To support programs designed to engage youth in activities that promote health, fitness and character development.

ELIGIBILITY:
Grants are made to organizations that have tax-exempt status under Section 501(c)(3) of the Internal Revenue Code. No unsolicited grants are accepted.

GEOGRAPHIC RESTRICTIONS:
The Greater St. Louis area, Missouri.

FINANCIAL DATA:
Since 1995, the Foundation has donated more than $6,000,000 in cash, grants, merchandise and tickets to area charities.
Amount of support per award: Varies based on program or project scope.
Total amount of support: Up to $200,000 annually.

NUMBER OF APPLICANTS MOST RECENT YEAR:
125 to 150.

NUMBER OF AWARDS: More than 15.

REPRESENTATIVE AWARDS:
St. Louis Public Schools Foundation;
Cooperating School Districts.

APPLICATION INFORMATION:
Proposals are accepted by invitation only; however, letters and collateral material from potential grant recipients are welcome.

ADDRESS INQUIRIES TO:
Michael Yarbrough
Director of Community Outreach
(See address above.)

THE SCHUMANN FUND FOR NEW JERSEY [1218]

21 Van Vleck Street
Montclair, NJ 07042
(973) 509-9883

FOUNDED: 1988

AREAS OF INTEREST:
Children and youth, education, environment and public policy (statewide) as well as social services in Essex County, NJ.

TYPE:
Demonstration grants; General operating grants; Project/program grants; Research grants. Priorities include early childhood development, supporting efforts to heighten the chances of academic and social success for young children, especially the urban poor. Other focus areas include environmental protection, public policy and local activities directed at solving community problems, with particular concern for families with young children and education.

YEAR PROGRAM STARTED: 1988

LEGAL BASIS:
Tax-exempt, private foundation.

ELIGIBILITY:
Organizations seeking grants must be designated 501(c)(3) by the IRS. No applications for capital campaigns, annual giving, endowment, direct support of individuals and local programs in counties other than Essex. Projects in the arts, health care and housing development normally fall outside the Schumann Fund priority areas.

GEOGRAPHIC RESTRICTIONS:
New Jersey, with special emphasis on Essex County.

FINANCIAL DATA:
Amount of support per award: $15,000 to $50,000.
Total amount of support: Approximately $1,000,000 to $1,500,000.

APPLICATION INFORMATION:
There is no standard application form to be used in presenting a request to the Schumann Fund. The Fund, however, encourages the use of the New York/New Jersey Common Application Form. A written proposal should be submitted which includes a detailed description of the purpose for which assistance is desired and the plan for accomplishment. The proposal should be accompanied by a copy of the organization's latest financial statement, an expense budget which identifies all sources of income, the project's time frame and future funding plans, a list of the organization's Board of Directors, IRS documents confirming the organization's status as a 501(c)(3) tax-exempt organization and not a private foundation, and the most recent audit.
Duration: Usually one year. Multiyear grants possible.
Deadline: January 15, April 15, July 15 and October 15.

PUBLICATIONS:
Annual report.

IRS IDENTIFICATION NUMBER: 52-1556076

TRUSTEES:
Aubin Z. Ames
Anthony Cicatello
Leonard S. Coleman, Jr.
Christopher J. Daggett
Martha Day
Roger Pratt

STAFF:
Barbara Reisman, Executive Director
Annette B. Strickland, Program and Administrative Officer

ADDRESS INQUIRIES TO:
Barbara Reisman, Executive Director
(See address above.)

*SPECIAL STIPULATIONS:
Grants are restricted to projects in New
Jersey.

THE SEYBERT FOUNDATION   [1219]
P.O. Box 1286
Doylestown, PA 18901
(215) 696-9336

E-MAIL ADDRESS:
admin@seybertfoundation.org

WEB SITE ADDRESS:
www.seybertfoundation.org

FOUNDED: 1914

AREAS OF INTEREST:
Projects and services for disadvantaged
children who are residents of the city of
Philadelphia. The Institution is limited under
the terms of the will setting up the fund to
disadvantaged boys and girls of the city of
Philadelphia only.

TYPE:
General operating grants; Project/program
grants. Grants to support a variety of projects
and services for disadvantaged youth in
Philadelphia, primarily through
community-based organizations.

LEGAL BASIS:
501(c)(3) charitable foundation.

ELIGIBILITY:
Grants are limited to projects and services for
disadvantaged young people through the high
school ages who are residents of the city of
Philadelphia. Grants are made to qualifying
tax-exempt organizations under Sections
501(c)(3) and 509(a) of the Internal Revenue
Code.

GEOGRAPHIC RESTRICTIONS:
Philadelphia, Pennsylvania.

FINANCIAL DATA:
Amount of support per award: Up to $7,500.
Total amount of support: $304,500 for the
year 2008.

NUMBER OF APPLICANTS MOST RECENT YEAR:
165.

NUMBER OF AWARDS: 61.

REPRESENTATIVE AWARDS:
Committee for Dignity and Fairness in
Housing, Juvenile Law Center, Taller
Puertorriqueno, Al-Bustan Seeds of Culture.

APPLICATION INFORMATION:
Applicants should submit nine copies with
the original application, including a budget
for the project, its necessity and one copy of
an IRS exemption letter. Application forms
and additional guidelines are available upon
request.
Duration: One year. Renewal possible.
Deadline: March 15. No more than one
request will be considered per calendar year
except under special circumstances.

PUBLICATIONS:
Annual report, including application
guidelines and procedures.

IRS IDENTIFICATION NUMBER: 23-6260105

OFFICERS AND BOARD OF DIRECTORS:
Sara S. Moran, President
Dwayne Wharton, Vice President

Dee Hillas, Treasurer
Julie Cousler-Emig, Secretary
William C. Bullitt, Esq.
C. Richard Cox
Susan C. Day, M.D.
Lucy Wolf Tuton, Ph.D.

ADDRESS INQUIRIES TO:
Diana Loukedis Doherty, Manager
(See address above.)

*SPECIAL STIPULATIONS:
Grants must benefit poor boys and girls of
the city of Philadelphia.

SIERRA HEALTH FOUNDATION
1321 Garden Highway
Sacramento, CA 95833
(916) 922-4755
Fax: (916) 922-4024

E-MAIL ADDRESS:
info@sierrahealth.org

WEB SITE ADDRESS:
www.sierrahealth.org

TYPE:
Matching gifts; Project/program grants.
Specific to funding opportunities - solicited.

See entry 1614 for full listing.

SILICON VALLEY COMMUNITY FOUNDATION
2440 West El Camino Real
Suite 300
Mountain View, CA 94040-1498
(650) 450-5400
Fax: (650) 450-5401

E-MAIL ADDRESS:
info@siliconvalleycf.org

WEB SITE ADDRESS:
www.siliconvalleycf.org

TYPE:
General operating grants; Project/program
grants; Scholarships; Seed money grants.
Nonprofit organizations that provide services
or programs related to the specific five
grantmaking strategies in San Mateo and
Santa Clara counties may be eligible to apply
for funding from the Foundation's
endowment. Scholarships for college-bound
students are also open to application.

See entry 1466 for full listing.

STUART FOUNDATION   [1220]
500 Washington Street
Eighth Floor
San Francisco, CA 94111
(415) 393-1551
Fax: (415) 393-1552

E-MAIL ADDRESS:
info@stuartfoundation.org

WEB SITE ADDRESS:
www.stuartfoundation.org

FOUNDED: 1985

NAME(S) OF PROGRAMS:
● **Child Welfare**
● **Public Education**

TYPE:
Conferences/seminars; Demonstration grants;
Development grants; General operating
grants; Project/program grants; Research
grants; Technical assistance; Training grants.
Systematic change and collaborative service
delivery.

YEAR PROGRAM STARTED: 1985

PURPOSE:
To provide a coordinated set of programs,
activities, research, and policy analysis that
improve opportunities for children and youth
in California and Washington to become
self-reliant, responsible and contributing
members of their communities.

LEGAL BASIS:
Private foundation.

ELIGIBILITY:
No grants to individuals.

GEOGRAPHIC RESTRICTIONS:
California and Washington.

FINANCIAL DATA:
Amount of support per award: $116,101
average grant for the year 2009.
Total amount of support: $13,583,826 in total
grants for the year 2009.

REPRESENTATIVE AWARDS:
Child Welfare: $250,000 over 12 months to
Foundation for California Community
Colleges, Sacramento, CA, for the
participation of eight to 10 California
campuses in Community College Pathways, a
learning community to deepen, embed and
expand services to foster youth enrolled in
community college; Education: $150,000
over 12 months to University of San
Diego-School of Leadership and Education
Studies, San Diego, CA, to provide coaches
and professional development for veteran
school principals and school leadership teams
in four small districts in San Diego County.

APPLICATION INFORMATION:
Duration: Grants are approved for one year
at a time, although projects can be funded for
several years.

IRS IDENTIFICATION NUMBER: 20-0882784

STAFF:
Christy Pichel, President
David Barlow, Vice President of Finance and
Administration
Rhonnel Sotelo, Vice President of Programs
and Operations
Teri Kook, Child Welfare Director
Michelle Francois, Child Welfare Program
Officer

BOARD MEMBERS:
Dwight L. Stuart, Jr., Chairman
Stuart Lucas, Vice Chairman
Elbridge H. Stuart, III, Vice Chairman and
Treasurer
Davis Campbell, Director

ADDRESS INQUIRIES TO:
Grants Manager
(See address above.)

SUBARU OF AMERICA FOUNDATION, INC.
2235 Route 70 West
Cherry Hill, NJ 08002
(856) 488-5099
Fax: (856) 488-3300

E-MAIL ADDRESS:
foundation@subaru.com

WEB SITE ADDRESS:
www.subaru.com

TYPE:
General operating grants; Project/program
grants. Special programs; Employee matching
gift program.

See entry 1699 for full listing.

THE FRANK M. TAIT FOUNDATION [1221]

1530 Kettering Tower
40 North Main Street
Dayton, OH 45423
(937) 222-2401
Fax: (937) 224-6015

E-MAIL ADDRESS:
taitfdn@earthlink.net

FOUNDED: 1955

AREAS OF INTEREST:
Youth development and cultural activities for underserved youth.

TYPE:
Project/program grants. Focus on youth development, particularly early childhood development.

YEAR PROGRAM STARTED: 1956

PURPOSE:
To provide programs that develop youth (particularly early childhood development programs); to provide cultural enrichment experiences for underserved youth.

LEGAL BASIS:
Ohio corporation, not for profit.

ELIGIBILITY:
Organizations must be exempt under 501(c)(3). No private foundations.

The Foundation does not fund:
(1) medical research or equipment;
(2) operating budgets or annual fund drives;
(3) emergency requests for crash programs;
(4) endowment funds;
(5) religious programs or activities or;
(6) lobbying or propaganda activities.

GEOGRAPHIC RESTRICTIONS:
Montgomery County, Ohio.

FINANCIAL DATA:
Amount of support per award: Typically $5,000 to $50,000.
Total amount of support: $285,000 for the year 2010.
Matching fund requirements: Varies.

APPLICATION INFORMATION:
Must contact the Executive Director at the phone number above to discuss the prospective grant proposal and to obtain approval for its subsequent submission.
Duration: Usually one year. Reapply for renewal.

PUBLICATIONS:
Guidelines.

IRS IDENTIFICATION NUMBER: 31-6037499

ADDRESS INQUIRIES TO:
Jenni Roer, Executive Director
(See address above.)

*SPECIAL STIPULATIONS:
Funding in Montgomery County, Ohio only.

TEAMMATES FOR KIDS FOUNDATION [1222]

4251 Kipling Street, Suite 370
Wheat Ridge, CO 80033
(303) 759-9777
Fax: (303) 759-9555

E-MAIL ADDRESS:
jason@tfkf.com

WEB SITE ADDRESS:
www.teammates4kids.com

FOUNDED: 1999

AREAS OF INTEREST:
Serving children's needs in the areas of health, education or providing inner-city services.

TYPE:
Grants-in-aid. Foundation grants are directed to nonprofit organizations that specialize in working with children.

PURPOSE:
To develop and implement innovative concepts that generate funds for the benefit of children's charities.

ELIGIBILITY:
To qualify for a grant from the Foundation, an organization must:
(1) be a 501(c)(3) tax-exempt nonprofit organization in good standing with the IRS;
(2) have a record of outstanding service in effectively and efficiently delivering programs and services that improve the lives of needy children;
(3) serve children's needs in the areas of health, education or providing inner-city services;
(4) deliver services which impact the lives of children, both short- and long-term and;
(5) ensure that 100% of grant monies received from the Foundation are used for the exclusive benefit of children.

FINANCIAL DATA:
Amount of support per award: Most grants are from $5,000 to $50,000. Average grant $10,000.

APPLICATION INFORMATION:
By invitation only.

ADDRESS INQUIRIES TO:
Jason Graham
Director of Charitable Giving
(See address above.)

TURRELL FUND [1223]

21 Van Vleck Street
Montclair, NJ 07042-2358
(973) 783-9358
Fax: (973) 783-9283

E-MAIL ADDRESS:
turrell@turrellfund.org

WEB SITE ADDRESS:
www.turrellfund.org

FOUNDED: 1935

AREAS OF INTEREST:
Youth organizations, such as the Boy Scouts and Girl Scouts, YMCAs and YWCAs, day programs and inner city programs, with a focus on children from infancy to three years old.

TYPE:
Capital grants; General operating grants; Project/program grants.

YEAR PROGRAM STARTED: 1935

PURPOSE:
To financially and strategically support organizations which directly provide or foster the creation and delivery of high-quality, developmental and educational services to at-risk children, especially the youngest and their families in Vermont and designated areas of New Jersey.

LEGAL BASIS:
Tax-exempt private foundation.

ELIGIBILITY:
Tax-exempt 501(c)(3) organizations in New Jersey and Vermont only may apply. In New Jersey, emphasis is on northern urban areas centered in Essex, Hudson, Passaic and Union counties only. No grants are awarded for lobbying, endowments or research. No grants to individuals and most hospital work and health delivery services. Only organizations providing direct services and advocacy for children and youth are eligible.

GEOGRAPHIC RESTRICTIONS:
Essex, Hudson, Passaic and Union counties, New Jersey and Vermont.

FINANCIAL DATA:
Amount of support per award: $1,000 to $100,000. $17,000 average grant.
Total amount of support: Approximately $6,000,000 for the year 2009; $4,959,321 for the year 2010.

NUMBER OF APPLICANTS MOST RECENT YEAR: 490 for the year 2010.

NUMBER OF AWARDS: 310 for the year 2010.

REPRESENTATIVE AWARDS:
NorthWard Center; St. Benedict's Preparatory School; Boys and Girls Clubs of Burlington, VT.

APPLICATION INFORMATION:
Applications are accepted online only. Accompanying a proposal should be the following:
(1) a brief letter describing the project;
(2) a statement of confirmation of the organization's tax-exempt status sent on the organization's letterhead, signed by an official on behalf of the governing board;
(3) a copy of the IRS letter granting tax exemption;
(4) operating and project budgets and;
(5) either a 990 form and audited statement from most recent year available.

The proposal should include:
(1) background information about the organization;
(2) identification of board members;
(3) staff qualifications;
(4) a financial report;
(5) current budget and;
(6) project costs.
Duration: One year.
Deadline: Proposals for organizations: August 1 and February 1. Announcement in late June and late December.

PUBLICATIONS:
Annual report.

IRS IDENTIFICATION NUMBER: 22-1551936

OFFICERS:
S. Lawrence Prendergast, Chairman of the Board
Sonyia Woloshyn, Vice President and Treasurer
Curtland E. Fields, Secretary

TRUSTEES:
Robert E. Angelica
Elizabeth W. Christie
Curtland E. Fields
Rev. William S. Gannon
Kim Keiser
Matthew E. Melmed
Dr. Julia A. Miller
John P. Mitchell
S. Lawrence Prendergast
Mark Sustic

ADDRESS INQUIRIES TO:
Curtland E. Fields, President and Chief Executive Officer
(See address above.)

U.S. DEPARTMENT OF EDUCATION [1224]

Office of Safe and Drug Free Schools
550 12th Street, S.W., 10th Floor
Washington, DC 20202-6450
(202) 245-7896
Fax: (202) 485-0013

E-MAIL ADDRESS:
osdfs.safeschl@ed.gov

WEB SITE ADDRESS:
www2.ed.gov/osdfs

AREAS OF INTEREST:
Drug abuse and violence prevention.

NAME(S) OF PROGRAMS:
- **Safe and Drug Free Schools Program**

TYPE:
Project/program grants. Discretionary grants
to prevent the illegal use of drugs and
violence among, and promote safety and
discipline for, students at all educational
levels from preschool through the
postsecondary level. The many discretionary
grants are listed on the *Federal Register*.

YEAR PROGRAM STARTED: 1987

PURPOSE:
To provide drug and alcohol abuse education
and prevention.

LEGAL BASIS:
Government agency.

ELIGIBILITY:
Grants are made to state educational
agencies, local educational agencies,
institutions of higher education and other
public and private nonprofit agencies.

GEOGRAPHIC RESTRICTIONS:
United States.

FINANCIAL DATA:
Amount of support per award: Varies.
Total amount of support: Varies.

APPLICATION INFORMATION:
Duration: Up to five years.

U.S. DEPARTMENT OF HEALTH AND HUMAN SERVICES [1225]

Administration for Children and Families
Office of Head Start
1250 Maryland Avenue, S.W., 8th Floor
Washington, DC 20024
(866) 763-6481
(202) 205-8573
(202) 205-8396
Fax: (202) 401-9721

WEB SITE ADDRESS:
www.acf.hhs.gov/programs/ohs/
www.eclkc.ohs.acf.hhs.gov

NAME(S) OF PROGRAMS:
- **Head Start**

TYPE:
Project/program grants. Grants for
comprehensive programs focused primarily
upon children from low-income families who
have not reached the age of compulsory
school attendance. Supported projects should
involve:
(1) comprehensive health (including medical
and dental examinations), nutritional, social,
psychological, educational and mental health
services;
(2) appropriate activities to encourage and
provide opportunities for participation of
parents and effective use of provided services
and;

(3) other pertinent training, technical
assistance, evaluation and follow-through
activities.

YEAR PROGRAM STARTED: 1965

PURPOSE:
To provide children from low-income
families with comprehensive health, nutrition,
educational, social and other services; to aid
children to attain their full potential.

LEGAL BASIS:
Omnibus Budget and Reconciliation Act of
1981 (Public Law 97-35).

ELIGIBILITY:
Local public and private nonprofit and
for-profit organizations are eligible to apply.
However, the actual operation of a Head Start
program may be delegated to an organization
qualified to and capable of operating such a
program.

FINANCIAL DATA:
Federal funds may not exceed 80% except in
certain limited situations where grantees may
be relieved of all or part of the non-federal
share.
Amount of support per award: Varies.
Total amount of support: $7,110,283,000
(federal appropriation) for fiscal year 2009.
Matching fund requirements: Grantees are
required to provide 20% of the total cost of
the project.

NUMBER OF APPLICANTS MOST RECENT YEAR:
1,305.

APPLICATION INFORMATION:
Applications from organizations which are
not current grantees are accepted only in
response to announcements in the *Federal
Register*. Applicants for a Head Start grant
should contact the Health and Human
Services regional office in their area. Parents
wishing to enroll their children should
consult the local Head Start Program in their
Community.

ADDRESS INQUIRIES TO:
Tel: (866) 763-6481
Web site: www.eclkc.ohs.acf.hhs.gov

U.S. DEPARTMENT OF HEALTH AND HUMAN SERVICES [1226]

Administration for Children and Families
Children's Bureau
1250 Maryland Avenue, S.W., 8th Floor
Washington, DC 20024
(202) 205-8618
Fax: (202) 260-9345

WEB SITE ADDRESS:
www.acf.hhs.gov/programs/cb

FOUNDED: 1912

AREAS OF INTEREST:
Child welfare, family preservation and
support, time-limited family reunification,
and adoption promotion and support.

NAME(S) OF PROGRAMS:
- **Stephanie Tubbs Jones Child Welfare
Services Program**

TYPE:
Formula grants. Funds may be used for the
following purposes:
(a) protecting the welfare of all children;
(b) preventing the abuse, neglect, or
exploitation of children;
(c) supporting at-risk families through
services that allow children to remain with
their families or return to their families in a

timely manner;
(d) promoting the safety, permanence, and
well-being of children in foster care and
adoptive families and;
(e) providing training, professional
development, and support to ensure a
well-qualified workforce.

YEAR PROGRAM STARTED: 1993

PURPOSE:
To promote State flexibility in the
development and expansion of a coordinated
child and family services program that
utilizes community-based agencies and
ensures all children are raised in safe, loving
families.

ELIGIBILITY:
Families and children in need of child
welfare services.

GEOGRAPHIC RESTRICTIONS:
District of Columbia, Indian Tribes, Puerto
Rico, Northern Marianas, Virgin Islands,
Guam, and American Samoa.

FINANCIAL DATA:
Funds will be awarded after the State plan, or
annual update, is submitted and approved.
Total amount of support: $281,744,000
estimated for the year 2010.

NUMBER OF AWARDS: Approximately 213.

APPLICATION INFORMATION:
Deadline: June 30.

ADDRESS INQUIRIES TO:
Eileen West, Program Officer
Tel: (202) 205-8438
E-mail: eileen.west@acf.hhs.gov

*SPECIAL STIPULATIONS:
States are required to maintain adequate
fiscal reports, and to make reports as required
by the Department of DHHS.

U.S. DEPARTMENT OF HEALTH AND HUMAN SERVICES [1227]

1250 Maryland Avenue, S.W.
Washington, DC 20024
(202) 205-8102
Fax: (202) 260-9333

E-MAIL ADDRESS:
ncfy@acf.hhs.gov

WEB SITE ADDRESS:
www.acf.hhs.
gov/grants/open/foa/office/acyf_fysb

FOUNDED: 1974

AREAS OF INTEREST:
Crisis and referral services for runaway and
homeless youth.

NAME(S) OF PROGRAMS:
- **Runaway and Homeless Youth Grants
Program**

TYPE:
Development grants; General operating
grants; Project/program grants; Technical
assistance. Title III of the Juvenile Justice
and Delinquency Prevention Act of 1974, et
seq., to authorize the Runaway and Homeless
Youth Program.

Basic Center, Street Outreach, and
Transitional Living are components of this
Program.

Through Basic Center, the Bureau provides
financial assistance to establish or strengthen
community-based programs that address the
immediate needs of runaway and homeless
youth and their families. These programs are

designed to provide youth with emergency shelter, food, clothing, counseling and referrals for health care.

Through Street Outreach, the Bureau awards grants to private, nonprofit agencies to conduct outreach designed to build relationships between grantee staff and street youth. These efforts are intended to help young people leave the streets.

Through Transitional Living, the Bureau supports projects that provide longer-term residential services to homeless youth, 16 to 21 years of age, for up to 18 months. Services are intended to help homeless youth make a successful transition to self-sufficient living.

YEAR PROGRAM STARTED: 1974

PURPOSE:
To establish or strengthen locally controlled community programs that address the immediate needs of runaway and homeless youth and their families. Services must be provided outside of the law enforcement, juvenile justice system, child welfare or mental health. The program is designed to alleviate problems of RHY youth, reunite youth with their families, and encourage the resolution of intrafamily problems through counseling and other services, strengthen family relationships and encourage stable living conditions for youth and help youth decide upon constructive courses of action.

LEGAL BASIS:
Grants under this program are authorized by the Runaway and Homeless Youth Act (the Act), 42 U.S.C. 5701 et seq. This Act was enacted as Title III of the Juvenile Justice and Delinquency Prevention Act of 1974 (Pub. L. 93-415), as amended by the Juvenile Justice Amendments of 1977 (Pub. L. 95-115), the Juvenile Justice Amendments of 1980 (Pub. L. 96-509), the Juvenile Justice Amendments of 1984 (Pub. L. 98-473), the Anti-Drug Abuse Act of 1988 (Pub. L. 100-690) and the Juvenile Justice and Delinquency Prevention Amendments of 1992 (Pub. L. 102-586).

ELIGIBILITY:
Grants are available to states, localities, nonprofit private agencies, coordinated networks and Indian Tribes.

GEOGRAPHIC RESTRICTIONS:
United States and its territories.

FINANCIAL DATA:
Amount of support per award: Maximum of $200,000 per year.

Total amount of support: Approximately $113,000,000 annually.

NUMBER OF APPLICANTS MOST RECENT YEAR:
182 Basic Center, 144 Street Outreach, 163 Transitional Living.

APPLICATION INFORMATION:
Guidelines available on the web site.

Duration: Three years for Basic Center and Street Outreach. Five years for Transitional Living.

ADDRESS INQUIRIES TO:
Curtis O. Porter, Director, Division of Youth Services
Family and Youth Services Bureau
Administration for Children, Youth and Families
(See address above.)

U.S. DEPARTMENT OF HEALTH AND HUMAN SERVICES [1228]
Administration for Children and Families
Children's Bureau
1250 Maryland Avenue, S.W.
Washington, DC 20024
(202) 205-8618
Fax: (202) 260-9345

WEB SITE ADDRESS:
www.acf.hhs.gov/programs/cb

NAME(S) OF PROGRAMS:
- **Discretionary Grant Programs**
- **Promoting Safe and Stable Families**
- **State & Tribal Grant Programs**
- **State Formula Grants**

TYPE:
Formula grants; Project/program grants. Discretionary Grants are awarded for research and program development, through a competitive peer-review process, to State, Tribal and local agencies, faith-based and community-based organizations, and other nonprofit and for profit groups.

Promoting Safe and Stable Families (PSSF) primarily aims to prevent the unnecessary separation of children from their families, improve the quality of care and services to children and their families, and ensure permanency for children by reuniting them with their parents, by adoption or by another permanent living arrangement.

State & Tribal Grant Programs provide matching funds to States and Tribes to help them operate every aspect of their child welfare systems–from prevention of child abuse and neglect to adoption–and the information systems necessary to support these programs.

State Formula Grants assist States and Territories in establishing, maintaining and expanding programs and projects to prevent family violence and to provide immediate shelter and related assistance for victims of family violence and their dependents.

PURPOSE:
To fund projects, programs and research that serve children, families or the community to states, territories and tribes.

ELIGIBILITY:
Discretionary Grants: States, local governments, tribes, public agencies or private agencies or organizations with expertise in providing technical assistance related to family preservation, family support, time-limited family reunification and adoption promotion and support.

Promoting Safe and Stable Families: Families and children who need services to assist them to stabilize their lives, strengthen family functioning, prevent out-of-home placement of children, enhance child development and increase competence in parenting abilities, facilitate timely reunification of the child and promote appropriate adoptions.

State & Tribal Grant Programs and State Formula Grants: States, territories and certain Indian Tribes are eligible.

FINANCIAL DATA:
Formula Grants: Funds will be approved after the State plan, or annual update is submitted and approved.

Amount of support per award: $180,239 to $34,757,984 with an average of $6,019,347 for states and territories; $10,244 to $1,858,864 with an average of $80,715 for

Tribes; $100,000 to $1,040,000 with an average award of $250,000 for Discretionary Grants.

APPLICATION INFORMATION:
Discretionary Grants: Announcement of availability of funds is published in the Federal Register. Eligible applicants submit applications by specified deadlines. Formula Grants: A five-year State plan must be submitted. The plan must be jointly developed by the Secretary and State or Indian Tribe and written after consultation by the agency.

Duration: Discretionary Grants are generally for a 12-, 24- or 36-month period; some may be renewed for up to five years. Formula Grants: Awards will be made quarterly on a fiscal year basis through a letter of credit.

Deadline: Formula Grants: June 30. Contact the headquarters or regional office, as appropriate, for other application deadlines.

ADDRESS INQUIRIES TO:
Catherine Heath, Program Specialist
(See address above.)

U.S. DEPARTMENT OF JUSTICE
Office of Juvenile Justice and Delinquency Prevention
810 Seventh Street, N.W., 5th Floor
Washington, DC 20531
(202) 307-5911
Fax: (202) 307-2093

WEB SITE ADDRESS:
www.ojjdp.ncjrs.gov/

TYPE:
Block grants; Challenge/matching grants; Demonstration grants; Formula grants; Internships; Project/program grants; Research grants; Technical assistance; Training grants. Grants to increase the capacity of state and local governments to conduct effective juvenile justice and delinquency prevention programs as developed in the state comprehensive action plan.

See entry 1505 for full listing.

U.S. DEPARTMENT OF JUSTICE
Office of Juvenile Justice and Delinquency Prevention
810 Seventh Street, N.W.
Washington, DC 20531
(202) 353-8734
Fax: (202) 307-2819

E-MAIL ADDRESS:
thomas.murphy@usdoj.gov

WEB SITE ADDRESS:
www.ojjdp.ncjrs.gov

TYPE:
Block grants. Grants awarded on a formula basis. Funds are available for 17 specific program purpose areas.

See entry 1508 for full listing.

USDA FOOD AND NUTRITION SERVICE [1229]
Child Nutrition Division
3101 Park Center Drive, Room 640
Alexandria, VA 22302
(703) 305-2590
Fax: (703) 305-2879

WEB SITE ADDRESS:
www.fns.usda.gov/cnd

FOUNDED: 1969

AREAS OF INTEREST:
Child nutrition.

NAME(S) OF PROGRAMS:
- **The Child and Adult Care Food Program**
- **The National School Lunch Program**
- **The School Breakfast Program**
- **The Special Milk Program for Children**
- **The Summer Food Service Program for Children**

TYPE:
Formula grants; Grants-in-aid; Project/program grants. Reimbursement for the support of food service in schools, child and adult care institutions to improve nutrition.

The Child and Adult Care Food Program helps child care facilities and institutions serve nutritious meals and snacks to pre-school and school-age children. To participate, facilities and institutions must be licensed or approved to provide child care services. They must also meet certain other eligibility requirements. The program operates in nonresidential day care centers, settlement houses, outside-school-hours care centers, family day care homes, institutions providing day care for handicapped children and others. Participating facilities and institutions get cash assistance, USDA-donated foods and technical guidance. In child care centers, the amount of cash assistance varies according to the family size and income of children served. In day care homes, the amount of cash assistance is based on a food service payment rate. Similar benefits are also now available to adult day care centers which serve functionally impaired adults or persons 60 years of age or older.

The National School Lunch Program makes well-planned nutritious meals available to school children. Any public or nonprofit private schools of high school grade or under and licensed public or nonprofit private residential child care institutions are eligible to participate in the National School Lunch and School Breakfast Programs. Schools that participate are required to provide free and reduced-price meals to children unable to pay the full price. Eligibility is based on application information submitted by a parent or guardian. The household income limit for free lunches is set at or below 130% of the federal poverty level and for reduced price lunches household income must be above 130% or at or below 185% of the federal poverty level. Children from households not eligible for free or reduced-price meals must pay the school's full price charge for lunch. Cash and donated commodities are provided to participating schools and institutions according to the number of meals served.

The School Breakfast Program makes nutritious breakfasts available to school children under the same eligibility guidelines and general requirements as the National School Lunch Program.

The Special Milk Program for Children makes it possible for all children attending a participating school or institution to purchase milk at a reduced price or receive it free, if they are eligible. Reimbursement is provided for each half-pint of milk served under the program. Schools and institutions that participate in other federal child nutrition programs authorized under the National School Lunch Act or the Child Nutrition Act of 1966 may not participate in the Special

Milk Program for Children, except for split-session kindergarten programs conducted in schools in which the children do not have access to the other meal program.

The Summer Food Service Program for Children helps communities serve meals to needy children when school is not in session. The program is sponsored by public or private nonprofit school food authorities or local, municipal, county or state governments. Public or private nonprofit residential camps, other private nonprofit organizations, colleges and universities which participate in the National Youth Sports Program also may be sponsors. The program operates in areas in which at least 50% of the children meet the income criteria for free and reduced-price school meals. USDA reimburses sponsors for operating costs of food services up to a specified maximum rate for each meal served. In addition, sponsors receive some reimbursement for planning, operating and supervising expenses.

YEAR PROGRAM STARTED: 1946

PURPOSE:
To help safeguard the health and well-being of the nation's children and to encourage the domestic consumption of nutritious agricultural commodities and other foods.

LEGAL BASIS:
The National School Lunch Act as amended and the Child Nutrition Act of 1966, as amended.

ELIGIBILITY:
Family size and number of children based on income poverty levels.

GEOGRAPHIC RESTRICTIONS:
United States and its territories.

FINANCIAL DATA:
Amount of support per award: Varies.
Matching fund requirements: Varies.

APPLICATION INFORMATION:
Official application materials are available upon request to state educational agencies or other state designated agency. In states where education agencies do not administer the programs for nonprofit private schools, contact the appropriate Food and Nutrition Service Regional Office of the Department of Agriculture for more information.
Deadline: Applications are accepted throughout the year.

FRANKLIN H. AND RUTH L. WELLS FOUNDATION [1230]

3607 Rosemont Avenue, Suite 404
Camp Hill, PA 17011
(717) 763-1157

E-MAIL ADDRESS:
mgibbons989@verizon.net

FOUNDED: 1981

AREAS OF INTEREST:
Health care, youth, human services and education.

TYPE:
Project/program grants; Seed money grants. Seed money grants are primarily for new programs.

PURPOSE:
To improve the quality of life in central Pennsylvania.

LEGAL BASIS:
Private foundation.

ELIGIBILITY:
Grants are made to organizations that have tax-exempt status under Section 501(c)(3) of the Internal Revenue Code. No grants are made to individuals. Non-sectarian religious programs may apply.

GEOGRAPHIC RESTRICTIONS:
Cumberland, Dauphin and Perry counties, Pennsylvania.

FINANCIAL DATA:
Amount of support per award: $500 to $20,000.
Total amount of support: Approximately $300,000 annually.

NUMBER OF AWARDS: 40 for the year 2010.

APPLICATION INFORMATION:
Send proposal to the address listed above.
Duration: One or two years. Renewal possible for third year.
Deadline: February 28 and September 30.

ADDRESS INQUIRIES TO:
Miles J. Gibbons, Jr., Executive Director (See address above.)

*PLEASE NOTE:
Applications should be submitted by mail.

JOSEPH B. WHITEHEAD FOUNDATION [1231]

50 Hurt Plaza, Suite 1200
Atlanta, GA 30303
(404) 522-6755
Fax: (404) 522-7026

E-MAIL ADDRESS:
fdns@woodruff.org

WEB SITE ADDRESS:
www.jbwhitehead.org

FOUNDED: 1937

AREAS OF INTEREST:
Human services, public education, children and youth services.

TYPE:
Capital grants; Challenge/matching grants.

LEGAL BASIS:
Supporting organization.

ELIGIBILITY:
Limited to a selected list of beneficiaries.

GEOGRAPHIC RESTRICTIONS:
Metropolitan Atlanta, Georgia.

FINANCIAL DATA:
Total amount of support: $25,000 to $2,000,000.

APPLICATION INFORMATION:
An application form is not required. Proposals should be made in letter form and should include the following information:
(1) a description of the organization, its purposes, programs, staffing and governing board;
(2) organization's latest financial statements, including the most recent report;
(3) a description of the proposed project and full justification for its funding;
(4) an itemized project budget, including other sources of support in hand anticipated and;
(5) evidence from the IRS of the organization's tax-exempt status and the applying organization itself is not a private foundation.
Deadline: February 1 and September 1.

THE WHO (WOMEN HELPING OTHERS) FOUNDATION

2121 Midway Road
Carrollton, TX 75006
(972) 458-0601
(800) 946-4663
Fax: (972) 341-3080

WEB SITE ADDRESS:
www.whofoundation.org

TYPE:
Development grants; Product donations; Project/program grants.

See entry 1164 for full listing.

WIDENER MEMORIAL FOUNDATION IN AID OF HANDICAPPED CHILDREN

4060 Butler Pike
Suite 225
Plymouth Meeting, PA 19462
(610) 825-8900
Fax: (610) 825-8904

TYPE:
Capital grants; Project/program grants.

See entry 1087 for full listing.

Community development and services

ABEL FOUNDATION [1232]

1815 Y Street
Lincoln, NE 68508
(402) 434-1212
Fax: (402) 434-1799

WEB SITE ADDRESS:
www.abelfoundation.org

AREAS OF INTEREST:
Health and human services, higher education and community development programs.

TYPE:
Capital grants; Matching gifts; Project/program grants.

PURPOSE:
To improve the quality of life, particularly in communities where the company has facilities.

ELIGIBILITY:
Grants are made to organizations that have tax-exempt status under Section 501(c)(3) of the Internal Revenue Code. No grants are made to individuals.

GEOGRAPHIC RESTRICTIONS:
Nebraska, particularly Lincoln.

FINANCIAL DATA:
Amount of support per award: Varies.

APPLICATION INFORMATION:
Please use the Lincoln/Lancaster County Grant Maker Common Application Form.
Duration: One year. Renewal possible.
Deadline: April 15 and November 15. Foundation meets in May and December, respectively, to review funding requests. It is possible that the Foundation will meet again in September, if funding requests warrant additional meetings.

ADDRESS INQUIRIES TO:
J. Ross McCown, Vice President
(See address above.)

ADCO FOUNDATION

c/o American Atlantic Co.
1060 First Avenue, Suite 400
King of Prussia, PA 19406
(610) 768-8020
Fax: (610) 337-3128

TYPE:
General operating grants; Project/program grants; Seed money grants.

See entry 1727 for full listing.

AKRON COMMUNITY FOUNDATION [1233]

345 West Cedar Street
Akron, OH 44307-2407
(330) 376-8522
Fax: (330) 376-0202

E-MAIL ADDRESS:
deckert@akroncommunityfdn.org

WEB SITE ADDRESS:
www.akroncommunityfdn.org

FOUNDED: 1955

AREAS OF INTEREST:
Arts and culture, civic affairs, health and human services, and education.

TYPE:
Capital grants; General operating grants; Project/program grants; Scholarships; Seed money grants.

LEGAL BASIS:
Community foundation.

ELIGIBILITY:
Organizations must be tax-exempt.

GEOGRAPHIC RESTRICTIONS:
Summit County, Ohio.

FINANCIAL DATA:
Assets of $132,000,000 for the year ended December 31, 2010.
Amount of support per award: Average $15,000 to $20,000.
Total amount of support: $7,000,000 for the year 2010.

COOPERATIVE FUNDING PROGRAMS: City of Akron Neighborhood Partnership.

NUMBER OF APPLICANTS MOST RECENT YEAR: 1,200.

NUMBER OF AWARDS: 850.

APPLICATION INFORMATION:
Applicants must complete pre-application on web site or contact the Foundation before submitting an application.
Deadline: Education: January 2; Arts and Culture: April 1; Civic Affairs: July 1; Health and Human Services: October 1.

PUBLICATIONS:
Guidelines.

IRS IDENTIFICATION NUMBER: 34-1087615

ADDRESS INQUIRIES TO:
Donae Eckert
Vice President of Community Investment
(See address above.)

*SPECIAL STIPULATIONS:
Complete pre-application on web site or contact the Foundation before submitting an application.

ALBION COMMUNITY FOUNDATION [1234]

P.O. Box 156
Albion, MI 49224-0156
(517) 629-3349
Fax: (517) 629-8027

E-MAIL ADDRESS:
foundation@albionfoundation.org

WEB SITE ADDRESS:
www.albionfoundation.org

FOUNDED: 1969

AREAS OF INTEREST:
Promoting philanthropy addressing community needs through grantmaking, and providing leadership on key community issues.

TYPE:
Capital grants; Challenge/matching grants; Development grants; Project/program grants.

PURPOSE:
To provide a favorable ratio between the amount of money requested and the number of people served, show innovation and creativity in addressing a community need that demonstrates careful planning that provides for successful completion of the project.

LEGAL BASIS:
501(c)(3).

GEOGRAPHIC RESTRICTIONS:
Greater Albion, Michigan area.

FINANCIAL DATA:
Amount of support per award: $250 to $5,000.
Total amount of support: Approximately $80,000 to $100,000 each year.

APPLICATION INFORMATION:
One complete, hard copy of the application and attachments, with original signatures, must be sent to the Foundation at the address above. An electronic version of the grant must also be submitted via e-mail or through the online system. Please refer to grant program guidelines for specifics. If the organization does not have computer access, please contact the Foundation to make special arrangements.
Deadline: Varies annually.

*PLEASE NOTE:
Certified by the Counsel of Foundations.

ALBUQUERQUE COMMUNITY FOUNDATION [1235]

3301 Menaul, N.E.
Suite 2
Albuquerque, NM 87107
(505) 883-6240
Fax: (505) 883-3629

E-MAIL ADDRESS:
foundation@albuquerquefoundation.org

WEB SITE ADDRESS:
www.albuquerquefoundation.org

FOUNDED: 1981

AREAS OF INTEREST:
Arts and culture, education, environmental and historic preservation, health and human services.

TYPE:
Challenge/matching grants; General operating grants; Project/program grants; Scholarships; Seed money grants; Technical assistance.

YEAR PROGRAM STARTED: 1983

PURPOSE:
To improve the quality of life in the greater Albuquerque area by providing support for projects and organizations that serve the community.

LEGAL BASIS:
Community foundation.

ELIGIBILITY:
Grants are made to nonprofit organizations. Foundation grants are generally not made to individuals, for political or religious purposes, to retire indebtedness, for the payment of interest or taxes, annual campaigns, endowments, emergency funding, to influence legislation or elections, to private foundations and other grantmaking organizations, or to organizations that discriminate on the basis of race, creed or sex.

GEOGRAPHIC RESTRICTIONS:
Albuquerque, New Mexico.

FINANCIAL DATA:
$59,179,081 in assets for fiscal year ended December 31, 2010.
Amount of support per award: Varies.
Total amount of support: $2,759,030 in grants and scholarships for fiscal year ended December 31, 2010.

APPLICATION INFORMATION:
Current guidelines and criteria are available on the web site.
Duration: One year.

PUBLICATIONS:
Report to the Community.

IRS IDENTIFICATION NUMBER: 85-0295444

STAFF:
Randy Royster, Esq., Executive Director
Kelli Cooper, Communications Director
Lissa Blaschke, Development Director
Cassidy Grantham, C.P.A., Finance Director
Nancy Johnson, Program Director
Colleen Frangos, Office Administrator

BOARD OF TRUSTEES:
Diane Harrison Ogawa, President
Ron Rivera, C.P.A., Treasurer
Julia B. Bowdich, Secretary
Karen Bard
Victor J. Chavez
Mark Gorham
James N. King
E. Larry Lujan
Bev McMillan
Kim Nunley, C.P.A.
George Stanfield
Jennifer Thomas
Vickie Wilcox
Kevin Yearout
Erin Young

ADDRESS INQUIRIES TO:
Nancy Johnson, Program Director
(See address above.)

ALGER REGIONAL COMMUNITY FOUNDATION   [1236]

100 West Munising Avenue
Munising, MI 49862
(906) 387-3900
Fax: (906) 387-2988

E-MAIL ADDRESS:
algercf@jamadots.com

WEB SITE ADDRESS:
www.algercounty.com/communityfoundation

AREAS OF INTEREST:
Cultural arts, community service, education, the environment and conservation, health and human services, and youth.

TYPE:
Project/program grants; Scholarships.

YEAR PROGRAM STARTED: 1995

PURPOSE:
To provide support to organizations that enhance the quality of life in Alger County.

ELIGIBILITY:
Grants are made to organizations that have tax-exempt status under Section 501(c)(3) of the Internal Revenue Code. Non-sectarian religious programs may apply. Organizations must serve or be located in Alger County, MI. No grants are made to individuals.

GEOGRAPHIC RESTRICTIONS:
Alger County, Michigan.

FINANCIAL DATA:
Amount of support per award: Varies.

APPLICATION INFORMATION:
Foundation staff members are available to talk with potential applicants who are interested in learning about opportunities and needs in the community.

ADDRESS INQUIRIES TO:
Paul Essinger
P.O. Box 39
Munising, MI 49862

ALLEGAN COUNTY COMMUNITY FOUNDATION   [1237]

524 Marshall Street
Allegan, MI 49010-1632
(269) 673-8344
Fax: (269) 673-8745

E-MAIL ADDRESS:
theresa.accf@gmail.com

WEB SITE ADDRESS:
www.alleganfoundation.org

FOUNDED: 1965

AREAS OF INTEREST:
Education, health and human services, culture, community development, environmental issues and art.

TYPE:
General operating grants; Project/program grants; Scholarships; Seed money grants; Technical assistance. Grants fall into the following categories: youth and general.

PURPOSE:
To impact the Allegan County community through the establishment of permanently endowed funds.

LEGAL BASIS:
Community foundation.

ELIGIBILITY:
Applications accepted from charitable organizations serving Allegan County, MI residents. No funding for individuals except for scholarships.

GEOGRAPHIC RESTRICTIONS:
Allegan County, Michigan.

FINANCIAL DATA:
Amount of support per award: $100 to $25,000.

NUMBER OF APPLICANTS MOST RECENT YEAR:
44 for the year 2010.

NUMBER OF AWARDS: 26 for the year 2010.

APPLICATION INFORMATION:
Applications must include a copy of the IRS 501(c)(3) tax determination letter.
Duration: One year.
Deadline: TAG Grants: First Friday in November; Legacy Grants: Second Friday in December.

PUBLICATIONS:
Annual report.

IRS IDENTIFICATION NUMBER: 38-6189947

ADDRESS INQUIRIES TO:
Theresa Bray, Executive Director
(See address above.)

*SPECIAL STIPULATIONS:
Potential applicants must meet with the Executive Director before receiving the grant application(s).

ALTMAN FOUNDATION   [1238]

521 Fifth Avenue
35th Floor
New York, NY 10175
(212) 682-0970

WEB SITE ADDRESS:
www.altmanfoundation.org

FOUNDED: 1913

AREAS OF INTEREST:
Strengthening communities, health, education (independent and non-public schools), arts and culture.

TYPE:
Project/program grants.

YEAR PROGRAM STARTED: 1913

PURPOSE:
To provide direct services grants to New York City-based organizations working in the Foundation's four program areas.

LEGAL BASIS:
Private foundation.

ELIGIBILITY:
Must have a current IRS 501(c)(3) tax-exemption letter. No grants to individuals. No grants for bricks and mortar or capital equipment.

GEOGRAPHIC RESTRICTIONS:
New York.

FINANCIAL DATA:
Amount of support per award: Average $75,899.
Total amount of support: $12,219,800 in grants authorized for the year 2010.

NUMBER OF APPLICANTS MOST RECENT YEAR:
369.

NUMBER OF AWARDS: 161 for the year 2010.

APPLICATION INFORMATION:
Application includes a three- to five-page proposal, project budget, organization budget,

list of corporate and foundation supporters with amounts, board of directors with affiliations, most recent audited financial statement and 501(c)(3) letter. The Foundation accepts the New York Area Common Application Form.

Duration: One year. Renewal possible.

PUBLICATIONS:
Annual report.

IRS IDENTIFICATION NUMBER: 13-1623879

STAFF:
Karen L. Rosa, Vice President and Executive Director
Deborah Thompson Velazquez, Senior Program Officer
Megan McAllister, Program Officer
Rachael Pine, Program Officer

ADDRESS INQUIRIES TO:
Karen L. Rosa
Vice President and Executive Director
(See address above.)

*PLEASE NOTE:
The Foundation's charter limits its grantmaking activities to New York State. Program focus is on New York City.

Send proposal. The Foundation will contact applicant if there is some interest.

AMARILLO AREA FOUNDATION [1239]

801 South Fillmore
Suite 700
Amarillo, TX 79101
(806) 376-4521
Fax: (806) 373-3656

E-MAIL ADDRESS:
kathie@aaf-hf.org

WEB SITE ADDRESS:
www.amarilloareafoundation.org

FOUNDED: 1957

AREAS OF INTEREST:
Community, arts and culture, education, health and human services, teen pregnancy prevention, youth-oriented programs and elderly services.

TYPE:
Project/program grants; Scholarships. Also discretionary grants.

PURPOSE:
To exercise leadership on charitable issues, advance the cause of philanthropy throughout the region and promote efficient and effective delivery of services from nonprofit organizations.

LEGAL BASIS:
501(c)(3).

ELIGIBILITY:
No grants to individuals. Scholarships go to educational institutions.

GEOGRAPHIC RESTRICTIONS:
26 northernmost counties in the Texas panhandle.

FINANCIAL DATA:
Total amount of support: Discretionary grants: $794,486 for the year 2010. The Foundation's public supporting organization, The Don and Sybil Harrington Foundation, awarded $2,578,767 for the year 2010.

NUMBER OF AWARDS: 36 for the year 2010.

APPLICATION INFORMATION:
Contact Grants Coordinator for counseling prior to submitting application. Application is available online for download as a Word document.

Duration: One year.

ADDRESS INQUIRIES TO:
Kathie Grant, Grants Coordinator
(See address above.)

AMERICA THE BEAUTIFUL FUND [1240]

725 15th Street, N.W.
Suite 605
Washington, DC 20005-6093
(202) 638-1649
Fax: (202) 638-2175

E-MAIL ADDRESS:
info@america-the-beautiful.org

WEB SITE ADDRESS:
www.america-the-beautiful.org

FOUNDED: 1965

AREAS OF INTEREST:
Community gardens, to grow food for the hungry, aged, children and youth, and beautification groups.

NAME(S) OF PROGRAMS:
● **Operation Green Plant**

TYPE:
Awards/prizes; Product donations; Technical assistance. Awards are given once or twice per year.

YEAR PROGRAM STARTED: 1965

PURPOSE:
To assist and encourage realistic grassroots efforts to save the natural and historic beauty of America.

LEGAL BASIS:
501(c)(3) organization.

ELIGIBILITY:
Local projects to protect, enhance or restore a community that have broad-scale participation.

GEOGRAPHIC RESTRICTIONS:
United States.

FINANCIAL DATA:
Amount of support per award: Up to $6,000.
Total amount of support: $5,000,000.

NUMBER OF APPLICANTS MOST RECENT YEAR:
10,000 average.

NUMBER OF AWARDS: Approximately 9,000 to 10,000 annually.

APPLICATION INFORMATION:
Guidelines and application form are available on the web site.

PUBLICATIONS:
Better Times; *Green Earth Guide*.

IRS IDENTIFICATION NUMBER: 52-0963138

OFFICERS:
Thomas Farrell, Chairman of the Board
Nanine Bilski, President
Dianne Mendez, Vice President
Nancy Johnson, Treasurer
Daniel Schneider, Secretary

ADDRESS INQUIRIES TO:
Katie Rehwaldt, Program Director
(See address above.)

AMERICAN PLANNING ASSOCIATION [1241]

205 North Michigan Avenue
Suite 1200
Chicago, IL 60601
(312) 786-6722
Fax: (312) 786-6727

E-MAIL ADDRESS:
kblank@planning.org

WEB SITE ADDRESS:
www.planning.org

FOUNDED: 1909

AREAS OF INTEREST:
Urban and regional planning and promotion of the art and science of planning.

NAME(S) OF PROGRAMS:
● **Charles Abrams Scholarship Program**

TYPE:
Scholarships. For a graduate student, majoring in Urban or Transportation Planning, who attends one of the following schools:
(1) Columbia University, Division of Urban Planning;
(2) Harvard University, City & Regional Planning Program of the Graduate School of Architecture and Design;
(3) Massachusetts Institute of Technology, Department of Urban Studies and Planning;
(4) The New School for Social Research, New York Department for Urban Affairs and Policy Analysis or;
(5) University of Pennsylvania, Department of City and Regional Planning.

PURPOSE:
To aid students who will pursue careers as practicing planners.

LEGAL BASIS:
Private, nonprofit educational association.

ELIGIBILITY:
An applicant must be a U.S. citizen and have been accepted into the graduate planning program of one of the five eligible schools. Incoming students are eligible. An applicant must be in need of financial assistance, as determined by a review of the applicant's financial needs. A nomination by the department chair is required.

FINANCIAL DATA:
Student also receives one-year membership in the American Planning Association.
Amount of support per award: $2,000 paid directly to the student's school to defray tuition costs.
Total amount of support: $2,000 each year.

NUMBER OF APPLICANTS MOST RECENT YEAR:
4.

NUMBER OF AWARDS: 1 each year.

APPLICATION INFORMATION:
An eligible applicant should apply through one of the five designated schools on forms supplied to the participating university by APA. Applicant needs to be nominated by Department Chair.

Duration: One academic year.
Deadline: April 30.

OFFICERS:
Bruce A. Knight, FAICP, President
W. Paul Farmer, FAICP, Executive Director

ADDRESS INQUIRIES TO:
Kriss Blank, Leadership Affairs Associate
(See address above.)

AMERICAN PLANNING ASSOCIATION

205 North Michigan Avenue
Suite 1200
Chicago, IL 60601
(312) 786-6722
Fax: (312) 786-6727

E-MAIL ADDRESS:
kblank@planning.org

WEB SITE ADDRESS:
www.planning.org

TYPE:
Fellowships; Scholarships.

See entry 1025 for full listing.

AMERIPRISE FINANCIAL   [1242]

64 Ameriprise Financial Center
Minneapolis, MN 55474
(612) 671-3131
Fax: (612) 671-5112

E-MAIL ADDRESS:
communityrelations@ampf.com

WEB SITE ADDRESS:
www.ameriprise.com

AREAS OF INTEREST:
Meeting basic needs, supporting community
vitality and volunteer-driven causes.

NAME(S) OF PROGRAMS:
- **Meeting Basic Needs**
- **Supporting Community Vitality**
- **Volunteer-Driven Causes**

TYPE:
General operating grants; Matching gifts;
Project/program grants. Project/program
grants are preferred.

PURPOSE:
To support organizations across the nation
where the corporation's employees and
advisors live and work.

FINANCIAL DATA:
Amount of support per award: $5,000 if
applying within Volunteer-Driven Causes
platform.

Total amount of support: $7,300,000.
Includes giftmatching.

Matching fund requirements: 501(c)(3)
organizations that meet funding requirements.

COOPERATIVE FUNDING PROGRAMS: Employee
Giving Campaign, Grants, Gift Matching.

NUMBER OF AWARDS: 181 for the year 2009.

REPRESENTATIVE AWARDS:
Feeding America; American Red Cross;
Habitat for Humanity.

APPLICATION INFORMATION:
Applications must be submitted via
Ameriprise Financial's online application
tool. No paper applications accepted.

Deadline: February 1, May 1 and September
1.

ADDRESS INQUIRIES TO:
Community Relations
(See e-mail address above.)

THE ANDERSEN CORPORATE FOUNDATION   [1243]

White Pine Building
342 Fifth Avenue North
Bayport, MN 55003
(651) 275-4450
Fax: (651) 439-9480

E-MAIL ADDRESS:
andersencorpfdn@srinc.biz

WEB SITE ADDRESS:
www.srinc.biz/foundations/andersen-
corporate-foundation/

FOUNDED: 1941

AREAS OF INTEREST:
Education and youth development, health and
safety, human services, civic support and
affordable housing.

TYPE:
Capital grants; General operating grants;
Project/program grants.

YEAR PROGRAM STARTED: 1941

PURPOSE:
To better people's lives and strengthen
communities, focusing primarily where
Andersen employees live and work.

LEGAL BASIS:
Private foundation.

ELIGIBILITY:
Qualified tax-exempt organizations.

GEOGRAPHIC RESTRICTIONS:
Primarily, Washington County, Minnesota
and portions of western Wisconsin.
Secondarily, the East Metro area of St. Paul,
Minnesota. Also, communities where
Andersen has facilities and employees,
including Des Moines and Dubuque, Iowa;
North Brunswick, New Jersey; Marion, Ohio;
Page County, Virginia; and Menomonie,
Wisconsin.

FINANCIAL DATA:
$37,000,000 in assets as of November 30,
2009.

Amount of support per award: $2,000 to
$100,000.

Total amount of support: $1,675,000.

NUMBER OF APPLICANTS MOST RECENT YEAR:
377.

NUMBER OF AWARDS: 150 for fiscal year ended
November 30, 2009.

REPRESENTATIVE AWARDS:
$20,000 (general operating) to Science
Museum of Minnesota; $37,500 (capital) to
Gillette Children's Hospital; $3,000 (general
operating) to Boys and Girls Clubs Twin
Cities.

APPLICATION INFORMATION:
Cover form and checklist are available
online.

Deadline: October 15, December 15, April
15 and July 15 for board meetings in
January, April, July and November,
respectively.

PUBLICATIONS:
Application guidelines and Form 990PF.

IRS IDENTIFICATION NUMBER: 41-6020912

OFFICERS AND BOARD OF DIRECTORS:
Keith Olson, President
Susan Roeder, Vice President
Phil Donaldson, Treasurer
Jim Humphrey
Randy Iles
Jay Lund
Jerry Redmond

ADDRESS INQUIRIES TO:
Chloette Haley, Program Officer
(See address above.)

*PLEASE NOTE:
Foundation prefers that the proposal be sent
to the address above.

FRED C. AND KATHERINE B. ANDERSEN FOUNDATION   [1244]

P.O. Box 80
Bayport, MN 55003
(651) 264-7355
Fax: (651) 264-5537

E-MAIL ADDRESS:
marygillstrom@sbcglobal.net

FOUNDED: 1959

AREAS OF INTEREST:
Education, youth, elderly and health
programs.

TYPE:
Capital grants; General operating grants;
Project/program grants. The Foundation
supports four-year accredited colleges and
universities that do not accept state or federal
funding.

YEAR PROGRAM STARTED: 1959

PURPOSE:
To support organizations of higher learning
that are four-year institutions that do not
accept state or federal funding.

LEGAL BASIS:
Private foundation.

ELIGIBILITY:
Grants are made to organizations that have
tax-exempt status under Section 501(c)(3) of
the Internal Revenue Code. No grants are
made to individuals.

GEOGRAPHIC RESTRICTIONS:
Washington County, Minnesota; Pierce, Polk
and St. Croix counties, Wisconsin.

FINANCIAL DATA:
Amount of support per award: Varies by
need.

Total amount of support: $23,805,752 for the
year 2010.

APPLICATION INFORMATION:
Organizations should submit a letter of intent
to the Foundation.

Duration: One year. Must reapply for future
grants.

Deadline: March 11, July 15 and October 14.

ADDRESS INQUIRIES TO:
Mary Gillstrom, Vice President/Secretary
(See address above.)

HUGH J. ANDERSEN FOUNDATION   [1245]

342 Fifth Avenue North
Bayport, MN 55003-1201
(651) 439-1557
Fax: (651) 439-9480

WEB SITE ADDRESS:
www.srinc.biz/foundations/hugh-j-andersen-
foundation/

FOUNDED: 1962

AREAS OF INTEREST:
Humanities, arts/culture, elementary and
secondary education, health care, human
services, women and homelessness.

TYPE:
Capital grants; General operating grants;
Project/program grants. Supports focused
efforts that foster inclusivity, promotes
equality, and lends to increased human
independence, self-sufficiency and dignity.

PURPOSE:
To improve the quality of life in the St. Croix Valley.

LEGAL BASIS:
Private organization.

ELIGIBILITY:
Eligible organizations must be IRS 501(c)(3) tax-exempt.

GEOGRAPHIC RESTRICTIONS:
Primary geographic focus: Washington County, Minnesota and Pierce, Polk, and St. Croix counties in Wisconsin. Secondary focus: St. Paul, Minnesota.

FINANCIAL DATA:
Total amount of support: $3,404,937 for fiscal year ended February 2009.

NUMBER OF AWARDS: 267.

REPRESENTATIVE AWARDS:
$9,000 to Human Services, Inc. in Washington County for general operating support; $20,000 to The Phipps Center for the Arts for general operating support; $18,000 to Store to Door for general operating support; $12,000 to The Raptor Center, University of Minnesota Foundation for education programs; $10,000 to Kinship of Polk County for general operating support.

APPLICATION INFORMATION:
Applicant organizations must use the Foundation's application form and include a copy of the IRS tax-exempt determination letter.
Duration: One year. Renewal by reapplication.
Deadline: March 15, June 15, September 15 and November 15.

PUBLICATIONS:
Annual report; application guidelines.

ADDRESS INQUIRIES TO:
Brad Kruse, Program Director
(See address above.)

ANDRUS FAMILY FUND   [1246]

330 Madison Avenue
Suite 30
New York, NY 10017
(212) 687-6975
Fax: (212) 687-6978

E-MAIL ADDRESS:
info@affund.org

WEB SITE ADDRESS:
www.affund.org

FOUNDED: 2000

AREAS OF INTEREST:
Community reconciliation and foster care.

NAME(S) OF PROGRAMS:
- **Community Reconciliation**
- **Foster Care to Independence**

TYPE:
Project/program grants; Research grants.

YEAR PROGRAM STARTED: 2000

PURPOSE:
To contribute to the body of knowledge and experience about what is necessary to create and sustain effective social change.

LEGAL BASIS:
501(c)(3).

ELIGIBILITY:
AFF does not fund endowments, capital improvements, fund-raising events/sponsorships, scholarships, or loans.

Nor does AFF make grants to individuals. Presently, AFF does not fund international projects.

GEOGRAPHIC RESTRICTIONS:
United States.

FINANCIAL DATA:
Amount of support per award: $20,000 to $200,000.
Total amount of support: $3,500,000 to $4,000,000.

NUMBER OF AWARDS: 40.

APPLICATION INFORMATION:
Applications may be submitted at any time. The first step in applying for a grant is to submit an Online AFF Application, which includes a two- or three-page letter of inquiry explaining the project for which funds are sought. The letter should include:
(1) a succinct description of the application organization;
(2) a brief description of the project and how it accomplishes AFF's program strategies;
(3) information about the key participants, including staff members and beneficiaries and;
(4) a section on how you envision the transition framework will be intentionally and consistently incorporated into your work.
Deadline: Grants are awarded by the trustees, who meet in September, January, April and June.

ADDRESS INQUIRIES TO:
Steven Kelban, Executive Director
(See address above.)

ANN ARBOR AREA COMMUNITY FOUNDATION   [1247]

301 North Main Street
Suite 300
Ann Arbor, MI 48104-1133
(734) 663-0401
Fax: (734) 663-3514

E-MAIL ADDRESS:
info@aaacf.org

WEB SITE ADDRESS:
www.aaacf.org

FOUNDED: 1963

AREAS OF INTEREST:
Environment, arts, health and human services, youth and seniors.

NAME(S) OF PROGRAMS:
- **The African American Endowment Fund**
- **The Ann Arbor Energy Fund**
- **The Anna Botsford Bach Fund**
- **Community Foundation of Plymouth Grantmaking Endowment**
- **The Healthy Youth/Healthy Senior Fund**
- **The Ypsilanti Area Community Fund**

TYPE:
Challenge/matching grants; Demonstration grants; Development grants; Project/program grants; Scholarships; Seed money grants; Technical assistance.

YEAR PROGRAM STARTED: 1963

PURPOSE:
To improve the quality of life in the Foundation's region.

ELIGIBILITY:
Eligible organizations must be nonprofit and located in the Ann Arbor, MI region.

GEOGRAPHIC RESTRICTIONS:
Plymouth and Washtenaw County, Michigan.

FINANCIAL DATA:
Amount of support per award: $500 to $20,000.
Total amount of support: $2,200,000 for the year 2010.

APPLICATION INFORMATION:
Applicants must apply online at www.communitygrants.org.
Deadline: February and October. Contact the Foundation for exact dates.

ADDRESS INQUIRIES TO:
Neel Hajra, Chief Operating Officer and Vice President for Community Investment
(See address above.)

ARIZONA COMMUNITY FOUNDATION   [1248]

2201 East Camelback Road
Suite 202
Phoenix, AZ 85016
(602) 381-1400
(800) 222-8221
Fax: (602) 381-1575

WEB SITE ADDRESS:
www.azfoundation.org

FOUNDED: 1978

AREAS OF INTEREST:
Children's mental health and prevention programs, economic development, arts and culture, youth agencies and health agencies.

NAME(S) OF PROGRAMS:
- **Campaign for Working Families**
- **Communities for All Ages**

TYPE:
Project/program grants.

YEAR PROGRAM STARTED: 1978

PURPOSE:
To benefit the quality of life in the Phoenix, AZ community and the surrounding area.

LEGAL BASIS:
Community foundation.

ELIGIBILITY:
Tax-exempt, nonprofit organizations. No grants are made to individuals.

GEOGRAPHIC RESTRICTIONS:
Arizona.

FINANCIAL DATA:
Amount of support per award: $10,000 average.

APPLICATION INFORMATION:
Duration: Typically, one year.

PUBLICATIONS:
Annual report.

OFFICERS:
Bill Hodges, Chairman

ADDRESS INQUIRIES TO:
Jill Christiansen, Junior Program Officer
(See address above.)

ARKANSAS COMMUNITY FOUNDATION   [1249]

1400 West Markham St
Suite 206
Little Rock, AR 72201
(501) 372-1116
Fax: (501) 372-1166

E-MAIL ADDRESS:
arcf@arcf.org

WEB SITE ADDRESS:
www.arcf.org

FOUNDED: 1976

AREAS OF INTEREST:
Grants are made in all fields. Most funds are restricted or designated for specific organizations. Very few unrestricted grants are made.

TYPE:
Project/program grants; Scholarships; Seed money grants.

YEAR PROGRAM STARTED: 1987

PURPOSE:
To serve as a vehicle for Arkansans in carrying out their long-term philanthropic plans; to exercise stewardship in the investment of and grantmaking from, both permanent and short-term charitable funds; to provide leadership to increase public understanding of emerging problems, issues and the importance of philanthropy to the future of the state.

LEGAL BASIS:
Community foundation.

ELIGIBILITY:
Applicants must be nonprofit organizations with projects to benefit Arkansans. Few unrestricted grants are made. Only Arkansas organizations need apply.

GEOGRAPHIC RESTRICTIONS:
Arkansas.

FINANCIAL DATA:
Amount of support per award: $20 to $200,000.
Total amount of support: $7,370,000 for fiscal year 2008.

APPLICATION INFORMATION:
Duration: One year.

PUBLICATIONS:
Annual report; newsletter.

IRS IDENTIFICATION NUMBER: 52-1055743

BOARD OF DIRECTORS:
Sharon Allen, Chairperson
Jerry Adams, Vice Chairperson
Jim Williamson, Finance Chairperson
Heather Larkin, President and Chief Executive Officer
Ted Belden
Murray Claycomb
Mary Elizabeth Eldridge
Glenn Freeman
Ted Gammill
Tina Green
Stacey Harral
Mahlon Maris
George E. McLeod
Sam Scruggs
Estella Tullgren
Peggy Wright

ADDRESS INQUIRIES TO:
Grants Coordinator
(See address above.)

THE AUSTIN COMMUNITY FOUNDATION FOR THE CAPITAL AREA [1250]

4315 Guadalupe, Suite 300
Austin, TX 78751
(512) 472-4483
Fax: (512) 472-4486

E-MAIL ADDRESS:
info@austincf.org

WEB SITE ADDRESS:
www.austincf.org

FOUNDED: 1977

AREAS OF INTEREST:
Arts and culture, community development, community service, education and training, environment, health and human services, recreation and animal-related services.

TYPE:
Project/program grants.

YEAR PROGRAM STARTED: 1977

PURPOSE:
To promote philanthropy in central Texas; to improve the quality of life now and in the future.

ELIGIBILITY:
Organizations must be 501(c)(3) or 170(b)(1)(a)(vi) and located in the central Texas area, including Travis and contiguous counties. Funds are not given to individuals.

GEOGRAPHIC RESTRICTIONS:
Central Texas.

FINANCIAL DATA:
Amount of support per award: Varies; average competitive grant is $17,500.

APPLICATION INFORMATION:
Applications must include the IRS letter ruling 501(c)(3) status.
Duration: One year. Must reapply.
Deadline: Proposals are reviewed on an ongoing basis; four- to six-month process.

IRS IDENTIFICATION NUMBER: 74-1934031

ADDRESS INQUIRIES TO:
MariBen Ramsey, Vice President
(See address above.)

AUTRY FOUNDATION [1251]

4383 Colfax Avenue
Studio City, CA 91604
(818) 752-7770
Fax: (818) 752-7779

AREAS OF INTEREST:
Culture, education, children's and seniors' groups, hunger and health.

TYPE:
Project/program grants.

PURPOSE:
To offer assistance to communities in southern California.

LEGAL BASIS:
Private foundation.

ELIGIBILITY:
Eligible organizations must be IRS 501(c)(3) tax-exempt.

GEOGRAPHIC RESTRICTIONS:
Southern California.

FINANCIAL DATA:
Amount of support per award: $200 to $5,000.
Total amount of support: Varies.

APPLICATION INFORMATION:
Applicants should submit a letter and include a copy of the IRS tax determination letter.
Duration: Depends on project. Renewable.

ADDRESS INQUIRIES TO:
Maxine Hansen, Secretary
(See address above.)

BADGER METER FOUNDATION, INC. [1252]

4545 West Brown Deer Road
Milwaukee, WI 53223-2479
(414) 355-0400
Fax: (414) 371-5956

AREAS OF INTEREST:
Social services, education, conservation and community funds.

TYPE:
General operating grants; Research grants; Seed money grants.

PURPOSE:
To support education and community service organizations, health associations, the handicapped, the arts and conservation.

ELIGIBILITY:
Organizations classified as 501(c)(3) by the IRS can apply. No grants to individuals and religious organizations.

GEOGRAPHIC RESTRICTIONS:
Milwaukee area, Wisconsin.

FINANCIAL DATA:
Amount of support per award: Varies.
Total amount of support: Varies.

NUMBER OF AWARDS: 50.

APPLICATION INFORMATION:
Request must be submitted on organization's letterhead paper.
Duration: One year. Grants are renewable.

ADDRESS INQUIRIES TO:
John Biever, Treasurer
(See address above.)

BALTIMORE COMMUNITY FOUNDATION

2 East Read Street, 9th Floor
Baltimore, MD 21202
(410) 332-4171
Fax: (410) 837-4701

E-MAIL ADDRESS:
info@bcf.org

WEB SITE ADDRESS:
www.bcf.org

TYPE:
Project/program grants; Scholarships; Technical assistance.

See entry 32 for full listing.

BARAGA COUNTY COMMUNITY FOUNDATION [1253]

100 Hemlock Street
Baraga, MI 49908
(906) 353-7898
Fax: (906) 353-7896

E-MAIL ADDRESS:
baragacf@up.net

WEB SITE ADDRESS:
www.baragacountyfoundation.org

FOUNDED: 1994

AREAS OF INTEREST:
Arts and culture, community development, education, senior well-being, and youth development.

TYPE:
Capital grants; Challenge/matching grants; Endowments; Project/program grants; Scholarships; Seed money grants; Technical assistance. Community convening.

PURPOSE:
To enhance the quality of life for the citizens of the community.

ELIGIBILITY:
Grants are made to organizations that have tax-exempt status under Section 501(c)(3) of the Internal Revenue Code. Grants are made to individuals. Nonsectarian religious programs may apply.

GEOGRAPHIC RESTRICTIONS:
Baraga County, Michigan.

FINANCIAL DATA:
Amount of support per award: $200 is a common grant amount. However, grants vary in amount depending upon the needs and nature of the request.
Total amount of support: $2,000.

NUMBER OF APPLICANTS MOST RECENT YEAR:
80.

NUMBER OF AWARDS: Varies.

APPLICATION INFORMATION:
Duration: One year. Renewal possible.
Deadline: Mid-October.

IRS IDENTIFICATION NUMBER: 38-3198122

ADDRESS INQUIRIES TO:
Gordette Marie Leutz, Executive Director
(See address above.)

BARNES GROUP FOUNDATION [1254]

123 Main Street
Bristol, CT 06010
(860) 583-7070
Fax: (860) 589-7466

WEB SITE ADDRESS:
www.bginc.com

AREAS OF INTEREST:
Cultural arts, education, and health and welfare.

TYPE:
General operating grants; Scholarships.

PURPOSE:
To support higher education, cultural arts, and health and welfare.

ELIGIBILITY:
Organizations classified as 501(c)(3) by the IRS can apply. Individuals and religious organizations are ineligible.

GEOGRAPHIC RESTRICTIONS:
United States, with emphasis on Connecticut and New England.

FINANCIAL DATA:
Amount of support per award: Varies.
Total amount of support: Varies.

APPLICATION INFORMATION:
Applicants must write to the Foundation for an application form.
Duration: One year. Grants are renewable.

ADDRESS INQUIRIES TO:
Tom Barnes, Secretary
(See address above.)

BARR FOUNDATION [1255]

The Pilot House
Lewis Wharf
Boston, MA 02110
(617) 854-3500
Fax: (617) 854-3501

E-MAIL ADDRESS:
info@barrfoundation.org

WEB SITE ADDRESS:
www.barrfoundation.org

FOUNDED: 1987

AREAS OF INTEREST:
Education, the environment, arts and cultural activities in Boston, MA.

TYPE:
The work of the Foundation focuses on three critical areas relating to Boston, MA:
(1) providing quality education;
(2) making a more livable city (quality of life issues) and;
(3) enhancing cultural vitality.

PURPOSE:
To enhance the quality of life for all of Boston's citizens.

ELIGIBILITY:
No unsolicited proposals.

GEOGRAPHIC RESTRICTIONS:
Boston, Massachusetts.

FINANCIAL DATA:
Amount of support per award: Varies.
Total amount of support: Approximately $50,118,907 for the year 2009.

NUMBER OF AWARDS: 334 grant approvals and 393 grants paid for fiscal year 2009.

APPLICATION INFORMATION:
By invitation only.
Deadline: Quarterly, in conjunction with quarterly meeting.

ADDRESS INQUIRIES TO:
Kerri Ann Hurley, Grants Manager
(See address above.)

*SPECIAL STIPULATIONS:
Unsolicited proposals are not accepted.

NORWIN S. AND ELIZABETH N. BEAN FOUNDATION [1256]

40 Stark Street
Manchester, NH 03101
(603) 493-7257

E-MAIL ADDRESS:
kcook@beanfoundation.org

WEB SITE ADDRESS:
www.beanfoundation.org

FOUNDED: 1957

AREAS OF INTEREST:
Arts and humanities, education, environment, health, social and community services and development of the voluntary sector.

TYPE:
Capital grants; Challenge/matching grants; Project/program grants. Grants to tax-exempt charitable organizations operating in Amherst or Manchester, NH, for broad charitable purposes. Generally, at least two-thirds of available funds are awarded as grants for programs undertaken by nonprofit organizations and public agencies. The remaining one-third is allocated for capital needs, including acquisition of equipment, renovation or construction of facilities and additions to endowment.

General operating support grants are not made to ongoing programs, nor are grants made to eliminate previously incurred deficits. Short-term operating support may be provided to new organizations or for new program initiatives of established organizations. Generally, grants are provided for expenditure over a period of one year.

PURPOSE:
To promote the general welfare.

LEGAL BASIS:
Private foundation.

ELIGIBILITY:
Applications are accepted from nonprofit 501(c)(3) organizations, municipal and public agencies serving the communities of Amherst or Manchester, NH. Priority consideration is given to organizations operating primarily in those two communities. However, the Foundation will consider applications from statewide or regional organizations which provide a substantial and documented level of service to Manchester and Amherst. The Foundation does not make grants to individuals or provide scholarship aid.

GEOGRAPHIC RESTRICTIONS:
Amherst or Manchester, New Hampshire.

FINANCIAL DATA:
Amount of support per award: $1,000 to $50,000.
Total amount of support: Approximately $650,000 annually.

NUMBER OF APPLICANTS MOST RECENT YEAR:
61 for the year 2008.

NUMBER OF AWARDS: 43 for the year 2008.

REPRESENTATIVE AWARDS:
$30,000 to the capital campaign for a wildlife sanctuary and educational facility to be built by the Audubon Society of New Hampshire; $7,000 to Child and Family Services of New Hampshire to establish a volunteer management position; $3,000 to the Franco-American Centre for the preservation and cataloging of historic documents; $15,000 for the Manchester Families in Transition program; $2,000 to The Caregivers, Inc. for an improved development tracking system.

APPLICATION INFORMATION:
Applications should include a completed cover letter sheet and proposal with appropriate enclosures explaining the purpose of the project, describing how the project will be accomplished, and indicating the amount of grant support sought.
Duration: Grants are usually awarded for a one-year period only. The Foundation does not consider multi-year grants except in very rare circumstances.
Deadline: April 1, September 1 and December 1 for decisions made in February, June and November, respectively.

PUBLICATIONS:
Guidelines.

TRUSTEES:
David Scannell, Chairperson
Jay Dinkel
Thomas J. Donovan
Selma Naccach-Hoff
William G. Steele

STAFF:
Kathleen D. Cook, Grant Manager

ADDRESS INQUIRIES TO:
Kathleen D. Cook, Grant Manager
(See address above.)

BENTON FOUNDATION

1250 Connecticut Avenue, N.W.
Suite 200
Washington, DC 20036
(202) 638-5770
Fax: (240) 235-5024

E-MAIL ADDRESS:
cgarcia@benton.org

WEB SITE ADDRESS:
www.benton.org

TYPE:
Technical assistance. Program is funded for preserving, protecting and strengthening the public benefits in America's media environment.

See entry 2047 for full listing.

BERKS COUNTY COMMUNITY FOUNDATION [1257]
237 Court Street
Reading, PA 19601
(610) 685-2223
Fax: (610) 685-2240

E-MAIL ADDRESS:
richardm@bccf.org

WEB SITE ADDRESS:
www.bccf.org

FOUNDED: 1994

AREAS OF INTEREST:
Community, health, energy, smart growth and public policy.

NAME(S) OF PROGRAMS:
- **Boyertown Area Grantmaking**
- **Metropolitan Edison Energy Fund**
- **Governor Mifflin Area Grantmaking**

TYPE:
Awards/prizes; Capital grants; Challenge/matching grants; Conferences/seminars; Demonstration grants; Development grants; Endowments; Fellowships; General operating grants; Grants-in-aid; Internships; Matching gifts; Product donations; Professorships; Project/program grants; Research grants; Residencies; Scholarships; Seed money grants; Technical assistance; Training grants; Travel grants; Visiting scholars; Work-study programs; Research contracts.

PURPOSE:
To promote philanthropy and improve the quality of life in Berks County; to encourage and nurture performing artists at critical points in their careers.

LEGAL BASIS:
501(c)(3).

GEOGRAPHIC RESTRICTIONS:
Berks County, Pennsylvania.

FINANCIAL DATA:
$50,000,000 in assets.
Amount of support per award: Varies, depending on fund.
Total amount of support: $2,635,000 for the year 2009.

APPLICATION INFORMATION:
Applicants must submit a letter of inquiry.

PUBLICATIONS:
Annual report.

ADDRESS INQUIRIES TO:
Richard Mappin, Vice President
(See address above.)

THE KATHRYNE BEYNON FOUNDATION [1258]
P.O. Box 90815
Pasadena, CA 91109
(626) 584-8800
Fax: (626) 584-8807

E-MAIL ADDRESS:
bob@bannonlawfirm.com

AREAS OF INTEREST:
Child welfare, alcohol and drug rehabilitation, children's clubs, welfare and education.

TYPE:
General operating grants; Project/program grants.

PURPOSE:
To improve the quality of life in southern California.

ELIGIBILITY:
Eligible organizations must be IRS 501(c)(3) tax-exempt. No funding to individuals.

GEOGRAPHIC RESTRICTIONS:
Southern California, preferably Pasadena area.

FINANCIAL DATA:
Amount of support per award: Average $2,000.
Total amount of support: Varies.

APPLICATION INFORMATION:
Applicant organizations must submit a copy of their IRS 501(c)(3) tax determination letter.
Duration: Varies.

ADDRESS INQUIRIES TO:
Robert D. Bannon, Trustee
(See address above.)

WILLIAM BLAIR AND COMPANY FOUNDATION [1259]
222 West Adams
Chicago, IL 60606
(312) 236-1600
Fax: (312) 236-3612

AREAS OF INTEREST:
Cultural programs, hospitals, education, social services, Jewish giving and Catholic giving.

TYPE:
Capital grants; Endowments; Fellowships; General operating grants.

ELIGIBILITY:
Organizations, including religious, must be classified as 501(c)(3) by the IRS and located in Illinois. No grants to individuals. Limited to employees or clients of William Blair. Not open to the public.

GEOGRAPHIC RESTRICTIONS:
Illinois.

FINANCIAL DATA:
Amount of support per award: $500 to $5,000.

APPLICATION INFORMATION:
Duration: One year.

ADDRESS INQUIRIES TO:
E. David Coolidge, III, Vice Chairman
(See address above.)

BLOWITZ-RIDGEWAY FOUNDATION [1260]
1701 East Woodfield Road
Suite 201
Schaumburg, IL 60173-5127
(847) 330-1020
Fax: (847) 330-1028

E-MAIL ADDRESS:
serena@blowitzridgeway.org

WEB SITE ADDRESS:
www.blowitzridgeway.org

FOUNDED: 1984

AREAS OF INTEREST:
Health and human services.

TYPE:
Capital grants; General operating grants; Project/program grants; Research grants; Scholarships. Scholarships are given through schools.

YEAR PROGRAM STARTED: 1984

PURPOSE:
To support advances in medical, psychiatric, psychological and/or residential care, and research programs in medicine, psychology, social science and education.

LEGAL BASIS:
Private independent foundation.

ELIGIBILITY:
Organizations classified as 501(c)(3) by the IRS can apply. Preference will be given to organizations in Illinois and to programs or services which benefit youth, seniors or individuals lacking sufficient resources to care for themselves. No grants to individuals, religious or political organizations, government agencies, organizations that subsist mainly on third-party funding nor for the production or writing of audio-visual materials.

GEOGRAPHIC RESTRICTIONS:
Illinois.

FINANCIAL DATA:
Assets of $22,400,000 for the year ended September 30, 2010.
Amount of support per award: $5,000 to $15,000.
Total amount of support: $1,300,000 for fiscal year 2010.

NUMBER OF APPLICANTS MOST RECENT YEAR:
248 for the year 2010.

NUMBER OF AWARDS: 108 grants for the year 2010.

APPLICATION INFORMATION:
The Blowitz-Ridgeway application form must accompany all grant requests. If declined, applicants may reapply the next year.
Duration: One year. Grants are renewable.

PUBLICATIONS:
Annual report; application guidelines.

IRS IDENTIFICATION NUMBER: 36-2488355

ADDRESS INQUIRIES TO:
Serena Moy, Administrator
(See address above.)

BLUE MOUNTAIN COMMUNITY FOUNDATION [1261]
8 South Second Street, Suite 618
Walla Walla, WA 99362
(509) 529-4371
Fax: (509) 529-5284

E-MAIL ADDRESS:
bmcf@bluemountainfoundation.org

WEB SITE ADDRESS:
www.bluemountainfoundation.org

FOUNDED: 1984

AREAS OF INTEREST:
Social and community services, education, health, and the arts and humanities.

TYPE:
Grants-in-aid; Scholarships.

PURPOSE:
To seek, steward and share charitable gifts in the Blue Mountain area, for good, forever.

ELIGIBILITY:
The Foundation awards grants to nonprofit, tax-exempt organizations in the Foundation's service area which includes the counties of Columbia, Garfield and Walla Walla in the state of Washington and the communities of Athena, Milton-Freewater and Weston in Umatilla County, OR. It strives to make awards to agencies and programs that meet community needs and bring the most benefit to people in the Blue Mountain area.

The Foundation also administers and awards scholarships to local area students to enable them to attend college, graduate school or trade school.

GEOGRAPHIC RESTRICTIONS:
Columbia, Garfield and Walla Walla counties in Washington, and the northern parts of Umatilla County in Oregon.

FINANCIAL DATA:
Amount of support per award: Varies.
Total amount of support: $1,500,000.

APPLICATION INFORMATION:
Grant guidelines and application forms can be obtained through the Foundation's web site. Grant applicants should submit an original and nine copies each of the completed Summary of Applicant Organization form and a one-page description of the program/project or idea on the organization's letterhead. Upon review, the Foundation may request additional information, including but not limited to financial statements, project budgets, 501(c)(3) verification and a list of members of the governing board.
Deadline: Grants: July 1; Scholarships: March 1.

ADDRESS INQUIRIES TO:
Lawson Knight, Executive Director
(See address above.)

THE BNY MELLON FOUNDATION OF SOUTHWESTERN PENNSYLVANIA   [1262]

BNY Mellon Center, Room 1830
Pittsburgh, PA 15258-0001
(412) 234-2732
Fax: (412) 234-0831

E-MAIL ADDRESS:
doreen.tumminello@bnymellon.com

WEB SITE ADDRESS:
www.bnymellon.com

FOUNDED: 1974

AREAS OF INTEREST:
Basic needs provisions: food, clothing, energy and housing assistance; Workforce development: access to employment through job training, education, mentoring and skills development.

TYPE:
Capital grants; Challenge/matching grants; General operating grants; Project/program grants; Technical assistance.

YEAR PROGRAM STARTED: 1974

PURPOSE:
To identify and support initiatives that improve the social and economic conditions of residents where the company does business and where employees live and work. Through powering potential, the company's strategic philanthropic investments will emphasize basic needs, provisions, and workforce development.

LEGAL BASIS:
Corporate foundation, part of BNY Mellon's Charitable Giving Program.

ELIGIBILITY:
Organizations requesting support must have 501(c)(3) tax-exempt charitable status and must be public charities as defined under Section 509(a)(1) of the Internal Revenue Code.

No support is available for loans or direct grants to individuals, religious programs of churches or other sectarian organizations and political parties, campaigns or candidates. As a general rule, support is not available for fraternal organizations, such as police or fire associations, scholarships, fellowships and travel grants, conference or seminar attendance, specialized health campaigns, endowment campaigns, individual United Way agencies which already benefit from the Corporation's gift to the United Way appeal, national organizations, projects or programs or those which operate outside the U.S. and multiyear commitments.

GEOGRAPHIC RESTRICTIONS:
Southwestern Pennsylvania.

FINANCIAL DATA:
Amount of support per award: $2,500 to $10,000 average.
Total amount of support: $3,300,000 for the year 2010.

NUMBER OF APPLICANTS MOST RECENT YEAR:
500.

NUMBER OF AWARDS: Approximately 125.

APPLICATION INFORMATION:
Duration: One year.
Deadline: Requests are considered upon receipt.

PUBLICATIONS:
Annual report which contains contributions policy and application guidelines; *Discover Total Resources: A Guide for Nonprofits.*

STAFF:
James P. McDonald, President
Doreen Tumminello, Administrator
Kenya Boswell, Secretary

ADDRESS INQUIRIES TO:
James P. McDonald, President
(See address above.)

BOSTON FOUNDATION   [1263]

75 Arlington Street, 10th Floor
Boston, MA 02116-3936
(617) 338-1700
Fax: (617) 338-1604

E-MAIL ADDRESS:
grantsinfo@tbf.org

WEB SITE ADDRESS:
www.tbf.org

FOUNDED: 1915

AREAS OF INTEREST:
Health, welfare, educational, cultural, planning and housing needs of the Boston metropolitan area community.

TYPE:
General operating grants; Project/program grants; Technical assistance. Capacity building. Grants for new or experimental programs of both new and established institutions.

LEGAL BASIS:
Community foundation established in 1915 in Massachusetts by agreement and declaration of trust. Incorporated in 1917.

ELIGIBILITY:
Grants are made to organizations or for programs in the Boston standard metropolitan statistical area only. Organizations must have federal tax-exempt status or a fiscal nonprofit agent. No grants are made to individuals. Grants are not made for scholarship, travel, medical or scientific research, religious purposes, publications or films or for national/international organizations.

GEOGRAPHIC RESTRICTIONS:
Greater Boston, Massachusetts.

FINANCIAL DATA:
Amount of support per award: Averages approximately $50,000 to $75,000.
Total amount of support: Approximately $17,000,000 annually.
Matching fund requirements: Varies.

NUMBER OF APPLICANTS MOST RECENT YEAR:
Approximately 1,100.

APPLICATION INFORMATION:
The Foundation requires submission of a Letter of Inquiry. It will review only proposals that have been invited based on its review.
Duration: Up to five years.

PUBLICATIONS:
Annual report; application guidelines; quarterly newsletters.

OFFICERS:
Michael Keating, Chairman
Catherine D'Amato, Vice Chairperson
George Wilson, Treasurer and Chief Investment Officer
Timothy Gassert, Secretary

BOARD MEMBERS:
Richard M. Burnes, Jr.
Gerald Chertavian
Sandra M. Edgerley
Michael R. Eisenson
Grace Fey
Atsuko Fish
Paul S. Grogan
Jackie Jenkins-Scott
Myra H. Kraft
Paul LaCamera
Claudio Martinez
Jack Meyer
Herbert Morse
Kevin Phelan
Greg Shell
Binkley C. Shorts
Micho Spring
Benaree P. Wiley

ADDRESS INQUIRIES TO:
Grants Manager or Program Officer
(See address above.)

OTTO BREMER FOUNDATION   [1264]

445 Minnesota Street, Suite 2250
St. Paul, MN 55101
(651) 227-8036
(888) 291-1123
Fax: (651) 312-3665

E-MAIL ADDRESS:
obf@ottobremer.org

WEB SITE ADDRESS:
www.ottobremer.org

AREAS OF INTEREST:
Community economic, civic, and social betterment.

TYPE:
Capital grants; Challenge/matching grants; General operating grants; Project/program grants.

PURPOSE:
To assist people in achieving full economic, civic and social participation in and for the betterment of their communities.

ELIGIBILITY:
Grants are restricted to private nonprofit or public tax-exempt organizations for purposes defined under Section 501(c)(3) of the Internal Revenue Code. Grants are only made to organizations whose beneficiaries are residents of Minnesota, North Dakota or Wisconsin. Grants are not made to individuals.

GEOGRAPHIC RESTRICTIONS:
Minnesota, North Dakota and Wisconsin.

FINANCIAL DATA:
Amount of support per award: $1,000 to $500,000; average $35,000.
Total amount of support: $24,000,000 for the year 2010.

APPLICATION INFORMATION:
Must include copy of IRS 501(c)(3) letter of determination.
Duration: One year. Must reapply.

THE HARRY B. AND JANE H. BROCK FOUNDATION   [1265]

2101 Highland Avenue, Suite 250
Birmingham, AL 35205
(205) 939-0236
Fax: (205) 939-0806

FOUNDED: 1987

AREAS OF INTEREST:
Higher education and community development.

TYPE:
Project/program grants.

YEAR PROGRAM STARTED: 1985

PURPOSE:
To support higher education and community development in Alabama.

LEGAL BASIS:
Private family foundation.

ELIGIBILITY:
Organizations must be IRS 501(c)(3) tax-exempt.

GEOGRAPHIC RESTRICTIONS:
Alabama, mainly Jefferson County.

FINANCIAL DATA:
Amount of support per award: $5,000 average.
Total amount of support: $301,352 for the year 2010.

NUMBER OF AWARDS: 48 for the year 2010.

REPRESENTATIVE AWARDS:
Samford University; University of Alabama; Cahaba River.

APPLICATION INFORMATION:
Applicants may submit a written proposal and must include a copy of the IRS tax determination letter.

Duration: One year. Renewable by reapplication.
Deadline: November 1.

ADDRESS INQUIRIES TO:
Harry B. Brock, Jr., President
(See address above.)

GLADYS BROOKS FOUNDATION   [1266]

1055 Franklin Avenue
Suite 208
Garden City, NY 11530-2903
(516) 746-6103

WEB SITE ADDRESS:
www.gladysbrooksfoundation.org

FOUNDED: 1981

AREAS OF INTEREST:
Libraries, education, hospitals and clinics.

TYPE:
Awards/prizes; Capital grants; Endowments; Professorships; Scholarships; Technical assistance. Grants to private, not-for-profit publicly supported libraries, educational institutions, hospitals and clinics in the eastern U.S.

YEAR PROGRAM STARTED: 1981

PURPOSE:
To provide for the intellectual, moral and physical welfare of the people of this country by establishing and supporting nonprofit libraries, educational institutions, hospitals and clinics.

ELIGIBILITY:
Applicants must be publicly supported, not-for-profit tax-exempt organizations. Generally speaking, grant applications will only be considered where outside funding, including governmental, is not available. The project will be largely funded by the grant unless the grant request covers a discrete component of a larger project. The funds will be used for capital projects including equipment or endowments. Applications for direct salary support will not be accepted.

Grant applications will be considered only for major expenditures generally between $50,000 and $100,000 and greater or lesser amounts in certain circumstances.

GEOGRAPHIC RESTRICTIONS:
Connecticut, Delaware, District of Columbia, Florida, Indiana, Louisiana, Maine, Maryland, Massachusetts, New Hampshire, New Jersey, New York, Ohio, Pennsylvania, Rhode Island, Tennessee and Vermont.

FINANCIAL DATA:
Amount of support per award: $50,000 to $100,000.

APPLICATION INFORMATION:
Foundation application form must be used and is available by contacting Ms. Jessica L. Rutledge. Applications must be completed and postmarked and sent with all supporting documents to the Foundation within 45 days from the date of the letter from the Foundation furnishing the application materials. The only exception to this is if the letter is dated after April 18, in which case application materials must be postmarked with all supporting materials before June 1. Applicants must furnish audited financial statements and include a specific budget for the project; also an annual report or a brief description of applicant organization.

Electronic submissions are not acceptable.

Duration: One year.
Deadline: June 1.

PUBLICATIONS:
Annual report.

GOVERNING BOARD:
James J. Daly, Chairman
Christopher R. Hawkins
Thomas Q. Morris, M.D.

ADDRESS INQUIRIES TO:
Jessica L. Rutledge
(See web site above.)

*PLEASE NOTE:
All grant awards are made on the condition that the entirety of the funds advanced shall be utilized in direct furtherance of the project and that no portion thereof shall be appropriated by the grantee as an administrative or processing fee, for overseeing the project or for its general overhead.

BRUNSWICK FOUNDATION, INC.   [1267]

One Northfield Court
Lake Forest, IL 60045
(847) 735-4344
Fax: (847) 735-4330

E-MAIL ADDRESS:
lisa.debartolo@brunswick.com

FOUNDED: 1957

AREAS OF INTEREST:
Organizations that support the company's products.

NAME(S) OF PROGRAMS:
● **Brunswick Employee Sons and Daughters Scholarship**
● **Dollars for Doers Volunteer Program**

TYPE:
General operating grants. Employee scholarships.

PURPOSE:
To support causes and/or projects that are related to boating and outdoor/indoor recreation activities.

LEGAL BASIS:
Private foundation.

ELIGIBILITY:
Organizations in areas of company operation classified as 501(c)(3) by the IRS will be considered. The Foundation does not have and is not able to donate equipment or products.

FINANCIAL DATA:
Amount of support per award: Dollars for Doers: $75 to $1,000.
Total amount of support: Approximately $500,000, including scholarships, for fiscal year 2010.

NUMBER OF APPLICANTS MOST RECENT YEAR:
450.

NUMBER OF AWARDS: Varies.

APPLICATION INFORMATION:
Applications are sent out by invitation only.
Duration: One year.
Deadline: February.

IRS IDENTIFICATION NUMBER: 36-6033576

STAFF:
Lisa DeBartolo, Coordinator

DIRECTORS:
Judith Zelisko, President
B. Russell Lockridge, Vice President

William L. Metzger, Treasurer
Marsha Vaughn, Secretary

ADDRESS INQUIRIES TO:
Lisa DeBartolo, Coordinator
(See address above.)

THE BUHL FOUNDATION [1268]

650 Smithfield Street
Suite 2300
Pittsburgh, PA 15222
(412) 566-2711
Fax: (412) 566-2714

E-MAIL ADDRESS:
buhl@buhlfoundation.org

WEB SITE ADDRESS:
www.buhlfoundation.org

FOUNDED: 1927

AREAS OF INTEREST:
Education, youth development, human
services and economic and community
development.

CONSULTING OR VOLUNTEER SERVICES:
Wide variety of community initiatives to
improve quality of life in greater Pittsburgh
area.

TYPE:
Demonstration grants; Development grants;
Grants-in-aid; Project/program grants; Seed
money grants; Training grants. Capacity
building. Grants-in-aid, primarily to
institutions in the Pittsburgh metropolitan
area, Allegheny County and western
Pennsylvania for developmental and
innovative projects in education, children and
youth, and community services.

YEAR PROGRAM STARTED: 1928

PURPOSE:
To support efforts that: (1) contribute to the
vibrancy and well-being of the North Side
and the Pittsburgh region; (2) create learning
environments so that young people will thrive
and be prepared for adulthood; (3) encourage
innovation and entrepreneurial solutions to
improve quality of life and; (4) make a
definitive difference in addressing persistent
community challenges or unmet needs of
at-risk neighborhoods.

LEGAL BASIS:
Independent private foundation established by
will probated on June 20, 1927.

ELIGIBILITY:
Tax-exempt, nonprofit institutions with
appropriate interests in southwestern
Pennsylvania are eligible to apply. Emphasis
is on grants to institutions in the Pittsburgh
metropolitan area. Programs and projects
which combine different professional
interests and relate agencies in cooperative
endeavors are often recognized as worthy of
a grant. Grants are not made to individuals.

GEOGRAPHIC RESTRICTIONS:
Southwestern Pennsylvania, including
Pittsburgh and Allegheny counties.

FINANCIAL DATA:
Total amount of support: $3,115,759 for the
year ended June 30, 2010.

NUMBER OF APPLICANTS MOST RECENT YEAR:
204.

NUMBER OF AWARDS: 117.

REPRESENTATIVE AWARDS:
$1,500,000 to Pittsburgh Promise for the first
five years of up to $3,000,000 for ten-year
support for the Pittsburgh Promise to ensure

that Pittsburgh Public School students are
"Promise Ready" and that scholarship funds
help students prepare to succeed in
postsecondary educational choices; $200,000
to Community College of Allegheny County
Educational Foundation to support a pilot
program to encourage unemployed young
adults, aged 17-25, to pursue training and
certificate programs as they seek gainful
employment; $100,000 to August Wilson
Center for African American Culture for
funding to deliver educational and public
programming celebrating African American
culture in Pittsburgh area schools and to
provide excitement for and transition in the
new Center; $100,000 to Pittsburgh Parks
Conservancy to support a complete
renovation and restoration of Mellon Square
to its original grandeur as a downtown park
that richly contributes to Pittsburgh's quality
of life.

APPLICATION INFORMATION:
The usual procedure is to write a letter of
inquiry to the President at the address above,
followed, if requested, by a formal proposal.
Interviews and other follow-up procedures
are then initiated by staff. Applications must
contain a statement of objectives and the
proposed means of attaining these, a
description of the program and budget as
well as information regarding the applicant
agency, its organization and structure, its tax
status and its capacity to implement the
project.
Duration: Usually one year although some
grants cover two or three years.

PUBLICATIONS:
Annual report; application procedures.

IRS IDENTIFICATION NUMBER: 25-0378910

OFFICERS:
Frederick W. Thieman, President
Cheryl L. Kubelick, Vice President, Senior
Program Officer

TRUSTEES:
Jean A. Robinson, Chairman
Peter F. Mathieson, Vice Chairman
Saleem H. Ghubril, Treasurer
Helen S. Faison, Secretary
Kim Tillotson Fleming
Alex Johnson

ADDRESS INQUIRIES TO:
Frederick W. Thieman, President
(See address above.)

PATRICK AND AIMEE BUTLER FAMILY FOUNDATION [1269]

332 Minnesota Street
Suite E-1420
St. Paul, MN 55101-1369
(651) 222-2565

E-MAIL ADDRESS:
info@butlerfamilyfoundation.org

WEB SITE ADDRESS:
www.butlerfamilyfoundation.org

FOUNDED: 1951

AREAS OF INTEREST:
Arts and culture, environment, human
services and philanthropy.

TYPE:
General operating grants; Project/program
grants.

YEAR PROGRAM STARTED: 1951

PURPOSE:
To support solid progressive ideas in art and
culture, the environment, social service and
social change.

LEGAL BASIS:
Private foundation.

ELIGIBILITY:
Eligible organizations must be IRS 501(c)(3)
tax-exempt. The Foundation does not fund
criminal justice, economic development or
education, employment or vocational
programs, films or videos, health, hospitals or
medical research, loans or grants to
individuals, secondary or elementary
education, theater or dance, or projects
outside the U.S.

GEOGRAPHIC RESTRICTIONS:
Twin Cities Metropolitan area, Minnesota.

FINANCIAL DATA:
Amount of support per award: Average
$15,000.
Total amount of support: $2,657,415 for the
year 2009.

NUMBER OF APPLICANTS MOST RECENT YEAR:
129 for the year 2009.

NUMBER OF AWARDS: 118 for the year 2009.

APPLICATION INFORMATION:
Application must include a copy of the IRS
tax determination letter.
Duration: Two years.

PUBLICATIONS:
Guidelines.

TRUSTEES:
Peter M. Butler, President
Patrick Butler, Vice President
John K. Butler, Treasurer
Brigid M. Butler
Katherine Butler
Patricia M. Butler
Paul S. Butler
Sandra K. Butler
Suzanne A. LeFevour
Melanie Martinez
Temple Peterson

STAFF:
Kerrie Blevins, Foundation Director
Nora McKinnon, Grants Administrator
Shehla Tauscher, Secretary

ADDRESS INQUIRIES TO:
Kerrie Blevins, Foundation Director
(See address above.)

CALIFORNIA COMMUNITY FOUNDATION [1270]

445 South Figueroa Street, Suite 3400
Los Angeles, CA 90071-1638
(213) 413-4130
Fax: (213) 383-2046

E-MAIL ADDRESS:
info@ccf-la.org

WEB SITE ADDRESS:
www.calfund.org

FOUNDED: 1915

AREAS OF INTEREST:
Education (preschool through fifth grade),
arts and culture, human development, health
prevention and treatment services, health care
coverage expansion, and affordable housing.

NAME(S) OF PROGRAMS:
- **Arts**
- **Civic Engagement**
- **Education**
- **Health Care**

- Housing and Neighborhoods
- Human Development

TYPE:
Capital grants; Fellowships; General operating grants; Project/program grants; Scholarships. Program-related investments. Policy analysis and advocacy.

YEAR PROGRAM STARTED: 1915

PURPOSE:
To strengthen Los Angeles communities through effective philanthropy and civic engagement.

LEGAL BASIS:
Community foundation, designated a public charity by the IRS.

ELIGIBILITY:
The Foundation will consider applications that are consistent with current program priorities and goals. Eligible organizations are:
(1) nonprofit agencies with evidence of tax-exempt status under Section 501(c)(3) of the Internal Revenue Code and not classified as a private foundation;
(2) located within and primarily serving residents of Los Angeles County, with the exception of regional, statewide or national public policy efforts that may benefit a substantial portion of the local population and;
(3) operated and organized so that they do not discriminate in the hiring of staff or the provision of services on the basis of race, religion, gender, sexual orientation, age, national origin or disability.

GEOGRAPHIC RESTRICTIONS:
Los Angeles County, California.

FINANCIAL DATA:
Amount of support per award: Nonprofit Organization Grants: Generally $75,000 to $100,000; Scholarships: Generally $250 to $15,000; Fellowship for Visual Artists Awards: $15,000 to $20,000.
Total amount of support: $129,000,000.

COOPERATIVE FUNDING PROGRAMS: Children's Health Initiative through LA Care; California Homeownership Preservation Initiative.

NUMBER OF APPLICANTS MOST RECENT YEAR:
Approximately 400 annually.

NUMBER OF AWARDS: 193.

APPLICATION INFORMATION:
Organizations seeking support from the Foundation must submit a letter of intent (LOI) to apply for a grant regardless of the requested amount. An online LOI can be accessed at www.calfund.org/how_to_apply_for_grants.php
Duration: Generally two years.

PUBLICATIONS:
Annual report; biannual newsletter; application form; application guidelines; philanthropic white papers; fund brochures.

IRS IDENTIFICATION NUMBER: 95-3510055

GOVERNING BOARD:
Sheldon M. Stone, Chairperson
David Bohnett
Reveta Bowers
Sonia Marie de Leon de Vega
Dr. Patrick Dowling
David W. Fleming
Dennis Gertmenian
Meloni M. Hallock
Antonia Hernandez
Preston Johnson

Joanne Corday Kozberg
Quan Phung
James M. Rosser
Paul Schulz
Jean Bixby Smith
Melanie Staggs
Cynthia Telles, Ph.D.
Catherine L. Unger
Tom Unterman
Ronald T. Vera

*PLEASE NOTE:
Online applications are preferred, though hard copies are accepted.

CALLAWAY FOUNDATION, INC.   [1271]
209 Broome Street
LaGrange, GA 30240
(706) 884-7348
Fax: (706) 884-0201

E-MAIL ADDRESS:
hsburdette@callaway-foundation.org

WEB SITE ADDRESS:
www.callawayfoundation.org

FOUNDED: 1943

AREAS OF INTEREST:
Charitable, religious and educational interests.

TYPE:
Capital grants; Challenge/matching grants; Matching gifts. Matching grants focus on construction.

YEAR PROGRAM STARTED: 1943

PURPOSE:
To improve the quality of life in the city of LaGrange and Troup County, Georgia.

LEGAL BASIS:
Private foundation.

ELIGIBILITY:
Eligible organizations must be IRS 501(c)(3). Each application is considered on its merits.

GEOGRAPHIC RESTRICTIONS:
City of LaGrange and Troup County, Georgia.

FINANCIAL DATA:
Amount of support per award: Varies.
Total amount of support: Varies.

NUMBER OF APPLICANTS MOST RECENT YEAR:
500.

NUMBER OF AWARDS: Varies.

REPRESENTATIVE AWARDS:
$3,000,000 to LaGrange College; $450,000 to Downtown LaGrange Development Authority; $155,000 to Lafayette Society for Performing Arts.

APPLICATION INFORMATION:
Applicants may submit a written proposal and must include a copy of the IRS tax determination letter.
Duration: Varies.
Deadline: March 31, June 30, September 30 and December 31.

PUBLICATIONS:
Annual report.

IRS IDENTIFICATION NUMBER: 58-0566147

ADDRESS INQUIRIES TO:
H. Speer Burdette, III
President and General Manager
(See address above.)

CAPITAL REGION COMMUNITY FOUNDATION   [1272]
6035 Executive Drive
Suite 104
Lansing, MI 48911
(517) 272-2870
Fax: (517) 272-2871

E-MAIL ADDRESS:
bpatterson@crcfoundation.org

WEB SITE ADDRESS:
crcfoundation.org

FOUNDED: 1987

AREAS OF INTEREST:
Education, environment, health care, human services, humanities and youth.

TYPE:
Capital grants; Challenge/matching grants; Development grants; General operating grants; Project/program grants; Scholarships; Seed money grants.

YEAR PROGRAM STARTED: 1989

PURPOSE:
To build a permanent endowment; to meet charitable needs in the tri-county area.

LEGAL BASIS:
Community foundation.

ELIGIBILITY:
Eligible organizations must be IRS 501(c)(3) tax-exempt and be located in the tri-county area.

GEOGRAPHIC RESTRICTIONS:
Clinton, Eaton and Ingham counties, Michigan.

FINANCIAL DATA:
Amount of support per award: $2,000 to $5,000.
Matching fund requirements: Given higher priority.

NUMBER OF APPLICANTS MOST RECENT YEAR:
230 for the year 2008.

NUMBER OF AWARDS: 592 for the year 2008.

APPLICATION INFORMATION:
Duration: One year. No renewals.
Deadline: April 1.

PUBLICATIONS:
Annual report; grant guidelines.

IRS IDENTIFICATION NUMBER: 38-2776652

ADDRESS INQUIRIES TO:
Brad Patterson, Vice President of Program (See address above.)

*PLEASE NOTE:
No grants are made to individuals. Do not apply for college scholarships.

THE CARPENTER FOUNDATION   [1273]
711 East Main Street
Suite 10
Medford, OR 97504
(541) 772-5851
(541) 772-5732
Fax: (541) 773-3970

E-MAIL ADDRESS:
pwilliams@carpenter-foundation.org

WEB SITE ADDRESS:
www.carpenter-foundation.org

FOUNDED: 1958

AREAS OF INTEREST:
Arts, education, human services and public interest issues.

TYPE:
Capital grants; Challenge/matching grants; Demonstration grants; Development grants; General operating grants; Matching gifts; Project/program grants; Scholarships; Technical assistance; Training grants.

YEAR PROGRAM STARTED: 1958

PURPOSE:
To add opportunity, choice, inclusiveness, enrichment and a climate for change for those living in the Rogue Valley. The Foundation works in partnership with other agencies, organizations and public entities.

LEGAL BASIS:
Private family foundation.

ELIGIBILITY:
Grant applications will be accepted only from tax-exempt agencies. No grants are made to individuals. Only one grant per year to any agency is usually considered. The Foundation makes grants only within Jackson and Josephine counties with the exception of a few statewide public interest issues directly affecting persons living in these counties. The Foundation rarely makes multiyear grants, grants for historical applications, hospital construction or equipment, group or individual trips, or activities for religious purposes.

GEOGRAPHIC RESTRICTIONS:
Jackson and Josephine counties, Oregon.

FINANCIAL DATA:
Total assets as of June 30, 2010: $15,836,975.
Amount of support per award: Varies.
Total amount of support: $675,896 in grants for fiscal year ended June 30, 2010.

NUMBER OF APPLICANTS MOST RECENT YEAR:
100.

NUMBER OF AWARDS: 90.

REPRESENTATIVE AWARDS:
Human Services: $15,000 to Boys & Girls Clubs of the Rogue Valley, Grants Pass, OR, in support of a program that provides free dinners and nutrition education to children. Education: $6,000 to Ashland Family YMCA, for support staff to help children in YMCA after-school programs with their homework. Arts: $20,000 to Britt Festivals, Medford, OR, for support for 2010 classical music season. Public Interest: $6,000 to Cascade Community Pool, White City, OR, for staff time to focus on various membership and fund development activities.

APPLICATION INFORMATION:
Cover letter (nor more than one page) from the applicant organization summarizing the scope of the project, the amount of the request, and the name, address, telephone number and e-mail address of the person to contact regarding the request.

Proposal information (no more than four pages) including:
(1) description of proposal or project, and the community needs or strengths that it addresses;
(2) review of the applicant agency, its purpose and services to the community, its staffing and use of volunteers;
(3) the project budget, showing specifically how the grant funds will be used, as well as other possible funding sources for this project;
(4) description of how the project will be funded in the future (if applicable);
(5) the planning process, staffing and timeline for the project;
(6) result expected and proposed evaluation method and;
(7) any recent independent board fund-raising efforts.

Required attachments (do not staple or clip):
(1) detailed budget for the agency's current year and the year for which the project is proposed (if different);
(2) income statement and balance sheet from the most recently completed fiscal year (or audit, if available); no 990s please;
(3) list of board of directors, occupations and addresses;
(4) approval of the application by the agency's board of directors and;
(5) copy of the IRS exemption letter under Section 501(c)(3).
Duration: One year.
Deadline: Applications are reviewed on a quarterly basis.

BOARD OF TRUSTEES:
Emily C. Mostue, President
Karen C. Allan, Vice President/Secretary
William Moffat, Treasurer
Jim DeCourcey
John Forsyth
Sue Naumes
Marc Sirinsky
Dan Thorndike

ADDRESS INQUIRIES TO:
Polly Williams, Program Officer
Tel: (541) 772-5732 or
(See e-mail address above.)

CATERPILLAR CORPORATE GIVING PROGRAM [1274]
100 N.E. Adams Street
Peoria, IL 61629-1480
(309) 675-1000
Fax: (309) 675-5815

WEB SITE ADDRESS:
www.caterpillar.com/foundation

AREAS OF INTEREST:
Basic human needs, education and environment.

TYPE:
General operating grants; Project/program grants.

PURPOSE:
To support local and community activities where the company has a major manufacturing presence, as well as national organizations.

ELIGIBILITY:
Organizations in areas of company manufacturing operations and classified as 501(c)(3) by the IRS can apply. No grants to individuals and religious organizations.

FINANCIAL DATA:
Amount of support per award: Varies.

APPLICATION INFORMATION:
Applications must be submitted online.
Duration: One year. Grants are renewable.

CATHOLIC CAMPAIGN FOR HUMAN DEVELOPMENT [1275]
3211 4th Street, N.E.
Washington, DC 20017
(202) 541-3210
Fax: (202) 541-3329

E-MAIL ADDRESS:
cchdgrants@usccb.org

WEB SITE ADDRESS:
www.usccb.org/cchd

FOUNDED: 1970

AREAS OF INTEREST:
Humanitarianism.

NAME(S) OF PROGRAMS:
● **Community Organizing Grants**
● **Economic Development Grants**

TYPE:
Project/program grants. Self-help social or economic development projects in the U.S. which will cause institutional change in economics, housing, health, education, communications, legal practices, etc. Fund community organizing grants.

YEAR PROGRAM STARTED: 1970

PURPOSE:
To change existing policies, practices and laws in ways which will lead to greater justice and opportunity for all.

LEGAL BASIS:
Roman Catholic Church-sponsored funding agency.

ELIGIBILITY:
Applicant groups must be clearly representative of poor and low-income people and must be tax-exempt.

GEOGRAPHIC RESTRICTIONS:
United States and territories.

FINANCIAL DATA:
Amount of support per award: $10,000 to $50,000.
Total amount of support: $8,200,000 for the year 2008.

NUMBER OF APPLICANTS MOST RECENT YEAR:
650.

NUMBER OF AWARDS: 300.

APPLICATION INFORMATION:
All applications for CCHD grants must be submitted online.
Duration: Up to six years.
Deadline: December 1 for current grantees; December 15 for new applicants.

ADDRESS INQUIRIES TO:
Grants Administrator
(See address above.)

*PLEASE NOTE:
The Catholic Campaign only funds projects that are in conformance with Roman Catholic social teachings, and that do not engage in partisan political activity.

CENTRAL INDIANA COMMUNITY FOUNDATION [1276]
615 North Alabama Street
Suite 119
Indianapolis, IN 46204
(317) 634-2423
Fax: (317) 684-0943

E-MAIL ADDRESS:
info@cicf.org

WEB SITE ADDRESS:
www.cicf.org

FOUNDED: 1997

AREAS OF INTEREST:
Arts, culture, civic affairs, education, environment, parks, and health and human services.

TYPE:
Capital grants; Endowments; General operating grants; Project/program grants; Research grants; Scholarships; Technical assistance; Training grants.

PURPOSE:
To strengthen Marion and Hamilton counties by attracting charitable endowments; to maximize benefits to donors; to make effective grants; to provide leadership to address community needs by developing productive citizens, building strong neighborhoods, embracing inclusiveness, and promoting community amenities.

LEGAL BASIS:
Community foundation.

ELIGIBILITY:
Grants are made to nonprofit charitable organizations exempt from federal taxation under Section 501(c)(3) of the Internal Revenue Code.

FINANCIAL DATA:
Amount of support per award: $250 to $1,000,000.

APPLICATION INFORMATION:
Contact the program officer prior to submitting a proposal.
Duration: One year.

PUBLICATIONS:
Annual report; newsletter.

IRS IDENTIFICATION NUMBER: 35-1793630

ADDRESS INQUIRIES TO:
Keri Snyder
Marketing and Communications Associate
(See address above.)

*PLEASE NOTE:
Priority is given to programs and projects which expect to have a positive effect on Marion and Hamilton counties.

CENTRAL MINNESOTA COMMUNITY FOUNDATION   [1277]
101 7th Avenue South, No. 100
St. Cloud, MN 56301
(320) 253-4380
(877) 253-4380
Fax: (320) 240-9215

E-MAIL ADDRESS:
slorenz@communitygiving.org

WEB SITE ADDRESS:
www.communitygiving.org

FOUNDED: 1985

AREAS OF INTEREST:
Philanthropy to support arts and culture, education, environment, youth and families, and human services.

TYPE:
Challenge/matching grants; Conferences/seminars; General operating grants; Project/program grants; Scholarships; Seed money grants; Technical assistance. Assistance to organizations working to strengthen youth and families through recognition and appreciation of diversity.

PURPOSE:
To attract and administer funds to improve the quality of life for citizens of central Minnesota.

LEGAL BASIS:
Community foundation.

ELIGIBILITY:
Eligible organizations must be IRS 501(c)(3) tax-exempt and located within Benton, Sherburne and Stearns counties, Minnesota. Funding to religious organizations of a nonsectarian nature, which benefits the entire community. No grants to individuals.

GEOGRAPHIC RESTRICTIONS:
Benton, Sherburne and Stearns counties, Minnesota.

FINANCIAL DATA:
$65,000,000 in assets as of June 30, 2010.
Total amount of support: $4,500,000 in grants paid as of June 30, 2010.

APPLICATION INFORMATION:
Applicants may use the Minnesota Common Grant application (online form only) and must include a copy of the IRS 501(c)(3) tax determination letter.

PUBLICATIONS:
Annual report; application guidelines.

IRS IDENTIFICATION NUMBER: 36-3412544

ADDRESS INQUIRIES TO:
Susan Lorenz, Director of Programs
(See address above.)

CENTRAL NEW YORK COMMUNITY FOUNDATION   [1278]
431 East Fayette Street
Suite 100
Syracuse, NY 13202-3314
(315) 422-9538
Fax: (315) 471-6031

WEB SITE ADDRESS:
www.cnycf.org

FOUNDED: 1927

AREAS OF INTEREST:
Literacy, capacity building, sabbaticals for nonprofit executives, and classroom leadership.

TYPE:
Capital grants; Project/program grants; Seed money grants; Training grants. Grants to help provide training to develop leadership and grantwriting skills and to help build neighborhood stability. Grants also help participants learn from each other and become keenly aware of the level of need in the community.

PURPOSE:
To identify and initiate effective, creative actions which enrich the community by receiving, managing and disbursing charitable funds.

LEGAL BASIS:
Community foundation.

ELIGIBILITY:
Applicants must be tax-exempt, 501(c)(3) not-for-profit organizations in Madison and Onondaga counties which will fund innovative programs that address unmet community needs.

The Foundation encourages proposals that:
(1) suggest practical solutions to community problems;
(2) promote cooperation among not-for-profits without duplicating existing services;
(3) generate community support, both professional and volunteer;
(4) strengthen the organization's effectiveness or stability;

(5) demonstrate the organization's ability to secure realistic funding and;
(6) address prevention as well as remediation.

The Foundation does not make grants for annual operating budgets, endowments, sectarian purposes, loans or assistance to individuals, medical or academic research except when directed by donor, or activities that occurred before the Community Foundation's decision date.

GEOGRAPHIC RESTRICTIONS:
Madison and Onondaga counties, New York.

FINANCIAL DATA:
Amount of support per award: Varies.

APPLICATION INFORMATION:
Standard application forms are available. Foundation staff is available to answer questions or discuss with any prospective applicant the appropriateness of a request.
Duration: Varies.
Deadline: July, September and April.

PUBLICATIONS:
Annual report.

OFFICERS:
Peter A. Dunn, President and Chief Executive Officer
Mary Meyer, Esq., Senior Vice President, Finance and Operations
John G. Eberley, Vice President, Grants and Community Initiatives
Gay M. Pomeroy, Esq., Counsel

ADDRESS INQUIRIES TO:
Peter A. Dunn
President and Chief Executive Officer
(See address above.)

THE CH FOUNDATION
P.O. Box 94038
Lubbock, TX 79493-4038
(806) 792-0448
Fax: (806) 792-7824

E-MAIL ADDRESS:
ksanford@chfoundation.com

WEB SITE ADDRESS:
www.chfoundationlubbock.com

TYPE:
Capital grants; Project/program grants.
See entry 2250 for full listing.

HARRY CHAPIN FOUNDATION   [1279]
16 Gerard Street
Huntington, NY 11743
(631) 423-7558
Fax: (631) 423-7596

E-MAIL ADDRESS:
harrychapinfound@aol.com

WEB SITE ADDRESS:
www.harrychapinfoundation.org

FOUNDED: 1981

AREAS OF INTEREST:
Community education, arts-in-education, agriculture and environment.

TYPE:
Challenge/matching grants; General operating grants.

PURPOSE:
To address the problems of the disadvantaged and promote educational programs that lead to a greater understanding of human suffering.

ELIGIBILITY:
Only programs operating in the U.S. will be funded. Applicants must be 501(c)(3) nonprofit. See web site for complete description of focus areas. No grants to individuals.

GEOGRAPHIC RESTRICTIONS:
United States.

FINANCIAL DATA:
Amount of support per award: Up to $10,000.

NUMBER OF APPLICANTS MOST RECENT YEAR:
More than 200.

NUMBER OF AWARDS: 20 for the year 2010.

APPLICATION INFORMATION:
Application should be made in a brief written proposal to Ms. Leslie Ramme, Executive Director, at the HCF Office. HCF also accepts the New York/New Jersey Area Common Grant Application Form.
Duration: One year. Must reapply.
Deadline: Applications are accepted on an ongoing basis.

EXECUTIVE DIRECTOR:
Leslie Ramme

ADDRESS INQUIRIES TO:
Leslie Ramme, Executive Director
(See address above.)

CHARLESTON AREA CHARITABLE FOUNDATION [1280]

c/o Gilbert, Metzger & Madigan
P.O. Box 677
Charleston, IL 61920
(217) 345-2128
Fax: (217) 345-2315

AREAS OF INTEREST:
Community and education.

TYPE:
Grants-in-aid; Project/program grants.

PURPOSE:
To enhance and support the quality of life in Charleston, IL area.

ELIGIBILITY:
Grants are made to organizations that have tax-exempt status under Section 501(c)(3) of the Internal Revenue Code. No grants are made to individuals.

GEOGRAPHIC RESTRICTIONS:
Charleston, Illinois and surrounding area.

FINANCIAL DATA:
Amount of support per award: Grants vary in amount, depending upon the needs and nature of the request.

APPLICATION INFORMATION:
Applicants must submit a brief letter outlining the purpose of the grant.
Deadline: Quarterly; two weeks prior to Board meetings to be held in February, May, August and November.

ADDRESS INQUIRIES TO:
Michael Metzger, President
(See address above.)

THE CHAUTAUQUA REGION COMMUNITY FOUNDATION [1281]

418 Spring Street
Jamestown, NY 14701
(716) 661-3390
Fax: (716) 488-0387

E-MAIL ADDRESS:
rsweeney@crcfonline.org

WEB SITE ADDRESS:
www.crcfonline.org

FOUNDED: 1978

AREAS OF INTEREST:
Community.

NAME(S) OF PROGRAMS:
● **Axel W. Carlson Award**
● **John D. Hamilton Community Service Award**

TYPE:
Awards/prizes; Capital grants; Challenge/matching grants; Matching gifts; Project/program grants; Scholarships; Seed money grants; Technical assistance; Training grants. The John D. Hamilton Community Service Award recognizes an individual's dedication, leadership and support in furthering community spirit and enhancing the quality of life in the Chautauqua Community.

Axel W. Carlson Award has been a tribute to the unsung heroes of our community. These individuals have made significant contributions through their efforts while neither receiving nor expecting reward or recognition.

YEAR PROGRAM STARTED: 1978

PURPOSE:
To enrich the quality of life in the Chautauqua region.

LEGAL BASIS:
501(c)(3).

GEOGRAPHIC RESTRICTIONS:
Chautauqua region, New York.

FINANCIAL DATA:
Amount of support per award: Varies.
Total amount of support: $2,500,000.
Matching fund requirements: Varies depending on the request.

NUMBER OF AWARDS: 1,400.

APPLICATION INFORMATION:
Nominations are to be submitted by letter or e-mail, with the full name, address and detailed explanation of that person's contributions and accomplishments, along with an explanation of why the nominee is deserving of the award. If the nominator is uncertain if they should submit the nomination or has additional questions, please contact the office via telephone for clarification.
Duration: One calendar year.
Deadline: March 1 for Carlson award. April for Hamilton award.

PUBLICATIONS:
Annual report; newsletters; scholarship booklet.

IRS IDENTIFICATION NUMBER: 16-1116837

STAFF:
Randall J. Sweeney, Executive Director
Joel Keefer, Community Relations Officer
Jacob S. Schrantz, Fiscal Officer
Lisa W. Lynde, Program Officer
Christine A. Ditz, Program Associate
June C. Diethrick, Executive Administrator

ADDRESS INQUIRIES TO:
Randall J. Sweeney, Executive Director
(See address above.)

CHESTER COUNTY COMMUNITY FOUNDATION [1282]

28 West Market Street
West Chester, PA 19382
(610) 696-8211
Fax: (610) 696-8213

E-MAIL ADDRESS:
info@chescocf.org

WEB SITE ADDRESS:
www.chescocf.org

FOUNDED: 1994

AREAS OF INTEREST:
Quality of life in the Chester County, Pennsylvania area.

TYPE:
Capital grants; Challenge/matching grants; General operating grants; Grants-in-aid; Project/program grants; Scholarships.

YEAR PROGRAM STARTED: 1994

PURPOSE:
To improve the quality of life in communities within Chester County, Pennsylvania.

LEGAL BASIS:
501(c)(3) public charity.

GEOGRAPHIC RESTRICTIONS:
Primarily Chester County, Pennsylvania.

FINANCIAL DATA:
$30,000,000 in assets.
Amount of support per award: $1,000 to $15,000.
Total amount of support: $1,800,000 for the year 2010.

NUMBER OF APPLICANTS MOST RECENT YEAR:
150 for the year 2010.

NUMBER OF AWARDS: 500 for the year 2010.

APPLICATION INFORMATION:
Information may be obtained from the web site above.
Duration: One year. Renewal by reapplication.
Deadline: Proposals are accepted year-round.

ADDRESS INQUIRIES TO:
Beth Harper Briglia, Vice President of Donor Services and Grantmaking
(See address above.)

THE CHICAGO COMMUNITY TRUST [1283]

111 East Wacker Drive
Suite 1400
Chicago, IL 60601
(312) 616-8000
Fax: (312) 616-7955

E-MAIL ADDRESS:
sandy@cct.org

WEB SITE ADDRESS:
www.cct.org

FOUNDED: 1915

AREAS OF INTEREST:
The well-being of the residents of Cook County, IL in the fields of health, basic human needs, community development, education and cultural arts.

TYPE:
General operating grants; Project/program grants; Technical assistance. Grants to

tax-exempt institutions and organizations for charitable purposes. Special initiatives are developed periodically.

YEAR PROGRAM STARTED: 1915

PURPOSE:
To provide for the broad charitable needs of the community in a manner which will assure response to the most pressing problems of the day.

LEGAL BASIS:
Community foundation.

ELIGIBILITY:
Applicants must be tax-exempt, 501(c)(3) organizations. Funded projects must benefit the residents of Cook County, IL. Some grants are made for the region.

GEOGRAPHIC RESTRICTIONS:
Cook County, Illinois.

FINANCIAL DATA:
Amount of support per award: Varies.
Total amount of support: $110,953,384 for the year 2009.

NUMBER OF APPLICANTS MOST RECENT YEAR:
700 to 800.

APPLICATION INFORMATION:
Applicants must register through the online grant system. Paper letters of inquiry will not be accepted.
Duration: One year.
Deadline: Letter of inquiry accepted in March, July and November.

PUBLICATIONS:
Guidelines; annual report.

STAFF:
Terry Mazany, President and Chief Executive Officer

ADDRESS INQUIRIES TO:
Sandy Phelps, Grants Manager
(See address above.)

CHICAGO SUN-TIMES CHARITY TRUST   [1284]
350 North Orleans-10 South
Chicago, IL 60654
(312) 321-2205
(312) 321-2213

E-MAIL ADDRESS:
pdudek@suntimes.com

WEB SITE ADDRESS:
www.suntimes.com

FOUNDED: 1936

AREAS OF INTEREST:
Youth reading and literacy, education, arts and cultural, human services, civic and community services.

TYPE:
Project/program grants.

YEAR PROGRAM STARTED: 1936

LEGAL BASIS:
Corporate contributions program.

ELIGIBILITY:
Grants are made only to tax-exempt organizations and are not made to organizations outside the Chicago metropolitan area. No grants are made to individuals, religious organizations for sectarian purposes, scholarships or fellowships, medical research or national health agency drives or to political activities. The Trust prefers to fund projects directed at

the solution of specific problems. No grants are made to governmental bodies or tax-supported educational institutions for services that fall within their normal responsibilities. No grants are awarded to organizations funded by United Way or receive more than 25% government funding.

GEOGRAPHIC RESTRICTIONS:
Chicago, Illinois metropolitan area.

FINANCIAL DATA:
Amount of support per award: $20,000 to $75,000.
Total amount of support: Approximately $250,000 for the year 2009.

NUMBER OF APPLICANTS MOST RECENT YEAR:
100.

NUMBER OF AWARDS: 25 to 50 for the year 2009.

APPLICATION INFORMATION:
Formal proposals should contain the following elements:
(1) a brief history of the organization, including a general statement of its primary functions and goals;
(2) a brief summary of the proposal including a statement of the need to be addressed, some indication of how the planned project will ameliorate the need, a project budget and a plan for the evaluation of the completed project;
(3) a copy of the organization's most recent audited financial report and approved operating budget. In addition, a statement of current and recent sources of support should be provided and;
(4) a copy of the organization's tax-exemption letter from the IRS.
Duration: Grants are rarely made in consecutive years.
Deadline: Grants are accepted and reviewed throughout the year, and awarded twice per year in March and September.

PUBLICATIONS:
Application guidelines.

IRS IDENTIFICATION NUMBER: 36-6059459

ADDRESS INQUIRIES TO:
Patricia L. Dudek, Manager, Community Relations
(See address above.)

ROBERT STERLING CLARK FOUNDATION   [1285]
135 East 64th Street
New York, NY 10065
(212) 288-8900
Fax: (212) 288-1033

E-MAIL ADDRESS:
rscf@rsclark.org

WEB SITE ADDRESS:
www.rsclark.org

FOUNDED: 1952

AREAS OF INTEREST:
Promoting international arts engagement nationally, improving the performance of government agencies in New York City and State, and protecting reproductive freedom and access to family planning services nationally.

TYPE:
Project/program grants; Research grants.

YEAR PROGRAM STARTED: 1976

PURPOSE:
For cultural institutions and improving performance of government programs.

LEGAL BASIS:
501(c)(3).

ELIGIBILITY:
Applicants must be nonprofit organizations in the U.S.

GEOGRAPHIC RESTRICTIONS:
New York City.

FINANCIAL DATA:
Amount of support per award:
Approximately $15,000 to $120,000.
Total amount of support: Approximately $4,155,000 allocated for the year 2010.

NUMBER OF APPLICANTS MOST RECENT YEAR:
700.

REPRESENTATIVE AWARDS:
$50,000 to Citizens Committee for Children; $100,000 to National Abortion Federation.

APPLICATION INFORMATION:
Applicant organization must submit budgets (past, current and projected), audited financial statements, IRS letter documenting tax status, names and occupations of trustees, project budget, expectations, plans for evaluations and plans for future support, as well as resumes of key personnel.
Duration: Usually one year.
Deadline: Proposals are accepted throughout the year.

PUBLICATIONS:
Annual report; guidelines.

STAFF:
Laura Wolff, Senior Program Officer
Roslyn Black, Program Officer

BOARD OF DIRECTORS:
James Allen Smith, Chairman
Margaret C. Ayers, President
Clara Miller, Treasurer
Joanna D. Underwood, Secretary
Paul Dolan
Winthrop R. Munyan
John Hoyt Stookey

ADDRESS INQUIRIES TO:
Margaret C. Ayers, President and Chief Executive Officer
(See address above.)

THE CLEVELAND FOUNDATION   [1286]
1422 Euclid Avenue
Suite 1300
Cleveland, OH 44115-2001
(216) 861-3810
Fax: (216) 589-9039; (216) 861-1729

E-MAIL ADDRESS:
grantsmgmt@clevefdn.org

WEB SITE ADDRESS:
www.clevelandfoundation.org

FOUNDED: 1914

AREAS OF INTEREST:
Economic development in advanced energy and international relations, public education reform, neighborhood and housing, human services and youth development strengthening the quality of life in early childhood, strengthening the arts and cultural community and greater university circle.

TYPE:
Awards/prizes; Research grants; Scholarships; Seed money grants; Technical assistance.

YEAR PROGRAM STARTED: 1914

PURPOSE:
To enhance the quality of life for all citizens of greater Cleveland, now and for generations to come, by building endowment, addressing needs through grantmaking and providing leadership on key community issues.

LEGAL BASIS:
Community foundation.

ELIGIBILITY:
Grantmaking is restricted to programs and services in the Greater Cleveland community, Cuyahoga, Geauga and Lake counties. Requests are considered from tax-exempt agencies in the following areas: civic affairs, economic development, education, health, social services, arts and culture and environment. Careful consideration is given to such criteria as benefit the entire community and applicant's ability to successfully carry out the proposed activity. Applicant must be a nonprofit organization.

Giving is limited to the Greater Cleveland area unless specified by the donor. No grants to individuals or religious institutions for religious purposes. No support for community services such as fire and police protection, fund-raising campaigns, memberships and travel. No support for publications or audiovisual materials unless they are an integral part of a key program. Capital support for buildings, major equipment, land or renovation is only provided when there is strong evidence that the project has high priority for the community.

GEOGRAPHIC RESTRICTIONS:
Greater Cleveland, Cuyahoga, Geauga and Lake counties, Ohio.

FINANCIAL DATA:
The Foundation has assets of $1.8 billion.
Amount of support per award: $200 to $4,000,000; average $50,000.
Total amount of support: $80,000,000 to $85,000,000 annually.
Matching fund requirements: Depending upon proposal, grants may be authorized contingent upon receipt of matching funds from agency's own or other sources.

COOPERATIVE FUNDING PROGRAMS: Fund for Our Economic Future; Literacy Cooperative of Greater Cleveland.

APPLICATION INFORMATION:
Inquiries and application must be made electronically.
Duration: Usually one to two years.

PUBLICATIONS:
Annual report; *Giving Voice*, quarterly; Grantee e-newsletter.

IRS IDENTIFICATION NUMBER: 34-0714588

COASTAL COMMUNITY FOUNDATION OF SOUTH CAROLINA [1287]
635 Rutledge Avenue
Suite 201
Charleston, SC 29403
(843) 723-3635
Fax: (843) 577-3671

E-MAIL ADDRESS:
info@coastalcommunityfoundation.org

WEB SITE ADDRESS:
www.coastalcommunityfoundation.org

FOUNDED: 1974

AREAS OF INTEREST:
Community development, health, education, human needs, environment and arts.

TYPE:
Awards/prizes; Challenge/matching grants; Endowments; Project/program grants; Scholarships; Technical assistance; Training grants.

ELIGIBILITY:
Generally, applicants must be charitable 501(c)(3) organizations in Beaufort, Berkeley, Charleston, Colleton, Dorchester, Georgetown, Hampton and Jasper counties, South Carolina.

GEOGRAPHIC RESTRICTIONS:
Coastal South Carolina.

FINANCIAL DATA:
Amount of support per award: Varies.
Total amount of support: Varies.

APPLICATION INFORMATION:
Contact the Foundation for instructions.
Deadline: Varies.

ADDRESS INQUIRIES TO:
Edie Blakeslee, Program Officer
(See address above.)

THE COLUMBUS FOUNDATION [1288]
1234 East Broad Street
Columbus, OH 43205
(614) 251-4000
Fax: (614) 251-4009

E-MAIL ADDRESS:
info@columbusfoundation.org

WEB SITE ADDRESS:
www.columbusfoundation.org

FOUNDED: 1943

AREAS OF INTEREST:
Advancing philanthropy, arts and humanities, urban affairs, conservation, education, health and social services.

NAME(S) OF PROGRAMS:
- **Community Improvement Project**
- **Fund for Financial Innovation**
- **Fund for Innovative Operations**
- **Fund for Targeted Needs**

TYPE:
Grants-in-aid; Project/program grants. The Foundation awards competitive grants from the unrestricted and field-of-interest funds created by donors.

The Community Improvement Project supports a concentrated initiative to advance progress over a longer term in an identified area of community need.

The Fund for Financial Innovation will support nonprofit leaders and their organizations to adapt to the new economic reality.

The Fund for Innovative Operations addresses significant needs of local organizations through grants supporting continuous improvement, capacity-building, and arts and cultural efforts.

The Fund for Targeted Needs addresses basic needs, disadvantaged children, developmental disabilities (traditional grants program), as well as more narrow and specific grant programs.

YEAR PROGRAM STARTED: 1943

PURPOSE:
To provide a pool of charitable funds for the development of community programs and services and to offer various ways of giving for citizens who wish to benefit the community.

LEGAL BASIS:
Community foundation, exempt under Section 501(c)(3) of the Internal Revenue Code.

ELIGIBILITY:
Organizations in the central Ohio region having recognition under Section 501(c)(3) of the Internal Revenue Code. No grants are made to individuals.

GEOGRAPHIC RESTRICTIONS:
Primarily Franklin County and surrounding area.

FINANCIAL DATA:
Amount of support per award: $250 to $1,250,000.

REPRESENTATIVE AWARDS:
Arts & Culture: $24,387 to Columbus Symphony Orchestra to support operations from April 1, 2010 to June 30, 2010; Capacity Building and Leadership Grants: $6,000 to Jeanne B. McCoy Community Center for the Arts Corporation to support the fund-raising planning component of the business plan; Innovative Operations-Continuous Improvement: $273,500 to Ohio Association of Second Harvest Foodbanks to support overall operations; Basic Needs: $95,000 to Community Shelter Board to support general operating expenses to address homelessness.

APPLICATION INFORMATION:
Those seeking grants may submit a Letter of Intent or a Full Proposal to the Foundation by accessing its online grant application system through its web site.
Deadline: Varies.

PUBLICATIONS:
Annual yearbook; application guidelines.

IRS IDENTIFICATION NUMBER: 31-6044264

STAFF:
Douglas F. Kridler, President and Chief Executive Officer
Lisa S. Courtice, Ph.D., Vice President, Community Research and Grants Management
Raymond J. Biddiscombe, Vice President, Finance and Administration

ADDRESS INQUIRIES TO:
Melissa Neely
Grants Management Administrator
(See address above.)

COLUMBUS JEWISH FOUNDATION [1289]
Robins Center for Philanthropy
1175 College Avenue
Columbus, OH 43209
(614) 338-2365
Fax: (614) 338-2361

E-MAIL ADDRESS:
jjacobs@tcjf.org

WEB SITE ADDRESS:
www.columbusjewishfoundation.org

FOUNDED: 1955

AREAS OF INTEREST:
Jewish education, Jewish leadership development and the preservation of the integrity of the Jewish family.

TYPE:
Challenge/matching grants; Demonstration grants; Seed money grants.

YEAR PROGRAM STARTED: 1955

PURPOSE:
To strengthen the Jewish community and establish a secure and vital future for Jewish life worldwide.

LEGAL BASIS:
Public charity.

ELIGIBILITY:
Applicants must be 501(c)(3) organizations. No grants to individuals. No operating support. Money will be designated for pilot projects or as seed money only.

GEOGRAPHIC RESTRICTIONS:
United States and international with particular emphasis on central Ohio Jewish organizations.

FINANCIAL DATA:
Amount of support per award: Varies depending on needs and nature of the request.

COOPERATIVE FUNDING PROGRAMS: The Foundation prefers to set up networks for funding with other organizations.

NUMBER OF APPLICANTS MOST RECENT YEAR: 30.

NUMBER OF AWARDS: 22.

REPRESENTATIVE AWARDS:
$40,000 to Mid-Ohio Foodbank; $20,000 to Jewish Family Services Short-Term Therapy.

APPLICATION INFORMATION:
Formal request forms are available from the address above.

PUBLICATIONS:
Annual report; guidelines.

IRS IDENTIFICATION NUMBER: 31-1384772

OFFICERS:
Judge Alan S. Acker, President
Bradley Kastan, President-Elect
Marcia Hershfield, Vice President
Laurence Ruben, Vice President
Reid Wassertrom, Treasurer
Ruth Ann Blank, Assistant Treasurer
Steven Schottenstein, Secretary
Jeff Meyer, Assistant Secretary

ADDRESS INQUIRIES TO:
Susan Tanur, Director of Grants
(See address above.)

COMMON COUNSEL FOUNDATION   [1290]
678 13th Street, Suite 100
Oakland, CA 94612
(510) 834-2995
Fax: (510) 834-2998

E-MAIL ADDRESS:
info@commoncounsel.org

WEB SITE ADDRESS:
www.commoncounsel.org

FOUNDED: 1988

AREAS OF INTEREST:
Economic, environmental and social justice.

TYPE:
General operating grants; Training grants; Travel grants.

PURPOSE:
To offer strategic philanthropic advisory services to donors and family foundations while serving the community at large.

ELIGIBILITY:
501(c)(3) nonprofit organizations. Religious organizations must be working in interfaith coalitions. Grants are not made to individuals. Also, must involve low- and moderate-income members in grassroots community organizing to bring about long-term policy change. Organizational budget must be $400,000 or less except for the small Grassroots Exchange Fund (travel grants), which considers requests from organizations with budgets up to $1,000,000 (higher priority is given to those with budgets less than $750,000).

GEOGRAPHIC RESTRICTIONS:
Primarily western states and Appalachia.

FINANCIAL DATA:
Amount of support per award: Travel and training grants: $500 to $1,000 with an average of approximately $800; General operating grants: $5,000 to $15,000.

COOPERATIVE FUNDING PROGRAMS: Abelard Foundation West; Acorn Foundation; Penney Family Fund; Victor and Lorraine Honig Fund; Grassroots Exchange Fund; Social and Economic Justice Fund.

NUMBER OF APPLICANTS MOST RECENT YEAR: 280.

NUMBER OF AWARDS: Grant support to over 200 community organizations each year.

APPLICATION INFORMATION:
Applicant should submit a letter of inquiry. Full proposals for most of the Funds are by invitation only.
Deadline: January 15 and June 15 (or February through November for Grassroots Exchange Fund).

THE COMMUNITY FOUNDATION   [1291]
7501 Boulders View Drive, Suite 110
Richmond, VA 23225-4047
(804) 330-7400
Fax: (804) 330-5992

E-MAIL ADDRESS:
info@tcfrichmond.org

WEB SITE ADDRESS:
www.tcfrichmond.org

FOUNDED: 1968

AREAS OF INTEREST:
Children, families, communities, health care, education and arts.

NAME(S) OF PROGRAMS:
● **Garland and Agnes Taylor Gray Foundation**
● **The Jenkins Foundation: Improving the Health of Greater Richmond**
● **R.E.B. Awards for Teaching Excellence**
● **Richmond Eye and Ear Fund**
● **Sheltering Arms Fund**

TYPE:
Project/program grants; Scholarships. Competitive grants.

YEAR PROGRAM STARTED: 1968

PURPOSE:
To improve life for generations of children; to improve public education; to support innovative health care projects.

LEGAL BASIS:
Charitable trust.

ELIGIBILITY:
Proposals are accepted from charitable organizations which serve Richmond and/or the tricities.

GEOGRAPHIC RESTRICTIONS:
Richmond and central Virginia.

FINANCIAL DATA:
Amount of support per award: Varies.

PUBLICATIONS:
Annual report; guidelines.

OFFICERS:
John Sherman, Chairman

ADDRESS INQUIRIES TO:
Susan Hallett, Vice President, Programs
(See address above.)

COMMUNITY FOUNDATION FOR GREATER ATLANTA, INC.   [1292]
50 Hurt Plaza, Suite 449
Atlanta, GA 30303
(404) 688-5525
Fax: (404) 688-3060

E-MAIL ADDRESS:
lgrady@cfgreateratlanta.org

WEB SITE ADDRESS:
www.cfgreateratlanta.org

FOUNDED: 1951

AREAS OF INTEREST:
Operational grants to nonprofits serving a 23-county region in Georgia.

NAME(S) OF PROGRAMS:
● **Arts Fund**
● **Common Good**
● **Grants to Green**
● **Neighborhood Fund**

TYPE:
General operating grants; Project/program grants; Scholarships; Technical assistance. Project/program grants are for community development only.

YEAR PROGRAM STARTED: 1951

PURPOSE:
To strengthen private philanthropy and promote the well-being of the people of the metropolitan Atlanta community.

LEGAL BASIS:
501(c)(3) community foundation.

ELIGIBILITY:
Applicant organizations must have 501(c)(3) status. Project must be within the metropolitan Atlanta area. No grants to individuals.

GEOGRAPHIC RESTRICTIONS:
23 counties in the metropolitan Atlanta area.

FINANCIAL DATA:
Amount of support per award: $25,500 to $75,000.

NUMBER OF APPLICANTS MOST RECENT YEAR: 300 for discretionary monies.

NUMBER OF AWARDS: 75 discretionary grants.

APPLICATION INFORMATION:
Grant application guidelines available. Initial approach by letter or phone.
Duration: No grants are awarded on a continuing basis.
Deadline: February and October. Board meets in January, May and September.

PUBLICATIONS:
Annual report; policy and application guidelines.

OFFICERS:
Christie Brown, Chief Operating Officer
Alicia Philipp, President
Benjamin T. White, Assistant Secretary and Legal Counsel

BOARD MEMBERS:
Ken Bernhardt, Chair
Suzanne Boas
Kenneth F. Britt
Deborah Hicks Ellis
Brian Friedman
Carol Hatfield
John Hatfield
Bob Jimenez
Michael Kay
Dr. James T. Laney
Donata Russell Major
Michael A. Nadal
Dr. David Satcher
Beverly Daniel Tatum
Isaiah Tidwell
Hon. Ronit Walker
Jeannie B. Wright

ADDRESS INQUIRIES TO:
Lesley Grady, Vice President of Community Partnerships
(See address above.)

COMMUNITY FOUNDATION FOR GREATER BUFFALO [1293]

712 Main Street
Buffalo, NY 14202
(716) 852-2857
Fax: (716) 852-2861

E-MAIL ADDRESS:
mail@cfgb.org

WEB SITE ADDRESS:
www.cfgb.org

FOUNDED: 1919

TYPE:
Grants-in-aid; Scholarships. Grants to organizations in the eight counties of western New York state.

YEAR PROGRAM STARTED: 1919

PURPOSE:
To connect people, ideas and resources to improve lives in western New York state. The four focus areas of the Foundation are:
(1) to increase economic self-sufficiency for low-income individuals and families;
(2) to reduce racial and ethnic disparities;
(3) to enhance and leverage significant natural, historic and architectural resources and;
(4) to strengthen the region as a center for arts and culture.

LEGAL BASIS:
Community trust; 501(c)(3) tax determination; public charity under Section 170(b)(1)(a)(vi).

ELIGIBILITY:
Programs and agencies must benefit residents of the eight counties of western New York state.

GEOGRAPHIC RESTRICTIONS:
8 counties of western New York state.

FINANCIAL DATA:
Amount of support per award: Approximately $3,000 to $90,000 in 2010.
Total amount of support: $437,000.

NUMBER OF APPLICANTS MOST RECENT YEAR:
189 for the year 2010.

NUMBER OF AWARDS: 22.

REPRESENTATIVE AWARDS:
Cradle Beach; Daemen College; Harvest House of South Buffalo; Child and Adolescent Treatment Services; Massachusetts Avenue Project.

APPLICATION INFORMATION:
Deadline: Letters of Intent accepted from January 1 until March 1. Selected Letters of Intent invited to submit a full proposal by June 1. Applicants notified in early August.

STAFF:
Clotilde Perez-Bode Dedecker, President/Chief Executive Officer
Myra Lawrence, Vice President, Finance & Administration
Cara Matteliano, Vice President, Program
Betsy Murrett Behrend, Communications Director
Jean McKeown, Senior Program Officer
Curtis Robbins, Knowledge Management Officer
Rebekah Williams, Environmental Program Coordinator
Darren Penoyer, Grants Administrator
Johanna Hess, Special Projects Associate
Betsy Constantine, Vice President, Giving Strategies

BOARD OF DIRECTORS:
Cindy Abbott-Letro
Charles Balbach
Gayle L. Eagan, Esq.
Ross Eckert
Danis Gehl, Ph.D.
Luke Jacobs, Esq.
Tim Kibler
Gerard Mazurkiewicz, C.P.A.
Katie Militello
John A. Mitchell
Gary Mucci
Mary Murphy
Alphonso O'Neil-White
Jennifer J. Parker, J.D.
Andrew J. Rudnick, Ph.D.
Anne Saldanha, M.D.
Katie Schneider
Hon. Hugh Scott
Richard Stockton, Ph.D.
Marsha Joy Sullivan
Francisco Vasquez, Ph.D.

ADDRESS INQUIRIES TO:
Jean McKeown, Senior Program Officer
(See address above.)

THE COMMUNITY FOUNDATION FOR GREATER NEW HAVEN [1294]

70 Audubon Street
New Haven, CT 06510
(203) 777-2386
Fax: (203) 787-6584

E-MAIL ADDRESS:
contactus@cfgnh.org

WEB SITE ADDRESS:
www.cfgnh.org

FOUNDED: 1928

AREAS OF INTEREST:
Health, education, community development, regional and economic development, arts and culture, youth, environment, and food and shelter.

TYPE:
Capital grants; General operating grants; Matching gifts; Project/program grants; Scholarships. Capacity building grants. Support for youth and welfare agencies, social services, hospitals and health agencies, educational institutions, community funds and the humanities, including music and art, to organizations serving the residents of greater New Haven.

LEGAL BASIS:
Community foundation established in Connecticut by Resolution and Declaration of Trust.

ELIGIBILITY:
The Foundation welcomes grant requests from greater New Haven area organizations that are defined as tax-exempt under Section 501(c)(3) or any applicable statute of the Internal Revenue Code. While grants are occasionally made to governmental agencies, local nonprofits receive priority.

GEOGRAPHIC RESTRICTIONS:
Greater New Haven, Connecticut: Ansonia, Bethany, Branford, Cheshire, Derby, East Haven, Guilford, Hamden, Madison, Milford, New Haven, North Branford, North Haven, Orange, Oxford, Seymour, Shelton, Wallingford, West Haven, and Woodbridge.

FINANCIAL DATA:
Amount of support per award: $250 to $100,000.
Total amount of support: Varies.

NUMBER OF APPLICANTS MOST RECENT YEAR:
1,188.

NUMBER OF AWARDS: 1,098.

REPRESENTATIVE AWARDS:
$35,000 to Housatonic Valley Association to support the stewardship manager position and to support the stream teams; $32,000 to Literacy Volunteers of Greater New Haven to support increasing the level of outreach to parents of school-age children in New Haven public schools and to provide literacy tutoring to at least 80 parents so they will participate more fully in their child's education; $18,000 to Downtown Evening Soup Kitchen to provide 28,000 free, nutritious meals to the homeless, unemployed, and working poor seven days a week, as well as to provide 4,000 bags of groceries to families on an emergency basis.

APPLICATION INFORMATION:
Nonprofit organizations that have been certified by the IRS as charitable organizations are encouraged to contact the Foundation staff to discuss a program and its funding requirements. If a strong need is shown in an area of concern to the region served by the Foundation, the applicant is asked to prepare a preliminary application.

Duration: One year with multiyears considered annually.

Deadline: Varies from year to year.

PUBLICATIONS:
Annual report; grant guidelines; newsletters.

IRS IDENTIFICATION NUMBER: 06-6032106

STAFF:
William W. Ginsberg, President and Chief Executive Officer
A.F. Drew Alden, Senior Vice President and Chief Financial Officer

ADDRESS INQUIRIES TO:
Denise Canning, Grants Manager
(See address above.)

THE COMMUNITY FOUNDATION FOR MONTEREY COUNTY [1295]

2354 Garden Road
Monterey, CA 93940
(831) 375-9712
Fax: (831) 375-4731

E-MAIL ADDRESS:
info@cfmco.org

WEB SITE ADDRESS:
www.cfmco.org

AREAS OF INTEREST:
Animal welfare, arts and culture, community services, education, environment, health, historic preservation, social services and technical assistance.

NAME(S) OF PROGRAMS:
● **General Endowment Fund**
● **Neighborhood Grants Program**

TYPE:
Capital grants; Challenge/matching grants; Project/program grants; Seed money grants.

PURPOSE:
To increase charitable giving to improve the quality of life for all residents of Monterey County and to strengthen the institutions which help build healthy communities.

LEGAL BASIS:
Community foundation.

ELIGIBILITY:
Community-based, nonprofit organizations whose programs benefit the residents of Monterey County, California.

The Foundation does not make General Endowment Grants to support individuals, for normal operating costs usually covered by operating income, for endowment funds, to support sectarian religious programs, for annual campaigns, dinners, or special events, to pay off past debts or existing obligations, for scholarships, fellowships or travel grants, or for technical or specialized research.

GEOGRAPHIC RESTRICTIONS:
Monterey County, California.

FINANCIAL DATA:
Amount of support per award: Varies.
Total amount of support: Varies.

APPLICATION INFORMATION:
Detailed guidelines and application form can be obtained at the Foundation web site.
Duration: One year. Reapplication annually.

ADDRESS INQUIRIES TO:
Director of Grants and
Donor Advisor Services
(See address above.)

COMMUNITY FOUNDATION FOR NORTHEAST GEORGIA [1296]

6500 Sugarloaf Parkway, Suite 220
Duluth, GA 30097
(770) 813-3380
Fax: (770) 813-3375

E-MAIL ADDRESS:
jwaters@cfneg.org

WEB SITE ADDRESS:
www.cfneg.org

FOUNDED: 1985

AREAS OF INTEREST:
The quality of life in northeast Georgia.

TYPE:
Grants-in-aid.

PURPOSE:
To improve the quality of life throughout northeast Georgia.

ELIGIBILITY:
Grants can be made to tax-exempt private agencies that the IRS classifies as 501(c)(3) organizations, public charities and government agencies. The Foundation will consider organizations that serve people in the areas of education, health and human services, community service and the arts.

GEOGRAPHIC RESTRICTIONS:
Northeast Georgia.

FINANCIAL DATA:
Total amount of support: $112,227 in unrestricted grants and $4,487,815 for all other grants for the year 2010.

APPLICATION INFORMATION:
The grant request must be completed according to the standard Grant Proposal Guidelines issued by the Foundation. Application can be downloaded from the web site.
Deadline: March 1.

ADDRESS INQUIRIES TO:
Beverly Estafen, Director of Finance
(See address above.)

COMMUNITY FOUNDATION FOR NORTHEAST MICHIGAN [1297]

111 Water Street
Alpena, MI 49707
(989) 354-6881
Fax: (989) 356-3319

E-MAIL ADDRESS:
bwillyard@cfnem.org

WEB SITE ADDRESS:
www.cfnem.org

FOUNDED: 1974

AREAS OF INTEREST:
Education, health, youth services, arts and community needs.

TYPE:
Endowments; Project/program grants; Scholarships. Tobacco-related programs/projects. Women's Giving Circle for issues important to women.

YEAR PROGRAM STARTED: 1974

PURPOSE:
To provide resources for community projects.

LEGAL BASIS:
Community foundation.

ELIGIBILITY:
Eligible organizations must be IRS 501(c)(3) tax-exempt, government schools or churches, providing the project is nonsectarian. No grants to individuals.

GEOGRAPHIC RESTRICTIONS:
Alcona, Alpena, Montmorency and Presque Isle counties, Michigan.

FINANCIAL DATA:
Amount of support per award: Up to $3,000.
Total amount of support: Over $100,000 for fiscal year 2010.

COOPERATIVE FUNDING PROGRAMS:
Collaboration between organizations is encouraged.

NUMBER OF APPLICANTS MOST RECENT YEAR:
136 Common Grant.

NUMBER OF AWARDS: 111.

REPRESENTATIVE AWARDS:
Alpena Public Schools; Thunder Bay Junior High School; Bullying Prevention Initiative.

APPLICATION INFORMATION:
Applications must include a copy of the IRS tax determination letter, except for schools, churches and government agencies.
Duration: One year, with the possibility of a six-month extension.
Deadline: Varies. Details are available online.

PUBLICATIONS:
Annual report; biannual newsletter; brochures; application guidelines.

IRS IDENTIFICATION NUMBER: 23-7384822

EXECUTIVE DIRECTOR:
Barbara Willyard

ADDRESS INQUIRIES TO:
Julie Wiesen, Program Director
(See address above.)

COMMUNITY FOUNDATION FOR PALM BEACH AND MARTIN COUNTIES [1298]

700 South Dixie Hwy
Suite 200
West Palm Beach, FL 33401-5854
(561) 659-6800 (Palm Beach County)
(888) 853-4438 (Florida only)
Fax: (561) 832-6542

E-MAIL ADDRESS:
info@cfpbmc.org

WEB SITE ADDRESS:
www.yourcommunityfoundation.org

FOUNDED: 1972

AREAS OF INTEREST:
Community development, social change and development, human relations, race relations, cultural events and intergenerational programs.

TYPE:
Challenge/matching grants; Development grants; Project/program grants; Scholarships; Technical assistance; Training grants.

PURPOSE:
To develop a shared vision of building a sense of community.

ELIGIBILITY:
501(c)(3) organizations are eligible to apply for grants.

GEOGRAPHIC RESTRICTIONS:
Martin and Palm Beach counties, Florida.

FINANCIAL DATA:
Total amount of support: $8,900,000, including $600,000 in scholarships, for the year ended June 30, 2009.

NUMBER OF APPLICANTS MOST RECENT YEAR:
114.

NUMBER OF AWARDS: 126 grants and 84 scholarships for the year ended June 30, 2008.

APPLICATION INFORMATION:
Write to the above address for application information. The Foundation uses a printed form for applications or proposals. Applicants must complete a proposal summary and budget form.
Deadline: Scholarships: February 1.

PUBLICATIONS:
Annual report; newsletter.

OFFICERS:
Leslie Lilly, President and Chief Executive
Officer

ADDRESS INQUIRIES TO:
Jillian Vukusich, Senior Program Officer
(See address above.)

COMMUNITY FOUNDATION FOR SOUTHERN ARIZONA [1299]

2250 East Broadway Boulevard
Tucson, AZ 85719
(520) 770-0800
Fax: (520) 770-1500

E-MAIL ADDRESS:
philanthropy@cfsoaz.org

WEB SITE ADDRESS:
www.cfsoaz.org

FOUNDED: 1980

AREAS OF INTEREST:
Addressing the needs of the citizens and
communities of southern Arizona.

NAME(S) OF PROGRAMS:
- **Community Investment Grants**
- **LBGT&S Alliance Fund**
- **Oro Valley Community Foundation**
- **Pro Neighborhoods**
- **Santa Cruz Community Foundation**
- **Southern Arizona HIV/AIDS Consortia**
- **Stone Canyon Community Foundation**

TYPE:
Awards/prizes; Challenge/matching grants;
General operating grants; Project/program
grants; Scholarships. Community Investment
Grants: This program promotes and identifies
community collaborations that build on
existing strengths to increase the capacity of
local nonprofit organizations to better serve
southern Arizona.

LBGT&S Alliance Fund: This program
provides grant opportunities for nonprofit
organizations addressing the needs of lesbian,
gay, bisexual and transgender individuals.

Oro Valley Community Foundation: The
Foundation provides grants to nonprofit
organizations in the Oro Valley area.

Pro Neighborhoods: This program provides
small grants to neighborhood organizations
involved in community efforts in Pima
County.

Santa Cruz Community Foundation: This
program provides grants to nonprofit
organizations serving Santa Cruz County.

Southern Arizona HIV/AIDS Consortia: This
program provides grant opportunities for
nonprofit organizations addressing the needs
of people living with and/or affected by
HIV/AIDS in Pima County and southeastern
Arizona.

Stone Canyon Community Foundation: This
Foundation provides grants to nonprofit
organizations in the Oro Valley and Tucson
communities.

The Foundation also offers a general
scholarship program and a number of awards
programs for nonprofit organizations and
individuals.

YEAR PROGRAM STARTED: 1980

PURPOSE:
To support donors making a difference now
and forever.

LEGAL BASIS:
Nonprofit, tax-exempt public charity
(community foundation).

ELIGIBILITY:
Grants are given to eligible 501(c)(3)
charitable organizations. Scholarships are
given to residents of southern Arizona.

GEOGRAPHIC RESTRICTIONS:
Southern Arizona, primarily Pima, Santa
Cruz and Yuma counties, south of the Gila
river.

FINANCIAL DATA:
Amount of support per award: Varies.
Total amount of support: $3,419,826.

REPRESENTATIVE AWARDS:
Four Community Collaboration Grants
involving more than 40 organizations at
$225,000 each over three years: (1) Ajo
Regional Food Partnership; (2) City of South
Tucson Neighborhood Revitalization; (3)
E.L.D.E.R. Project: Empowered Leaders
Directing Elder Resources and; (4) Project:
Women and Girls.

APPLICATION INFORMATION:
Detailed information is available online.
Duration: Varies.
Deadline: Varies.

IRS IDENTIFICATION NUMBER: 94-2681765

STAFF:
Evan Mendelson, Vice President, Donor
Relations and Program Services
Marthena Maley, Grants and Donor Services
Administrator

ADDRESS INQUIRIES TO:
Evan Mendelson, Vice President
Donor Relations and Program Services
(See address above.)

THE COMMUNITY FOUNDATION FOR THE GREATER CAPITAL REGION [1300]

6 Tower Place
Albany, NY 12203
(518) 446-9638
Fax: (518) 446-9708

E-MAIL ADDRESS:
jmahoney@cfgcr.org

WEB SITE ADDRESS:
www.cfgcr.org

FOUNDED: 1968

AREAS OF INTEREST:
Health, science, education, youth and
environment.

NAME(S) OF PROGRAMS:
- **Capacity-Building Grant Initiative**
- **Regular Competitive Grants**

TYPE:
Capital grants; Challenge/matching grants;
General operating grants; Matching gifts;
Project/program grants; Research grants;
Scholarships; Technical assistance. Small,
flexible grants to support some of the costs
associated with organizational
capacity-building.

The Foundation creates networks of
opportunity–opportunities to bring together
interested donors and community service
providers to address a particular problem or
need in the local community served. It serves
the Capital Region of New York state by
funding creative, visionary and sensitive

projects–often seed money for innovative
programs–that address the evolving needs of
the community. The Foundation also serves
as a vehicle for individuals, families,
corporations, private foundations and
nonprofit organizations to use in carrying out
their long-term philanthropic plans.

Homelessness: Grants are designed to
eliminate homelessness in the Capital
Region.

Disabilities: The purpose of these grants is to
serve the needs of the mentally and/or
physically disabled, including the hearing-
and sight-impaired.

Health: Program and capital grants are
available for health care organizations
working to improve the health of residents of
the four-county region around Albany, NY.

Science: This program makes grants to
support and promote discovery and
development in medicine, science and
technology in the Capital District.

PURPOSE:
To support capacity-building efforts of
organizations including projects that are
designed to generate new thinking about
ways to improve an organization's ability to
serve the community, more effectively carry
out its mission, and plan for the future.

LEGAL BASIS:
Classified by the Internal Revenue Code as a
public charity.

ELIGIBILITY:
Grants are made to applicants that qualify
under Section 501(c)(3) of the Internal
Revenue Code as a nonprofit organization, or
operate under the fiscal sponsorship of an
organization that does, and serve residents
and be located in Albany, Rensselaer,
Schenectady and/or Saratoga counties. No
grants are made to individuals. Nonsectarian
religious programs may apply.

The Foundation's competitive grants support
organizations that do not discriminate in their
employment practices, volunteer
opportunities, or delivery of programs or
services on the basis of race, color, religion,
gender, national origin, ancestry, age, medical
condition, disability, veteran status, marital
status, sexual orientation, or any other
characteristic protected by law.

GEOGRAPHIC RESTRICTIONS:
Albany, Rensselaer, Saratoga or Schenectady
counties, New York.

FINANCIAL DATA:
Assets of over $40,000,000.
Amount of support per award: Homelessness
Grants: Usually $5,000 to $10,000;
Disabilities Grants: Usually $2,500 to
$20,000; Health Care Grants: Up to $30,000;
Science Grants: Up to $10,000; Youth
Grants: Up to $30,000.
Total amount of support: More than
$2,000,000 in grant distributions annually.

NUMBER OF APPLICANTS MOST RECENT YEAR:
Over 800.

NUMBER OF AWARDS: 700 grants awarded.

APPLICATION INFORMATION:
An application form is required and may be
obtained by e-mailing the Community
Foundation. Prospective applicants are
encouraged to discuss their plans with the
Foundation's program staff prior to
submitting an application.

Duration: With the exception of operating grants, grant periods do not exceed one year in duration. Applicants may submit only one application to the Foundation's regular competitive grantmaking program per year. Organizations that have been funded by the Foundation must wait one year from denial date until they can reapply.

PUBLICATIONS:
Grantmaking Guidelines.

ADDRESS INQUIRIES TO:
Jackie Mahoney, Director of Grantmaking
(See address above.)

THE COMMUNITY FOUNDATION IN JACKSONVILLE   [1301]
245 Riverside Avenue
Suite 310
Jacksonville, FL 32202
(904) 356-4483
Fax: (904) 356-7910

E-MAIL ADDRESS:
criddick@jaxcf.org

WEB SITE ADDRESS:
www.jaxcf.org

AREAS OF INTEREST:
Children, youth, families, seniors, neighborhoods, community values and the arts.

TYPE:
Challenge/matching grants; Development grants; Endowments; Matching gifts; Project/program grants; Seed money grants.

PURPOSE:
To stimulate philanthropy to build a better community.

ELIGIBILITY:
Eligible organizations must be IRS 501(c)(3) tax-exempt.

GEOGRAPHIC RESTRICTIONS:
Baker, Clay, Duval, Nassau and St. Johns counties in northern Florida.

FINANCIAL DATA:
Amount of support per award: Approximately $250 to $150,000.
Total amount of support: $17,000,000 for the year 2010.

APPLICATION INFORMATION:
Duration: Up to 24 months.

PUBLICATIONS:
Newsletter; annual report.

STAFF:
John Zell, Vice President, Donor Services
Cheryl Riddick, Vice President, Grantmaking Services

ADDRESS INQUIRIES TO:
Cheryl Riddick, Vice President
Grantmaking Services
(See address above.)

COMMUNITY FOUNDATION OF ABILENE   [1302]
500 Chestnut, Suite 1634
Abilene, TX 79604
(325) 676-3883
Fax: (325) 676-4206

E-MAIL ADDRESS:
cf@abilene.org

WEB SITE ADDRESS:
www.cfabilene.org

FOUNDED: 1986

AREAS OF INTEREST:
Human services, arts and culture, education, health, community development and civic affairs.

TYPE:
Capital grants; Challenge/matching grants; Project/program grants; Technical assistance.

PURPOSE:
To increase the quality of life in Abilene, TX; to increase the awareness to philanthropy in the area.

ELIGIBILITY:
Eligible organizations must be IRS 501(c)(3) tax-exempt and be located in the immediate Abilene, TX area.

GEOGRAPHIC RESTRICTIONS:
Abilene, Texas.

FINANCIAL DATA:
Amount of support per award: $1,000 to $50,000.
Total amount of support: Approximately $6,000,000.

NUMBER OF APPLICANTS MOST RECENT YEAR: 56.

NUMBER OF AWARDS: 36.

APPLICATION INFORMATION:
Applicants may submit a letter of intent and include a copy of the IRS tax determination letter.
Duration: One year.
Deadline: February 4 and September 3.

COMMUNITY FOUNDATION OF COLLIER COUNTY   [1303]
2400 Tamiami Trail North, Suite 300
Naples, FL 34103
(239) 649-5000
Fax: (239) 649-5337

E-MAIL ADDRESS:
akirk@cfcollier.org

WEB SITE ADDRESS:
cfcollier.org

FOUNDED: 1987

AREAS OF INTEREST:
Health, human services, education, civic affairs, environment, arts and humanities.

NAME(S) OF PROGRAMS:
- **Fred Coyle ROTC Leaders Scholarship**
- **The Daphne Vocational Fund**
- **Joel A. Deifik Memorial Scholarship Fund**
- **Diano-Tougas Memorial Scholarship Fund**
- **Dorothy Edwards Vocational Scholarship Fund**
- **Ashley Kelly Memorial Scholarship Fund**
- **Louise Prothero Leadership Fund - Women's Club**
- **Jimmy Schneeberger Scholarship Fund**
- **Raymond D. and Sara Thomas Fund**

TYPE:
Conferences/seminars; Matching gifts; Project/program grants; Scholarships. Community Grant Programs in the area of professional development.

YEAR PROGRAM STARTED: 1987

PURPOSE:
To establish a perpetual endowment and to improve the quality of life in Collier County.

LEGAL BASIS:
Public foundation.

ELIGIBILITY:
Eligible organizations must be IRS 501(c)(3) tax-exempt.

GEOGRAPHIC RESTRICTIONS:
Collier County, Florida.

FINANCIAL DATA:
Amount of support per award: Professional Development: Up to $2,000.

APPLICATION INFORMATION:
Request guidelines two to three months prior to deadlines.
Duration: Renewal applications may be considered.
Deadline: Scholarships: Postmarked March 1.

PUBLICATIONS:
Guidelines.

STAFF:
Colleen Murphy, President and Chief Executive Officer
Bill Franz, Chief Operating Officer
Mary Ellen Barrett, Vice President of Programs

ADDRESS INQUIRIES TO:
Annette Kirk
Financial Services Representative
(See address above.)

COMMUNITY FOUNDATION OF DELAWARE COUNTY   [1304]
3954 North Hampton Drive
Powell, OH 43065
(614) 764-2332
Fax: (614) 764-2333

E-MAIL ADDRESS:
cfdc@midohio.net

WEB SITE ADDRESS:
www.delawarecf.org

FOUNDED: 1995

AREAS OF INTEREST:
Arts, civic affairs, community needs, culture, education, environment, health and human services.

NAME(S) OF PROGRAMS:
- **Designated Funds**
- **Donor Advised Funds**
- **Field of Interest Funds**
- **Organizational Endowment Funds**
- **Scholarship Funds**
- **Special Project Funds**
- **Unrestricted Funds**

TYPE:
Scholarships.

PURPOSE:
To enhance the quality of life for Delaware County residents.

ELIGIBILITY:
Grants are made to organizations that have tax-exempt status under Section 501(c)(3) of the Internal Revenue Code that serve Delaware County. No grants are made to individuals, religious programs, political groups or for deficit reduction.

GEOGRAPHIC RESTRICTIONS:
Delaware County, Ohio.

FINANCIAL DATA:
Amount of support per award: $500 to $100,000. Gooding Memorial Scholarships do not exceed $15,000.
Total amount of support: $539,498 in grants and scholarships for the year 2010.

APPLICATION INFORMATION:
Information may be obtained from the Foundation web site.

Deadline: Scholarships: Mid-April and mid-June.

STAFF:
Marlene A. Casini, President and Chief Executive Officer

COMMUNITY FOUNDATION OF EASTERN CONNECTICUT [1305]

147 State Street
New London, CT 06320
(860) 442-3572
Fax: (860) 442-0584

E-MAIL ADDRESS:
jennob@cfect.org

WEB SITE ADDRESS:
www.cfect.org

FOUNDED: 1982

AREAS OF INTEREST:
Arts, charity, civic affairs, community needs and development, culture, education, environment, health and human services.

NAME(S) OF PROGRAMS:
• **Community Foundation Grants**
• **Community Foundation Scholarship Awards**
• **Women and Girls Fund**

TYPE:
General operating grants; Project/program grants; Scholarships.

YEAR PROGRAM STARTED: 1982

PURPOSE:
To connect the generosity of private donors with the changing needs of the residents of eastern Connecticut by promoting local philanthropy and funding local projects.

ELIGIBILITY:
Federally recognized 501(c)(3) organizations and most charitable, educational and civic institution organizations that serve the towns listed below.

GEOGRAPHIC RESTRICTIONS:
Towns of East Lyme, Groton, Ledyard, Lyme, Montville, New London, North Stonington, Old Lyme, Salem, Stonington, and Waterford, Connecticut.

FINANCIAL DATA:
Amount of support per award: Grants: $1,000 to $10,000; Scholarships: $500 to $5,000.

Total amount of support: $2,500,000 for fiscal year 2009.

NUMBER OF APPLICANTS MOST RECENT YEAR:
170.

NUMBER OF AWARDS: 100.

APPLICATION INFORMATION:
Contact the Foundation for specific details on the various grant programs.

Deadline: Women and Girls Fund: August 15; General grants: November 15; Scholarships: April 1.

ADDRESS INQUIRIES TO:
Jennifer O'Brien, Program Director
(See address above.)

THE COMMUNITY FOUNDATION OF FREDERICK COUNTY, MD, INC. [1306]

312 East Church Street
Frederick, MD 21701
(301) 695-7660
Fax: (301) 695-7775

E-MAIL ADDRESS:
info@cffredco.org

WEB SITE ADDRESS:
www.cffredco.org

FOUNDED: 1986

AREAS OF INTEREST:
Community development.

TYPE:
Capital grants; Development grants; Endowments; Grants-in-aid; Scholarships; Seed money grants. One-time grants for capital expenditures, one-time purchases and new or innovative projects.

YEAR PROGRAM STARTED: 1986

PURPOSE:
To make charitable dreams come true by working with donors to establish funds that award grants and scholarships.

ELIGIBILITY:
For some grants, applicant organizations must have 501(c)(3) not-for-profit status.

GEOGRAPHIC RESTRICTIONS:
Frederick County, Maryland.

FINANCIAL DATA:
Amount of support per award: Varies depending on need.

Total amount of support: Varies.

NUMBER OF AWARDS: More than 200 scholarships for the academic year 2010-11; More than 270 grants for fiscal year ended June 30, 2010.

APPLICATION INFORMATION:
Applications are available after August 15 and must include a copy of the 501(c)(3) IRS letter, if applicable, when submitted.

Duration: One year.

Deadline: Varies.

PUBLICATIONS:
Annual report; newsletters; grant applications.

IRS IDENTIFICATION NUMBER: 52-2028247

ADDRESS INQUIRIES TO:
Gayle Sutch, Director of Donor Services
(See address above.)

THE COMMUNITY FOUNDATION OF GREATER CHATTANOOGA, INC. [1307]

1270 Market Street
Chattanooga, TN 37402
(423) 265-0586
Fax: (423) 265-0587

E-MAIL ADDRESS:
info@cfgc.org

WEB SITE ADDRESS:
www.cfgc.org

FOUNDED: 1963

AREAS OF INTEREST:
Nonprofit organizations.

NAME(S) OF PROGRAMS:
• **Coca-Cola Centennial Scholarship Fund**
• **Japanese-American Understanding Fund**
• **Together We Can Scholarship Fund**

TYPE:
Scholarships.

YEAR PROGRAM STARTED: 1963

PURPOSE:
To encourage giving and inspire action to improve lives in the Chattanooga area.

LEGAL BASIS:
501(c)(3).

ELIGIBILITY:
Must be a nonprofit corporation with 501(c)(3) tax-exempt status based in or primarily serving Hamilton County, Tennessee.

Students for Together We Can Scholarship Fund must live in Chattanooga and attend a public high school.

GEOGRAPHIC RESTRICTIONS:
Hamilton County, Tennessee.

FINANCIAL DATA:
Amount of support per award: Coca-Cola Centennial Scholarship Fund: $1,500 to $2,500; Japanese-American Understanding Fund: $8,000 for payment of trip to Japan; Together We Can Scholarship Fund: $500 to $3,000.

APPLICATION INFORMATION:
Prior to submitting an application, potential applicants are required to submit a letter of intent form and receive written approval from the Foundation to continue the application process. A completed application can then be submitted along with required documentation.

Duration: Coca-Cola Centennial Scholarship Fund: Renewable up to four academic years; Japanese-American Understanding Fund: One year. No renewals; Together We Can Scholarship Fund: Up to four years.

IRS IDENTIFICATION NUMBER: 62-6045999

STAFF:
Peter T. Cooper, President
Marty Robinson, Vice President
Rebecca Smith, Director of Scholarships

BOARD OF DIRECTORS:
Max Bahner
Charlie Brock
Paul Campbell, III
Jeff Cannon
Clif Cleveland, M.D.
Ann Coulter
Mike Feely
Patsy Hazlewood
Wade Hinton
Helen Johnson
Dallas Joseph
Alison Lebovitz
Susan O'Hare
Michelle Ruest
Lynn Schmissrauter
Mary Tanner
Carolyn Thompson
Edna Varner
Charlesettta Woodard-Thompson

EXECUTIVE COMMITTEE:
Edna Varner, Chairperson
Paul Campbell, III, Vice Chairperson
Grant Law, Vice Chairperson
Dallas Joseph, Treasurer
Ansley Moses, Corporate Secretary

ADDRESS INQUIRIES TO:
Rebecca Smith
Director of Scholarships
(See address above.)

*SPECIAL STIPULATIONS:
All grants limited to students from or programs in Hamilton County, Tennessee.

COMMUNITY FOUNDATION OF GREATER GREENSBORO   [1308]
330 South Greene Street
Suite 100
Greensboro, NC 27401
(336) 379-9100
Fax: (336) 378-0725

E-MAIL ADDRESS:
info@cfgg.org

WEB SITE ADDRESS:
www.cfgg.org

FOUNDED: 1983

AREAS OF INTEREST:
Serving the Greater Greensboro, NC area.

NAME(S) OF PROGRAMS:
● **Thornton H. Brooks Award**
● **Community Service Award**
● **Hugh Humphrey Award**

TYPE:
Challenge/matching grants; Conferences/seminars; Demonstration grants; Development grants; Endowments; General operating grants; Project/program grants; Scholarships. Recognition Awards.

Brooks Award recognizes individuals for outstanding leadership to the Foundation and its mission.

Community Service Award recognizes individuals who have exhibited outstanding community service.

Hugh Humphrey Award recognizes the most improved high school in Guilford County, NC.

GEOGRAPHIC RESTRICTIONS:
Greater Greensboro, North Carolina area.

APPLICATION INFORMATION:
Nomination only.
Deadline: Varies.

IRS IDENTIFICATION NUMBER: 56-1380249

ADDRESS INQUIRIES TO:
Tara Sandercock
Vice President, Grants and Initiatives
(See address above.)

COMMUNITY FOUNDATION OF GREATER ROCHESTER   [1309]
P.O. Box 80431
Rochester, MI 48308-0431
(248) 608-2804
Fax: (248) 608-2826

E-MAIL ADDRESS:
cfound@cfound.org

WEB SITE ADDRESS:
www.cfound.org

FOUNDED: 1983

AREAS OF INTEREST:
Arts, conservation of natural resources, community needs and development, culture, education, environment, health, historic preservation and human services.

TYPE:
Endowments; Project/program grants; Scholarships; Travel grants. Community grants.

PURPOSE:
To enhance the quality of life for the citizens of Greater Rochester area by serving as a community endowment builder, grantmaker and leader.

ELIGIBILITY:
Grants are made to organizations that have tax-exempt status under Section 501(c)(3) of the Internal Revenue Code. Nonsectarian religious programs may apply.

GEOGRAPHIC RESTRICTIONS:
Greater Rochester, Michigan and surrounding area.

FINANCIAL DATA:
Amount of support per award: Varies.
Total amount of support: Varies.

APPLICATION INFORMATION:
Contact the Foundation for application procedures.

ADDRESS INQUIRIES TO:
Peggy Hamilton, Executive Director
(See address above.)

THE COMMUNITY FOUNDATION OF HERKIMER & ONEIDA COUNTIES, INC.   [1310]
1222 State Street
Utica, NY 13502
(315) 735-8212
Fax: (315) 735-9363

E-MAIL ADDRESS:
info@foundationhoc.org

WEB SITE ADDRESS:
foundationhoc.org

FOUNDED: 1952

AREAS OF INTEREST:
Community development.

TYPE:
Capital grants; Challenge/matching grants; Project/program grants; Scholarships; Seed money grants; Technical assistance; Training grants.

PURPOSE:
To improve the quality of life of the residents of Herkimer and Oneida counties in New York.

LEGAL BASIS:
Community Foundation.

ELIGIBILITY:
Applications are entertained from organizations that are tax-exempt under Section 501(c)(3) of the Internal Revenue Code. Grants may be made for program or capital expenses. Operating funds will receive consideration on a short-term or emergency basis, with the understanding that applicants must submit a clear, realistic plan to secure alternative funding at the end of a specific time.

The Community Foundation does not make grants for religious purposes, nor does it provide financial assistance or scholarships directly to individuals, support for non-emergency expenses already incurred, requests over $100,000, or ongoing operating support.

GEOGRAPHIC RESTRICTIONS:
Herkimer and Oneida counties, New York.

FINANCIAL DATA:
Amount of support per award: $1,000 to $100,000; average $5,000 to $15,000.

Total amount of support: $5,835,383 for the year 2009.

NUMBER OF AWARDS: 313 grants for the year 2009.

APPLICATION INFORMATION:
Applicants should call the Senior Program Officer prior to submitting a written request.
Duration: One year.
Deadline: Grant requests are accepted on an ongoing basis.

PUBLICATIONS:
Annual report; newsletter for applicants/grantees; application guidelines; foundation brochure; history book.

ADDRESS INQUIRIES TO:
Jan Squadrito, Senior Program Officer
(See address above.)

COMMUNITY FOUNDATION OF JACKSON HOLE   [1311]
255 East Simpson Street
Jackson, WY 83001
(307) 739-1026
Fax: (307) 734-2841

E-MAIL ADDRESS:
info@cfjacksonhole.org

WEB SITE ADDRESS:
www.cfjacksonhole.org

FOUNDED: 1989

AREAS OF INTEREST:
Art, education, environment, health and social services.

TYPE:
Grants-in-aid; Project/program grants; Research grants.

PURPOSE:
To improve lives through philanthropic leadership.

LEGAL BASIS:
501(c)(3).

ELIGIBILITY:
Must be a 501(c)(3) corporation.

GEOGRAPHIC RESTRICTIONS:
Teton County, Wyoming.

FINANCIAL DATA:
Total amount of support: $15,900,000 for the year 2009.

IRS IDENTIFICATION NUMBER: 83-0308856

ADDRESS INQUIRIES TO:
Katharine Conover, President
(See address above.)

THE COMMUNITY FOUNDATION OF LORAIN COUNTY   [1312]
9080 Leavitt Road
Elyria, OH 44035
(440) 984-7390
Fax: (440) 984-7399

E-MAIL ADDRESS:
foundation@peoplewhocare.org

WEB SITE ADDRESS:
www.peoplewhocare.org

FOUNDED: 1980

AREAS OF INTEREST:
Community of Lorain County, OH.

TYPE:
General operating grants; Project/program grants. Grants are given to improve the quality of life in Lorain County.

YEAR PROGRAM STARTED: 1980

PURPOSE:
To connect people who care with causes that matter.

ELIGIBILITY:
Organization or sponsor must be 501(c)(3). Funding must serve the people of Lorain County.

GEOGRAPHIC RESTRICTIONS:
Lorain County, Ohio.

FINANCIAL DATA:
Total amount of support: Varies.

APPLICATION INFORMATION:
Application can be downloaded at the web site.
Deadline: February 1 and July 1.

ADDRESS INQUIRIES TO:
Linda Styer, Senior Program Officer
E-mail: lstyer@peoplewhocare.org

THE COMMUNITY FOUNDATION OF MUNCIE AND DELAWARE COUNTY, INC. [1313]
201 East Jackson Street
Muncie, IN 47305
(765) 747-7181
Fax: (765) 289-7770

E-MAIL ADDRESS:
commfound@cfmdin.org

WEB SITE ADDRESS:
www.cfmdin.org

FOUNDED: 1985

AREAS OF INTEREST:
Arts and culture, education, human services, economic development and community betterment.

TYPE:
Challenge/matching grants; Scholarships; Seed money grants; Technical assistance.

PURPOSE:
To improve the quality of life in the city of Muncie and Delaware County, IN.

ELIGIBILITY:
Organizations must be IRS 501(c)(3) tax-exempt. The Foundation does not make grants to individuals, for religious purposes, for covering budget deficits, for endowments or for projects normally the responsibility of a government agency.

GEOGRAPHIC RESTRICTIONS:
The city of Muncie and Delaware County, Indiana.

FINANCIAL DATA:
Total amount of support: $1,608,839 for the year 2010.

NUMBER OF APPLICANTS MOST RECENT YEAR: 400.

NUMBER OF AWARDS: 367.

APPLICATION INFORMATION:
Applicant organizations should secure an application from the address above. Applicants should submit 17 copies of the application and also include supporting material, goals and objectives, method of evaluation, how the proposal benefits the community, a list of officers and board of directors, the most recent financial report, and a copy of the IRS tax-exempt determination letter.
Deadline: Mid-January, April, July and October.

PUBLICATIONS:
Guidelines.

IRS IDENTIFICATION NUMBER: 35-1640051

ADDRESS INQUIRIES TO:
Roni Johnson, President
P.O. Box 807
Muncie, IN 47308

*SPECIAL STIPULATIONS:
The Foundation will periodically review each grant awarded and will request a final postgrant report from each grantee.

COMMUNITY FOUNDATION OF NORTH CENTRAL WISCONSIN [1314]
500 First Street
Suite 2600
Wausau, WI 54403
(715) 845-9555
Fax: (715) 845-5423

E-MAIL ADDRESS:
info@cfoncw.org

WEB SITE ADDRESS:
www.cfoncw.org

FOUNDED: 1987

AREAS OF INTEREST:
Arts, education, health and human services, and resource preservation.

TYPE:
Awards/prizes; Capital grants; Development grants; Project/program grants; Scholarships; Seed money grants; Technical assistance.

YEAR PROGRAM STARTED: 1987

PURPOSE:
To enhance the quality of the greater Wausau (WI) area.

ELIGIBILITY:
Consideration is given primarily to those organizations that are tax-exempt under Section 501(c)(3) of the Internal Revenue Code.

GEOGRAPHIC RESTRICTIONS:
Greater Wausau area, Marathon County, Wisconsin.

FINANCIAL DATA:
Amount of support per award: $2,500 to $10,000.

NUMBER OF APPLICANTS MOST RECENT YEAR: 35.

NUMBER OF AWARDS: 26.

REPRESENTATIVE AWARDS:
Marathon County Historical Society; Bridge Community Health Clinic; Dairyland State Academy; Center for the Visual Arts; The Women's Community.

APPLICATION INFORMATION:
Duration: One year.
Deadline: Applications are due the first business day of March, June, September and December.

STAFF:
Jean Tehan, Executive Director
Sue Nelson, Program Manager
Pauline Zweck, Accountant

ADDRESS INQUIRIES TO:
Jean Tehan, Executive Director
(See address above.)

COMMUNITY FOUNDATION OF NORTHEAST ALABAMA [1315]
1130 Quintard Avenue
Suite 100
Anniston, AL 36201
(256) 231-5160
Fax: (256) 231-5161

E-MAIL ADDRESS:
etatman@yourcommunityfirst.org

WEB SITE ADDRESS:
www.yourcommunityfirst.org

AREAS OF INTEREST:
Arts, community needs, culture, education, health and human services.

TYPE:
Project/program grants; Scholarships; Technical assistance. Mini-Grants.

PURPOSE:
To support the most discernible needs and most promising opportunities within Calhoun County and northeast Alabama.

ELIGIBILITY:
Grants are made to organizations that have tax-exempt status under Section 501(c)(3) of the Internal Revenue Code. No grants are made to individuals. Nonsectarian religious programs may apply.

GEOGRAPHIC RESTRICTIONS:
Calhoun County, Alabama.

FINANCIAL DATA:
Amount of support per award: Maximum $50,000 per year.
Total amount of support: $1,065,572 in grants and $63,500 in scholarships for the year 2010.

NUMBER OF AWARDS: 75 grants and 19 scholarships for the year 2010.

APPLICATION INFORMATION:
Grant request must be completed online. To improve chance of a positive response, applicants are encouraged to review the Mini-Grant Guidelines and the Core Operating Standards for Nonprofits before applying.
Duration: One year. Renewal possible.
Deadline: Grants: March 1 and September 1; Scholarships: March 1.

ADDRESS INQUIRIES TO:
Eula Tatman, Interim President and Chief Executive Officer
(See address above.)

COMMUNITY FOUNDATION OF SAINT JOSEPH COUNTY [1316]
P.O. Box 837
South Bend, IN 46624
(574) 232-0041
Fax: (574) 233-1906

E-MAIL ADDRESS:
info@cfsjc.org

WEB SITE ADDRESS:
www.cfsjc.org

AREAS OF INTEREST:
Arts and culture; community development and urban affairs; health and human services; parks, recreation, and environment; youth and education.

NAME(S) OF PROGRAMS:
- **African American Community Fund**
- **ArtsEverywhere Fund**
- **Leighton Award for Nonprofit Excellence**

- **Robert P. and Clara I. Milton Fund for Senior Housing**
- **Special Project Challenge Grant**

TYPE:
Capital grants; Challenge/matching grants; Project/program grants; Scholarships; Seed money grants. Donor-advised grants.

PURPOSE:
To promote organizations whose programs benefit the residents of St. Joseph County; to assist existing agencies to better respond to the needs of the community.

ELIGIBILITY:
Grants are made to organizations that have tax-exempt status under Section 501(c)(3) of the Internal Revenue Code. No grants are made to individuals. Non-sectarian religious programs may apply. Funded projects should benefit a significant constituency within the community and the organization must exhibit the ability to raise the required matching funds, if applicable.

GEOGRAPHIC RESTRICTIONS:
Saint Joseph County, Indiana.

FINANCIAL DATA:
Amount of support per award: Varies per award.

Total amount of support: $6,400,000 for the year 2010.

Matching fund requirements: Some programs require matching funds.

APPLICATION INFORMATION:
Deadline: Special Project Challenge Grant and African American Community Fund: March 1 and October 1; Robert P. and Clara I. Milton Fund and ArtsEverywhere Fund: May 1 and November 1; Leighton Award for Nonprofit Excellence: July 1.

STAFF:
Rose Meissner, President

ADDRESS INQUIRIES TO:
Angela Butiste, Senior Program Officer
(See address above.)

THE COMMUNITY FOUNDATION OF SHELBY COUNTY   [1317]
Courtview Center, Suite 202
100 South Main Avenue
Sidney, OH 45365-2771
(937) 497-7800
Fax: (937) 497-7799

E-MAIL ADDRESS:
info@commfoun.com

WEB SITE ADDRESS:
www.commfoun.com

FOUNDED: 1952

AREAS OF INTEREST:
Arts and culture, family and community, education, environment, and health.

TYPE:
Capital grants; Scholarships; Seed money grants.

PURPOSE:
To improve the quality of life and to cultivate, administer and distribute legacy gifts for the benefit of its local community.

ELIGIBILITY:
Organizations must have 501(c)(3) status.

GEOGRAPHIC RESTRICTIONS:
Shelby County, Ohio.

FINANCIAL DATA:
Amount of support per award: Discretionary grants: $500 to $2,000.

Total amount of support: $12,000 in discretionary grants for the year 2009; Approximately $700,000 in total grantmaking for fiscal year 2009.

NUMBER OF APPLICANTS MOST RECENT YEAR:
29.

NUMBER OF AWARDS: 10.

APPLICATION INFORMATION:
Applicants must call the Executive Director of the Foundation to discuss the grant request idea and whether the project appears to fit within the Foundation's guidelines. Preliminary Grant Proposals and Full Proposals will not be accepted if they have not been requested by the Executive Director.

Applications for most of the scholarships are available to be printed online. Submissions cannot be made by e-mail, because original signatures are required.

Deadline: Discretionary grants: March 15. Designated purpose grants: Varies.

ADDRESS INQUIRIES TO:
Marian Spicer, Executive Director
(See address above.)

THE COMMUNITY FOUNDATION OF SOUTH ALABAMA   [1318]
212 St. Joseph Street
Mobile, AL 36602
(251) 438-5591
Fax: (251) 438-5592

E-MAIL ADDRESS:
info@communityendowment.org

WEB SITE ADDRESS:
www.communityendowment.org

FOUNDED: 1976

AREAS OF INTEREST:
Community, health, social services, arts and education.

TYPE:
Challenge/matching grants; Development grants; General operating grants; Project/program grants; Scholarships; Seed money grants.

PURPOSE:
To strengthen the future of nonprofit organizations in southwest Alabama by encouraging gifts, large and small, from all segments of the community.

LEGAL BASIS:
Alabama not-for-profit corporation/community foundation.

ELIGIBILITY:
Eligible organizations must be IRS 501(c)(3) tax-exempt and located in southwest Alabama.

GEOGRAPHIC RESTRICTIONS:
Southwestern Alabama (Baldwin, Choctaw, Clarke, Conecah, Escambia, Mobile, Monroe and Washington counties).

FINANCIAL DATA:
Amount of support per award: Varies.

Total amount of support: $3,300,000 for the year 2009.

APPLICATION INFORMATION:
Request for Proposals will be issued by the Foundation to announce when funding is available. Applications are to be submitted electronically using the Common Grant Application form. Applicants must include a copy of the IRS tax determination letter.

Duration: One year. Renewal by reapplication.

PUBLICATIONS:
Annual report; newsletter; application guidelines; *Charitable Gift Annuity*; *Real Estate Gifts.*

IRS IDENTIFICATION NUMBER: 63-0695166

STAFF:
Thomas H. Davis, Jr., President
Christina Cooley, Vice President of Accounting
Danny Patterson, Community Economic Development Director
Stephanie Ryan, Communications Officer
Janine Phillips, Program Officer
Carolyn Douglas, Community Economic Development Project Manager
Michael Dillaber, Project Manager

ADDRESS INQUIRIES TO:
Janine Phillips, Program Officer
(See address above.)

COMMUNITY FOUNDATION OF THE EASTERN SHORE   [1319]
1324 Belmont Avenue, Suite 401
Salisbury, MD 21804
(410) 742-9911
Fax: (410) 742-6638

E-MAIL ADDRESS:
cfes@cfes.org

WEB SITE ADDRESS:
www.cfes.org

FOUNDED: 1984

AREAS OF INTEREST:
Arts, civic affairs, community needs, conservation, culture, education, health and historic preservation.

CONSULTING OR VOLUNTEER SERVICES:
ShoreCAN Regional Volunteer Center.

NAME(S) OF PROGRAMS:
- **Chairman's Award**
- **Community Needs Grants**
- **Excellence in Education Program**
- **Field of Interest Grants**
- **Richard A. Henson Award of Excellence**
- **Frank H. Morris Humanitarian Award**
- **Nonprofit Support Program**

TYPE:
Awards/prizes; Challenge/matching grants; Demonstration grants; Project/program grants; Scholarships; Seed money grants; Technical assistance; Training grants.

YEAR PROGRAM STARTED: 1984

PURPOSE:
To improve the quality of life in the area by acting as a funding source for present and future generations.

ELIGIBILITY:
Grants are made to organizations that have tax-exempt status under Section 501(c)(3) of the Internal Revenue Code and not classified as a private foundation that is located or serves the residents of the counties. No grants are made to individuals. Nonsectarian religious programs may apply. Agencies must be operated and organized so that they do not discriminate in the hiring of staff on the basis of race, religion, gender, sexual orientation, age, national origin or disability.

GEOGRAPHIC RESTRICTIONS:
Somerset, Wicomico and Worcester counties, Maryland.

FINANCIAL DATA:
Total amount of support: $4,100,000 for the year 2010.

APPLICATION INFORMATION:
Duration: One year.

STAFF:
Erica Joseph, Program Director

ADDRESS INQUIRIES TO:
Erica Joseph, Program Director
(See address above.)

COMMUNITY FOUNDATION OF THE FOX RIVER VALLEY [1320]
111 West Downer Place
Suite 312
Aurora, IL 60506
(630) 896-7800
Fax: (630) 896-7811

E-MAIL ADDRESS:
info@communityfoundationfrv.org

WEB SITE ADDRESS:
www.communityfoundationfrv.org

AREAS OF INTEREST:
Education, health care, social services, the arts, and other charitable fields.

TYPE:
Capital grants; Scholarships.

PURPOSE:
To support worthwhile projects in the served communities.

ELIGIBILITY:
Grants are made to organizations that have tax-exempt status under Section 501(c)(3) of the Internal Revenue Code. No grants are made to individuals.

GEOGRAPHIC RESTRICTIONS:
Aurora, southern Kane County, and Kendall County, Illinois.

FINANCIAL DATA:
Amount of support per award: $1,000 to $10,000.
Total amount of support: Varies.

NUMBER OF APPLICANTS MOST RECENT YEAR:
Scholarships: 518.

NUMBER OF AWARDS: Scholarships: 242.

APPLICATION INFORMATION:
Applications may be obtained from the Foundation web site.
Duration: Varies.
Deadline: Grant proposals: First business day in June and December. Scholarships: January.

COMMUNITY FOUNDATION OF THE OZARKS [1321]
425 East Trafficway
Springfield, MO 65806
(417) 864-6199
Fax: (417) 864-8344

E-MAIL ADDRESS:
jleeth@cfozarks.org

WEB SITE ADDRESS:
www.cfozarks.org

AREAS OF INTEREST:
Health and social services; arts, culture and environment; education and community development.

TYPE:
Capital grants; Challenge/matching grants; Demonstration grants; Development grants; Endowments; Project/program grants; Scholarships. Initiative grants and Technical/Capacity-building grants.

PURPOSE:
To build a community endowment; to provide leadership; to prompt collaboration on community issues; to improve the quality of life for citizens in Greene County, MO and the surrounding region.

LEGAL BASIS:
Community foundation.

ELIGIBILITY:
Eligible organizations must be IRS 501(c)(3) tax-exempt and located in Greene County, MO or counties represented by our affiliate organizations which are located throughout the southern half of Missouri.

GEOGRAPHIC RESTRICTIONS:
Missouri.

FINANCIAL DATA:
Amount of support per award: Grants: $1,500 to $80,000; Initiative Awards: $100,000 to $1,000,000.
Total amount of support: Discretionary Grants Program: $15,000,000.

APPLICATION INFORMATION:
Complete application information is available online.

ADDRESS INQUIRIES TO:
Randy Russell, Senior Program Officer
(See address above.)

COMMUNITY FOUNDATION OF THE TEXAS HILL COUNTRY [1322]
301 Junction Highway, Suite 345
Kerrville, TX 78028
(830) 896-8811
Fax: (830) 792-5956

E-MAIL ADDRESS:
rick@communityfoundation.net

WEB SITE ADDRESS:
www.communityfoundation.net

FOUNDED: 1982

AREAS OF INTEREST:
Community development.

NAME(S) OF PROGRAMS:
- **Arts**
- **Children and Education**
- **Community**
- **Designated and Donor Advised Funds**
- **Healers**
- **Pass Through Grants**

TYPE:
Grants-in-aid.

PURPOSE:
To improve the quality of life in the Texas Hill Country of Texas.

ELIGIBILITY:
Grants are generally not awarded to individuals or to religious organizations.

GEOGRAPHIC RESTRICTIONS:
Bandera, Gillespie, Kendell and Kerr counties, Texas.

FINANCIAL DATA:
More than $6,000,000 in assets.
Amount of support per award: Varies.
Total amount of support: $810,000 for the year 2009.

APPLICATION INFORMATION:
Applicants must submit a cover letter, signed by the Board Chairman and the Executive Director, describing the proposal and need for the project in the community. Grant application must also include:
(1) completed application form including project description;
(2) detailed project budget along with indication of what portion of the project is funded or expected to be funded by other sources;
(3) organizational budget for the current fiscal year;
(4) financial statements, including balance sheet and statement of activity for the organization for the fiscal year most recently completed, or certified audit for the fiscal year most recently completed;
(5) most recent 990 tax return filed by the organization;
(6) copy of IRS 501(c)(3) letter of determination;
(7) list of board of directors and executive staff;
(8) board and staff training for previous 12-month period and;
(9) letters of support for cooperative projects between organizations (if applicable).

First time applicants should include a one- to two-page history of their organization. A plan for the evaluation of the project's results and dissemination of its findings must be included. Provide one original and two copies of the grant proposal and all attachments.

ADDRESS INQUIRIES TO:
Rick McManigle, Executive Director
(See address above.)

COMMUNITY FOUNDATION OF WESTERN MASSACHUSETTS (CFWM) [1323]
1500 Main Street
Springfield, MA 01115
(413) 732-2858
Fax: (413) 733-8565

E-MAIL ADDRESS:
wmass@communityfoundation.org

WEB SITE ADDRESS:
www.communityfoundation.org

FOUNDED: 1990

AREAS OF INTEREST:
Human services, education, arts and culture, health, housing and environment.

TYPE:
Capital grants; Challenge/matching grants; Demonstration grants; Project/program grants; Scholarships; Seed money grants; Technical assistance; Training grants. Arts and equipment.

YEAR PROGRAM STARTED: 1990

PURPOSE:
To support charitable programs in developing and expanding their services.

ELIGIBILITY:
Grants are restricted to worthy public charities located within Franklin, Hampden and Hampshire counties in Massachusetts.

GEOGRAPHIC RESTRICTIONS:
Franklin, Hampden and Hampshire counties, Massachusetts.

FINANCIAL DATA:
Amount of support per award: Average
$9,000.

Total amount of support: Approximately
$8,200,000 for fiscal year 2010.

COOPERATIVE FUNDING PROGRAMS: Informal
linkages as well as funds established by
family foundations within the community
foundation.

APPLICATION INFORMATION:
Applicant must submit short, two-page
application form and three copies of the
following elements:
(1) one- to two-page narrative and budget;
(2) 501(c)(3) and 509(a)(1) status;
(3) annual operating budget and audit;
(4) board of directors;
(5) signature of authorized individual and;
(6) evaluation plan.

Upon completion of the project, a Grant
Report form must be completed and returned
to the Community Foundation within 60
days.
Duration: One year. Nonrenewable.
Deadline: January and August.

PUBLICATIONS:
Annual report; newsletter; application with
guidelines; brochures for donors and
applicants.

STAFF:
Ron Ancrum, President
Nancy Reiche, Vice President for Programs

ADDRESS INQUIRIES TO:
Nancy Reiche
Vice President for Programs
(See address above.)

COMMUNITY FOUNDATION
SANTA CRUZ COUNTY   [1324]
7807 Soquel Drive
Aptos, CA 95003
(831) 662-2000

E-MAIL ADDRESS:
cfhelp@cfscc.org

WEB SITE ADDRESS:
www.cfscc.org

FOUNDED: 1982

AREAS OF INTEREST:
General projects and management assistance,
arts and humanities, community development,
education, environment, health, historic
preservation and human services.

NAME(S) OF PROGRAMS:
- **R.H. Beel Memorial Scholarship**
- **Ernest V. Cowell Scholarship**
- **Emmett and Elsie Geiser Scholarship**
- **The Matt's Climb Scholarship**
- **Louis J. and Mary Ellen Shultz
  Scholarship**
- **The Simunovich Family Agricultural
  Scholarship**
- **The Barbara J. Thompson Scholarship**
- **John L. Turner Scholarship**
- **Dan Wood Scholarship**

TYPE:
Awards/prizes; Conferences/seminars;
Fellowships; General operating grants;
Matching gifts; Project/program grants;
Scholarships; Technical assistance; Training
grants.

YEAR PROGRAM STARTED: 1982

PURPOSE:
To improve the quality of life in Santa Cruz
County; to make Santa Cruz County a better
place to live, now and in the future.

LEGAL BASIS:
Nonprofit, community foundation.

ELIGIBILITY:
Eligible organizations must be IRS 501(c)(3)
tax-exempt.

GEOGRAPHIC RESTRICTIONS:
Santa Cruz County, California.

FINANCIAL DATA:
Amount of support per award: Varies by
program. Average $15,000.

Total amount of support: $4,000,000 for the
year 2010.

NUMBER OF AWARDS: 11.

APPLICATION INFORMATION:
Applications are available at the Foundation
web site.
Duration: One year. Must reapply for
additional funding.

PUBLICATIONS:
Annual reports; list of grants; application
guidelines.

IRS IDENTIFICATION NUMBER: 94-2808039

ADDRESS INQUIRIES TO:
Christina Cuevas, Program Director
(See address above.)

THE COMMUNITY
FOUNDATIONS OF THE
HUDSON VALLEY   [1325]
80 Washington Street, Suite 201
Poughkeepsie, NY 12601
(845) 452-3077
Fax: (845) 452-3083

E-MAIL ADDRESS:
areynolds@cfhvny.org

WEB SITE ADDRESS:
www.cfhvny.org

FOUNDED: 1969

AREAS OF INTEREST:
Health, education and social services.

NAME(S) OF PROGRAMS:
- **Community Response Grants of the
  Hudson Valley**
- **Community Response Grants of Ulster
  County**

TYPE:
Project/program grants; Training grants.
Equipment to improve office operations.

PURPOSE:
To improve the quality of life in Dutchess
County.

ELIGIBILITY:
Eligible organizations must be IRS 501(c)(3)
tax-exempt.

GEOGRAPHIC RESTRICTIONS:
Primarily Dutchess County, New York.

FINANCIAL DATA:
Amount of support per award: Varies.

Total amount of support: $1,600,000 for
fiscal year ended June 30, 2010.

APPLICATION INFORMATION:
Applications are submitted through the online
application system.

PUBLICATIONS:
Annual report; newsletters.

IRS IDENTIFICATION NUMBER: 23-7026859

ADDRESS INQUIRIES TO:
Andrea L. Reynolds
President and Chief Executive Officer
(See address above.)

CONNECTICUT COMMUNITY
FOUNDATION   [1326]
43 Field Street
Waterbury, CT 06702
(203) 753-1315
Fax: (203) 756-3054

E-MAIL ADDRESS:
info@conncf.org

WEB SITE ADDRESS:
www.conncf.org

FOUNDED: 1923

AREAS OF INTEREST:
The arts, education, environment, health care
and human services.

CONSULTING OR VOLUNTEER SERVICES:
Nonprofit advisor services available.

NAME(S) OF PROGRAMS:
- **Capacity Building Grants**
- **Nonprofit Assistance Initiative**
- **Program Grants**

TYPE:
Capital grants; Challenge/matching grants;
Project/program grants; Scholarships; Seed
money grants. Organizational development.

YEAR PROGRAM STARTED: 1923

PURPOSE:
To serve the people of the Greater Waterbury
and Litchfield Hills to improve the quality of
life.

LEGAL BASIS:
Community foundation.

ELIGIBILITY:
The following requirements apply:
(1) Applicant is either a public institution or
a private tax-exempt organization under
Sections 501(c)(3) or 501(c)(4) of the
Internal Revenue Code. Individuals may
apply for scholarships or awards only;
(2) political, lobbying or religious activities
are ineligible. Religiously affiliated
organizations may propose nonsectarian
projects;
(3) organization must have a minimum
six-member board, representative of the
community, of which a majority are neither
employees nor relatives of employees and;
(4) organization or proposed program must
be located in Beacon Falls, Bethlehem,
Bridgewater, Cheshire, Goshen, Litchfield,
Middlebury, Morris, Naugatuck, New
Milford, Oxford, Prospect, Roxbury,
Southbury, Thomaston, Warren, Washington,
Waterbury, Watertown, Wolcott or Woodbury.

GEOGRAPHIC RESTRICTIONS:
Greater Waterbury and Litchfield Hills,
Connecticut.

FINANCIAL DATA:
Total amount of support: $1,900,000 in
grants and scholarships for the year 2009.

REPRESENTATIVE AWARDS:
Waterbury Health Access Project;
Connecticut Association for Human Services
for Earned Benefits Online Program.

APPLICATION INFORMATION:
Applicants must submit a letter of inquiry
before making a final submission. Guidelines
and letter of inquiry form may be obtained
online.

Duration: One year. Multiyear funding must be applied for at the outset and is subject to review.

Deadline: Letters of Inquiry: January 14 and September 16.

PUBLICATIONS:
Annual report.

ADDRESS INQUIRIES TO:
Carol O'Donnell
Associate Chief Executive Officer and Director of Programs
Josh Carey, Program Officer
(See address above.)

COOK FAMILY FOUNDATION [1327]

P.O. Box 278
Owosso, MI 48867-0278
(989) 725-1621
Fax: (989) 936-5910

E-MAIL ADDRESS:
tom@cookfamilyfoundation.org

WEB SITE ADDRESS:
www.cookfamilyfoundation.org

FOUNDED: 1978

AREAS OF INTEREST:
Education and community development.

TYPE:
Capital grants; Challenge/matching grants; Demonstration grants; Development grants; Matching gifts; Project/program grants; Scholarships; Seed money grants; Technical assistance. Educational support.

YEAR PROGRAM STARTED: 1978

PURPOSE:
To strengthen community institutions in Shiawassee County; to support the University of Michigan.

LEGAL BASIS:
Family (private) foundation.

ELIGIBILITY:
Eligible organizations must be IRS 501(c)(3) tax-exempt.

GEOGRAPHIC RESTRICTIONS:
Shiawassee County, Michigan.

FINANCIAL DATA:
Amount of support per award: $500 to $50,000.
Total amount of support: $500,000.
Matching fund requirements: Varies based on grant; average 20% cash/in-kind.

APPLICATION INFORMATION:
Applicants should submit a short letter of inquiry.

STAFF:
Robin Grinnell, Program Officer

ADDRESS INQUIRIES TO:
Thomas Cook, Executive Director
(See address above.)

COOPERATIVE DEVELOPMENT FOUNDATION [1328]

2011 Crystal Drive
Suite 800
Arlington, VA 22202
(703) 302-8094

E-MAIL ADDRESS:
equinn@cdf.coop

WEB SITE ADDRESS:
www.cdf.coop

FOUNDED: 1944

AREAS OF INTEREST:
Community, economic and social development through cooperative enterprise.

TYPE:
Grants-in-aid. The Foundation makes grants and loans for cooperative development through its various funds.

PURPOSE:
To promote self-help and mutual aid in community, economic and social development through cooperative enterprise.

LEGAL BASIS:
501(c)(3) organization.

ELIGIBILITY:
The Foundation does not award grants for purely personal needs. It works only in the cooperative sector.

GEOGRAPHIC RESTRICTIONS:
United States.

FINANCIAL DATA:
Amount of support per award: Varies.
Total amount of support: Varies.

NUMBER OF APPLICANTS MOST RECENT YEAR:
Approximately 30.

NUMBER OF AWARDS: 26.

APPLICATION INFORMATION:
Contact the Foundation after reviewing the various fund descriptions to determine if the proposed project fits within the Foundation's funding priorities. The Foundation supports cooperative development only.

PUBLICATIONS:
Annual report.

STAFF:
Elizabeth Bailey, Executive Director
Terence Buen, Programs Director
Ellen Quinn, Funds Manager

ADDRESS INQUIRIES TO:
See e-mail address above.

*SPECIAL STIPULATIONS:
The Foundation supports cooperative development only.

ADOLPH COORS FOUNDATION

4100 East Mississippi Avenue, Suite 1850
Denver, CO 80246
(303) 388-1636
Fax: (303) 388-1684

E-MAIL ADDRESS:
generalinfo@acoorsfdn.org

WEB SITE ADDRESS:
www.coorsfoundation.org

TYPE:
Capital grants; General operating grants; Project/program grants.

See entry 1184 for full listing.

CORPORATION FOR NATIONAL AND COMMUNITY SERVICE [1329]

1201 New York Avenue, N.W.
Washington, DC 20525
(202) 606-5000
(202) 606-6608
Fax: (202) 565-3475

E-MAIL ADDRESS:
vista@americorps.gov

WEB SITE ADDRESS:
www.nationalservice.gov

FOUNDED: 1964

AREAS OF INTEREST:
Anti-poverty or poverty-related activities.

NAME(S) OF PROGRAMS:
• **AmeriCorps VISTA**

TYPE:
Project/program grants. Provides full-time, full-year volunteers at the request of community groups to work on clearly defined tasks that lead to mobilization of the community's resources. The volunteers live among the people they serve at subsistence levels of support.

YEAR PROGRAM STARTED: 1965

PURPOSE:
To supplement efforts to eliminate poverty and poverty-related problems.

LEGAL BASIS:
Domestic Volunteer Service Act of 1973, as amended (P.L. 93-113).

ELIGIBILITY:
Sponsors applying for AmeriCorps VISTA must be nonprofit organizations. They may be public or private and include state and local governments.

GEOGRAPHIC RESTRICTIONS:
United States and its territories.

FINANCIAL DATA:
Volunteers receive a basic monthly subsistence allowance. An additional stipend is paid upon completion of service or the Americorps educational award.
Amount of support per award:
Approximately $16,000 per volunteer service year.
Total amount of support: Varies.

NUMBER OF APPLICANTS MOST RECENT YEAR:
Approximately 6,000.

NUMBER OF AWARDS: 1,200.

APPLICATION INFORMATION:
Duration: Varies.

THE DALLAS FOUNDATION [1330]

900 Jackson Street, Suite 705
Dallas, TX 75202
(214) 741-9898
Fax: (214) 741-9848

E-MAIL ADDRESS:
mjalonick@dallasfoundation.org

WEB SITE ADDRESS:
www.dallasfoundation.org

FOUNDED: 1929

AREAS OF INTEREST:
Arts, education, health and human services, and social services.

TYPE:
Capital grants; Project/program grants; Scholarships.

YEAR PROGRAM STARTED: 1929

PURPOSE:
To improve the quality of life for residents of the city and county of Dallas.

LEGAL BASIS:
Community foundation.

ELIGIBILITY:
Applicant organizations must be tax-exempt nonprofit focused on needs within Dallas County. Grants from the field of interest

funds require a match between the purpose of the grant and the purpose of the available funds. Grants from the unrestricted funds may be given to any type of need within Dallas County.

Funds are not available from discretionary funds for individuals, endowments, research, debt retirement, annual campaigns, underwriting of fund-raising events, or for organizations that have received support within the preceding three to five years.

GEOGRAPHIC RESTRICTIONS:
City and county of Dallas, Texas.

FINANCIAL DATA:
Since its inception, the Foundation has given more than $330,000,000 in grants to more than 2,400 organizations.

APPLICATION INFORMATION:
The application form is available on the Foundation web site, or by request. Unrestricted funds must have a letter of inquiry submitted by August 1.
Deadline: Interest funds: April 1 with announcement in June. Unrestricted funds: October 1 with announcement in December.

PUBLICATIONS:
Annual report; application guidelines.

ADDRESS INQUIRIES TO:
Laura Smith
Director of Community Philanthropy
(See address above.)

IRENE E. AND GEORGE A. DAVIS FOUNDATION   [1331]
One Monarch Place
Suite 1450
Springfield, MA 01144-1450
(413) 734-8336
Fax: (413) 734-7845

E-MAIL ADDRESS:
info@davisfdn.org

WEB SITE ADDRESS:
www.davisfdn.org

FOUNDED: 1970

AREAS OF INTEREST:
Community, social services and early education.

TYPE:
Project/program grants.

PURPOSE:
To make strategically significant investments in organizations and projects that promise demonstrable long-range benefits improving the quality of life of citizens residing in Hampden County, MA.

LEGAL BASIS:
Private foundation.

ELIGIBILITY:
Grants are made to organizations that have tax-exempt status under Section 501(c)(3) of the Internal Revenue Code. No grants are made to individuals. Catholic organizations may apply.

GEOGRAPHIC RESTRICTIONS:
Hampden County, Massachusetts.

FINANCIAL DATA:
Amount of support per award: Varies.

APPLICATION INFORMATION:
Submit a letter of intent to the Foundation to determine the interest and appropriateness of a full proposal.
Duration: One year.

Deadline: February 1, May 1, August 1 and November 1.

ADDRESS INQUIRIES TO:
Mary E. Walachy, Executive Director
(See address above.)

DEARBORN COMMUNITY FOUNDATION, INC.   [1332]
322 Walnut Street
Lawrenceburg, IN 47025
(812) 539-4115
Fax: (812) 539-4119

E-MAIL ADDRESS:
dcfgrants@comcast.net

WEB SITE ADDRESS:
www.dearborncf.org

FOUNDED: 1997

AREAS OF INTEREST:
Art, culture and humanities, community and public benefit, education, environmental and animal protection, and human services and youth.

TYPE:
Capital grants; Challenge/matching grants; Development grants; General operating grants; Project/program grants; Scholarships; Seed money grants; Technical assistance; Training grants.

YEAR PROGRAM STARTED: 1997

PURPOSE:
To connect people who care with causes that improve the quality of life in the community by advancing cultural, educational and social opportunities, while preserving the community's heritage and helping donors create a permanent legacy in Dearborn County, IN.

ELIGIBILITY:
Grants are made to organizations that are tax-exempt under Section 501(c)(3) of the Internal Revenue Code and recognized by the state of Indiana as current and active not-for-profit organizations. No grants are made to individuals outside of scholarships and/or educational grants. Non-sectarian religious programs may apply.

GEOGRAPHIC RESTRICTIONS:
Dearborn County, Indiana.

FINANCIAL DATA:
Amount of support per award: Varies.
Total amount of support: Maximum $100,000.

APPLICATION INFORMATION:
Duration: One year.

STAFF:
Fred McCarter, Executive Director
Denise Sedler, Program Director

ADDRESS INQUIRIES TO:
Denise Sedler, Program Director
(See address above.)

ROGER L. AND AGNES C. DELL CHARITABLE TRUST   [1333]
U.S. Bank Charitable Services Group
800 Nicollet Mall, BC-MN-H16A
Minneapolis, MN 55402
(612) 303-3208
Fax: (612) 303-3219

E-MAIL ADDRESS:
sarah.godfrey@usbank.com

AREAS OF INTEREST:
Arts and culture, education and youth in the Fergus Falls, MN region.

TYPE:
Capital grants; General operating grants; Project/program grants.

PURPOSE:
To improve the quality of life in Fergus Falls, MN and the surrounding area.

ELIGIBILITY:
Eligible organizations must be IRS 501(c)(3) tax-exempt.

GEOGRAPHIC RESTRICTIONS:
Fergus Falls, Minnesota and the surrounding area.

FINANCIAL DATA:
Total amount of support: $36,788 for the year 2008.

APPLICATION INFORMATION:
Application should be submitted in writing form outlining nature of the request.

ADDRESS INQUIRIES TO:
Matt McGovern
Pemberton Sorlie Rufer Kershner PLLP
110 North Mill Street
P.O. Box 866
Fergus Falls, MN 56538-0866

*SPECIAL STIPULATIONS:
Unsolicited proposals not accepted.

DEPAUW UNIVERSITY KEY CLUB INTERNATIONAL BONNER/WRIGHT SCHOLARSHIP   [1334]
101 East Seminary Street
Greencastle, IN 46135
(765) 658-4030
(800) 447-2495
Fax: (765) 658-4137

E-MAIL ADDRESS:
jenniecoy@depauw.edu

WEB SITE ADDRESS:
www.keyclub.org

AREAS OF INTEREST:
Leadership and community service.

NAME(S) OF PROGRAMS:
• **Bonner Scholarship**
• **John Ellis Wright Award**

TYPE:
Scholarships.

PURPOSE:
To encourage youth to become actively involved in the community around them.

ELIGIBILITY:
Applicant must be a college-bound graduating high school senior with a grade point average of B or higher and have been an active Key Club member for two years, not serving as International Board member or governor.

Selection is based on academic achievement, commitment to community service, and leadership.

Women, ethnic minorities, and high-need students are encouraged to apply.

GEOGRAPHIC RESTRICTIONS:
United States.

FINANCIAL DATA:
Amount of support per award: Recipient receives $10,000 annual John Ellis Wright award and $2,500 Bonner Scholarship.

COOPERATIVE FUNDING PROGRAMS: Corella and Bertram F. Bonner Foundation.

APPLICATION INFORMATION:
No special application is required. Applicants involved in Key Club will be identified via their admissions application.

Duration: Four years.

Deadline: March 1 for early consideration; however, applications will be received until all selections are made.

ADDRESS INQUIRIES TO:
DePauw University Office of Admission
Bonner/Wright Scholarship Program
Greencastle, IN 46135-1778

*SPECIAL STIPULATIONS:
Bonner scholars are expected to maintain good academic standing at DePauw (2.5 grade point average or better), participate in educational and enrichment activities, successfully complete the Bonner Program First-Year Student Seminar, as well as participate in community-service programs for an average of 10 hours per week during the school year, and complete two summer internships consisting of 280 hours each.

RICHARD AND HELEN DEVOS FOUNDATION [1335]

P.O. Box 230257
Grand Rapids, MI 49523-0257
(616) 643-4700
Fax: (616) 774-0116

E-MAIL ADDRESS:
foundations@pdbcorp.com

AREAS OF INTEREST:
Christian ministry and outreach and local community support.

TYPE:
General operating grants; Project/program grants.

PURPOSE:
To improve the quality of people's lives and to build a stronger community.

LEGAL BASIS:
Private foundation.

ELIGIBILITY:
Primarily, organizations that have prior affiliation with the family of DeVos and are located in Western Michigan or Central Florida. Also, they must have evidence of tax-exempt status as an IRS 501(c)(3) public charity.

GEOGRAPHIC RESTRICTIONS:
Central Florida and western Michigan.

FINANCIAL DATA:
Amount of support per award: Varies as to need and project.

APPLICATION INFORMATION:
Organizations should submit a statement of purpose and history of organization, budget, sources of support, goals and specifics regarding the program to be funded, annual report (if available) and copy of the organization's tax-exempt letter.

Duration: One year. Renewal possible.

Deadline: Proposals are reviewed quarterly.

ADDRESS INQUIRIES TO:
Ginny VanderHart, Executive Director
(See address above.)

DICKINSON AREA COMMUNITY FOUNDATION [1336]

333 South Stephenson Avenue
Suite 204
Iron Mountain, MI 49801
(906) 774-3131
Fax: (906) 774-7640

E-MAIL ADDRESS:
dacf@uplogon.com

WEB SITE ADDRESS:
www.dickinsonareacommunityfoundation.org

AREAS OF INTEREST:
Arts, community needs and development, culture, education, environment, health and human services.

TYPE:
Grants-in-aid; Scholarships.

PURPOSE:
To encourage philanthropic investment in Dickinson County and surrounding Wisconsin communities.

ELIGIBILITY:
Grants are made to organizations that have tax-exempt status under Section 501(c)(3) of the Internal Revenue Code. No grants are made to individuals. Nonsectarian religious programs may apply.

GEOGRAPHIC RESTRICTIONS:
Dickinson County, Michigan and surrounding Wisconsin and Michigan communities.

FINANCIAL DATA:
Amount of support per award: $200 to $5,000.

Total amount of support: Approximately $150,000 for the year 2011.

NUMBER OF AWARDS: 54 for the year 2010; 60 for the year 2011.

APPLICATION INFORMATION:
Duration: One year.
Deadline: March 15.

PUBLICATIONS:
Brochures.

ADDRESS INQUIRIES TO:
Tamara Juul, Executive Director
(See address above.)

THE DIXON FOUNDATION [1337]

One Chase Corporate Drive
Suite 400
Birmingham, AL 35244-7001
(205) 313-6501
Fax: (205) 313-6502

E-MAIL ADDRESS:
joy@dixon-group.com

FOUNDED: 1986

TYPE:
General operating grants.

PURPOSE:
To support social services in northern Alabama and northern Georgia.

ELIGIBILITY:
Eligible organizations must be IRS 501(c)(3) tax-exempt. No funding to individuals.

GEOGRAPHIC RESTRICTIONS:
Northern Alabama and northern Georgia.

FINANCIAL DATA:
Amount of support per award: Varies.
Total amount of support: Up to $400,000.

APPLICATION INFORMATION:
Applicants should send in a brief summary, budget, and copy of IRS 501(c)(3) tax determination letter.

Duration: One year. Grants renewable by reapplication.

ADDRESS INQUIRIES TO:
Joy Levio, Operations Manager
(See address above.)

THE JEAN AND LOUIS DREYFUS FOUNDATION, INC. [1338]

315 Madison Avenue, Suite 900
New York, NY 10017
(212) 599-1931
Fax: (212) 599-2956

E-MAIL ADDRESS:
info@jldreyfus.org

WEB SITE ADDRESS:
www.foundationcenter.org/grantmaker/dreyfus

FOUNDED: 1979

AREAS OF INTEREST:
Aging and disadvantaged, arts-in-education, education and literacy, and social services.

TYPE:
Challenge/matching grants; General operating grants; Project/program grants. Funding to direct service organizations and those projects which will produce systemic change.

PURPOSE:
To enhance the quality of life of New Yorkers, particularly the aging and disadvantaged.

ELIGIBILITY:
Nonprofit 501(c)(3) direct service organizations focusing on enhancing the quality of life of New Yorkers.

GEOGRAPHIC RESTRICTIONS:
New York City (five boroughs), New York.

FINANCIAL DATA:
Amount of support per award: $5,000 to $20,000.

Total amount of support: $649,500.

APPLICATION INFORMATION:
Initially, a one- to two-page letter of inquiry describing the grantee organization and outlining the project in question. Letters should be sent by mail to the attention of Ms. Edmee de M. Firth, Executive Director.

Letters of inquiry from organizations not previously funded are not being accepted at this time.

Duration: One year. Must reapply.

Deadline: Letter of inquiry: January 15 and July 15.

PUBLICATIONS:
Annual report.

ADDRESS INQUIRIES TO:
Edmee de M. Firth, Executive Director
(See address above.)

*PLEASE NOTE:
Letters of inquiry from organizations not previously funded are not being accepted at this time.

DULUTH SUPERIOR AREA COMMUNITY FOUNDATION   [1339]

222 East Superior Street
Suite 302
Duluth, MN 55802
(218) 726-0232
Fax: (218) 726-0257

E-MAIL ADDRESS:
grantsinfo@dsacommunityfoundation.com

WEB SITE ADDRESS:
www.dsacommunityfoundation.com

FOUNDED: 1982

AREAS OF INTEREST:
Arts, community and economic development,
education, environment and human services.

TYPE:
Challenge/matching grants; Development
grants; Project/program grants; Seed money
grants.

YEAR PROGRAM STARTED: 1983

PURPOSE:
To improve the quality of life in Duluth,
Superior and surrounding counties.

LEGAL BASIS:
Community foundation.

ELIGIBILITY:
Eligible organizations must be IRS 501(c)(3)
tax-exempt.

GEOGRAPHIC RESTRICTIONS:
Aitkin, Carlton, Cook, Itasca, Koochiching,
Lake, and St. Louis counties, Minnesota;
Bayfield and Douglas counties, Wisconsin.

FINANCIAL DATA:
Amount of support per award: $200 to
$25,000.

APPLICATION INFORMATION:
Information regarding the inquiry process is
available online.
Duration: Usually one year.
Deadline: Varies according to program.

PUBLICATIONS:
Elements, newsletter; annual report.

THE JOHN G. DUNCAN TRUST   [1340]

c/o Wells Fargo Bank, N.A.
1740 Broadway
MAC C7300-483
Denver, CO 80274
(720) 947-6752
Fax: (303) 864-9244

E-MAIL ADDRESS:
colleen.f.lynch@wellsfargo.com

FOUNDED: 1955

AREAS OF INTEREST:
Human services, health, education, religion
and arts.

TYPE:
Project/program grants.

YEAR PROGRAM STARTED: 1956

PURPOSE:
To support education and health care,
including dental care, food, children and
youth, social, blind and aging services.

LEGAL BASIS:
Private foundation.

ELIGIBILITY:
501(c)(3) tax-exempt organizations in
Colorado only may apply. Grants are not

made for individuals, general operating
expenses, endowments, organizations outside
of Colorado, or other grantmaking
organizations.

Organizations receiving a grant are not
eligible to apply for a grant in the following
calendar year.

GEOGRAPHIC RESTRICTIONS:
Colorado.

FINANCIAL DATA:
Amount of support per award: Typically
$1,000 to $10,000.
Total amount of support: Approximately
$300,000 per year.

APPLICATION INFORMATION:
Proposals should include standard summary
and budget information, evidence of
tax-exempt status, and written information
deemed appropriate by the applicant
organizations to be helpful in evaluating their
proposal. Mission statement is required. Do
not include audio or video materials.

Applicants are strongly urged to contact
Colleen Lynch by e-mail for current
guidelines, application and program/project
budget.
Duration: No grants are made on a
continuing basis.
Deadline: The last day of January, April,
July and October.

ADDRESS INQUIRIES TO:
Colleen Lynch
(See e-mail address above.)

THE EAST BAY COMMUNITY FOUNDATION   [1341]

DeDomenico Building
200 Frank H. Ogawa Plaza
Oakland, CA 94612
(510) 836-3223
Fax: (510) 836-7418

E-MAIL ADDRESS:
communityinvestment@eastbaycf.org

WEB SITE ADDRESS:
www.eastbaycf.org

FOUNDED: 1928

AREAS OF INTEREST:
Preparing young people for success in the
educational system and providing economic
opportunities for the underprivileged and
families.

TYPE:
Project/program grants. Building leadership
capacity grants.

YEAR PROGRAM STARTED: 1928

PURPOSE:
To transform the lives of people in the East
Bay with pressing needs.

LEGAL BASIS:
Public foundation.

ELIGIBILITY:
Eligible organizations must be IRS 501(c)(3)
tax-exempt.

GEOGRAPHIC RESTRICTIONS:
Alameda and Contra Costa counties,
California.

FINANCIAL DATA:
Amount of support per award: Varies.
Total amount of support: $1,000,000
annually.

APPLICATION INFORMATION:
Guidelines and applications are available
online.

PUBLICATIONS:
Guidelines.

ADDRESS INQUIRIES TO:
Community Investment Department
(See web site above.)

EAST TEXAS COMMUNITIES FOUNDATION   [1342]

315 North Broadway Avenue
Tyler, TX 75702-5712
(903) 533-0208
Fax: (903) 533-0258

E-MAIL ADDRESS:
info@etcf.org

WEB SITE ADDRESS:
www.etcf.org/about.htm

FOUNDED: 1989

AREAS OF INTEREST:
Community development.

TYPE:
Grants-in-aid; Scholarships. The Foundation
administers scholarship funds for donors,
nonprofit organizations, civic clubs, service
groups and businesses.

PURPOSE:
To promote charitable giving which enhances
the quality of life for the people of east
Texas.

ELIGIBILITY:
Grants are made to 501(c)(3) organizations.
Scholarship applicants must be citizens or
permanent residents of the U.S.

GEOGRAPHIC RESTRICTIONS:
East Texas.

FINANCIAL DATA:
Amount of support per award: Varies.
Total amount of support: Varies.

APPLICATION INFORMATION:
Deadline: Varies.

ADDRESS INQUIRIES TO:
Dana Durman, Program Officer
(See address above.)

EAU CLAIRE COMMUNITY FOUNDATION   [1343]

306 South Barstow Street, Suite 104
Eau Claire, WI 54701
(715) 552-3801
Fax: (715) 552-3802

E-MAIL ADDRESS:
suebornick@eccommunityfoundation.org

WEB SITE ADDRESS:
www.eccommunityfoundation.org

FOUNDED: 1997

AREAS OF INTEREST:
Serving the charitable needs of the Eau
Claire, WI community.

TYPE:
Project/program grants.

YEAR PROGRAM STARTED: 1997

PURPOSE:
To strengthen our community by offering
donors opportunities to establish charitable
legacies, by making grants, and by serving as
a catalyst to address community needs.

LEGAL BASIS:
Nonprofit community foundation.

ELIGIBILITY:
Eligible organizations must have 501(c)(3) status. Grants are available to religious organizations when recipients of services are not required to profess membership or belief in the religious organization.

GEOGRAPHIC RESTRICTIONS:
Eau Claire County, Wisconsin.

FINANCIAL DATA:
Net assets of $6,251,194 as of December 31, 2010.
Amount of support per award: Varies.
Total amount of support: $2,253,449 in grants from 1999 to 2010.

NUMBER OF APPLICANTS MOST RECENT YEAR:
54 for the year 2010.

NUMBER OF AWARDS: 36.

APPLICATION INFORMATION:
Submit original application and cover letter, plus 15 copies (three-hole punched). Include one copy of each of the following:
(1) most recent audited financial statement or form 990 tax return;
(2) list of Board of Directors and;
(3) copy of current IRS determination letter indicating 501(c)(3) or 509(a) tax-exempt status, or evidence the organization is not a private foundation as defined in Section 509(a). If not available, explain status.

Applications must be delivered or mailed. Applications sent by fax or e-mail are not accepted.
Duration: Varies. Grants are renewable.
Deadline: March 10.

STAFF:
Sue Bornick, Executive Director

ADDRESS INQUIRIES TO:
Sue Bornick, Executive Director
(See address above.)

ECOLAB FOUNDATION   [1344]
370 North Wabasha Street, EUC/11
St. Paul, MN 55102
(651) 293-2923
Fax: (651) 225-3191

E-MAIL ADDRESS:
ecolabfoundation@ecolab.com

WEB SITE ADDRESS:
www.ecolab.com

FOUNDED: 1986

AREAS OF INTEREST:
Arts and culture, education, environment and community development.

CONSULTING OR VOLUNTEER SERVICES:
501(c)(3) organizations.

TYPE:
General operating grants; Project/program grants. Employee matching gifts.

YEAR PROGRAM STARTED: 1986

PURPOSE:
To enrich the quality of life in communities where Ecolab operates.

LEGAL BASIS:
Corporate foundation.

ELIGIBILITY:
Eligible organizations must be IRS 501(c)(3) tax-exempt.

GEOGRAPHIC RESTRICTIONS:
City of Industry, California; Atlanta, Georgia; Elk Grove Village and Joliet, Illinois;

Huntington, Indiana; St. Paul, Minnesota; Columbus, Mississippi; Greensboro, North Carolina; Grand Forks, North Dakota; Fort Worth and Garland, Texas; Martinsburg, West Virginia; and Beloit, Wisconsin.

FINANCIAL DATA:
Amount of support per award: $5,000 to $60,000.
Total amount of support: $4,560,000 in grants as of fiscal year 2010.
Matching fund requirements: Must be an Ecolab employee.

NUMBER OF APPLICANTS MOST RECENT YEAR:
300.

NUMBER OF AWARDS: 203.

APPLICATION INFORMATION:
Application form is available online.
Duration: One year.
Deadline: September 1.

PUBLICATIONS:
Guidelines (on web site).

ADDRESS INQUIRIES TO:
Lisa Maloney-Vinz
Community Relations Specialist
(See address above.)

EL PASO COMMUNITY FOUNDATION   [1345]
123 West Mills Avenue
Suite 520
El Paso, TX 79901
(915) 533-4020
Fax: (915) 532-0716

E-MAIL ADDRESS:
info@epcf.org

WEB SITE ADDRESS:
www.epcf.org

FOUNDED: 1977

AREAS OF INTEREST:
Arts and humanities, education, public benefit, health and disabilities, environment and animals, and human services.

TYPE:
General operating grants; Scholarships. A charitable fund established at the Foundation by individuals, corporations or organizations.

YEAR PROGRAM STARTED: 1972

PURPOSE:
To improve the quality of life in the El Paso region, TX.

LEGAL BASIS:
501(c)(3) agencies.

ELIGIBILITY:
Grant request will be considered only from 501(c)(3) agencies located within or offering services to the community which includes far west Texas, southern New Mexico and northern Chihuahua, Mexico. Grants are not made to individuals or religious organizations.

GEOGRAPHIC RESTRICTIONS:
Far west Texas, southern New Mexico and northern Chihuahua, Mexico.

FINANCIAL DATA:
Amount of support per award: $4,000 to $40,000.
Total amount of support: Varies.

APPLICATION INFORMATION:
Applicant must submit a Letter of Inquiry to the Foundation.

Deadline: Grants: February 1 and August 1.

ADDRESS INQUIRIES TO:
Virginia Martinez, President
(See address above.)

FRED L. EMERSON FOUNDATION, INC.   [1346]
5654 South Street Road
Auburn, NY 13021
(315) 253-9621 ext. 222
Fax: (315) 253-5235

E-MAIL ADDRESS:
info@emersonfoundation.com

WEB SITE ADDRESS:
www.emersonfoundation.com

AREAS OF INTEREST:
Education (primarily private higher education), hospital and health programs, community agencies, cultural institutions, youth and community service programs, and social welfare agencies.

TYPE:
Capital grants; Challenge/matching grants; Endowments; Project/program grants; Research grants.

PURPOSE:
To improve the quality of life in Auburn, Cayuga County and upstate New York.

ELIGIBILITY:
Organizations must be tax-exempt. No grants are made to individuals; no loans or funding of operating expenses.

GEOGRAPHIC RESTRICTIONS:
Community of Auburn, Cayuga County and upstate New York.

FINANCIAL DATA:
Amount of support per award: Varies.
Total amount of support: Varies.

APPLICATION INFORMATION:
Proposals may be submitted in letter form, detailing the project for which support is being sought, along with a copy of the 501(c)(3) IRS tax-exempt determination letter, project budget and fund-raising plan, list of board of directors, and most recent copy of financial statement.
Duration: Varies.
Deadline: Proposals are accepted on an ongoing basis.

PUBLICATIONS:
Guidelines.

ADDRESS INQUIRIES TO:
Daniel Fessenden
Executive Director and Secretary
(See address above.)

ENTERPRISE COMMUNITY PARTNERS
10227 Wincopin Circle, Suite 500
American City Building
Columbia, MD 21044
(410) 964-1230
(434) 960-2484
Fax: (410) 964-1376

WEB SITE ADDRESS:
www.enterprisecommunity.org

TYPE:
Fellowships.

See entry 443 for full listing.

ESSEX COUNTY COMMUNITY FOUNDATION   [1347]

175 Andover Street
Suite 101
Danvers, MA 01923
(978) 777-8876 ext. 28
Fax: (978) 777-9454

E-MAIL ADDRESS:
j.bishop@eccf.org

WEB SITE ADDRESS:
www.eccf.org

FOUNDED: 1999

AREAS OF INTEREST:
Arts and culture, education, environment, health, social and community services and youth services.

CONSULTING OR VOLUNTEER SERVICES:
Nonprofit organizations in Essex County, MA.

NAME(S) OF PROGRAMS:
● **Arts Forum**
● **Essex County Youth-at-Risk**
● **First Jobs**
● **Greater Lawrence Summer Fund**
● **The Hunger Project**
● **The Women's Fund of Essex County**

TYPE:
Capital grants; Conferences/seminars; Endowments; General operating grants; Project/program grants; Scholarships; Technical assistance. Capacity-building grants. Various grantmaking funds. Mostly project/program grants. Agencies can establish endowment funds.

YEAR PROGRAM STARTED: 1999

PURPOSE:
To promote local philanthropy and to strengthen the nonprofit organizations of Essex County.

LEGAL BASIS:
Public 501(c)(3) charity.

ELIGIBILITY:
Organizations offering programs and services in Essex County (MA) communities, recognized as tax-exempt under Section 501(c)(3) of the Internal Revenue Code and, in some cases, to agencies of local or state government. Organizations with a qualified fiscal sponsor are also considered.

FINANCIAL DATA:
$17,000,000 in assets under management.
Amount of support per award: $1,000 to $20,000.
Total amount of support: $2,597,072 in grants and scholarships for fiscal year 2010.

COOPERATIVE FUNDING PROGRAMS: The Foundation has eight competitive grant funds and 17 scholarship programs. There are 80 donor-advised funds.

NUMBER OF AWARDS: 517.

REPRESENTATIVE AWARDS:
$20,000 to Greater Lawrence Community Boating Program for summer programming; $3,806 to Marblehead Middle School for a SMART Board (interactive whiteboard).

APPLICATION INFORMATION:
Duration: Some two-year awards, but mostly one-year.
Deadline: Varies.

PUBLICATIONS:
Annual report; newsletter; brochure.

IRS IDENTIFICATION NUMBER: 04-3407816

STAFF:
David Welbourn, President and Chief Executive Officer

ADDRESS INQUIRIES TO:
Julie Bishop, Vice President
Grants and Services
(See address above.)

EURASIA FOUNDATION   [1348]

1350 Connecticut Avenue, N.W.
Suite 1000
Washington, DC 20036-1206
(202) 234-7370
Fax: (202) 234-7377

E-MAIL ADDRESS:
eurasia@eurasia.org

WEB SITE ADDRESS:
www.eurasia.org

FOUNDED: 1992

AREAS OF INTEREST:
International development and the former Soviet Union.

TYPE:
Conferences/seminars; Development grants; General operating grants; Project/program grants; Seed money grants.

YEAR PROGRAM STARTED: 1993

PURPOSE:
To promote private enterprise and civil society in the former Soviet Union.

LEGAL BASIS:
Nonprofit.

ELIGIBILITY:
Legally registered organizations are eligible for grants.

FINANCIAL DATA:
Amount of support per award: Up to $20,000.
Total amount of support: Annual budget under $20,000,000.

APPLICATION INFORMATION:
No application form required. Submit a two- to three-page letter of inquiry describing the objectives of the program.
Duration: One to three years. Renewal possible.

PUBLICATIONS:
Annual report; regional newsletter; foundationwide newsletter.

ADDRESS INQUIRIES TO:
Angie Woodward, Human Resources and Administration Officer
(See address above.)

FAIR OAKS FOUNDATION   [1349]

600 Grant Street, Suite 4600
Pittsburgh, PA 15219
(412) 456-4418
(412) 456-4400
Fax: (412) 456-4404

AREAS OF INTEREST:
United Way, universities and community funds.

TYPE:
Cash contributions.

PURPOSE:
To provide support for community funds and higher education.

ELIGIBILITY:
Organizations classified as 501(c)(3) by the IRS can apply. No grants to individuals.

FINANCIAL DATA:
Amount of support per award: $250 to $1,000.
Total amount of support: $400,000 per year.

APPLICATION INFORMATION:
Contact the Foundation for application procedures. Request should be in letter format.
Deadline: November 1.

ADDRESS INQUIRIES TO:
Rose Hoover, Secretary
(See address above.)

FAIRFIELD COUNTY COMMUNITY FOUNDATION   [1350]

383 Main Avenue
Norwalk, CT 06851
(203) 750-3200
Fax: (203) 750-3232

E-MAIL ADDRESS:
info@fccfoundation.org

WEB SITE ADDRESS:
www.fccfoundation.org

FOUNDED: 1992

AREAS OF INTEREST:
Community development, housing, education, youth development, health and human services.

TYPE:
Challenge/matching grants; Demonstration grants; Development grants; Endowments; General operating grants; Project/program grants; Scholarships; Seed money grants. Scholarships are for high school students pursuing college or postsecondary training.

YEAR PROGRAM STARTED: 1992

PURPOSE:
To promote the growth of philanthropy in order to strengthen the communities of Fairfield County, CT.

ELIGIBILITY:
Grants are made to organizations that have tax-exempt status under Section 501(c)(3) of the Internal Revenue Code. No grants are made to individuals. Discretionary grants are only made to organizations serving Fairfield County, CT.

GEOGRAPHIC RESTRICTIONS:
Fairfield County, Connecticut.

FINANCIAL DATA:
Amount of support per award: Grants vary in amount, depending upon the needs and nature of the request.
Total amount of support: $11,000,000 annually.

APPLICATION INFORMATION:
Duration: One year. Renewal possible.

ADDRESS INQUIRIES TO:
Sharon Jones, Program Assistant
E-mail: sjones@fccfoundation.org
(See address above.)

THE FEINSTEIN FOUNDATION

37 Alhambra Circle
Cranston, RI 02905
(401) 467-5155
(401) 941-5913
Fax: (401) 941-0988

E-MAIL ADDRESS:
asf@feinsteinfoundation.org

WEB SITE ADDRESS:
www.feinsteinfoundation.org

TYPE:
Challenge/matching grants. Each participating agency receives a share of $1,000,000 that represents their portion of the total amount reported to the Foundation that was raised by anti-hunger agencies using the Foundation's challenge in their fight to end hunger fund-raising.

See entry 1582 for full listing.

SAMUEL S. FELS FUND [1351]
1616 Walnut Street, Suite 800
Philadelphia, PA 19103
(215) 731-9455
Fax: (215) 731-9457

WEB SITE ADDRESS:
www.samfels.org

FOUNDED: 1936

AREAS OF INTEREST:
Public education, community services and arts.

NAME(S) OF PROGRAMS:
- **Arts and Culture**
- **Community Concerns**
- **Public Education**

TYPE:
Challenge/matching grants; Demonstration grants; Development grants; General operating grants; Project/program grants; Seed money grants; Technical assistance.

YEAR PROGRAM STARTED: 1936

PURPOSE:
To improve the quality of life for the citizens of Philadelphia, especially the least fortunate.

LEGAL BASIS:
Private foundation.

ELIGIBILITY:
Applicants must be agencies located in the city of Philadelphia. Excluded from the Fund's program of grants are contributions to national organizations, capital campaigns, general support, scholarships, fellowships and grants-in-aid for travel, research and publication; grants to individual day care or afterschool programs. No grants are made to individuals.

GEOGRAPHIC RESTRICTIONS:
Philadelphia, Pennsylvania.

FINANCIAL DATA:
Amount of support per award: $3,000 to $30,000.
Total amount of support: $2,000,000 for the year 2010.

NUMBER OF APPLICANTS MOST RECENT YEAR:
Approximately 500.

NUMBER OF AWARDS: Approximately 200.

APPLICATION INFORMATION:
Guidelines are available from the web site above.
Duration: Primarily one year.
Deadline: Arts: January 15 and May 15.

PUBLICATIONS:
Annual report; guidelines for applicants.

TRUSTEES:
Mindy Posoff, President
Valerie Clayton, Vice President
Beverly Coleman, Treasurer
Helen Cunningham, Secretary
Phoebe Haddon, Member Director
Ida Chen
Sandra Featherman
John H. Rice
Len Rieser
David Wice

ADDRESS INQUIRIES TO:
Helen Cunningham, Executive Director
(See telephone number above.)

FIREMAN'S FUND INSURANCE COMPANY [1352]
777 San Marin Drive
Novato, CA 94998
(415) 899-2000

E-MAIL ADDRESS:
heritage@ffic.com

WEB SITE ADDRESS:
www.firemansfund.com

FOUNDED: 1863

AREAS OF INTEREST:
Fire service organizations and fire and burn prevention programs.

NAME(S) OF PROGRAMS:
- **Heritage Program**

TYPE:
Project/program grants.

YEAR PROGRAM STARTED: 2004

PURPOSE:
To support firefighters for safer communities; to provide awards to fire departments for needed equipment, training and community education programs.

LEGAL BASIS:
Company corporate giving program.

ELIGIBILITY:
Must be a nonprofit, tax-exempt 501(c)(3) organization. No grants to individuals, fraternal, veteran, sectarian, religious or political organizations.

GEOGRAPHIC RESTRICTIONS:
United States.

FINANCIAL DATA:
Amount of support per award: Varies.

NUMBER OF AWARDS: 300.

REPRESENTATIVE AWARDS:
$12,330 to Berea Fire Department, Berea, OH, for critical protective gear and clothing; $7,500 to Fort Washington Fire Company, Fort Washington, PA, for extrication equipment.

APPLICATION INFORMATION:
Employees and independent agencies nominate fire departments for grants.
Duration: One year.

*PLEASE NOTE:
No request considered by phone call.

FIRST HORIZON NATIONAL CORPORATION [1353]
P.O. Box 84
Memphis, TN 38101-0084
(901) 523-4444
(901) 523-4357
Fax: (901) 523-4354

E-MAIL ADDRESS:
pwaviotti@firsthorizon.com

WEB SITE ADDRESS:
www.fhnc.com

FOUNDED: 1864

AREAS OF INTEREST:
Economic development, health and human services, education, arts and community-based programs and organizations in Shelby County, TN.

TYPE:
Matching gifts.

PURPOSE:
To generate economic development in core market; to preserve and enhance what is special about core market and its communities; to leverage additional resources for the community.

LEGAL BASIS:
Corporate contributions program.

ELIGIBILITY:
Grants are made to tax-exempt organizations whose activities meet the objectives outlined above. First Horizon National Corp. does not use corporate contributions to support individuals, charities sponsored solely by a single civic organization, charities which redistribute funds to other charitable organizations, except in the case of recognized united fund-type organizations, bank "clearing-house" organizations, agencies supported by United Way or united arts funds, religious, veteran, social, athletic or fraternal organizations, political organizations or those having the primary purpose of influencing legislation or promoting a particular ideological point of view, trips and tours, operating budget deficits, multiyear commitments of four years or more and/or endowments.

GEOGRAPHIC RESTRICTIONS:
Tennessee, with emphasis on Shelby County.

FINANCIAL DATA:
Amount of support per award: $1,000 per award.
Total amount of support: Varies.

APPLICATION INFORMATION:
There is no standard application form. If an organization wishes to apply for support, contact should be made through a telephone call or letter of inquiry before a full proposal is submitted. Inquiries should describe the organization's name, address, phone number and contact person, a brief description of the organization's history, accomplishments and goals, the objectives of the program to be funded and the amount sought from First Horizon National Corp. in relation to the total need. Organizations will be notified within four weeks of receipt of an inquiry if a written proposal will be sought.
Duration: Funding is not automatically renewed. Recipients desiring continued support should submit a request for review in the fall.
Deadline: November 1 prior to the year for which funds are being requested.

PUBLICATIONS:
Program guidelines and application procedures.

STAFF:
Penny Aviotti, Community Investment Manager, First Tennessee Foundation

ADDRESS INQUIRIES TO:
Penny Aviotti, Community Investment Manager
First Tennessee Foundation
(See address above.)

THE FOUNDATION FOR ENHANCING COMMUNITIES [1354]

200 North Third Street, 8th Floor
Harrisburg, PA 17108
(717) 236-5040
Fax: (717) 231-4463

E-MAIL ADDRESS:
info@tfec.org

WEB SITE ADDRESS:
www.tfec.org

FOUNDED: 1920

AREAS OF INTEREST:
Education, human services, arts and culture, children and youth.

CONSULTING OR VOLUNTEER SERVICES:
Consulting services available.

NAME(S) OF PROGRAMS:
● **AIDS**
● **Lesbian and Gay Partnership**
● **Women's Fund**

TYPE:
Challenge/matching grants; Conferences/seminars; Endowments; Project/program grants; Scholarships; Seed money grants; Technical assistance; Travel grants. Management agreements; Back room services and projects; Management of other foundations.

YEAR PROGRAM STARTED: 1920

PURPOSE:
To stimulate philanthropy and enhance the quality of life in the community through accumulating, managing and disbursing financial assets and by serving as a catalyst and neutral convener to meet a wide range of community needs in south central Pennsylvania counties of Cumberland, Dauphin, Franklin, Lebanon and Perry.

LEGAL BASIS:
Community foundation.

ELIGIBILITY:
Eligible organizations must have 501(c)(3) status. No grants are made to individuals or religious organizations for religious purposes.

GEOGRAPHIC RESTRICTIONS:
Discretionary Grants: Cumberland, Dauphin, Franklin, Lebanon and Perry counties, Pennsylvania.

FINANCIAL DATA:
Amount of support per award: $500 to $10,000.

APPLICATION INFORMATION:
Applicants should:
(1) review the grantmaking guidelines for each regional foundation;
(2) contact the Program Officer to determine eligibility to apply and discuss the proposal and;
(3) submit a grant application according to the guidelines provided on the Foundation's web site.
Duration: One year. Nonrenewable.

PUBLICATIONS:
Annual report.

IRS IDENTIFICATION NUMBER: 01-0564355

STAFF:
Janice R. Black, President and Chief Executive Officer
Kirk C. Demyan, Chief Financial Officer
Dr. Steve Messner, Capital Beginnings Project Director

Rosemary Browne, Director of Programs and Community Investment
Jennifer Doyle, Associate Director of Development and Donor Services
Lisa Miller, Program Officer
Jennifer Kuntch, Program Associate
Jim Martin, Financial Services Associate
Stacey Romberger, Financial Services Associate

ADDRESS INQUIRIES TO:
Director of Programs and Community Investment
The Foundation for Enhancing Communities
(See address above.)

FOUNDATION FOR THE CAROLINAS [1355]

217 South Tryon Street
Charlotte, NC 28202
(704) 973-4556
Fax: (704) 973-4956

E-MAIL ADDRESS:
bcollier@fftc.org

WEB SITE ADDRESS:
www.fftc.org

FOUNDED: 1958

AREAS OF INTEREST:
Education, human services, health and medical research, arts, environment and historical preservation, youth, senior programs and social capital.

TYPE:
Demonstration grants; General operating grants; Project/program grants; Scholarships; Seed money grants.

YEAR PROGRAM STARTED: 1958

PURPOSE:
To advance philanthropy by serving donors, increasing charitable giving and improving communities in its area of service.

LEGAL BASIS:
Community foundation.

ELIGIBILITY:
Grants will be made only to organizations recognized by the IRS as 501(c)(3) in the greater Charlotte area.

The Foundation generally does not fund capital campaigns and buildings, computers, vehicles and similar equipment, publication of books and production of videos, conferences and travel, grants to individuals or endowment funds.

GEOGRAPHIC RESTRICTIONS:
Greater Charlotte, North Carolina area.

FINANCIAL DATA:
Amount of support per award: $2,500 to $100,000.

Total amount of support: $139,000,000 for the year 2010.

APPLICATION INFORMATION:
Contact the Foundation.
Duration: One year.
Deadline: Varies.

BOARD OF DIRECTORS:
Cathy Bessant, Chairperson
Angela Bower
Ron Carter
Mike Coltrane
Alan Dickson
W. Barnes Hauptfuhrer
Polly Jackson
Chris Kearney

Ray Kennedy
Todd Mansfield
Cynthia Marshall
James E. Rogers
Laura Schulte
Bertram Scott
Ruth Shaw
Lori Levine Sklut
Tom Smith

ADDRESS INQUIRIES TO:
Brian Collier, Senior Vice President
(See address above.)

FOUNDATION FOR THE MID SOUTH [1356]

134 East Amite Street
Jackson, MS 39201
(601) 355-8167
Fax: (601) 355-6499

E-MAIL ADDRESS:
iallen@fndmidsouth.org

WEB SITE ADDRESS:
www.fndmidsouth.org

FOUNDED: 1989

AREAS OF INTEREST:
Improving the quality of life for residents in the states of Arkansas, Louisiana and Mississippi, with a primary focus on education, community development, health and wellness, and wealth building.

NAME(S) OF PROGRAMS:
● **Communities of Opportunity**
● **Community Philanthropy**
● **Mid South Health Initiative**
● **Mid South Wealth Building**

TYPE:
Conferences/seminars; Fellowships; General operating grants; Internships; Training grants. Communities of Opportunity is a comprehensive community change model designed to transform distressed areas into healthy communities for individuals, families and institutions.

Community Philanthropy invests in select communities throughout the Mississippi Delta and Gulf Coast regions to increase regional philanthropic resources, build permanent community-asset bases, expand stakeholder representation, and identify and invite new organizations to actively participate in regional community-building efforts.

Mid South Health Initiative is exploring both the challenges and the opportunities to effectively address regional health issues identified by experts in Arkansas, Louisiana and Mississippi.

PURPOSE:
To nurture families and children; to improve schools; to build the economy for all people in the region.

GEOGRAPHIC RESTRICTIONS:
Arkansas, Louisiana and Mississippi.

FINANCIAL DATA:
Amount of support per award: Varies.
Total amount of support: $2,627,468 for the year 2010.

APPLICATION INFORMATION:
The Foundation awards most grants by issuing Requests for Proposals (RFPs). If an RFP is not available and a project is within the scope and strategy of the Foundation's priorities, an eligible organization may submit an initial inquiry using the Grant Inquiry Form. The form seeks basic

information about the organization and a brief overview of the concept and request. If the inquiry is deemed favorable after review, applicants will be contacted by the appropriate program officer to discuss the request in greater detail.

Duration: One to three years.

Deadline: Varies.

ADDRESS INQUIRIES TO:
Grants Department
(See address above.)

FOUNDATION FOR THE TRI-STATE COMMUNITY, INC. [1357]

1999 Winchester Avenue
Second Floor
Ashland, KY 41101
(606) 324-3888
Fax: (606) 324-5961

E-MAIL ADDRESS:
ftsc_mwwiseman@yahoo.com

WEB SITE ADDRESS:
www.tristatefoundation.org

FOUNDED: 1972

AREAS OF INTEREST:
Arts and cultural programs, education, science and charity.

NAME(S) OF PROGRAMS:
● **21st Century Endowment Fund**

TYPE:
Challenge/matching grants; Project/program grants; Scholarships; Seed money grants; Technical assistance.

YEAR PROGRAM STARTED: 1980

PURPOSE:
To improve the quality of life in the tri-state area by encouraging, raising, administering and distributing gifts for charitable, cultural, educational and scientific purposes.

LEGAL BASIS:
Community foundation.

ELIGIBILITY:
Priority will be given to organizations who are 501(c)(3) and other organizations that meet the Foundation's special charitable grant guidelines. The Foundation does not fund sectarian activities or individuals.

GEOGRAPHIC RESTRICTIONS:
Boyd and Greenup counties, Kentucky; Lawrence County, Ohio; Cabell and Wayne counties, West Virginia.

FINANCIAL DATA:
Amount of support per award: $500 to $5,000.

Total amount of support: Typically, around $13,500 per quarter.

NUMBER OF APPLICANTS MOST RECENT YEAR: 17.

NUMBER OF AWARDS: 15 for the year 2010.

REPRESENTATIVE AWARDS:
$2,000 to American Foundation for the Blind; $2,000 to Little Victories Animal Rescue; $4,000 to Huntington Area Food Bank; $2,058 to CASA of Northeast Kentucky.

APPLICATION INFORMATION:
Applicants must submit the application form and IRS tax determination letter.

Duration: One-time award. Applicants may reapply after a one-year period.

Deadline: Applications are accepted at any time and are currently reviewed on a quarterly basis.

PUBLICATIONS:
Annual report; *How We've Grown*, grant guidelines; 35th anniversary report.

IRS IDENTIFICATION NUMBER: 61-0729266

STAFF:
Mary Witten Wiseman, President

ADDRESS INQUIRIES TO:
Mary Witten Wiseman, President
(See address above.)

THE FREMONT AREA COMMUNITY FOUNDATION [1358]

4424 West 48th Street
Fremont, MI 49412
(231) 924-5350
Fax: (231) 924-5391

E-MAIL ADDRESS:
jjahr@tfacf.org

WEB SITE ADDRESS:
www.tfacf.org

AREAS OF INTEREST:
Arts and culture, children, community development, community health, education, environment and natural resources, family and youth.

TYPE:
Challenge/matching grants; Project/program grants.

YEAR PROGRAM STARTED: 1951

PURPOSE:
To bring community development to life in Newaygo County.

LEGAL BASIS:
Public community foundation.

ELIGIBILITY:
Eligible organizations must be IRS 501(c)(3) tax-exempt.

GEOGRAPHIC RESTRICTIONS:
Newaygo County, Michigan.

FINANCIAL DATA:
Amount of support per award: Varies.

Total amount of support: $7,500,000 for the year 2010.

APPLICATION INFORMATION:
Applications are available from the Foundation and must include a copy of the IRS tax determination letter.

Duration: One year. Renewal by reapplication.

Deadline: February 15, May 15 and September 15.

STAFF:
Carla A. Roberts, President and Chief Executive Officer

ADDRESS INQUIRIES TO:
Jeff Jahr, Vice President of Program
(See address above.)

THE FRIST FOUNDATION [1359]

3100 West End Avenue, Suite 1200
Nashville, TN 37203
(615) 292-3868
Fax: (615) 292-5843

E-MAIL ADDRESS:
askfrist@fristfoundation.org

WEB SITE ADDRESS:
www.fristfoundation.org

FOUNDED: 1982

AREAS OF INTEREST:
Health, human services, education, technology, civic affairs and the arts.

NAME(S) OF PROGRAMS:
● **The Frist Foundation Awards of Achievement**
● **The Frist Foundation Technology Grants Program**

TYPE:
Capital grants; General operating grants; Project/program grants; Technical assistance. The Foundation makes direct grants to tax-exempt organizations in the greater Nashville area in the fields of health, human services, education, civic affairs and the arts.

In addition to conducting a grantmaking program responsive to external requests, the Frist Foundation actively seeks out and initiates programs addressing particular needs. Among these programs are the Center for Nonprofit Management, a community-wide effort to provide specialized management training and consulting to nonprofit community organizations.

Operating grants are given to organizations that offer management assistance, training, volunteers, goods or services to large numbers of Nashville agencies.

YEAR PROGRAM STARTED: 1983

PURPOSE:
To invest its resources in selected not-for-profit organizations in the greater Nashville area in ways that strengthen their ability to provide services.

LEGAL BASIS:
501(c)(3) private foundation.

ELIGIBILITY:
Grantees must be tax-exempt under Section 501(c)(3) of the Internal Revenue Code and not private foundations as described in Section 509(a). The Foundation ordinarily does not make grants or provide support to:
(1) international, regional or local organizations outside the Nashville area;
(2) projects, programs or organizations that serve a limited audience or a relatively small number of people;
(3) hospitals, biomedical or clinical research, or disease-specific organizations seeking support for national projects and programs;
(4) organizations during their first three years of operation;
(5) endowments;
(6) social events, fund-raising activities or telethons;
(7) individuals or their projects;
(8) political activities;
(9) religious organizations for religious purposes;
(10) private foundations;
(11) advertising sponsorships or;
(12) schools below the college level, except for projects intended to serve the broader community.

GEOGRAPHIC RESTRICTIONS:
Nashville, Tennessee area.

FINANCIAL DATA:
Amount of support per award: $500 to $100,000. Average $3,000.

Total amount of support: $7,500,000 for the year 2010.

NUMBER OF APPLICANTS MOST RECENT YEAR:
150 requests for the year 2010.

NUMBER OF AWARDS: 110 awards for the year 2010.

APPLICATION INFORMATION:
If an organization wishes to apply for support, it should make contact by phone, by letter of inquiry, or by completing an application through the web site. If you apply by mail, the letter should describe in no more than two pages:
(1) the organization and its record of accomplishment;
(2) the objectives of the program to be funded and whom it would benefit;
(3) the amount sought from the Foundation in relation to the total need;
(4) exactly how Foundation funds would be used and;
(5) the proposed method to evaluate the program's success.

The initial inquiry should also include an annual report, if available, and a copy of the IRS letter confirming that the organization is tax-exempt under Section 501(c)(3) of the Internal Revenue Code and not a private foundation as described in Section 509(a).
Duration: Up to three years. Renewals are not automatic, and applications from organizations supported in the past will be considered new requests.

IRS IDENTIFICATION NUMBER: 62-1134070

STAFF:
Peter F. Bird, Jr., President and Chief Executive Officer
Colette R. Easter, Treasurer
Barbara W. Baker, Program Assistant and Corporate Secretary

DIRECTORS:
Thomas F. Frist, Jr., Chairman
Peter F. Bird, Jr.
Frank F. Drowota, III
Patricia Frist Elcan
Patricia C. Frist
Thomas F. Frist, III
William R. Frist
Kenneth L. Roberts

ADDRESS INQUIRIES TO:
Peter F. Bird, Jr., President and Chief Executive Officer
(See address above.)

THE ROSAMOND GIFFORD CHARITABLE CORPORATION   [1360]
100 Clinton Square
126 North Salina Street, 3rd Floor
Syracuse, NY 13202
(315) 474-2489
Fax: (315) 475-4983

E-MAIL ADDRESS:
hholtz@giffordfd.org

WEB SITE ADDRESS:
www.giffordfoundation.org

FOUNDED: 1954

AREAS OF INTEREST:
Youth development, education and job readiness, and capacity building.

TYPE:
Capital grants; Challenge/matching grants; Conferences/seminars; Demonstration grants; Development grants; General operating grants; Project/program grants; Research grants; Seed money grants; Training grants. Grants to support educational, scientific, religious and general charitable organizations

and programs in Syracuse and Onondaga County, NY. Emphasis is on grants which deal with capacity building in Onondaga County, and neighborhood-based grants near West and Southside of Syracuse.

YEAR PROGRAM STARTED: 1954

PURPOSE:
To provide funds for education, scientific, religious and general charitable purposes.

LEGAL BASIS:
Private.

ELIGIBILITY:
Only tax-exempt organizations may apply. Organizations must show evidence of problems to be solved and how proposed solution will benefit constituency and the community. No grants to individuals.

GEOGRAPHIC RESTRICTIONS:
Madison, Onondaga and Oswego counties, New York.

FINANCIAL DATA:
Amount of support per award: $900 to $150,000; average $15,000.
Total amount of support: $1,800,000 for the year 2008.

APPLICATION INFORMATION:
Duration: One year.

PUBLICATIONS:
Application guidelines; statement of policies; mission statement.

STAFF:
Dirk E. Sonneborn, Executive Director
Heidi Holtz, Program Director
Lindsay McClung, Grants Manager, Program Associate
Sheena Solomon, Program Officer

TRUSTEES AND OFFICERS:
M. Catherine Richardson, President
Billy Harper, Vice President
Jack H. Webb, Treasurer
Ben Walsh, Secretary
Sharon C. Northrup, Assistant Secretary
Jaime Alicea
Eric Allyn
Jennifer Baskerville-Burrows
Nancy Bellow
Laurence G. Bousquet
Michael Connor
Edward Green
Mark D. Muhammad
Kathy O'Connell

ADDRESS INQUIRIES TO:
Heidi Holtz, Program Director
(See address above.)

LISA AND DOUGLAS GOLDMAN FUND   [1361]
One Daniel Burnham Court, Suite 330C
San Francisco, CA 94109-5460
(415) 771-1717

WEB SITE ADDRESS:
www.ldgfund.org

FOUNDED: 1992

AREAS OF INTEREST:
Jewish affairs, social and human services, health, environment, civic affairs, children's literacy and education.

TYPE:
Capital grants; Project/program grants.

YEAR PROGRAM STARTED: 1992

PURPOSE:
To improve the quality of life, primarily in San Francisco.

LEGAL BASIS:
Private foundation.

ELIGIBILITY:
Eligible organizations must be IRS 501(c)(3) tax-exempt.

GEOGRAPHIC RESTRICTIONS:
San Francisco area, California.

FINANCIAL DATA:
Amount of support per award: $10,000 to $100,000.
Total amount of support: $2,449,500 for the year 2009.

NUMBER OF AWARDS: 184 for the year 2009.

REPRESENTATIVE AWARDS:
$15,000 to Project Vote Smart; $5,000 to Build On; $10,000 to Teach for America, Bay Area; $15,000 to Canopy; $15,000 to Breast Cancer Action.

APPLICATION INFORMATION:
Applicants must include a copy of the IRS tax determination letter. Letter of inquiry must be submitted before proposal.
Duration: Varies.

PUBLICATIONS:
Annual report; application guidelines.

ADDRESS INQUIRIES TO:
Nancy S. Kami, Executive Director
(See address above.)

GOLDSEKER FOUNDATION   [1362]
1040 Park Avenue
Suite 310
Baltimore, MD 21201
(410) 837-5100
Fax: (410) 837-7927

E-MAIL ADDRESS:
tdarmbruster@goldsekerfoundation.org

WEB SITE ADDRESS:
www.goldsekerfoundation.org

FOUNDED: 1973

AREAS OF INTEREST:
Three priority areas for grantmaking: community development, regionalism, and the nonprofit sector.

TYPE:
General operating grants; Matching gifts; Project/program grants; Scholarships; Seed money grants; Technical assistance. Project grants and ongoing operating support.

The Foundation maintains a two-track grantmaking program that designates three priority areas, but retains the ability to initiate and respond to new ideas and opportunities within our established program areas. In each of the priority grant areas-community development, regionalism, and the nonprofit sector-the Foundation is a directly engaged and active partner. Grants include a mix of Foundation initiatives and projects submitted independently by potential grantees. The Foundation's established program areas are community affairs, education, and human services.

YEAR PROGRAM STARTED: 1976

PURPOSE:
To support programs which directly benefit the people of the Baltimore metropolitan area.

LEGAL BASIS:
Private, nonprofit.

ELIGIBILITY:
Qualified nonprofit, charitable and educational organizations as defined under federal and state laws as permissible grantees of private foundations. Support is limited to institutions in the Baltimore metropolitan area with special emphasis on disadvantaged persons, giving priority to programs intended to assist children and families and to strengthen neighborhoods.

No support for endowment, capital, deficits, annual giving, publications, religious purposes, arts and culture, specific diseases or disabilities or projects typically supported with public funds.

GEOGRAPHIC RESTRICTIONS:
Metropolitan Baltimore, Maryland.

FINANCIAL DATA:
No distribution in any calendar year to any single institution is to exceed five percent of the Foundation's net income for that year.

Amount of support per award: $1,500 to $175,000 for the year 2011.

Total amount of support: Approximately $3,000,000 for the year 2010.

Matching fund requirements: Varies with specific request.

NUMBER OF APPLICANTS MOST RECENT YEAR:
169 requests received.

NUMBER OF AWARDS: 66.

REPRESENTATIVE AWARDS:
$160,000 to Central Baltimore Partnership; $35,000 to Downtown Baltimore Family Alliance; $215,000 to Healthy Neighborhoods, Inc.

APPLICATION INFORMATION:
Preliminary proposals submitted should include details as outlined in the Annual Report, available upon request. Program guidelines also available, and phone calls are welcomed.

Duration: Typically one year. Occasional multiyear grants.

Deadline: February 1, May 1 and September 1.

PUBLICATIONS:
Annual report; program guidelines.

IRS IDENTIFICATION NUMBER: 52-0983502

OFFICERS:
Sheldon Goldseker, Chairman
Simon Goldseker, Vice Chairman
Timothy D. Armbruster, Ph.D., President and Chief Executive Officer
Sheila L. Purkey, Vice President, Secretary, Treasurer, Controller

STAFF:
Laurie M. Latuda, Program Officer

BOARD OF DIRECTORS:
Ana Goldseker
Deby Goldseker
Sharna Goldseker
Sheldon Goldseker
Simon Goldseker
Susan B. Katzenberg
Howard M. Weiss

ADDRESS INQUIRIES TO:
Program Officer
(See address above.)

*SPECIAL STIPULATIONS:
Grantmaking is limited to the metropolitan area of Baltimore, Maryland.

THE GRACO FOUNDATION [1363]

88 Eleventh Avenue, N.E.
Minneapolis, MN 55413
(612) 623-6684
Fax: (612) 623-6944

E-MAIL ADDRESS:
kridley@graco.com

WEB SITE ADDRESS:
www.graco.com

FOUNDED: 1956

AREAS OF INTEREST:
Education, workforce development, youth development and civic projects.

CONSULTING OR VOLUNTEER SERVICES:
Through established community programs.

NAME(S) OF PROGRAMS:
● **Financial Grants of Support**

TYPE:
Capital grants; Development grants; Matching gifts; Scholarships. Grants for a variety of local programs concerning education and social problems. Emphasis is on support of local community programs. Employee Matching gifts are for education only. Scholarships are for children of Graco employees only.

YEAR PROGRAM STARTED: 1956

PURPOSE:
To provide financial support to well-screened and evaluated community programs for making the community a better place in which to live.

LEGAL BASIS:
Established under the Minnesota Nonprofit Corporation Act as a nonprofit corporation under the provisions of Chapter 317, Minnesota Statutes 1953 and Acts amendatory thereof.

ELIGIBILITY:
Accredited institutions of higher education and other nonprofit organizations which have been validated by the IRS as charitable organizations under 501(c)(3) and not a private foundation as defined in 509(a). No grants are awarded to individuals or to churches and schools of religion.

GEOGRAPHIC RESTRICTIONS:
In Minnesota, emphasis on the Twin Cities, in particular, north and northeast Minneapolis and the northern suburbs, as well as North Canton, Ohio and Sioux Falls, South Dakota.

FINANCIAL DATA:
Amount of support per award: Varies.

Total amount of support: $596,334 for the year 2010.

Matching fund requirements: Limited to educational institutions.

REPRESENTATIVE AWARDS:
$100,000 to North Community YMCA; $60,000 to Metro Deaf School; $20,000 to Twin Cities Rise!

APPLICATION INFORMATION:
No official application forms are used. Applicants should submit a brief outline of the program with their agency background, objectives and their IRS validation as a qualified applicant.

Duration: One-time grants may apply again after two years for other campaigns.

Deadline: Proposals are reviewed four times per year. Board meetings are in March, June, September and December.

PUBLICATIONS:
Annual report/guidelines available on web site.

IRS IDENTIFICATION NUMBER: 41-6023537

BOARD OF DIRECTORS:
Patrick J. McHale, President
Karen P. Gallivan, Director
Janel W. French, Treasurer
Kristin R. Ridley, Secretary

ADDRESS INQUIRIES TO:
Kristin R. Ridley
Manager, Community Relations
(See address above.)

GRAND HAVEN AREA COMMUNITY FOUNDATION [1364]

One South Harbor Drive
Grand Haven, MI 49417
(616) 842-6378
Fax: (616) 842-9518

E-MAIL ADDRESS:
bpost@ghacf.org

WEB SITE ADDRESS:
www.ghacf.org

FOUNDED: 1971

AREAS OF INTEREST:
Arts, environment, social services, education and support of local nonprofit organizations.

TYPE:
Project/program grants; Scholarships; Seed money grants. Pool of funds contributed by donors for the benefit of the Tri-Cities area.

YEAR PROGRAM STARTED: 1971

PURPOSE:
To enrich and enhance the quality of life in the Tri-Cities area; to link donors' interests with the needs of the community.

LEGAL BASIS:
Community foundation.

ELIGIBILITY:
Grant applicants must have a charitable 501(c)(3) classification by the IRS. The Foundation will consider grant requests submitted by religious organizations if the proposed project meets a general need in the community. Grants are generally given one-time only for specific purposes. The Foundation has no obligation or commitment to provide ongoing or additional support to the grantee. No grants to individuals, except in the form of scholarships. Grants are not given to fund an organization's continued operating support or expenses, including salaries.

GEOGRAPHIC RESTRICTIONS:
Grand Haven, Michigan and greater Tri-Cities area.

FINANCIAL DATA:
Amount of support per award: Varies depending on needs and nature of the request.

Total amount of support: $3,027,000 for the year 2009.

NUMBER OF APPLICANTS MOST RECENT YEAR:
1,150.

NUMBER OF AWARDS: 1,100.

REPRESENTATIVE AWARDS:
$4,000 to Bluebird Cancer Retreats to assist in offering a weekend retreat; $25,000 to Greater Ottawa County United Way to provide a comprehensive community needs analysis; $15,000 to OAR to initiate a Family

Education/Outreach Program for those with a loved one with a substance abuse problem; $23,000 to provide enhancements to Robinson Township Park; $2,500 to YMCA to support Healthy Kids Day.

APPLICATION INFORMATION:
Application form required. Please contact Foundation for specific requirements.
Duration: Varies.
Deadline: Call for specific dates.

PUBLICATIONS:
Annual report; application.

STAFF:
Ann Tabor, President
Holly Johnson, Development Director
Barbara Post, Donor Services and Scholarship Director
Janet Tomhave, Finance Director
Carol Bedient, Grants and Program Director

BOARD OF TRUSTEES:
Shirley Poulton, Chairperson
Tom Creswell, Vice Chairperson
Cal Bosman, Treasurer
Tim Parker, Secretary
Melinda Brink
Lana Jacobson
Sheila Steffel
Bonnie Suchecki
L.J. Verplank

ADDRESS INQUIRIES TO:
Carol Bedient
Grants and Program Director
(See address above.)

THE GREATER CEDAR RAPIDS COMMUNITY FOUNDATION   [1365]
324 Third Street, S.E.
Cedar Rapids, IA 52401
(319) 366-2862
Fax: (319) 366-2912

E-MAIL ADDRESS:
karla.twedt-ball@gcrcf.org

WEB SITE ADDRESS:
www.gcrcf.org

FOUNDED: 1948

AREAS OF INTEREST:
Arts and culture, community development, education, environment, health and human services.

NAME(S) OF PROGRAMS:
• **Linn County Nonprofit Resource Center**
• **Youth Power**

TYPE:
Demonstration grants; Project/program grants; Scholarships; Seed money grants; Technical assistance; Training grants.

YEAR PROGRAM STARTED: 1989

PURPOSE:
To enrich the quality of life in Linn County, IA.

LEGAL BASIS:
Community foundation.

ELIGIBILITY:
Eligible organizations must be IRS 501(c)(3) tax-exempt, public agencies/units of government or have a fiscal sponsor.

GEOGRAPHIC RESTRICTIONS:
Cedar Rapids and surrounding Linn County, Iowa.

FINANCIAL DATA:
Amount of support per award: $700 to $50,000. Average: $6,500.
Total amount of support: $5,900,000 for the year 2010.

COOPERATIVE FUNDING PROGRAMS: A variety of donor advisors operate competitive funds.

NUMBER OF APPLICANTS MOST RECENT YEAR: 670 competitive applications received.

NUMBER OF AWARDS: 1,054 grants awarded: 484 competitive awards, 72 scholarships and 498 other grants (233 of the "other grants" are designated funds for particular organizations).

APPLICATION INFORMATION:
Applications must include a copy of the IRS tax determination letter.
Duration: One year for most funds. Renewal by reapplication.
Deadline: Approximately February 15, June 15 and October 15.

PUBLICATIONS:
Annual report; "Community" newsletter; guidelines.

STAFF:
Dr. Leslie Garner, President/Chief Executive Officer
Karla Twedt-Ball, M.P.P., Vice President of Programs
Jean Brenneman, Director of Finance
Amber Mulnik, Director of Communications
Josie Velles, Foundation Services Manager
Elizabeth Cwik, Program Associate
Rochelle Naylor, Program Assistant
Bob Untiedt, Executive Director, Linn County Nonprofit Resource Center
Katie Giorgio, Marketing Assistant, Linn County Nonprofit Resource Center
Emmy Ball, Accountant

ADDRESS INQUIRIES TO:
Karla Twedt-Ball
Vice President of Programs
(See address above.)

*SPECIAL STIPULATIONS:
The Foundation makes competitive grant awards only within Linn County, Iowa and its immediate vicinity.

THE GREATER CINCINNATI FOUNDATION   [1366]
200 West 4th Street
Cincinnati, OH 45202-2602
(513) 241-2880
Fax: (513) 768-6122

WEB SITE ADDRESS:
www.gcfdn.org

FOUNDED: 1963

AREAS OF INTEREST:
Arts and culture, community economic development, education, environment, health and human services.

CONSULTING OR VOLUNTEER SERVICES:
General staff support provided by volunteers.

TYPE:
Capital grants; Development grants. Funds for capital improvements, one-time needs, demonstration projects, demands normally outside the reach of philanthropic budgets. Funds may not be used for operating budgets.

LEGAL BASIS:
Tax-exempt under Section 501(c)(3) of IRS code.

ELIGIBILITY:
Recipient must be a local agency in the Greater Cincinnati area and must be tax-exempt under Section 501(c)(3) of the IRS code.

No unsolicited proposals accepted.

GEOGRAPHIC RESTRICTIONS:
Greater Cincinnati, Ohio, northern Kentucky and southeast Indiana.

FINANCIAL DATA:
Amount of support per award: $5,000 to $150,000.
Total amount of support: $66,686,000 for the year 2009.

NUMBER OF APPLICANTS MOST RECENT YEAR: 141.

NUMBER OF AWARDS: 108 to agencies from unrestricted funds.

REPRESENTATIVE AWARDS:
Dan Beard Council, Boy Scouts of America; Children's Protective Service, Cincinnati Association for the Blind.

APPLICATION INFORMATION:
Duration: One to three years.
Deadline: February 1 and August 1.

IRS IDENTIFICATION NUMBER: 31-0669700

STAFF:
Kathryn E. Merchant, President and Chief Executive Officer
Elizabeth Bower Benson, Vice President for Communications and Marketing
Shiloh Turner, Vice President for Community Investment
Scott McReynolds, Vice President for Finance and Administration
Amy Cheney, Vice President for Giving Strategies
Daniel J. Hoffheimer, Legal Counsel

GOVERNING BOARD:
David W. Ellis, III, Chairperson
Peter S. Strange, Vice Chairperson
Thomas G. Cody
Neil Comber
Cathy T. Crain
Alva Jean Crawford
Jane V. Domaschko
Linda C. Fath
Christopher L. Fister
John L. Henderson, Ph.D.
Molly A. Katz, M.D.
Teri L. List-Stoll
Dianne M. Rosenberg
Nancy K. Swanson
Joseph P. Tomain
Kathryn E. Merchant, President and Chief Executive Officer
Daniel J. Hoffheimer, Legal Counsel

ADDRESS INQUIRIES TO:
Kay Pennington
Community Investment Coordinator
(See address above.)

GREATER GREEN BAY COMMUNITY FOUNDATION   [1367]
310 West Walnut Street
Suite 350
Green Bay, WI 54303-2734
(920) 432-0800
Fax: (920) 432-5577

E-MAIL ADDRESS:
martha@ggbcf.org

WEB SITE ADDRESS:
www.ggbcf.org

FOUNDED: 1990

AREAS OF INTEREST:
Improving the quality of life for the residents of the Greater Green Bay, WI area.

TYPE:
Project/program grants; Scholarships. Donor-advised funds.

PURPOSE:
To improve the quality of life in the local area.

ELIGIBILITY:
Eligible organizations must have 501(c)(3) not-for-profit status. No grants are made to individuals.

GEOGRAPHIC RESTRICTIONS:
Brown, Kewaunee and Oconto counties, Wisconsin.

FINANCIAL DATA:
Net assets of $55,000,000 for fiscal year ended June 30, 2010.
Amount of support per award: Varies by need.
Total amount of support: $2,000,000 to $3,000,000 per year.

APPLICATION INFORMATION:
All applicants should share their ideas with the Foundation prior to the submission of a formal application.
Duration: Varies by grant program; usually one year.
Deadline: Varies by grant program.

ADDRESS INQUIRIES TO:
Martha Ahrendt, Vice President, Programs (See address above.)

THE GREATER KANAWHA VALLEY FOUNDATION [1368]

Huntington Square, Suite 1600
900 Lee Street East
Charleston, WV 25301
(304) 346-3620
Fax: (304) 346-3640

E-MAIL ADDRESS:
sryder@tgkvf.org

WEB SITE ADDRESS:
www.tgkvf.org

FOUNDED: 1962

AREAS OF INTEREST:
Arts and culture, education, health, human services, land use, recreation, community development, and scholarship program.

TYPE:
Project/program grants; Scholarships.

YEAR PROGRAM STARTED: 1964

PURPOSE:
To serve the greater Kanawha Valley and surrounding areas.

LEGAL BASIS:
501(c)(3).

ELIGIBILITY:
Applicant must be a charitable organization located in or directly benefiting residents of the Greater Kanawha Valley.

GEOGRAPHIC RESTRICTIONS:
Scholarships: West Virginia residents only. Other grants are restricted to six-county region: Boone, Clay, Fayette, Kanawha, Lincoln and Putnam.

FINANCIAL DATA:
Amount of support per award: Grants: Average $10,000; Scholarships: Usually $1,000.
Total amount of support: $3,346,853 in grants and $604,638 in scholarships for the year ended December 31, 2009.
Matching fund requirements: Must have a match, not a specific percent.

NUMBER OF APPLICANTS MOST RECENT YEAR:
105 grant applicants for the year 2010; 601 scholarship applicants for the academic year 2010-11.

NUMBER OF AWARDS: 87 grants for the year 2010; 374 scholarships for the academic year 2010-11.

APPLICATION INFORMATION:
Applications are accepted online only.
Duration: Grants: One year. Nonrenewable; Scholarships: Varies.
Deadline: Grants: February 1, May 1 and August 1. Scholarships: January 15.

PUBLICATIONS:
Annual report.

IRS IDENTIFICATION NUMBER: 55-6024430

STAFF:
Sheri Ryder, Senior Program Officer
Susan Hoover, Scholarship Program Officer

ADDRESS INQUIRIES TO:
For grants:
Sheri Ryder, Senior Program Officer
(See address and e-mail above.)
For scholarships:
Susan Hoover, Scholarship Program Officer
(See address above.)
E-mail: shoover@tgkvf.org

THE GREATER KANSAS CITY COMMUNITY FOUNDATION AND AFFILIATED TRUSTS [1369]

1055 Broadway, Suite 130
Kansas City, MO 64105
(816) 842-0944
(866) 719-7886
Fax: (816) 842-8079; (816) 842-0318

E-MAIL ADDRESS:
info@gkccf.org

WEB SITE ADDRESS:
www.gkccf.org

FOUNDED: 1978

AREAS OF INTEREST:
Public education and life sciences.

CONSULTING OR VOLUNTEER SERVICES:
Grantmaking services.

TYPE:
Project/program grants; Scholarships. Grants in the areas of public education and life sciences and scholarships are given to make a positive support of the nonprofit sector and to promote philanthropy for the benefit of the community.

PURPOSE:
To improve the quality of life in greater Kansas City by increasing charitable giving, connecting donors to community needs they care about, and providing leadership on critical community issues.

LEGAL BASIS:
Public foundation.

ELIGIBILITY:
Nonprofit charitable organizations in the five-county Kansas City area are eligible for support from unrestricted funds.

The Community Foundation does not ordinarily fund endowment campaigns, debt reduction, annual appeals and membership contributions, operating expenses and fund-raising projects of religious organizations, capital fund drives, including brick and mortar, land acquisition, equipment purchases, renovation or purchase of buildings, construction or the improvement of public spaces or financial assistance for individuals.

FINANCIAL DATA:
Amount of support per award: $25 to $1,000,000. Average $50,000.
Total amount of support: $147,000,000 for the year 2008.

NUMBER OF APPLICANTS MOST RECENT YEAR:
10 for the year 2008.

NUMBER OF AWARDS: 8,300.

REPRESENTATIVE AWARDS:
$100,000 over three years to the University of Missouri-Kansas City Institute for Urban Education.

PUBLICATIONS:
Annual report.

IRS IDENTIFICATION NUMBER: 43-1152398

OFFICERS:
Laura McKnight, President and Chief Executive Officer
George S. Bittner, Executive Vice President
Brenda Chumley, Senior Vice President of Administration
Jean-Paul Chaurand, Senior Vice President of Community Investment
Roxie Jerde, Vice President of Donor and Nonprofit Relations

ADDRESS INQUIRIES TO:
grants@gkccf.org

THE GREATER LANSING FOUNDATION [1370]

120 North Washington Square
Suite 650
Lansing, MI 48933
(517) 334-5299
Fax: (517) 334-5445

FOUNDED: 1947

AREAS OF INTEREST:
Arts, education, general charitable giving, handicapped and health.

NAME(S) OF PROGRAMS:
● **The Greater Lansing Foundation General Fund**

TYPE:
Capital grants; Development grants; Project/program grants; Scholarships; Seed money grants; Training grants; Work-study programs. General support for seed money and capital funds.

YEAR PROGRAM STARTED: 1947

PURPOSE:
To promote the well-being of the inhabitants of Clinton, Eaton and Ingham counties by distributing income to local charitable, public or educational institutions.

LEGAL BASIS:
Private foundation.

ELIGIBILITY:
Applicants must have a 501(c)(3) IRS exemption and be a public charity.

GEOGRAPHIC RESTRICTIONS:
Greater Lansing, Michigan counties.

FINANCIAL DATA:
Amount of support per award: Up to $10,000.

Total amount of support: Approximately $50,000 annually.

APPLICATION INFORMATION:
Duration: One year.
Deadline: April 1.

IRS IDENTIFICATION NUMBER: 38-6057513

DISTRIBUTION COMMITTEE:
Melissa Alford
Wayne Buletza
Rishan Butler
Janet Groves
Robert Hotchkiss
John Thelen

ADDRESS INQUIRIES TO:
Steven J. Peters, Secretary
(See address above.)

*SPECIAL STIPULATIONS:
The Foundation does not usually make grants to fund normal operating costs. The Committee prefers to consider grants in the nature of capital expenditures, expansion or improvement of existing programs or grants of a nonrecurring nature.

GREATER LOWELL COMMUNITY FOUNDATION   [1371]

100 Merrimack Street
Suite 202
Lowell, MA 01852-1707
(978) 970-1600
Fax: (978) 970-2444

WEB SITE ADDRESS:
www.glcfoundation.org

FOUNDED: 1997

AREAS OF INTEREST:
The quality of life in the Greater Lowell, Massachusetts area.

TYPE:
The usual type of grant is a capacity grant: It has to benefit the capacity or structure of the applicant organization (e.g., installing a new phone or e-mail system, purchasing a new computer, hiring a consultant to strengthen a short-term project in an organizational capacity, etc.).

PURPOSE:
To improve the quality of life in the Greater Lowell, Massachusetts area.

LEGAL BASIS:
501(c)(3) organization.

ELIGIBILITY:
Grants are not given to individuals. Eligible organizations must have 501(c)(3) status.

GEOGRAPHIC RESTRICTIONS:
Western Merrimack Valley/Northern Middlesex County, Massachusetts area.

FINANCIAL DATA:
Total assets of $22,000,000 for fiscal year ended December 31, 2010.

Amount of support per award: $500 to $10,000.

Total amount of support: $900,000 for the year 2010.

APPLICATION INFORMATION:
Applications are posted on the web site and can be accessed from August 31 until early October.

Duration: One year. Nonrenewable.

Deadline: October 5 for receiving grant application. Grants are distributed the following October.

GREATER MILWAUKEE FOUNDATION   [1372]

101 West Pleasant Street
Suite 210
Milwaukee, WI 53212
(414) 272-5805
Fax: (414) 272-6235

E-MAIL ADDRESS:
info@greatermilwaukeefoundation.org

WEB SITE ADDRESS:
www.greatermilwaukeefoundation.org

FOUNDED: 1915

AREAS OF INTEREST:
A broad-spectrum community foundation, the main focus of the Foundation's unrestricted grantmaking focuses on poverty. Specifically, it is targeted to programs assisting families with asset building, those that promote success in school and access to higher education and quality early childhood programs. Other areas of interest include employment and training, health and human services, arts and culture, conservation and historic preservation, youth development, children, youth and families, and community development.

TYPE:
Awards/prizes; Capital grants; Challenge/matching grants; Demonstration grants; Development grants; Matching gifts; Professorships; Project/program grants; Scholarships; Seed money grants; Technical assistance; Training grants. The Foundation's unrestricted grantmaking does not support general operations.

The Foundation operates as a community trust, a public nonprofit organization established to administer charitable funds for the benefit of the people of the community. It is composed of over 1,000 funds, each with its own charitable purpose and most identified with the name of the donor whose gift established it. Donors make grants in the metropolitan area and around the world.

The component funds are of several types, depending upon the wishes of the donor expressed at the time the originating gift or bequest was made.

Unrestricted funds are those in which the Board is given full discretion in determining how income can best be disbursed each year for charitable purposes. Funds usually used for special projects, usually non-recurring, for which other funds are not available.

Field of Interest Funds are administered with a particular charitable purpose in mind, such as support of the arts, child welfare or education.

Designated Funds have been established to favor specific charitable agencies and institutions serving the Milwaukee community. The income earned by this type of fund is paid annually to a particular agency or agencies named by the donor.

Grants are usually intended to provide general sustaining support for current agency operations.

Donor Advised Funds are those established by gifts from individuals, foundations or corporations in which the original contributors, from time to time, make suggestions to the board about grant distributions.

YEAR PROGRAM STARTED: 1915

PURPOSE:
To strengthen communities through effective partnerships.

LEGAL BASIS:
Public nonprofit organization exempt from federal taxation under Section 501(c)(3) of the Internal Revenue Code.

ELIGIBILITY:
The Greater Milwaukee Foundation Board welcomes grant applications from agencies serving the people of the greater Milwaukee community. Details regarding grantmaking criteria are available online.

GEOGRAPHIC RESTRICTIONS:
Grants are primarily made in Greater Milwaukee, Wisconsin, including Milwaukee, Ozaukee, Washington and Waukesha counties. Donor-advised funds may also make grants outside the metropolitan area and throughout the United States and the world.

FINANCIAL DATA:
The funds vary in size from $10,000 to $24,000,000.

Amount of support per award: $15,000 to $30,000 average. Most funds are handled as endowments with the principal kept intact.

Total amount of support: $27,400,000 for the year 2010.

COOPERATIVE FUNDING PROGRAMS: Nonprofit Management Fund.

NUMBER OF AWARDS: 3,931 grants for the year 2010.

APPLICATION INFORMATION:
To facilitate fair and equitable consideration, grant applicants are expected to use a prescribed proposal format. The application process is as follows:
(1) applicant organization should update (or add) its information on the Philanthropy Online database (see Grantseekers section of Foundation web site);
(2) organization must then submit a Letter of Inquiry to the Foundation (again, see Foundation web site);
(3) Foundation staff will then review applicant's proposal for merit;
(4) if encouraged by staff to apply, the applicant must complete a detailed online proposal;
(5) Foundation staff will thoroughly review the proposal;
(6) the Foundation Board's Program Committee will review the proposal and make recommendations to the full Board, which must approve all grant awards and;
(7) each applicant will receive written notification of the Board's action; those selected for grants must adhere to the stipulated terms.

Grant seekers are strongly encouraged to consult with a program officer at the Foundation prior to submitting a Letter of Inquiry. Details for grant seekers are available online.

Duration: Generally one year. Multiyear grants are considered but rarely for a period of more than three years.

Deadline: Letters of Inquiry are accepted year-round and reviewed on a continual basis. Funding decisions are made quarterly.

PUBLICATIONS:
Newsletters; annual report.

IRS IDENTIFICATION NUMBER: 39-6036407

STAFF:
Patti Dew, Vice President and Chief Financial Officer
Karen Rogers, Vice President, Development and Donor Services
Marcus White, Vice President, Community Partnerships
Doris Heiser, Director, Donor Services
James A. Marks, Director, Special Projects
Craig Nuechterlein, Director, Operations
Maureen Siwula, Director, Human Resources

BOARD OF DIRECTORS:
John W. Daniels, Jr., Chairperson
Thomas L. Spero, Vice Chairperson
Wendy Reed Bosworth
Peter W. Bruce
Ness Flores
Hon. Janine P. Geske, (Retired)
Franklyn M. Gimbel
Jacqueline Herd-Barber
Judy Jorgensen
David J. Kundert
David J. Lubar
Mary B. Read

OFFICER:
Ellen M. Gilligan, President and Chief Executive Officer

ADDRESS INQUIRIES TO:
Ellen M. Gilligan
President and Chief Executive Officer
(See address above.)

THE GREATER NEW ORLEANS FOUNDATION [1373]

K & B Plaza, Suite 100
1055 St. Charles Street
New Orleans, LA 70130
(504) 598-4663
Fax: (504) 598-4676

E-MAIL ADDRESS:
richard@gnof.org

WEB SITE ADDRESS:
www.gnof.org

AREAS OF INTEREST:
Housing, environment, workforce development, and children and youth.

TYPE:
Project/program grants. The Foundation provides start-up funds for promising new organizations or programs. It also funds demonstration grants to new or established organizations with innovative program models and offers transition grants to nonprofit organizations moving into a new state of organizational development.

PURPOSE:
To create a thriving community for all in the greater New Orleans region.

ELIGIBILITY:
The Foundation makes grants only to nonprofit, tax-exempt organizations that serve the greater New Orleans area.

GEOGRAPHIC RESTRICTIONS:
Southeastern Louisiana and greater New Orleans region.

FINANCIAL DATA:
Amount of support per award: Varies.

APPLICATION INFORMATION:
Guidelines are available online.
Duration: Renewal by reapplication.
Deadline: Varies.

PUBLICATIONS:
Guidelines.

*SPECIAL STIPULATIONS:
Upon completion of the funded project, or within one year, grant recipients must provide an end-of-grant report based on their proposed program evaluation.

ALLEN P. AND JOSEPHINE B. GREEN FOUNDATION [1374]

200 West Boulevard
Mexico, MO 65265
(573) 581-5568
Fax: (573) 581-1714

E-MAIL ADDRESS:
carlf@greenfdn.org

WEB SITE ADDRESS:
www.greenfdn.org

FOUNDED: 1941

AREAS OF INTEREST:
Welfare of children, environment, health care and educational services.

TYPE:
Capital grants; Challenge/matching grants; Conferences/seminars; Demonstration grants; Development grants; Endowments; Matching gifts; Project/program grants; Seed money grants; Training grants; Work-study programs.

YEAR PROGRAM STARTED: 1941

PURPOSE:
To improve the quality of life, primarily of Missourians.

LEGAL BASIS:
Nonprofit private charitable foundation.

ELIGIBILITY:
Applicants must be tax-exempt entities. A copy of the organization's federal tax-exempt letter should accompany the grant request. Special consideration will be given to qualified projects within the immediate geographical area of Mexico, MO.

No grants to individuals for graduate work, scholarships, fellowships or other purposes. No grants to projects outside of the U.S.

GEOGRAPHIC RESTRICTIONS:
Preferably, Missouri.

FINANCIAL DATA:
Amount of support per award: $2,500 to $50,000.

Total amount of support: $211,200 for the year 2010.

NUMBER OF APPLICANTS MOST RECENT YEAR: 222 for the year 2009.

NUMBER OF AWARDS: 39 for the year 2009.

APPLICATION INFORMATION:
No application forms are provided. Letters of request should be limited to two pages and clearly state the complete financial planning and costs involved, as well as other material information substantiating the validity of the project. If additional information, verification or interviews are considered necessary, notification will be given.

Letter should outline the project and include the amount requested, budget figures, period of time and a copy of exemption letter.

Duration: Normally, one year.

Deadline: March 15 and September 15. Notification to grantees following May and November meetings of the Board.

PUBLICATIONS:
Annual report.

IRS IDENTIFICATION NUMBER: 43-6030135

OFFICERS:
Laura W. Erdel, President
Carl Fuemmeler, Assistant Secretary and Assistant Treasurer

ADDRESS INQUIRIES TO:
Carl Fuemmeler, Assistant Secretary and Assistant Treasurer
(See address above.)

THE GRUNDY FOUNDATION [1375]

680 Radcliffe Street
Bristol, PA 19007
(215) 788-5460
Fax: (215) 788-0915

E-MAIL ADDRESS:
ejw@grundyfoundation.com

WEB SITE ADDRESS:
www.grundyfoundation.com

FOUNDED: 1961

AREAS OF INTEREST:
Arts and culture, education and human services.

TYPE:
Capital grants; General operating grants. Capital grants for 501(c)(3) organizations throughout Bucks County, PA, primarily Lower Bucks County. Operating/programmatic support only for pre-selected organizations primarily in Bristol, PA and other parts of Lower Bucks County.

YEAR PROGRAM STARTED: 1961

PURPOSE:
To promote the well-being of the Commonwealth of Pennsylvania, with a particular emphasis in Bucks County.

LEGAL BASIS:
501(c)(3) private foundation.

ELIGIBILITY:
Applicants must be nonprofit organizations that have public charity status. No grants to individuals or for fellowships or loans.

GEOGRAPHIC RESTRICTIONS:
Primarily Lower Bucks County, Pennsylvania.

FINANCIAL DATA:
Amount of support per award: Average $2,530 for the calendar year 2010.

Total amount of support: $202,200 for the calendar year 2010.

Matching fund requirements: Stipulated with specific programs.

NUMBER OF AWARDS: 29 for fiscal year 2010.

APPLICATION INFORMATION:
Letter of request and related documentation should be submitted to Eugene J. Williams, Executive Director.

Duration: No grants are awarded on a continuing basis.

PUBLICATIONS:
Application guidelines.

ADDRESS INQUIRIES TO:
Eugene J. Williams, Executive Director
(See address above.)

GULF COAST COMMUNITY FOUNDATION OF VENICE [1376]
601 Tamiami Trail South
Venice, FL 34285
(941) 486-4600
Fax: (941) 486-4699

E-MAIL ADDRESS:
cpfahler@gulfcoastcf.org

WEB SITE ADDRESS:
www.gulfcoastcf.org

FOUNDED: 1995

AREAS OF INTEREST:
Arts and culture, civic affairs, the
environment, education, health and human
services, and economic development.

TYPE:
General operating grants; Project/program
grants; Scholarships; Technical assistance;
Training grants. Scholarships for individuals
living in Sarasota County, FL.

YEAR PROGRAM STARTED: 1995

PURPOSE:
To improve the quality of life in communities
the Foundation serves.

LEGAL BASIS:
Community foundation.

ELIGIBILITY:
Nonprofit organizations are eligible to apply,
501(c)(3) tax-exempt.

GEOGRAPHIC RESTRICTIONS:
Charlotte, DeSoto, Lee and Sarasota counties,
Florida.

FINANCIAL DATA:
Amount of support per award: Varies.
Total amount of support: Varies.
Matching fund requirements: Varies.

REPRESENTATIVE AWARDS:
$19,500 to Charlotte County Homeless
Coalition to provide first-year operating
support for Safe House Shelter; $114,000 to
Legal Aid of Manasota to provide free legal
representation for southern Sarasota County
homeowners facing foreclosure on their
homes; $10,000 to United Way of Sarasota
County to fund site coordinators who will
facilitate the new Volunteer Income Tax
Assistance Program.

APPLICATION INFORMATION:
Duration: Varies.

PUBLICATIONS:
Annual report; application guidelines.

ADDRESS INQUIRIES TO:
Chris Pfahler
Director of Community Investment
(See address above.)

HAMILTON COMMUNITY FOUNDATION [1377]
120 King Street West, Suite 700
Hamilton ON L8P 4V2 Canada
(905) 523-5600
Fax: (905) 523-0741

E-MAIL ADDRESS:
information@hcf.on.ca

WEB SITE ADDRESS:
www.hcf.on.ca

FOUNDED: 1954

AREAS OF INTEREST:
Community development and services for
Hamilton, ON.

TYPE:
Project/program grants.

YEAR PROGRAM STARTED: 1954

PURPOSE:
To foster the growth of community
philanthropy; to build and prudently manage
community endowments; to provide
exceptional services to donors; to address
needs through strategic grantmaking and
organizational support; to provide leadership
on key community issues.

LEGAL BASIS:
Community foundation.

GEOGRAPHIC RESTRICTIONS:
Community of Hamilton, Ontario, Canada.

FINANCIAL DATA:
Total amount of support: $6,000,000 for the
year 2008-09.

APPLICATION INFORMATION:
Duration: One year or multiyear grants.

STAFF:
Carolyn Milne, President and Chief
Executive Officer

ADDRESS INQUIRIES TO:
Anne Lupkoski, Executive Assistant
(See address above.)

THE HAMPTON ROADS COMMUNITY FOUNDATION [1378]
101 West Main Street
Suite 4500
Norfolk, VA 23510
(757) 622-7951
Fax: (757) 622-1751

E-MAIL ADDRESS:
info@hamptonroadscf.org

WEB SITE ADDRESS:
www.hamptonroadscf.org

FOUNDED: 1950

AREAS OF INTEREST:
Community development, education and
social welfare.

TYPE:
Capital grants; Challenge/matching grants;
Seed money grants; Technical assistance.
Capital projects. Grants for scholarships,
educational institutions, family, child and
social welfare, cultural and civic affairs.

YEAR PROGRAM STARTED: 1950

PURPOSE:
To make grants that transform the quality of
life and inspire philanthropy in southeastern
Virginia.

LEGAL BASIS:
Nonprofit corporation.

ELIGIBILITY:
501(c)(3) nonprofit organizations that provide
benefits to the residents.

GEOGRAPHIC RESTRICTIONS:
Southeastern Virginia.

FINANCIAL DATA:
Amount of support per award: $250 to
$1,000,000.

Total amount of support: $10,000,000 in
grants for the year 2009.

NUMBER OF AWARDS: 63 grants and 260
scholarships for the year 2009.

APPLICATION INFORMATION:
Duration: Grants: One year to multiyear;
Scholarships: One to four years.
Deadline: Varies depending upon program.

PUBLICATIONS:
Annual report; application guidelines;
quarterly newsletter.

IRS IDENTIFICATION NUMBER: 54-2035996

STAFF:
Angelica D. Light, President and Chief
Executive Officer
Christine Morris, Director of Initiatives
Leigh Evans Davis, Director of Programs and
Donor Services
Robin Foreman, Director of Scholarships and
Administration
Vivian Oden, Program and Donor Services
Manager

ADDRESS INQUIRIES TO:
Leigh Evans Davis
Director of Programs and Donor Services
(See address above.)

*SPECIAL STIPULATIONS:
All discretionary grants are to charitable
organizations for capital or special purposes
only.

HANCOCK COUNTY COMMUNITY FOUNDATION [1379]
312 East Main Street
Greenfield, IN 46140
(317) 462-8870
Fax: (317) 467-3330

E-MAIL ADDRESS:
mgibble@hccf.cc

WEB SITE ADDRESS:
www.hccf.cc

FOUNDED: 1992

AREAS OF INTEREST:
Arts, civic affairs, culture, education, youth,
and health and human services.

TYPE:
Project/program grants; Scholarships.

PURPOSE:
To build and improve the quality of life
within the community.

ELIGIBILITY:
Grants are made to organizations that have
tax-exempt status under Section 501(c)(3) of
the Internal Revenue Code. No grants are
made to individuals. Nonsectarian religious
programs may apply.

GEOGRAPHIC RESTRICTIONS:
Hancock County, Indiana.

FINANCIAL DATA:
Amount of support per award: $500 to
$7,500.
Total amount of support: Approximately
$475,000.

NUMBER OF APPLICANTS MOST RECENT YEAR:
23.

NUMBER OF AWARDS: 16.

APPLICATION INFORMATION:
Send a Letter of Intent, which outlines the
request and projected request amount. Upon
receiving the Letter of Intent, the Program

Officer will follow up with the applicant organization to discuss the submission of a formal grant application.

Duration: One year. Extension possible.

ADDRESS INQUIRIES TO:
Alyse Vail, Program Officer
(See address above.)

HARTFORD FOUNDATION FOR PUBLIC GIVING   [1380]

10 Columbus Boulevard, 8th Floor
Hartford, CT 06106-1976
(860) 548-1888
Fax: (860) 524-8346

E-MAIL ADDRESS:
hfpg@hfpg.org

WEB SITE ADDRESS:
www.hfpg.org

FOUNDED: 1925

AREAS OF INTEREST:
Community and economic development, education, summer programs, health, family and social services, and arts and culture.

TYPE:
Capital grants; Project/program grants. Grants for programs and capital purposes, with emphasis on the Foundation's areas of interest, to organizations in the greater Hartford, CT region and 28 surrounding towns.

LEGAL BASIS:
Community foundation established in Connecticut by resolution and declaration of trust.

ELIGIBILITY:
No grants are made directly to individuals or to organizations outside the greater Hartford, CT region.

GEOGRAPHIC RESTRICTIONS:
Hartford, Connecticut and surrounding area.

FINANCIAL DATA:
Amount of support per award: Varies.

APPLICATION INFORMATION:
Formal application available after staff discussion. Board of Directors meets nine times per year.
Duration: Generally, three-year grants.

PUBLICATIONS:
Yearbook; application package; newsletters.

ADDRESS INQUIRIES TO:
Linda J. Kelly, President
(See address above.)

HAWAII COMMUNITY FOUNDATION   [1381]

827 Port Street Mall
Honolulu, HI 96813
(808) 537-6333
(888) 731-3863 (Hawaii)
Fax: (808) 521-6286

E-MAIL ADDRESS:
info@hcf-hawaii.org

WEB SITE ADDRESS:
www.hawaiicommunityfoundation.org

FOUNDED: 1916

AREAS OF INTEREST:
Culture and art, natural resources conservation, education, health and medical research, human services, disability,

mentoring and media, scholarships, neighbor island assistance, persons in need and organizational capacity building.

TYPE:
Conferences/seminars; Development grants; Project/program grants; Scholarships; Seed money grants; Technical assistance; Training grants; Travel grants.

PURPOSE:
To build community among the people of Hawaii.

LEGAL BASIS:
Community foundation.

ELIGIBILITY:
Grantseeker must be a tax-exempt organization, either a unit of government or one classified by the IRS as a 501(c)(3) charity which is not a private foundation. The organization must serve Hawaii's people and environment and have leadership which represents the community served. It must make a request that is time-limited or has other source of future funding.

The Foundation supports innovative and creative programs that fit within specific areas. It also provides scholarships for college studies.

GEOGRAPHIC RESTRICTIONS:
Hawaii.

FINANCIAL DATA:
Foundation has more than $284,000,000 in charitable assets.
Amount of support per award: Varies.

APPLICATION INFORMATION:
Applicant must submit a written proposal describing the proposed project.
Duration: Varies.
Deadline: Varies by program.

PUBLICATIONS:
Annual report; *Grantseeker's Guide*; *Scholarship Seeker's Guide*; *The Power of Giving*; *The Giving Study*.

ADDRESS INQUIRIES TO:
Kalowena Komeiji, Communications Director
(See address above.)

THE HEALTH FOUNDATION OF GREATER INDIANAPOLIS

429 East Vermont Street, Suite 300
Indianapolis, IN 46202-3698
(317) 630-1805
Fax: (317) 630-1806

E-MAIL ADDRESS:
bwilson@thfgi.org

WEB SITE ADDRESS:
www.thfgi.org

TYPE:
Project/program grants.

See entry 1584 for full listing.

THE HEALTHCARE FOUNDATION FOR ORANGE COUNTY

1450 North Tustin Avenue
Suite 209
Santa Ana, CA 92705-8641
(714) 245-1650
Fax: (714) 245-1653

E-MAIL ADDRESS:
ckoenig@hfoc.org

WEB SITE ADDRESS:
www.hfoc.org

TYPE:
Awards/prizes; Demonstration grants; Development grants; General operating grants; Project/program grants; Technical assistance; Training grants.

See entry 1537 for full listing.

HILLSDALE COUNTY COMMUNITY FOUNDATION   [1382]

2 South Howell
Hillsdale, MI 49242-1634
(517) 439-5101
Fax: (517) 439-5109

E-MAIL ADDRESS:
s.bisher@abouthccf.org

WEB SITE ADDRESS:
www.abouthccf.org

FOUNDED: 1991

AREAS OF INTEREST:
Arts, education, community needs, scholarships and philanthropy.

TYPE:
Project/program grants; Scholarships.

YEAR PROGRAM STARTED: 1991

PURPOSE:
To improve the quality of life in Hillsdale County.

LEGAL BASIS:
Community foundation.

ELIGIBILITY:
For grants, organizations must be in and benefit Hillsdale County and be IRS 501(c)(3) tax-exempt. For scholarships, students must be graduates of Hillsdale County High School, residents of Hillsdale County and citizens of the U.S.

GEOGRAPHIC RESTRICTIONS:
Hillsdale County, Michigan.

FINANCIAL DATA:
Amount of support per award: $300 to $25,000.

APPLICATION INFORMATION:
Applications are available at the address above and must include all required documentation, completed application according to requirements, and a copy of the IRS 501(c)(3) tax determination letter.
Duration: One year.
Deadline: Foundation Grants: May 1 and November 1.

ADDRESS INQUIRIES TO:
Sharon Bisher, Executive Director
(See address above.)

THE HOME DEPOT FOUNDATION   [1383]

2455 Paces Ferry Road, C-17
Atlanta, GA 30339
(770) 384-3889
(866) 593-7019
Fax: (770) 384-3908; (866) 593-7027

E-MAIL ADDRESS:
hd_foundation@homedepot.com

WEB SITE ADDRESS:
www.homedepotfoundation.org

FOUNDED: 1978

AREAS OF INTEREST:
Affordable housing, sustainable community development and community affairs.

CONSULTING OR VOLUNTEER SERVICES:
Team Depot volunteer program.

NAME(S) OF PROGRAMS:
- **Affordable Housing Built Responsibly Program**
- **Framing Hope Program**
- **Sustainable Community Development Program**
- **Team Depot**

TYPE:
Challenge/matching grants; Development grants; Product donations; Project/program grants. Environmental research grants.

YEAR PROGRAM STARTED: 2002

PURPOSE:
To contribute to the development of affordable housing in communities where The Home Depot does business; to support employee participation in the community; to promote economic development in The Home Depot communities.

LEGAL BASIS:
Corporate giving program.

ELIGIBILITY:
Most grants are made in communities where The Home Depot operates stores. No grants to individuals, religious, fraternal, political, labor, athletic, social or veterans groups, fund-raising benefits, dinners, exhibits, conferences and sports events, charities sponsored solely by a single civic organization, courtesy or journal advertising campaigns, multiyear commitments, or organizations that are not 501(c)(3) or Revenue Canada designated charities.

GEOGRAPHIC RESTRICTIONS:
United States, Canada and Mexico.

FINANCIAL DATA:
Amount of support per award: Varies depending on needs and nature of the request.

Total amount of support: $37,000,000 for the year 2009.

Matching fund requirements: Employees making contributions to recognized nonprofits may apply for matching gifts up to $500 through The Home Depot Matching Gift Program.

APPLICATION INFORMATION:
Contact the Foundation for application guidelines.

Duration: Varies.

Deadline: Letters of Inquiry: January 15 and July 1. Full Project Description: March 15 and September 15.

PUBLICATIONS:
Brochure; *Social Responsibility Report.*

ADDRESS INQUIRIES TO:
See e-mail address above.

HOUSING EDUCATION AND RESEARCH ASSOCIATION (HERA)   [1384]
Montana State University, 102 Taylor Hall
P.O. Box 173580
Bozeman, MT 59717-3580
(406) 994-3451
Fax: (406) 994-5417

E-MAIL ADDRESS:
mvogel@montana.edu

WEB SITE ADDRESS:
www.housingeducators.org

AREAS OF INTEREST:
Housing education.

NAME(S) OF PROGRAMS:
- **Tessie Agan Award Competition**

TYPE:
Awards/prizes.

ELIGIBILITY:
Open to graduate and undergraduate students.

FINANCIAL DATA:
Amount of support per award: Graduate Award: $750 presented at the HERA Annual Meeting; Undergraduate Award: $250 and opportunity to present paper at the HERA Annual Conference.

APPLICATION INFORMATION:
Information and specific guidelines pertaining to all grants can be found online.

Duration: One-time award.

ADDRESS INQUIRIES TO:
Michael P. Vogel, Executive Director
(See address above.)

*SPECIAL STIPULATIONS:
Award is contingent upon attending the meeting and presenting the paper. Conference registration fees are waived.

HUDSON-WEBBER FOUNDATION   [1385]
333 West Fort Street
Suite 1310
Detroit, MI 48226-3134
(313) 963-7777
Fax: (313) 963-2818

WEB SITE ADDRESS:
www.hudson-webber.org

FOUNDED: 1943

AREAS OF INTEREST:
The primary concern of the Foundation is the vitality of the metropolitan Detroit community. The Foundation's Trustees have defined four specific program missions in which they will concentrate their efforts and resources: the physical revitalization of downtown Detroit, the enhancement of major art and cultural resources in Detroit, the reduction of crime in Detroit and the economic development of Detroit, with emphasis on the creation of additional employment opportunities.

TYPE:
Capital grants; Challenge/matching grants; General operating grants; Project/program grants.

YEAR PROGRAM STARTED: 1943

PURPOSE:
To improve the vitality and quality of life of the metropolitan Detroit community.

LEGAL BASIS:
Private foundation.

ELIGIBILITY:
The Foundation assigns highest priority of support to programs in the city of Detroit. Programs outside of Detroit within the Wayne, Oakland and Macomb tri-county area of southeastern Michigan are included as a much lower priority. Programs outside of the tri-county area of southeastern Michigan generally are not supported.

The Foundation does not make grants for endowments, fund-raising social events, conferences or exhibits. With the exception

of the Foundation's program for Hudsonians, the Foundation does not make grants to individuals.

GEOGRAPHIC RESTRICTIONS:
Southeastern Michigan, specifically the city of Detroit.

FINANCIAL DATA:
Amount of support per award: $5,000 to $500,000.

Total amount of support: $6,255,548 for the year 2010.

APPLICATION INFORMATION:
Information may be obtained from the Foundation's web site.

ADDRESS INQUIRIES TO:
Stephanie Armes
Grants/Finance Associate
(See address above.)

HUMBOLDT AREA FOUNDATION   [1386]
373 Indianola Road
Bayside, CA 95524
(707) 442-2993 ext. 302
Fax: (707) 442-3811

E-MAIL ADDRESS:
chrisw@hafoundation.org

WEB SITE ADDRESS:
www.hafoundation.org

FOUNDED: 1972

AREAS OF INTEREST:
Children, youth and families; community, economy and the environment; health and well-being; arts and humanities; native cultures.

NAME(S) OF PROGRAMS:
- **Community Building Grants**
- **Community Response Grants**
- **Field of Interest Grant Program**
- **Summer Youth Program**

TYPE:
Capital grants; Project/program grants; Scholarships; Seed money grants; Technical assistance.

YEAR PROGRAM STARTED: 1972

PURPOSE:
To improve the quality of life on the north coast of California.

ELIGIBILITY:
Eligible organizations must be IRS 501(c)(3) tax-exempt. Applications will be evaluated using the following criteria: need, planning and management, leadership and collaboration.

The Foundation will not fund projects outside of its service area, projects without sound planning and development, deferred maintenance, annual operating costs, travel, scholarships and fellowships, or projects which violate the nonprofit public laws.

GEOGRAPHIC RESTRICTIONS:
Del Norte, Humboldt and Trinity counties, California.

FINANCIAL DATA:
Amount of support per award: Varies.

APPLICATION INFORMATION:
Information, guidelines and applications are available online.

PUBLICATIONS:
Guidelines.

ADDRESS INQUIRIES TO:
Chris Witt, Director of Grantmaking and Donor Services
(See address above.)

INTERNATIONAL DEVELOPMENT RESEARCH CENTRE (IDRC)   [1387]
150 Kent Street
Mailroom Suite 990
Ottawa ON K1P 0B2 Canada
(613) 236-6163 ext. 2098
Fax: (613) 236-4026

E-MAIL ADDRESS:
cta@idrc.ca

WEB SITE ADDRESS:
www.idrc.ca/awards

FOUNDED: 1970

NAME(S) OF PROGRAMS:
● **IDRC Doctoral Research Awards**

TYPE:
Awards/prizes.

PURPOSE:
To support the field research of Canadian graduate students and developing country nationals enrolled in a Canadian university for doctoral research on a topic of relevance to sustainable and equitable development.

ELIGIBILITY:
Applicants must meet the following conditions for eligibility:
(1) hold Canadian citizenship (or permanent residency status), or hold citizenship of a developing country;
(2) be registered at a Canadian university;
(3) research proposal is for a doctoral thesis and has been approved by the thesis supervisor;
(4) provide evidence of affiliation with an institution or organization in the region in which the research will take place and;
(5) have completed course work and passed comprehensive examinations by the time of award tenure.

Program can involve research in any developing region of the world, excluding Burma, Central Asia, Cuba, Eastern Europe, Iran and Iraq.

FINANCIAL DATA:
Total amount of support: Up to $20,000 (CAN).

NUMBER OF AWARDS: 35 to 38 per year (2 competitions per year).

APPLICATION INFORMATION:
Duration: Up to 12 months.
Deadline: April 1 and November 1.

ADDRESS INQUIRIES TO:
Fellowships and Awards
(See address above.)

INTERNATIONAL DEVELOPMENT RESEARCH CENTRE (IDRC)   [1388]
150 Kent Street
Mailroom Suite 990
Ottawa ON K1P 0B2 Canada
(613) 236-6163 ext. 2098
Fax: (613) 236-4026

E-MAIL ADDRESS:
cta@idrc.ca

WEB SITE ADDRESS:
www.idrc.ca/awards

FOUNDED: 1970

AREAS OF INTEREST:
Research for international development.

NAME(S) OF PROGRAMS:
● **The Internship Award Program**

TYPE:
Awards/prizes. The Internship award program provides exposure to research for international development through a program of training in research management and grant administration under the guidance of Centre program staff. The intern will undertake a program of research on the topic submitted when competing for the internship and will be trained in the techniques of research management through hands-on experience with the Centre's policies and practices for grant administration under the mentorship of a program officer.

PURPOSE:
To provide exposure to research for international development through a program of training in research management and grant administration.

ELIGIBILITY:
Canadian citizens, permanent residents of Canada, and citizens of developing countries are eligible. Applicant must be registered in a Master's program or have completed a Master's degree in a recognized university.

Program can involve research in any developing region of the world, excluding Burma, Central Asia, Cuba, Eastern Europe, Iran and Iraq.

NUMBER OF APPLICANTS MOST RECENT YEAR:
150 or more.

NUMBER OF AWARDS: 10 to 19.

APPLICATION INFORMATION:
Duration: One year.
Deadline: September 12.

ADDRESS INQUIRIES TO:
Fellowships and Awards
(See address above.)

INTERNATIONAL DEVELOPMENT RESEARCH CENTRE (IDRC)
150 Kent Street
Mailroom Suite 990
Ottawa ON K1P 0B2 Canada
(613) 236-6163 ext. 2098
Fax: (613) 236-4026

E-MAIL ADDRESS:
cta@idrc.ca

WEB SITE ADDRESS:
www.idrc.ca/awards

TYPE:
Awards/prizes. The Centre offers one award for doctoral research that explores the relationship between Canadian aid, trade, immigration and diplomatic policy, and international development and the alleviation of global poverty. A second award will be granted for doctoral or Master's research into a problem that is common to First Nations or Inuit communities in Canada and a developing region of the world.

See entry 898 for full listing.

AUDREY AND SYDNEY IRMAS CHARITABLE FOUNDATION   [1389]
5045 Rubio Avenue
Encino, CA 91436
(818) 382-3313
Fax: (818) 382-3315

E-MAIL ADDRESS:
robirm@gmail.com

AREAS OF INTEREST:
Arts, religious organizations, homeless and urban issues.

TYPE:
Challenge/matching grants; Matching gifts. Long-term pledges.

LEGAL BASIS:
501(c)(3).

ELIGIBILITY:
Organizations classified as 501(c)(3) by the IRS can apply. Individuals are ineligible.

GEOGRAPHIC RESTRICTIONS:
Los Angeles County, California.

APPLICATION INFORMATION:
Contact the Foundation by mail for application procedures. Telephone calls will not be accepted.

ADDRESS INQUIRIES TO:
Robert Irmas, Trustee and Administrator
(See address above.)

JEWEL-OSCO   [1390]
150 Pearce Road
Suite 200
Itasca, IL 60143
(630) 948-6000

WEB SITE ADDRESS:
www.jewelosco.com

FOUNDED: 1899

AREAS OF INTEREST:
Education, health, hunger and nutrition.

TYPE:
Capital grants; Conferences/seminars; Project/program grants.

YEAR PROGRAM STARTED: 1943

PURPOSE:
To support programs that meet the needs of society and improve the quality of life, particularly in communities where the company has facilities.

LEGAL BASIS:
Corporate giving program.

ELIGIBILITY:
Grants are made to organizations that have tax-exempt status under Section 501(c)(3) of the Internal Revenue Code. No grants are made to individuals.

GEOGRAPHIC RESTRICTIONS:
Illinois, Indiana and Iowa.

FINANCIAL DATA:
Amount of support per award: Grants vary in amount, depending upon the needs and nature of the request.

APPLICATION INFORMATION:
Contact the Community Relations office for application procedures.
Duration: One year. Renewal possible.

ADDRESS INQUIRIES TO:
Miguel Alba, Director of Public Affairs
(See address above.)

JEWISH COMMUNITY FOUNDATION OF LOS ANGELES [1391]

6505 Wilshire Boulevard
Suite 1200
Los Angeles, CA 90048
(323) 761-8700
Fax: (323) 761-8666

E-MAIL ADDRESS:
grants@jewishfoundationla.org

WEB SITE ADDRESS:
www.jewishfoundationla.org

FOUNDED: 1954

AREAS OF INTEREST:
Jewish life, community and health services, education, social services, arts and culture, and civic life.

CONSULTING OR VOLUNTEER SERVICES:
Family Foundation Center - consultation with family foundations and individual funders regarding the effectiveness of their grantmaking.

NAME(S) OF PROGRAMS:
● **Capital Grants**
● **Cutting Edge Grants**
● **Israel Grants**
● **Los Angeles Collaborative Grants**

TYPE:
Awards/prizes; Capital grants; Project/program grants; Seed money grants.

YEAR PROGRAM STARTED: 1976

PURPOSE:
To provide endowment resources to enable the community to initiate model programs, assist agencies to address the diverse and demanding challenges to face emergencies and the needs of the Jewish community and the Los Angeles community at large.

LEGAL BASIS:
Jewish community foundation.

ELIGIBILITY:
Grants are made to nonprofit 501(c)(3) organizations.

GEOGRAPHIC RESTRICTIONS:
Primarily Los Angeles and Israel.

FINANCIAL DATA:
Amount of support per award: Varies.
Total amount of support: $61,000,000 for the year ended December 31, 2009.

REPRESENTATIVE AWARDS:
$250,000 to LimmudLA; $25,000 to Advancement Project to launch Mothers Against Gang Violence program.

APPLICATION INFORMATION:
Contact the Foundation for details.
Duration: One to three years. No renewals.
Deadline: Varies.

PUBLICATIONS:
Annual report.

OFFICERS:
Lorin M. Fife, Chairperson
Kenneth A. August, Vice President

Leah M. Bishop, Vice President
Anthony Chanin, Vice President
Max Factor, III, Vice President
Bertrand I. Ginsberg, Vice President
Harold J. Masor, Vice President
Scott H. Richland, Vice President
Alan Stern, Vice President
Lawrence Rauch, Treasurer
Selwyn Gerber, Secretary

EXECUTIVE STAFF:
Marvin I. Schotland, President and Chief Executive Officer
Daniel M. Rothblatt, Senior Vice President, Philanthropic Services
Elliot B. Kristal, Vice President, Charitable Gift Planning
Baruch S. Littman, Vice President, Development
Michael J. Januzik, Vice President, Finance and Administration
Amelia Xann, Vice President, Family Foundation Center and Grant Programs

ADDRESS INQUIRIES TO:
Amelia Xann
Vice President, Family Foundation Center and Grant Programs
(See address above.)

J. SEWARD JOHNSON, SR. 1963 CHARITABLE TRUST [1392]

100 Albany Street
Suite 200
New Brunswick, NJ 08901
(732) 524-1020
Fax: (732) 524-1019

FOUNDED: 1963

AREAS OF INTEREST:
Oceanography, drugs and alcohol abuse prevention, cultural enrichment, preventive family health, water and the environment, education, law and public broadcasting.

TYPE:
Project/program grants; Research grants.

LEGAL BASIS:
Charitable trust.

ELIGIBILITY:
Grants are limited to applicants which are tax-exempt under Section 501(c)(3) of the Internal Revenue Code.

The Trust does not generally support grants or gifts to individuals, conferences, symposia, dinners, publications, requests for funds to offset deficits and/or requests for long-term support.

GEOGRAPHIC RESTRICTIONS:
New Jersey, specifically New Brunswick and Princeton.

FINANCIAL DATA:
Amount of support per award: $1,000 to $100,000.

APPLICATION INFORMATION:
Organizations wishing to apply for funds not in response to requests for proposals (RFPs) are advised to submit a preliminary one-page letter of inquiry before submitting a fully developed proposal. This allows the Trust to determine whether a proposed project meets its interests without requiring a significant time commitment on the applicant's part.

Inquiries to the Trust should include a brief explanation of the project/program and should include budget information and expected outcomes.
Duration: One year.

PUBLICATIONS:
Guidelines.

ADDRESS INQUIRIES TO:
Robert E. Campbell, Consultant
(See address above.)

THE KAHANOFF FOUNDATION [1393]

101 Sixth Street, S.W., Suite 105
Calgary AB T2P 5K7 Canada
(403) 237-7896
Fax: (403) 261-9614

E-MAIL ADDRESS:
info@kahanoff.com

WEB SITE ADDRESS:
www.kahanoff.com

FOUNDED: 1979

AREAS OF INTEREST:
Community development and research, culture, education, health and social services.

YEAR PROGRAM STARTED: 1979

PURPOSE:
To fund traditional and innovative charitable programs in Canada and Israel.

LEGAL BASIS:
Private foundation.

ELIGIBILITY:
Must be a charitable program in Canada and/or Israel.

GEOGRAPHIC RESTRICTIONS:
Alberta, Canada and Israel.

FINANCIAL DATA:
Amount of support per award: Small grants: $1,000 to $10,000. Large grants: $100,000 to $1,000,000.

APPLICATION INFORMATION:
Applications should include:
(1) a brief description of the organization's history, objectives, and activities;
(2) latest audited financial statement;
(3) current financial statement and budget;
(4) membership of board;
(5) charitable registration number;
(6) funding requirements;
(7) anticipated additional sources of funding and;
(8) current status of the program (if relevant).

ADDRESS INQUIRIES TO:
Shira Herzog, President
(See address above.)

KALAMAZOO COMMUNITY FOUNDATION [1394]

151 South Rose Street
Suite 332
Kalamazoo, MI 49007-4775
(269) 381-4416
Fax: (269) 381-3146

E-MAIL ADDRESS:
info@kalfound.org

WEB SITE ADDRESS:
www.kalfound.org

FOUNDED: 1930

AREAS OF INTEREST:
Community investment and leadership priorities in Kalamazoo County: individuals and families, community engagement and youth development, education and learning, economic development.

TYPE:
Capital grants; Project/program grants; Scholarships; Seed money grants.

LEGAL BASIS:
Community foundation established in 1925. Incorporated in 1930.

ELIGIBILITY:
Grants are available to institutions with 501(c)(3) status and charitable activities operating in Kalamazoo County, MI.

GEOGRAPHIC RESTRICTIONS:
Kalamazoo County, Michigan.

FINANCIAL DATA:
Amount of support per award: $250 to $100,000.
Total amount of support: $17,300,000 for the year 2009.

APPLICATION INFORMATION:
eGrant application is available at the Foundation web site.
Duration: One year.
Deadline: First working day of each quarter: January, April, July and October.

OFFICERS:
Juan R. Olivarez, President and Chief Executive Officer
Carrie Pickett-Erway, Vice President, Community Investment
David D. Gardiner, Community Relations Advisor

TRUSTEES:
Barbara L. James, Chairperson
Ronda E. Stryker, Vice Chairperson
Si Johnson
Donald J. Vander Kooy
Hon. Carolyn H. Williams
Dr. Eileen Wilson-Oyelaran

ADDRESS INQUIRIES TO:
Carrie Pickett-Erway
Vice President, Community Investment
(See address above.)

THE KANTZLER FOUNDATION [1395]
Pere Marquette Depot
1000 Adams Street, Suite 200
Bay City, MI 48708
(989) 893-4438
Fax: (989) 893-4448

E-MAIL ADDRESS:
kathyc@bayfoundation.org

FOUNDED: 1974

AREAS OF INTEREST:
Initial funding for educational, recreational and charitable projects in the Bay City area.

TYPE:
Development grants; Project/program grants.

YEAR PROGRAM STARTED: 1974

PURPOSE:
To increase the quality of life in the Bay City area.

LEGAL BASIS:
Michigan nonprofit corporation.

ELIGIBILITY:
Organizations must be IRS 501(c)(3) tax-exempt. Priority is given to projects that will have a multiplier effect upon the community. The grants must be used to finance the cost of special projects and capital improvements and not to defray current operating expenses. The Foundation will not provide the entire support for a project and will expect that others will share the costs.

GEOGRAPHIC RESTRICTIONS:
Bay City area, Michigan.

FINANCIAL DATA:
Amount of support per award: $1,000 to $250,000.
Total amount of support: $230,000 for the year 2009.

APPLICATION INFORMATION:
Grant requests must include 10 copies of the following:
(1) cover letter, including the amount being requested;
(2) organizational mission;
(3) executive summary, which includes the benefits to the community and anticipated outcomes;
(4) project description, funding goal with names of all sources and dollar amounts, benefit to organization/community and segment of community served;
(5) financial data including program budget with all sources of revenue, current balance sheet, current income statement, copy of federal tax-exempt ruling from the IRS, copy of form 990, and primary sources of revenue for the organization;
(6) board of directors/trustees names and occupations and;
(7) letters of support.

Also include additional information or documentation deemed pertinent to the grant request. If the information requested is not available, please explain.

Grant requests are to be mailed to The Kantzler Foundation at the address listed above.
Duration: Usually one year. In appropriate circumstances, however, a commitment may be made on an extended basis.
Deadline: Two weeks prior to trustees meetings in mid-April, mid-July and mid-November.

PUBLICATIONS:
Brochure.

BOARD OF TRUSTEES:
Andrea Hales
Linda Heemstra
Ruth Jaffe
D. Brian Law
Dominic Monastiere
Valerie Roof
Robert Sarow
Clifford Van Dyke
Jerome Yantz

ADDRESS INQUIRIES TO:
Administrator for the Board of Trustees
(See address above.)

*SPECIAL STIPULATIONS:
The Board of Trustees requires the grant recipient to furnish a written report, ordinarily within a year of the grant's payment, regarding the results of the project which has been supported.

EDWARD BANGS KELLEY & ELZA KELLEY FOUNDATION, INC. [1396]
243 South Street
Hyannis, MA 02601
(508) 775-3117
Fax: (508) 775-3720

E-MAIL ADDRESS:
contact@kelleyfoundation.org

WEB SITE ADDRESS:
www.kelleyfoundation.org

FOUNDED: 1954

AREAS OF INTEREST:
Health, psychology, sociology, education, culture, and environment.

TYPE:
Capital grants; Challenge/matching grants; Development grants; Matching gifts; Project/program grants.

YEAR PROGRAM STARTED: 1954

PURPOSE:
To promote the health and welfare of the residents of Barnstable County.

LEGAL BASIS:
Private foundation.

ELIGIBILITY:
Applicants must be U.S. citizens, residents of Barnstable County, or organizations who serve Barnstable County. Grants must benefit health and welfare of Barnstable County (MA) residents.

GEOGRAPHIC RESTRICTIONS:
Barnstable County, Massachusetts.

FINANCIAL DATA:
Amount of support per award: Varies.
Total amount of support: $250,000.

COOPERATIVE FUNDING PROGRAMS: Cape Cod Grantmakers Collaborative, other foundations.

NUMBER OF APPLICANTS MOST RECENT YEAR: 37.

NUMBER OF AWARDS: 29.

APPLICATION INFORMATION:
Contact the Foundation.
Duration: One year. Renewals by reapplication.

IRS IDENTIFICATION NUMBER: 04-6039660

ADDRESS INQUIRIES TO:
Henry L. Murphy, Jr., President
(See address above.)

THE KETTERING FUND [1397]
1480 Kettering Tower
Dayton, OH 45423
(937) 228-1021
Fax: (937) 228-2399

E-MAIL ADDRESS:
info@ketteringfamilyphilanthropies.org

WEB SITE ADDRESS:
www.ketteringfamilyphilanthropies.org

FOUNDED: 1958

AREAS OF INTEREST:
The environment, medical research, teaching, the arts and higher education.

TYPE:
Capital grants; Challenge/matching grants; Development grants; Endowments; Matching gifts; Project/program grants; Research grants.

YEAR PROGRAM STARTED: 1958

PURPOSE:
To support scientific, medical, social and educational studies and research conducted by nonprofit, charitable organizations that are located in Ohio.

LEGAL BASIS:
Private foundation.

ELIGIBILITY:
Applicants must be tax-exempt 501(c)(3) nonprofit organizations. The Fund does not support individuals, partisan political causes or candidates, public elementary or secondary schools, scholarships or travel.

GEOGRAPHIC RESTRICTIONS:
Ohio.

FINANCIAL DATA:
Amount of support per award: Varies.
Total amount of support: $2,200,000 for fiscal year 2010.

NUMBER OF APPLICANTS MOST RECENT YEAR:
25.

NUMBER OF AWARDS: 23.

REPRESENTATIVE AWARDS:
$500,000 to Wright State University; $2,000,000 to U.S. Air Force Museum.

APPLICATION INFORMATION:
The Kettering Fund requires a letter of inquiry, to be submitted online, as a preliminary step before an application is requested. Check online for availability of funding.
Duration: Varies with project.
Deadline: Letter of inquiry: Generally late January and July.

PUBLICATIONS:
Application guidelines.

ADDRESS INQUIRIES TO:
Judy Thompson, Executive Director
(See address above.)

KEWEENAW COMMUNITY FOUNDATION   [1398]
236 Quincy Street
Hancock, MI 49930
(906) 482-9673
Fax: (906) 482-9679

E-MAIL ADDRESS:
mail@k-c-f.org

WEB SITE ADDRESS:
www.k-c-f.org

FOUNDED: 1994

AREAS OF INTEREST:
Environment, health and youth.

TYPE:
Awards/prizes; Challenge/matching grants; Development grants; Endowments; Project/program grants; Scholarships.

YEAR PROGRAM STARTED: 1994

PURPOSE:
To enhance and support the quality of life in the Keweenaw area.

ELIGIBILITY:
Grants are made to organizations that have tax-exempt status under Section 501(c)(3) of the Internal Revenue Code. No grants are made to individuals. Religious programs may apply. Grants can also be given to governmental units or eligible educational institutions.

GEOGRAPHIC RESTRICTIONS:
Houghton and Keweenaw counties, Michigan.

FINANCIAL DATA:
Amount of support per award: Grants vary in amount, depending upon the needs and nature of the request.

NUMBER OF APPLICANTS MOST RECENT YEAR:
50.

NUMBER OF AWARDS: 18.

APPLICATION INFORMATION:
Duration: One year. Renewal possible.

ADDRESS INQUIRIES TO:
Heather McCloksey, Office Manager
(See address above.)

KITSAP COMMUNITY FOUNDATION   [1399]
9657 Levin Road, N.W.
Suite 260
Silverdale, WA 98383
(360) 698-3622
Fax: (360) 698-6043

E-MAIL ADDRESS:
kcf@kitsapfoundation.org

WEB SITE ADDRESS:
www.kitsapfoundation.org

FOUNDED: 1993

AREAS OF INTEREST:
Social welfare, environment, cultural development and community development.

TYPE:
General operating grants; Project/program grants; Scholarships.

YEAR PROGRAM STARTED: 1999

PURPOSE:
To improve the quality of life in the community. Specifically, to address basic human needs by working to eliminate ignorance, hopelessness and suffering; to protect the environment; to provide cultural enrichment; to encourage excellence; to promote understanding and cooperation.

LEGAL BASIS:
501(c)(3).

ELIGIBILITY:
Grant support mostly for nonprofit organizations serving Kitsap County, Washington and surrounding areas.

GEOGRAPHIC RESTRICTIONS:
Kitsap County, Washington and its surrounding areas.

FINANCIAL DATA:
$2,000,000 in assets for the year 2010.
Amount of support per award: $500 to $2,500.
Total amount of support: $130,000 in grants and $5,000 in scholarships for the year 2010.

NUMBER OF AWARDS: 37 grants and 5 scholarships for the year 2010.

REPRESENTATIVE AWARDS:
Boys & Girls Clubs; Great Peninsula Conservancy; Joy of Freedom; Kitsap Community Resources; Washington CASH.

APPLICATION INFORMATION:
Two complete copies of the application packet are required, except only one copy of the most recent audited financial statement need be included. A complete packet includes:
(1) Grant Summary page;
(2) narrative (four-page limit) on how the organization plans to use the funds;
(3) verification of tax-exempt status under Section 501(c)(3), or other such proof of charitable activities;
(4) list of current board members, including member affilitiations and any other pertinent information;
(5) list of key organizational staff, including titles and main functions;

(6) one-page summary of current year revenue and expense budget (operating budget). Note status (committed or requested) of each revenue source;
(7) one-page summary of actual operating revenue and expenses for the past two complete fiscal years, including a list of funding sources and amounts received over the past two years. Group sources in broad categories. Do not include individual donor names or amount of donations;
(8) proposed project income and expense budget, if applicable. Note status (committed or requested) of each revenue source;
(9) if the project for which funds are sought is a collaboration with other agencies, include letters of commitment or other documentation of support from the collaborating agencies and;
(10) one copy of the most recent audited financial statement. If organization does not conduct an annual audit, provide a copy of the most recent IRS Form 990 or 990EZ, if available. If those are not available, provide documentation to demonstrate organization is in compliance with any regulatory agencies (State of Washington).

PUBLICATIONS:
Newsletter; annual report.

IRS IDENTIFICATION NUMBER: 94-3205217

STAFF:
Pete Atha, Executive Director

ADDRESS INQUIRIES TO:
Pete Atha, Executive Director
(See address above.)

KOHL'S CORPORATION
N56 W17000 Ridgewood Drive
Menomonee Falls, WI 53051
(262) 703-7000
Fax: (262) 703-6305

E-MAIL ADDRESS:
community.relations@kohls.com

WEB SITE ADDRESS:
www.kohlscorporation.com

TYPE:
Awards/prizes; Scholarships. Nomination reward/scholarship program in two age categories: 6-12 and 13-18 at three progressive levels: store level, regional and national.
See entry 1828 for full listing.

THE KROGER COMPANY FOUNDATION   [1400]
1014 Vine Street
Cincinnati, OH 45202-1100
(513) 762-4000
Fax: (513) 762-1100

WEB SITE ADDRESS:
www.thekrogerco.com

FOUNDED: 1987

AREAS OF INTEREST:
Education, human services, hunger relief and women's health.

TYPE:
General operating grants.

YEAR PROGRAM STARTED: 1987

PURPOSE:
To feed the hungry, support breast cancer initiatives, provide disaster relief and assist local grassroots organizations.

LEGAL BASIS:
Corporate giving program.

ELIGIBILITY:
Only proposals from 501(c)(3) organizations located in communities where the Kroger Company has operations are considered. No international funding.

FINANCIAL DATA:
Amount of support per award: Typically $1,000 to $5,000.
Total amount of support: Approximately $8,000,000 for the year 2010.

APPLICATION INFORMATION:
Eligible organizations may submit proposals at any time through the community relations department of the local retail division office. Proposals must include an IRS tax-exempt determination letter and should include a statement of the reason for the request.
Duration: Application must be made each year. Grants not automatically renewed.
Deadline: Grants are reviewed year-round.

PUBLICATIONS:
Program announcement; application guidelines.

ADDRESS INQUIRIES TO:
Foundation Administrator
(See address above.)

*PLEASE NOTE:
The Foundation does not support international projects or national organizations, except when local chapter is active in a community served by the Kroger Company.

LAWRENCE COUNTY COMMUNITY FOUNDATION   [1401]
1016 15th Street
Bedford, IN 47421
(812) 279-2215
Fax: (812) 279-1984

E-MAIL ADDRESS:
hope@cfpartner.org

WEB SITE ADDRESS:
www.cfpartner.org

AREAS OF INTEREST:
Community improvement.

TYPE:
Challenge/matching grants; Endowments; Project/program grants; Scholarships.

PURPOSE:
To be proactive in creating and growing an enduring source of charitable assets that will help to identify and respond to the emerging and changing needs of the community.

ELIGIBILITY:
Organizations and agencies who may or may not be tax-exempt according to Section 501(c)(3) of the Internal Revenue Code or for-profit entities interested in funding a charitable, not-for profit program are eligible. Population served by the program must be within Lawrence County, IN.

GEOGRAPHIC RESTRICTIONS:
Lawrence County, Indiana.

FINANCIAL DATA:
Amount of support per award: Varies.

APPLICATION INFORMATION:
Application form can be requested from the Foundation or downloaded from the web site above. Applicants must submit the following

documents with the application form:
(1) concise summary of the proposed project, two or three paragraphs in length, stating the community need to be addressed by the project and why the organization is qualified to address the need, the target population and estimated number to be served, the organization's experience with similar projects, and a description of how the project will fit into and further the organization's overall mission;
(2) description of the activities or steps that will be taken to carry out the project, including project timeline;
(3) summary of funding details, including how the funds will be used, as well as other funding sources. Attach a detailed budget sheet showing projected income and expenses for the project;
(4) an explanation of how the success of this project will be evaluated. If the organization plans to continue the project, explain how will it be sustained after grant funding is expended and;
(5) list of names and amounts from sources contributing 10% or more of the organization's budget in the past two years. Also list affiliations with religious groups.

Application must be signed by the organization President or another non-paid board officer. Staple or clip each grant application copy.
Duration: Funding for a multiyear project will usually be considered on an annual basis and not extend beyond three years.

ADDRESS INQUIRIES TO:
Hope Flores, Executive Director
(See address above.)

THE LEARY FIREFIGHTERS FOUNDATION   [1402]
594 Broadway, Suite 409
New York, NY 10012-3234
(212) 343-0240
Fax: (212) 343-1762

E-MAIL ADDRESS:
info@learyfirefighters.org

WEB SITE ADDRESS:
www.learyfirefighters.org

FOUNDED: 2000

AREAS OF INTEREST:
Firefighting.

NAME(S) OF PROGRAMS:
● **The Jeremiah Lucey Grant Program**

TYPE:
Grants-in-aid; Project/program grants; Training grants. Grant program to assist professional fire departments.

YEAR PROGRAM STARTED: 2000

PURPOSE:
To provide funding and resources for fire departments to obtain the highest level of equipment, training and technology.

LEGAL BASIS:
Publicly funded tax-exempt organization under Section 501(c)(3) of the Internal Revenue Code.

ELIGIBILITY:
Fire departments with a financial need not covered by a municipal budget in order to maintain the highest level of public safety.

GEOGRAPHIC RESTRICTIONS:
Massachusetts, New York and Gulf Coast region affected by Hurricane Katrina.

FINANCIAL DATA:
Amount of support per award: $25,000 to $50,000.
Total amount of support: $70,000 for the year 2008.

APPLICATION INFORMATION:
Initial letter of inquiry, up to two pages, and project budget.

IRS IDENTIFICATION NUMBER: 13-4125074

ADDRESS INQUIRIES TO:
Mardi Grant, Executive Director
(See address above.)

THE JOHN J. LEIDY FOUNDATION   [1403]
305 West Chesapeake Avenue
Suite 308
Towson, MD 21204
(410) 821-3006
Fax: (410) 821-3007

E-MAIL ADDRESS:
info@leidyfoundation.org

WEB SITE ADDRESS:
www.leidyfoundation.org

FOUNDED: 1957

AREAS OF INTEREST:
Education, health care, arts/culture, food services, human services, children and youth.

TYPE:
General operating grants; Scholarships.

PURPOSE:
To improve the quality of life in the Baltimore area.

LEGAL BASIS:
Private foundation.

ELIGIBILITY:
Organizations must be IRS 501(c)(3) tax-exempt and be located in Maryland. The Foundation does not fund individuals.

GEOGRAPHIC RESTRICTIONS:
Baltimore metropolitan area.

FINANCIAL DATA:
Amount of support per award: $350 to $20,000.
Total amount of support: $523,280 for the year 2010.

NUMBER OF APPLICANTS MOST RECENT YEAR:
120.

NUMBER OF AWARDS: 97.

APPLICATION INFORMATION:
Applications must include the proposed budget and a copy of the IRS tax-exempt letter. Please submit an original and four copies.

PUBLICATIONS:
Application guidelines.

OFFICER:
Robert L. Pierson, President

ADDRESS INQUIRIES TO:
Lu Pierson, Grants Administrator
(See address above.)

THE LES CHENEAUX COMMUNITY FOUNDATION   [1404]
P.O. Box 249
Cedarville, MI 49719
(906) 484-2256 ext. 215
Fax: (906) 484-2072

E-MAIL ADDRESS:
lccommunityfoundation@gmail.com

WEB SITE ADDRESS:
www.lescheneauxcommunityfoundation.org

AREAS OF INTEREST:
Education, culture and recreation,
environment and youth.

TYPE:
Grants-in-aid; Project/program grants;
Scholarships.

PURPOSE:
To support programs that improve the quality
of life in the community.

LEGAL BASIS:
Community foundation.

ELIGIBILITY:
Grants are made to organizations that have
tax-exempt status under Section 501(c)(3) of
the Internal Revenue Code. Nonsectarian
religious programs may apply. No grants are
made to individuals.

GEOGRAPHIC RESTRICTIONS:
Les Cheneaux, Michigan.

FINANCIAL DATA:
Amount of support per award: Grants vary in
amount, depending upon the needs and
nature of the request.
Total amount of support: Varies.

NUMBER OF APPLICANTS MOST RECENT YEAR:
Approximately 30.

NUMBER OF AWARDS: Approximately 24.

APPLICATION INFORMATION:
Deadline: May 1 and October 1.

LOCAL INITIATIVES SUPPORT
CORPORATION   [1405]
1825 K Street, N.W., Suite 1100
Washington, DC 20006
(202) 785-2908
Fax: (202) 835-8931

WEB SITE ADDRESS:
www.lisc.org

FOUNDED: 1980

AREAS OF INTEREST:
Urban and rural community revitalization.

TYPE:
Project/program grants; Technical assistance.
Organization was formed to help existing
community development corporations
revitalize urban and rural communities
throughout the country. Since 1980, LISC has
aggregated and invested more than $7.8
billion in equity, loans and grants, which has
leveraged more than $22 billion for
development projects and programs directed
at lower-income communities. LISC's
investments have helped finance more than
215,000 affordable homes and apartments
and 30 million square feet of retail and
commercial space, including schools, day
care centers, health clinics and recreational
facilities. Along with these efforts has been
the creation of 74,000 jobs for lower-income
residents in communities throughout urban
and rural America.

YEAR PROGRAM STARTED: 1980

PURPOSE:
To build sustainable communities, which are
good places to work, do business and raise
children.

ELIGIBILITY:
Nonprofit 501(c)(3) IRS status.

GEOGRAPHIC RESTRICTIONS:
United States.

FINANCIAL DATA:
Total amount of support: Varies.
Matching fund requirements: A strict
matching requirement, dollar-for-dollar of
new money from local private sources.

IRS IDENTIFICATION NUMBER: 13-3030229

BOARD OF DIRECTORS:
Robert E. Rubin, Chairman
Michael Rubinger, President and Chief
Executive Officer

LONG ISLAND COMMUNITY
FOUNDATION   [1406]
Nassau Hall
1864 Muttontown Road
Syosset, NY 11791
(516) 348-0575 ext. 222
Fax: (516) 348-0570

E-MAIL ADDRESS:
vgreene@licf.org

WEB SITE ADDRESS:
www.licf.org

FOUNDED: 1978

AREAS OF INTEREST:
Environment, arts, education, health and the
community.

NAME(S) OF PROGRAMS:
● **Community Response-Critical Issues,
  Critical Communities, Critical
  Organizations**
● **Henry Phillip Kraft Memorial
  Fund-Environmental Grants**
● **LIUU Fund-Progressive Social Change
  Grants**

TYPE:
Challenge/matching grants; Demonstration
grants; Development grants; General
operating grants; Project/program grants;
Seed money grants; Technical assistance;
Research contracts.

YEAR PROGRAM STARTED: 1978

PURPOSE:
To provide leadership in identifying current
and future community needs, and building a
permanent endowment to address these
needs.

LEGAL BASIS:
501(c)(3) or fiscal agent.

ELIGIBILITY:
Programs and projects benefiting Nassau and
Suffolk counties, NY.

GEOGRAPHIC RESTRICTIONS:
Nassau and Suffolk counties, New York.

FINANCIAL DATA:
Amount of support per award: Varies.
Total amount of support: Approximately
$10,000,000 to $11,000,000 for the year
2009. Competitive Grants: $1,300,000.

NUMBER OF AWARDS: Over 60.

APPLICATION INFORMATION:
The Foundation has three grant cycles
throughout the year. Detailed instructions are
provided on the Foundation's web site.
Applicants should review the instructions
carefully before submitting an application.

STAFF:
Sol Marie Alfonso-Jones, Program Officer
Vanessa Greene, Program Officer
Nancy Arnold, Grants Administrator

EXECUTIVE DIRECTOR:
David Okorn

ADDRESS INQUIRIES TO:
Vanessa Greene, Program Officer
(See address above.)

LUBBOCK AREA FOUNDATION,
INC.   [1407]
2509 80th Street
Lubbock, TX 79423
(806) 762-8061
Fax: (806) 762-8551

E-MAIL ADDRESS:
tami@lubbockareafoundation.org

WEB SITE ADDRESS:
www.lubbockareafoundation.org

FOUNDED: 1981

AREAS OF INTEREST:
Charitable organizations and community
development.

NAME(S) OF PROGRAMS:
● **Mini Grant for Teachers Program**

TYPE:
Grants-in-aid; Scholarships. Responsiveness
to changing or emerging community needs
approach for solving community problems in
South Plains area.

YEAR PROGRAM STARTED: 1981

PURPOSE:
To improve the quality of life in the South
Plains area of Texas.

ELIGIBILITY:
Organizations must be 501(c)(3)
not-for-profit.

GEOGRAPHIC RESTRICTIONS:
South Plains area of Texas.

FINANCIAL DATA:
Amount of support per award: Grant awards:
Typically $3,000 to $5,000.
Total amount of support: Varies.

COOPERATIVE FUNDING PROGRAMS: Community
Endowment Challenge, Mini Grants for
Teachers.

NUMBER OF APPLICANTS MOST RECENT YEAR:
350.

NUMBER OF AWARDS: 284.

APPLICATION INFORMATION:
Deadline: June 15.

ADDRESS INQUIRIES TO:
Michelle Stephens
Director, Educational Initiatives
(See address above.)

M & M AREA COMMUNITY
FOUNDATION   [1408]
1101 11th Avenue
Menominee, MI 49858
(906) 864-3599
Fax: (906) 864-3657

E-MAIL ADDRESS:
mmfoundation@czwireless.net

WEB SITE ADDRESS:
www.mmcommunityfoundation.org

FOUNDED: 1994

AREAS OF INTEREST:
Arts, charity, civic affairs, community
development, culture, education, health,
historic preservation and human services.

TYPE:
Project/program grants; Scholarships;
Training grants.

YEAR PROGRAM STARTED: 1997

PURPOSE:
To make people's lives better: more
meaningful, secure, and safe.

ELIGIBILITY:
Grants are made to organizations that have
tax-exempt status under Section 501(c)(3) of
the Internal Revenue Code. No grants are
made to individuals. Nonsectarian religious
programs may apply.

GEOGRAPHIC RESTRICTIONS:
Menominee County, Michigan and Marinette
County, Wisconsin.

FINANCIAL DATA:
Amount of support per award: Up to
$10,000.
Total amount of support: $327,000 for the
year 2010.

NUMBER OF APPLICANTS MOST RECENT YEAR:
82.

NUMBER OF AWARDS: 44.

APPLICATION INFORMATION:
Applications must be submitted online.
Duration: One year. Renewal possible.

ADDRESS INQUIRIES TO:
Richard O'Farrell, Executive Director
P.O. Box 846
Menominee, MI 49858-0846
(See e-mail address above.)

MADISON COMMUNITY
FOUNDATION   [1409]

2 Science Court
Madison, WI 53711
(608) 232-1763
Fax: (608) 232-1772

E-MAIL ADDRESS:
tlinfield@madisoncommunityfoundation.org

WEB SITE ADDRESS:
www.madisoncommunityfoundation.org

FOUNDED: 1942

AREAS OF INTEREST:
Children, arts and culture, community
development, environment, elderly, learning
and youth.

TYPE:
Capital grants; Project/program grants.
Program grants support new programs or
expansion of existing programs. Capital
grants support the construction, acquisition
and renovation of facilities and the purchase
of equipment. Investments in technology are
given to significantly enhance the
organization's ability to operate or to
improve services.

PURPOSE:
To enhance the quality of life for residents in
Dane County.

LEGAL BASIS:
Community foundation.

ELIGIBILITY:
Organizations must be nonprofit IRS
501(c)(3) tax-exempt, serve the people of
Dane County, employ a staff, elect a
governing board, and conduct business
without discrimination on the basis of race,
religion, gender, sexual preference, age,
marital status, disability or national origin.

Generally grants are not made for operating
expenses, individuals, endowments, debt
retirement, lobbying, annual campaigns,
scholarships, religious organizations for
religious purposes, conferences, fund-raising,
celebrations or substance abuse treatment.

GEOGRAPHIC RESTRICTIONS:
Dane County, Wisconsin.

FINANCIAL DATA:
Approximately 30% of grant applications are
funded at some level. The Foundation is
rarely the sole funder of projects; other
sources will be sought to accomplish project
goals.
Amount of support per award: Program
average: $35,000; Capital average: $55,000.
Total amount of support: Approximately
$1,245,000 in unrestricted and
field-of-interest grants for the year 2010.

NUMBER OF APPLICANTS MOST RECENT YEAR:
90 for the year 2010.

NUMBER OF AWARDS: 18 for the year 2010.

REPRESENTATIVE AWARDS:
$75,000 to Fitchburg Public Library toward
the construction of a LEED gold certified
public library; $25,000 to Madison Music
Collective for the Mary Lou Williams
Centennial Youth Engagement program;
$50,000 to Porchlight, Inc. for the Madison
Cares capital campaign, an initiative to build
two new facilities to support and house
homeless people with serious mental illness.

APPLICATION INFORMATION:
Guidelines and applications are available
from the Foundation. Proposals must be
submitted in both paper and electronic form.
Proposals by fax are not accepted. An online
letter of inquiry (LOI) is required.
Duration: One to two years.
Deadline: Letter of Inquiry: January 15 and
July 15. Those asked to submit a full
proposal: March 1 and September 1.

PUBLICATIONS:
Grantmaking Guidelines.

ADDRESS INQUIRIES TO:
Tom Linfield
Vice President, Grantmaking
(See address above.)

MARIETTA COMMUNITY
FOUNDATION   [1410]

Putnam Commons
121 Putnam Street, Suite 105
Marietta, OH 45750
(740) 373-3286
Fax: (740) 373-3937

E-MAIL ADDRESS:
carol@mcfohio.org

WEB SITE ADDRESS:
mariettacommunityfoundation.org

FOUNDED: 1974

AREAS OF INTEREST:
Civic affairs, the elderly, community needs
and education.

TYPE:
Challenge/matching grants;
Conferences/seminars; Development grants;
Endowments; Grants-in-aid; Matching gifts;
Scholarships; Seed money grants; Technical
assistance; Training grants.

YEAR PROGRAM STARTED: 1974

PURPOSE:
To support philanthropy and the efforts of
citizens to improve natural, human and civic
resources.

LEGAL BASIS:
Community foundation.

ELIGIBILITY:
Must be a 501(c)(3) organization in or
serving Washington County, Ohio.

GEOGRAPHIC RESTRICTIONS:
Greater Washington County, Ohio, and
surrounding area.

FINANCIAL DATA:
Amount of support per award: $3,000 to
$25,000.
Total amount of support: $123,000
unrestricted for the year 2010.

NUMBER OF APPLICANTS MOST RECENT YEAR:
60.

NUMBER OF AWARDS: 35.

APPLICATION INFORMATION:
Organizations may either send a one-page
letter of inquiry or submit a formal
application form.
Deadline: Proposals are accepted at any time
during the year. To be considered in a
particular quarter, the in-hand deadlines are
February 7, June 7 and October 7. Applicants
should allow 45 to 75 days for processing
and response.

PUBLICATIONS:
Annual report; grant guidelines; memorial
brochure.

FREDA MAYTAG-GRACE
CRAWFORD TRUST

c/o JPMorgan Private Client Services
402 North Tejon Street, Suite 200
Colorado Springs, CO 80903
(719) 227-6445
Fax: (719) 227-6448

E-MAIL ADDRESS:
julie.golden@jpmorgan.com

WEB SITE ADDRESS:
www.jpmorgan.com/onlinegrants

TYPE:
Project/program grants.
See entry 1547 for full listing.

LUTHER T. MCCAULEY
CHARITABLE TRUST   [1411]

c/o JPMorgan Private Client Services
402 North Tejon Street, Suite 200
Colorado Springs, CO 80903
(719) 227-6445
Fax: (719) 227-6448

E-MAIL ADDRESS:
julie.golden@jpmorgan.com

WEB SITE ADDRESS:
www.jpmorgan.com/onlinegrants

AREAS OF INTEREST:
Economically deprived, the socially
disadvantaged, mentally and physically
handicapped citizens, with preference made
toward the youth of the community for their
educational, social, recreational and medical
needs.

TYPE:
Project/program grants.

ELIGIBILITY:
Qualifying charities, agencies and institutions
which direct their attention to the

economically deprived, the socially disadvantaged and the mentally and physically handicapped citizens of El Paso County, CO. No grants to individuals.

Organization must provide copy of current IRS determination letter showing tax-exempt status under Section 501(c)(3) and public charity status under Section 509(a).

GEOGRAPHIC RESTRICTIONS:
El Paso County, Colorado.

FINANCIAL DATA:
Total amount of support: Average: $3,000 to $5,000.

APPLICATION INFORMATION:
Application and guidelines are available online.
Duration: One year. No renewals.
Deadline: March 31, June 30 and October 31.

ADDRESS INQUIRIES TO:
Julie Golden, Trust Advisor
(See address above.)

RICHARD KING MELLON FOUNDATION   [1412]
BNY/Mellon Center
500 Grant Street, Suite 4106
Pittsburgh, PA 15219-2502
(412) 392-2800
Fax: (412) 392-2837

E-MAIL ADDRESS:
lreed@rkmf.org

WEB SITE ADDRESS:
www.fdncenter.org/grantmaker/rkmellon

FOUNDED: 1947

AREAS OF INTEREST:
Conservation; regional economic development; children, youth and young adults; education; human services and nonprofit capacity building.

TYPE:
Capital grants; Challenge/matching grants; Grants-in-aid; Project/program grants. Grant program for improving the quality of life in southwestern Pennsylvania.

PURPOSE:
To promote conservation, economic development, education, human services and programs in the public interest.

ELIGIBILITY:
Must be 501(c)(3) nonprofit organizations. Priority is given to projects and programs that have clearly defined outcomes and an evaluation component. Funding is almost exclusively committed to southwestern Pennsylvania. Preference is given for support of established organizations with specific objectives, and for partnering with other donors rather than solely underwriting the entire cost of projects.

GEOGRAPHIC RESTRICTIONS:
Southwestern Pennsylvania.

FINANCIAL DATA:
Total amount of support: Varies.

APPLICATION INFORMATION:
Applications must be mailed; faxes are not accepted. Current IRS determination letter indicating 501(c)(3) tax-exempt status required.

ADDRESS INQUIRIES TO:
Lisa Reed, Grant Manager
(See address above.)

EUGENE AND AGNES E. MEYER FOUNDATION   [1413]
1250 Connecticut Avenue, N.W.
Suite 800
Washington, DC 20036
(202) 483-8294
Fax: (202) 328-6850

E-MAIL ADDRESS:
meyer@meyerfdn.org

WEB SITE ADDRESS:
www.meyerfoundation.org

FOUNDED: 1944

AREAS OF INTEREST:
Arts, heritage and culture; children, youth and families; civic engagement; education; employment and skills training; health and mental health; homelessness and hunger; housing and community development; immigrant communities; law and justice.

TYPE:
Capital grants; Challenge/matching grants; General operating grants; Project/program grants; Technical assistance. Grants for a wide variety of projects in the above areas of interest in the Washington, DC metropolitan area.

YEAR PROGRAM STARTED: 1944

PURPOSE:
To develop the Washington, DC area as a community by supporting capable, community-based nonprofit organizations that can foster the well-being of all people in the region; to help low-income people and create healthy neighborhoods; to promote the region's diversity.

LEGAL BASIS:
Private foundation.

ELIGIBILITY:
The Foundation distributes its funds to and through tax-exempt corporations. It also prefers not to make grants for projects that are primarily sectarian in character. Grants are seldom made for projects outside the geographical boundaries of Greater Washington and are never made to individuals. The Foundation does not support endowment drives, scientific or medical research, scholarship programs, special or annual events or conferences.

GEOGRAPHIC RESTRICTIONS:
Restricted to the metropolitan DC region, which is defined as: District of Columbia; Montgomery and Prince George's counties in Maryland; Arlington, Fairfax and Prince William counties in Virginia; and the cities of Alexandria, Falls Church, Manassas and Manassas Park, Virginia.

FINANCIAL DATA:
Amount of support per award: $1,000 to $500,000; $25,000 average.
Total amount of support: $6,294,000 in grants authorized for the year 2008.

COOPERATIVE FUNDING PROGRAMS: Occasional joint funding.

NUMBER OF APPLICANTS MOST RECENT YEAR:
Approximately 750.

NUMBER OF AWARDS: 246 grants for the year ended December 31, 2008.

APPLICATION INFORMATION:
The Foundation uses a two-step application process:
Step One: Eligible candidates interested in requesting a grant from the Foundation are required to first submit a letter of inquiry.

Step Two: The letter of inquiry will be reviewed by the Foundation. A full proposal may thereafter be invited and a submission date will be agreed upon.

All letters of inquiry (cover sheet, letter and required attachments) must be received in the Foundation's offices no later than 5 P.M. of the day of the deadline. Materials must also be submitted in duplicate.
Duration: Generally one-year support from date of award.
Deadline: June 9.

PUBLICATIONS:
Annual report; e-newsletter.

IRS IDENTIFICATION NUMBER: 53-0241716

STAFF:
Julie L. Rogers, President and Chief Executive Officer
Kristen Conte, Vice President of Finance and Administration
Richard L. Moyers, Vice President, Programs and Communications
Karen FitzGerald, Senior Program Officer
Carmen James Lane, Senior Program Officer
Danielle Reyes, Senior Program Officer
Jane Ward, Grants Manager and Program Officer
Maegan Scott, Program and Communications Associate
Alegneta Asfaw, Program Assistant
Andrew Brown, Program Assistant
Jennifer Burke, Business Operations Assistant

OFFICERS AND BOARD OF DIRECTORS:
Barbara Krumsiek, Chairperson
Julie L. Rogers, President and Chief Executive Officer
Maria Gomez, R.N., M.P.H., Secretary-Treasurer
Newman T. Halvorson, Jr., Assistant Secretary-Treasurer
Joshua Bernstein
Antoinette Cook Bush
James Dyke, Jr.
Barbara Lang
Ginger Lew
Deborah Ratner Salzberg
James Sandman
Dr. Robert G. Templin, Jr.
Kerrie B. Wilson

ADDRESS INQUIRIES TO:
Julie L. Rogers, President and Chief Executive Officer
(See address above.)

MICHIGAN GATEWAY COMMUNITY FOUNDATION   [1414]
111 Days Avenue
Buchanan, MI 49107-1609
(269) 695-3521
Fax: (269) 695-4250

E-MAIL ADDRESS:
info@mgcf.org

WEB SITE ADDRESS:
www.mgcf.org

FOUNDED: 1978

AREAS OF INTEREST:
Health, culture, education and community development.

TYPE:
Challenge/matching grants; Development grants; Project/program grants; Scholarships; Seed money grants.

YEAR PROGRAM STARTED: 1978

PURPOSE:
To address the changing needs of the community in Cass and South Berrien counties.

LEGAL BASIS:
501(c)(3) nonprofit foundation.

ELIGIBILITY:
Eligible organizations must be IRS 501(c)(3) tax-exempt.

GEOGRAPHIC RESTRICTIONS:
Cass and South Berrien counties, Michigan.

FINANCIAL DATA:
Amount of support per award: Varies.
Total amount of support: Varies.

REPRESENTATIVE AWARDS:
$2,500 over six weeks for Group Counseling "Life on a Tightrope" for High School Girls at risk for low self-esteem and peer pressure.

APPLICATION INFORMATION:
Applicants may use the Common Grant Application Form of the Council of Michigan Foundations. Applications must include a copy of the IRS tax determination letter.
Duration: One year. Most grants not renewable.
Deadline: February 1, May 1, August 1 and November 1.

PUBLICATIONS:
Annual report; scholarship programs.

IRS IDENTIFICATION NUMBER: 38-2180730

ADDRESS INQUIRIES TO:
Rob Habicht
President and Chief Executive Officer
(See address above.)

THE MINNEAPOLIS FOUNDATION   [1415]
800 IDS Center
80 South Eighth Street
Minneapolis, MN 55402
(612) 672-3878
Fax: (612) 672-3846

E-MAIL ADDRESS:
e-mail@mplsfoundation.org

WEB SITE ADDRESS:
www.minneapolisfoundation.org

FOUNDED: 1915

AREAS OF INTEREST:
Education, housing and homelessness, racial and economic equity, immigration and youth violence.

CONSULTING OR VOLUNTEER SERVICES:
Philanthropic services for other foundations.

NAME(S) OF PROGRAMS:
● **Community Action Funds**
● **Designated Beneficiary Funds**
● **Donor-Advised Funds**
● **Field of Interest Funds**
● **Investment Management Services**
● **Nonprofit Assistance Fund**
● **Robins, Kaplan, Miller and Ciresi Foundation for Children**

TYPE:
General operating grants; Project/program grants.

PURPOSE:
To connect resources with opportunities to benefit Minnesota; to effect positive change in the quality of life for all Minnesotans by leveraging the assets of individual funds, supporting organizations and community partnerships; to engage the community on critical social issues through public information campaigns and convenings.

LEGAL BASIS:
Community foundation incorporated in Minnesota.

ELIGIBILITY:
Organizations must advance social, economic, and/or racial equity to be eligible for funding. The Foundation grants to 501(c)(3) organizations, some 501(c)(4) nonprofits, governmental or tribal organizations, and groups organized for nonprofit purposes (informal, emerging or collaborative groups).

The Foundation does not fund individuals, organizations/activities outside of Minnesota, conference registration fees, memberships, direct religious activities, political organizations or candidates' fund-raising efforts, conferences, events or sponsorships, financial deficits, replacement of public sector funds, emergency/safety net services, regranting/loans, production of housing units, or purchase or repair of vehicles.

GEOGRAPHIC RESTRICTIONS:
Primarily Minneapolis, Minnesota.

FINANCIAL DATA:
Amount of support per award: Competitive grants: $10,000 to $75,000; average approximately $41,574.
Total amount of support: $33,958,000 total grants for fiscal year 2009-10; $4,157,400 in competitive grants for fiscal year 2010-11.

NUMBER OF APPLICANTS MOST RECENT YEAR:
Competitive Community Grants: 266 for fiscal year 2010-11.

NUMBER OF AWARDS: Competitive Community Grants: 105 for fiscal year 2010-11.

REPRESENTATIVE AWARDS:
$45,000 to Admission Possible for program services for 40 low-income high school seniors in Minneapolis in their second year; $40,000 to Emerge Community Development for the Northside Job Connection ex-offender program in North Minneapolis; $50,000 to Immigrant Law Center for its legal, advocacy and education services.

APPLICATION INFORMATION:
Duration: Annual. Must reapply for additional funding. No multiyear grants.
Deadline: March 15 and September 1, with grant decisions in June and December.

IRS IDENTIFICATION NUMBER: 41-6029402

OFFICERS:
Sandra Vargas, President and Chief Executive Officer
Jean Adams, Vice President-Finance and Administration

ADDRESS INQUIRIES TO:
Community Grantmaking
(See address above.)

*PLEASE NOTE:
Through its competitive grantmaking, the Foundation invests its community resources to increase social, economic, and racial equity in our community.

MIZUHO USA FOUNDATION, INC.   [1416]
Mizuho Corporate Bank, Ltd.
1251 Avenue of the Americas
31st Floor
New York, NY 10020-1104
(212) 282-4192
Fax: (212) 282-4250

E-MAIL ADDRESS:
mizuho.usa.foundation@mizuhocbus.com

WEB SITE ADDRESS:
www.mizuhocbk.com/americas/community/foundation/index.html

FOUNDED: 2003

AREAS OF INTEREST:
Community development, with a focus on affordable housing, economic development and workforce development.

NAME(S) OF PROGRAMS:
● **Fostering Economic Self-Sufficiency**
● **Mizuho Community Involvement Grants Program**
● **Mizuho Matching Gifts Program**
● **Promoting Economic Development**
● **Strengthening Affordable Housing**

TYPE:
Demonstration grants; Matching gifts; Project/program grants; Seed money grants. The Foundation awards grants to not-for-profit charitable organizations for community development programs that help sustain and revitalize economically distressed urban communities, and assist individuals who live in these neighborhoods.

Fostering Economic Self-Sufficiency funds programs that strengthen the workforce development field through the provision of technical assistance and/or training to not-for-profit organizations.

Mizuho Community Involvement Grants Program makes small grants available to the not-for-profit charitable organizations with which Mizuho Corporate Bank volunteer activities take place.

Mizuho Matching Gifts Program is for qualifying contributions made by eligible Mizuho Financial Group U.S. employees to qualifying not-for-profit charitable organizations in the areas of education, arts and culture, health and community affairs.

Promoting Economic Development supports programs that promote economic and commercial revitalization of communities by fostering small business development, entrepreneurship, job creation and job retention.

Strengthening Affordable Housing provides funding for programs that facilitate access to affordable housing for low- and moderate-income individuals and families.

YEAR PROGRAM STARTED: 2003

PURPOSE:
To provide grants to not-for-profit charitable organizations to support community development programs that contribute to the strength and vitality of urban neighborhoods; to serve as a catalyst for innovative programs in the U.S. that strengthen urban communities.

LEGAL BASIS:
Corporate foundation.

ELIGIBILITY:
Organizations applying to the Foundation must:

(1) be recognized as tax-exempt under Section 501(c)(3) of the Internal Revenue Code and classified as a public charity under Section 509(a)(1) or (2) of the Internal Revenue Code and not a supporting organization under Section 509(a)(3);
(2) present a proposal that satisfies the Foundation's guidelines;
(3) not discriminate against a person or group on the basis of age, race, national origin, ethnicity, gender, disability, sexual orientation, political affiliation or religious belief and;
(4) be in full compliance with U.S. anti-terrorism laws and regulations, including the USA Patriot Act and Executive Order 13224, pertaining to U.S.-based, not-for-profit charitable organizations conducting activities outside of the U.S.

The Foundation does not fund:
(1) general operating support;
(2) individuals;
(3) religious, sectarian, fraternal, veteran, athletic or labor groups;
(4) organizations or programs outside the U.S.;
(5) political organizations, political candidates or political activity;
(6) organizations whose primary purpose is to influence legislation;
(7) fund-raising activities such as charitable dinners, benefits, courtesy advertising, telethons, races or other sporting events;
(8) advertising and;
(9) endowment or capital campaigns.

GEOGRAPHIC RESTRICTIONS:
New York City, New York and Los Angeles, California.

FINANCIAL DATA:
Foundation's endowment is approximately $13,000,000. Since its establishment, the Foundation has made over $4,500,000 in grant commitments.
Amount of support per award: $10,000 to $100,000; average $40,000.
Total amount of support: $560,000 in grants for the year 2010.
Matching fund requirements: Mizuho Matching Gifts Program: 1:1 match for qualifying contributions. Requests for matching gifts must come from eligible employees of the Mizuho Financial Group in the U.S.

COOPERATIVE FUNDING PROGRAMS:
Neighborhood Opportunities Fund (New York City, NY) and New York City Workforce Development Fund.

NUMBER OF APPLICANTS MOST RECENT YEAR: 50.

NUMBER OF AWARDS: 25 for the year 2010, in addition to matching gifts.

REPRESENTATIVE AWARDS:
Program Grants 2010: $50,000 to ACCION USA, New York, NY, for a Women's Program for the development and launch of a dedicated microlending and financial education program for female borrowers; $5,000 to Esperanza Community Housing Corporation, CA, for a Community Health Promoters' Training Program for a community health training and internship program for economically disadvantaged residents, increasing their access to both employment opportunities and health information and services.

Community Involvement Grants 2010: $1,000 to Atlanta Habitat for Humanity.

APPLICATION INFORMATION:
Qualifying organizations must submit a short concept paper of up to three pages for preliminary review. The concept paper should include:
(1) a brief description of the organization including its legal name, history, mission/goals, activities and, if applicable, web address;
(2) copy of the IRS determination letter indicating 501(c)(3) tax-exempt status and 509(a) public charity classification and;
(3) a description of the program for which funding is sought, including statement of need, goals and activities of the program, expected outcomes and evaluation methods, projected time frame, population(s)/geographies served, grant amount requested, and a preliminary program budget, with projected expenses and revenues, including funding commitments received to date for the program as well as pending requests (may be provided in attachment form).

The Foundation staff will review all initial submissions and invite organizations on a selective basis to submit more detailed proposals. Each applicant will be notified of the Foundation's interest within eight weeks of the annual deadline. Selected proposals are presented to the Foundation's Board of Directors, which makes funding decisions each fall.
Duration: Usually one year; some multiyear grants may be awarded.
Deadline: First weekday in July, to be considered for funding in the same year.

PUBLICATIONS:
Brochure; application guidelines.

IRS IDENTIFICATION NUMBER: 13-3550008

OFFICERS:
Merlin E. Nelson, Chairman
Tsuyoshi Monri, President
Paul Dankers, Treasurer
Hajime Fukuzawa, Secretary
Lesley H. Palmer, Executive Director
Albert Scarola, Assistant Treasurer
Leah Markham, Program Officer

BOARD OF DIRECTORS:
John H. Higgs
Takashi Horie
Tsuyoshi Monri
Merlin E. Nelson
Shinya Wako

ADDRESS INQUIRIES TO:
Lesley H. Palmer, Executive Director
(See address above.)

MONTANA COMMUNITY FOUNDATION   [1417]
One North Last Chance Gulch
Suite 1
Helena, MT 59601
(406) 443-8313
Fax: (406) 442-0482

E-MAIL ADDRESS:
info@mtcf.org

WEB SITE ADDRESS:
www.mtcf.org

FOUNDED: 1988

AREAS OF INTEREST:
General charitable purposes.

NAME(S) OF PROGRAMS:
• **Social Justice Montana**
• **Women's Foundation of Montana**

TYPE:
Grants-in-aid. The Foundation does almost no competitive grantmaking. Although it provides $2,000,000 yearly in grants and scholarships, almost all of that money is designated. It also has a large number of donor-advised and scholarship funds. The only competitive granting programs are the following:
Social Justice Montana: the mission of this Fund is to promote tolerance and combat bigotry and discrimination, with a focus on youth, ages elementary through high school and;
Women's Foundation of Montana: its mission is to promote economic self-sufficiency and a brighter future for girls.

All of the Foundation's other unrestricted grant funds are devoted to matching programs, technical assistance programs and other supportive services for building local community foundations.

PURPOSE:
To cultivate a culture of giving so Montana communities can flourish.

LEGAL BASIS:
501(c)(3) organization.

GEOGRAPHIC RESTRICTIONS:
Montana.

FINANCIAL DATA:
Amount of support per award: Women's Foundation of Montana: Up to $10,000.
Total amount of support: $2,000,000 per year in grants and scholarships; almost all of this money is designated funding.
Women's Foundation of Montana: Up to $55,000 per year.

ADDRESS INQUIRIES TO:
Linda Reed
President/Chief Executive Officer
(See address above.)

THE MORTON-KELLY CHARITABLE TRUST   [1418]
c/o Jensen Baird Gardner & Henry
10 Free Street
Portland, ME 04101
(207) 775-7271
Fax: (207) 775-7935

E-MAIL ADDRESS:
mquinlan@jbgh.com

FOUNDED: 1988

AREAS OF INTEREST:
The arts, education, environment and history.

TYPE:
Capital grants; Challenge/matching grants; Development grants; Endowments; General operating grants; Internships; Matching gifts; Project/program grants; Research grants; Seed money grants. One-time cash award.

YEAR PROGRAM STARTED: 1988

PURPOSE:
To support organizations in the arts, education, environment and history.

LEGAL BASIS:
Private foundation.

ELIGIBILITY:
Organizations must be IRS 501(c)(3) tax-exempt and be located in Maine.

GEOGRAPHIC RESTRICTIONS:
Maine.

FINANCIAL DATA:
Amount of support per award: Varies.

Total amount of support: $205,500 for the year 2010.

NUMBER OF APPLICANTS MOST RECENT YEAR: 80.

NUMBER OF AWARDS: 30 for the year 2010.

REPRESENTATIVE AWARDS:
$4,250 to Dead River Area Historical Society; $5,000 to Friends of Casco Bay; $5,000 to Penobscot Theatre Company.

APPLICATION INFORMATION:
Applicants may submit a written proposal and must include a copy of the IRS tax determination letter.

Duration: One year.

Deadline: November 1.

IRS IDENTIFICATION NUMBER: 01-0442078

ADDRESS INQUIRIES TO:
Michael J. Quinlan, Secretary
(See address above.)

*PLEASE NOTE:
Applications not accepted before July 1 each year.

SAMUEL B. AND MARGARET C. MOSHER FOUNDATION [1419]

1114 State Street, Suite 254
Santa Barbara, CA 93101
(805) 962-1700
Fax: (805) 962-1792

E-MAIL ADDRESS:
ygiller@mosherfdn.com

WEB SITE ADDRESS:
www.mosher-foundation.org

FOUNDED: 1951

AREAS OF INTEREST:
Performing arts, health care and education.

TYPE:
Grants-in-aid.

PURPOSE:
To improve the quality of life in Santa Barbara County.

ELIGIBILITY:
Eligible organizations must be IRS 501(c)(3) tax-exempt. No grants to individuals.

GEOGRAPHIC RESTRICTIONS:
Southern Santa Barbara County, California.

FINANCIAL DATA:
Amount of support per award: $5,000 to $10,000.

Total amount of support: $1,200,000 for the year 2009.

APPLICATION INFORMATION:
Application by invitation only.

Duration: One year. Nonrenewable.

STAFF:
Yvette Giller, Director

ADDRESS INQUIRIES TO:
Yvette Giller, Director
(See address above.)

*PLEASE NOTE:
The Foundation will initiate contact with local nonprofit organizations.

CHARLES STEWART MOTT FOUNDATION [1420]

Mott Foundation Building
503 South Saginaw Street, Suite 1200
Flint, MI 48502-1851
(810) 238-5651
Fax: (810) 766-1753

E-MAIL ADDRESS:
info@mott.org

WEB SITE ADDRESS:
www.mott.org

FOUNDED: 1926

AREAS OF INTEREST:
Civil society, environment, pathways out of poverty and Flint, MI, besides exploratory interests.

TYPE:
Challenge/matching grants; Conferences/seminars; Demonstration grants; General operating grants; Project/program grants; Seed money grants; Technical assistance; Training grants. Grants for improvement of the quality of living in the community through pilot ventures in a number of human service areas. Emphasis is on improving opportunity for the individual, partnership with the community, effectiveness of community systems and leadership.

PURPOSE:
To support efforts that promote a just, equitable and sustainable society.

LEGAL BASIS:
Private foundation.

ELIGIBILITY:
Applicants must be organizations and institutions with appropriate interests. No grants to individuals. Tax-exempt status is required.

FINANCIAL DATA:
Amount of support per award: $15,000 to $250,000.

Total amount of support: $92,898,581 for the year 2010.

NUMBER OF AWARDS: 492 grants for the year 2010.

APPLICATION INFORMATION:
Information on application procedures is available online.

PUBLICATIONS:
Annual report.

TRUSTEES:
William S. White, Chairman, President and Chief Executive Officer
A. Marshall Acuff, Jr.
Rushworth M. Kidder
Frederick S. Kirkpatrick
Tiffany W. Lovett
Webb F. Martin
Olivia P. Maynard
John Morning
Maryanne Mott
Charlie Nelms
William H. Piper
John W. Porter
Marise M.M. Stewart
Claire M. White

ADDRESS INQUIRIES TO:
Office of Proposal Entry
(See address above.)

MUSKINGUM COUNTY COMMUNITY FOUNDATION [1421]

534 Putnam Avenue
Zanesville, OH 43701
(740) 453-5192
Fax: (740) 453-5734

E-MAIL ADDRESS:
giving@mccf.org

WEB SITE ADDRESS:
www.mccf.org

FOUNDED: 1985

AREAS OF INTEREST:
Improving the quality of life in Muskingum County, OH.

CONSULTING OR VOLUNTEER SERVICES:
Assistance to grantseekers and grantmakers in the Muskingum County, OH area.

TYPE:
Awards/prizes; Conferences/seminars; Internships; Project/program grants; Research grants; Scholarships; Seed money grants. Scholarships for Muskingum County, OH residents and others designated in fund agreements.

YEAR PROGRAM STARTED: 1985

PURPOSE:
To improve the quality of life and to serve the charitable needs of the community by attracting and administering charitable funds.

GEOGRAPHIC RESTRICTIONS:
Muskingum and contiguous counties, Ohio.

FINANCIAL DATA:
Amount of support per award: Varies.

Total amount of support: $1,000,000 for the year 2009.

APPLICATION INFORMATION:
Deadline: March 1.

ADDRESS INQUIRIES TO:
David P. Mitzel, Executive Director
(See address above.)

NATIONAL BLACK MBA ASSOCIATION [1422]

180 North Michigan
Suite 1400
Chicago, IL 60601
(312) 236-2622
Fax: (312) 236-0390

E-MAIL ADDRESS:
lori.johnson@nbmbaa.org

WEB SITE ADDRESS:
www.nbmbaa.org

AREAS OF INTEREST:
The economic and intellectual wealth of the black community.

NAME(S) OF PROGRAMS:
- **NBMBAA Graduate Scholarship Program**

TYPE:
Scholarships.

PURPOSE:
To help create economic and intellectual wealth for the black community; to identify and increase the pool of Black talent for business, public, private and nonprofit sectors.

ELIGIBILITY:
Open to qualified business students enrolled full-time in an accredited Association to Advance Collegiate Schools of Business

(AACSB) graduate business program in the U.S. This Program identifies students who have demonstrated potential to make significant contributions in the field of business in the public and private sectors. Applicants must demonstrate academic excellence, exceptional leadership potential and be actively involved in their local communities through service to others.

GEOGRAPHIC RESTRICTIONS:
United States and Canada.

FINANCIAL DATA:
Amount of support per award: Up to $15,000.

Total amount of support: Over $500,000.

NUMBER OF APPLICANTS MOST RECENT YEAR:
550.

NUMBER OF AWARDS: Minimum of 25.

APPLICATION INFORMATION:
Applicants must submit a two-page essay (with applicant's name omitted entirely from document), resume (not to exceed two pages), and official transcripts for all college coursework or the current graduate program. Essay and resume must be submitted through Association's online process only.

Deadline: May 15.

NATIONAL TRUST FOR HISTORIC PRESERVATION

1785 Massachusetts Avenue, N.W.
Washington, DC 20036
(202) 588-6315
Fax: (202) 588-6223

E-MAIL ADDRESS:
grants@nthp.org

WEB SITE ADDRESS:
www.preservationnation.org

TYPE:
Challenge/matching grants; Conferences/seminars; Project/program grants; Seed money grants; Technical assistance; Training grants. Education program curricula. Project grants to support consultants with professional expertise in areas such as architecture, law, planning, economics, archeology and graphic design. Conferences that address subjects of particular importance to historic preservation also are funded. In addition, grants are made for curriculum development in preservation education directed at select audiences.

See entry 650 for full listing.

NEW MEXICO COMMUNITY FOUNDATION   [1423]

502 West Cordova Road, Suite 1
Santa Fe, NM 87505
(505) 820-6860
Fax: (505) 820-7860

E-MAIL ADDRESS:
nmcf@nmcf.org

WEB SITE ADDRESS:
www.nmcf.org

FOUNDED: 1983

AREAS OF INTEREST:
New Mexico's communities and their people.

NAME(S) OF PROGRAMS:
• **New Mexico Community AIDS Partnership Initiative (NMCAP)**

TYPE:
Endowments; Grants-in-aid. Supports community-based projects and organizations around the state that provide HIV/AIDS prevention, education, harm reduction and direct services.

GEOGRAPHIC RESTRICTIONS:
New Mexico.

FINANCIAL DATA:
Amount of support per award: $100 to $300,000.

APPLICATION INFORMATION:
Applicants must first submit the online Letter of Inquiry. This letter must provide brief, but basic, information about the project, its mission, planned activity or delivery of services, its current stage of development, and the proposed budget/funding. If the project meets the necessary preliminary criteria, the Foundation will then invite a detailed application.

ADDRESS INQUIRIES TO:
Denise Gonzales
Director, Community Philanthropy
(See address above.)

THE NEW YORK COMMUNITY TRUST   [1424]

909 Third Avenue, 22nd Floor
New York, NY 10022
(212) 686-0010
Fax: (212) 532-8528

WEB SITE ADDRESS:
www.nycommunitytrust.org

FOUNDED: 1924

AREAS OF INTEREST:
Children, youth and families, community development and the environment, education, arts and humanities, health, people with special needs and special projects.

TYPE:
Project/program grants. The New York Community Trust is the community foundation of the greater New York area. It administers almost 2,000 charitable funds created by individuals, families, corporations and other entities to benefit the world around them.

YEAR PROGRAM STARTED: 1924

PURPOSE:
To benefit mankind, especially citizens of New York and vicinity.

LEGAL BASIS:
Public nonprofit foundation.

ELIGIBILITY:
Priority is given to grant proposals from nonprofit organizations which deal with the problems of the New York metropolitan region. Preference is given to proposals for support for specific programs or projects. Grants are not normally made for endowments or building fund campaigns, deficit financing or annual giving, religious purposes or financial assistance or to individual applicants.

GEOGRAPHIC RESTRICTIONS:
New York, New York.

FINANCIAL DATA:
Amount of support per award: $10,000 to $65,000.

APPLICATION INFORMATION:
A cover letter should be submitted in writing on the organization's letterhead, signed by its

chief executive officer on behalf of its governing body, along with a written proposal providing the following:
(1) the need that will be met by the actions for which funds are requested;
(2) how the need will be met by the project or program proposed;
(3) why the organization requesting a grant is the logical one to carry out the project;
(4) what the qualifications are of its staff leadership;
(5) what the budget for the project is and what other potential sources of support may be forthcoming;
(6) what evaluation of the project is planned;
(7) how the program will be supported after the requested grant expires and;
(8) brief background on the organization.

The proposal should be accompanied by a list of board members, a copy of the organization's most recent audited financial statement, a copy of the organization's current operating budget and evidence of tax-exempt status.
Duration: Usually one year.

PUBLICATIONS:
Annual report; application and individual program guidelines; proposal cover sheet.

OFFICERS:
Lorie A. Slutsky, President
Joyce M. Bove, Senior Vice President, Grants and Special Projects
Mercedes Leon, Vice President, Administration
Alan Holzer, Chief Financial Officer

DISTRIBUTION COMMITTEE:
Charlynn Goins, Chairman
Anthony Carvette
Ernest J. Collazo
Jamie Drake
Roger J. Maldonado
Anne Moore, M.D.
Valerie Peltier
Samuel S. Polk
Lorie A. Slutsky
Estelle N. Tanner
Ann Unterberg

ADDRESS INQUIRIES TO:
Joyce M. Bove, Senior Vice President, Grants and Special Projects
(See address above.)

THE NORCLIFFE FOUNDATION

Wells Fargo Center
999 Third Avenue, Suite 1006
Seattle, WA 98104
(206) 682-4820
Fax: (206) 682-4821

E-MAIL ADDRESS:
arline@thenorcliffefoundation.com

WEB SITE ADDRESS:
www.thenorcliffefoundation.com

TYPE:
Capital grants; Challenge/matching grants; Conferences/seminars; Endowments; General operating grants; Research grants; Seed money grants.

See entry 270 for full listing.

NORTHEAST AGRICULTURAL EDUCATION FOUNDATION

101 South Salina Street
Suite 400
Syracuse, NY 13202
(315) 671-0588
Fax: (315) 671-0589

E-MAIL ADDRESS:
mhabib@rockbridgeinvest.com

TYPE:
Project/program grants.

See entry 2259 for full listing.

THE NORTHERN TRUST COMPANY [1425]

50 South LaSalle Street, L7
Chicago, IL 60603
(312) 444-4059
Fax: (312) 630-1809

E-MAIL ADDRESS:
communityaffairs@northerntrust.com

WEB SITE ADDRESS:
www.northerntrust.com

FOUNDED: 1889

AREAS OF INTEREST:
Education, social welfare, and culture and the arts.

NAME(S) OF PROGRAMS:
- **The Northern Trust Company Charitable Trust**
- **The Northern Trust Matching Gift Program**
- **Volunteer Grants Program**

TYPE:
Capital grants; Endowments; General operating grants; Matching gifts; Project/program grants; Technical assistance; Training grants. Grants within the Bank's areas of interest, including matching gifts to hospitals, educational institutions, cultural institutions and social welfare organizations.

YEAR PROGRAM STARTED: 1966

PURPOSE:
To reach out to people in the Chicago area who are in need or face obstacles that impede their full participation in society.

LEGAL BASIS:
Northern Trust Corporation is a multi-bank holding company.

ELIGIBILITY:
Applicant must be a not-for-profit organization, tax-exempt under IRS requirements and located in the U.S., Chicago metropolitan area.

Normally, contributions will not be made to support individuals, fraternal groups, individual churches or sectarian organizations, political activity, research, tickets or advertising for fund-raising benefits and agencies receiving more than 5% of their funding from the United Way.

GEOGRAPHIC RESTRICTIONS:
Chicago, Illinois.

FINANCIAL DATA:
Amount of support per award: Largest single grant goes to United Way. Other grants generally $1,000 to $25,000; typical grant is $3,000 to $7,500.
Total amount of support: $14,200,000 for the year 2010.
Matching fund requirements: Will match 100% of any gifts at least $25 to a maximum of $2,000 per person per year.

NUMBER OF APPLICANTS MOST RECENT YEAR:
500.

NUMBER OF AWARDS: 300.

APPLICATION INFORMATION:
New applicants must submit an online letter of inquiry six weeks before application deadline. If proposal is approved, then applicant must submit:
(1) a completed application form;
(2) a copy of organization's IRS 501(c)(3) notification letter;
(3) a copy of organization's operating budget and specific project budget, if applicable;
(4) financial information for previous two years;
(5) a list of Chicago-area corporate and foundation contributors and amounts given in the last and the current year;
(6) a list of board members, with affiliations and;
(7) a list of organization's management staff and their qualifications.

Prior successful applicants are not required to submit the letter of inquiry.
Duration: Grants are annual. Multiyear pledges for capital or endowments. Requests for renewals are considered annually.
Deadline: Varies.

PUBLICATIONS:
Annual report.

IRS IDENTIFICATION NUMBER: 36-6147253

STAFF:
K. Kelly Mannard, Executive Vice President
Deborah Liverette, Senior Vice President and Director of Community Affairs
Jerome Harper, Second Vice President
Chastity Davis, Coordinator
Dawn McGovern, Coordinator
Katie Stobbe, Officer

ADDRESS INQUIRIES TO:
Deborah Liverette, Senior Vice President and Director of Community Affairs
(See address above.)

THE NORTHWEST MINNESOTA FOUNDATION [1426]

4225 Technology Drive, N.W.
Bemidji, MN 56601
(218) 759-2057
Fax: (218) 759-2328

E-MAIL ADDRESS:
nwmf@nwmf.org

WEB SITE ADDRESS:
www.nwmf.org

FOUNDED: 1986

TYPE:
Development grants; Endowments; Project/program grants; Training grants.

PURPOSE:
To improve the quality of life for the people of the region.

ELIGIBILITY:
Applicants must be a public agency or private nonprofit organization with a 501(c)(3) federal tax-exempt status. If an organization does not meet these criteria, it may work with an affiliated tax-exempt organization that may be the applicant and fiscal agent for the project. The affiliate must be a parent organization, provide similar services and/or define in writing its participation in project implementation. No grants are made to individuals.

GEOGRAPHIC RESTRICTIONS:
Beltrami, Clearwater, Hubbard, Kittson, Lake of the Woods, Mahnomen, Marshall, Norman, Pennington, Polk, Red Lake and Roseau counties, Minnesota.

FINANCIAL DATA:
Amount of support per award: Up to $25,000, depending on the grant type.
Matching fund requirements: 50% typically required.

APPLICATION INFORMATION:
A pre-proposal must be submitted on the NMF pre-proposal application form. Applicants are encouraged to contact NMF staff to discuss projects prior to submission. Once a project has been determined to be eligible, a full application is invited and NMF staff will explain the process for submitting additional information.
Duration: Up to two years.
Deadline: Pre-proposals may be submitted at any time.

ADDRESS INQUIRIES TO:
Jim Steenerson
Senior Program Officer-Grants
(See address above.)

THE NORTHWESTERN MUTUAL FOUNDATION [1427]

720 East Wisconsin Avenue
Milwaukee, WI 53202
(414) 665-4305
Fax: (414) 665-2199

E-MAIL ADDRESS:
deannatillisch@northwesternmutual.com

WEB SITE ADDRESS:
www.nmfoundation.com

FOUNDED: 1992

AREAS OF INTEREST:
Education, health and human services, and arts and culture.

CONSULTING OR VOLUNTEER SERVICES:
Mutual Friends.

NAME(S) OF PROGRAMS:
- **Greater Milwaukee Program**

TYPE:
Capital grants; Challenge/matching grants; Conferences/seminars; General operating grants; Matching gifts; Project/program grants; Research grants; Scholarships; Technical assistance; Training grants. Grant program focusing especially on the Greater Milwaukee area, where the company is headquartered.

PURPOSE:
To inspire human potential through lifelong learning and community commitment.

ELIGIBILITY:
Applying organizations must be nonprofit 501(c)(3) in the Milwaukee, WI area, with programs centered on education, health and human services, or arts and culture. Grants are not given to religious organizations.

GEOGRAPHIC RESTRICTIONS:
Greater Milwaukee, Wisconsin area.

FINANCIAL DATA:
Amount of support per award: Varies.
Total amount of support: $15,000,000 for the year 2009.

NUMBER OF APPLICANTS MOST RECENT YEAR:
1,200.

NUMBER OF AWARDS: 750.

APPLICATION INFORMATION:
Organizations that are new to the Foundation are encouraged to request modest grants. Foundation accepts electronic applications only.
Duration: One year. Must reapply.

ADDRESS INQUIRIES TO:
Deanna Tillisch, Vice President
(See address above.)

OKLAHOMA CITY COMMUNITY FOUNDATION, INC. [1428]

P.O. Box 1146
Oklahoma City, OK 73101-1146
(405) 235-5603
Fax: (405) 235-5612

E-MAIL ADDRESS:
info@occf.org

WEB SITE ADDRESS:
www.occf.org

FOUNDED: 1969

AREAS OF INTEREST:
Beautification, education, the arts, social services and civic organizations.

TYPE:
Project/program grants; Scholarships. Support for philanthropic agencies designated by donors. Discretionary grants by the Foundation's trustees are relatively modest.

PURPOSE:
To serve the charitable purposes of its donors and the charitable needs of the Oklahoma City area through the development and administration of endowment and other charitable funds with the goal of preserving capital and enhancing value.

LEGAL BASIS:
Public foundation.

ELIGIBILITY:
Applicants can be any IRS 501(c)(3) organization.

GEOGRAPHIC RESTRICTIONS:
Oklahoma City, Oklahoma and surrounding area.

FINANCIAL DATA:
Assets of $465,000,000 for the year ended June 30, 2009.
Amount of support per award: Varies.
Total amount of support: $20,900,000 in grant distributions for fiscal year ended June 30, 2009.

IRS IDENTIFICATION NUMBER: 23-7024262

ADDRESS INQUIRIES TO:
Nancy Anthony, Executive Director
(See address above.)

OMAHA COMMUNITY FOUNDATION

302 South 36th Street
Suite 100
Omaha, NE 68131
(402) 342-3458
Fax: (402) 342-3582

E-MAIL ADDRESS:
sarah@omahafoundation.org

WEB SITE ADDRESS:
www.omahafoundation.org

TYPE:
Capital grants; Project/program grants; Scholarships. Donors can contribute through the Omaha Community Foundation to any nonprofit agency. The OCF also has five discretionary grant programs.

See entry 277 for full listing.

OMNOVA SOLUTIONS FOUNDATION [1429]

175 Ghent Road
Fairlawn, OH 44333-3300
(330) 869-4289
Fax: (330) 869-4345

E-MAIL ADDRESS:
theresa.carter@omnova.com

WEB SITE ADDRESS:
www.omnova.com

FOUNDED: 1999

AREAS OF INTEREST:
Support of educational, cultural and 501(c)(3) organizations in areas where OMNOVA Solutions has large concentrations of employment.

TYPE:
Capital grants; Development grants; Endowments; General operating grants; Matching gifts; Project/program grants; Scholarships.

YEAR PROGRAM STARTED: 1999

PURPOSE:
To support education and other charitable organizations in the communities where OMNOVA Solutions has facilities.

LEGAL BASIS:
Nonprofit corporation, private foundation.

ELIGIBILITY:
Tax-exempt organizations are eligible.

FINANCIAL DATA:
Amount of support per award: $100 to $35,000. Average $5,000.
Total amount of support: $1,684,500 for the year 2010.
Matching fund requirements: Education only.

NUMBER OF AWARDS: 569 for the year 2010.

REPRESENTATIVE AWARDS:
American Red Cross; Akron Community Service Center and Urban League; E.J. Thomas Performing Arts Hall.

APPLICATION INFORMATION:
A brief letter is required.
Duration: One-time grants. Renewable.
Deadline: Applications are reviewed and grants awarded throughout the year.

PUBLICATIONS:
Application guidelines; annual report.

TRUSTEES:
Michael E. Hicks, President
Frank Robers, Treasurer
Kristine Syrvalin, Secretary
Robin McCain
Nick Triantafillopoulos

ADDRESS INQUIRIES TO:
Theresa Carter, President
(See address above.)

OPEN SOCIETY INSTITUTE - BALTIMORE [1430]

201 North Charles Street
Suite 1300
Baltimore, MD 21201
(410) 234-1091
Fax: (410) 234-2816

WEB SITE ADDRESS:
www.soros.org/baltimore

AREAS OF INTEREST:
Drug addiction.

NAME(S) OF PROGRAMS:
● **The Drug Addiction Treatment Program**

TYPE:
Project/program grants.

YEAR PROGRAM STARTED: 1998

PURPOSE:
To focus on critical national urban issues as they are expressed locally.

LEGAL BASIS:
Foundation.

ELIGIBILITY:
Grants are made to organizations that have tax-exempt status under Section 501(c)(3) of the Internal Revenue Code. No grants are made to individuals. Nonsectarian religious programs may apply.

GEOGRAPHIC RESTRICTIONS:
Baltimore City, Maryland.

FINANCIAL DATA:
Amount of support per award: Varies.
Total amount of support: Varies.

APPLICATION INFORMATION:
Applicants should submit a letter of inquiry of two to three pages which includes:
(1) a description of the program to be funded;
(2) the qualifications of the organization to carry out the program;
(3) the ways in which the program reflects the priorities of The Drug Addiction Treatment Program and;
(4) the amount requested.
Duration: Varies.

ADDRESS INQUIRIES TO:
Kima Taylor, Program Director
(See address above.)

THE ORDEAN FOUNDATION [1431]

501 Ordean Building
424 West Superior Street
Duluth, MN 55802
(218) 726-4785
Fax: (218) 726-4848

E-MAIL ADDRESS:
smangan@ordean.org

FOUNDED: 1933

AREAS OF INTEREST:
Social services, education and health, services to low-income, mentally and physically handicapped, elderly, mentally ill, chemically dependent, prevention of delinquency, and scholarships for certain health-related majors at Duluth colleges.

TYPE:
Capital grants; Challenge/matching grants; Demonstration grants; General operating grants; Project/program grants; Scholarships. Grants, occasional low-interest loans and scholarships in the Foundation's areas of interest in Duluth, MN.

YEAR PROGRAM STARTED: 1933

LEGAL BASIS:
Private foundation.

ELIGIBILITY:
Applicants must be nonprofit, tax-exempt IRS 501(c)(3) organizations located or providing services in Greater City of Duluth, MN.

GEOGRAPHIC RESTRICTIONS:
Greater City of Duluth, Minnesota.

FINANCIAL DATA:
Amount of support per award: $5,000 to $350,000.
Total amount of support: $2,000,000 for fiscal year 2010.

NUMBER OF AWARDS: Approximately 50.

REPRESENTATIVE AWARDS:
$350,000 to Lake Superior Community Health Center; $150,000 to Mentor Duluth to match caring adults with at-risk youths.

APPLICATION INFORMATION:
Guidelines are available from the Foundation office at the address above.
Duration: One year. Renewal possible up to three years.

STAFF:
Stephen Mangan, Executive Director
Joe Everett, Program Director

BOARD OF DIRECTORS:
Lauren Larson, President
Lonnie Swartz, Treasurer
Ann Niedringhaus, Secretary
Marge Bray
Carl Crawford
Beth Kelly
Tom Patnoe
Mary Beth Santori
Ben Stromberg

ADDRESS INQUIRIES TO:
Joe Everett, Program Director
(See address above.)

THE OREGON COMMUNITY FOUNDATION [1432]
1221 S.W. Yamhill Street, Suite 100
Portland, OR 97205-2108
(503) 227-6846
Fax: (503) 274-7771

E-MAIL ADDRESS:
info@oregoncf.org

WEB SITE ADDRESS:
www.oregoncf.org

FOUNDED: 1973

AREAS OF INTEREST:
Children, families, culture, education and community involvement.

NAME(S) OF PROGRAMS:
● **Community Grants Program**

TYPE:
Project/program grants.

PURPOSE:
To help communities achieve goals identified by a broad cross section of community members for which local support has been clearly demonstrated; to build a strong, inclusive spirit of community where all Oregonians are involved in community life.

LEGAL BASIS:
Community foundation.

ELIGIBILITY:
Applicants for programs must be nonprofit, tax-exempt organizations in Oregon.

Applicants must have received a community grant only once during the previous 12 months and must have completed evaluation reports for all prior grants. The Foundation gives preference to projects that demonstrate strong local support and promise tangible benefits or means of solving community problems or concerns.

GEOGRAPHIC RESTRICTIONS:
Oregon.

FINANCIAL DATA:
Amount of support per award: $5,000 to $40,000.

NUMBER OF APPLICANTS MOST RECENT YEAR: 587.

NUMBER OF AWARDS: 200 annually.

APPLICATION INFORMATION:
Duration: Small grants: One year; Large grants: One to three years.
Deadline: August 1 and February 1.

PUBLICATIONS:
Brochure.

IRS IDENTIFICATION NUMBER: 23-7315673

STAFF:
Jeff Anderson, Chief Operating Officer

ADDRESS INQUIRIES TO:
Megan Schumaker
Senior Administrative Officer
(See address above.)

*SPECIAL STIPULATIONS:
Generally funds only in Oregon.

OUTER BANKS COMMUNITY FOUNDATION [1433]
13 Skyline Road
Southern Shores, NC 27949
(252) 261-8839
Fax: (252) 261-0371

E-MAIL ADDRESS:
info@obcf.org

WEB SITE ADDRESS:
www.obcf.org

FOUNDED: 1982

TYPE:
Project/program grants; Scholarships. 30 different scholarship funds available to local students. Grants available for local nonprofit programs and projects.

PURPOSE:
To help meet local needs in the Corolla area of Currituck County, Dare County and Ocracoke Island in Hyde County, NC.

LEGAL BASIS:
501(c)(3).

GEOGRAPHIC RESTRICTIONS:
Corolla area of Currituck County, Dare County and Ocracoke Island in Hyde County, North Carolina.

FINANCIAL DATA:
Amount of support per award: Varies.
Total amount of support: Varies.

APPLICATION INFORMATION:
Deadline: February 10, May 10, August 10 and November 10 for grants; April 15 for scholarships.

ADDRESS INQUIRIES TO:
Barbara Bingham, Executive Director
(See address above.)

*PLEASE NOTE:
Very limited geographic area. Applicants restricted to Corolla area of Currituck County, Dare County and Ocracoke Island in Hyde County, NC.

PERMIAN BASIN AREA FOUNDATION [1434]
200 North Loraine, Suite 500
Midland, TX 79701
(432) 617-3213
Fax: (432) 617-0151

E-MAIL ADDRESS:
gmccrary@pbaf.org

WEB SITE ADDRESS:
www.pbaf.org

FOUNDED: 1989

AREAS OF INTEREST:
Community development.

TYPE:
Grants-in-aid; Scholarships.

PURPOSE:
To enrich the quality of life for the communities of the Permian Basin area of Texas.

LEGAL BASIS:
501(c)(3) organization.

GEOGRAPHIC RESTRICTIONS:
Communities of the Permian Basin region of Texas.

FINANCIAL DATA:
$63,800,000 in assets as of December 31, 2010.
Amount of support per award: Varies.

APPLICATION INFORMATION:
Organizations wishing to apply for a grant must fully complete and submit one copy of the Pre-Application Summary (SF-1). Organizations that have received funding during a previous grant cycle must also complete and submit the Grant Award Follow-up Form (SF-FW). Do not include a cover letter with the application.

A full application will be complete when one copy of the appropriate Standard Forms and additional documents indicated on the Standard Form Checklist are completed and submitted to the Foundation by the full application due date. (The list of required forms differs depending on the purpose of the grant request.) Upon receiving a full application, the Foundation will conduct a full application review which may include an applicant interview, a site visit, and/or a request for additional information.

All scholarship applications must contain the following:
(1) transcript with fall semester grades;
(2) college transcript if student is enrolled in concurrent college courses and;
(3) at least one letter of recommendation, but not more than three.

Some applications require an essay. Check the individual scholarship criteria to determine if an essay is required and the designated topic.
Duration: Grants: Usually one year.
Deadline: Grant proposals: April 1 for Spring and October 1 for Fall.

ADDRESS INQUIRIES TO:
Louren Young, Grants and Administration
(See address above.)

PETOSKEY-HARBOR SPRINGS AREA COMMUNITY FOUNDATION [1435]
616 Petoskey Street, Suite 300
Petoskey, MI 49770
(231) 348-5820
Fax: (231) 348-5883

E-MAIL ADDRESS:
info@phsacf.org

WEB SITE ADDRESS:
www.petoskey-harborspringsfoundation.org

FOUNDED: 1992

AREAS OF INTEREST:
Arts, education, environment, health, human service and community development.

TYPE:
Grants-in-aid; Scholarships. Grants are given for scholarships or for charitable needs.

YEAR PROGRAM STARTED: 1992

PURPOSE:
To build an endowment to serve community needs.

LEGAL BASIS:
Community foundation.

ELIGIBILITY:
Grants must be for charitable purposes, but not for individuals.

GEOGRAPHIC RESTRICTIONS:
Emmet County, Michigan.

FINANCIAL DATA:
Over $17,000,000 in assets.
Amount of support per award: $500 to $10,000.
Total amount of support: Varies.

APPLICATION INFORMATION:
Applications are available at the address above and must include a copy of the IRS tax determination letter. Call before you apply.
Duration: One year.
Deadline: March 1 and October 1.

PUBLICATIONS:
Annual report; application guidelines.

ADDRESS INQUIRIES TO:
Sara Ward, Program Officer
(See address above.)

THE PHILADELPHIA FOUNDATION [1436]

1234 Market Street
Suite 1800
Philadelphia, PA 19107
(215) 563-6417
Fax: (215) 563-6882

WEB SITE ADDRESS:
www.philafound.org

FOUNDED: 1918

AREAS OF INTEREST:
Arts, culture, humanities, education, environment, health, human services and public/community development.

TYPE:
General operating grants; Scholarships. The Philadelphia Foundation's grantmaking strategies are sensitive to the needs of diverse population groups in the community and reflect a commitment to stabilizing the infrastructure of nonprofit organizations.

The Foundation encourages applicants to address:
(1) empowering people and groups;
(2) building community assets or;
(3) managing current issues or preparing for future trends when submitting grant requests.

YEAR PROGRAM STARTED: 1918

PURPOSE:
To serve as a vehicle and resource for philanthropy in Bucks, Chester, Delaware, Montgomery and Philadelphia counties, PA;

to develop, manage and allocate community resources in partnership with donors and grantees to build on community assets, to respond to the needs of the entire community, and to promote empowerment, leadership, and civic participation among underserved groups; to practice and encourage diversity, equity, and inclusiveness as fundamental values of community life.

LEGAL BASIS:
Community foundation established in Pennsylvania by bank resolution.

ELIGIBILITY:
Organization must be IRS 501(c)(3), located in five-county area of southeastern Pennsylvania.

GEOGRAPHIC RESTRICTIONS:
Bucks, Chester, Delaware, Montgomery, and Philadelphia counties, Pennsylvania.

FINANCIAL DATA:
Amount of support per award: $3,000 to $50,000.

PUBLICATIONS:
Newsletters; annual report.

OFFICERS:
R. Andrew Swinney, President
Beatriz Vieira, Vice President for Philanthropic Services
Patricia Meller, Vice President of Finance and Administration

ADDRESS INQUIRIES TO:
Grantmaking Services Department
(See address above.)

PIEDMONT HEALTH CARE FOUNDATION

P.O. Box 9303
Greenville, SC 29604
(864) 370-0212
Fax: (864) 370-0212

E-MAIL ADDRESS:
katypughsmith@bellsouth.net

WEB SITE ADDRESS:
www.piedmonthealthcarefdn.org

TYPE:
Demonstration grants; Project/program grants; Research grants; Seed money grants.

See entry 1557 for full listing.

VIRGINIA G. PIPER CHARITABLE TRUST [1437]

1202 East Missouri Avenue
Phoenix, AZ 85014-2921
(480) 948-5853
Fax: (480) 348-1316

E-MAIL ADDRESS:
info@pipertrust.org

WEB SITE ADDRESS:
www.pipertrust.org

FOUNDED: 2000

AREAS OF INTEREST:
Health care and medical research, children, older adults, arts and culture, education and religious organizations.

NAME(S) OF PROGRAMS:
● **Piper Fellows Program**

TYPE:
Grants-in-aid. The Piper Fellows program recognizes the contributions of the

community's exemplary nonprofit leaders and helps them and their organizations maintain and strengthen their professional vitality.

PURPOSE:
To improve the quality of life in Maricopa County, AZ, through programs that support children, older adults, arts and culture, health care and medical research, education and religious organizations.

ELIGIBILITY:
To be eligible to receive a grant, a nonprofit must have been actively operating in Maricopa County, AZ as a 501(c)(3) organization for at least 10 years.

Executives with significant responsibilities for the programmatic or operational activities of a 501(c)(3) nonprofit organization serving the areas of human services, health care, education, religion, or arts and culture in Maricopa County, AZ may apply. Applicants must have worked a minimum of 10 years in the nonprofit sector and must be a full-time employee of the applicant's organization. Executives from organizations classified as private foundations under Section 509(a) are not eligible.

GEOGRAPHIC RESTRICTIONS:
Maricopa County, Arizona.

FINANCIAL DATA:
Amount of support per award: Up to $30,000.

APPLICATION INFORMATION:
Complete application details are available online.
Deadline: September.

ADDRESS INQUIRIES TO:
Judy Jolley Mohraz, Ph.D.
President and Chief Executive Officer
(See address above.)

THE PITTSBURGH FOUNDATION [1438]

5 PPG Place
Suite 250
Pittsburgh, PA 15222
(412) 391-5122
Fax: (412) 391-7259

E-MAIL ADDRESS:
email@pghfdn.org

WEB SITE ADDRESS:
www.pittsburghfoundation.org

FOUNDED: 1945

AREAS OF INTEREST:
Education, family life, economic development, health care and the arts.

TYPE:
Capital grants; General operating grants; Project/program grants; Research grants; Scholarships. The Foundation promotes and champions the betterment of the greater Pittsburgh community and the quality of life for all its citizens by helping a wide variety of donors fulfill significant community needs and providing a vehicle to make giving easy, personally satisfying and effective. The Foundation awards grants through restricted and unrestricted funds. Purposes for which unrestricted grants are awarded include: organizational capacity building; systemic change; improved service delivery; planning and program development; capital and equipment (in limited and special circumstances) through one targeted fund;

operating (in very limited and defined circumstances); research (in special circumstances).

Scholarships and medical research grants are awarded from specific funds established for this purpose.

PURPOSE:
To achieve educational excellence and equity; to support families; to foster economic development; to eliminate disparities in health outcomes; to advance the arts.

LEGAL BASIS:
Community foundation established in Pennsylvania by bank resolution and declaration of trust.

ELIGIBILITY:
Grant applicants must be tax-exempt, public charitable organizations and institutions located in Pittsburgh or Allegheny County. Generally, grants are nonrecurring and are not granted for operating budgets and not made to individuals.

GEOGRAPHIC RESTRICTIONS:
Pittsburgh and Allegheny County, Pennsylvania.

FINANCIAL DATA:
Amount of support per award: $30 to $700,000.

Total amount of support: Approximately $9,000,000 in unrestricted funds; $9,000,000 in restricted funds.

NUMBER OF APPLICANTS MOST RECENT YEAR:
2,581.

NUMBER OF AWARDS: 2,255.

APPLICATION INFORMATION:
Applicants must submit grant application and IRS tax-exemption letter. Prior to sending a full proposal, applicants are encouraged to send a letter of inquiry that includes a brief statement about the organization, the proposed project, its intended results, and a general idea of costs.

Duration: Up to three years.

PUBLICATIONS:
Annual report; newsletter; donor information; application guidelines; scholarship brochure.

IRS IDENTIFICATION NUMBER: 25-0965466

STAFF:
Grant Oliphant, President and Chief Executive Officer
Jonathan Brelsford, Director of Investments
Marianne Cola, Executive Secretary

BOARD OF DIRECTORS:
Gregory D. Curtis, Chairman
John C. Harmon, Vice Chairman
David McL. Hillman, Treasurer
George A. Davidson
Mark R. Hornak
William E. Hunt
Jui M. Joshi
Maxwell E. King
Claudette R. Lewis
Peter F. Mathieson
Vincent J. Quatrini
Nancy L. Rackoff
James C. Roddey
Elizabeth Schroeder
Edith L. Shapira, M.D.
Dr. Howard Slaughter, Jr.
Walter H. Smith, Jr., Ph.D.

ADDRESS INQUIRIES TO:
Grant Oliphant
President and Chief Executive Officer
(See address above.)

PRINCETON AREA COMMUNITY FOUNDATION   [1439]
15 Princess Road
Lawrenceville, NJ 08648
(609) 219-1800
Fax: (609) 219-1850

E-MAIL ADDRESS:
info@pacf.org

WEB SITE ADDRESS:
www.pacf.org

FOUNDED: 1991

AREAS OF INTEREST:
Connecting people who care with causes that matter across central New Jersey.

NAME(S) OF PROGRAMS:
● **The Fund for Women and Girls**
● **Greater Mercer Grants**

TYPE:
General operating grants; Project/program grants; Scholarships. The Fund for Women and Girls supports efforts that help girls and women develop special talents, build character and self-esteem, and expand their abilities.

Greater Mercer Grants focus support on current priorities with the greatest impact within Mercer County, NJ. There are two grant categories: one provides program and/or operating support for nonprofit organizations addressing the needs of low-income individuals and families; the other provides program support for building community within and among municipalities in Mercer County, NJ.

PURPOSE:
To connect people who care with causes that matter across central New Jersey.

LEGAL BASIS:
A public benefit (nonprofit) organization.

ELIGIBILITY:
Eligible organizations must have 501(c)(3) status.

GEOGRAPHIC RESTRICTIONS:
Trenton, the 12 other Mercer County (New Jersey) municipalities and surrounding communities in Burlington, Hunterdon, Middlesex, Monmouth and Somerset counties.

FINANCIAL DATA:
Since its founding, the Foundation has granted nearly $18,000,000 to its community area of service.

Amount of support per award: Varies.

Total amount of support: $3,400,000 in grants awarded for the year 2010.

APPLICATION INFORMATION:
Duration: One year. Renewable.

STAFF:
Nancy W. Kieling, President and Executive Director
Ralph Serpe, Vice President
Michelle Cash, Vice President of Grants and Programs
Maria Santisi, C.P.A., Chief Financial Officer
Trisha Volk, Director of Donor Services
Myriam Padro, Administrator

ADDRESS INQUIRIES TO:
Michelle Cash
Vice President of Grants and Programs
(See address above.)

PROLITERACY WORLDWIDE   [1440]
1320 Jamesville Avenue
Syracuse, NY 13210-4241
(315) 422-9121
Fax: (315) 422-6369

E-MAIL ADDRESS:
mdiecuch@proliteracy.org

WEB SITE ADDRESS:
www.proliteracy.org

FOUNDED: 1955

AREAS OF INTEREST:
Literacy, adult basic education, English as a second language, and family literacy.

NAME(S) OF PROGRAMS:
● **National Book Fund (NBF)**

TYPE:
Project/program grants; Technical assistance.

YEAR PROGRAM STARTED: 1995

PURPOSE:
To provide grants for books and other materials local programs can use to expand their current volunteer literacy programs and to develop, promote and expand literacy programs in the U.S. that target the needs of women.

LEGAL BASIS:
Nonprofit organization.

ELIGIBILITY:
Adult literacy and adult basic education programs only.

GEOGRAPHIC RESTRICTIONS:
United States.

FINANCIAL DATA:
Amount of support per award: Typically $500 to $2,000.

Total amount of support: $106,000 for the year 2010.

Matching fund requirements: 10% to 20% match required.

NUMBER OF APPLICANTS MOST RECENT YEAR:
180 for the year 2008.

NUMBER OF AWARDS: 65 for the year 2008.

APPLICATION INFORMATION:
Duration: One year. NBF grantee eligible again in three years.

Deadline: Mid-April to early May.

PUBLICATIONS:
Guidelines.

IRS IDENTIFICATION NUMBER: 16-1214734

ADDRESS INQUIRIES TO:
Michele Diecuch, Program Administrator
National Book Fund
(See address above.)

PUBLIC SERVICE ENTERPRISE GROUP   [1441]
80 Park Plaza, 10 C
Newark, NJ 07102
(973) 430-8325
Fax: (973) 297-1480

E-MAIL ADDRESS:
marion.oneill@pseg.com

WEB SITE ADDRESS:
www.pseg.com

AREAS OF INTEREST:
Children and family, environment and community-economic development.

NAME(S) OF PROGRAMS:
- **Contributions Program**

TYPE:
Project/program grants.

PURPOSE:
To support children's issues, economic development and the environment.

LEGAL BASIS:
Corporation foundation.

ELIGIBILITY:
Organizations must be exempt under Section 501(c)(3) of the Internal Revenue Code. Priority is given to organizations located in New Jersey or other PSEG operating territories.

FINANCIAL DATA:
Amount of support per award: Average: $5,000.

APPLICATION INFORMATION:
Complete request for Financial Contributions Forms.
Duration: One year.

PUBLICATIONS:
Contribution guidelines.

IRS IDENTIFICATION NUMBER: 22-3125880

ADDRESS INQUIRIES TO:
Vaughn L. McKoy, Director, Corporate Responsibility and Sustainability
(See address above.)

RANCHO SANTA FE FOUNDATION   [1442]
6004-A Paseo Delicias
Rancho Santa Fe, CA 92067
(858) 756-6557
Fax: (858) 756-6561

E-MAIL ADDRESS:
christy@rsffoundation.org

WEB SITE ADDRESS:
www.rsffoundation.org

FOUNDED: 1981

AREAS OF INTEREST:
Charity, education, literature or science.

NAME(S) OF PROGRAMS:
- **Armed Forces Interest Group**
- **Rancho Santa Fe Women's Fund**

TYPE:
Challenge/matching grants; Development grants; Endowments; General operating grants; Project/program grants; Scholarships.

YEAR PROGRAM STARTED: 1981

PURPOSE:
To promote and sustain effective community philanthropy by assisting donors to build charitable endowments that strategically support worthy local and regional needs.

LEGAL BASIS:
Community foundation.

ELIGIBILITY:
Rancho Santa Fe organizations or those who have been asked to submit a grant request are eligible for support.

Organizations must have tax-exempt status under Section 501(c)(3) of the Internal Revenue Code.

FINANCIAL DATA:
Amount of support per award: $500 to $1,000,000.

Total amount of support: $350,000 in grants from designated and discretionary funds. Nearly $5,000,000 from donor-advised funds.

NUMBER OF APPLICANTS MOST RECENT YEAR: 635 for the year 2010.

NUMBER OF AWARDS: 635 for the year 2010.

APPLICATION INFORMATION:
The Foundation accepts the San Diego Grantmakers Common Grant Application, by invitation only. Applications are invited in April.
Deadline: June 1.

PUBLICATIONS:
Annual report.

IRS IDENTIFICATION NUMBER: 95-3709639

STAFF:
Christina P. Wilson, Executive Director
Debbie Anderson, Programs Manager
Dan Beals, Finance Manager

ADDRESS INQUIRIES TO:
Christina P. Wilson, Executive Director
(See address above.)

RBC FOUNDATION-U.S.A.   [1443]
RBC Plaza
60 South Sixth Street
Minneapolis, MN 55402-4422
(612) 371-2765
Fax: (612) 371-7933

E-MAIL ADDRESS:
sherry.koster@rbc.com

WEB SITE ADDRESS:
www.rbcwm-usa.com/communityinvolvement

AREAS OF INTEREST:
Arts and culture, youth education and human services.

NAME(S) OF PROGRAMS:
- **Regional Program**
- **Twin Cities Grants Program**

TYPE:
General operating grants; Project/program grants.

PURPOSE:
To improve the quality of life in communities where the company has facilities.

LEGAL BASIS:
Corporate foundation.

ELIGIBILITY:
Organizations must have tax-exempt status according to Internal Revenue Code 501(c)(3). Grants are made to organizations where RBC Wealth Management has employees actively involved.

FINANCIAL DATA:
Amount of support per award: Minimum $2,000.

Total amount of support: $2,000,000 for fiscal year 2010.

APPLICATION INFORMATION:
Organizations interested in applying must complete the online eligibility questionnaire.
Duration: One year.

ADDRESS INQUIRIES TO:
Liz Thatcher
E-mail: liz.thatcher@rbc.com

THE REINBERGER FOUNDATION   [1444]
27600 Chagrin Boulevard, Suite 355
Cleveland, OH 44122
(216) 292-2790
Fax: (216) 292-4466

E-MAIL ADDRESS:
info@reinbergerfoundation.org

WEB SITE ADDRESS:
www.reinbergerfoundation.org

FOUNDED: 1968

AREAS OF INTEREST:
Arts, education, health care and social service.

TYPE:
Capital grants; Challenge/matching grants; General operating grants; Matching gifts; Project/program grants; Research grants; Scholarships.

PURPOSE:
To enhance quality of life for individuals from all walks of life.

LEGAL BASIS:
Private foundation.

ELIGIBILITY:
Eligible organizations must be IRS 501(c)(3) tax-exempt.

GEOGRAPHIC RESTRICTIONS:
Northeast Ohio or greater Columbus area.

FINANCIAL DATA:
Amount of support per award: $5,000 to $500,000.

Total amount of support: $2,466,700 for the year 2010.

NUMBER OF APPLICANTS MOST RECENT YEAR: 267 for the year 2010.

NUMBER OF AWARDS: 96 for the year 2010.

APPLICATION INFORMATION:
Applicants should send a letter of inquiry on the organization's letterhead.
Duration: Up to seven years.
Deadline: March, June, September and December.

ADDRESS INQUIRIES TO:
Karen L. Hooser, President
(See address above.)

LUTHER I. REPLOGLE FOUNDATION   [1445]
1720 N Street, N.W.
Washington, DC 20036-2907
(202) 679-0677
Fax: (202) 580-6579

E-MAIL ADDRESS:
gwenn@lirf.org

WEB SITE ADDRESS:
www.lirf.org

FOUNDED: 1966

AREAS OF INTEREST:
At-risk youth and children, educational opportunities for inner-city children, and affordable and supportive housing.

TYPE:
Challenge/matching grants; General operating grants; Project/program grants; Seed money grants. The Foundation supports programs that:
(1) address the needs of youth and children living in, or at risk of, long-term poverty, especially children of inner-city residents. Of particular interest are programs for teen pregnancy prevention, counseling, broad-spectrum social services, and other programs that help young people improve their own lives;
(2) improve educational opportunities for inner-city children, including enrichment

programs in the arts and sciences, alternative schools, after-school tutoring and mentoring, and scholarship programs and; (3) provide for affordable and supportive housing that reaches people frequently left out of traditional shelter programs, including single mothers and families with children, the elderly, ex-offenders, and youth. An emphasis is placed on programs that enable individuals to help themselves and become self-sufficient over the long-term.

PURPOSE:
To address the needs of youth and children living in, or at risk of, long-term poverty; to improve educational opportunities for inner-city children; to support programs for affordable and supportive housing that reaches groups of people frequently left out of traditional shelter programs.

ELIGIBILITY:
Organizations must be not-for-profit 501(c)(3). Grants are given to religious organizations only for social services programs, not for religious programs, buildings or bibles. No grants to individuals.

GEOGRAPHIC RESTRICTIONS:
Washington, District of Columbia; Chicago, Illinois; Minneapolis, Minnesota.

FINANCIAL DATA:
Amount of support per award: Usually $5,000 to $10,000.

APPLICATION INFORMATION:
Applicants meeting the grant criteria through the online eligibility quiz will be prompted to complete the Letter of Inquiry form.
Duration: Renewable if grantee sends report.
Deadline: March 15 and September 15.

IRS IDENTIFICATION NUMBER: 36-6141697

ADDRESS INQUIRIES TO:
Gwenn H.S. Gebhard, Executive Director
(See address above.)

DONALD W. REYNOLDS FOUNDATION [1446]
1701 Village Center Circle
Las Vegas, NV 89134
(702) 804-6000
Fax: (702) 804-6099

E-MAIL ADDRESS:
generalquestions@dwrf.org

WEB SITE ADDRESS:
www.dwreynolds.org

FOUNDED: 1954

AREAS OF INTEREST:
Arts and culture, humanities, education, health and human services, welfare of the public and society.

NAME(S) OF PROGRAMS:
- **Aging and Quality of Life**
- **Capital Grants**
- **Cardiovascular Clinical Research**
- **Journalism Grants**

TYPE:
Capital grants; Challenge/matching grants; General operating grants; Matching gifts; Project/program grants; Research grants. Capital construction/renovation of agency facilities; Medical research; Medical training.

National programs support cardiovascular clinical research and strengthened geriatrics training of physicians. Aging and Quality of Life and Cardiovascular Clinical Research programs are national programs.

PURPOSE:
To support The Donald W. Reynolds Foundation which is dedicated to honoring the memory of its benefactor through charitable giving in areas designated by its trustees.

LEGAL BASIS:
Private foundation.

ELIGIBILITY:
Organizations classified as 501(c)(3) by the IRS and located in Arkansas, Nevada and Oklahoma may apply. No grants to individuals, religious organizations or hospitals.

GEOGRAPHIC RESTRICTIONS:
Arkansas, Nevada and Oklahoma.

FINANCIAL DATA:
Amount of support per award: Varies.
Total amount of support: Varies.

APPLICATION INFORMATION:
Contact the Foundation for application procedures.
Duration: Grants are not renewable.

PUBLICATIONS:
Application guidelines.

IRS IDENTIFICATION NUMBER: 71-6053383

ADDRESS INQUIRIES TO:
Karina Mayer, Grants Manager
(See address above.)

*SPECIAL STIPULATIONS:
Preapplication visits are discouraged. Staff is eager to respond to specific questions by phone or in writing.

J.B. REYNOLDS FOUNDATION [1447]
3520 Broadway
Kansas City, MO 64111
(816) 753-7000
Fax: (816) 561-2415

AREAS OF INTEREST:
Education, research, civic affairs, youth training and cultural organizations.

TYPE:
Capital grants; General operating grants; Project/program grants; Research grants.

ELIGIBILITY:
Eligible organizations must be IRS 501(c)(3) tax-exempt and be located within the local Kansas City area. No grants to individuals.

GEOGRAPHIC RESTRICTIONS:
Kansas City, Missouri area.

FINANCIAL DATA:
Amount of support per award: Varies.

APPLICATION INFORMATION:
There is no application form. Applicants should send a letter of two pages or less. Send submissions to smorehead@kclife.com.
Duration: One year. Renewal on a yearly basis.
Deadline: July and December.

ADDRESS INQUIRIES TO:
Phillip Bixby, President and Chief Executive Officer
(See address above.)

RGK FOUNDATION [1448]
1301 West 25th Street
Suite 300
Austin, TX 78705-4236
(512) 474-9298
Fax: (512) 474-7281

E-MAIL ADDRESS:
shaffey@rgkfoundation.org

WEB SITE ADDRESS:
www.rgkfoundation.org

FOUNDED: 1966

AREAS OF INTEREST:
Education, community and medicine/health.

TYPE:
Challenge/matching grants; Project/program grants. The Foundation awards grants in the broad areas of education, community and medicine/health; its primary interests within education include programs that focus on formal K-12 education (particularly mathematics, science and reading/literacy), after-school tutoring and enrichment, integrating technology into curriculum, teacher development and higher education. The Foundation is particularly interested in programs that attract female and minority students into the fields of mathematics, science and technology. Within community, the Foundation supports a broad range of human services programs, youth development programs, community improvement programs and cultural arts programs. Its current interests in the area of medicine/health are programs that promote the health and well-being of children and families, access to health care and ALS.

LEGAL BASIS:
Private foundation.

ELIGIBILITY:
The Foundation prefers to provide programmatic support for new programs or expansion of ongoing successful programs. While the Foundation occasionally awards grants for operating expenses and capital campaigns, such grants are infrequent and usually initiated by the Foundation.

Grants are made only to nonprofit organizations certified as tax-exempt under Sections 501(c)(3) or 170(c) of the Internal Revenue Code and are classified as "not a private foundation" under Section 509(a). Hospitals, educational institutions and governmental institutions meeting these requirements are eligible to apply. Organizations that have completed and filed Form 1023 but not yet received an IRS determination letter are not eligible to apply. The Foundation does not make grants or loans to individuals.

GEOGRAPHIC RESTRICTIONS:
United States.

FINANCIAL DATA:
Amount of support per award: Average grant to new organization: $25,000.
Total amount of support: $4,400,000 for all programs for the year 2010.

NUMBER OF AWARDS: Varies.

APPLICATION INFORMATION:
Application is available online.
Duration: Most grants are awarded for a one-year period; multiyear grants are extremely rare.
Deadline: Proposals are reviewed on an ongoing basis.

IRS IDENTIFICATION NUMBER: 74-6077587

STAFF:
Suzanne Haffey, Grants Associate

OFFICERS AND DIRECTORS:
Gregory A. Kozmetsky, Chairman and President
Nadya K. Scott, Vice Chairman
Cynthia H. Kozmetsky, Vice President and Secretary
Lois J. Cox
Charles E. Hurwitz
Aaron W. Kozmetsky
Daniel Kozmetsky
Ronya Kozmetsky
Mary Beth Rogers
Laila P. Scott
M. Jordan Scott

ADDRESS INQUIRIES TO:
Suzanne Haffey, Grants Associate
(See address above.)

ROCHESTER AREA FOUNDATION [1449]

400 South Broadway
Suite 300
Rochester, MN 55904
(507) 282-0203
Fax: (507) 282-4938

E-MAIL ADDRESS:
raf-info@rochesterarea.org

WEB SITE ADDRESS:
www.rochesterarea.org

FOUNDED: 1944

AREAS OF INTEREST:
General grants to benefit residents of the Greater Rochester area.

TYPE:
Capital grants; Challenge/matching grants; Project/program grants; Seed money grants.

YEAR PROGRAM STARTED: 1944

PURPOSE:
To use its resources to improve the quality of life, promote greater equality of opportunities and to support development of effective methods to assist those in need in the Greater Rochester area.

LEGAL BASIS:
Community foundation.

ELIGIBILITY:
Applicants must be 501(c)(3) organizations or units of government agencies or government-created public agencies located in or serving the Greater Rochester area. Grants are not given to individuals.

GEOGRAPHIC RESTRICTIONS:
Greater Rochester, Minnesota.

FINANCIAL DATA:
Total amount of support: $2,100,000 for the year 2010.

APPLICATION INFORMATION:
Pre-approved and approved application forms are required. Applicant organizations must include an IRS letter of tax determination.
Duration: One-time grants.
Deadline: Pre-approved: January 1 and September 1.
Approved: Last week of April, August and December.

ADDRESS INQUIRIES TO:
Steve Thornton, Executive Director
(See address above.)

ROSE COMMUNITY FOUNDATION [1450]

600 South Cherry Street
Suite 1200
Denver, CO 80246-1712
(303) 398-7400
(303) 398-7446
Fax: (303) 398-7430

E-MAIL ADDRESS:
grantsmanager@rcfdenver.org

WEB SITE ADDRESS:
www.rcfdenver.org

FOUNDED: 1995

AREAS OF INTEREST:
Child and family development, education, the elderly, health of the community, Jewish life, human service, palliative end-of-life care, transportation (aging only), early childhood education, family self-sufficiency, health preventive, low-income health access and health policy leadership.

TYPE:
Capital grants; Challenge/matching grants; General operating grants; Project/program grants; Seed money grants; Technical assistance. Capacity-building grants.

YEAR PROGRAM STARTED: 1995

PURPOSE:
To enhance the quality of life of the greater Denver community through leadership, resources, traditions and values.

ELIGIBILITY:
Applicants must be charitable, nonprofit organizations classified as 501(c)(3) by the IRS or be a tax-supported institution, such as a school or government agency. New or emerging organizations are permitted to apply through a sponsoring tax-exempt organization. Applicants (including university departments) may have only one proposal pending at any given time. Individual schools are welcome to apply.

The Foundation will not support grants to individuals or endowments, including academic chairs, grants to one organization to be passed to another, annual appeals or membership drives, fund-raising events, or political candidates.

GEOGRAPHIC RESTRICTIONS:
Denver metropolitan area, specifically Adams, Arapahoe, Boulder, Broomfield, Denver, Douglas and Jefferson counties, Colorado.

FINANCIAL DATA:
Amount of support per award: Varies depending on needs and nature of the request.
Total amount of support: $9,403,000 in grants for the year 2009.
Matching fund requirements: Varies by nature of award.

NUMBER OF AWARDS: 220 in priority areas for the year 2009.

APPLICATION INFORMATION:
It is recommended to contact the Grants Manager prior to applying if the organization is new to the Foundation.
Duration: Varies.

IRS IDENTIFICATION NUMBER: 84-0920862

STAFF:
Sheila Bugdanowitz, President and Chief Executive Officer
Cheryl McDonald, Grants Manager

ADDRESS INQUIRIES TO:
Cheryl McDonald, Grants Manager
(See address above.)

HENRY AND RUTH BLAUSTEIN ROSENBERG FOUNDATION [1451]

10 East Baltimore Street, Suite 1111
Baltimore, MD 21202
(410) 347-7201
Fax: (410) 347-7210

E-MAIL ADDRESS:
info@blaufund.org

WEB SITE ADDRESS:
www.blaufund.org

AREAS OF INTEREST:
Arts and culture, youth development and adult self-sufficiency.

TYPE:
Capital grants; General operating grants; Project/program grants. Programs of benefit to the underserved community in the Baltimore, MD area.

PURPOSE:
To promote arts and culture, youth development, and adult self-sufficiency within the underserved community.

ELIGIBILITY:
501(c)(3) nonprofit organizations. No grants to individuals.

GEOGRAPHIC RESTRICTIONS:
Baltimore, Maryland.

FINANCIAL DATA:
Amount of support per award: $5,000 to $25,000.

APPLICATION INFORMATION:
Send two- to three-page letter of intent or application. IRS tax status determination letter is required. Faxed and e-mailed letters of intent are not accepted.
Duration: One to two years. Prior grantee organizations may be renewable.

ADDRESS INQUIRIES TO:
Betsy F. Ringel, Executive Director
(See address above.)

ROSS FOUNDATION [1452]

202 Fifth Street
Arkadelphia, AR 71923
(870) 246-9881
Fax: (870) 246-9674

E-MAIL ADDRESS:
meeldridge@rossfoundation.us

FOUNDED: 1966

AREAS OF INTEREST:
Education, culture, conservation and community activities.

TYPE:
Project/program grants.

LEGAL BASIS:
Private foundation.

ELIGIBILITY:
Applicants must be IRS 501(c)(3) organizations located in Clark County or Arkadelphia, AR. No grants to individuals.

GEOGRAPHIC RESTRICTIONS:
Clark County or Arkadelphia, Arkansas.

FINANCIAL DATA:
Amount of support per award: Generally $1,000 to $25,000.
Total amount of support: $600,000 for the year 2010.

NUMBER OF APPLICANTS MOST RECENT YEAR:
Approximately 30 for the year 2010.

NUMBER OF AWARDS: 20 to 25.

APPLICATION INFORMATION:
Contact the Foundation for an application form.
Duration: Typically one year.
Deadline: Proposals are reviewed in May, July and November.

ADDRESS INQUIRIES TO:
Mary Elizabeth Eldridge
Director of Programs
(See address above.)

THE RUSSELL FAMILY FOUNDATION [1453]

3025 Harborview Drive
Gig Harbor, WA 98335
(253) 858-5050
Fax: (253) 851-0460

E-MAIL ADDRESS:
info@trff.org

WEB SITE ADDRESS:
www.trff.org

FOUNDED: 1999

AREAS OF INTEREST:
Elimination of poverty, healthy educational and extracurricular activities for youth, and social justice.

NAME(S) OF PROGRAMS:
● **Jane's Fellowship Program**

TYPE:
Fellowships. Fellowship program for individuals who plan to work in the Foundation's areas of interest.

YEAR PROGRAM STARTED: 2004

PURPOSE:
To support grassroots leaders in Pierce County and Tacoma, WA.

ELIGIBILITY:
Must be a grassroots leader who has demonstrated exceptional creativity, courage and commitment in serving diverse needs in Tacoma and countywide.

GEOGRAPHIC RESTRICTIONS:
Pierce County and Tacoma, Washington.

FINANCIAL DATA:
Amount of support per award: Varies.

APPLICATION INFORMATION:
Duration: Two years. Nonrenewable.
Deadline: Every two years.

SAGINAW COMMUNITY FOUNDATION [1454]

100 South Jefferson Avenue, Suite 201
Saginaw, MI 48607
(989) 755-0545
Fax; (989) 755-6524

E-MAIL ADDRESS:
brian@saginawfoundation.org

WEB SITE ADDRESS:
www.saginawfoundation.org

FOUNDED: 1984

AREAS OF INTEREST:
Arts, community development, culture, education, health, youth and human services.

CONSULTING OR VOLUNTEER SERVICES:
Seminars, group presentations and one-on-one consultation.

TYPE:
Grants-in-aid; Project/program grants; Scholarships.

YEAR PROGRAM STARTED: 1984

PURPOSE:
To enhance and support the quality of life in Saginaw County.

ELIGIBILITY:
Typically, grants are made to organizations that have tax-exempt status under Section 501(c)(3) of the Internal Revenue Code. Except for scholarships, no grants are made to individuals. Nonsectarian religious programs may apply.

GEOGRAPHIC RESTRICTIONS:
Saginaw County, Michigan.

FINANCIAL DATA:
Amount of support per award: Grants vary in amount, depending upon the needs and nature of the request.
Total amount of support: $1,282,421 for the year 2009.
Matching fund requirements: Varies by program.

NUMBER OF APPLICANTS MOST RECENT YEAR:
4,886 for the year 2009.

NUMBER OF AWARDS: 444 for the year 2009.

ADDRESS INQUIRIES TO:
Program Officer
(See address above.)

SAINT CROIX VALLEY FOUNDATION [1455]

516 Second Street, Suite 214
Hudson, WI 54016
(715) 386-9490
Fax: (715) 386-1250

E-MAIL ADDRESS:
info@scvfoundation.org

WEB SITE ADDRESS:
www.scvfoundation.org

FOUNDED: 1995

AREAS OF INTEREST:
Arts, civic affairs, community needs and development, environment, health and human services, and education.

NAME(S) OF PROGRAMS:
● **Health and Wellness Grant**
● **Music Education Grant**
● **Nonprofit Management Assistance Grants**
● **Valley Arts Initiative Grant**

TYPE:
Project/program grants; Scholarships.

YEAR PROGRAM STARTED: 1995

PURPOSE:
To advance the quality of life in the Saint Croix Valley of Wisconsin and Minnesota.

LEGAL BASIS:
501(c)(3).

ELIGIBILITY:
Grants are made to organizations that have tax-exempt status under Section 501(c)(3) of the Internal Revenue Code or serving the Saint Croix Valley of Wisconsin and Minnesota. Nonsectarian religious programs may apply.

FINANCIAL DATA:
Amount of support per award: $2,250 average per grant. Scholarships: $1,000.

Total amount of support: $1,355,260 in grants for fiscal year ended June 30, 2010. Scholarships: $132,274 for the year 2010.

APPLICATION INFORMATION:
Applicants must submit eight copies of the following (original and seven copies, except financial attachments which require only one copy):
(1) cover sheet signed by board chair and/or school principal/headmaster (and fiscal agent if necessary);
(2) a one- to three-page proposal narrative;
(3) project budget;
(4) 501(c)(3) tax determination letter (required for all organizations, except public schools);
(5) for Nonprofit Management Assistance Grants: If requesting funds for a consultant, include the consultant's resume and their cost estimate. If a consultant has not been identified, include a description of the intended process for selecting a consultant and;
(6) organization financial statement for year most recently completed and organization budget and financial statement for year to date (not required for Music Education grant applications).

Applications without signatures will not be considered.
Duration: Varies depending on the field of interest. One year for the Valley Arts Initiative Grant. Grants are renewable upon review.

STAFF:
Jill Shannon, Director of Community Partnerships

ADDRESS INQUIRIES TO:
Jane Hetland Stevenson, President
(See address above.)

SAINT-GOBAIN CORPORATION FOUNDATION [1456]

750 East Swedesford Road
P.O. Box 860
Valley Forge, PA 19482-0101
(610) 341-6937
Fax: (610) 341-7777

WEB SITE ADDRESS:
www.saint-gobain-northamerica.com/people/foundation.asp

FOUNDED: 2001

AREAS OF INTEREST:
Housing and community development, energy conservation and environmental concerns.

TYPE:
Project/program grants.

PURPOSE:
To play a vital role in the economic, social and educational development of the community.

LEGAL BASIS:
Corporation foundation.

ELIGIBILITY:
Eligible organizations must be IRS 501(c)(3) tax-exempt and be located in areas where Saint-Gobain Corporation has manufacturing locations.

GEOGRAPHIC RESTRICTIONS:
Alabama, Arizona, Arkansas, California, Colorado, Connecticut, Florida, Georgia, Illinois, Indiana, Kentucky, Maine, Massachusetts, Michigan, New Hampshire, New Jersey, New Mexico, New York, North

Carolina, Ohio, Pennsylvania, South
Carolina, Tennessee, Texas, Utah, Vermont,
Washington and West Virginia.

APPLICATION INFORMATION:
Applications are available from the
Foundation.

SAN ANGELO AREA
FOUNDATION   [1457]
2201 Sherwood Way, Suite 205
San Angelo, TX 76901
(325) 947-7071
Fax: (325) 947-7322

E-MAIL ADDRESS:
infosaaf@saafound.org

WEB SITE ADDRESS:
www.saafound.org

FOUNDED: 2002

AREAS OF INTEREST:
Community development.

TYPE:
Grants-in-aid; Scholarships. To build a legacy
of philanthropy by attracting and prudently
managing endowed gifts in order to match
donor interests with community needs of the
area.

PURPOSE:
To improve the quality of life in the San
Angelo, TX area.

LEGAL BASIS:
Community foundation.

ELIGIBILITY:
Must be a 501(c)(3) nonprofit organization.
Grant funds must be used within and for the
benefit of residents and communities of the
17 counties of the San Angelo area.

GEOGRAPHIC RESTRICTIONS:
San Angelo area, Texas.

FINANCIAL DATA:
Amount of support per award: Varies.
Total amount of support: $11,473,550 for the
year 2010.

APPLICATION INFORMATION:
Application and proposal forms are available
online.
Deadline: Scholarships: Due in Foundation's
office by 5 P.M., March 1. Grants: Executive
summary due September 1.

ADDRESS INQUIRIES TO:
Matt Lewis, President and
Chief Executive Officer
(See address above.)

SAN ANTONIO AREA
FOUNDATION   [1458]
110 Broadway
Suite 230
San Antonio, TX 78205
(210) 225-2243
Fax: (210) 225-1980

E-MAIL ADDRESS:
gift@saafdn.org

WEB SITE ADDRESS:
www.saafdn.org

FOUNDED: 1964

AREAS OF INTEREST:
Animal services, arts and culture, biomedical
research, community services, education,
medical services, social services, and visual
research/services.

NAME(S) OF PROGRAMS:
● **Discretionary Grant Process**

TYPE:
Capital grants; Challenge/matching grants;
General operating grants; Project/program
grants; Research grants; Seed money grants;
Technical assistance. Capital grants are only
given after 75% of the goal has been met.
General operating grants are for nonsalary
expenses. Research grants are for biomedical
and visual research only.

YEAR PROGRAM STARTED: 1964

PURPOSE:
To help donors achieve their charitable goals
for the greater benefit of the community.

LEGAL BASIS:
Community foundation.

ELIGIBILITY:
Eligible organizations must be IRS 501(c)(3)
tax-exempt and located in Bexar County or
surrounding counties. Endowments, salaries,
scholarships, and debt reduction will not be
funded. The Foundation does not provide
grants to individuals.

GEOGRAPHIC RESTRICTIONS:
Bexar County and surrounding counties,
Texas.

FINANCIAL DATA:
Amount of support per award: Varies.

NUMBER OF APPLICANTS MOST RECENT YEAR:
400.

NUMBER OF AWARDS: 93 for the year 2010.

APPLICATION INFORMATION:
Application and guidelines are available on
the web site in September.
Duration: One year. Must reapply for
additional funding.

PUBLICATIONS:
Newsletter; annual report.

IRS IDENTIFICATION NUMBER: 74-6065414

ADDRESS INQUIRIES TO:
Lydia Rodriguez
Program Officer, Discretionary Funds
(See address above.)

*SPECIAL STIPULATIONS:
The Foundation does not fund statewide;
only in Bexar County and surrounding
counties.

THE SAN DIEGO
FOUNDATION   [1459]
2508 Historic Decatur Road
Suite 200
San Diego, CA 92106-6138
(619) 235-2300
Fax: (619) 239-1710

E-MAIL ADDRESS:
info@sdfoundation.org

WEB SITE ADDRESS:
www.sdfoundation.org

FOUNDED: 1975

AREAS OF INTEREST:
Civil society, economic/employment
development, education, health and human
services, environment, arts and culture,
capacity building, science and technology.

TYPE:
Awards/prizes; Capital grants;
Challenge/matching grants; Demonstration
grants; Development grants; Fellowships;
General operating grants; Matching gifts;

Project/program grants; Research grants;
Scholarships; Seed money grants; Technical
assistance; Training grants.

YEAR PROGRAM STARTED: 1975

PURPOSE:
To improve the quality of life for all San
Diegans through effective responsible
philanthropy.

LEGAL BASIS:
Community foundation.

ELIGIBILITY:
Applicant organizations must be IRS
501(c)(3).

GEOGRAPHIC RESTRICTIONS:
San Diego County, California.

FINANCIAL DATA:
Amount of support per award: Varies.
Total amount of support: $44,292,559 for the
year ended June 30, 2010.
Matching fund requirements: On a
case-by-case basis.

NUMBER OF AWARDS: 2,800.

APPLICATION INFORMATION:
Requests for proposals in the area of
Community Partnerships must include a
project budget, organization budget, and letter
of qualification.
Duration: Generally, one year.
Deadline: Varies.

PUBLICATIONS:
Annual report; newsletters.

IRS IDENTIFICATION NUMBER: 95-2942582

OFFICERS:
Bob Kelly, President and Chief Executive
Officer

*SPECIAL STIPULATIONS:
Most grants made only in San Diego region.

THE SAN FRANCISCO
FOUNDATION   [1460]
225 Bush Street
Suite 500
San Francisco, CA 94104
(415) 733-8500
Fax: (415) 477-2783

E-MAIL ADDRESS:
info@sff.org

WEB SITE ADDRESS:
www.sff.org

FOUNDED: 1948

AREAS OF INTEREST:
Societal and civic issues, health and
environment, and arts and humanities.

NAME(S) OF PROGRAMS:
● **Community Leadership Awards**

TYPE:
Awards/prizes.

PURPOSE:
To recognize individuals and organizations
whose leadership has made a significant
impact in their particular Bay Area
communities.

LEGAL BASIS:
Community foundation.

ELIGIBILITY:
Organizations must be 501(c)(3).

GEOGRAPHIC RESTRICTIONS:
Alameda, Contra Costa, Marin, San
Francisco and San Mateo counties,
California.

FINANCIAL DATA:
Amount of support per award: Individual leaders: $10,000; Organizations: $20,000.

NUMBER OF APPLICANTS MOST RECENT YEAR: 275.

ADDRESS INQUIRIES TO:
Community Leadership Award Program (See address above.)

SANTA BARBARA FOUNDATION [1461]

1111 Chapala Street, Suite 200
Santa Barbara, CA 93101
(805) 963-1873
Fax: (805) 966-2345

E-MAIL ADDRESS:
info@sbfoundation.org

WEB SITE ADDRESS:
www.sbfoundation.org

FOUNDED: 1928

AREAS OF INTEREST:
Arts and culture expression, living and dying with dignity, lifelong learning, safety, civic engagement, sustainable protection of environment/historic places.

NAME(S) OF PROGRAMS:
- **Express Grant**
- **Strategy Grant**

TYPE:
Challenge/matching grants; Development grants; General operating grants; Project/program grants.

YEAR PROGRAM STARTED: 1928

PURPOSE:
To enrich the lives of the people of Santa Barbara County, CA.

LEGAL BASIS:
Community foundation incorporated in California.

ELIGIBILITY:
501(c)(3) organizations only. Funds must be used to benefit the people of Santa Barbara County, CA.

GEOGRAPHIC RESTRICTIONS:
Santa Barbara County, California.

FINANCIAL DATA:
Amount of support per award: Express Grant: Up to $5,000; Strategy Grant: $5,000 to $75,000.
Total amount of support: $2,370,000 in discretionary grants for the year ended December 31, 2010.
Matching fund requirements: Varies.

APPLICATION INFORMATION:
Contact the Foundation for guidelines.
Duration: One year. No guarantee for continuation.
Deadline: Strategy Grant Letters of Inquiry: April 15; full proposal early August. Express Grant: First Monday of each month.

PUBLICATIONS:
Annual report; application guidelines; quarterly newsletter.

IRS IDENTIFICATION NUMBER: 95-1866094

STAFF:
Ron Gallo, President and Chief Executive Officer
Martha Harmon, Senior Vice President of Community Investments
Dee Jennings, Senior Vice President of Finance and Administration

ADDRESS INQUIRIES TO:
Bronwen Fitzsimons, Grants Administrator (See address above.)

CHARLES AND LYNN SCHUSTERMAN FAMILY FOUNDATION [1462]

Two West Second Street
20th Floor
Tulsa, OK 74103
(918) 591-1090
Fax: (918) 591-1758

E-MAIL ADDRESS:
ahughes@schusterman.org

WEB SITE ADDRESS:
www.schusterman.org
www.tulsa.schusterman.org

FOUNDED: 1987

AREAS OF INTEREST:
Child advocacy, Jewish life, education, and community service.

TYPE:
Capital grants; General operating grants; Project/program grants.

PURPOSE:
To fund projects of interest to the Foundation including, but not limited to, those working with education, community life and Jewish affairs.

LEGAL BASIS:
Family foundation.

ELIGIBILITY:
Tax-exempt U.S. and international organizations that enhance Jewish life and nonsectarian Oklahoma-based organizations focused on child advocacy, education and youth leadership through service are eligible.

FINANCIAL DATA:
Amount of support per award: Varies.
Total amount of support: Varies.

NUMBER OF APPLICANTS MOST RECENT YEAR: 697.

NUMBER OF AWARDS: 378.

APPLICATION INFORMATION:
Grants are by invitation only.
Duration: One year; seldom more than three years. Must reapply for renewal based on performance.

PUBLICATIONS:
Inaugural Report, 2002; 20th Anniversary Report, 2007.

ADDRESS INQUIRIES TO:
Alana Hughes, Director of Administration (See address above.)

SCRANTON AREA FOUNDATION [1463]

321 Spruce Street, Suite 608
Scranton, PA 18503
(570) 347-6203
Fax: (570) 347-7587

E-MAIL ADDRESS:
safinfo@safdn.org

WEB SITE ADDRESS:
www.safdn.org

FOUNDED: 1954

AREAS OF INTEREST:
The people and community of the city of Scranton and Lackawanna County, PA.

TYPE:
Challenge/matching grants; Demonstration grants; Grants-in-aid; Project/program grants; Scholarships; Seed money grants; Training grants.

PURPOSE:
To strengthen the local community; to enrich the lives of the people of Scranton and Lackawanna County, PA.

ELIGIBILITY:
Grants to 501(c)(3) nonprofits serving Lackawanna County, PA.

GEOGRAPHIC RESTRICTIONS:
The city of Scranton and Lackawanna County, Pennsylvania.

FINANCIAL DATA:
Amount of support per award: Varies.
Total amount of support: Approximately $700,000 for the year 2010.

APPLICATION INFORMATION:
Before a grant application is submitted to the Foundation, it is strongly recommended that the applicant submit a letter of intent (one to two pages maximum).

THE SELF FAMILY FOUNDATION [1464]

120 Main Street
Greenwood, SC 29646
(864) 941-4011
Fax: (864) 941-4091

E-MAIL ADDRESS:
fwideman@selffoundation.org

WEB SITE ADDRESS:
www.selffoundation.org

FOUNDED: 1942

AREAS OF INTEREST:
Community wellness, education, with emphasis on early childhood development and youth, and health with emphasis on prevention.

TYPE:
Challenge/matching grants; Development grants; Endowments; Internships; Project/program grants; Training grants. Project grants in areas of the Foundation's interest.

YEAR PROGRAM STARTED: 1942

PURPOSE:
To help people to help themselves in South Carolina.

LEGAL BASIS:
Tax-exempt, private foundation.

ELIGIBILITY:
Applicants must be tax-exempt organizations in South Carolina only. No grants are awarded directly to individuals.

GEOGRAPHIC RESTRICTIONS:
South Carolina, with preference to Greenwood.

FINANCIAL DATA:
Amount of support per award: $1,000 to $500,000.
Matching fund requirements: Stipulated with specific programs.

NUMBER OF APPLICANTS MOST RECENT YEAR: 65.

NUMBER OF AWARDS: 34.

REPRESENTATIVE AWARDS:
$50,000 to Greenwood Community Children's Center; $75,230 to Independent

Colleges and Universities of South Carolina;
$7,500 to Ed Venture Children's Museum;
$15,000 to Greater Greenwood United
Ministries.

APPLICATION INFORMATION:
There is no application form. Applicants are
requested to submit a written proposal,
leadership list, a description of the
organization's activities and objectives and a
description of the purpose for which funding
is sought. Include copy of IRS tax
determination letter, expense budget of the
organization and copy of latest financial
statement.

Duration: No grants on a continuing basis.

Deadline: February 15, May 15, August 15
and November 15. Announcements in March,
June, September and December.

IRS IDENTIFICATION NUMBER: 57-0400594

OFFICERS:
Virginia P. Self, Chairman
Frank J. Wideman, III, President
Furman C. Self, Treasurer
Dr. Sally E. Self, Secretary

TRUSTEES:
J. Welborn Adams
George Kennedy
Julian Nexsen
Furman C. Self
Dr. Sally E. Self
Virginia P. Self
W.M. Self
W.M. Self, Jr.

ADDRESS INQUIRIES TO:
Frank J. Wideman, III, President
(See address above.)

SHASTA REGIONAL COMMUNITY FOUNDATION   [1465]

1335B Arboretum Drive
Redding, CA 96003
(530) 244-1219
Fax: (530) 244-0905

E-MAIL ADDRESS:
info@shastacf.org

WEB SITE ADDRESS:
www.shastacf.org

FOUNDED: 2000

AREAS OF INTEREST:
Arts and culture, community development,
education, health and human services.

NAME(S) OF PROGRAMS:
• **The McConnell Foundation Fund**
• **Redding Rancheria Community Fund**

TYPE:
Project/program grants.

PURPOSE:
To enhance the quality of life of Shasta and
Siskiyou communities through philanthropy,
education and information.

ELIGIBILITY:
To be eligible for funding, the applicant
must:
(1) be a nonprofit 501(c)(3) organization or
public agency and;
(2) provide specific and direct benefits to
residents of Shasta and/or Siskiyou counties,
primarily, or to Modoc, Tehema, or Trinity
counties.

GEOGRAPHIC RESTRICTIONS:
Primarily Shasta and Siskiyou counties,
California. Limited funding to Modoc,
Tehema and Trinity counties, California.

FINANCIAL DATA:
Amount of support per award: Varies.

Total amount of support: $1,400,000 for the
year 2009.

APPLICATION INFORMATION:
Application is available on the Foundation's
web site.

Deadline: Varies.

ADDRESS INQUIRIES TO:
Kerry Caranci, Program Officer
(See address above.)

SILICON VALLEY COMMUNITY FOUNDATION   [1466]

2440 West El Camino Real
Suite 300
Mountain View, CA 94040-1498
(650) 450-5400
Fax: (650) 450-5401

E-MAIL ADDRESS:
info@siliconvalleycf.org

WEB SITE ADDRESS:
www.siliconvalleycf.org

FOUNDED: 2007

AREAS OF INTEREST:
This community foundation utilizes five
grantmaking strategies: economic security;
education (closing the middle school
achievement gap in mathematics); immigrant
integration; regional planning (land use and
transportation planning); and a community
opportunity fund currently focused on
safety-net services of food and shelter.

TYPE:
General operating grants; Project/program
grants; Scholarships; Seed money grants.
Nonprofit organizations that provide services
or programs related to the specific five
grantmaking strategies in San Mateo and
Santa Clara counties may be eligible to apply
for funding from the Foundation's
endowment. Scholarships for college-bound
students are also open to application.

YEAR PROGRAM STARTED: 2008

PURPOSE:
To strengthen the common good, improve
quality of life and address the most
challenging problems; this is accomplished
through visionary community leadership,
world-class donor services and effective
grantmaking.

LEGAL BASIS:
Community foundation.

ELIGIBILITY:
To be eligible for a grant, an organization
should have current evidence of tax-exempt
status under Section 501(c)(3) from the IRS,
be a public entity or have a fiscal sponsor
with tax-exempt status.

In general, the Foundation does not make
grants from its endowment for or to:
(1) activities not directly benefiting the
residents of San Mateo and Santa Clara
counties;
(2) organizations that are discriminatory;
(3) individuals (contact the Foundation for
exceptions to this rule);
(4) costs already incurred;
(5) fraternal organizations, unless sponsoring
a specific program open to the entire
community;
(6) religious purposes; however, organizations
with religious affiliations will be considered
for grants if their programs seek to address

the needs of the wider community without
regard to religious beliefs;
(7) fund-raising events such as walk-a-thons,
tournaments and fashion shows and general
fund-raising solicitations;
(8) organizations and programs designed to
elect candidates to public office or;
(9) out-of-area travel.

GEOGRAPHIC RESTRICTIONS:
Endowment grants are restricted to nonprofit
and public agencies that serve San Mateo and
Santa Clara counties only.

FINANCIAL DATA:
Amount of support per award: $10,000 to
$250,000, with average grant size less than
$100,000. Grant size varies according to the
type of project, needs of the organization,
and the Foundation's annual giving budget
and program concentration.

Total amount of support: Dependent on the
Foundation's annual giving budget.

NUMBER OF APPLICANTS MOST RECENT YEAR:
360.

NUMBER OF AWARDS: 250.

APPLICATION INFORMATION:
The first step for any potential applicant is to
learn the specific components of the
grantmaking strategies. If the potential
applicant's organization does work or plans
to do work related to one of the grantmaking
strategies and a Request for Proposal (RFP)
regarding that strategy is open for
application, then a representative should
attend a grant information session. This will
give the potential applicant an opportunity to
learn more about the grantmaking strategy,
the RFP process and talk with a program
officer.

Step two would be to submit a proposal with
all the required information outlined in the
RFP application checklist. The Foundation
encourages submission of proposals via
e-mail and accepts proposals postmarked and
submitted electronically by the respective
deadline date.

Duration: Grants are usually for one year,
and should not be considered a source of
ongoing support.

Deadline: Contact the Foundation for the
appropriate grantmaking strategy application.

PUBLICATIONS:
Annual report; RFP guidelines; research
papers; *One Magazine.*

IRS IDENTIFICATION NUMBER: 20-5205488

BOARD OF DIRECTORS:
John M. Sobrato, Chairperson
Thomas J. Friel, Vice Chairperson
Jayne Battey
Gloria Brown
Emmett D. Carson, Ph.D.
Caretha Coleman
Gregory M. Gallo
Narendra Gupta
Nancy H. Handel
Susan M. Hyatt
Samuel Johnson, Jr.
William S. Johnson
Robert A. Keller
Anne F. Macdonald
Ivonne Montes de Oca
C.S. Park
Eduardo Rallo
Sanjay Vaswani
Richard Wilkolaski

Erika Williams
Gordon Yamate

ADDRESS INQUIRIES TO:
Ellen Clear
Vice President of Grantmaking
(See address above.)

*SPECIAL STIPULATIONS:
Please note the geographical restriction
(above).

THE SOUTHFIELD COMMUNITY FOUNDATION [1467]

25630 Evergreen Road
Southfield, MI 48075
(248) 327-6125
Fax: (248) 327-6127

E-MAIL ADDRESS:
rrrobinson@scfmi.org

WEB SITE ADDRESS:
www.scfmi.org

AREAS OF INTEREST:
Diversity, youth and Southfield public
schools.

TYPE:
Grants-in-aid; Project/program grants;
Scholarships.

PURPOSE:
To enhance the quality of life for those who
work or live in the community.

ELIGIBILITY:
Grants are made to organizations that have
tax-exempt status under Section 501(c)(3) of
the Internal Revenue Code. No grants are
made to individuals. Nonsectarian religious
programs may apply.

GEOGRAPHIC RESTRICTIONS:
Southfield or Lathrup Village, Michigan.

FINANCIAL DATA:
Amount of support per award: $500 to
$5,000.

Total amount of support: Approximately
$60,000 per year.

NUMBER OF APPLICANTS MOST RECENT YEAR:
Approximately 45 for the year 2010.

NUMBER OF AWARDS: Approximately 15 for the
year 2010.

APPLICATION INFORMATION:
Duration: One year.

ADDRESS INQUIRIES TO:
Raquel Robinson, Executive Director
(See address above.)

SOUTHWEST FLORIDA COMMUNITY FOUNDATION [1468]

8260 College Parkway
Suite 101
Fort Myers, FL 33919
(239) 274-5900
Fax: (239) 274-5930

E-MAIL ADDRESS:
info@floridacommunity.com

WEB SITE ADDRESS:
www.floridacommunity.com

FOUNDED: 1977

AREAS OF INTEREST:
Arts, animal welfare and rights, community
needs and development, culture, education,
environment, health and human services.

NAME(S) OF PROGRAMS:
● **Leadership Seminar Series**

TYPE:
Capital grants; Challenge/matching grants;
Conferences/seminars; Demonstration grants;
Project/program grants; Scholarships; Seed
money grants; Technical assistance; Training
grants.

PURPOSE:
To connect donors and their philanthropic
aspirations with evolving community needs.

LEGAL BASIS:
501(c)(3).

ELIGIBILITY:
Grants are made to organizations that have
tax-exempt status under Section 501(c)(3) of
the Internal Revenue Code. No grants are
made to individuals. Nonsectarian religious
programs may apply. Must serve the needs of
the communities listed below.

GEOGRAPHIC RESTRICTIONS:
Charlotte, Collier, Glades, Hendry and Lee
counties, Florida.

FINANCIAL DATA:
Amount of support per award: $1,500 to
$25,000; Initiative Grant Awards: Up to
$100,000.

Total amount of support: $2,830,064 for the
year 2009-10.

NUMBER OF APPLICANTS MOST RECENT YEAR:
1,200.

NUMBER OF AWARDS: 300.

APPLICATION INFORMATION:
Contact the Foundation for application
procedures.
Duration: One year.

PUBLICATIONS:
Annual report; quarterly newsletter.

IRS IDENTIFICATION NUMBER: 59-6580974

ADMINISTRATORS:
Julia East, President and Chief Executive
Officer

ADDRESS INQUIRIES TO:
Anne Douglas, Director of Programs
(See address above.)

STARK COMMUNITY FOUNDATION [1469]

400 Market Avenue North
Suite 200
Canton, OH 44702-2107
(330) 454-3426
Fax: (330) 454-5855

WEB SITE ADDRESS:
www.starkcommunityfoundation.org

FOUNDED: 1963

AREAS OF INTEREST:
Advancement of the health, social welfare,
education, culture or civic improvement of
the community.

TYPE:
Capital grants; Challenge/matching grants;
Demonstration grants; Development grants;
General operating grants; Matching gifts;
Project/program grants; Research grants;
Scholarships; Seed money grants; Technical
assistance; Training grants; Loan forgiveness
programs.

YEAR PROGRAM STARTED: 1965

LEGAL BASIS:
Community foundation.

ELIGIBILITY:
Organizations with 501(c)(3) status serving
Stark County, OH, are eligible. The
Foundation will not support operating
expenses of well established organizations,
deficit programs, or capital expenditures,
endowment funds, religious organizations or
religious purposes, annual appeal or
membership contributions, conferences or
recognition events.

GEOGRAPHIC RESTRICTIONS:
Stark County, Ohio.

FINANCIAL DATA:
Total assets $160,000,000 as of December
31, 2010.

Amount of support per award: $1,000 to
$225,000.

Total amount of support: Approximately
$5,500,000 annually.

Matching fund requirements: No general
requirements.

NUMBER OF APPLICANTS MOST RECENT YEAR:
Approximately 200.

NUMBER OF AWARDS: 130 Discretionary Field
of Interest and 60 Pro-Active Initiatives.

APPLICATION INFORMATION:
Duration: One year.
Deadline: January 5. August 1 for
discretionary funds.

PUBLICATIONS:
Annual report; guidelines and policies;
Community and Commitment, newsletter.

STAFF:
Mark Samolczyk, President

ADDRESS INQUIRIES TO:
Mark Samolczyk, President
(See address above.)

THE STEELE-REESE FOUNDATION [1470]

32 Washington Square West
New York, NY 10011
(212) 557-0905
Fax: (212) 286-8513

E-MAIL ADDRESS:
charlesbuice@hotmail.com

WEB SITE ADDRESS:
www.steele-reese.org

FOUNDED: 1955

AREAS OF INTEREST:
Education, health, social welfare, the
humanities and the environment.

TYPE:
Endowments; Matching gifts;
Project/program grants; Scholarships.
Charities.

Funding is provided for rural projects of
interest to the Foundation. The projects must
serve people in the geographic area served by
the Foundation.

YEAR PROGRAM STARTED: 1955

LEGAL BASIS:
Private foundation.

ELIGIBILITY:
Scholarship applicants must be conscientious
high school students from Lemhi and Custer
counties, Idaho.

Grant applications must be for rural, modest
and essential projects with community
financial support. The Foundation makes no

grants to individuals, to community chest or similar drives, for conferences or workshops, for efforts to influence elections or legislation, for planning purposes or experimental projects, for emergencies, or for permanent support except for occasional endowment grants to organizations where stability is critically important. Few grants are made for construction or for economic development and none for sectarian religious purposes.

GEOGRAPHIC RESTRICTIONS:
Idaho and Montana, and in the southern Appalachian mountain region of eastern Kentucky.

FINANCIAL DATA:
Amount of support per award: $5,000 to over $150,000 (multiyear grant).
Matching fund requirements: Grants often require that an organization raise a matching amount.

APPLICATION INFORMATION:
The Foundation welcomes proposals that are accurately aimed. Full proposal should be sent if an organization believes its needs are aligned with the Foundation's policies and funding interests. The Foundation's policies and guidelines in detail are available for review online.
Duration: Grants payable over one to four years. Absolutely no renewals.
Deadline: March 1 for consideration during the current fiscal year.

PUBLICATIONS:
Annual report.

ADDRESS INQUIRIES TO:
For general inquiries about Foundation policies:
William T. Buice
The Steele-Reese Foundation
32 Washington Square West
New York, NY 10011 or

Charles U. Buice
The Steele-Reese Foundation
39 Plaza Street West, 5-A
Brooklyn, NY 11217
E-mail: charlesbuice@hotmail.com

For Kentucky:
Judy Owens, Appalachian Director
2613 Clubside Court
Lexington, KY 40513
Tel & Fax: (859) 313-5225
E-mail: jkowensjd@aol.com

For Idaho or Montana:
Linda Tracy, Western Program Director
P.O. Box 8311
Missoula, MT 59807-8311
Tel: (406) 207-7984
Fax: (207) 470-3872

IRVIN STERN FOUNDATION   [1471]
4 East Ohio Street
Studio 6
Chicago, IL 60611
(312) 321-9402

E-MAIL ADDRESS:
christine@irvinstern.org

WEB SITE ADDRESS:
www.irvinstern.org

FOUNDED: 1957

AREAS OF INTEREST:
Human services, civic affairs and Jewish welfare.

TYPE:
General operating grants; Project/program grants.

PURPOSE:
To benefit social service organizations and enhance the welfare of Jewish communities.

LEGAL BASIS:
Family foundation.

ELIGIBILITY:
Applicants must be 501(c)(3) organizations operating in Chicago, IL. No grants to individuals, endowments, capital campaigns, capital construction projects, and academic or medical research programs.

GEOGRAPHIC RESTRICTIONS:
Rogers Park neighborhood of Chicago, Illinois.

APPLICATION INFORMATION:
Submit an online Letter of Inquiry or download a form and mail it to the Foundation at the address listed above.
Deadline: March 1 and September 1.

ADDRESS INQUIRIES TO:
Christine Flood, Grants Administrator
(See address and e-mail above.)

THE ABBOT AND DOROTHY H. STEVENS FOUNDATION   [1472]
P.O. Box 111
North Andover, MA 01845
(978) 688-7211

AREAS OF INTEREST:
Education, community welfare, arts and youth programs.

TYPE:
Capital grants; General operating grants; Project/program grants.

PURPOSE:
To improve the quality of life in greater Lawrence and Merrimack Valley.

ELIGIBILITY:
Eligible organizations must be IRS 501(c)(3) tax-exempt.

GEOGRAPHIC RESTRICTIONS:
Greater Lawrence and Merrimack Valley, Massachusetts.

FINANCIAL DATA:
Amount of support per award: $8,000 average.
Total amount of support: Varies.

APPLICATION INFORMATION:
Applicants must include a copy of their IRS 501(c)(3) tax determination letter.
Duration: One year.
Deadline: Trustees meet monthly with the exception of July and August.

PUBLICATIONS:
Guidelines.

ADDRESS INQUIRIES TO:
Joshua Miner, Administrator
(See address above.)

THE NATHANIEL AND ELIZABETH P. STEVENS FOUNDATION   [1473]
P.O. Box 111
North Andover, MA 01845
(978) 688-7211

E-MAIL ADDRESS:
grantprocess@stevensfoundation.com

AREAS OF INTEREST:
Education, community welfare, arts and youth programs.

TYPE:
Capital grants; General operating grants; Project/program grants.

PURPOSE:
To improve the quality of life in the greater Lawrence and Merrimack Valley.

ELIGIBILITY:
Eligible organizations must be IRS 501(c)(3) tax-exempt.

GEOGRAPHIC RESTRICTIONS:
Greater Lawrence and Merrimack Valley, Massachusetts.

FINANCIAL DATA:
Amount of support per award: $8,000 average.
Total amount of support: Varies.

APPLICATION INFORMATION:
Applications must include a copy of the IRS 501(c)(3) tax determination letter.
Duration: One year.
Deadline: Trustees meet monthly with the exception of July and August.

PUBLICATIONS:
Guidelines.

ADDRESS INQUIRIES TO:
Joshua Miner, Administrator
(See address above.)

H. CHASE STONE TRUST
c/o JPMorgan Private Client Services
402 North Tejon Street, Suite 200
Colorado Springs, CO 80903
(719) 227-6445
Fax: (719) 227-6448

E-MAIL ADDRESS:
julie.golden@jpmorgan.com

WEB SITE ADDRESS:
www.jpmorgan.com/onlinegrants

TYPE:
Project/program grants.

See entry 536 for full listing.

SUDBURY FOUNDATION   [1474]
326 Concord Road
Sudbury, MA 01776
(978) 443-0849
Fax: (978) 579-9536

E-MAIL ADDRESS:
contact@sudburyfoundation.org

WEB SITE ADDRESS:
www.sudburyfoundation.org

FOUNDED: 1952

AREAS OF INTEREST:
Scholarships, environment, and charitable grants for communities in the Sudbury area.

NAME(S) OF PROGRAMS:
● **The Atkinson Scholarship Program**
● **The Environmental Program**
● **The Regional Program**
● **The Sudbury Program**

TYPE:
Project/program grants; Scholarships.

YEAR PROGRAM STARTED: 1952

PURPOSE:
To improve the quality of life in Sudbury and the surrounding communities.

ELIGIBILITY:
Eligible organizations must be IRS 501(c)(3) tax-exempt. The Foundation funds projects in Sudbury and the 10 communities surrounding Sudbury that address the issues of Youth Development and Opportunity, Community Building, Preservation of Community Character and Assets, and/or Organizational Capacity and Effectiveness.

The Environmental Program focuses on Northern Forest of New York, Vermont, New Hampshire and Maine, and the fisheries and coastal communities of the Gulf of Maine.

The Atkinson Scholarship program provides college financial aid to students connected to Sudbury, MA.

GEOGRAPHIC RESTRICTIONS:
Sudbury, Massachusetts and surrounding areas.

FINANCIAL DATA:
Scholarships are administered to the schools earmarked for specific students.
Amount of support per award: Scholarships: Up to $5,000; Grants: $5,000 to $50,000.
Total amount of support: Varies.

NUMBER OF AWARDS: Scholarships: 15 new awards per year; Grants to nonprofits: 50 per year.

APPLICATION INFORMATION:
Applicants should write to the Foundation at the address above. Must include a copy of the IRS tax determination letter.

ADDRESS INQUIRIES TO:
Marilyn Martino, Executive Director
(See address above.)

*SPECIAL STIPULATIONS:
Scholarship program open to local high school seniors only for undergraduate education.

THE SUMMERLEE FOUNDATION [1475]
5556 Caruth Haven Lane
Dallas, TX 75225
(214) 363-9000
Fax: (214) 363-1941

E-MAIL ADDRESS:
info@summerlee.org

WEB SITE ADDRESS:
www.summerlee.org

FOUNDED: 1988

AREAS OF INTEREST:
Animal protection and Texas history.

NAME(S) OF PROGRAMS:
- **Animal Protection Program**
- **Texas History**

TYPE:
Project/program grants; Research grants.

YEAR PROGRAM STARTED: 1988

PURPOSE:
To promote animal protection and the prevention of cruelty to animals; to research and document all facts of Texas history.

LEGAL BASIS:
Charitable foundation.

ELIGIBILITY:
No grants are made for religious purposes or to individuals. Must be 501(c)(3).

GEOGRAPHIC RESTRICTIONS:
North America.

FINANCIAL DATA:
Amount of support per award: $5,000 to $10,000.

APPLICATION INFORMATION:
Applications should include:
(1) a brief history of the organization;
(2) a statement of organizational goals and purposes;
(3) a list of board of trustees and officers of the organization;
(4) the most recent audited financial statement;
(5) the most recent copy of the IRS determination letter which grants the organization 501(c)(3 status);
(6) the most recent copy of the 990 IRS information return;
(7) vitae of key personnel;
(8) the amount of time needed to complete the project;
(9) a budget forecast and;
(10) a plan of work to complete project.
Applications should be submitted in writing and signed by the chief executive officer of the applicant organization.
Duration: One year.
Deadline: The Foundation meets quarterly to review grant proposals.

IRS IDENTIFICATION NUMBER: 75-2252355

OFFICERS:
John W. Crain, President and Program Director-Texas History
Hon. David D. Jackson, Vice President
Melanie A. Lambert, Vice President and Program Director-Animal Protection
Martha L. Benson, Treasurer
Hon. Nikki DeShazo, Secretary

BOARD OF DIRECTORS:
Martha L. Benson
Michael H. Collins
John W. Crain
Hon. Nikki DeShazo
Hon. David D. Jackson
Melanie A. Lambert
Ron Tyler, Ph.D.

ADDRESS INQUIRIES TO:
For Animal Protection:
Melanie A. Lambert, Program Director

For Texas History:
John W. Crain, Program Director
(See address above.)

THE SUMMIT FOUNDATION [1476]
111 A Lincoln Street
Breckenridge, CO 80424
(970) 453-5970
Fax: (970) 453-1423

E-MAIL ADDRESS:
tsfdirector@summitfoundation.org

WEB SITE ADDRESS:
summitfoundation.org

FOUNDED: 1984

AREAS OF INTEREST:
Art and culture, health and human service, education, environment and sports.

TYPE:
Capital grants; Challenge/matching grants; General operating grants; Matching gifts; Project/program grants; Scholarships; Seed money grants; Technical assistance; Training grants. The Foundation supports scholarship programs at Summit High School and neighboring community high schools. Scholarships are available to graduating seniors each year.

YEAR PROGRAM STARTED: 1984

PURPOSE:
To improve the quality of life for residents and guests of Summit County and neighboring communities.

LEGAL BASIS:
Community foundation.

ELIGIBILITY:
Grants are made to organizations that have tax-exempt status under Section 501(c)(3) of the Internal Revenue Code. No grants are made to individuals. Nonsectarian religious programs may apply.

GEOGRAPHIC RESTRICTIONS:
Summit County and neighboring communities of Alma, Fairplay, Kremmling and Leadville, Colorado.

FINANCIAL DATA:
Amount of support per award: Varies.
Total amount of support: Approximately $1,250,000 for the year 2010.

NUMBER OF APPLICANTS MOST RECENT YEAR: 95.

NUMBER OF AWARDS: 83.

APPLICATION INFORMATION:
Contact the Foundation for specific details on the various grant programs.
Deadline: Typically April and September.

IRS IDENTIFICATION NUMBER: 74-2341399

ADDRESS INQUIRIES TO:
Lee Zimmerman, Executive Director
(See address above.)

TECHFOUNDATION [1477]
30 Brattle Street, Third Floor
Cambridge, MA 02138
(617) 354-7500
Fax: (617) 354-7510

E-MAIL ADDRESS:
info@techfoundation.org

WEB SITE ADDRESS:
www.techfoundation.org

AREAS OF INTEREST:
Helping nonprofit organizations utilize information technology.

NAME(S) OF PROGRAMS:
- **TechConnect**
- **TechGrants**
- **TechMarketplace**

TYPE:
Conferences/seminars; Fellowships; Grants-in-aid; Product donations.
TechConnect: A series of educational seminars designed to bring needed technology expertise to the nonprofit community.

TechGrants: A newsletter and a grant program that provides nonprofit organizations with access to capital to help fulfill their technology needs.

TechMarketplace: A business-to-nonprofit program that provides discounted and donated technology hardware, software and services to nonprofit organizations.

PURPOSE:
To deliver technology, expertise and capital to help nonprofit organizations serve humanity; to help nonprofit organizations access the same resources to serve humanity that businesses use to create wealth.

LEGAL BASIS:
Nonprofit organization.

ELIGIBILITY:
To participate in TechMarketplace,
organizations must meet the requirements
laid out in Section 501(c)(3) of the Internal
Revenue Code and be designated as exempt
from federal income tax under Section
501(a). Applicant organization must provide
services without discrimination on the basis
of race, color, sex, sexual orientation, age,
religion, national or ethnic origin, or physical
disability. Organization is also required to be
a member of TechFoundation to use this
program.

FINANCIAL DATA:
Amount of support per award: Varies.

NUMBER OF AWARDS: Varies.

APPLICATION INFORMATION:
Guidelines become available in September.

THOMAS THOMPSON TRUST   [1478]

c/o Rackemann, Sawyer and Brewster
160 Federal Street, 15th Floor
Boston, MA 02110-1700
(617) 951-1108
Fax: (617) 542-7437

E-MAIL ADDRESS:
smonahan@rackemann.com

WEB SITE ADDRESS:
www.cybergrants.com/thompson

AREAS OF INTEREST:
Education, health/mental health, social
services and cultural.

TYPE:
Capital grants; Challenge/matching grants;
Conferences/seminars; Demonstration grants;
Development grants; Endowments;
Professorships; Project/program grants; Seed
money grants; Technical assistance; Training
grants; Research contracts. Support for
special programs, capital support, new
construction, renovation and equipment.

PURPOSE:
To promote health, education, or general
social and civic betterment.

LEGAL BASIS:
Private foundation.

ELIGIBILITY:
Eligible organizations must be in operation
for three consecutive years prior to
submitting an application.

GEOGRAPHIC RESTRICTIONS:
Dutchess County, New York, particularly in
Rhinebeck; and Windham County, Vermont,
particularly in Brattleboro.

FINANCIAL DATA:
Amount of support per award: $5,000 to
$15,000.
Total amount of support: $500,255 for the
year 2010.
Matching fund requirements: Determined on
case-by-case basis.

REPRESENTATIVE AWARDS:
Brattleboro Boys and Girls Club; Windham
Housing Trust; Young Rhinebeck.

APPLICATION INFORMATION:
Applications must be submitted online.

PUBLICATIONS:
Application guidelines.

TRUSTEES:
Daniel W. Fawcett
Albert M. Fortier, Jr., Esq.
William B. Tyler, Esq.

ADDRESS INQUIRIES TO:
Susan T. Monahan, Grants Coordinator
(See address or e-mail above.)

TIDES FOUNDATION   [1479]

Presidio Building 1014
Lincoln Boulevard at Torney Avenue
San Francisco, CA 94129
(415) 561-6400
Fax: (415) 561-6401

E-MAIL ADDRESS:
info@tides.org

WEB SITE ADDRESS:
www.tides.org

FOUNDED: 1976

AREAS OF INTEREST:
Civic participation, economic development,
economic and racial justice, environment,
environmental justice, LGBTIQ communities,
HIV/AIDS, native communities, progressive
media, arts and culture, violence prevention,
women's empowerment and reproductive
health, and youth organizing and
development.

TYPE:
General operating grants; Internships;
Project/program grants.

YEAR PROGRAM STARTED: 1976

PURPOSE:
To partner with donors to increase and
organize resources for social change.

LEGAL BASIS:
Public foundation.

FINANCIAL DATA:
Amount of support per award: Varies.

APPLICATION INFORMATION:
Tides fund advisors direct their own
grantmaking and most do not accept
unsolicited proposals.

IRS IDENTIFICATION NUMBER: 51-0198509

ADDRESS INQUIRIES TO:
Mary Claire Hubert
Director of Grants Management
(See address above.)

For internships:
E-mail: intern@tides.org

TOLEDO COMMUNITY FOUNDATION   [1480]

300 Madison Avenue, Suite 1300
Toledo, OH 43604
(419) 241-5049
Fax: (419) 242-5549

E-MAIL ADDRESS:
toledocf@toledocf.org

WEB SITE ADDRESS:
www.toledocf.org

FOUNDED: 1973

AREAS OF INTEREST:
Education, social services, physical and
mental health, neighborhood and urban
affairs, natural resources and the arts.

TYPE:
Challenge/matching grants; Project/program
grants; Seed money grants. The Foundation
has a particular interest in providing seed

money for new programs designed to meet
emerging community needs or to expand
existing successful programs. Emphasis is
placed on programs that will:
(a) create safe, positive living environments;
(b) enable families to develop the
skills/resources needed to support and nurture
each member and;
(c) foster the development of responsible
young people who are capable of achieving
their fullest potential.

PURPOSE:
To enrich the quality of life for individuals
and families in the greater Toledo service
area.

ELIGIBILITY:
Grants are awarded only to nonprofit,
charitable organizations that are IRS
501(c)(3) tax-exempt. The Foundation usually
will not make grants from its unrestricted
funds to support general operating budgets
(or budget deficits) of established
organizations, annual campaigns, capital
campaigns, purchase of equipment such as
computer hardware/software or motor
vehicles, production of films, videos,
television programs, etc., or for sectarian
activities of religious organizations.

GEOGRAPHIC RESTRICTIONS:
Northwest Ohio and southeast Michigan,
with particular emphasis on the greater
Toledo, Ohio area.

FINANCIAL DATA:
Amount of support per award: Varies.

APPLICATION INFORMATION:
Online grant application must be completed.
No hard copies accepted.
Duration: Varies.
Deadline: January 15, May 15 and
September 1.

PUBLICATIONS:
Guidelines.

ADDRESS INQUIRIES TO:
Sarah Harrison, Senior Program Officer
(See address above.)

THE TRULL FOUNDATION [1481]

404 Fourth Street
Palacios, TX 77465
(361) 972-5241
Fax: (361) 972-1109

E-MAIL ADDRESS:
info@trullfoundation.org

WEB SITE ADDRESS:
www.trullfoundation.org

FOUNDED: 1967

AREAS OF INTEREST:
Four main focus areas are: The Palacios,
Matagorda County area; children and
families; substance abuse problems; Texas
coastal environment.

CONSULTING OR VOLUNTEER SERVICES:
Assists local projects and to some extent,
organizations in other geographical areas.

TYPE:
Challenge/matching grants;
Conferences/seminars; Development grants;
General operating grants; Matching gifts;
Project/program grants; Scholarships; Seed
money grants.

YEAR PROGRAM STARTED: 1948

PURPOSE:
To support religious, charitable and
educational programs.

LEGAL BASIS:
Private (family) foundation.

ELIGIBILITY:
Applicants must have federal tax-exemption letter from IRS.

GEOGRAPHIC RESTRICTIONS:
Primarily in rural Texas.

FINANCIAL DATA:
Amount of support per award: $2,000 to $5,000 average.
Total amount of support: $1,600,000 for the year 2010.

NUMBER OF APPLICANTS MOST RECENT YEAR:
400 for the year 2010.

NUMBER OF AWARDS: 250 for the year 2010.

REPRESENTATIVE AWARDS:
$5,000 to Bay City, TX, Volunteer Fire Department, for purchase of a fire truck; $2,500 to Boys and Girls Clubs of Rusk County; $4,500 to Council on Substance Abuse of Southeast Texas; $5,000 to Environmental Defense Fund, Texas.

APPLICATION INFORMATION:
Each applicant should submit the following in triplicate (original and two copies):
(1) cover letter (two-page maximum);
(2) proposal fact sheet (two-page maximum);
(3) current agency budget (one to three pages), including sources of income;
(4) one-page project budget, if different from operating budget;
(5) documentation of IRS status 501(c)(3). If there is any matter which might affect the IRS status to cause the revocation of the exemption, include information about this matter and;
(6) selected additional material or information (limit five pages) (optional).

Proposals sent by fax or e-mail are not accepted.

The Foundation may request additional information if there is an interest in the proposal.

Duration: Usually no more than three years per project.
Deadline: Announcement within two months after receipt of proposal.

PUBLICATIONS:
Biennial report; application guidelines; proposal fact sheet.

IRS IDENTIFICATION NUMBER: 23-7423943

TRUSTEES:
Colleen Claybourn, Chairman
R. Scott Trull, Vice Chairman
Susan Herlin, Advisory Trustee
Kristan Olfers, Advisory Trustee
Cara P. Herlin, Trustee
Sarah H. Olfers, Trustee
Mike McAllister, Associate Trustee
Craig Wallis, Associate Trustee

STAFF:
E. Gail Purvis, Executive Director

ADDRESS INQUIRIES TO:
E. Gail Purvis, Executive Director
(See address above.)

TWENTY-FIRST CENTURY FOUNDATION

132 West 112th Street
Lower Level No. 1
New York, NY 10026
(212) 662-3700
Fax: (212) 662-6690

E-MAIL ADDRESS:
info@21cf.org

WEB SITE ADDRESS:
www.21cf.org

TYPE:
Challenge/matching grants; General operating grants; Project/program grants; Seed money grants. Donor-advised fund grants.

See entry 1098 for full listing.

U.S. BANCORP FOUNDATION [1482]

800 Nicollet Mall
BC-MN-H21B
Minneapolis, MN 55402
(612) 303-7870
Fax: (612) 303-0787

WEB SITE ADDRESS:
www.usbank.com

FOUNDED: 1979

AREAS OF INTEREST:
Arts and culture, education, affordable housing and economic opportunity.

TYPE:
Capital grants; Development grants; General operating grants; Matching gifts; Project/program grants.

PURPOSE:
To improve the quality of life in communities where U.S. Bancorp employees live and work.

LEGAL BASIS:
Corporate foundation.

ELIGIBILITY:
Organizations must be IRS 501(c)(3) tax-exempt and must be located in communities where U.S. Bank operates.

The Foundation charitable contributions program will not provide funding for:
(1) organizations not tax-exempt under Internal Revenue Code Section 501(c)(3);
(2) fraternal organizations, merchant associations, chamber memberships or programs, or 501(c)(4) or (6) organizations;
(3) fund-raising events or sponsorships, "pass through" organizations or private foundations;
(4) organizations outside U.S. Bancorp communities;
(5) programs operated by religious organizations for religious purposes;
(6) political organizations or organizations designed primarily to lobby;
(7) individuals;
(8) travel and related expenses;
(9) endowment campaigns;
(10) deficit reduction;
(11) organizations receiving primary funding from the United Way or;
(12) organizations whose practices are not in keeping with the Company's equal opportunity policy.

GEOGRAPHIC RESTRICTIONS:
Arizona, Arkansas, California, Colorado, Idaho, Illinois, Indiana, Iowa, Kansas, Kentucky, Minnesota, Missouri, Montana, Nebraska, Nevada, North Dakota, Ohio, Oregon, South Dakota, Tennessee, Utah, Washington, Wisconsin and Wyoming.

FINANCIAL DATA:
Amount of support per award: Varies.
Total amount of support: Companywide grants and matching contributions of $20,600,000 for the year 2009.

Matching fund requirements: Through the Foundation, U.S. Bancorp matches qualifying contributions of cash and stock made by U.S. Bancorp employees to nonprofit organizations or higher education institutions on a dollar-for-dollar basis from a minimum of $50 to an annual maximum of $1,000 per person per year.

APPLICATION INFORMATION:
Application and guidelines are available online.

PUBLICATIONS:
Guidelines; Corporate Citizenship Report.

IRS IDENTIFICATION NUMBER: 41-1359579

ADDRESS INQUIRIES TO:
Local contact information is available online.

U.S. DEPARTMENT OF EDUCATION

Office of Safe and Drug Free Schools
550 12th Street, S.W., 10th Floor
Washington, DC 20202-6450
(202) 245-7896
Fax: (202) 485-0013

E-MAIL ADDRESS:
osdfs.safeschl@ed.gov

WEB SITE ADDRESS:
www2.ed.gov/osdfs

TYPE:
Project/program grants. Discretionary grants to prevent the illegal use of drugs and violence among, and promote safety and discipline for, students at all educational levels from preschool through the postsecondary level. The many discretionary grants are listed on the *Federal Register*.

See entry 1224 for full listing.

U.S. DEPARTMENT OF HEALTH AND HUMAN SERVICES [1483]

200 Independence Avenue, S.W.
Washington, DC 20201
(202) 690-6590
Fax: (202) 205-8037

WEB SITE ADDRESS:
www.acf.hhs.gov/programs/add

AREAS OF INTEREST:
Developmental disabilities.

NAME(S) OF PROGRAMS:
- **Projects of National Significance for Persons with Developmental Disabilities**

TYPE:
Demonstration grants; Technical assistance; Training grants. Model demonstration grants. Support for persons with developmental disabilities.

YEAR PROGRAM STARTED: 1975

PURPOSE:
To provide grants and contracts for projects of national significance that increase and support the independence, productivity and integration of persons with developmental disabilities into the community.

LEGAL BASIS:
Government agency.

ELIGIBILITY:
Applicants must be nonprofit organizations, state agencies, or consortia.

GEOGRAPHIC RESTRICTIONS:
United States and its territories.

FINANCIAL DATA:
Amount of support per award: Up to $200,000. Average award is $100,000.

Total amount of support: $14,162,000 for the year 2009.

Matching fund requirements: 25% local match.

NUMBER OF AWARDS: 59 for the year 2009.

APPLICATION INFORMATION:
Duration: 12 to 60 months.

OFFICERS:
Sharon Lewis, Commissioner, Administration on Developmental Disabilities
Jamie Kendall, Deputy Commissioner

ADDRESS INQUIRIES TO:
Ophelia McLain, Program Specialist
(See address above.)

U.S. DEPARTMENT OF HOUSING AND URBAN DEVELOPMENT [1484]

451 7th Street, S.W.
Room 7286
Washington, DC 20410
(202) 708-3587 (Office of Block Grant Assistance)
(202) 708-1577 (Entitlement Division)
(202) 708-1322 (State/Small Cities Division)
Fax: (202) 401-2044

WEB SITE ADDRESS:
www.hud.
gov/offices/cpd/communitydevelopment

FOUNDED: 1974

AREAS OF INTEREST:
Community development.

NAME(S) OF PROGRAMS:
- **Community Development Block Grant Program: Entitlement Communities Program**
- **State Community Development Block Grant Program**

TYPE:
Block grants; Project/program grants. Acquisition, construction of certain public works, facilities and improvements, clearance, housing rehabilitation, relocation and demolition, public services (limited), activities relating to conservation and renewable energy resources, neighborhood revitalization and economic development projects, including assistance to micro enterprises.

YEAR PROGRAM STARTED: 1975

PURPOSE:
To develop viable urban communities, including decent housing and a suitable living environment and expand economic opportunities, principally for persons of low and moderate income.

LEGAL BASIS:
Units of general local government under Title I of the Housing and Community Development Act of 1974 (PL 93-383).

ELIGIBILITY:
The following units of general local government and states are all entitled to receive block grants from the CDBG Entitlement Communities Program and State and Small Cities Program. Grant amounts are determined by a statutory formula:
(1) principal cities of Metropolitan Statistical Areas (MSAs);
(2) other metropolitan cities with a

population of at least 50,000 and;
(3) qualified urban counties, as defined in the Act, with populations of at least 200,000 (excluding the population of entitled cities).

Under the State CDBG Program, HUD provides grant assistance to 49 states and Puerto Rico that in turn award grants to units of general local government not eligible to receive grants from the Entitlement Communities Program. Grant amounts to states are determined by statutory formula.

Under the HUD Administered Small Cities Program, HUD directly awards grants to non-entitled units of general local government within the state of Hawaii by formula. The total value of grants awarded through this Program is determined by statutory formula.

FINANCIAL DATA:
Amount of support per award: Varies from city to city.

Total amount of support: $3.9 billion in formula grants for fiscal year 2010.

NUMBER OF AWARDS: 1,145 entitlement grantees for the year 2008.

APPLICATION INFORMATION:
For the CDBG Entitlement Communities Program, a grantee must develop and submit to HUD its consolidated plan, which is a jurisdiction's comprehensive planning document and application for funding under the Community Planning and Development formula grant programs: CDBG, HOME, Emergency Shelter Grants (ESG) and Housing Opportunities for Persons with AIDS (HOPWA). In its consolidated plan, the jurisdiction must identify its goals for these community planning and development programs, as well as for housing programs. These goals will serve as the criteria against which HUD will evaluate a jurisdiction's plan and its performance under the plan. In addition, the consolidated plan must include required certifications, including that not less than 70% of the CDBG funds expended over a one-, two- or three-year period specified by the grantee, will be used for activities that benefit low- and moderate-income persons. A consolidated plan submission will be approved by HUD unless the plan (or a portion of it) is inconsistent with the purposes of the National Affordable Housing Act or it is substantially incomplete.

Under the State CDBG Program, to receive a grant from HUD, a state must certify that it:
(1) is following a detailed citizen participation plan and that each funded unit of general local government is following a detailed citizen participation plan;
(2) has consulted with affected units of general local government in the nonentitled area in determining the method of distribution of funding; it engages or will engage in planning for community development activities; it will provide assistance to units of general local government; it will not refuse to distribute funds to any unit of general local government based on the particular eligible activity chosen by the unit of general local government, except that a state is not prevented from establishing priorities based on the activities selected;
(3) has a consolidated plan that identifies community development and housing needs and short-term and long-term community development objectives;
(4) will conduct its program in accordance

with the Civil Rights Act of 1964 and the Fair Housing Act of 1988 and will affirmatively further fair housing;
(5) will set forth a method of distribution that ensures that each of the funded activities will meet one or more of the program's three broad, national objectives (grant maximum feasible priority to activities which benefit low- and moderate-income families, aid in the prevention or elimination of slums or blight or, in unique circumstances, meet urgent community development needs) and at least 70% of the amount expended for activities over a period of one, two or three consecutive program years will benefit low- and moderate-income families, and that the state will not attempt to recover any capital costs of public improvements assisted with CDBG funds, except for certain exceptions found in 24 CFR 91.325(b)(4);
(6) will require units of general local government to certify that they are adapting and enforcing laws to prohibit the use of excessive force against nonviolent civil rights demonstrations, and they will enforce laws against barring entrance and exit from facilities that are the targets of nonviolent civil rights demonstrations in their jurisdiction and;
(7) will comply with Title I of the HCD Act and all other applicable laws.

Under the HUD Administered Small Cities Program, to receive a grant, the counties of Hawaii, Maui and Kauai in Hawaii must prepare and submit a consolidated plan to HUD.

ADDRESS INQUIRIES TO:
Office of Block Grant Assistance
(See address above.)

*SPECIAL STIPULATIONS:
Block grants made to states and local governments, not individuals.

U.S. DEPARTMENT OF JUSTICE
OJJDP
810 Seventh Street, N.W.
Washington, DC 20531
(202) 514-4158
Fax: (202) 353-9093

E-MAIL ADDRESS:
patrick.dunckhorst@usdoj.gov

WEB SITE ADDRESS:
www.ojjdp.ncjrs.org
www.tribaljusticeandsafety.gov

TYPE:
Demonstration grants; Project/program grants; Training grants.

See entry 1506 for full listing.

THE UNITY FOUNDATION OF LAPORTE COUNTY [1485]

619 Franklin Street
Michigan City, IN 46360
(219) 879-0327
Fax: (219) 873-2416

E-MAIL ADDRESS:
unity@uflc.net

WEB SITE ADDRESS:
www.uflc.net

FOUNDED: 1992

AREAS OF INTEREST:
Community development in LaPorte County, IN.

CONSULTING OR VOLUNTEER SERVICES:
Technical assistance to nonprofits and donors.

NAME(S) OF PROGRAMS:
● **Community Fund**

TYPE:
Challenge/matching grants; Grants-in-aid; Project/program grants; Scholarships; Technical assistance. Community Fund makes grants to education, the arts, health and human services, and the environment to the whole community. Grants are based on what the community needs at a given time.

YEAR PROGRAM STARTED: 1992

PURPOSE:
To improve the quality of life in LaPorte County, IN.

LEGAL BASIS:
Indiana corporation 501(c)(3).

ELIGIBILITY:
Nonprofits serving people of LaPorte County, IN.

GEOGRAPHIC RESTRICTIONS:
LaPorte County, Indiana.

FINANCIAL DATA:
Amount of support per award: $3,000.
Total amount of support: $800,000 in grants and $92,000 in scholarships each year.

NUMBER OF APPLICANTS MOST RECENT YEAR: 75.

NUMBER OF AWARDS: 42.

APPLICATION INFORMATION:
Applications should follow the format outlined in the Grant Packet. The following information is required:
(1) narrative describing the program or specific need to be addressed, its significance to the community and its particular benefit to those living in the LaPorte County area, and the names and qualifications of those persons who will carry it out;
(2) complete budget for the project, including funding plan, amount of the request, and names of other funding sources the organization has applied to for assistance and;
(3) description of applicant organization(s) including the name, address, telephone and fax number of the contact person, a list of the officers and board members, a copy of the IRS letter designating the organization as 501(c)(3) federal tax-exempt, latest annual financial report, and any descriptive brochures or promotional literature.
Deadline: Mid-July.

PUBLICATIONS:
Report to Community.

STAFF:
Maggi Spartz, President
Sue Korte Regetz, Vice President

ADDRESS INQUIRIES TO:
Maggi Spartz, President
(See address above.)

VAN LOEBENSELS/REMBEROCK FOUNDATION [1486]

131 Steuart Street
Suite 301
San Francisco, CA 94105
(415) 512-0500
Fax: (415) 371-0227

E-MAIL ADDRESS:
info@vlsrr.org

WEB SITE ADDRESS:
www.vlsrr.org

FOUNDED: 1964

AREAS OF INTEREST:
Public interest law, juvenile justice reform, incarcerated and formerly incarcerated individuals, and selected immigration organizations and programs.

TYPE:
General operating grants; Project/program grants; Seed money grants.

YEAR PROGRAM STARTED: 1964

PURPOSE:
To support projects that will test potentially useful innovations in the areas of public interest law.

LEGAL BASIS:
Private independent foundation.

ELIGIBILITY:
Grants are restricted to Northern California. Grants are not ordinarily made for projects requiring medical, scientific or other technical knowledge for evaluation, operating budgets of well-established organizations, capital expenditures, to national organizations unless for a specific local project, to individuals or for scholarships.

GEOGRAPHIC RESTRICTIONS:
Northern California.

FINANCIAL DATA:
Amount of support per award: Average grant: $10,000.
Total amount of support: $2,005,500 for the year 2010.

NUMBER OF AWARDS: 150 for the year 2010.

REPRESENTATIVE AWARDS:
$25,000 to East Bay Community Law Center; $32,000 to Immigrant Legal Resource Center.

APPLICATION INFORMATION:
Duration: Most grants are awarded on a single-year basis, but may be renewed if warranted.
Deadline: Proposals are considered every six to eight weeks. Announcement one to two weeks after Board meetings.

STAFF:
Katherine Armstrong, Executive Director
Gail Shuster, Program Administrator

BOARD OF DIRECTORS:
Toni Rembe, President
Dan Corsello, Treasurer
Richard W. Odgers, Secretary
Julie Divola

ADDRESS INQUIRIES TO:
Toni Rembe, President
(See address above.)

VENTURA COUNTY COMMUNITY FOUNDATION [1487]

1317 Del Norte Road
Suite 150
Camarillo, CA 93010
(805) 988-0196
Fax: (805) 485-5537

E-MAIL ADDRESS:
vccf@vccf.org

WEB SITE ADDRESS:
www.vccf.org

FOUNDED: 1986

AREAS OF INTEREST:
Community needs and development, culture, education, health, human services, women's issues and Latino issues.

TYPE:
Project/program grants; Scholarships.

YEAR PROGRAM STARTED: 1987

PURPOSE:
To promote and enable philanthropy to improve our community, for good, forever.

ELIGIBILITY:
Must qualify under the Internal Revenue Code Section 501(c)(3) as a nonprofit organization, or operate under the fiscal sponsorship of an organization that does, and serve residents of Ventura County, CA.

GEOGRAPHIC RESTRICTIONS:
Ventura County, California.

FINANCIAL DATA:
Amount of support per award: Varies.
Total amount of support: Varies.

NUMBER OF AWARDS: 716.

APPLICATION INFORMATION:
Applications accepted only in response to an open request for proposals. See web site for details.

ADDRESS INQUIRIES TO:
Appropriate program officer, as outlined in the Request for Proposals.

VICTORIA FOUNDATION, INC. [1488]

946 Bloomfield Avenue
Glen Ridge, NJ 07028
(973) 748-5300
Fax: (973) 748-0016

E-MAIL ADDRESS:
info@victoriafoundation.org

WEB SITE ADDRESS:
www.victoriafoundation.org

FOUNDED: 1924

AREAS OF INTEREST:
Education, neighborhood revitalization, youth and families in Newark, NJ, as well as statewide environmental issues.

TYPE:
Capital grants; Challenge/matching grants; Demonstration grants; Development grants; General operating grants; Project/program grants; Seed money grants; Technical assistance; Training grants. The focus in Education includes after-school programs, educational enrichment, teacher training and curriculum development.

Neighborhood Revitalization includes community development, employment training, housing programs and community organizing.

The focus in Youth and Families includes youth development programs and efforts to strengthen families.

The concentration in Environment includes open space preservation in New Jersey, particularly in the Highlands and Pinelands.

YEAR PROGRAM STARTED: 1924

PURPOSE:
To promote education, urban environment, neighborhood development and urban revitalization, and youth and families in the city of Newark; to preserve and conserve

resources including land, water and energy in the state of New Jersey and within the city of Newark.

LEGAL BASIS:
Independent foundation.

ELIGIBILITY:
Organizations must be nonprofit per Internal Revenue Code 501(c)(3) and must address the Foundation's interests. No grants are made to individuals or for programs dealing with specific diseases, afflictions or geriatric needs. Proposals from arts organizations will be considered only if they directly bear on education.

GEOGRAPHIC RESTRICTIONS:
Newark, New Jersey for general programs and the entire state of New Jersey for environmental programs.

FINANCIAL DATA:
Amount of support per award: $50,000.
Total amount of support: $9,295,000 in total grants paid for the year ended December 31, 2009.

NUMBER OF APPLICANTS MOST RECENT YEAR:
229.

NUMBER OF AWARDS: 155 for the year ended December 31, 2009.

REPRESENTATIVE AWARDS:
$75,000 to New Jersey Symphony Orchestra to support the Newark Early Strings Program, which provides Suzuki violin instruction to over 500 elementary school children; $130,000 to Ironbound Community Corporation towards general operating support; $40,000 to Planned Parenthood to support a peer-to-peer health education program in the Newark Public Schools.

APPLICATION INFORMATION:
Duration: One year. Renewal based upon careful trustee and staff review of subsequent proposal submissions.
Deadline: Current grantees: January 15 and July 15; New applicants: February 1 and August 1; March 1 for school applications; Summer camp: September 1. Announcements in late June and December.

PUBLICATIONS:
Annual report.

IRS IDENTIFICATION NUMBER: 22-1554541

OFFICERS:
Percy Chubb, III, President
Margaret H. Parker, Vice President
Kevin Shanley, Treasurer
Gordon A. Millspaugh, Jr., Assistant Treasurer
Irene Cooper-Basch, Executive Officer and Secretary

TRUSTEES:
Frank Alvarez
Charles M. Chapin, III
Percy Chubb, III
Sally Chubb
Sara Chubb-Sauvayre
Robert Holmes
Robert L. Johnson, M.D.
Gordon A. Millspaugh, Jr.
Franklin Parker, IV
John E. Parker
Margaret H. Parker
Helen Frye Parr
Kevin Shanley
A. Zachery Yamba

ADDRESS INQUIRIES TO:
Irene Cooper-Basch, Executive Officer
(See address above.)

THE WACO FOUNDATION [1489]
900 Austin Avenue, Ninth Floor
Waco, TX 76701
(254) 754-3404
Fax: (254) 752-9457

E-MAIL ADDRESS:
info@wacofdn.org

WEB SITE ADDRESS:
www.wacofoundation.org

FOUNDED: 1958

AREAS OF INTEREST:
Residents of McLennan County, TX.

NAME(S) OF PROGRAMS:
● **MAC Program Scholarship Fund**

TYPE:
Scholarships. Intended to promote postsecondary educational opportunities in the community, and thereby promote greater employment opportunities for those of working age.

YEAR PROGRAM STARTED: 1995

PURPOSE:
To make a positive difference in the lives and future of the people who live in Waco and McLennan County through grantmaking, promotion of community philanthropy, and support of the not-for-profit sector.

ELIGIBILITY:
Must have graduated from McLennan County high schools and have family income of less than $50,000.

GEOGRAPHIC RESTRICTIONS:
McLennan County, Texas.

FINANCIAL DATA:
Amount of support per award: Varies.
Total amount of support: $500,000 in contributions annually.

APPLICATION INFORMATION:
High school seniors must submit completed application form and FAFSA.
Duration: One year. Renewable.
Deadline: May 1.

ADDRESS INQUIRIES TO:
Robbie Stabeno, Director of Scholarships
(See address above.)

DENNIS & PHYLLIS WASHINGTON FOUNDATION [1490]
P.O. Box 16630
Missoula, MT 59808
(406) 523-1300
Fax: (406) 523-1399

WEB SITE ADDRESS:
www.dpwfoundation.org

FOUNDED: 1987

AREAS OF INTEREST:
Youth-focused programs in arts and culture, community service, health and human services and education.

TYPE:
Project/program grants; Scholarships. Scholarship monies awarded to Montana's nine colleges and universities and seven Indian reservations.

YEAR PROGRAM STARTED: 1987

PURPOSE:
To invest in people to improve the quality of their lives.

LEGAL BASIS:
Private foundation.

ELIGIBILITY:
Eligible organizations must be IRS 501(c)(3) tax-exempt. Low administrative costs.

FINANCIAL DATA:
Amount of support per award: Average grant: $8,500.

NUMBER OF APPLICANTS MOST RECENT YEAR:
567 for the year 2009.

NUMBER OF AWARDS: 250 for the year 2009.

APPLICATION INFORMATION:
Grant applicants must complete the online application process which includes reading grant guidelines, completion of a short eligibility review and submission of a preliminary application form. If qualified, the organization will be invited to submit a full application online.

Scholarship applicants can review application guidelines on the Foundation's web site.
Duration: One year. Renewals are rare but possible upon reapplication.

ADDRESS INQUIRIES TO:
Mike Halligan, Executive Director
(See address above.)

WASHINGTON FORREST FOUNDATION [1491]
2300 Ninth Street South
Arlington, VA 22204-2387
(703) 920-3688
Fax: (703) 920-0130

E-MAIL ADDRESS:
washforr@aol.com

FOUNDED: 1968

AREAS OF INTEREST:
Health and human services, education, religion and the arts.

TYPE:
Capital grants; Challenge/matching grants; General operating grants; Matching gifts; Project/program grants; Scholarships; Seed money grants.

PURPOSE:
To improve and enhance the quality of life in Arlington and especially South Arlington, VA.

LEGAL BASIS:
Public foundation.

ELIGIBILITY:
Eligible organizations must be IRS 501(c)(3) tax-exempt and be located in northern Virginia.

GEOGRAPHIC RESTRICTIONS:
Arlington and northern Virginia.

FINANCIAL DATA:
Amount of support per award: $500 to $25,000.
Total amount of support: $724,547 for the year 2009.

NUMBER OF AWARDS: 122 for the year 2009.

APPLICATION INFORMATION:
Applicants should first call the Foundation to discuss the proposal. Applications must include a copy of the IRS tax determination letter.
Duration: One year. Renewal by reapplication.

Deadline: August 1, November 1, February 1 and May 1.

ADDRESS INQUIRIES TO:
Deborah Lucckese
President and Executive Director
(See address above.)

THOMAS H. WHITE FOUNDATION [1492]

1422 Euclid Avenue, Suite 627
Cleveland, OH 44115-1952
(216) 696-7273
Fax: (216) 621-8198

E-MAIL ADDRESS:
salthans@fmscleveland.com

WEB SITE ADDRESS:
www.fmscleveland.com/thomaswhite

FOUNDED: 1913

AREAS OF INTEREST:
Early childhood education, middle school to high school education, and high school to higher education.

TYPE:
Project/program grants. The Foundation will focus its grantmaking in two major areas: Education and Human Services. Specifically, the Foundation is interested in supporting programs that address three critical areas: (1) Workforce readiness: programs that emphasize science and technology education, adequate employment preparation, support systems and the relationship to earning potential;
(2) School retention: programs that emphasize the critical transition issues that occur during early teenage years and affect family relationships and school attendance and;
(3) Early childhood enrichment: programs which enhance the learning environment; provide support, training and ancillary services to parents; and /or enhance the recruitment and training of day care providers.
Organizations and programs that contribute generally to the quality of life in Greater Cleveland may also be considered at the Foundation's discretion.

YEAR PROGRAM STARTED: 1913

PURPOSE:
To improve educational resources and support charitable purposes in the city of Cleveland, OH.

LEGAL BASIS:
Private foundation.

ELIGIBILITY:
Grants awarded to tax-exempt, nonprofit charitable and educational institutions located within Cuyahoga County, OH, if such organizations, and their services and facilities, primarily serve residents of the City of Cleveland.

Applicants are discouraged from submitting requests for endowment, general operating support, research, symposia or seminars. No grants are awarded to individuals. The Foundation does not respond to general solicitations or annual fund-raising campaigns.

GEOGRAPHIC RESTRICTIONS:
Cuyahoga County, Ohio.

FINANCIAL DATA:
Amount of support per award: $1,000 to $100,000.

Total amount of support: $999,768 in grants approved for the year 2010.

Matching fund requirements: Stipulated with individual programs.

NUMBER OF APPLICANTS MOST RECENT YEAR: 112.

NUMBER OF AWARDS: 70.

REPRESENTATIVE AWARDS:
$54,000 over three years to Baldwin Wallace for the Barbara Byrd-Bennett Scholars Program; $20,000 to The Center for Community Solutions for Ohio Early Care and Education Campaign; $7,500 to Hunger Network of Greater Cleveland to provide support and referral services to clients.

APPLICATION INFORMATION:
Submit the following:
(1) a brief history of the organization;
(2) explanation of request;
(3) evaluation plan and future funding plan;
(4) its total budget, other funding sources and its importance to the people of Cleveland;
(5) the amount requested;
(6) the organization's tax-exempt status;
(7) a list of the organization's trustees and;
(8) the proposal, plus one copy.

Foundation staff is available to assist applicants and/or to further clarify the Foundation's grantmaking policies and procedures.
Duration: Most grants are made for one year only. Two- to three-year grants are made occasionally.
Deadline: Six weeks prior to distribution meetings, which are held in February, May and September. Announcement is made within three weeks of meeting.

PUBLICATIONS:
Annual report.

DISTRIBUTION COMMITTEE:
Margot James Copeland
Robin Cottingham
Jan Culver
Michael S. Galland
Catherine O'Malley Kearny
Cynthia Koury
Susan S. Locke
Robert S. Reitman, Advisory Member

ADDRESS INQUIRIES TO:
Susan Althans, Consultant
(See address above.)

*SPECIAL STIPULATIONS:
Local giving only.

WICHITA COMMUNITY FOUNDATION [1493]

301 North Main Street
Suite 100
Wichita, KS 67202
(316) 264-4880
Fax: (316) 264-7592

E-MAIL ADDRESS:
wcf@wichitacf.org

WEB SITE ADDRESS:
www.wichitacf.org

FOUNDED: 1986

AREAS OF INTEREST:
Arts, conservation, education, environmental health, humanities and social services.

TYPE:
Project/program grants; Scholarships; Seed money grants.

PURPOSE:
To provide a permanent resource for building community philanthropy.

LEGAL BASIS:
Community foundation.

ELIGIBILITY:
Grants are made to organizations that have tax-exempt status under Section 501(c)(3) of the Internal Revenue Code. No grants are made to individuals. High school students may apply for scholarships on the Foundation's web site.

GEOGRAPHIC RESTRICTIONS:
Sedgwick County, Kansas.

FINANCIAL DATA:
Amount of support per award: $10,000 to $100,000.
Total amount of support: $3,100,000 for the year 2010.

APPLICATION INFORMATION:
Duration: Typically one year.
Deadline: Applications accepted throughout the year.

ADDRESS INQUIRIES TO:
Carol Nazar, Grants Administrator
(See address above.)

HARVEY RANDALL WICKES FOUNDATION [1494]

Plaza North, Suite 472
4800 Fashion Square Boulevard
Saginaw, MI 48604
(989) 799-1850
Fax: (989) 799-3327

E-MAIL ADDRESS:
hrwickes@att.net

FOUNDED: 1945

AREAS OF INTEREST:
Arts, health, education, recreation, civic improvement and human services.

TYPE:
Matching gifts; Project/program grants.

YEAR PROGRAM STARTED: 1945

PURPOSE:
To improve the quality of life in Saginaw County.

ELIGIBILITY:
Eligible organizations must be IRS 501(c)(3) tax-exempt.

GEOGRAPHIC RESTRICTIONS:
Saginaw County, Michigan.

FINANCIAL DATA:
Amount of support per award: $10,000 average grant.
Total amount of support: $1,500,000 for the year 2010.

NUMBER OF AWARDS: Approximately 63 awards for the year 2008.

APPLICATION INFORMATION:
Applicants may send a written proposal and must include a copy of the IRS tax determination letter.
Duration: One year. Renewal possible by reapplication.
Deadline: Two weeks prior to board meetings. The board meets on the second Tuesday in March, June and September and the first Tuesday in December.

PUBLICATIONS:
Annual report; grant guidelines.

IRS IDENTIFICATION NUMBER: 38-6061470

ADDRESS INQUIRIES TO:
Hugo E. Braun, Jr., President
(See address above.)

*SPECIAL STIPULATIONS:
No grants to individuals.

THE WINSTON-SALEM
FOUNDATION   [1495]
860 West 5th Street
Winston-Salem, NC 27101
(336) 725-2382
Fax: (336) 727-0581

E-MAIL ADDRESS:
info@wsfoundation.org

WEB SITE ADDRESS:
www.wsfoundation.org

FOUNDED: 1919

AREAS OF INTEREST:
Human services, education, youth, arts,
culture and health.

NAME(S) OF PROGRAMS:
- **Black Philanthropy Grants**
- **Community Grants**
- **Elkin/Tri-County Grants**
- **Stokes County Grants**
- **Student Aid Grants, Scholarship, and**
  Loans
- **Teacher Grants**
- **Victim Assistance Grants**
- **Women's Fund Grants**
- **Youth Philanthropy Grants**

TYPE:
Capital grants; Challenge/matching grants;
Development grants; Endowments;
Project/program grants; Scholarships; Seed
money grants; Training grants. Discretionary
grants given to organizations providing
benefit to citizens within the greater Forsyth
County, NC area, subject to limitations on
program areas expressed by the donor of the
source fund. Student aid primarily for
Forsyth County residents.

YEAR PROGRAM STARTED: 1919

PURPOSE:
To help agencies initiate, innovate and
experiment, as well as to provide other types
of support as appropriate.

LEGAL BASIS:
Community foundation.

ELIGIBILITY:
Applicants must be charitable organizations
and publicly supported charities. No grants
are made to individuals.

GEOGRAPHIC RESTRICTIONS:
Forsyth County, North Carolina and
contiguous counties.

FINANCIAL DATA:
Amount of support per award: $500 to
$2,000,000; average $25,000.
Total amount of support: $18,000,000 for the
year 2010.

NUMBER OF APPLICANTS MOST RECENT YEAR:
173.

NUMBER OF AWARDS: 100.

APPLICATION INFORMATION:
Duration: Generally, grants are for one year.
Deadline: Preliminary applications accepted
on the first of each month.

PUBLICATIONS:
Annual report; guidelines for donors and
grantseekers; newsletters.

IRS IDENTIFICATION NUMBER: 56-6037615

STAFF:
Scott F. Wierman, President
Lisa Purcell, Executive Vice President

ADDRESS INQUIRIES TO:
Grants Manager
(See address above.)

WOODS CHARITABLE FUND,
INC.   [1496]
1440 M Street
Lincoln, NE 68508
(402) 436-5971
Fax: (402) 742-0123

E-MAIL ADDRESS:
pbaker@woodscharitable.org

WEB SITE ADDRESS:
www.woodscharitable.org

FOUNDED: 1941

AREAS OF INTEREST:
Children, youth and families, education,
community development and housing, arts
and humanities.

TYPE:
Challenge/matching grants; Demonstration
grants; General operating grants;
Project/program grants; Seed money grants;
Technical assistance. Grants to support
organizations and projects located in and
directly serving the residents of Lincoln, NE.

YEAR PROGRAM STARTED: 1941

PURPOSE:
To strengthen the community by improving
opportunities and life outcomes for all people
in Lincoln, NE.

LEGAL BASIS:
Private foundation.

ELIGIBILITY:
Grants are made only to tax-exempt
organizations described in Section 501(c)(3)
of the IRS Code and which have a written
ruling from the IRS that they also qualify
under 509(a)(1), (2) or (3) of the code
(publicly supported organizations and their
affiliates).

Geographically, grants are limited to
organizations in Lincoln. Occasionally, the
Fund reviews proposals from outside the city
if the proposed activities have statewide
impact and a significant Lincoln component.
While the Fund makes grants in very diverse
fields, fund-raising benefits or program
advertising, individual needs, endowments,
scholarships or fellowships are not eligible
for grant review.

GEOGRAPHIC RESTRICTIONS:
Lincoln, Nebraska.

FINANCIAL DATA:
Amount of support per award: Average
payment: $21,804 for the year 2010.
Total amount of support: $1,439,040 grants
paid for the year 2010.

NUMBER OF APPLICANTS MOST RECENT YEAR:
200.

NUMBER OF AWARDS: 53 for the year 2010.

REPRESENTATIVE AWARDS:
$5,000 to Angels Theatre Company for "In
My Daughter's Name" production focusing
on domestic violence murder; $30,000 to
Voices for Children in Nebraska for capacity
building for this child advocate organization
during leadership transition period; $50,000

to University of Nebraska Lincoln, Center for
Research on Children, Youth, Families and
Schools to increase student engagement,
motivation and achievement among ninth
graders at risk of dropping out of high
school.

APPLICATION INFORMATION:
Guidelines are available on request. Before
submitting a full proposal, applicants should
contact the Fund with a two-page summary
request and budget or a phone call. If the
request appears suitable, a full proposal will
be requested.
Deadline: March 1 to 15 for June Board
Meeting. July 1 to 15 for November Board
Meeting. November 1 to 15 for March Board
Meeting. Proposals that arrive well before the
deadline have a better chance for careful
review.

PUBLICATIONS:
Annual report.

IRS IDENTIFICATION NUMBER: 47-6032847

STAFF:
Pam Baker, Secretary and Executive Director
Joan Stolle, Operations and Information
Manager
Tom Woods, Senior Program Officer
Angie Zmarzly, Program Associate

DIRECTORS:
Donna W. Woods, President
Jose J. Soto, Vice President
Hank Woods, Treasurer
Lynn Roper, Assistant Treasurer
Michael J. Tavlin, Assistant Treasurer
Nelle Jamison
Orville Jones
T.J. McDowell, Jr.
Kathleen Rutledge

ADDRESS INQUIRIES TO:
Pam Baker, Executive Director
(See address above.)

WOODS FUND OF
CHICAGO   [1497]
35 East Wacker Drive
Suite 1760
Chicago, IL 60601
(312) 782-2698
Fax: (312) 782-4155

E-MAIL ADDRESS:
application@woodsfund.org

WEB SITE ADDRESS:
www.woodsfund.org

FOUNDED: 1941

AREAS OF INTEREST:
Arts and culture, community organizing,
intersection of community organizing and
public policy.

TYPE:
General operating grants; Project/program
grants.

PURPOSE:
To increase opportunities for less advantaged
people and communities in the metropolitan
area, including the opportunity to contribute
to decisions affecting them.

LEGAL BASIS:
Nonprofit.

ELIGIBILITY:
Grants are made to cultural organizations that
have tax-exempt status under Section
501(c)(3) of the Internal Revenue Code. No
grants are made to individuals.

GEOGRAPHIC RESTRICTIONS:
Metropolitan Chicago, Illinois.

FINANCIAL DATA:
Amount of support per award: $10,000 to
$35,000.

APPLICATION INFORMATION:
The Woods Fund requires that prospective
grantees first submit a completed Inquiry
Form. If the Fund responds positively,
applicants will be asked to submit a full
application. Form and application instructions
are available at the Fund web site.

Deadline: For June grants, letter of inquiry
should be received by the last business day in
January. For December grants, letter of
inquiry should be received by the last
business day in July.

ADDRESS INQUIRIES TO:
Grant Processing
(See e-mail address above.)

WILLIAM C. WOOLF FOUNDATION   [1498]

333 Texas Street, LASH30202T
Shreveport, LA 71101
(318) 429-1705
Fax: (318) 429-1021

FOUNDED: 1959

AREAS OF INTEREST:
Northwestern Louisiana.

TYPE:
Grants-in-aid.

PURPOSE:
To better the lives of citizens in Shreveport,
LA.

ELIGIBILITY:
Eligible organizations must be IRS 501(c)(3)
tax-exempt and be located in northwestern
Louisiana.

GEOGRAPHIC RESTRICTIONS:
Northwestern Louisiana.

FINANCIAL DATA:
Amount of support per award: $150 to
$50,000.

APPLICATION INFORMATION:
Applicants may send a written proposal and
must include a copy of the IRS tax
determination letter.

Duration: One year. Renewals by
reapplication.

Deadline: Submit by February 1.
Determination at board meeting end of
February.

ADDRESS INQUIRIES TO:
Barbara R. York, Secretary
(See address above.)

WYOMING COMMUNITY FOUNDATION   [1499]

313 South 2nd Street
Laramie, WY 82070
(307) 721-8300
(866) 708-7878
Fax: (307) 721-8333

E-MAIL ADDRESS:
wcf@wycf.org

WEB SITE ADDRESS:
www.wycf.org

FOUNDED: 1989

NAME(S) OF PROGRAMS:
- **McMurry Continuing Staff Education Library Grants**
- **Hazel Patterson Memorial Donor Advised Fund**
- **Gordon and Edna Sykes Endowment Fund**
- **Upper Green River Sustainable Community Endowment Fund**
- **Wyoming Women's Foundation Grants**
- **Wyoming Youth in Natural Resources Grants**

TYPE:
Conferences/seminars; Development grants;
General operating grants; Grants-in-aid;
Matching gifts; Project/program grants;
Research grants; Scholarships; Seed money
grants; Technical assistance; Training grants.
McMurry Continuing Staff Education Library
Grants: Available for employees of Wyoming
public libraries in order to enhance the
applicants' level of education.

Wyoming Women's Foundation Grants: Made
to nonprofit organizations with programs to
enhance the economic self-sufficiency of
women in Wyoming.

YEAR PROGRAM STARTED: 1986

PURPOSE:
To connect people who care with causes that
matter to build a better Wyoming.

ELIGIBILITY:
Except for the McMurry Grants, grants are
not made to individuals. Nonprofit 501(c)(3)
organizations or public/governmental
agencies are eligible to apply. Grants are
given to religious organizations, as long as
the program to be funded is of a
nonproselytizing nature.

Organization must be registered in the state
of Wyoming. For McMurry Grants,
applicants must be residents of Wyoming.

GEOGRAPHIC RESTRICTIONS:
Wyoming.

FINANCIAL DATA:
Amount of support per award: $500 to
$50,000. Average $5,000.

Total amount of support: $2,500,000 for the
year 2009.

COOPERATIVE FUNDING PROGRAMS: Community
Assessment grants in conjunction with the
Wyoming Rural Development Association.

NUMBER OF APPLICANTS MOST RECENT YEAR:
750.

NUMBER OF AWARDS: 500.

APPLICATION INFORMATION:
Organizations applying must include IRS
501(c)(3) documentation.

Duration: One year. Grants are renewable,
but a full application would have to be
resubmitted.

Deadline: March 1, July 1 and November 1.

STAFF:
George Gault, President
Cheryl Welegala, Vice President of Finance
Press Stephens, Development Officer
Samin Dadelahi, Senior Program Officer
Vickie Quisenberry, Database Administrator
Jason S. Clark, Grants Administrator
Richelle Keinath, Executive Director,
Wyoming Women's Foundation
Katie Boysen, Program Assistant, Wyoming
Women's Foundation

ADDRESS INQUIRIES TO:
Samin Dadelahi, Senior Program Officer
Wyoming Community Foundation
(See address above.)

Crime prevention

INTERNATIONAL CENTRE FOR COMPARATIVE CRIMINOLOGY   [1500]

University of Montreal
C.P. 6128, Succursale Centre-Ville
Montreal QC H3C 3J7 Canada
(514) 343-7065
Fax: (514) 343-2269

E-MAIL ADDRESS:
cicc@umontreal.ca

WEB SITE ADDRESS:
www.cicc.umontreal.ca

FOUNDED: 1969

AREAS OF INTEREST:
Sociology of crime and deviance,
comparative studies on criminal justice,
police, courts, prisons, victims, national and
international research, terrorism and
counter-terrorism.

CONSULTING OR VOLUNTEER SERVICES:
In all the fields of criminal justice.

NAME(S) OF PROGRAMS:
- **Research Fieldwork**

TYPE:
Conferences/seminars; Exchange programs;
Fellowships. Postdoctoral scholarship. The
Centre brings visiting professors and
specialists to confer on projects and
cooperate on research investigation and
invites graduate and postgraduate students to
do fieldwork at the Centre.

YEAR PROGRAM STARTED: 1969

PURPOSE:
To provide funding to encourage continued
study in the field of crime and criminal
justice.

LEGAL BASIS:
University.

ELIGIBILITY:
Applicants must have a Ph.D. from any
country.

FINANCIAL DATA:
Amount of support per award: Postdoctoral
scholarships: $30,000 (CAN) per year. Fixed
sum for living expenses.

NUMBER OF APPLICANTS MOST RECENT YEAR:
6.

NUMBER OF AWARDS: Postdoctoral scholarships:
2 per year.

APPLICATION INFORMATION:
Submit research project, curriculum vitae,
three letters from researchers who know the
candidate and an abstract of the Ph.D. thesis.

Duration: One year.

Deadline: June 30.

PUBLICATIONS:
Annual report; Revue *Criminologie.*

OFFICERS:
Benoit Dupont, Director

ADDRESS INQUIRIES TO:
Benoit Dupont, Director
(See address above.)

NATIONAL INSTITUTE OF JUSTICE [1501]

810 Seventh Street, N.W.
Washington, DC 20531
(202) 307-2942
Fax: (202) 307-6394

WEB SITE ADDRESS:
www.ncjrs.org
www.ojp.usdoj.gov/nij/funding.htm

FOUNDED: 1968

AREAS OF INTEREST:
Criminal justice and evaluation, program development, dissemination of research-based criminal justice, and fellowships.

NAME(S) OF PROGRAMS:
● **Research Grants**

TYPE:
Research grants. Research grants and contracts, including those for evaluative research; research and development grants and contracts in science and technology for criminal justice applications.

The focus of NIJ research is on generating information that is useful to state and local public officials in developing policies related to crime reduction.

YEAR PROGRAM STARTED: 1968

PURPOSE:
To increase knowledge of the causes, prevention, and control of crime, the effectiveness and efficiency of the criminal justice system, and the responsiveness of the nation's law enforcement and justice administration systems; to disseminate this knowledge to the federal, state, and local policymakers.

LEGAL BASIS:
Anti-Drug Abuse Act of 1988 (42 U.S.C. 3721).

ELIGIBILITY:
NIJ awards grants to or enters into cooperative agreements with educational institutions, nonprofit organizations, public agencies, individuals, and profit-making organizations that are willing to waive their fees. Special eligibility criteria are indicated in NIJ's solicitations for proposals.

GEOGRAPHIC RESTRICTIONS:
United States.

FINANCIAL DATA:
All NIJ awards must be used to supplement existing funds, not to replace those already appropriated for the same purpose.
Amount of support per award: $10,000 to more than $1,000,000.
Total amount of support: Varies.
Matching fund requirements: Units of state and local governments are encouraged to contribute matching funds and other applicants are encouraged to seek matching contributions from government agencies or private organizations.

REPRESENTATIVE AWARDS:
Kenneth R. Freeman, Judge, Municipal Court Bench for Los Angeles, "A Study to Find More Effective Ways to Investigate and Prosecute Child Sexual Abuse Cases;" Lt. John Buchanan, II, Phoenix Police Department, "Assessing the Current Status of Police-Prosecutor Team Efforts;" Dr. Wesley G. Skogan, Professor, Northwestern University, "Crime and the Survival of Small Business."

APPLICATION INFORMATION:
Guidelines, applications, and information about specific solicitations for proposals is available from National Criminal Justice Reference Service.
Duration: Normally two years maximum. Renewal possible.

PUBLICATIONS:
Guidelines; application; *Building Knowledge about Crime and Justice: The Research Prospectus of the National Institute of Justice.*

ADDRESS INQUIRIES TO:
National Criminal Justice Reference Service
P.O. Box 6000
Rockville, MD 20849-6000
Tel: (800) 851-3420
E-mail: askncjrt@ncjrs.org

GARDINER HOWLAND SHAW FOUNDATION [1502]

355 Boylston St.
Boston, MA 02116
(781) 455-8303
Fax: (781) 433-8090

E-MAIL ADDRESS:
admin@shawfoundation.org

WEB SITE ADDRESS:
shawfoundation.org

FOUNDED: 1959

AREAS OF INTEREST:
Criminal justice, the study, prevention, correction and alleviation of crime and delinquency and the rehabilitation of juvenile and adult offenders.

CONSULTING OR VOLUNTEER SERVICES:
Technical assistance to grantees and other human service agencies on request.

NAME(S) OF PROGRAMS:
● **Grantee Workshops**
● **Participating Foundation of Grantmakers for Public Safety**
● **Shaw Foundation Grants**

TYPE:
Conferences/seminars; Demonstration grants; Development grants; General operating grants; Seed money grants; Technical assistance. Priorities for funding include programs which can effectively divert court-involved youth and juvenile offenders from escalating involvement in the criminal justice system, programs which promote the use and acceptance of alternatives to incarceration and intermediate criminal sanctions, innovative and effective approaches to rehabilitation for detained and incarcerated juvenile and adult offenders, methods which improve the administration of justice and the quality of services for individuals appearing before the criminal court, and initiatives which can impact current public policy in the field of criminal justice through education, training and effective advocacy. Added weight will be given to proposals which clearly demonstrate the ability to utilize Shaw Foundation support to attract new public and private resources to the field of criminal justice.

YEAR PROGRAM STARTED: 1959

PURPOSE:
To aid the study, prevention, correction and alleviation of crime and delinquency and the rehabilitation of adult and juvenile offenders.

LEGAL BASIS:
Private foundation.

ELIGIBILITY:
Applicant must have tax-exempt public charitable status from the IRS and must operate within Massachusetts. The Foundation does not support capital requests, the arts, endowments, grants to individuals or scholarships.

GEOGRAPHIC RESTRICTIONS:
Massachusetts.

FINANCIAL DATA:
Total amount of support: $686,000 for fiscal year ended April 30, 2008.

COOPERATIVE FUNDING PROGRAMS: The Shaw Foundation does, from time to time, work with other sources for the purpose of cooperative fundings.

NUMBER OF AWARDS: 46 grantees for fiscal year ended April 30, 2008.

REPRESENTATIVE AWARDS:
$30,000 to Criminal Justice Policy Coalition for public education; $10,000 to Advocacy City Mission Society for prison services program; $20,000 to Span Inc., service for ex-offenders in transition from prison to the community.

APPLICATION INFORMATION:
Potential applicants are encouraged to telephone the Foundation to discuss their ideas prior to submitting a proposal. Also, all new applicants should submit a concept paper describing their organization and the purposes for which funds are being sought, along with a budget and evidence of tax-exempt status. The applicant will be informed if the work being proposed fits with the current interests of the Foundation.
Duration: Typically, the Foundation will provide support up to three years, with renewal dependent upon grantee performance and program need.
Deadline: February 1. Decision by May.

PUBLICATIONS:
Annual report; guidelines.

TRUSTEES:
Peter P. Brown
Theodore E. Ober
Benjamin Williams, Jr.

ADDRESS INQUIRIES TO:
Thomas E. Coury, Executive Director
(See address above.)

U.S. DEPARTMENT OF JUSTICE [1503]

Bureau of Justice Statistics
810 7th Street, N.W.
Washington, DC 20531
(202) 514-9012
(202) 307-0765
Fax: (202) 616-1351

E-MAIL ADDRESS:
stephanie.burroughs@usdoj.gov

WEB SITE ADDRESS:
bjs.ojp.usdoj.gov

FOUNDED: 1969

AREAS OF INTEREST:
Statistics on crime, victims of crime, criminal offenders and operations of justice systems at all levels of government throughout the U.S.

NAME(S) OF PROGRAMS:
● **State Justice Statistics for Statistical Analysis Centers**

TYPE:
Development grants; Research grants.
Cooperative agreements for the development
of statistical methods and techniques and the
aggregation and analysis of statistical
information on crime and criminal justice in
the states.

YEAR PROGRAM STARTED: 1972

PURPOSE:
To develop and enhance the capabilities of
the states in gathering, analyzing and using
statistical information pertaining to crime and
the criminal justice system and to obtain
selected types of data for multistate
aggregation.

LEGAL BASIS:
Government agency formed under the Justice
System Improvement Act of 1979.

ELIGIBILITY:
Applicants must be state agencies whose
activities include statistical analysis at the
state level.

FINANCIAL DATA:
Amount of support per award: Usually
$50,000.
Total amount of support: Varies.

NUMBER OF APPLICANTS MOST RECENT YEAR:
75.

APPLICATION INFORMATION:
Duration: 12 months.
Deadline: Varies.

ADDRESS INQUIRIES TO:
Stephanie Burroughs, Program Manager
(See address above.)

U.S. DEPARTMENT OF
JUSTICE   [1504]
Office of Juvenile Justice and
Delinquency Prevention
810 7th Street, N.W., 5th Floor
Washington, DC 20531
(202) 307-5911
Fax: (202) 307-2093

WEB SITE ADDRESS:
www.ojjdp.ncjrs.gov

FOUNDED: 1975

AREAS OF INTEREST:
Delinquency prevention research, juvenile
gangs, serious violent juvenile offenders and
juvenile justice statistics.

NAME(S) OF PROGRAMS:
● **Juvenile Justice and Delinquency
Prevention Program**

TYPE:
Conferences/seminars; Development grants;
Fellowships; Internships; Project/program
grants; Research grants; Residencies; Visiting
scholars; Research contracts. Grants to
conduct research, evaluation and development
on juvenile justice and delinquency
prevention activities, including the
development of new or improved approaches,
techniques, systems and program models to
conduct behavioral research on the causes of
juvenile crime, means of, intervention and
prevention, and to evaluate juvenile programs
and procedures.

YEAR PROGRAM STARTED: 1975

PURPOSE:
To encourage, coordinate and conduct
research and evaluation of juvenile justice
and delinquency prevention activities; to

provide a clearinghouse and information
center for collecting, publishing and
distributing information on juvenile
delinquency; to conduct a national training
program; to establish standards for the
administration on juvenile justice. Current
emphasis is work in the area of serious and
violent juvenile crime, drug involvement by
youth and missing children.

LEGAL BASIS:
Juvenile Justice and Delinquency Prevention
Act of 1974, Public Law 93-415, 42 U.S.C.
5601, as amended.

ELIGIBILITY:
Public or private agencies, organizations,
including institutions of higher learning, or
individuals.

GEOGRAPHIC RESTRICTIONS:
United States and its territories.

FINANCIAL DATA:
Amount of support per award: Varies.

NUMBER OF APPLICANTS MOST RECENT YEAR:
100.

NUMBER OF AWARDS: 80.

REPRESENTATIVE AWARDS:
Law Enforcement Agencies Policies
Regarding Missing Children; School Crime
and Discipline Research and Discipline;
Causes and Correlates of Delinquency.

APPLICATION INFORMATION:
Duration: Generally one to three years.

PUBLICATIONS:
Annual report; annual program plan; various
project reports.

ADDRESS INQUIRIES TO:
Juvenile Justice Clearinghouse
National Criminal Justice
Reference Service
P.O. Box 6000
Rockville, MD 20849-6000
Tel: (800) 851-3420
Fax: (301) 519-5600

U.S. DEPARTMENT OF
JUSTICE   [1505]
Office of Juvenile Justice and
Delinquency Prevention
810 Seventh Street, N.W., 5th Floor
Washington, DC 20531
(202) 307-5911
Fax: (202) 307-2093

WEB SITE ADDRESS:
www.ojjdp.ncjrs.gov/

AREAS OF INTEREST:
Juvenile justice, delinquency prevention and
child protection.

NAME(S) OF PROGRAMS:
● **Juvenile Justice and Delinquency
Prevention Allocation to States**

TYPE:
Block grants; Challenge/matching grants;
Demonstration grants; Formula grants;
Internships; Project/program grants; Research
grants; Technical assistance; Training grants.
Grants to increase the capacity of state and
local governments to conduct effective
juvenile justice and delinquency prevention
programs as developed in the state
comprehensive action plan.

YEAR PROGRAM STARTED: 1974

LEGAL BASIS:
Juvenile Justice and Delinquency Prevention
Act of 1974, Public Law 93-415, 42 U.S.C.
5601 as amended (JJDP Act).

ELIGIBILITY:
All states as defined by Section 103(7) of the
JJDP Act and meeting the requirements of
Section 223 of the Act.

GEOGRAPHIC RESTRICTIONS:
United States and its territories.

FINANCIAL DATA:
Amount of support per award: Varies.
Matching fund requirements: Formula is
based upon population of people under age
18. No match is required except for
construction programs, where the match is
50%. Seven and one half percent
administrative funds are matched 100%.

NUMBER OF APPLICANTS MOST RECENT YEAR:
60.

NUMBER OF AWARDS: 60.

APPLICATION INFORMATION:
Duration: One to three years from the fiscal
year of awards.
Deadline: Varies.

ADDRESS INQUIRIES TO:
Juvenile Justice Clearinghouse
National Criminal Justice
Reference Service
P.O. Box 6000
Rockville, MD 20849-6000
Tel: (800) 851-3420
Fax: (301) 519-5600

U.S. DEPARTMENT OF
JUSTICE   [1506]
OJJDP
810 Seventh Street, N.W.
Washington, DC 20531
(202) 514-4158
Fax: (202) 353-9093

E-MAIL ADDRESS:
patrick.dunckhorst@usdoj.gov

WEB SITE ADDRESS:
www.ojjdp.ncjrs.org
www.tribaljusticeandsafety.gov

AREAS OF INTEREST:
American Indian/Alaska Native juvenile
justice and delinquency prevention.

NAME(S) OF PROGRAMS:
● **Tribal Youth Program**

TYPE:
Demonstration grants; Project/program
grants; Training grants.

YEAR PROGRAM STARTED: 1999

PURPOSE:
To support and enhance tribal efforts for
comprehensive delinquency prevention and
control and for juvenile justice system
improvement for Native American youth; to
improve the quality of life in tribal
communities by addressing the problem of
violent crime among Native American youth.

ELIGIBILITY:
Only tribal governments or federally
recognized tribal organizations with the
endorsement of the tribal government are
eligible.

GEOGRAPHIC RESTRICTIONS:
United States.

FINANCIAL DATA:
Amount of support per award: Varies.
Total amount of support: Approximately
$25,000,000 annually.

APPLICATION INFORMATION:
Duration: Up to five years.

ADDRESS INQUIRIES TO:
Patrick Dunckhorst, Program Manager
(See address above.)

U.S. DEPARTMENT OF JUSTICE   [1507]

Office of Juvenile Justice and
Delinquency Prevention
810 Seventh Street, N.W.
Washington, DC 20531
(202) 307-5911
(202) 514-5655
Fax: (202) 307-2819

E-MAIL ADDRESS:
askjj@ncjrs.gov

WEB SITE ADDRESS:
www.ojjdp.ncjrs.gov
www.ojp.usdoj.gov

FOUNDED: 1974

AREAS OF INTEREST:
Juvenile justice, delinquency prevention and
child protection.

NAME(S) OF PROGRAMS:
● **Enforcing the Underage Drinking Laws
Program**

TYPE:
Block grants; Demonstration grants.

YEAR PROGRAM STARTED: 1998

PURPOSE:
To support and enhance State efforts, in
cooperation with local jurisdictions, to
enforce laws prohibiting the sale of alcoholic
beverages to, or the consumption of alcoholic
beverages by, minors.

LEGAL BASIS:
Government grant program.

ELIGIBILITY:
Agencies designated by the Chief Executive
of the State.

GEOGRAPHIC RESTRICTIONS:
United States and its territories.

FINANCIAL DATA:
Amount of support per award: $350,000.
Total amount of support: Approximately
$25,000,000 annually.

APPLICATION INFORMATION:
Contact the Department of Justice.
Duration: Two years from June 1.

ADDRESS INQUIRIES TO:
Scott Pestridge, Program Manager
Tel: (202) 514-5655
(See address above.)

U.S. DEPARTMENT OF JUSTICE   [1508]

Office of Juvenile Justice and
Delinquency Prevention
810 Seventh Street, N.W.
Washington, DC 20531
(202) 353-8734
Fax: (202) 307-2819

E-MAIL ADDRESS:
thomas.murphy@usdoj.gov

WEB SITE ADDRESS:
www.ojjdp.ncjrs.gov

FOUNDED: 1974

AREAS OF INTEREST:
Accountability-based programs, graduated
sanctions, reentry, drug courts, and judiciary
and prosecutorial staffing and training.

NAME(S) OF PROGRAMS:
● **Juvenile Accountability Block Grants
Program**

TYPE:
Block grants. Grants awarded on a formula
basis. Funds are available for 17 specific
program purpose areas.

YEAR PROGRAM STARTED: 1986

PURPOSE:
To provide states and units of local
government with funds to develop programs
to promote greater accountability in the
juvenile justice system.

LEGAL BASIS:
The Omnibus Safe Streets and Crime Control
Act of 2002.

ELIGIBILITY:
In order to receive JABG funds, the chief
executive officer of the state must designate
the appropriate agency.

GEOGRAPHIC RESTRICTIONS:
United States and its territories.

FINANCIAL DATA:
Amount of support per award: Varies.
Total amount of support: $55,000,000 for the
year 2010.
Matching fund requirements: The state or
local government recipient of a JABG award
must contribute (in the form of a cash match)
10% of the total program cost (other than
costs of construction of permanent
corrections facilities, which require a 50%
match).

NUMBER OF APPLICANTS MOST RECENT YEAR:
55.

NUMBER OF AWARDS: 55.

APPLICATION INFORMATION:
Duration: Three years.

ADDRESS INQUIRIES TO:
Thomas Murphy, State Representative
(See address above.)

Public health

AAA FOUNDATION FOR TRAFFIC SAFETY   [1509]

607 14th Street, N.W.
Suite 201
Washington, DC 20005
(202) 638-5944 ext. 7
Fax: (202) 638-5943

E-MAIL ADDRESS:
jgrabowski@aaafoundation.org

WEB SITE ADDRESS:
www.aaafoundation.org

FOUNDED: 1947

AREAS OF INTEREST:
Traffic safety.

TYPE:
Demonstration grants; Project/program
grants; Research grants; Research contracts.

YEAR PROGRAM STARTED: 1947

PURPOSE:
To save lives and reduce injuries by
preventing traffic crashes; to reduce injuries
when crashes do occur.

LEGAL BASIS:
Publicly supported not-for-profit 501(c)(3).

ELIGIBILITY:
Organizations only.

The Foundation does not fund research to
develop new devices, grants for community
action initiatives or other purely local traffic
safety programs, or projects outside the field
of traffic safety.

GEOGRAPHIC RESTRICTIONS:
Primarily United States and Canada.

FINANCIAL DATA:
Amount of support per award: $5,000 to
$600,000.
Total amount of support: $1,200,000 per
year.
Matching fund requirements: Encourage
co-funding, but not required.

NUMBER OF APPLICANTS MOST RECENT YEAR:
100.

NUMBER OF AWARDS: 5.

APPLICATION INFORMATION:
Contact the Foundation for application
procedures.
Duration: Six months to five years.
Deadline: August 15.

PUBLICATIONS:
Annual report.

IRS IDENTIFICATION NUMBER: 52-0794368

ADDRESS INQUIRIES TO:
Jurek Grabowski, Director of Research
(See address above.)

ABMRF/THE FOUNDATION FOR ALCOHOL RESEARCH   [1510]

1122 Kenilworth Drive
Suite 407
Baltimore, MD 21204-2189
(410) 821-7066
Fax: (410) 821-7065

E-MAIL ADDRESS:
grantinfo@abmrf.org

WEB SITE ADDRESS:
www.abmrf.org

FOUNDED: 1981

AREAS OF INTEREST:
Medical research on alcoholic beverages and
their proper use.

TYPE:
Research grants. Major research interests
include factors influencing transitions in
drinking patterns and behavior, the effects of
moderate use of alcohol on health and
well-being, mechanisms underlying the
behavioral and biomedical effects of alcohol
and biobehavioral/interdisciplinary research
on the etiology of alcohol misuse.

YEAR PROGRAM STARTED: 1982

PURPOSE:
To provide support for scientific studies on
the use, and prevention of misuse, of alcohol.

LEGAL BASIS:
Private foundation.

ELIGIBILITY:
Applicants must be U.S. or Canadian
universities and research institutions.

Nonresearch activities such as education projects, public awareness efforts and treatment or referral services are not eligible for support.

GEOGRAPHIC RESTRICTIONS:
United States and Canada.

FINANCIAL DATA:
Approximately $2,000,000 (U.S.) is available each year to fund newly approved applications and continuation of previously funded projects. Funds may be requested in U.S. or Canadian currency for a period of up to two years. Funding of the second year depends on the availability of funds and satisfactory research progress during the first year.
Amount of support per award: Most annual awards do not exceed $50,000 (U.S.); this includes a maximum of 15% indirect costs.

NUMBER OF APPLICANTS MOST RECENT YEAR:
119.

NUMBER OF AWARDS: 28.

REPRESENTATIVE AWARDS:
Grant Proposals Approved in 2010: $50,000 (for the first of two years) to Eleni Anni, Ph.D., Thomas Jefferson University, "Alcohol regulates self-renewal and differentiation capacity of embryonic stem cells;" $50,000 (for the first of two years) to Beth M. Anderson, Ph.D., Hartford Hospital, "Alcohol cue reactivity as a predictor of future alcohol use disorders;" $50,000 (for the second of two years) to Ludmila Bakhireva, M.D., Ph.D., University of New Mexico, "Traditional and novel biomarkers in identification of moderate prenatal alcohol exposure;" $50,000 (for the second of two years) to Sean Barrett, Ph.D., Dalhousie University, for "The effects of alcohol on the reinforcing and subjective effects of nicotine-containing and denicotinized tobacco in drinkers that smoke."

APPLICATION INFORMATION:
Applicants must submit form with institutional approval.
Duration: One year. Two years if justified.
Deadline: February 1 and September 1.

PUBLICATIONS:
Annual report; application guidelines.

IRS IDENTIFICATION NUMBER: 52-1234277

OFFICERS:
Mack C. Mitchell, Jr., M.D., President

ADDRESS INQUIRIES TO:
Grants Program Administrator
(See address above.)

AGENCY FOR HEALTHCARE RESEARCH AND QUALITY (AHRQ)　[1511]
Office of Communications
and Knowledge Transfer
540 Gaither Road, 2nd Floor
Rockville, MD 20850
(301) 427-1447
Fax: (301) 427-1562

WEB SITE ADDRESS:
www.ahrq.gov

FOUNDED: 1968

AREAS OF INTEREST:
AHRQ is the primary source of federal support for research on problems related to the quality and delivery of health services.

NAME(S) OF PROGRAMS:
● **AHRQ Research Grants**

TYPE:
Conferences/seminars; Development grants; Fellowships; Project/program grants; Research grants; Training grants. Dissertation support highlighting primary care, market forces, cost containment, managed care, the cost of treating AIDS, the improvement of treatment for persons with HIV, rural health care, infant mortality, medical liability, malpractice reform, health care of the aged and disabled and policy studies.

YEAR PROGRAM STARTED: 1969

PURPOSE:
To develop knowledge concerning cost, quality, effectiveness, access and distribution of health services.

LEGAL BASIS:
AHCPR Research Grants: Section 304, 5, 7, 8, of the Public Health Service Act.

ELIGIBILITY:
Any academic institution, agency of a state or local government, nonprofit organization or individual is eligible to submit grant proposals under this program. For-profit entities are not eligible.

FINANCIAL DATA:
Amount of support per award: Varies according to the project type and nature of the individual research proposal.
Total amount of support: Varies.

APPLICATION INFORMATION:
Duration: One to five years.
Deadline: Varies.

STAFF:
Kishna Wadhwani, Scientific Review Division

ADDRESS INQUIRIES TO:
Office of Communications
and Knowledge Transfer
(See address above.)

THE AMERICAN FOUNDATION FOR SUICIDE PREVENTION
120 Wall Street
22nd Floor
New York, NY 10005
(212) 363-3500 ext. 15
Fax: (212) 363-6237

E-MAIL ADDRESS:
lspaulding@afsp.org

WEB SITE ADDRESS:
www.afsp.org

TYPE:
Research grants.

See entry 1620 for full listing.

THE AMERICAN FOUNDATION FOR SUICIDE PREVENTION
120 Wall Street
22nd Floor
New York, NY 10005
(212) 363-3500 ext. 15
Fax: (212) 363-6237

E-MAIL ADDRESS:
lspaulding@afsp.org

WEB SITE ADDRESS:
www.afsp.org

TYPE:
Fellowships; Research grants.

See entry 1621 for full listing.

THE AMERICAN FOUNDATION FOR SUICIDE PREVENTION
120 Wall Street
22nd Floor
New York, NY 10005
(212) 363-3500 ext. 15
Fax: (212) 363-6237

E-MAIL ADDRESS:
lspaulding@afsp.org

WEB SITE ADDRESS:
www.afsp.org

TYPE:
Research grants.

See entry 1622 for full listing.

THE AMERICAN FOUNDATION FOR SUICIDE PREVENTION
120 Wall Street
22nd Floor
New York, NY 10005
(212) 363-3500 ext. 15
Fax: (212) 363-6237

E-MAIL ADDRESS:
lspaulding@afsp.org

WEB SITE ADDRESS:
www.afsp.org

TYPE:
Research grants. Standard Research Grants are awarded to individual investigators. An additional annual stipend is available for mentors on Young Investigator Awards in which the investigator is at the level of Assistant Professor or lower.

See entry 1623 for full listing.

AMERICAN HEALTH ASSISTANCE FOUNDATION　[1512]
22512 Gateway Center Drive
Clarksburg, MD 20871
(301) 948-3244
Fax: (301) 948-4403

E-MAIL ADDRESS:
drg@ahaf.org

WEB SITE ADDRESS:
www.ahaf.org

FOUNDED: 1997

AREAS OF INTEREST:
Macular degeneration.

NAME(S) OF PROGRAMS:
● **Macular Degeneration Research Program**

TYPE:
Research grants.

YEAR PROGRAM STARTED: 1998

PURPOSE:
To fund research on and educate the public about macular degeneration.

LEGAL BASIS:
501(c)(3) nonprofit charitable organization.

ELIGIBILITY:
Grants are awarded on the basis of the proposal's scientific merit and its relevance to understanding the diseases studied. No funds for large equipment, institutional overhead cost, construction or building expenses.

The Foundation is particularly interested in receiving letters from new investigators and from established investigators seeking to explore new directions in macular degeneration research.

FINANCIAL DATA:
Amount of support per award: Up to $50,000 per year.

NUMBER OF APPLICANTS MOST RECENT YEAR:
81.

NUMBER OF AWARDS: 12.

APPLICATION INFORMATION:
Must send initial letter of intent. Subsequent proposal by invitation.
Duration: Up to two years.

PUBLICATIONS:
Annual report; newsletters; clinical brochures.

ADDRESS INQUIRIES TO:
E-mail: researchgrants@ahaf.org

AMERICAN MEDICAL WOMEN'S ASSOCIATION, INC.

100 North 20th Street, 4th Floor
Philadelphia, PA 19103
(215) 320-3716
Fax: (215) 564-2175

E-MAIL ADDRESS:
associatedirector@amwa-doc.org

WEB SITE ADDRESS:
www.amwa-doc.org

TYPE:
Awards/prizes; Conferences/seminars; General operating grants; Project/program grants; Training grants; Travel grants. Support for clinics serving the poor in medically underserved areas, scholarships and loans to qualifying women medical students, and continuing medical education for physicians in areas related to women's health.

See entry 2377 for full listing.

AMERICAN PSYCHOLOGICAL ASSOCIATION

Government Relations Office
Public Interest Directorate
750 First Street, N.E.
Washington, DC 20002-4242
(202) 336-6104
Fax: (202) 336-6063

E-MAIL ADDRESS:
delmore@apa.org

WEB SITE ADDRESS:
www.apa.org/about/gr/fellows

TYPE:
Fellowships. Program provides trained scientists and practitioners an opportunity for enhanced understanding of and involvement in the federal policy-making process by serving as Congressional staff in Washington, DC.

See entry 2726 for full listing.

AMERICAN SOCIETY FOR HEALTHCARE RISK MANAGEMENT [1513]

155 North Wacker Drive
Suite 400
Chicago, IL 60606
(312) 422-3980
Fax: (312) 422-4580

E-MAIL ADDRESS:
kclark@aha.org

WEB SITE ADDRESS:
www.ashrm.org

FOUNDED: 2004

AREAS OF INTEREST:
Health care risk management.

TYPE:
Awards/prizes; Conferences/seminars; Development grants; Fellowships; Project/program grants; Research grants; Scholarships; Training grants. Education grants.

YEAR PROGRAM STARTED: 2004

PURPOSE:
To help facilitate the advancement of the health care risk management profession by funding education, research and scholarship programs; to promote professional development of hospital risk managers; to provide educational resources and programs on health care risk management; to address risk management issues affecting the health care industry; to foster research and innovation among professionals and graduate students; to identify and reward exemplary writing in the *Journal of Healthcare Risk Management* and encourage other members to write in it.

ELIGIBILITY:
Open to individual professionals in risk management or a related field, as well as graduate students in health care risk management, health law, or health administration programs that wish to develop original research studies that enhance the profession of health care risk management. Must be original work related to health care risk management research and innovation for consideration.

FINANCIAL DATA:
Since inception, the Society has awarded more than $90,000.
Amount of support per award: Education Grants $1,000; Scholarship Grants $2,500; Research Grants $10,000.

APPLICATION INFORMATION:
Deadline: Education and Scholarship Grants: April 2, June 4 and August 6. Research Grants: February, June and September.

ADDRESS INQUIRIES TO:
Kara Clark, Executive Director
(See address above.)

ANDALUSIA HEALTH SERVICES, INC. [1514]

P.O. Box 56
Andalusia, AL 36420-1200
(334) 488-5990

E-MAIL ADDRESS:
healthservices@andycable.com

AREAS OF INTEREST:
Health care.

NAME(S) OF PROGRAMS:
● **Emergency Medicine (Basic and Paramedic)**
● **Lab Technician**
● **Medicine**
● **Nursing (Practitioner, Registered, Licensed Practical)**
● **Physical Therapy**
● **Physical Therapy Assistant**
● **Radiology Tech/Imaging**
● **Speech Pathology (Master's)**
● **Surgical Technology**

TYPE:
Scholarships.

PURPOSE:
To improve the health care in the local area.

LEGAL BASIS:
Private foundation.

ELIGIBILITY:
Eligible organizations must be IRS 501(c)(3) tax-exempt and serve the residents of Covington County, Alabama. To apply, person must be a resident of and must intend to work in Covington County, Alabama.

GEOGRAPHIC RESTRICTIONS:
Covington County, Alabama.

FINANCIAL DATA:
Amount of support per award: $1,500 to $13,125.

NUMBER OF AWARDS: 25.

APPLICATION INFORMATION:
Applications are available from the organization.
Deadline: March 31.

ADDRESS INQUIRIES TO:
Gwen Ryland, Scholarship Coordinator
(See address above.)

ARCHSTONE FOUNDATION [1515]

401 East Ocean Boulevard
Suite 1000
Long Beach, CA 90802
(562) 590-8655
Fax: (562) 495-0317

E-MAIL ADDRESS:
archstone@archstone.org

WEB SITE ADDRESS:
www.archstone.org

FOUNDED: 1985

AREAS OF INTEREST:
Health and aging.

TYPE:
Demonstration grants; Development grants; Project/program grants.

YEAR PROGRAM STARTED: 1985

PURPOSE:
To contribute toward the preparation of the society in meeting the needs of an aging population.

ELIGIBILITY:
501(c)(3) organizations. Individuals may not apply. No funding available for capital expenditures, fundraisers, research or general operating funds.

GEOGRAPHIC RESTRICTIONS:
Southern California.

FINANCIAL DATA:
Limited indirect costs to 10%.
Amount of support per award: $15,000 to $400,000.
Total amount of support: $5,000,000.

NUMBER OF APPLICANTS MOST RECENT YEAR:
120.

NUMBER OF AWARDS: 13 for fiscal year ended June 30, 2009.

APPLICATION INFORMATION:
Application forms and reporting guidelines are available on the Foundation's web site.

Duration: One year. May be renewed for up to three years.

IRS IDENTIFICATION NUMBER: 33-0133359

BOARD OF DIRECTORS:
Robert C. Maxson, Chairman
Joseph F. Prevratil, President and Chief Executive Officer
Diana M. Bonta, Dr.PH, R.N.
Lynn Daucher
Amye L. Leong, MBA
Renee B. Simon
Mark D. Smith, M.D.
Rocky Suares, C.F.P.
Peter C. Szutu, M.P.H.

ADDRESS INQUIRIES TO:
E. Thomas Brewer
Director of Programs
(See address above.)

MAX BELL FOUNDATION   [1516]
1201 5th Street, S.W.
Suite 380
Calgary AB T2R 0Y6 Canada
(403) 215-7310
Fax: (403) 215-7319

E-MAIL ADDRESS:
northcotta@maxbell.org

WEB SITE ADDRESS:
www.maxbell.org

FOUNDED: 1972

AREAS OF INTEREST:
Health, education and environment.

TYPE:
Challenge/matching grants; Development grants; Internships; Project/program grants.

YEAR PROGRAM STARTED: 1972

PURPOSE:
To develop innovative ideas that impact public policies and practices.

LEGAL BASIS:
Private foundation.

ELIGIBILITY:
Organizations must have a registered Canadian charitable number issued by Revenue Canada. Grants are not made for conferences and workshops, scholarships, individuals, sabbaticals, equipment purchases, capital campaigns, fund-raising drives or annual charitable appeals.

GEOGRAPHIC RESTRICTIONS:
Canada.

FINANCIAL DATA:
Amount of support per award: Varies.
Total amount of support: Approximately $1,800,000.
Matching fund requirements: Varies.

APPLICATION INFORMATION:
For Internship Grants: Interested applicants should initiate the process by outlining:
(1) tentative details, including objectives, intended output/deliverables, and summary work plan showing activities and outputs by month;
(2) process by which applicant would search for and hire an intern and;
(3) budget with line items for intern stipend, administration/overhead and mentoring/supervision.

This information should be forwarded by post or fax to Allan Northcott, Senior Program Officer.

Applicants for Project/Program Grants should submit a letter of intent to Alida White, Office Administrator.
Duration: One to three years. Nonrenewable.

OFFICERS:
Dr. David Elton, President
Alida White, Secretary and Treasurer

STAFF:
Alida White, Office Administrator
Allan Northcott, Senior Program Officer
Ralph Strother, Senior Program Officer

BOARD OF DIRECTORS:
Carolyn Hursh, Chairman
Ken Marra, Vice Chairman
Tom D'Aquino
Brenda Eaton
Jim Gray
Carol Hill
Dr. Morton Mendelson

ADDRESS INQUIRIES TO:
Allan Northcott, Senior Program Officer
(See address above.)

BRIGHAM AND WOMEN'S HOSPITAL   [1517]
75 Francis Street
Boston, MA 02115
(617) 732-8422
Fax: (617) 582-6112

WEB SITE ADDRESS:
www.brighamandwomens.org/delandfellowship

AREAS OF INTEREST:
Health care.

NAME(S) OF PROGRAMS:
● **Deland Fellowship Program in Health Care and Society**

TYPE:
Fellowships.

PURPOSE:
To train outstanding future leaders in health care.

ELIGIBILITY:
It is anticipated that candidates will come from a variety of careers and educational backgrounds including business, law, economics, public policy and medicine. Candidates are required to have an advanced degree.

FINANCIAL DATA:
Amount of support per award: Stipends are commensurate with the seniority and prior educational experience of the appointees.

NUMBER OF APPLICANTS MOST RECENT YEAR:
69 for the year 2009.

NUMBER OF AWARDS: 2 for the year 2009.

APPLICATION INFORMATION:
Complete applications must be submitted electronically to bwhdeland@partners.org by the deadline and must include the following items:
(1) completed application form;
(2) copy of curriculum vitae;
(3) list of individuals to provide references and;
(4) candidates statement (application provides additional information).
Duration: One year.
Deadline: First Monday in November. Notification in January.

ADDRESS INQUIRIES TO:
Trishia Lichauco, Administrative Director
(See address above.)

THE CALIFORNIA ENDOWMENT   [1518]
1000 North Alameda Street
Los Angeles, CA 90012
(213) 928-8645
(800) 449-4149
Fax: (213) 928-8818

E-MAIL ADDRESS:
destrada@calendow.org

WEB SITE ADDRESS:
www.calendow.org

FOUNDED: 1996

AREAS OF INTEREST:
Health care access, disparities in health, public health, multicultural health, health and well-being, cultural competency and work force diversity.

NAME(S) OF PROGRAMS:
● **Building Healthy Communities Initiative**

TYPE:
Challenge/matching grants; Conferences/seminars; General operating grants; Project/program grants; Technical assistance.

YEAR PROGRAM STARTED: 1998

PURPOSE:
To improve access to affordable, quality health care for underserved individuals and communities; to promote fundamental improvements in the health status of the people of California; to improve the health of Californians through community-based programs, collaborations and partnerships that strengthen leadership, stimulate policy development and contribute to systems change.

ELIGIBILITY:
Grants are awarded to tax-exempt organizations only. No grants to individuals.

GEOGRAPHIC RESTRICTIONS:
California.

FINANCIAL DATA:
Amount of support per award: Varies.
Total amount of support: $165,825,874 for the year ended February 28, 2009.

NUMBER OF APPLICANTS MOST RECENT YEAR:
981 for the year ended March 2010.

NUMBER OF AWARDS: 877 for the year ended March 2010.

APPLICATION INFORMATION:
The Grant Application Guide, located online, serves as the single-point-of-entry to all of the Endowment's funding.

IRS IDENTIFICATION NUMBER: 95-4523232

CALIFORNIA HEALTHCARE FOUNDATION   [1519]
1438 Webster Street
Suite 400
Oakland, CA 94612
(510) 238-1040
Fax: (510) 238-1388

E-MAIL ADDRESS:
info@chcf.org

WEB SITE ADDRESS:
www.chcf.org

FOUNDED: 1996

AREAS OF INTEREST:
Better chronic disease care, market and policy monitor innovations for the underserved.

TYPE:
Project/program grants; Research grants.

PURPOSE:
To commission research and analysis; to publish and disseminate information; to convene stakeholders and fund development of programs and models aimed at improving the health care delivery and financing systems.

GEOGRAPHIC RESTRICTIONS:
California.

FINANCIAL DATA:
Amount of support per award: Varies.
Total amount of support: Varies.

APPLICATION INFORMATION:
Many projects are solicited through RFP process. Letters of inquiry are preferred for unsolicited projects with description, timeline and estimated budget.
Duration: Varies.

ADDRESS INQUIRIES TO:
Lisa Kang
Director, Grants Administration
(See address above.)

THE CALIFORNIA WELLNESS FOUNDATION   [1520]

6320 Canoga Avenue
Suite 1700
Woodland Hills, CA 91367-7111
(818) 702-1900
Fax: (818) 702-1999

WEB SITE ADDRESS:
www.tcwf.org

FOUNDED: 1991

AREAS OF INTEREST:
Diversity in the health professions, environmental health, healthy aging, mental health, teenage pregnancy prevention, violence prevention, women's health, and work and health.

TYPE:
Conferences/seminars; Demonstration grants; General operating grants; Project/program grants; Seed money grants. The Foundation makes grants within the scope of its eight health issues (above), plus in the category of special projects.

YEAR PROGRAM STARTED: 1992

PURPOSE:
To improve the health of the people of California by making grants for health promotion, wellness education and disease prevention.

LEGAL BASIS:
Private foundation.

ELIGIBILITY:
Applicants must be nonprofit organizations that are exempt under Section 501(c)(3) of the IRS and are defined as "not a private foundation" under Section 509(a)(1). The Foundation also funds government agencies.

The Foundation does not fund Section 509(a)(3) Type III non-functionally integrated supporting organizations and does not provide international funding or fund organizations located outside of the U.S. Grants are not made for annual fund drives,

building campaigns, major equipment, biomedical research or to activities that exclusively benefit members of sectarian or religious organizations.

GEOGRAPHIC RESTRICTIONS:
California.

FINANCIAL DATA:
Amount of support per award: Varies depending on needs and nature of the request.
Total amount of support: $50,062,305 for the year 2009.

NUMBER OF APPLICANTS MOST RECENT YEAR:
1,554 for the year 2009.

NUMBER OF AWARDS: 410 for the year 2009.

APPLICATION INFORMATION:
Application process begins with a succinct, two-page maximum letter of interest including a summary of the proposed program, its objectives and anticipated outcomes, its leadership, the organization(s) involved, region to be served, the project duration and the funds requested. Inquiries will be reviewed by the Foundation staff. Eligible organizations with programs that are consistent with current priorities and most closely meet the Foundation's selection criteria will be invited to submit a proposal. Review of the initial materials may require additional information, a meeting or a site visit. Applicants will be notified of the results of the initial review normally within three months. Those encouraged to submit a proposal will receive guidance as to what information is required and how best to present it.
Duration: Varies.

PUBLICATIONS:
Annual report; brochure; quarterly newsletter.

IRS IDENTIFICATION NUMBER: 95-4292101

STAFF:
Cristina M. Regalado, Vice President of Programs
Fatima Angeles, Director of Evaluation and Organizational Learning
Amy B. Scop, Director of Grants Management
Saba S. Brelvi, Program Director
Jeffrey Seungkyu Kim, Program Director
Frank A. Lalle, Program Director
Earl Lui, Program Director
Julio Marcial, Program Director
Sandra J. Martinez, Program Director

BOARD OF DIRECTORS:
Elizabeth M. Gomez, Chairperson
David S. Barlow, Vice Chairperson
Gary L. Yates, President and Chief Executive Officer
M. Isabel Becerra
Elisabeth Hallman, R.N.
Barbara C. Staggers, M.D.
Eugene Washington, M.D.

ADMINISTRATIVE STAFF:
Margaret W. Minnich, Vice President of Administration and Finance
Magdalena Beltran-del Olmo, Vice President of Communications
Bruce Minnich, Director of Information Systems

EXECUTIVE STAFF:
Gary L. Yates, President and Chief Executive Officer
Peggy E. Graham, Senior Executive Assistant

ADDRESS INQUIRIES TO:
Amy B. Scop
Director of Grants Management
(See address above.)

CENTER FOR SCIENCE IN THE PUBLIC INTEREST

1220 L Street, N.W.
Suite 300
Washington, DC 20005
(202) 332-9110
Fax: (202) 265-4954

E-MAIL ADDRESS:
coday@cspinet.org

WEB SITE ADDRESS:
www.cspinet.org

TYPE:
Internships. Stipends allow interns to work on specific projects under the direction of a Project Director or the Executive Director.

See entry 2838 for full listing.

CENTERS FOR MEDICARE & MEDICAID SERVICES   [1521]

C2-21-15 Central Building
7500 Security Boulevard
Baltimore, MD 21244
(410) 786-3000
Fax: (410) 786-9088

WEB SITE ADDRESS:
www.cms.gov

FOUNDED: 1977

AREAS OF INTEREST:
Health care research.

NAME(S) OF PROGRAMS:
- **Hispanic Health Services Research**
- **Historically Black Colleges and Universities**
- **Real Choice Systems Changes**
- **State Health Insurance Assistance Program**
- **Ticket to Work**

TYPE:
Demonstration grants; Project/program grants; Research grants; Seed money grants; Research contracts.

PURPOSE:
To assist in the resolution of major health financing issues, particularly as they affect the Medicare and Medicaid programs and beneficiaries.

LEGAL BASIS:
Government agency.

FINANCIAL DATA:
Amount of support per award: $100,000 to $3,000,000.
Matching fund requirements: Section 1110 SSA.

NUMBER OF APPLICANTS MOST RECENT YEAR:
308.

NUMBER OF AWARDS: 293.

APPLICATION INFORMATION:
Duration: One to three years.
Deadline: Varies by program.

ADDRESS INQUIRIES TO:
Bill Tate, Grants Management Officer
(See address above.)

CHICAGO BOARD OF TRADE FOUNDATION [1522]
20 South Wacker Drive
Chicago, IL 60606
(312) 435-3609
Fax: (312) 341-3392

E-MAIL ADDRESS:
ellen.paparelli@cmegroup.com

WEB SITE ADDRESS:
www.cmegroup.
com/company/foundations/cbot-foundation.html

AREAS OF INTEREST:
Hospitals, handicapped, arts, education, youth and wildlife.

TYPE:
General operating grants; Project/program grants.

PURPOSE:
To support health care, education, arts and culture.

ELIGIBILITY:
Organizations classified as 501(c)(3) by the IRS can apply. Individuals and religious organizations are ineligible. Must be nondiscriminatory in its practices and may not give funds to ancillary organizations.

GEOGRAPHIC RESTRICTIONS:
Greater Chicago, Illinois metropolitan area.

FINANCIAL DATA:
Amount of support per award: $1,000 to $20,000.

APPLICATION INFORMATION:
Applicant must submit copy of proposal, 501(c)(3), (4) or (10) documentation, and a recent financial statement.
Duration: One year. Grants are renewable.

ADDRESS INQUIRIES TO:
Ellen Paparelli, Foundation Administrator
(See address above.)

THE COLORADO TRUST [1523]
1600 Sherman Street
Denver, CO 80203-1604
(303) 837-1200
(888) 847-9140
Fax: (303) 839-9034

E-MAIL ADDRESS:
christie@coloradotrust.org

WEB SITE ADDRESS:
www.coloradotrust.org

FOUNDED: 1985

AREAS OF INTEREST:
Access to health for all Coloradans by supporting policies, programs and services that expand health coverage, and improve and expand health care.

TYPE:
General operating grants; Project/program grants; Research grants; Technical assistance.

YEAR PROGRAM STARTED: 1985

PURPOSE:
To advance the health and well-being of the people of Colorado.

LEGAL BASIS:
Private foundation.

GEOGRAPHIC RESTRICTIONS:
Colorado.

FINANCIAL DATA:
Amount of support per award: Varies.

Total amount of support: Approximately $21,000,000 (unaudited) in total grantmaking for the year 2010.

COOPERATIVE FUNDING PROGRAMS: Building Public Will to Achieve Access to Health is a three-year, multifaceted effort intended to help build the necessary awareness, understanding, support and demand for the kind of policy and system changes that will help to achieve access to health for all Coloradans. Co-funded with Colorado Health Foundation.

REPRESENTATIVE AWARDS:
Grants of approximately $400,000 each to 14 grantee partners over a three-year period to conduct a variety of communications, advocacy, network-building, leadership development and media activities to help build public will to achieve access to health.

APPLICATION INFORMATION:
Applications are accepted following the release of Requests for Proposals issued by The Colorado Trust. Application requirements are detailed specifically in Requests for Proposals.
Duration: Varies.

PUBLICATIONS:
Annual report; community connections blog; evaluation reports; program reports.

IRS IDENTIFICATION NUMBER: 84-0994055

BOARD OF TRUSTEES:
Ned Calonge, M.D., President and Chief Executive Officer
Patricia Baca, Ed.D.
Ned Calonge, M.D.
John P. Hopkins
Jennifer Paquette, C.F.A.
Rev. R. J. Ross
Gail Schoettler, Ph.D.
Colleen Schwarz, M.B.A.
Alan Synn, M.D.
Reginald Washington, M.D.
William Wright, M.D.

ADDRESS INQUIRIES TO:
Christie McElhinney, Vice President of Communications and Public Affairs
(See e-mail and address above.)

COMMUNITY MEMORIAL FOUNDATION [1524]
15 Spinning Wheel Road, Suite 326
Hinsdale, IL 60521
(630) 654-4729
Fax: (630) 654-3402

E-MAIL ADDRESS:
info@cmfdn.org

WEB SITE ADDRESS:
www.cmfdn.org

FOUNDED: 1995

AREAS OF INTEREST:
Community services, health, youth, older adults and families.

TYPE:
Challenge/matching grants; Project/program grants; Technical assistance.

PURPOSE:
To improve the health of people who live and work in 27 west suburban Chicago communities.

ELIGIBILITY:
Eligible organizations must be IRS 501(c)(3) tax-exempt. No grants are made to individuals. The Foundation focuses on

communities in Illinois, such as: Argo, Bridgeview, Broadview, Brookfield, Burr Ridge, Clarendon Hills, Countryside, Darien, Downers Grove, Hickory Hills, Hinsdale, Hodgkins, Indian Head Park, Justice, La Grange, La Grange Park, Lyons, McCook, North Riverside, Oak Brook, Riverside, Stickney, Summit, Westchester, Western Springs, Westmont, Willow Springs and Willowbrook.

GEOGRAPHIC RESTRICTIONS:
Illinois.

FINANCIAL DATA:
Amount of support per award: Varies.
Total amount of support: $4,000,000 annually.

APPLICATION INFORMATION:
Applications must include a copy of the IRS tax determination letter.
Deadline: March 31 and September 30.

PUBLICATIONS:
Annual report; funding guidelines; Community Needs and Assets Assessment.

STAFF:
Greg DiDomenico, Vice President
Thomas Fuechtmann, Program Officer
Nanette Silva, Program Officer
Deborah Kustra, Grants Manager

ADDRESS INQUIRIES TO:
Deborah Kustra, Grants Manager
(See address above.)

CONGRESSIONAL BLACK CAUCUS FOUNDATION, INC.
1720 Massachusetts Avenue, N.W.
Washington, DC 20036
(202) 263-2800
Fax: (202) 775-0773

E-MAIL ADDRESS:
info@cbcfinc.org

WEB SITE ADDRESS:
www.cbcfinc.org

TYPE:
Fellowships. This Fellowship is designed around three components: public policy training, educational enrichment and leadership development.

The centerpiece of the public policy training component is a 20-month Congressional office/committee placement. Fellows are assigned to the office of CBC Members who sit on the House Committee on Energy and Commerce for a period of two months at the beginning of the Fellowship year. This initial placement is designed to allow the Fellows to acclimate to the Congressional work environment and obtain a general understanding of the legislative process and minority health policy issues. Following the office placement, Fellows are assigned to the House Committee on Energy and Commerce where they stay for the remainder of the program. Fellows work 40 hours per week on a range of staff assignments, including conducting research and analysis, drafting legislation, and coordinating logistics and public testimony for Congressional hearings. Additionally, Fellows are required to write a public policy research paper, legislative briefing paper, and op-ed article on a matter of mutual interest to themselves and the Member for whom they work.

During the fall and summer recesses, Fellows leave Capitol Hill to conduct site visits at national public and private health-related organizations. The site visits are designed to expose Fellows to the inner workings of the institutions that influence Congress during the policymaking process and/or execute the will of Congress. These site visits will last for one week each.

Fellows also participate in a rigorous educational program centered around monthly seminars on policy and politics. These seminars explore topics such as African Americans'relationship with the two major parties, the history of the CBC, and relevant policy issues. The seminars are supplemented by a series of lectures and briefings by Members of the CBC and other Congressional leaders, federal government officials, and public policy experts.

Participants in the Fellowship must reside in or relocate to the Washington, DC metropolitan area. Fellows receive health and dental insurance and are responsible for all relocation, housing and transportation costs.

See entry 1090 for full listing.

THE CULLEN TRUST FOR HEALTH CARE [1525]

601 Jefferson, Suite 4000
Houston, TX 77002
(713) 651-8860
Fax: (713) 651-8993

E-MAIL ADDRESS:
julie@werinterests.com

FOUNDED: 1978

AREAS OF INTEREST:
Health care.

TYPE:
Capital grants; Development grants; Endowments; General operating grants; Project/program grants. Clinical-based research grants.

YEAR PROGRAM STARTED: 1978

PURPOSE:
To provide financial assistance and to benefit institutions providing health care.

LEGAL BASIS:
Charitable trust.

ELIGIBILITY:
Applicants must be tax-exempt 501(c)(3).

GEOGRAPHIC RESTRICTIONS:
Primarily Houston, Texas area.

FINANCIAL DATA:
Amount of support per award: Average $50,000.
Total amount of support: Varies.

APPLICATION INFORMATION:
Applicants must submit the following (in duplicate):
(1) purpose and scope of the grant;
(2) amount of the grant request;
(3) other sources of funding received or anticipated;
(4) list of trustees, directors and staff;
(5) financial statements and tax returns of last two years and;
(6) anticipated budget.

If the grant is for building construction or purchase of real estate, the applicant must submit an architectural drawing or photograph of the property, a detailed description and cost estimate. Evidence is required from the IRS to prove the applicant organization is a tax-exempt public charity. If request is for multiyear funding, applicant must specify.

Duration: One to five years.
Deadline: February 1 and September 1.

ADDRESS INQUIRIES TO:
Julie Mitchell, Executive Administrator
(See address above.)

RAY EDWARDS MEMORIAL TRUST [1526]

U.S. Bank Charitable Services Group
800 Nicollet Mall, BC-MN-H16A
Minneapolis, MN 55402
(612) 303-4513
Fax: (612) 303-3219
sarah.godfrey@usbank.com

FOUNDED: 1961

AREAS OF INTEREST:
Hospital-based health care delivery, direct health care services to indigent.

TYPE:
Capital grants; General operating grants; Project/program grants.

YEAR PROGRAM STARTED: 1961

PURPOSE:
To provide hospital-based health care services for those who are in greatest financial need and are enduring or experiencing serious illnesses.

LEGAL BASIS:
Private foundation.

ELIGIBILITY:
Eligible organizations must be IRS 501(c)(3) tax-exempt.

GEOGRAPHIC RESTRICTIONS:
Greater St. Paul, Minnesota and the metropolitan area to the east.

FINANCIAL DATA:
Amount of support per award: $5,000 to $150,000.
Total amount of support: Up to $845,000 annually.

NUMBER OF APPLICANTS MOST RECENT YEAR:
Approximately 200.

NUMBER OF AWARDS: 15 to 25.

REPRESENTATIVE AWARDS:
$30,000 ($15,000 per year for two years) to Children's Hospitals and Clinics.

APPLICATION INFORMATION:
Applications must include four copies of the following:
(1) one-page cover letter signed by Chief Executive Officer or Board Chair;
(2) Minnesota Common Grant Application (cover page only);
(3) audited financial statement from most recent fiscal year;
(4) IRS tax-exempt determination letter;
(5) Board of Directors listing and;
(6) report describing use and impact of any recent grants from the Trust.

The Foundation does not accept letters of inquiry.
Deadline: May 1.

PUBLICATIONS:
Application guidelines.

FIRST CANDLE/SIDS ALLIANCE

1314 Bedford Avenue
Suite 210
Baltimore, MD 21208
(410) 653-8226
(800) 221-7437
Fax: (410) 653-8709

E-MAIL ADDRESS:
info@firstcandle.org

WEB SITE ADDRESS:
www.firstcandle.org

TYPE:
Conferences/seminars; Research grants. Professional medical research for SIDS, stillbirths and related issues.

See entry 2690 for full listing.

THE FOUNDATION FOR SPIRITUALITY AND MEDICINE [1527]

13500 Fork Road
Baldwin, MD 21013
(410) 592-3583
Fax: (410) 592-3583 (Call ahead)

E-MAIL ADDRESS:
smdcdaneker@comcast.net

WEB SITE ADDRESS:
www.foundationspiritmed.org

FOUNDED: 1981

AREAS OF INTEREST:
Health, health education and spirituality.

TYPE:
Challenge/matching grants; Conferences/seminars; Demonstration grants; Development grants; General operating grants; Project/program grants; Research grants; Seed money grants; Training grants.

YEAR PROGRAM STARTED: 1995

PURPOSE:
To promote the integration of spirituality into health care.

ELIGIBILITY:
Grants are given to any nonprofit organization whose mission is the training of professionals in the healing arts, the delivery of health care, or the provision of spiritual services. Preference may be given to applicants who demonstrate matching funds by their organization or from other sources.

GEOGRAPHIC RESTRICTIONS:
Primarily Maryland.

FINANCIAL DATA:
Net worth as of December 31, 2010: $1,741,000.
Amount of support per award: Maximum $25,000 per year.
Total amount of support: $50,000.

NUMBER OF APPLICANTS MOST RECENT YEAR: 8 for the year 2010.

NUMBER OF AWARDS: 9 for the year 2010.

APPLICATION INFORMATION:
Applications must be no more than 10 pages in length (double-spaced) and should include the following:
(1) description and history of the project;
(2) description of organization and personnel;
(3) rationale for proposed project;
(4) goals and objectives of the project;
(5) short-term and long-term benefits expected from the project;
(6) plans for a continuation of the project;
(7) timetable and;
(8) budget.

Grantees must meet Foundation requirements for regular financial and project reporting, and submit an annual and final written report. An oral presentation to the board of directors of the Foundation may be requested as part of the application process and/or as part of the report.

Submit applications in triplicate if possible.

Duration: Two years.

Deadline: January 15 and July 15. Announcements April 1 and October 1.

PUBLICATIONS:
Form 990-PF; brochure.

IRS IDENTIFICATION NUMBER: 52-1238713

ADDRESS INQUIRIES TO:
David C. Daneker, Chairman
(See address above.)

THE FOUNDATION OF THE AMERICAN COLLEGE OF HEALTHCARE EXECUTIVES [1528]

One North Franklin Street
Suite 1700
Chicago, IL 60606-3529
(312) 424-9400
Fax: (312) 424-9405

E-MAIL ADDRESS:
contact@ache.org

WEB SITE ADDRESS:
www.ache.org

FOUNDED: 1933

AREAS OF INTEREST:
Healthcare management.

NAME(S) OF PROGRAMS:
- **Albert W. Dent Graduate Student Scholarship**
- **Foster G. McGaw Graduate Student Scholarship**

TYPE:
Scholarships. Offered annually, the Albert W. Dent and the Foster G. McGaw Graduate Student Scholarships are designated for students enrolled in their final year of classroom work in a health care management graduate program.

Albert W. Dent Graduate Student Scholarship is only available to minority students.

YEAR PROGRAM STARTED: 1969

PURPOSE:
To provide financial aid, increase the enrollment in health care management graduate programs and to encourage students to obtain positions in the middle and upper levels of health care management.

ELIGIBILITY:
An applicant must:
(1) be a Student Associate in good standing in ACHE;
(2) be a full-time student entering the final year of classroom work in a health care management graduate program;
(3) be able to demonstrate financial need;
(4) be a U.S. or Canadian citizen;
(5) have not been a previous recipient of the scholarship and;
(6) be a minority if applying for the Albert W. Dent Graduate Student Scholarship.

GEOGRAPHIC RESTRICTIONS:
United States and Canada.

FINANCIAL DATA:
Amount of support per award: $5,000.
Total amount of support: Varies.

COOPERATIVE FUNDING PROGRAMS: The initial gift for the McGaw Student Scholarship was from the Foster G. McGaw Charitable Fund.

Additional gifts were made by Mr. McGaw from his personal funds before his death in 1986.

NUMBER OF APPLICANTS MOST RECENT YEAR:
75 to 100.

NUMBER OF AWARDS: 15 to 20 scholarships awarded per year.

APPLICATION INFORMATION:
Applications can be downloaded from the web site, under the "Faculty and Students" section.

Duration: One year. Renewal by reapplication.

Deadline: March 31.

ADDRESS INQUIRIES TO:
Scholarship Committee
Division of Membership
(See address above.)

THE DAVID GEFFEN FOUNDATION [1529]

12011 San Vicente Boulevard
Suite 606
Los Angeles, CA 90049
(310) 581-5955
Fax: (310) 581-5949

E-MAIL ADDRESS:
ddishman@geffenco.com

FOUNDED: 1986

AREAS OF INTEREST:
AIDS/HIV, civil liberties, health and health care, the arts and issues of concern to the Jewish community.

TYPE:
Capital grants; General operating grants; Project/program grants.

PURPOSE:
To support the arts, health care, issues of concern to the Jewish community, HIV/AIDS and civil liberties.

LEGAL BASIS:
Private foundation.

ELIGIBILITY:
Applicants must be 501(c)(3) organizations. No grants for documentaries, audio-visual programming or publications. No grants to individuals.

GEOGRAPHIC RESTRICTIONS:
Primarily New York City and Los Angeles, California.

FINANCIAL DATA:
Amount of support per award: Varies depending on needs and nature of the request.

APPLICATION INFORMATION:
No application form. Proposals should include summary and description of the project or program, background information of the organization, description of key staff, list of Board of Directors, IRS letter confirming tax-exempt status and financial information including annual operating and project budgets. Applicants should not send videotapes or additional materials unless otherwise requested.

Duration: One-time grant and multiyear support. Renewal possible.

Deadline: Applications accepted throughout the year. Each request may take up to three months to evaluate.

PUBLICATIONS:
Application guidelines.

IRS IDENTIFICATION NUMBER: 95-4085811

STAFF:
J. Dallas Dishman, Ph.D., Executive Director

ADDRESS INQUIRIES TO:
J. Dallas Dishman, Ph.D., Executive Director
(See address above.)

GLAXOSMITHKLINE [1530]

5 Moore Drive
Research Triangle Park, NC 27709
(919) 483-2719

E-MAIL ADDRESS:
community.partnership@gsk.com

WEB SITE ADDRESS:
www.gsk.com

AREAS OF INTEREST:
Health care practice and education, mental health and welfare and science education.

TYPE:
Project/program grants.

PURPOSE:
To support health-related organizations working to improve health care practices and education; to promote the physical welfare of the disadvantaged, minorities, disabled persons, women and the aged; to promote interest and experience in science.

LEGAL BASIS:
Corporate foundation.

ELIGIBILITY:
Applicants must be nonprofit organizations with proposals consistent with guidelines and interest areas. No grants for capital projects, operating expenses, multiyear grants, conferences, symposia, publications, fund-raising events, lobbying to influence legislation, religious organizations, sporting events, universities, free-standing research centers, scholar aid, expeditions or individuals.

GEOGRAPHIC RESTRICTIONS:
United States.

FINANCIAL DATA:
Amount of support per award: Varies depending on needs and nature of the request.

APPLICATION INFORMATION:
Applications must include a brief summary of the organization and the proposed project, amount requested, relevant interest area and reasoning for proposal and contact name, telephone number and fax number if available. If GlaxoSmithKline is interested in the project, the applicant will be contacted to request a formal proposal. All applications will be acknowledged.

Duration: One year. Multiyear requests are not funded.

Deadline: Applications accepted throughout the year.

ADDRESS INQUIRIES TO:
Bill Shore, Director or
Dawn Winters
Community Partnership
(See address above.)

HCR MANOR CARE FOUNDATION [1531]

333 North Summit Street
Toledo, OH 43604
(419) 252-5989
Fax: (419) 252-5521

E-MAIL ADDRESS:
foundation@hcr-manorcare.com

WEB SITE ADDRESS:
www.hcr-manorcare.org

FOUNDED: 1997

AREAS OF INTEREST:
Community service and outreach, hospice-related programs, research and public education for diseases and disorders that affect the elderly, those requiring post-acute services and those requiring hospice or end-of-life care.

TYPE:
Challenge/matching grants; Project/program grants.

YEAR PROGRAM STARTED: 1997

PURPOSE:
To support organizations involved in research and public education about diseases and disorders affecting the elderly, and organizations which provide community service and outreach to such individuals; to provide support to programs addressing end-of-life care; to provide support for hospice and palliative like-related programs.

LEGAL BASIS:
Corporate foundation.

ELIGIBILITY:
Preference is given to organizations in states where HCR Manor Care Corporation has strategic operations. Organizations must be IRS 501(c)(3) tax-exempt and have one other source of support.

HCR Manor Care will not fund advertising or fund-raising events, individuals, for-profit organizations, building or capital campaigns, endowments, organizations with primary service areas in non-HCR Manor Care states, multiyear commitments, research projects with overhead fees in excess of 10% or organizations that have applied for funding within the last 12 months.

GEOGRAPHIC RESTRICTIONS:
United States.

FINANCIAL DATA:
Amount of support per award: $2,000 to $10,000 average.
Total amount of support: $100,000 for the year 2007-08.

NUMBER OF APPLICANTS MOST RECENT YEAR:
300.

NUMBER OF AWARDS: 150.

APPLICATION INFORMATION:
The Foundation does not accept unsolicited applications, and grants are only given through HCR Manor Care Corporation locations.
Duration: One year.

IRS IDENTIFICATION NUMBER: 52-2031975

ADDRESS INQUIRIES TO:
Bill White, Executive Director
(See address above.)

HEALTH EFFECTS INSTITUTE (HEI)   [1532]
101 Federal Street
Suite 500
Boston, MA 02110-1817
(617) 488-2338
Fax: (617) 488-2335

E-MAIL ADDRESS:
jrutledge@healtheffects.org

WEB SITE ADDRESS:
www.healtheffects.org

FOUNDED: 1980

AREAS OF INTEREST:
Health effects of air pollution.

NAME(S) OF PROGRAMS:
● **Health Effects of Air Pollution**
● **Walter A. Rosenblith New Investigator Award**

TYPE:
Research contracts.

YEAR PROGRAM STARTED: 1980

PURPOSE:
To provide high quality, impartial, and relevant science on the health effects of air pollution.

LEGAL BASIS:
Public/Private partnership.

ELIGIBILITY:
Requirements vary according to program. Detailed information is available on the web site.

FINANCIAL DATA:
Amount of support per award: Varies.
Total amount of support: Varies.

APPLICATION INFORMATION:
Application information is available online.
Deadline: Varies.

ADDRESS INQUIRIES TO:
For Health Effects
Dr. Kate Adams
Tel: (617) 488-2330
(See address above.)

THE HEALTH FOUNDATION OF GREATER INDIANAPOLIS [1533]
429 East Vermont Street, Suite 300
Indianapolis, IN 46202-3698
(317) 630-1805
Fax: (317) 630-1806

E-MAIL ADDRESS:
bwilson@thfgi.org

WEB SITE ADDRESS:
www.indianaaidsfund.org

AREAS OF INTEREST:
AIDS education and prevention.

NAME(S) OF PROGRAMS:
● **Indiana AIDS Fund**

TYPE:
Grants-in-aid.

PURPOSE:
To support HIV prevention and services programs throughout Indiana.

ELIGIBILITY:
Any Indiana-based nonprofit 501(c)(3) group, organization or agency that provides HIV/AIDS-related programs or services to local constituencies may apply for funding.

GEOGRAPHIC RESTRICTIONS:
Indiana.

FINANCIAL DATA:
Total amount of support: $500,000 for the year 2011.

NUMBER OF AWARDS: Varies.

APPLICATION INFORMATION:
Submit one master copy of the proposal with all attachments and 10 copies of the proposal without attachments. Proposal must contain the following elements:

(1) the provided Proposal Cover Sheet;
(2) brief description of the organization and its qualifications for this project, no longer than two pages;
(3) proposal narrative which should describe need, target population, geographic area served by this project, project objectives and prospects for future funding, no longer than five pages;
(4) budget statement and justification, no longer than three pages, which should include form provided;
(5) evaluation component, no longer than two pages, which (a) describes the behavior change evaluation component; (b) explains what it will measure; (c) lists the expected outcomes and; (d) explains the rationale for choosing this component and;
(6) attachments.
Duration: One year.
Deadline: Varies.

ADDRESS INQUIRIES TO:
Betty Wilson, President and
Chief Executive Officer
(See address above.)

HEALTH FOUNDATION OF SOUTH FLORIDA   [1534]
One Biscayne Tower
2 South Biscayne Boulevard, Suite 1710
Miami, FL 33131
(305) 374-7200
Fax: (305) 374-7003

E-MAIL ADDRESS:
pwood@hfsf.org

WEB SITE ADDRESS:
www.hfsf.org

FOUNDED: 1993

AREAS OF INTEREST:
Primary care, healthy lifestyles, oral health and preventive health measures.

TYPE:
Challenge/matching grants; General operating grants; Project/program grants; Technical assistance; Training grants.

PURPOSE:
For charitable, scientific and educational purposes to advance the health and well-being of the people of Broward, Miami-Dade and Monroe counties, FL; to facilitate and support efforts at the neighborhood, county and regional levels to improve the health status of underserved individuals and families.

ELIGIBILITY:
Eligible organizations must be IRS 501(c)(3) tax-exempt and be located in south Florida.

GEOGRAPHIC RESTRICTIONS:
South Florida counties of Broward, Miami-Dade and Monroe.

FINANCIAL DATA:
Amount of support per award: Typically $50,000 to $100,000.
Total amount of support: $7,000,000.

NUMBER OF APPLICANTS MOST RECENT YEAR:
160 for the year 2010.

NUMBER OF AWARDS: 41 for the year 2011.

APPLICATION INFORMATION:
Preliminary proposal must be submitted electronically through the Foundation's web site.
Duration: One year.

ADDRESS INQUIRIES TO:
Peter N. Wood
Vice President of Programs
and Community Investments
(See address above.)

THE HEALTH TRUST [1535]

2105 South Bascom Avenue
Suite 220
Campbell, CA 95008-3292
(408) 559-9385 ext. 5590
Fax: (408) 559-9515

E-MAIL ADDRESS:
grants@healthtrust.org

WEB SITE ADDRESS:
www.healthtrust.org

FOUNDED: 1996

AREAS OF INTEREST:
Public health.

NAME(S) OF PROGRAMS:
● **Event Grants**

TYPE:
Project/program grants.

YEAR PROGRAM STARTED: 1996

PURPOSE:
To lead the Silicon Valley community to
advance wellness.

LEGAL BASIS:
Nonprofit, public charity, qualifying as IRS
501(c)(3) organization.

ELIGIBILITY:
The organization must be tax-exempt and
nonprofit. Health services must be provided
within Santa Clara County and the following
three zip codes of San Benito County: 95045,
95023 and 95024.

GEOGRAPHIC RESTRICTIONS:
Santa Clara and northern San Benito
counties, California.

FINANCIAL DATA:
Amount of support per award: $250 to
$5,000.

NUMBER OF APPLICANTS MOST RECENT YEAR:
Approximately 110.

APPLICATION INFORMATION:
Submit Event Grant application form written
on organization's letterhead (not to exceed
two pages) including:
(1) event name;
(2) requested amount;
(3) event purpose;
(4) one-page, line item project budget and;
(5) IRS letter.
Duration: One year.

ADDRESS INQUIRIES TO:
Grants Administrator
(See address above.)

THE HEALTH TRUST [1536]

2105 South Bascom Avenue
Suite 220
Campbell, CA 95008-3292
(408) 559-9385
Fax: (408) 559-9515

E-MAIL ADDRESS:
grants@healthtrust.org

WEB SITE ADDRESS:
www.healthtrust.org

FOUNDED: 1996

AREAS OF INTEREST:
Public health.

NAME(S) OF PROGRAMS:
● **Health Partnership Grants**

TYPE:
Project/program grants.

PURPOSE:
To make grants to programs and projects that
advance specific strategies under three
initiatives: Healthy Living, Healthy Aging
and Healthy Communities.

LEGAL BASIS:
Nonprofit, public charity.

ELIGIBILITY:
Organization must be tax-exempt and
nonprofit. Health services must be provided
within Santa Clara County and the following
three zip codes of San Benito County: 95045,
95023 and 95024.

GEOGRAPHIC RESTRICTIONS:
Santa Clara and northern San Benito
counties, California.

FINANCIAL DATA:
Amount of support per award: Varies.
Total amount of support: Varies.

APPLICATION INFORMATION:
Duration: Varies.

ADDRESS INQUIRIES TO:
Grants Administrator
(See address above.)

THE HEALTHCARE FOUNDATION FOR ORANGE COUNTY [1537]

1450 North Tustin Avenue
Suite 209
Santa Ana, CA 92705-8641
(714) 245-1650
Fax: (714) 245-1653

E-MAIL ADDRESS:
ckoenig@hfoc.org

WEB SITE ADDRESS:
www.hfoc.org

FOUNDED: 1996

AREAS OF INTEREST:
Health care and community health.

CONSULTING OR VOLUNTEER SERVICES:
Some training and technical assistance.

NAME(S) OF PROGRAMS:
● **Gold Fund for Health**
● **Healthy Orange County**
● **Partners for Health**

TYPE:
Awards/prizes; Demonstration grants;
Development grants; General operating
grants; Project/program grants; Technical
assistance; Training grants.

YEAR PROGRAM STARTED: 1999

PURPOSE:
To promote health and support health care
for the benefit of the people of Orange
County, CA; to improve the health of the
neediest and most underserved residents of
the county.

LEGAL BASIS:
Private 501(c)(3) foundation.

ELIGIBILITY:
Grants are made to nonprofit organizations
that are exempt from taxation under Section
501(c)(3) of the Internal Revenue Code and
that are defined as "not a private foundation"
under Section 509(a). Government agencies
may also be funded.

Grants are not generally awarded for annual
fund drives, building campaigns, major
equipment or biomedical research. Activities
that exclusively benefit the members of a
religious or fraternal organization are not
funded.

GEOGRAPHIC RESTRICTIONS:
Primarily Anaheim, Orange, Santa Ana and
Tustin, California.

FINANCIAL DATA:
Amount of support per award: Gold Fund for
Health: $25,000; Healthy Orange County:
$75,000; Partners for Health: $550,000.
Total amount of support: Under $650,000.

COOPERATIVE FUNDING PROGRAMS: Health
Funders Partnership.

NUMBER OF APPLICANTS MOST RECENT YEAR:
Approximately 35.

NUMBER OF AWARDS: Approximately 10.

REPRESENTATIVE AWARDS:
$245,250 to Children's Hospital of Orange
County to develop multidisciplinary treatment
center for pediatric obesity; $75,000 to Hoag
Memorial Hospital/MOMS Orange County
for postpartum depression.

APPLICATION INFORMATION:
Requests for proposals may be obtained from
the Foundation.
Duration: One year; multiyear funding at the
Board's discretion.

IRS IDENTIFICATION NUMBER: 33-0644620

ADDRESS INQUIRIES TO:
Catherine Koenig, Foundation Coordinator
(See address above.)

HUGOTON FOUNDATION [1538]

900 Park Avenue, Suite 17E
New York, NY 10075
(212) 734-5447
Fax: (212) 734-5447

AREAS OF INTEREST:
Patient care and health.

TYPE:
Project/program grants.

PURPOSE:
To improve patient care.

LEGAL BASIS:
Nonprofit organization.

ELIGIBILITY:
Eligible organizations must be IRS 501(c)(3)
tax-exempt and be located in Miami, FL or
the borough of Manhattan, NY.

GEOGRAPHIC RESTRICTIONS:
Miami, Florida and borough of Manhattan,
New York.

FINANCIAL DATA:
Amount of support per award: $1,000 to
$100,000.
Total amount of support: $1,750,000 for the
year 2008.

APPLICATION INFORMATION:
Application should be made by letter and
include a copy of the IRS tax determination
letter.
Duration: One year. Nonrenewable.

ADDRESS INQUIRIES TO:
Joan K. Stout, President
(See address above.)

THE JENKINS FOUNDATION [1539]

7501 Boulders View Drive, Suite 110
Richmond, VA 23225
(804) 330-7400
Fax: (804) 330-5992

WEB SITE ADDRESS:
www.jenkinsfoundation-va.org

FOUNDED: 1995

AREAS OF INTEREST:
Health care services for the uninsured and
underserved, violence prevention and
substance abuse prevention in the greater
Richmond, VA area.

TYPE:
General operating grants; Project/program
grants.

YEAR PROGRAM STARTED: 1996

PURPOSE:
To expand access to community-based health
care programs and improved health care in
the greater Richmond area.

LEGAL BASIS:
Supporting organization of The Community
Foundation Serving Richmond and Central
Virginia.

ELIGIBILITY:
Eligible organizations must be IRS 501(c)(3)
tax-exempt and serve the greater Richmond,
VA area.

GEOGRAPHIC RESTRICTIONS:
Richmond and the counties of Chesterfield,
Goochland, Hanover, Henrico and Powhatan,
Virginia.

FINANCIAL DATA:
The Foundation's investments now total over
$13,000,000 towards improving the future
health of the Richmond community.
Amount of support per award: $20,000 to
$100,000.
Total amount of support: $1,625,000 for the
year 2010.

APPLICATION INFORMATION:
Application forms are available online.
Duration: Annually. May reapply.
Deadline: May 5 and November 5.

PUBLICATIONS:
Guidelines; annual report (online).

ADDRESS INQUIRIES TO:
Elaine Summerfield
Vice President of Programs
(See address above.)

THE JEWISH HEALTHCARE FOUNDATION OF PITTSBURGH [1540]

Centre City Tower, Suite 2400
650 Smithfield Street
Pittsburgh, PA 15222
(412) 594-2550
Fax: (412) 232-6240

E-MAIL ADDRESS:
feinstein@jhf.org

WEB SITE ADDRESS:
www.jhf.org

FOUNDED: 1990

AREAS OF INTEREST:
Health care.

CONSULTING OR VOLUNTEER SERVICES:
Research, planning, convening and technical
assistance.

TYPE:
Challenge/matching grants; Demonstration
grants; Project/program grants; Research
grants; Seed money grants; Technical
assistance.

YEAR PROGRAM STARTED: 1991

PURPOSE:
To provide for the health care needs of the
Jewish and general community in
southwestern Pennsylvania.

LEGAL BASIS:
Public charity.

ELIGIBILITY:
Applicants must be 501(c)(3) organizations.
No grants to programs without a health care
component, general operations, endowments,
capital campaigns, retirement of debt,
scholarships, fellowships, travel or individual
research grants.

GEOGRAPHIC RESTRICTIONS:
Southwestern Pennsylvania.

FINANCIAL DATA:
Assets of $106,000,000 for the year ended
December 31, 2010.
Amount of support per award: Average
$50,000.
Total amount of support: $4,461,207 for the
year ended December 31, 2010.

NUMBER OF APPLICANTS MOST RECENT YEAR:
200.

NUMBER OF AWARDS: 95 for the year 2010.

REPRESENTATIVE AWARDS:
Pittsburgh Regional Health Initiative;
Brandeis University; University of Pittsburgh
Institute to Enhance Palliative Care.

APPLICATION INFORMATION:
Send letter of intent (not to exceed six
pages), including program objectives,
timetable, long-term plans, board of directors
list, budget, documentation of 501(c)(3)
status and most recent financial statements.
Duration: Varies.
Deadline: Applications accepted on a
continual basis.

PUBLICATIONS:
Annual report.

IRS IDENTIFICATION NUMBER: 25-1624347

STAFF:
Karen Wolk Feinstein, Ph.D., President
Nancy Zionts, M.B.A., Chief Program Officer

ADDRESS INQUIRIES TO:
Karen Wolk Feinstein, Ph.D., President
(See address above.)

THE JOHNS HOPKINS CENTER FOR ALTERNATIVES TO ANIMAL TESTING [1541]

Johns Hopkins University
615 North Wolfe Street, Room W7032
Baltimore, MD 21205
(410) 516-8000
(410) 614-4983
Fax: (410) 223-1603

E-MAIL ADDRESS:
caat@jhsph.edu

WEB SITE ADDRESS:
altweb.jhsph.edu

FOUNDED: 1981

AREAS OF INTEREST:
Health and safety.

TYPE:
Development grants; Research grants.

YEAR PROGRAM STARTED: 1982

PURPOSE:
To develop innovative non-whole animal
methods to evaluate fully commercial and/or
therapeutic products to ensure the health and
safety of the public. CAAT accomplishes this
goal by funding research which will lead to
the refinement, replacement or reduction of
animals in toxicity testing and by
disseminating scientifically correct
information about these methods and their
applications.

LEGAL BASIS:
University research program.

ELIGIBILITY:
Grants are made to institutions which have
an established mechanism for handling
private funding. Grant proposals should
provide the fundamental knowledge base to
develop alternative methods to whole animals
for the safety evaluation of commercial
products. CAAT encourages the development
of in vitro approaches to toxicity evaluation
including, but not limited to, methods using
human cells/cell lines and studies in the areas
of skin hypersensitivity/toxicity,
phototoxicity, target organ toxicity (e.g.,
neurotoxicity) and structure-activity
relationships.

FINANCIAL DATA:
Amount of support per award: $25,000
maximum per year, including 15% overhead
or actual costs, whichever is less. Refinement
Developmental Toxicology Award and
Immunology Toxicology Award: Up to
$50,000 per year.
Total amount of support: $25,000 to $50,000
maximum per year, per award.

APPLICATION INFORMATION:
Applicants must submit and receive approval
of preproposal by deadline date using CAAT
preproposal form.
Duration: One year. Renewal possible.
Deadline: March 10 for preproposal
abstracts.

PUBLICATIONS:
CAAT Newsletter; technical reports;
Alternatives in Toxicology, book series.

IRS IDENTIFICATION NUMBER: 52-0595110

STAFF:
Thomas Hartung, Director

ADDRESS INQUIRIES TO:
Ruth Brady, Grant Coordinator
(See address above.)

KANSAS HEALTH FOUNDATION [1542]

309 East Douglas
Wichita, KS 67202
(316) 262-7676
(800) 373-7681
Fax: (316) 262-2044

E-MAIL ADDRESS:
ghess@khf.org

WEB SITE ADDRESS:
www.kansashealth.org

FOUNDED: 1985

AREAS OF INTEREST:
Improvement in the health of Kansans.

NAME(S) OF PROGRAMS:
- **Recognition Grants**

TYPE:
Project/program grants.

YEAR PROGRAM STARTED: 1994

PURPOSE:
To fund competitive grants to grassroots nonprofits and government entities doing innovative and meaningful work that fits within the Kansas Health Foundation's mission to improve the health of all Kansans. Recognition Grants expand the Foundation's support to a broad range of health-related organizations throughout the state.

ELIGIBILITY:
Applicants must be tax-exempt 501(c)(3) organizations located within the state and must not have been a previous recipient of a Recognition Grant within the calendar year.

GEOGRAPHIC RESTRICTIONS:
Kansas.

FINANCIAL DATA:
Amount of support per award: Up to $25,000 per organization.

Total amount of support: Up to $1,700,000 annually in two cycles per year.

NUMBER OF AWARDS: Varies.

APPLICATION INFORMATION:
Applications are only accepted online. Projects are selected based on the following:
(1) focus on prevention;
(2) meeting a clear, identifiable need;
(3) creativity;
(4) operational strength of the applicant organization, including project leadership and;
(5) ranking when compared with other applications received during the funding cycle.

Duration: One year.

Deadline: September 1 and March 1. Announcement December 1 and June 1, respectively.

PUBLICATIONS:
Grant announcement press release.

IRS IDENTIFICATION NUMBER: 48-0873431

ADDRESS INQUIRIES TO:
Gina Hess, Grants Assistant
(See address above.)

LA84 FOUNDATION   [1543]
2141 West Adams Boulevard
Los Angeles, CA 90018
(323) 730-4600
Fax: (323) 730-9637

E-MAIL ADDRESS:
info@la84foundation.org

WEB SITE ADDRESS:
www.la84foundation.org

FOUNDED: 1984

AREAS OF INTEREST:
Youth sports.

TYPE:
Capital grants; Project/program grants. Field of play activities.

PURPOSE:
To promote and enhance youth sports opportunities in southern California.

LEGAL BASIS:
Private foundation.

ELIGIBILITY:
Grants are made only to organizations with nonrestrictive membership operating open to all, regardless of race, creed, sex, sexual orientation, religious affiliation, or nationality. No grants to individuals. Grants are discouraged for endowments, travel outside of southern California, general operating expenses, land purchases, or debt recovery and liability. Grants are need-based.

GEOGRAPHIC RESTRICTIONS:
Imperial, Los Angeles, Orange, Riverside, San Bernardino, San Diego, Santa Barbara and Ventura counties, California.

FINANCIAL DATA:
Amount of support per award: $5,000 to $561,980 for the year 2010.

Total amount of support: $3,381,461 for the year 2010.

NUMBER OF APPLICANTS MOST RECENT YEAR: 235 for the year 2010.

NUMBER OF AWARDS: 80 for the year 2010.

REPRESENTATIVE AWARDS:
Kids In Sports; LAUSD; LA's BEST; Students Run LA; Southern California Tennis Association.

APPLICATION INFORMATION:
Applicants are urged to carefully read the Grant Guidelines before completing the online grant application. Applicants will be asked to:
(1) state clearly the purpose for which funding is requested;
(2) briefly describe the organization, its history, status (nonprofit or for profit, etc.), and connection to youth and sport;
(3) describe in detail how the program would work and whom it would serve. Include an estimate of the number of participants to be served by the grant;
(4) describe the personnel who would be carrying out the program, and include brief biographical statements of those who would be most centrally involved;
(5) describe efforts already made or underway to find matching grant funds and;
(6) provide a clear time schedule for the program.

Additionally, applicants may be asked to make available the following documents:
(1) the organization's most current annual operating budget;
(2) the most recent completed financial statement;
(3) the most recent IRS Form 990;
(4) IRS tax status determination letter;
(5) California tax status determination letter;
(6) a detailed program budget with justifications for each budget item and;
(7) list of board of directors.

Duration: One year.

Deadline: Applications are accepted year-round.

PUBLICATIONS:
Biannual report.

IRS IDENTIFICATION NUMBER: 95-3792725

OFFICERS:
Anita L. DeFrantz, President
Conrad Freund, Chief Operating Officer, Finance and Administration
F. Patrick Escobar, Vice President, Grants and Programs
Wayne Wilson, Vice President, Education Services

ADDRESS INQUIRIES TO:
F. Patrick Escobar, Vice President Grants and Programs
(See address above.)

LIVINGSTON MEMORIAL FOUNDATION   [1544]
c/o Musick, Peeler and Garrett
2801 Townsgate Road, Suite 200
Westlake Village, CA 91361-5842
(805) 418-3115
Fax: (805) 418-3101

E-MAIL ADDRESS:
l.mcavoy@mpglaw.com

WEB SITE ADDRESS:
www.livingstonmemorialfoundation.org

FOUNDED: 1974

AREAS OF INTEREST:
Medical and health care in Ventura County, CA.

NAME(S) OF PROGRAMS:
- **Operational Program Grants**
- **Special Project Grants**

TYPE:
Capital grants; General operating grants; Project/program grants. Capital grants are for medical and health care services.

Operational grants support well established programs that continue to provide positive results.

Special project grants support those agencies and institutions that can demonstrate the need for assistance in funding a special project or with the cost of medical equipment that promises significant positive results.

YEAR PROGRAM STARTED: 1976

PURPOSE:
To promote medical and health-related services of benefit to the underserved and uninsured people of Ventura County, CA.

ELIGIBILITY:
Grant applications are assessed according to criteria that include giving preferential treatment to programs or projects that offer measurable medical benefits, are patient-specific or involve hands-on care.

Grants are not usually made to individuals, for projects or programs normally financed from government sources, conferences, seminars, workshops, exhibits, travel, or publishing activities.

GEOGRAPHIC RESTRICTIONS:
Ventura County, California.

FINANCIAL DATA:
Amount of support per award: $1,000 to $149,000 for the year 2009-10.

Total amount of support: $313,500 for the year ended April 30, 2010. $370,000 in estimated grants for the 2010-11 cycle.

NUMBER OF APPLICANTS MOST RECENT YEAR: 35 for the 2010-11 cycle.

APPLICATION INFORMATION:
Organizations should first submit a brief introductory letter, not to exceed three pages. The letter should include a concise statement of the need for the funds, the amount requested, pertinent factual information, and state the desired type of grant. Current verification of tax-exempt status should also be included. After review, eligible organizations may be invited to submit a formal grant application.

Duration: One year.

Deadline: Introductory letters may be submitted at any time. Formal applications are reviewed in mid-October. Awards announced after the first of the year.

PUBLICATIONS:
Brochure.

IRS IDENTIFICATION NUMBER: 23-7364623

DIRECTORS AND OFFICERS:
Charles M. Hair, M.D., President and Chairman
W. Cloyce Huff, M.D., Vice President and Vice Chairman
Richard M. Loft, M.D., Vice President and Vice Chairman
Marcia Donlon, Secretary
Laura K. McAvoy, Esq., Chief Financial Officer and Assistant Secretary
John R. Walters, M.D., Assistant Chief Financial Officer
Thomas F. McGrath, III, Director

ADDRESS INQUIRIES TO:
Laura K. McAvoy, Esq., Director
(See address above.)

JOHN M. LLOYD FOUNDATION [1545]

11777 San Vicente Boulevard
Suite 745
Los Angeles, CA 90049
(310) 622-1050
Fax: (424) 625-0740

E-MAIL ADDRESS:
info@johnmlloyd.org

WEB SITE ADDRESS:
www.johnmlloyd.org

FOUNDED: 1991

AREAS OF INTEREST:
Education, prevention and public policy around HIV/AIDS.

TYPE:
Awards/prizes; Conferences/seminars; Demonstration grants; General operating grants; Project/program grants; Seed money grants; Training grants.

YEAR PROGRAM STARTED: 1992

PURPOSE:
To increase funding from public and private sectors to address the HIV/AIDS pandemic, both globally and domestically; to improve domestic and international policies; to amplify global awareness of HIV/AIDS and to facilitate broad-based change in attitudes to reduce stigma and change behavior; to develop the leadership of organizations that fight HIV/AIDS, as well as foster collaborations among those organizations and leaders.

LEGAL BASIS:
Private, family foundation.

ELIGIBILITY:
The Foundation makes contributions to U.S.-based projects with a national or global scope and to international projects. The Foundation does not fund annual campaigns, operating budgets of established organizations, capital expenditures (physical plant, equipment, endowment), indirect costs, individuals, locally focused projects in the U.S., organizations that have annual budgets of $5,000,000 or more, lobbying (as per federal restrictions on private foundations), health care or service provision, or general support.

FINANCIAL DATA:
Amount of support per award: $20,000.
Total amount of support: $400,000 annually.

NUMBER OF APPLICANTS MOST RECENT YEAR:
300.

NUMBER OF AWARDS: 30.

APPLICATION INFORMATION:
Applicants are urged to review the guidelines carefully to be sure their project fits within the Foundation's specific funding objectives. Applicants may call or e-mail the Foundation to discuss a particular proposal if they are uncertain as to whether it falls within the guidelines.

Applicants must submit a Concept Letter via e-mail or fax describing the specific project for which funding is sought. Applicants whose Concept Letters are reviewed favorably by the Board will be asked to submit a Formal Proposal.

Duration: One year.
Deadline: Concept Letter must be received by December 15 (for the Spring Cycle) in order to be considered.

IRS IDENTIFICATION NUMBER: 36-3766003

BOARD OF DIRECTORS:
Jesse Estrin
Mary Lloyd Estrin
Robert L. Estrin
Zoe Lloyd Estrin
Sharon Gelman
Trish Devine Karlin
Linda Dorn Klein
Heidi Mage Lloyd

ADDRESS INQUIRIES TO:
Melanie Havelin, Executive Director
(See address above.)

*SPECIAL STIPULATIONS:
Unsolicited Formal Proposals will not be considered.

THE DR. JOHN T. MACDONALD FOUNDATION, INC.

1550 Madruga Avenue, Suite 215
Coral Gables, FL 33146
(305) 667-6017
Fax: (305) 667-9135

E-MAIL ADDRESS:
info@jtmacdonaldfdn.org

WEB SITE ADDRESS:
www.jtmacdonaldfdn.org

TYPE:
Capital grants; Challenge/matching grants; Project/program grants; Seed money grants; Training grants.

See entry 1202 for full listing.

MANITOBA HEALTH RESEARCH COUNCIL [1546]

Room P-216, 770 Bannatyne Avenue
Winnipeg MB R3E 0W3 Canada
(204) 775-1096
Fax: (204) 786-5401

E-MAIL ADDRESS:
info@mhrc.mb.ca

WEB SITE ADDRESS:
www.mhrc.mb.ca

FOUNDED: 1980

AREAS OF INTEREST:
Health-related basic, clinical and applied scientific research in the Province of Manitoba.

CONSULTING OR VOLUNTEER SERVICES:
The Council advises the provincial Minister of Health on matters relating to health research, as the Minister may refer to the Council for its consideration.

TYPE:
Awards/prizes; Fellowships; General operating grants; Professorships; Research grants. Operating Grants are for new investigators only. Establishment grants are given out over a three-year period.

Postdoctoral Fellowships are meant to allow recent doctoral degree recipients, with considerable research training and accomplishments, to further their training to allow them to become independent investigators.

Graduate Studentships are offered to qualified graduate students who are undertaking full-time Master's or doctoral programs in the province of Manitoba.

Ph.D. Dissertation Awards are for graduate students in population and health-related social sciences fields.

Operating Grants are for investigators who have held an academic appointment at the rank of assistant professor or above (or equivalent) in Manitoba for a period of not more than five years.

Establishment Grants are intended to allow recently recruited faculty members in the province of Manitoba to focus on research and to establish their research programs.

Bridge Funding awards are intended to allow investigators who have recently lost funding, after a sustained period of support from a major agency, to maintain their research program while attempting to regain their funding by reapplication.

YEAR PROGRAM STARTED: 1981

PURPOSE:
To provide support for health-related research in the Province of Manitoba.

LEGAL BASIS:
Established by an Act of the Provincial Legislature and provincially funded.

ELIGIBILITY:
Grants are awarded to individuals in the Province of Manitoba.

GEOGRAPHIC RESTRICTIONS:
Manitoba, Canada.

FINANCIAL DATA:
Amount of support per award: Establishment Grants: $100,000; Fellowships: $36,750; Operating Grants: Up to $100,000; Studentships: $17,850.
Total amount of support: Varies.
Matching fund requirements: For Regional Partnership Grants.

NUMBER OF APPLICANTS MOST RECENT YEAR:
238 for the year 2009.

APPLICATION INFORMATION:
Applications must be made on the appropriate Manitoba Health Research Council forms.
Duration: Establishment Grants: Three years. Operating Grants: Up to five years.
Deadline: Clinical Fellows, Fellowships and Studentships: January 29. Establishment Grants, Operating Grants and Research Chairs: March 2.

PUBLICATIONS:
Annual report; awards guide; EGMS user guide.

STAFF:
Shannon Rogalski, Manager, Funding Programs
Liz Ford, Administrative Officer

COUNCIL MEMBERS:
Dr. Dean Sandham, Chairperson
Dr. Judith Bartlett
Mr. F. Lynn Bishop
John Clarkson
Dr. Albert Friesen
Dr. Henry Friesen
Bob Gannon
Ray Hoemsen
Dr. Digvir Jayas
Dr. Arnold Naimark
Dr. Brian Postl
Dr. Brent Schacter
Dr. Ian Smith
Arlene Wilgosh

ADDRESS INQUIRIES TO:
The Administrative Officer or Executive Director
(See address above.)

FREDA MAYTAG-GRACE CRAWFORD TRUST [1547]

c/o JPMorgan Private Client Services
402 North Tejon Street, Suite 200
Colorado Springs, CO 80903
(719) 227-6445
Fax: (719) 227-6448

E-MAIL ADDRESS:
julie.golden@jpmorgan.com

WEB SITE ADDRESS:
www.jpmorgan.com/onlinegrants

AREAS OF INTEREST:
Tuberculosis and other respiratory diseases; preservation of a clean and healthy environment.

TYPE:
Project/program grants.

PURPOSE:
To provide medical and nursing care for individuals in the Colorado Springs community who are afflicted with tuberculosis or other respiratory diseases.

ELIGIBILITY:
Grants to 501(c)(3) nonprofit organizations. No grants to individuals.

GEOGRAPHIC RESTRICTIONS:
Colorado Springs, CO.

FINANCIAL DATA:
Amount of support per award: $3,000 to $5,000.

APPLICATION INFORMATION:
Application and guidelines are available online.
Duration: One year. No renewals.
Deadline: March 20, June 20, September 20 and December 20.

ADDRESS INQUIRIES TO:
Julie Golden, Trust Advisor
(See address above.)

MT. SINAI HEALTH CARE FOUNDATION [1548]

11000 Euclid Avenue
Cleveland, OH 44106-1714
(216) 421-5500
Fax: (216) 421-5633

E-MAIL ADDRESS:
msb12@case.edu

WEB SITE ADDRESS:
www.mtsinaifoundation.org

FOUNDED: 1996

AREAS OF INTEREST:
Urban health, Jewish community, health policy, academic medicine and bioscience.

TYPE:
Challenge/matching grants; Demonstration grants; Development grants; Project/program grants; Seed money grants.

YEAR PROGRAM STARTED: 1997

PURPOSE:
To improve the health of the citizens in the greater Cleveland, OH area.

LEGAL BASIS:
Public charity.

ELIGIBILITY:
Eligible organizations must be IRS 501(c)(3) tax-exempt.

GEOGRAPHIC RESTRICTIONS:
Greater Cleveland, Ohio.

FINANCIAL DATA:
Total amount of support: $6,000,000 annually.

APPLICATION INFORMATION:
Deadline: January 1, April 1, July 1 and October 1.

PUBLICATIONS:
Guidelines; annual report; *Legacy*, newsletter.

IRS IDENTIFICATION NUMBER: 34-1777878

ADDRESS INQUIRIES TO:
Mitchell Balk, President
(See address above.)

NATIONAL HEALTH SERVICE CORPS (NHSC) [1549]

U.S. Department of Health and Human Services
Health Resources and Services Administration
Bureau of Clinicians and Recruitment Services
5600 Fishers Lane
Rockville, MD 20857
(800) 221-9393

E-MAIL ADDRESS:
callcenter@hrsa.gov

WEB SITE ADDRESS:
nhsc.bhpr.hrsa.gov
nhsc.hrsa.gov

AREAS OF INTEREST:
Competitive scholarships for students enrolled in schools of osteopathic and allopathic medicine, family nurse practitioner, nurse midwifery and physician assistant training programs and dental school.

NAME(S) OF PROGRAMS:
- **National Health Service Corps Scholarship Program**

TYPE:
Scholarships. The scholarship award includes the payment of a monthly stipend, an amount for other reasonable educational expenses, tuition and required fees. Recipients owe one year of professional clinical service in a health professional shortage area (HPSA) for each year of support, with a two-year service minimum.

YEAR PROGRAM STARTED: 1973

PURPOSE:
To provide the National Health Service Corps with an adequate supply of trained health professionals to serve in health professional shortage areas.

ELIGIBILITY:
All applicants must be citizens or nationals of the U.S. at the time they apply, enrolled or accepted for enrollment in an accredited health professions education program.

FINANCIAL DATA:
Scholarship recipients receive a monthly stipend, one annual payment for other reasonable educational expenses, and payment to the school, on their behalf, of tuition and required fees. The stipend only is taxable.
Amount of support per award: Based on costs for every student in the program.
Total amount of support: Varies.

COOPERATIVE FUNDING PROGRAMS: Educational benefits from the Veterans Administration (G.I. Bill) may continue along with Scholarship Program funds since these benefits were earned by prior active duty in a uniformed service.

APPLICATION INFORMATION:
Application form is to be submitted online. Students must submit on paper proof of U.S. citizenship, transcript, resume detailing volunteer and work experience (no more than five pages), verifications and evaluations from their school, and essays in response to prompts.

Applications submitted after the deadline are not reviewed.
Duration: The scholarship award is only for the year(s) that the contract is signed with a two-year minimum service obligation.

PUBLICATIONS:
Applicant information bulletin.

*SPECIAL STIPULATIONS:
Recipients must serve where needed in a designated Health Professional Shortage Area (HPSA).

NATIONAL INSTITUTE ON AGING [1550]

Division of Extramural Activities
7201 Wisconsin Avenue, Room 2C218
Bethesda, MD 20892
(301) 496-9322
Fax: (301) 402-2945

E-MAIL ADDRESS:
barrr@mail.nih.gov

WEB SITE ADDRESS:
www.nia.nih.gov

FOUNDED: 1975

AREAS OF INTEREST:
Biology of aging research, geriatrics research, neuroscience and neuropsychology of aging research, behavioral and social research on aging.

NAME(S) OF PROGRAMS:
- **Aging Research**

TYPE:
Conferences/seminars; Fellowships; Grants-in-aid; Project/program grants; Research grants; Technical assistance; Training grants; Loan forgiveness programs; Research contracts.

PURPOSE:
To support biomedical, clinical, social, neuroscience, neuropsychology and behavioral research and research training directed toward greater understanding of the aging process and the needs and problems of older people. The primary goal is to improve the health and well-being of older people through the development of new knowledge.

LEGAL BASIS:
Government agency.

ELIGIBILITY:
Grants and contracts are available to universities, colleges, medical, dental and nursing schools, schools of public health, laboratories, hospitals, state and local health departments and other public or private profit or nonprofit institutions.

NRSA awards are provided for individual postdoctoral and institutional pre-and postdoctoral research training in health and health-related areas which are periodically specified by the National Institutes of Health. Individuals with a professional or scientific degree are eligible. Applicants must be citizens of the U.S. or be admitted for permanent residency.

GEOGRAPHIC RESTRICTIONS:
United States.

FINANCIAL DATA:
Amount of support per award: Average: $392,500.

NUMBER OF APPLICANTS MOST RECENT YEAR:
2,000.

NUMBER OF AWARDS: 1,400.

APPLICATION INFORMATION:
Duration: One year to multiyear.
Deadline: Varies.

OFFICERS:
Robin A. Barr, D.Phil., Director

ADDRESS INQUIRIES TO:
Division of Extramural Activities
(See address above.)

NATIONAL INSTITUTE ON ALCOHOL ABUSE AND ALCOHOLISM [1551]

Office of Extramural Activities
5635 Fishers Lane
MSC 9304
Bethesda, MD 20892-9304
(301) 443-9737
Fax: (301) 443-6077

E-MAIL ADDRESS:
bautista@mail.nih.gov

WEB SITE ADDRESS:
www.niaaa.nih.gov

FOUNDED: 1971

NAME(S) OF PROGRAMS:
- **Academic Career Awards (K07)**
- **Career Enhancement Award for Stem Cell Research (K18)**
- **Independent Scientist Awards (K02)**
- **Mentored Patient-Oriented Research Career Development Award (K23)**
- **Mentored Quantitative Research Career Development Award (K25)**
- **Midcareer Investigator Award in Patient-Oriented Research (K24)**
- **Scientist Development Awards for Mentored Clinical (K08)**
- **Scientist Development Awards for Mentored Research (K01)**
- **Senior Scientist Awards (K05)**

TYPE:
Research grants. Support for full-time research on a long-term (five years) basis for research scientists.

Academic Career Awards (K07) support development of clinical faculty in clinical research and teaching related to alcohol problems. Developmental award only.

Career Enhancement Award for Stem Cell Research (K18) is to encourage investigators to obtain the training they need to appropriately use stem cells in their research.

Independent Scientist Awards (K02) support advanced research experience.

Scientist Development Awards for Mentored Research (K01) and Scientist Development Awards for Mentored Clinical (K08) support individuals with one to four years of postdoctoral training or experience, but no extensive research experience.

Senior Scientist Awards (K05) support exceptional senior investigators to conduct full-time research.

PURPOSE:
To provide salary support to talented investigators so that they can engage in full-time research on a long-term basis and develop their full research potential.

LEGAL BASIS:
PHS Act, Section 301 as amended (42 U.S.C. 241).

ELIGIBILITY:
Applicants can either be public or nonprofit private organizations and institutions located in the U.S. or its territories and possessions or U.S. citizens or permanent residents. Citizenship is mandatory for renewal beyond the initial five-year award.

APPLICATION INFORMATION:
Application kits are available at most institutional offices of sponsored research and may be obtained from the Grants Information Office.

Duration: All awards five years. Renewal possible.

Deadline: February 12, June 12 and October 12.

PUBLICATIONS:
NIAAA additional information to the NIH Career Development Program Announcements (K Awards).

ADDRESS INQUIRIES TO:
Dr. Bob Huebner, Acting Director
Division of Treatment
and Recovery Research
Tel: (301) 443-4344 or

Dr. Ralph Hingson, Director
Division of Epidemiology
and Prevention Research
Tel: (301) 443-1274 or

Dr. Sameer Zakhari
Division of Metabolism
and Health Effects
Tel: (301) 443-0799 or

Dr. Antonio Noronha
Division of Neuroscience and Behavior
Tel: (301) 443-7722
(See address above.)

NATIONAL INSTITUTE ON ALCOHOL ABUSE AND ALCOHOLISM [1552]

Division of Metabolism and Health Effect
5635 Fishers Lane, Room 2034
MSC 9304
Bethesda, MD 20892-9304
(301) 443-9940
Fax: (301) 594-0673

E-MAIL ADDRESS:
murrayg@mail.nih.gov

WEB SITE ADDRESS:
www.niaaa.nih.gov

FOUNDED: 1971

AREAS OF INTEREST:
Pharmaceuticals, diagnostic instruments, and the prevention and treatment of alcoholism.

NAME(S) OF PROGRAMS:
- **Small Business Innovation Research Program**

TYPE:
Research grants; Research contracts. Separate grant applications are awarded for Phase I and Phase II of the program. Phase I is designed to establish the feasibility of the technological innovation and determine the quality of performance. The objective of Phase II is to further demonstrate the efficacy of the product for commercial exploitation. Only funded applicants from Phase I are eligible to apply for Phase II.

YEAR PROGRAM STARTED: 1983

PURPOSE:
To stimulate technological innovation in the alcohol field, increase private-sector commercialization of innovations derived from federal research and development and foster and encourage participation by minority and disadvantaged firms in technological innovation.

LEGAL BASIS:
The Small Business Innovation Development Act, P.L. 97-219.

ELIGIBILITY:
Each organization must qualify as a small business in accordance with the stipulations set forth in the Omnibus Solicitation of the PHS Small Business Innovation Research Program. In general, the organization must be independently owned and operated, must be located in the U.S. and at least 51% of the ownership must be by U.S. citizens or lawfully admitted permanent resident aliens. The primary employment of the principal investigator must be with the firm at the time of award and during the conduct of the proposed project. The performance site must be in the U.S.

GEOGRAPHIC RESTRICTIONS:
United States.

FINANCIAL DATA:
Amount of support per award: May not exceed $150,000 for both direct and indirect costs, for a maximum period of six months, for Phase I. May not exceed $1,000,000 for two years in total costs for Phase II.

APPLICATION INFORMATION:
Applications may be obtained from www.nih.gov/grants/funding/sbir.htm.
Duration: Six months for Phase I. Two years for Phase II.
Deadline: December.

PUBLICATIONS:
Omnibus solicitation for SBIR grant applications.

NATIONAL INSTITUTES OF HEALTH [1553]

Center for Population Research
National Institute of Child Health and Human Development
6100 Executive Boulevard, Room 8B-07
MSC-7510
Bethesda, MD 20892
(301) 496-1101
Fax: (301) 496-0962

E-MAIL ADDRESS:
haseltif@mail.nih.gov

WEB SITE ADDRESS:
www.nichd.nih.gov/about/cpr/cpr.htm

FOUNDED: 1968

AREAS OF INTEREST:
Population research.

NAME(S) OF PROGRAMS:
- **Center for Population Research (CPR)**
- **Contraception and Reproductive Health Branch (CRH)**
- **Demographic and Behavioral Sciences Branch (DBS)**
- **Reproductive Sciences Branch (RS)**

TYPE:
Fellowships; Project/program grants; Research grants; Training grants; Loan forgiveness programs; Research contracts. Project grants and research contracts. Population research encompasses three large and complex research objectives including contraceptive development and evaluation, demographic and behavioral research on population, and reproductive sciences.

YEAR PROGRAM STARTED: 1968

PURPOSE:
To support population research.

LEGAL BASIS:
Public Health Service Act, Sections 301(c), 444, 472.

ELIGIBILITY:
Universities, colleges, medical, dental, nursing schools, schools of public health, laboratories, hospitals, state and local health departments, other public or private nonprofit institutions and commercial organizations are eligible. Individuals may apply for grants for biomedical, behavioral, and clinical research training.

ADDRESS INQUIRIES TO:
Office of Grants and Management
Tel: (301) 496-5001 or

Office of Contracts
Tel: (301) 496-4611
(See address above.)

NATIONAL INSTITUTES OF HEALTH

Division of International Relations
Fogarty International Center
Building 31, Room B2C11
31 Center Drive, MSC 2220
Bethesda, MD 20892-2220
(301) 496-4784
(301) 496-1653
Fax: (301) 480-3414

E-MAIL ADDRESS:
chungt@mail.nih.gov
mili.ferreira@nih.gov
ficjspsextramural@mail.nih.gov

WEB SITE ADDRESS:
www.fic.nih.gov/programs

TYPE:
Fellowships. A limited number of postdoctoral research fellowships are provided by the Japan Science and Technology Agency (JSTA) to U.S. scientists to conduct research in Japan. Types of activity supported include collaboration in basic or clinical research and familiarization with or utilization of special techniques and equipment not otherwise available to the applicant.

See entry 1017 for full listing.

NATIONAL INSTITUTES OF HEALTH [1554]

Division of International Services
9000 Rockville Pike, MSC-2028
Bethesda, MD 20892-2028
(301) 496-6166
Fax: (301) 496-0847

E-MAIL ADDRESS:
dis@mail.nih.gov

WEB SITE ADDRESS:
www.training.nih.gov
dis.ors.od.nih.gov

FOUNDED: 1950

AREAS OF INTEREST:
Biomedical and behavioral sciences.

NAME(S) OF PROGRAMS:
- **The NIH Visiting Program**

TYPE:
Fellowships; Visiting scholars. Visiting foreign scholars.

YEAR PROGRAM STARTED: 1950

PURPOSE:
To provide talented scientists throughout the world an opportunity to participate in the varied research activities of the National Institutes of Health. Two categories of Visiting Program participants include Visiting Fellows for obtaining research training experience and Visiting Scientists for conducting health-related research.

LEGAL BASIS:
Government agency.

ELIGIBILITY:
Visiting Fellows must have a doctoral degree or its equivalent and not more than five years of relevant postdoctoral research experience when the fellowship begins. Visiting Fellows may be resident or nonresident aliens. U.S. citizens are not eligible for the Visiting Fellow award.

Visiting Scientists must have a doctoral degree or its equivalent and more than three years of postdoctoral research experience.

All Visiting Program participants must be proficient in the use and understanding of the English language, both written and spoken.

FINANCIAL DATA:
Visiting Fellows receive a monthly stipend during the award period to cover living expenses. The stipend level is determined by the number of years of relevant postdoctoral research experience. Visiting Scientists receive a salary based on the candidate's qualifications and several of the benefits available to employees of the U.S. Government.

Amount of support per award: Visiting Fellows: $41,200 to $78,700. Visiting Scientists start at $45,461. Funding may be increased annually by $1,500 to $2,000 per year.

NUMBER OF AWARDS: 1,700.

APPLICATION INFORMATION:
Individuals interested in a Visiting Program fellowship award or appointment should write to NIH, enclosing a resume and brief description of their particular research area.

Duration: Generally, two years. Renewable for a total of five years, based upon merit and depending on visa restrictions.

PUBLICATIONS:
Program description.

ADDRESS INQUIRIES TO:
Candelario Zapata
(See address above.)

THE PATRON SAINTS FOUNDATION [1555]

260 South Los Robles Avenue, No. 201
Pasadena, CA 91101
(626) 564-0444
Fax: (626) 564-0444

E-MAIL ADDRESS:
patronsaintsfdn@sbcglobal.net

WEB SITE ADDRESS:
www.patronsaintsfoundation.org

FOUNDED: 1986

AREAS OF INTEREST:
Health care.

TYPE:
Capital grants; Project/program grants; Research grants. Limited operating support will be awarded at the discretion of the Board of Directors.

YEAR PROGRAM STARTED: 1986

PURPOSE:
To improve the health of individuals residing in the West San Gabriel Valley through health care programs that are consistent with the moral and religious teachings of the Roman Catholic Church.

LEGAL BASIS:
Private foundation.

ELIGIBILITY:
Organizations must be IRS 501(c)(3) tax-exempt.

GEOGRAPHIC RESTRICTIONS:
West San Gabriel Valley, California.

FINANCIAL DATA:
Amount of support per award: $5,000 to $15,000.

Total amount of support: $483,247 for fiscal year ended June 30, 2010.

NUMBER OF APPLICANTS MOST RECENT YEAR: 45.

NUMBER OF AWARDS: 31 for fiscal year ended June 30, 2010.

APPLICATION INFORMATION:
Two copies of the application (not to exceed three pages, no less than 11-point type, one stapled and one paper-clipped) must be mailed to the Foundation, along with other required documents including financial statements, copy of the organization's 501(c)(3) determination letter and IRS Form 990.

Duration: One year. Renewal by reapplication.

Deadline: First Friday in March and first Friday in October.

PUBLICATIONS:
Grant guidelines; grant application form; brochure.

IRS IDENTIFICATION NUMBER: 95-3484257

EXECUTIVE DIRECTOR:
Kathleen T. Shannon

ADDRESS INQUIRIES TO:
Kathleen T. Shannon, Executive Director
(See address above.)

CHARLES H. PEARSON FOUNDATION FUND [1556]
Bank of America
225 Franklin Street
Boston, MA 02110
(866) 778-6859

WEB SITE ADDRESS:
www.bankofamerica.com/grantmaking

AREAS OF INTEREST:
Health care, family services and education.

TYPE:
General operating grants; Project/program grants.

LEGAL BASIS:
Trust fund.

ELIGIBILITY:
Eligible organizations must be IRS 501(c)(3) tax-exempt.

GEOGRAPHIC RESTRICTIONS:
Massachusetts.

FINANCIAL DATA:
Amount of support per award: $6,235 to $20,000.
Total amount of support: $114,500 for the year 2010.

APPLICATION INFORMATION:
Duration: One year. Occasionally multiyear.
Deadline: July 1.

PUBLICATIONS:
Guidelines.

ADDRESS INQUIRIES TO:
Michealle Larkins, Senior Programs Officer
(See address above.)

PIEDMONT HEALTH CARE FOUNDATION [1557]
P.O. Box 9303
Greenville, SC 29604
(864) 370-0212
Fax: (864) 370-0212

E-MAIL ADDRESS:
katypughsmith@bellsouth.net

WEB SITE ADDRESS:
www.piedmonthealthcarefdn.org

FOUNDED: 1985

AREAS OF INTEREST:
Health service and education in the health field.

TYPE:
Demonstration grants; Project/program grants; Research grants; Seed money grants.

YEAR PROGRAM STARTED: 1986

PURPOSE:
To improve health in Greenville County, SC.

LEGAL BASIS:
Private foundation.

ELIGIBILITY:
Organizations must be nonprofit 501(c)(3). No grants to individuals.

GEOGRAPHIC RESTRICTIONS:
Greenville, South Carolina.

FINANCIAL DATA:
Amount of support per award: Grants typically $2,000 to $25,000.
Total amount of support: $50,000 for the year 2010.

NUMBER OF APPLICANTS MOST RECENT YEAR: 5.

NUMBER OF AWARDS: 5.

REPRESENTATIVE AWARDS:
Safe Kids Upstate for Cribs for Kids program; New Horizon Family Health Services for small business initiative; Cancer Society of Greenville County for computer services.

APPLICATION INFORMATION:
Application form required along with copy of IRS tax-exempt certificate. Contact the Foundation for specific guidelines and form.
Duration: One year.
Deadline: Varies.

OFFICERS:
Robert R. Morgan, Jr., M.D., Chairman
Jennifer Graf Smith, Vice Chairman
Mark Cooter, Treasurer
Helene Edwards, Secretary

ADDRESS INQUIRIES TO:
Katy Pugh Smith, Executive Director
(See address above.)

THE DOROTHY RIDER POOL HEALTH CARE TRUST [1558]
1050 South Cedar Crest Boulevard
Suite 202
Allentown, PA 18103
(610) 770-9346
Fax: (610) 770-9361

E-MAIL ADDRESS:
drpool@ptd.net

WEB SITE ADDRESS:
www.pooltrust.org

FOUNDED: 1975

AREAS OF INTEREST:
Community health, health services research, leadership development and medical education, recruitment and retention of outstanding health care providers, access to care, health studies, and clinical innovation.

TYPE:
Awards/prizes; Challenge/matching grants; Development grants; Endowments; Fellowships; Project/program grants. Grants addressing at least one of the key components of the Trust's Philanthropic Agenda: improved health status of the citizens of the region, recruitment and retention of outstanding health care providers, clinical innovation, access to care, medical education, community health and health service research.

PURPOSE:
To serve as a resource that enables Lehigh Valley Hospital to be a superior regional hospital and improve the health of the citizens of the region it serves.

ELIGIBILITY:
The Trust considers proposals from nonprofit organizations and institutions within the Trust's interest areas.

GEOGRAPHIC RESTRICTIONS:
Allentown, Pennsylvania and surrounding area.

FINANCIAL DATA:
Amount of support per award: Varies.
Total amount of support: $4,033,608 for the year 2010.

REPRESENTATIVE AWARDS:
$4,317,074 to Lehigh Valley Hospital Network, Department of Community Health, Health Studies and Education-Division of Education-Essential Infrastructure and Project Support; $2,700,000 to Lehigh Valley Hospital Network, Department of Community Health, Health Studies and Education, Division of Community Health and Health Studies-Reorganization of Community Health and Health Studies; $915,000 to Lehigh Valley Hospital Network, Department of Family Medicine-Transforming Primary Care: Leadership in Education, Access and Quality (P4); $165,793 to Lehigh Valley Hospital Network, Department of Community Health and Health Studies and the Department of Pediatrics-Pediatric Asthma; $50,000 to Lehigh Valley Hospital Network, Telehealth Services-Telehealth Evaluation; $30,000 to Lehigh Valley Hospital Network, Organizational Development-Crucial Conversations for Case Managers and Patient Care Specialists.

APPLICATION INFORMATION:
Funding requests should be initiated with a letter of intent from the applicant. The letter should be two to four pages summarizing the need, objective, strategy, evaluation, budget and duration.
Duration: Varies.
Deadline: Submit letter of intent by August 1 and March 1. Funding notification by early March and October, respectively.

PUBLICATIONS:
Annual report.

IRS IDENTIFICATION NUMBER: 23-6627932

TRUSTEES:
Denise M. Gargan
John P. Jones, III
Lawrence P. Levitt, M.D.
Carol M. McCarthy, Ph.D., J.D.
James O. Wolliscroft, M.D.

STAFF:
Edward F. Meehan, M.P.H., Executive Director
Ronald C. Dendas, M.S., Program Officer
Joseph J. Napolitano, Ph.D., M.P.H., Program Officer
Bridget I. Rassler, Administrative Manager
Regina M. Marks, Program Secretary

ADDRESS INQUIRIES TO:
Edward F. Meehan, Executive Director
(See address above.)

QUANTUM FOUNDATION [1559]
2701 North Australian Avenue, Suite 200
West Palm Beach, FL 33407
(561) 832-7497
Fax: (561) 832-5794

E-MAIL ADDRESS:
eric@quantumfnd.org

WEB SITE ADDRESS:
www.quantumfnd.org

FOUNDED: 1995

AREAS OF INTEREST:
Health care access, science and health education, and health care workforce.

TYPE:
Capital grants; Challenge/matching grants; Demonstration grants; Matching gifts; Project/program grants; Seed money grants.

YEAR PROGRAM STARTED: 1997

PURPOSE:
To increase health care access, improve science and health education, and enhance the health care workforce.

LEGAL BASIS:
Private foundation.

ELIGIBILITY:
Eligible organizations must be IRS 501(c)(3) tax-exempt or state or local governments providing services in Palm Beach County.

GEOGRAPHIC RESTRICTIONS:
Palm Beach County, Florida.

FINANCIAL DATA:
Amount of support per award: Varies.
Total amount of support: Approximately $6,000,000 annually.

NUMBER OF APPLICANTS MOST RECENT YEAR:
199.

NUMBER OF AWARDS: 105 for the year 2009.

APPLICATION INFORMATION:
Submit a Letter of Inquiry at the Foundation's web site.

STAFF:
Stacey Amodio, Program Officer

ADDRESS INQUIRIES TO:
Stacey Amodio, Program Officer
E-mail: stacey@quantumfnd.org

JOSEPHINE G. RUSSELL TRUST [1560]

59 Lucerne Drive
Andover, MA 01810
(978) 500-3171

E-MAIL ADDRESS:
russelltrust@yahoo.com

FOUNDED: 1933

AREAS OF INTEREST:
Education, health care, poverty and social services.

TYPE:
General operating grants; Scholarships.

PURPOSE:
To provide care, healing and nursing of the sick and injured; to provide relief and aid to the poor; to provide training and education of the young; to assist in any other manner of social service in the City of Lawrence.

LEGAL BASIS:
Private charitable trust.

ELIGIBILITY:
Eligible organizations must be IRS 501(c)(3) tax-exempt and serve the Lawrence area. No grants to individuals. No grants are made for endowments, equipment, capital campaigns, construction or renovations of buildings and facilities. No matching gifts.

Organizations intending to submit applications for funds must be able to demonstrate that, if funds are awarded by the Trust, the program will confer a direct benefit to Lawrence residents who are sick, injured or poor; or for education or in any other manner of social services upon the people of the city of Lawrence, MA.

GEOGRAPHIC RESTRICTIONS:
Lawrence, Massachusetts.

FINANCIAL DATA:
Amount of support per award: Minimum $1,000.
Total amount of support: $390,000 for the year 2010.

NUMBER OF APPLICANTS MOST RECENT YEAR:
43.

NUMBER OF AWARDS: 38.

APPLICATION INFORMATION:
Guidelines are available upon request. Applicants may submit a written proposal and must include a copy of the IRS tax determination letter, budget and list of trustees in the organization.

Once application is completed, individual copies must be sent to all designated trustees.
Duration: One year. Renewal possible.
Deadline: January 31.

PUBLICATIONS:
Guidelines.

ADDRESS INQUIRIES TO:
Marsha Rich
(See phone number and e-mail address above.)

EUNICE KENNEDY SHRIVER NATIONAL INSTITUTE OF CHILD HEALTH AND HUMAN DEVELOPMENT [1561]

Executive Building, Room 4B05
6100 Executive Boulevard
MSC 7510
Bethesda, MD 20852-7510
(301) 496-5098
Fax: (301) 480-9791

WEB SITE ADDRESS:
www.nichd.nih.gov

FOUNDED: 1963

AREAS OF INTEREST:
All health sciences pertaining to mothers and children.

NAME(S) OF PROGRAMS:
● **Child Development and Behavior Branch**
● **Endocrinology, Nutrition and Growth Branch**
● **Global Network for Women's and Children's Health Research**
● **Obstetric and Pediatric Pharmacology Branch**
● **Pediatric, Adolescent and Maternal AIDS Branch**

TYPE:
Conferences/seminars; Development grants; Fellowships; General operating grants; Project/program grants; Training grants; Research contracts. Project grants and research contracts to expand the health and well-being of individuals from the moment of conception and extending through the later teenage years.

PURPOSE:
To discover new knowledge through research.

LEGAL BASIS:
Public Health Service Act, Sections 301(c), 444 and 472.

ELIGIBILITY:
Universities, colleges, medical, dental and nursing schools, schools of public health, laboratories, hospitals, state and local health departments, other public or private nonprofit institutions and commercial organizations are eligible. Individuals may apply for grants for academic and research training. They must have a professional or scientific degree and be citizens or permanent residents of the U.S.

FINANCIAL DATA:
Amount of support per award: Varies.

APPLICATION INFORMATION:
Duration: One-year to multiyear funding.

SICKKIDS FOUNDATION [1562]

525 University Avenue, 14th Floor
Toronto ON M5G 2L3 Canada
(416) 813-6166 ext. 2354
(800) 661-1083
Fax: (416) 813-7311

E-MAIL ADDRESS:
national.grants@sickkidsfoundation.com

WEB SITE ADDRESS:
www.sickkidsfoundation.com/grants

FOUNDED: 1973

AREAS OF INTEREST:
Healthier children; a better world.

NAME(S) OF PROGRAMS:
● **Community Conference Grants Program**
● **New Investigator Research Grants**

TYPE:
Awards/prizes; Conferences/seminars; Project/program grants; Research grants. Grants for research for subspecialty training of career physicians and scientists to equip them for work in child health disciplines that are underdeveloped in Canada.

YEAR PROGRAM STARTED: 1974

PURPOSE:
To promote quality programs in child health, research and public health education in the field.

LEGAL BASIS:
Public foundation with charitable registration.

ELIGIBILITY:
Grants are paid to recognized Canadian charitable organizations. Institutions, agencies and other groups working in the field of child health in Canada may apply. Applications are subjected to peer assessment as to the merits of the project, feasibility, and significance for child health and study design criteria as appropriate.

GEOGRAPHIC RESTRICTIONS:
Canada.

FINANCIAL DATA:
Amount of support per award: $5,000 to $100,000 per year.
Total amount of support: Varies.

NUMBER OF APPLICANTS MOST RECENT YEAR:
100 for the year 2010-11.

NUMBER OF AWARDS: 15 for the year 2010-11.

APPLICATION INFORMATION:
Application guidelines are available online. To discuss eligibility, contact grants office directly.
Duration: Maximum of three years with annual review of progress. Limited renewal possibilities.
Deadline: Community Conference Grants: January 31, May 31 and September 30. New Investigator Research Grant: Fall.

ADDRESS INQUIRIES TO:
National Grants Program
(See address above.)

SISTERS OF ST. JOSEPH HEALTHCARE FOUNDATION [1563]

440 South Batavia
Orange, CA 92868-3998
(714) 633-8121 ext. 7109
Fax: (714) 744-3135

E-MAIL ADDRESS:
rfox@csjorange.org

WEB SITE ADDRESS:
www.csjorange.org

FOUNDED: 1992

AREAS OF INTEREST:
Health care and health access.

TYPE:
General operating grants; Project/program grants. The Foundation sponsors or supports long-term efforts which are closely identified with the Sisters of St. Joseph of Orange and their mission of bringing unity and healing where divisiveness and oppression exist.

PURPOSE:
To fund programs which directly serve the needs of the underserved, especially families and children at risk.

LEGAL BASIS:
Public foundation.

ELIGIBILITY:
Applicants must be nonprofit organizations operating in Humbolt County, southern California and San Francisco Bay area which have programs that directly serve the needs of the underserved, especially families and children at risk, as well as programs of education and advocacy which are directed at improving health and access to health care. Religious organizations also receive support. A Sister of St. Joseph of Orange endorsement or Vice President for Mission Integration endorsement and/or involvement is required. Capital projects will not be considered.

The Foundation supports the concept of Healthy Communities, and desires to fund programs and organizations that:
(1) provide direct health-related services;
(2) support and transform the individual, social, economic, institutional, and cultural aspects of communities;
(3) provide change within larger societal systems to benefit low-income and at-risk populations and;
(4) develop the leadership and capacity for self-determination of those served by the Foundation's funding.

GEOGRAPHIC RESTRICTIONS:
Southern California, Humbolt County and San Francisco Bay area.

APPLICATION INFORMATION:
Duration: One year.
Deadline: Contact Foundation for exact dates.

ADDRESS INQUIRIES TO:
Sister Regina Fox, S.S.N.D.
Program Director
(See address above.)

GERTRUDE E. SKELLY CHARITABLE FOUNDATION

4600 North Ocean Boulevard
Suite 206
Boynton Beach, FL 33435
(561) 276-1008
Fax: (561) 272-2793

E-MAIL ADDRESS:
skelly@hhk.com

TYPE:
Challenge/matching grants;
Conferences/seminars; Internships;
Project/program grants; Research grants;
Scholarships; Training grants.

See entry 1758 for full listing.

THE CHRISTOPHER D. SMITHERS FOUNDATION, INC. [1564]

P.O. Box 67
Mill Neck, NY 11765
(516) 676-0067
Fax: (516) 676-0323

E-MAIL ADDRESS:
info@smithersfoundation.org

WEB SITE ADDRESS:
www.smithersfoundation.org

FOUNDED: 1952

AREAS OF INTEREST:
Education and prevention of alcoholism.

NAME(S) OF PROGRAMS:
● **The Ambassador of Hope Award**
● **The Adele C. Smithers Award**
● **The R. Brinkley Smithers Annual Award**
● **The R. Brinkley Smithers Distinguished Scientist Award**
● **The R. Brinkley Smithers Lifetime Achievement Award**

TYPE:
Conferences/seminars; Project/program grants; Research grants; Technical assistance; Training grants.

YEAR PROGRAM STARTED: 1952

PURPOSE:
To prevent alcoholism through education.

REPRESENTATIVE AWARDS:
$28,252 to Alcoholism Council of New York, New York, NY; $12,500 to American Society of Addiction Medicine (ASAM), Chevy Chase, MD; $50,000 to Grenville Baker Boys & Girls Club, Locust Valley, NY.

APPLICATION INFORMATION:
Grant proposal must include:
(1) brief description of the program and grant amount requested (budget);
(2) copy of 501(c)(3) nonprofit status and;
(3) copy of most recent annual report.

PUBLICATIONS:
Annual report.

OFFICERS:
Adele C. Smithers, President
Thomas D. Croci, M.S., Ph.D., Vice President/Treasurer
Thomas D.A. Croci, Esq., Secretary

DIRECTORS:
Joseph J. Calandra, M.D.
Thomas D. Croci, M.S., Ph.D.
Thomas D.A. Croci, Esq.
M. Elizabeth Brothers, Honorary Director

ARTEMAS W. STEARNS TRUST [1565]

59 Lucerne Drive
Andover, MA 01810
(978) 500-3171

E-MAIL ADDRESS:
stearnstrust@yahoo.com

FOUNDED: 1896

AREAS OF INTEREST:
The aged and poor, health care in the greater Lawrence area, social services and education.

TYPE:
General operating grants; Project/program grants; Scholarships. Elder and infirm support.

YEAR PROGRAM STARTED: 1896

PURPOSE:
To pay income to such nonprofit and charitable homes, nursing homes, convalescent homes, retirement homes, sanitaria, homes for the aged, hospitals, agencies and such other similar institutions, organizations and agencies as may provide for or care, in whole or in part, for the indigent aged people of both sexes; to provide relief of the deserving poor of the City of Lawrence, without distinction of nationality or religious belief.

LEGAL BASIS:
Private charitable trust.

ELIGIBILITY:
Eligible organizations must be IRS 501(c)(3) tax-exempt. No grants to individuals. No grants are made for endowments, equipment, capital campaigns, construction or renovations of buildings and facilities.

Organizations intending to submit applications for funds must be able to demonstrate that, if funds are awarded by the Trust, the program will confer a direct benefit upon the indigent aged people or to the deserving poor of the city of Lawrence, MA exclusively.

GEOGRAPHIC RESTRICTIONS:
Lawrence, Massachusetts.

FINANCIAL DATA:
Amount of support per award: Minimum $1,000.
Total amount of support: $194,000 for the year 2010.

NUMBER OF APPLICANTS MOST RECENT YEAR: 33.

NUMBER OF AWARDS: 28.

APPLICATION INFORMATION:
Guidelines are sent upon request. Applicants may submit a written proposal and must include a copy of the IRS tax determination letter, budget and list of trustees in the organization.

Once application is completed, individual copies must be sent to all designated trustees. Contact the Trust for complete guidelines.
Duration: One year. Renewal possible.
Deadline: January 31.

PUBLICATIONS:
Application guidelines.

ADDRESS INQUIRIES TO:
Marsha Rich
(See phone number and e-mail address above.)

U.S. DEPARTMENT OF HEALTH AND HUMAN SERVICES [1566]

Health Resources and Services Administration
Bureau of Primary Health Care
Parklawn Building, 5600 Fishers Lane
Room 17C26
Rockville, MD 20857
(301) 594-4300
(301) 594-4329
Fax: (301) 594-4997

WEB SITE ADDRESS:
www.hrsa.gov
www.bphc.hrsa.gov

FOUNDED: 1976

AREAS OF INTEREST:
Assisting communities located in medically underserved areas to develop needed primary health care services.

CONSULTING OR VOLUNTEER SERVICES:
Information and technical assistance is available from U.S. Public Health Service Regional Office staff.

NAME(S) OF PROGRAMS:
● **The Health Center Program**

TYPE:
Project/program grants. Grants may be made for planning and development of a community health center and for operations.

YEAR PROGRAM STARTED: 1975

PURPOSE:
To provide primary health care in ambulatory care settings located in severely medically underserved areas and to develop a network of services involving as many other health programs and facilities operating in the area as possible; to arrange for other federal programs not operating in the area to establish services within the federally funded primary care center whenever possible.

LEGAL BASIS:
Government agency.

ELIGIBILITY:
Grants may be made to public or private not-for-profit entities. Area to be served must be medically underserved. Priority will be given to areas of highest need.

GEOGRAPHIC RESTRICTIONS:
United States.

FINANCIAL DATA:
Amount of support per award: Approximately $600,000.

Total amount of support: Approximately $1.6 billion per fiscal year.

Matching fund requirements: The applicant must assume part of the project costs determined on a case-by-case basis.

COOPERATIVE FUNDING PROGRAMS: Cooperative funding with other federal programs, such as Migrant Health Centers, National Health Service Corps, MCH, or Mental Health Alcohol and Drug Abuse are encouraged, as well as cooperation with state and local programs.

APPLICATION INFORMATION:
Information available from HRSA Grant Application Center, 901 Russell Avenue, Suite 450, Gaithersburg, MD 20879, or call (877) 477-2123.

Duration: Project periods may be up to five years, with annual budget periods. The project may be renewed for additional years of support based on its performance and the need for additional federal support.

PUBLICATIONS:
Application guidelines.

STAFF:
Dr. Jim Macrae, Associate Administrator to Bureau of Primary Health Care Director

ADDRESS INQUIRIES TO:
Tonya Bowers
Director of Policy and Program Development
(See address above.)

U.S. DEPARTMENT OF HEALTH AND HUMAN SERVICES   [1567]
Centers for Medicare and Medicaid Services
7500 Security Boulevard
Baltimore, MD 21244-1850
(410) 786-3000
(877) 267-2323
Fax: (410) 786-1008

WEB SITE ADDRESS:
www.cms.gov

FOUNDED: 1967

NAME(S) OF PROGRAMS:
● **Medicaid**

TYPE:
Formula grants. Financial assistance to states for in-and outpatient hospital services, other laboratory services, home health care, family planning, physicians' services and early diagnosis and treatment for persons who are medically needy.

LEGAL BASIS:
Title XIX, Social Security Act as amended; Public Law 89-97; Public Law 90-248; Public Law 91-56; 42 U.S.C. 1396, et seq. Public Law 92-223; Public Law 92-603.

ELIGIBILITY:
State and local welfare agencies operating under an approved Medicaid plan are eligible for support.

GEOGRAPHIC RESTRICTIONS:
United States.

FINANCIAL DATA:
Matching grants, with Federal share ranging from 50 to 76.29% for fiscal year 2008.

Amount of support per award: Varies.

Total amount of support: Varies.

APPLICATION INFORMATION:
Application forms are available from the address above or from regional or local offices of the Medical Services Administration to whom applications should be submitted.

Duration: Quarterly.

Deadline: States must submit quarterly estimates of funds no later than May 15, August 15, November 15 and February 15 in order to receive quarterly grant awards.

UNITED HOSPITAL FUND OF NEW YORK   [1568]
1411 Broadway, 12th Floor
New York, NY 10018
(212) 494-0761
Fax: (212) 494-0801

E-MAIL ADDRESS:
hholmes@uhfnyc.org

WEB SITE ADDRESS:
www.uhfnyc.org

FOUNDED: 1879

AREAS OF INTEREST:
Strengthening health care finances, expanding health insurance coverage, improving quality of care, redesigning health care services and promoting health care volunteerism.

NAME(S) OF PROGRAMS:
● **Health Care Improvement Grant Program**

TYPE:
Project/program grants; Seed money grants.

YEAR PROGRAM STARTED: 1938

PURPOSE:
To provide support to innovative projects by nonprofit hospitals and health care and other organizations to improve the quality of health care for all New Yorkers.

LEGAL BASIS:
Public charity.

ELIGIBILITY:
Nonprofit 501(c)(3) tax-exempt organizations are eligible for support. No grants to individuals, capital or endowment campaigns or general operating grants.

GEOGRAPHIC RESTRICTIONS:
New York, New York.

FINANCIAL DATA:
Amount of support per award: $30,000 to $75,000.

Total amount of support: Approximately $1,500,000 for the year 2010-11.

NUMBER OF APPLICANTS MOST RECENT YEAR: 75.

NUMBER OF AWARDS: 30.

REPRESENTATIVE AWARDS:
$40,000 to Charles B. Wang Community Health Center; $75,000 to New Yorkers for Accessible Health Coverage; $50,000 to New York City Health and Hospitals Corporation.

APPLICATION INFORMATION:
Required documentation includes grant application form, budget, specifics regarding the particular project to be funded and sources of support.

Duration: One year. Nonrenewable.

Deadline: March 1, July 2 and November 1. Notification one week after board meets.

PUBLICATIONS:
Annual report; application guidelines.

OFFICERS:
J. Barclay Collins, II, Chairman
James R. Tallon, Jr., President
Sheila M. Abrams, Senior Vice President and Treasurer
William M. Evarts, Jr., Vice Chairman
Patricia S. Levinson, Vice Chairman
David A. Gould, Senior Vice President
Sally J. Rogers, Senior Vice President
Michael Birnbaum, Vice President
Deborah E. Halper, Vice President
Stephanie L. Davis, Corporate Secretary

BOARD OF DIRECTORS:
Richard A. Berman
Jo Ivey Boufford, M.D.
Rev. John E. Carrington
Philip Chapman
J. Barclay Collins, II
Richard Cotton
Richard K. De Scherer
William M. Evarts, Jr.
Michael R. Golding, M.D.
Josh N. Kuriloff
Patricia S. Levinson
Howard P. Milstein
Susana R. Morales, M.D.
Robert C. Osborne
Peter J. Powers
Katherine Osborn Roberts
Mary H. Schachne
John C. Simons
Howard Smith
Michael A. Stocker, M.D.
Most Rev. Joseph M. Sullivan
James R. Tallon, Jr.
Frederick W. Telling, Ph.D.
Mary Beth Tully

ADDRESS INQUIRIES TO:
Hollis Holmes, Grants Manager
(See address above.)

*SPECIAL STIPULATIONS:
Grants to New York City organizations for
projects of primary benefit to the city.

THE WHITEHORSE FOUNDATION   [1569]

1200 Fifth Avenue, Suite 1300
Seattle, WA 98101-3151
(206) 515-2131
Fax: (206) 622-7673

E-MAIL ADDRESS:
c.erickson@seattlefoundation.org

WEB SITE ADDRESS:
www.seattlefoundation.org

FOUNDED: 1989

AREAS OF INTEREST:
Preventative human services.

TYPE:
Capital grants; Development grants;
Project/program grants; Training grants.
Program development.

YEAR PROGRAM STARTED: 1990

PURPOSE:
To fund comprehensive preventive social
service programs in Snohomish County, WA.

LEGAL BASIS:
Community foundation.

ELIGIBILITY:
Applicant organizations must be IRS
501(c)(3) tax-exempt. No grants to
individuals.

GEOGRAPHIC RESTRICTIONS:
Snohomish County, Washington.

FINANCIAL DATA:
Amount of support per award: $40,000 to
$150,000.

NUMBER OF APPLICANTS MOST RECENT YEAR:
10.

NUMBER OF AWARDS: 5.

APPLICATION INFORMATION:
Applications must include a copy of the IRS
tax determination letter. Applications are by
invitation only.
Duration: One year.

STAFF:
Ceil Erickson, Program Director

ADDRESS INQUIRIES TO:
Ceil Erickson, Program Director
(See address above.)

MR. AND MRS. P.A. WOODWARD'S FOUNDATION   [1570]

1155 West Pender Street, Suite 710
Vancouver BC V6E 2P4 Canada
(604) 682-8116
Fax: (604) 682-8153

E-MAIL ADDRESS:
woodwds@telus.net

WEB SITE ADDRESS:
www.woodwardfoundation.ca

FOUNDED: 1951

AREAS OF INTEREST:
Health care.

TYPE:
The Foundation supports those projects
which primarily affect the people of the
Province of British Columbia where there is
clear indication of the health benefit
anticipated. The Foundation is charged with
aiding in the purchase of the latest medical
equipment of proven performance that would
permit clinical studies to be carried out for
the direct benefit of the patient. A preference
was expressed for clinical research for and
with the patient as contrasted to that done
primarily in the laboratory with consequent
uncertain or delayed benefits.

PURPOSE:
To assist in projects which could contribute
to better health care.

LEGAL BASIS:
Charitable foundation.

ELIGIBILITY:
Organizations applying for funding must be
domiciled within the Province of British
Columbia. All individuals and organizations
applying must be in possession of a
Charitable Gift Registration Number as
issued by the Department of National
Revenue of Canada.

The Foundation will consider applications in
the following general areas:
(1) health care equipment of proven
effectiveness and;
(2) special projects which will benefit the
health of British Columbians.

The Foundation will not support routine
operational budgets, fundamental research not
directly related to patient care, conferences or
annual meetings, endowments or capital
building costs.

GEOGRAPHIC RESTRICTIONS:
British Columbia, Canada.

FINANCIAL DATA:
Amount of support per award: Grants vary in
amount, depending upon the needs and
nature of the request.

NUMBER OF AWARDS: Up to 30.

APPLICATION INFORMATION:
Letter of application, in duplicate, should
contain the following:
(1) name and executive officer of applicant
organization and membership of its board of
directors;
(2) the organization's charitable gift
registration number from the Department of
National Revenue of Canada;
(3) name, title, address and telephone number
of person in charge of the project;
(4) description and budget of the project;
(5) dates project will be started and
completed and;
(6) a copy of the applicant's latest year-end
audited financial statements.
Duration: Projects will be supported on an
annual basis with continuation of support, if
required, based on a satisfactory annual
progress report.
Deadline: Prior to mid-January for April
Board of Directors meeting and prior to
mid-July for October meeting.

PUBLICATIONS:
Mr. and Mrs. P.A. Woodward's Foundation,
booklet.

OFFICERS:
Leo P. Sauve, President
E. Wallace Campbell, First Vice President
Christopher C. Woodward, Second Vice
President

Christine Alexander, Secretary-Treasurer
Dr. J. Wm. Ibbott, Medical Advisor

MEMBERS AND DIRECTORS:
Robert J. Buchanan
E. Wallace Campbell
Jill Leversage
Gregory J.D. McKinstry
Hon. Madam Justice Mary V. Newbury
Don Potvin
Leo P. Sauve
Christopher C. Woodward

ADDRESS INQUIRIES TO:
Dr. J. Wm. Ibbott, Medical Advisor
(See address above.)

Social welfare

AAA FOUNDATION FOR TRAFFIC SAFETY

607 14th Street, N.W.
Suite 201
Washington, DC 20005
(202) 638-5944 ext. 7
Fax: (202) 638-5943

E-MAIL ADDRESS:
jgrabowski@aaafoundation.org

WEB SITE ADDRESS:
www.aaafoundation.org

TYPE:
Demonstration grants; Project/program
grants; Research grants; Research contracts.

See entry 1509 for full listing.

THE ABELARD FOUNDATION-EAST   [1571]

P.O. Box 148
Lincoln, MA 01773

E-MAIL ADDRESS:
eastabel@aol.com

WEB SITE ADDRESS:
foundationcenter.org/grantmaker/abelardeast/

AREAS OF INTEREST:
Progressive social change, community
organizing, civil and human rights.

TYPE:
General operating grants; Project/program
grants.

PURPOSE:
To support local progressive social change
activities that expand and protect civil
liberties and civil and human rights, and
promote and strengthen community
involvement in, and control over, the
decisions that affect their lives.

ELIGIBILITY:
Applicants must represent or be associated
with a nonprofit, 501(c)(3) tax-exempt
organization. Priority is given to projects that
are in their first years of development and
have budgets less than $300,000.

GEOGRAPHIC RESTRICTIONS:
Eastern United States, east of the Mississippi
River.

FINANCIAL DATA:
Amount of support per award: Average
$10,000.
Total amount of support: Approximately
$140,000 annually.

APPLICATION INFORMATION:
Applicants should submit one copy of a proposal (no more than seven to 10 pages) which includes:
(1) background of the organization;
(2) description of the work for which funds are being sought;
(3) explanation of need and;
(4) impact the project will have.

Proposals prepared in a "common application" format will also be accepted.

Applying organizations must include IRS 501(c)(3) determination letter.

Duration: One year. Up to two renewals possible.

Deadline: Applications mailed by March 15 will be reviewed for the spring meeting, and applications mailed by September 15 will be reviewed for the fall meeting.

ADDRESS INQUIRIES TO:
Susan Collins, Trustee
The Abelard Foundation-East
(See address above.)

THE ABELARD FOUNDATION-WEST [1572]

c/o Common Counsel Foundation
405 14th Street, Suite 809
Oakland, CA 94612
(510) 834-2995
Fax: (510) 834-2998

E-MAIL ADDRESS:
grantsadmin@commoncounsel.org

WEB SITE ADDRESS:
www.commoncounsel.org

FOUNDED: 1958

AREAS OF INTEREST:
Social change, community development, environment, public policy and empowerment.

TYPE:
General operating grants; Project/program grants.

YEAR PROGRAM STARTED: 1953

PURPOSE:
To support grassroots social change organizations which reflect the communities in which they are based; to expand community control over economic, social and environmental decisions affecting the communities' well-being; to build a strong informed voice on public policy issues.

LEGAL BASIS:
Family foundation.

ELIGIBILITY:
Grants made only to IRS 501(c)(3) tax-exempt organizations. No grants are made to social service programs offering ongoing or direct delivery of services, medical, educational or cultural institutions, emergency funding, scholarship funds or other aids to individuals, organizations which have sophisticated fund-raising capabilities, capital expenditure, construction or renovation programs or programs undertaken at government initiative. Priority is given to grassroots community organizations in low-income areas. Organizational budget must be $400,000 or less.

GEOGRAPHIC RESTRICTIONS:
Western United States, west of the Mississippi.

FINANCIAL DATA:
Amount of support per award: $6,000 to $12,000.
Total amount of support: $260,000 for the year 2010.

NUMBER OF APPLICANTS MOST RECENT YEAR:
300.

NUMBER OF AWARDS: 30.

REPRESENTATIVE AWARDS:
East Bay Alliance for a Sustainable Economy; Montana People's Action; Young Workers United.

APPLICATION INFORMATION:
The Foundation has an open Letter of Inquiry (LOI) process. However, full proposals are accepted by invitation only. The first step in submitting a letter of inquiry is to thoroughly review the eligibility criteria and grantmaking guidelines to ensure that your organization is a good fit for the grant program. Organizations that meet the eligibility and funding criteria are encouraged to submit the letter of inquiry form.

The Foundation's western office, at the address listed above, reviews grants from groups located in the Northern Rockies, the Great Basin, the Northwest, the Southwest and California. Organizations based east of the Mississippi should contact the Foundation's eastern office at Abelard Foundation/East, P.O. Box 148, Lincoln, MA 01773.

Duration: Most grants are for one year.

Deadline: January 15 and June 15.

ADDRESS INQUIRIES TO:
Grants Administrator
Common Counsel Foundation
(See address above.)

EMMA J. ADAMS MEMORIAL FUND, INC. [1573]

860 Park Avenue
New York, NY 10075
(212) 327-0493
Fax: (212) 327-0593

FOUNDED: 1936

AREAS OF INTEREST:
Geriatric institutions, welfare, elderly, and needy, mostly through organizations.

TYPE:
Grants-in-aid. Financial support and organized aid to geriatric, needy and/or elderly institutional agencies and occasionally to referred respectable, aged indigent persons in financial difficulty through no fault of their own, in the greater New York City area.

YEAR PROGRAM STARTED: 1936

PURPOSE:
To aid elderly, needy and indigent people and geriatric institutions.

LEGAL BASIS:
Nonprofit corporation.

ELIGIBILITY:
Most grants are awarded to operating geriatric institutions.

No scholarships, program grants, administrative expenses, and no brick-and-mortar grants.

GEOGRAPHIC RESTRICTIONS:
Greater New York area.

FINANCIAL DATA:
Amount of support per award: $500 average.

Total amount of support: Average $125,000 per year; $193,965 for the year 2008.

NUMBER OF APPLICANTS MOST RECENT YEAR:
Over 200.

NUMBER OF AWARDS: Approximately 35.

REPRESENTATIVE AWARDS:
Stanley M. Isaacs Center; Episcopal Mission Society; St. Bartholomew's Outreach Service; Meals on Wheels, Inc.

APPLICATION INFORMATION:
Application forms available upon request. The letter must indicate the referral source. No telephone requests honored.

Deadline: September 1.

IRS IDENTIFICATION NUMBER: 13-6116503

DIRECTORS:
Jill Arkwright
Dr. Mat D. Finch
Rev. Bruce Forbes
Rev. Elizabeth Jacks
Betsy Rowe
Sally Saran
Carolyn Swayze

ADDRESS INQUIRIES TO:
Edward R. Finch, Jr., President
(See address above.)

JUDD S. ALEXANDER FOUNDATION [1574]

500 First Street, Suite 10
Wausau, WI 54403
(715) 845-4556
Fax: (715) 843-9018

E-MAIL ADDRESS:
office@alexanderprop.org

WEB SITE ADDRESS:
juddsalexanderfoundation.org

FOUNDED: 1978

AREAS OF INTEREST:
Education, recreation, human services, children's services and economic development.

TYPE:
Capital grants; Challenge/matching grants; Project/program grants; Seed money grants. Support is provided for capital building and emergency funds.

YEAR PROGRAM STARTED: 1978

LEGAL BASIS:
Private foundation.

ELIGIBILITY:
Organizations classified as 501(c)(3) by the IRS can apply. The Foundation does not make grants to individuals or private businesses.

GEOGRAPHIC RESTRICTIONS:
Marathon County, Wisconsin.

APPLICATION INFORMATION:
Five copies, unbound, of the proposal should be submitted. The Foundation has an application form available, should the applicant prefer to use a form. A fully reviewable proposal will include:
(1) a cover page with the exact name and location of the proposed grant recipient, along with the name, title, address and phone number of a contact at the organization;
(2) an application narrative, which includes a description of the organization's main activities and whether it is a public, private or not-for-profit entity, a description of the project or activity for which funding is requested, and the specific outcomes and

goals of the project and;
(3) a project budget which includes revenue and expense pages and a budget narrative.

The following items must also be attached:
(1) the organization's current annual operating budget, including revenues and expenses;
(2) a list of the organization's governing body and its officers, showing business, professional and/or community affiliations;
(3) letters of support and letters from other agencies indicating their intent to collaborate (as appropriate);
(4) other documents the applicant feels supplement the above information, provided it is not duplicative of other material or information contained in the narratives or budget presentation;
(5) the most recent audited financial statements and;
(6) the most recent IRS determination letter.

ADDRESS INQUIRIES TO:
Gary W. Freels, President
(See address above.)

THE ALLSTATE FOUNDATION [1575]

2775 Sanders Road
Suite F-4
Northbrook, IL 60062-6127

E-MAIL ADDRESS:
grants@allstate.com

WEB SITE ADDRESS:
allstatefoundation.org

FOUNDED: 1952

AREAS OF INTEREST:
Teen safe drivers and economic empowerment for victims of domestic violence.

TYPE:
Matching gifts; Project/program grants. Program support in the Foundation's areas of focus; matching gifts for higher education only.

YEAR PROGRAM STARTED: 1952

PURPOSE:
To assist deserving organizations serving the fields of teen safe drivers and economic empowerment for victims of domestic violence.

LEGAL BASIS:
Corporate foundation.

ELIGIBILITY:
Grants are made only to nonprofit 501(c)(3) organizations.

GEOGRAPHIC RESTRICTIONS:
United States.

FINANCIAL DATA:
Amount of support per award: National programs: $100,000; Local/regional grants: $5,000 to $20,000.
Total amount of support: $18,300,000 for the year 2011.
Matching fund requirements: For colleges and universities.

APPLICATION INFORMATION:
Information and guidelines are available online.
Duration: One year. Renewal based on program outcome and results.

PUBLICATIONS:
Guidelines.

IRS IDENTIFICATION NUMBER: 36-6116535

STAFF:
Jan Epstein, Executive Director

ADDRESS INQUIRIES TO:
See e-mail address above.

*SPECIAL STIPULATIONS:
Funding for domestic programs only.

THE CALIFORNIA ENDOWMENT

1000 North Alameda Street
Los Angeles, CA 90012
(213) 928-8645
(800) 449-4149
Fax: (213) 928-8818

E-MAIL ADDRESS:
destrada@calendow.org

WEB SITE ADDRESS:
www.calendow.org

TYPE:
Challenge/matching grants; Conferences/seminars; General operating grants; Project/program grants; Technical assistance.

See entry 1518 for full listing.

CAMPBELL FOUNDATION, INC.

705 York Road
Towson, MD 21204
(410) 828-1961
Fax: (410) 821-8814

E-MAIL ADDRESS:
lsperato@stoycpa.com

TYPE:
Capital grants; General operating grants; Project/program grants.

See entry 1178 for full listing.

CATHOLIC CHARITIES USA [1576]

66 Canal Center Plaza, Suite 600
Alexandria, VA 22314
(703) 549-1390
Fax: (703) 549-1656

WEB SITE ADDRESS:
www.catholiccharitiesusa.org

AREAS OF INTEREST:
The aged, community services, homeless, emergency relief and family services.

TYPE:
Assistantships; Project/program grants.

PURPOSE:
To provide service to those in need and to advocate justice in societal structures.

LEGAL BASIS:
Nonprofit organization.

ELIGIBILITY:
Grants are only offered to the 1,700 Catholic Charities member agencies. Any organization which is not affiliated with Catholic Charities is ineligible for support.

GEOGRAPHIC RESTRICTIONS:
United States.

FINANCIAL DATA:
Amount of support per award: Varies depending on project and need of the geographic area being served.
Total amount of support: Varies.

APPLICATION INFORMATION:
Organizations should contact their local or diocesan chapters of Catholic Charities for application information and materials.
Duration: Up to five years.

CHRISTOPHER COLUMBUS FELLOWSHIP FOUNDATION [1577]

110 Genesee Street
Suite 390
Auburn, NY 13021
(315) 258-0090
Fax: (315) 258-0093

E-MAIL ADDRESS:
judithmscolumbus@cs.com

WEB SITE ADDRESS:
www.columbusfdn.org

FOUNDED: 1992

AREAS OF INTEREST:
To encourage and support research, study and labor designed to produce new discoveries in all fields of endeavor for the benefit of mankind.

NAME(S) OF PROGRAMS:
● **Agriscience Awards**
● **Christopher Columbus Awards**
● **Homeland Security Awards**
● **Life Sciences Awards**

TYPE:
Project/program grants; Research grants; Seed money grants. In partnership with the American Farm Bureau Federation, the Foundation presents eight Agriscience Awards and research funds. The mission of this partnership is to recognize, through monetary awards, two adult scientists and provide research funds; three current secondary school educators; and three current secondary school students who are judged to exemplify excellence in the field of agriscience and to highlight the importance of agriculture in the 21st century.

Christopher Columbus Awards are given to eight finalist teams of middle school students. The competition asks the students to identify a problem in their community and then solve it using the scientific method. The eight teams and their coaches win an all-expense paid trip to Walt Disney World®, attend the Christopher Columbus Academy, vie for savings bonds and the $25,000 community grant.

In partnership with AgustaWestland North America, the Foundation presents four $25,000 Homeland Security Awards. To honor "cutting edge" innovations in the vast arena of homeland security, a $25,000 award will be presented in each of the following four fields: (1) Biological, Radiological, Nuclear, Chemical and Explosive Attacks; (2) Border and Transportation Security; (3) Cyber Security and Information Sharing and; (4) Emergency Responses to Natural and Man-made Disasters.

In partnership with the U.S. Chamber of Commerce, the Foundation presents seven Life Sciences Awards and research funds. The mission of this partnership is to recognize, through monetary awards, an adult scientist and provide research funds; three current secondary school educators, and three current secondary school students who are judged to exemplify excellence in life sciences.

YEAR PROGRAM STARTED: 1996

PURPOSE:
To honor individuals whose accomplishments have had a significant impact on mankind, and encourage the youth in the U.S.

LEGAL BASIS:
Federal government agency.

GEOGRAPHIC RESTRICTIONS:
United States.

FINANCIAL DATA:
Amount of support per award: Agriscience Awards: Two $25,000 awards, plus $25,000 each in research funds; three $10,000 and three $5,000. Christopher Columbus Awards: Two teams win $2,000 U.S. Savings Bonds and gold medals (three- to four-member teams); one team wins a $25,000 grant for a practical community innovation. Homeland Security Awards: $25,000 each. Life Sciences Awards: One $25,000 plus $25,000 in research funds, three $10,000 and three $5,000.
Total amount of support: Approximately $381,000 per year.

NUMBER OF AWARDS: Agriscience: 8; Christopher Columbus: 8; Homeland Security: 4; Life Sciences: 7.

APPLICATION INFORMATION:
Contact the Foundation for information on each individual program application process.

TRUSTEES:
James H. Herring, Vice Chairman
Judith M. Shellenberger, Executive Director
Anthony C. Wisniewski

ADDRESS INQUIRIES TO:
Judith M. Shellenberger
Executive Director
(See address above.)

THE COMMONWEALTH FUND [1578]

One East 75th Street
New York, NY 10021
(212) 606-3800
Fax: (212) 606-3508

E-MAIL ADDRESS:
info@cmwf.org

WEB SITE ADDRESS:
www.commonwealthfund.org

FOUNDED: 1918

AREAS OF INTEREST:
Supporting independent research on health care issues, and making grants to improve health care practice and policy.

NAME(S) OF PROGRAMS:
- **Affordable Health Insurance**
- **Commission on a High Performance Health System**
- **Health System Improvement & Efficiency**
- **International Health Policy & Innovation**
- **Patient-Centered Coordinated Care**
- **Payment System Reform**
- **Policy Development & Convening**

TYPE:
Project/program grants; Research grants; Research contracts.

YEAR PROGRAM STARTED: 1918

PURPOSE:
To promote a high performing health care system that achieves better access, improved quality, and greater efficiency, particularly for society's most vulnerable, including low-income people, the uninsured, minority Americans, young children and elderly adults.

The Fund carries out this mandate by supporting independent research on health care issues and making grants to improve health care practice and policy. An international program in health policy is designed to stimulate innovative policies and practices in the U.S. and other industrialized countries.

LEGAL BASIS:
Private foundation.

ELIGIBILITY:
The Fund makes grants only to tax-exempt organizations and public agencies. No grants to individuals.

FINANCIAL DATA:
Amount of support per award: Varies.
Total amount of support: Projected $19,554,843 in grants for fiscal year 2010-11.

NUMBER OF APPLICANTS MOST RECENT YEAR: 870.

NUMBER OF AWARDS: 186.

REPRESENTATIVE AWARDS:
$258,582 to Harvard University to analyze the relationship between quality and efficiency in hospital care; $72,936 to Massachusetts General Hospital to assess the role of pay-for-performance in reducing racial and ethnic inequalities in health care.

APPLICATION INFORMATION:
The Fund requests letters of inquiry to initiate the grant application process. Applicants are encouraged to submit letters of inquiry using the online form. While the Fund will continue to accept letters of inquiry via regular mail and fax, such submissions will take longer to process than those received online. Letters of inquiry are acknowledged when received. Applicants are typically advised of the results of an initial staff review within two months. Program staff will contact applicants if more detailed information is required.
Duration: Typically one year, although some multiyear funding available.
Deadline: Applications may be submitted at any time.

IRS IDENTIFICATION NUMBER: 13-1635260

STAFF:
Karen Davis, President
John E. Craig, Jr., Executive Vice President and Chief Operating Officer
Anthony Shih, Executive Vice President for Programs
Cathy A. Schoen, Senior Vice President for Policy, Research and Evaluation
Robin Osborn, Vice President and Director, International Program in Health Policy and Innovation
Barry A. Scholl, Vice President for Communications and Publishing
Edward L. Schor, Vice President of State Health Policy and Practices
Andrea Landes, Director of Grants Management

BOARD OF DIRECTORS:
James R. Tallon, Jr., Chairman
Cristine Russell, Vice Chairman
William R. Brody, M.D.
Benjamin K. Chu, M.D.
Karen Davis
Michael V. Drake, M.D.
Samuel C. Fleming
Glen M. Hackbarth, J.D.
Jane E. Henney, M.D.
James J. Mongan, M.D.
Robert C. Pozen
William Y. Yun

ADDRESS INQUIRIES TO:
Andrea Landes
Director of Grants Management
(See address above.)

COMMUNITY FOUNDATION OF THE VERDUGOS [1579]

330 Arden Avenue, Suite 130
Glendale, CA 91203-1176
(818) 241-8040
Fax: (818) 241-8045

E-MAIL ADDRESS:
info@communityfoundationoftheverdugos.org

WEB SITE ADDRESS:
www.communityfoundationoftheverdugos.org

FOUNDED: 1956

AREAS OF INTEREST:
Arts and culture, children, education, health, homeless services, human services, senior services and environment.

TYPE:
Capital grants; Challenge/matching grants; Development grants; General operating grants; Project/program grants; Scholarships.

YEAR PROGRAM STARTED: 1956

PURPOSE:
To meet current and changing needs in the community.

LEGAL BASIS:
Community foundation.

ELIGIBILITY:
Eligible organizations must be schools or IRS 501(c)(3) tax-exempt.

GEOGRAPHIC RESTRICTIONS:
Burbank, Flintridge, Glendale, La Canada, La Crescenta, Montrose and Verdugo City, California.

FINANCIAL DATA:
Total amount of support: $20,000 each grant cycle; $60,000 annually.

COOPERATIVE FUNDING PROGRAMS: Through restricted, donor-advised funds within the Foundation.

NUMBER OF APPLICANTS MOST RECENT YEAR: 42.

REPRESENTATIVE AWARDS:
$10,000 to The Salvation Army for ZONE afterschool program; $15,000 to Glendale Adventist Medical Center toward cost of Omni Giraffe Bed for NICU; $10,000 to College View School toward cost of playground equipment for developmentally disabled children.

APPLICATION INFORMATION:
Applicants must submit a written proposal, including a copy of the IRS tax determination letter.
Duration: One year. Agency can reapply one year after the grant is made.
Deadline: February 1, June 1 and September 1.

PUBLICATIONS:
Annual report; quarterly newsletters.

IRS IDENTIFICATION NUMBER: 95-6068137

ADDRESS INQUIRIES TO:
Executive Director
(See address above.)

COMMUNITY MEMORIAL FOUNDATION

15 Spinning Wheel Road, Suite 326
Hinsdale, IL 60521
(630) 654-4729
Fax: (630) 654-3402

E-MAIL ADDRESS:
info@cmfdn.org

WEB SITE ADDRESS:
www.cmfdn.org

TYPE:
Challenge/matching grants; Project/program grants; Technical assistance.

See entry 1524 for full listing.

CORPORATION FOR NATIONAL AND COMMUNITY SERVICE [1580]

1201 New York Avenue, N.W.
Washington, DC 20525
(202) 606-5000 ext. 6822
(800) 424-8867
Fax: (202) 606-3475

WEB SITE ADDRESS:
www.nationalservice.gov
www.seniorcorps.gov

FOUNDED: 1971

AREAS OF INTEREST:
Volunteer service.

NAME(S) OF PROGRAMS:
● **Foster Grandparent Program**
● **Retired and Senior Volunteer Program (RSVP)**
● **Senior Companion Program**

TYPE:
Demonstration grants; General operating grants; Grants-in-aid; Project/program grants; Technical assistance. Grants to provide meaningful opportunities for low-income persons age 55 years and over, specifically providing person-to-person service to children with special needs as Foster Grandparents and providing services to adults with special needs as Senior Companions. The Retired and Senior Volunteer Program helps people 55 and older put their skills and life experience to work in their communities.

YEAR PROGRAM STARTED: 1965

PURPOSE:
To provide service opportunities for older Americans.

LEGAL BASIS:
Federal agency.

ELIGIBILITY:
State and local public agencies and private nonprofit organizations may apply.

GEOGRAPHIC RESTRICTIONS:
United States and territories.

FINANCIAL DATA:
Amount of support per award: Foster Grandparent Program: $328,000 average. Retired Senior Volunteer Program: $77,000 average. Senior Companion Program: $204,000 average.
Total amount of support: For the fiscal year 2010, Foster Grandparent Program: $110,000,000; Retired Senior Volunteer Program: $63,000,000; Senior Companion Program: $47,000,000.
Matching fund requirements: 10% for Foster Grandparent Program and Senior Companion Program. For Retired Senior Volunteer Program, 10-20-30%.

COOPERATIVE FUNDING PROGRAMS: Local public and private nonprofit agencies receive grants to sponsor and operate FGP, RSVP and SCP.

APPLICATION INFORMATION:
Duration: Three years with opportunity to amend annually.
Deadline: Varies.

PUBLICATIONS:
Grant application; guidelines.

IRS IDENTIFICATION NUMBER: 53-0260397

ENTERPRISE COMMUNITY PARTNERS [1581]

10227 Wincopin Circle, Suite 500
Columbia, MD 21044-3400
(410) 772-2450
Fax: (410) 964-1918

E-MAIL ADDRESS:
mail@enterprisecommunity.org

WEB SITE ADDRESS:
www.enterprisecommunity.org

FOUNDED: 1982

AREAS OF INTEREST:
Affordable housing.

NAME(S) OF PROGRAMS:
● **MetLife Foundation Awards for Excellence in Affordable Housing**
● **Jim and Patty Rouse Awards for Excellence in Community Revitalization**

TYPE:
Awards/prizes; General operating grants. MetLife Awards will be made in two categories: 1) Supportive Housing and 2) Property and Asset Management.

YEAR PROGRAM STARTED: 1996

PURPOSE:
To see that all low-income people in the U.S. have the opportunity for fit and affordable housing and to move up and out of poverty into the mainstream of American life; to promote development and quality management of affordable housing.

GEOGRAPHIC RESTRICTIONS:
United States.

FINANCIAL DATA:
Amount of support per award: MetLife Awards of $35,000, $15,000 and $10,000 will be made in each category.
Total amount of support: MetLife Awards: $120,000.

COOPERATIVE FUNDING PROGRAMS: MetLife Foundation.

NUMBER OF AWARDS: 6 each year.

APPLICATION INFORMATION:
Contact the Foundation for application procedures.
Deadline: Varies.

PUBLICATIONS:
Annual report.

ADDRESS INQUIRIES TO:
metlifeawards@enterprisecommunity.org
rouseawards@enterprisecommunity.org

THE FEINSTEIN FOUNDATION [1582]

37 Alhambra Circle
Cranston, RI 02905
(401) 467-5155
(401) 941-5913
Fax: (401) 941-0988

E-MAIL ADDRESS:
asf@feinsteinfoundation.org

WEB SITE ADDRESS:
www.feinsteinfoundation.org

AREAS OF INTEREST:
Ending hunger.

NAME(S) OF PROGRAMS:
● **Feinstein $1 Million Giveaway to Fight Hunger**

TYPE:
Challenge/matching grants. Each participating agency receives a share of $1,000,000 that represents their portion of the total amount reported to the Foundation that was raised by anti-hunger agencies using the Foundation's challenge in their fight to end hunger fund-raising.

PURPOSE:
To help nonprofit anti-hunger agencies nationwide raise funds.

LEGAL BASIS:
Nonprofit foundation.

ELIGIBILITY:
U.S. registered nonprofit 501(c)(3) agencies.

FINANCIAL DATA:
Amount of support per award: Divided proportionately among all complying agencies with a maximum of $40,000 going to any one agency.
Total amount of support: $1,000,000.

NUMBER OF AWARDS: Varies.

APPLICATION INFORMATION:
The Foundation does not accept unsolicited requests for funding except from nonprofit agencies feeding the hungry.
Deadline: March 1 to April 30.

EXECUTIVE STAFF:
Alan Shawn Feinstein, Chief Executive Officer

ADDRESS INQUIRIES TO:
Alan Shawn Feinstein
Chief Executive Officer
(See address above.)

CARL M. FREEMAN FOUNDATION

18330 Village Center Drive
Second Floor
Olney, MD 20832
(302) 436-3555
Fax: (302) 436-3080

E-MAIL ADDRESS:
info@freemanfoundation.org

WEB SITE ADDRESS:
www.freemanfoundation.org

TYPE:
Capital grants; Challenge/matching grants; General operating grants.

See entry 483 for full listing.

FUNDING EXCHANGE

666 Broadway
Suite 500
New York, NY 10012
(212) 529-5300

E-MAIL ADDRESS:
information@fex.org

WEB SITE ADDRESS:
www.fex.org

TYPE:
General operating grants; Project/program grants; Seed money grants. Out Fund supports lesbian/gay/bisexual/transgender issues. Saguaro Fund supports communities of color.

See entry 1049 for full listing.

THE GREAT BAY FOUNDATION [1583]

111 Commercial Street, Suite 201
Portland, ME 04101
(207) 899-2820
Fax: (207) 899-2927

E-MAIL ADDRESS:
info@greatbayfoundation.org

WEB SITE ADDRESS:
www.greatbayfoundation.org

FOUNDED: 1998

AREAS OF INTEREST:
Social change.

TYPE:
General operating grants; Grants-in-aid; Project/program grants; Seed money grants. Grant program limited to projects that seek change on a fundamental systemic, institutional or community basis.

PURPOSE:
To improve the lives of children and families in Maine communities.

ELIGIBILITY:
Applicants must be 501(c)(3) organizations led by individuals who have an entrepreneurial attitude, drive and vision, and who work toward social change in the areas of economic development, education and health care. Grants are not made to individuals or religious organizations.

GEOGRAPHIC RESTRICTIONS:
Maine, Massachusetts, New Hampshire, Rhode Island and Vermont.

FINANCIAL DATA:
Amount of support per award: Up to $150,000.

APPLICATION INFORMATION:
Grant requests are considered only in response to an invitation by the Foundation. Unsolicited applications will not be accepted or considered.
Duration: One year.

ADDRESS INQUIRIES TO:
Anne Dinsmore, Executive Director
(See address above.)

THE HEALTH FOUNDATION OF GREATER INDIANAPOLIS [1584]

429 East Vermont Street, Suite 300
Indianapolis, IN 46202-3698
(317) 630-1805
Fax: (317) 630-1806

E-MAIL ADDRESS:
bwilson@thfgi.org

WEB SITE ADDRESS:
www.thfgi.org

AREAS OF INTEREST:
Childhood obesity, HIV/AIDS and school-based health.

TYPE:
Project/program grants.

PURPOSE:
To encourage organizations to improve the health of people in greater Indianapolis, especially those who are disadvantaged.

ELIGIBILITY:
Applicant must be a 501(c)(3) group, organization or agency that provides health-related programs or services within Marion and the seven contiguous counties. Must also function without discrimination or segregation based on race, gender, age, religion, national origin, sexual orientation, disability, military or marital status in hiring, termination, assignment and promotion of staff, selection of board members or provisions of services. No grants are made to individuals. Non-sectarian religious programs may apply.

GEOGRAPHIC RESTRICTIONS:
Marion County, Indiana and the seven contiguous counties.

FINANCIAL DATA:
Total amount of support: Approximately $1,400,000 for the year 2009.

NUMBER OF APPLICANTS MOST RECENT YEAR:
20.

NUMBER OF AWARDS: 15.

APPLICATION INFORMATION:
Contact the Foundation prior to applying to determine appropriateness of the proposal.
Duration: One year.
Deadline: March 1 for Spring cycle; September 1 for Fall cycle.

ADDRESS INQUIRIES TO:
Jason Grisell, Program Manager
(See address above.)

HEBREW IMMIGRANT AID SOCIETY (HIAS)

333 Seventh Avenue, 16th Floor
New York, NY 10001-5004
(212) 613-1358
Fax: (212) 967-4483

E-MAIL ADDRESS:
scholarship@hias.org

WEB SITE ADDRESS:
www.hias.org/scholarships

TYPE:
Awards/prizes; Scholarships. Cash awards made annually to refugees assisted by HIAS in recognition of their academic excellence, financial need and community service.

See entry 1056 for full listing.

GROVER HERMANN FOUNDATION [1585]

c/o Rhoads
908 Kenmare Drive
Burr Ridge, IL 60527-7091
(630) 908-7800

AREAS OF INTEREST:
Community within Chicago metropolitan area, education, health, public policy, and religion for nonsecular uses.

TYPE:
Project/program grants.

LEGAL BASIS:
Private foundation.

ELIGIBILITY:
Grants are made to organizations that have tax-exempt status under Section 501(c)(3) of the Internal Revenue Code. No grants are made to individuals. Grants may be made to religious organizations for nonsectarian programs in the Chicago area.

GEOGRAPHIC RESTRICTIONS:
United States, with an emphasis on Chicago, Illinois.

FINANCIAL DATA:
Amount of support per award: Varies.
Total amount of support: Varies.

APPLICATION INFORMATION:
Contact the Foundation for application procedures.
Duration: One year.

ADDRESS INQUIRIES TO:
Kay Vee Rhoads, Executive Director
(See address above.)

VICTOR AND LORRAINE HONIG FUND [1586]

405 14th Street, Suite 809
Oakland, CA 94612
(510) 834-2995
Fax: (510) 834-2998

E-MAIL ADDRESS:
grantsadmin@commoncounsel.org

WEB SITE ADDRESS:
www.commoncounsel.org

AREAS OF INTEREST:
Social change, community development, environment, public policy and empowerment.

TYPE:
General operating grants; Project/program grants.

PURPOSE:
To support social change organizations which reflect the communities in which they are based; to expand community control over economic, social and environmental decisions affecting the communities' well-being; to build a strong informed voice on public policy issues.

LEGAL BASIS:
Family foundation.

ELIGIBILITY:
Grants made only to IRS 501(c)(3) tax-exempt organizations. No grants are made to social service programs offering ongoing or direct delivery of services, medical, educational or cultural institutions, emergency funding, scholarship funds or other aids to individuals, organizations which have sophisticated fund-raising capabilities, capital expenditure, construction or renovation programs or programs undertaken at government initiative. Priority is given to grassroots community organizations in low-income areas.

GEOGRAPHIC RESTRICTIONS:
California.

FINANCIAL DATA:
Amount of support per award: $1,000 to $25,000.
Total amount of support: $468,000 for the year 2010.

NUMBER OF APPLICANTS MOST RECENT YEAR:
50 to 100.

NUMBER OF AWARDS: 53 for the year 2010.

APPLICATION INFORMATION:
Letters of Inquiry and Proposals are by invitation only.

Duration: Most grants are for one year.

ADDRESS INQUIRIES TO:
Grants Administrator
(See address above.)

A.V. HUNTER TRUST, INC. [1587]

650 South Cherry Street
Suite 535
Glendale, CO 80246
(303) 399-5450
Fax: (303) 399-5499

E-MAIL ADDRESS:
barbarahowie@avhuntertrust.org

WEB SITE ADDRESS:
www.avhuntertrust.org

FOUNDED: 1924

AREAS OF INTEREST:
Disabled, seniors, youth, and indigent.

TYPE:
General operating grants. Grants to
Colorado-based organizations in the priority
areas listed above.

YEAR PROGRAM STARTED: 1924

PURPOSE:
To give aid, comfort, support or assistance to
children or aged persons or indigent adults.

LEGAL BASIS:
Private foundation.

ELIGIBILITY:
Applicants must be organizations classified as
501(c)(3) by the IRS. The Trust will consider
only one request from an organization during
any 12-month period. Institutions or
organizations supported by tax-derived
monies, including those which have lost
governmental funding, will not be
considered. The Trustees will not consider
grants or loans to individuals, developmental
or start-up funds, research, publications, films
or other media projects, capital campaigns or
acquisitions, including construction and
renovations, education or scholarship aid,
grants to cover deficits or retirement of debt,
purchase of memberships or blocks of
tickets, endowments, recruiting and training
of staff or gathering and disseminating
information.

GEOGRAPHIC RESTRICTIONS:
Colorado.

FINANCIAL DATA:
Amount of support per award: $5,000 to
$60,000. Average: $15,000.
Total amount of support: $2,668,980 for the
year 2009.

REPRESENTATIVE AWARDS:
$7,500 to Families First, Denver; $25,000 to
Food Bank of the Rockies; $16,000 to Easter
Seals Colorado; $15,000 to SafeHouse
Denver, Inc.; $35,000 to Step 13, Denver.

APPLICATION INFORMATION:
Detailed application information can be
obtained at the Trust web site or by calling
the telephone number listed above.

STAFF:
Barbara L. Howie, Executive Director
Charlotte A. Gillespie, Senior Program
Officer

BOARD OF TRUSTEES:
Bruce K. Alexander, President
Allan B. Adams, Vice President
Mary K. Anstine, Treasurer
W. Robert Alexander
George C. Gibson

ADDRESS INQUIRIES TO:
Barbara L. Howie, Executive Director
(See address above.)

THE STEWART HUSTON CHARITABLE TRUST

50 South First Avenue
Coatesville, PA 19320
(610) 384-2666
Fax: (610) 384-3396

E-MAIL ADDRESS:
admin@stewarthuston.org

WEB SITE ADDRESS:
www.stewarthuston.org

TYPE:
Capital grants; Challenge/matching grants;
General operating grants; Matching gifts;
Project/program grants; Seed money grants.

See entry 858 for full listing.

THE HYAMS FOUNDATION [1588]

50 Federal Street, 9th Floor
Boston, MA 02110
(617) 426-5600
Fax: (617) 426-5696

E-MAIL ADDRESS:
info@hyamsfoundation.org

WEB SITE ADDRESS:
www.hyamsfoundation.org

FOUNDED: 1921

AREAS OF INTEREST:
Low-income and underserved populations;
low-income youth.

TYPE:
General operating grants; Project/program
grants; Technical assistance. General
operating, multiyear pledges, special projects,
technical assistance/consulting, unrestricted
grants in the following program areas:
(1) Affordable Housing: Public
policy/community organizing;
(2) Civic Engagement: Grassroots leadership
development, including teen organizing,
public policy/community organizing, voter
engagement and;
(3) Teen Development: Public
policy/community organizing.

PURPOSE:
To increase economic and social justice and
power within low-income communities in
Boston and Chelsea, MA.

LEGAL BASIS:
Nonprofit foundation.

ELIGIBILITY:
Applicants must be Massachusetts charitable
corporations, must be tax-exempt under
Section 501(c)(3) and designated as not a
private foundation under Section 509(a). No
grants will be made to one organization for
the programs of another organization which
has not itself received both such
determinations. The Foundation ordinarily
will consider only one application from an
organization in any given 12-month period.
However, a single application may include a
request for more than one program or
purpose.

Grants are not given to individuals,
educational institutions for standard
educational or capital programs, any

municipal, state or federal agency, hospital
capital campaigns, endowments and religious
organizations for sectarian religious purposes.

Grants are rarely made for curriculum
development, conferences, film production,
scholarships or to national or international
organizations.

GEOGRAPHIC RESTRICTIONS:
Boston and Chelsea, Massachusetts.

FINANCIAL DATA:
Amount of support per award: $30,000 to
$50,000.
Total amount of support: $5,500,000 for the
year 2010.

NUMBER OF APPLICANTS MOST RECENT YEAR:
205 for the year 2009.

NUMBER OF AWARDS: 161 grants for the year
2009.

APPLICATION INFORMATION:
Application form required. Organizations
which are unsure about whether they meet
the Foundation's funding priorities and
criteria are encouraged to submit a one-page
letter of interest to the Foundation. This letter
should describe the reason for seeking
support and the geographic area(s) and
population(s) to be served.

One copy of applicant's proposal should be
mailed or delivered to the Executive Director
at the address above.

Duration: Typically one year. Multiyear
grants also given.

Deadline: March 1, September 1 and
December 1.

PUBLICATIONS:
Annual report; guidelines for preparing a
proposal.

TRUSTEES:
Barbara Casey, Chairman
Iris Gomez
Karen Mapp
John Sarvey
Adam Seitchik
Edward Swan
Martella Wilson-Taylor

STAFF:
Elizabeth B. Smith, Executive Director
Angela Brown, Senior Program Officer
David Moy, Program Officer
Tammy Tai, Program Officer

ADDRESS INQUIRIES TO:
Susan Perry, Administrative Manager
(See address above.)

ITTLESON FOUNDATION, INC. [1589]

15 East 67th Street
New York, NY 10065
(212) 794-2008
Fax: (212) 794-0351

WEB SITE ADDRESS:
www.ittlesonfoundation.org

FOUNDED: 1932

AREAS OF INTEREST:
Mental health, environment and AIDS.

TYPE:
Demonstration grants; Project/program
grants; Seed money grants. Seed money for
the start-up of innovative programs that will
improve the social welfare of citizens of the
U.S.

In the area of AIDS, the Foundation supports cutting-edge prevention efforts. It is also particularly interested in new model, pilot, and demonstration efforts: addressing the needs of underserved at-risk populations; responding to the challenges facing community-based AIDS service organizations; providing meaningful school-based sex education; making treatment information accessible, available, and easily understandable to those in need of it; and addressing the psycho-social needs of those infected and affected by AIDS, especially adolescents.

In the area of environment, the Foundation supports innovative pilot, model and demonstration projects that will help move individuals, communities and organizations from environmental awareness to environmental activism. The Foundation seeks to: support the present generation of environmental activists; educate and engage the next generation; strengthen the infrastructure of the environmental movement with a particular focus on efforts at the grassroots and statewide levels; and activate new constituencies.

In the area of mental health, the Foundation continues to support efforts to address the needs of underserved populations. It also seeks pilot, model and demonstration projects: fighting the stigma associated with mental illness; utilizing new knowledge and current technological advances to improve programs and services for people with mental illness; bringing the full benefits of this new knowledge and technology to those who presently do not have access to them; and advancing preventative mental health efforts, especially those targeted to youth and adolescents.

PURPOSE:
To launch innovative projects in the areas of mental health, AIDS and the environment.

ELIGIBILITY:
Grants are available to nonprofit organizations within the U.S. Preference is given to pilot projects, test and demonstration projects and applied research which ideally should inform public policy, if successful. The Foundation also supports dissemination projects.

The Foundation does not usually support capital building projects, endowments, grants to individuals, scholarships or internships (except as part of a program), or continuing support to existing programs. Moreover, the Foundation does not support programs of direct service to individuals with only a local focus or constituency. The Foundation does not make international grants.

GEOGRAPHIC RESTRICTIONS:
United States.

FINANCIAL DATA:
Amount of support per award: Average $20,000 to $70,000.

NUMBER OF APPLICANTS MOST RECENT YEAR:
Approximately 500.

APPLICATION INFORMATION:
There are no application forms. Applicants should write a brief letter to the Executive Director describing the basic organization and the work for which funds are being sought, along with a budget and evidence of tax-exempt status. If the activity falls within the current scope of the Foundation's interests, the applicant will be asked to supply additional information as required.

Duration: Generally one year. Multiyear when appropriate. No renewals.

Deadline: Letters of inquiry must be received by September 1 for December meeting.

OFFICERS AND DIRECTORS:
H. Anthony Ittleson, Chairman and President
Pamela Syrmis, Vice President and Director
H. Davidson, Treasurer
Anthony C. Wood, Secretary and Executive Director
Andrew Auchincloss, Director
H. Philip Ittleson, Director
Stephanie Ittleson, Director
Christina Ittleson Smith, Director
Victor Syrmis, M.D., Director

ADDRESS INQUIRIES TO:
Anthony C. Wood, Executive Director
(See address above.)

JACKSONVILLE JAGUARS FOUNDATION

One Everbank Field Drive
Jacksonville, FL 32202
(904) 633-5437
Fax: (904) 633-5683

WEB SITE ADDRESS:
www.jaguars.com

TYPE:
General operating grants; Project/program grants. Limited capital grants that target economically and socially "at-risk" youths in northeast Florida.

See entry 194 for full listing.

THE CARL W. AND CARRIE MAE JOSLYN CHARITABLE TRUST [1590]

c/o JPMorgan Private Client Services
402 North Tejon Street, Suite 200
Colorado Springs, CO 80903
(719) 227-6445
Fax: (719) 227-6448

E-MAIL ADDRESS:
julie.golden@jpmorgan.com

WEB SITE ADDRESS:
www.jpmorgan.com/onlinegrants

FOUNDED: 1975

AREAS OF INTEREST:
Children, elderly and handicapped persons of El Paso County, CO.

TYPE:
Project/program grants. Small project grants and general operating support.

YEAR PROGRAM STARTED: 1975

LEGAL BASIS:
Tax-exempt charitable trust.

ELIGIBILITY:
Organizations and individuals serving children, the elderly and handicapped persons in El Paso County, CO, are eligible to apply.

GEOGRAPHIC RESTRICTIONS:
El Paso County, Colorado.

FINANCIAL DATA:
Amount of support per award: $500 to $15,000.

Total amount of support: Approximately $55,000 to $65,000 annually.

NUMBER OF APPLICANTS MOST RECENT YEAR:
150.

NUMBER OF AWARDS: 30.

APPLICATION INFORMATION:
Application must be in writing. There is no specified form.

Duration: One year. Nonrenewable.

Deadline: November 1.

ADDRESS INQUIRIES TO:
Julie Golden
Trust Advisor and Trust Officer
JPMorgan
(See address above.)

LIBERTY HILL FOUNDATION [1591]

2121 Cloverfield Boulevard
Suite 113
Santa Monica, CA 90404
(310) 453-3611
Fax: (310) 453-7806

E-MAIL ADDRESS:
info@libertyhill.org

WEB SITE ADDRESS:
www.libertyhill.org

FOUNDED: 1976

AREAS OF INTEREST:
Economic justice and environmental justice.

NAME(S) OF PROGRAMS:
• **Fund for Change**
• **Wally Marks Leadership Institute for Change**
• **Queer Youth Fund**

TYPE:
General operating grants; Project/program grants; Seed money grants; Technical assistance; Training grants. Fund for Change supports high-impact social change through cultivating effective community leaders, seeding emerging organizations, and developing a base of grassroots activists within the areas of economic and racial justice, environmental justice and LGBTQ justice.

The Wally Marks Leadership Institute for Change invests in community leaders at the front lines of change with intensive on-the-job training for community organizers.

The Queer Youth Fund supports local, state and national nonprofit organizations that empower youth to improve their societal condition, promoting equality and justice. Youth are defined as 24 years old and younger.

YEAR PROGRAM STARTED: 1976

PURPOSE:
To promote progressive social change by funding grassroots community organizations who are empowering the disenfranchised and challenging institutions and attitudes which create economic, social and racial inequalities.

LEGAL BASIS:
Public foundation.

ELIGIBILITY:
Fund for Change: The Foundation considers applications from nonprofit 501(c)(3) organizations, or those organizations having a fiscal sponsorship agreement with a nonprofit organization which complies with Liberty Hill's policy on fiscal sponsorship, in Los Angeles County, CA that actively work toward a more just distribution of resources and power, develop grassroots activism and

leadership, are building their organizational infrastructure and promote a society free from discrimination.

The Foundation does not fund capital campaigns for land or buildings, individual efforts, films or video projects, profit making ventures, direct union organizing, electioneering for candidates in public office, one-time events or conferences that are not linked to social change organizing strategies, or projects that only serve communities outside Los Angeles County.

FINANCIAL DATA:
Amount of support per award: Fund for Change: $10,000 to $50,000. Queer Youth Fund: $100,000.
Total amount of support: $3,500,000 for the year 2008.

COOPERATIVE FUNDING PROGRAMS:
Donor-advised program.

APPLICATION INFORMATION:
Applications for Fund for Change must be submitted by mail or in person. Applications by e-mail or fax will not be accepted. Queer Youth Fund requires initial letter of intent.
Duration: One to five years.
Deadline: Varies.

PUBLICATIONS:
Guidelines; newsletter.

IRS IDENTIFICATION NUMBER: 51-0181191

STAFF:
Shane Goldsmith, Director of Programs
Margarita Ramirez, Deputy Director of Grantmaking

ADDRESS INQUIRIES TO:
Shane Goldsmith, Director of Programs
(See address above.)

THE AGNES M. LINDSAY TRUST

660 Chestnut Street
Manchester, NH 03104
(603) 669-1366
(866) 669-1366
Fax: (603) 665-8114

E-MAIL ADDRESS:
admin@lindsaytrust.org

WEB SITE ADDRESS:
www.lindsaytrust.org

TYPE:
Capital grants; Scholarships. Awards grants for capital campaigns, capital items and renovation needs. Also, supports a number of health and welfare organizations, health projects, dental projects, special needs including blind, deaf and learning-disabled, elderly, children's hospitals, children's homes, youth organizations, youth and family services and summer camperships (summer enrichment programs). In addition, Trust supports colleges and universities and private secondary schools through scholarship aid.

See entry 1200 for full listing.

LUTHERAN FOUNDATION OF ST. LOUIS

8860 Ladue Road
Suite 200
St. Louis, MO 63124
(314) 231-2244
Fax: (314) 727-7688

E-MAIL ADDRESS:
info@lutheranfoundation.org

WEB SITE ADDRESS:
www.lutheranfoundation.org

TYPE:
Capital grants; Challenge/matching grants; General operating grants; Project/program grants; Technical assistance.

See entry 861 for full listing.

M & M AREA COMMUNITY FOUNDATION

1101 11th Avenue
Menominee, MI 49858
(906) 864-3599
Fax: (906) 864-3657

E-MAIL ADDRESS:
mmfoundation@czwireless.net

WEB SITE ADDRESS:
www.mmcommunityfoundation.org

TYPE:
Project/program grants; Scholarships; Training grants.

See entry 1408 for full listing.

RODERICK MACARTHUR FOUNDATION   [1592]

9333 North Milwaukee Avenue
Niles, IL 60714
(847) 966-0143
Fax: (847) 581-8730

FOUNDED: 1976

AREAS OF INTEREST:
Protecting and encouraging freedom of expression, human rights, civil liberties and social justice.

TYPE:
Project/program grants. Project budgets, litigation and special projects.

YEAR PROGRAM STARTED: 1976

PURPOSE:
To support those working on programs and projects of interest to the Foundation, especially to maintain individual freedoms of expression and correct social injustices.

LEGAL BASIS:
Independent private foundation.

FINANCIAL DATA:
Amount of support per award: Varies.
Total amount of support: $6,281,445 for the year ended December 31, 2010.

NUMBER OF APPLICANTS MOST RECENT YEAR:
50.

NUMBER OF AWARDS: 7 for the year ended December 31, 2010.

REPRESENTATIVE AWARDS:
$4,500,000 to Harper's Magazine Foundation; $800,000 to American Dance Institute; $151,814 to Death Penalty Information Center; $829,632 to MacArthur Justice Center.

APPLICATION INFORMATION:
Board-initiated only.
Duration: Varies according to project.

PUBLICATIONS:
Grants list.

IRS IDENTIFICATION NUMBER: 51-0214450

STAFF:
Marylou Bane, Administrator and Treasurer

BOARD OF DIRECTORS:
Solange D. MacArthur, Chairperson

John R. MacArthur, Vice Chairman
James Liggett, Director

ADDRESS INQUIRIES TO:
Marylou Bane
Administrator and Treasurer
(See address above.)

MAINE INITIATIVES   [1593]

P.O. Box 2248
Augusta, ME 04338
(207) 622-6294
Fax: (207) 622-6295

E-MAIL ADDRESS:
info@maineinitiatives.org

WEB SITE ADDRESS:
www.maineinitiatives.org

FOUNDED: 1993

AREAS OF INTEREST:
Supporting social change in Maine.

NAME(S) OF PROGRAMS:
- **Grants for Change**
- **Rapid Response "Lightning" Grants**

TYPE:
General operating grants; Seed money grants; Technical assistance. Grants provide funding to Maine groups advancing social, economic, and environmental justice at the grassroots level.

YEAR PROGRAM STARTED: 1994

PURPOSE:
To cultivate social, economic and environmental justice through grants and other support to grassroots organizations in Maine communities.

ELIGIBILITY:
501(c)(3) organizations and groups with tax-exempt sponsors. Religious organizations are eligible but not for religious purposes.

GEOGRAPHIC RESTRICTIONS:
Maine.

FINANCIAL DATA:
Amount of support per award: Grants for Change: Up to $25,000 per year.

NUMBER OF APPLICANTS MOST RECENT YEAR:
Grants for Change: 50.

NUMBER OF AWARDS: 10.

APPLICATION INFORMATION:
Copies of IRS 501(c)(3) designation letters are requested. Contact the organization for application.
Duration: Grants for Change: Up to three years.
Deadline: First Friday of October. Rapid Response Grants are reviewed on an ongoing basis.

PUBLICATIONS:
Newsletter; annual report.

IRS IDENTIFICATION NUMBER: 01-0484310

STAFF:
Charlie Bernstein, Executive Director

MAZON: A JEWISH RESPONSE TO HUNGER   [1594]

10495 Santa Monica Boulevard
Suite 100
Los Angeles, CA 90025
(310) 442-0020
Fax: (310) 442-0030

E-MAIL ADDRESS:
mazonmail@mazon.org

WEB SITE ADDRESS:
www.mazon.org

FOUNDED: 1986

AREAS OF INTEREST:
Advocacy, education and research pertaining
to hunger, emergency food assistance and
food banks.

NAME(S) OF PROGRAMS:
● **Healthy Options Healthy Meals**
● **Healthy Snack Sack Program for Kids**

TYPE:
General operating grants; Project/program
grants.

YEAR PROGRAM STARTED: 1986

PURPOSE:
To provide for people who are hungry while
advocating for other ways to end hunger and
its causes.

GEOGRAPHIC RESTRICTIONS:
United States.

APPLICATION INFORMATION:
Applicants must submit a letter (maximum
two pages) describing the agency and/or
project, and request a grant application. A
full grant application packet will be sent to
organizations that best match the funding
criteria and grantmaking priorities.
Duration: One year.

PUBLICATIONS:
Program announcement; guidelines.

ADDRESS INQUIRIES TO:
Marla Feldman, California Program Director
(See address above.)

FAYE MCBEATH
FOUNDATION   [1595]
101 West Pleasant Street, Suite 210
Milwaukee, WI 53212
(414) 272-2626
Fax: (414) 272-6235

E-MAIL ADDRESS:
info@fayemcbeath.org

WEB SITE ADDRESS:
www.fayemcbeath.org

FOUNDED: 1964

AREAS OF INTEREST:
Children, health, health education, aging and
elders, civic and governmental affairs.

TYPE:
Challenge/matching grants; Demonstration
grants; General operating grants;
Project/program grants; Seed money grants.
The Foundation's major areas of interest
remain fixed: children, the elderly, health,
health education, and civic/governmental
affairs. However, specific grantmaking
interests within each of these major
categories change periodically.

Grants are made within the state of
Wisconsin and principally to support
projects/programs having primary focus on
the welfare of the residents of the greater
Milwaukee community. Project/program
grants are the most frequent types of grants
awarded. Capital grants are limited to
projects with community-wide impact that
reflect the program interests of the
Foundation.

YEAR PROGRAM STARTED: 1964

LEGAL BASIS:
Private foundation.

ELIGIBILITY:
Grants are made only to nonprofit,
tax-exempt 501(c)(3) organizations and
agencies for projects having a primary focus
on the welfare of the residents of the greater
Milwaukee community including Milwaukee,
Ozaukee, Washington and Waukesha
counties. No grants are made to individuals.
Grants will not ordinarily be made for annual
fund drives or endowment funds.

GEOGRAPHIC RESTRICTIONS:
Milwaukee, Ozaukee, Washington and
Waukesha counties, Wisconsin.

FINANCIAL DATA:
Amount of support per award: Varies.
Total amount of support: $1,100,000 for the
year 2010.

COOPERATIVE FUNDING PROGRAMS: Nonprofit
Management Fund.

NUMBER OF APPLICANTS MOST RECENT YEAR:
225.

NUMBER OF AWARDS: 55 to 65 per year.

REPRESENTATIVE AWARDS:
$25,000 to Milwaukee Renaissance
Academy; $25,000 to St. Ann Center for
Intergenerational Care; $25,000 to Grand
Avenue Club, Inc.; $34,500 to Guest House
of Milwaukee, Inc.; $15,000 to Milwaukee
Turners, Inc.

APPLICATION INFORMATION:
Applicants should review the Foundation's
latest guidelines and information prior to
submitting proposals. Requests should
initially take the form of a brief written
inquiry which gives basic information about
the applicant organization and its tax-exempt
status, the project in terms of its concrete
objectives, anticipated costs and significance.
Letter of intent is required.
Duration: One to two years.
Deadline: Letters of Intent accepted
throughout the year.

TRUSTEES:
Sara E. Aster, Chairperson
P. Michael Mahoney, Vice Chairperson
Mary T. Kellner, Secretary
Steven J. Smith
Gregory Wesley

STAFF:
Scott E. Gelzer, Executive Director

ADDRESS INQUIRIES TO:
Scott E. Gelzer, Executive Director
(See address above.)

MCKENZIE RIVER GATHERING
FOUNDATION   [1596]
2705 East Burnside Street
Suite 210
Portland, OR 97214
(503) 234-2338
Fax: (503) 232-1731

E-MAIL ADDRESS:
info@mrgfoundation.org

WEB SITE ADDRESS:
www.mrgfoundation.org

FOUNDED: 1976

AREAS OF INTEREST:
Community-based groups working for
progressive social change, women, racial
justice, low-income organizing, lesbian/gay,
bi/trans, peace, international solidarity,
environmental protection, economic justice
and anti-bigotry.

NAME(S) OF PROGRAMS:
● **Critical Response Grants**
● **Public Interest Grants (General Fund)**
● **Travel Grants**

TYPE:
General operating grants; Project/program
grants; Seed money grants; Travel grants.
Funds special project grants and general
support.

Critical Response Grants provide
community-based groups with the additional
capacity needed to organize a progressive
response to an unexpected crisis or
opportunity for organizing.

Travel Grants help MRG grantees make
national and regional connections and
develop the leadership and skills needed for
effective organizational development and
organizing.

YEAR PROGRAM STARTED: 1976

PURPOSE:
Social change.

LEGAL BASIS:
Nonprofit, tax-exempt 501(c)(3) public
foundation.

ELIGIBILITY:
Organizations must do tax-exempt activities
in the state of Oregon and fit criteria of
social change work listed in fields of interest.
No grants to individuals. The Foundation
does not fund food co-ops, health centers or
social services.

Travel Grants: Group applicant must have
received an MRG General Fund or Peace
Fund grant within the prior two years.

Grant applicants for the Critical Response
Grant and the Travel Grant must have an
organizational budget under $500,000 to be
eligible.

GEOGRAPHIC RESTRICTIONS:
Oregon.

FINANCIAL DATA:
Amount of support per award: Critical
Response Grants: Up to $2,000; General
Fund: $2,000 to $20,000; Travel Grants: Up
to $1,000.
Total amount of support: $470,000.

NUMBER OF APPLICANTS MOST RECENT YEAR:
100.

NUMBER OF AWARDS: 40.

REPRESENTATIVE AWARDS:
Community Alliance of Lane County;
Community Alliance of Tenants;
Salem/Keizer Coalition for Equality.

APPLICATION INFORMATION:
Application forms and information are
available upon request.
Duration: Six to 12 months.
Deadline: Critical Response Grants and
Travel Grants have no application deadline,
but are subject to exhaustion of annual
funding monies. General Fund: August and
February.

PUBLICATIONS:
Applying for a Grant from MRG.

OFFICERS:
Arbrella Luvert, Board Co-Chair
Guadalupe Quinn, Board Co-Chair

ADDRESS INQUIRIES TO:
Anita Rodgers, Program Director
(See address above.)

THE MCKNIGHT FOUNDATION [1597]

710 South Second Street
Suite 400
Minneapolis, MN 55401
(612) 333-4220
Fax: (612) 332-3833

E-MAIL ADDRESS:
info@mcknight.org

WEB SITE ADDRESS:
www.mcknight.org

FOUNDED: 1953

AREAS OF INTEREST:
Youth, early literacy, region and
communities, arts, international, environment,
and research and applied sciences.

NAME(S) OF PROGRAMS:
● The Arts Program
● Education and Learning
● The Environment Program
● International
● Region and Communities
● Research and Applied Sciences

TYPE:
General operating grants; Project/program
grants. The Research and Applied Sciences
Program is by invitation only.

YEAR PROGRAM STARTED: 1953

LEGAL BASIS:
Family foundation.

GEOGRAPHIC RESTRICTIONS:
Minnesota, with emphasis on the
Minneapolis-St. Paul area and Mississippi.

FINANCIAL DATA:
Total amount of support: $96,686,049
(unaudited) for the year 2010.

NUMBER OF APPLICANTS MOST RECENT YEAR:
883.

NUMBER OF AWARDS: 540 for the year 2010.

APPLICATION INFORMATION:
Applications are available online.
Deadline: Initial Inquiry - Arts and Region
and Communities: October 15, January 15,
April 15 and July 15; Environment:
November 1, February 1, May 1 and August
1.

PUBLICATIONS:
Annual report, including grants list;
grantmaking guidelines for all programs.

OFFICERS:
Kate Wolford, President
Richard J. Scott, Vice President of Finance
and Compliance

DIRECTORS:
Robert Struyk, Chairperson
Patricia S. Binger, Assistant Treasurer and
Assistant Secretary
Anne Binger
Erika Binger
Cynthia Binger Boynton
Meghan Binger Brown
Bill Gregg
Richard McFarland
John Natoli
Noa Staryk
Ted Staryk

ADDRESS INQUIRIES TO:
Stephanie Duffy
Grants Administration Manager
(See address above.)

METRO HEALTH FOUNDATION [1598]

333 West Fort Street
Suite 1370
Detroit, MI 48226-3134
(313) 965-4220
Fax: (313) 965-3626

E-MAIL ADDRESS:
theresasondys@aol.com

WEB SITE ADDRESS:
www.sitekreator.com/metrohealthfoundation

FOUNDED: 1988

AREAS OF INTEREST:
Primary health care and health care-related
services, with priority to the city of Detroit.

TYPE:
Challenge/matching grants; Project/program
grants; Scholarships.

PURPOSE:
To support a wide variety of health-related
services within the city of Detroit and the
surrounding tri-county area (Wayne, Oakland
and Macomb counties).

LEGAL BASIS:
Private foundation.

ELIGIBILITY:
Priority is given to projects in collaboration
with other organizations and those serving
needy urban populations. The Foundation
supports grants for restricted projects,
operating support, start-up/seed money,
matching/challenge grants, and scholarships.

No grant support for program-related
investments, loans, endorsements, multiyear
pledges, underwriting special events,
sponsorships, grants to individuals,
educational loans, travel grants or research
grants.

MHF will not provide loans, support
religious organizations, indulge in lobbying,
or support organizations which discriminate
because of race, ethnic origins, religion,
sexual orientation, handicap or sex.

GEOGRAPHIC RESTRICTIONS:
Greater Detroit, Michigan area.

FINANCIAL DATA:
Amount of support per award: $1,000 to
$30,000.
Total amount of support: $208,932 for the
year 2010.

NUMBER OF APPLICANTS MOST RECENT YEAR:
33 for the year 2010.

NUMBER OF AWARDS: 16 for the year 2010.

REPRESENTATIVE AWARDS:
$20,000 to Optometric Institute and Clinic of
Detroit, Detroit, MI, to pay for retinal
surgery for the Clinic's low-income,
uninsured clients, who have no other way to
obtain/pay for the procedure; $22,242 to
Hope Medical Clinic, Ypsilanti, MI, to
support the part-time Medical Clinic
Coordinator as she works to expand the
services provided at the Hope-Wayne
Medical Clinic in the new facility; $10,000 to
World Medical Relief, Detroit, MI, to support
the Prescription Assistance Program through
the purchase of medications not available by
donation of good-dated samples.

APPLICATION INFORMATION:
Applicants must use the *Common Grant
Application* form available from the
Foundation.
Duration: One year. Renewal possible.

Deadline: August 1 and February 1.

PUBLICATIONS:
Grant-making Policies, Areas of Program
Interest; *Grant Application Procedures*;
Proposal Review Process.

IRS IDENTIFICATION NUMBER: 38-2100939

ADDRESS INQUIRIES TO:
Theresa L. Sondys, Senior Program Officer
(See address above.)

MARIETTA MCNEILL MORGAN AND SAMUEL TATE MORGAN, JR. FOUNDATION [1599]

Bank of America
Philanthropic Management VA2-300-12-99
1111 East Main Street, 12th Floor
P.O. Box 26688
Richmond, VA 23261-6688
(804) 788-2963
Fax: (804) 788-2700

FOUNDED: 1959

AREAS OF INTEREST:
Specific capital projects of organizations only
in the Commonwealth of Virginia.

TYPE:
Capital grants; Challenge/matching grants.
Grants for capital only. No grants to
individuals, for endowment funds or
operating funds.

YEAR PROGRAM STARTED: 1959

LEGAL BASIS:
Private foundation.

ELIGIBILITY:
Nonprofit organizations in the
Commonwealth of Virginia who are classified
by IRS as tax-exempt and are not private
foundations.

GEOGRAPHIC RESTRICTIONS:
Virginia.

FINANCIAL DATA:
Amount of support per award: $5,000 to
$75,000 dispersed in a single payment;
average $25,000.
Total amount of support: Varies.

COOPERATIVE FUNDING PROGRAMS: Other
funding sources encouraged.

APPLICATION INFORMATION:
Applicant should write to the Foundation,
requesting guidelines for application.
Duration: One year.
Deadline: May 1 and November 1. Award
announcements late June and early February.

ADDRESS INQUIRIES TO:
Elizabeth D. Seaman, Advisor
(See address above.)

A.J. MUSTE MEMORIAL INSTITUTE [1600]

339 Lafayette Street
New York, NY 10012
(212) 533-4335
Fax: (212) 228-6193

E-MAIL ADDRESS:
info@ajmuste.org

WEB SITE ADDRESS:
www.ajmuste.org

FOUNDED: 1974

AREAS OF INTEREST:
Peace and disarmament, social and economic
justice, racial and sexual equality, and the
labor movement.

TYPE:
Grants-in-aid. The Institute's regular grant fund annually funds international, national and local projects in the U.S. and around the world. It gives priority to those with small budgets and little chance of funding from more traditional sources. The Institute does not provide academic scholarships.

YEAR PROGRAM STARTED: 1974

PURPOSE:
To promote peace and disarmament, social and economic justice, racial and sexual equality, and the labor movement.

ELIGIBILITY:
The Institute funds projects which seek to advance nonviolent grassroots education and action for social and economic justice. The Institute does not make grants for general support of ongoing operations. It does not generally accept proposals from organizations with annual budgets over $500,000 or for projects with budgets over $50,000. It will also not accept a new request from a previously funded group for two years after a grant. Grants are not made to individuals and generally not to religious organizations.

FINANCIAL DATA:
Amount of support per award: Up to $2,000.

NUMBER OF AWARDS: 20 to 30 annually.

ADDRESS INQUIRIES TO:
Jane Guskin, Program Director
(See address above.)

NATIONAL COUNCIL ON FAMILY RELATIONS [1601]

1201 West River Parkway
Suite 200
Minneapolis, MN 55454
(763) 781-9331
Fax: (763) 781-9348

E-MAIL ADDRESS:
jeannestrand@ncfr.org

WEB SITE ADDRESS:
www.ncfr.org

FOUNDED: 1938

AREAS OF INTEREST:
Social work, family life education, child development, family studies, sociology, psychology, family health, human ecology and religion.

NAME(S) OF PROGRAMS:
- **Affiliate Councils Award for Meritorious Service**
- **Margaret E. Arcus Outstanding Family Life Educator Award**
- **Felix Berardo Mentoring Award**
- **Jessie Bernard Outstanding Contribution to Feminist Scholarship Paper**
- **Jessie Bernard Outstanding Research Proposal**
- **Ernest W. Burgess Award**
- **Czaplewski Fellowship Award**
- **Reuben Hill Award**
- **Ruth Jewson Award**
- **John L. and Harriet P. McAdoo Award**
- **NCFR Student Award**
- **Ernest G. Osborne Award**
- **Marie Peters Award**
- **Anselm Straus Award for Qualitative Family Research**
- **Jan Trost Award**
- **Cindy Winter Award**

TYPE:
Awards/prizes. Awards given for contributions to the area of family relations. All of the awards, except the Reuben Hill Award, require NCFR membership. The Ruben Hill Award is a juried award.

YEAR PROGRAM STARTED: 1938

PURPOSE:
To support contributions in teaching, research and distinguished service in the area of family relations.

LEGAL BASIS:
501(c)(3) education and research association.

ELIGIBILITY:
Awardees must be nominated by NCFR members. No other applications are accepted.

FINANCIAL DATA:
Amount of support per award: $200 to $1,500.

NUMBER OF AWARDS: 1 award each annually.

APPLICATION INFORMATION:
Awards are by nomination only.
Duration: One year.
Deadline: May 1 for most awards.

PUBLICATIONS:
Journal of Marriage and the Family; Family Relations; Journal of Family Theory and Review.

OFFICERS:
Gary L. Bowen, President

ADDRESS INQUIRIES TO:
Jeanne Strand, Manager of Governance and Operations
(See address above.)

NATIONAL HIGHWAY TRAFFIC SAFETY ADMINISTRATION [1602]

1200 New Jersey Avenue, S.E.
NTI-200
Washington, DC 20590
(202) 366-0144
Fax: (202) 366-7394

WEB SITE ADDRESS:
www.nhtsa.gov

FOUNDED: 1966

AREAS OF INTEREST:
Highway safety.

NAME(S) OF PROGRAMS:
- **State and Community Highway Safety Program-Section 402**

TYPE:
Formula grants. Formula grants to states for highway and transportation-related safety purposes.

YEAR PROGRAM STARTED: 1967

PURPOSE:
To promote a coordinated national highway safety program to reduce traffic crashes, deaths, injuries and property damage.

LEGAL BASIS:
Highway Safety Acts of 1966 as amended, 23 U.S.C. 401 et seq.

ELIGIBILITY:
All applicants must be state, American Indian and certain territorial highway safety programs, approved by the Secretary of Transportation. Political subdivisions are eligible through the State Highway Safety Program.

GEOGRAPHIC RESTRICTIONS:
United States and territories.

FINANCIAL DATA:
Grants vary according to a formula based on population and public road miles.
Amount of support per award: $562,000 to $21,300,000 for fiscal year 2010.
Total amount of support: $235,000,000 for the year 2010.
Matching fund requirements: Requires 20% match from outside sources.

NUMBER OF AWARDS: 57.

APPLICATION INFORMATION:
Submission of Highway Safety Plans and performance plans covering state and community highway safety activities for the year to National Highway Traffic Safety Administration (NHTSA) region and Federal Highway Administration (FHWA) Division Offices.
Duration: One year.
Deadline: September 1.

ADDRESS INQUIRIES TO:
Regional Offices or
State Highway Safety Office
(See address above.)

OPEN SOCIETY INSTITUTE - BALTIMORE [1603]

201 North Charles Street
Suite 1300
Baltimore, MD 21201
(410) 234-1091
Fax: (410) 234-2816

WEB SITE ADDRESS:
www.soros.org/baltimore

AREAS OF INTEREST:
Criminal rehabilitation.

NAME(S) OF PROGRAMS:
- **Criminal Justice Program**

TYPE:
Project/program grants.

YEAR PROGRAM STARTED: 1998

PURPOSE:
To reduce Maryland's overuse of incarceration and its social and economic costs without compromising public safety.

LEGAL BASIS:
Foundation.

ELIGIBILITY:
Grants are made to organizations that have tax-exempt status under Section 501(c)(3) of the Internal Revenue Code. No grants are made to individuals.

GEOGRAPHIC RESTRICTIONS:
Baltimore City, Maryland.

FINANCIAL DATA:
Amount of support per award: Varies.

APPLICATION INFORMATION:
Applicants should submit a letter of inquiry of two to three pages which includes:
(1) a description of the program to be funded;
(2) the qualifications of the organization to carry out the program;
(3) the ways in which the program reflects the priorities of the Criminal Justice Program;
(4) the amount of the budget and the funds requested and;
(5) a copy of the IRS letter stating the organization's tax-exempt status.
Duration: Varies.

ADDRESS INQUIRIES TO:
Monique Dixon, Program Director
(See address above.)

OPEN SOCIETY INSTITUTE - NEW YORK
400 West 59th Street
New York, NY 10019
(212) 548-0600
Fax: (212) 548-4600

E-MAIL ADDRESS:
grants@sorosny.org
osfellows@sorosny.org

WEB SITE ADDRESS:
www.soros.org

TYPE:
Fellowships; Project/program grants;
Scholarships; Technical assistance; Training
grants.

See entry 1990 for full listing.

PASADENA COMMUNITY FOUNDATION   [1604]
260 South Los Robles Avenue, Suite 119
Pasadena, CA 91101
(626) 796-2097
Fax: (626) 583-4738

E-MAIL ADDRESS:
jdevoll@pasadenacf.org

WEB SITE ADDRESS:
www.pasadenacf.org

FOUNDED: 1954

AREAS OF INTEREST:
Charitable organizations (Pasadena area
only), children, youth and family, community
development, environment education, arts and
the humanities, health and people with
special needs.

TYPE:
Capital grants; Project/program grants. Grants
for non-recurring capital needs, such as
equipment, building repairs and vehicles.

YEAR PROGRAM STARTED: 1954

PURPOSE:
To support charitable organizations in the
Pasadena area.

LEGAL BASIS:
Nonprofit public benefit corporation.

ELIGIBILITY:
Applicants must be 501(c)(3) organizations.
No personal grants to individuals, churches
or schools. No grants out of the Pasadena
area.

GEOGRAPHIC RESTRICTIONS:
Greater Pasadena area, California.

FINANCIAL DATA:
Amount of support per award: $1,725 to
$50,000.
Total amount of support: $650,000 in grants
for the year 2010.

NUMBER OF APPLICANTS MOST RECENT YEAR:
132.

NUMBER OF AWARDS: 50.

REPRESENTATIVE AWARDS:
$8,000 to Bishop Gooden Home, for kitchen
improvements; $25,000 to Rosemary
Children's Center, for passenger van; $40,000
to Pasadena Enterprise Center, for new roof
and air conditioning.

APPLICATION INFORMATION:
Duration: One year.
Deadline: February 1.

PUBLICATIONS:
Application guidelines; formal application
form; newsletter.

IRS IDENTIFICATION NUMBER: 20-0253310

ADDRESS INQUIRIES TO:
Jennifer Fleming DeVoll
Executive Director
(See address above.)

JAY AND ROSE PHILLIPS FAMILY FOUNDATION OF MINNESOTA   [1605]
10 Second Street, N.E., Suite 200
Minneapolis, MN 55413
(612) 623-1654
Fax: (612) 623-1653

E-MAIL ADDRESS:
info@phillipsfamilyfoundationmn.org

WEB SITE ADDRESS:
www.phillipsfamilyfoundationmn.org

FOUNDED: 1944

AREAS OF INTEREST:
Human services, health, education,
employment, housing, transit, programs for
people with disabilities, programs to combat
discrimination, and programs to help people
in poverty attain economic stability.

TYPE:
Project/program grants. Grants to improve
organizational effectiveness.

YEAR PROGRAM STARTED: 1944

PURPOSE:
To provide support for organizations and
projects that address unmet human and social
needs; to help people in poverty attain
economic stability.

LEGAL BASIS:
Private foundation.

ELIGIBILITY:
Grants are made to organizations that have
tax-exempt status under Section 501(c)(3) of
the Internal Revenue Code. No grants are
made to individuals.

During times of severe economic hardship
and financial distress, the Foundation's
primary concern is in providing support for
projects addressing unmet human and social
needs.

Additional Funding Considerations: The
Foundation's preference is to support projects
that represent new thinking about community
needs and innovative efforts that have the
potential for long-term solutions to the
problems being addressed.

GEOGRAPHIC RESTRICTIONS:
Minnesota.

FINANCIAL DATA:
Amount of support per award: $15,000 to
$50,000.
Total amount of support: $9,187,910 for the
year 2010.

NUMBER OF AWARDS: 317.

PUBLICATIONS:
Annual report; application guidelines.

IRS IDENTIFICATION NUMBER: 27-4196509

ADDRESS INQUIRIES TO:
Tracy Lamparty
Grants and Operations Manager
(See address above.)

*SPECIAL STIPULATIONS:
Unsolicited requests are not accepted from
organizations located outside of Minnesota.

PLOUGH FOUNDATION   [1606]
62 North Main, Suite 201
Memphis, TN 38103
(901) 521-2779
Fax: (901) 529-4063

E-MAIL ADDRESS:
mail@plough.org

FOUNDED: 1960

AREAS OF INTEREST:
Families in crisis, public education and
youth, crime, health and economic
development.

TYPE:
Capital grants; Challenge/matching grants;
Development grants; Endowments;
Professorships; Project/program grants; Seed
money grants; Technical assistance.

YEAR PROGRAM STARTED: 1960

PURPOSE:
To make payments or distributions to
charitable organizations or for charitable
purposes which will benefit the greatest
number of people in the City of Memphis
and/or Shelby County, TN.

LEGAL BASIS:
Private, independent foundation.

ELIGIBILITY:
No grants for assistance to address a crisis
management situation caused by poor initial
planning, individuals and projects outside the
Memphis/Shelby County (TN) area. No
grants for funding for private schools K-12,
funding for annual fund-raising, or to
individuals.

GEOGRAPHIC RESTRICTIONS:
Shelby County, Tennessee with particular
emphasis on Memphis.

FINANCIAL DATA:
Amount of support per award: Varies.
Total amount of support: $10,600,000 in
grants for the year 2009.

REPRESENTATIVE AWARDS:
Community Institute for Early Childhood;
University of Memphis; Alzheimer's Day
Services; Church Health Center; Memphis
Child Advocacy Center.

APPLICATION INFORMATION:
A brief letter of three pages or less should be
sent to the Foundation explaining the specific
project for which funds are needed and the
results anticipated if the funding is received.
Organizations whose projects appear to fall
within the focus of the Foundation will be
invited to submit a full grant proposal.
Duration: One to three years.
Deadline: Concept letter must be received by
January 1, April 1, July 1 and October 1 for
review at quarterly board meetings.

PUBLICATIONS:
Brochure.

IRS IDENTIFICATION NUMBER: 23-7175983

BOARD OF TRUSTEES:
Diane Rudner, Chairperson
Patricia R. Burnham

Eugene J. Callahan
D.D. Eisenberg
Roger T. Knox
Johnny B. Moore
Peter Pettit
Jocelyn P. Rudner
James F. Springfield
Steven Wishnia

ADDRESS INQUIRIES TO:
Barbara Jacobs, Program Director
(See address above.)

PRITCHETT TRUST

Marshall & Ilsley Trust Company
417 North Broadway
Pittsburg, KS 66762
(620) 231-2000
Fax: (620) 231-3974

TYPE:
Project/program grants; Seed money grants.

See entry 1215 for full listing.

KATE B. REYNOLDS CHARITABLE TRUST [1607]

128 Reynolda Village
Winston-Salem, NC 27106-5123
(336) 397-5500
Fax: (336) 723-7765

E-MAIL ADDRESS:
karenmm@kbr.org

WEB SITE ADDRESS:
www.kbr.org

FOUNDED: 1947

AREAS OF INTEREST:
Human services and health care for the
financially disadvantaged.

NAME(S) OF PROGRAMS:
- **Health Care Division**
- **Poor and Needy Division**

TYPE:
Capital grants; Challenge/matching grants;
Conferences/seminars; Demonstration grants;
Fellowships; Project/program grants;
Scholarships; Seed money grants; Technical
assistance; Training grants; Research
contracts. Capacity building. Through the
Health Care Division, the Trust responds to
health and wellness needs and invests in
solutions that improve the quality of health
for financially needy residents of North
Carolina. This Division seeks impact through
two program areas: Supporting Prevention
and Providing Treatment.

Through the Poor and Needy Division, the
Trust responds to basic life needs and invests
in solutions that improve the quality of life
for financially needy residents of Forsyth
County. This Division seeks impact through
two program areas: Increasing Self Reliance
and Providing Basic Needs.

YEAR PROGRAM STARTED: 1947

PURPOSE:
To improve the quality of life and quality of
health for the financially needy of North
Carolina; to accelerate positive movement on
critical community issues and to effect
enduring systemic change.

LEGAL BASIS:
Private foundation.

ELIGIBILITY:
Organizations eligible for grants are those
that have qualified for exemption under
Section 501(c)(3) and are not private
foundations or a Type III supporting
organization. Grants are not made to
individuals or for medical research. Advance
consultations are required prior to accepting
an application.

GEOGRAPHIC RESTRICTIONS:
North Carolina.

FINANCIAL DATA:
Asset value of $485,356,765 as of February
28, 2010.

Amount of support per award: Average
$20,000 to $200,000.

Total amount of support: $24,850,634 in
grants paid for the year ended August 31,
2009.

APPLICATION INFORMATION:
The Trust requires prospective applicants to
call for an advance consultation prior to
submitting an application. Applications are
only accepted electronically.

Duration: One to seven years.

Deadline: Health Care: March 15 and
September 15. Poor and Needy: January 15
and July 15.

PUBLICATIONS:
Annual report; *CATALYST,* newsletter.

IRS IDENTIFICATION NUMBER: 56-6036515

STAFF:
Karen McNeil-Miller, President
Allen J. Smart, Director, Health Care
Division
Joe D. Crocker, Director, Poor and Needy
Division
Joel T. Beeson, Director, Operations and
Administration
Lori V. Fuller, Director, Evaluation and
Research
Alan G. Welch, Information Systems
Manager
Abena K. Asante, Program Officer
Susan J. Richardson, Program Officer
Edgar G. Villanueva, Program Officer
Shinika M. McKiever, Program Associate
Emily R. Richardson, Research Associate

ADDRESS INQUIRIES TO:
Health Care Division:
Shinika McKiever, Program Associate
Tel: (866) 551-0690

RURITAN NATIONAL FOUNDATION

5451 Lyons Road
Dublin, VA 24084
(540) 674-5431
Fax: (540) 674-2304

E-MAIL ADDRESS:
office@ruritan.org

WEB SITE ADDRESS:
www.ruritan.org

TYPE:
Grants-in-aid; Matching gifts. These
programs allow Ruritan clubs to increase
their financial assistance to a student of the
club's choice. Ruritan clubs contribute $300
to the Foundation and, in turn, the
Foundation will add to this amount for
grants.

See entry 1696 for full listing.

RURITAN NATIONAL FOUNDATION [1608]

5451 Lyons Road
Dublin, VA 24084
(540) 674-5431
(877) 787-8727
Fax: (540) 674-2304

E-MAIL ADDRESS:
office@ruritan.org

WEB SITE ADDRESS:
www.ruritan.org

AREAS OF INTEREST:
Disaster relief.

NAME(S) OF PROGRAMS:
- **Operation We Care**

TYPE:
Project/program grants.

PURPOSE:
To provide aid to victims of situations
officially declared disasters by the state and
federal governments.

ELIGIBILITY:
Available to individuals in areas that are
officially declared disasters by the state and
federal governments.

FINANCIAL DATA:
Amount of support per award: Grants vary in
amount, depending upon the needs and
nature of the request.

Total amount of support: Varies.

APPLICATION INFORMATION:
Application must be made to the local
Ruritan District Governor.

ADDRESS INQUIRIES TO:
Michael Chrisley, Executive Director
(See address above.)

SAILORS' SNUG HARBOR OF BOSTON [1609]

c/o GMA Foundations
77 Summer Street, 8th Floor
Boston, MA 02110-1006
(617) 426-7080
Fax: (617) 426-7087

E-MAIL ADDRESS:
info@gmafoundations.com

WEB SITE ADDRESS:
www.sailorssnugharbor.org

FOUNDED: 1852

AREAS OF INTEREST:
Elderly and fishing families.

TYPE:
Challenge/matching grants; Project/program
grants.

PURPOSE:
To help current and former Massachusetts
fishing families achieve sustainable
self-sufficiency during the current transition
period in their industry; to help Greater
Boston's low-income elderly population live
independently.

LEGAL BASIS:
Private foundation.

ELIGIBILITY:
Grants are made to organizations that have
tax-exempt status under Section 501(c)(3) of
the Internal Revenue Code. No grants are
made to individuals. Non-sectarian religious
programs may apply.

FINANCIAL DATA:
Amount of support per award: $5,000 to
$25,000; typical grant $10,000.

Total amount of support: Varies.

COOPERATIVE FUNDING PROGRAMS: Fishing Communities Initiative of Island Foundation.

NUMBER OF APPLICANTS MOST RECENT YEAR: 60.

NUMBER OF AWARDS: 30 to 40.

APPLICATION INFORMATION:
Applications must be submitted online.

Duration: One year. Renewal by reapplication.

Deadline: Late August for programs with a fishing communities focus and mid-December for programs with an elderly focus.

ADDRESS INQUIRIES TO:
Gracelaw Simmons, Foundation Administrator
(See address above.)

SAINT LUKE'S EPISCOPAL HEALTH CHARITIES   [1610]
3100 Main, Suite 865
MC3-206
Houston, TX 77002
(832) 355-4984
(832) 355-7701
Fax: (832) 355-7223

E-MAIL ADDRESS:
charities@sleh.com

WEB SITE ADDRESS:
www.slehc.org

FOUNDED: 1997

AREAS OF INTEREST:
Physical health, dental health, mental health, Congregational Health Ministries, wellness and disease prevention.

TYPE:
Capital grants; General operating grants; Research grants; Seed money grants.

YEAR PROGRAM STARTED: 1997

PURPOSE:
To assess and enhance community health, including targeting the needs of the underserved, not just for ill-care, but for lifelong health and well-being.

LEGAL BASIS:
Public charity.

ELIGIBILITY:
Grants are made to organizations that have tax-exempt status under Section 501(c)(3) or 170(c) of the Internal Revenue Code. No grants are made to individuals.

GEOGRAPHIC RESTRICTIONS:
Texas.

FINANCIAL DATA:
Amount of support per award: $500 to $100,000.

Total amount of support: Typically $2,000,000.

APPLICATION INFORMATION:
Applicants should submit their application online.

Duration: One year.

Deadline: First working day of January, April and July.

ADDRESS INQUIRIES TO:
Celene Meyer
Director for Grants and Evaluation
(See address above.)

GEORGE J. AND EFFIE L. SEAY MEMORIAL TRUST   [1611]
1111 East Main Street, 12th Floor
Richmond, VA 23219
(804) 788-2963
Fax: (804) 788-2700

FOUNDED: 1959

AREAS OF INTEREST:
General philanthropic purposes with emphasis on direct service projects in Virginia.

TYPE:
Project/program grants. Grants for specific needs.

PURPOSE:
To enhance the quality of life in the Commonwealth of Virginia.

LEGAL BASIS:
Private foundation.

ELIGIBILITY:
Nonprofit organizations only in the Commonwealth of Virginia. No grants to individuals or to endowment funds.

GEOGRAPHIC RESTRICTIONS:
Virginia.

FINANCIAL DATA:
Amount of support per award: $5,000 to $15,000.

Total amount of support: Varies.

Matching fund requirements: Stipulated for specific grants.

COOPERATIVE FUNDING PROGRAMS: Other funding sources are encouraged.

APPLICATION INFORMATION:
Applicants should write to the Trust for application guidelines.

Duration: Single payment grants made for one year.

Deadline: May 1 and November 1. Award announcement made in late June and early February.

PUBLICATIONS:
Application guidelines.

ADDRESS INQUIRIES TO:
Elizabeth D. Seaman, Advisor
(See address above.)

*SPECIAL STIPULATIONS:
Grants made only to organizations in Virginia.

WILLIAM G. AND MARIE SELBY FOUNDATION   [1612]
1800 Second Street
Suite 750
Sarasota, FL 34236
(941) 957-0442
Fax: (941) 957-3135

E-MAIL ADDRESS:
ejones@selbyfdn.org

WEB SITE ADDRESS:
www.selbyfdn.org

FOUNDED: 1955

AREAS OF INTEREST:
Education, human services, the arts and community improvement.

TYPE:
Capital grants; Scholarships.

YEAR PROGRAM STARTED: 1955

PURPOSE:
To improve the quality of life in the Sarasota County area.

LEGAL BASIS:
Private foundation.

ELIGIBILITY:
501(c)(3) organizations.

GEOGRAPHIC RESTRICTIONS:
Charlotte, DeSoto, Manatee and Sarasota counties, Florida.

FINANCIAL DATA:
Amount of support per award: Minimum request: $10,000. Average grant size: $100,000. Scholarships: Up to $7,000 per year.

Total amount of support: $3,300,000 for fiscal year 2010.

NUMBER OF AWARDS: Grants: 31 for fiscal year 2009.

APPLICATION INFORMATION:
Duration: Typically one year.

Deadline: Grant Applications: February 1 and August 1. Notification dates: May 15 and December 15. Scholarships: April 1.

PUBLICATIONS:
Guidelines.

STAFF:
Sarah H. Pappas, President and Chief Executive Officer
Evan G. Jones, Grants and Scholarship Manager

ADDRESS INQUIRIES TO:
Evan G. Jones
Grants and Scholarship Manager
(See address above.)

SHARE OUR STRENGTH   [1613]
1730 M Street, N.W.
Suite 700
Washington, DC 20036
(202) 393-2925
(800) 969-4767
Fax: (202) 347-5868

E-MAIL ADDRESS:
grants@strength.org

WEB SITE ADDRESS:
www.strength.org

FOUNDED: 1984

AREAS OF INTEREST:
Domestic childhood hunger, hunger prevention and alleviation limited to summer meals, after school meals, SNAP/WIC outreach, school breakfast and nutrition education.

NAME(S) OF PROGRAMS:
● No Kid Hungry

TYPE:
Project/program grants. Grants are focused on increasing participation in the federal nutrition programs, including summer meals, after school meals, SNAP, WIC, school breakfast, and on nutrition education.

YEAR PROGRAM STARTED: 1984

PURPOSE:
To end childhood hunger in the United States.

LEGAL BASIS:
Nonprofit organization.

ELIGIBILITY:
Applicants must be 501(c)(3) organizations, schools/school districts, churches/faith-based organizations or other organizations/agencies eligible to receive grants.

GEOGRAPHIC RESTRICTIONS:
United States.

FINANCIAL DATA:
Amount of support per award: Average grant size $5,000 to $10,000.

APPLICATION INFORMATION:
Duration: One year. Renewal possible.
Deadline: Varies.

PUBLICATIONS:
Annual report.

ADDRESS INQUIRIES TO:
Susan Berkun, Director, Grants
(See address above.)

SIERRA HEALTH FOUNDATION   [1614]

1321 Garden Highway
Sacramento, CA 95833
(916) 922-4755
Fax: (916) 922-4024

E-MAIL ADDRESS:
info@sierrahealth.org

WEB SITE ADDRESS:
www.sierrahealth.org

FOUNDED: 1984

AREAS OF INTEREST:
Health-related programs and services.

NAME(S) OF PROGRAMS:
- **Conference and Convening Program**
- **Grizzly Creek Ranch Camp and Conference Center**
- **Health Leadership Program**
- **Responsive Grants Program**

TYPE:
Matching gifts; Project/program grants. Specific to funding opportunities - solicited.

YEAR PROGRAM STARTED: 1984

PURPOSE:
To invest in and serve as a catalyst for ideas, partnerships and programs that improve health and quality of life in northern California through convening, educating and strategic grantmaking.

LEGAL BASIS:
Private foundation.

ELIGIBILITY:
Applicant must be a designated 501(c)(3) organization or public entity by the IRS with 509(a)(1) or 509(a)(2) status. No grants to individuals, endowments or activities which exclusively benefit members of private or religious organizations.

GEOGRAPHIC RESTRICTIONS:
Northern California counties.

FINANCIAL DATA:
Amount of support per award: $1,000 to $100,000. Average $25,000.
Total amount of support: $3,281,131 for the year ended December 31, 2010.

NUMBER OF APPLICANTS MOST RECENT YEAR:
697 for the year 2010.

NUMBER OF AWARDS: 114 for the year 2010.

IRS IDENTIFICATION NUMBER: 68-0050036

OFFICERS:
Chet P. Hewitt, President and Chief Executive Officer
Gil Alvarado, Vice President of Administration and Chief Financial Officer

BOARD OF DIRECTORS:
Earl Washburn, M.D., Chairperson
Jose Hermocillo, Vice Chairperson
David Gordon
Chet P. Hewitt
Nancy Lee
Robert Petersen, C.P.A.
Claire Pomeroy
Carol G. Whiteside

ADDRESS INQUIRIES TO:
Grants Administrator
(See address above.)

SOCIAL JUSTICE FUND NORTHWEST   [1615]

603 Stewart Street, Suite 1007
Seattle, WA 98101-1264
(206) 624-4081
Fax: (206) 382-2640

E-MAIL ADDRESS:
grants@socialjusticefund.org

WEB SITE ADDRESS:
www.socialjusticefund.org

FOUNDED: 1978

AREAS OF INTEREST:
Funding community-based groups to promote social justice activities and organizations attempting to establish a society that is politically and economically democratic, equitable and environmentally sound. Also funds technical assistance support and small grants for arts/cultural work promoting social justice.

CONSULTING OR VOLUNTEER SERVICES:
Facilitates regional networking and general foundation information.

TYPE:
General operating grants; Project/program grants; Seed money grants; Technical assistance; Training grants. Rapid response grants.

YEAR PROGRAM STARTED: 1978

PURPOSE:
To be a resource for organizations working for social justice in the states of Idaho, Montana, Oregon, Washington and/or Wyoming; attempting to establish a society that is politically and economically democratic, equitable and environmentally just.

LEGAL BASIS:
Nonprofit, 501(c)(3), public foundation.

ELIGIBILITY:
Applicant must address fundamental issues facing Northwest/Northern Rockies or any organizations that work in and have a direct impact on the people of Idaho, Montana, Oregon, Washington and/or Wyoming. Applicants must also be sponsored by a 501(c)(3) organization.

GEOGRAPHIC RESTRICTIONS:
Idaho, Montana, Oregon, Washington and/or Wyoming.

FINANCIAL DATA:
Amount of support per award: Average grant: $10,000.
Total amount of support: Approximately $500,000 for the year 2010.

PUBLICATIONS:
Guidelines; monthly e-mail newsletter; annual report.

IRS IDENTIFICATION NUMBER: 91-1036971

BOARD OF DIRECTORS:
Dana Arviso
George Cheung
Tracy Cosgrove
Vickie Goodwin
Esther Handy
Eli Hastings
Jessan Hutchinson-Quillian
Abel Vallardes

ADDRESS INQUIRIES TO:
Mijo Lee, Program Director
(See address above.)

THE STODDARD CHARITABLE TRUST   [1616]

370 Main Street
Suite 1250
Worcester, MA 01608
(508) 798-8621
Fax: (508) 791-6454

FOUNDED: 1939

AREAS OF INTEREST:
General charitable activities.

TYPE:
Project/program grants. Grants to support activities in the Trustees' areas of interest.

YEAR PROGRAM STARTED: 1939

PURPOSE:
To provide funding to worthy causes in the Worcester, MA area and to help that community during times of need.

LEGAL BASIS:
Private, charitable foundation.

ELIGIBILITY:
Nonprofit organizations.

GEOGRAPHIC RESTRICTIONS:
Worcester, Massachusetts.

FINANCIAL DATA:
Amount of support per award: $5,000 to $2,000,000; average grant $10,000.
Total amount of support: $3,000,000 annually.

APPLICATION INFORMATION:
Submit requests for application procedures to the address above.
Duration: One year.
Deadline: March 1, June 1, September 1, and December 1.

OFFICERS AND TRUSTEES:
Warner S. Fletcher, Chairman
Judith S. King, Treasurer
Valerie S. Loring, Secretary

TRUSTEE:
Allen W. Fletcher, Trustee

ADDRESS INQUIRIES TO:
Warner S. Fletcher, Chairman
(See address above.)

THE SUMMIT FOUNDATION

111 A Lincoln Street
Breckenridge, CO 80424
(970) 453-5970
Fax: (970) 453-1423

E-MAIL ADDRESS:
tsfdirector@summitfoundation.org

WEB SITE ADDRESS:
summitfoundation.org

TYPE:
Capital grants; Challenge/matching grants;
General operating grants; Matching gifts;
Project/program grants; Scholarships; Seed
money grants; Technical assistance; Training
grants. The Foundation supports scholarship
programs at Summit High School and
neighboring community high schools.
Scholarships are available to graduating
seniors each year.

See entry 1476 for full listing.

SUNNEN FOUNDATION   [1617]
7910 Manchester Avenue
St. Louis, MO 63143
(314) 781-2100

FOUNDED: 1953

AREAS OF INTEREST:
Grants for specific goal-oriented activities to
protect reproductive and First Amendment
rights and for youth and family services.

TYPE:
Capital grants; Challenge/matching grants;
Development grants; Matching gifts;
Project/program grants.

YEAR PROGRAM STARTED: 1953

LEGAL BASIS:
Private foundation.

ELIGIBILITY:
Limited to those organizations having
tax-exempt status. No scholarship, research
or travel grants are made to or for specific
individuals.

GEOGRAPHIC RESTRICTIONS:
St. Louis, Missouri.

FINANCIAL DATA:
Assets of $12,345,000 (unaudited) as of
December 31, 2010.
Amount of support per award: $3,000 to
$100,000 for the year 2010.
Total amount of support: $933,000 for the
year 2010.

NUMBER OF APPLICANTS MOST RECENT YEAR:
Approximately 30.

NUMBER OF AWARDS: 11 for the year 2010.

REPRESENTATIVE AWARDS:
$140,000 to Planned Parenthood Agencies.

APPLICATION INFORMATION:
The Sunnen Foundation has no formal
application form. Proposal should include:
(1) summary page that describes the project
and amount of funds requested;
(2) organizational background that includes
mission, history, types of programs offered
and constituencies served;
(3) project description that justifies the need,
outlines specific goals, objectives and
activities planned to meet the goals and
objectives, a project time-line and specific
methods of evaluation;
(4) project budget that notes anticipated
expenses, including details of how the
Sunnen Foundation funds will be used and
anticipated income, including information
about other grantmakers approached for
funding;
(5) organizational budget that notes the
current year budget and proposed budget for
project year(s) showing income and expenses,
the organization's most recent audited
financial statement and public and private
sources of funds and;

(6) supporting documents that should include
a list of current board members, annual
report and evidence of 501(c)(3) status.
Six copies of the proposal should be
submitted.
Duration: Varies.
Deadline: August 1. Proposals should be
submitted in June or July.

PUBLICATIONS:
Guidelines.

IRS IDENTIFICATION NUMBER: 43-6029156

OFFICERS:
Kurt J. Kallaus, President and Director
Matthew S. Kreider, Vice President and
Director
Susan S. Brasel, Treasurer and Director
Ruth Cardinale, Secretary and Director
Helen S. Sly, Director

ADDRESS INQUIRIES TO:
Kurt J. Kallaus, President
(See address above.)

SUPERVALU
FOUNDATION   [1618]
P.O. Box 990
Minneapolis, MN 55440
(952) 828-4000
Fax: (952) 828-4838

WEB SITE ADDRESS:
www.supervalu.com

FOUNDED: 1939

AREAS OF INTEREST:
Environmental stewardship, hunger relief,
health and nutrition.

TYPE:
General operating grants; Product donations;
Project/program grants. Capital grants for
hunger relief. Scholarships available through
Pharmacy Division for pharmacology
education.

PURPOSE:
To promote the health and well-being of the
communities that the company serves.

LEGAL BASIS:
Corporate giving program.

ELIGIBILITY:
Applicant must be an IRS tax-exempt
501(c)(3) organization. No grants are made to
individuals.

FINANCIAL DATA:
Amount of support per award: $1,000 and
up.

APPLICATION INFORMATION:
Requests are only accepted through the
online submission form.
Duration: One year.
Deadline: February 15, May 15, August 15
and November 15.

PUBLICATIONS:
Annual report; contributions guidelines.

TEAMMATES FOR KIDS
FOUNDATION
4251 Kipling Street, Suite 370
Wheat Ridge, CO 80033
(303) 759-9777
Fax: (303) 759-9555

E-MAIL ADDRESS:
jason@tfkf.com

WEB SITE ADDRESS:
www.teammates4kids.com

TYPE:
Grants-in-aid. Foundation grants are directed
to nonprofit organizations that specialize in
working with children.

See entry 1222 for full listing.

TIDES FOUNDATION
Presidio Building 1014
Lincoln Boulevard at Torney Avenue
San Francisco, CA 94129
(415) 561-6400
Fax: (415) 561-6401

E-MAIL ADDRESS:
info@tides.org

WEB SITE ADDRESS:
www.tides.org

TYPE:
General operating grants; Internships;
Project/program grants.

See entry 1479 for full listing.

UNITED METHODIST HEALTH
MINISTRY FUND   [1619]
100 East First Street
Hutchinson, KS 67501
(620) 662-8586
Fax: (620) 662-8597

E-MAIL ADDRESS:
healthfund@healthfund.org

WEB SITE ADDRESS:
www.healthfund.org

FOUNDED: 1986

AREAS OF INTEREST:
Health care.

NAME(S) OF PROGRAMS:
- **Access to Health Care-System Change
  and Advocacy**
- **Healthy Congregations Program**
- **Healthy Nutrition and Physical Activity
  for Young Children**
- **Mental Health for Young Children**

TYPE:
Challenge/matching grants;
Conferences/seminars; Demonstration grants;
General operating grants; Project/program
grants; Seed money grants; Technical
assistance; Training grants.

YEAR PROGRAM STARTED: 1986

PURPOSE:
To advance health, healing and wholeness for
persons within and beyond the bounds of the
Kansas West Conference of the United
Methodist Church.

LEGAL BASIS:
Church foundation.

ELIGIBILITY:
Grants are made:
(1) to organizations exempt from income tax
under Section 501(c)(3) of the IRS Code;
(2) to governmental entities;
(3) for health care services and;
(4) for projects located in Kansas.

GEOGRAPHIC RESTRICTIONS:
Kansas.

FINANCIAL DATA:
Amount of support per award: Average grant
$51,857 for the year 2009.

Total amount of support: $2,564,614 for the year 2009.

NUMBER OF APPLICANTS MOST RECENT YEAR: Approximately 150.

NUMBER OF AWARDS: 49 for the year 2009.

REPRESENTATIVE AWARDS:
$75,000 to Community Health Center of Southeast Kansas to integrate mental health services for young children into primary care; $40,000 to Kansas Association for Infant and Early Childhood Mental Health for mental health endorsement trainings; $150,000 to Kansas Chapter of the American Academy of Pediatrics for private medical practice trainings and support of fluoride varnish applications; $53,599 to Healthy Kids Challenge to implement healthy lifestyles education and behavior change through Kansas libraries.

APPLICATION INFORMATION:
Application information is available by contacting the Fund.
Duration: Varies.

PUBLICATIONS:
Annual report; special publications.

IRS IDENTIFICATION NUMBER: 48-1019578

STAFF:
Kim Moore, President
Virginia Elliott, Vice President for Programs
Jeff Gamber, Technology Manager
Michael Gray, Program Assistant

ADDRESS INQUIRIES TO:
Virginia Elliott
Vice President for Programs
(See address above.)

*SPECIAL STIPULATIONS:
Preference for United Methodist Churches and agencies in Kansas.

WICHITA COMMUNITY FOUNDATION
301 North Main Street
Suite 100
Wichita, KS 67202
(316) 264-4880
Fax: (316) 264-7592

E-MAIL ADDRESS:
wcf@wichitacf.org

WEB SITE ADDRESS:
www.wichitacf.org

TYPE:
Project/program grants; Scholarships; Seed money grants.

See entry 1493 for full listing.

EDUCATION

Educational projects and research (general)

AMERICAN ASSOCIATION OF UNIVERSITY WOMEN EDUCATIONAL FOUNDATION

101 ACT Drive
Iowa City, IA 52243
(319) 337-1716

E-MAIL ADDRESS:
aauw@act.org

WEB SITE ADDRESS:
www.aauw.org

TYPE:
Project/program grants; Seed money grants.

See entry 1137 for full listing.

THE AMERICAN FOUNDATION FOR SUICIDE PREVENTION [1620]

120 Wall Street
22nd Floor
New York, NY 10005
(212) 363-3500 ext. 15
Fax: (212) 363-6237

E-MAIL ADDRESS:
lspaulding@afsp.org

WEB SITE ADDRESS:
www.afsp.org

FOUNDED: 1987

AREAS OF INTEREST:
Suicide prevention.

NAME(S) OF PROGRAMS:
● **Pilot Grant**

TYPE:
Research grants.

PURPOSE:
To enable established investigators to pursue promising leads that emerge from their investigations and help develop preliminary data for the submission of larger funding requests to granting agencies.

ELIGIBILITY:
Grants are awarded to individuals affiliated with not-for-profit institutions or organizations in the U.S. and abroad. Grant applications are not accepted from for-profit organizations. Grant payments are made to the grantee institution and not the individual investigator.

FINANCIAL DATA:
Amount of support per award: Up to $30,000.

NUMBER OF APPLICANTS MOST RECENT YEAR: 14.

APPLICATION INFORMATION:
Applications for a Pilot Grant must be submitted on the appropriate AFSP forms and must follow the format specified. Completed grant applications must be submitted electronically to the e-mail address above. A compact disc (CD) containing the completed application must also be submitted to the Foundation.

Care should be taken to comply with the page restrictions noted for each section of the application on the application forms. Material submitted that exceeds the specified maximum number of pages, or that is not specifically requested, may not be considered

by the reviewers. The entire application should be typed using a font size no smaller than 11-point.

Duration: One or two years.

Deadline: December 1.

ADDRESS INQUIRIES TO:
Vinita Ling, Research Administrator
(See address above.)

THE AMERICAN FOUNDATION FOR SUICIDE PREVENTION [1621]

120 Wall Street
22nd Floor
New York, NY 10005
(212) 363-3500 ext. 15
Fax: (212) 363-6237

E-MAIL ADDRESS:
lspaulding@afsp.org

WEB SITE ADDRESS:
www.afsp.org

FOUNDED: 1987

AREAS OF INTEREST:
Suicide prevention.

NAME(S) OF PROGRAMS:
● **Postdoctoral Research Fellowships**

TYPE:
Fellowships; Research grants.

PURPOSE:
To sponsor full-time training projects by investigators who have recently received a Ph.D. degree.

ELIGIBILITY:
Postdoctoral Research Fellowships are awarded for full-time training projects by investigators who have received a Ph.D. degree within the preceding three years and have not had more than three years of fellowship support.

FINANCIAL DATA:
Amount of support per award: Up to $100,000 (progressive stipend $42,000 first year, $46,000 second year and $6,000 per year institutional allowance).

Total amount of support: Up to $100,000.

NUMBER OF APPLICANTS MOST RECENT YEAR: 7.

NUMBER OF AWARDS: 1.

APPLICATION INFORMATION:
Applications must be submitted on the appropriate AFSP forms and must follow the format specified. Completed grant applications must be submitted electronically to the e-mail address above. A compact disc (CD) containing the completed application must also be submitted to the Foundation.

Care should be taken to comply with the page restrictions noted for each section of the application on the application forms. Material submitted that exceeds the specified maximum number of pages, or that is not specifically requested, may not be considered by the reviewers. The entire application should be typed using a font size no smaller than 11-point.

Duration: Two years.

Deadline: December 1.

ADDRESS INQUIRIES TO:
Vinita Ling, Research Administrator
(See address above.)

THE AMERICAN FOUNDATION FOR SUICIDE PREVENTION [1622]

120 Wall Street
22nd Floor
New York, NY 10005
(212) 363-3500 ext. 15
Fax: (212) 363-6237

E-MAIL ADDRESS:
lspaulding@afsp.org

WEB SITE ADDRESS:
www.afsp.org

FOUNDED: 1987

AREAS OF INTEREST:
Suicide prevention.

NAME(S) OF PROGRAMS:
● **Distinguished Investigator Award**

TYPE:
Research grants.

PURPOSE:
To advance knowledge of suicide and the ability to prevent it; to fund new directions and initiatives in suicidology.

ELIGIBILITY:
Applicant must be an associate professor or higher with a proven history of research in the area of suicide.

FINANCIAL DATA:
Amount of support per award: $100,000 ($50,000 per year).

NUMBER OF APPLICANTS MOST RECENT YEAR: 10.

NUMBER OF AWARDS: 2.

APPLICATION INFORMATION:
Applications must be submitted on the appropriate AFSP forms and must follow the format specified. Completed grant applications must be submitted electronically to the e-mail address above. A compact disc (CD) containing the completed application must also be submitted to the Foundation.

Care should be taken to comply with the page restrictions noted for each section of the application on the application forms. Material submitted that exceeds the specified maximum number of pages, or that is not specifically requested, may not be considered by the reviewers. The entire application should be typed using a font size no smaller than 11-point.

Duration: Up to two years.

Deadline: December 1.

ADDRESS INQUIRIES TO:
Vinita Ling, Research Administrator
(See address above.)

THE AMERICAN FOUNDATION FOR SUICIDE PREVENTION [1623]

120 Wall Street
22nd Floor
New York, NY 10005
(212) 363-3500 ext. 15
Fax: (212) 363-6237

E-MAIL ADDRESS:
lspaulding@afsp.org

WEB SITE ADDRESS:
www.afsp.org

FOUNDED: 1987

AREAS OF INTEREST:
Suicide prevention.

NAME(S) OF PROGRAMS:
- **Standard Research Grants**
- **Young Investigator Grants**

TYPE:
Research grants. Standard Research Grants are awarded to individual investigators. An additional annual stipend is available for mentors on Young Investigator Awards in which the investigator is at the level of Assistant Professor or lower.

PURPOSE:
To advance the knowledge of suicide and the ability to prevent it; to promote the study of clinical, biological and psychosocial aspects of suicide.

ELIGIBILITY:
Grants are awarded to not-for-profit organizations.

FINANCIAL DATA:
Amount of support per award: Up to $75,000. An additional $10,000 over two years to mentor on Young Investigator Grant.

NUMBER OF APPLICANTS MOST RECENT YEAR:
Standard Research Grants: 33; Young Investigator Awards: 34.

NUMBER OF AWARDS: Standard Research Grants: 1; Young Investigator Grants: 2.

APPLICATION INFORMATION:
Applications must be submitted on the appropriate AFSP forms and must follow the format specified. Completed grant applications must be submitted electronically to the e-mail address above. A compact disc (CD) containing the completed application must also be submitted to the Foundation.

Care should be taken to comply with the page restrictions noted for each section of the application on the application forms. Material submitted that exceeds the specified maximum number of pages, or that is not specifically requested, may not be considered by the reviewers. The entire application should be typed using a font size no smaller than 11-point.

Duration: One or two years.

Deadline: December 1.

ADDRESS INQUIRIES TO:
Vinita Ling, Research Administrator
(See address above.)

AMERICAN HONDA FOUNDATION   [1624]

1919 Torrance Boulevard
Building 100
Torrance, CA 90501-2746
(310) 781-4090
Fax: (310) 781-4270

WEB SITE ADDRESS:
www.honda.com
www.foundation.honda.com

FOUNDED: 1984

AREAS OF INTEREST:
Youth, education, career training, math, science, technology, engineering and environment.

TYPE:
Challenge/matching grants; Development grants; General operating grants; Project/program grants.

YEAR PROGRAM STARTED: 1984

PURPOSE:
To fund programs which strive to educate communities in the process of problem solving and planning; to educate minority youth in the areas of science and math.

LEGAL BASIS:
501(c)(3) corporate foundation.

ELIGIBILITY:
Applicants must be 501(c)(3) organizations, national in scope, impact and outreach and focused on youth and scientific education. To be considered for possible funding, programs related to youth and scientific education should be dedicated to improving the human condition of all mankind, soundly managed and administered by enthusiastic and dedicated individuals who approach their jobs in a youthful way, look to the future or foresightful programs, innovative and creative programs that propose untried methods which ultimately may result in providing solutions to the complex cultural, educational, scientific and social concerns currently facing American society, broad in scope, intent, impact and outreach, possess a high potential for success with a relatively low incidence of duplication of effort, operate from a position of financial soundness, in urgent need of funding from a priority basis (not necessarily financial need), i.e., the relative importance of the program or project to the public and represent a minimal risk in terms of venture capital investment.

Grants are not given to individuals or for scholarships, politics, fund-raising activities, religious activities, arts and culture, medical or educational research, sponsorships for nonprofit, or disaster relief.

No in-kind contributions from the Foundation. No donations of Honda products.

GEOGRAPHIC RESTRICTIONS:
United States.

FINANCIAL DATA:
Amount of support per award: $20,000 to $60,000 per year; $25,000 to $45,000 average.

Total amount of support: $1,400,000 for fiscal year 2011.

APPLICATION INFORMATION:
Grant application is accessible online. Grant requests should include:
(1) a description of the program for which the grant will be used;
(2) a copy of the IRS determination letter, 501(c)(3), designating the organization as a nonprofit, tax-exempt, public supported charity;
(3) a copy of the organization's most recent Form 990 to the IRS;
(4) a list of the Board of Directors and a resolution from the Board which authorizes the request for a grant;
(5) a copy of the current budget for the entire organization, with comparisons to the last previous budget;
(6) a proposed budget utilizing the grant funds requested with line item detail;
(7) audited financial statements for the last two years;
(8) a list of current contributions, with giving levels, particularly of other corporate sponsors and/or corporate foundations;
(9) a three to five-year plan from the organization and;
(10) support materials (i.e., annual reports, press kits, brochures, flyers, press clippings, photos, etc.).

Duration: One year.

Deadline: November 1, February 1, May 1 and August 1.

PUBLICATIONS:
Contributions Policy, brochure.

ADDRESS INQUIRIES TO:
Alexandra Warnier, Manager
(See address above.)

*SPECIAL STIPULATIONS:
One proposal per year, per grant seeker.

AMERICAN INSTITUTE OF CERTIFIED PUBLIC ACCOUNTANTS (AICPA)   [1625]

220 Leigh Farm Road
Durham, NC 27707
(919) 402-4931
Fax: (919) 419-4705

E-MAIL ADDRESS:
mic_programs@aicpa.org

WEB SITE ADDRESS:
www.aicpa.org

AREAS OF INTEREST:
Accounting.

NAME(S) OF PROGRAMS:
- **AICPA Scholarship for Minority Accounting Students**

TYPE:
Scholarships.

YEAR PROGRAM STARTED: 1969

PURPOSE:
To provide financial assistance to minority students who show significant potential to become CPAs.

ELIGIBILITY:
An applicant must meet the following requirements:
(1) be an underrepresented minority in the accounting profession (e.g., Black/African American; Hispanic/Latino; Native American; or Asian American);
(2) be planning to pursue the CPA credential;
(3) be full-time undergraduate student (12 semester-hours or equivalent) or graduate student (nine semester-hours or equivalent). An exception is made for a student completing their final semester of study. Have completed at least 30 semester-hours (or equivalent) of college coursework, including at least six semester-hours (or equivalent) in accounting. Undergraduate students level must be declared accounting majors (as indicated on the transcript or by a signed letter from the department of school of business head indicating major). Graduate level must have been accepted to a Masters-level accounting, finance, taxation or other related Masters-level program. Have maintained a minimum of 3.3 grade point average (both cumulative and in major courses);
(4) be a AICPA Student Affiliate member (or have recently submitted a new member application).
(5) be currently enrolled in a regionally accredited, public or private, 501(c)(3), four-year college or university located in the U.S. and offering accounting degrees and;
(6) be a U.S. citizen or permanent resident (green-card holder).

GEOGRAPHIC RESTRICTIONS:
United States and its territories.

FINANCIAL DATA:
Amount of support per award: Up to $3,000.

Total amount of support: Approximately $390,000 for the academic year 2008-09.

NUMBER OF AWARDS: Up to 140 per academic year.

APPLICATION INFORMATION:
Information is available online.
Deadline: April 1.

AMERICAN INSTITUTE OF CERTIFIED PUBLIC ACCOUNTANTS (AICPA)
220 Leigh Farm Road
Durham, NC 27707
(919) 402-4931
Fax: (919) 419-4705

E-MAIL ADDRESS:
mic_programs@aicpa.org

WEB SITE ADDRESS:
www.aicpa.org

TYPE:
Fellowships. Awarded annually to full-time minority accounting scholars who demonstrate significant potential to become accounting educators.

See entry 1772 for full listing.

THE AMERICAN SOCIETY FOR NONDESTRUCTIVE TESTING, INC.   [1626]
1711 Arlingate Lane
Columbus, OH 43228
(614) 274-6003
(800) 222-2768 ext. 223 (U.S. and Canada)
Fax: (614) 274-6899

WEB SITE ADDRESS:
www.asnt.org

FOUNDED: 1997

AREAS OF INTEREST:
Promotion of nondestructive testing.

NAME(S) OF PROGRAMS:
● **ASNT Faculty Grant Award**

TYPE:
Development grants. The Society sponsors an annual award that will provide grants to foster the development of nondestructive testing and evaluation courses (NDT & NDE) as an integral part of its engineering curricula.

PURPOSE:
To support research and education in nondestructive testing; to increase public awareness of nondestructive testing's critical role in ensuring the safety and well-being of mankind.

LEGAL BASIS:
501(c)(3) corporation.

ELIGIBILITY:
Faculty members from ABET-accredited engineering programs are encouraged to submit proposals for this award.

FINANCIAL DATA:
Amount of support per award: $8,000.
Total amount of support: Up to $16,000.

NUMBER OF AWARDS: Up to 2.

APPLICATION INFORMATION:
Contact the ASNT administrative assistant for an application.
Duration: One year.
Deadline: December 1. Funding will begin the following July.

ADDRESS INQUIRIES TO:
Stephanie Dille
Administrative Assistant
(See address above.)

THE KATHRYN AMES FOUNDATION
c/o Pierson & Pierson
305 West Chesapeake Avenue, Suite 308
Towson, MD 21204
(410) 821-3004
Fax: (410) 821-3007

E-MAIL ADDRESS:
info@kathrynames.org

WEB SITE ADDRESS:
www.kathrynames.org

TYPE:
General operating grants; Project/program grants.

See entry 875 for full listing.

ARCHAEOLOGICAL INSTITUTE OF AMERICA
656 Beacon Street, 6th Floor
Boston, MA 02215
(617) 358-4184
Fax: (617) 353-6550

E-MAIL ADDRESS:
lsparks@aia.bu.edu

WEB SITE ADDRESS:
www.archaeological.org

TYPE:
Fellowships. The Fellowship supports projects pertaining to the archaeology of Portugal. These include, but are not limited to, research projects, colloquia, symposia, publication, research-related travel, or travel to academic meetings for the purpose of presenting papers on the archaeology of Portugal.

See entry 876 for full listing.

ARIZONA STATE UNIVERSITY   [1627]
P.O. Box 870112
Tempe, AZ 85287-0112
(480) 965-3040
Fax: (480) 965-3610

E-MAIL ADDRESS:
kimberly.jones@asu.edu

WEB SITE ADDRESS:
www.asu.edu

AREAS OF INTEREST:
Leadership.

NAME(S) OF PROGRAMS:
● **ASU Leadership Scholarship Program**

TYPE:
Scholarships.

PURPOSE:
To recognize outstanding high school graduating seniors who have achieved excellence in leadership.

ELIGIBILITY:
Must have demonstrated leadership abilities, responsibilities, and potential in Key Club leadership and high school activities.

FINANCIAL DATA:
Amount of support per award: In-state: $9,000 per year; Out-of-state: $17,500 per year.

NUMBER OF AWARDS: 25 per year.

APPLICATION INFORMATION:
Duration: Four years. Renewable.
Deadline: December.

ADDRESS INQUIRIES TO:
Kimberly Jones, Program Coordinator
(See address above.)

AXE-HOUGHTON FOUNDATION
c/o Foundation Source
55 Walls Drive, 3rd Floor
Fairfield, CT 06824
(800) 839-1754
Fax: (800) 839-1764

WEB SITE ADDRESS:
www.foundationcenter.
org/grantmaker/axehoughton

TYPE:
Project/program grants.

See entry 691 for full listing.

BAT CONSERVATION INTERNATIONAL   [1628]
P.O. Box 162603
Austin, TX 78716
(512) 327-9721
Fax: (512) 327-9724

E-MAIL ADDRESS:
grants2@batcon.org

WEB SITE ADDRESS:
www.batcon.org

AREAS OF INTEREST:
Mammals, ecology, conservation and biology; specifically bats.

NAME(S) OF PROGRAMS:
● **BCI Student Scholarship**

TYPE:
Scholarships. Support graduate students in research.

YEAR PROGRAM STARTED: 1990

PURPOSE:
To conserve bats and their habitat worldwide; to support research that specifically provides for bat conservation progress.

ELIGIBILITY:
Must be currently enrolled in a degree-granting program.

FINANCIAL DATA:
Amount of support per award: Up to $5,000.

NUMBER OF APPLICANTS MOST RECENT YEAR: 77.

NUMBER OF AWARDS: 19 for the year 2011.

APPLICATION INFORMATION:
Applications must be completed online.
Duration: One year.
Deadline: December 15.

IRS IDENTIFICATION NUMBER: 74-2553144

ADDRESS INQUIRIES TO:
Robert Locke, Scholarship Coordinator
(See address above.)

BATON ROUGE AREA FOUNDATION
402 North Fourth Street
Baton Rouge, LA 70802
(225) 387-6126
Fax: (225) 387-6153

E-MAIL ADDRESS:
ghobdy@braf.org

WEB SITE ADDRESS:
www.braf.org

TYPE:
Capital grants; Challenge/matching grants;
Conferences/seminars; Demonstration grants;
Development grants; Matching gifts;
Project/program grants; Scholarships; Seed
money grants; Technical assistance; Training
grants; Visiting scholars.

See entry 466 for full listing.

THE BAY AND PAUL FOUNDATIONS [1629]

17 West 94th Street, 1st Floor
New York, NY 10025
(212) 663-1115
Fax: (212) 932-0316

WEB SITE ADDRESS:
www.bayandpaulfoundations.org

FOUNDED: 1962

AREAS OF INTEREST:
Arts in education and educational reform.

TYPE:
Challenge/matching grants; General operating
grants; Project/program grants.

YEAR PROGRAM STARTED: 1962

PURPOSE:
To support a variety of programs that
empower students through democracy,
environmental stewardship, meaningful
community service and the arts.

LEGAL BASIS:
Private foundation.

ELIGIBILITY:
Grants are made to organizations that have
tax-exempt status under Section 501(c)(3) of
the Internal Revenue Code. No grants are
made to individuals and no grants are made
to building campaigns or sectarian religious
programs.

Pre-collegiate arts-in-education and
science/health grants are available in the New
York City metropolitan area only.

FINANCIAL DATA:
Amount of support per award: $4,000 to
$10,000.

NUMBER OF AWARDS: 70 to 80.

APPLICATION INFORMATION:
There is no application form. Proposals
should include:
(1) a brief description of the applicant
organization;
(2) an outline of the program or project for
which funding is being sought, including
objectives and population served;
(3) the qualifications of key personnel;
(4) a project budget and/or financials,
including projected sources of support and;
(5) evidence of U.S. tax-exempt status.
Duration: One year; some multiyear.
Deadline: March 1 for May meeting,
September 1 for November meeting and
December 1 for February meeting.

IRS IDENTIFICATION NUMBER: 13-1991717

STAFF:
Dianne J. Daniels, Program Director
Michelle Graham, Program Officer

BOARD OF DIRECTORS:
Frederick Bay, Executive Director
Robert W. Ashton, Chairman
Synnova B. Hayes, Vice
President-Administration and Treasurer

Corinne Steel, Secretary and Assistant
Treasurer
Rebecca Adamson
David Bury
Kenneth Hurwitz

ADDRESS INQUIRIES TO:
Frederick Bay, Executive Director
(See address above.)

BAYER USA FOUNDATION

100 Bayer Road
Pittsburgh, PA 15205
(412) 777-2000
Fax: (412) 778-4430

E-MAIL ADDRESS:
karen.wirth@bayer.com

WEB SITE ADDRESS:
www.bayerus.
com/foundation/foundation_home.aspx

TYPE:
Challenge/matching grants; General operating
grants; Grants-in-aid; Project/program grants.

See entry 1935 for full listing.

BETHESDA LUTHERAN COMMUNITIES, INC. [1630]

600 Hoffmann Drive
Watertown, WI 53094
(920) 206-4410
Fax: (920) 206-7706 (Attn.: Pam Bergen)

E-MAIL ADDRESS:
pam.bergen@mailblc.org

WEB SITE ADDRESS:
bethesdalutherancommunities.org

AREAS OF INTEREST:
Developmental disabilities.

NAME(S) OF PROGRAMS:
● **Developmental Disabilities Scholastic
Achievement Scholarships**

TYPE:
Scholarships.

PURPOSE:
To encourage Lutheran youth to develop
God-pleasing attitudes and actions toward
people with individual differences, and to
consider careers in the field of developmental
disabilities services.

ELIGIBILITY:
Must be an active communicant member of a
Lutheran church, have achieved sophomore
status at a college or university, have a
minimum 3.0 overall grade point average and
have a career objective in the field of
developmental disabilities services.

GEOGRAPHIC RESTRICTIONS:
United States and Canada.

FINANCIAL DATA:
Amount of support per award: $3,000.
Total amount of support: $6,000.

NUMBER OF APPLICANTS MOST RECENT YEAR:
21.

APPLICATION INFORMATION:
The application process includes a short,
relevant essay, 100 hours of paid or volunteer
work in the field of developmental
disabilities, services, and letters of reference.
Deadline: April 15.

ADDRESS INQUIRIES TO:
Pam Bergen, Coordinator
(See address above.)

BIBLIOGRAPHICAL SOCIETY OF AMERICA [1631]

P.O. Box 1537
Lenox Hill Station, NY 10021
(212) 734-2500
Fax: (212) 452-2710

E-MAIL ADDRESS:
bsa@bibsocamer.org

WEB SITE ADDRESS:
www.bibsocamer.org

FOUNDED: 1904

AREAS OF INTEREST:
Study of books and manuscripts.

NAME(S) OF PROGRAMS:
● **BSA Fellowship Program**

TYPE:
Fellowships. Stipend in support of travel,
living and research expenses.

YEAR PROGRAM STARTED: 1983

PURPOSE:
To support bibliographical inquiry as well as
research in the history of the book trades and
in publishing history.

ELIGIBILITY:
Open to doctorates, postdoctorates and
postgraduates. Applicants of any nationality
can apply. Eligible topics may concentrate on
books and documents in any field, but should
focus on the book or manuscript (the
physical object) as historical evidence. Such
topics may include establishing a text or
studying the history of book production,
publication, distribution, collecting, or
reading. Enumerative listings do not fall
within the scope of this program.

FINANCIAL DATA:
Amount of support per award: Up to $2,000
per month.

APPLICATION INFORMATION:
Instructions on how to apply and application
form are available on the Society's web site
Duration: One to two months. Nonrenewable.
Deadline: December 1.

ADDRESS INQUIRIES TO:
Michele Randall, Executive Secretary
(See address above.)

THE BROWARD EDUCATION FOUNDATION, INC. [1632]

KC Wright Administration Building, 1st Floor
600 S.E. Third Avenue
Fort Lauderdale, FL 33301
(754) 321-2030
Fax: (754) 321-2706

E-MAIL ADDRESS:
jorene.jameson@browardschools.com

WEB SITE ADDRESS:
www.browardedfoundation.net

FOUNDED: 1983

AREAS OF INTEREST:
Education.

NAME(S) OF PROGRAMS:
● **Broward Advisors for Continuing
Education (BRACE) Scholarship Fund**
● **Citigroup/Citibank Teacher Grants**
● **The Florida Prepaid College Tuition
Program**
● **Impact II Teacher Grants**
● **Kids in Need Resource Center**
● **Project Opportunity Scholarship Fund**

TYPE:
Grants-in-aid; Scholarships. Broward Advisors for Continuing Education (BRACE) Scholarship Fund awards last-dollar scholarships to qualifying students who have exhausted all avenues for financial aid and still fall short of their monetary need to pursue a postsecondary education, including community college, university and vocational school.

The Florida Prepaid College Tuition Program purchases prepaid contracts through the state of Florida's Prepaid College Foundation. It provides a defined benefit college tuition contract for state universities, community colleges, and vocational/technical centers.

Project Opportunity Scholarship Fund consists of scholarships awarded to public school paraprofessionals and support services personnel who want to become future educators.

YEAR PROGRAM STARTED: 1983

PURPOSE:
To provide resources for students, teachers and other employees to help them achieve educational success.

LEGAL BASIS:
501(c)(3) education foundation.

GEOGRAPHIC RESTRICTIONS:
Broward County, Florida.

FINANCIAL DATA:
Amount of support per award: Varies.

APPLICATION INFORMATION:
Contact the Foundation for specific application forms.
Duration: Varies.
Deadline: Varies.

PUBLICATIONS:
Financial report.

STAFF:
Jorene Jameson, Chief Executive Officer and President

ADDRESS INQUIRIES TO:
Jorene Jameson
Chief Executive Officer and President
(See address above.)

THE BROWN FOUNDATION, INC. [1633]

P.O. Box 130646
Houston, TX 77219-0646
(713) 523-6867
Fax: (713) 523-2917

E-MAIL ADDRESS:
bfi@brownfoundation.org

WEB SITE ADDRESS:
www.brownfoundation.org

FOUNDED: 1951

AREAS OF INTEREST:
Education, arts and humanities, civic/public affairs, medicine and science, and human services.

TYPE:
Assistantships; Capital grants; Challenge/matching grants; Fellowships; General operating grants; Matching gifts; Professorships; Project/program grants; Scholarships; Seed money grants.

YEAR PROGRAM STARTED: 1951

PURPOSE:
To distribute funds for public charitable purposes, principally for the support, encouragement and assistance to education, the arts and community service.

LEGAL BASIS:
Private foundation.

ELIGIBILITY:
Funding given to 501(c)(3) nonprofit institutions only. No grants to individuals.

GEOGRAPHIC RESTRICTIONS:
Primarily Texas.

FINANCIAL DATA:
Amount of support per award: Varies.
Total amount of support: $44,264,169 for fiscal year ended June 30, 2010.

APPLICATION INFORMATION:
Grant proposals must include the purpose of the organization requesting funds, tax-exempt determination letter, audited financial statement, summary of proposed project, budget and letter of approval from a chief administrator. Applications will not be processed until all required information is included.
Duration: Typically one year.

PUBLICATIONS:
Application guidelines.

OFFICERS AND TRUSTEES:
Isabel Wilson, Chairman
Herman L. Stude, President
Nancy Negley, Vice President
Maconda Brown O'Connor, Vice President
Louisa Stude Sarofim, Secretary
Holbrook Dorn
Will Mathis
John O'Connor
Elisa Pye
Christopher B. Sarofim

ADDRESS INQUIRIES TO:
Katy Hays, Chief Grants Officer
(See address above.)

FRITZ B. BURNS FOUNDATION [1634]

4001 West Alameda Avenue
Suite 203
Burbank, CA 91505
(818) 840-8802
Fax: (818) 840-0468

FOUNDED: 1955

AREAS OF INTEREST:
Education.

TYPE:
Capital grants; Scholarships. Grants are educational in nature. The emphasis is on buildings, equipment, endowments (not for operational expenses), scholarships, faculty fellowships, hospitals and hospital equipment and medical research.

YEAR PROGRAM STARTED: 1955

LEGAL BASIS:
Private foundation.

ELIGIBILITY:
Eligible organizations must have IRS 501(c)(3) not-for-profit status. Grants are not made to individuals or to religious organizations.

GEOGRAPHIC RESTRICTIONS:
Southern California, primarily Los Angeles County.

FINANCIAL DATA:
Amount of support per award: $500 to $100,000.

APPLICATION INFORMATION:
Applicant organizations must provide IRS 501(c)(3) documentation. Financial statements and a list of the organization's board of directors must be included with the application.
Duration: One year.
Deadline: October 1.

OFFICER:
Rex Rawlinson, President

ADDRESS INQUIRIES TO:
Rex Rawlinson, President
(See address above.)

BUSINESS SOLUTIONS ASSOCIATION EDUCATIONAL FOUNDATION [1635]

5024-R Campbell Boulevard
Baltimore, MD 21236
(410) 931-8100
Fax: (410) 931-8111

E-MAIL ADDRESS:
taylor@businesssolutionsassociation.com

WEB SITE ADDRESS:
www.businesssolutionsassociation.com

AREAS OF INTEREST:
Education.

NAME(S) OF PROGRAMS:
● **Business Solutions Association Educational Foundation Scholarships**

TYPE:
Scholarships.

PURPOSE:
To assist students that are working in the office products industry with educational needs.

ELIGIBILITY:
Open to students that are already at college or starting in the fall, who are:
(1) employed by Business Solutions Association member company;
(2) a relative of an employee of Business Solutions Association member company;
(3) a member of a group affiliated with the office products industry or;
(4) a relative of a member of a group affiliated with the office products industry.

FINANCIAL DATA:
Amount of support per award: Up to $5,000.
Total amount of support: $16,500 for fiscal year 2009.

APPLICATION INFORMATION:
Applicant must complete a Scholarship Application Form and mail it, along with attachments, to the address above. Form is available on the web site. The attachments which must accompany the completed form are:
(1) transcript of grades and credits through the most recent grading period (high school applicants) or transcripts covering a minimum of the previous two scholastic years;
(2) letter of recommendation from a person employed by a firm in the office products industry. This person should hold an executive or managerial position and;
(3) letter of recommendation from a teacher, professor or other educational professional.
Duration: One year. Renewal possible.
Deadline: March 31.

ADDRESS INQUIRIES TO:
Taylor Flynn, Meetings and
Member Services Manager
(See address above.)

THE CAYL INSTITUTE [1636]

60 Gore Street
Cambridge, MA 02141
(617) 354-3820
Fax: (617) 354-3823

E-MAIL ADDRESS:
info@cayl.org

WEB SITE ADDRESS:
www.cayl.org

FOUNDED: 2004

NAME(S) OF PROGRAMS:
● **The CAYL Principals Fellowship**

TYPE:
Fellowships. Established to help early
education professionals develop the skills,
relationships, and knowledge needed to bring
about public policy change in early care and
education.

YEAR PROGRAM STARTED: 2004

PURPOSE:
To develop and strengthen the movement for
equity in education and childcare.

ELIGIBILITY:
Applicants must be citizens or permanent
residents of the U.S.

GEOGRAPHIC RESTRICTIONS:
Massachusetts.

FINANCIAL DATA:
No stipend is granted; instead, six college
credits from Cambridge College are awarded.

APPLICATION INFORMATION:
Applications are available online.
Duration: One calendar year.
Deadline: September 30.

STAFF:
Jessica D'Amico, Operations Manager

ADDRESS INQUIRIES TO:
Dr. Valora Washington
Fellowship Director
(See address above.)

CEMALA FOUNDATION [1637]

330 South Greene Street, Suite 101
Greensboro, NC 27401
(336) 274-3541
Fax: (336) 272-8153

E-MAIL ADDRESS:
cemala@cemala.org

WEB SITE ADDRESS:
www.cemala.org

FOUNDED: 1986

AREAS OF INTEREST:
Education, arts, health, human services,
environment and public interest.

TYPE:
Capital grants; Challenge/matching grants;
Conferences/seminars; Development grants;
Fellowships; Grants-in-aid; Project/program
grants; Seed money grants; Technical
assistance; Training grants.

PURPOSE:
To better the quality of life for the citizens of
Guilford County.

LEGAL BASIS:
Private foundation.

ELIGIBILITY:
Eligible organizations must be IRS 501(c)(3)
tax-exempt.

GEOGRAPHIC RESTRICTIONS:
Primarily Guilford County, North Carolina.

NUMBER OF APPLICANTS MOST RECENT YEAR:
78.

NUMBER OF AWARDS: 33.

APPLICATION INFORMATION:
Application is available online. A copy of
IRS tax determination letter should be
included.
Duration: Annual. Renewal possible.
Deadline: March 1 and September 1.

PUBLICATIONS:
Application guidelines.

STAFF:
Susan Schwartz, Executive Director
Betty Day, Assistant Treasurer

THE COCA-COLA FOUNDATION, INC. [1638]

P.O. Box 1734
Atlanta, GA 30301
(404) 676-2121

E-MAIL ADDRESS:
cocacolacommunityrequest@na.ko.com

WEB SITE ADDRESS:
www.cocacolacommunityrequest.com

FOUNDED: 1984

AREAS OF INTEREST:
Water stewardship, healthy and active
lifestyles, community recycling and
education.

TYPE:
Project/program grants.

PURPOSE:
To help develop and maintain vibrant,
sustainable and local communities; to support
initiatives and programs that respond in a
meaningful way to community needs and
priorities.

LEGAL BASIS:
Corporate foundation.

ELIGIBILITY:
Grants are made only to nonprofit 501(c)(3)
or equivalent organizations. No grants to
individuals, religious organizations or
endeavors, or political, legislative, lobbying
or fraternal organizations.

FINANCIAL DATA:
Amount of support per award: Varies.
Total amount of support: Varies.

APPLICATION INFORMATION:
Detailed instructions and application form is
available online.
Duration: Typically, one year.
Deadline: Requests accepted and reviewed on
a year-round basis.

PUBLICATIONS:
Annual report.

COMMUNITY FOUNDATION OF THE LOWCOUNTRY, INC. [1639]

4 Northridge Drive, Suite A
Hilton Head Island, SC 29926
(843) 681-9100
Fax: (843) 681-9101

E-MAIL ADDRESS:
foundation@cf-lowcountry.org

WEB SITE ADDRESS:
www.cf-lowcountry.org

FOUNDED: 1994

TYPE:
Community impact grants. Investment grants.
Organization development grants.

PURPOSE:
To maintain and enhance the educational,
social, culture, health, civic and
environmental resources of the community.

LEGAL BASIS:
501(c)(3).

ELIGIBILITY:
501(c)(3) organizations.

GEOGRAPHIC RESTRICTIONS:
Hilton Head area, South Carolina.

FINANCIAL DATA:
Amount of support per award: Community
Impact Grants: $5,000 to $50,000;
Community Investment Grants: $100,000 up;
Organizational Development Grants: Not to
exceed $5,000.
Total amount of support: Approximately
$2,000,000 for fiscal year 2010-11.

NUMBER OF APPLICANTS MOST RECENT YEAR:
Approximately 30 for Community Impact
Grants, 3 for Community Investment Grants,
and 12 for Organizational Development
Grants for fiscal year 2010-11.

APPLICATION INFORMATION:
Applicants must attend a grants information
session and register. In order to determine
project eligibility, applicants are then
required to meet with the Vice President for
Grantmaking. Those eligible are invited to
apply.
Duration: One year.
Deadline: April 1, August 1 and December
1.

ADDRESS INQUIRIES TO:
Dr. Cynthia Smith, Vice President
for Grantmaking and Community Leadership
(See address above.)

CONSORTIUM OF COLLEGE AND UNIVERSITY MEDIA CENTERS [1640]

601 East Kirkwood Avenue
Franklin Hall 0009
Bloomington, IN 47405-1223
(812) 855-6049
Fax: (812) 855-2103

E-MAIL ADDRESS:
ccumc@ccumc.org

WEB SITE ADDRESS:
www.ccumc.org

FOUNDED: 1971

AREAS OF INTEREST:
Media and technology services in higher
education.

CONSULTING OR VOLUNTEER SERVICES:
Operation of media services.

NAME(S) OF PROGRAMS:
● **Donald A. Rieck Research Grant**

TYPE:
Awards/prizes; Demonstration grants;
Research grants. Financial support for
research related to the production, selection,

collection development, information retrieval, utilization, distribution, or management of instructional media, equipment or technology.

Faculty, staff and students at constituent member institutions are eligible to apply for the annual Donald A. Rieck Research Grant. Research reports are presented at conferences.

YEAR PROGRAM STARTED: 1978

PURPOSE:
To encourage the development of new knowledge and practices that will lead to the increased accessibility to and utilization of educational media, equipment or technology.

LEGAL BASIS:
University nonprofit association.

ELIGIBILITY:
The submission must be from an undergraduate or graduate student, faculty, or staff person in a member organization of the Consortium. The research must be in progress or expected to be completed within 18 months of the submission of the proposal.

FINANCIAL DATA:
Amount of support per award: Up to $2,000.

NUMBER OF APPLICANTS MOST RECENT YEAR:
3.

NUMBER OF AWARDS: 1 to 3 per year.

APPLICATION INFORMATION:
The application must include a one- to two-page description of the study, a proposed budget and a resume of the investigator. Budget should be directly related to research. Mail or fax three copies of the required materials.

Duration: One year.

Deadline: May 1. Announcement at the CCUMC Summer Board Meeting in July. Notification in August.

PUBLICATIONS:
Leader (CCUMC newsletter); *College & University Media Review* (CCUMC journal); Consortium directory; conference proceedings; annual report.

IRS IDENTIFICATION NUMBER: 51-0168225

BOARD OF DIRECTORS:
Mark McCallister, President
Susan Zvacek, President-elect
Jim Twetten, Treasurer
Pat Poet, Secretary
Aileen Scales, Executive Director
Carleton Jackson, Editor-in-Chief
Brian Burns
Chris Dedrick
Jane Hutchison
Andrew Lokie
Jim Pierret
Daniel Pyne
Bruce Ritchie

EXECUTIVE DIRECTOR:
Aileen Scales

*SPECIAL STIPULATIONS:
Recipients of the Research Grant are expected to provide the Consortium with a progress report within six months of receipt of the grant and a copy of the finished research within 18 months of the award. In addition, recipients are encouraged to present the results of their research at a Consortium conference.

COUNCIL ON TECHNOLOGY TEACHER EDUCATION   [1641]
Department of Engineering and
Technology Education
Utah State University
Logan, UT 84322-6000
(435) 797-3642
Fax: (435) 797-2567

E-MAIL ADDRESS:
ed.reeve@usu.edu

WEB SITE ADDRESS:
www.ctte.iweb.bsu.edu

FOUNDED: 1951

AREAS OF INTEREST:
Technology teacher education.

CONSULTING OR VOLUNTEER SERVICES:
NCATE state guideline preparation found on web site.

NAME(S) OF PROGRAMS:
● **Engineering and Technology Education**

TYPE:
Challenge/matching grants; Conferences/seminars; Project/program grants; Research grants; Research contracts. Field study support and curriculum development.

YEAR PROGRAM STARTED: 1996

PURPOSE:
To discover philosophical rationales, theoretical models, principles and/or practices that potentially increase the effectiveness and efficiency of pre-service or in-service engineering and technology teacher education.

LEGAL BASIS:
Special-interest foundation.

ELIGIBILITY:
Applicants must be members of the Council on Technology Teacher Education.

FINANCIAL DATA:
Amount of support per award: Average $1,000.
Total amount of support: Varies.

NUMBER OF AWARDS: Varies.

APPLICATION INFORMATION:
Duration: Typically one year.
Deadline: Varies.

ADDRESS INQUIRIES TO:
Dr. Edward Reeve, President
(See address above.)

THE DANA FOUNDATION
505 Fifth Avenue, Sixth Floor
New York, NY 10017
(212) 223-4040
Fax: (212) 317-8721

E-MAIL ADDRESS:
amarin@dana.org

WEB SITE ADDRESS:
www.dana.org

TYPE:
Awards/prizes; Challenge/matching grants; Project/program grants; Research grants. For the decade of the 1990s, the Foundation focused on brain research. In 2001, interests expanded to include research in immunology. Grants in these areas are made principally through competitive Clinical Hypotheses Programs in immuno-imaging, neuroimmunology, neuroimaging and brain-cardiovascular system interactions.

These competitive grants programs support pilot testing of experimental and innovative ideas that in immunology and neuroscience research have the potential of advancing clinical applications. The Foundation also supports an invitational program in which leading scientists are invited to compete for research grants designed to improve immune system responses to biological agents.

The Foundation has supported advances in education throughout its history. Its current interest is focused primarily on professional development programs that foster improved teaching of the performing arts in public schools. Programs emphasize innovative training projects that are exported from, or imported to, New York City, Washington, DC, Los Angeles and their surrounding areas. Letters of intent are accepted on a rolling basis. Grantees are selected through a competitive process.

See entry 2403 for full listing.

FREDERICK DOUGLASS INSTITUTE FOR AFRICAN AND AFRICAN-AMERICAN STUDIES   [1642]
University of Rochester
302 Morey Hall
Rochester, NY 14627-0440
(585) 275-7235
Fax: (585) 256-2594

E-MAIL ADDRESS:
fdi@mail.rochester.edu

WEB SITE ADDRESS:
www.cc.rochester.edu/college/aas

FOUNDED: 1986

AREAS OF INTEREST:
African and African-American studies and graduate education through advanced research at the University of Rochester.

NAME(S) OF PROGRAMS:
● **FDI Postdoctoral Fellowship**
● **FDI Predoctoral Dissertation Fellowship**

TYPE:
Awards/prizes; Conferences/seminars; Fellowships.

PURPOSE:
To promote the development of African and African-American studies and graduate education through advanced research at the University of Rochester; specifically, to support the completion of a project (FDI Postdoctoral Fellowship) and to support the completion of a dissertation (FDI Predoctoral Dissertation Fellowship).

ELIGIBILITY:
FDI Postdoctoral Fellowship: Open to scholars who hold a Ph.D. degree in a field related to the African and African-American experience.

FDI Predoctoral Dissertation Fellowship: Open to graduate students of any university who study aspects of the African and African-American experience.

FINANCIAL DATA:
Amount of support per award: FDI Postdoctoral Fellowship: $40,000; FDI Predoctoral Dissertation Fellowship: $26,000.

NUMBER OF APPLICANTS MOST RECENT YEAR:
60.

NUMBER OF AWARDS: 2.

APPLICATION INFORMATION:
Applicants to the Postdoctoral Fellowship must submit:
(1) a completed FDI fellowship application form;
(2) a curriculum vitae;
(3) a three- to five-page description of the project (plus a short bibliography);
(4) a sample of published or unpublished writing on a topic related to the proposal and;
(5) three letters of recommendation that comment upon the value and feasibility of the work proposed, to be sent by the referees.

Applicants to the Predoctoral Dissertation Fellowship must submit:
(1) a completed FDI fellowship application form;
(2) a curriculum vitae;
(3) an official transcript showing completion of all preliminary coursework and qualifying examinations;
(4) the dissertation prospectus;
(5) a sample chapter from the dissertation and;
(6) three letters of recommendation to be sent out by the referees, including one from the dissertation supervisor, assessing the candidate's prospects for completing the project within a year.
Duration: September 1 to May 31.
Deadline: January 31.

EDUCATIONAL TESTING SERVICE [1643]
660 Rosedale Road, MS 19-T
Princeton, NJ 08541
(609) 734-5543
Fax: (609) 734-5010

E-MAIL ADDRESS:
internfellowships@ets.org

WEB SITE ADDRESS:
www.ets.org/research/fellowships.html

FOUNDED: 1947

AREAS OF INTEREST:
Educational measurement and psychometrics, validity, natural language processing and speech technologies, cognitive psychology, learning theory, linguistics and computational linguistics, teaching and classroom research, statistics and international large-scale assessments.

NAME(S) OF PROGRAMS:
• **Summer Internship Program for Graduate Students**

TYPE:
Internships. Interns in this eight- or 12-week program participate in research under the guidance of a senior ETS staff member in one of the areas of interest listed above. Interns also participate in seminars and workshops on a variety of topics.

YEAR PROGRAM STARTED: 1963

PURPOSE:
To provide research opportunities to individuals enrolled in a doctoral program in the fields described above; to increase the number of women and underrepresented minority professionals conducting research in educational measurement and related fields.

LEGAL BASIS:
Not-for-profit organization.

ELIGIBILITY:
Graduate students who are currently enrolled in a full-time doctoral program in one of the areas listed above and who have completed a minimum of two years of coursework toward their Ph.D. or Ed.D. prior to the program start date are eligible to apply.

GEOGRAPHIC RESTRICTIONS:
Princeton, New Jersey.

FINANCIAL DATA:
Amount of support per award: $5,000 stipend, round-trip travel reimbursement up to $1,000 from the intern's university to Princeton (consistent with ETS travel policy), and $1,500 housing allowance for interns residing outside a 50-mile radius of ETS's facilities for eight-week internship. 12-week internship carries a stipend of $7,500 and housing allowance of $2,250, along with up to $1,000 travel reimbursement as above.

NUMBER OF APPLICANTS MOST RECENT YEAR:
More than 200.

NUMBER OF AWARDS: 15 to 20.

APPLICATION INFORMATION:
The application process opens in November. Applications accepted online.
Duration: Eight weeks in June and July, or 12 weeks in June, July and August, each summer.
Deadline: All application materials must be postmarked on or before February 1. Applicants will be notified by April 5.

PUBLICATIONS:
Program announcement.

STAFF:
Georgiana Weingart, Fellowship Program Administrator

ADDRESS INQUIRIES TO:
See e-mail address above.

EDUCATIONAL TESTING SERVICE [1644]
660 Rosedale Road, MS 19-T
Princeton, NJ 08541
(609) 734-5543
Fax: (609) 734-5010

E-MAIL ADDRESS:
internfellowships@ets.org

WEB SITE ADDRESS:
www.ets.org

FOUNDED: 1947

AREAS OF INTEREST:
Educational measurement and psychometrics, validity, natural language processing and speech technologies, cognitive psychology, learning theory, linguistics and computational linguistics, assessment design and development, teaching and classroom research, and statistics.

NAME(S) OF PROGRAMS:
• **ETS Postdoctoral Fellowship Award Program**

TYPE:
Fellowships.

YEAR PROGRAM STARTED: 1958

PURPOSE:
To provide research opportunities to individuals who hold a Doctorate in the fields indicated above; to increase the number of women and underrepresented minority professionals conducting research in educational measurement and related fields.

LEGAL BASIS:
Not-for-profit organization.

ELIGIBILITY:
Open to early career scholars who hold a Ph.D. or Ed.D. in one of the areas listed above. Individuals who have recently earned their doctoral degrees are invited to apply for a unique fellowship experience which combines working on cutting-edge ETS research projects and conducting independent research that is relevant to ETS goals.

FINANCIAL DATA:
Fellowship includes employee benefits, vacation, holidays and other paid leave in accordance with ETS policies. Also includes a $5,000 one-time relocation incentive for round-trip relocation expenses.
Total amount of support: Varies.

NUMBER OF APPLICANTS MOST RECENT YEAR:
12.

NUMBER OF AWARDS: Up to 2.

APPLICATION INFORMATION:
Application accepted online.
Duration: 12 months, with an option for second-year renewal upon mutual agreement.
Deadline: All application materials must be postmarked on or before February 1.

ADDRESS INQUIRIES TO:
See e-mail address above.

FALK FOUNDATION
3315 Grant Building
330 Grant Street
Pittsburgh, PA 15219
(412) 261-2485
Fax: (412) 471-7739

E-MAIL ADDRESS:
kerryo@falkfund.org

WEB SITE ADDRESS:
www.falkfund.org

TYPE:
Challenge/matching grants; Conferences/seminars; Demonstration grants; Project/program grants; Seed money grants; Technical assistance; Training grants; Travel grants.

See entry 1046 for full listing.

FEDERATION OF AMERICAN CONSUMERS AND TRAVELERS [1645]
318 Hillsboro Avenue
P.O. Box 104
Edwardsville, IL 62025
(618) 656-0454
Fax: (618) 656-5369

E-MAIL ADDRESS:
vrolens@usafact.org

WEB SITE ADDRESS:
www.usafact.org

FOUNDED: 1984

AREAS OF INTEREST:
Education.

NAME(S) OF PROGRAMS:
• **Classroom and Community Grants**
• **Continuing Education Scholarships**

TYPE:
Project/program grants.

PURPOSE:
To help provide supplies or to otherwise support a classroom project for which funds

may not be readily available somewhere else; to improve the teacher's ability to teach and the students' opportunity to learn.

ELIGIBILITY:
Classroom Grants: Any dues paying member of FACT may nominate any teacher to apply for a grant. Only one nomination per year per member.

Continuing Education Scholarships: All applicants must be FACT members, their children or grandchildren.

Scholarships available to:
(1) current high school seniors;
(2) people who graduated from high school four or more years ago and are now planning to enroll in an undergraduate college, university or trade school program;
(3) students currently enrolled in an undergraduate college or university and;
(4) people who wish to attend a trade school or technical college.

GEOGRAPHIC RESTRICTIONS:
United States.

FINANCIAL DATA:
Amount of support per award: Classroom and Community Grants: $100 to $2,500; Continuing Education Scholarships: One $10,000 and one $2,500 award available in each of the four categories of eligibility for scholarships.
Total amount of support: Classroom and Community Grants: Approximately $110,000 since 1999; Continuing Education Scholarships: $729,000 since 1992.

APPLICATION INFORMATION:
Duration: Annual awards.
Deadline: Classroom and Community Grants: January, April, July and October; Continuing Education Scholarships: January 15.

ADDRESS INQUIRIES TO:
Vicki Rolens, Managing Director
(See address above.)

FLORIDA EDUCATION FUND   [1646]
201 East Kennedy Boulevard
Suite 1525
Tampa, FL 33602
(813) 272-2772 ext. 203
Fax: (813) 272-2784

E-MAIL ADDRESS:
fef.jackson@verizon.net

WEB SITE ADDRESS:
www.fefonline.org

FOUNDED: 1984

AREAS OF INTEREST:
Arts and sciences, mathematics, business, engineering, health sciences, nursing, visual and performing arts.

NAME(S) OF PROGRAMS:
● **McKnight Doctoral Fellowship**

TYPE:
Fellowships.

YEAR PROGRAM STARTED: 1984

PURPOSE:
To address the under-representation of African American and Hispanic faculty at colleges and universities in the state of Florida by increasing the pool of citizens qualified with Ph.D. degrees to teach at the college and university levels, thus expanding employment opportunities in the industry.

LEGAL BASIS:
Corporation.

ELIGIBILITY:
Applicants must be African American or Hispanic, U.S. citizens, and hold a minimum of a bachelor's degree from a regionally accredited college or university. The Fellowship will be awarded only to persons who intend to seek the Ph.D. degree in one of the disciplines in the arts and sciences, mathematics, business or engineering.

FINANCIAL DATA:
Fellowships include a $12,000 stipend, plus up to $5,000 for tuition and fees. Any tuition and fees over $5,000 are waived.
Amount of support per award: $17,000 per year.
Total amount of support: Approximately $680,000.

NUMBER OF APPLICANTS MOST RECENT YEAR:
300.

NUMBER OF AWARDS: Up to 40 per academic year.

APPLICATION INFORMATION:
Online application is available at the web site.
Duration: Three years, with fourth and fifth years supported by the institution if necessary.
Deadline: January 15.

PUBLICATIONS:
Annual report.

ADDRESS INQUIRIES TO:
Charles Jackson, Program Manager
(See address above.)

FLORIDA STATE UNIVERSITY FOUNDATION   [1647]
2010 Levy Avenue
Building B, Suite 300
Tallahassee, FL 32310
(850) 644-6000
Fax: (850) 644-6211

WEB SITE ADDRESS:
www.foundation.fsu.edu

FOUNDED: 1851

AREAS OF INTEREST:
Information studies.

TYPE:
Assistantships; Awards/prizes; Conferences/seminars; Fellowships; Internships; Scholarships; Visiting scholars.

YEAR PROGRAM STARTED: 1973

PURPOSE:
To support educational excellence.

LEGAL BASIS:
University.

FINANCIAL DATA:
Amount of support per award: $500 to $6,300 per year.
Total amount of support: Varies.

NUMBER OF APPLICANTS MOST RECENT YEAR:
30.

NUMBER OF AWARDS: 1 of each scholarship each year.

APPLICATION INFORMATION:
Detailed information and application forms may be obtained from the web site.
Duration: Normally one year. Renewable for one year.

Deadline: January to March annually.

PUBLICATIONS:
Catalogs; brochures.

THE FOUNDATION FOR INDEPENDENT HIGHER EDUCATION   [1648]
1920 N Street, N.W.
Suite 210
Washington, DC 20036
(202) 367-0333
Fax: (202) 367-0334

E-MAIL ADDRESS:
info@fihe.org

WEB SITE ADDRESS:
www.fihe.org

FOUNDED: 1958

AREAS OF INTEREST:
Collaboration among private colleges; access and success for first-generation, low-income, minority and new American students.

TYPE:
Project/program grants; Scholarships.

PURPOSE:
To secure philanthropic support and other resources on behalf of private colleges and universities; to develop and implement programs of mutual interest to the business, philanthropic and education communities; to make known and celebrate the unique characteristics and contributions of private colleges and universities.

LEGAL BASIS:
501(c)(3) organization.

ELIGIBILITY:
Grants are made to member private colleges and universities to support their students. No grants are made to individuals.

FINANCIAL DATA:
Amount of support per award: Up to $50,000.

NUMBER OF APPLICANTS MOST RECENT YEAR:
20.

NUMBER OF AWARDS: 6.

APPLICATION INFORMATION:
Contact the Foundation for current grants and application procedures.
Deadline: Varies.

IRS IDENTIFICATION NUMBER: 13-5674610

STAFF:
Ned Moore, Executive Director
Jacalyn Cox, Director of State Fund Programs

ADDRESS INQUIRIES TO:
Ned Moore, Executive Director
(See address above.)

*SPECIAL STIPULATIONS:
Grants only awarded to affiliated State Associations of Private Colleges and their member colleges and universities.

FOUNDATION FOR TECHNOLOGY EDUCATION   [1649]
1914 Association Drive
Suite 201
Reston, VA 20191-1539
(703) 860-2100
Fax: (703) 860-0353

E-MAIL ADDRESS:
tmacdonald@iteea.org

WEB SITE ADDRESS:
www.iteea.org

FOUNDED: 1939

AREAS OF INTEREST:
Technology education.

NAME(S) OF PROGRAMS:
- **Pittsco/Hearlihy/FTE Grant Excellence in Teaching Technology**

TYPE:
Grants-in-aid.

PURPOSE:
To encourage the integration of a quality technology program within the school curriculum.

ELIGIBILITY:
Applicant must be a teacher, elementary or secondary, who is successfully integrating technology education within the school curriculum and is a member of the ITEEA. An application above the elementary school level must be from a technology teacher.

FINANCIAL DATA:
Amount of support per award: $2,000.

NUMBER OF AWARDS: 1.

APPLICATION INFORMATION:
Applicants must submit an application package with three copies of the following required items:
(1) letter with explanation of the technology education program, how technology education is integrated with other academic projects, plans for using the grant and name, address, telephone, grade level and home address;
(2) school-based curriculum materials and/or a five- to 10-minute video (1/2-inch VHS) illustrating how technology education is integrated with other academic subjects in the school and;
(3) three letters of recommendation which confirm the success of integrating technology education with other subjects. One letter must be from the principal and at least two from other academic teachers.
Deadline: December 1.

ADDRESS INQUIRIES TO:
Tamara MacDonald, Publications Services
(See address above.)

*SPECIAL STIPULATIONS:
Applicant must be a member of the ITEEA.

FOUNDATION FOR TECHNOLOGY EDUCATION   [1650]
1914 Association Drive
Suite 201
Reston, VA 20191-1539
(703) 860-2100
Fax: (703) 860-0353

E-MAIL ADDRESS:
tmacdonald@iteea.org

WEB SITE ADDRESS:
www.iteea.org

FOUNDED: 1939

AREAS OF INTEREST:
Technology education.

NAME(S) OF PROGRAMS:
- **Maley/FTE Scholarship Technology Teacher Professional Development**

TYPE:
Scholarships.

PURPOSE:
To support teachers in their preparation to increase the positive outcomes of technology education.

ELIGIBILITY:
Criteria includes evidence of teaching success, plans for action research, recommendations, plans for professional development, ITEEA membership and the applicant's needs.

FINANCIAL DATA:
Amount of support per award: $1,000.

NUMBER OF AWARDS: 1.

APPLICATION INFORMATION:
Applicant must send an application package with four copies of the following required items:
(1) letter of application explaining plans for graduate study, plans for action research, the applicant's need and the school's name, address, telephone, grade level, and home address;
(2) official college transcript(s);
(3) documentation of acceptance into graduate school and;
(4) three letters of recommendation from among the following: undergraduate faculty, graduate faculty and school administration.
Deadline: December 1.

ADDRESS INQUIRIES TO:
Tamara MacDonald, Publications Services
(See address above.)

*SPECIAL STIPULATIONS:
Applicant must be a member of the ITEEA.

THE GAMBLE FOUNDATION   [1651]
1660 Bush Street, Suite 300
San Francisco, CA 94109
(415) 561-6540
Fax: (415) 561-6477

WEB SITE ADDRESS:
www.pfs-llc.net/gamble/gamble.html

FOUNDED: 1968

AREAS OF INTEREST:
Youth development and environment.

TYPE:
Project/program grants.

YEAR PROGRAM STARTED: 1968

PURPOSE:
To support academic enrichment programs and environmental education for disadvantaged youths; to promote a healthy and productive lifestyle.

LEGAL BASIS:
Private foundation.

ELIGIBILITY:
Grants are made to organizations that have tax-exempt status under Section 501(c)(3) of the Internal Revenue Code. No grants are made to individuals.

GEOGRAPHIC RESTRICTIONS:
San Francisco, Marin and Napa counties, California.

FINANCIAL DATA:
Amount of support per award: $10,000 to $30,000.
Total amount of support: Varies.

APPLICATION INFORMATION:
The Foundation encourages submission of proposals and attachments by e-mail. The proposal and required attachments should be e-mailed in PDF format only. Send proposals to Fiona Barrett at fbarrett@pfs-llc.net. Additional instructions, such as required attachments, are available on the Foundation web site.
Duration: One year. Renewal by reapplication.

ADDRESS INQUIRIES TO:
Eric Sloan, Senior Program Officer
(See address above.)

THE GOODRICH FOUNDATION   [1652]
2730 West Tyvola Road
4 Coliseum Centre
Charlotte, NC 28217-4578
(704) 423-7000
Fax: (704) 423-7011

E-MAIL ADDRESS:
grantinfo@goodrich.com

WEB SITE ADDRESS:
www.goodrich.com

FOUNDED: 1988

AREAS OF INTEREST:
Arts and culture, civic and community, health and human services, and K-12 education (with an emphasis on STEM).

TYPE:
Capital grants; Development grants; Endowments; General operating grants; Grants-in-aid; Matching gifts; Project/program grants; Technical assistance; Training grants.

YEAR PROGRAM STARTED: 1988

PURPOSE:
To provide support to charitable organizations serving the public where Goodrich employees live and work.

LEGAL BASIS:
Corporate foundation.

ELIGIBILITY:
Grant applicants must be tax-exempt 501(c)(3) organizations as defined by the IRS. No grants to individuals.

GEOGRAPHIC RESTRICTIONS:
United States.

FINANCIAL DATA:
Amount of support per award: Varies depending on needs and nature of the request.

COOPERATIVE FUNDING PROGRAMS: Volunteer Bonus Program.

NUMBER OF APPLICANTS MOST RECENT YEAR: 1,500.

NUMBER OF AWARDS: 100.

APPLICATION INFORMATION:
Online application only.
Duration: Varies depending on project.
Deadline: February 1 and August 1.

OFFICERS:
Terrence Linnert, President
Jack Carmola, Vice President
Scott Kuechle, Treasurer
Kelly Chopus, Secretary

ADDRESS INQUIRIES TO:
See e-mail address above.

HAMILTON FAMILY FOUNDATION [1653]

200 Eagle Road
Suite 316
Wayne, PA 19087
(610) 293-2225
Fax: (610) 293-0967

E-MAIL ADDRESS:
nwingo@218enterprises.com

WEB SITE ADDRESS:
www.hamiltonfamilyfoundation.org

FOUNDED: 1992

AREAS OF INTEREST:
Education, youth and literacy-based education programs for underserved children and youth.

TYPE:
Challenge/matching grants; General operating grants; Project/program grants.

YEAR PROGRAM STARTED: 1996

PURPOSE:
To promote quality programs of education for economically underserved youth.

LEGAL BASIS:
Private foundation.

ELIGIBILITY:
Grants are made to organizations that have tax-exempt status under Section 501(c)(3) of the Internal Revenue Code. No grants are made to individuals.

GEOGRAPHIC RESTRICTIONS:
Philadelphia, Pennsylvania and surrounding counties.

FINANCIAL DATA:
Amount of support per award: $5,000 to $100,000.
Total amount of support: $2,442,000 for fiscal year ended December 31, 2010.

NUMBER OF APPLICANTS MOST RECENT YEAR:
164.

NUMBER OF AWARDS: 81.

APPLICATION INFORMATION:
The following items must be included with the Grant Application form:
(1) cover letter addressed to Nancy Wingo, Executive Director;
(2) list of Board of Directors;
(3) organization and project budgets;
(4) two-year comparative financial statements and;
(5) copy of 501(c)(3) tax-exempt letter.
Duration: One calendar year.

STAFF:
Nancy Wingo, Executive Director

ADDRESS INQUIRIES TO:
Nancy Wingo, Executive Director
(See address above.)

HANNAFORD CHARITABLE FOUNDATION [1654]

145 Pleasant Hill Road
Scarborough, ME 04074
(207) 885-3834
Fax: (207) 885-3051

WEB SITE ADDRESS:
www.hannaford.com

AREAS OF INTEREST:
Higher education.

TYPE:
Scholarships.

PURPOSE:
To provide financial support to nonprofit organizations dedicated to improving the communities where Hannaford operates.

LEGAL BASIS:
Private foundation.

ELIGIBILITY:
Preference for funding is given to organizations or programs that involve Hannaford associates and are located in Hannaford's marketing area, and have the potential to provide ongoing services to Foundation customers.

The Foundation does not offer support to individuals, tax-supported institutions or scholarship programs outside of their marketing area.

GEOGRAPHIC RESTRICTIONS:
Maine, Massachusetts, New Hampshire, New York and Vermont.

FINANCIAL DATA:
Total amount of support: $200,000.

NUMBER OF AWARDS: 50 annually.

APPLICATION INFORMATION:
Instructions on how to apply and what is required are available on the Foundation web site.

HARBUS FOUNDATION [1655]

Harvard Business School
Gallatin Hall E
Boston, MA 02163
(617) 495-6528
Fax: (617) 495-8619

E-MAIL ADDRESS:
info@harbusfoundation.org

WEB SITE ADDRESS:
www.harbusfoundation.org

FOUNDED: 1997

AREAS OF INTEREST:
Education, journalism and literacy.

TYPE:
Project/program grants. The Foundation, which was formed by the student-run Harbus News Corporation at Harvard Business School, seeks to give back to the community by supporting programs of educational development in the communities where students live and learn.

PURPOSE:
To support small, community-based organizations, individuals, or local schools with limited resources to establish and sustain new and innovative programs in the areas of literacy, journalism, and/or education.

ELIGIBILITY:
Proposals will be accepted from individuals and tax-exempt organizations as defined by Section 501(c)(3) of the Internal Revenue Code for purposes to be carried out within the greater Boston area.

The Foundation does not fund scholarships and fellowships, religious organizations for religious purposes, city or state governments, capital campaigns, for-profit organizations or purely personal needs.

GEOGRAPHIC RESTRICTIONS:
Greater Boston, Massachusetts area with priority given to the communities of Allston and Brighton.

FINANCIAL DATA:
Amount of support per award: $10,000.

Total amount of support: Varies.

APPLICATION INFORMATION:
Application for funding is by invitation only. However, if your organization aligns with the Foundation mission, send e-mail with a brief description of your organization and desire use of the Foundation resources.
Duration: One year. Renewal possible by reapplication for a maximum of three years.
Deadline: January 31.

PUBLICATIONS:
Brochure.

ADDRESS INQUIRIES TO:
Trustees
(See address above.)

THE PHIL HARDIN FOUNDATION [1656]

2750 North Park Drive
Meridian, MS 39305
(601) 483-4282
Fax: (601) 483-5665

E-MAIL ADDRESS:
info@philhardin.org

WEB SITE ADDRESS:
www.philhardin.org

FOUNDED: 1964

AREAS OF INTEREST:
Education with special (but not exclusive) emphasis on pre-kindergarten.

TYPE:
Challenge/matching grants; Conferences/seminars; Development grants; Endowments; Fellowships; Project/program grants; Research grants; Training grants. Foundation's current primary focus is pre-kindergarten.

YEAR PROGRAM STARTED: 1964

PURPOSE:
To improve teaching and learning for Mississippians from grades preK-12.

LEGAL BASIS:
Tax-exempt, private foundation.

ELIGIBILITY:
Tax-exempt organizations in and out of Mississippi for projects to improve the education of Mississippians. No individual grants.

GEOGRAPHIC RESTRICTIONS:
Mississippi.

FINANCIAL DATA:
Amount of support per award: $2,000 to $500,000.
Total amount of support: $1,900,000 per year for all programs.
Matching fund requirements: Stipulated with specific program.

COOPERATIVE FUNDING PROGRAMS: Economic Development Administration, Kresge Foundation, Mississippi Governor's Office of Job Development and Training, Texas Educational Association, Chisholm Foundation and CREATE.

NUMBER OF APPLICANTS MOST RECENT YEAR:
25 for the year 2009.

NUMBER OF AWARDS: 19.

APPLICATION INFORMATION:
Proposals are to be based on current research and best practices. If not available, then prior approval to submit proposal must be obtained. Applications must be submitted in

the prescribed format and include the following:
(1) IRS tax-exempt determination letter;
(2) list of board members, affiliations and contact information;
(3) most recent audited financial statement, including 990;
(4) copy of operating budget and;
(5) list of past and present funders.

Proposals are to be no longer than three pages in length and may include three additional pages of supporting documents. Include the following:
(1) mission statement;
(2) project summary (two or three sentences);
(3) project details (include identified need and how it was determined, length of project, actions to be taken, resources, goals);
(4) expected outcomes;
(5) measurements and evaluation process and how the project will be sustained and;
(6) date the report will be filed with the Foundation.

Do not staple or bind. The Foundation does not accept videotapes, faxed or e-mailed proposals.
Duration: One-time, one-year or multiyear grants and loans. Some renewals possible.

OFFICERS:
Robert Ward, President
R.B. Deen, Jr., Vice President
Steve Moore, Treasurer
Ronnie L. Walton, Secretary

DIRECTORS:
Dr. J.S. Covington
Marty Davidson
R.B. Deen, Jr.
Jim McGinnis
Steve Moore
Ronnie L. Walton
Robert Ward

ADDRESS INQUIRIES TO:
Rebecca Combs, Chief Executive Officer
(See address above.)

EDWARD W. HAZEN FOUNDATION
333 Seventh Avenue, 14th Floor
New York, NY 10001
(212) 889-3034
Fax: (212) 889-3039

E-MAIL ADDRESS:
hazen@hazenfoundation.org

WEB SITE ADDRESS:
www.hazenfoundation.org

TYPE:
Grants-in-aid; Project/program grants. In the area of Public Education, current programs support the strengthening of the connection between schools and community organizations, including school reform. The Foundation is primarily interested in parent organizing and training initiatives.

In the area of Youth Organizing, there is support for youth organizing around concrete social issues or issues of concern to youth.

For both Public Education and Youth Organizing, community-based projects directed toward middle and high school-age minority and low-income youth are given priority consideration.

There is limited support for Philanthropy and Special Projects including support for collaborative projects that encourage the growth of grantmaking.
See entry 1199 for full listing.

HEALTH RESOURCES AND SERVICES ADMINISTRATION [1657]
5600 Fishers Lane, Room 9-105
Rockville, MD 20857
(301) 443-4776
Fax: (301) 443-0846

E-MAIL ADDRESS:
dpolicy@hrsa.gov

WEB SITE ADDRESS:
www.bhpr.hrsa.gov/dsa

AREAS OF INTEREST:
Health professions and nursing education.

NAME(S) OF PROGRAMS:
● **Scholarships for Disadvantaged Students**

TYPE:
Scholarships. Funds made available to eligible schools for the purpose of providing scholarships to full-time financially needy students from disadvantaged backgrounds. Students must apply at the financial aid office of school where enrolled or admitted for enrollment.

YEAR PROGRAM STARTED: 1991

LEGAL BASIS:
Government agency.

ELIGIBILITY:
Must be a citizen or permanent resident of the U.S. enrolled in a health profession or nursing program and be from a disadvantaged background.

GEOGRAPHIC RESTRICTIONS:
United States.

FINANCIAL DATA:
Amount of support per award: Varies.
Total amount of support: Varies.

NUMBER OF AWARDS: 308 from regular appropriations and 273 from American Recovery and Reinvestment Act (ARRA) for the year 2010.

APPLICATION INFORMATION:
Contact student financial aid office at the school attended for application procedure.
Duration: One year. Must reapply for additional funding.

WILLIAM G. AND MYRTLE E. HESS CHARITABLE TRUST [1658]
c/o JPMorgan
1116 West Long Lake Road
Bloomfield Hills, MI 48302
Fax: (248) 645-8448

E-MAIL ADDRESS:
nayda.schwartz@jpmorgan.com

WEB SITE ADDRESS:
www.jpmorgan.com/onlinegrants

FOUNDED: 1969

AREAS OF INTEREST:
Science, education and charity.

TYPE:
General operating grants; Grants-in-aid; Project/program grants.

YEAR PROGRAM STARTED: 1969

PURPOSE:
To benefit organizations in Oakland County.

ELIGIBILITY:
Eligible organizations must be nonprofit, 501(c)(3) tax-exempt. Grants are not given to individuals or for religious or political purposes.

GEOGRAPHIC RESTRICTIONS:
Waterford and White Lake Townships in Oakland County, Michigan.

FINANCIAL DATA:
Amount of support per award: $1,000 to $10,000.
Total amount of support: $182,000 for the year 2010.

NUMBER OF APPLICANTS MOST RECENT YEAR: 34.

NUMBER OF AWARDS: 27.

APPLICATION INFORMATION:
Applications are to be submitted online.
Deadline: April 30. Decisions on grant requests made annually in May.

ADDRESS INQUIRIES TO:
Nayda Schwartz, Vice President
(See address above.)

*PLEASE NOTE:
Applications received late will be held until the following year.

HILGENFELD FOUNDATION FOR MORTUARY EDUCATION
120 East Broadway
Anaheim, CA 92805
(714) 535-4105
Fax: (714) 635-6842

E-MAIL ADDRESS:
becky@hilgenfeldmortuary.com

WEB SITE ADDRESS:
www.hilgenfeldmortuary.com

TYPE:
Challenge/matching grants; Conferences/seminars; Demonstration grants; Development grants; Project/program grants; Research grants; Technical assistance; Training grants. Entry-level scholarships; Graduate scholarship awards; Research studies. The Foundation has a broad interest in research which shows a promise of improving the practice of funeral service.
See entry 1944 for full listing.

HUTCHINSON COMMUNITY FOUNDATION
One North Main Street
Suite 501
Hutchinson, KS 67501
(620) 663-5293
Fax: (620) 663-9277

E-MAIL ADDRESS:
info@hutchcf.org

WEB SITE ADDRESS:
www.hutchcf.org

TYPE:
Project/program grants; Seed money grants.
See entry 490 for full listing.

INTERNATIONAL ASSOCIATION OF ICE CREAM DISTRIBUTORS AND VENDORS [1659]

5024 Campbell Boulevard
Suite R
Baltimore, MD 21236
(410) 931-8100
Fax: (410) 931-8111

E-MAIL ADDRESS:
shannon@iaicdv.org

WEB SITE ADDRESS:
www.iaicdv.org

AREAS OF INTEREST:
The ice cream vending industry.

TYPE:
Scholarships.

YEAR PROGRAM STARTED: 1994

PURPOSE:
To cooperate for the improvement and stabilization of the ice cream vending industry.

ELIGIBILITY:
Applicant must be either an employee or child of an employee that is currently an IAICV member.

FINANCIAL DATA:
Amount of support per award: $1,000 to $5,000.
Total amount of support: $5,000.

NUMBER OF APPLICANTS MOST RECENT YEAR:
26.

NUMBER OF AWARDS: 3.

APPLICATION INFORMATION:
Deadline: October 1.

ADDRESS INQUIRIES TO:
Shannon Stamm, Associate Director
(See address above.)

INTERNATIONAL READING ASSOCIATION [1660]

800 Barksdale Road
Newark, DE 19714
(302) 731-1600
Fax: (302) 731-1057

E-MAIL ADDRESS:
exec@reading.org

WEB SITE ADDRESS:
www.reading.org

FOUNDED: 1956

AREAS OF INTEREST:
Reading and literacy through professional development, advocacy, partnership, research, and global literacy development.

NAME(S) OF PROGRAMS:
- **Grants for Literacy Projects in Countries with Developing Economies**
- **IRA Jerry Johns Outstanding Teacher Educator in Reading Award**
- **IRA Regie Routman Teacher Recognition Grant**
- **IRA Paul A. Witty Short Story Award**
- **IRA/Weekly Reader Eleanor M. Johnson Award**
- **National Affiliate Conference Grants**

TYPE:
Awards/prizes; Conferences/seminars; Project/program grants. Grants for Literacy Projects in Countries with Developing Economies is to assist in the funding of literacy projects and in the professional development of literacy educators. The fund

also offers annual one-time grants to International Reading Association members from countries with developing economies who seek support for a literacy project in their own countries.
IRA Jerry Johns Outstanding Teacher Educator in Reading Award: Honors an outstanding college or university teacher of reading methods or reading-related courses. Nominees must be Association members, affiliated with a college or a university, and engaged in teacher preparation in reading at the undergraduate and/or graduate levels.
IRA Regie Routman Teacher Recognition Grant: Honors an outstanding mainstream, elementary classroom teacher dedicated to improving the teaching and learning of reading and writing, across the curriculum in real world contexts in grades K-6 (ages 5-12). The grant may not be used for purchase of commercial programs.
IRA Paul A. Witty Short Story: Given to the author of an original short story published for the first time, in a periodical for children. The short story should serve as a literacy standard that encourages young readers to read periodicals.
IRA/Weekly Reader Eleanor M. Johnson Award: Recognizes an outstanding elementary classroom teacher of reading/language arts.
National Affiliate Conference Grants: To assist national affiliates in good standing located in the countries the World Bank classifies as "economically developing" at the time of the application. The Grant is to support pre-conference planning, actual conference expenses, and/or post-conference publication and reporting.

PURPOSE:
To promote reading by continuously advancing the quality of literacy instruction and research worldwide.

FINANCIAL DATA:
Amount of support per award: Grants for Literacy Projects: up to $2,500; Jerry Johns: $1,000; Regie Routman: $2,500; Paul A. Witty: $1,000; Weekly Reader Eleanor M. Johnson: $1,000; National Affiliate Conference: $5,000.

APPLICATION INFORMATION:
Forms and guidelines can be obtained at the Association web site.
Deadline: Jerry Johns: October 15; Regie Routman: November 1; Paul A. Witty: December 1; Weekly Reader Eleanor M. Johnson: November 15; National Affiliate Conference: October 1 (twelve months prior to the conference).

INTERNATIONAL READING ASSOCIATION [1661]

800 Barksdale Road
Newark, DE 19714
(302) 731-1600 ext. 423
Fax: (302) 731-1057

E-MAIL ADDRESS:
research@reading.org

WEB SITE ADDRESS:
www.reading.org

FOUNDED: 1956

AREAS OF INTEREST:
Reading and literacy through professional development, advocacy, partnership, research, and global literacy development.

NAME(S) OF PROGRAMS:
- **Jeanne S. Chall Research Fellowship**
- **Dina Feitelson Research Award**
- **Elva Knight Research Grant**
- **Outstanding Dissertation of the Year Award**
- **Helen M. Robinson Grant**
- **Steven A. Stahl Research Grant**
- **Teacher as Researcher Grant**

TYPE:
Awards/prizes; Fellowships; Grants-in-aid; Research grants. Jeanne S. Chall Research Fellowship is established to encourage and support reading research by promising scholars. Its special emphasis is to support research efforts in the following areas:
(1) beginning reading;
(2) readability;
(3) reading difficulty;
(4) stages of reading development;
(5) the relation of vocabulary to reading and;
(6) diagnosing and teaching adults with limited reading ability.

Dina Feitelson Research Award is established to recognize an outstanding empirical study published in English in a refereed journal. The work should report on one or more aspects of literacy acquisition, such as phonemic awareness, the alphabetic principle, bilingualism, or cross-cultural studies of beginning reading. Works may be submitted by the author or anyone else.

Elva Knight Research Grant provides research in reading and literacy. Projects should be completed within two years and may be carried out using any research method or approach so long as the focus of the project is on research in reading or literacy.

Outstanding Dissertation of the Year Award is a grant from Scott Foresman. Dissertations in reading or related fields are eligible for the competition. Studies using any research approach (ethnographic, experimental, historical, survey, etc.) are encouraged.

Helen M. Robinson Grant is given annually to assist doctoral students at the early stages of their dissertation research in the areas of reading and literacy.

Steven A. Stahl Research Grant was established to encourage and support promising graduate students in their research. The grant will be awarded annually to a recipient with at least three years of teaching experience who is conducting classroom research (including action research) focused on improving reading instruction and children's reading achievement.

Teacher as Researcher Grant supports classroom teachers who undertake action research inquiries about literacy and instruction.

PURPOSE:
To promote reading by continuously advancing the quality of literacy instruction and research worldwide.

FINANCIAL DATA:
Amount of support per award: Jeanne S. Chall: $6,000; Dina Feitelson $500; Elva Knight $8,000; Outstanding Dissertation and Steven A. Stahl: $1,000; Helen M. Robinson: $1,200; Teacher as Researcher: Up to $4,000.

NUMBER OF AWARDS: 1 each annually. Research grants can be up to 5.

APPLICATION INFORMATION:
Application guidelines are available online.

Deadline: Jeanne S. Chall, Elva Knight, Helen M. Robinson, Steven A. Stahl and Teacher as Researcher: November 1; Dina Feitelson: September 1; Outstanding Dissertation: October 1.

PUBLICATIONS:
Application guidelines.

ADDRESS INQUIRIES TO:
Marcella Moore
Administrative Assistant, Research Division
(See mailing address above.)

JELLISON BENEVOLENT SOCIETY [1662]
P.O. Box 145
Junction City, KS 66441-0145
(785) 762-5566

E-MAIL ADDRESS:
s_williams1948@yahoo.com

FOUNDED: 1947

AREAS OF INTEREST:
Higher education.

TYPE:
Scholarships.

PURPOSE:
To aid area students in pursuit of higher education.

LEGAL BASIS:
Private foundation.

ELIGIBILITY:
Must be a high school senior or older, preferably a resident of Geary County, KS.

GEOGRAPHIC RESTRICTIONS:
Geary County, Kansas.

FINANCIAL DATA:
Amount of support per award: $500 to $1,500 per semester.

NUMBER OF APPLICANTS MOST RECENT YEAR:
79.

NUMBER OF AWARDS: 76.

APPLICATION INFORMATION:
Duration: One year. Renewable by supplying copy of grades above 2.0.
Deadline: June 20 and November 20.

IRS IDENTIFICATION NUMBER: 48-6106092

STAFF:
Dale Ann Clore, President
Susan E. Williams, Secretary

ADDRESS INQUIRIES TO:
Susan E. Williams, Secretary
(See address above.)

JEWISH COMMUNAL SERVICE ASSOCIATION OF NORTH AMERICA [1663]
25 Broadway
New York, NY 10004
(212) 532-0167
Fax: (212) 532-1461

E-MAIL ADDRESS:
info@jcsana.org

WEB SITE ADDRESS:
www.jcsana.org

FOUNDED: 1899

AREAS OF INTEREST:
Jewish communal services.

NAME(S) OF PROGRAMS:
● **Graduate Student Network**

● **Outstanding Journal Article**
● **Professional Development Programs**
● **Young Professional Award**

TYPE:
Awards/prizes; Conferences/seminars; Internships. Support of local groups of Jewish professionals.

YEAR PROGRAM STARTED: 1899

PURPOSE:
To enrich Jewish education in the communal service field.

LEGAL BASIS:
Nonprofit corporation.

GEOGRAPHIC RESTRICTIONS:
United States and Canada.

FINANCIAL DATA:
Amount of support per award: Varies.

NUMBER OF AWARDS: 5.

APPLICATION INFORMATION:
Contact the organization for application procedures.

PUBLICATIONS:
Journal of Jewish Communal Service.

EXECUTIVE DIRECTOR:
Brenda Gevertz, Executive Director

ADDRESS INQUIRIES TO:
Brenda Gevertz, Executive Director
(See address above.)

WALTER S. JOHNSON FOUNDATION [1664]
1660 Bush Street, Suite 300
San Francisco, CA 94109
(415) 561-6540 ext. 224
Fax: (415) 561-6477

E-MAIL ADDRESS:
info@wsjf.org

WEB SITE ADDRESS:
www.wsjf.org

AREAS OF INTEREST:
Children and education.

NAME(S) OF PROGRAMS:
● **High Risk & Adjudicated Youth**
● **School Reform**
● **Youth Development**

TYPE:
General operating grants; Project/program grants; Seed money grants; Technical assistance.

PURPOSE:
To strengthen public education and enhance the well-being of children and youth.

LEGAL BASIS:
Private foundation.

ELIGIBILITY:
The Foundation does not consider proposals for grants to individuals or religious organizations for sectarian purposes. It also does not provide funds for capital projects.

GEOGRAPHIC RESTRICTIONS:
Northern California and Washoe County, Nevada.

FINANCIAL DATA:
Amount of support per award: $30,000 to $100,000.
Total amount of support: Varies.

APPLICATION INFORMATION:
Applicant must review the Foundation's guidelines on its web site or call for the guidelines before submitting a full proposal.

Organizations may call the Foundation to discuss a proposed project with a staff member before submitting a letter of inquiry.
Duration: Multiyear.

ADDRESS INQUIRIES TO:
Amy Freeman, Program Officer
(See address above.)

WILLIAM R. KENAN, JR. CHARITABLE TRUST [1665]
300 Kenan Center Drive
Chapel Hill, NC 27599
(919) 962-0343
Fax: (919) 962-3331

FOUNDED: 1965

AREAS OF INTEREST:
Education.

PURPOSE:
To support educational programs of interest to the Trust.

LEGAL BASIS:
Private foundation.

ELIGIBILITY:
The Foundation does not accept unsolicited proposals.

GEOGRAPHIC RESTRICTIONS:
United States.

FINANCIAL DATA:
Amount of support per award: Varies.
Total amount of support: Varies.

APPLICATION INFORMATION:
Trustee's statement of guidelines, areas of interest and required procedures are available on request.

ADDRESS INQUIRIES TO:
Executive Director
William R. Kenan, Jr. Charitable Trust
P.O. Box 3858
Chapel Hill, NC 27515-3858

CHARLES G. KOCH CHARITABLE FOUNDATION [1666]
15-15 North Courthouse Road
Suite 200
Arlington, VA 22201
(703) 875-1600
Fax: (703) 875-1601

E-MAIL ADDRESS:
email@cgkfoundation.org

WEB SITE ADDRESS:
www.cgkfoundation.org

FOUNDED: 1980

AREAS OF INTEREST:
Public interest.

TYPE:
Project/program grants; Seed money grants.

YEAR PROGRAM STARTED: 1980

LEGAL BASIS:
Private foundation.

ELIGIBILITY:
The Foundation primarily makes grants to Section 501(c)(3) public charities. The Foundation does not support for-profit corporations or individuals. Grant proposals for capital construction, debt reduction, or general fund-raising drives or events are discouraged. The Foundation does not make

grants intended to support lobbying activities or candidates for political office, and rarely funds endowments.

GEOGRAPHIC RESTRICTIONS:
United States.

FINANCIAL DATA:
Amount of support per award: Varies depending on program.

APPLICATION INFORMATION:
Organizations seeking grants from the Foundation and which meet the aforementioned criteria should submit a short letter (no more than three pages) outlining their request. The letter should clearly and succinctly state:
(1) prospective grantee's mission and goals;
(2) specific project for which support is being sought;
(3) amount of funding requested;
(4) name, title, address, telephone number, and e-mail address of the primary contact person and;
(5) current annual budget or audited financial statements.

If applicable, also include a list of other support (e.g., funding, in-kind contributions) secured for the project.

Because the Foundation only supports Section 501(c)(3) public charities, it also requires that you submit verification from the IRS that your organization is exempt from federal income tax as a Section 501(c)(3) organization and is classified as a public charity under Section 509(a) of the Internal Revenue Code. The Foundation requests that no materials beyond what are described above be included.

Duration: Varies depending on needs and nature of the request.

Deadline: Proposals are evaluated on a rolling basis.

STAFF:
Richard Fink, President
Vonda Holliman, Secretary and Treasurer
Logan Moore, Administrator
Matthew Brown, Policy Research Director
Elizabeth Brannen, Human Resource Coordinator
Christopher Cardiff, Program Officer
Ryan Stowers, Program Officer

ADDRESS INQUIRIES TO:
Logan Moore, Foundation Administrator
(See address above.)

THE JEAN AND E. FLOYD KVAMME FOUNDATION   [1667]
P.O. Box 2494
Saratoga, CA 95070
(408) 395-2829
Fax: (408) 354-0804

AREAS OF INTEREST:
Arts, charitable and cultural, education, engineering school, health, medical research and Christian religious organizations.

TYPE:
Capital grants; Development grants; General operating grants; Project/program grants.

PURPOSE:
To support organizations and institutes that promote arts, cultural, education, health, medical, scientific and social advancement of the international communities.

LEGAL BASIS:
Corporate contributions.

ELIGIBILITY:
Grants are made to organizations that have tax-exempt status under Section 501(c)(3) of the Internal Revenue Code and international Christian organizations. No grants are made to individuals.

GEOGRAPHIC RESTRICTIONS:
Northern California.

FINANCIAL DATA:
Amount of support per award: Varies.
Total amount of support: Varies.

APPLICATION INFORMATION:
Applicants must submit a brief (one-page) letter outlining the purpose of the grant. Further information may be obtained from the address above.
Duration: One year. Renewal possible.

EXECUTIVE STAFF:
Jean Kvamme, President and Director

ADDRESS INQUIRIES TO:
Jean Kvamme, President and Director
(See address above.)

LEARNING FOR LIFE   [1668]
1325 West Walnut Hill Lane
P.O. Box 152079
Irving, TX 75015-2079
(972) 580-2433
Fax: (972) 580-2137

WEB SITE ADDRESS:
www.learningforlife.org/exploring

AREAS OF INTEREST:
Career opportunities, life skills, service learning, character education and leadership experience.

NAME(S) OF PROGRAMS:
- **Exploring Program**

TYPE:
Awards/prizes; Scholarships.

PURPOSE:
To provide experiences to help young people mature and to prepare them to become responsible and caring adults; to provide an opportunity for youth to investigate the meaning of interdependence in their personal relationships and communities.

ELIGIBILITY:
Young men and women 15 to 20 years old or 14 years old, if they have completed the eighth grade. Must be a participant in the Learning for Life Exploring Program to receive scholarship.

GEOGRAPHIC RESTRICTIONS:
United States.

FINANCIAL DATA:
Amount of support per award: Varies per award.

MARSHALL COMMUNITY FOUNDATION   [1669]
126 West Michigan Avenue
Suite 202
Marshall, MI 49068
(269) 781-2273
Fax: (269) 781-9747

E-MAIL ADDRESS:
info@marshallcf.org

WEB SITE ADDRESS:
www.marshallcf.org

FOUNDED: 1970

AREAS OF INTEREST:
Culture, education, environment and recreation.

TYPE:
Project/program grants.

YEAR PROGRAM STARTED: 1985

PURPOSE:
To support projects that promote the educational, recreational, environmental and cultural development of the Marshall area and Calhoun County.

LEGAL BASIS:
Community foundation.

ELIGIBILITY:
Grants are made to organizations that have tax-exempt status under Section 501(c)(3) and 509(a)(1) or (2) of the Internal Revenue Code. Nonsectarian religious programs meeting a general community need may apply. No grants are made to individuals.

GEOGRAPHIC RESTRICTIONS:
Calhoun County, Michigan.

FINANCIAL DATA:
Amount of support per award: Varies.
Total amount of support: Varies.

APPLICATION INFORMATION:
Contact the Foundation for application.
Duration: One year.
Deadline: January 1, April 1, July 1 and October 1.

ADDRESS INQUIRIES TO:
Sherry Anderson, Executive Director
(See address above.)

THE MCGRAW-HILL COMPANIES CORPORATE CONTRIBUTIONS AND COMMUNITY RELATIONS
1221 Avenue of the Americas, 47th Floor
New York, NY 10020-1095
(212) 512-6480
Fax: (212) 512-3611

E-MAIL ADDRESS:
susan_wallman@mcgraw-hill.com

WEB SITE ADDRESS:
www.mcgraw-hill.com

TYPE:
Matching gifts; Project/program grants. Matching gift program for McGraw-Hill employees and retirees.

The grants program places its strongest emphasis on financial literacy and economic empowerment. Contributions through matching gifts are to colleges and universities, to financial literacy, to adult literacy organizations whose sole purpose is the delivery or advancement of adult basic skills instruction, and to arts and cultural organizations providing matching gifts on a 1:1 basis.

See entry 2028 for full listing.

THE MUSTARD SEED FOUNDATION   [1670]
7115 Leesburg Pike, Suite 304
Falls Church, VA 22043
(703) 524-5620

E-MAIL ADDRESS:
ljackson@msfdn.org

WEB SITE ADDRESS:
www.harveyfellows.org

FOUNDED: 1983

AREAS OF INTEREST:
Education and religion.

NAME(S) OF PROGRAMS:
- **Harvey Fellows Program**

TYPE:
Fellowships.

YEAR PROGRAM STARTED: 1992

PURPOSE:
To encourage students who are committed to Jesus Christ to pursue vocations that are culturally influential and to pursue vocational credentials in the most prestigious graduate programs; to validate exceptional abilities in academics and leadership as gifts from God worthy of cultivation and development.

LEGAL BASIS:
Nonprofit.

ELIGIBILITY:
The Harvey Fellows must be Christian graduate students and attend a graduate school program that is considered to be one of the top five in a given subject area or specialty in the world.

FINANCIAL DATA:
Amount of support per award: $16,000.

NUMBER OF AWARDS: 25 to 30.

APPLICATION INFORMATION:
The application process has two stages. First, the application must be completed and submitted through the Online Application system. No paper applications are accepted. The online application does not need to be completed all at once. Secondly, specific required materials must be submitted via mail (e.g., official transcripts, letters of recommendation, test scores). All required materials must be collected by the applicant, bundled, and sent directly to the Foundation. A complete list of the required documents can be found on the Foundation's web site.
Duration: One year. Optional renewal.
Deadline: November 1.

THE NAACP LEGAL DEFENSE AND EDUCATIONAL FUND, INC.

99 Hudson Street, Suite 1600
New York, NY 10013
(212) 965-2225
Fax: (212) 219-1595

E-MAIL ADDRESS:
scholarships@naacpldf.org
kthompson@naacpldf.org
mcorro@naacpldf.org

WEB SITE ADDRESS:
www.naacpldf.org/scholarships

TYPE:
Awards/prizes; Grants-in-aid; Internships; Scholarships. LDF Herbert Lehman Education Fund Scholarship Program: Scholarships for African-American high school seniors, high school graduates and college freshmen to attend four-year accredited colleges and universities.

LDF Earl Warren Legal Training Program: Scholarships for law students to attend three-year accredited law schools. Law students already enrolled in law school are ineligible to apply.

See entry 1094 for full listing.

THE NATIONAL ACADEMY OF EDUCATION   [1671]

500 Fifth Street, N.W., No. 333
Washington, DC 20001
(202) 334-2341
Fax: (202) 334-2350

E-MAIL ADDRESS:
info@naeducation.org

WEB SITE ADDRESS:
www.naeducation.org

FOUNDED: 1965

AREAS OF INTEREST:
All aspects of educational research.

NAME(S) OF PROGRAMS:
- **National Academy of Education/Spencer Postdoctoral Fellowship Program**

TYPE:
Fellowships. This nonresidential postdoctoral fellowship funds proposals that make significant scholarly contributions to the field of education. The program also develops the careers of its recipients through professional development activities involving National Academy of Education members.

PURPOSE:
To support early career scholars working in critical areas of education research.

LEGAL BASIS:
Private operating foundation.

ELIGIBILITY:
Primary criterion for selection is promise as a research scholar, with special emphasis on potential to make a significant contribution to our understanding of education. Applicant must have received Ph.D., Ed.D. or equivalent degree in the past five years.

FINANCIAL DATA:
Terms of the award do not permit institutional overhead. If the scholar transfers institutions, the grant transfers with him or her. The money may be spent toward any salary, supplies, etc., that aid the grantee in pursuing research described in the fellowship application.
Amount of support per award: $55,000.

NUMBER OF APPLICANTS MOST RECENT YEAR:
Approximately 200 each year.

NUMBER OF AWARDS: Up to 20.

APPLICATION INFORMATION:
Application material is available in July.
Duration: Up to two years.
Deadline: Early November.

NATIONAL CENTER FOR LEARNING DISABILITIES   [1672]

381 Park Avenue South
Suite 1401
New York, NY 10016
(212) 545-7510
(888) 575-7373
Fax: (212) 545-9665

E-MAIL ADDRESS:
afscholarship@ncld.org

WEB SITE ADDRESS:
www.ld.org

FOUNDED: 2001

AREAS OF INTEREST:
Education and learning disabilities.

NAME(S) OF PROGRAMS:
- **Anne Ford & Allegra Ford Scholarship**

TYPE:
Scholarships.

YEAR PROGRAM STARTED: 2001

PURPOSE:
To support a high school senior of high merit with an identified learning disability, who is pursuing an undergraduate degree.

LEGAL BASIS:
Nonprofit organization.

ELIGIBILITY:
Students (seniors in high school) of high merit in public or private secondary schools with an identified learning disability (LD), pursuing an undergraduate university degree. The ideal candidate is a person who has faced the challenges of having a learning disability and who, through perseverance and academic endeavor, has created a life of purpose and achievement. Financial need will be strongly considered. Minorities and women are encouraged to apply. Only U.S. citizens are eligible.

GEOGRAPHIC RESTRICTIONS:
United States.

FINANCIAL DATA:
Amount of support per award: $10,000, paid in four yearly installments of $2,500.
Total amount of support: $10,000.

NUMBER OF APPLICANTS MOST RECENT YEAR:
950.

NUMBER OF AWARDS: 1 award per year.

APPLICATION INFORMATION:
Deadline: December 31.

ADDRESS INQUIRIES TO:
Sheldon H. Horowitz, Ed.D.
Director, Professional Services
E-mail: shhorowitz@ncld.org

*SPECIAL STIPULATIONS:
The scholars will be required to submit annual reports detailing their progress in school and describing their insights about their personal growth.

NATIONAL CENTER FOR LEARNING DISABILITIES   [1673]

381 Park Avenue South
Suite 1401
New York, NY 10016
(212) 545-7510
(888) 575-7373
Fax: (212) 545-9665

E-MAIL ADDRESS:
programs@ncld.org

WEB SITE ADDRESS:
www.ld.org

FOUNDED: 2000

AREAS OF INTEREST:
Education and learning disabilities.

NAME(S) OF PROGRAMS:
- **Pete and Carrie Rozelle Award**

TYPE:
Awards/prizes.

YEAR PROGRAM STARTED: 1977

PURPOSE:
To recognize a school or school-related program that addresses the educational and social/emotional needs of all children, including those with learning disabilities. The award will allow for expanded programmatic and staff development opportunities that focus on incorporating effective

research-based practices into classroom and schoolwide practice with preference given to programs that serve underprivileged and underserved communities, or programs that have demonstrated unique impact for students with learning disabilities.

LEGAL BASIS:
Nonprofit organization.

GEOGRAPHIC RESTRICTIONS:
United States.

FINANCIAL DATA:
Amount of support per award: $5,000.
Total amount of support: $5,000 annually.

NUMBER OF AWARDS: 1.

APPLICATION INFORMATION:
Contact the Organization for application procedures.
Deadline: February 1.

ADDRESS INQUIRIES TO:
Sheldon H. Horowitz, Ed.D.
Director, Professional Services
E-mail: shhorowitz@ncld.org

NATIONAL CENTER FOR LEARNING DISABILITIES [1674]
381 Park Avenue South
Suite 1401
New York, NY 10016
(212) 545-7510 ext. 1233
(888) 575-7373
Fax: (212) 545-9665

E-MAIL ADDRESS:
programs@ncld.org

WEB SITE ADDRESS:
www.ncld.org

FOUNDED: 1977

AREAS OF INTEREST:
Education and learning disabilities.

NAME(S) OF PROGRAMS:
● **Bill Ellis Teacher Preparation Award**

TYPE:
Awards/prizes.

YEAR PROGRAM STARTED: 1996

PURPOSE:
To recognize and award excellence in teaching by a general education teacher committed to helping all students, including those with learning disabilities, to learn successfully; to increase opportunities for all individuals with learning disabilities to achieve their potential.

LEGAL BASIS:
Nonprofit organization.

ELIGIBILITY:
Applicants must be general educators who would not otherwise be able to participate in professional meetings that focus on the needs of individuals with learning disabilities.

GEOGRAPHIC RESTRICTIONS:
United States.

FINANCIAL DATA:
Amount of support per award: $500.
Total amount of support: $500 annually.

NUMBER OF AWARDS: 1.

ADDRESS INQUIRIES TO:
Sheldon H. Horowitz, Ed.D.
Director, Professional Services
E-mail: shhorowitz@ncld.org

NATIONAL COALITION OF BLACK MEETING PLANNERS (NCBMP) [1675]
4401 Huntchase Drive
Suite 126
Bowie, MD 20720
(301) 860-0200
Fax: (301) 860-0500

E-MAIL ADDRESS:
ncbmp.hq@verizon.net

WEB SITE ADDRESS:
www.ncbmp.com

AREAS OF INTEREST:
Professional meeting planning.

TYPE:
Scholarships.

YEAR PROGRAM STARTED: 1983

PURPOSE:
To be the preeminent organization in educating the African American meeting planner in all aspects of the meeting planning profession; to improve the meetings, conferences, exhibitions, and convocations that African Americans manage.

ELIGIBILITY:
Students seeking careers in meeting planning and enrolled in a hospitality management program.

GEOGRAPHIC RESTRICTIONS:
United States.

FINANCIAL DATA:
Amount of support per award: $1,000 to $2,500.
Total amount of support: $8,500 annually.

NUMBER OF AWARDS: 7.

APPLICATION INFORMATION:
Contact the Coalition for application procedures.
Duration: One-time award.
Deadline: Mid-May.

ADDRESS INQUIRIES TO:
Mrs. Ozzie Jenkins, Executive Director
(See address above.)

NATIONAL COUNCIL FOR THE SOCIAL STUDIES
8555 16th Street, Suite 500
Silver Spring, MD 20910
(301) 588-1800
Fax: (301) 588-2049

E-MAIL ADDRESS:
excellence@ncss.org

WEB SITE ADDRESS:
www.socialstudies.org

TYPE:
Awards/prizes; Grants-in-aid.
See entry 1983 for full listing.

NATIONAL COUNCIL FOR THE SOCIAL STUDIES
8555 16th Street, Suite 500
Silver Spring, MD 20910
(301) 588-1800 ext. 106
Fax: (301) 588-2049

E-MAIL ADDRESS:
excellence@ncss.org

WEB SITE ADDRESS:
www.socialstudies.org

TYPE:
Awards/prizes. Annual award for projects representing excellence and innovation in social studies education and having the potential of serving as a model for other teachers.
See entry 1984 for full listing.

NATIONAL COUNCIL FOR THE SOCIAL STUDIES
8555 16th Street, Suite 500
Silver Spring, MD 20910
(301) 588-1800 ext. 106
Fax: (301) 588-2049

E-MAIL ADDRESS:
excellence@ncss.org

WEB SITE ADDRESS:
www.socialstudies.org

TYPE:
Awards/prizes. Annual award honoring the outstanding performance of teachers, researchers, and other worthy individuals and programs.
See entry 1985 for full listing.

NATIONAL COUNCIL FOR THE SOCIAL STUDIES
8555 16th Street, Suite 500
Silver Spring, MD 20910
(301) 588-1800 ext. 106
Fax: (301) 588-2049

E-MAIL ADDRESS:
excellence@ncss.org

WEB SITE ADDRESS:
www.socialstudies.org

TYPE:
Awards/prizes. Annual award recognizing those who have distinguished themselves in defending the principles of academic freedom.
See entry 1986 for full listing.

NATIONAL COUNCIL FOR THE SOCIAL STUDIES
8555 16th Street, Suite 500
Silver Spring, MD 20910
(301) 588-1800 ext. 106
Fax: (301) 588-2049

E-MAIL ADDRESS:
excellence@ncss.org

WEB SITE ADDRESS:
www.socialstudies.org

TYPE:
Awards/prizes.
See entry 1987 for full listing.

NATIONAL COUNCIL OF TEACHERS OF ENGLISH RESEARCH FOUNDATION [1676]
1111 West Kenyon Road
Urbana, IL 61801
(217) 328-3870 ext. 3675
Fax: (217) 328-0977

E-MAIL ADDRESS:
sgallivan@ncte.org

WEB SITE ADDRESS:
www.ncte.org/grants

FOUNDED: 1911

AREAS OF INTEREST:
Materials, methods, curriculum patterns in English and studies related to the teaching of English.

TYPE:
Research grants. Support for individuals and groups engaged in theoretical, basic or applied research that has significance for the teaching or learning of English/Language Arts or related fields.

YEAR PROGRAM STARTED: 1960

PURPOSE:
To encourage research, experimentation and investigation in the teaching of English.

LEGAL BASIS:
Separate entity within nonprofit, tax-exempt organization.

ELIGIBILITY:
Applicants must be members of NCTE.

GEOGRAPHIC RESTRICTIONS:
United States.

FINANCIAL DATA:
Funds are not available for travel costs or subsidies for loss of salary unless cooperating agencies are willing to bear a substantial part of the cost.
Amount of support per award: Up to $12,500.

NUMBER OF APPLICANTS MOST RECENT YEAR:
25.

APPLICATION INFORMATION:
Further information is available from the address above.
Duration: Generally one year. Applicants may reapply to Trustees for extension.
Deadline: June 15. Notification August 1.

PUBLICATIONS:
Application guidelines.

ADDRESS INQUIRIES TO:
Susan Gallivan, Meeting Planner
(See address above.)

*SPECIAL STIPULATIONS:
Must be members of NCTE.

NATIONAL EMERGENCY MEDICINE ASSOCIATION [1677]
P.O. Box 1039
Edgewood, MD 21040
(443) 922-7533
Fax: (888) 682-7947

E-MAIL ADDRESS:
info@nemahealth.org

WEB SITE ADDRESS:
www.nemahealth.org

FOUNDED: 1982

AREAS OF INTEREST:
Emergency medicine.

NAME(S) OF PROGRAMS:
• **Kids Do Matter (KDM)**
• **National Alzheimer's Council (NAC)**
• **National Heart Council (NHC)**
• **National Stroke Council (NSC)**

TYPE:
Awards/prizes; Capital grants; Project/program grants; Research grants.

YEAR PROGRAM STARTED: 1982

PURPOSE:
To prevent injury or illness by addressing health and social issues through education, applied research, technology, and equipment.

LEGAL BASIS:
Educational nonprofit 501(c)(3).

ELIGIBILITY:
The granting of funds to applicants is considered according to the following priorities:
(1) first consideration to grants relating to coronary trauma and heart wellness program;
(2) second consideration to grants relating to all other types of trauma, vehicular trauma and strokes and;
(3) third consideration to grants relating to trauma prevention and the cause of trauma.

GEOGRAPHIC RESTRICTIONS:
United States.

FINANCIAL DATA:
Amount of support per award: Varies.

NUMBER OF APPLICANTS MOST RECENT YEAR:
5.

NUMBER OF AWARDS: 1.

REPRESENTATIVE AWARDS:
St. Agnes Hospital, Catonsville, MD, for Chest Pain Emergency Clinic; National Institute of Health, Bethesda, MD, for research into coronary ischemia; Beth Israel Medical Center, New York, NY, for research in reversing effects of heart disease.

APPLICATION INFORMATION:
The proposal should be written in clear, concise language with all technical terms defined and should give a full description of the project. The proposal should also include:
(1) purpose and services;
(2) a history of other similar projects and their results;
(3) activities, benefits and desired results;
(4) amount requested, anticipated costs, budget, and funding sources;
(5) annual report, financial statements and background information of the sponsoring organization;
(6) proof of tax-exempt status;
(7) qualifications of staff;
(8) list of Board members and;
(9) a plan for how information on the project will be communicated to the public and how NEMA will be credited.
Duration: Varies.
Deadline: Applications considered as received.

PUBLICATIONS:
Five Minute Guide to Heart Attack Prevention and Survival; Five Minute Guide to Stroke (Brain Attack) Prevention and Survival; wallet cards for Heart, Stroke and Alzheimer's.

IRS IDENTIFICATION NUMBER: 52-1257429

OFFICERS:
Kelly Herzog, President/Chief Executive Officer

ADDRESS INQUIRIES TO:
Kelly Herzog
President/Chief Executive Officer
(See address above.)

NATIONAL ENDOWMENT FOR THE HUMANITIES [1678]
1100 Pennsylvania Avenue, N.W.
Office of Communications, Room 510
Washington, DC 20506
(202) 606-8446
Fax: (202) 606-8240

E-MAIL ADDRESS:
info@neh.gov

WEB SITE ADDRESS:
www.neh.gov

FOUNDED: 1965

AREAS OF INTEREST:
Scholarship, research, education and public programs in the humanities. In the act that established the Endowment, the term humanities includes, but is not limited to, the study of history, philosophy, languages, linguistics, literature, archaeology, jurisprudence, the history, theory and criticism of the arts, ethics, comparative religion and those aspects of the social sciences that employ historical or philosophical approaches.

NAME(S) OF PROGRAMS:
• **Grants for Teaching and Learning Resources**

TYPE:
Conferences/seminars; Development grants; Fellowships; Project/program grants. Grants, including Humanities Initiatives for Historically Black Colleges and Universities, Institutions with High Hispanic Enrollment, and Tribal Colleges and Universities, support curriculum and materials development efforts and faculty study programs within and among educational institutions and networks of institutions. The Endowment is interested in projects that help teachers use new electronic technologies to enhance students' understanding of humanities subjects.

YEAR PROGRAM STARTED: 1973

PURPOSE:
To improve the quality of humanities education in the nation's schools by strengthening humanities curriculum and providing opportunities for teachers and administrators to increase their knowledge in the humanities.

LEGAL BASIS:
Federal agency, established by act of Congress: the National Foundation on the Arts and Humanities Act of 1965, Public Law 89-209, as amended.

ELIGIBILITY:
U.S. colleges and universities and other nonprofit educational and cultural organizations are eligible.

FINANCIAL DATA:
Amount of support per award: Up to $100,000.
Total amount of support: $1,000,000.

COOPERATIVE FUNDING PROGRAMS: Division of Education–Professional Development Programs: Seminars and Institutes, Landmarks of American History and Culture, and Digital Humanities Workshops.

NUMBER OF APPLICANTS MOST RECENT YEAR:
139.

NUMBER OF AWARDS: 19.

APPLICATION INFORMATION:
For application forms, applicants should contact the Office of Public Affairs at the address, e-mail or web site listed above. Well before the deadline, applicants should send a preliminary letter outlining the proposed project. Staff suggestions can enable the applicant to prepare a more competitive proposal.
Duration: Varies.
Deadline: Varies.

PUBLICATIONS:
Annual report; *Grant Programs*; *Humanities Magazine*.

IRS IDENTIFICATION NUMBER: 52-1098584

ADDRESS INQUIRIES TO:
Public Affairs Specialist
(See address above.)

NATIONAL FASTENER DISTRIBUTORS ASSOCIATION [1679]
401 North Michigan Avenue, 22nd Floor
Chicago, IL 60611
(312) 527-6671
Fax: (312) 673-6740

E-MAIL ADDRESS:
nfda@nfda-fastener.org

WEB SITE ADDRESS:
www.nfda-fastener.org

AREAS OF INTEREST:
Education.

TYPE:
Scholarships.

PURPOSE:
To provide assistance to employees and children of NFDA member companies; to promote the continued education of people employed in the fastener industry.

ELIGIBILITY:
Must be a student who is the child of NFDA member company employees entering their first year of college as full-time students or an employee of NFDA member companies who work at least 20 hours per week and take at least six credit hours of college-level course work per semester.

FINANCIAL DATA:
Amount of support per award: $500 to $2,500.
Total amount of support: Varies.

NUMBER OF APPLICANTS MOST RECENT YEAR:
50.

NUMBER OF AWARDS: Varies.

APPLICATION INFORMATION:
Contact the Association for application procedures.
Deadline: Usually mid-May.

ADDRESS INQUIRIES TO:
Kari Aylward
Membership Services Coordinator
(See address above.)

NATIONAL FOOTBALL LEAGUE CHARITIES [1680]
280 Park Avenue
New York, NY 10017
(212) 450-2000

E-MAIL ADDRESS:
lynda.hamilton@nfl.com

WEB SITE ADDRESS:
www.nflcharities.org

FOUNDED: 1973

AREAS OF INTEREST:
Education, football, public service, sports medicine research and youth.

NAME(S) OF PROGRAMS:
- **Medical Research Grant**
- **Player Foundation Grant**
- **Pro Bowl Grants**

TYPE:
Awards/prizes; Challenge/matching grants; General operating grants; Project/program grants; Research grants; Seed money grants; Training grants. Through its grants, NFL Charities seeks to support education, mentoring, or youth-centered programming that show potential for national impact.

YEAR PROGRAM STARTED: 1973

PURPOSE:
To support youth-oriented programs that promote education, physical fitness and the value of a healthy lifestyle.

LEGAL BASIS:
Private foundation.

ELIGIBILITY:
Grants will be awarded to organizations that focus on youth-centered educational and recreational programming on a national scale.

GEOGRAPHIC RESTRICTIONS:
United States.

FINANCIAL DATA:
Amount of support per award: Varies.
Total amount of support: Varies.

NUMBER OF APPLICANTS MOST RECENT YEAR:
Approximately 1,200.

NUMBER OF AWARDS: Varies.

IRS IDENTIFICATION NUMBER: 23-7315236

ADDRESS INQUIRIES TO:
Lynda Hamilton, Manager
(See address above.)

NATIONAL FOSTER PARENT ASSOCIATION
1102 Prairie Ridge Trail
Pflugerville, TX 78660
(512) 706-7513
Fax: (253) 238-4252

E-MAIL ADDRESS:
info@nfpaonline.org

WEB SITE ADDRESS:
www.nfpaonline.org

TYPE:
Scholarships.

See entry 1209 for full listing.

NATIONAL INSTITUTE ON DRUG ABUSE [1681]
6001 Executive Boulevard, Room 5232
MSC 9591
Bethesda, MD 20892-9591
(301) 443-6071
Fax: (301) 480-2485

E-MAIL ADDRESS:
ghimm@nida.nih.gov

WEB SITE ADDRESS:
www.nida.nih.gov

AREAS OF INTEREST:
Drug abuse and addiction.

TYPE:
Awards/prizes. The Institute supports a variety of training and career development grant awards. See www.drugabuse.gov/researchtraining for a complete listing.

PURPOSE:
To support research training and/or career development.

ELIGIBILITY:
Specific eligibility criteria vary based on the award.

GEOGRAPHIC RESTRICTIONS:
United States.

FINANCIAL DATA:
Amount of support per award: Varies.

ADDRESS INQUIRIES TO:
Mimi Ghim, Ph.D.
Deputy Coordinator of Research Training
(See address above.)

NATIONAL INSTITUTE ON DRUG ABUSE [1682]
6001 Executive Boulevard, Room 4216
MSC 9567
Bethesda, MD 20892-9567
(301) 443-0441
Fax: (301) 480-8179

E-MAIL ADDRESS:
lb75x@nih.gov

WEB SITE ADDRESS:
www.nida.nih.gov

AREAS OF INTEREST:
Drug abuse, medicine and health disparity.

NAME(S) OF PROGRAMS:
- **Diversity-Promoting Institutions Drug Abuse Research Program**

TYPE:
Project/program grants; Research grants.

PURPOSE:
To broaden and strengthen drug abuse research in diversity-promoting; to achieve health promotion and disease prevention.

ELIGIBILITY:
Organizations classified as 501(c)(3) by the IRS can apply. No grants to individuals.

FINANCIAL DATA:
Amount of support per award: Varies, but not to exceed direct costs of $350,000 per year.

APPLICATION INFORMATION:
Program Announcement (PA) Number: PAR-09-011. Application form required. Applicants should submit Public Health Service Form 398. Additional information and appropriate forms can be obtained online.

ADDRESS INQUIRIES TO:
Lula Beatty, Director
Special Populations Office
(See address above.)

NATIONAL INSTITUTE ON DRUG ABUSE [1683]
6001 Executive Boulevard, Room 5195
MSC 9589
Bethesda, MD 20892-9589
(301) 451-4998
Fax: (301) 443-2636

E-MAIL ADDRESS:
duffys@nida.nih.gov

WEB SITE ADDRESS:
www.nida.nih.gov

AREAS OF INTEREST:
Economics of drug treatment services.

NAME(S) OF PROGRAMS:
- **Economics of Drug Abuse Treatment and Prevention Services**

TYPE:
Research grants.

YEAR PROGRAM STARTED: 1996

PURPOSE:
To enhance public health through biomedical and behaviorial research.

ELIGIBILITY:
Organizations, including religious, universities and research institutions, can apply. No grants to individuals.

FINANCIAL DATA:
Amount of support per award: Varies.
Total amount of support: Varies.

APPLICATION INFORMATION:
Instructions and guidelines are available at www.grants.gov.
Duration: One year. Renewable after submission of progress report.

ADDRESS INQUIRIES TO:
Dr. Sarah Duffy, Economist
(See address above.)

NATIONAL INVESTMENT COMPANY SERVICE ASSOCIATION   [1684]
8400 Westpark Drive, 2nd Floor
McLean, VA 22102
(508) 485-1500
Fax: (508) 485-1560

E-MAIL ADDRESS:
info@nicsa.org

WEB SITE ADDRESS:
www.nicsa.org

AREAS OF INTEREST:
Education.

NAME(S) OF PROGRAMS:
● **The NICSA/William T. Blackwell Scholarship Fund**

TYPE:
Scholarships.

PURPOSE:
To provide leadership and innovation in educational programming and information exchange within the operations sector of the mutual fund industry worldwide; to recognize outstanding students of the NICSA Family with financial support for postsecondary education.

ELIGIBILITY:
Applicants must be dependent children of full-time employees of NICSA member companies and be enrolled in or planning to pursue a Bachelor's degree from an accredited four-year college or university.

FINANCIAL DATA:
Amount of support per award: $2,000 to $5,000.
Total amount of support: $30,000 annually.

APPLICATION INFORMATION:
Send a letter of inquiry outlining the organization's goal and purposes, and the intended use and amount of the grant requested.
Duration: One-time award.
Deadline: January.

ADDRESS INQUIRIES TO:
Teresa Hamacher, President
(See address above.)

NATIONAL MOLE DAY FOUNDATION
P.O. Box 602
Millersport, OH 43046
(740) 928-8455
Fax: (740) 928-8455

E-MAIL ADDRESS:
mole@avolve.net

WEB SITE ADDRESS:
www.moleday.org

TYPE:
Grants-in-aid. The George Hague Memorial Travel Award is given to financially support a young chemistry instructor (with two to five years of chemistry experience) in attending a biennial ChemEd conference.

The Maury Award is given to teachers to support student-centered Mole Day activities (promoting chemistry education).

The National Mole of the Year Award (MOTY) is given to a member of the National Mole Day Foundation who has contributed the most to furthering the cause of Mole Day and chemistry education.

See entry 2199 for full listing.

NATIONAL OCEANIC AND ATMOSPHERIC ADMINISTRATION   [1685]
NOAA Chesapeake Bay Office
410 Severn Avenue, Suite 107-A
Annapolis, MD 21403
(410) 267-5660
Fax: (410) 267-5666

E-MAIL ADDRESS:
derek.orner@noaa.gov

WEB SITE ADDRESS:
noaa.chesapeakebay.net

FOUNDED: 1985

AREAS OF INTEREST:
Stock assessment, multispecies, and ecosystem-based fisheries research in Chesapeake Bay.

NAME(S) OF PROGRAMS:
● **Chesapeake Bay Fisheries Research Program**

TYPE:
Project/program grants; Research grants; Research contracts.

YEAR PROGRAM STARTED: 1985

PURPOSE:
To support stock assessment, multispecies and ecosystem-based fisheries research in Chesapeake Bay.

LEGAL BASIS:
Government agency.

ELIGIBILITY:
Individuals who are U.S. citizens or residents and organizations, including religious, classified as 501(c)(3) by the IRS can apply.

GEOGRAPHIC RESTRICTIONS:
United States, with a focus on Chesapeake Bay/mid-Atlantic.

FINANCIAL DATA:
Amount of support per award: $100,000 average.

NUMBER OF APPLICANTS MOST RECENT YEAR: 27.

NUMBER OF AWARDS: 15.

REPRESENTATIVE AWARDS:
Menhaden Analyses; Blue Crab Benchmark Assessment.

APPLICATION INFORMATION:
Duration: One year. Grants are usually renewable.

Deadline: March/April time frame; varies each year.

PUBLICATIONS:
Application guidelines; annual report.

ADDRESS INQUIRIES TO:
Derek Orner, Research Fishery Biologist
(See address above.)

NATIONAL SCIENCE FOUNDATION
Division of Research on Learning in Formal and Informal Settings
4201 Wilson Boulevard, Suite 885
Arlington, VA 22230
(703) 292-8620
Fax: (703) 292-9044; (703) 292-9046

E-MAIL ADDRESS:
acarroll@nsf.gov

WEB SITE ADDRESS:
www.nsf.gov

TYPE:
Conferences/seminars; Demonstration grants; Development grants; Project/program grants; Research grants; Training grants. Through the Advanced Learning Technologies (ALT) program, the CISE and EHR Directorates of NSF support research that (1) enables radical improvements in learning through innovative computer and information technologies, and (2) advances research in computer science, information technology, learning and cognitive science through the unique challenges posed by learning environments and learning technology platforms.

With an emphasis on two-year colleges, the Advanced Technological Education (ATE) program focuses on the education of technicians for the high-technology fields that drive the nation's economy.

Communicating Research to Public Audiences is a component of the Informal Science Education program (ISE) in the Division of Elementary, Secondary, and Informal Education. ISE projects provide rich and stimulating contexts and experiences for individuals of all ages, interests and backgrounds to increase their appreciation for, and understanding of, science, technology, engineering and mathematics (STEM) in out-of-school settings.

Discovery Research K-12 (DR-K12) funds research, development and evaluation activities through knowledge generation and application to improve K-12 learning and teaching.

Informal Science Education (ISE) program invests in projects that develop and implement informal learning experiences designed to increase interest, engagement and understanding of science, technology, engineering and mathematics (STEM) by individuals of all ages and backgrounds, as well as projects that advance knowledge and practice of informal science education.

Innovative Technology Experiences for Students and Teachers (ITEST) is designed to increase the opportunities for students and teachers to learn about, experience, and use information technologies within the context of science, technology, engineering and mathematics (STEM), including Information Technology (IT) courses. It is in direct response to the concern about shortages of information technology workers in the U.S.

Research and Evaluation on Education in Science and Engineering (REESE) supports basic and applied research and evaluation that enhances science, technology, engineering and mathematics (STEM) learning and teaching.

See entry 1718 for full listing.

NATIVE AMERICAN COMMUNITY BOARD (NACB)   [1686]

P.O. Box 572
Lake Andes, SD 57356-0572
(605) 487-7072
Fax: (605) 487-7964

E-MAIL ADDRESS:
charon@charles-mix.com

WEB SITE ADDRESS:
www.nativeshop.org

AREAS OF INTEREST:
Native American women.

NAME(S) OF PROGRAMS:
● **NACB Scholarship Fund**

TYPE:
Scholarships.

PURPOSE:
To support young women who show high potential and future promise and that are likely to have an impact on the community.

LEGAL BASIS:
Nonprofit tax-exempt 501(c)(3) organization.

ELIGIBILITY:
Must be a Yankton Sioux Tribally enrolled woman attending a college off of the reservation majoring in the fields of business, education, environmental studies, health, law/criminal justice or sociology.

GEOGRAPHIC RESTRICTIONS:
United States.

FINANCIAL DATA:
Amount of support per award: Varies.
Total amount of support: Varies.

NUMBER OF AWARDS: 4 or more per year.

APPLICATION INFORMATION:
Contact the NACB for application procedures.
Deadline: March 15 for Spring. November 15 for Fall.

ADDRESS INQUIRIES TO:
Charon Asetoyer, Executive Director
(See address above.)

THE NEA FOUNDATION   [1687]

1201 16th Street, N.W.
Washington, DC 20036
(202) 822-7840
Fax: (202) 822-7779

E-MAIL ADDRESS:
info@neafoundation.org

WEB SITE ADDRESS:
www.neafoundation.org

AREAS OF INTEREST:
Public education.

TYPE:
Awards/prizes. Recognizes and awards the excellence demonstrated by educators nationwide.

PURPOSE:
To advance student achievement, through the unique strength of the Foundation's

partnership with educators, by investing in public education that will prepare each of America's children to learn and thrive in a rapidly changing world.

ELIGIBILITY:
Details are available online at the Foundation web site.

FINANCIAL DATA:
Amount of support per award: State level: $750 gift to teacher's school and travel to Annual Salute to Excellence in Education Gala. Five finalists from the state level: $10,000 courtesy of the Horace Mann Educators Corporation. National awardee: $25,000 total from NEA Member Benefits Company.

APPLICATION INFORMATION:
Applications are through the NEA State Affiliates. The Foundation receives a nomination from each state. Guidelines and applications are available online.
Deadline: May 1, 2012.

THE NEA FOUNDATION   [1688]

1201 16th Street, N.W., Suite 416
Washington, DC 20036-3207
(202) 822-7840
Fax: (202) 822-7779

E-MAIL ADDRESS:
foundation_info@nea.org

WEB SITE ADDRESS:
www.neafoundation.org

FOUNDED: 1969

AREAS OF INTEREST:
Education.

NAME(S) OF PROGRAMS:
● **NEA Foundation Learning and Leadership Grants**
● **NEA Foundation Student Achievement Grants**

YEAR PROGRAM STARTED: 1999

PURPOSE:
To improve the academic achievement of students in U.S. public schools and public higher education institutions in any subject area(s); to support public school teachers, public education support professionals, and/or faculty and staff in public institutions of higher education.

ELIGIBILITY:
Applicants must be practicing U.S. public school teachers in grades PreK-12, public school education support professionals, or faculty or staff at public higher education institutions.

Preference will be given to members of the National Education Association. The NEA Foundation encourages grant applications from teachers with less than seven years of experience in the profession and from education support professionals.

Learning and Leadership Grant: All professional development must improve practice, curriculum, and student achievement. "One-shot" professional growth experiences, such as attending a national conference or engaging a professional speaker, are discouraged. Decisions regarding the content of the professional growth activities must be based upon an assessment of student work undertaken with colleagues, and must be integrated into the institutional planning process. Funds may not be used to pursue degrees, pay direct costs, grant

administration fees, or salaries, or support travel costs or conference fees for more than one person.

Student Achievement Grant: The proposed work should engage students in critical thinking and problem solving that deepens their knowledge of standards-based subject matter. The work should also improve students' habits of inquiry, self-directed learning, and critical reflection. Proposals for work resulting in low-income and minority student success with honors, advanced placement, or other challenging curricula are particularly encouraged. Funds may be used for resource materials, supplies, equipment, transportation, software, or scholars-in-residence. Although some funds may be used to support the professional development necessary to implement the project, the majority of grant funds must be spent on materials or educational experiences for students.

With the exception of study groups, applicants may not use grant funds to pay themselves stipends. Funds may not be used for lobbying or religious purposes. Identical applications will not be considered.

GEOGRAPHIC RESTRICTIONS:
United States.

FINANCIAL DATA:
Amount of support per award: Learning and Leadership Grants: $2,000 (individuals), $5,000 (groups engaged in collegial study); Student Achievement Grants: $5,000.

APPLICATION INFORMATION:
Applications may be submitted at any time and are reviewed three times per year, every year. Applicants are encouraged to plan ahead.

Please give careful attention to the timelines of your grant. Applications that include activities scheduled prior to the date of notification will not be considered. A list of grant recipients will be posted on the NEA Foundation's web site. Please do not contact the Foundation regarding the status of your application.
Duration: Annual. Nonrenewable.
Deadline: February 1, June 1, October 15.

ADDRESS INQUIRIES TO:
Jesse Graytock, Grants Manager
(See address above.)

*SPECIAL STIPULATIONS:
Preference is given to members of NEA. For Student Achievement Grants, additionally, preference is given to educators who serve the economically disadvantaged and/or underserved students.

NELLIE MAE EDUCATION FOUNDATION   [1689]

1250 Hancock Street, Suite 205N
Quincy, MA 02169-4331
(781) 348-4200
Fax: (781) 348-4299

E-MAIL ADDRESS:
info@nmefdn.org

WEB SITE ADDRESS:
www.nmefdn.org

FOUNDED: 1998

AREAS OF INTEREST:
Early learning, time for learning, pathways to higher learning, adult learning and systems building.

TYPE:
General operating grants; Matching gifts; Project/program grants; Research grants.

YEAR PROGRAM STARTED: 1998

PURPOSE:
To promote accessibilty, quality and effectiveness of education, especially for underserved populations in the six New England states.

LEGAL BASIS:
Public charity.

ELIGIBILITY:
Organizations must be 501(c)(3) or public schools. Religious organizations may apply. No grants are made to individuals.

GEOGRAPHIC RESTRICTIONS:
The six New England states.

FINANCIAL DATA:
Total amount of support: Approximately $13,000,000 for the year 2010.

ADDRESS INQUIRIES TO:
See e-mail address above.

NORTH CAROLINA GLAXOSMITHKLINE FOUNDATION [1690]

5 Moore Drive
Research Triangle Park, NC 27709
(919) 483-2140
Fax: (919) 315-3015

WEB SITE ADDRESS:
www.gsk.com

FOUNDED: 1986

AREAS OF INTEREST:
Mathematics, science and health at all educational and professional levels.

NAME(S) OF PROGRAMS:
- **Ribbon of Hope**
- **Traditional Grants**

TYPE:
Fellowships; Professorships; Project/program grants; Seed money grants. Support for activities which help meet the educational and health needs of today's society and future generations.

Ribbon of Hope provides one-time grants to nonprofits for projects furthering health, science and education in their communities.

The Traditional Grants program provides for larger grants that may be multiyear in nature, to support programs advancing health, science and education throughout the state of North Carolina.

YEAR PROGRAM STARTED: 1986

PURPOSE:
To provide programs that emphasize the understanding and applications of health, science and education at all academic and professional levels; to seek out grant recipients representative of worthy causes that contribute to all well-being and quality of life.

LEGAL BASIS:
Corporate foundation.

ELIGIBILITY:
Ribbon of Hope: North Carolina community-based nonprofit, charitable organizations and institutions exempt under Section 501(c)(3) of the Internal Revenue Code are eligible to apply. Individuals may

not apply. Nonprofits with proposals pertaining to health, science and education are encouraged to apply.

Traditional Grants: Grant applicants must be nonprofit, charitable organizations and institutions exempt under Section 501(c)(3) of the Internal Revenue Code. No grants are made to individuals, for construction or restoration projects, or for international programs. The primary focus of the Foundation is to provide seed funds for new and worthwhile educational programs. This policy does not preclude the consideration and possible funding of ongoing projects.

GEOGRAPHIC RESTRICTIONS:
North Carolina.

FINANCIAL DATA:
Amount of support per award: Ribbon of Hope: $25,000; Traditional Grants: $25,000 and up.

Total amount of support: Awards granted: $2,347,527 in 2009.

APPLICATION INFORMATION:
Traditional Grants: Proposals should be accompanied by a cover letter signed by the president, director or equivalent official of the applicant organization. The application should also include an official certification from the IRS or other documentation of the applicant institution's tax-exempt 501(c)(3) status, an executive summary of the planned activities (not exceeding two double-spaced pages), a description and explanation of the overall strategy of the proposed activities, and a detailed statement on the types of expenses for each activity proposed. Also, the applying organization should provide a summary of general information regarding itself, resumes of its program director and key personnel, and a summary of the organization's revenues and support during the past three fiscal years.

Duration: Ribbon of Hope: One-time grant; Traditional Grants: Up to five years.

Deadline: Ribbon of Hope: April 1 and October 1. Traditional Grants: January 1, April 1, July 1 and October 1.

PUBLICATIONS:
Annual report; application; brochure.

OFFICERS:
Robert A. Ingram, Chairman
Margaret B. Dardess, President
Paul A. Holcombe, Jr., Secretary
Marilyn E. Foote-Hudson, Executive Director

ADDRESS INQUIRIES TO:
Marilyn E. Foote-Hudson, Executive Director
(See address above.)

OAK GROVE SCHOOL FOUNDATION [1691]

P.O. Box 150
South China, ME 04358
(207) 445-3333
Fax: (207) 445-4477

E-MAIL ADDRESS:
austinlaw@fairpoint.net

FOUNDED: 1989

AREAS OF INTEREST:
Education, secondary school curriculum development and limited secondary school scholarships.

NAME(S) OF PROGRAMS:
- **Grants Program**
- **Tuition Assistance**

TYPE:
Project/program grants; Scholarships.

YEAR PROGRAM STARTED: 1991

PURPOSE:
To foster secondary education innovation in proximate geographic area; to provide tuition assistance.

LEGAL BASIS:
Private foundation.

ELIGIBILITY:
Secondary schools and 501(c)(3) organizations in Central Maine. For tuition assistance, candidates may be either currently enrolled or accepted for enrollment in a Quaker secondary school and must be a resident of Maine or children or grandchildren of Oak Grove School or Oak Grove-Coburn School alumni/ae. In addition, children and grandchildren of former Oak Grove or Oak Grove-Coburn faculty and staff are eligible applicants.

GEOGRAPHIC RESTRICTIONS:
Central Maine.

FINANCIAL DATA:
Amount of support per award: $2,000 to $5,000.

Total amount of support: $100,000.

NUMBER OF APPLICANTS MOST RECENT YEAR:
37.

NUMBER OF AWARDS: 22.

APPLICATION INFORMATION:
Application available from Foundation.
Duration: Up to four years.
Deadline: April 1.

IRS IDENTIFICATION NUMBER: 01-0211537

ADDRESS INQUIRIES TO:
Joann Clark Austin, President
(See address above.)

ORPHAN FOUNDATION OF AMERICA [1692]

21351 Gentry Drive, Suite 130
Sterling, VA 20166
(571) 203-0270
Fax: (571) 203-0273

E-MAIL ADDRESS:
scholarships@orphan.org
office@orphan.org

WEB SITE ADDRESS:
www.orphan.org

FOUNDED: 1981

AREAS OF INTEREST:
Foster children.

NAME(S) OF PROGRAMS:
- **Casey Family Scholars**
- **OFA Scholarship Fund**

TYPE:
Scholarships.

YEAR PROGRAM STARTED: 1986

PURPOSE:
To recognize outstanding scholarship and community service by a college student who has no family supporting their goals and efforts.

LEGAL BASIS:
501(c)(3), nonprofit organization.

ELIGIBILITY:
Applicants must be currently entering or enrolled in college or a vocational training program and:
(1) be currently in foster care or in foster

care for one year at the time of their 18th birthday or high school graduation;
(2) have been adopted or taken into legal guardianship out of foster care after their 16th birthday or;
(3) have lost both parents to death before the age of 18 and not been subsequently adopted. In this instance, copies of the death certificate must be provided.

Applicants must be under the age of 25 on March 31 of the year in which they apply.

GEOGRAPHIC RESTRICTIONS:
United States.

FINANCIAL DATA:
Funds may be used for tuition, books, and approved living expenses.
Amount of support per award: $1,000 to $6,000.

NUMBER OF APPLICANTS MOST RECENT YEAR: 2,200.

NUMBER OF AWARDS: 75 new; 300 repeat recipients.

APPLICATION INFORMATION:
Information may be obtained from the address above or online from January 1 to March 31.
Duration: Annual awards. Recipients can reapply.
Deadline: March 31 if applying online; April 15 if applying by mail.

IRS IDENTIFICATION NUMBER: 52-1238437

STAFF:
Eileen McCaffrey, Chief Executive Officer

ADDRESS INQUIRIES TO:
Tina Raheem, Scholarship Director
(See address above.)

PANASONIC FOUNDATION, INC. [1693]
3 Panasonic Way, 2I-1
Secaucus, NJ 07094
(201) 392-4132
Fax: (201) 392-4126

E-MAIL ADDRESS:
info@foundation.us.panasonic.com

WEB SITE ADDRESS:
www.panasonic.
com/MECA/foundation/foundation.html
www.panasonicfoundation.net

FOUNDED: 1984

AREAS OF INTEREST:
Pre-collegiate education and school reform.

NAME(S) OF PROGRAMS:
- **New Jersey Network of Superintendents**
- **Panasonic Foundation Partnership Program for School Reform**

TYPE:
Technical assistance. The New Jersey Network of Superintendents, established December 2008, supports monthly meetings of district superintendents focused on improving teaching and learning.

The Partnership Program was established with urban school districts serving large proportions of disadvantaged youth. The Foundation does not make grants, but rather it provides technical assistance to school districts with which it has formed a partnership.

YEAR PROGRAM STARTED: 1987

PURPOSE:
To support systemic, school-based, whole-school reform.

LEGAL BASIS:
Corporate foundation.

GEOGRAPHIC RESTRICTIONS:
United States.

FINANCIAL DATA:
Amount of support per award: $35,000 to $70,000 per site.
Matching fund requirements: Districts in the Panasonic Partnership Program participate in the Foundation Leadership Associates Program, which requires the district to assume the travel and lodging of at least four participants in two three-day long events.

APPLICATION INFORMATION:
The Foundation does not accept proposals.

PUBLICATIONS:
Newsletter; brochure.

OFFICERS:
Michael Riccio, Treasurer
Robert Ohme, Assistant Treasurer
Sandra Karriem, Secretary

STAFF:
Larry Leverett, Executive Director
Scott Thompson, Assistant Executive Director
Kathleen Archetti, Planning Coordinator

BOARD OF DIRECTORS:
Masaharu Matsushita, Honorary Chairman
Milton Chen, Chairman
Megan Lee
Robert Marin
Kent McGuire
Deborah Meier
Ira Perlman
Sophie Sa

ADDRESS INQUIRIES TO:
Larry Leverett, Executive Director
(See address above.)

PARENTS WITHOUT PARTNERS [1694]
1100-H Brandywine Boulevard
Zanesville, OH 43701
(740) 450-1332
Fax: (740) 452-2552

E-MAIL ADDRESS:
pwppn@parentswithoutpartners.org

WEB SITE ADDRESS:
www.parentswithoutpartners.org

FOUNDED: 1957

AREAS OF INTEREST:
Education of children of single parents belonging to the organization.

NAME(S) OF PROGRAMS:
- **Parents Without Partners International Scholarship**

TYPE:
Scholarships.

PURPOSE:
To provide single parents and their children with an opportunity for enhancing personal growth, self-confidence, and sensitivity towards others by offering an environment for support, friendship and the exchange of parenting techniques.

LEGAL BASIS:
Nonprofit.

ELIGIBILITY:
Applicants must be dependent children, up to 25 years of age, of PWP members. Also, must be either in the senior class of any high school and planning to enter and have applied to a school of higher education for the following year, or be an undergraduate student at a college or trade school.

GEOGRAPHIC RESTRICTIONS:
United States and Canada.

FINANCIAL DATA:
Amount of support per award: Varies.

THE MABEL LOUISE RILEY FOUNDATION [1695]
77 Summer Street, Eighth Floor
Boston, MA 02110
(617) 399-1850
Fax: (617) 399-1851

E-MAIL ADDRESS:
info@rileyfoundation.com

WEB SITE ADDRESS:
www.rileyfoundation.com

FOUNDED: 1972

AREAS OF INTEREST:
Emphasis on priority needs in social services and education, especially for youth, community development including cultural, housing and urban environmental programs.

TYPE:
Capital grants; Challenge/matching grants; Development grants; Project/program grants; Seed money grants; Training grants.

LEGAL BASIS:
Private foundation.

ELIGIBILITY:
Requests are considered only from corporations organized under the laws of Massachusetts for purposes to be carried out within Massachusetts and those who have a 501(c)(3) IRS determination.

GEOGRAPHIC RESTRICTIONS:
Greater Boston area, with a primary focus on the city of Boston, Massachusetts.

FINANCIAL DATA:
Amount of support per award: $50,000 to $100,000.
Total amount of support: $2,092,000 for the year 2010.

NUMBER OF APPLICANTS MOST RECENT YEAR:
Approximately 350 for the year 2009.

NUMBER OF AWARDS: 34 for the year 2009.

APPLICATION INFORMATION:
A brief two-page summary of proposal should be submitted before full proposal is submitted. If, after review of letter, the Trustees wish to see full proposal, applicant will be asked to submit one. All proposals should be prepared using the Common Proposal Format supplied by Associated Grantmakers of Massachusetts. However, all proposals should include a separate concise statement of purpose for which the grant is sought and of the program, staff, and specific budget necessary for its achievement. In addition, proposals should include:
(1) the organization's history, mission and services;
(2) current year's operating budget;
(3) the most recent audited financial statements;
(4) a complete copy of Form 990;
(5) a roster of the board of directors;
(6) a copy of the IRS tax-exemption letter

and;

(7) where applicable, the resumes of the key staff people involved in the project.

Duration: One year. Renewals possible. Two-year waiting period is requested before applying again for those who have been awarded a grant.

Deadline: Meetings are held in March, June, September and December with deadlines for receipt of full grant proposals set 30 to 45 days prior to each meeting.

PUBLICATIONS:
Guidelines.

IRS IDENTIFICATION NUMBER: 04-6278857

TRUSTEES:
Andrew C. Bailey
Grace Fey
Robert W. Holmes, Jr.

ADDRESS INQUIRIES TO:
Nancy A. Saunders, Administrative Manager
(See address above.)

RURITAN NATIONAL FOUNDATION   [1696]

5451 Lyons Road
Dublin, VA 24084
(540) 674-5431
Fax: (540) 674-2304

E-MAIL ADDRESS:
office@ruritan.org

WEB SITE ADDRESS:
www.ruritan.org

AREAS OF INTEREST:
Education.

NAME(S) OF PROGRAMS:
- **Build Your Dollars Grant**
- **Educational Grant Program**

TYPE:
Grants-in-aid; Matching gifts. These programs allow Ruritan clubs to increase their financial assistance to a student of the club's choice. Ruritan clubs contribute $300 to the Foundation and, in turn, the Foundation will add to this amount for grants.

PURPOSE:
To manage and maintain a trust for the encouragement, promotion, and financing of the charitable, educational, and benevolent principles and activities of Ruritan Clubs and of Ruritan National.

ELIGIBILITY:
Must be sponsored by a local Ruritan Club and have the endorsement of two members. Applicant should be pursuing a postsecondary education. Selection is based on financial need, character, scholarship and applicant's desire for higher education.

GEOGRAPHIC RESTRICTIONS:
United States.

FINANCIAL DATA:
Amount of support per award: Varies.
Total amount of support: Varies.

NUMBER OF AWARDS: 388 for the year 2010.

APPLICATION INFORMATION:
Applications for grant programs are available online.

Duration: Applicants must reapply each year.

Deadline: April 1.

ADDRESS INQUIRIES TO:
Michael Chrisley, Executive Director
(See address above.)

THE SCHOTT FOUNDATION FOR PUBLIC EDUCATION [1697]

678 Massachusetts Avenue, 8th Floor
Cambridge, MA 02139
(617) 876-7700
Fax: (617) 876-7702

E-MAIL ADDRESS:
info@schottfoundation.org

WEB SITE ADDRESS:
www.schottfoundation.org

FOUNDED: 1999

AREAS OF INTEREST:
K-12 education, early education, resource and fiscal equity.

TYPE:
General operating grants.

PURPOSE:
To develop and strengthen a broad-based and representative movement to achieve fully resourced and adequately funded high-quality preK-12 public education in Massachusetts and New York.

LEGAL BASIS:
501(c)(3).

ELIGIBILITY:
Funding to grassroots and other nonprofit organizations working to improve public education.

GEOGRAPHIC RESTRICTIONS:
Massachusetts and New York.

FINANCIAL DATA:
Amount of support per award: Varies.
Total amount of support: Varies.

COOPERATIVE FUNDING PROGRAMS: Yes.

NUMBER OF AWARDS: 50.

ADDRESS INQUIRIES TO:
Nakisha Lewis, Project Manager
(See address above.)

GEORGE J. AND EFFIE L. SEAY MEMORIAL TRUST

1111 East Main Street, 12th Floor
Richmond, VA 23219
(804) 788-2963
Fax: (804) 788-2700

TYPE:
Project/program grants. Grants for specific needs.

See entry 1611 for full listing.

SMITHSONIAN ENVIRONMENTAL RESEARCH CENTER

647 Contees Wharf Road
Edgewater, MD 21037
(443) 482-2217
Fax: (443) 482-2380

E-MAIL ADDRESS:
sercintern@si.edu

WEB SITE ADDRESS:
www.serc.si.
edu/pro_training/internships/internships.aspx

TYPE:
Challenge/matching grants; Fellowships; Internships; Research grants. The Program enables undergraduate and graduate students to work on specific projects under the direction of the Center's professional staff and is tailored to provide the maximum educational benefit to each participant.

Graduate students and undergraduates may conduct independent projects with the approval of the staff member with whom they plan to study.

Subject matter of the projects includes terrestrial and estuarine environmental research within the disciplines of mathematics, chemistry, microbiology, botany, zoology, and environmental education.

Fellowships are offered annually at the postdoctoral, predoctoral and graduate levels.

Internships are offered three times per year at the undergraduate levels, recent graduate, or beginning Master's student.

See entry 2344 for full listing.

SPENCER FOUNDATION   [1698]

625 North Michigan Avenue
Suite 1600
Chicago, IL 60611
(312) 337-7000
Fax: (312) 337-0282

E-MAIL ADDRESS:
abrinkman@spencer.org
fellows@spencer.org

WEB SITE ADDRESS:
www.spencer.org

FOUNDED: 1962

AREAS OF INTEREST:
Research on education as approached from scholars in the sciences, social sciences and humanities.

NAME(S) OF PROGRAMS:
- **Dissertation Fellowship Program**
- **Research Grant Program**

TYPE:
Fellowships; Research grants. Grants for research to expand knowledge and understanding of the problems and processes of education.

YEAR PROGRAM STARTED: 1970

PURPOSE:
To support research that gives promise of yielding new knowledge leading to the improvement of education, broadly defined.

LEGAL BASIS:
Independent foundation.

ELIGIBILITY:
The Foundation is interested in a wide variety of disciplinary and interdisciplinary approaches to the study of education. The principal investigator ordinarily must have an earned Doctorate in an academic discipline or in the field of education and must have an affiliation with a college or university, a research facility, or a cultural institution.

Dissertation Fellowship applicants must be candidates for the doctoral degree at a graduate school within the U.S., though they need not be citizens of the U.S.

FINANCIAL DATA:
Amount of support per award: Varies.
Total amount of support: Approximately $14,000,000 annually.

NUMBER OF APPLICANTS MOST RECENT YEAR:
Approximately 1,000.

REPRESENTATIVE AWARDS:
$40,000 over one year to the University of Wisconsin-Madison, Mary Haywood Metz, for "Models of School Organization: Comparing Understandings of School Organization Grounded in Ethnographics, Survey Research and the Federal 'No Child Left Behind Act';" $300,000 over two years to the University of North Carolina at Chapel Hill, Jill V. Hamm et al., for "Correlations and Consequences of Growth in Mathematics Conceptual Understanding in Middle and High School."

APPLICATION INFORMATION:
Application procedures differ by program. Researchers seeking support should telephone for general program information.
Duration: Varies.
Deadline: Initial research proposals are accepted throughout the year. Dissertation Fellowship applications have an annual deadline each fall.

PUBLICATIONS:
Annual report.

OFFICERS:
Michael McPherson, President

BOARD OF DIRECTORS:
Derek C. Bok, Chairman
Deborah Loewenberg Ball, Vice Chairman
Christopher Jencks
Carol Johnson
Lyle Logan, Sr.
Stephen Raudenbush
Cybele Raver
Richard J. Shavelson
T. Dennis Sullivan

ADDRESS INQUIRIES TO:
Annie Brinkman, Grants Manager
(See address above.)

SUBARU OF AMERICA FOUNDATION, INC.   [1699]
2235 Route 70 West
Cherry Hill, NJ 08002
(856) 488-5099
Fax: (856) 488-3300

E-MAIL ADDRESS:
foundation@subaru.com

WEB SITE ADDRESS:
www.subaru.com

FOUNDED: 1984

AREAS OF INTEREST:
Education for children and youth and environmental stewardship for youth.

TYPE:
General operating grants; Project/program grants. Special programs; Employee matching gift program.

YEAR PROGRAM STARTED: 1984

PURPOSE:
To make a difference in the lives of young people by offering them enrichment and educational programs that support their academic needs.

LEGAL BASIS:
Corporate foundation.

ELIGIBILITY:
Consideration will be given primarily to nonprofit 501(c)(3) organizations in the communities located in and around National Headquarters and in the immediate surrounding areas of regional offices.

The Foundation does not permit contributions to religious, fraternal, veterans' or political associations, individual schools or special events, nor does it make grants to individuals, fund organizations outside the U.S., programs that benefit residents outside the U.S., or consider donation of vehicles.

FINANCIAL DATA:
Amount of support per award: Varies.
Matching fund requirements: Contributions for the matching gift program must be made by Subaru of America employees at a $25 minimum or $2,000 maximum per employee per fiscal year.

APPLICATION INFORMATION:
Application form is available online as a Word document. Grant application and all required supporting documentation must be submitted at the same time as one package and should be mailed to the address above to arrive by the deadline (not postmarked by the deadline). Grant applications with missing information or documentation will not be considered.
Deadline: Educational: April 2; Environmental: July 31.

IRS IDENTIFICATION NUMBER: 22-2531774

STAFF:
Sandra E. Capell, Community Services Manager

ADDRESS INQUIRIES TO:
Sandra E. Capell
Community Services Manager
(See address above.)

TAILHOOK EDUCATIONAL FOUNDATION   [1700]
9696 Business Park Avenue
San Diego, CA 92131
(858) 689-9223
Fax: (858) 578-8839

E-MAIL ADDRESS:
tag@tailhook.net

WEB SITE ADDRESS:
www.tailhook.org

FOUNDED: 1992

AREAS OF INTEREST:
Education.

NAME(S) OF PROGRAMS:
● **Tailhook Educational Foundation Scholarship Award**

TYPE:
Scholarships. The Foundation awards merit-based scholarships.

YEAR PROGRAM STARTED: 1992

PURPOSE:
To support dependents of the Naval Aviation community with their educational needs.

LEGAL BASIS:
501(c)(3).

ELIGIBILITY:
The applicant or the applicant's parent/grandparent/guardian must have served in the U.S. Navy, U.S. Marine Corps, or U.S. Coast Guard as a Naval Aviator, Naval Flight Officer, or Designated Naval Aircrewman, or served on board a U.S. Navy aircraft carrier in any capacity as a member of ship's company or assigned air wing.

GEOGRAPHIC RESTRICTIONS:
United States.

FINANCIAL DATA:
Amount of support per award: $2,000 to $15,000.

NUMBER OF APPLICANTS MOST RECENT YEAR: 285.

NUMBER OF AWARDS: 87.

APPLICATION INFORMATION:
Duration: Multiyear.
Deadline: March 15.

IRS IDENTIFICATION NUMBER: 33-0487778

ADDRESS INQUIRIES TO:
The Tailhook Educational Foundation
P.O. Box 26626
San Diego, CA 92196-0626

TRIANGLE COMMUNITY FOUNDATION   [1701]
324 Blackwell Street, Suite 1220
Durham, NC 27701
(919) 474-8370
Fax: (919) 941-9208

E-MAIL ADDRESS:
libby@trianglecf.org

WEB SITE ADDRESS:
www.trianglecf.org

AREAS OF INTEREST:
Projects of excellence.

TYPE:
Grants-in-aid; Scholarships. General grantmaking.

YEAR PROGRAM STARTED: 1984

PURPOSE:
To expand philanthropy.

ELIGIBILITY:
Organizations, including religious, classified as 501(c)(3) by the IRS can apply. No grants to individuals.

GEOGRAPHIC RESTRICTIONS:
Chatham, Durham, Orange and Wake counties, North Carolina.

FINANCIAL DATA:
Amount of support per award: Minimum $250; Maximum dependent on donor.
Total amount of support: Varies.

APPLICATION INFORMATION:
Application available online.
Duration: Grants are not renewable.

PUBLICATIONS:
Annual report.

ADDRESS INQUIRIES TO:
Libby Richards, Scholarships
and Special Projects Coordinator
(See address above.)

U.S. DEPARTMENT OF EDUCATION   [1702]
Management/Program Analyst
Institute of Education Sciences, Room 602C
555 New Jersey Avenue, N.W.
Washington, DC 20208
(202) 219-1310
Fax: (202) 219-1466

E-MAIL ADDRESS:
Elizabeth.Payer@ed.gov

WEB SITE ADDRESS:
ies.ed.gov

FOUNDED: 1972

AREAS OF INTEREST:
Basic and applied research, evaluations and analyses in education practice and policy.

NAME(S) OF PROGRAMS:
- **National Education Research and Development Centers**

TYPE:
Project/program grants; Research grants. Grants competitions.

Education research and development centers conduct research in teaching, learning, teacher education, reading, writing, education and employment, education for at-risk students, postsecondary teaching and learning, postsecondary governance and finance, state and local policy development and leadership, and evaluation and standards.

PURPOSE:
To help solve problems of American education through both basic and applied research and development activities.

LEGAL BASIS:
Public Law 92-318, as amended.

ELIGIBILITY:
Applicants must be colleges, universities, state departments of education, local education agencies, other public or private profit and nonprofit agencies, organizations, groups and individuals. Support is restricted to basic and applied research, planning studies, evaluations, investigations, experiments and developmental activities directly related to research in the field of education.

Most funds provide continuing support for long-term research and development programs. The remaining funds are used for new projects, announced as Grants Competitions in specific areas of interest.

GEOGRAPHIC RESTRICTIONS:
United States.

FINANCIAL DATA:
Amount of support per award: $1,500,000 average to research centers.
Total amount of support: Varies.

APPLICATION INFORMATION:
Deadline: Varies with grant, but all deadlines fall between March and April.

U.S. DEPARTMENT OF EDUCATION   [1703]
Office of Vocational and Adult Education
550 12th Street, S.W.
Potomac Center Plaza, 11th Floor
Washington, DC 20202-7240
(202) 245-7721
Fax: (202) 245-7171

WEB SITE ADDRESS:
www2.ed.
gov/about/offices/list/ovae/pi/AdultEd/index.
html

FOUNDED: 1965

AREAS OF INTEREST:
Adult basic education, basic literacy skills, English as a second language and adult secondary education.

CONSULTING OR VOLUNTEER SERVICES:
Technical assistance is provided to state educational agencies.

TYPE:
Grants-in-aid. This program provides grants to states to fund local programs of adult education and literacy services, including workplace literacy services, family literacy services, English language learning and integrated English literacy/civics education

programs. Basic grants to all states including the District of Columbia as well as the Virgin Islands, American Samoa, Guam, Northern Mariana Islands and Palau.

YEAR PROGRAM STARTED: 1965

PURPOSE:
To provide educational opportunities for educationally disadvantaged adults.

LEGAL BASIS:
The Adult Education and Family Literacy Act (AEFLA), enacted as Title II of the Workforce Investment Act (WIA) of 1998, is the principal source of federal support for adult basic and literacy education programs for adults who lack basic skills, a high school diploma, or proficiency in English.

ELIGIBILITY:
Individuals and local providers cannot receive grant money directly from the Office of Vocational and Adult Education (OVAE).

Adult education and literacy programs are funded through federal grants to the states. The amount each state receives is based on a formula established by Congress. States, in turn, distribute funds to local eligible entities to provide adult education and literacy services.

The Division provides assistance to states to improve program quality and capacity.

GEOGRAPHIC RESTRICTIONS:
United States and its territories.

FINANCIAL DATA:
AEFLA funds are distributed by formula to states using census data on the number of adults (ages 16 and older) in each state who lack a high school diploma and who are not enrolled in school. States must match 25% of the federal contribution with state or local funds, but many states contribute considerably more.
Amount of support per award: Varies.
Matching fund requirements: 25% of grant award.

NUMBER OF APPLICANTS MOST RECENT YEAR:
57.

NUMBER OF AWARDS: 57.

APPLICATION INFORMATION:
Applicants interested in participating in the State-Administered Program should contact the appropriate state educational agency for information.
Duration: One year and continuing based on appropriations.

ADDRESS INQUIRIES TO:
Office of Vocational and Adult Education
(See address above.)

U.S. DEPARTMENT OF EDUCATION   [1704]
Office of English Language Acquisition, Language Enhancement and Academic Achievement
LBJ Education Building, Room 5C-132, MS-6510
400 Maryland Avenue, S.W.
Washington, DC 20202
(202) 401-1402
(202) 401-1436
Fax: (202) 260-5496

E-MAIL ADDRESS:
oela@ed.gov

WEB SITE ADDRESS:
www.ed.gov/offices/oela

AREAS OF INTEREST:
English language acquisition, language enhancement and academic achievement for Limited English Proficient (LEP) children.

NAME(S) OF PROGRAMS:
- **Foreign Language Assistance Program - LEA Grants**
- **Foreign Language Assistance Program - SEA Grants**
- **National Professional Development Program**
- **Native American and Alaska Native Children in School Program**

TYPE:
Formula grants. Foreign Language Assistance Program - LEA Grants: This program provides grants to establish, improve or expand innovative foreign language programs for elementary and secondary school students.

Foreign Language Assistance Program - SEA Grants: This program provides grants to establish, improve or expand innovative foreign language programs for elementary and secondary school students.

National Professional Development Program: This program provides professional development activities intended to improve instruction for students with limited English proficiency (LEP) and assists education personnel working with such children to meet high professional standards.

Native American and Alaska Native Children in School Program: This program provides grants to eligible entities that support language instruction education projects for limited English proficient (LEP) children from Native American, Alaska Native, native Hawaiian, and Pacific Islander backgrounds. The program is designed to ensure that LEP children master English and meet the same rigorous standards for academic achievement that all children are expected to meet. Funds may support the study of Native American languages.

YEAR PROGRAM STARTED: 1968

LEGAL BASIS:
Elementary and Secondary Education Act of 1965, as amended by No Child Left Behind Act of 2001.

ELIGIBILITY:
Foreign Language Assistance Program - LEA Grants: In awarding grants under this program, the Secretary of Education supports projects that: (a) show the promise of being continued beyond their project period and; (b) demonstrate approaches that can be disseminated and duplicated by other LEAs.

Foreign Language Assistance Program - SEA Grants: In awarding grants under this program, the Secretary of Education supports projects that promote systemic approaches to improving foreign language learning in the state.

National Professional Development Program: Institutions of higher education in consortia with local education agencies or state education agencies may apply.

Native American and Alaska Native Children in School Program: Entities that operate the following kinds of elementary, secondary and postsecondary schools primarily for Native American children (including Alaska Native children) are eligible applicants under this program:
(1) Indian tribes;

(2) tribally sanctioned educational authorities;
(3) Native Hawaiian or Native American Pacific Islander native language educational organizations;
(4) elementary schools or secondary schools that are operated or funded by the Bureau of Indian Affairs (BIA), or a consortium of such schools;
(5) elementary schools or secondary schools operated under a contract with or grant from the BIA in consortium with another such school or a tribal or community organization and;
(6) elementary schools or secondary schools operated by the BIA and an institution of higher education (IHE), in consortium with elementary schools or secondary schools operated under a contract with or a grant from the BIA or a tribal or community organization.

GEOGRAPHIC RESTRICTIONS:
United States and its Commonwealths and territories.

STAFF:
Cynthia Ryan, Division Director

ADDRESS INQUIRIES TO:
Foreign Language Assistance Programs - (LEA and SEA Grants) :
Rebecca Richey
Tel: (202) 402-1443

National Professional Development Program:
Cynthia Ryan
Tel: (202) 401-1436

Native American and Alaska Native Children in School Program:
Trini Torres-Carrion
Tel: (202) 401-1445

U.S. DEPARTMENT OF STATE, FULBRIGHT TEACHER EXCHANGE PROGRAM   [1705]
c/o Academy for Educational Development
1825 Connecticut Avenue, N.W.
Washington, DC 20009-5721
(202) 884-8228

E-MAIL ADDRESS:
fulbrightcte@aed.org

WEB SITE ADDRESS:
www.fulbrightteacherexchange.org

FOUNDED: 1946

AREAS OF INTEREST:
All subjects, including mathematics, science, English, English as a Second Language (ESL), foreign language and history. Subject and grade levels vary with each country.

NAME(S) OF PROGRAMS:
● **Fulbright Teacher Exchange Program**

TYPE:
Exchange programs; Travel grants.

YEAR PROGRAM STARTED: 1946

PURPOSE:
To increase mutual understanding between the people of the U.S. and the people of other countries through the funding of teacher and administrator exchanges.

LEGAL BASIS:
Mutual Educational and Cultural Exchange Act (Fulbright Hays Act) of 1961.

ELIGIBILITY:
Applicants must meet the following general requirements:
(1) current full-time teaching position;
(2) three years full-time teaching experience;

(3) U.S. citizenship;
(4) Bachelor's degree or higher and;
(5) English language fluency.

In addition, applicants must meet the specific subject and level requirements of the countries to which they apply. For some countries, fluency in the host country's language is required. Country-specific requirements are detailed in the application booklet.

FINANCIAL DATA:
In most cases, the U.S. teacher secures a leave of absence with pay from his or her home institution (as does the foreign teacher). Exchange grants include a summer orientation program and includes round-trip transportation for grantee only.
Amount of support per award: Varies.
Total amount of support: Varies.

APPLICATION INFORMATION:
Applications are available online.
Duration: Most programs last one academic year. Semester-long programs in India and the U.K.
Deadline: October 15 of the year preceding the grant year.

PUBLICATIONS:
Application booklet.

STAFF:
Stephen Money, Program Officer
Shenandoah Sampson, Program Officer

ADDRESS INQUIRIES TO:
See e-mail address above.

*SPECIAL STIPULATIONS:
All programs are tentative and are subject to the availability of funds.

UNIVERSITY OF MANITOBA   [1706]
Faculty of Graduate Studies
500 University Centre
Winnipeg MB R3T 2N2 Canada
(204) 474-9836
Fax: (204) 474-7553

E-MAIL ADDRESS:
marcia_yoshida@umanitoba.ca

WEB SITE ADDRESS:
www.umanitoba.
ca/faculties/graduate_studies/awards

AREAS OF INTEREST:
Teaching and cutting edge research.

NAME(S) OF PROGRAMS:
● **University of Manitoba Graduate Fellowships**

TYPE:
Fellowships. Any discipline taught at graduate level at the university.

PURPOSE:
To reward academic excellence.

ELIGIBILITY:
At the time of application, students do not need to have been accepted by the department or faculty, but at the time of taking up the award must be regular full-time graduate students who have been admitted to and registered in advanced degree programmes, e.g., Master's or Ph.D., but not pre-Master's in any field of study or faculty of the University of Manitoba. Students beyond the second year in the Master's programme or beyond the fourth year in the Ph.D. programme are not eligible to apply

for or hold a University of Manitoba Fellowship. Part-time Ph.D. students enrolled for a four-year course will be eligible for two years of funding.

FINANCIAL DATA:
Amount of support per award: $16,000 for Ph.D.; $12,000 for Master's.

APPLICATION INFORMATION:
Applicant must request application forms from the department to which they are applying at the University of Manitoba and must be returned to that department. Forms are available beginning in December.
Deadline: February 1, with earlier departmental deadlines.

ADDRESS INQUIRIES TO:
Marcia Yoshida, Awards Officer
(See address above.)

THE UNIVERSITY OF SYDNEY   [1707]
Scholarships Office
Level 5, Jane Foss Russell Building G02
The University of Sydney N.S.W. 2006
Australia
(02) 8627 8112
Fax: (02) 8627 8145

E-MAIL ADDRESS:
research.training@sydney.edu.au

WEB SITE ADDRESS:
www.sydney.edu.au/scholarships/research

FOUNDED: 1850

AREAS OF INTEREST:
Veterinary science and diseases of domestic animals.

NAME(S) OF PROGRAMS:
● **Lionel Lonsdale Clinical Fellowship**

TYPE:
Fellowships. Awarded for research and training in the diseases of domestic animals and their treatment in the University Veterinary Centre.

YEAR PROGRAM STARTED: 1977

LEGAL BASIS:
University.

ELIGIBILITY:
Open to graduates in veterinary science who are candidates for the Master of Veterinary Clinical Studies or for the degree of Ph.D. at the University of Sydney.

FINANCIAL DATA:
Amount of support per award: $22,860 (AUD) per annum for the year 2011.

NUMBER OF AWARDS: Offered as funds are available.

APPLICATION INFORMATION:
Duration: Master level: Two years; Ph.D. level: Three years.
Deadline: As advertised, when funds are available.

ADDRESS INQUIRIES TO:
The Faculty of Veterinary Science
The University of Sydney
N.S.W. 2006 Australia
Tel: (02) 9351 2441
Fax: (02) 9351 3056
E-mail: lee@vetsci.usyd.edu.au

*PLEASE NOTE:
Very few awards are available, and competition for them is extremely keen. They are awarded strictly on academic merit and

only graduates with First Class Honours or equivalent qualifications (e.g., graduation magna cum laude) will be considered.

VIETNOW NATIONAL   [1708]
1835 Broadway
Rockford, IL 61104
(815) 227-5100
Fax: (815) 227-5127

E-MAIL ADDRESS:
nationalhq@vietnow.com

WEB SITE ADDRESS:
www.vietnow.com

AREAS OF INTEREST:
Veterans.

TYPE:
Scholarships.

PURPOSE:
To provide financial assistance to college students of VietNow members.

ELIGIBILITY:
Applicant must be a child of a full member of VietNow.

FINANCIAL DATA:
Amount of support per award: Up to $2,000.
Total amount of support: Varies.

APPLICATION INFORMATION:
Contact the Organization for application procedures.
Duration: One year. Renewal by reapplication.
Deadline: April 1.

ADDRESS INQUIRIES TO:
Eileen Shoemaker, Executive Assistant, or Scholarship Committee
(See address above.)

DENNIS & PHYLLIS WASHINGTON FOUNDATION
P.O. Box 16630
Missoula, MT 59808
(406) 523-1300
Fax: (406) 523-1399

WEB SITE ADDRESS:
www.dpwfoundation.org

TYPE:
Project/program grants; Scholarships. Scholarship monies awarded to Montana's nine colleges and universities and seven Indian reservations.

See entry 1490 for full listing.

FRED B. AND RUTH B. ZIGLER FOUNDATION   [1709]
P.O. Box 986
Jennings, LA 70546-0986
(337) 824-2413
Fax: (337) 824-2414

E-MAIL ADDRESS:
frzigler@bellsouth.net

WEB SITE ADDRESS:
www.ziglerfoundation.org

AREAS OF INTEREST:
Education.

TYPE:
Project/program grants; Scholarships.

PURPOSE:
To benefit Jefferson-Davis Parish area.

LEGAL BASIS:
Private foundation.

ELIGIBILITY:
Grants are made to organizations that have tax-exempt status under Section 501(c)(3) of the Internal Revenue Code. No grants are made to individuals.

GEOGRAPHIC RESTRICTIONS:
Jefferson-Davis Parish area, Louisiana.

FINANCIAL DATA:
Amount of support per award: $10,000.
Total amount of support: $380,000 for the year 2010.

NUMBER OF AWARDS: 30 for the year 2010.

APPLICATION INFORMATION:
Applicants must submit a brief letter outlining the purpose of the grant.
Duration: Up to four years.
Deadline: 30 days prior to the Board meeting. The Board meets every other month starting in January.

ADDRESS INQUIRIES TO:
Julie Berry, President
(See address above.)

Elementary and secondary education

ALTMAN FOUNDATION
521 Fifth Avenue
35th Floor
New York, NY 10175
(212) 682-0970

WEB SITE ADDRESS:
www.altmanfoundation.org

TYPE:
Project/program grants.

See entry 1238 for full listing.

THE LOUIS CALDER FOUNDATION
175 Elm Street
New Canaan, CT 06840
(203) 966-8925
Fax: (203) 966-5785

E-MAIL ADDRESS:
proposals@calderfdn.org

WEB SITE ADDRESS:
www.louiscalderfdn.org

TYPE:
Capital grants; Project/program grants. Curriculum development.

See entry 1177 for full listing.

SAMUEL N. AND MARY CASTLE FOUNDATION   [1710]
733 Bishop Street, Suite 1275
Honolulu, HI 96813
(808) 522-1101
Fax: (808) 522-1103

E-MAIL ADDRESS:
snandmarycastle@hawaii.rr.com

WEB SITE ADDRESS:
foundationcenter.org/grantmaker/castle

FOUNDED: 1894

AREAS OF INTEREST:
Early education and childcare, elementary education to grade 3, cultural arts, and human services for children.

CONSULTING OR VOLUNTEER SERVICES:
Castle colleagues training for directors of early childhood centers.

TYPE:
Capital grants; Challenge/matching grants; Project/program grants.

YEAR PROGRAM STARTED: 1894

PURPOSE:
To support training for early childhood education professionals; to support early education, preschools, K-three schools, K-12 Christian schools, and select higher education programs in teacher training; to support select arts and culture projects.

LEGAL BASIS:
Private family foundation.

GEOGRAPHIC RESTRICTIONS:
Hawaii.

FINANCIAL DATA:
Amount of support per award: Typically $5,000 to $250,000.
Total amount of support: $1,568,909 for the year 2010.
Matching fund requirements: Varies.

NUMBER OF APPLICANTS MOST RECENT YEAR: 280.

NUMBER OF AWARDS: 55.

REPRESENTATIVE AWARDS:
$100,000 to Seabury Hall; $100,000 to Mission Houses Museum; $25,000 to Star of the Sea Early Learning Center.

APPLICATION INFORMATION:
The applicant organization should review the Foundation's priorities and policies to determine whether it is eligible to be considered for funding and whether the type of activity proposed is in one of the Foundation's funding areas. Applicants are required to contact the Foundation's Executive Director by letter, e-mail, phone or personal visit before making fund application.

Proposals may be hand delivered or mailed and should include the following:
(1) proposal (one copy);
(2) one copy of each of the additional materials as defined on the Foundation's web site (e.g. IRS determination letter, audited financial statements);
(3) one- to two-page executive summary (two copies);
(4) budget (two copies) and;
(5) Board of Directors list (two copies).

Organizations which have submitted their charters, bylaws and 501(c)(3) may submit complete applications by e-mail attachment.

Applicant organizations should not bind their proposals or submit videos or other items which have not been requested by the Foundation.
Duration: One year. Renewal possible up to three years.
Deadline: February 1, June 1 and October 1.

PUBLICATIONS:
Annual report.

BOARD OF TRUSTEES:
Randy Moore, President
James C. McIntosh, Vice President
Alfred L. Castle, Treasurer and Executive Director
Cynthia Quisenberry, Secretary

ADDRESS INQUIRIES TO:
Alfred L. Castle, Executive Director
(See address above.)

HUGH AND HAZEL DARLING FOUNDATION

500 South Grand Avenue, 19th Floor
Los Angeles, CA 90071
(213) 683-5200
Fax: (213) 627-7795

TYPE:
Block grants; Capital grants;
Challenge/matching grants; Scholarships;
Training grants.

See entry 1742 for full listing.

FIRSTENERGY [1711]

76 South Main Street
Akron, OH 44308
(330) 384-5022
Fax: (330) 761-4203

E-MAIL ADDRESS:
delores.jones@firstenergycorp.com

WEB SITE ADDRESS:
www.firstenergycorp.com/community

AREAS OF INTEREST:
Mathematics, science and technology
education.

NAME(S) OF PROGRAMS:
• **Mathematics, Science and Technology
Education Grants Program**

TYPE:
Project/program grants. Project/program
grants primarily in the classroom setting.

YEAR PROGRAM STARTED: 1985

PURPOSE:
To encourage education in mathematics, the
sciences and technology.

ELIGIBILITY:
Educators (grades preK-12) and youth group
leaders in the service areas of FirstEnergy
and communities where FirstEnergy has
facilities are encouraged to apply. Any
creative project dealing with mathematics,
science and technology is eligible. Projects
that involve students directly, incorporate
matching funds, community resources,
interdisciplinary or team-teaching and involve
various age groups are preferred. Teacher
training projects are highly favored.
Completed projects or those previously
funded are not eligible.

GEOGRAPHIC RESTRICTIONS:
Maryland, New Jersey, Ohio, Pennsylvania
and West Virginia.

FINANCIAL DATA:
Grants may be used to compensate experts
who come to work with the students, but not
to pay teachers or staff.
Amount of support per award: $500
maximum.
Total amount of support: Varies.

APPLICATION INFORMATION:
Submission must be filed on the appropriate
application form. Contact the External Affairs
Manager at your FirstEnergy office or the
Community Initiatives Department of
FirstEnergy at the address listed above. A
downloadable application is available online.
Duration: One school year.
Deadline: Usually third week in September.

PUBLICATIONS:
Bright Ideas for Educators.

ADDRESS INQUIRIES TO:
Community Initiatives Department
(See address above.)

*SPECIAL STIPULATIONS:
Grants are only available to schools or
groups in the FirstEnergy service area or in
communities where it has facilities.

CHARLES HAYDEN FOUNDATION

140 Broadway, 51st Floor
New York, NY 10005
(212) 785-3677
Fax: (212) 785-3689

E-MAIL ADDRESS:
fdn@chf.org

WEB SITE ADDRESS:
www.charleshaydenfoundation.org

TYPE:
Capital grants; Challenge/matching grants;
Project/program grants. Grant priorities focus
on institutions and programs primarily
serving youth at risk of not reaching their
full potential, especially youth in low-income
communities. Support is provided for youth
development programs, charter schools,
independent and parochial schools, and
informal educational enrichment programs in
institutions such as zoos, museums or
libraries.

See entry 1198 for full listing.

HOWARD HUGHES MEDICAL INSTITUTE [1712]

Office of Science Education
Precollege and Undergraduate Grants
4000 Jones Bridge Road
Chevy Chase, MD 20815-6789
(301) 215-8818
Fax: (301) 215-8888

E-MAIL ADDRESS:
grantprc@hhmi.org

WEB SITE ADDRESS:
www.hhmi.org/grants

FOUNDED: 1953

AREAS OF INTEREST:
Precollege and undergraduate science
education.

NAME(S) OF PROGRAMS:
• **Precollege and Undergraduate Science
Education Program**

TYPE:
Project/program grants. Offered to leverage
the resources of science-based organizations.

YEAR PROGRAM STARTED: 1992

PURPOSE:
To leverage the resources of science-based
organizations in order to increase science
literacy among children and the general
population.

LEGAL BASIS:
Medical research organization.

ELIGIBILITY:
Most awards are made through national
competitions in which selected institutions
are invited to submit proposals according to
prescribed criteria.

GEOGRAPHIC RESTRICTIONS:
United States and its territories.

FINANCIAL DATA:
Total amount of support: Varies.

NUMBER OF APPLICANTS MOST RECENT YEAR:
Varies by initiative.

NUMBER OF AWARDS: 2.

REPRESENTATIVE AWARDS:
$50,000 to University of Mississippi Medical
Center, Jackson, MS.

APPLICATION INFORMATION:
Required forms will be issued by the Institute
when new competitions are announced.
Applications by invitation only.
Duration: Two years.

PUBLICATIONS:
Program announcement.

IRS IDENTIFICATION NUMBER: 59-0735717

OFFICERS:
Robert Tjian, Ph.D., President
Craig A. Alexander, Vice President and
General Counsel
Sean Carroll, Ph.D., Vice President for
Grants and Special Programs
Jack E. Dixon, Ph.D., Vice President and
Chief Scientific Officer
Mohamoud Jibrell, Vice President for
Information Technology
Avice A. Meehan, Vice President for
Communications and Public Affairs
Edward J. Palmerino, Vice President for
Finance and Treasurer
Gerald M. Rubin, Ph.D., Vice President and
Director, Janelia Farm Research Campus
Landis P. Zimmerman, Vice President and
Chief Investment Officer

ADDRESS INQUIRIES TO:
Deb Felix, Senior Program Officer
Precollege and Undergraduate Grants
(See address above.)

INVESTED [1713]

911 Eighth Avenue North
Seattle, WA 98109
(206) 352-1199
Fax: (206) 352-1203

E-MAIL ADDRESS:
support@invested.org

WEB SITE ADDRESS:
www.invested.org

FOUNDED: 1963

AREAS OF INTEREST:
Secondary education and personal needs for
disadvantaged students.

NAME(S) OF PROGRAMS:
• **InvestED School Fund Program**

TYPE:
Grants-in-aid; Matching gifts.

YEAR PROGRAM STARTED: 1963

PURPOSE:
To support middle and senior high school aid
program providing for grants to both
accredited public and private schools (grades
6-12) within the state of Washington to
enable these schools to assist individual
students who have needs their families
cannot afford.

LEGAL BASIS:
Public charity.

ELIGIBILITY:
Grants are restricted to a program aiding
students in Washington state secondary
schools. Check web site to confirm if "new"
schools are being accepted.

GEOGRAPHIC RESTRICTIONS:
Washington state.

FINANCIAL DATA:
Amount of support per award: $200 to more than $5,500 per school.

Total amount of support: $356,528 for the year 2010.

APPLICATION INFORMATION:
School must submit year-end report May 1 to June 30 to be eligible for grant the following year.

Duration: One year. Renewable.

Deadline: June 30.

IRS IDENTIFICATION NUMBER: 23-7189670

DIRECTORS:
Dan Barritt, President
Kate Janeway, Vice President
Emory Bundy
Paul Condrat
Nancy Fike
Hon. Betty B. Fletcher
Tom Gleason
Danner Graves
Joel Groen
Pamela J. Hughes
Paul Ishii
Jim Menzies
George Moynihan
Martin Need
Roger Percy
Tom Rath
Lisa Schaures
Steven Sherman
Debbie Williams

ADDRESS INQUIRIES TO:
Executive Director
(See address above.)

MARTHA HOLDEN JENNINGS FOUNDATION   [1714]

The Halle Building
1228 Euclid Avenue, Suite 710
Cleveland, OH 44115-1811
(216) 589-5700
Fax: (216) 589-5730

WEB SITE ADDRESS:
www.mhjf.org

FOUNDED: 1959

AREAS OF INTEREST:
Elementary and secondary education.

NAME(S) OF PROGRAMS:
● **Grants-to-Educators Program**
● **Open Grants**

TYPE:
Project/program grants. Project/program grants are for education only. Support to aide the improvement of elementary and secondary public school education in Ohio.

YEAR PROGRAM STARTED: 1959

PURPOSE:
To foster the development of individual capabilities of young people to the maximum extent through improving the quality of teaching in secular primary and secondary schools; to provide a means for greater accomplishment on the part of Ohio's teachers by encouraging creativity in teaching and bringing greater recognition to the teaching profession.

LEGAL BASIS:
Nonprofit foundation.

ELIGIBILITY:
For Grants-to-Educators, applicants must be teachers or public school administrators. For other grants, applicants must be tax-exempt with 501(c)(3) status from the IRS.

Open Grants are available to any public school district, nonreligious private school working with public schools, or tax-exempt organization that assists elementary and secondary schools in Ohio. No grants for capital improvements or graduate study, and generally no grants for equipment or travel.

GEOGRAPHIC RESTRICTIONS:
Ohio.

FINANCIAL DATA:
Amount of support per award:
Grants-to-Educators: Up to $3,000; Open Grants: Varies depending on needs and nature of the request. Average $12,000.

Total amount of support: $3,860,000 for the year 2010.

NUMBER OF AWARDS: 431 for the year 2010.

REPRESENTATIVE AWARDS:
$6,560 to River Valley Local Schools for Transforming Student Instruction; $9,000 to Clermont County ESC for Process-Oriented Guided-Inquiry Program; $15,880 to Kent State University Foundation for Math Academy.

APPLICATION INFORMATION:
For Grants-to-Educators, specific application forms are required. The original application form, signed by the superintendent, and nine copies need to be submitted. The application forms can be found on the Foundation's web site.

The Foundation has established the following six categories within the Open Grants program. Applicants must indicate the particular grant category for which they are seeking funds:
(1) improving learning in math, science and technology;
(2) improving language literacy;
(3) improving learning in the arts;
(4) supporting the recruitment, retention and development of teachers;
(5) strengthening teachers' and administrators' leadership skills and;
(6) providing other services to students (e.g., citizenship education, character education, early intervention, special needs and transition to college or work).

For grant proposals, there is no prescribed form for applications. Only the original grant proposal should be submitted for consideration. The following items must be included with all grant proposals:
(1) a one-page cover letter on the organization's letterhead, signed by the chief executive of the organization requesting funds;
(2) a one-page executive summary of the proposed project including which grant category the proposal addresses; include program coordinator contact information;
(3) no more than a six-page detailed proposal in as brief a form as possible giving the amount requested, the specific purpose, its need, plan of action, and projected outcomes, the number of participants, schools, etc., to be involved; if applicable, the sources of other funding for this specific project (a copy of applicant organization's financial audit or list of trustees not needed);
(4) a detailed one-page budget for the entire project specific to the Foundation, indicating

how the requested funds would be used and, if other funds will be used to support the project, their amount and source; include narrative description of budget items;
(5) in the case of institutions that propose to provide services to schools, a letter indicating a need for the services and support for the project signed by the superintendent of schools of the targeted district;
(6) grant requests must not exceed 10 pages and;
(7) a copy of the organization's IRS ruling; only organizations exempt from tax under Section 501(c)(3) may be considered for grants. (No IRS ruling is needed for public schools.) The IRS ruling is not considered part of the 10-page maximum.

Duration: One year. Proposal may be resubmitted for a second or third year.

Deadline: Proposals should be in by the 20th of the month preceding the month in which they are to be considered.

PUBLICATIONS:
Guidelines; *Pro-Excellentia*.

STAFF:
Dr. William T. Hiller, Executive Director

ADDRESS INQUIRIES TO:
Chairperson, Distribution Committee
(See address above.)

LOUIS G. KAUFMAN ENDOWMENT FUND   [1715]

c/o Wells Fargo Bank
101 West Washington Street
Marquette, MI 49855
(906) 228-1244
Fax: (906) 228-1479

TYPE:
Project/program grants.

PURPOSE:
To provide benefits for the children of Marquette schools.

LEGAL BASIS:
Trust fund.

ELIGIBILITY:
Eligible organizations must be IRS 501(c)(3) tax-exempt.

GEOGRAPHIC RESTRICTIONS:
Marquette, Michigan.

FINANCIAL DATA:
Amount of support per award: $250 to $50,000.

Total amount of support: Varies.

APPLICATION INFORMATION:
Applicants may send a letter with a copy of the IRS tax determination letter and the budget. Applicants must demonstrate how the proposal benefits youth of the Marquette area.

Duration: One year. Renewal possible.

Deadline: May 1.

ADDRESS INQUIRIES TO:
Michael Kolasa, Trust Administrator
(See address above.)

*SPECIAL STIPULATIONS:
Funds are only for youth of the Marquette, Michigan area.

KLINGENSTEIN CENTER FOR INDEPENDENT SCHOOL LEADERSHIP [1716]

Teachers College, Columbia University
525 West 120th Street, Box 125
New York, NY 10027-6696
(212) 678-3156
Fax: (212) 678-3254

E-MAIL ADDRESS:
klingenstein@tc.columbia.edu

WEB SITE ADDRESS:
www.klingenstein.org

FOUNDED: 1977

AREAS OF INTEREST:
Leadership development for independent education.

NAME(S) OF PROGRAMS:
- **Klingenstein Heads Program**
- **Klingenstein Summer Institute**
- **Master's Degree in Educational Leadership**

TYPE:
Scholarships. The Klingenstein Heads Program gathers heads of independent schools from throughout the nation and the world for two weeks of intensive study among professional peers.

The Klingenstein Summer Institute gathers teachers in the beginning years of their careers for an exploration of teaching styles, educational philosophies and issues, and personal development.

The Master's Degree in Educational Leadership, with a focus in private school leadership, gathers independent school teachers and administrators for a rigorous degree program. The Leadership Academy is the two-summer version of the full-time degree program. The majority of students get generous tuition scholarships.

YEAR PROGRAM STARTED: 1978

PURPOSE:
To draw attention to outstanding leadership.

LEGAL BASIS:
Private foundation.

ELIGIBILITY:
Teachers and administrators working in an independent school with a nondiscriminatory admissions policy are eligible to apply. All programs are open to international applicants.

FINANCIAL DATA:
Some programs offer tuition and stipend. All programs offer tuition funding.
Amount of support per award: Varies.

APPLICATION INFORMATION:
Applicant must submit application, autobiographical information and recommendations from sponsoring school.
Duration: Varies.
Deadline: Summer Institute and Master's Degree: January 15; Klingenstein Heads: May 1; Leadership Academy: November 1 of even-numbered years.

ADDRESS INQUIRIES TO:
Assistant Director
(See address above.)

MEBANE CHARITABLE FOUNDATION, INC.

232 South Main Street
Mocksville, NC 27028
(336) 936-0041
Fax: (336) 936-0038

E-MAIL ADDRESS:
lcolbourne@mebanefoundation.com

WEB SITE ADDRESS:
www.mebanefoundation.com

TYPE:
Endowments.

See entry 1207 for full listing.

MITSUBISHI ELECTRIC AMERICA FOUNDATION [1717]

1560 Wilson Boulevard
Suite 1150
Arlington, VA 22209
(703) 276-8240
Fax: (703) 276-8260

E-MAIL ADDRESS:
mea.foundation@meus.mea.com

WEB SITE ADDRESS:
www.meaf.org

FOUNDED: 1991

AREAS OF INTEREST:
People with disabilities, including education, employment, independence and community inclusion.

TYPE:
Demonstration grants; General operating grants; Internships; Matching gifts; Project/program grants; Seed money grants; Technical assistance; Training grants. Grants are offered to make a better world for all by helping young people with disabilities to maximize their potential and participation in society.

YEAR PROGRAM STARTED: 1991

PURPOSE:
To help young people with disabilities maximize their potential and participation in society.

LEGAL BASIS:
Foundation.

ELIGIBILITY:
Applicants must meet criteria as stated in foundation guidelines brochure. Priority given to applicants in communities where MEUS facilities are located.

GEOGRAPHIC RESTRICTIONS:
United States.

FINANCIAL DATA:
Amount of support per award: Average: $30,000.
Total amount of support: $483,980 for the year 2009.

NUMBER OF APPLICANTS MOST RECENT YEAR:
300.

NUMBER OF AWARDS: 9 for the year 2009.

REPRESENTATIVE AWARDS:
$93,000 to American Association of People with Disabilities to expand its Congressional internship program; $100,000 to Girls Scouts of the USA for an Include All Girls initiative; $200,000 to Kids Included Together to promote the development of inclusive programming in after-school programs.

APPLICATION INFORMATION:
Submit a two-page concept paper including a budget summary and description of the need and objectives for the funds requested. Instructions for full proposals will be sent after initial screening. Concept papers are reviewed throughout the year.

Applicants are requested not to telephone the Foundation during the application process.
Duration: One to three years. Renewal possible on a case-by-case basis.
Deadline: June 1 to be considered for following year funding.

PUBLICATIONS:
Annual report; guidelines.

BOARD OF DIRECTORS:
Roger Barna
Cayce Blanchard
Bruce Brenizer
Veronica Clark
Mike DeLano
Jack Greaf
LaShetha Hayes
Yasushi Moriyama
Perry Pappous
David Rebmann
Katsuya Takamia
Susumu Ujino
Dick Waters
Kenichiro Yamanishi

ADDRESS INQUIRIES TO:
Kevin R. Webb, Director
(See address above.)

NATIONAL ENDOWMENT FOR THE HUMANITIES

1100 Pennsylvania Avenue, N.W.
Room 510
Washington, DC 20506
(202) 606-8400
Fax: (202) 606-8240

E-MAIL ADDRESS:
info@neh.gov

WEB SITE ADDRESS:
www.neh.gov

TYPE:
Conferences/seminars. Grants support summer seminars and national institutes in the humanities for college and school teachers. These faculty development activities are conducted at colleges and universities across the country. Lists of pending seminars and institutes are available from the program.

See entry 416 for full listing.

NATIONAL SCIENCE FOUNDATION [1718]

Division of Research on Learning in Formal and Informal Settings
4201 Wilson Boulevard, Suite 885
Arlington, VA 22230
(703) 292-8620
Fax: (703) 292-9044; (703) 292-9046

E-MAIL ADDRESS:
acarroll@nsf.gov

WEB SITE ADDRESS:
www.nsf.gov

FOUNDED: 1950

AREAS OF INTEREST:
Science, mathematics, technology education content; pedagogy; applied research; development of resources and tools for instruction, assessment, evaluation and informal science.

NAME(S) OF PROGRAMS:
- **Advanced Learning Technologies (ALT)**
- **Advanced Technological Education**
- **Communicating Research to Public Audiences**

- **Discovery Research K-12 (DR-K12)**
- **Informal Science Education (ISE)**
- **Innovative Technology Experiences for Students and Teachers (ITEST)**
- **Research and Evaluation on Education in Science and Engineering (REESE)**

TYPE:
Conferences/seminars; Demonstration grants; Development grants; Project/program grants; Research grants; Training grants. Through the Advanced Learning Technologies (ALT) program, the CISE and EHR Directorates of NSF support research that (1) enables radical improvements in learning through innovative computer and information technologies, and (2) advances research in computer science, information technology, learning and cognitive science through the unique challenges posed by learning environments and learning technology platforms.

With an emphasis on two-year colleges, the Advanced Technological Education (ATE) program focuses on the education of technicians for the high-technology fields that drive the nation's economy.

Communicating Research to Public Audiences is a component of the Informal Science Education program (ISE) in the Division of Elementary, Secondary, and Informal Education. ISE projects provide rich and stimulating contexts and experiences for individuals of all ages, interests and backgrounds to increase their appreciation for, and understanding of, science, technology, engineering and mathematics (STEM) in out-of-school settings.

Discovery Research K-12 (DR-K12) funds research, development and evaluation activities through knowledge generation and application to improve K-12 learning and teaching.

Informal Science Education (ISE) program invests in projects that develop and implement informal learning experiences designed to increase interest, engagement and understanding of science, technology, engineering and mathematics (STEM) by individuals of all ages and backgrounds, as well as projects that advance knowledge and practice of informal science education.

Innovative Technology Experiences for Students and Teachers (ITEST) is designed to increase the opportunities for students and teachers to learn about, experience, and use information technologies within the context of science, technology, engineering and mathematics (STEM), including Information Technology (IT) courses. It is in direct response to the concern about shortages of information technology workers in the U.S.

Research and Evaluation on Education in Science and Engineering (REESE) supports basic and applied research and evaluation that enhances science, technology, engineering and mathematics (STEM) learning and teaching.

PURPOSE:
To promote quality programs of education in mathematics, science and technology for all the nation's youth, and informal learning opportunities in these fields for youth and adults.

LEGAL BASIS:
The National Science Foundation Act of 1950, Public Law 81-507, as amended.

GEOGRAPHIC RESTRICTIONS:
United States.

FINANCIAL DATA:
Amount of support per award: Grants vary in amount, depending upon the needs and nature of the request and availability of funds.
Total amount of support: $180,000,000.

NUMBER OF APPLICANTS MOST RECENT YEAR:
Estimated 800.

NUMBER OF AWARDS: Estimated 200.

APPLICATION INFORMATION:
Duration: One to five years.
Deadline: Varies.

THE RADIANT PEACE FOUNDATION INTERNATIONAL, INC.   [1719]
P.O. Box 40822
St. Petersburg, FL 33743-0822
(727) 343-8212
Fax: (727) 343-8212

E-MAIL ADDRESS:
radiantpeaceintl@gmail.com

WEB SITE ADDRESS:
www.radiantpeace.org

FOUNDED: 1986

NAME(S) OF PROGRAMS:
- **Radiant Peace Education Awards**

TYPE:
Awards/prizes. Recognizes and awards children, teachers and schools for Radiant Peace essays, art, projects, and videos.

YEAR PROGRAM STARTED: 1990

PURPOSE:
To inspire, promote and encourage Radiant Peace worldwide.

LEGAL BASIS:
A 501(c)(3) nonprofit educational organization.

ELIGIBILITY:
All students grades one-12 including home schools and youth groups.

FINANCIAL DATA:
Amount of support per award: $25 to $500.
Total amount of support: Varies by year.

NUMBER OF AWARDS: Varies.

APPLICATION INFORMATION:
Invitations and guidelines posted online.
Deadline: December and April.

ADDRESS INQUIRIES TO:
Office Manager
(See address above.)

THE ROCHE FOUNDATION   [1720]
340 Kingsland Street
Nutley, NJ 07110-1199
(973) 562-2055
Fax: (973) 562-2999

WEB SITE ADDRESS:
www.rocheusa.com

FOUNDED: 1945

AREAS OF INTEREST:
Math and science education (K-12), health education and health promotion (not medical delivery).

ELIGIBILITY:
Contributions will be made only to domestic, nonprofit charitable and IRS 501(c)(3)

organizations engaged in programs in the areas of health and education, in communities where Roche has a significant presence and interest.

GEOGRAPHIC RESTRICTIONS:
New Jersey.

FINANCIAL DATA:
Amount of support per award: Varies according to need.
Matching fund requirements: Volunteer matching programs: The company will match employee contributions of $25 to a maximum of $5,000 per full-time employee.

APPLICATION INFORMATION:
Specific information on application procedures is available on the web site.
Duration: One year. Renewal possible.

ADDRESS INQUIRIES TO:
Patricia Hughes, Executive Director
(See address above.)

*SPECIAL STIPULATIONS:
A funded project must be scheduled for completion within a 12-month period.

THOMAS B. AND ELIZABETH M. SHERIDAN FOUNDATION   [1721]
Executive Plaza II, Suite 704
11350 McCormick Road
Hunt Valley, MD 21031
(410) 771-0475

AREAS OF INTEREST:
Education.

TYPE:
Awards/prizes. Awards are financial in nature.

PURPOSE:
To support private secondary schools and cultural organizations.

ELIGIBILITY:
Organizations, including parochial schools, classified as 501(c)(3) by the IRS can apply. No grants to individuals.

GEOGRAPHIC RESTRICTIONS:
Baltimore, Maryland.

FINANCIAL DATA:
Amount of support per award: $5,000 to $150,000.

SONY USA FOUNDATION, INC.   [1722]
550 Madison Avenue, 33rd Floor
New York, NY 10022-3211
(212) 833-6851

E-MAIL ADDRESS:
erin_amaty@sonyusa.com

WEB SITE ADDRESS:
www.sony.com/sca/philanthropy.shtml

FOUNDED: 1972

AREAS OF INTEREST:
Arts, culture and technology, with primary focus in education; environmental issues; civic affairs; health and welfare.

TYPE:
General operating grants; Matching gifts; Product donations; Project/program grants.

YEAR PROGRAM STARTED: 1972

PURPOSE:
To meet the needs of the communities where Sony has a presence; to support national organizations which extend into Sony presence areas.

LEGAL BASIS:
Corporate foundation.

ELIGIBILITY:
No grants to individuals, political or religious organizations, labor unions, endowments, capital campaigns, lobbying groups, testimonial dinners, for-profit publications seeking advertisements and foreign or non-U.S. organizations.

GEOGRAPHIC RESTRICTIONS:
United States.

FINANCIAL DATA:
Amount of support per award: Varies.
Total amount of support: Varies.
Matching fund requirements: Sony matches contributions made by full-time employees to educational institutions, hospitals and cultural organizations.

APPLICATION INFORMATION:
Send brief letter describing organization, amount requested, objectives of organization, recent audited financial statement and proof of tax-exempt status. Phone calls not accepted, only written requests.
Duration: One year. Must reapply for continued support.
Deadline: Requests accepted throughout the year. Notification within three months.

PUBLICATIONS:
Contribution guidelines.

OFFICERS:
Mark Khalil, President

ADDRESS INQUIRIES TO:
Erin Amaty
Public Affairs Administrator
(See address above.)

STATE LIBRARY AND ARCHIVES OF FLORIDA
R.A. Gray Building
500 South Bronough Street
Tallahassee, FL 32399-0250
(850) 245-6600
Fax: (850) 245-6282

E-MAIL ADDRESS:
mdeeney@dos.state.fl.us

WEB SITE ADDRESS:
www.fllibraries.org

TYPE:
Project/program grants. Project grants congruent with the state long-range plan.

See entry 784 for full listing.

W. CLEMENT & JESSIE V. STONE FOUNDATION [1723]
The Presidio
1016 Lincoln Boulevard, Suite 111
San Francisco, CA 94129
(415) 561-6691
Fax: (415) 561-6695

E-MAIL ADDRESS:
anita@wcstonefnd.org

WEB SITE ADDRESS:
www.wcstonefnd.org

FOUNDED: 1958

AREAS OF INTEREST:
Education, early childhood and youth development.

TYPE:
Demonstration grants; Development grants; General operating grants; Project/program grants; Technical assistance; Training grants.

YEAR PROGRAM STARTED: 1958

PURPOSE:
To make the world a better place by supporting programs in education, early childhood and youth development.

ELIGIBILITY:
Grants are made to organizations that have tax-exempt status under Section 501(c)(3) of the Internal Revenue Code. Nonsectarian religious programs may apply. No grants are made to individuals.

GEOGRAPHIC RESTRICTIONS:
San Francisco Bay area, California; Chicago, Illinois; Boston, Massachusetts and New York City.

FINANCIAL DATA:
Amount of support per award: $10,000 to $100,000, depending upon the program.
Total amount of support: $3,800,000 for the year 2009.

NUMBER OF AWARDS: 100.

REPRESENTATIVE AWARDS:
$30,000 to the Community Network for Youth Development; $40,000 to the Boston Plan for Excellence; $20,000 to Chicago Health Connection.

APPLICATION INFORMATION:
The Foundation does not accept unsolicited proposals. Organizations may call if they feel there is a strong match between their work and the Foundation's grantmaking priorities.

IRS IDENTIFICATION NUMBER: 36-2498125

OFFICERS AND DIRECTORS:
Norman C. Stone, President
Barbara Samuels, Vice President
Steven M. Stone, Vice President and Treasurer
Michael A. Stone, Secretary
Sandra Treacy, Executive Director
Alex Knecht
Amy Stone
Barbara Stone
David Stone
Debbie Stone
Jennifer Stone
Norah Stone
Sandra Stone
Sara Stone
Chad Tingley

ADDRESS INQUIRIES TO:
Sandra Treacy, Executive Director
(See address above.)

THE ROBERT A. TAFT INSTITUTE OF GOVERNMENT
Taft Institute at Queen's College
Powdermaker Hall, Room 150
65-30 Kissena Boulevard
Flushing, NY 11367-1597
(718) 997-5164
(718) 997-5000
Fax: (718) 997-5333

E-MAIL ADDRESS:
jack.zevin@gmail.com

WEB SITE ADDRESS:
taftinstitute.org

TYPE:
Conferences/seminars; Demonstration grants; Development grants; Endowments; Fellowships; Project/program grants; Scholarships; Seed money grants; Training grants. Grants are given to colleges and universities to conduct Taft Seminars for Teachers.

Scholarships are awarded to elementary and secondary school teachers, administrators, librarians, community college instructors, graduate students in social studies education, and ESL teachers to participate for graduate credit for two to three weeks.

See entry 2143 for full listing.

TOSHIBA AMERICA FOUNDATION [1724]
1251 Avenue of the Americas, 41st Floor
New York, NY 10020
(212) 596-0620

E-MAIL ADDRESS:
foundation@tai.toshiba.com

WEB SITE ADDRESS:
www.taf.toshiba.com

FOUNDED: 1990

AREAS OF INTEREST:
Mathematics and science education for grades K-12.

TYPE:
Project/program grants.

YEAR PROGRAM STARTED: 1990

PURPOSE:
To improve science and math education at the pre-college level (grades K-12 only).

LEGAL BASIS:
Corporate foundation.

ELIGIBILITY:
Grants are made to 501(c)(3) organizations. Preference is given to programs or projects that take place in science or math classrooms. The Foundation does not fund grants for general operating costs, endowment, scholarships, conferences, summer programs, purchase of equipment (product or donations), sponsorships, or individuals.

GEOGRAPHIC RESTRICTIONS:
United States.

FINANCIAL DATA:
Amount of support per award: $1,000 to $20,000.
Total amount of support: Approximately $500,000.

NUMBER OF AWARDS: 150 annually.

APPLICATION INFORMATION:
All applicants must obtain a copy of the guidelines before submitting a proposal.
Duration: One year.
Deadline: Grades K-6: October 1. Grades 7-12: February 1 and August 1 for requests more than $5,000.

PUBLICATIONS:
Guidelines; program report; annual brochure.

IRS IDENTIFICATION NUMBER: 13-3596612

ADDRESS INQUIRIES TO:
Program Officer
(See address above.)

TOYOTA USA FOUNDATION   [1725]

601 Lexington Avenue, 49th Floor
New York, NY 10022
(212) 715-7440
Fax: (212) 750-3564

WEB SITE ADDRESS:
www.toyota.com/community

FOUNDED: 1987

AREAS OF INTEREST:
K-12 education, with a focus on math,
science and environmental science.

TYPE:
Challenge/matching grants; Demonstration
grants; Development grants; Seed money
grants; Training grants. Develop and
implement programs.

YEAR PROGRAM STARTED: 1987

PURPOSE:
To improve the quality of American
education in grades K-12.

LEGAL BASIS:
Foundation.

ELIGIBILITY:
Applicants must be 501(c)(3) organizations
located in communities where Toyota has
major operations.

No grants directly to public schools. No
funds for operating costs, endowments,
capital campaigns, annual drives, deficit
reductions, fraternal groups or religious
organizations. Government agencies,
individuals, and for-profit businesses are not
eligible.

FINANCIAL DATA:
Amount of support per award: $30,000 to
$400,000.

Total amount of support: Approximately
$2,000,000.

REPRESENTATIVE AWARDS:
$200,000 to Academy for Educational
Development for After-School PLUS
Program; $249,875 to The Greening of
Detroit for Life Sciences Program for K-5th
grade students; $50,000 to Girls Inc. for the
Thinking SMART program to sharpen math,
science, engineering and technology skills
among young girls ages 12 to 18.

APPLICATION INFORMATION:
Application forms are available online. The
Foundation does not accept mail-in
applications.
Duration: One to three years.

PUBLICATIONS:
Guidelines; brochure; press releases.

IRS IDENTIFICATION NUMBER: 95-3255038

OFFICERS:
Yukitoshi Funo, President
Jim Press, Executive Vice President
A. Yamaguchi, Treasurer
Chuck Brown
Gary Condis
Dennis Cueno
Dave Illingworth
Irv Miller
Dian Ogilvie
Harry Otaka
Seiichi Sudo
Jim Wiseman

ADDRESS INQUIRIES TO:
Jaye Corvino, Foundation Administrator
(See address above.)

U.S. DEPARTMENT OF EDUCATION

Office of Indian Education
Office of Elementary and Secondary Education
400 Maryland Avenue, S.W.
Washington, DC 20202
(202) 401-0113
(202) 260-1454
Fax: (202) 260-7779

E-MAIL ADDRESS:
bernard.garcia@ed.gov

WEB SITE ADDRESS:
www.ed.gov

TYPE:
Formula grants. Grants to provide financial
assistance to LEAs and tribal schools to
develop and carry out elementary and
secondary school programs specially
designed to meet the special educational and
culturally related educational needs of Indian
children.

See entry 1123 for full listing.

U.S. DEPARTMENT OF EDUCATION

Office of Federal TRIO Programs
1990 K Street, N.W., Suite 7000
Washington, DC 20006-8510
(202) 502-7600
Fax: (202) 502-7857; (202) 219-7074

E-MAIL ADDRESS:
OPE_TRIO@ed.gov

WEB SITE ADDRESS:
www.ed.gov/ope/trio

TYPE:
Project/program grants. There are three types
of grants under the Upward Bound program:
Regular Upward Bound Grants; Veterans
Upward Bound Grants; and Upward Bound
Math and Science Grants.

The Regular Upward Bound projects are
designed to generate in participants the skills
and motivation necessary for success in
education beyond secondary school. The
Veterans Upward Bound projects are
designed to assist veterans in preparing for a
program of postsecondary education. The
Upward Bound Math and Science projects
are designed to prepare high school students
for postsecondary education programs that
lead to careers in the fields of math and
science.

See entry 1760 for full listing.

THE WALTON FAMILY FOUNDATION, INC.   [1726]

P.O. Box 2030
Bentonville, AR 72712
(479) 464-1570
Fax: (479) 464-1580

E-MAIL ADDRESS:
info@wffmail.com

WEB SITE ADDRESS:
www.waltonfamilyfoundation.org

AREAS OF INTEREST:
Educational reform, with emphasis on
primary and secondary education;
environment; Delta region of Arkansas and
Mississippi; northwest Arkansas.

NAME(S) OF PROGRAMS:
● **Public Charter School Grants**

● **Walton International Scholarship
  Program**
● **Walton Scholarship**

TYPE:
Scholarships. Grants to charter schools and
charter school developers for planning,
start-up and expansion or operation.

PURPOSE:
To promote reform in education; to support
university-level programs that involve K-12
education issues; to support the initiation of
charter schools; to fund scholarships.

LEGAL BASIS:
Family foundation.

ELIGIBILITY:
The Foundation seeks applicants on a
pro-active basis for charter school developers
or organizations that aim to improve the
quality of charter schools. The Foundation
funds only IRS 501(c)(3) organizations or
public entities. Requests from the same
organization will be considered only once
every 12 months.

Walton International Scholarship Program:
Students from Central America who will
attend one of three private universities in
Arkansas to study the American enterprise
system.

Walton Scholarship: Students who are
children of Wal-Mart Stores, Inc., associates
with a superior academic and leadership
record.

FINANCIAL DATA:
Amount of support per award: Varies.

PUBLICATIONS:
Annual report.

ADDRESS INQUIRIES TO:
Buddy D. Philpot, Executive Director
(See address above.)

YOUTH FOR UNDERSTANDING USA

6400 Goldsboro Road
Suite 100
Bethesda, MD 20817
(240) 235-2100
(800) 833-6243
(866) 493-8872
Fax: (240) 235-2188

E-MAIL ADDRESS:
admissions@yfu.org

WEB SITE ADDRESS:
www.yfu-usa.org

TYPE:
Exchange programs; Grants-in-aid;
Scholarships; Travel grants. Students on
summer semester and year programs live
with volunteer host families overseas.
Students on semester and academic year
programs also attend school. International
students live and study at U.S. high schools
or community colleges. Competitive, full and
partial scholarships for Corporate,
Finland-U.S. Senate, Japan-U.S. Senate
Programs and Japan-America Friendship
Scholars Program.

See entry 1005 for full listing.

Higher education projects and research

ABEL FOUNDATION

1815 Y Street
Lincoln, NE 68508
(402) 434-1212
Fax: (402) 434-1799

WEB SITE ADDRESS:
www.abelfoundation.org

TYPE:
Capital grants; Matching gifts;
Project/program grants.

See entry 1232 for full listing.

ADCO FOUNDATION   [1727]

c/o American Atlantic Co.
1060 First Avenue, Suite 400
King of Prussia, PA 19406
(610) 768-8020
Fax: (610) 337-3128

AREAS OF INTEREST:
Higher education, communications, civic
affairs, community funds, health and mental
health.

TYPE:
General operating grants; Project/program
grants; Seed money grants.

PURPOSE:
To promote higher education, physical and
mental health.

ELIGIBILITY:
Grants are made to organizations that have
tax-exempt status under Section 501(c)(3) of
the Internal Revenue Code. No grants are
made to individuals.

GEOGRAPHIC RESTRICTIONS:
Primarily New Jersey, New York and
Pennsylvania.

FINANCIAL DATA:
Amount of support per award: $500 to
$12,000.
Total amount of support: $36,000 for the
year 2010.

NUMBER OF AWARDS: 5 for the year 2009.

APPLICATION INFORMATION:
Send a letter of inquiry to the Foundation,
outlining the organization's goal and
purposes, and the intended use and amount
of the grant requested.
Duration: One year. Renewal possible.
Deadline: November.

ADDRESS INQUIRIES TO:
Barry Doney, Administrator
(See address above.)

AMERICAN FLORAL ENDOWMENT

1601 Duke Street
Alexandria, VA 22314
(703) 838-5211
Fax: (703) 838-5212

E-MAIL ADDRESS:
afe@endowment.org

WEB SITE ADDRESS:
www.endowment.org

TYPE:
Internships; Project/program grants; Research
grants; Scholarships. The Endowment funds
research and educational development in
floriculture and environmental horticulture
designed to produce solutions to industry
needs and promote the growth and
improvement of the floral industry for the
benefit of the grower, wholesale, retail, allied
segments and the general public.

The Endowment supports educational
programs focused on attracting young people
to the industry, and educational endeavors to
identify and solve industry needs and/or
challenges. The programs are divided into
two major areas:
(1) paid floriculture internships/scholarships
for full-time college students and;
(2) general educational grants to national
programs.

See entry 2247 for full listing.

AMERICAN FOUNDATION FOR PHARMACEUTICAL EDUCATION

One Church Street, Suite 400
Rockville, MD 20850
(301) 738-2160
Fax: (301) 738-2161

E-MAIL ADDRESS:
afpe@att.net

WEB SITE ADDRESS:
www.afpenet.org

TYPE:
Fellowships.

See entry 2698 for full listing.

AMERICAN FOUNDATION FOR PHARMACEUTICAL EDUCATION   [1728]

One Church Street, Suite 400
Rockville, MD 20850
(301) 738-2160
Fax: (301) 738-2161

E-MAIL ADDRESS:
info@afpenet.org

WEB SITE ADDRESS:
www.afpenet.org

FOUNDED: 1942

AREAS OF INTEREST:
Education.

NAME(S) OF PROGRAMS:
● **AACP-AFPE New Investigator
  Program for Pharmacy Faculty (NIP)**
● **AFPE Gateway to Research
  Scholarship**
● **AFPE Predoctoral Fellowships in the
  Pharmaceutical Sciences**

TYPE:
Scholarships.

YEAR PROGRAM STARTED: 1942

PURPOSE:
To encourage an outstanding pharmacy
school graduate to pursue an advanced
degree in the pharmaceutical sciences.

ELIGIBILITY:
Applicants must be in the final year of a
pharmacy college B.S. or Pharm.D. program
or have completed a pharmacy degree.
Consideration is given to those who need
financial assistance to further their education
in pharmacy. At the time of application, the
applicant must be in good financial and
academic standing and planning to pursue a
Ph.D., a Master's degree or a combined
Residency/Master's degree program at a U.S.
college or school of pharmacy. Applicants
may apply annually and receive up to three
years of financial support.

GEOGRAPHIC RESTRICTIONS:
United States.

FINANCIAL DATA:
Amount of support per award: $4,000 to
$25,000.
Total amount of support: Varies.

NUMBER OF APPLICANTS MOST RECENT YEAR:
200.

NUMBER OF AWARDS: 60.

APPLICATION INFORMATION:
Application guidelines are available from the
Foundation. Application forms are available
from Kappa Epsilon faculty advisors or from
the Kappa Epsilon Executive Office: 5800
Foxridge Drive, Suite 115, Mission, KS
66202-4510. Completed applications are to
be mailed to the Mission, KS address.
Duration: Six months to one year.
Deadline: Varies.

ADDRESS INQUIRIES TO:
Yona Mead, Grants Manager
(See address above.)

AMERICAN FRIENDS OF THE ALEXANDER VON HUMBOLDT FOUNDATION   [1729]

1012 14th Street, N.W.
Suite 300
Washington, DC 20005
(202) 783-1907
Fax: (202) 783-1908

E-MAIL ADDRESS:
info@americanfriends-of-avh.org

WEB SITE ADDRESS:
www.humboldt-foundation.de
americanfriends-of-avh.org

FOUNDED: 1953

AREAS OF INTEREST:
Postgraduate research in Germany.

NAME(S) OF PROGRAMS:
● **Humboldt Research Fellowship for
  Postdoctoral Researchers**

TYPE:
Fellowships. This program supports highly
qualified scholars and scientists of all
nationalities and disciplines so that they may
carry out long-term research projects that the
applicant has selected in cooperation with an
academic host the applicant has selected at a
research institution in Germany.

PURPOSE:
To support highly qualified scholars and
scientists of all nationalities and disciplines
so that they may carry out long-term research
projects in Germany.

ELIGIBILITY:
Open to scientists and scholars who
completed a doctoral degree within four
years prior to the application submission
date.

Fellowships are awarded on the basis of
academic achievement, the quality and
feasibility of the proposed research and the
candidate's publications.

FINANCIAL DATA:
In addition to a monthly stipend, special
allowances are available for accompanying
family members, travel expenses and German
language instruction.

Amount of support per award: EUR 2,250 monthly.

NUMBER OF AWARDS: Approximately 600 total fellowships for postdoctoral researchers and experienced researchers each year.

APPLICATION INFORMATION:
Duration: Six to 24 months in Germany.
Deadline: Continuous. The review process takes several months, and the selection committee meets three times a year to review applications.

ADDRESS INQUIRIES TO:
Program Coordination
(See address above.) or

Alexander von Humboldt Stiftung
Jean-Paul-Strasse 12
D-53173 Bonn
Germany
Tel: 49 (0228) 833-0
Fax: 49 (0228) 833-199
E-mail: info@avh.de

AMERICAN LIBRARY ASSOCIATION (ALA)   [1730]
50 East Huron Street
Chicago, IL 60611-2795
(312) 280-4279
(800) 545-2433 ext. 4277
Fax: (312) 280-3256

E-MAIL ADDRESS:
scholarships@ala.org

WEB SITE ADDRESS:
www.ala.org/scholarships

AREAS OF INTEREST:
Library science.

NAME(S) OF PROGRAMS:
- **ALSC/Bound-to-Stay-Bound Books Scholarship**
- **ALSC/Frederic G. Melcher Scholarship**
- **ASCLA/Century Scholarship**
- **Marshall Cavendish Scholarship**
- **David H. Clift Scholarship**
- **Tom and Roberta Drewes Scholarship**
- **Mary V. Gaver Scholarship**
- **Miriam L. Hornback Scholarship**
- **Christopher J. Hoy/ERT Scholarship**
- **Tony B. Leisner Scholarship**
- **LITA/Christian Larew Memorial Scholarship**
- **LITA/LSSI Minority Scholarship**
- **LITA/OCLC Minority Scholarship**
- **Peter Lyman Memorial/SAGE Scholarships**
- **Cicely Phippen Marks Scholarship**
- **Spectrum Initiative Scholarship Program**

TYPE:
Scholarships. ALSC and Gaver Scholarships are for a youth services librarian.

ASCLA Scholarship is for an individual with a disability entering a Master's degree or Ph.D. program.

Clift, Cavendish and Hoy/ERT are general scholarships.

Drewes, Hornback and Leisner Scholarships are for library support staff currently working in a library.

LITA/Christian Larew Memorial, LITA/LSSI Minority and LITA/OCLC Minority Scholarships are for librarians entering a Master's degree program.

Marks Scholarship is for a federal services librarian.

SAGE Scholarship is for a new media services librarian.

YEAR PROGRAM STARTED: 1996

PURPOSE:
To support library staff education.

ELIGIBILITY:
Applicants must be U.S. or Canadian citizens, or permanent residents thereof.

Applicants must demonstrate academic excellence, leadership qualities and evidence of commitment to a career in library service. Applicants may not have completed more than 12 semester hours or the equivalent towards a Master's degree in library science prior to June 1.

FINANCIAL DATA:
Amount of support per award: Varies.

NUMBER OF APPLICANTS MOST RECENT YEAR: 800.

NUMBER OF AWARDS: 1.

APPLICATION INFORMATION:
Deadline: March 1.

STAFF:
Kimberly Sanders, Program Officer

ADDRESS INQUIRIES TO:
Kimberly Sanders, Program Officer
(See address above.)

ARCHAEOLOGICAL INSTITUTE OF AMERICA   [1731]
656 Beacon Street, 6th Floor
Boston, MA 02215
(617) 358-4184
Fax: (617) 353-6550

E-MAIL ADDRESS:
lsparks@aia.bu.edu

WEB SITE ADDRESS:
www.archaeological.org

FOUNDED: 1879

AREAS OF INTEREST:
Archaeological research and publication.

NAME(S) OF PROGRAMS:
- **Helen M. Woodruff Fellowship**

TYPE:
Fellowships. A predoctoral or postdoctoral fellowship for study of archaeology and classical studies has been established by the Institute at the American Academy in Rome.

PURPOSE:
To promote the study of archaeology and classical studies.

ELIGIBILITY:
Applicant must be a citizen or permanent resident of the U.S.

GEOGRAPHIC RESTRICTIONS:
United States.

FINANCIAL DATA:
Amount of support per award: $10,000.
Total amount of support: $10,000.

NUMBER OF AWARDS: 1.

APPLICATION INFORMATION:
Applications must be sent to the American Academy in Rome.
Duration: One year.
Deadline: November 1.

ADDRESS INQUIRIES TO:
Laurel Nilsen Sparks
Lecture and Fellowship Coordinator
(See address above.)

ARCHITECTURAL LEAGUE OF NEW YORK
594 Broadway, Suite 607
New York, NY 10012
(212) 753-1722
Fax: (212) 486-9173

E-MAIL ADDRESS:
info@archleague.org

WEB SITE ADDRESS:
www.archleague.org

TYPE:
Research grants; Travel grants. The Deborah J. Norden Fund, established in 1995 in memory of architect and arts administrator Deborah Norden, awards travel/study grants to students and recent graduates in the field of architecture, architectural history, and urban studies.

See entry 441 for full listing.

ARCTIC INSTITUTE OF NORTH AMERICA   [1732]
The University of Calgary
2500 University Drive, N.W.
Calgary AB T2N 1N4 Canada
(403) 220-7515
Fax: (403) 282-4609

E-MAIL ADDRESS:
arctic@ucalgary.ca

WEB SITE ADDRESS:
www.arctic.ucalgary.ca

FOUNDED: 1945

AREAS OF INTEREST:
Arctic natural and social sciences.

NAME(S) OF PROGRAMS:
- **AINA Grants-in-Aid**

TYPE:
Grants-in-aid; Scholarships.

YEAR PROGRAM STARTED: 1945

PURPOSE:
To provide funding to young investigators, especially graduate students, to augment their research.

ELIGIBILITY:
Proposed projects can include field, library or office-intensive investigations. Although there is no limitation on the area of investigation, the Institute encourages applications focused on the natural sciences and social sciences, including anthropology and economics, in the North.

FINANCIAL DATA:
Funding can be used for travel, supplies, equipment and services, but not for salary or wages.
Amount of support per award: $1,000.
Total amount of support: Varies each year, depending on applications received.

NUMBER OF AWARDS: 6.

APPLICATION INFORMATION:
Applications must be mailed to:
Dr. Erich H. Follmann
Institute of Arctic Biology
University of Alaska, Fairbanks
P.O. Box 757000
Fairbanks, AK 99775-7000.
Deadline: February 1 (postmark).

PUBLICATIONS:
Arctic Journal.

ADDRESS INQUIRIES TO:
Dr. Erich Follman
Tel: (907) 474-7338
E-mail: ffehf@uaf.edu

BARNES GROUP FOUNDATION
123 Main Street
Bristol, CT 06010
(860) 583-7070
Fax: (860) 589-7466

WEB SITE ADDRESS:
www.bginc.com

TYPE:
General operating grants; Scholarships.

See entry 1254 for full listing.

BOSQUE FOUNDATION [1733]
5950 Cedar Springs Road, Suite 210
Dallas, TX 75235
(214) 357-0333
Fax: (214) 357-9358

E-MAIL ADDRESS:
lbeecherl@beecherl.com

FOUNDED: 1983

AREAS OF INTEREST:
Higher education and medical research.

TYPE:
Capital grants; Research grants.

PURPOSE:
To promote medical research and higher education development.

ELIGIBILITY:
No grants to individuals. Organizations do not have to be tax-exempt.

GEOGRAPHIC RESTRICTIONS:
Primarily Texas.

FINANCIAL DATA:
Amount of support per award: Varies.
Total amount of support: Varies.
Matching fund requirements: Varies.

APPLICATION INFORMATION:
Applicants should submit a one-page letter explaining purpose and reasoning for the request of funds.
Duration: Varies depending on grant.
Deadline: Applications accepted all year.

ADDRESS INQUIRIES TO:
Louis Beecherl III
(See address above.)

CAESAR'S ENTERTAINMENT CORPORATION [1734]
One Caesar's Palace Drive
Las Vegas, NV 89109
(702) 407-6300
Fax: (702) 407-6520

WEB SITE ADDRESS:
www.caesars.com

AREAS OF INTEREST:
Education.

TYPE:
Matching gifts. The corporation matches employee contributions, dollar-for-dollar, to eligible colleges or universities.

YEAR PROGRAM STARTED: 1983

PURPOSE:
To encourage employees to support higher education by matching their gifts to institutions of greatest importance to them.

LEGAL BASIS:
Corporation.

ELIGIBILITY:
Regular, full-time employees of Caesar's or one of its operating units are eligible. Eligible institutions are postsecondary and meet the following requirements: must have a nonprofit tax status, an appropriate regional or professional accreditation or licensing, a policy of nondiscrimination on the basis of sex, age, race or religion and location within the U.S. or its possessions.

FINANCIAL DATA:
Amount of support per award: Up to $1,000 per employee, per year.
Total amount of support: Varies.

PUBLICATIONS:
Annual report.

OFFICERS:
Gary Loveman, Chairman and Chief Executive Officer

ADDRESS INQUIRIES TO:
Meredith Hartstern, Political Affairs and CSR Program Manager
(See address above.)

CANADIAN EMBASSY
Academic Relations Office
501 Pennsylvania Avenue, N.W.
Washington, DC 20001
(202) 682-7727
Fax: (202) 682-7791

E-MAIL ADDRESS:
academicrelations@canadianembassy.org

WEB SITE ADDRESS:
www.washington.gc.ca

TYPE:
Development grants; Research grants; Travel grants. Faculty Enrichment (Course Development) Program provides faculty members with an opportunity to develop or update a course(s) with substantial Canadian content that will be offered as part of their regular teaching load. Submissions from all fields in the social sciences and humanities are welcomed.

See entry 881 for full listing.

ROY J. CARVER CHARITABLE TRUST [1735]
202 Iowa Avenue
Muscatine, IA 52761-3733
(563) 263-4010
Fax: (563) 263-1547

E-MAIL ADDRESS:
info@carvertrust.org

WEB SITE ADDRESS:
www.carvertrust.org

FOUNDED: 1982

AREAS OF INTEREST:
Biomedical and scientific research; elementary, secondary and higher education; youth recreation.

TYPE:
Capital grants; Challenge/matching grants; Professorships; Project/program grants; Research grants; Scholarships.

YEAR PROGRAM STARTED: 1982

PURPOSE:
To support medical and scientific research, scholarships, general education and programs addressing the needs of youth.

LEGAL BASIS:
Trust.

ELIGIBILITY:
Eligible organizations must be IRS 501(c)(3) tax-exempt.

GEOGRAPHIC RESTRICTIONS:
Iowa and portions of western Illinois.

FINANCIAL DATA:
Amount of support per award: Varies.
Total amount of support: Varies.

NUMBER OF APPLICANTS MOST RECENT YEAR:
207 for fiscal year 2009-10.

NUMBER OF AWARDS: 109 for fiscal year 2009-10.

APPLICATION INFORMATION:
Detailed information is available online.
Duration: Varies.
Deadline: February 15, May 15, August 15 and November 15.

ADDRESS INQUIRIES TO:
Troy K. Ross, Ph.D.
Executive Administrator
(See address above.)

CENTER FOR CALIFORNIA STUDIES, CAPITAL FELLOWS PROGRAMS
California State University, Sacramento
6000 J Street
Sacramento, CA 95819-6081
(916) 278-6906
(916) 278-4487

E-MAIL ADDRESS:
calstudies@csus.edu
hoenigco@csus.edu

WEB SITE ADDRESS:
www.csus.edu/calst/judicial

TYPE:
Fellowships. Jointly sponsored by the Center for California Studies at California State University, Sacramento and the California Judicial Council. Full-time fellowships for 10 fellows, 10 months and graduate units earned from California State University, Sacramento.

See entry 2117 for full listing.

CENTER FOR CALIFORNIA STUDIES, CAPITAL FELLOWS PROGRAMS
California State University, Sacramento
6000 J Street
Sacramento, CA 95819-6081
(916) 278-6906

E-MAIL ADDRESS:
calstudies@csus.edu

WEB SITE ADDRESS:
www.csus.edu/calst/senate

TYPE:
Fellowships. Jointly sponsored by the Center for California Studies at California State University, Sacramento and the California State Senate. Full-time fellowships for 18 fellows, 11 months and graduate units earned from California State University, Sacramento.

See entry 2118 for full listing.

CENTER FOR CALIFORNIA STUDIES, CAPITAL FELLOWS PROGRAMS
California State University, Sacramento
6000 J Street
Sacramento, CA 95819-6081
(916) 278-6906

E-MAIL ADDRESS:
calstudies@csus.edu

WEB SITE ADDRESS:
www.csus.edu/calst/executive

TYPE:
Fellowships. Jointly sponsored by the Center for California Studies at California State University, Sacramento and the California governor. Full-time fellowships for 18 fellows, 10 months and six units of graduate study through California State University, Sacramento.

See entry 2119 for full listing.

CENTER FOR CALIFORNIA STUDIES, CAPITAL FELLOWS PROGRAMS
California State University, Sacramento
6000 J Street
Sacramento, CA 95819-6081
(916) 278-6906
Fax: (916) 278-5199

E-MAIL ADDRESS:
calstudies@csus.edu

WEB SITE ADDRESS:
www.csus.edu/calst/assembly_fellowship_program

TYPE:
Fellowships. Jointly sponsored by the Center for California Studies at California State University, Sacramento and the California State Assembly. Full-time fellowships for 18 fellows, 11 months and units of graduate study through California State University, Sacramento.

See entry 2116 for full listing.

CENTER FOR COMPARATIVE IMMIGRATION STUDIES AT THE UNIVERSITY OF CALIFORNIA-SAN DIEGO [1736]
9500 Gilman Drive, MC 0548
La Jolla, CA 92093-0548
(858) 822-4447
Fax: (858) 822-4432

E-MAIL ADDRESS:
ccis@ucsd.edu

WEB SITE ADDRESS:
ccis-ucsd.org

FOUNDED: 1999

AREAS OF INTEREST:
International and internal migration and refugee flows in all countries and immigrant ethnic minorities.

NAME(S) OF PROGRAMS:
● **Visiting Research Fellowship Program**

TYPE:
Fellowships.

YEAR PROGRAM STARTED: 1999

PURPOSE:
To systematically compare the historical and contemporary U.S. immigration experience with that of other labor-importing countries

in other regions such as the Asia-Pacific, Latin America, Western Europe and Western Africa.

ELIGIBILITY:
Must be an advanced predoctoral or postdoctoral scholar researching and writing on any aspect of international migration and refugee flows, in any field of the social sciences, history, law and comparative literature. Must have current or former affiliation with a University of California campus.

NUMBER OF APPLICANTS MOST RECENT YEAR: 40.

NUMBER OF AWARDS: 3.

APPLICATION INFORMATION:
The applicant must complete a Fellowship Application Form and mail it, along with required attachments, to the address above.
Duration: Three to 10 months, depending on the requirements of the project. Full academic year projects that are nine to 10 months are preferred.
Deadline: January 15.

STAFF:
Prof. David Fitzgerald, Director of Mexican Migration Field Research Program
Prof. John Skrentny

ADDRESS INQUIRIES TO:
Fellowship Program
(See address above.)

*SPECIAL STIPULATIONS:
Fellowships must be held in residence at CCIS.

CORNELL UNIVERSITY
Society for the Humanities
A.D. White House
27 East Avenue
Ithaca, NY 14853-1101
(607) 255-9274
Fax: (607) 255-1422

E-MAIL ADDRESS:
humctr-mailbox@cornell.edu

WEB SITE ADDRESS:
www.arts.cornell.edu/sochum

TYPE:
Fellowships. Postdoctoral teaching-research fellowships in the humanities, each awarded for a two-year period. While in residence at Cornell, postdoctoral fellows hold department affiliation and have limited teaching duties and the opportunity for scholarly work.

See entry 396 for full listing.

COUNCIL FOR INTERNATIONAL EXCHANGE OF SCHOLARS (CIES) [1737]
3007 Tilden Street, N.W.
Suite 5L
Washington, DC 20008-3009
(202) 686-6232
Fax: (202) 362-3442; (202) 686-6258

E-MAIL ADDRESS:
tjanes@iie.org

WEB SITE ADDRESS:
www.cies.org

FOUNDED: 1947

AREAS OF INTEREST:
Scholarly exchange.

NAME(S) OF PROGRAMS:
● **Fulbright Scholar Program-German Studies Seminar**

TYPE:
Exchange programs; Project/program grants; Travel grants. The annual two-week German Studies Seminar focuses on current German society and culture and examines political, social and economic institutions.

YEAR PROGRAM STARTED: 1947

PURPOSE:
To promote mutual understanding and scholarship.

LEGAL BASIS:
U.S. government funding and German Commission.

ELIGIBILITY:
Applicants must be U.S. citizens and be in German area studies or in a field related to the current topic.

FINANCIAL DATA:
Award benefits include round-trip transportation and per diem allowance.

NUMBER OF AWARDS: Up to 25.

APPLICATION INFORMATION:
Application materials are available online.
Duration: Two weeks.
Deadline: November 1.

PUBLICATIONS:
Annual awards catalog; descriptive brochure.

ADDRESS INQUIRIES TO:
Tanya Janes, Senior Program Officer
(See address above.)

COUNCIL FOR INTERNATIONAL EXCHANGE OF SCHOLARS (CIES) [1738]
1400 K Street, N.W.
Washington, DC 20005
(202) 686-6232
Fax: (202) 362-3442

E-MAIL ADDRESS:
mbettua@iie.org

WEB SITE ADDRESS:
www.cies.org

FOUNDED: 1947

AREAS OF INTEREST:
Distinguished chair lecturing awards.

NAME(S) OF PROGRAMS:
● **Fulbright Distinguished Chairs**

TYPE:
Awards/prizes. There are approximately 40 distinguished chair awards in 18 countries. Awards available in a wide variety of disciplines.

PURPOSE:
To promote mutual understanding and scholarship.

ELIGIBILITY:
Applicants must have a Ph.D. or equivalent professional degree; a terminal degree is required. Applicants should have a record of prominent scholarly achievement. U.S. citizenship required. Lecturing is in English.

FINANCIAL DATA:
Award benefits vary by country and generally include a monthly stipend, travel, and possibly housing.
Amount of support per award: Varies.
Total amount of support: Varies.

APPLICATION INFORMATION:
Application must be submitted online.

Deadline: August 1.

ADDRESS INQUIRIES TO:
Distinguished Chair Program
(See address above.)

COUNCIL FOR INTERNATIONAL EXCHANGE OF SCHOLARS (CIES) [1739]

3007 Tilden Street, N.W.
Suite 5L
Washington, DC 20008-3009
(202) 686-4000
Fax: (202) 362-3442

E-MAIL ADDRESS:
scholars@iie.org

WEB SITE ADDRESS:
www.iie.org/cies

FOUNDED: 1947

AREAS OF INTEREST:
Scholarly exchange.

NAME(S) OF PROGRAMS:
● **Fulbright International Education Administrators Awards**

TYPE:
Conferences/seminars; Exchange programs; Project/program grants; Research grants; Travel grants. Three special programs are currently being offered under Fulbright auspices for college, university and community college administrators:

U.S.-German International Education Administrators Program supports participation in a three-week seminar in Germany on the educational, cultural and political issues involved in international education.

U.S.-Japan International Education Administrators Program supports participation in a three-week group program in Japan on higher education, society and culture in Japan.

U.S.-Korea International Education Administrators Program supports participation in a two and one-half week group program in Korea on higher education, society and culture in Korea.

YEAR PROGRAM STARTED: 1947

PURPOSE:
To promote mutual understanding between people of the U.S. and people of other nations.

LEGAL BASIS:
Public Law 87-256, as amended, The Mutual Educational and Cultural Exchange Act of 1961.

ELIGIBILITY:
Applicants must be U.S. citizens.

Applicants for the German IEA Program must be full-time administrators of two- or four-year colleges, universities or nonprofit international education exchange organizations. They should have significant involvement with at least one of the following areas: student or faculty exchanges; foreign student admissions/advising; study abroad programs; and international exchanges. Academic administrators whose current responsibilities have a direct relation to international exchange in higher education are also encouraged to participate. Preference is for applicants with at least three years of administrative experience and supervisory responsibility who have been at their current institutions for at least one year.

Applicants for the Japan IEA Program must be international education administrators or senior-level university administrators with substantial (at least 25%) responsibility for international activities at their institutions and must be affiliated with a four-year college or university or a nonprofit international education exchange organization. They must also have a minimum of three years of full-time work experience. Grantees are expected to attend an orientation program held in conjunction with the annual NAFSA Conference, at their own expense.

Applicants for the U.S.-Korea IEA Program must be international education administrators or senior-level university administrators with substantial (at least 25%) responsibility for international activities at their institutions and must be affiliated with a two- or four-year college or university or a nonprofit international education exchange organization. They must also have a minimum of three years of full-time work experience. This program is not a vehicle for initiating or developing an American institution's linkage programs, for student recruitment, or for establishment of branch campuses. Grantees are expected to attend an orientation program held in conjunction with the annual NAFSA Conference, at their own expense.

GEOGRAPHIC RESTRICTIONS:
United States.

FINANCIAL DATA:
Amount of support per award: Varies.

NUMBER OF APPLICANTS MOST RECENT YEAR:
Approximately 75.

NUMBER OF AWARDS: German IEA: 25; Japan IEA: 5; Korea IEA: 4.

APPLICATION INFORMATION:
Applicants must submit:
(1) adapted application form;
(2) project statement (not to exceed five single-spaced pages);
(3) institutional statement (one to two pages);
(4) curriculum vitae (not to exceed six pages) and;
(5) three references.
Duration: German IEA: Two weeks beginning in late October; Japan IEA: Three weeks beginning in mid-June; Korea IEA: Two weeks beginning in mid-June.
Deadline: November 1; Germany IEA: February 1.

PUBLICATIONS:
Descriptive brochure; annual awards catalog; annual report.

STAFF:
David Adams, Senior Program Officer for Korea and Japan
Alisha Scott, Program Officer for Europe

ADDRESS INQUIRIES TO:
Fulbright International Education Administrators Program
(See e-mail and address above.)

COUNCIL OF INDEPENDENT COLLEGES [1740]

One Dupont Circle, N.W.
Suite 320
Washington, DC 20036
(202) 466-7230
Fax: (202) 466-7238

E-MAIL ADDRESS:
cic@cic.nche.edu

WEB SITE ADDRESS:
www.cic.edu

FOUNDED: 1956

AREAS OF INTEREST:
Nation's private liberal arts colleges and universities.

NAME(S) OF PROGRAMS:
● **Tuition Exchange Program**

TYPE:
Technical assistance. Consists of a network of CIC colleges and universities willing to accept tuition-free students from families of full-time employees of other CIC institutions. The program encourages students from employee families of private colleges and universities to attend similar institutions and assists these families in meeting the partial cost of college attendance.

PURPOSE:
To support college leadership, advance institutional excellence, and enhance private higher education's contributions to society.

LEGAL BASIS:
Association of independent colleges and universities.

GEOGRAPHIC RESTRICTIONS:
United States.

PUBLICATIONS:
Independent, newsletter.

STAFF:
Richard Ekman, President
Laura Wilcox, Vice President, Communications
Ed Clark, Senior Advisor

BOARD OF DIRECTORS:
Antoine Garibaldi, Chairperson

ADDRESS INQUIRIES TO:
Richard Ekman, President
(See address above.)

GARDNER AND FLORENCE CALL COWLES FOUNDATION [1741]

1915 Grand Avenue
Des Moines, IA 50309
(515) 284-8117
Fax: (515) 309-0704

AREAS OF INTEREST:
Higher education and private four-year colleges in Iowa.

TYPE:
Capital grants; Project/program grants.

YEAR PROGRAM STARTED: 1936

PURPOSE:
To support four-year colleges in Iowa.

ELIGIBILITY:
Eligible organizations must be IRS 501(c)(3) tax-exempt. No individual grants are given.

GEOGRAPHIC RESTRICTIONS:
Iowa.

FINANCIAL DATA:
Amount of support per award: Varies.

APPLICATION INFORMATION:
Contact the Foundation.
Duration: Varies.
Deadline: Spring and Fall. Call for dates.

STAFF:
Phyllis Mumford, Administrator

ADDRESS INQUIRIES TO:
Charles Edward, Jr., President
(See address above.)

HUGH AND HAZEL DARLING FOUNDATION   [1742]
500 South Grand Avenue, 19th Floor
Los Angeles, CA 90071
(213) 683-5200
Fax: (213) 627-7795

FOUNDED: 1987

AREAS OF INTEREST:
Education.

TYPE:
Block grants; Capital grants;
Challenge/matching grants; Scholarships;
Training grants.

YEAR PROGRAM STARTED: 1987

PURPOSE:
To support education in California, with
principle emphasis on legal education.

LEGAL BASIS:
Private foundation.

ELIGIBILITY:
Grants are made only to tax-exempt
501(c)(3) organizations. No grants are made
to individuals.

GEOGRAPHIC RESTRICTIONS:
California.

FINANCIAL DATA:
Amount of support per award: Varies.
Total amount of support: Varies.

NUMBER OF APPLICANTS MOST RECENT YEAR:
100.

NUMBER OF AWARDS: 47 for the year 2010.

REPRESENTATIVE AWARDS:
$125,000 to Pepperdine University; $200,000
to Azusa Pacific University; $20,000 to Deep
Springs College; $100,000 to Loyola Law
School; $50,000 to Hope International
University.

APPLICATION INFORMATION:
Send letter and literature.
Deadline: Announcement in November and
December.

OFFICERS:
Richard L. Stack, Trustee

ADDRESS INQUIRIES TO:
Richard L. Stack, Trustee
(See address above.)

DELOITTE FOUNDATION   [1743]
10 Westport Road
Wilton, CT 06897
(203) 761-3413
Fax: (203) 423-6413

E-MAIL ADDRESS:
plevine@deloitte.com

WEB SITE ADDRESS:
www.deloitte.com/us/df

FOUNDED: 1928

AREAS OF INTEREST:
Higher education, specializing in accounting
and business.

TYPE:
Conferences/seminars; Fellowships; Matching
gifts; Professorships; Research grants.

YEAR PROGRAM STARTED: 1956

PURPOSE:
To support teaching and research in
accounting, business and related fields.

LEGAL BASIS:
Foundation.

ELIGIBILITY:
Doctoral Fellowship Program applicants must
be doctoral candidates pursuing a Ph.D. in
accounting at U.S. colleges and universities.

GEOGRAPHIC RESTRICTIONS:
United States.

FINANCIAL DATA:
Amount of support per award: Doctoral
Fellowship Program: $25,000.
Total amount of support: Fellowship:
$250,000 each year.
Matching fund requirements: Match gifts of
partners and employees to academic
programs at degree- granting colleges and
universities in the U.S. and Puerto Rico.

NUMBER OF APPLICANTS MOST RECENT YEAR:
42 for the year 2009.

NUMBER OF AWARDS: Doctoral Fellowship
Program: Up to 10.

APPLICATION INFORMATION:
Application required only for Doctoral
Fellowship Program and can be obtained
through head of university accounting
program. Send letter for other grant requests.
Duration: Doctoral Fellowship Program: Up
to two years.
Deadline: Doctoral Fellowships: October 15.
Announcement in January. No deadline for
Research Grants.

PUBLICATIONS:
Information brochure.

BOARD OF DIRECTORS:
Sharon Allen, Chairman
Shaun Budnik, President
James Jaeger, Secretary and Treasurer

ADDRESS INQUIRIES TO:
Peg Levine, Specialist
(See address above.)

FUND FOR THE IMPROVEMENT OF POSTSECONDARY EDUCATION   [1744]
1990 K Street, N.W.
6th Floor
Washington, DC 20006-8544
(202) 502-7500
Fax: (202) 502-7621

E-MAIL ADDRESS:
sarah.beaton@ed.gov

WEB SITE ADDRESS:
www.ed.gov/fipse

FOUNDED: 1972

AREAS OF INTEREST:
Postsecondary education.

NAME(S) OF PROGRAMS:
● **Comprehensive Program**

TYPE:
Development grants; Project/program grants;
Seed money grants; Technical assistance.
Annual program (occasionally targeted
competitions are held). Project grants for
activities sponsored by institutions, agencies
and organizations which develop and
demonstrate innovative approaches that
improve postsecondary education. All
proposals are tested against criteria published
in the *Federal Register.*

YEAR PROGRAM STARTED: 1972

PURPOSE:
To provide grants and cooperative agreements
for innovative programs in postsecondary
education.

LEGAL BASIS:
Title VII, Part B of the Higher Education Act
as amended in 1998 (Public Law 105-244).

ELIGIBILITY:
All nonprofit institutions, agencies and
organizations providing postsecondary
educational services are eligible.

No funds for facilities development. Funds
for equipment are not encouraged.

GEOGRAPHIC RESTRICTIONS:
United States.

FINANCIAL DATA:
Amount of support per award: $400,000 to
$600,000 for a four-year grant.
Total amount of support: $2,584,000.
Matching fund requirements: The Fund
suggests that institutional funds be included
as part of program support, but this is not
required by legislation or regulation.

APPLICATION INFORMATION:
Application consists of a two-stage proposal
process. A five-page preliminary application
is submitted; then a number of applicants are
invited to submit a longer final proposal.
Preliminary applications should state the
problem being addressed, explain the
intended outcomes and describe the proposed
project activities.
Duration: The Fund will support multiyear
projects on a declining fund basis. Grants are
awarded on a one-, two- and three-year basis,
with phasing of assistance as required.

PUBLICATIONS:
Application guidelines; abstracts of projects
funded.

ADDRESS INQUIRIES TO:
Sarah Beaton
Program Officer and Coordinator
(See address above.)

HALBERT CENTRE FOR CANADIAN STUDIES   [1745]
Canadian Friends of the Hebrew University
3080 Yonge Street, Suite 3020
P.O. Box 65
Toronto ON M4N 3N1 Canada
(416) 485-8000
(888) 432-7398 (Canada only)
Fax: (416) 485-8565

E-MAIL ADDRESS:
inquiry@cfhu.org

WEB SITE ADDRESS:
www.cfhu.org

FOUNDED: 1944

AREAS OF INTEREST:
Canadian studies.

NAME(S) OF PROGRAMS:
● **Halbert Centre for Canadian Studies
Visiting Appointment**

TYPE:
Awards/prizes; Research grants; Visiting
scholars.

YEAR PROGRAM STARTED: 1945

PURPOSE:
To emphasize the development of joint
Israel-Canada research.

LEGAL BASIS:
Nonprofit.

ELIGIBILITY:
Applicants should hold university teaching positions in the social sciences, humanities or law. Applicants will be expected to combine broad teaching and research experience in their field with an ability to emphasize Canadian content. An expression of interest in participating in cooperative work to emphasize the development of joint Israel-Canada research will be of advantage to the applicant.

GEOGRAPHIC RESTRICTIONS:
Canada.

FINANCIAL DATA:
Remuneration includes economy-class return airfare, salary for four, five or nine months (as appropriate) at the rate of the Hebrew University equivalent to Canadian position and other benefits accruing to the position.
Total amount of support: Varies.

NUMBER OF AWARDS: 1.

PUBLICATIONS:
Program announcement.

STAFF:
Rami Kleinmann, National Director

ADDRESS INQUIRIES TO:
Merle Goldman, Associate National Director
(See address above.)

THE HALLETT CHARITABLE TRUSTS [1746]
P.O. Box 39045
Edina, MN 55439
(952) 946-1229

E-MAIL ADDRESS:
halletttrusts@aol.com

WEB SITE ADDRESS:
www.halletttrusts.org

AREAS OF INTEREST:
Higher education, social services, children's services, health, economic and cultural services.

TYPE:
Project/program grants.

PURPOSE:
To directly impact the population of the community in a manner that will measurably enrich its educational, health, economic and cultural opportunities.

ELIGIBILITY:
Grants are made to organizations that have tax-exempt status under Section 501(c)(3) of the Internal Revenue Code. Nonsectarian religious programs may apply. No grants are made to individuals.

GEOGRAPHIC RESTRICTIONS:
Cuyuna Range area, Minnesota.

APPLICATION INFORMATION:
Minnesota Common Grant application form must be submitted to the address above.
Duration: Two years.
Deadline: October 1.

ADDRESS INQUIRIES TO:
Margaret M. Poley, Executive Director
(See address above.)

HALLIBURTON FOUNDATION, INC. [1747]
10200 Bellaire Boulevard
Houston, TX 77072-5206
(281) 575-3558
Fax: (281) 575-3570

E-MAIL ADDRESS:
brinda.maxwell@halliburton.com

WEB SITE ADDRESS:
www.halliburton.com

AREAS OF INTEREST:
Higher education and elementary/secondary education.

TYPE:
Matching gifts; Project/program grants.

LEGAL BASIS:
Corporate giving program.

ELIGIBILITY:
Applicants should be accredited junior colleges, colleges and universities or accredited elementary/secondary schools. Direct Grants are typically awarded to engineering departments or schools of colleges and universities. Grants include awards for faculty support.

No grants are awarded for building programs, financial assistance to students or support of student activities and organizations.

Grants are by invitation only.

GEOGRAPHIC RESTRICTIONS:
United States.

FINANCIAL DATA:
Amount of support per award: Varies.
Total amount of support: Varies.
Matching fund requirements: Contributions of directors, officers and employees of the Halliburton companies to accredited junior colleges, colleges/universities and elementary/secondary schools are matched 2:1 under certain conditions.

NUMBER OF AWARDS: Over 500.

APPLICATION INFORMATION:
Requests for support should be mailed to the address listed above. Lengthy proposals are not required.
Duration: One year.

PUBLICATIONS:
Guidelines.

ADDRESS INQUIRIES TO:
Brinda Maxwell, Administrator
(See address above.)

THE JOHN RANDOLPH HAYNES AND DORA HAYNES FOUNDATION [1748]
888 West Sixth Street, Suite 1150
Los Angeles, CA 90017-2737
(213) 623-9151
Fax: (213) 623-3951

E-MAIL ADDRESS:
info@haynesfoundation.org

WEB SITE ADDRESS:
www.haynesfoundation.org

FOUNDED: 1926

AREAS OF INTEREST:
Education and research in social sciences.

TYPE:
Fellowships; Research grants.

YEAR PROGRAM STARTED: 1926

PURPOSE:
To strengthen education and research in the social sciences into issues of the Los Angeles region.

LEGAL BASIS:
Independent private foundation.

ELIGIBILITY:
501(c)(3) organizations only.

GEOGRAPHIC RESTRICTIONS:
Los Angeles, California.

FINANCIAL DATA:
Amount of support per award: $5,000 to $400,000.
Total amount of support: Up to $3,000,000.

NUMBER OF APPLICANTS MOST RECENT YEAR:
50.

NUMBER OF AWARDS: 12.

REPRESENTATIVE AWARDS:
$50,000 to Center for the Study of Political Graphics; $30,000 to KPCC Southern California Public Radio; $18,800 to Los Angeles City Historical Society.

APPLICATION INFORMATION:
Duration: One to two years.
Deadline: Varies.

PUBLICATIONS:
Annual report.

IRS IDENTIFICATION NUMBER: 95-1644020

ADDRESS INQUIRIES TO:
William J. Burke, Administrative Director
(See address above.)

THE HOROWITZ FOUNDATION FOR SOCIAL POLICY
P.O. Box 7
Rocky Hill, NJ 08553-0007
(732) 445-2280

E-MAIL ADDRESS:
info@horowitz-foundation.org
applications@horowitz-foundation.org

WEB SITE ADDRESS:
www.horowitz-foundation.org

TYPE:
Awards/prizes; Research grants. Grant giving direct assistance to individual scholars who require small grants to further their research with emphasis on policy-oriented studies.

See entry 1978 for full listing.

THE GEORGE A. AND ELIZA GARDNER HOWARD FOUNDATION [1749]
194 Meeting Street
Providence, RI 02912
(401) 863-2640
Fax: (401) 863-6280

E-MAIL ADDRESS:
howard_foundation@brown.edu

WEB SITE ADDRESS:
www.brown.edu/Howard_Foundation

FOUNDED: 1952

TYPE:
Fellowships. The Foundation awards a limited number of fellowships each year for independent projects in fields selected on a rotational basis.

YEAR PROGRAM STARTED: 1952

PURPOSE:
To aid the personal development of promising individuals at the crucial middle stages of their careers.

LEGAL BASIS:
Private foundation.

ELIGIBILITY:
Nominees should normally have the rank of assistant or associate professor or their non-academic equivalents. Support is intended to augment paid sabbatical leaves, making it financially possible for grantees to have time off in which to pursue their projects, free of any other professional responsibilities. Accepted nominees should therefore be eligible for sabbaticals or other leave with guaranteed additional support.

The project undertaken by a Howard Fellow should also be comprehensible to persons outside the immediate field of specialization. Candidates, regardless of their country of citizenship, must be professionally based in the U.S. either by affiliation with an institution or by residence.

GEOGRAPHIC RESTRICTIONS:
United States.

FINANCIAL DATA:
Amount of support per award: $25,000 for the year 2009-10.

Total amount of support: Approximately $250,000.

NUMBER OF APPLICANTS MOST RECENT YEAR:
160.

NUMBER OF AWARDS: Approximately 10 per year.

APPLICATION INFORMATION:
Duration: One academic year, July 1 to June 30.

Deadline: November 1.

ADMINISTRATION:
Ruth J. Simmons, President of the University
Prof. William C. Crossgrove, Administrative Director
Peter Weber, Dean of the Graduate School
Robert W. Kenyon, Representative of the Trustees to the Board of Administration
Prof. Svetlana Evdokimova
Prof. Kenneth Sacks
Prof. Michael Steinberg

BOARD OF TRUSTEES:
Bradford Gorham
Jane G. Gurzenda
Robert W. Kenyon
William W. Kenyon
Arthur H. Parker

ADDRESS INQUIRIES TO:
Prof. William C. Crossgrove
Administrative Director
George A. and Eliza
Gardner Howard Foundation
Box 1945
Brown University
Providence, RI 02912

HOWARD HUGHES MEDICAL INSTITUTE
Office of Grants and Special Programs
4000 Jones Bridge Road
Chevy Chase, MD 20815
(301) 215-8895
Fax: (301) 347-3053

E-MAIL ADDRESS:
biederma@hhmi.org

WEB SITE ADDRESS:
www.hhmi.org/grants

TYPE:
Project/program grants.

See entry 2283 for full listing.

THE FLETCHER JONES FOUNDATION   [1750]
117 East Colorado Boulevard
Suite 403
Pasadena, CA 91105
(626) 535-9506
Fax: (626) 535-9508

E-MAIL ADDRESS:
chris@fletcherjonesfdn.org

WEB SITE ADDRESS:
www.fletcherjonesfdn.org

FOUNDED: 1969

AREAS OF INTEREST:
Primarily, support to private independent colleges and universities in California.

TYPE:
Capital grants; Endowments; Fellowships; Grants-in-aid; Internships; Professorships; Project/program grants; Scholarships. Equipment grants. Academic programs.

YEAR PROGRAM STARTED: 1969

PURPOSE:
To assist private higher education in California.

LEGAL BASIS:
Private foundation.

ELIGIBILITY:
Grants are made to nonprofit, 501(c)(3) organizations. 90% of grants are for private colleges and universities in California. Grants are not made to carry on propaganda, to influence legislation or elections, to promote voter registration, to political candidates, to political campaigns, or to organizations engaged in such activities. Grants are not made to individuals.

The Foundation generally does not favor requests for projects which should be financed by government agencies, nor does it normally make grants to operating funds, elementary or secondary schools, deficit financing, or contingencies. It does not make grants for conferences, seminars, workshops, travel exhibits or surveys.

GEOGRAPHIC RESTRICTIONS:
California.

FINANCIAL DATA:
Amount of support per award: Varies.

APPLICATION INFORMATION:
A qualified, nonprofit organization which believes it meets the Foundation's criteria for a grant may wish to contact the Executive Director.

Deadline: Applications are accepted throughout the year and reviewed quarterly.

IRS IDENTIFICATION NUMBER: 23-7030155

OFFICERS:
Peter Barker, President
Samuel P. Bell, Vice President
Patrick C. Hayden, Vice President
Parker S. Kennedy, Vice President
Robert W. Kummer, Jr., Vice President
Dan Lungren, Vice President
Donald E. Nickelson, Vice President
John P. Pollock, Vice President
Dickinson C. Ross, Vice President
Rockwell Schnabel, Vice President
Stewart R. Smith, Vice President

TRUSTEES:
Peter Barker
Samuel P. Bell
Patrick C. Hayden
Parker S. Kennedy
Robert W. Kummer, Jr.
Dan Lungren
Donald E. Nickelson
John P. Pollock
Dickinson C. Ross
Rockwell Schnabel
Stewart R. Smith

STAFF:
Christine Sisley, Executive Director and Treasurer

ADDRESS INQUIRIES TO:
Christine Sisley
Executive Director and Treasurer
(See address above.)

ALICE AND JULIUS KANTOR CHARITABLE TRUST
809 North Bedford Drive
Beverly Hills, CA 90210
(310) 360-7541
Fax: (310) 360-7580

TYPE:
Development grants; Project/program grants; Research grants.

See entry 204 for full listing.

KCC JAPAN EDUCATION EXCHANGE   [1751]
2100 Sanders Road, Suite 190
Northbrook, IL 60062
(847) 715-9859
Fax: (847) 715-9860

E-MAIL ADDRESS:
kccjee@comcast.net

WEB SITE ADDRESS:
www.kccjee.org

FOUNDED: 1920

NAME(S) OF PROGRAMS:
- **Graduate Fellowships**

TYPE:
Fellowships; Research grants. Fellowships on the Master's and doctoral level. Preparations for studies of a postdoctoral nature in Japan.

YEAR PROGRAM STARTED: 1994

PURPOSE:
To promote education and teaching about Japan in the U.S.

ELIGIBILITY:
Individuals who are U.S. citizens can apply.

FINANCIAL DATA:
Amount of support per award: $24,000.
Total amount of support: $24,000.

NUMBER OF APPLICANTS MOST RECENT YEAR:
13.

NUMBER OF AWARDS: 1.

APPLICATION INFORMATION:
Contact KCC-JEE for an application.
Duration: One year.

ADDRESS INQUIRIES TO:
Barbara Pulsifer, Administrator
(See address above.)

*SPECIAL STIPULATIONS:
Applicants must be currently enrolled in a
Ph.D. program in Japanese studies. Awards
are granted for research year in Japan only
and do not support language study.

MONROE-BROWN
FOUNDATION   [1752]
7950 Moorsbridge Road
Portage, MI 49024
(269) 324-5586
Fax: (269) 324-0686

E-MAIL ADDRESS:
jbaker@monroebrown.org

WEB SITE ADDRESS:
www.monroebrown.org

FOUNDED: 1984

AREAS OF INTEREST:
Higher education and economic development.

TYPE:
Development grants; Internships;
Project/program grants; Scholarships.

PURPOSE:
To advance the public well-being through
higher education and economic development.

LEGAL BASIS:
Private foundation.

ELIGIBILITY:
Organizations must qualify as a nonprofit
under Section 501(c)(3) of the Internal
Revenue Code.

GEOGRAPHIC RESTRICTIONS:
Kalamazoo, Michigan.

FINANCIAL DATA:
Amount of support per award: Varies.

APPLICATION INFORMATION:
Duration: Varies.
Deadline: March 15, June 15, September 15
and December 15.

ADDRESS INQUIRIES TO:
Jane Baker, Director
(See address above.)

NATIONAL ASSOCIATION OF
SCHOLARS   [1753]
One Airport Place
Suites 7 and 8
Princeton, NJ 08540-1532
(609) 683-7878
Fax: (609) 683-0316

E-MAIL ADDRESS:
nas@nas.org

WEB SITE ADDRESS:
www.nas.org

NAME(S) OF PROGRAMS:
● **The Barry R. Gross Memorial Award**
● **The Sidney Hook Memorial Award**
● **The Peter Shaw Memorial Award**

TYPE:
Awards/prizes. The Barry R. Gross Memorial
Award rewards an NAS member for
outstanding service to the cause of academic
reform.

The Sidney Hook Memorial Award is given
to an individual for distinguished
contributions to the defense of academic
freedom and the integrity of academic life.

The Peter Shaw Memorial Award recognizes
exemplary writing on issues pertaining to
higher education and American intellectual
culture.

PURPOSE:
To enrich the substance and strengthen the
integrity of scholarship and teaching.

ELIGIBILITY:
Candidates must be chosen by the
Association.

FINANCIAL DATA:
Amount of support per award: Gross and
Shaw Memorial Awards: $1,000; Hook
Memorial Award: $2,500; for all three in
addition, a plaque and travel expenses to
attend the Association's National Conference
and present a speech.

NATIONAL WILDLIFE
FEDERATION
11100 Wildlife Center Drive
Reston, VA 20190-5362
(703) 438-6265
Fax: (703) 438-6468

E-MAIL ADDRESS:
campus@nwf.org

WEB SITE ADDRESS:
www.nwf.org/campusecology/fellowships

TYPE:
Fellowships.

See entry 2335 for full listing.

SAMUEL ROBERTS NOBLE
FOUNDATION, INC.   [1754]
2510 Sam Noble Parkway
Ardmore, OK 73402
(580) 223-5810
Fax: (580) 224-6212

E-MAIL ADDRESS:
mkwilson@noble.org

WEB SITE ADDRESS:
www.noble.org

FOUNDED: 1945

AREAS OF INTEREST:
Higher education (primarily in Oklahoma)
and health research.

TYPE:
Capital grants; Challenge/matching grants;
General operating grants. Focus on capital
funding for higher education and on health
research and delivery systems.

LEGAL BASIS:
Private foundation.

ELIGIBILITY:
Organizations must be classified as 501(c)(3)
by the IRS and are primarily located in
Oklahoma. No loans or grants are made to
individuals.

GEOGRAPHIC RESTRICTIONS:
Oklahoma.

NUMBER OF APPLICANTS MOST RECENT YEAR:
300 requests received.

NUMBER OF AWARDS: 29 grants awarded.

APPLICATION INFORMATION:
Applicant organizations must send a letter of
request summarizing the project prior to

making a formal grant application. This letter
should be addressed to Michael Cawley,
President, at the address above. If the
proposed project falls within Foundation
interests and parameters, a formal grant
application will be sent to the organization.
Deadline: March 1, June 1, September 1 and
December 1.

ADDRESS INQUIRIES TO:
Mary Kate Wilson, Director of Granting
(See address above.)

NORTH CAROLINA
ASSOCIATION OF
EDUCATORS   [1755]
700 South Salisbury Street
Raleigh, NC 27601
(919) 832-3000 ext. 214
Fax: (919) 829-1626

E-MAIL ADDRESS:
karen.archia@ncae.org

WEB SITE ADDRESS:
www.ncae.org

FOUNDED: 1970

AREAS OF INTEREST:
Teaching.

NAME(S) OF PROGRAMS:
● **Mary Morrow/Edna Richards
Scholarship Fund**

TYPE:
Scholarships. To be used for college expenses
in senior year.

YEAR PROGRAM STARTED: 1994

PURPOSE:
To aid worthy students who plan to teach in
North Carolina after graduation.

LEGAL BASIS:
Nonprofit organization.

ELIGIBILITY:
The applicant must be in their junior year in
a North Carolina college or university,
planning to teach and willing to teach in the
public schools of North Carolina for at least
two years following graduation. Selection is
based on character, personality, scholastic
achievement, evidence of promise as a
teacher and financial need.

GEOGRAPHIC RESTRICTIONS:
North Carolina.

FINANCIAL DATA:
Amount of support per award: $1,000 for the
senior year, payable to the college where
enrolled, to be applied toward expenses of
the student. Amount varies each year
according to earnings of the trust fund.
Total amount of support: Varies.

NUMBER OF APPLICANTS MOST RECENT YEAR:
50.

NUMBER OF AWARDS: 4.

APPLICATION INFORMATION:
Application forms are available from NCAE
Office at the address above. They are mailed
in Fall to the heads of the department of
education in colleges in North Carolina, both
state-supported and private. The department
head is requested to give the application
forms to two juniors of his or her selection.
Duration: One year.
Deadline: Second Monday in January.

STAFF:
Karen Archia, Media Coordinator

PACIFIC FOUNDATION SERVICES   [1756]

1660 Bush Street, Suite 300
San Francisco, CA 94109
(415) 561-6540
Fax: (415) 561-6477

FOUNDED: 1984

AREAS OF INTEREST:
Minority education.

TYPE:
Challenge/matching grants; Demonstration grants; Project/program grants; Seed money grants.

YEAR PROGRAM STARTED: 1984

PURPOSE:
To support higher education, particularly within the minority and underprivileged community.

ELIGIBILITY:
Funding is available for eligible organizations who are IRS 501(c)(3) tax-exempt.

GEOGRAPHIC RESTRICTIONS:
San Francisco Bay area, California.

FINANCIAL DATA:
Amount of support per award: $10,000 to $25,000.
Total amount of support: $176,000.
Matching fund requirements: Generally 1:1.

NUMBER OF AWARDS: 10 to 12.

APPLICATION INFORMATION:
Applications must include a copy of the IRS tax determination letter.
Duration: Multiyear funding is subject to review.
Deadline: April 15 and October 15.

IRS IDENTIFICATION NUMBER: 94-2955164

ADDRESS INQUIRIES TO:
Hector Menendez, Managing Director
(See address above.)

RADCLIFFE INSTITUTE FOR ADVANCED STUDY, HARVARD UNIVERSITY   [1757]

Radcliffe Institute Fellowship Program
Byerly Hall
8 Garden Street
Cambridge, MA 02138
(617) 496-1324
Fax: (617) 495-8136

E-MAIL ADDRESS:
fellowships@radcliffe.edu

WEB SITE ADDRESS:
www.radcliffe.edu/fellowships

FOUNDED: 1960

NAME(S) OF PROGRAMS:
● **Radcliffe Institute Fellowship Program**

TYPE:
Fellowships. The Radcliffe Institute for Advanced Study is a scholarly community where individuals pursue advanced work across a wide range of academic disciplines, professions or creative arts. Within this broad purpose, and in recognition of Radcliffe's historic contributions to the education of women and to the study of issues related to women, the Radcliffe Institute sustains a continuing commitment to the study of women, gender and society, although applicants' projects need not focus on gender.

Radcliffe Institute Fellowships are designed to support scholars, scientists, artists and writers of exceptional promise and demonstrated accomplishment who wish to pursue independent work in academic and professional fields, and in the creative arts.

YEAR PROGRAM STARTED: 1961

PURPOSE:
To offer support to The Radcliffe Institute for Advanced Study Fellowship programs for a scholarly community where individuals pursue advanced work across a wide range of academic disciplines, professions and creative arts.

LEGAL BASIS:
Department of Harvard University, nonprofit.

ELIGIBILITY:
For all programs, residence in the Boston area and participation in the Institute community are required during the fellowship appointment.

GEOGRAPHIC RESTRICTIONS:
Boston and Cambridge, Massachusetts.

FINANCIAL DATA:
Additional funds provided for project expenses. Some support for relocation expenses provided when relevant. If so directed, Radcliffe will pay stipend to home institution.
Amount of support per award: Stipends up to $65,000 for one year.
Total amount of support: Varies.

NUMBER OF APPLICANTS MOST RECENT YEAR:
Over 800.

NUMBER OF AWARDS: Up to 45 fellowships.

APPLICATION INFORMATION:
Applications are available online in late Spring.
Duration: September 1 to May 31.
Deadline: October 1. For scientists: November 15.

ADDRESS INQUIRIES TO:
Fellowships at Radcliffe
(See address above.)

*SPECIAL STIPULATIONS:
Fellows are expected to present their work-in-progress and to attend other fellows' events.

THE NELL J. REDFIELD FOUNDATION

P.O. Box 61
Reno, NV 89504
(775) 323-1373
Fax: (775) 323-4476

E-MAIL ADDRESS:
redfieldfoundation@yahoo.com

TYPE:
Capital grants; Challenge/matching grants; Development grants; Matching gifts; Project/program grants. Grants for higher education. Medical and social welfare for disadvantaged children and seniors.

See entry 304 for full listing.

GERTRUDE E. SKELLY CHARITABLE FOUNDATION   [1758]

4600 North Ocean Boulevard
Suite 206
Boynton Beach, FL 33435
(561) 276-1008
Fax: (561) 272-2793

E-MAIL ADDRESS:
skelly@hhk.com

FOUNDED: 1991

AREAS OF INTEREST:
Education and medical care for indigents.

TYPE:
Challenge/matching grants; Conferences/seminars; Internships; Project/program grants; Research grants; Scholarships; Training grants.

YEAR PROGRAM STARTED: 1991

PURPOSE:
To provide scholarships for individuals to obtain educational opportunities and/or medical care.

LEGAL BASIS:
Private foundation.

ELIGIBILITY:
Eligible applicants are colleges and universities, and other IRS 501(c)(3) tax-exempt organizations. No grants are given to agencies which do not provide direct services or scholarships.

GEOGRAPHIC RESTRICTIONS:
United States.

FINANCIAL DATA:
Amount of support per award: Up to $50,000.
Total amount of support: $765,500 for the year 2009.
Matching fund requirements: Tailored to specific projects.

NUMBER OF APPLICANTS MOST RECENT YEAR:
98.

NUMBER OF AWARDS: 50.

APPLICATION INFORMATION:
Write to the address above for application guidelines and additional information.
Duration: One year.
Deadline: July 31. Award announcement the following January.

TRUSTEES:
Erik Edward Joh

ADDRESS INQUIRIES TO:
Erik Edward Joh, Trustee
(See address above.)

TARAKNATH DAS FOUNDATION   [1759]

South Asian Institute
Columbia University
606 West 122nd Street
New York, NY 10027
(212) 666-4282

E-MAIL ADDRESS:
lg17@columbia.edu

WEB SITE ADDRESS:
www.sipa.columbia.edu/sai/tdas.html

FOUNDED: 1930

AREAS OF INTEREST:
South Asian graduate students and social and research activities in India.

TYPE:
Grants-in-aid.

YEAR PROGRAM STARTED: 1935

PURPOSE:
To promote friendly relations and cultural cooperation among nations.

LEGAL BASIS:
Special interest foundation.

ELIGIBILITY:
Applicants are not limited by discipline or subject area. Applicants must be Indian nationals (holding Indian passports) and must have completed at least one year of graduate study in the U.S.

FINANCIAL DATA:
Amount of support per award: Up to $4,000.
Total amount of support: $25,000.

NUMBER OF APPLICANTS MOST RECENT YEAR:
25 to 30.

NUMBER OF AWARDS: 4 to 6 annually.

APPLICATION INFORMATION:
Applicants must submit all application materials together. Only complete applications will be judged for the awards. Complete applications include:
(1) completed application form;
(2) transcript from most recent academic institution;
(3) three sealed letters of recommendation, including one from the applicant's academic advisor;
(4) academic plans of applicant and;
(5) photocopy of applicant's passport.
Duration: One year.
Deadline: August 1. Award announcement in late October.

U.S. DEPARTMENT OF EDUCATION [1760]

Office of Federal TRIO Programs
1990 K Street, N.W., Suite 7000
Washington, DC 20006-8510
(202) 502-7600
Fax: (202) 502-7857; (202) 219-7074

E-MAIL ADDRESS:
OPE_TRIO@ed.gov

WEB SITE ADDRESS:
www.ed.gov/ope/trio

AREAS OF INTEREST:
Education for low-income youth.

NAME(S) OF PROGRAMS:
● **Upward Bound**

TYPE:
Project/program grants. There are three types of grants under the Upward Bound program: Regular Upward Bound Grants; Veterans Upward Bound Grants; and Upward Bound Math and Science Grants.

The Regular Upward Bound projects are designed to generate in participants the skills and motivation necessary for success in education beyond secondary school. The Veterans Upward Bound projects are designed to assist veterans in preparing for a program of postsecondary education. The Upward Bound Math and Science projects are designed to prepare high school students for postsecondary education programs that lead to careers in the fields of math and science.

YEAR PROGRAM STARTED: 1966

PURPOSE:
To generate participation skills and the motivation necessary for success in education beyond school.

LEGAL BASIS:
Title IV of the Higher Education Act of 1965, as amended.

GEOGRAPHIC RESTRICTIONS:
United States.

FINANCIAL DATA:
Amount of support per award: Estimated - Regular Upward Bound: $250,000 to $853,000 for year one. Average $350,000; Veterans Upward Bound: $250,000 to $543,000 for year one. Average $300,000; Upward Bound Math and Science: $250,000 to $354,000 for year one. Average $270,000.

NUMBER OF APPLICANTS MOST RECENT YEAR:
1,148.

NUMBER OF AWARDS: 791. Upward Bound Award for Math and Science: 130.

APPLICATION INFORMATION:
Official application materials are available from the address above.
Duration: Project periods of up to 60 months.

ADDRESS INQUIRIES TO:
Gaby Watts
(See address above.)

U.S. DEPARTMENT OF EDUCATION

International Education Programs Service
1990 K Street, N.W.
Washington, DC 20006
(202) 502-7626
Fax: (202) 502-7859

E-MAIL ADDRESS:
tanyelle.richardson@ed.gov

WEB SITE ADDRESS:
www.ed.gov

TYPE:
Conferences/seminars; Demonstration grants; Development grants; Project/program grants; Research grants; Seed money grants; Training grants; Travel grants. The program assists institutions of higher learning in:
(1) innovation and improvement of international education curricula to serve the needs of the business community, including the development of new programs for nontraditional, midcareer or part-time students;
(2) development of programs to inform the public of increasing international economic interdependence and the role of U.S. business within the international economic system;
(3) internationalization of curricula at junior and community colleges, and at undergraduate and graduate schools of business;
(4) development of area studies programs and interdisciplinary international programs;
(5) establishment of export education programs through cooperative arrangements with regional and world trade centers and councils and with bilateral and multilateral trade associations;
(6) research for and development of teaching materials relating to international education, including language materials and facilities appropriate to business-oriented students;
(7) establishment of student and faculty fellowships and internships for training and education in international business activities;
(8) development of opportunities for business and other professional school junior faculty to acquire or strengthen international skills and perspectives and;
(9) development of research programs on issues of common interest to institutions of

higher education and private- sector organizations and associations engaged in promoting international economic activity.

See entry 2039 for full listing.

U.S. DEPARTMENT OF EDUCATION

Centers for International Business Education
1990 K Street, N.W., 6th Floor
Washington, DC 20006-8521
(202) 502-7628

E-MAIL ADDRESS:
susanna.easton@ed.gov

WEB SITE ADDRESS:
www.ed.gov/about/offices/list/ope/iegps/index.html

TYPE:
Project/program grants. The program provides grants to eligible institutions of higher education or combinations of these institutions for planning, establishing and operating Centers for International Business Education.

See entry 2040 for full listing.

UCLA INSTITUTE OF AMERICAN CULTURES (IAC)

1237 Murphy Hall, Box 951419
Los Angeles, CA 90095-1419
(310) 794-5115
Fax: (310) 825-8099

E-MAIL ADDRESS:
iaccoordinator@gdnet.ucla.edu

WEB SITE ADDRESS:
www.gdnet.ucla.edu/iacweb/iachome.htm

TYPE:
Fellowships. Deals with arts and humanities, education and teacher training, fine arts, applied arts, law, social sciences, and sciences. The IAC, in cooperation with UCLA's four Ethnic Studies Research Centers (American Indian Studies Center, Asian American Studies Center, Bunche Center for African American Studies Center, and Chicano Studies Research Center) offers awards to visiting scholars to support research on African Americans, American Indians, Asian Americans and Chicanas/os.

See entry 1082 for full listing.

THE UNIVERSITY OF CALGARY [1761]

Faculty of Graduate Studies
Earth Sciences Building, Room 720
2500 University Drive, N.W.
Calgary AB T2N 1N4 Canada
(403) 220-4938
Fax: (403) 289-7635

E-MAIL ADDRESS:
gsaward@ucalgary.ca

WEB SITE ADDRESS:
www.grad.ucalgary.ca

AREAS OF INTEREST:
Management.

NAME(S) OF PROGRAMS:
● **Robert A. Willson Doctoral Management Scholarship**

TYPE:
Awards/prizes; Scholarships.

PURPOSE:
To produce a noteworthy leader in management teaching and research who has a broad appreciation of management's role in society.

ELIGIBILITY:
Open to candidates who are registered in or admissible to a full-time program leading to a doctoral degree in management at the University of Calgary. While academic excellence is essential, candidates should also present evidence of leadership in their academic or professional background.

FINANCIAL DATA:
Amount of support per award: Up to $10,000.
Total amount of support: $10,000.

NUMBER OF AWARDS: 1 per annum.

APPLICATION INFORMATION:
Duration: One year.
Deadline: May 30.

PUBLICATIONS:
Academic calendar.

ADDRESS INQUIRIES TO:
Graduate Scholarship Office
(See address above.)

UNIVERSITY OF CALIFORNIA
President's Postdoctoral Fellowship Program
403 Sproul
Berkeley, CA 94720-5920
(510) 643-6566
Fax: (510) 642-1811

E-MAIL ADDRESS:
kadkinson@berkeley.edu

WEB SITE ADDRESS:
www.ucop.edu/acadadv/ppfp

TYPE:
Fellowships. Awarded for research conducted under faculty sponsorship on any one of the University of California's 10 campuses.

See entry 1084 for full listing.

UNIVERSITY OF TEXAS AT AUSTIN [1762]
LBJ School of Public Affairs
P.O. Box Y
Austin, TX 78713-8925
(512) 471-4292
Fax: (512) 471-8455

E-MAIL ADDRESS:
lbjadmit@mail.utexas.edu

WEB SITE ADDRESS:
www.utexas.edu/lbj

AREAS OF INTEREST:
Public policy.

NAME(S) OF PROGRAMS:
● **Lyndon B. Johnson School of Public Affairs**

TYPE:
Assistantships; Fellowships. Merit fellowships are provided to assist graduate students with paying for education at the Master's and doctoral level.

ELIGIBILITY:
Applicants must be graduate students enrolled in Lyndon B. Johnson School of Public Affairs.

FINANCIAL DATA:
Amount of support per award: $4,000 to $25,000.

NUMBER OF AWARDS: 150.

APPLICATION INFORMATION:
Contact the University for application procedures.
Duration: One to two years. Grants not renewable.
Deadline: January 5.

ADDRESS INQUIRIES TO:
Office of Student Affairs and Programs
(See address above.)

THE WABASH CENTER FOR TEACHING AND LEARNING IN THEOLOGY AND RELIGION
301 West Wabash Avenue
Crawfordsville, IN 47933
(765) 361-6047
Fax: (765) 361-6051

E-MAIL ADDRESS:
wabashcenter@wabash.edu

WEB SITE ADDRESS:
www.wabashcenter.wabash.edu

TYPE:
Conferences/seminars; Fellowships; Project/program grants; Research grants.

See entry 872 for full listing.

JEANNETTE K. WATSON FELLOWSHIP [1763]
11 Park Place, Suite 1503
New York, NY 10007
(212) 655-0201
Fax: (212) 843-0370

E-MAIL ADDRESS:
fwolf@jkwatson.org

WEB SITE ADDRESS:
www.jkwatson.org

TYPE:
Fellowships. The program offers 15 students each year, from 12 New York City colleges, the opportunity for paid internships for three consecutive summers. The internships offer closely supervised, challenging work from which the student can learn. The expectation is that three summers in different sectors (nonprofit organizations, public service and for-profit firms) in New York City and overseas will make fellows more compelling candidates for national fellowships, graduate admissions and good jobs.

YEAR PROGRAM STARTED: 2000

PURPOSE:
To develop talent, leadership and motivation for service.

ELIGIBILITY:
Applicant must:
(1) be enrolled at one of the invited colleges (Baruch College, Brooklyn College, City College, College of Staten Island, Hunter College, John Jay College, Lehman College, Long Island University-Brooklyn Campus, Marymount Manhattan College, Pace University-Manhattan Campus, Queens College, and St. John's University);
(2) be a second semester freshman or a sophomore;
(3) not be older than 25 on March 1 of application year;
(4) be enrolled in a liberal arts program;
(5) be a U.S. citizen or a "green card" holder and;

---

(6) be willing to participate in three successive summer internships and their collateral summer and term-time seminars.

FINANCIAL DATA:
Amount of support per award: $5,000 for the first summer; $6,000 for each of the second and third summers.
Total amount of support: $255,000 annually.

APPLICATION INFORMATION:
Duration: Three consecutive summer internships of 10 weeks plus year-round activities.
Deadline: February.

STAFF:
Frank Wolf, Director
Jennifer Betancourt, Associate Director

THOMAS J. WATSON FELLOWSHIP PROGRAM [1764]
11 Park Place, Suite 1503
New York, NY 10017
(212) 245-8859
Fax: (212) 245-8860

E-MAIL ADDRESS:
tjw@watsonfellowship.org

WEB SITE ADDRESS:
watsonfellowship.org

FOUNDED: 1968

AREAS OF INTEREST:
Independent study outside of the U.S. for graduating college seniors.

TYPE:
Fellowships. The Foundation provides Fellows an opportunity for a focused and disciplined "Wanderjahr" of their own devising or design-time in which to explore with thoroughly a particular interest, test their aspirations and abilities, view their lives and American society in greater perspective and concomitantly, to develop a more informed sense of international concern. The Fellowship experience is intended to provide Fellows an opportunity to immerse themselves in cultures other than their own for an entire year. The candidate's proposed project should involve investigation into an area of demonstrated concern and personal interest.

YEAR PROGRAM STARTED: 1968

PURPOSE:
To give exceptional college graduates the freedom to engage in a year of independent study, purposeful exploration and travel outside of the U.S. in order to enhance their capacity for resourcefulness, imagination, openness and leadership, and to foster their humane and effective participation in the world community.

LEGAL BASIS:
Private foundation.

ELIGIBILITY:
The Foundation welcomes applicants from a diverse range of backgrounds and academic disciplines. Only graduating seniors at participating institutions are eligible for nomination by their institution.

GEOGRAPHIC RESTRICTIONS:
United States.

FINANCIAL DATA:
Amount of support per award: $25,000 for single fellow; up to $35,000 if accompanied by a legal dependent.
Total amount of support: Varies.

NUMBER OF APPLICANTS MOST RECENT YEAR:
180.

NUMBER OF AWARDS: 40 each year.

APPLICATION INFORMATION:
Students must first be nominated by their
college or university, and then compete on a
national level. Application form required.

Duration: One year.

Deadline: Nominations and nominees'
completed applications should arrive by first
Tuesday in November. Announcement made
in mid-March.

PUBLICATIONS:
Guidelines.

IRS IDENTIFICATION NUMBER: 13-6038151

STAFF:
Jennifer Ludovici, Assistant Director
Michele Amar, Project Manager

ADDRESS INQUIRIES TO:
Michele Amar, Project Manager
(See address above.)

*SPECIAL STIPULATIONS:
All Fellows are required to maintain contact
with the fellowship office during their year
abroad. In addition to quarterly progress
reports, they must submit a final evaluation
of the Fellowship year together with a
financial accounting of the expenditure of
Fellowship funds. The Fellowship is taxable
and must be reported by recipients as
income. Taxes are not withheld by the
Foundation.

Scholar aid programs (all disciplines)

ALABAMA COMMISSION ON HIGHER EDUCATION [1765]
100 North Union Street
Montgomery, AL 36104-3702
(334) 242-2273
Fax: (334) 242-2269

E-MAIL ADDRESS:
cheryl.newton@ache.alabama.gov

WEB SITE ADDRESS:
www.ache.alabama.gov

FOUNDED: 1977

AREAS OF INTEREST:
Continuing higher education.

NAME(S) OF PROGRAMS:
● **Senior Adult Scholarship Program**

TYPE:
Grants-in-aid; Scholarships. A free tuition
program for senior citizens who meet the
admission requirements.

ELIGIBILITY:
Alabama residents who are 60 years of age
or older and who attend public two-year
postsecondary educational institutions in
Alabama are eligible to apply.

GEOGRAPHIC RESTRICTIONS:
Alabama.

APPLICATION INFORMATION:
Applications can be obtained by contacting
the financial aid office at any public two-year
postsecondary educational institution in
Alabama.

ADDRESS INQUIRIES TO:
Cheryl B. Newton, Grants Coordinator
(See address above.)

ALABAMA COMMISSION ON HIGHER EDUCATION [1766]
100 North Union Street
Montgomery, AL 36104-3702
(334) 242-2273
Fax: (334) 242-2269

E-MAIL ADDRESS:
cheryl.newton@ache.alabama.gov

WEB SITE ADDRESS:
www.ache.alabama.gov

FOUNDED: 1977

AREAS OF INTEREST:
Higher education.

NAME(S) OF PROGRAMS:
● **Alabama National Guard Educational Assistance Program**

TYPE:
Awards/prizes. An award to be used for
tuition, educational fees and books/supplies
for Alabama National Guard members to
attend a public or private postsecondary
educational institution in Alabama.

YEAR PROGRAM STARTED: 1984

ELIGIBILITY:
Students who are active members in good
standing with a federally recognized unit of
the Alabama National Guard are eligible to
apply. Participants may receive federal
veterans benefits, but must show a
cost-less-aid amount of at least $25. Awards
are based on need.

GEOGRAPHIC RESTRICTIONS:
Alabama.

FINANCIAL DATA:
Amount of support per award: Awards are
limited to $500 per term and no more than
$1,000 per year.

NUMBER OF AWARDS: 704 for the year 2009-10.

APPLICATION INFORMATION:
Application forms are available from
Alabama National Guard Units. Funds are
limited, so students who are Guard members
are encouraged to apply early. Forms must be
signed by a representative of the Alabama
Military Department and the financial aid
officer at the college or university the student
plans to attend.

ADDRESS INQUIRIES TO:
Cheryl B. Newton, Grants Coordinator
(See address above.)

ALABAMA COMMISSION ON HIGHER EDUCATION [1767]
100 North Union Street
Montgomery, AL 36104-3702
(334) 242-2273
Fax: (334) 242-2269

E-MAIL ADDRESS:
cheryl.newton@ache.alabama.gov

WEB SITE ADDRESS:
www.ache.alabama.gov

FOUNDED: 1977

AREAS OF INTEREST:
Higher education.

NAME(S) OF PROGRAMS:
● **Alabama Student Assistance Program**
● **Alabama Student Grant Program**

ADDRESS INQUIRIES TO:
Cheryl B. Newton, Grants Coordinator
(See address above.)

TYPE:
Awards/prizes; Grants-in-aid; Scholarships.
The Alabama Student Assistance Program is
a need-based, state/federal grant. Awards are
limited to undergraduate work.

The Alabama Student Grant Program is an
award of grant assistance at an eligible
independent Alabama college or university.
Award is not based on need. Maximum
amount available only when sufficient funds
are available.

ELIGIBILITY:
Applicants for the Alabama Student
Assistance Program must be undergraduate
students who are Alabama residents attending
eligible Alabama institutions. 55 Alabama
institutions participate in the program.

Applicants for the Alabama Student Grant
Program must be undergraduate students
either half-time or full-time who are Alabama
residents attending Amridge University,
Birmingham-Southern College, Concordia
College, Faulkner University, Huntington
College, Judson College, Miles College,
Oakwood College, Samford University, South
University, Spring Hill College, Stillman
College, U.S. Sports Academy or the
University of Mobile.

GEOGRAPHIC RESTRICTIONS:
Alabama.

FINANCIAL DATA:
Amount of support per award: Student
Assistance Program: $300 to $5,000; Student
Grant Program: Up to $1,200.

Total amount of support: ASAP: $5,204,129;
ASGP: $2,299,025 for the year 2009-10.

NUMBER OF AWARDS: ASAP: 11,520; ASGP:
7,312 for the year 2008-09.

APPLICATION INFORMATION:
Application forms are available at the
institution that the applicant is planning on
attending.

ADDRESS INQUIRIES TO:
Cheryl B. Newton, Grants Coordinator
(See address above.)

THE ISABEL ALLENDE FOUNDATION [1768]
116 Caledonia Street
Sausalito, CA 94965
(415) 289-0992
Fax: (415) 289-1154

E-MAIL ADDRESS:
lori@isabelallendefoundation.org

WEB SITE ADDRESS:
www.isabelallendefoundation.org

FOUNDED: 1996

NAME(S) OF PROGRAMS:
● **Paula Scholarships**

TYPE:
Scholarships.

PURPOSE:
To help dedicated individuals pursue their
educational dreams.

ELIGIBILITY:
Selected male and female students who
would otherwise be unable to afford their
education. Applicants must be U.S. citizens
or residents. Students from all races and
religions are eligible.

GEOGRAPHIC RESTRICTIONS:
San Francisco Bay area, California and Chile.

FINANCIAL DATA:
Amount of support per award: $500 to
$2,500.

Total amount of support: $1,000 to $5,000.

COOPERATIVE FUNDING PROGRAMS: Marin
Education Fund.

APPLICATION INFORMATION:
Unsolicited requests are not accepted.

ADDRESS INQUIRIES TO:
Lori Barra, Executive Director
(See address above.)

AMERICAN ASSOCIATION OF UNIVERSITY WOMEN EDUCATIONAL FOUNDATION

301 ACT Drive
Iowa City, IA 52243-4030
(319) 337-1716
(800) 326-2289
Fax: (319) 337-1204

E-MAIL ADDRESS:
aauw@act.org

WEB SITE ADDRESS:
www.aauw.org

TYPE:
Fellowships. Awarded to women who are
U.S. citizens or permanent residents and who
intend to pursue a full-time course of study
(during the fellowship year) in designated
degree programs where women's
participation has been traditionally low.

See entry 1134 for full listing.

AMERICAN COLLEGE OF MEDICAL PRACTICE EXECUTIVES   [1769]

104 Inverness Terrace East
Englewood, CO 80112-5306
(303) 799-1111 ext. 1869
Fax: (303) 784-6098

E-MAIL ADDRESS:
acmpe@mgma.com

WEB SITE ADDRESS:
www.mgma.com

FOUNDED: 1956

AREAS OF INTEREST:
Medical practice management.

TYPE:
Scholarships. Undergraduate and/or Graduate
Scholarships are for individuals pursuing a
degree relevant to medical practice
management at accredited universities and
colleges.

PURPOSE:
To support the continuous personal
development of professionals in medical
practice management and credentialing.

ELIGIBILITY:
Scholarships are available to individuals in
graduate or undergraduate programs in health
care administration. Preference in the
selection of all scholarship recipients is given
to individuals who either by past experience,
current position, or future plans, demonstrate
potential for contributing to the medical
practice management profession. Applicants
must be enrolled for the fall semester in
which the award is made. The scholarship
program is not intended to support clinical
professions such as medicine, nursing, or
physical therapy.

FINANCIAL DATA:
Amount of support per award: $1,000 to
$5,000.

Total amount of support: Up to $45,000 per
year.

APPLICATION INFORMATION:
Applicants must apply online.

Duration: Varies.

Deadline: May 1.

ADDRESS INQUIRIES TO:
International Scholarship and
Tuition Services, Inc.
Tel: (800) 310-4053 or

ACMPE Scholarship Fund, Inc.
Tel: (877) 275-6462 ext. 1869

AMERICAN COUNCIL OF THE BLIND   [1770]

2200 Wilson Boulevard, Suite 650
Arlington, VA 22201
(202) 467-5081
(800) 424-8666
Fax: (703) 465-5085

E-MAIL ADDRESS:
info@acb.org

WEB SITE ADDRESS:
www.acb.org

FOUNDED: 1961

AREAS OF INTEREST:
The needs, interests and concerns of blind
and visually impaired people on the local,
state and national level.

CONSULTING OR VOLUNTEER SERVICES:
The Council offers the following services:
(1) information and referral on all aspects of
blindness;
(2) legal consultation and representation;
(3) support to consumer advocates working
on issues related to visual handicaps;
(4) assistance in chapter development;
(5) assistance in program development;
(6) employment opportunities information;
(7) speaker referral;
(8) monitoring of existing service delivery
systems, with advocacy for improvement
when necessary;
(9) representation on boards and advisory
committees, both governmental and private;
(10) consultation and assistance in
technological research and;
(11) national legislative hotline.

NAME(S) OF PROGRAMS:
● **American Council of the Blind
   Scholarships**

TYPE:
Assistantships; Awards/prizes; Internships;
Scholarships. Scholarships for outstanding
blind students enrolled in academic,
vocational, technical or professional training
programs beyond the high school level.

YEAR PROGRAM STARTED: 1982

PURPOSE:
To assist blind postsecondary students with
educational expenses.

LEGAL BASIS:
Nonprofit membership organization.

ELIGIBILITY:
Applicants must be legally blind persons
admitted or under consideration for
admission to postsecondary training programs
for the next school year, who are U.S.

citizens or resident aliens and who have
submitted a completed application and the
required supporting materials.

GEOGRAPHIC RESTRICTIONS:
United States.

FINANCIAL DATA:
Amount of support per award: $500 to
$4,000.

Total amount of support: $49,500.

NUMBER OF APPLICANTS MOST RECENT YEAR:
300.

NUMBER OF AWARDS: 25.

APPLICATION INFORMATION:
Submit completed application, certified
transcript, autobiographical sketch, letter of
recommendation from instructor, proof of
acceptance by postsecondary school and
proof of legal blindness.

Duration: One academic year. Nonrenewable,
but recipient may reapply.

Deadline: Postmarked by March 1.
Announcement June 1.

PUBLICATIONS:
Annual report; *Braille Forum*; *Student
Advocate*.

IRS IDENTIFICATION NUMBER: 58-0914436

OFFICERS:
Mitch Pomerantz, President
Brenda Dillon, Second Vice President

ADDRESS INQUIRIES TO:
Scholarship Coordinator
(See address above.)

AMERICAN FRIENDS OF THE ALEXANDER VON HUMBOLDT FOUNDATION   [1771]

1012 14th Street, N.W.
Suite 300
Washington, DC 20005
(202) 783-1907
Fax: (202) 783-1908

E-MAIL ADDRESS:
info@americanfriends-of-avh.org

WEB SITE ADDRESS:
www.humboldt-
foundation.de/en/programme/preise/pt.htm

FOUNDED: 1953

AREAS OF INTEREST:
Scholarly research and academic cooperation
through provision of awards and fellowships.
All countries and all disciplines.

NAME(S) OF PROGRAMS:
● **Humboldt Research Awards for
   Foreign Scholars**

TYPE:
Awards/prizes. Research awards for
outstanding achievements in the fields of
humanities and social sciences, natural
sciences, medicine and engineering sciences
providing for visits to German research
institutes.

YEAR PROGRAM STARTED: 1972

PURPOSE:
To strengthen scientific cooperation between
foreign and German researchers.

LEGAL BASIS:
Government agency run according to private
law.

ELIGIBILITY:
Open to internationally renowned scientists
and scholars having full professor or
equivalent standing.

FINANCIAL DATA:
Amount of support per award: Up to EUR 60,000, plus travel expenses for awardee and accompanying family members.
Total amount of support: Varies.

NUMBER OF AWARDS: Varies.

APPLICATION INFORMATION:
Awards are made by nomination and by eminent German scholars only. No direct applications are allowed.
Duration: Visits to German institutes from six to 12 months. No renewal of the award is possible, but recipient may be invited to Germany again.
Deadline: Nominations may be submitted at any time.

OFFICERS:
Dr. Thomas Hesse, Director, Selection Department

AMERICAN INDIAN GRADUATE CENTER

4520 Montgomery Boulevard, N.E.
Suite 1-B
Albuquerque, NM 87109-1291
(505) 881-4584
Fax: (505) 884-0427

E-MAIL ADDRESS:
marveline@aigcs.org

WEB SITE ADDRESS:
www.aigcs.org

TYPE:
Fellowships; Grants-in-aid; Scholarships. Grants on an academic year basis. Summer funding available to continuing students only; these are students who are currently in the fellowship program.

See entry 1100 for full listing.

AMERICAN INDIAN SCIENCE AND ENGINEERING SOCIETY (AISES)

P.O. Box 9828
Albuquerque, NM 87119-9828
(505) 765-1052

E-MAIL ADDRESS:
scholarship@aises.org

WEB SITE ADDRESS:
www.aises.org

TYPE:
Scholarships. AISES scholarships are intended to partially defray tuition and other educational expenses, thereby increasing access to higher education and improving college retention rates for AISES members.

AISES scholarships are made possible by corporations, government agencies, foundations, and individuals who wish to support the advancement of American Indian/Alaskan Natives. Scholarships are distributed in two disbursements and awarded for one academic year, unless otherwise specified. Recipients cannot receive more than one scholarship in any of the five programs.

Scholarships are also awarded to members of AISES who are American Indian/Alaskan Native college students who meet the eligibility requirements for each scholarship.

See entry 1101 for full listing.

AMERICAN INSTITUTE OF CERTIFIED PUBLIC ACCOUNTANTS (AICPA)

220 Leigh Farm Road
Durham, NC 27707
(919) 402-4931
Fax: (919) 419-4705

E-MAIL ADDRESS:
mic_programs@aicpa.org

WEB SITE ADDRESS:
www.aicpa.org

TYPE:
Scholarships.

See entry 1625 for full listing.

AMERICAN INSTITUTE OF CERTIFIED PUBLIC ACCOUNTANTS (AICPA)   [1772]

220 Leigh Farm Road
Durham, NC 27707
(919) 402-4931
Fax: (919) 419-4705

E-MAIL ADDRESS:
mic_programs@aicpa.org

WEB SITE ADDRESS:
www.aicpa.org

AREAS OF INTEREST:
Accounting/doctoral program.

NAME(S) OF PROGRAMS:
● **AICPA Fellowship for Minority Doctoral Students**

TYPE:
Fellowships. Awarded annually to full-time minority accounting scholars who demonstrate significant potential to become accounting educators.

PURPOSE:
To ensure that C.P.As. of diverse backgrounds are visible in college and university classrooms to serve as role models and mentors to young people in planning their education and careers.

ELIGIBILITY:
Applicants must meet the following requirements to be considered:
(1) has applied to and/or been accepted into a doctoral program with a concentration in accounting;
(2) has earned a Master's degree and/or completed a minimum of three years of full-time experience in the practice of accounting;
(3) be a minority student of Black or African American, Hispanic or Latino, or Native American ethnicity;
(4) attends school on a full-time basis and remains enrolled full-time until attaining one's doctoral degree;
(5) agrees not to work full-time in a paid position or accept responsibility for teaching more than one course per semester as a teaching assistant, or dedicate more than one-quarter of the time as a research assistant;
(6) be a C.P.A. or plan to pursue the C.P.A. credential and;
(7) be a U.S. citizen or permanent resident (green card holder).

GEOGRAPHIC RESTRICTIONS:
United States or its territories.

FINANCIAL DATA:
The AICPA has assisted approximately 100 students in attaining their accounting doctoral designations.

Amount of support per award: Up to $12,000.

NUMBER OF AWARDS: 21 for the academic year 2010-11.

APPLICATION INFORMATION:
Instructions are available online, or send an e-mail to the Institute.
Deadline: April 1.

ADDRESS INQUIRIES TO:
AICPA Minority Doctoral Fellowship Program
(See address above.)

AMERICAN LEGION AUXILIARY - DEPARTMENT OF INDIANA   [1773]

777 North Meridian Street
Room 107
Indianapolis, IN 46204
(317) 630-1390
Fax: (317) 630-1277

E-MAIL ADDRESS:
ala777@sbcglobal.net

WEB SITE ADDRESS:
www.amlegauxin.org

AREAS OF INTEREST:
Indiana's youth who are children, grandchildren or great-grandchildren of veterans.

NAME(S) OF PROGRAMS:
● **Edna M. Barcus Memorial/Hoosier Schoolhouse Scholarship**

TYPE:
Scholarships.

LEGAL BASIS:
Society.

ELIGIBILITY:
The applicant must be the child, grandchild or great-grandchild of a veteran of World War I, World War II, Korean, Vietnam, Beirut, Grenada, Panama or Persian Gulf Wars or any current conflict who is financially unable to attend college or a school for special training after graduation from high school. The applicant must not be under 16 nor over 22 years old and must be in their senior year or be a graduate of an accredited high school, but cannot have attended an institution of higher learning.

Students receiving a scholarship must be Indiana residents who will be attending an Indiana school approved by the Scholarship Committee.

GEOGRAPHIC RESTRICTIONS:
Indiana.

FINANCIAL DATA:
Funds are sent to school to be used for books, tuition or other incidentals.
Amount of support per award: $250 first semester, $250 second semester.
Total amount of support: Up to $2,500.

NUMBER OF APPLICANTS MOST RECENT YEAR: 500.

NUMBER OF AWARDS: 5.

APPLICATION INFORMATION:
The applicant must complete an application form and provide letters of recommendation from the superintendent or principal of the school from which the applicant is a graduate and an adult citizen, other than relatives, who knows the applicant in the community and

home. In addition, a transcript of credits must be included as well as an essay of no more than 1,000 words on the topic "My Obligation as a Hoosier." Enclose self-addressed, stamped envelope.

Duration: One year. No renewals.

Deadline: April 1.

ADDRESS INQUIRIES TO:
Judy Otey
Department Secretary/Treasurer
(See address above.)

AMERICAN LEGION AUXILIARY - DEPARTMENT OF WISCONSIN [1774]

2930 American Legion Drive
Portage, WI 53901
(608) 745-0124
Fax: (608) 745-1947

E-MAIL ADDRESS:
alawi@amlegionauxwi.org

WEB SITE ADDRESS:
www.amlegionauxwi.org

FOUNDED: 1921

AREAS OF INTEREST:
Scholar aid programs for children of Veterans.

NAME(S) OF PROGRAMS:
- **Child Welfare Scholarship**
- **Health Careers Scholarships**
- **H.S. and Angeline Lewis Scholarships**
- **Merit and Memorial Scholarships**
- **State President's Scholarships**
- **Della Van Deuren Scholarships**

TYPE:
Scholarships.

PURPOSE:
To enable students to secure Baccalaureate degrees.

ELIGIBILITY:
(1) Applicant must be a daughter, son, stepdaughter, stepson, wife or widow of a veteran;
(2) Granddaughters, grandsons, great-granddaughters, great-grandsons, step-granddaughters, step-grandsons, step-great-granddaughters, step-great-grandsons of a Wisconsin American Legion Auxiliary member may also apply;
(2a) If the applicant is a member of a Wisconsin American Legion Auxiliary Unit, a Wisconsin American Legion Post or a Wisconsin Sons of The American Legion Squadron, they do not need to reside in Wisconsin;
(3) Applicant must be in need of financial help to continue their education;
(4) Applicant must have at least a 3.5 grade point average on a 4.0 grade base and;
(5) Applicant must be a resident of Wisconsin, except as noted in (2a) above.

Applicant may apply for more than one scholarship, but can only receive one scholarship from the American Legion Auxiliary-Department of Wisconsin, awarded on a one-time only basis, nonrenewable. School selected to attend must be an accredited school, but need not be located in Wisconsin. Judges reserve the right to determine the type of scholarship awarded and their decision is final.

GEOGRAPHIC RESTRICTIONS:
Wisconsin.

FINANCIAL DATA:
Amount of support per award: Varies depending on available funds.
Total amount of support: $26,500 for the year 2010.

NUMBER OF APPLICANTS MOST RECENT YEAR: 200.

NUMBER OF AWARDS: 27 for the year 2010.

APPLICATION INFORMATION:
Applicants must use only the application form designated for the year that they are applying for. For the Lewis, State President's, Merit and Memorial, Child Welfare, Health Careers and Registered Nurse Scholarships, one application form may be used regardless of how many programs an applicant may be eligible for.

Duration: One year.

Deadline: March 15.

PUBLICATIONS:
Need a Lift.

ADDRESS INQUIRIES TO:
Bonnie Dorniak
Executive Secretary/Treasurer
(See address above.)

AMERICAN MEDICAL ASSOCIATION FOUNDATION [1775]

515 North State Street
Chicago, IL 60654
(312) 464-4200
Fax: (312) 464-4142

E-MAIL ADDRESS:
amafoundation@ama-assn.org

WEB SITE ADDRESS:
www.amafoundation.org

FOUNDED: 1950

AREAS OF INTEREST:
Public health and medical education.

CONSULTING OR VOLUNTEER SERVICES:
Raising awareness about low-health literacy.

NAME(S) OF PROGRAMS:
- **Excellence in Medicine**
- **Joan F. Giambalvo Memorial Scholarship**
- **Health Literacy Initiative**
- **Healthy Communities/Healthy America**
- **Healthy Living Grant Program**
- **Minority Scholars Award**
- **Physicians of Tomorrow Scholarship**
- **Scholars Fund**
- **Seed Grant Research Program**
- **Arthur N. Wilson, M.D. Scholarship**

TYPE:
Awards/prizes; Project/program grants; Research grants; Scholarships; Seed money grants. Excellence in Medicine Awards are given to recognize physicians and medical students who are improving the health of their communities and the lives of those who are most in need.

The Joan F. Giambalvo Memorial Scholarship is presented in conjunction with the AMA's Women Physicians Congress to provide a research grant to help researchers advance the progress of women in the medical profession and identify and address the needs of women physicians and medical students.

Health Literacy Initiative seeks to provide awareness among physicians and health care providers to understand healthy literacy and its impact on patient safety.

Healthy Communities/Healthy America awards grants to existing, physician-led free clinics that provide free or low-cost medical care to underserved and uninsured populations.

Healthy Living Grant Program provides grants to support healthy lifestyles projects in the areas of nutrition, physical fitness, prescription medication safety and violence prevention.

The Minority Scholars Awards are given in collaboration with the AMA Minority Affairs Consortium to first- and second-year medical students from historically underrepresented minority groups in the medical profession.

The Physicians of Tomorrow Scholarships are awarded to promising fourth-year medical students based on financial need and academic excellence.

In partnership with the AMA Alliance, the Scholars Fund distributes tuition assistance funds to medical schools across the country.

The Seed Grant Research Program provides medical students, physician residents and fellows with grants to help them conduct basic science or clinical research.

The Arthur N. Wilson, M.D. Scholarship is awarded to a medical student who is a graduate of a high school in southeast Alaska.

PURPOSE:
To improve the health of Americans through philanthropic support of quality programs in public health and medical education.

LEGAL BASIS:
Public foundation.

GEOGRAPHIC RESTRICTIONS:
United States.

FINANCIAL DATA:
Amount of support per award: Joan F. Giambalvo Memorial Scholarship, Minority Scholars Award and Physicians of Tomorrow Scholarship: $10,000; Healthy Communities/Healthy America: $10,000 to $25,000; Healthy Living Grant Program and Arthur N. Wilson, M.D. Scholarship: $5,000; Scholars Fund: $1,000 up; Seed Grant Research Program: $2,500.

PUBLICATIONS:
Brochure; program announcement; e-newsletter; quarterly newsletter.

ADDRESS INQUIRIES TO:
Louella Hung, Program Officer or
Dina Lindenberg, Program Officer
(See address above.)

AMERICAN OSTEOPATHIC FOUNDATION

142 East Ontario Street, Suite 1450
Chicago, IL 60611-2864
(312) 202-8232
Fax: (312) 202-8216

E-MAIL ADDRESS:
vheck@aof-foundation.org

WEB SITE ADDRESS:
www.aof-foundation.org

TYPE:
Awards/prizes; Scholarships. Grants.

See entry 2681 for full listing.

AMERICAN OSTEOPATHIC FOUNDATION [1776]

142 East Ontario Street, Suite 1450
Chicago, IL 60611-2864
(312) 202-8232
(312) 202-8234
Fax: (312) 202-8216

E-MAIL ADDRESS:
vheck@aof-foundation.org

WEB SITE ADDRESS:
www.aof-foundation.org

FOUNDED: 1949

AREAS OF INTEREST:
Osteopathic medical education.

NAME(S) OF PROGRAMS:
● **Russell C. McCaughan, D.O., Education Scholarship**

TYPE:
Scholarships. Awarded annually to one rising second-year student at each of the accredited U.S. colleges of osteopathic medicine.

PURPOSE:
To ensure the ideals of osteopathic medicine by initiating and supporting programs that enhance the profession, advance the quality of people's health, and recognize excellence in the areas of education and research.

LEGAL BASIS:
Private foundation.

ELIGIBILITY:
Candidates for the Russell C. McCaughan Education Scholarship must demonstrate financial need, outstanding academic and extracurricular accomplishments, and strong commitment to osteopathic philosophy during the first year of school. Student must possess ability to work harmoniously with fellow students and faculty and show promise as an osteopathic physician. The Foundation solicits nominations from each school of osteopathic medicine.

FINANCIAL DATA:
Amount of support per award: $400.

NUMBER OF AWARDS: 1.

APPLICATION INFORMATION:
Selections are made by the Dean and faculty.

STAFF:
Stephen S. Downey, Executive Director
Vicki Heck, Associate Director of Communications
Maggie K. Burton, Senior Development Officer
Jacqui Golding, Program Specialist
Susan Laslie, Controller

ADDRESS INQUIRIES TO:
Vicki Heck
Associate Director of Communications
(See address above.)

THE AMERICAN SOCIETY FOR NONDESTRUCTIVE TESTING, INC. [1777]

1711 Arlingate Lane
Columbus, OH 43228
(614) 274-6003
(800) 222-2768
Fax: (614) 274-6899

E-MAIL ADDRESS:
sdille@asnt.org

WEB SITE ADDRESS:
www.asnt.org

FOUNDED: 1941

AREAS OF INTEREST:
Nondestructive testing and engineering.

NAME(S) OF PROGRAMS:
● **Engineering Undergraduate Award**
● **Robert B. Oliver Scholarship**

TYPE:
Scholarships.

YEAR PROGRAM STARTED: 1998

PURPOSE:
To support research and education in nondestructive testing and to increase public awareness of nondestructive testing's critical role in ensuring the safety and well-being of mankind.

LEGAL BASIS:
501(c)(3) corporation.

ELIGIBILITY:
Engineering Undergraduate Award: Students must be enrolled in an engineering program of a university accredited by ABET or its equivalent and choosing NDT as their field of specialization.

Oliver Scholarship: Students must be officially enrolled in an undergraduate degree, associate degree, or postsecondary certificate program, which includes studies in NDT.

FINANCIAL DATA:
Amount of support per award: Engineering Undergraduate Award: $3,000; Oliver Scholarship: $2,500.

Total amount of support: Engineering Undergraduate Award: $9,000; Oliver Scholarship: $7,500.

NUMBER OF AWARDS: 3 per award.

APPLICATION INFORMATION:
Contact ASNT Executive Assistant for application.
Deadline: Engineering Undergraduate Award: December 15. Oliver Scholarship: February 15.

ADDRESS INQUIRIES TO:
Stephanie Dille, ASNT Executive Assistant
(See address above.)

AMERICAN SOCIETY OF HEMATOLOGY

2021 L Street, N.W.
Suite 900
Washington, DC 20036
(202) 776-0544
Fax: (888) 719-7814

E-MAIL ADDRESS:
awards@hematology.org

WEB SITE ADDRESS:
www.hematology.org

TYPE:
Awards/prizes; Fellowships; Research grants; Scholarships.

See entry 2381 for full listing.

THE AMERICAN SWEDISH INSTITUTE

2600 Park Avenue
Minneapolis, MN 55407
(612) 871-4907
Fax: (612) 871-8682

E-MAIL ADDRESS:
info@americanswedishinst.org

WEB SITE ADDRESS:
www.americanswedishinst.org

TYPE:
Scholarships; Travel grants. The Malmberg Scholarship is awarded for up to one academic year of study in Sweden.

See entry 944 for full listing.

AMVETS [1778]

4647 Forbes Boulevard
Lanham, MD 20706-4380
(301) 459-9600
(877) 726-8387
Fax: (301) 459-7924

E-MAIL ADDRESS:
scholarships@amvets.org

WEB SITE ADDRESS:
www.amvets.org

FOUNDED: 1944

NAME(S) OF PROGRAMS:
● **AMVETS National Scholarship Program: Entering College Freshman Scholarship**
● **AMVETS National Scholarship Program: JROTC Scholarship**

TYPE:
Scholarships. National scholarship program for high school seniors who are children or grandchildren of veterans.

PURPOSE:
To make the goal of postsecondary education more attainable for the children and grandchildren of veterans by assisting deserving students who might not otherwise have the financial means to achieve their educational goals.

ELIGIBILITY:
Applicant must:
(1) be a graduating high school senior entering at the college freshman level in the upcoming fall or be an active JROTC cadet and currently a high school senior;
(2) have a minimum grade point average of 3.0 (or documented evidence of extenuating circumstances that caused a lower grade point average);
(3) be the child or grandchild of a U.S. veteran who is an AMVETS member, or if deceased, would have been eligible for AMVETS membership;
(4) be a U.S. citizen;
(5) demonstrate academic promise and financial need and;
(6) agree to authorize AMVETS to publicize their scholarship award, if they are selected.

GEOGRAPHIC RESTRICTIONS:
United States.

FINANCIAL DATA:
Amount of support per award: Entering College Freshman Scholarship: $4,000 ($1,000 per year of a four-year program); JROTC Scholarship: $1,000.

NUMBER OF AWARDS: Entering College Freshman Scholarship: 6; JROTC Scholarship: 1.

APPLICATION INFORMATION:
Applications must be sent via regular mail.
Duration: One to four years. Nonrenewable.
Deadline: April 15.

ADDRESS INQUIRIES TO:
Tiffany Hilton
National Programs Associate
(See address above.)

AMVETS   [1779]
4647 Forbes Boulevard
Lanham, MD 20706-4380
(301) 459-9600
(877) 726-8387
Fax: (301) 459-7924

E-MAIL ADDRESS:
scholarships@amvets.org

WEB SITE ADDRESS:
www.amvets.org

FOUNDED: 1944

NAME(S) OF PROGRAMS:
● **AMVETS/University of Phoenix Scholarship**

TYPE:
Scholarships. Scholarships for U.S. veterans, active-duty service members, reservists, Guardsmen and their family members.

YEAR PROGRAM STARTED: 2007

PURPOSE:
To enable members of the active military, veterans, and their families to be successful and have a better quality of life for themselves and their families, starting with education.

ELIGIBILITY:
All veterans, service members, and family members are eligible to apply. Applicant must be a current member of the active military or an honorably discharged veteran or spouse, child or grandchild of these two groups and not be receiving 100% tuition reimbursement.

GEOGRAPHIC RESTRICTIONS:
United States.

FINANCIAL DATA:
Amount of support per award: $4,000 scholarship in the form of a non-cash credit to the awardee's University Account to be used for tuition and fees only.

NUMBER OF AWARDS: Approximately 25 annually.

APPLICATION INFORMATION:
Applicants must submit a complete essay on one of the listed topics. All materials must be submitted by mail. Recipients will be selected by the Scholarship Committee, consisting of representatives from the University of Phoenix and AMVETS.
Duration: Varies. Nonrenewable.
Deadline: July 1.

ADDRESS INQUIRIES TO:
Tiffany Hilton
National Programs Associate
(See address above.)

ARCHAEOLOGICAL INSTITUTE OF AMERICA   [1780]
656 Beacon Street, 6th Floor
Boston, MA 02215
(617) 358-4184
Fax: (617) 353-6550

E-MAIL ADDRESS:
lsparks@aia.bu.edu

WEB SITE ADDRESS:
www.archaeological.org

FOUNDED: 1879

AREAS OF INTEREST:
Archaeological research and publication.

NAME(S) OF PROGRAMS:
● **Publications Preparation Grant**

TYPE:
Grants-in-aid. Publication Grant offers a stipend to assist scholars in preparing, completing, and publishing results of their field research.

YEAR PROGRAM STARTED: 2002

PURPOSE:
To support the scholarly publication of already excavated achaeological material in a peer-reviewed outlet.

ELIGIBILITY:
Open to graduate students and scholars with a Ph.D. To be eligible, applicants must be members of the AIA at the time of application and until the end of the grant term.

FINANCIAL DATA:
Amount of support per award: $5,000 distributed over two years in annual installments of $2,500.
Total amount of support: $5,000.

NUMBER OF APPLICANTS MOST RECENT YEAR:
8.

NUMBER OF AWARDS: 1.

APPLICATION INFORMATION:
Applicants must submit a dissertation title or graduate transcript, three letters of reference, and a summary statement of the proposed project. Applicants may request funds to work on archaeological material of any period from anywhere in the world. Material may already reside in international or North American museums or institutions, or still remain in storerooms on site. Recipients are expected to submit a report to the AIA Fellowship Committee after the first year of funding and are also encouraged to submit an abstract to the AIA's Annual Meeting during the second. At the conclusion of the fellowship tenure, the recipient must submit two copies of the following items for the AIA Fellowship Committee and the President of the AIA:
(1) a budgetary report on the use of the stipend;
(2) a summary of the research;
(3) the completed manuscript and;
(4) evidence that the manuscript has been submitted to an appropriate venue for publication.
Duration: Two years.
Deadline: November 1. Announcement by February 1.

ADDRESS INQUIRIES TO:
Laurel Nilsen Sparks
Lecture and Fellowship Coordinator
(See address above.)

*SPECIAL STIPULATIONS:
After the tenure of their fellowship, fellows are expected to submit an abstract to the Program Committee within two years in accordance with that committee's guidelines, in order to present a paper on their research at the Institute Annual Meeting.

ARMENIAN GENERAL BENEVOLENT UNION   [1781]
55 East 59th Street
New York, NY 10022-1112
(212) 319-6383
Fax: (212) 319-6507

E-MAIL ADDRESS:
scholarship@agbu.org

WEB SITE ADDRESS:
www.agbu.org

AREAS OF INTEREST:
Education.

NAME(S) OF PROGRAMS:
● **A.G.B.U. Scholarship Program**
● **Fellowship for U.S.-Based Study**
● **International Scholarships**
● **Performing Arts Fellowship**
● **Religious Studies Fellowship**

TYPE:
Fellowships; Scholarships.

PURPOSE:
To provide financial assistance to students of Armenian descent.

ELIGIBILITY:
Students must be of Armenian descent enrolled in college or university.

FINANCIAL DATA:
Amount of support per award: $1,000 to $7,500.
Total amount of support: Approximately $500,000 annually.

NUMBER OF APPLICANTS MOST RECENT YEAR:
Over 500.

NUMBER OF AWARDS: Over 500.

APPLICATION INFORMATION:
Applications are available online.
Deadline: U.S. Fellowship: April 15; Performing Arts and Religious Studies Fellowships: May 15; International Scholarship: May 31.

ADDRESS INQUIRIES TO:
Scholarship Program
(See address above.)

ASIAN AMERICAN JOURNALISTS ASSOCIATION   [1782]
5 Third Street
Suite 1108
San Francisco, CA 94103
(415) 346-2051
Fax: (415) 346-6343

E-MAIL ADDRESS:
naov@aaja.org

WEB SITE ADDRESS:
www.aaja.org

FOUNDED: 1981

AREAS OF INTEREST:
Journalism.

NAME(S) OF PROGRAMS:
● **Broadcast News Grant**
● **Stanford Chen Grant**
● **Vincent Ching Scholarships**
● **Mary Moy Quon Ing Memorial Scholarships**
● **Print & Online News Grant**

TYPE:
Internships; Scholarships.

PURPOSE:
To encourage Asian-American students to pursue journalism careers.

ELIGIBILITY:
Must be a full-time college student or high school senior pursuing journalism as a major.

FINANCIAL DATA:
Amount of support per award: Broadcast News Grant: $1,000 to $2,500; Stanford Chen Grant: $1,750; Vincent Ching

Scholarships: $500; Mary Moy Quon Ing Memorial Scholarships: $2,000; Print & Online News Grant: $1,000.

NUMBER OF APPLICANTS MOST RECENT YEAR: 100.

NUMBER OF AWARDS: 20.

APPLICATION INFORMATION:
Duration: One year. Renewal possible.
Deadline: Broadcast News Grant and Print & Online News Grant: May 16; Stanford Chen Grant and Mary Moy Quon Ing Memorial Scholarships: May 2; Vincent Ching Scholarships: May 13.

ADDRESS INQUIRIES TO:
Nao Vang, Student Programs Coordinator
(See address above.)

ASSOCIATION OF UNIVERSITIES AND COLLEGES OF CANADA   [1783]

350 Albert Street, Suite 600
Ottawa ON K1R 1B1 Canada
(613) 563-1236
Fax: (613) 563-9745

E-MAIL ADDRESS:
awards@aucc.ca

WEB SITE ADDRESS:
www.aucc.ca

FOUNDED: 1911

AREAS OF INTEREST:
Undergraduate education at a Canadian university.

NAME(S) OF PROGRAMS:
● **C.D. Howe Scholarships**

TYPE:
Scholarships. Awards for undergraduate study in any discipline. Recipients may attend any university or degree-granting college which is a member or affiliated to a member of the Association of Universities and Colleges of Canada. Community colleges are not eligible institutions.

YEAR PROGRAM STARTED: 1987

PURPOSE:
To assist Canadian students from Thunder Bay and the former federal constituency of Port Arthur to pursue an undergraduate degree in any field at a Canadian university.

LEGAL BASIS:
Nonprofit foundation.

ELIGIBILITY:
Candidates must be Canadian citizens or permanent residents and must be graduating or have graduated within the last year, with a minimum average of A minus in their top six Ontario Academy Credits or Grade 13 subjects. Award holders must enter first-year university full-time in the year of application, be enrolled in a course of study leading to an undergraduate degree and remain in good academic and disciplinary standing.

Students must be residents of Thunder Bay or the former constituency of Port Arthur.

The Thunder Bay area includes the following school boards:
(1) Thunder Bay Catholic District School Board;
(2) Red Lake Combined Roman Catholic Separate School Board and;
(3) Superior North Catholic District School Board.

The former constituency of Port Arthur includes the following school boards:
(1) Lakehead District School Board;
(2) Superior Greenstone District School Board and;
(3) Conseil scolaire de district catholique des Aurores Boreales.

To be considered for renewal, award holders must maintain a full-time status, as defined by the institution, and obtain a B average in each year of study. Students must request an official transcript from their educational institution as well as complete a renewal report; both should be sent to the AUCC at the end of each academic year. Any changes of personal or academic status must also be transmitted to the AUCC.

GEOGRAPHIC RESTRICTIONS:
Canada.

FINANCIAL DATA:
Payment will be made by AUCC to the universities attended. Payment by the university will be according to the usual practice of the university.
Amount of support per award: $5,500 (CAN) annually.
Total amount of support: $11,000 (CAN) annually.

NUMBER OF AWARDS: 2 annually; one to a Thunder Bay student and one to a student from C.D. Howe's former constituency of Port Arthur.

APPLICATION INFORMATION:
Application forms are available from the high schools or school boards in the relevant districts or directly from AUCC. Applicants must have their schools send the official transcript directly to AUCC. In addition, applicants must enclose two letters of reference with their application.
Duration: Maximum of four years or until first degree is obtained, whichever occurs first.
Deadline: Postmarked by June 1. Announcement by mid-August.

PUBLICATIONS:
Program announcement.

ADDRESS INQUIRIES TO:
Linda Balaton
Customer Relations Officer, Scholarships
(See address above.)

ASSOCIATION ON AMERICAN INDIAN AFFAIRS

966 Hungerford Drive, Suite 12-B
Rockville, MD 20850
(240) 314-7155
Fax: (240) 314-7159

E-MAIL ADDRESS:
lw.aaia@verizon.net

WEB SITE ADDRESS:
www.indian-affairs.org

TYPE:
Grants-in-aid; Scholarships. Emergency Aid Scholarships are for full-time graduate and undergraduate students. This program is limited by the availability of scholarship funds.

See entry 1104 for full listing.

ASSOCIATION ON AMERICAN INDIAN AFFAIRS

966 Hungerford Drive, Suite 12-B
Rockville, MD 20850
(240) 314-7155
Fax: (240) 314-7159

E-MAIL ADDRESS:
lw.aaia@verizon.net

WEB SITE ADDRESS:
www.indian-affairs.org

TYPE:
Scholarships.

See entry 1105 for full listing.

ASSOCIATION ON AMERICAN INDIAN AFFAIRS

966 Hungerford Drive, Suite 12-B
Rockville, MD 20850
(240) 314-7155
Fax: (240) 314-7159

E-MAIL ADDRESS:
lw.aaia@verizon.net

WEB SITE ADDRESS:
www.indian-affairs.org

TYPE:
Scholarships. Intended for those men and women who would not otherwise be able to complete their educational goals due to family responsibilities.

See entry 1107 for full listing.

ASSOCIATION ON AMERICAN INDIAN AFFAIRS

966 Hungerford Drive, Suite 12-B
Rockville, MD 20850
(240) 314-7155
Fax: (240) 314-7159

E-MAIL ADDRESS:
lw.aaia@verizon.net

WEB SITE ADDRESS:
www.indian-affairs.org

TYPE:
Scholarships. Offered to American Indian and Alaskan Native graduate and undergraduate students who are members of tribes that are not federally recognized.

See entry 1108 for full listing.

ASSOCIATION ON AMERICAN INDIAN AFFAIRS

966 Hungerford Drive, Suite 12-B
Rockville, MD 20850
(240) 314-7155
Fax: (240) 314-7159

E-MAIL ADDRESS:
lw.aaia@verizon.net

WEB SITE ADDRESS:
www.indian-affairs.org

TYPE:
Scholarships. Offered to American Indian or Alaskan Native graduate students pursuing a Master's in the arts, law or public health.

See entry 1109 for full listing.

ASSOCIATION ON AMERICAN INDIAN AFFAIRS

966 Hungerford Drive, Suite 12-B
Rockville, MD 20850
(240) 314-7155
Fax: (240) 314-7159

E-MAIL ADDRESS:
lw.aaia@verizon.net

WEB SITE ADDRESS:
www.indian-affairs.org

TYPE:
Scholarships. Offered to graduate and undergraduate students pursuing a major in public health and science.

See entry 1110 for full listing.

ASSOCIATION ON AMERICAN INDIAN AFFAIRS
966 Hungerford Drive, Suite 12-B
Rockville, MD 20850
(240) 314-7155
Fax: (240) 314-7159

E-MAIL ADDRESS:
lw.aaia@verizon.net

WEB SITE ADDRESS:
www.indian-affairs.org

TYPE:
Scholarships.

See entry 1111 for full listing.

ALEXANDER GRAHAM BELL ASSOCIATION FOR THE DEAF AND HARD OF HEARING
3417 Volta Place, N.W.
Washington, DC 20007
(202) 337-5220
Fax: (202) 337-8314

E-MAIL ADDRESS:
financialaid@agbell.org

WEB SITE ADDRESS:
www.agbell.org

TYPE:
Scholarships.

See entry 1035 for full listing.

BNSF FOUNDATION
2650 Lou Menk Drive
Fort Worth, TX 76131-2830
(817) 867-6458
Fax: (817) 352-7925

E-MAIL ADDRESS:
bnsffoundation@bnsf.com

WEB SITE ADDRESS:
www.bnsffoundation.org

TYPE:
Scholarships. Awarded annually to outstanding Native American high school seniors from funds provided by the Foundation, for up to four years or until undergraduate degree requirements are completed, whichever occurs first. Scholarship winners may attend any accredited college (two-year leading to a four-year degree) or university in the U.S.

See entry 1112 for full listing.

BNSF FOUNDATION
2650 Lou Menk Drive
Fort Worth, TX 76131-2830
(817) 867-6458
Fax: (817) 352-7925

E-MAIL ADDRESS:
bnsffoundation@bnsf.com

WEB SITE ADDRESS:
www.bnsffoundation.org

TYPE:
Scholarships. Scholarships awarded to high school graduates of Hispanic origin through the Hispanic College Fund (HCF).

See entry 1129 for full listing.

THE LYNDE AND HARRY BRADLEY FOUNDATION, INC.   [1784]
1241 North Franklin Place
Milwaukee, WI 53202-2901
(414) 291-9915
Fax: (414) 291-9991

WEB SITE ADDRESS:
www.bradleyfdn.org

FOUNDED: 1942

AREAS OF INTEREST:
Humanities, social sciences and law.

NAME(S) OF PROGRAMS:
- **Bradley Fellowship Program**

TYPE:
Fellowships. To strengthen America's "intellectual infrastructure" at a higher-education level, providing useful assistance to young scholars during a critical phase in their education.

YEAR PROGRAM STARTED: 1986

PURPOSE:
To assist candidates to complete their studies, prepare manuscripts for publication, conduct research, and enhance their competitiveness in the job market.

ELIGIBILITY:
Selected candidates must be intelligent doctoral and postdoctoral fellows within the discretion of participating professors or nominators. The principal consideration is excellence and merit. Candidates must also be U.S. citizens or residents.

GEOGRAPHIC RESTRICTIONS:
United States.

FINANCIAL DATA:
Amount of support per award: Up to $25,000 per academic year.

APPLICATION INFORMATION:
Recipients must be nominated by participating professors or nominators.

ADDRESS INQUIRIES TO:
Dianne Sehler, Director of Academic, International and Cultural Programs
(See address above.)

BROADCAST EDUCATION ASSOCIATION
1771 N Street, N.W.
Washington, DC 20036-2891
(888) 380-7222
(202) 429-3935
Fax: (202) 775-2981

E-MAIL ADDRESS:
beamemberservices@nab.org

WEB SITE ADDRESS:
www.beaweb.org

TYPE:
Scholarships. BEA is the professional development association for professors, industry professionals and students involved in teaching and research related to radio, television and other electronic media. BEA

administers 14 scholarships annually, to honor broadcasters and the electronic media profession.

The BEA Two Year Award is for study at member schools offering only freshman and sophomore instruction, or for use at a four-year member school by a graduate of a BEA two-year campus. All other scholarships are awarded to juniors, seniors and graduate students at BEA Member institutions.

Helen J. Sioussat/Fay Wells, Alexander M. Tanger, and Vincent T. Wasilewski Scholarships: Study in any area of broadcasting.

Walter S. Patterson and Abe Voron Scholarships: Study toward a career in radio.

See entry 2048 for full listing.

BUREAU OF INDIAN EDUCATION
215 Dean A. McGee
Suite 610
Oklahoma City, OK 73102
(405) 605-6001
Fax: (405) 605-6010

E-MAIL ADDRESS:
alicia.henson@bie.edu

WEB SITE ADDRESS:
www.bie.edu

TYPE:
Fellowships; Scholarships.

See entry 1113 for full listing.

CALIFORNIA STUDENT AID COMMISSION   [1785]
P.O. Box 419027
Rancho Cordova, CA 95741-9027
(888) 224-7268
Fax: (916) 464-8002

E-MAIL ADDRESS:
studentsupport@csac.ca.gov

WEB SITE ADDRESS:
www.calgrants.org

FOUNDED: 1955

NAME(S) OF PROGRAMS:
- **Cal Grants A, B and C**

TYPE:
Assistantships; Grants-in-aid. Grant A will help pay for tuition and fees at public and private colleges, and some private career colleges. Grant B provides low-income students with a living allowance and assistance with tuition and fees. Most five-year students receive an allowance for books and living expenses. Grant C helps pay for tuition and training costs at occupational or career technical schools.

YEAR PROGRAM STARTED: 1956

PURPOSE:
To assist with tuition and books for students attending college in California.

LEGAL BASIS:
California Education Code.

ELIGIBILITY:
Students must be U.S. citizen or eligible non-citizen and a California resident.

GEOGRAPHIC RESTRICTIONS:
California.

FINANCIAL DATA:
Amount of support per award: Grant A: $4,882; Grant B: $1,551; Grant C: $576.

NUMBER OF APPLICANTS MOST RECENT YEAR: 350,000.

NUMBER OF AWARDS: 75,000.

APPLICATION INFORMATION:
Students should submit the Free Application for Federal Student Aid (FAFSA) and a verified Cal Grant GPA. The FAFSA is available online.

Duration: Up to four years.

PUBLICATIONS:
Fund Your Future; *Financial Aid for Students*, booklet.

CALIFORNIA STUDENT AID COMMISSION [1786]

P.O. Box 419029
Rancho Cordova, CA 95741-9029
(888) 224-7268 Option 3
Fax: (916) 464-7977

E-MAIL ADDRESS:
specialized@csac.ca.gov

WEB SITE ADDRESS:
www.csac.ca.gov

FOUNDED: 1955

AREAS OF INTEREST:
Dependents of law enforcement personnel.

NAME(S) OF PROGRAMS:
● **Law Enforcement Personnel Dependents' Grant Program (LEPD)**

TYPE:
General operating grants. The program provides need-based educational grants to dependents and spouses of California peace officers (Highway Patrol, police officers), Department of Corrections and California Youth Authority employees and permanent/full-time firefighters, employed by public entities who have been killed in the performance of duty or totally disabled as a result of an accident or injury caused by external violence or physical force incurred in the performance of duty.

Grant awards are for attendance at WASC accredited colleges in California.

YEAR PROGRAM STARTED: 1969

LEGAL BASIS:
California Labor Code, Section 4709. State agency.

ELIGIBILITY:
Dependents and spouses of California peace officers.

GEOGRAPHIC RESTRICTIONS:
California.

FINANCIAL DATA:
Amount of support per award: $100 to $11,000.

Total amount of support: $52,320 for the year 2007-08.

NUMBER OF APPLICANTS MOST RECENT YEAR: 10.

APPLICATION INFORMATION:
Eligible students must file the following documents with the Specialized Programs Branch:
(1) a Law Enforcement Personnel Dependent's Grant application;
(2) a copy of the Student Aid Report (SAR), which is generated after filing a FAFSA;
(3) birth certificate (not required for spouse);
(4) the death certificate of the parent or spouse and the coroner's report (if appropriate), police report, and any other

documentation that shows evidence that the death or total disability was caused by external violence or physical force incurred in the line of duty (for peace and law enforcement officers), by the direct action of an inmate (for officers and employees of the Department of Corrections and Rehabilitation), or in the performance of duty (for firefighters);
(5) findings of the Workers' Compensation Appeals Board or other evidence that the fatality or 100% disabling accident or injury was compensable under Division 4.0 and 4.5 (commencing with Section 6100) of the Labor Code and;
(6) proof of enrollment at a California postsecondary institution as described above for the applicable academic year.

Duration: Up to four years.

PUBLICATIONS:
Financial Aid for Students, booklet.

STAFF:
Diana Fuentes-Michel, Executive Director

ADDRESS INQUIRIES TO:
Diana Fuentes-Michel, Executive Director
(See address above.)

CALIFORNIA STUDENT AID COMMISSION [1787]

P.O. Box 419026
Rancho Cordova, CA 95741-9026
(888) 224-7268
Fax: (916) 464-8002

E-MAIL ADDRESS:
specialized@csac.ca.gov

WEB SITE ADDRESS:
www.csac.ca.gov
www.calgrants.org

FOUNDED: 1955

AREAS OF INTEREST:
Students pursuing teaching careers in critical teacher shortage areas and designated low-income schools.

NAME(S) OF PROGRAMS:
● **Assumption Program of Loans for Education (APLE)**

TYPE:
Loan forgiveness programs. Assumption of outstanding educational loan balances in return for the participant's service as a public school teacher in California designated shortage areas.

YEAR PROGRAM STARTED: 1986

PURPOSE:
To encourage outstanding students to become teachers and serve in critical teacher shortage areas.

LEGAL BASIS:
California Education Code.

ELIGIBILITY:
Applicants must:
(1) be legal residents of California;
(2) have completed a minimum of 60 semester or 90 quarter units prior to the fall term of the year of application;
(3) enroll in a program leading to a Baccalaureate degree or in an approved program of professional teacher preparation;
(4) have received, or have been approved to receive, Stafford Student Loans/Guaranteed Student Loans (GSL), Consolidation Loan Program loans or privately funded educational loans issued to students through institutions of higher education;

(5) be free of any obligation to repay any state or federal educational grant and not be in default on any state or federally insured educational loan;
(6) not have completed the coursework necessary to obtain an initial teaching credential;
(7) student must teach in a California public school within 36 months from the date they become eligible to receive their initial teaching credential and;
(8) student must provide eligible full-time teaching service under a regular full-time contract at a California public school for four consecutive years in their designated service area.

Additionally, credential teachers must teach at a public school ranked in the lowest two deciles on the Academic Performance Index, possess a clear multiple subject or single subject teaching credential or level II education specialist credential and be nominated through California County Office of Education. Service provided prior to entering into the program will not count towards assumption benefits.

GEOGRAPHIC RESTRICTIONS:
California.

FINANCIAL DATA:
Amount of support per award: Up to $19,000 to be issued by the Commission directly to lenders in the following manner: Up to $4,000 after completion of the first full school year of eligible full-time teaching service; Up to $5,000 for each of the second, third and fourth years of eligible teaching service.

Total amount of support: Based on the number of eligible teachers.

NUMBER OF AWARDS: 7,500 annually, pending legislative changes.

APPLICATION INFORMATION:
Applications may be obtained after April 1 through participating California colleges and universities offering approved teaching credential programs. Participating postsecondary institutions distribute applications, assess academic ability, select applicants, and are encouraged to promote applications by population underrepresented in the teaching profession.

Duration: Participants must maintain satisfactory progress and half-time enrollment to renew.

Deadline: June 30; however, will continue to receive applications after deadline until all allocations have been met.

PUBLICATIONS:
Program announcement.

ADDRESS INQUIRIES TO:
APLE
California Student Aid Commission
Specialized Programs Branch
(See address above.)

CANADIAN FRIENDS OF THE HEBREW UNIVERSITY [1788]

3080 Yonge Street, Suite 3020
Toronto ON M4N 3N1 Canada
(416) 485-8000
(888) 432-7398 (Canada only)
Fax: (416) 485-8565

E-MAIL ADDRESS:
mgoldman@cfhu.org
inquiry@cfhu.org

WEB SITE ADDRESS:
www.cfhu.org

FOUNDED: 1944

AREAS OF INTEREST:
Law, dentistry, social sciences, economics, humanities and the sciences.

TYPE:
Awards/prizes; Scholarships. The Canadian Friends of the Hebrew University sponsors Canadian college students who participate in programs at the Hebrew University of Jerusalem.

YEAR PROGRAM STARTED: 1944

PURPOSE:
To give the financial support necessary for Canadian students to study at Hebrew University in Jerusalem, Israel.

LEGAL BASIS:
Nonprofit.

ELIGIBILITY:
Applicants must be Canadian citizens or landed immigrants. Awards are given based on need.

GEOGRAPHIC RESTRICTIONS:
Canada.

FINANCIAL DATA:
Amount of support per award: $1,500 to $5,000.
Total amount of support: Varies.

NUMBER OF AWARDS: Varies per program.

APPLICATION INFORMATION:
Contact the Office of Academic Affairs at the address above.
Duration: At least one year.
Deadline: Announcement in May.

STAFF:
Rami Kleinmann, National Director

ADDRESS INQUIRIES TO:
Merle Goldman, Associate National Director
(See address above.)

CANADIAN MERIT SCHOLARSHIP FOUNDATION   [1789]
460 Richmond Street West, Suite 502
Toronto ON M5V 1Y1 Canada
(416) 646-2120
(866) 544-2673
Fax: (416) 646-0846

E-MAIL ADDRESS:
info@cmsf.ca

WEB SITE ADDRESS:
www.cmsf.ca
www.loranaward.ca

FOUNDED: 1988

AREAS OF INTEREST:
Higher education.

NAME(S) OF PROGRAMS:
• **Loran Awards**

TYPE:
Scholarships. Scholarship grants for high school graduates about to enter a university in Canada.

PURPOSE:
To identify and support talented students who show promise of leadership and a strong commitment to service in the community; to fund these citizens to study on Canadian campuses, to the benefit of their future and ours.

ELIGIBILITY:
Applicant must:
(1) be in the graduating year of uninterrupted full-time studies in high school or CEGEP. Exceptions may be considered for those who have undertaken a gap year for academic pursuits or community service-based activities;
(2) present a minimum cumulative average of 85% and;
(3) hold Canadian citizenship or permanent resident status.

GEOGRAPHIC RESTRICTIONS:
Canada.

FINANCIAL DATA:
Amount of support per award: Varies.

APPLICATION INFORMATION:
Applications are available early September and can be downloaded from the Loran Award web site. Students should speak to their guidance counselor about their school's nomination process.
Duration: Up to four years.

ADDRESS INQUIRIES TO:
Franca Gucciardi, Executive Director
(See address above.)

*PLEASE NOTE:
Loran Award Finalist and Provincial Awards are tenable at any public university in Canada. Loran Awards are tenable at participating Canadian consortium universities only.

CATCHING THE DREAM
8200 Mountain Road, N.E.
Suite 203
Albuquerque, NM 87110
(505) 262-2351
Fax: (505) 262-0534

E-MAIL ADDRESS:
NScholarsh@aol.com

WEB SITE ADDRESS:
www.catchingthedream.org

TYPE:
Conferences/seminars; Project/program grants; Scholarships; Technical assistance. CTD also works to improve Indian schools through a program of grants and technical assistance. This work has led to the development of 35 Exemplary Programs in Indian education since 1988. The annual Exemplary Institute is a meeting of these Exemplary Programs, where they teach other people how to develop similar programs.

MESBEC Program consists of competitive scholarships for high-potential Native Americans studying in math, engineering, science, business, education and computers.

NALE Program consists of competitive scholarships for high-potential paraprofessional Native Americans who plan to complete their degrees and obtain credentials as teachers, counselors or administrators.

Tribal Business Management (TBM) Program consists of competitive scholarships for native students in all fields of business.

See entry 1114 for full listing.

CHATHAM UNIVERSITY   [1790]
Woodland Road
Pittsburgh, PA 15232-9987
(412) 365-1825
Fax: (412) 365-1609

E-MAIL ADDRESS:
admission@chatham.edu

WEB SITE ADDRESS:
www.chatham.edu

FOUNDED: 1869

AREAS OF INTEREST:
Provision of scholarship to young women who have shown academic promise during their high school career and who must be enrolled at Chatham.

NAME(S) OF PROGRAMS:
• **The Chatham University Merit Scholarship Programs**

TYPE:
Awards/prizes; Endowments; Formula grants; General operating grants; Grants-in-aid; Internships; Scholarships. The Chatham University Merit Scholarship Programs include the Presidential, Trustee, Founders, and Dean Scholarship.

YEAR PROGRAM STARTED: 1978

PURPOSE:
To attract outstanding women to Chatham University and to provide recognition of their academic performance.

ELIGIBILITY:
Chatham University Merit Scholars are chosen based on their performance in high school, grades, and SAT or ACT scores.

Grants are based strictly on need; many of the scholars are from families for whom the choice of a college such as Chatham would not be possible without this support.

FINANCIAL DATA:
Presidential Scholarship pays full tuition, including room and board.
Amount of support per award: Dean: Up to $9,000 per year; Founders: Up to $7,000 per year; Trustee: Up to $12,000 per year.
Total amount of support: Varies.

NUMBER OF APPLICANTS MOST RECENT YEAR: 700.

APPLICATION INFORMATION:
All applicants must complete an application for admission to Chatham University which includes SAT or ACT scores, high school transcript, and application.

First-year students who choose not to submit the SAT/ACT will be required to submit a graded writing sample and resume or list of activities. Applicants will also have the option to submit a portfolio or special project/activity.
Duration: Four years of the undergraduate career, provided the high academic criteria expected of such scholars is maintained. Renewable annually based on grade point average of 3.0 or higher for Presidential Scholarship and 2.0 or higher for the other scholarships, and full-time enrollment.
Deadline: March 1.

ADDRESS INQUIRIES TO:
Office of Admissions and Financial Aid
(See address above.)

CHILD LANGUAGE DOCTORAL PROGRAM   [1791]
University of Kansas
1000 Sunnyside Avenue
Room 3031, Dole Center
Lawrence, KS 66045-7555
(785) 864-4570
Fax: (785) 864-4571

E-MAIL ADDRESS:
childlang@ku.edu

WEB SITE ADDRESS:
www.clp.ku.edu

AREAS OF INTEREST:
Early childhood education and language research.

NAME(S) OF PROGRAMS:
- **Child Language Doctoral Program**

TYPE:
Conferences/seminars; Research grants; Scholarships.

PURPOSE:
To train individuals on language impairment across the life span.

ELIGIBILITY:
Applicants must have U.S. citizenship or permanent residency status, admission to the Child Language Doctoral Program or Intercampus Program in Speech-Language-Hearing or a related program, submission of a significant research plan of high quality, demonstrated high academic achievements and potential, and research interests congruent with those of one or more of the training program faculty members.

FINANCIAL DATA:
Amount of support per award: $21,180 per year predoctoral award.

APPLICATION INFORMATION:
Applicants must submit:
(1) a curriculum vitae;
(2) a list of all courses taken in relevant areas such as language impairment of children, linguistics, psychology, special education, and speech and hearing sciences;
(3) a research plan describing the applicant's plans for research on language impairments of children;
(4) two official transcripts;
(5) names and phone numbers of three references who can evaluate the applicant's research potential;
(6) scores from the Graduate Record Examinations and;
(7) letter of intent stating willingness to participate in continuous research practicum.
Duration: One year.
Deadline: Beginning of February.

DIRECTORS:
Dr. Mabel L. Rice, Director

ADMINISTRATORS:
Patsy Woods, Program Administrator

ADDRESS INQUIRIES TO:
Dr. Mabel L. Rice, Director
(See address above.)

CHINESE AMERICAN CITIZENS ALLIANCE FOUNDATION
763 Yale Street
Los Angeles, CA 90012
(213) 628-6368

E-MAIL ADDRESS:
cacafoundation@gmail.com

WEB SITE ADDRESS:
www.cacafoundation.org

TYPE:
Scholarships. For college students of Chinese descent attending a college or university in California.

See entry 1040 for full listing.

CHINESE AMERICAN CITIZENS ALLIANCE FOUNDATION
Los Angeles Lodge
415 Bamboo Lane
Los Angeles, CA 90012
(213) 628-8015

WEB SITE ADDRESS:
www.cacala.org

TYPE:
Scholarships. Scholarship for high school seniors of Chinese descent planning to attend a junior/community college in California.

See entry 1041 for full listing.

CHINESE AMERICAN MEDICAL SOCIETY
281 Edgewood Avenue
Teaneck, NJ 07666
(201) 833-1506
Fax: (201) 833-8252

E-MAIL ADDRESS:
hw5@columbia.edu

WEB SITE ADDRESS:
www.camsociety.org

TYPE:
Research grants; Scholarships.

See entry 2401 for full listing.

THE CLARK FOUNDATION   [1792]
One Rockefeller Plaza
New York, NY 10020
(607) 547-9927 (Cooperstown)
(212) 977-6900 (New York City)
Fax: (607) 547-8598

FOUNDED: 1931

NAME(S) OF PROGRAMS:
- **Clark Foundation Scholarship Program**

TYPE:
Scholarships. Undergraduate college scholarships.

YEAR PROGRAM STARTED: 1961

PURPOSE:
To assist Cooperstown area students in their pursuit of higher education.

LEGAL BASIS:
Nonprofit foundation.

ELIGIBILITY:
Individual undergraduate college scholarships are awarded to graduates of Central School, Cooperstown, New York and nine surrounding rural central school districts.

GEOGRAPHIC RESTRICTIONS:
Cooperstown and the nine surrounding New York rural central school districts of Cherry Valley-Springfield, Edmeston, Laurens, Milford, Mount Markham, Richfield Springs, Schenevus, Worcester and Owen D. Young.

FINANCIAL DATA:
Amount of support per award:
Approximately $3,800.
Total amount of support: $3,660,000 for the year ended June 30, 2011.

NUMBER OF APPLICANTS MOST RECENT YEAR:
347.

NUMBER OF AWARDS: 183 new scholarships.

APPLICATION INFORMATION:
Students are recommended by their respective schools.

Duration: One year. Possible renewal each year for duration of undergraduate education.
Deadline: First week in February.

OFFICERS:
Jane Forbes Clark, President
Kevin S. Moore, Treasurer
Douglas Bauer, Executive Director and Secretary

ADDRESS INQUIRIES TO:
Peter Severud
Clark Foundation Scholarship Office
P.O. Box 427
Cooperstown, NY 13326

COCA-COLA SCHOLARS FOUNDATION   [1793]
P.O. Box 442
Atlanta, GA 30301-0442
(800) 306-2653
Fax: (404) 733-5439

E-MAIL ADDRESS:
scholars@na.ko.com

WEB SITE ADDRESS:
www.coca-colascholars.org

FOUNDED: 1986

AREAS OF INTEREST:
Enhancing educational opportunities in the U.S.

NAME(S) OF PROGRAMS:
- **Coca-Cola Scholars Program**

TYPE:
Scholarships. Coca-Cola Scholars Program is in two categories: National Scholars and Regional Scholars. They are awarded based on leadership, academics and community service.

YEAR PROGRAM STARTED: 1989

PURPOSE:
To enhance educational opportunities in the U.S. through scholarship awards and enrichment programs for young people who demonstrate, through academic excellence and leadership in their communities, their capacity for and commitment to making a difference in the world.

ELIGIBILITY:
Current high school (or home-schooled) seniors attending school in the U.S. (or select DoD schools). Applicant must not graduate prior to deadline.

GEOGRAPHIC RESTRICTIONS:
United States.

FINANCIAL DATA:
Program has awarded $39,000,000 in scholarships since inception.
Amount of support per award: $10,000 regional and $20,000 national.

NUMBER OF APPLICANTS MOST RECENT YEAR:
250.

APPLICATION INFORMATION:
Application must be submitted online.
Duration: Four or six years.
Deadline: October 31.

ADDRESS INQUIRIES TO:
Ryan Rodriguez, Program Coordinator
(See address above.)

CONCORDIA UNIVERSITY [1794]

1455 de Maisonneuve Boulevard West
Graduate Awards Office, Room M102
Montreal QC H3G 1M8 Canada
(514) 848-2424 ext. 3809
(514) 848-2424 ext. 3801
Fax: (514) 848-2812

E-MAIL ADDRESS:
awardsgs@alcor.concordia.ca

WEB SITE ADDRESS:
graduatestudies.concordia.ca

FOUNDED: 1974

AREAS OF INTEREST:
All disciplines.

NAME(S) OF PROGRAMS:
* **Concordia University Graduate
Fellowships**

TYPE:
Fellowships. Postgraduate full-time
fellowships.

PURPOSE:
To recruit highly qualified graduate students
to Master's and doctoral programs.

ELIGIBILITY:
All new admissions will be considered for
awards.

Candidates must be planning to pursue
full-time Master's or doctoral studies at
Concordia University. Academic merit is the
prime consideration in the granting of the
award. Candidate must have a minimum
cumulative grade point average in all their
university studies.

Recipients must maintain a minimum grade
point average of 3.7 at the Master's level or
4.3 at the doctoral level, satisfactory progress
and good academic standing throughout
tenure of their award.

FINANCIAL DATA:
Amount of support per award: $10,000
(CAN) at the Master's level; $10,800 (CAN)
per term at the doctoral level.

NUMBER OF APPLICANTS MOST RECENT YEAR:
Over 1,000.

NUMBER OF AWARDS: 30.

APPLICATION INFORMATION:
Applicants must submit a completed
application form, statement of purpose, three
letters of recommendation, and official
transcripts of all university studies.

Duration: First three terms of the Master's,
nonrenewable; first nine terms of the
doctoral.

COOK FAMILY FOUNDATION

P.O. Box 278
Owosso, MI 48867-0278
(989) 725-1621
Fax: (989) 936-5910

E-MAIL ADDRESS:
tom@cookfamilyfoundation.org

WEB SITE ADDRESS:
www.cookfamilyfoundation.org

TYPE:
Capital grants; Challenge/matching grants;
Demonstration grants; Development grants;
Matching gifts; Project/program grants;
Scholarships; Seed money grants; Technical
assistance. Educational support.

See entry 1327 for full listing.

THE RICHARD AND JEAN COYNE FAMILY FOUNDATION [1795]

110 Constitution Drive
Menlo Park, CA 94025-1107
(650) 326-6040
Fax: (650) 326-1648

E-MAIL ADDRESS:
jeanc@commarts.com

FOUNDED: 1990

AREAS OF INTEREST:
Education in graphic design.

TYPE:
Project/program grants; Scholarships.

YEAR PROGRAM STARTED: 1990

PURPOSE:
To help high school students develop
portfolios for admission to art schools; to
provide college scholarships in graphic
design.

LEGAL BASIS:
Private foundation.

ELIGIBILITY:
Eligible organizations must be IRS 501(c)(3)
tax-exempt.

GEOGRAPHIC RESTRICTIONS:
United States.

FINANCIAL DATA:
Amount of support per award: $15,000 to
$50,000.

Total amount of support: $492,500 for the
year 2010.

NUMBER OF AWARDS: 19 for the year 2010.

REPRESENTATIVE AWARDS:
$15,000 to WorldStudio Foundation for
scholarships in the graphic design and
graphic arts disciplines to economically
disadvantaged and minority students (New
York); $25,000 to Osmosis
Education/Mentoring Initiative for creating
interest and awareness of the graphic design
profession in high schools through hands-on
seminars, contests and career days where
professionals pair with students and develop
personal mentorships, and for providing
annual college scholarships in graphic design
for at least three minority students per year
(Chicago); $50,000 to Seattle Link Program
for funding graphic design workshops, art
college tours, student internships in graphic
design, portfolio preparation advice and
graphic design scholarships for inner-city
high school students in Seattle.

APPLICATION INFORMATION:
Applicants must submit a written proposal.

Duration: Annual support.

Deadline: September.

IRS IDENTIFICATION NUMBER: 77-0259860

ADDRESS INQUIRIES TO:
Jean Coyne, President
(See address above.)

*SPECIAL STIPULATIONS:
Foundation funding is always given to the
managing organization and not to individuals.

Grants are made only in graphic design
education, not fine arts.

No phone calls.

DARTMOUTH COLLEGE

Office of Graduate Studies
Chavez/Eastman/Marshall
Dissertation Fellowship Committee
6062 Wentworth Hall, Room 304
Hanover, NH 03755-3526
(603) 646-6578
Fax: (603) 646-8762

E-MAIL ADDRESS:
jane.b.seibel@dartmouth.edu

WEB SITE ADDRESS:
www.dartmouth.
edu/~gradstdy/funding/fellowships

TYPE:
Exchange programs; Fellowships.

See entry 1043 for full listing.

DATATEL SCHOLARS FOUNDATION [1796]

4375 Fair Lakes Court
Fairfax, VA 22033
(800) 486-4332

E-MAIL ADDRESS:
scholars@datatel.com

WEB SITE ADDRESS:
www.datatelscholars.org

FOUNDED: 1990

AREAS OF INTEREST:
Scholarships for higher education.

NAME(S) OF PROGRAMS:
* **Angelfire Scholarship**
* **Datatel Scholars Foundation
Scholarship**
* **Russ Griffith Memorial Scholarship**

TYPE:
Scholarships. Support for eligible students to
attend higher learning institutions selected
from Datatel's more than 700 college and
university client site.

Angelfire Scholarship: for outstanding
students currently attending (at least six
credit hours) an eligible Datatel client
institution, who are veterans of the Vietnam
War, or are spouses or children of veterans of
the Vietnam War. Veterans must have served
in the Asian Theater during the 1964-1975
time frame. Also for those serving in the
U.S. military during Operations Desert
Storm, Enduring Freedom and/or Iraqi
Freedom.

Datatel Scholars Foundation Scholarship: for
outstanding students currently attending an
eligible Datatel client institution.

Russ Griffith Memorial Scholarship: for
outstanding students currently attending an
eligible Datatel client institution, who have
returned to school after a five-year or more
absence.

YEAR PROGRAM STARTED: 1990

PURPOSE:
To give back to the Datatel client base by
focusing on scholarships.

LEGAL BASIS:
Tax-exempt foundation.

ELIGIBILITY:
The criteria is a mix of academic merit,
personal motivation and achievements,
including employment and extracurricular
activities. Scholarships are open to
undergraduate and graduate students who are
enrolled in at least six credit hours
(part-time). Applicants must attend a school
which uses Datatel's software solutions.

Eligible client institutions maintain a current user and maintenance agreement. A list of eligible institutions can be found at the Foundation web site.

FINANCIAL DATA:
All scholarship payments are made to the institution of study for credit to the student's account. Funds may be used for tuition, books and education-related expenses. All unused funds are to be returned to the Foundation at the end of the academic year for which it was awarded.
Amount of support per award: $1,000 to $2,400, based on type of scholarship and tuition costs.

COOPERATIVE FUNDING PROGRAMS: Corporate gifts, employee contributions, vendor contributions and a matching gift program fund The Datatel Scholars Foundation scholarship program.

NUMBER OF APPLICANTS MOST RECENT YEAR: 2,500.

NUMBER OF AWARDS: 334.

APPLICATION INFORMATION:
Applicants must apply using online application form. Institution will review applications and nominate top applicants between February 1 and February 15. Nominated applications are then forwarded to the Foundation's board of directors for evaluation and awards determination. Paper applications are neither provided nor accepted.
Duration: One year. Nonrenewable; however, students may reapply.
Deadline: January 31.

PUBLICATIONS:
Fact sheet.

STAFF:
Jane Roth, Executive Director
Stacey Fessler, Project Leader

DAUGHTERS OF ITALY LODGE #2825 [1797]
14 South Jupiter Avenue
Clearwater, FL 33755
(727) 447-6890

E-MAIL ADDRESS:
vincenzad@verizon.net

WEB SITE ADDRESS:
www.daughtersofitaly.com

AREAS OF INTEREST:
Furtherance of education of Floridian students of Italian descent.

NAME(S) OF PROGRAMS:
● **Daughters of Italy Lodge #2825 Scholarship**
● **Filomena Genovese Meo Scholarship**

TYPE:
Scholarships. Open to full-time students at a Florida-accredited junior college, college or university or students graduating from high school.

Filomena Genovese Meo Scholarship is open to female students. Scholarships are awarded on the basis of eligibility, scholastic achievement, financial need and participation in school and community programs.

PURPOSE:
To benefit worthy students of Italian descent that display academic excellence, leadership qualities and a financial need.

ELIGIBILITY:
Applicant must:
(1) be a Florida resident of Italian descent and a U.S. citizen;
(2) have a minimum grade point average of 3.0 (unweighted) and a minimum SAT total score of 1100, or must have an ACT Composite Score of 23 and;
(3) be a full-time student at a Florida-accredited junior college, college or university or a student graduating from high school.

GEOGRAPHIC RESTRICTIONS:
Florida.

FINANCIAL DATA:
Scholarship funds will not be released to any school until the Daughters of Italy Lodge #2825 Scholarship Chairperson receives a letter of acceptance from an accredited school and the recipient notifies the Chairperson in writing of her/his intent to enroll in the fall semester.
Amount of support per award: $1,000 each.

NUMBER OF AWARDS: 1 each.

APPLICATION INFORMATION:
Application, checklist and procedures may be accessed online. Applicants must include a 500-word essay on student's current and futuristic academic goals. Applicants for the Filomena Genovese Meo Scholarship must include an additional 500-word essay regarding their Italian heritage, the importance of living in America, and how their mother or father influenced them to seek an education.
Duration: One year; not renewable.
Deadline: End of March; exact date available online.

DAUGHTERS OF PENELOPE FOUNDATION, INC.
Supreme Headquarters
1909 Q Street, N.W., Suite 500
Washington, DC 20009
(770) 365-2488
Fax: (202) 483-6983

E-MAIL ADDRESS:
cmondore@mindspring.com

WEB SITE ADDRESS:
www.ahepa.org/dop
www.dopfoundationinc.com

TYPE:
Scholarships.

See entry 1144 for full listing.

DAUGHTERS OF THE CINCINNATI [1798]
20 West 44th Street, Room 508
New York, NY 10036
(212) 991-9945

E-MAIL ADDRESS:
scholarships@daughters1894.org

WEB SITE ADDRESS:
fdncenter.org/grantmaker/cincinnati
www.daughters1894.org

FOUNDED: 1894

NAME(S) OF PROGRAMS:
● **Daughters of the Cincinnati Scholarship Program**

TYPE:
Scholarships. Undergraduate scholarships.

YEAR PROGRAM STARTED: 1906

PURPOSE:
To assist high school seniors entering college with financial aid (annually for the four years).

LEGAL BASIS:
Nonprofit, tax-exempt organization.

ELIGIBILITY:
Applicant must be a senior in high school who is the daughter of a career officer commissioned in the regular Army, Navy, Air Force, Coast Guard or Marine Corps (active, retired or deceased). The daughters of officers in the Reserves, National Guard and State Militia are not eligible to apply for this scholarship.

FINANCIAL DATA:
Financial aid for tuition and/or living expense.
Amount of support per award: Average $3,000 to $5,000 annually.

NUMBER OF APPLICANTS MOST RECENT YEAR: Approximately 200.

NUMBER OF AWARDS: Approximately 4 annually.

APPLICATION INFORMATION:
The application is accessible from the web site after supplying the parent's branch of service and rank.
Duration: Four years, or as long as the student attends college up to that length of time. Reviewed annually.
Deadline: March 15 (postmark). Announcement in mid-May.

PUBLICATIONS:
Information sheet.

ADDRESS INQUIRIES TO:
Scholarship Administrator
(See address above.)

MICHAEL AND SUSAN DELL FOUNDATION [1799]
P.O. Box 163867
Austin, TX 78716-3867
(512) 600-5586
Fax: (512) 600-5501

E-MAIL ADDRESS:
info@msdf.org

WEB SITE ADDRESS:
www.msdf.org

NAME(S) OF PROGRAMS:
● **Dell Scholars Program**

TYPE:
Scholarships. Need-based scholarship that recognizes academic potential in lower-income and underserved students. Applicants must demonstrate a drive to succeed while overcoming personal obstacles.

PURPOSE:
To assist students who have worked hard to prepare themselves for higher education yet may have lower grade point averages and test scores because of adverse personal situations or surroundings.

ELIGIBILITY:
Applicants must:
(1) be high school seniors who have participated in a Michael and Susan Dell Foundation-approved college readiness program;
(2) be a U.S. citizen or legal permanent resident;
(3) have financial need confirmed through

eligibility for a Federal Pell Grant and; (4) have a minimum 2.4 grade point average on a 4.0 scale.

Scholarship may be used at any accredited two- or four-year institution in the U.S. where credits can be earned towards a Baccalaureate degree, including community and junior colleges. Technical colleges and vocational programs are not eligible.

GEOGRAPHIC RESTRICTIONS:
United States.

FINANCIAL DATA:
Award may be applied to any cost of acquiring an education. Also provide other means of support, such as mentoring.
Amount of support per award: $20,000 over a maximum of six years.

APPLICATION INFORMATION:
All applications must be completed at www.dellscholars.org. No paper applications will be accepted.
Duration: Up to six years.
Deadline: Application process opens in November and closes the following January 15.

EBELL OF LOS ANGELES SCHOLARSHIP ENDOWMENT FUND   [1800]

The Ebell of Los Angeles
743 South Lucerne Boulevard
Los Angeles, CA 90005
(323) 931-1277
Fax: (323) 937-0272

E-MAIL ADDRESS:
scholarship@ebellla.com

WEB SITE ADDRESS:
www.ebellla.org

FOUNDED: 1894

AREAS OF INTEREST:
Higher education.

NAME(S) OF PROGRAMS:
• **Ebell Scholarship Program**

TYPE:
Scholarships.

YEAR PROGRAM STARTED: 1921

PURPOSE:
To support scholarships for qualified college students.

LEGAL BASIS:
Private foundation.

ELIGIBILITY:
Students must attend school in Los Angeles County at the school of his or her choice, be a sophomore, maintain a 3.25 grade point average or above, carry a minimum of 24 units per year, and be a U.S. citizen.

GEOGRAPHIC RESTRICTIONS:
Los Angeles, California.

FINANCIAL DATA:
Amount of support per award: Four-year colleges: $5,000 per year (12 months) paid semi-annually in September and January; Two-year colleges: $2,500 per year.
Total amount of support: Over $200,000 annually.

NUMBER OF APPLICANTS MOST RECENT YEAR:
162.

NUMBER OF AWARDS: 58.

APPLICATION INFORMATION:
Applicant must submit:
(1) completed application form;
(2) one-page autobiographical essay;
(3) Ebell Scholarship Applicant Financial Aid Profile;
(4) official transcripts to date from the higher educational institutions the applicant has attended and;
(5) three letters of recommendation (faculty member, professional or work associate, personal reference, e.g. teacher, counselor, supervisor).
Duration: Three years or when the student graduates, whichever comes first.
Deadline: March 31, 2012.

IRS IDENTIFICATION NUMBER: 23-7049580

ADDRESS INQUIRIES TO:
Scholarship Department
(See address above.)

THE JAMES MARSTON FITCH CHARITABLE FOUNDATION

c/o The Neighborhood Preservation Center
232 East 11th Street
New York, NY 10003
(212) 252-6809
Fax: (212) 471-9987

E-MAIL ADDRESS:
info@fitchfoundation.org

WEB SITE ADDRESS:
www.fitchfoundation.org

TYPE:
Research grants. Richard Blinder Award was created to promote studies that explore the architecture of cultural buildings which integrate historic preservation and new construction–past, present and future; presented biennially.

Mid-Career Grant Program: This grant is the primary mission and the signature grant of this Foundation. The grants are intended to support projects of innovative original research or creative design that advance the practice of historic preservation in the U.S.

See entry 444 for full listing.

FLORIDA DEPARTMENT OF EDUCATION

Office of Student Financial Assistance
325 West Gaines Street, Suite 1314
Tallahassee, FL 32399-0400
(850) 410-5200
(888) 827-2004
Fax: (850) 487-1809

E-MAIL ADDRESS:
osfa@fldoe.org

WEB SITE ADDRESS:
www.FloridaStudentFinancialAid.org

TYPE:
Scholarships. Financial assistance for descendants of the Rosewood family to attend a state university, public community college or public postsecondary vocational-technical school.

See entry 1092 for full listing.

FLORIDA DEPARTMENT OF EDUCATION   [1801]

Office of Student Financial Assistance
Turlington Building, Suite 1314
325 West Gaines Street
Tallahassee, FL 32399-0400
(850) 410-5200
(888) 827-2004
Fax: (850) 487-1809

E-MAIL ADDRESS:
osfa@fldoe.org

WEB SITE ADDRESS:
www.floridastudentfinancialaid.org

AREAS OF INTEREST:
Financial aid for Florida undergraduate students.

NAME(S) OF PROGRAMS:
• **Access to Better Learning and Education Grant Program (ABLE)**
• **Mary McLeod Bethune Scholarship Program**
• **First Generation Matching Grant Program (FGMG)**
• **Florida Resident Access Grant**
• **Florida Student Assistance Grant Program**
• **Florida Work Experience Program**
• **Scholarships for Children and Spouses of Deceased or Disabled Veterans and Servicemembers**

TYPE:
Scholarships. The Access to Better Learning and Education (ABLE) Grant Program provides tuition assistance to Florida undergraduate students enrolled in degree programs at eligible private Florida colleges or universities. ABLE is a decentralized program, and each participating institution determines application procedures, deadlines and student eligibility.

The Mary McLeod Bethune Scholarships are awarded to undergraduate students attending Bethune-Cookman University, Edward Waters College, Florida A&M University, or Florida Memorial University.

The First Generation Matching Grant Program (FGMG) provides need-based grants to degree-seeking, resident, undergraduate students who are enrolled in participating postsecondary institutions, and whose parents have not earned Baccalaureate or higher degrees.

Florida Resident Access Grants are provided to full-time Florida undergraduates attending an eligible private, nonprofit Florida college or university.

The Florida Student Assistance Grant Program is a need-based grant program available to degree-seeking, resident, undergraduate students who demonstrate substantial financial need and are enrolled in participating postsecondary institutions.

The Florida Work Experience Program provides eligible Florida students the opportunity to secure work experiences that will complement and reinforce the students' educational and career goals.

Scholarships for Children and Spouses of Deceased or Disabled Veterans and Servicemembers provides scholarships for dependent children or unremarried spouses of Florida veterans or service members who died as a result of service-connected injuries, diseases, or disabilities sustained while on active duty or have been verified by the

Florida Department of Veterans' Affairs as having service-connected 100% total and permanent disabilities.

PURPOSE:
To provide financial assistance to Florida students continuing their education.

LEGAL BASIS:
State agency.

GEOGRAPHIC RESTRICTIONS:
Florida.

FINANCIAL DATA:
Amount of support per award: Varies per program.
Total amount of support: Varies.

APPLICATION INFORMATION:
Detailed program information can be found on the web site.

ADDRESS INQUIRIES TO:
Barbara Dombrowski
Director, Training and Information Unit
(See address above.)

FLORIDA DEPARTMENT OF EDUCATION   [1802]
Office of Student Financial Assistance
325 West Gaines Street, Suite 1314
Tallahassee, FL 32399-0400
(850) 410-5200
(888) 827-2004
Fax: (850) 487-1809

E-MAIL ADDRESS:
osfa@fldoe.org

WEB SITE ADDRESS:
www.FloridaStudentFinancialAid.org

NAME(S) OF PROGRAMS:
- **Robert C. Byrd Honors Scholarship Program**
- **Florida Bright Futures Scholarship Program**

TYPE:
Scholarships. The Robert C. Byrd Honors Scholarship Program, established by the U.S. Congress, awards scholarships to outstanding high school seniors who show promise of continued academic achievement.

The Florida Bright Futures Scholarship Program is the umbrella program for three state-funded scholarships based on academic achievement in high school: Florida Academic Scholars Award, Florida Medallion Scholars Award and Florida Gold Seal Vocational Scholars Award.

PURPOSE:
To reward Florida's high school graduates who merit recognition of high academic achievement.

LEGAL BASIS:
State agency.

GEOGRAPHIC RESTRICTIONS:
Florida.

FINANCIAL DATA:
Total amount of support: Varies.

APPLICATION INFORMATION:
Deadline: Robert C. Byrd Honors Scholarship Program: April 15. Florida Bright Futures Scholarship: Prior to high school graduation.

ADDRESS INQUIRIES TO:
State Scholarship and Grant Programs
(See address above.)

FLORIDA DEPARTMENT OF EDUCATION
Office of Student Financial Assistance
325 West Gaines Street, Suite 1314
Tallahassee, FL 32399-0400
(888) 827-2004
Fax: (850) 487-1809

E-MAIL ADDRESS:
osfa@fldoe.org

WEB SITE ADDRESS:
www.FloridaStudentFinancialAid.org

TYPE:
Challenge/matching grants; Grants-in-aid. Jose Marti Scholarship Challenge Grant Fund is a need-based merit scholarship that provides financial assistance to eligible students of Hispanic origin who will attend Florida public or eligible private institutions.

See entry 1130 for full listing.

THE FOUNDATION FOR INDEPENDENT HIGHER EDUCATION
1920 N Street, N.W.
Suite 210
Washington, DC 20036
(202) 367-0333
Fax: (202) 367-0334

E-MAIL ADDRESS:
info@fihe.org

WEB SITE ADDRESS:
www.fihe.org

TYPE:
Project/program grants; Scholarships.

See entry 1648 for full listing.

FOUNDATION FOR TECHNOLOGY EDUCATION   [1803]
1914 Association Drive
Suite 201
Reston, VA 20191-1539
(703) 860-2100
Fax: (703) 860-0353

E-MAIL ADDRESS:
tmacdonald@iteea.org

WEB SITE ADDRESS:
www.iteea.org

FOUNDED: 1939

AREAS OF INTEREST:
Technology education.

NAME(S) OF PROGRAMS:
- **FTE Undergraduate Scholarship**

TYPE:
Scholarships. The scholarship is for an undergraduate student majoring in technology education teacher preparation.

PURPOSE:
To support teacher preparation in technology education.

ELIGIBILITY:
Applicant must be a member of the International Technology and Engineering Educators Association and be a current, full-time undergraduate majoring in technology education teacher preparation. Applicant must not be a senior by application deadline.

FINANCIAL DATA:
Amount of support per award: $1,000.

NUMBER OF AWARDS: 1.

APPLICATION INFORMATION:
Applicants must submit the application package which consists of four copies of the following required items:
(1) letter of transmittal that includes a statement about personal interest in teaching technology and applicant's address with day and evening telephone numbers;
(2) resume or vitae which indicate career goals, current professional and college activities and achievements (maximum three pages);
(3) photocopy of college transcript (required 2.5 grade point average on 4.0 scale) and;
(4) three faculty letters of recommendation from among his or her professors and/or advisor.
Deadline: December 1.

ADDRESS INQUIRIES TO:
Tamara MacDonald, Publications Services
(See address above.)

*SPECIAL STIPULATIONS:
Applicant must be a member of the ITEEA.

The scholarship will be presented in the spring during the ITEEA Conference Awards Banquet. The winner does not have to be present to receive the scholarship.

FOUNDATION FOR TECHNOLOGY EDUCATION   [1804]
1914 Association Drive
Suite 201
Reston, VA 20191-1539
(703) 860-2100
Fax: (703) 860-0353

E-MAIL ADDRESS:
tmacdonald@iteea.org

WEB SITE ADDRESS:
www.iteea.org

FOUNDED: 1939

AREAS OF INTEREST:
Technology education.

NAME(S) OF PROGRAMS:
- **Litherland/FTE Scholarship Undergraduate Major in Technology Education**

TYPE:
Scholarships.

PURPOSE:
To assist an undergraduate student majoring in technology education teacher preparation.

ELIGIBILITY:
Applicant must be member of the International Technology and Engineering Educators Association and a current, full-time undergraduate majoring in technology education teacher preparation. The student must not be a senior by application deadline. The award is based upon interest in teaching, academic ability, need and faculty recommendations.

FINANCIAL DATA:
Amount of support per award: $1,000.

NUMBER OF AWARDS: 1.

APPLICATION INFORMATION:
Applicants must submit an application package including four copies of the following required items:
(1) a letter of transmittal that includes a statement about his or her personal interest in teaching technology and applicant's address

with day and evening telephone numbers;
(2) resume or vitae identifying career goals, current professional activities and achievements;
(3) photocopy of college transcript and;
(4) three faculty letters of recommendation from among his or her professors and/or advisor.

Deadline: December 1.

ADDRESS INQUIRIES TO:
Tamara MacDonald, Publications Services
(See address above.)

*SPECIAL STIPULATIONS:
Applicant must be a member of the ITEEA.

FREEDOM ALLIANCE   [1805]

22570 Markey Court, Suite 240
Dulles, VA 20166
(703) 444-7940
(800) 475-6620
Fax: (703) 444-9893

E-MAIL ADDRESS:
info@fascholarship.com

WEB SITE ADDRESS:
www.fascholarship.com

FOUNDED: 1990

AREAS OF INTEREST:
Scholarship aid to the children of American military personnel who have been killed or injured in military service.

NAME(S) OF PROGRAMS:
● **Freedom Alliance Scholarship Fund**

TYPE:
Scholarships. Freedom Alliance Scholarship Fund provides college scholarships to the sons and daughters of America's military heroes–those who sacrifice life or limb in defense of America's freedom.

YEAR PROGRAM STARTED: 1990

PURPOSE:
To honor the bravery and dedication exhibited by Americans in the U.S. armed forces who have sacrificed life and limb by providing educational scholarships to their children.

LEGAL BASIS:
501(c)(3) educational and charitable foundation.

ELIGIBILITY:
Students must be dependent child of a service member who died or was permanently disabled (100% rating) in the line of duty, or who is currently certified as POW or MIA. The applicant must also be a senior in high school, a high school graduate, or enrolled in an institution of higher learning, including colleges, universities or vocational schools.

FINANCIAL DATA:
Amount of support per award: Varies.

NUMBER OF AWARDS: 225.

APPLICATION INFORMATION:
Eligible students seeking a Freedom Alliance scholarship must first complete an application form. Applications will not be considered by the scholarship committee unless all required materials listed below accompany the application package:
(1) certificate of death/disability or proof of POW/MIA status as defined in the instructions;
(2) proof of dependency as defined in the instructions;

(3) 500-word essay as explained in the instructions;
(4) official transcripts from high school and all post-high school educational institutions;
(5) photo of applicant and;
(6) photo of parent.

Duration: Scholarships are awarded annually and are renewable for a total of four scholarships.

STAFF:
Thomas Kilgannon, President
Calvin Coolidge, Executive Director

BOARD OF DIRECTORS:
Robert Eichenberg, Chairman
Thomas Cook, Treasurer
Hon. Ralph Smith, Secretary
Michael Mason
Jerry Morris

FOUNDERS:
Lt Col Oliver L. North, USMC (Ret.), Honorary Chairman
Lt Gen Edward J. Bronars, USMC

ADDRESS INQUIRIES TO:
Adam Morgan, Program Officer
(See address above.)

*PLEASE NOTE:
Applications are currently being accepted for the 2011-12 school year.

GOLDEN KEY INTERNATIONAL HONOUR SOCIETY   [1806]

1040 Crown Pointe Parkway
Suite 900
Atlanta, GA 30319
(800) 377-2401

E-MAIL ADDRESS:
awards@goldenkey.org

WEB SITE ADDRESS:
www.goldenkey.org

AREAS OF INTEREST:
Nonprofit academic honors organization that recognizes the top 15% of juniors and seniors in all undergraduate fields.

NAME(S) OF PROGRAMS:
● **Business Achievement Awards**
● **Community Service Award**
● **Education Achievement Awards**
● **Engineering/Technology Achievement Awards**
● **GEICO Life Scholarship**
● **The Golden Key Graduate Scholarship Award**
● **Golden Key Research Grants**
● **Literary Achievement Awards**
● **Student Leader Award (Regional and International)**
● **Study Abroad Scholarships**
● **Visual and Performing Arts Achievement Awards**

TYPE:
Awards/prizes; Scholarships; Travel grants. Business Achievement Awards: Recognize members who excel in the study of business.

Community Service Award: Recognizes one member for outstanding service to the community.

Education Achievement Awards: Recognize members who excel in the study of education.

Engineering/Technology Achievement Awards: Recognize members who excel in the study of engineering or technology.

GEICO Life Scholarship: Recognizes outstanding members who achieve academic excellence while balancing additional commitments such as family and/or career.

The Golden Key Graduate Scholar Award: Golden Key's premier scholarship program. Supports members' post-baccalaureate study at accredited universities anywhere in the world.

Golden Key Research Grants: Allow members to conduct thesis research and/or present their research at professional conferences or student research symposia.

Literary Achievement Awards: Recognize the literary talents of members in four categories: fiction, nonfiction, poetry and news writing.

Student Leader Awards: Regional Student Leader Awards recognizes one member in each region (10 U.S. regions) for outstanding commitment to the Society and display of effective campus and community leadership while maintaining superior academic performance.

Study Abroad Scholarships: Assists members who participate in a study abroad program.

Visual and Performance Arts Achievement Awards: Recognize the visual art talents of members in nine categories: painting, drawing, photography, sculpture, computer-generated art/graphic design/illustration, mixed media, instrumental performance, vocal performance, and dance.

PURPOSE:
To enable members to realize their potential.

ELIGIBILITY:
Open to Golden Key members.

FINANCIAL DATA:
Amount of support per award: $1,000 to $10,000.

APPLICATION INFORMATION:
Golden Key's scholarships and awards require a formal application. Each scholarship has a unique submission deadline and application process. Details about each of the scholarship programs can be found under the Scholarship and Award Listing on the web site. All scholarship submissions must be written in English.

ADDRESS INQUIRIES TO:
Crystal Hunter, Program Manager
(See address above.)

*SPECIAL STIPULATIONS:
Only Golden Key members may apply for these scholarships and awards.

GRADUATE EDUCATION OPPORTUNITY PROGRAM

Michigan State University
The Graduate School, 116 Linton Hall
East Lansing, MI 48824-1044
(517) 353-3262
Fax: (517) 353-3355

WEB SITE ADDRESS:
www.grad.msu.edu

TYPE:
Assistantships; Fellowships.

See entry 1053 for full listing.

THE GREATER KANAWHA VALLEY FOUNDATION

Huntington Square, Suite 1600
900 Lee Street East
Charleston, WV 25301
(304) 346-3620
Fax: (304) 346-3640

E-MAIL ADDRESS:
sryder@tgkvf.org

WEB SITE ADDRESS:
www.tgkvf.org

TYPE:
Project/program grants; Scholarships.

See entry 1368 for full listing.

THE HIGHER EDUCATION STUDENT ASSISTANCE AUTHORITY   [1807]

P.O. Box 540
Trenton, NJ 08625
(609) 588-3266
(800) 792-8670
Fax: (609) 588-2390

WEB SITE ADDRESS:
www.hesaa.org

FOUNDED: 1959

AREAS OF INTEREST:
State financial assistance for college students.

NAME(S) OF PROGRAMS:
• **Urban Scholars**

TYPE:
Scholarships. The Higher Education Student Assistance Authority (HESAA) is a New Jersey authority that provides students and families with the financial and informational resources for students to pursue their education beyond high school. With roots dating back to 1959, HESAA's singular focus has always been to benefit the students it serves. HESAA provides state supplemental loans, grants and scholarships. HESAA also administers the state's college savings plan.

YEAR PROGRAM STARTED: 1978

PURPOSE:
To provide financial assistance to college students demonstrating academic proficiency.

ELIGIBILITY:
Students must demonstrate academic achievement based upon secondary school records and SAT scores at the end of the junior year. Applicants must be U.S. citizens or eligible non-citizens and residents of New Jersey for at least the 12 consecutive months prior to receiving an award. Students must be enrolled full-time in an approved New Jersey college or university and in a curriculum leading to a degree or certificate and be registered with the Selective Service, if applicable. Renewals are based on satisfactory academic progress.

GEOGRAPHIC RESTRICTIONS:
New Jersey.

FINANCIAL DATA:
Amount of support per award: Up to $1,000 per year during the student's undergraduate program.

NUMBER OF AWARDS: Based upon appropriations.

APPLICATION INFORMATION:
Students may not apply directly to the program. Candidates will be selected for consideration by their secondary schools based upon standard academic criteria. A committee will review selections received from secondary schools in the fall of the student's senior year in high school and will identify award recipients in October for the next academic year. Students should file the FAFSA after January 1, in order to be considered for additional need-based financial aid. Interested students should see their guidance counselor for more information.

Duration: Renewable for four years of undergraduate study, providing eligibility for each program continues.

Deadline: September 30.

PUBLICATIONS:
State and Federal Financial Aid Programs for New Jersey Students, brochure.

THE HIGHER EDUCATION STUDENT ASSISTANCE AUTHORITY   [1808]

P.O. Box 540
Trenton, NJ 08625
(609) 588-3266
(800) 792-8670
Fax: (609) 588-2390

WEB SITE ADDRESS:
www.hesaa.org

FOUNDED: 1959

AREAS OF INTEREST:
State financial assistance for college students.

NAME(S) OF PROGRAMS:
• **Tuition Aid Grant (TAG)**

TYPE:
Grants-in-aid. The Higher Education Student Assistance Authority (HESAA) is a New Jersey authority that provides students and families with the financial and informational resources for students to pursue their education beyond high school. With roots dating back to 1959, HESAA's singular focus has always been to benefit the students it serves. HESAA provides state supplemental loans, grants and scholarships. HESAA also administers the state's college savings plan.

YEAR PROGRAM STARTED: 1969

PURPOSE:
To provide financial assistance to needy students attending approved New Jersey institutions. This is calculated by estimating what a family can contribute from income and assets plus a contribution from the student's earnings and savings. The amount and type of aid will depend upon program eligibility, available funds and the degree of need.

LEGAL BASIS:
New Jersey Higher Education Tuition Aid Act.

ELIGIBILITY:
Applicants must be New Jersey residents for at least 12 consecutive months prior to receiving an award, and will be enrolled in an approved New Jersey institution. Student must be a U.S. citizen or eligible non-citizen and be registered with the Selective Service, if applicable. Grants are renewable annually based upon satisfactory academic progress and continued financial need. Students who have received a Baccalaureate degree are not eligible.

GEOGRAPHIC RESTRICTIONS:
New Jersey.

FINANCIAL DATA:
Amount of support per award: Award amounts are based on the student's New Jersey Eligibility Index, tuition charged and appropriated funds.

NUMBER OF AWARDS: Based upon appropriations.

APPLICATION INFORMATION:
Applicants must file the Free Application for Federal Student Aid (FAFSA), which is available through high school guidance and financial aid offices or by calling, Tel: (800) 792-8670, available from any location in New Jersey, Monday through Friday, 9 A.M. to 5 P.M.

Duration: Renewable for four years of undergraduate study providing eligibility continues and an application is filed.

Deadline: October 1 for fall and spring terms. Renewals June 1 for fall and spring terms.

PUBLICATIONS:
State and Federal Financial Aid Programs for New Jersey Students, brochure.

THE HIGHER EDUCATION STUDENT ASSISTANCE AUTHORITY   [1809]

P.O. Box 540
Trenton, NJ 08625
(609) 588-3266
(800) 792-8670
Fax: (609) 588-2390

WEB SITE ADDRESS:
www.hesaa.org

FOUNDED: 1959

AREAS OF INTEREST:
State financial assistance for college students.

NAME(S) OF PROGRAMS:
• **Educational Opportunity Fund Grants (EOF)**

TYPE:
Grants-in-aid. The Higher Education Student Assistance Authority (HESAA) is a New Jersey authority that provides students and families with the financial and informational resources for students to pursue their education beyond high school. With roots dating back to 1959, HESAA's singular focus has always been to benefit the students it serves. HESAA provides state supplemental loans, grants and scholarships. HESAA also administers the state's college savings plan.

Educational Opportunity Fund Grants (EOF) provide financial aid to eligible students from educationally and economically disadvantaged backgrounds at participating in-state institutions.

YEAR PROGRAM STARTED: 1968

PURPOSE:
To grant assistance to students from educationally disadvantaged backgrounds with demonstrated financial need.

LEGAL BASIS:
New Jersey Educational Opportunity Act of 1968.

ELIGIBILITY:
Applicants must be New Jersey residents for at least 12 consecutive months prior to receiving an award. Applicants must be full-time, matriculated students in an approved New Jersey college or university in an approved program of study. Household income cannot exceed established guidelines.

The amount of the grant varies based on financial need, cost of attendance and available funding.

GEOGRAPHIC RESTRICTIONS:
New Jersey.

FINANCIAL DATA:
Amount of support per award: Dependent upon annual appropriations, financial need, and cost of attendance.

APPLICATION INFORMATION:
All applicants for New Jersey grant assistance must file the Free Application for Federal Student Aid (FAFSA). Applications are available at high school guidance and college financial aid offices or by calling toll free number, Tel: (800) 792-8670, available from any location in New Jersey, Monday through Friday, 9 A.M. to 5 P.M.
Duration: Financial assistance is renewable for four years of undergraduate study providing eligibility for each program continues and an application is filed.
Deadline: October 1 for fall and spring terms.

PUBLICATIONS:
State and Federal Financial Aid Programs for New Jersey Students, brochure.

THE HIGHER EDUCATION STUDENT ASSISTANCE AUTHORITY   [1810]
P.O. Box 540
Trenton, NJ 08625
(609) 588-3266
(800) 792-8670
Fax: (609) 588-2390

WEB SITE ADDRESS:
www.hesaa.org

FOUNDED: 1959

AREAS OF INTEREST:
State financial assistance for college students.

NAME(S) OF PROGRAMS:
- **Survivor Tuition Benefits Program**

TYPE:
Grants-in-aid; Scholarships. The Higher Education Student Assistance Authority (HESAA) is a New Jersey authority that provides students and families with the financial and informational resources for students to pursue their education beyond high school. With roots dating back to 1959, HESAA's singular focus has always been to benefit the students it serves. HESAA provides state supplemental loans, grants and scholarships. HESAA also administers the state's college savings plan.

YEAR PROGRAM STARTED: 1980

PURPOSE:
This scholarship benefits dependent children and surviving spouses of New Jersey firefighters, emergency service workers or law enforcement officers who were killed in the line of duty.

ELIGIBILITY:
Student must be a child or spouse of a New Jersey firefighter, emergency service worker or law enforcement officer killed in the line of duty, who is resident of New Jersey, attending an independent New Jersey institution of higher education as an undergraduate. Student must be a U.S. citizen or eligible non-citizen.

GEOGRAPHIC RESTRICTIONS:
New Jersey.

FINANCIAL DATA:
Covers the cost of tuition at any New Jersey public college or university. Students enrolled at an independent New Jersey college or university may receive up to the highest tuition charged at a New Jersey public institution.

APPLICATION INFORMATION:
Applications are available by calling the New Jersey Financial Aid Hotline, Tel: (800) 792-8670, available from any location in New Jersey, Monday through Friday, 9 A.M. to 5 P.M.
Duration: Financial assistance is renewable for four years of undergraduate study providing eligibility for each program continues and an application is filed.
Deadline: October 1 for fall and spring terms. March 1 for spring term only.

PUBLICATIONS:
State and Federal Financial Aid Programs for New Jersey Students, brochure.

ADDRESS INQUIRIES TO:
Carol Muka
Assistant Director of Client Services
(See address above.)

THE HIGHER EDUCATION STUDENT ASSISTANCE AUTHORITY   [1811]
P.O. Box 540
Trenton, NJ 08625
(609) 588-3266
(800) 792-8670
Fax: (609) 588-2390

WEB SITE ADDRESS:
www.hesaa.org

FOUNDED: 1959

AREAS OF INTEREST:
State financial assistance for college students.

NAME(S) OF PROGRAMS:
- **Edward J. Bloustein Distinguished Scholars Program**

TYPE:
Scholarships. The Higher Education Student Assistance Authority (HESAA) is a New Jersey authority that provides students and families with the financial and informational resources for students to pursue their education beyond high school. With roots dating back to 1959, HESAA's singular focus has always been to benefit the students it serves. HESAA provides state supplemental loans, grants and scholarships. HESAA also administers the state's college savings plan.

Edward J. Bloustein Distinguished Scholars Program is a merit-based college financial aid program.

YEAR PROGRAM STARTED: 1984

PURPOSE:
To recognize New Jersey secondary students demonstrating the highest level of academic achievement.

LEGAL BASIS:
New Jersey state agency.

ELIGIBILITY:
Secondary schools select students for award consideration based on the secondary school records and SAT scores. From these selections, awards will be offered to secondary school seniors meeting minimum criteria established by the department. Recipients must be U.S. citizens or eligible

non-citizens and residents of New Jersey for at least 12 consecutive months prior to receiving an award and must enroll at an approved New Jersey college or university as full-time undergraduate students. Students must register for the Selective Service, if applicable and maintain satisfactory academic progress to renew the award.

GEOGRAPHIC RESTRICTIONS:
New Jersey.

FINANCIAL DATA:
Amount of support per award: Up to $1,000 per year throughout the student's undergraduate program. Scholar awards are renewable based upon satisfactory academic progress, continued undergraduate enrollment in a New Jersey college or university and continued program funding.

NUMBER OF AWARDS: Based upon appropriations.

APPLICATION INFORMATION:
Students are selected for consideration by their secondary school and final determination is made by the department. Interested students should see their guidance counselor for more information.
Duration: Renewable for four years of undergraduate study at approved New Jersey colleges and universities.
Deadline: Selections submitted by secondary schools by October 1. Announcements made to students in November of their senior year.

PUBLICATIONS:
State and Federal Financial Aid Programs for New Jersey Students, brochure.

THE HIGHER EDUCATION STUDENT ASSISTANCE AUTHORITY   [1812]
4 Quakerbridge Plaza
Trenton, NJ 08625-0540
(800) 792-8670
Fax: (609) 588-2228

WEB SITE ADDRESS:
www.hesaa.org

FOUNDED: 1959

AREAS OF INTEREST:
State financial assistance for college students.

NAME(S) OF PROGRAMS:
- **Dana Christmas Scholarship for Heroism**
- **Law Enforcement Officer Memorial Scholarship**
- **New Jersey Student Tuition Assistance Reward Scholarship**
- **New Jersey Student Tuition Assistance Reward Scholarship II**
- **New Jersey World Trade Center Scholarship**

TYPE:
Dana Christmas Scholarship for Heroism honors the Seton Hall student who saved lives during the dormitory fire in 2001.

Law Enforcement Officer Memorial Scholarship provides financial aid for eligible children of law enforcement officers killed in the line of duty.

New Jersey Student Tuition Assistance Reward Scholarship provides access to higher education for the state's highest achieving students.

New Jersey Student Tuition Assistance Reward Scholarship II enables successful NJ scholars to transfer to a New Jersey four-year public college or university and earn a Bachelor's degree.

New Jersey World Trade Center Scholarship benefits dependent children and surviving spouses of New Jersey residents who were killed in or who died of the terrorist attacks against the U.S. on September 11, 2001.

PURPOSE:
To provide financial assistance to college students demonstrating academic proficiency.

GEOGRAPHIC RESTRICTIONS:
New Jersey.

APPLICATION INFORMATION:
Deadline: New Jersey World Trade Scholarship: October 1 for Fall or full academic year; March 1 for Spring semester.

HISPANIC COLLEGE FUND [1813]
1300 L Street, N.W.
Suite 975
Washington, DC 20005
(202) 296-5400
(800) 644-4223
Fax: (202) 296-3774

E-MAIL ADDRESS:
hcf-info@hispanicfund.org

WEB SITE ADDRESS:
www.hispanicfund.org

FOUNDED: 1993

NAME(S) OF PROGRAMS:
● **Hispanic College Fund Scholarship Programs**

TYPE:
Scholarships. Merit and need-based scholarships to Latino students.

PURPOSE:
To educate and develop the next generation of Hispanic professionals.

ELIGIBILITY:
Applicants must:
(1) be Hispanic or of Hispanic descent;
(2) be a U.S. citizen or permanent resident;
(3) be studying at an accredited university in the U.S. or Puerto Rico for the upcoming year;
(4) be (or plan to be) enrolled full-time as an undergraduate student for the upcoming academic year;
(5) have earned and maintained a cumulative grade point average of no less than 3.0 on a 4.0 scale;
(6) have graduated from a U.S. high school, to which the student attended for a minimum of three years by June 12 and;
(7) demonstrate financial need.

GEOGRAPHIC RESTRICTIONS:
United States.

FINANCIAL DATA:
Amount of support per award: $500 to $10,000.

APPLICATION INFORMATION:
All documents for application must be uploaded to the web site above.
Duration: One academic year. Must reapply.
Deadline: March 1.

ADDRESS INQUIRIES TO:
Erika Viramontes
Scholarship Program Manager
(See address above.)

HISPANIC COLLEGE FUND [1814]
1300 L Street, N.W.
Suite 975
Washington, DC 20005
(202) 296-5400
(800) 644-4223
Fax: (202) 296-3774

E-MAIL ADDRESS:
hcf-info@hispanicfund.org

WEB SITE ADDRESS:
www.hispanicfund.org

FOUNDED: 1993

AREAS OF INTEREST:
Hospitality management, hotel management, culinary or food and beverage field.

NAME(S) OF PROGRAMS:
● **Marriott Scholars Program**

TYPE:
Scholarships. Scholarship support for up to four years coupled with opportunities for ongoing career guidance and mentoring by Marriott hotel managers and corporate executives.

PURPOSE:
To educate and develop the next generation of Hispanic professionals.

ELIGIBILITY:
Applicants must:
(1) be a U.S. citizen or permanent resident residing in the U.S. or Puerto Rico;
(2) be enrolled full-time in an accredited four-year college or university in the U.S. or Puerto Rico with a hospitality management program as an incoming college freshman, first-year freshman or community college transfer;
(3) be pursuing or planning to pursue a degree within the hospitality management, hotel management, culinary or food and beverage field and;
(4) possess a cumulative grade point average of 3.0 or better on a 4.0 scale.

GEOGRAPHIC RESTRICTIONS:
United States.

FINANCIAL DATA:
Amount of support per award: Full tuition up to $9,000.

APPLICATION INFORMATION:
All documents for application must be uploaded to the web site above.
Duration: One academic year. Renewable.
Deadline: March 1.

ADDRESS INQUIRIES TO:
Erika Viramontes
Scholarship Program Manager
(See address above.)

HISPANIC COLLEGE FUND [1815]
1300 L Street, N.W.
Suite 975
Washington, DC 20005
(202) 296-5400
(800) 644-4223
Fax: (202) 296-3774

E-MAIL ADDRESS:
hcf-info@hispanicfund.org

WEB SITE ADDRESS:
www.hispanicfund.org

FOUNDED: 1993

AREAS OF INTEREST:
Computer science and computer engineering.

NAME(S) OF PROGRAMS:
● **Google Scholarship Program**

TYPE:
Scholarships. Need-based scholarships to Latino juniors or seniors in college or pursuing a Master's or Ph.D.

PURPOSE:
To educate and develop the next generation of Hispanic professionals.

ELIGIBILITY:
Applicants must:
(1) be Hispanic or of Hispanic background;
(2) be a U.S. citizen or permanent resident residing in the U.S.;
(3) be studying full-time in the U.S. or Puerto Rico;
(4) have a minimum grade point average of 3.5 on a 4.0 scale;
(5) demonstrate financial need and;
(6) be a junior or senior undergraduate or graduate student pursuing a degree in computer science or computer engineering for the next academic year.

GEOGRAPHIC RESTRICTIONS:
United States.

FINANCIAL DATA:
Amount of support per award: $10,000.

APPLICATION INFORMATION:
All documents for application must be uploaded to the web site above.
Duration: One academic year. Must reapply.
Deadline: March 1.

ADDRESS INQUIRIES TO:
Erika Viramontes
Scholarship Program Manager
(See address above.)

HISPANIC SCHOLARSHIP FUND
55 Second Street
Suite 1500
San Francisco, CA 94105
(877) 473-4636
(415) 808-2355
Fax: (415) 808-2301

E-MAIL ADDRESS:
info@hsf.net
gmsinfo@hsf.net

WEB SITE ADDRESS:
www.hsf.net
www.gmsp.org

TYPE:
Scholarships. Awarded to Hispanic community college, undergraduate and graduate students.

See entry 1131 for full listing.

THE HONOR SOCIETY OF PHI KAPPA PHI [1816]
7576 Goodwood Boulevard
Baton Rouge, LA 70806
(225) 388-4917 ext. 35
(800) 804-9880 ext. 35
Fax: (225) 388-4900

E-MAIL ADDRESS:
info@phikappaphi.org

WEB SITE ADDRESS:
www.phikappaphi.org

FOUNDED: 1897

AREAS OF INTEREST:
Phi Kappa Phi recognizes scholastic excellence in all academic fields.

NAME(S) OF PROGRAMS:
- **The Phi Kappa Phi Fellowship**

TYPE:
Fellowships. Support for the first year of graduate or professional school.

YEAR PROGRAM STARTED: 1932

PURPOSE:
To stimulate members of Phi Kappa Phi to go to graduate or professional school.

LEGAL BASIS:
Honor Society incorporated in Michigan, May 20, 1972. Authorized to operate in Louisiana, September 1978. Tax-exempt under IRS 501(c)(3). Companion organization, the Phi Kappa Phi Foundation, incorporated in California, December 17, 1969, as a Public Benefit Foundation, tax-exempt under IRS 501(c)(3).

ELIGIBILITY:
Applicant must be a member of Phi Kappa Phi, maintain high scholastic standing and be recommended by a chapter of Phi Kappa Phi.

GEOGRAPHIC RESTRICTIONS:
United States.

FINANCIAL DATA:
Amount of support per award: $5,000 or $15,000.
Total amount of support: $330,000.

COOPERATIVE FUNDING PROGRAMS: Awards made through Phi Kappa Phi Foundation, a companion organization to the Society.

NUMBER OF APPLICANTS MOST RECENT YEAR: 170.

NUMBER OF AWARDS: 60 (57 valued at $5,000 and 3 valued at $15,000) for the year 2010.

APPLICATION INFORMATION:
Completed application packet must be returned to the local chapter on or before the deadline.
Duration: One academic year. Nonrenewable.

IRS IDENTIFICATION NUMBER: 95-1856406

ADDRESS INQUIRIES TO:
Maria C. Davis
National Marketing Development Manager
(See address above.)

HORIZONS FOUNDATION

WID HORIZONS
2111 Wilson Boulevard, Suite 400
Arlington, VA 22201
(703) 247-2552
Fax: (703) 527-6945

E-MAIL ADDRESS:
jcasey@ndia.org

WEB SITE ADDRESS:
wid.ndia.org

TYPE:
Scholarships. The Horizons Foundation Scholarship Program is supported by accredited colleges and universities. Awards are made on an annual basis. The Foundation selects all scholarship recipients based on criteria it sets. Scholarships are awarded to applicants who require financial assistance, demonstrate strong academic credentials and a commitment to a career in national security.

See entry 1148 for full listing.

HORTICULTURAL RESEARCH INSTITUTE, INC.   [1817]

1000 Vermont Avenue, N.W.
Suite 300
Washington, DC 20005
(202) 741-4852
Fax: (202) 478-7288

WEB SITE ADDRESS:
www.hriresearch.org

AREAS OF INTEREST:
Nursery, landscape research and horticulture.

NAME(S) OF PROGRAMS:
- **Carville M. Akehurst Memorial Scholarship**
- **Timothy and Palmer Bigelow, Jr. Scholarship**
- **Muggets Scholarship**
- **Spring Meadow Nursery Scholarship**

TYPE:
Scholarships. The Carville M. Akehurst Memorial Scholarship was established by the Mid-Atlantic Nursery Trade Show, Inc. (MANTS) to provide scholarship opportunity to qualified students from Maryland, Virginia or West Virginia to help ensure the continuity of the nursery and landscape profession.

The Bigelow Scholarships provide aid to students from New England.

The Muggets Scholarship and the Spring Meadow Nursery Scholarship are intended to help aspiring students from across the U.S. obtain a degree in horticulture (nursery industry).

YEAR PROGRAM STARTED: 1988

PURPOSE:
To aid students seeking a career in the horticulture/nursery industry.

LEGAL BASIS:
Nonprofit organization.

ELIGIBILITY:
Carville M. Akehurst Memorial Scholarship: Applicant must be a resident of Maryland, Virginia or West Virginia, must be enrolled in an accredited undergraduate or graduate landscape/horticulture program or related discipline at a two- or four-year institution, must be currently enrolled in good standing, with a good academic record, carry a full-time course load and must have at least a junior standing (four-year curriculum) or senior standing (two-year curriculum).

Bigelow Scholarship: Applicant must be a resident of one of the six New England states and be enrolled full-time in an accredited undergraduate or graduate landscape/horticulture program. Preference will be given to an applicant who plans to work in any aspect of the nursery industry following graduation. Preference will also be given to an applicant in financial need. Previous winners are not eligible for additional funding.

Muggets and Spring Meadow Nursery Scholarships: Applicant must be enrolled in an accredited undergraduate or graduate landscape horticulture program or related discipline at a two- or four-year institution (students in vocational agriculture programs are also eligible), must be currently enrolled in good standing, with a good academic record, and carry a full-time course load. Applicant must be a sophomore or senior at the start of the fall semester.

FINANCIAL DATA:
Since 1962, the Institute has directed over $5,700,000 of industry funds to some 600 research projects covering the full range of production, environmental and business issues important to trade.
Amount of support per award: Carville M. Akehurst Memorial Scholarship and Muggets Scholarship: $1,000; Bigelow Scholarship: $2,000; Spring Meadow Nursery Scholarship: $1,500.

NUMBER OF APPLICANTS MOST RECENT YEAR:
Akehurst Memorial Scholarship: 10; Bigelow Scholarship: 10; Muggets Scholarship: 35; Spring Meadow Nursery Scholarship: 34.

NUMBER OF AWARDS: Carville M. Akehurst Memorial Scholarship: 2; All other scholarships: 1.

APPLICATION INFORMATION:
Applications are available online.
Duration: Bigelow Scholarship: One-time award.
Deadline: May 31.

IRS IDENTIFICATION NUMBER: 52-1052547

ADDRESS INQUIRIES TO:
Teresa Jodon, Executive Director
(See address above.)

ILLINOIS RESTAURANT ASSOCIATION EDUCATIONAL FOUNDATION, INC.   [1818]

33 West Monroe, Suite 250
Chicago, IL 60603
(312) 787-4000
Fax: (312) 845-1956

E-MAIL ADDRESS:
edfound@illinoisrestaurants.org

WEB SITE ADDRESS:
www.illinoisrestaurants.org

FOUNDED: 1973

AREAS OF INTEREST:
Food service/restaurant/hospitality.

NAME(S) OF PROGRAMS:
- **IRA Educational Foundation Scholarship Program**

TYPE:
Scholarships.

YEAR PROGRAM STARTED: 1973

PURPOSE:
To build Illinois' hospitality work force through career exploration and development programs, scholarships and image enhancement.

LEGAL BASIS:
Not-for-profit organization.

ELIGIBILITY:
Applicants must be permanent residents of the state of Illinois who are applying to or enrolled in an accredited culinary school, college or university and who are enrolled full-time or substantial part-time, taking a minimum of nine credit hours each term, majoring in a culinary restaurant management or foodservice related program.

GEOGRAPHIC RESTRICTIONS:
Illinois.

FINANCIAL DATA:
Scholarships provide assistance toward tuition and materials.
Amount of support per award: Minimum $1,000.

NUMBER OF AWARDS: 60.

APPLICATION INFORMATION:
Application forms are available upon request from the Foundation or can be downloaded from the web site.

Duration: One academic year. Renewal is not automatic.

Deadline: June 10.

IRS IDENTIFICATION NUMBER: 36-3271510

EXECUTIVE COMMITTEE:
Sara Rowe
Gary Salvestrini

OFFICERS AND TRUSTEES:
Dave Yanda, Chairperson
Nancy Rotunno, Vice Chairperson
Dan Gilroy, Treasurer
John Meyers, IRA Chairman

EXECUTIVE DIRECTOR:
Kathy Summers

ADDRESS INQUIRIES TO:
Kathy Summers, Executive Director
(See address above.)

INSTITUTE FOR THE INTERNATIONAL EDUCATION OF STUDENTS (IES) [1819]

33 North LaSalle Street
15th Floor
Chicago, IL 60602
(312) 944-1750
(800) 995-2300
Fax: (312) 944-1448

E-MAIL ADDRESS:
info@IESabroad.org

WEB SITE ADDRESS:
www.IESabroad.org

FOUNDED: 1950

AREAS OF INTEREST:
International education (JYA).

NAME(S) OF PROGRAMS:
● **IES Achievement Scholarship Program**

TYPE:
Scholarships. IES Merit-Based Scholarships supplement U.S. college and university awards for undergraduates studying with IES in Argentina, Australia, Austria, Chile, China, Ecuador, England, France, Germany, India, Ireland, Italy, Japan, Morocco, the Netherlands, New Zealand, South Africa and Spain. Merit-Based Scholarships are available for proven strength and interest in cross-cultural and comparative studies, fine arts, foreign language, high achievement, IES Asia programs, IES South American programs, international business, international relations, leadership, science and urban issues. Diversity Scholarships are also available as are scholarships for students who attend historically Black colleges/universities.

Need-based grants available to students with demonstrated financial need.

All IES Abroad aid is available only to students from schools within the IES Abroad Consortium and who attend an IES Abroad program.

YEAR PROGRAM STARTED: 1950

PURPOSE:
To provide study opportunities abroad for qualified American undergraduate students.

LEGAL BASIS:
Not-for-profit educational organization organized under the laws of Illinois.

ELIGIBILITY:
To be eligible, candidates must have been accepted (or have made application) to an IES program, be at least 18 years of age, be working toward an academic degree, have approval of his or her home college or university and submit a merit-based scholarship application along with its accompanying pieces.

FINANCIAL DATA:
Amount of support per award: Up to $3,000.

Total amount of support: $2,331,136 in financial aid and scholarships for the 2010-11 academic year.

NUMBER OF APPLICANTS MOST RECENT YEAR:
Summer 2010: need-based aid, 97. Fall 2010: need-based aid, 229; merit-based aid, 473. Spring 2011: need-based aid, 310; merit-based aid, 552.

NUMBER OF AWARDS: Summer 2010: need-based aid, 63. Fall 2010: need-based aid, 185; merit-based aid, 62. Spring 2011: need-based aid, 220; merit-based aid, 55.

APPLICATION INFORMATION:
Applications may be submitted online or downloaded from the IES web site.

Duration: Academic year, one semester, or summer (need-based only). Nonrenewable.

Deadline: May 1 for fall semester and academic year; October 25 for spring semester; April 1 for summer.

PUBLICATIONS:
Annual report; IES Alumni Exchange Newsletter; IES catalogs; IES MAP©.

IRS IDENTIFICATION NUMBER: 36-2251912

GOVERNING BOARD:
Dr. Kathryn M. Moore, Chairperson
Dr. Danielle Allen
Dr. Loren J. Anderson
Mary Cahillane
John Coblentz
James Crawford
Kenneth W. Cunningham
Debora de Hoyos
Dr. Mark H. Erickson
Dr. Pamela Brooks Gann
John J. Gearen
Dr. Homer J. Holland
Regge Life
Thomas McDonald
Robert McNeill
Dr. Marla Salmon
Alan Schwartz
Ian H. Turvill
Monica Vachher
Ezio Vergani
Dr. Kristi A. Wormhoudt

ADDRESS INQUIRIES TO:
Joseph Sevigny, Associate Vice President of Enrollment Management
(See address above.)

*SPECIAL STIPULATIONS:
Applicants must be admitted to an IES program and must attend a college or university that is part of the IES Abroad Consortium.

INTERNATIONAL ASSOCIATION OF FIRE CHIEFS FOUNDATION, INC. [1820]

4025 Fair Ridge Drive
Suite 300
Fairfax, VA 22033-2868
(703) 896-4822
Fax: (703) 273-9363

E-MAIL ADDRESS:
jcooke@iafc.org

WEB SITE ADDRESS:
www.iafcf.org

FOUNDED: 1974

NAME(S) OF PROGRAMS:
● **International Association of Fire Chiefs Foundation (IAFC Foundation) Scholarship Program**

TYPE:
Scholarships. Scholarships for advanced study in fire science, fire department administration and operation, public administration or any fire-related program.

YEAR PROGRAM STARTED: 1974

PURPOSE:
To aid in better fire service administration and to support training in this area.

ELIGIBILITY:
Under the regulations, any member of the fire service who is a member of a state, county, provincial, municipal, community, industrial or federal fire department, and who has demonstrated proficiency as a member, is eligible to apply for a scholarship to a recognized institution of higher education of his or her choice. Applicants must have the approval of their department chiefs. Dependents are not eligible.

FINANCIAL DATA:
Amount of support per award: Generally $500 to $2,000, providing a maximum of this dollar amount toward tuition costs.

Total amount of support: Approximately $25,000 per year.

NUMBER OF APPLICANTS MOST RECENT YEAR:
Approximately 60.

NUMBER OF AWARDS: Approximately 15 awards annually.

APPLICATION INFORMATION:
Duration: One year.

Deadline: June 1.

PUBLICATIONS:
Application guidelines.

ADDRESS INQUIRIES TO:
Jennifer Cooke
Association Manager for Foundation
(See address above.)

INTERNATIONAL DEVELOPMENT RESEARCH CENTRE (IDRC)

150 Kent Street
Mailroom Suite 990
Ottawa ON K1P 0B2 Canada
(613) 236-6163 ext. 2098
Fax: (613) 236-4026

E-MAIL ADDRESS:
cta@idrc.ca

WEB SITE ADDRESS:
www.idrc.ca/awards

TYPE:
Awards/prizes.

See entry 1387 for full listing.

IODE [1821]

40 Orchard View Boulevard, Suite 254
Toronto ON M4R 1B9 Canada
(416) 487-4416
Fax: (416) 487-4417

E-MAIL ADDRESS:
 iodecanada@bellnet.ca

WEB SITE ADDRESS:
 www.iode.ca

FOUNDED: 1900

AREAS OF INTEREST:
 Education, social service and citizenship.

NAME(S) OF PROGRAMS:
 • **War Memorial Scholarships**

TYPE:
 Scholarships. Postgraduate scholarships
 tenable in any university in Canada and the
 Commonwealth.

YEAR PROGRAM STARTED: 1920

PURPOSE:
 To provide scholarships for educational
 purposes as a memorial to Canadian men and
 women who gave their lives in defense of
 freedom during World Wars I and II.

LEGAL BASIS:
 Charitable organization.

ELIGIBILITY:
 Candidates must be Canadian citizens. At the
 time of application, candidates must be
 enrolled in the second year of a doctoral
 program.

GEOGRAPHIC RESTRICTIONS:
 Canada and the Commonwealth.

FINANCIAL DATA:
 Amount of support per award: $15,000
 (CAN) for study in Canada and for study
 overseas within the Commonwealth.

NUMBER OF AWARDS: 5 annually.

APPLICATION INFORMATION:
 A candidate must apply to the War Memorial
 Convener in the province in which the first
 degree was obtained. The names of
 Conveners change from year to year, but
 appear in the scholarship folder.
 Duration: One year.
 Deadline: Applications must reach the
 Convenor of the Province from which the
 first degree was obtained by December 1.

OFFICERS:
 Marie Locke, National War Memorial Officer

TRUSTEES:
 Catherine Moore, National President

THE JAPAN FOUNDATION, LOS ANGELES   [1822]

333 South Grand Avenue, Suite 2250
Los Angeles, CA 90071
(213) 621-2267 ext. 109
Fax: (213) 621-2590

E-MAIL ADDRESS:
 jflainfo@jflalc.org

WEB SITE ADDRESS:
 www.jflalc.org

FOUNDED: 1983

AREAS OF INTEREST:
 Japanese arts, culture and language
 education.

NAME(S) OF PROGRAMS:
 • **Exhibitions Abroad Support Program**
 • **Film and TV Program Production Support Program**
 • **Program for the Donation of Japanese Language Teaching Materials (for the United States)**
 • **Translation and Publication Support Program**

TYPE:
 Conferences/seminars; Exchange programs;
 Fellowships; Grants-in-aid; Product
 donations; Project/program grants; Research
 grants; Training grants; Visiting scholars.

PURPOSE:
 To support grants that promote Japanese arts,
 culture, language and education.

ELIGIBILITY:
 Candidates must be citizens or permanent
 residents of the U.S.

GEOGRAPHIC RESTRICTIONS:
 United States.

FINANCIAL DATA:
 Amount of support per award: Varies.
 Total amount of support: Varies.

APPLICATION INFORMATION:
 Guidelines are available online.
 Duration: One year. No renewals.
 Deadline: Varies.

THE JAPANESE AMERICAN CITIZENS LEAGUE (JACL) [1823]

1765 Sutter Street
San Francisco, CA 94115
(415) 921-5225
Fax: (415) 931-4671

E-MAIL ADDRESS:
 jacl-ncwnpro@msn.com

WEB SITE ADDRESS:
 www.jacl.org

FOUNDED: 1929

AREAS OF INTEREST:
 Education and hate crimes.

NAME(S) OF PROGRAMS:
 • **JACL National Scholarship and Awards Program**

TYPE:
 Scholarships. Scholarships and student aid
 awards (financial aid).

 Scholarship categories: Entering Freshman
 (High School Senior), Undergraduate,
 Graduate, Law, Creative and Performing
 Arts, Hagiwara Financial Aid.

YEAR PROGRAM STARTED: 1946

PURPOSE:
 To recognize education as a key to greater
 opportunities for its members.

ELIGIBILITY:
 Applicant must be a current National JACL
 member at either an individual or
 student/youth level. Applicants must be
 enrolled at an institution of higher learning
 within the U.S. at the undergraduate or
 graduate school level. Applicants may apply
 under only one scholarship category. Entering
 freshman applicants must be high school
 seniors. Creative and performing arts
 applicants cannot be professional artists.

FINANCIAL DATA:
 Amount of support per award: $1,000 to
 $5,000.
 Total amount of support: $60,000.

NUMBER OF AWARDS: Over 30 awards offered.

APPLICATION INFORMATION:
 Information brochure and applications are
 posted on the JACL web site annually in
 October.
 Duration: One year. Limited to a total of two
 awards.

 Deadline: April 1.

ADDRESS INQUIRIES TO:
 Scholarships Department
 (See address above.)

JEWISH FAMILY AND CHILDREN'S SERVICES   [1824]

JFCS Financial Aid Center
2150 Post Street
San Francisco, CA 94115
(415) 449-1226
Fax: (415) 449-1229
TDD: (415) 567-1044

E-MAIL ADDRESS:
 erics@jfcs.org

WEB SITE ADDRESS:
 www.jfcs.org

FOUNDED: 1850

AREAS OF INTEREST:
 Jewish individuals and their families, college
 tuition and expenses, vocational training and
 business and professional endeavors.

TYPE:
 Scholarships. Loans.

PURPOSE:
 To provide college scholarships and loans to
 Jewish students.

LEGAL BASIS:
 Nonprofit.

ELIGIBILITY:
 Applicants must be Jewish students who have
 demonstrated academic achievement
 (generally demonstrated by a 2.75 grade
 point average on a 4.0 scale), financial need,
 broad-based extracurricular activities and
 in-depth community involvement and
 acceptance to a college, university or
 vocational school.

GEOGRAPHIC RESTRICTIONS:
 San Francisco, the Peninsula, Marin or
 Sonoma counties, California. For Loans,
 Alameda and Contra Costa County,
 California residents are eligible.

FINANCIAL DATA:
 Amount of support per award: Loans: $4,500
 to $5,000; Scholarships: $1,000 to $1,500.

NUMBER OF APPLICANTS MOST RECENT YEAR:
 167.

NUMBER OF AWARDS: Varies per year.

APPLICATION INFORMATION:
 Contact local JFCS office for forms, list of
 required documents and other information.
 Duration: One academic year.
 Deadline: August 1 for fall term. November
 1 for spring term.

PUBLICATIONS:
 Program announcement.

STAFF:
 Eric Singer, Director

ADDRESS INQUIRIES TO:
 Eric Singer, Director
 JFCS Financial Aid Center
 (See address above.)

MACKENZIE KING SCHOLARSHIP TRUST   [1825]

c/o J. Blom, Faculty of Law
1822 East Mall, University of British Columbia
Vancouver BC V6T 1Z1 Canada
(604) 822-4564
Fax: (604) 822-8108

E-MAIL ADDRESS:
mkingscholarships@law.ubc.ca

WEB SITE ADDRESS:
www.mkingscholarships.ca

FOUNDED: 1950

AREAS OF INTEREST:
Industrial and international relations.

NAME(S) OF PROGRAMS:
- **The Mackenzie King Traveling Scholarships**

TYPE:
Scholarships. For graduate study, either in the U.S. or the U.K., in the field of international or industrial relations (including the international or industrial aspects of law, history, politics or economics).

YEAR PROGRAM STARTED: 1950

LEGAL BASIS:
Private charitable trust.

ELIGIBILITY:
Applicants must be graduates of any Canadian university.

FINANCIAL DATA:
Amount of support per award: $10,000 (CAN).
Total amount of support: $40,000 (CAN).

NUMBER OF APPLICANTS MOST RECENT YEAR:
160 for the 2010-11 academic year.

NUMBER OF AWARDS: 4 scholarships awarded annually.

APPLICATION INFORMATION:
Applicants must submit completed application forms, all official transcripts and three letters of reference to the Canadian university from which they received their most recent degree, c/o the Faculty of Graduate Studies.
Deadline: February 1.

ADDRESS INQUIRIES TO:
Graduate department of Canadian university from which applicant received most recent Canadian degree, or see e-mail address above.

MACKENZIE KING SCHOLARSHIP TRUST [1826]
c/o J. Blom, Faculty of Law
1822 East Mall, University of British Columbia
Vancouver BC V6T 1Z1 Canada
(604) 822-4564
Fax: (604) 822-8108

E-MAIL ADDRESS:
mkingscholarships@law.ubc.ca

WEB SITE ADDRESS:
www.mkingscholarships.ca

FOUNDED: 1950

AREAS OF INTEREST:
Graduate studies.

NAME(S) OF PROGRAMS:
- **The Mackenzie King Open Scholarship**

TYPE:
Scholarships. For full-time graduate studies in Canada or elsewhere, in any field.

YEAR PROGRAM STARTED: 1950

PURPOSE:
To assist graduates of Canadian universities pursue graduate study in any discipline anywhere in the world.

LEGAL BASIS:
Private charitable trust.

ELIGIBILITY:
Applicants must be graduates of any Canadian university.

FINANCIAL DATA:
Amount of support per award: $10,000 (CAN).
Total amount of support: $10,000 (CAN) available annually.

NUMBER OF APPLICANTS MOST RECENT YEAR:
300 for the 2010-11 academic year.

NUMBER OF AWARDS: 1 for the 2010-11 academic year.

APPLICATION INFORMATION:
Applicants must submit completed application forms, all official transcripts and three letters of reference to the Canadian university from which they received their most recent degree, c/o Faculty of Graduate Studies.
Duration: Scholarships are tenable for one year.
Deadline: February 1.

ADDRESS INQUIRIES TO:
Graduate department of Canadian university from which applicant received most recent Canadian degree, or see e-mail address above.

KNIGHTS OF COLUMBUS [1827]
P.O. Box 1670
New Haven, CT 06507-0901
(203) 752-4332
Fax: (203) 752-4103

WEB SITE ADDRESS:
www.kofc.org/scholarships

AREAS OF INTEREST:
Educational support.

NAME(S) OF PROGRAMS:
- **Educational Trust Scholarships**
- **Bishop Charles P. Greco Graduate Fellowships**
- **John W. McDevitt (Fourth Degree) Scholarships**
- **Pro Deo and Pro Patria Scholarships**

TYPE:
Fellowships; Project/program grants; Scholarships. Scholarships and fellowships are awarded to members of The Knights of Columbus in good standing, a son or daughter of such a member or deceased member, or to a member of the Columbian Squires.

The Educational Trust provides scholarships to sons and daughters of members who died or became permanently and totally disabled while serving in the military during a period of conflict or who died as a result of criminal violence directed against them while performing duties of full-time law enforcement officers or full-time firemen. The awards are for undergraduate studies in a four-year program leading to a Bachelor's degree at a Catholic college and include the amount not covered by other financial aid for tuition up to $25,000 per year.

The Bishop Greco Graduate Fellowships are for full-time graduate study leading to a Master's degree in a program for classroom teachers of persons with intellectual disabilities.

The John W. McDevitt (Fourth Degree) Scholarships are awarded to students entering the freshman class of undergraduate study at a Catholic college or university in the U.S.

For the Pro Deo and Pro Patria Scholarships, students must be entering the freshman class in a college program leading to a Bachelor's degree. Twelve scholarships are available at The Catholic University of America in Washington, DC; 50 scholarships are available to students entering other Catholic colleges in the United States.

PURPOSE:
To provide support for community activities, education, the elderly, poor, disabled and victims of disasters; to provide financial assistance to children of members in good standing.

ELIGIBILITY:
For the Pro Deo and Pro Patria Scholarships, applicants must be students entering in the freshman class in a Catholic college program leading to a Bachelor's degree. An applicant must be a member in good standing of the Knights of Columbus or the son or daughter of such a member, a deceased member or a member in good standing of the Columbian Squires.

To be eligible for the Bishop Greco Graduate Fellowships, applicants must be enrolled in a graduate study program leading to a Master's degree in a program designed for the preparation of classroom teachers of persons with intellectual disabilities. Membership requirements as listed for the scholarship above also apply for this award.

For Educational Trust Scholarships:
(1) Children of a member in good standing who, while serving in the military forces of his country in a combat zone, specifically designated as such by the Board of Directors, is killed by hostile action or wounded by hostile action resulting within two years thereof in permanent and total disability; an application must be filed within two years of the death or determination of total and permanent disability of the member or;
(2) Children of a member in good standing who, while in the lawful performance of his duties as a full-time law enforcement officer or full-time firefighter, died as the result of criminal violence directed at him; an application must be filed within two years of the date of the death of the member.
A candidate for benefits is required to submit documents to establish eligibility.

McDevitt (Fourth Degree) Scholarships: An applicant must be a member in good standing of the Knights of Columbus or the wife, widow, son or daughter of such a member or deceased member.

GEOGRAPHIC RESTRICTIONS:
United States.

FINANCIAL DATA:
Amount of support per award: Bishop Greco Graduate Fellowships: $1,000 maximum per year; Educational Trust Scholarship: Up to $25,000 per year; McDevitt (Fourth Degree) Scholarships: $1,500; Pro Deo and Pro Patria Scholarships: $1,500 per year.

NUMBER OF AWARDS: McDevitt (Fourth Degree) Scholarships: Approximately 36; Pro Deo and Pro Patria Scholarships: 62.

APPLICATION INFORMATION:
Application form required. Candidates are required to submit supporting documents to substantiate eligibility.

Duration: Pro Deo and Pro Patria and Educational Trust Scholarships: Up to four years. Greco Graduate Fellowship: Up to two years.

Deadline: May 1 for filing fellowship applications for the Bishop Greco Graduate Fellowships. March 1 for filing scholarship applications for the Pro Deo and Pro Patria Scholarships and McDevitt (Fourth Degree) Scholarships.

ADDRESS INQUIRIES TO:
Department of Scholarships
(See address above.)

*SPECIAL STIPULATIONS:
Candidates for Educational Trust Fund scholarships will be required to submit supporting documents to substantiate the claim.

KOHL'S CORPORATION   [1828]

N56 W17000 Ridgewood Drive
Menomonee Falls, WI 53051
(262) 703-7000
Fax: (262) 703-6305

E-MAIL ADDRESS:
community.relations@kohls.com

WEB SITE ADDRESS:
www.kohlscorporation.com

AREAS OF INTEREST:
Education assistance and/or rewards for children who volunteer in the communities Kohl's serves.

NAME(S) OF PROGRAMS:
● **Kohl's Kids Who Care® Scholarship Program**

TYPE:
Awards/prizes; Scholarships. Nomination reward/scholarship program in two age categories: 6-12 and 13-18 at three progressive levels: store level, regional and national.

PURPOSE:
To recognize and reward youths whose volunteer efforts are making a difference in local communities Kohl's serves.

ELIGIBILITY:
Parents, educators and community members must nominate a child, 6 to 18 years of age, who is volunteering in their community and making a difference in the lives of friends, neighbors and even strangers, transforming their hometowns into more caring communities. Nominee must be within a Kohl's market area and be a U.S. citizen/resident.

FINANCIAL DATA:
Amount of support per award: Store Level: $50 Kohl's gift card and certificate; Regional Level: $1,000 scholarship; National Level: $9,000 scholarship and $1,000 donation in winner's name to the charity of their choice.
Total amount of support: $415,000 anticipated for the year 2011.

APPLICATION INFORMATION:
Nominations accepted February 1 to March 15.
Deadline: Nominations: March 15. Store winners announced in June. Regional and National winners posted in July.

ADDRESS INQUIRIES TO:
Community Relations Department
(See address above.)

THE KOREAN AMERICAN SCHOLARSHIP FOUNDATION   [1829]

1952 Gallows Road, Suite 204
Vienna, VA 22182
(703) 748-5935
Fax: (703) 748-1874

E-MAIL ADDRESS:
eastern@kasf.org

WEB SITE ADDRESS:
www.kasf.org

FOUNDED: 1969

AREAS OF INTEREST:
Helping to meet the financial needs of Korean American students seeking higher education.

TYPE:
Awards/prizes; Scholarships.

YEAR PROGRAM STARTED: 1969

PURPOSE:
To assist Korean American students in pursuit of academic and personal achievement; to encourage community and civic service as an integral part of leadership development; to nurture the sense of pride and confidence in Korean cultural heritage and tradition.

ELIGIBILITY:
Scholarships: Students currently enrolled in a full-time undergraduate or graduate program. Recipients are selected on the basis of financial need, academic achievement, school activities and community services.

FINANCIAL DATA:
Amount of support per award: Varies depending on type of scholarship.
Total amount of support: $1,000 to $5,000.

NUMBER OF APPLICANTS MOST RECENT YEAR:
320.

NUMBER OF AWARDS: 62.

APPLICATION INFORMATION:
Each applicant must submit an application to the respective KASF region, in which each region is designated by the state where the school is located.
Deadline: Varies by region.

THE KOSCIUSZKO FOUNDATION, INC.   [1830]

15 East 65th Street
New York, NY 10065
(212) 734-2130

E-MAIL ADDRESS:
addy@thekf.org

WEB SITE ADDRESS:
www.thekf.org

FOUNDED: 1925

AREAS OF INTEREST:
Scholarships and grants for graduate and postgraduate studies in the U.S.

NAME(S) OF PROGRAMS:
● **The Kosciuszko Foundation Tuition Scholarship**

TYPE:
Scholarships. Offers funding to American citizens of Polish descent and to Polish citizens who have permanent residency status in the U.S. Scholarships are for Master's and Ph.D. students for full-time studies only. Undergraduate seniors may apply for a scholarship towards their first year of

Master's-level studies. Americans (non-Polish descent) are eligible for graduate-level studies when majoring in Polish language, history or culture.

Special funding is allocated for law and engineering studies at DePaul University; Bayonne, NJ residents for studies in nursing, teaching and business; and residents of Amsterdam, NY, Chicopee, MA and New Hampshire.

Contact Foundation for additional funding opportunities.

YEAR PROGRAM STARTED: 1950

PURPOSE:
To foster knowledge and appreciation of Polish culture, history and traditions among Americans; to enhance knowledge of the Polish contribution to world civilization in general and to America in particular; to encourage the study of Polish culture, history and language in the U.S; to foster deeper understanding of Polish culture among Americans.

LEGAL BASIS:
501(c)(3) not-for-profit organization.

ELIGIBILITY:
Applicants must:
(1) be U.S. citizens of Polish descent or;
(2) be Polish citizens who are permanent legal residents of the U.S. or;
(3) be Americans of non-Polish descent who are pursuing studies relating to Polish subjects and;
(4) have a minimum grade point average of 3.0.

Scholarships will be awarded on the basis of academic excellence and evidence of identification with the Polish-American community. Financial need is taken into consideration. Scholarships are for full-time graduate study in the U.S. and certain programs in Poland.

GEOGRAPHIC RESTRICTIONS:
United States and Poland (limited to certain programs).

FINANCIAL DATA:
Amount of support per award: $1,000 to $7,000. Average $3,000.
Total amount of support: $88,125 for the academic year 2009-10.

NUMBER OF APPLICANTS MOST RECENT YEAR:
Over 100.

NUMBER OF AWARDS: 83.

APPLICATION INFORMATION:
Financial Information Form is required. Completed applications must be accompanied by a nonrefundable $35 application fee. Faxed and e-mailed applications and supporting materials are not accepted. Applications posted to the Internet in October are available through December 31. Application and supporting documents must be submitted as a complete packet, not separately, prior to or on the deadline date.
Duration: One academic year. Possible renewal for a second year upon reapplication.
Deadline: January 5. Notification in May. Funding for the following academic year.

PUBLICATIONS:
Guidelines; *KF Newsletter*; grants brochure; annual report.

IRS IDENTIFICATION NUMBER: 13-1628179

ADDRESS INQUIRIES TO:
Tuition Scholarships
(See address above.)

*SPECIAL STIPULATIONS:
Students who receive scholarships are required to submit proof of full-time studies during the grant period.

MARCUS AND THERESA LEVIE EDUCATION FUND [1831]

Jewish Vocational Service
216 West Jackson Boulevard, Suite 700
Chicago, IL 60606-6921
(312) 673-3444
Fax: (312) 553-5544
TTY: (312) 444-2877

E-MAIL ADDRESS:
jvsscholarship@jvschicago.org

WEB SITE ADDRESS:
www.jvschicago.org

FOUNDED: 1959

AREAS OF INTEREST:
Higher education for Jewish students in full-time academic programs in the helping professions, legally domiciled in the metropolitan Chicago (IL) area.

TYPE:
Awards/prizes; Scholarships. Awards to individuals for the academic year.

YEAR PROGRAM STARTED: 1959

PURPOSE:
To provide financial support to Jewish men and women for their full-time academic programs.

LEGAL BASIS:
Tax-exempt private foundation.

ELIGIBILITY:
Scholarships are awarded on the basis of financial need. Applicants must be full-time students of Jewish background, predominately those legally domiciled in the metropolitan Chicago area. Applicants must have demonstrated career promise. Assistance is available for the fields listed below, including but not limited to:
(1) the helping professions such as medicine, dentistry, social work, education, psychology, the rabbinate and noncorporate areas of law;
(2) mathematics, engineering and other sciences and;
(3) communications within the College of Communications at the University of Illinois at Urbana-Champaign.

Additional requirements:
(1) undergraduates entering or who have entered the junior year in career-specific programs which require no postgraduate education for professional-level employment in one of the professional areas mentioned above or;
(2) students entering or who have entered a graduate or professional school in a helping profession described above or;
(3) students in a vocational training program with a specific educational goal in the helping professions.

Newcomers who are refugees or asylees are encouraged to apply. Citizenship is not a prerequisite.

FINANCIAL DATA:
Total amount of support: More than $500,000 per year.

COOPERATIVE FUNDING PROGRAMS: This program is administered by the Jewish Vocational Service.

NUMBER OF APPLICANTS MOST RECENT YEAR:
150 for the year 2010.

NUMBER OF AWARDS: 105.

APPLICATION INFORMATION:
Application submission must include application form, budget worksheet, personal and financial data, IRS 1040 form, proof of (Cook County) legal domicility, two reference letters, autobiography and official academic transcript. In-person interview is required prior to April 20.

Applications are available in the fall and can be downloaded from the Jewish Vocational Service web site. (Click on "Scholarship Services.")
Duration: One academic year. Recipients may reapply for renewal.
Deadline: February 15 for submission of applications. Applicants must be available for a personal interview at Jewish Vocational Service offices located throughout the Chicago metropolitan area prior to April 20.

OFFICERS:
Sally Yarberry, Scholarship Secretary

ADDRESS INQUIRIES TO:
Scholarship Secretary
(See address and phone number above.)

*SPECIAL STIPULATIONS:
All applicants must be available for a personal interview at the Jewish Vocational Service offices located throughout the Chicago metropolitan area prior to April 20.

LOUISIANA DIVISION OF THE ARTS, DEPARTMENT OF CULTURE, RECREATION AND TOURISM

1051 North Third Street, Room 420
Baton Rouge, LA 70802
(225) 342-8180
Fax: (225) 342-8173

E-MAIL ADDRESS:
arts@crt.state.la.us

WEB SITE ADDRESS:
www.crt.state.la.us/arts

TYPE:
Awards/prizes; Conferences/seminars; Training grants. Stabilization grants. Grants in a variety of programs are offered to arts organizations across the state.

Stabilization grants are offered in four levels of operating support to nonprofit arts organizations.

See entry 500 for full listing.

MANITOBA STUDENT AID PROGRAM [1832]

401-1181 Portage Avenue
Winnipeg MB R3G 0T3 Canada
(204) 945-6383
Fax: (204) 948-3421

WEB SITE ADDRESS:
www.manitobastudentaid.ca

FOUNDED: 1940

AREAS OF INTEREST:
To provide financial assistance to Manitobans whose finances limit their pursuit of postsecondary education.

CONSULTING OR VOLUNTEER SERVICES:
Informational services are provided to high schools, universities, community colleges, private organizations and others who request this service. Service referrals and advocacy.

NAME(S) OF PROGRAMS:
● **Aboriginal Education Awards**
● **Grant for Services and Equipment for Students with Permanent Disabilities**
● **Medical Students/Resident Financial Assistance Program**
● **The Prince of Wales/Princess Anne Award**

TYPE:
Grants-in-aid. Aboriginal Education Awards help with the cost of tuition, books and school supplies for the program year.

Grant for Services and Equipment for Students with Permanent Disabilities is for specialized equipment and services needed for students to take part in postsecondary education.

Medical Students/Resident Financial Assistance Program is a conditional grant. After completing training, medical physicians are required to work in Manitoba for one year for each grant received.

Prince of Wales/Princess Anne Awards are available to Canadian Aboriginal students studying anywhere in Canada with an assessed need of $1 or more.

YEAR PROGRAM STARTED: 1964

PURPOSE:
To increase educational opportunities for Manitobans with limited financial resources.

FINANCIAL DATA:
Amount of support per award: Aboriginal Education Awards: Up to $3,000 (CAN) for university attendance and up to $1,500 (CAN) for college; Grant for Services and Equipment for Students with Permanent Disabilities: Up to $8,000 (CAN) per year for equipment/services; Medical Students/Resident Financial Assistance Program: $15,000 (CAN) for third- and fourth-year medical students; $20,000 (CAN) for residents; Prince of Wales/Princess Anne Award: $250 (CAN) per year.

APPLICATION INFORMATION:
Applications may be obtained from Student Financial Assistance at the address above, or from high schools, universities and human resource centers in Manitoba.
Deadline: Varies with program.

PUBLICATIONS:
Application guidelines.

STAFF:
Alain Comeau, Manager of Information Services

ADDRESS INQUIRIES TO:
Berrina Dequier, Information Officer
(See address above.)

MARINE CORPS SCHOLARSHIP FOUNDATION, INC. [1833]

121 South Saint Asaph Street
Alexandria, VA 22314
(703) 549-0060
Fax: (703) 549-9474

E-MAIL ADDRESS:
info@mcsf.org

WEB SITE ADDRESS:
www.mcsf.org

FOUNDED: 1962

AREAS OF INTEREST:
Scholarships to children of Marines and children of former Marines.

TYPE:
Scholarships. Scholarships are for higher education (post high school) college, trade or vocational school. Family income limit is $86,000 for the 2010 tax year.

The Foundation has pledged to award scholarships worth up to $20,000 each for higher education to the children of Marines and former Marines who lost their lives in the tragic events of September 11, 2001. The Foundation will also award similar $20,000 scholarships to the children of any Marine who is killed in combat in the declared war on terrorism, as well as to the children of any Navy Corpsman who is killed in combat while serving with the Marines.

YEAR PROGRAM STARTED: 1962

PURPOSE:
To encourage needy and deserving children of Marines and former children of Marines to develop their spiritual, intellectual and physical capabilities through a college, vocational or technical school education; to focus on the "youth, education, and values" that have made the U.S. strong.

LEGAL BASIS:
Nonprofit, tax-exempt corporation.

ELIGIBILITY:
Sons or daughters of Marines or children of former Marines. College or trade school. No graduate study.

The Foundation has made a special commitment to the sons and daughters of Marines and Navy Corpsmen whose parent is wounded or killed in combat.

Scholarships are for postsecondary education, including vocational and technical schools as well as college. No scholarships for graduate work.

FINANCIAL DATA:
The Foundation has provided over 24,000 scholarships worth approximately $50,000,000 since its inception.
Amount of support per award: $1,000 to $10,000 per year; average $3,500.
Total amount of support: $3,500,000 for the academic year 2009-10.

NUMBER OF AWARDS: 1,405 for the academic year 2009-10.

APPLICATION INFORMATION:
Request application from address above beginning in January for the following academic year. Applications will be sent out from January through March.
Duration: One year. Renewable for up to four years. Recipients must reapply.
Deadline: Graduating high school seniors and first-time freshmen: March 1. All other applicants: April 15.

PUBLICATIONS:
Annual report; guidelines; yearbook; trifold; newsletter.

IRS IDENTIFICATION NUMBER: 22-1905062

STAFF:
Julia Hill, Director of Scholarship Programs

ADDRESS INQUIRIES TO:
Julia Hill
Director of Scholarship Programs
(See address above.)

*SPECIAL STIPULATIONS:
Cannot violate civil or campus law.

THURGOOD MARSHALL COLLEGE FUND [1834]
80 Maiden Lane, Suite 2204
New York, NY 10038
(212) 573-8888
Fax: (212) 573-8497

E-MAIL ADDRESS:
tamekia.jackson@tmcfund.org

WEB SITE ADDRESS:
www.thurgoodmarshallfund.org

FOUNDED: 1987

NAME(S) OF PROGRAMS:
● **TMCF Scholarships**

TYPE:
Scholarships. Scholarship for full-time students pursuing a degree at one of the 47 TMCF "member schools."

ELIGIBILITY:
Students must:
(1) be U.S. citizen pursuing a degree in any discipline at one of the 47 TMCF "member schools" on a full-time basis;
(2) demonstrate financial need and;
(3) demonstrate academic excellence and a commitment to community service with a high school or college grade point average of 3.0.

Awards are merit-based.

GEOGRAPHIC RESTRICTIONS:
United States.

FINANCIAL DATA:
Amount of support per award: Usually $4,400 split into two semesters: fall $2,200; spring $2,200.

NUMBER OF AWARDS: Approximately 300 per year.

APPLICATION INFORMATION:
Apply online only.
Duration: One academic year.

ADDRESS INQUIRIES TO:
Tamekia Jackson, Scholarship Manager
(See address above.)

MARYLAND HIGHER EDUCATION COMMISSION [1835]
Office of Student Financial Assistance
839 Bestgate Road, Suite 400
Annapolis, MD 21401
(410) 260-4565
(800) 974-1024
Fax: (410) 260-3202; (410) 260-3200

E-MAIL ADDRESS:
osfamail@mhec.state.md.us

WEB SITE ADDRESS:
www.mhec.state.md.us

FOUNDED: 1961

NAME(S) OF PROGRAMS:
● **Maryland State Scholarships**

TYPE:
Grants-in-aid; Scholarships; Loan forgiveness programs. The Educational Excellence Awards program is the state's largest need-based program. It has two components: the Educational Assistance Grant and the Guaranteed Access Grant. The Educational Assistance Grant is targeted to low- to moderate-income families and is based on financial need (40% of calculated financial need for four-year institutions, 60% for community colleges). The Guaranteed Access

Grant is for very low-income high school students and requires a 2.5 high school grade point average (100% of student need up to a maximum of $14,300).

The Part-Time Grant supports part-time, degree-seeking, undergraduate students.

The Graduate and Professional School Scholarship provides support to full-time and part-time graduate and professional students in nursing, pharmacy, dentistry, law, medicine, veterinary science, and social work.

Senatorial Scholarships: Each member of the state senate may award $34,500 in scholarships each year.

Delegate Scholarships: Each member of the House of Delegates may award scholarships to students attending approved Maryland postsecondary institutions.

Distinguished Scholars Program is designed to keep exceptionally talented students in Maryland.

Maryland also offers a number of career/occupational and unique population financial assistance programs.

LEGAL BASIS:
Government agency.

ELIGIBILITY:
Candidate must be a resident of the state and generally enrolled or intending to enroll in a college or university in Maryland.

GEOGRAPHIC RESTRICTIONS:
Maryland.

FINANCIAL DATA:
Amount of support per award: Educational Assistance Grant: $400 to $3,000; Guaranteed Access Grant: Up to $14,300; Part-Time Grant: Up to $2,000; Graduate and Professional School Scholarship: Up to $5,000; Senatorial Scholarships: $400 to $34,500 per member of the state senate; Delegate Scholarships: $200 minimum award per member of the House of Delegates; Distinguished Scholars Program: $3,000 per year.
Total amount of support: Approximately $110,000,000 for all programs.

NUMBER OF APPLICANTS MOST RECENT YEAR: 109,000.

NUMBER OF AWARDS: 57,000 for all programs.

APPLICATION INFORMATION:
Use the Free Application for Federal Student Aid (FAFSA) or special program application.
Duration: Up to four years. Renewable.
Deadline: March 1 for state-administered, need-based aid program; other deadlines vary throughout the year.

PUBLICATIONS:
A Quick Guide to Cash for College and How to Get it; *Student Guide to Higher Education and Financial Aid In Maryland*; *6 Steps to Choosing the Right School.*

ADDRESS INQUIRIES TO:
See e-mail address above.

MASSACHUSETTS MEDICAL SOCIETY (MMS) [1836]
860 Winter Street
Waltham, MA 02451-1411
(800) 944-5562
Fax: (781) 464-4823

E-MAIL ADDRESS:
nero@mms.org

WEB SITE ADDRESS:
www.massmed.org

FOUNDED: 1954

NAME(S) OF PROGRAMS:
- **Massachusetts Medical Society International Health Studies Grant Program**
- **Massachusetts Medical Society (MMS) Scholars Program**
- **MMS Medical Information Technology Awards**
- **MMS Student Section Community Service Grants**

TYPE:
Awards/prizes; Grants-in-aid; Research grants; Scholarships. Massachusetts Medical Society International Health Studies Grant Program: Grants to defray the costs of study abroad.

Massachusetts Medical Society (MMS) Scholars Program: Awarded to two students from each of the four Massachusetts medical schools.

MMS Medical Information Technology Awards: Given annually to one medical student and one resident physician.

MMS Student Section Community Service Grants: Funding for each of two service projects per medical school chapter of the Section, per calendar year.

PURPOSE:
To advance medical knowledge; to develop and maintain the highest professional and ethical standards of medical practice and health care; to promote medical institutions formed on liberal principles for the health, benefit, and welfare of the citizens of the Commonwealth.

ELIGIBILITY:
Massachusetts Medical Society International Health Studies Grant Program: MMS member; preference given to applicants planning a career serving underprivileged populations. Massachusetts Medical Society (MMS) Scholars Program: MMS member; fourth-year students enrolled in a Massachusetts medical school. MMS Medical Information Technology Awards: MMS member; medical students, residents or fellows enrolled in one of the four Massachusetts Medical Schools or a Massachusetts hospital or training program. MMS Student Section Community Service Grants: Current medical student members of the MMS whose projects meet objectives in community and social service, public health activism and education or volunteer mentorship activities.

FINANCIAL DATA:
Amount of support per award: Massachusetts Medical Society International Health Studies Grant Program: $750. Massachusetts Medical Society (MMS) Scholars Program: $10,000. MMS Medical Information Technology Awards: $3,000 annually. MMS Student Section Community Service Grants: Up to $250.

NUMBER OF AWARDS: Massachusetts Medical Society International Health Studies Grant Program: 4. Massachusetts Medical Society (MMS) Scholars Program: 8. MMS Medical Information Technology Awards: 1 medical student and 1 resident physician. MMS

Student Section Community Service Grants: 2 service projects per medical school chapter of the Section, per calendar year.

APPLICATION INFORMATION:
Deadline: Massachusetts Medical Society International Health Studies Grant Program: September 15. Massachusetts Medical Society (MMS) Scholars Program: January 14. MMS Medical Information Technology Awards: Mid-November annually.

PUBLICATIONS:
Application guidelines.

ADDRESS INQUIRIES TO:
Linda Howard, Regional Manager
Massachusetts Medical Society (MMS)
(See address above.)

MMS International Health Studies
Grant Program:
Jennifer Day, MMS and Alliance
Charitable Foundation Director
Tel: (781) 434-7044
E-mail: jday@mms.org.

MMS Scholars Program:
Applicant's Office of Student Affairs or
Thelma Tatten
MMS Department of Continuing Education
and Certification
Tel: (781) 434-7305
E-mail: ttatten@mms.org

MMS Medical Information Technology
Awards
Leon Q. Barzin, MMS Technical Program
Portfolio Director
Tel: (800) 322-2303 ext. 7048
E-mail: lbarzin@mms.org

MASSACHUSETTS OFFICE OF STUDENT FINANCIAL ASSISTANCE [1837]

Office of Student Financial Assistance
454 Broadway, Suite 200
Revere, MA 02151
(617) 727-9420
Fax: (617) 727-0667

E-MAIL ADDRESS:
cmccurdy@osfa.mass.edu

WEB SITE ADDRESS:
www.osfa.mass.edu

FOUNDED: 1980

AREAS OF INTEREST:
Financial assistance to Massachusetts students.

NAME(S) OF PROGRAMS:
- **Gilbert Grants**
- **MASSGrants**
- **Public Service Grant**

TYPE:
Grants-in-aid. Gilbert Grants are based on financial need and awarded to Massachusetts residents enrolled in nonprofit and private colleges.

MASSGrants: State grants in all undergraduate fields, based solely on financial need, renewable for up to four years of undergraduate study. State grants must be used at accredited institutions in Massachusetts and reciprocal states.

Public Service Grants provide scholarships for children and/or spouses of deceased members of fire, police and corrections departments and children of deceased veterans whose death was service-related, for undergraduate study in any institution of higher education in Massachusetts.

PURPOSE:
To assist those who are unable to meet the costs of postsecondary education.

ELIGIBILITY:
For Gilbert Grants, applicants must be permanent Massachusetts residents for at least one year, attending full-time in Massachusetts. For Public Service Grants, applicant must be the child and/or widowed spouse of a duty deceased Massachusetts fire, police or corrections officer, POW/MIA or duty deceased veteran. MASSGrant applicants may attend school in Connecticut, Maine, Massachusetts, New Hampshire, Pennsylvania, Rhode Island, Vermont or Washington, DC.

GEOGRAPHIC RESTRICTIONS:
Primarily Massachusetts.

FINANCIAL DATA:
Amount of support per award: Gilbert Grants: $200 to $2,500; MASSGrant: $300 to $1,900; Public Service Grants: varies.

Total amount of support: Gilbert Grant: $20,000,000; approximately $28,000,000 for MASSGrant; less than $100,000 for Public Service Grants annually.

NUMBER OF APPLICANTS MOST RECENT YEAR:
MASSGrant: 300,000. Public Service Grants: 30.

NUMBER OF AWARDS: MASSGrant: 29,000 for the year 2008-09. Public Service Grants: Approximately 17 for the 2008-09 academic year.

APPLICATION INFORMATION:
Applicants must file the Free Application for Federal Student Aid (FAFSA) after January 1.

Deadline: Gilbert Grant deadline is determined by college. MASSGrant and Public Service Grants: May 1.

PUBLICATIONS:
Guidelines.

ADDRESS INQUIRIES TO:
Clantha McCurdy
Senior Deputy Commissioner
(See address above.)

MEXICAN AMERICAN LEGAL DEFENSE AND EDUCATIONAL FUND

634 South Spring Street, 11th Floor
Los Angeles, CA 90014
(213) 629-2512
Fax: (213) 629-0266

WEB SITE ADDRESS:
www.maldef.org

TYPE:
Awards/prizes; Internships; Scholarships. Awarded annually to law students who have a demonstrated commitment to serving the Latino community with their law degree.

See entry 2110 for full listing.

MISSOURI DEPARTMENT OF HIGHER EDUCATION [1838]

P.O. Box 1469
Jefferson City, MO 65102
(573) 751-2361
(800) 473-6757, option 4
Fax: (573) 751-6635

E-MAIL ADDRESS:
leroy.wade@dhe.mo.gov

WEB SITE ADDRESS:
www.dhe.mo.gov

FOUNDED: 1986

NAME(S) OF PROGRAMS:
● **Missouri Higher Education Academic Scholarship Program ("Bright Flight")**

TYPE:
Scholarships. Provides undergraduate student financial aid to qualified Missouri students who wish to attend qualified Missouri institutions of higher education, both public and private.

PURPOSE:
To enable qualified full-time students to attend a participating postsecondary institution (public and private).

LEGAL BASIS:
RSMO Supp. 173.250. Government agency.

ELIGIBILITY:
Applicant must be a Missouri resident enrolled in an eligible Missouri institution, be a high school senior who plans to enroll as a first-time, full-time student and have a composite score on the American College Testing Program (ACT) or the Scholastic Aptitude Test (SAT) in the top three percent of all Missouri students taking the tests.

GEOGRAPHIC RESTRICTIONS:
Missouri.

FINANCIAL DATA:
Amount of support per award: Maximum award for an academic year is $2,000 and not to exceed $1,000 per semester.
Total amount of support: Varies.

APPLICATION INFORMATION:
Student must take the ACT or SAT assessment and receive the required test score on or before the June test date. The Missouri Department of Higher Education will obtain the ACT or SAT assessment records, whichever the student has taken, and will notify students, high schools and postsecondary institutions of scholarship awards.
Duration: One academic year. Renewable annually until students have obtained a Baccalaureate degree or completed a total of 10 semesters.

ADDRESS INQUIRIES TO:
Information Center
(See address above.)

MISSOURI DEPARTMENT OF HIGHER EDUCATION   [1839]

P.O. Box 1469
Jefferson City, MO 65102-1469
(573) 751-2361
(800) 473-6757, option 4
Fax: (573) 751-6635

E-MAIL ADDRESS:
leroy.wade@dhe.mo.gov

WEB SITE ADDRESS:
www.dhe.mo.gov

FOUNDED: 1986

NAME(S) OF PROGRAMS:
● **Access Missouri Financial Assistance Program**

TYPE:
Grants-in-aid. Undergraduate student financial aid to qualified Missouri students who wish to attend qualified Missouri institutions of higher education, both public and private.

YEAR PROGRAM STARTED: 2007

PURPOSE:
To enable full-time students to attend a participating postsecondary institution (public and private).

LEGAL BASIS:
Section 173.1101-173.1107, RSMo. Government agency.

ELIGIBILITY:
Initially, applicants must meet the following requirements:
(1) have a FAFSA on file by April 1;
(2) have any FAFSA corrections made by July 31 (school choices may be added until September 30);
(3) be a U.S. citizen or permanent resident and a Missouri resident;
(4) be enrolled full-time at a participating Missouri school;
(5) have an EFC of $12,000 or less and;
(6) not be pursuing a degree or certificate in theology or divinity.

Renewal students must continue to meet the eligibility requirements for initial students and additionally:
(1) be an undergraduate student enrolled full-time at a participating Missouri school. (Students with disabilities who are enrolled in at least six credit hours may be considered to be enrolled full-time);
(2) not have received the first Bachelor's degree, completed the required hours for a Bachelor's degree, or completed 150 semester credit hours;
(3) maintain a minimum cumulative grade point average of 2.5 and otherwise maintain satisfactory academic progress as defined by the applicant's school and;
(4) not have received an Access Missouri award for a maximum of five semesters at a two-year school or 10 semesters at any combination of two-year or four-year schools, whichever occurs first. (If Charles Gallagher or Missouri College Guarantee awardee in past semesters, those semesters are counted in the 10-semester limit, along with any semester in which the applicant has received an Access Missouri award).

GEOGRAPHIC RESTRICTIONS:
Missouri.

FINANCIAL DATA:
Amount of support per award: Award amounts are based on the type of school one is attending when award is received. If applicant transfers to a different school, his or her award amount may change based on the type of school to which he or she transfers. Public two-year: $300 to $1,000. Public four-year and Linn State Technical College: $1,000 to $2,150. Private: $2,000 to $4,600. (Note: Maximum award amounts may be less than these figures; it depends on the amount of funding that is available for the program.)

NUMBER OF APPLICANTS MOST RECENT YEAR: 74,394.

NUMBER OF AWARDS: 43,000.

APPLICATION INFORMATION:
Duration: One academic year. Renewable.
Deadline: FAFSA on file by April 1.

ADDRESS INQUIRIES TO:
Information Center
(See address above.)

MONSANTO COMPANY/NATIONAL ASSOCIATION OF FARM BROADCASTERS   [1840]

c/o National FFA Organization
Scholarship Office
P.O. Box 68960
Indianapolis, IN 46268-0960

E-MAIL ADDRESS:
scholarships@ffa.org

WEB SITE ADDRESS:
www.monsanto.com
www.ffa.org

AREAS OF INTEREST:
Agriculture.

NAME(S) OF PROGRAMS:
● **Commitment to Agriculture Scholarship Program**

TYPE:
Scholarships. Open to high school seniors who have long-term interests in agriculture.

YEAR PROGRAM STARTED: 1999

PURPOSE:
To recognize deserving students with a long-term career interest in agriculture and reward them with funding for their college education.

ELIGIBILITY:
Applicant must:
(1) be a high school student senior in the U.S. with an immediate family actively engaged in production agriculture;
(2) plan to enroll, in the fall of the next academic year, in an accredited two- or four-year college, university or vocational-technical school;
(3) plan on pursuing a career in agriculture in any field related to agriculture and;
(4) have an average to above-average academic record.

Applicant must not have an immediate family member employed by Monsanto or be a member of the National Association of Farm Broadcasting.

GEOGRAPHIC RESTRICTIONS:
United States.

FINANCIAL DATA:
Amount of support per award: $1,500.

NUMBER OF AWARDS: 100 annually.

APPLICATION INFORMATION:
Application available online.
Duration: One year. Nonrenewable.
Deadline: February 15.

ADDRESS INQUIRIES TO:
Teri Buchholtz
Scholarship Program Manager
(See e-mail address above.)

THE NATIONAL COLLEGIATE ATHLETIC ASSOCIATION [1841]

1802 Alonzo Watford Sr. Drive
Indianapolis, IN 46202
(317) 917-6683
Fax: (317) 917-6336

E-MAIL ADDRESS:
lthomas@ncaa.org

WEB SITE ADDRESS:
www.ncaa.org

FOUNDED: 1906

AREAS OF INTEREST:
Intercollegiate athletics administration.

NAME(S) OF PROGRAMS:
- **NCAA Postgraduate Scholarship Program**

TYPE:
Scholarships. Awarded annually to student-athletes who have excelled academically and athletically and are in their final season of intercollegiate varsity athletics competition under NCAA legislation for the sport in which the student-athlete is nominated. Athletics participation is limited to those sports for which the NCAA conducts a championship or designates as an emerging sport. Each sports season (fall, winter and spring) there are 29 scholarships available for men and 29 scholarships available for women.

YEAR PROGRAM STARTED: 1964

PURPOSE:
To promote and encourage postgraduate education by rewarding the Association's most accomplished student-athletes through their participation in NCAA championship and/or emerging sports; to reward those individuals whose dedication and effort are reflective of those characteristics necessary to succeed and thrive through postgraduate study in an accredited graduate degree program.

LEGAL BASIS:
Nonprofit and voluntary association of more than 1,000 institutions, conferences, organizations and individuals devoted to the sound administration of intercollegiate athletics. The NCAA is the organization through which the nation's colleges and universities speak and act on athletic matters at the national level.

ELIGIBILITY:
To be eligible for consideration, a nominee:
(1) shall have excelled academically with an overall minimum accumulative grade point average of 3.2 (based on a maximum 4.0) or its equivalent;
(2) must be nominated in the academic year in which they complete the final season of eligibility in the sport they are nominated;
(3) shall have performed with distinction as a member of the varsity team in the sport in which the student has declared candidacy;
(4) shall have signified the intention to continue academic work beyond the Baccalaureate degree as a full-time or part-time graduate student and have been judged capable of graduate study by the major professor, major department head or dean of the college in which the nominee is enrolled;
(5) be enrolled at an NCAA member institution and have been nominated by the faculty athletics representative of an NCAA member institution;
(6) shall have conducted himself or herself, both on and off the field, in a manner that has brought credit to the student, the institution, intercollegiate athletics and the ideals and objectives of American higher education and;
(7) after satisfying the above requirements, consideration shall be given to participation in campus activities other than academic and athletic in which the student has had the opportunity to demonstrate qualities of leadership and serve as an example to fellow students.

FINANCIAL DATA:
Award must be used within three years as full-time ($7,500) or part-time ($3,750 at start, $3,750 with 6 hours remaining) student in the accredited graduate degree program of choice.
Amount of support per award: $7,500.

NUMBER OF APPLICANTS MOST RECENT YEAR: 854.

NUMBER OF AWARDS: 174 awards annually.

APPLICATION INFORMATION:
The Association requests that each member institution nominate not more than 10 candidates per season (five per gender). Applications can be requested from the NCAA at the address above or can be downloaded from the web site.

Application must have the signature of the FAR (Faculty Athletic Representative) or designee before being submitted.
Duration: One-time grants. Nonrenewable.

ADDRESS INQUIRIES TO:
Postgraduate Scholarship Program
(See address above.)

*SPECIAL STIPULATIONS:
Candidates must be nominated by a member institution's faculty athletics representative or designee.

NATIONAL FEDERATION OF THE BLIND
200 East Wells Street
Baltimore, MD 21230
(410) 659-9314 ext. 2415

E-MAIL ADDRESS:
scholarships@nfb.org

WEB SITE ADDRESS:
www.nfb.org/scholarships

TYPE:
Conferences/seminars; Scholarships. Awarded on the basis of academic excellence and service to the community. Provides a one-time grant plus a continuing program of mentors and seminars for blind college students.

See entry 1066 for full listing.

NATIONAL INSTITUTE FOR LABOR RELATIONS RESEARCH   [1842]
5211 Port Royal Road
Suite 510
Springfield, VA 22151
(703) 321-9606 ext. 2231
Fax: (703) 321-7143

E-MAIL ADDRESS:
research@nilrr.org

WEB SITE ADDRESS:
www.nilrr.org

FOUNDED: 1975

AREAS OF INTEREST:
Organization of public opposition to compulsory unionism in the education community.

NAME(S) OF PROGRAMS:
- **Future Teacher Scholarship**

TYPE:
Scholarships. Scholarship awarded annually to the education student who exemplifies dedication to principle and high professional standards.

YEAR PROGRAM STARTED: 1989

PURPOSE:
To promote awareness of compulsory unionism.

LEGAL BASIS:
Nonprofit 501(c)(3) organization.

ELIGIBILITY:
Applicants are limited to undergraduates and graduate students majoring in education in institutions of higher learning throughout the U.S. Applicants who will be considered must demonstrate potential for successful completion of educational requirements in a college or university Department of Education program and the potential of successful application for a teaching license and demonstrate, by means of a written essay, an understanding of the individual freedom issue as it applies to the problem of compulsory unionism in the education community.

GEOGRAPHIC RESTRICTIONS:
United States.

FINANCIAL DATA:
Amount of support per award: $1,000 per scholarship.
Total amount of support: $1,000.

NUMBER OF APPLICANTS MOST RECENT YEAR:
Approximately 212.

NUMBER OF AWARDS: 1.

APPLICATION INFORMATION:
A total application will consist of a completed application form and a typewritten essay of approximately 500 words clearly demonstrating an interest in and a knowledge of the Right to Work principle as it applies to educators. All finalists will be requested to submit an official copy of his or her most recent transcript of grades.
Duration: One year. Nonrenewable.
Deadline: Applications must be postmarked on or by December 31 of calendar year.

ADDRESS INQUIRIES TO:
Cathy Jones, Scholarship Administrator
(See address above.)

*SPECIAL STIPULATIONS:
Applicant must be education major attending college or have been admitted to an institution of higher learning in the U.S.

THE NATIONAL ITALIAN AMERICAN FOUNDATION [1843]
1860 19th Street, N.W.
Washington, DC 20009-5501
(202) 939-3118
Fax: (202) 483-2618

E-MAIL ADDRESS:
scholarships@niaf.org

WEB SITE ADDRESS:
www.niaf.org/scholarships

NAME(S) OF PROGRAMS:
- **NIAF Scholarship Program**

TYPE:
Scholarships. The National Italian American Foundation (NIAF) will award scholarships and grants to outstanding students for use during the following academic year. The awards will be made on the basis of academic merit and divided between two groups of students.

PURPOSE:
To assist Italian American students or those interested in Italian studies.

ELIGIBILITY:
Italian Americans studying any field, or students of any ethnic background studying Italian or Italian studies.

Italian American students who demonstrate outstanding potential and high academic achievements. The area of study is open.

Students from any ethnic background majoring or minoring in Italian language, Italian studies, Italian American studies or a related field, who demonstrate outstanding potential and high academic achievements.

GEOGRAPHIC RESTRICTIONS:
United States.

FINANCIAL DATA:
Each scholarship award can only cover tuition and university-provided room and board. Scholarship monies not used during one academic year are not transferable to the following academic year.
Amount of support per award: $2,000 to $10,000.
Total amount of support: Varies.

APPLICATION INFORMATION:
In order to be complete, an application must include the following:
(1) completed student application submitted online;
(2) Teacher Evaluation Form submitted online;
(3) an official school transcript submitted by mail and;
(4) FAFSA Financial Aid Form submitted by mail (optional).
Duration: One academic year.
Deadline: First Friday in March.

PUBLICATIONS:
Scholarship brochure.

ADDRESS INQUIRIES TO:
See e-mail address above.

NATIONAL JEWISH COMMITTEE ON SCOUTING [1844]

1325 West Walnut Hill Lane
Irving, TX 75015
(972) 580-2091
Fax: (972) 580 2535

E-MAIL ADDRESS:
lee.shaw@scouting.org

WEB SITE ADDRESS:
www.jewishscouting.org

NAME(S) OF PROGRAMS:
• **Rick Arkans Eagle Scout Scholarship**
• **Chester M. Vernon Memorial Eagle Scout Scholarship**
• **Frank L. Weil Memorial Eagle Scout Scholarship**

TYPE:
Scholarships. Awarded annually.

PURPOSE:
To promote Boy Scouting among Jewish youth; to help Jewish institutions and local council Jewish committees to provide Scouting opportunities for Jewish youth; to promote Jewish values in Scouting.

ELIGIBILITY:
Applicants must:
(1) be a registered, active member of a Boy Scout troop, Varsity Scout team, or Venturing crew;
(2) have received the Eagle Scout Award;
(3) be an active member of a synagogue and

must have received the Ner Tamid or Etz Chaim religious emblem;
(4) have demonstrated practical citizenship in his synagogue, school, Scouting unit, and community and;
(5) be enrolled in an accredited high school and in his final year at the time of selection, except Scouts whose Eagle Scout boards of review are held the same year of their high school graduation may apply in that calendar year. They may receive a scholarship one time only.

GEOGRAPHIC RESTRICTIONS:
United States.

FINANCIAL DATA:
Amount of support per award: Rick Arkans Eagle Scout Scholarship: $1,000; Chester M. Vernon Memorial Eagle Scout Scholarship: $1,000 per year for four years; Frank L. Weil Memorial Eagle Scout Scholarship: $1,000 first place award and two $500 second place awards.

NUMBER OF AWARDS: 6.

APPLICATION INFORMATION:
Applicants for the Arkans and Vernon Scholarships must submit a copy of the Free Application for Federal Student Assistance (FAFSA).

All sections of the scholarship application should be completed with as much information as possible. However, except for the required letter of recommendation (and FAFSA), no additional pages may be attached.
Deadline: Application submitted no later than February 28. Announcements by June 1.

ADDRESS INQUIRIES TO:
Keith Walton, Staff Advisor
(See address above.)

NATIONAL SOCIETY DAUGHTERS OF THE AMERICAN REVOLUTION [1845]

1776 D Street, N.W.
Washington, DC 20006-5303
(202) 879-3292
Fax: (202) 879-3348

WEB SITE ADDRESS:
www.dar.org

FOUNDED: 1890

AREAS OF INTEREST:
Furthering the education of Native Americans.

NAME(S) OF PROGRAMS:
• **American Indian Scholarship**

TYPE:
Scholarships. Intended to help Native American college/university and technical school students at the undergraduate or graduate level.

PURPOSE:
To provide scholarship assistance to Native American students of any age or tribe, in any state, striving to get an education.

ELIGIBILITY:
Applicants must:
(1) be Native Americans (proof required by letter or proof papers) in financial need;
(2) be U.S. citizens/residents and;
(3) have a grade point average of 2.75 or higher.

Graduate students are eligible; however, undergraduate students are given preference.

GEOGRAPHIC RESTRICTIONS:
United States.

FINANCIAL DATA:
Amount of support per award: $1,000.

NUMBER OF AWARDS: Up to 20.

APPLICATION INFORMATION:
No phone or fax inquiries. Send self-addressed, stamped envelope specifying American Indian Scholarships for information. Applications should be sent to the National Vice Chairman of the American Indians Committee.
Duration: No renewals.
Deadline: April 1.

NATIONAL SOCIETY DAUGHTERS OF THE AMERICAN REVOLUTION [1846]

1776 D Street, N.W.
Washington, DC 20006-5303
(202) 879-3292
Fax: (202) 879-3348

WEB SITE ADDRESS:
www.dar.org

FOUNDED: 1890

AREAS OF INTEREST:
Furthering the education of Native Americans.

NAME(S) OF PROGRAMS:
• **Frances Crawford Marvin American Indian Scholarship**

TYPE:
Scholarships. Intended to help Native American students enrolled full-time at a two- or four-year college or university.

PURPOSE:
To provide scholarship assistance to Native American students.

ELIGIBILITY:
Applicants must:
(1) be enrolled full-time at a two- or four-year college or university;
(2) be Native Americans (proof required by letter or proof papers);
(3) be U.S. citizens/residents;
(4) demonstrate financial need and academic achievement and;
(5) have a grade point average of 3.0 or higher.

A recipient may reapply and be considered along with members of the applicant pool.

GEOGRAPHIC RESTRICTIONS:
United States.

FINANCIAL DATA:
Amount of support per award: Up to $1,500.

APPLICATION INFORMATION:
No phone or fax inquiries. Send self-addressed, stamped envelope specifying American Indian Scholarships for information. Applications should be sent to the National Vice Chairman of the American Indians Committee.
Duration: Renewable upon reapplication.
Deadline: February 1.

NATIONAL SOCIETY OF ACCOUNTANTS SCHOLARSHIP FOUNDATION [1847]

1010 North Fairfax Street
Alexandria, VA 22314-1574
(703) 549-6400
(800) 966-6679
Fax: (703) 549-2984

E-MAIL ADDRESS:
sbrasse@nsacct.org

WEB SITE ADDRESS:
www.nsacct.org

AREAS OF INTEREST:
Accounting.

NAME(S) OF PROGRAMS:
- **The Stanley H. Stearman Award**

TYPE:
Scholarships.

PURPOSE:
To provide financial encouragement to students who select accounting as a career.

LEGAL BASIS:
501(c)(3) charitable organization.

ELIGIBILITY:
Must be an undergraduate accounting major who is a U.S. or Canadian citizen that attends a U.S. accredited school and maintains a "B" or better overall grade point average. Also, must be the spouse, son, daughter, grandchild, niece, nephew, daughter-in-law or son-in-law of an active or retired NSA living or deceased member. The member must have held membership for at least one year prior to the annual distribution of applications in October.

GEOGRAPHIC RESTRICTIONS:
United States.

FINANCIAL DATA:
Amount of support per award: $2,000 per year.
Total amount of support: Up to $6,000 per recipient.

NUMBER OF AWARDS: 1.

APPLICATION INFORMATION:
Applications and appraisal forms may be obtained by contacting the Foundation at the address above.
Duration: Not to exceed three years. This renewable award may extend through graduate studies.
Deadline: March 10 (postmark).

ADDRESS INQUIRIES TO:
National Society of Accountants
Scholarship Program
Scholarship America
One Scholarship Way
P.O. Box 297
St. Peter, MN 56082
Tel: (507) 931-1682

NATIONAL SOCIETY OF ACCOUNTANTS SCHOLARSHIP FOUNDATION [1848]

1010 North Fairfax Street
Alexandria, VA 22314-1574
(703) 549-6400
(800) 966-6679
Fax: (703) 549-2984

E-MAIL ADDRESS:
sbrasse@nsacct.org

WEB SITE ADDRESS:
www.nsacct.org

AREAS OF INTEREST:
Accounting.

NAME(S) OF PROGRAMS:
- **The Louis and Fannie Sager Memorial Scholarship**

TYPE:
Scholarships. This annual award honors retired Legal Counsel William H. Sager, the youngest son of Louis and Fannie Sager.

PURPOSE:
To provide financial encouragement to students who select accounting as a career.

LEGAL BASIS:
501(c)(3) charitable organization.

ELIGIBILITY:
Must be a Virginia public high school graduate who is enrolled as an undergraduate in a Virginia college or university, majoring in accounting.

GEOGRAPHIC RESTRICTIONS:
United States.

FINANCIAL DATA:
Amount of support per award: $500 to $1,000.

NUMBER OF AWARDS: 1.

APPLICATION INFORMATION:
Applications and appraisal forms may be obtained by contacting the Foundation at the above address. Completed application must be mailed along with a current, complete official transcript of grades to Scholarship America at the address given below.
Deadline: March 10 (postmark).

ADDRESS INQUIRIES TO:
National Society of Accountants
Scholarship Program
Scholarship America
One Scholarship Way
P.O. Box 297
St. Peter, MN 56082
Tel: (507) 931-1682

NATSO FOUNDATION [1849]

1737 King Street
Suite 200
Alexandria, VA 22314
(703) 549-2100
Fax: (703) 684-4525

E-MAIL ADDRESS:
foundation@natsofoundation.org

WEB SITE ADDRESS:
www.natsofoundation.org

FOUNDED: 1989

AREAS OF INTEREST:
Research, scholarships and public outreach.

NAME(S) OF PROGRAMS:
- **Bill Moon Scholarships**

TYPE:
Scholarships.

PURPOSE:
To aid travel plaza employees and their dependents with educational expenses.

ELIGIBILITY:
Must be an employee or a dependent of an employee of a travel plaza facility.

FINANCIAL DATA:
Amount of support per award: $2,500.

NUMBER OF APPLICANTS MOST RECENT YEAR:
30.

NUMBER OF AWARDS: 8 for the year 2009.

APPLICATION INFORMATION:
Must submit application including transcript, essay, letter(s) of recommendation, and demonstration of need.
Duration: One semester.

Deadline: Varies.

ADDRESS INQUIRIES TO:
Taryn Brice-Rowland
(See address above.)

NEED

Warner Centre
332 Fifth Avenue, 1st Floor
Pittsburgh, PA 15222
(412) 566-2760
Fax: (412) 471-6643

E-MAIL ADDRESS:
atyler@needld.org

WEB SITE ADDRESS:
www.needld.org

TYPE:
Scholarships. Supplemental grants for postsecondary education at colleges and business, trade and technical schools.

See entry 1096 for full listing.

NEW JERSEY DEPARTMENT OF MILITARY AND VETERANS AFFAIRS [1850]

DVP-VBB
P.O. Box 340
Trenton, NJ 08625-0340
(609) 530-6854
Fax: (609) 530-6970

E-MAIL ADDRESS:
patty.richter@njdmava.state.nj.us

WEB SITE ADDRESS:
www.state.nj.us/military

FOUNDED: 1959

AREAS OF INTEREST:
State financial assistance for postsecondary students.

NAME(S) OF PROGRAMS:
- **Veterans Tuition Credit Program (VTCP)**

TYPE:
Grants-in-aid. Tuition assistance grant for attendance at any eligible undergraduate, graduate or vocational institution in the U.S.

YEAR PROGRAM STARTED: 1977

PURPOSE:
To provide tuition assistance to U.S. veterans of the Armed Forces of the U.S. who served on active duty between December 31, 1960 and May 7, 1975 who were, or are, eligible for federal veterans' educational assistance (G.I. Bill).

LEGAL BASIS:
Entitlement.

ELIGIBILITY:
Applicant must be a veteran of the armed forces of the U.S. who is or was eligible for veterans educational assistance pursuant to federal law and served on active duty in the armed forces of the U.S. between December 31, 1960 and May 7, 1975. Applicant must have been a legal New Jersey resident at the time of induction into the armed forces, or at the time of discharge from active duty or for at least one year prior to the time of application, excluding the time spent in active duty. If a veteran was not a New Jersey resident at time of induction or separation, veteran must provide documentation reflecting residency–copy of NJ Income Tax Return, letter from postmaster, home mortgage or apartment lease. Applicant must be currently enrolled in

an approved state approving agency course of study at any eligible academic, professional or vocational institution in the U.S.

GEOGRAPHIC RESTRICTIONS:
New Jersey.

FINANCIAL DATA:
Amount of support per award: Eligible veterans may receive a maximum award of $400 a year for full-time attendance or $200 a year for half-time attendance as provided by regulations and available appropriations.

NUMBER OF APPLICANTS MOST RECENT YEAR:
17.

NUMBER OF AWARDS: Based upon appropriations.

APPLICATION INFORMATION:
Applications are available at campus Veterans Affairs offices or by calling the New Jersey Department of Military and Veterans Information Number, Tel: (888) 865-8387, available from any location in New Jersey, Monday through Friday, 8:30 A.M. to 4:30 P.M.
Duration: Eligible veterans may receive up to four academic years of payment.
Deadline: October 1 for fall and spring terms. March 1 for spring term only.

OFFICERS:
Robert Hughes, FD-FMB-BA

ADDRESS INQUIRIES TO:
Patricia Richter, Bureau Chief, VBB
(See address above.)

NEW JERSEY DEPARTMENT OF MILITARY AND VETERANS AFFAIRS [1851]

DVP-VBB
P.O. Box 340
Trenton, NJ 08625-0340
(609) 530-6854
Fax: (609) 530-6970

E-MAIL ADDRESS:
patty.richter@njdmava.state.nj.us

WEB SITE ADDRESS:
www.state.nj.us/military

FOUNDED: 1959

AREAS OF INTEREST:
State financial assistance for college students, 16 to 21 years of age.

NAME(S) OF PROGRAMS:
● **Prisoner of War/Missing in Action (POW/MIA) Program**

TYPE:
Grants-in-aid; Scholarships.

YEAR PROGRAM STARTED: 1978

LEGAL BASIS:
Entitlement.

ELIGIBILITY:
Applicants must be dependent children (any child born before, during or after the period of time its parent was a POW/MIA) of military service personnel who were officially declared "Prisoner of War" or "Person Missing in Action" after January 1, 1960. The POW or MIA must have been a resident of New Jersey at the time he or she entered the Armed Forces of the U.S. or whose official residence is New Jersey.

GEOGRAPHIC RESTRICTIONS:
New Jersey.

FINANCIAL DATA:
Amount of support per award: Full tuition costs will be paid on behalf of the eligible dependent to any New Jersey public or independent college or university upon certification of full-time enrollment.

APPLICATION INFORMATION:
Applications are available by contacting the New Jersey Department of Military and Veterans Affairs, Veterans Service Office, located in Mercer County.
Deadline: October 1 for fall and spring term benefits. March 1 for spring term benefits only.

OFFICERS:
Robert Hughes, FD-FMB-BA

ADDRESS INQUIRIES TO:
Patricia Richter, Bureau Chief, VBB
(See address above.)

NEW YORK STATE EDUCATION DEPARTMENT [1852]

Scholarships and Grants
Room 967 EBA
Albany, NY 12234
(518) 486-1319
Fax: (518) 486-5346

WEB SITE ADDRESS:
www.highered.nysed.
gov/kiap/scholarships/home.htm

NAME(S) OF PROGRAMS:
● **Robert C. Byrd Honors Scholarship**
● **Regents Physician Loan Forgiveness Award Program**
● **Scholarships for Academic Excellence**

TYPE:
Scholarships. Robert C. Byrd Honors Scholarship: Federally funded scholarships designed to promote student excellence and achievement and to recognize exceptionally able students who show promise of continued excellence. Scholarships may be used at any accredited postsecondary institution in the U.S. These awards may be held concurrently with any other type of scholarship.

Regents Physician Loan Forgiveness Award Program: Designed to increase the number of physicians practicing in areas of New York state designated by the Regents as having a shortage of physicians. Emphasis is placed on primary care.

Scholarships for Academic Excellence: For use only at colleges and universities within New York state. Students are nominated by their high schools for this award.

PURPOSE:
To encourage specially talented youth to continue their education.

ELIGIBILITY:
Robert C. Byrd Honors Scholarship:
Candidates must:
(1) be U.S. citizens, nationals, permanent residents or selected refugees approved by the U.S. Attorney General;
(2) be legal residents of New York state for at least one year immediately preceding the effective date of the award;
(3) be students in their senior year in high school, or be students earning a GED diploma by the end of February of the academic year prior to the effective date of the award and;
(4) have a minimum SAT score of 1875 at one sitting and a minimum unweighted GPA

of 95.00 in selected academic courses, or a 3100 GED score and a SAT score of 1875 at one sitting.

This is a federally funded program and is restricted to New York State residents who are in the 12th grade. Individual applications are available from the high schools.

Eligibility requirements for State Education Department scholarships are subject to change.

GEOGRAPHIC RESTRICTIONS:
New York state.

FINANCIAL DATA:
Amount of support per award: Robert C. Byrd Honors Scholarship: $1,500 per year for up to four years of undergraduate study; Regents Physician Loan Forgiveness Award Program: Up to $10,000 per year for two years; Scholarships for Academic Excellence: $500 to $1,500.
Total amount of support: Varies.

NUMBER OF AWARDS: Robert C. Byrd Honors Scholarship: Dependent on federal funding; Regents Physician Loan Forgiveness Award Program: Minimum of 80; Scholarships for Academic Excellence; 2,000 $1,500 scholarships, 6,000 $500 scholarships.

Actual number of awards depends on legislative approval.

APPLICATION INFORMATION:
Students must apply directly to the state education agency in their state of legal residence. Application forms are available through student's guidance counselor.
Duration: Robert C. Byrd Honors Scholarship: One year. Renewable for up to four years of undergraduate study. Regents Physician Loan Forgiveness Award Program: Two years.

NEW YORK STATE EDUCATION DEPARTMENT [1853]

Office of K-16 Initiatives and Access Programs, Scholarships and Grants
Administration Unit, Room 967 EBA
Albany, NY 12234
(518) 486-1319
Fax: (518) 486-5346

WEB SITE ADDRESS:
www.highered.nysed.
gov/kiap/scholarships/home.htm

FOUNDED: 1975

AREAS OF INTEREST:
Postsecondary student financial aid.

NAME(S) OF PROGRAMS:
● **New York State Regents Professional Opportunity Scholarships**

TYPE:
Scholarships. Support for students pursuing a professional career in an approved program in New York state. Eligible professions include accounting, architecture, chiropractic, dental hygiene, engineering, law, nursing, occupational therapy, occupational therapy assistant, ophthalmic dispensing, optometry, pharmacy, physical therapy, physical therapy assistant, podiatry, psychology, social work, speech language pathology/audiology, veterinary medicine, landscape architecture and physician's assistant.

YEAR PROGRAM STARTED: 1976

PURPOSE:
To give financial support to New York state residents seeking higher education.

LEGAL BASIS:
State agency.

ELIGIBILITY:
Scholarships will be awarded to eligible students beginning or already enrolled in an approved, licensure-qualifying program leading to a degree at a New York State postsecondary institution.

GEOGRAPHIC RESTRICTIONS:
New York state.

FINANCIAL DATA:
Upon completion of study, recipients must work one year for each annual payment received. Employment must be in the studied profession and must be in New York state. Recipients who do not begin practice within one year of program completion will be required to repay twice the amount of all scholarship monies received plus interest.

Amount of support per award: Awards range from $1,000 to $5,000 per year for up to four years of study. Students in an approved program usually requiring more than four years of study will be eligible for payments for the required duration of study.

Total amount of support: Varies.

NUMBER OF AWARDS: Depends on the amount of yearly support given by the New York state government.

APPLICATION INFORMATION:
Applications and further information may be obtained from NYS Education Department, Scholarship Processing Unit, EBA Room 967, Albany, NY 12234.
Duration: Up to four years of study or longer if required by the program.
Deadline: May 31.

ADDRESS INQUIRIES TO:
Student Information
(See address above.)

NEW YORK STATE HIGHER EDUCATION SERVICES CORPORATION [1854]

99 Washington Avenue
Albany, NY 12255
(888) 697-4372
Fax: (518) 473-3749

E-MAIL ADDRESS:
bhochberg@hesc.com

WEB SITE ADDRESS:
www.hesc.org

FOUNDED: 1975

AREAS OF INTEREST:
Postsecondary student financial aid.

NAME(S) OF PROGRAMS:
- **Military Service Recognition Scholarship (MSRS)**
- **NYS Memorial Scholarships**

TYPE:
Grants-in-aid; Scholarships. Military Service Recognition Scholarship (MSRS) provides financial aid to children, spouses and financial dependents of members of the armed forces of the U.S. or of a state-organized militia who, at any time on or after August 2, 1990, while a New York state resident, died or became severely and permanently disabled while engaged in hostilities or training for hostilities. It is for study in New York state.

NYS Memorial Scholarships (Full name: NYS Memorial Scholarships for Families of Deceased Firefighters, Volunteer Firefighters, Police Officers, Peace Officers, and Emergency Medical Service Workers) provides financial aid to children, spouses and financial dependents of deceased members of these branches of public service who have died as the result of injuries sustained in the line of duty in service to the state of New York. It is for study in New York state.

The Corporation administers more than 25 grant, scholarship, award and other programs providing college financial aid for New York state residents.

YEAR PROGRAM STARTED: 2004

PURPOSE:
To provide special financial assistance for postsecondary study for children in certain categories.

LEGAL BASIS:
Article 13 of the Education Law. New York state agency.

ELIGIBILITY:
Students must:
(1) study at an approved postsecondary institution in New York state;
(2) have graduated from high school in the U.S., earned a GED, or passed a federally approved "Ability to Benefit" test as defined by the Commissioner of the State Education Department;
(3) be enrolled as a full-time student taking 12 or more credits per semester;
(4) be matriculated in an approved program of study and be in good academic standing;
(5) have at least a cumulative "C" average after receipt of two annual payments and;
(6) not be in default on a student loan guaranteed by HESC or any repayment of state awards.

GEOGRAPHIC RESTRICTIONS:
New York state.

APPLICATION INFORMATION:
Applicants must complete and submit either the Military Service Recognition Scholarship Web Supplement or the NYS Memorial Scholarship Web Supplement. Be sure to print the Web Supplement confirmation, sign the supplement, and submit it along with the required documentation according to the instructions. FAFSA must be completed after eligibility is established and applicant has been assigned an account number.
Duration: Four years of full-time undergraduate study or five years of undergraduate study if the student is enrolled in an approved five-year program.
Deadline: June 30.

OFFICERS:
Elsa McGee, Acting President

NEW YORK STATE HIGHER EDUCATION SERVICES CORPORATION [1855]

99 Washington Avenue
Albany, NY 12255
(518) 473-3259
(888) 697-4372

E-MAIL ADDRESS:
dfreeman@hesc.org

WEB SITE ADDRESS:
www.hesc.org

FOUNDED: 1975

AREAS OF INTEREST:
Postsecondary student financial aid.

NAME(S) OF PROGRAMS:
- **NYS Aid for Part-Time Study (APTS)**

TYPE:
Grants-in-aid. College-based program providing grant assistance for eligible part-time students enrolled in approved undergraduate studies.

YEAR PROGRAM STARTED: 1984

PURPOSE:
To help pay tuition for eligible students enrolled in approved certificate or degree programs.

LEGAL BASIS:
State agency.

ELIGIBILITY:
To be considered for an award, a student must enroll part-time in a degree or an approved certificate program at a degree-granting institution, meet specific income limits, be a New York state resident, be either a U.S. citizen or eligible noncitizen, have a tuition charge of at least $100 per year, and not have used up Tuition Assistance Program (TAP) eligibility.

For this program, part-time study means being enrolled for at least three, but less than 12, semester hours per semester, or four, but less than eight, credit hours per trimester. A participating college selects recipients from among eligible students.

GEOGRAPHIC RESTRICTIONS:
New York state.

FINANCIAL DATA:
Award amount is based on the student's need and the amount of money available at the institution.
Amount of support per award: Up to $2,000 per year.

APPLICATION INFORMATION:
Awards are made through each college offering this program. Students should contact the college financial aid office to find out how to apply at their school.
Duration: Renewable.

OFFICERS:
Elsa McGee, Acting President

ADDRESS INQUIRIES TO:
Student Information
(See address above.)

NEW YORK STATE HIGHER EDUCATION SERVICES CORPORATION [1856]

99 Washington Avenue
Albany, NY 12255
(888) 697-4372
Fax: (518) 473-3749

E-MAIL ADDRESS:
bhochberg@hesc.com

WEB SITE ADDRESS:
www.hesc.org

FOUNDED: 1975

AREAS OF INTEREST:
Postsecondary student financial aid.

NAME(S) OF PROGRAMS:
- **New York State Tuition Assistance Program (TAP)**

TYPE:
Grants-in-aid. New York's largest grant program, the Tuition Assistance Program

helps eligible New York residents attending in-state postsecondary institutions pay for tuition. TAP grants are based on the applicant's and his or her family's New York state net taxable income.

YEAR PROGRAM STARTED: 1976

PURPOSE:
To partially defray tuition charges to students.

LEGAL BASIS:
Article 13 of the Education Law.

ELIGIBILITY:
Legal New York state residents who are U.S. citizens or eligible noncitizens, who are full-time students at an approved postsecondary institution in New York state, and who meet income eligibility limitations are eligible to apply.

GEOGRAPHIC RESTRICTIONS:
New York state.

FINANCIAL DATA:
Grant varies according to New York net taxable income of the applicant and the family. Student must attend an institution charging at least $200 annual tuition.
Amount of support per award: Up to $5,000.

NUMBER OF AWARDS: Unlimited.

APPLICATION INFORMATION:
Annual application is required. Applications will be sent to applicant after filing the Free Application for Federal Student Aid (FAFSA).
Duration: One year.
Deadline: June 30 of the current school year.

OFFICERS:
Elsa McGee, Acting President

ADDRESS INQUIRIES TO:
Student Information
(See address above.)

THE CHARLOTTE W. NEWCOMBE FOUNDATION   [1857]

35 Park Place
Princeton, NJ 08542-6918
(609) 924-7022
Fax: (609) 252-1773

E-MAIL ADDRESS:
info@newcombefoundation.org

WEB SITE ADDRESS:
www.newcombefoundation.org

FOUNDED: 1979

AREAS OF INTEREST:
College scholarship funds to colleges and universities.

NAME(S) OF PROGRAMS:
● **Newcombe Fellowships**
● **Newcombe Scholarships for Mature Women**
● **Newcombe Scholarships for Students with Disabilities**
● **Special Scholarship Endowment Grants**

TYPE:
Challenge/matching grants; Endowments; Fellowships; Internships; Scholarships. Endowment challenges build up current Newcombe Scholarship Endowments at colleges in a Newcombe program.

Newcombe Fellowships are designed to encourage original and significant study of ethical and religious values in all areas of

human endeavor. The selection process and all administration for this continuing fellowship program are handled by the Woodrow Wilson National Fellowship Foundation of Princeton, NJ. All doctoral requirements except the dissertation must be completed by November of the year preceding the Fellowship award. Student must be attending a graduate school in the U.S.

Newcombe Scholarships for Students with Disabilities are intended to recognize the extraordinary expenses these students incur because of their disabilities and to supplement other sources of aid. The Newcombe Foundation offers special disability expense scholarships, internship scholarships and partial tuition scholarships through the counseling offices of colleges which provide excellent support services for disabled students. Preference in this program is given to four-year colleges which render exceptional service to large numbers of disabled students. Nine colleges are in the Newcombe Program.

Newcombe Scholarships for Mature Women are for women age 25 and older who have completed half the credits required for their Bachelor's degrees. These scholarships are available at selected colleges which offer support services for mature women. Preference in this program is given to four-year colleges with excellent support services for mature women students. It is Foundation policy not to provide grants in this program to professional schools, including theological seminaries and those training health care professionals; 30 colleges are in this program.

Special Scholarship Endowment Grants are awarded to selected institutions to benefit students from a specified economically disadvantaged population that the institution serves.

The Foundation makes no awards to individual students. All grants are made to colleges, universities and other institutions of higher education.

YEAR PROGRAM STARTED: 1981

PURPOSE:
To provide selected colleges and universities with scholarship funds for specifically targeted groups of students.

LEGAL BASIS:
Private.

ELIGIBILITY:
No grants to individuals. Scholarship aid only. No funds for program development staffing or support. The Foundation provides grants to colleges, universities and foundations to create scholarships for designated undergraduate and graduate students. No aid is available for postdoctoral fellowships.

GEOGRAPHIC RESTRICTIONS:
Scholarships for Disabled Students and Mature Women Scholarships are limited to Colleges in Delaware, Maryland, New Jersey, New York City, New York, Pennsylvania and Washington, DC.

FINANCIAL DATA:
Amount of support per award: In three scholarship programs: $15,000 to $48,000.
Total amount of support: $1,938,217 for the year 2010-11.
Matching fund requirements: Varies.

NUMBER OF APPLICANTS MOST RECENT YEAR:
42 (by invitation).

NUMBER OF AWARDS: 40.

REPRESENTATIVE AWARDS:
$41,000 to Misericordia University; $37,000 to Gwynedd-Mercy College; $44,000 to LaSalle University; $25,000 to Brooklyn College.

APPLICATION INFORMATION:
For Newcombe Fellowships, contact Woodrow Wilson National Fellowship Foundation, P.O. Box 5281, Princeton, NJ 08543-5281 for application materials. Tel: (609) 452-7007. Web site: www.woodrow.org.

For Newcombe Scholarships for Students with Disabilities and Mature Women Scholarships, colleges within geographic area should contact the Foundation for applications. Individuals should contact their college of choice for availability of these scholarships.
Duration: Varies.
Deadline: Receipt of proposals: Mid-November for Newcombe Fellowships and November 1 for Students with Disabilities and Mature Women Scholarships.

PUBLICATIONS:
Annual report.

IRS IDENTIFICATION NUMBER: 23-2120614

STAFF:
Thomas N. Wilfrid, Executive Director
Catherine Thomas, Program Officer
Diane Wilfrid, Program Associate

BOARD OF TRUSTEES:
Robert M. Adams
Janet A. Fearon
Elizabeth T. Frank
Aaron E. Gast
J. Barton Luedeke

ADDRESS INQUIRIES TO:
Thomas N. Wilfrid, Executive Director
(See address above.)

*PLEASE NOTE:
No grants to individuals.

*SPECIAL STIPULATIONS:
Grants are made to colleges and universities exclusively for student scholarships. Two programs (Mature Women and Students with Disabilities) are limited to colleges in Delaware, Maryland, New Jersey, New York City, Pennsylvania, and Washington, DC.

NORTH CAROLINA STATE EDUCATION ASSISTANCE AUTHORITY/COLLEGE FOUNDATION OF NORTH CAROLINA   [1858]

P.O. Box 13663
Research Triangle Park, NC 27709-3663
(866) 866-2362
Fax: (919) 248-4687

E-MAIL ADDRESS:
programinformation@cfnc.org

WEB SITE ADDRESS:
www.cfnc.org

AREAS OF INTEREST:
Financial aid for North Carolina students.

TYPE:
Grants-in-aid; Scholarships.

PURPOSE:
To provide access to higher education and information for the citizens of North Carolina.

ELIGIBILITY:
Varies with program. All applicants must be North Carolina residents.

GEOGRAPHIC RESTRICTIONS:
North Carolina.

FINANCIAL DATA:
Amount of support per award: Varies.
Total amount of support: Varies.

APPLICATION INFORMATION:
Applications may be obtained online or by telephone request.
Duration: Varies.
Deadline: Varies.

ADDRESS INQUIRIES TO:
NCSEAA Grants Training and Outreach
(See address above.)

NORTH DAKOTA STATE BOARD FOR INDIAN SCHOLARSHIPS

1815 Schafer Street
Suite 202
Bismarck, ND 58501-1217
(701) 224-2501
Fax: (701) 224-2500

E-MAIL ADDRESS:
rhonda.schauer@ndus.nodak.edu

WEB SITE ADDRESS:
www.ndus.nodak.edu

TYPE:
Scholarships. Grants to undergraduate and graduate Indian students in North Dakota colleges.

See entry 1120 for full listing.

NORTHERN CHAUTAUQUA COMMUNITY FOUNDATION [1859]

212 Lake Shore Drive West
Dunkirk, NY 14048
(716) 366-4892
Fax: (716) 366-3905

E-MAIL ADDRESS:
nccf@nccfoundation.org

WEB SITE ADDRESS:
www.nccfoundation.org

FOUNDED: 1986

AREAS OF INTEREST:
Youth development and economic development.

TYPE:
Challenge/matching grants; Project/program grants; Scholarships. Youth Development and Economic Development grants.

PURPOSE:
To enhance the northern Chautauqua community.

LEGAL BASIS:
Community foundation.

ELIGIBILITY:
Applicants must be registered 501(c)(3) organizations that serve the northern Chautauqua County community.

GEOGRAPHIC RESTRICTIONS:
Northern Chautauqua County, New York.

FINANCIAL DATA:
Amount of support per award: $25 to $10,000.
Total amount of support: Approximately $400,000.

APPLICATION INFORMATION:
Call the Foundation for information.
Deadline: Grants: March 1 and September 1.

PUBLICATIONS:
Annual report; Spring and Fall newsletters.

IRS IDENTIFICATION NUMBER: 16-1271663

STAFF:
Diane E. Hannum, Executive Director
Eileen Dunn, Program Coordinator
Nancy Mosier, Administrative Scholarship Coordinator
John O. Wrigley, Accountant

ADDRESS INQUIRIES TO:
Eileen Dunn, Program Coordinator
(See address above.)

*SPECIAL STIPULATIONS:
Scholarships to Northern Chautauqua County residents only.

THE NRA FOUNDATION, INC. [1860]

11250 Waples Mill Road
Fairfax, VA 22030
(703) 267-1131
Fax: (703) 267-1083

E-MAIL ADDRESS:
grantprogram@nrahq.org

WEB SITE ADDRESS:
www.nrafoundation.org

NAME(S) OF PROGRAMS:
● **Jeanne E. Bray Memorial Scholarship**

TYPE:
Scholarships. For children of peace officers.

YEAR PROGRAM STARTED: 1988

PURPOSE:
To assist children of peace officers, who are current NRA members, in furthering their education.

ELIGIBILITY:
Must be an adult or junior member of the NRA and the son or daughter of a currently serving, full-time/deceased, full-time/retired, full-time, or disabled and retired commissioned peace officer who is also a current NRA member or was at the time of death. Eligible students can be senior high school students through senior college students. Applicants must have a satisfactory academic record and be enrolled full-time. Must be U.S. citizens or residents.

GEOGRAPHIC RESTRICTIONS:
United States.

FINANCIAL DATA:
Amount of support per award: Up to $8,000 or four years, whichever comes first.

APPLICATION INFORMATION:
Applicant will need to contact Sandy Elkin, Secretary of the Scholarship Committee, to receive the personal reference forms.
Duration: Up to four years.
Deadline: November 15.

ADDRESS INQUIRIES TO:
Sandy S. Elkin, Secretary
Jeanne E. Bray Memorial
Scholarship Committee
(See address above.)

OHIO BOARD OF REGENTS [1861]

Office of Financial Aid
30 East Broad Street, 36th Floor
Columbus, OH 43215-3414
(888) 833-1133
Fax: (614) 752-5903

E-MAIL ADDRESS:
wo_admin@regents.state.oh.us

WEB SITE ADDRESS:
regents.ohio.gov/sgs/war_orphans

NAME(S) OF PROGRAMS:
● **Ohio War Orphans Scholarship**

TYPE:
Scholarships. Full-time undergraduate scholarships.

YEAR PROGRAM STARTED: 1954

PURPOSE:
To enable children of disabled or deceased Ohio war veterans or children of Vietnam conflict MIAs or POWs to attend college.

LEGAL BASIS:
State agency.

ELIGIBILITY:
Applicant must be 16 to 25 years of age and a child of disabled or deceased Ohio war veteran or child of Vietnam conflict MIA or POW. Veteran parent must have a 60% combined disability rating. Applicant must also be enrolled as a full-time student in an eligible institution of higher education.

GEOGRAPHIC RESTRICTIONS:
Ohio.

FINANCIAL DATA:
Students attending Ohio nonprofit and profitmaking institutions of higher education will receive amounts no greater than the average amount paid for students attending public institutions. Children of Vietnam conflict MIAs and POWs also receive assistance with room, board and books.
Total amount of support: $3,969,912 for the year 2010.

NUMBER OF APPLICANTS MOST RECENT YEAR:
803 for the year 2010.

NUMBER OF AWARDS: 803 for the year 2010.

APPLICATION INFORMATION:
Student must submit a completed application form.
Duration: Scholarships are automatically renewable for up to four years of undergraduate education.
Deadline: July 1. Announcements in early August.

STAFF:
Jathiya Abdullah-Simmons, Program Manager

ADDRESS INQUIRIES TO:
Jathiya Abdullah-Simmons
Program Manager
(See address above.)

OHIO BOARD OF REGENTS [1862]

Office of Financial Aid
30 East Broad Street, 36th Floor
Columbus, OH 43215-3414
(888) 833-1133
Fax: (614) 752-5903

E-MAIL ADDRESS:
ocog_admin@regents.state.oh.us

WEB SITE ADDRESS:
regents.ohio.gov/sgs/ocog

FOUNDED: 1963

NAME(S) OF PROGRAMS:
- **Ohio College Opportunity Grant Program (OCOG)**

TYPE:
General operating grants. Grants for college-bound students or current undergraduate students.

YEAR PROGRAM STARTED: 2006

PURPOSE:
To assist in achieving the goals of access and choice for low-income and middle-income students.

LEGAL BASIS:
State agency.

ELIGIBILITY:
Applicant must be an Ohio resident, demonstrate financial need, and be seeking an Associate's degree, a Bachelor's degree, or nursing diploma at an eligible institution.

GEOGRAPHIC RESTRICTIONS:
Ohio and Pennsylvania.

FINANCIAL DATA:
Amount of support per award: Varies.
Total amount of support: $76,301,177 for the year 2010.

NUMBER OF AWARDS: 66,779 for the year 2010.

APPLICATION INFORMATION:
Student must submit a Free Application for Federal Student Aid (FAFSA).
Duration: One academic year. Renewable for a maximum of five years of full-time study.
Deadline: October 1.

ADDRESS INQUIRIES TO:
Tamika Braswell, Program Manager
(See address above.)

OHIO NATIONAL GUARD SCHOLARSHIP PROGRAM [1863]

2825 West Dublin Granville Road
AGOH-SP
Columbus, OH 43235-2789
(614) 336-7032
(614) 336-7053
(888) 400-6484 ext. 1
Fax: (614) 336-7318

E-MAIL ADDRESS:
toni.davis7@us.army.mil

WEB SITE ADDRESS:
ongsp.org

FOUNDED: 1977

AREAS OF INTEREST:
General education.

TYPE:
Scholarships. Grants for undergraduate students attending six credit hours or more.

YEAR PROGRAM STARTED: 1978

PURPOSE:
To encourage enlistment in Ohio National Guard.

LEGAL BASIS:
Ohio Revised Code. Nonprofit.

ELIGIBILITY:
Applicants must possess a high school diploma or a GED certificate and enlist, re-enlist or extend their current enlistment in a valid authorized or required MTOE/TDA

(ARNG) or UMD (ANG) position for six years of Selective Reserve duty in the Ohio National Guard.

GEOGRAPHIC RESTRICTIONS:
Ohio.

FINANCIAL DATA:
Instructional and general fees paid 100% for student attending public institution.
Amount of support per award: Private Institution: $4,311 maximum per semester; $2,874 maximum per quarter. Public Institution: Varies.

NUMBER OF APPLICANTS MOST RECENT YEAR:
3,500.

APPLICATION INFORMATION:
An applicant must apply each term so that the application is received in the Scholarship Program Office no later than the established deadlines, which are no later than the close of business (4:30 P.M.).
Duration: Scholarships are renewable for up to four years of undergraduate education.
Deadline: July 1 for fall; November 1 for winter/quarter, semester, trimester/spring semester; February 1 for spring quarter; April 1 for summer.

PUBLICATIONS:
Regulation AGOR 621-1 (Army); *35-1* (Air).

STAFF:
Toni E. Davis, Administrator

ADDRESS INQUIRIES TO:
Toni E. Davis, Administrator
(See address above.)

*SPECIAL STIPULATIONS:
Applicant must enlist in Ohio National Guard for not less than six years. Must enroll minimum six credit hours in degree-granting program.

PARAPSYCHOLOGY FOUNDATION, INC.

P.O. Box 1562
New York, NY 10021
(212) 628-1550
Fax: (212) 628-1559

E-MAIL ADDRESS:
info@parapsychology.org

WEB SITE ADDRESS:
www.parapsychology.org

TYPE:
Scholarships. Assists students attending an accredited college or university in pursuing the academic study of the science of parapsychology.

See entry 2747 for full listing.

PENNSYLVANIA HIGHER EDUCATION ASSISTANCE AGENCY   [1864]

Communications Office
1200 North Seventh Street
Harrisburg, PA 17102-1398
(717) 720-2800
(800) 692-7392 (Pennsylvania only)
Fax: (717) 720-3903

E-MAIL ADDRESS:
knew@pheaa.org

WEB SITE ADDRESS:
www.pheaa.org

FOUNDED: 1964

NAME(S) OF PROGRAMS:
- **Pennsylvania State Grant Program**

TYPE:
Grants-in-aid. The Pennsylvania State Grant Program allows eligible Pennsylvania residents to obtain financial assistance for undergraduate study at any PHEAA-approved institution of higher education. The Free Application for Federal Student Aid (FAFSA) serves as the program's application.

YEAR PROGRAM STARTED: 1964

PURPOSE:
To assist needy students in obtaining higher education.

LEGAL BASIS:
Government agency.

ELIGIBILITY:
The student applying for Pennsylvania State Grants must:
(1) meet criteria for financial need;
(2) be enrolled on at least a half-time basis in a PHEAA-approved undergraduate program of study and not already have a four-year (or more) undergraduate degree;
(3) be a high school graduate or the recipient of a GED;
(4) demonstrate academic progress (for continued aid) and;
(5) be a Pennsylvania resident (domiciliary).

Summer school students may also qualify for State Grant funds.

GEOGRAPHIC RESTRICTIONS:
Pennsylvania.

FINANCIAL DATA:
Amount of support per award: Varies annually; maximum award $3,541 for full-time students for academic year 2010-11.
Total amount of support: Varies annually due to appropriations, number of applicants, and financial strength of applying families.

NUMBER OF AWARDS: Approximately 185,000.

APPLICATION INFORMATION:
Submit the Free Application for Federal Student Aid (FAFSA). For faster processing, those applying can find out what they need to fill out the FAFSA and how to complete it by going online.
Duration: One academic year. Renewal contingent upon continued eligibility and financial need.
Deadline: May 1.

EXECUTIVE OFFICERS:
James L. Preston, President and Chief Executive Officer
Christine Zuzack, Vice President of State Grants and Special Programs

ADDRESS INQUIRIES TO:
Christine Zuzack, Vice President of State Grants and Special Programs
(See address above.)

THE PHI BETA KAPPA SOCIETY   [1865]

1606 New Hampshire Avenue, N.W.
Washington, DC 20009
(202) 745-3235
Fax: (202) 986-1601

E-MAIL ADDRESS:
awards@pbk.org

WEB SITE ADDRESS:
www.pbk.org

AREAS OF INTEREST:
Philosophy.

NAME(S) OF PROGRAMS:
- **The Romanell-Phi Beta Kappa Professorship in Philosophy**

TYPE:
Fellowships. Professorship awarded to scholars in the field of philosophy, without restriction to any one school of philosophical thought.

YEAR PROGRAM STARTED: 1983

PURPOSE:
To recognize not only distinguished achievement, but also the recipient's contribution or potential contribution to public understanding of philosophy.

ELIGIBILITY:
Scholar need not be a member of Phi Beta Kappa, but must be on the faculty of an institution sheltering a chapter of Phi Beta Kappa and must be nominated by that chapter.

GEOGRAPHIC RESTRICTIONS:
United States.

FINANCIAL DATA:
Amount of support per award: $7,500 stipend.

NUMBER OF AWARDS: 1 annually.

APPLICATION INFORMATION:
Recipient must be nominated by the chapter of Phi Beta Kappa at the institution in which they are on faculty.
Duration: One year. Nonrenewable.
Deadline: June 1.

ADDRESS INQUIRIES TO:
Lucinda Morales
Director of Society Affairs
(See address above.)

*SPECIAL STIPULATIONS:
Recipient will be expected to give a series of three special lectures during the year of the Professorship, such lectures to be given at the sheltering institution and to be open to the general public as well as to the academic community.

PI GAMMA MU, INTERNATIONAL HONOR SOCIETY IN SOCIAL SCIENCE [1866]
1001 Millington, Suite B
Winfield, KS 67156
(620) 221-3128
Fax: (620) 221-7124

E-MAIL ADDRESS:
pgm@sckans.edu

WEB SITE ADDRESS:
www.pigammamu.org

FOUNDED: 1924

AREAS OF INTEREST:
Economics, history, political science, sociology, anthropology, international relations, social work, psychology, social philosophy, history of education and criminal justice, law and human/cultural geography.

NAME(S) OF PROGRAMS:
- **Pi Gamma Mu Scholarships**

TYPE:
Scholarships. Awarded principally for first-year graduate study.

YEAR PROGRAM STARTED: 1951

PURPOSE:
To promote scholarship in the above fields.

LEGAL BASIS:
Nonprofit.

ELIGIBILITY:
Applicants must be a member of Pi Gamma Mu.

FINANCIAL DATA:
Amount of support per award: $1,000 or $2,000.
Total amount of support: $13,000 annually.

NUMBER OF APPLICANTS MOST RECENT YEAR: 24.

NUMBER OF AWARDS: 8.

APPLICATION INFORMATION:
Resume, personal statement, transcript and three letters of recommendation required.
Duration: One year.
Deadline: January 30. Announcement April 1.

PUBLICATIONS:
Application guidelines.

OFFICERS:
Gordon Mercer, President
Barry Friedman, First Vice President
Charles W. McClellan, Second Vice President
C. Laurence Heck, Secretary and Treasurer
Charles Hartwig, Chancellor
Wendell Hester, Chancellor
Amy Orr, Chancellor
Clara L. Small, Chancellor

MINNIE STEVENS PIPER FOUNDATION [1867]
1250 N.E. Loop 410, Suite 810
San Antonio, TX 78209-1539
(210) 525-8494
Fax: (210) 341-6627

E-MAIL ADDRESS:
mspf@mspf.org

WEB SITE ADDRESS:
www.mspf.org

FOUNDED: 1950

NAME(S) OF PROGRAMS:
- **Piper Professor Program**
- **Piper Scholar Program**
- **Student Loan Program**

TYPE:
Awards/prizes; Scholarships. Piper Professor Program: Annual awards to professors for superior teaching at the college level.

Piper Scholars: Four-year scholarships awarded to academically promising and superior high school seniors in amounts that assist them in attending the college or university of their choice within the state of Texas.

Student Loan Program: Loans to worthy and needy students at the junior, senior, undergraduate or graduate college level. Must be full-time status. Restricted to Texas residents attending a college or university within the State of Texas.

PURPOSE:
To support charitable, scientific, or educational undertakings by providing for, or contributing toward, the education of financially limited but worthy students; to assist young men and women residents of Texas, attending or wishing to attend colleges and universities in the state of Texas, to complete their education and obtain degrees; to contribute to community chests; to support

any other nonprofit organization or activity dedicated to promoting the general welfare within the state of Texas.

LEGAL BASIS:
Private foundation with Letter Ruling under Section 4945 of the Tax Reform Act of 1969.

ELIGIBILITY:
Participation is by invitation only to high schools in certain geographic areas. Candidates must be U.S. citizens and nominated through college/university President's office.

GEOGRAPHIC RESTRICTIONS:
Texas.

FINANCIAL DATA:
Amount of support per award: Piper Professor Program: $5,000.

NUMBER OF AWARDS: Piper Professional Program: 10; Piper Scholar Program: 25.

APPLICATION INFORMATION:
Duration: Piper Scholar Program: Four years.

ADDRESS INQUIRIES TO:
Joyce M. Ellis, Executive Director
(See address above.)

*SPECIAL STIPULATIONS:
Piper Professor and Piper Scholars Programs are by invitation only.

THE PLANNING AND VISUAL EDUCATION PARTNERSHIP (PAVE) [1868]
4651 Sheridan Street, Suite 470
Hollywood, FL 33021
(954) 893-7225
Fax: (954) 893-8375

E-MAIL ADDRESS:
pave@paveinfo.org

WEB SITE ADDRESS:
www.paveinfo.org

FOUNDED: 1992

AREAS OF INTEREST:
Retail design planning and visual merchandising.

TYPE:
Awards/prizes; Capital grants; Conferences/seminars; Internships; Product donations; Project/program grants; Scholarships. Student educational support.

PURPOSE:
To encourage students to study in the field of retail design and planning and visual merchandising.

FINANCIAL DATA:
Amount of support per award: PAVE the Way 3D Design Challenge: $13,500; Student Aid Program: $10,000; Student Design Competition: $5,000 for first place, $2,500 for second place, $1,500 for third place and $500 for honorable mention.
Total amount of support: $65,000 for the year 2010.

NUMBER OF AWARDS: 13.

ADDRESS INQUIRIES TO:
Catharine Scott, Managing Director
(See address above.)

PRESBYTERIAN CHURCH
(U.S.A.)   [1869]
Office of Financial Aid for Studies
100 Witherspoon Street
Louisville, KY 40202-1396
(888) 728-7228 ext. 5224
Fax: (502) 569-8766

E-MAIL ADDRESS:
 finaid@pcusa.org

WEB SITE ADDRESS:
 www.pcusa.org/financialaid

AREAS OF INTEREST:
 Majors in health services/sciences, religious
 studies, sacred music, social services and
 social sciences.

NAME(S) OF PROGRAMS:
 ● **Student Opportunity Scholarship**

TYPE:
 Scholarships. Need-based.

YEAR PROGRAM STARTED: 1956

PURPOSE:
 To assist undergraduate juniors and seniors
 already in college, with preference to racial
 ethnic students seeking a degree with
 emphasis on the mission of PCUSA in the
 following disciplines: health
 services/sciences, religious studies, sacred
 music, social services and social sciences.

ELIGIBILITY:
 Scholarship is open to African Americans,
 Asian Americans, Middle Eastern Americans,
 Hispanic Americans and Caucasians.
 Applicants must:
 (1) demonstrate financial need;
 (2) be a member of the Presbyterian Church
 (U.S.A.);
 (3) be a junior or senior already in college
 and;
 (4) have a 2.5 grade point average to get in
 the program and a 2.5 grade point average to
 stay in.

FINANCIAL DATA:
 Amount of support per award: Up to $2,500
 per academic year.

NUMBER OF APPLICANTS MOST RECENT YEAR:
 120.

NUMBER OF AWARDS: 65.

APPLICATION INFORMATION:
 Applications can be downloaded from the
 web site, beginning April 1.
 Duration: Renewable up to three years
 depending on need and maintenance of a 2.5
 grade point average.
 Deadline: June 15.

PUBLICATIONS:
 Financial Aid Programs.

ADDRESS INQUIRIES TO:
 Financial Aid for Studies
 (See address above.)

PRESBYTERIAN CHURCH
(U.S.A.)   [1870]
Office of Financial Aid for Studies
100 Witherspoon Street
Louisville, KY 40202-1396
(888) 728-7228 ext. 5224
Fax: (502) 569-8766

E-MAIL ADDRESS:
 finaid@pcusa.org

WEB SITE ADDRESS:
 www.pcusa.org/financialaid

NAME(S) OF PROGRAMS:
 ● **Samuel Robinson Essay Contest**

TYPE:
 Awards/prizes. Essay contest, awarded to
 junior or senior undergraduate students
 enrolled full-time in one of the
 colleges/universities related to the
 Presbyterian Church (U.S.A.).

YEAR PROGRAM STARTED: 1940

PURPOSE:
 To instill an interest in the work of the
 Presbyterian Church throughout the U.S.

LEGAL BASIS:
 Nonprofit.

FINANCIAL DATA:
 Amount of support per award: $2,500 to
 $5,000.

NUMBER OF APPLICANTS MOST RECENT YEAR:
 15.

NUMBER OF AWARDS: 12.

APPLICATION INFORMATION:
 Duration: One-time award.
 Deadline: April 1.

PUBLICATIONS:
 Financial Aid Brochure.

ADDRESS INQUIRIES TO:
 Financial Aid for Studies
 (See address above.)

*SPECIAL STIPULATIONS:
 Open to Presbyterian students attending a
 Presbyterian-related school.

THE PRESS CLUB OF
METROPOLITAN ST. LOUIS
AND JOURNALISM
FOUNDATION OF
METROPOLITAN ST.
LOUIS   [1871]
c/o The Press Club of Metropolitan St. Louis
P.O. Box 410522
St. Louis, MO 63141
(636) 230-1973
Fax: (636) 203-2441

E-MAIL ADDRESS:
 info@stlpressclub.org

WEB SITE ADDRESS:
 stlpressclub.org

FOUNDED: 1969

AREAS OF INTEREST:
 Journalism.

NAME(S) OF PROGRAMS:
 ● **Association of Black Journalists**
 ● **Baseball Writers of America**
 ● **Enterprise Journalism Fellowships**
 ● **Fleishman-Hillard, Inc.**
 ● **International Association of Business
   Communicators**
 ● **Journalism Foundation**
 ● **Missouri Press Women**
 ● **Newspaper Guild**
 ● **Press Club of Metropolitan St. Louis**
 ● **Society of Professional Journalists**

TYPE:
 Awards/prizes; Conferences/seminars;
 Fellowships; Internships; Scholarships; Seed
 money grants.

YEAR PROGRAM STARTED: 1970

PURPOSE:
 To award scholarships to those entering
 junior and senior years of college or graduate

school preparing for
journalism/communications careers at
recognized schools, majoring in journalism,
English or related fields; to award
fellowships for journalists to do investigative
stories for publication.

LEGAL BASIS:
 Incorporated as nonprofit organization in
 state of Missouri.

ELIGIBILITY:
 Applicant for scholarships must be at least a
 sophomore in college interested in a career in
 journalism and a St. Louis metropolitan area
 resident. Enterprise Journalism Fellowships:
 Journalists with an investigative project
 concerning the St. Louis region.

GEOGRAPHIC RESTRICTIONS:
 St. Louis, Missouri and counties of Franklin,
 Jefferson, Lincoln, St. Charles, St. Louis and
 Warren, and Illinois counties of Bond,
 Clinton, Jersey, Madison, Monroe and St.
 Clair.

FINANCIAL DATA:
 Amount of support per award: Varies.
 Total amount of support: $30,000.

COOPERATIVE FUNDING PROGRAMS: Grants from
 member organizations.

NUMBER OF APPLICANTS MOST RECENT YEAR:
 35.

NUMBER OF AWARDS: 19.

APPLICATION INFORMATION:
 Scholarship applicant should submit an
 application from Journalism Foundation,
 college transcript, two letters of reference,
 writing samples and financial data.

 Enterprise Journalism Fellowships: Journalist
 applicants prepare a description of story
 project, budget and where to be published.
 Duration: One year. Renewable.
 Deadline: May 2 for scholarships. Enterprise
 Journalism Fellowships applications are
 accepted on an ongoing basis.

IRS IDENTIFICATION NUMBER: 43-1489003

STAFF:
 Glenda Partlow, Executive Director
 Laura Schnarr, Social Media Coordinator

ADDRESS INQUIRIES TO:
 Glenda Partlow
 Executive Director, Press Club
 (See address above.)

*SPECIAL STIPULATIONS:
 Applicant must live in St. Louis metropolitan
 statistical area (MSA).

SID W. RICHARDSON
MEMORIAL FUND   [1872]
309 Main Street
Fort Worth, TX 76102
(817) 336-0494
Fax: (817) 332-2176

E-MAIL ADDRESS:
 plaskoski@sidrichardson.org

FOUNDED: 1965

AREAS OF INTEREST:
 Academic scholarships.

TYPE:
 Scholarships.

YEAR PROGRAM STARTED: 1965

LEGAL BASIS:
 Tax-exempt.

ELIGIBILITY:
Limited funds are available to assist in defraying the cost of college education or of vocational training. These scholarships are awarded on a competitive basis according to academic achievement and financial need.

Those eligible to apply for a Memorial Fund scholarship are direct descendants (children or grandchildren) of persons who qualified for Early Retirement, Normal Retirement, Disability Retirement, or Death Benefits from The Bass Retirement Plan (formerly The Retirement Plan For Employees of Bass Enterprises Production Co.), Retirement Plan for Employees of Barbnet/San Jose Cattle, Retirement Plan for Employees of City Center Development Co., City Club Retirement Plan, Retirement Plan for Employees of Richardson Aviation, G.P., Retirement Plan for Employees of Sid W. Richardson Foundation, or Retirement Plan for Employees of Sundance Square. Those eligible also include direct descendants (children or grandchildren) of persons presently employed with a minimum of three years' full-time service with any of the following employers: Barbnet Investment Co., BEPCO, L.P., BOPCO, L.P., City Club of Fort Worth, Richardson Aviation, San Jose Cattle Co., Sid Richardson Carbon Co. (SRCE, L.P.), Sid W. Richardson Foundation, and Sundance Square Management, L.P.

FINANCIAL DATA:
Amount of support per award: $1,000 to $7,000 per student per academic year for 2009-10.
Total amount of support: $252,000 for the academic year 2009-10.

NUMBER OF APPLICANTS MOST RECENT YEAR: 82.

NUMBER OF AWARDS: 54 for the year 2009-10.

APPLICATION INFORMATION:
Direct a written request for an application to Peggy Laskoski, Sid Richardson Memorial Fund, at the street address above or the above e-mail address. The request may also be sent to the above fax number. Include student name and address, qualifying employee name, Social Security number of employee, qualifying company name and dates of employment.

Inquirers must provide proof of eligibility, i.e., name of employee, etc., with their letter of request for an application. Renewal applicants must maintain a 2.0 grade point average on a possible scale of 4.0.
Duration: Considered for renewal annually if a 2.0 grade point average is maintained for each semester.
Deadline: March 31 annually. Announcement of awards by May 31.

OFFICERS:
Robert Kolba, President and Director
Ken McCarty, Vice President and Director
Tom White, Vice President and Director
Cindy Alexander, Treasurer
Peggy Laskoski, Secretary

ADDRESS INQUIRIES TO:
Peggy Laskoski, Coordinator
(See address above.)

JACKIE ROBINSON FOUNDATION
75 Varick Street, 2nd Floor
New York, NY 10013-1917
(212) 290-8600
Fax: (212) 290-8081

E-MAIL ADDRESS:
general@jackierobinson.org

WEB SITE ADDRESS:
www.jackierobinson.org

TYPE:
Conferences/seminars; Internships; Scholarships.

See entry 1075 for full listing.

THE ROTARY CLUB OF BRYN MAWR   [1873]
P.O. Box 84
Bryn Mawr, PA 19010
(610) 525-8585

FOUNDED: 1969

AREAS OF INTEREST:
To serve others and satisfy Rotary principles.

NAME(S) OF PROGRAMS:
● **Harry H. Cabell Scholarship Program**

TYPE:
Awards/prizes; Scholarships.

YEAR PROGRAM STARTED: 1985

PURPOSE:
To recognize and reward college students who meet trust requirements.

LEGAL BASIS:
Not-for-profit society.

ELIGIBILITY:
Financial need, high academic standards and leadership qualities, service to others and achievement qualities are important factors in the decision process. Applicants must be in an area college or university.

GEOGRAPHIC RESTRICTIONS:
Metropolitan Philadelphia and surrounding counties.

FINANCIAL DATA:
Amount of support per award: $1,500 to $2,000.
Total amount of support: Varies.

NUMBER OF AWARDS: 3 to 4 annually.

APPLICATION INFORMATION:
Application form must include recommendation from faculty, statement of good standing from dean, transcript of grades and 300-word essay.
Duration: One year. No renewals.
Deadline: Early March. Announcement approximately April 30.

ADDRESS INQUIRIES TO:
Richard Cuff, Scholarship Committee
Harry H. Cabell Scholarship Awards
(See address above.)

SACHS FOUNDATION
90 South Cascade Avenue
Suite 1410
Colorado Springs, CO 80903
(719) 633-2353
Fax: (719) 633-3663

E-MAIL ADDRESS:
lisa@sachsfoundation.org

WEB SITE ADDRESS:
sachsfoundation.org

TYPE:
Grants-in-aid; Scholarships.

See entry 1097 for full listing.

ST. PETERSBURG TIMES FUND, INC.   [1874]
490 First Avenue South
St. Petersburg, FL 33701
(727) 893-8780
Fax: (727) 892-2257

E-MAIL ADDRESS:
waclawek@sptimes.com

WEB SITE ADDRESS:
www.tampabay.com/scholarships

AREAS OF INTEREST:
Journalism.

NAME(S) OF PROGRAMS:
● **Career Journalism Scholarship**

TYPE:
Scholarships.

PURPOSE:
To identify worthy students who need additional resources to support their education in pursuing a journalism major in college and career after graduation.

ELIGIBILITY:
High school seniors in the Times' circulation area.

GEOGRAPHIC RESTRICTIONS:
Citrus, Hernando, Hillsborough, Pasco and Pinellas counties, Florida.

FINANCIAL DATA:
Amount of support per award: $2,500 annually.
Total amount of support: Average $10,000.

NUMBER OF AWARDS: Average 4 annually.

APPLICATION INFORMATION:
Applicant must submit:
(1) completed Questionnaire (two pages);
(2) short essay (500 to 800 words) describing journalism experience; if applicant does not have such experience, explain why interested in journalism as a career; also provide, on another sheet of paper, resume of achievements/awards;
(3) essay (1,000 to 1,500 words) reflecting how applicant has been affected by the work of journalists;
(4) letter detailing which college applicant plans to attend, total cost of education for that institution, other financial aid applied for or known to be received, and anything else pertinent to family's financial situation;
(5) portfolio of work (writing, web site, photography, design); no more than six examples and do not send originals; if applicant has no previous experience, send three samples of writing for class assignments and;
(6) three letters of recommendation, written and signed by teachers or others for whom applicant has done a substantial amount of writing, discussing the applicant's writing ability, strengths as a student, character, areas for improvement, and how applicant has demonstrated interest in journalism; each letter should have, at the top, applicant's name, teacher's name and teacher's phone number.
Duration: Up to four years. Must reapply.
Deadline: January 5.

ADDRESS INQUIRIES TO:
Nancy Waclawek, Director
(See address above.)

ST. PETERSBURG TIMES FUND, INC. [1875]

490 First Avenue South
St. Petersburg, FL 33701
(727) 893-8780
Fax: (727) 892-2257

E-MAIL ADDRESS:
waclawek@sptimes.com

WEB SITE ADDRESS:
www.tampabay.com/scholarships

NAME(S) OF PROGRAMS:
● **Barnes Scholarship**

TYPE:
Scholarships.

YEAR PROGRAM STARTED: 1999

PURPOSE:
To provide assistance to college-bound teens who have overcome significant obstacles in their lives while remaining committed to academic achievement and community involvement.

ELIGIBILITY:
Applicants must be U.S. citizens or permanent residents, high school seniors in public or private schools in specific counties of Florida. Preference will be given to students whose parents have not graduated from a college or university and also to students who are applying to schools outside of Florida.

GEOGRAPHIC RESTRICTIONS:
Citrus, Hernando, Hillsborough, Pasco and Pinellas counties, Florida.

FINANCIAL DATA:
Amount of support per award: Up to $15,000 per year.
Total amount of support: Up to $60,000.

NUMBER OF AWARDS: 4 annually.

APPLICATION INFORMATION:
There are three parts to the application:

The first part includes basic information about the applicant, e.g., addresses of applicant and parents or guardians, phone numbers, e-mails, test scores, high school information, and colleges to which applicant has applied to or intends to apply.

The second part is a resume providing information about academic honors, classes taken, community service performed, extracurricular activities, employment, awards, athletics, and other activities that have been key in forming the applicant's life experience thus far.

The third part is an essay (250 to 1,000 words) describing the applicant's greatest obstacle in life and how it has been overcome.
Duration: Up to four years.
Deadline: October 15.

ADDRESS INQUIRIES TO:
Nancy Waclawek, Director
(See address above.)

SCHOOL FOR ADVANCED RESEARCH [1876]

P.O. Box 2188
Santa Fe, NM 87504-2188
(505) 954-7201
Fax: (505) 954-7214

E-MAIL ADDRESS:
scholar@sarsf.org

WEB SITE ADDRESS:
www.sarweb.org

FOUNDED: 1907

AREAS OF INTEREST:
Anthropology and allied disciplines in the humanities and social sciences.

NAME(S) OF PROGRAMS:
● **Summer Scholar Fellowships**

TYPE:
Fellowships. Eight-week summer residency program.

PURPOSE:
To promote the pursuit of research or writing projects that promote understanding of human behavior, culture, society, and the history of anthropology.

ELIGIBILITY:
Scholars in anthropology and related disciplines are invited to apply in order to pursue research or writing projects. Scholars whose projects relate to anthropological linguistics or to the history of anthropology are especially encouraged to apply.

FINANCIAL DATA:
Scholars are provided with a small stipend, free housing and office space, an allowance account and other benefits.
Amount of support per award: Stipend up to $1,000 and an allowance up to $160.

COOPERATIVE FUNDING PROGRAMS: Ethel-Jane Westfeldt Bunting Foundation, William Y. and Nettie K. Adams Fellowship in the History of Anthropology, Cotsen Institute of Archaeology, and Christopher Smeall Fellowship in Anthropological Linguistics.

NUMBER OF APPLICANTS MOST RECENT YEAR: 48.

NUMBER OF AWARDS: 6.

APPLICATION INFORMATION:
Applicants should submit the following:
(1) cover sheet;
(2) letter describing the project, its significance, the status of the research, and what will be accomplished during the residency and;
(3) curriculum vitae.
Duration: Up to eight weeks, June 20 to August 10.
Deadline: December 15.

ADDRESS INQUIRIES TO:
Nancy Owen Lewis
Director of Scholar Programs
(See address above.)

SHASTRI INDO-CANADIAN INSTITUTE (SICI)

Room 1402, Education Tower
2500 University Drive, N.W.
Calgary AB T2N 1N4 Canada
(403) 220-7467
Fax: (403) 289-0100

E-MAIL ADDRESS:
sici@ucalgary.ca
maldeen@ucalgary.ca

WEB SITE ADDRESS:
www.sici.org

TYPE:
Fellowships. India Studies Fellowship Competition is intended to support candidates wishing to undertake research or training in India. The focus of study is subjects relating to India in the social sciences and

humanities, including education, law, management, the arts, science, and technology.
See entry 991 for full listing.

HORACE SMITH FUND [1877]

1441 Main Street, 6th Floor
Suite 620
Springfield, MA 01103
(413) 739-4222
Fax: (413) 739-1108

E-MAIL ADDRESS:
info@horacesmithfund.org

WEB SITE ADDRESS:
www.horacesmithfund.org

FOUNDED: 1899

AREAS OF INTEREST:
Education, scholarships and fellowships.

TYPE:
Fellowships; Scholarships.

YEAR PROGRAM STARTED: 1899

PURPOSE:
To help students obtain scholarships and fellowships.

ELIGIBILITY:
For scholarships, students must have graduated from a high school in Hampden County. For fellowships, students must be legal residents of Hampden County.

GEOGRAPHIC RESTRICTIONS:
Hampden County, Massachusetts.

FINANCIAL DATA:
Amount of support per award: Scholarships: $2,500 per year for four years; Fellowships: $4,000 per year for up to three years.
Total amount of support: Scholarships: $65,000; Fellowships: $16,000.

NUMBER OF APPLICANTS MOST RECENT YEAR: 110.

NUMBER OF AWARDS: 26 Scholarships and 4 Fellowships for the year 2010.

APPLICATION INFORMATION:
Applications are available in September.
Duration: One year. Renewable up to four years.
Deadline: Scholarships: January 10; Fellowships: February 1.

PUBLICATIONS:
Annual report; contributions policy; application guidelines.

ADDRESS INQUIRIES TO:
Benjamin Bump, Executive Secretary
(See address above.)

*SPECIAL STIPULATIONS:
Hampden County, Massachusetts residents only.

SOCIETY OF DAUGHTERS OF THE U.S. ARMY [1878]

11804 Grey Birch Place
Reston, VA 20191-4223

FOUNDED: 1928

NAME(S) OF PROGRAMS:
● **Society of Daughters of the United States Army Scholarships**

TYPE:
Scholarships.

PURPOSE:
To help daughters or granddaughters (including adopted or step) of career warrant

and commissioned Army officers (Warrant Officers through General) who are on active duty, retired after at least 20 years of active service, were medically retired, or died while on active duty or after eligible retirement.

LEGAL BASIS:
Nonprofit corporation.

ELIGIBILITY:
For the Roberts, Wagner, Prickett, Simpson and DUSA Scholarships, applicants must be a daughter or granddaughter (including step or adopted) of a career warrant (WO 1-5) or commissioned (2nd & 1st LT, CPT, MAJ, LTC, COL and BG, MG, LT or full General) officer of the U.S. Army who either:
(1) is currently on active duty;
(2) retired after at least 20 years of active service;
(3) was medically retired before 20 years of active service;
(4) died while on active duty or;
(5) died after retiring with 20 or more years of active service.

U.S. Army must have been the officer's primary occupation. These scholarships are for undergraduate study only and cover academic expenses only. Minimum grade point average is 3.0.

FINANCIAL DATA:
Amount of support per award: $1,000 per year.

NUMBER OF APPLICANTS MOST RECENT YEAR:
150.

NUMBER OF AWARDS: 12.

APPLICATION INFORMATION:
Mail one request with the officer's name, rank, component (active, reserve, retired), inclusive dates of active duty, and the relationship to the applicant, along with a stamped, self-addressed envelope, to the Scholarship Chairman. Do not send any documentation. Requests for applications must be postmarked between November 1 and March 1 for awards in the next academic year. Office is closed between March 2 and October 31. Application is not available when office is closed. Application will not be sent without qualifying information.

Do not send by registered/certified or commercial mail; delivery will be delayed. All application submissions become the property of DUSA.

Duration: One year. The scholarships may be renewed annually for four years, provided a student maintains eligibility.

Deadline: March 1.

STAFF:
Mary P. Maroney, Chairman, Memorial and Scholarship Funds

ADDRESS INQUIRIES TO:
Mary P. Maroney, Scholarship Chairman Daughters of the United States Army
(See address above.)

SOCIETY OF PHYSICS STUDENTS [1879]
One Physics Ellipse
College Park, MD 20740-3843
(301) 209-3007
Fax: (301) 209-0839

E-MAIL ADDRESS:
sps@aip.org

WEB SITE ADDRESS:
www.spsnational.org

FOUNDED: 1968

AREAS OF INTEREST:
Physics.

NAME(S) OF PROGRAMS:
● **Society of Physics Students Leadership Scholarship**

TYPE:
Scholarships.

YEAR PROGRAM STARTED: 1985

PURPOSE:
To encourage the study of physics and the pursuit of high scholarship.

LEGAL BASIS:
Not-for-profit, 501(c)(3).

ELIGIBILITY:
Applicants must be full-time undergraduate students applying in at least their junior year (except for two-year college applicants who should apply after completing one semester of physics). Only Society of Physics Students members are eligible.

GEOGRAPHIC RESTRICTIONS:
United States.

FINANCIAL DATA:
Amount of support per award: $2,000 to $5,000.

Total amount of support: $21,000.

NUMBER OF APPLICANTS MOST RECENT YEAR:
45.

NUMBER OF AWARDS: 18.

APPLICATION INFORMATION:
Completed application form, official transcript of grades, and two letters of recommendation required.
Duration: One year. No renewals.
Deadline: February 15.

STAFF:
Dr. Gary White, Director

ADDRESS INQUIRIES TO:
Dr. Thomas Olsen, Assistant Director
(See address above.)

*SPECIAL STIPULATIONS:
Applicant must be an active member of the Society of Physics Students.

THE PAUL & DAISY SOROS FELLOWSHIPS FOR NEW AMERICANS [1880]
400 West 59th Street, 4th Floor
New York, NY 10019
(212) 547-6926
Fax: (212) 548-4623

E-MAIL ADDRESS:
pdsoros_fellows@sorosny.org

WEB SITE ADDRESS:
www.pdsoros.org

FOUNDED: 1997

AREAS OF INTEREST:
Financial aid for New Americans.

TYPE:
Fellowships.

PURPOSE:
To provide opportunities for continuing generations of able and accomplished New Americans to achieve leadership in their chosen fields.

ELIGIBILITY:
A New American is defined as an individual who:

(1) is a resident alien (i.e., holds a Green Card) or;
(2) has been naturalized as a U.S. citizen or;
(3) is the child of two parents who are both naturalized citizens.

The applicant must either have a Bachelor's degree or be in his or her final year of undergraduate study.

Upper age limit is 30 years by deadline.

FINANCIAL DATA:
Amount of support per award: Fellow receives maintenance grant of $25,000 and a tuition grant of one-half tuition cost of U.S. graduate program attended, up to a maximum of $20,000 per annum.

NUMBER OF AWARDS: 30 per year.

APPLICATION INFORMATION:
Applications can be submitted via the online application system, or downloaded from the web site and submitted by mail.
Duration: Two years.
Deadline: November 1.

ADDRESS INQUIRIES TO:
Ellen Eng, Program Associate
(See address above.)

*SPECIAL STIPULATIONS:
Must be 30 years old or younger by deadline in order to be eligible.

SOUTH CAROLINA HIGHER EDUCATION TUITION GRANTS COMMISSION [1881]
800 Dutch Square Boulevard
Suite 260A
Columbia, SC 29210
(803) 896-1120
Fax: (803) 896-1126

E-MAIL ADDRESS:
toni@sctuitiongrants.org

WEB SITE ADDRESS:
www.sctuitiongrants.com

FOUNDED: 1970

AREAS OF INTEREST:
Undergraduate student financial aid to eligible South Carolina residents attending in-state, independent colleges on a full-time basis.

CONSULTING OR VOLUNTEER SERVICES:
Assistance to South Carolina high schools and colleges with questions and problems pertaining to student financial aid.

NAME(S) OF PROGRAMS:
● **South Carolina Tuition Grants Program**

TYPE:
Grants-in-aid.

YEAR PROGRAM STARTED: 1970

PURPOSE:
To increase the level of college attendance in South Carolina and to better utilize the existing educational resources of the state; to give students a choice of attending the college that best meets their academic needs.

LEGAL BASIS:
Established by state statute.

ELIGIBILITY:
Applicant must be a South Carolina resident, demonstrate good moral character, be accepted by or enrolled full-time in an eligible South Carolina private college and have financial need. Incoming freshmen must

rank in the upper three-quarters of their class or score 900 or higher on the re-centered SAT. Renewal applicants must complete at least 24 semester-hours per year.

GEOGRAPHIC RESTRICTIONS:
South Carolina.

FINANCIAL DATA:
Awards cannot exceed tuition and fees at the institution, the need of the student and the average per-pupil expenditure by the state at a public college.

Amount of support per award: $100 to $3,150 per year. Average grant $2,217 for the year 2010-11.

Total amount of support: $35,002,000 total state appropriation for the 2010-11 academic year.

NUMBER OF APPLICANTS MOST RECENT YEAR:
31,800 for the year 2010-11.

NUMBER OF AWARDS: 15,200 for the year 2010-11.

APPLICATION INFORMATION:
Application available online.

Duration: One year. Renewable if need continues for up to four years. Must reapply each year.

Deadline: June 30.

PUBLICATIONS:
Annual report; general brochure.

GRANTS COMMITTEE:
Dr. Charles Young, Chairman
Dr. Betsy Fleming, Vice Chairman
Dr. Evans Whitaker, Secretary
Dr. Bill Jones
Dr. Stephen Jones
Dr. David Shi
Dr. Henry Tisdale
Dr. Garrison Walters

ADDRESS INQUIRIES TO:
Earl L. Mayo, Jr.
(See address above.)

STATE COUNCIL OF HIGHER EDUCATION FOR VIRGINIA [1882]

James Monroe Building, 10th Floor
101 North 14th Street
Richmond, VA 23219
(804) 225-2600
Fax: (804) 225-2604

E-MAIL ADDRESS:
fainfo@schev.edu

WEB SITE ADDRESS:
www.schev.edu

FOUNDED: 1956

AREAS OF INTEREST:
Statewide coordination of higher education.

NAME(S) OF PROGRAMS:
• **Virginia Tuition Assistance Grant Program (TAGP)**

TYPE:
Grants-in-aid.

YEAR PROGRAM STARTED: 1973

PURPOSE:
To provide grants to all Virginia domiciliary residents who are undergraduate students enrolled full-time in participating private nonprofit colleges and universities in Virginia, regardless of financial need; to provide grants to graduate students in selected health-related degree programs.

LEGAL BASIS:
State agency. Program mandated by state law.

ELIGIBILITY:
Recipients must be domiciliary residents of Virginia who are enrolled full-time at an approved private college or university within the state. Not available at Virginia public institutions, for-profit institutions or non-Virginia institutions. Awards are not based on financial need. Students may not be enrolled in a program of religious training or theological education.

GEOGRAPHIC RESTRICTIONS:
Virginia.

FINANCIAL DATA:
Funding is specified biennially by the Appropriations Act.

Amount of support per award: Up to $3,200 per academic year, depending on amount of appropriation and number of recipients; $2,600 for the academic year 2010-11.

Total amount of support: $53,500,000 for the year 2010-11.

NUMBER OF APPLICANTS MOST RECENT YEAR:
Approximately 22,000.

NUMBER OF AWARDS: Approximately 21,000.

APPLICATION INFORMATION:
Application is available from participating private colleges or universities in Virginia.

Duration: Nine months (academic year). Renewals are reviewed by the institutions.

Deadline: July 31. September 14 for late applications.

ADDRESS INQUIRIES TO:
Applicants should contact the financial aid officer at the private Virginia college or university they plan to attend or see web site above.

STATE STUDENT ASSISTANCE COMMISSION OF INDIANA [1883]

The Indiana Government Center South, Room W 462
402 West Washington Street
Indianapolis, IN 46204
(317) 232-2350
Fax: (317) 232-3260

E-MAIL ADDRESS:
grants@ssaci.in.gov

WEB SITE ADDRESS:
www.ssaci.in.gov

FOUNDED: 1965

AREAS OF INTEREST:
Student financial aid.

NAME(S) OF PROGRAMS:
• **Robert C. Byrd Honors Scholarship**
• **Indiana College Work-Study Program**
• **Minority Teacher and Special Education Scholarship**
• **National Guard Grant**
• **Nursing Scholarship**
• **The Frank O'Bannon Grant**
• **21st Century Scholars Program**

TYPE:
Grants-in-aid; Project/program grants; Scholarships; Work-study programs. Monetary grants awarded annually toward the cost of tuition.

Indiana College Work-Study Program offers work opportunities for students who receive and use the Frank O'Bannon Grant and are

not graduating seniors. State and local government entities and private not-for-profit organizations are eligible to apply for funding and receive 50% reimbursement for student earnings.

The Minority Teacher Scholarship was created by the 1988 Indiana General Assembly to address the critical shortage of Black and Hispanic teachers in Indiana. The Special Education Teacher Scholarship is designed to encourage individuals to pursue a teaching career in the shortage area of special education.

The Frank O'Bannon Grant ranges from $200 upward, but may not exceed the cost of tuition and regularly assessed fees. Payments are made directly to the institution.

21st Century Scholars Program was created in 1990 as Indiana's way of raising the educational aspirations of low- and moderate-income families.

YEAR PROGRAM STARTED: 1971

PURPOSE:
To provide financial assistance to students attending colleges within the state of Indiana.

LEGAL BASIS:
Indiana Scholarship Act, I.C. 20-12-21. I.C. 20-12-21.1.

ELIGIBILITY:
An applicant must be an Indiana resident, a U.S. citizen or eligible non-citizen and must attend an eligible institution located within the state of Indiana as a full-time undergraduate student (12 to 15 hours per term).

GEOGRAPHIC RESTRICTIONS:
Indiana.

FINANCIAL DATA:
Amount of support per award: Varies.

Matching fund requirements: Only in Work-Study.

APPLICATION INFORMATION:
Free Application for Federal Student Aid (FAFSA) must be received by deadline for The Frank O'Bannon Grant.

21st Century Scholars Program: Must sign and mail pledge affirmation before March 10. File for state and federal financial aid by completing the FAFSA on time. Apply for admission and institutional financial aid at the Indiana college attending by the deadline for each college. Enroll as a full-time college student and maintain Indiana residency.

Duration: Four years. Reapplication required annually.

Deadline: Robert C. Byrd Honors Scholarship: April 26. The Frank O'Bannon Grant and Work-Study: March 10. Announcement in May. Minority Teacher and Special Education Scholarship: May 1. Nursing Scholarship: July 1. 21st Century Scholars Program: March 10.

PUBLICATIONS:
Application guidelines.

STAFF:
Claudia Braman, Executive Director
Laurie Gavrin, Director of Policy and Research
Kathi Graves, Grant Director

ADDRESS INQUIRIES TO:
State Student Assistance Commission
(See address above.)

SUDBURY FOUNDATION

326 Concord Road
Sudbury, MA 01776
(978) 443-0849
Fax: (978) 579-9536

E-MAIL ADDRESS:
contact@sudburyfoundation.org

WEB SITE ADDRESS:
www.sudburyfoundation.org

TYPE:
Project/program grants; Scholarships.

See entry 1474 for full listing.

SYRACUSE UNIVERSITY   [1884]

Enrollment Management
212 Bowne Hall
Syracuse, NY 13244-1200
(315) 443-4492
(315) 443-2298
Fax: (315) 443-3423

E-MAIL ADDRESS:
grad@syr.edu
ljmason@syr.edu

WEB SITE ADDRESS:
www.syr.edu

AREAS OF INTEREST:
Student work/study programs.

NAME(S) OF PROGRAMS:
- **Syracuse University Graduate Assistantships**

TYPE:
Assistantships. Syracuse University Graduate Assistantships are of a teaching, research or administrative nature.

ELIGIBILITY:
Open to all nationals.

FINANCIAL DATA:
Amount of support per award: $11,455 minimum stipend plus up to 24 credit hours of tuition scholarship.

NUMBER OF AWARDS: Approximately 1,600 annually.

APPLICATION INFORMATION:
Applicants must apply through departments.
Duration: One year. Renewable.

SYRACUSE UNIVERSITY   [1885]

Enrollment Management
212 Bowne Hall
Syracuse, NY 13244-1200
(315) 443-4492
(315) 443-2298
Fax: (315) 443-3423

E-MAIL ADDRESS:
grad@syr.edu
ljmason@syr.edu

WEB SITE ADDRESS:
www.syr.edu

AREAS OF INTEREST:
Graduate university education.

NAME(S) OF PROGRAMS:
- **African American Graduate Fellowship**
- **Hursky Fellowship**
- **McNair Graduate Fellowship**
- **STEM Doctoral Fellowships**
- **Syracuse University Fellowship**

TYPE:
Fellowships.

PURPOSE:
To provide a full support package during a student's term of study.

ELIGIBILITY:
African American Graduate Fellowships: Awarded annually to new and continuing students across disciplines whose work supports that of the African American Studies Program.

Hursky Fellowships: Open to graduate students with a Ukrainian background enrolled in Maxwell School of Citizenship and Public Affairs or the College of Arts and Sciences, or any SU graduate student whose area of study is the Ukraine or includes Ukrainian topics.

McNair Graduate Fellowship: Students must be either from an underrepresented group (African American, Hispanic or Native American) or a McNair Scholar at their undergraduate institution. Preference will be given to those in doctoral programs. Students will have already been admitted into a Syracuse University graduate program and must be formally nominated by their department for the award.

STEM Doctoral Fellowships: Science, technology, engineering and math disciplines. Open to members of an underrepresented group who are U.S. citizens or permanent residents.

Syracuse University Fellowships: Open to nationals of any country.

FINANCIAL DATA:
Amount of support per award: African American Graduate Fellowship, McNair Graduate Fellowship and Syracuse University Fellowship: $13,040 M.S. stipend plus full tuition; $21,805 Ph.D. stipend plus full tuition; Hursky Fellowship: $13,040 stipend plus full tuition; STEM Doctoral Fellowships: $21,170.

NUMBER OF AWARDS: African American Graduate Fellowship: 6 new per year; Hursky Fellowship: 1 new per year; McNair Graduate Fellowship: Up to 6 new per year; Syracuse University Fellowship: 25 new per year (number of these fellowships may vary from year to year); STEM Doctoral Fellowships: Up to 5 new per year (number of these fellowships may vary from year to year).

APPLICATION INFORMATION:
Applicants must apply through admission application.
Duration: One to six years.
Deadline: January 1, unless earlier date determined by specific department.

ADDRESS INQUIRIES TO:
Lynda Mason
Director of Graduate Awards
(See address above.)

TENNESSEE STUDENT ASSISTANCE CORPORATION   [1886]

Parkway Towers, Suite 1510
404 James Robertson Parkway
Nashville, TN 37243-0820
(615) 741-1346
(800) 342-1663
Fax: (615) 741-6101

E-MAIL ADDRESS:
tsac.aidinfo@tn.gov

WEB SITE ADDRESS:
www.tn.gov/collegepays

FOUNDED: 1976

NAME(S) OF PROGRAMS:
- **Robert C. Byrd Honors Scholarship Program**
- **Dependent Children Scholarship Program**
- **Graduate Nursing Loan-Forgiveness Program**
- **Christa McAuliffe Scholarship Program**
- **Ned McWherter Scholars Program**
- **Minority Teaching Fellows Program**
- **Tennessee Education Lottery Scholarship Program**
- **Tennessee Math & Science Teachers Loan Forgiveness Program**
- **Tennessee Rural Health Loan Forgiveness Program**
- **Tennessee Student Assistance Award**
- **Tennessee Teaching Scholars Program**

TYPE:
Grants-in-aid; Scholarships; Loan forgiveness programs. Need-based grants for undergraduate Tennessee residents enrolled in an eligible Tennessee institution.

Robert C. Byrd Honors Scholarship Program is intended to promote student excellence and achievement and to recognize exceptional students who show promise of continued excellence.

Dependent Children Scholarship Program provides aid for Tennessee residents who are dependent children of a Tennessee law enforcement officer, fireman or an emergency medical service technician who has been killed or totally and permanently disabled while performing duties within the scope of such employment.

Graduate Nursing Loan-Forgiveness Program is designed to encourage Tennessee residents who are nurses to become teachers and administrators in Tennessee nursing education programs. Participants in this program incur an obligation to enter a faculty or administrative position in a nursing education program, in Tennessee, immediately upon completion of the education program.

Christa McAuliffe Scholarship Program was established to encourage promising Tennesseans who have a commitment to teaching and inspiring young minds to explore and achieve their highest potential.

The Ned McWherter Scholars Program is intended to encourage academically superior Tennessee high school graduates to attend college in Tennessee.

Minority Teaching Fellows Program is intended to encourage talented minority Tennesseans to enter the teaching field in Tennessee.

Tennessee Education Lottery Scholarship Program is for those who have been a Tennessee resident for one year by September 1 of the year of application date.

Tennessee Math & Science Teachers Loan Forgiveness Program provides financial assistance to Tennessee public school teachers seeking an advanced degree in a math or a science, or a certification to teach a math or a science. Loan forgiveness requires employment in a Tennessee public school system two years for each year of the loan funding received.

Tennessee Rural Health Loan Forgiveness Program awards those who agree to practice medicine in a health resource shortage area after becoming a Tennessee-licensed physician, osteopathic physician, physician assistant, nurse practitioner or licensed dentist for one year for each year of funding received.

Tennessee Student Assistance Award provides nonrepayable financial assistance to financially needy undergraduate students who are residents of Tennessee.

Tennessee Teaching Scholars Program is intended to encourage exemplary students to enter the teaching field in Tennessee.

YEAR PROGRAM STARTED: 1976

PURPOSE:
To provide grants based on financial need for Tennessee residents.

LEGAL BASIS:
State agency.

ELIGIBILITY:
Applicants for the Tennessee Teaching Scholars Program must be college juniors or seniors or post-Baccalaureate students admitted to teacher education programs in Tennessee colleges or universities and U.S. citizens.

Applicants for the Ned McWherter Scholars Program must be high school seniors with a 3.5 grade point average, a GED score of 570 and 29 ACT or 1280 SAT, and planning to attend an eligible Tennessee institution.

Applicants for the Robert C. Byrd Honors Scholarship must be high school seniors with a 3.0 grade point average and 24 ACT, 1090 SAT, or 3.5 grade point average planning to attend an eligible U.S. institution.

Applicants for the Minority Teaching Fellows Program are preferably high school seniors with a 2.75 grade point average and 18 ACT or be at the top 25% of their graduating class. Undergraduate applicants must have a 2.5 college grade point average.

Applicants for the Tennessee Education Lottery Scholarship Program must:
(1) be entering freshmen who are Tennessee residents for one year prior to application;
(2) enroll in a Tennessee public college/university or enroll in a Tennessee private college/university that is accredited by the Southern Association of Colleges and Schools and;
(3) be enrolled full-time (part-time prorated), leading to a certificate in the Tennessee Technology Centers or degree in approved colleges and universities. Satisfactory academic progress required.

GEOGRAPHIC RESTRICTIONS:
Tennessee.

FINANCIAL DATA:
Amount of support per award: Varies.
Matching fund requirements: For Ned McWherter Scholars Program, the institution must match $3,000.

NUMBER OF APPLICANTS MOST RECENT YEAR:
Ned McWherter Scholars: 900; Robert C. Byrd Honors: 3,800; Minority Teaching Fellows: 150; Tennessee Teaching Scholars: 400.

NUMBER OF AWARDS: Ned McWherter Scholars: 50; Robert C. Byrd Honors: 125; Minority Teaching Fellows: 29; Tennessee Teaching Scholars: 160; Tennessee Education Lottery Scholarship Program: 40,000.

APPLICATION INFORMATION:
Detailed information is available online.
Duration: Renewable each academic year.
Deadline: Tennessee Teaching Scholars: April 15. Ned McWherter Scholars: February 15. Robert C. Byrd Honors: March 1. Minority Teaching Fellows: April 15. Tennessee Education Lottery Scholarship Program: September 1 for fall term, February 1 for spring and summer terms.

ADDRESS INQUIRIES TO:
See telephone numbers above.

*SPECIAL STIPULATIONS:
Tennessee Teaching Scholars and Minority Teaching Fellows: Recipients agree to teach one year for each year of funding in a public Tennessee grades K-12 school or repayment will be required.

TOURISM CARES   [1887]
275 Turnpike Street
Suite 307
Canton, MA 02021
(781) 821-5990 ext. 208
Fax: (781) 821-8949

E-MAIL ADDRESS:
carolyn@tourismcares.org

WEB SITE ADDRESS:
www.tourismcares.org/scholarships

FOUNDED: 2005

AREAS OF INTEREST:
Travel and tourism, hospitality, sustainable tourism, conservation, preservation, or restoration and cultural heritage tourism.

NAME(S) OF PROGRAMS:
- **Academic Scholarship Program**
- **Professional Development Internship**
- **Professional Development Scholarship Program**
- **Undergraduate or Graduate Internship**

TYPE:
Internships; Scholarships. Academic and Professional Development. Graduate Research Scholarships.

YEAR PROGRAM STARTED: 2005

PURPOSE:
To benefit society by preserving the travel experience for future generations by awarding academic, professional, and service-learning scholarships to students of travel, tourism, and hospitality; by giving grants to cultural, historic and natural tourism-related sites worldwide; and by organizing volunteer efforts to clean up and restore tourism-related sites in need of care and rejuvenation.

LEGAL BASIS:
Nonprofit, tax-exempt 501(c)(3) public charity.

FINANCIAL DATA:
Amount of support per award: $1,000 to $5,000.
Total amount of support: $87,000 in 2010; more than $2,000,000 cumulative total since the beginning of the program.

NUMBER OF AWARDS: 54 Undergraduate and Graduate Scholarships and Internships, and 11 Professional Development Scholarships and Internships.

APPLICATION INFORMATION:
Detailed information and application form are available at the web site.

PUBLICATIONS:
e-newsletter.

ADDRESS INQUIRIES TO:
Tourism Cares Scholarship Department at scholarships@tourismcares.org.

TUSKEGEE UNIVERSITY
1200 West Montgomery Road
Tuskegee, AL 36088
(334) 727-8375
Fax: (334) 724-4224

E-MAIL ADDRESS:
bufford@tuskegee.edu

WEB SITE ADDRESS:
www.tuskegee.edu

TYPE:
Fellowships.

See entry 2172 for full listing.

TWO TEN FOOTWEAR FOUNDATION   [1888]
Scholarship Department
1466 Main Street
Waltham, MA 02451
(800) 346-3210 ext. 1512
Fax: (781) 736-1555

E-MAIL ADDRESS:
scholarship@twoten.org

WEB SITE ADDRESS:
www.twoten.org

FOUNDED: 1939

AREAS OF INTEREST:
Footwear industry.

NAME(S) OF PROGRAMS:
- **Two Ten Footwear Foundation College Scholarship Program**

TYPE:
Scholarships. Offered to students affiliated with the footwear, leather or allied industries.

YEAR PROGRAM STARTED: 1969

PURPOSE:
To provide financial assistance to people in the footwear, leather and allied industries.

LEGAL BASIS:
Private foundation.

ELIGIBILITY:
Scholarship applicant must be affiliated with the footwear, leather or allied industries:
(1) either the student must be employed in the above industries, or have a parent (natural, step, or adopted) who must be employed in these industries for a minimum of two years prior to January 1 (student must be considered a dependent);
(2) student must display financial need for college costs as calculated by the federal method of need analysis and the Two Ten Selection Committee;
(3) student must be a U.S. citizen or eligible noncitizen and;
(4) student must enroll at an accredited college, university, nursing or vocational/technical school, earning a two- or four-year undergraduate degree.

FINANCIAL DATA:
Amount of support per award: Generally, up to $3,000. There are also several larger awards available, as well as one super scholarship award of up to $15,000 of unmet need annually.

Total amount of support: More than $700,000 for the year 2009-10.

NUMBER OF AWARDS: 450 for the year 2009-10.

APPLICATION INFORMATION:
Duration: Up to four years.
Deadline: February 16.

ADDRESS INQUIRIES TO:
Scholarship Department
(See address above.)

*SPECIAL STIPULATIONS:
Eligible companies must do at least 50% of their business in footwear, or applicant or parent must work in a specific footwear division.

TWO TEN FOOTWEAR FOUNDATION   [1889]
1466 Main Street
Waltham, MA 02451
(800) 346-3210 ext. 1512
Fax: (781) 736-1555

E-MAIL ADDRESS:
scholarship@twoten.org

WEB SITE ADDRESS:
www.twoten.org

AREAS OF INTEREST:
Footwear design.

NAME(S) OF PROGRAMS:
● **Two Ten Foundation Footwear Design Scholarship Program**

TYPE:
Scholarships. Intended for students who are interested in pursuing a career in footwear design.

PURPOSE:
To provide financial aid to those studying footwear design.

ELIGIBILITY:
Applicant must:
(1) demonstrate an interest and commitment to a career in footwear design;
(2) be a U.S. citizen or eligible non-citizen;
(3) display financial need as calculated by the federal method of need analysis and the Design Scholarship Selection Committee (applicant can estimate Expected Family Contribution at www.finaid.com) and;
(4) attend or plan to attend an approved postsecondary institution.

APPLICATION INFORMATION:
Applicants for consideration must submit a portfolio. Interested candidates must contact the director of scholarship for further information.

ADDRESS INQUIRIES TO:
Phyllis Molta, Director
(See address above.)

U.S. DEPARTMENT OF EDUCATION   [1890]
7th and D Streets, S.W.
ROB3, Room 4004
Washington, DC 20202
(800) 433-3243
Fax: (202) 275-0916
TTY: (800) 730-8913

E-MAIL ADDRESS:
studentaid@ed.gov

WEB SITE ADDRESS:
www.federalstudentaid.ed.gov

AREAS OF INTEREST:
Student financial aid.

NAME(S) OF PROGRAMS:
● **Federal Work-Study**

TYPE:
Work-study programs. Federal Work-Study program provides jobs for undergraduate and graduate students with financial need. Jobs can be on or off-campus. Students are paid at least federal minimum wage. The money earned does not have to be repaid.

PURPOSE:
To enable students to earn a part of educational expenses.

LEGAL BASIS:
Government agency.

ELIGIBILITY:
In general, the aid recipient must:
(1) show financial need;
(2) be a U.S. citizen or eligible noncitizen with a valid Social Security number (SSN);
(3) be working toward a degree or certificate in an eligible program;
(4) demonstrate one is qualified to obtain a postsecondary education;
(5) register (if not already done so) with the Selective Service, if one is a male between the ages of 18 and 25 and;
(6) maintain satisfactory academic progress once in school.

FINANCIAL DATA:
Federal Work-Study wages will be at least the current federal minimum wage, but may be higher, depending on the type of work and the skills required. The total Federal Work-Study award depends on when a student applies, one's level of need, and the funding level of one's school.
Amount of support per award: Varies.
Total amount of support: Varies.

APPLICATION INFORMATION:
Duration: One year. Renewable.

PUBLICATIONS:
Funding Education Beyond High School: The Guide to Federal Student Aid.

U.S. DEPARTMENT OF EDUCATION   [1891]
7th and D Streets, S.W.
ROB3, Room 4004
Washington, DC 20202
(800) 433-3243
Fax: (202) 275-0916
TTY: 800-730-8913

E-MAIL ADDRESS:
studentaid@ed.gov

WEB SITE ADDRESS:
www.federalstudentaid.ed.gov

AREAS OF INTEREST:
Student financial aid.

NAME(S) OF PROGRAMS:
● **Pell Grant**

TYPE:
Grants-in-aid. Student aid grants for higher education.

YEAR PROGRAM STARTED: 1973

PURPOSE:
To help undergraduates pay for education after high school.

LEGAL BASIS:
Title IV, Higher Education Act of 1965, as amended.

ELIGIBILITY:
In general, the aid recipient must:
(1) show financial need;
(2) enroll as a regular student in an eligible program;
(3) be a U.S. citizen or eligible noncitizen and;
(4) meet the school's satisfactory academic progress standards in his or her course of study.

The student also must register with the Selective Service, if required.

FINANCIAL DATA:
Amount of support per award: Up to $5,500 per year for the 2010-11 award year depending on Expected Family Contribution (EFC), the cost of attendance at the student's school, status as full-time or part-time student and how long the student will be enrolled in the academic year in question.

APPLICATION INFORMATION:
Applicants should contact the financial aid office at each school they are considering attending to determine which forms must be submitted. Students can request a copy of the *Student Guide* at the toll-free phone number.
Duration: One year. Renewable.

PUBLICATIONS:
Funding Education Beyond High School: The Guide to Federal Student Aid.

*PLEASE NOTE:
Applicant may receive only one Pell Grant in an award year, and may not receive Pell Grant funds from more than one school at a time.

THE MORRIS K. UDALL AND STEWART L. UDALL FOUNDATION   [1892]
130 South Scott Avenue
Tucson, AZ 85701
(520) 901-8564
Fax: (520) 901-8570

E-MAIL ADDRESS:
ibarra@udall.gov

WEB SITE ADDRESS:
www.udall.gov

FOUNDED: 1992

AREAS OF INTEREST:
Environment, including policy, engineering, science, education, urban planning and renewal, business, health, justice and economics; Native American health care and tribal public policy.

NAME(S) OF PROGRAMS:
● **Udall Scholarship**

TYPE:
Scholarships. The Udall Foundation seeks future leaders across a wide spectrum of environmental fields, including policy, engineering, science, education, urban planning and renewal, business, health, justice and economics.

The Udall Foundation also seeks future Native American and Alaska Native leaders in Native American health care and tribal public policy. Tribal policy includes fields related to tribal sovereignty, tribal governance, tribal law, Native American education, Native American justice, natural resource management, cultural preservation and revitalization, Native American economic development and other areas affecting Native American communities. Native American health care includes health care administration, social work, medicine and research into health conditions affecting Native American communities.

YEAR PROGRAM STARTED: 1996

PURPOSE:
To educate a new generation of Americans to preserve and protect their national heritage through studies in the environment, Native American health and tribal policy and effective public policy conflict resolution.

LEGAL BASIS:
The Foundation is an executive branch agency. The President of the U.S. appoints its board of trustees with the advice and consent of the U.S. Senate.

ELIGIBILITY:
The scholarship awards are made on the basis of merit to two groups of students: (1) those who are college sophomores or juniors in the current academic year, have outstanding potential and who study the environment and related fields and; (2) Native American and Alaska Native students who are college sophomores or juniors in the current academic year, have outstanding potential and are in fields related to health care or tribal public policy.

FINANCIAL DATA:
Amount of support per award: Up to $5,000.
Total amount of support: Varies.

NUMBER OF APPLICANTS MOST RECENT YEAR:
510 for the year 2011.

NUMBER OF AWARDS: Approximately 80.

APPLICATION INFORMATION:
Duration: One year.

STAFF:
Mia Ibarra, Program Manager

ADDRESS INQUIRIES TO:
Mia Ibarra, Program Manager
(See address above.)

THE MORRIS K. UDALL AND STEWART L. UDALL FOUNDATION   [1893]
130 South Scott Avenue
Tucson, AZ 85701
(520) 901-8500
Fax: (520) 901-8570

E-MAIL ADDRESS:
curlin@udall.gov

WEB SITE ADDRESS:
www.udall.gov

FOUNDED: 1992

AREAS OF INTEREST:
Educating young Americans in our nation's heritage, environmental studies, Native American affairs and public policy conflict resolution.

NAME(S) OF PROGRAMS:
● **Environmental Public Policy and Conflict Resolution Fellowships**

TYPE:
Fellowships. Each year the Foundation awards dissertation fellowships to students whose work is in the areas of U.S. environmental public policy or U.S. environmental conflict resolution.

YEAR PROGRAM STARTED: 1997

PURPOSE:
To educate a new generation of Americans to preserve and protect their national heritage

through studies in the environment, Native American health and tribal policy and effective public policy conflict resolution.

LEGAL BASIS:
The Foundation is an executive branch agency. The President of the U.S. appoints its board of trustees with the advice and consent of the U.S. Senate.

ELIGIBILITY:
Fellowship recipients must be in the final, writing year of their Ph.D. work and must submit a copy of their dissertation to the Foundation at the end of the award year.

Dissertation fellowships are awarded to men and women who have achieved or show promise of achieving distinction in their scholarly research. Applicants must be U.S. citizens, permanent residents, or, in the case of applicants from American Samoa or the Commonwealth of the Mariana Islands, U.S. Nationals.

GEOGRAPHIC RESTRICTIONS:
United States.

FINANCIAL DATA:
Amount of support per award: $24,000.

NUMBER OF APPLICANTS MOST RECENT YEAR:
37.

NUMBER OF AWARDS: 2.

APPLICATION INFORMATION:
Duration: One year.
Deadline: Mid- to late February.

STAFF:
Jane Curlin, Senior Program Manager

ADDRESS INQUIRIES TO:
Morris K. Udall Dissertation Fellowship
Jane Curlin, Senior Program Manager
Tel: (520) 901-8565
(See address above.)

UNICO NATIONAL, INC.   [1894]
271 U.S. Highway 46 West
Suite A-108
Fairfield, NJ 07003
(973) 808-0035
Fax: (973) 808-0043

E-MAIL ADDRESS:
uniconational@unico.org

WEB SITE ADDRESS:
www.unico.org

FOUNDED: 1922

NAME(S) OF PROGRAMS:
● **Basilone Postgraduate Scholarship**
● **Cottone Postgraduate Scholarship (Medical Only)**
● **William C. Davini Scholarship**
● **Major Don S. Gentile Scholarship**
● **Theodore Mazza Scholarship**
● **Alphonse A. Miele Scholarship**

TYPE:
Scholarships. Postgraduate scholarships and undergraduate scholarships.

PURPOSE:
To give financial aid to students of outstanding merit so they may complete their education.

ELIGIBILITY:
Candidates must reside in the corporate limits of a city wherein an active chapter of UNICO National is located. A graduating senior at any public or private school who is commencing undergraduate studies and who demonstrates financial need is eligible.

Scholarship candidates must be of Italian heritage, i.e., must have one parent or grandparent of Italian heritage. The extent to which a candidate has contributed to the life and welfare of school and/or community will be taken into account in the assessment of merit. UNICO member's children are eligible. Each chapter of UNICO National may submit applications for each of the UNICO Foundation scholarships.

A candidate for the undergraduate scholarships must be a citizen of the U.S. and have Italian heritage. An applicant must be a graduating senior at a public or private secondary school.

The Basilone Scholarship requires that the applicant be a senior in college or a graduate beginning postgraduate studies.

The Cottone Scholarship requires that a candidate be a college senior or graduate who is beginning postgraduate studies in the field of medicine or is currently enrolled in an accredited medical school in the U.S.

A candidate for either postgraduate program (Basilone or Cottone Scholarship) must be a U.S. citizen of Italian heritage.

FINANCIAL DATA:
Amount of support per award: Undergraduate and Basilone Postgraduate Scholarships: $1,500 per year for a maximum of four years; Cottone Postgraduate Scholarship: $5,000.

Total amount of support: $35,000 (Total amount paid out per year: $12,500).

NUMBER OF APPLICANTS MOST RECENT YEAR:
Approximately 140.

NUMBER OF AWARDS: 6.

APPLICATION INFORMATION:
Applications for scholarships are available and must be acquired from and submitted through a participating, local UNICO chapter.

Undergraduate scholarships: A candidate should apply for all four scholarships. To do so requires that they submit the original application and three complete copies, including attachments. Multiple copies are necessary because scholarships are judged in separate locations.
Duration: Undergraduate and Basilone Postgraduate Scholarships: Maximum of four years; Cottone Postgraduate Scholarship: One-time only.
Deadline: April 15. Announcement prior to August 1.

ADDRESS INQUIRIES TO:
National Scholarship Awards
(See address above.)

UNITED NEGRO COLLEGE FUND
8260 Willow Oaks Corporate Drive
Fairfax, VA 22031-4503
(703) 205-3400
(800) 331-2244
Fax: (703) 205-3550

E-MAIL ADDRESS:
scholarships@uncf.org

WEB SITE ADDRESS:
www.uncf.org

TYPE:
Fellowships; Internships; Scholarships; Technical assistance. The Fund, since its founding, has raised money for 39 private, historically Black colleges.

Faculty fellowship programs make it possible for hundreds of instructors to earn doctoral degrees.

Mentoring and internship opportunities are provided for hundreds of UNCF students.

Scholarships are offered to a pool of more than 60,000 talented students attending UNCF colleges and universities. The Fund oversees more than 450 scholarship programs in the following general categories:
(1) geographically based scholarships;
(2) scholarships based on academic major;
(3) scholarships based on merit and need and;
(4) financial aid for graduate study

See entry 1099 for full listing.

UNIVERSITY OF ALBERTA [1895]

Killam Centre for Advanced Studies
2-1B1 University Hall
Edmonton AB T6G 2J9 Canada
(780) 492-3264

E-MAIL ADDRESS:
janna.isabelle@ualberta.ca

WEB SITE ADDRESS:
www.postdoc.ualberta.ca

FOUNDED: 1906

NAME(S) OF PROGRAMS:
● **Izaak Walton Killam Memorial Postdoctoral Fellowship**

TYPE:
Fellowships. Postdoctoral fellowships available in most fields to allow new or recent Ph.Ds. to undertake research at the University of Alberta.

YEAR PROGRAM STARTED: 1967

PURPOSE:
To contribute to the advancement of learning.

ELIGIBILITY:
Applicants must have recently completed a Ph.D. program or will do so in the immediate future. Applicants who have received their Ph.D. degree from the University of Alberta or who will be on sabbatical leave or who hold or have held named postdoctoral fellowships at other institutions are not eligible. No restriction exists as to citizenship. No award can be taken up prior to completion of the Doctorate. Tenable only at the University of Alberta.

Killam Scholars should not be one-sided, and a sound character should complement their intellect.

FINANCIAL DATA:
Amount of support per award: $46,000 (CAN) per year, plus a one-time travel/research allowance of $4,000 (CAN).

NUMBER OF APPLICANTS MOST RECENT YEAR:
165.

NUMBER OF AWARDS: 4 for the year 2010-11.

APPLICATION INFORMATION:
Duration: Two years.
Deadline: December 15.

UNIVERSITY OF ALBERTA [1896]

Killam Centre for Advanced Studies
2-1B1 University Hall
Edmonton AB T6G 2J9 Canada
(780) 492-3264

E-MAIL ADDRESS:
janna.isabelle@ualberta.ca

WEB SITE ADDRESS:
www.postdoc.ualberta.ca

FOUNDED: 1906

NAME(S) OF PROGRAMS:
● **Grant Notley Memorial Postdoctoral Fellowship**

TYPE:
Fellowships. Postdoctoral fellowships for research in the politics, history, economy or society of western Canada or related fields. The Fellow may teach one course per year but must be primarily an investigative scholar.

PURPOSE:
To honor an illustrious Albertan by bringing to the University of Alberta active and promising young scholars who will do significant work in an area encompassed by Grant Notley's broad interests.

ELIGIBILITY:
Applicants must have recently completed a Ph.D. degree or will do so in the immediate future. No award can be taken up prior to completion of the Doctorate. Applicants should be active and promising young scholars who will perform significantly in fields associated with Grant Notley's broad interests in the politics, history, economy or society of western Canada or related fields. Applicants who have received their Ph.D. degree from the University of Alberta or who will be on sabbatical leave or who hold or have held named postdoctoral fellowships at other institutions are not eligible. Tenable only at the University of Alberta.

FINANCIAL DATA:
Amount of support per award: $46,000 (CAN) per year, plus a one-time travel/research allowance of $4,000 (CAN).

NUMBER OF AWARDS: 1 award offered annually.

APPLICATION INFORMATION:
Duration: Two years.
Deadline: December 15.

THE UNIVERSITY OF BRITISH COLUMBIA [1897]

Faculty of Graduate Studies
170-6371 Crescent Road
Vancouver BC V6T 1Z2 Canada
(604) 822-2080
Fax: (604) 822-5802

E-MAIL ADDRESS:
killam@interchange.ubc.ca

WEB SITE ADDRESS:
www.grad.ubc.ca/awards

NAME(S) OF PROGRAMS:
● **Izaak Walton Killam Memorial Postdoctoral Research Fellowships**

TYPE:
Fellowships. Offered to allow researchers holding a Ph.D. or equivalent to devote full-time to research at the University of British Columbia.

YEAR PROGRAM STARTED: 1967

LEGAL BASIS:
University.

ELIGIBILITY:
Open to persons who have shown superior ability in research and have obtained, within two academic years of the anticipated

commencement date of the Fellowship, a Ph.D. or equivalent at a university other than the University of British Columbia and who wish to pursue further study.

Fellowships are tenable only at the University of British Columbia. Applicants must not currently be employed or have been employed at any campus of UBC prior to commencement of the fellowship, and must not have current or prior research or employment affiliations with a faculty or adjunct faculty member of any campus of UBC. People holding faculty positions at universities or colleges are not eligible to apply.

Killam Postdoctoral Research Fellows are permitted to undertake teaching or other academic duties up to the equivalent of one six-credit (two-term) course over the two-year term of the Fellowship.

Citizens of any country may apply.

FINANCIAL DATA:
Amount of support per award: Stipend of up to $50,000 per annum plus a research/travel allowance of $6,000 over two years.
Total amount of support: Approximately $700,000 per year.

NUMBER OF APPLICANTS MOST RECENT YEAR:
150.

NUMBER OF AWARDS: 4 to 6 per year.

APPLICATION INFORMATION:
Applicant must first contact department of interest. Fellowships are awarded on the basis of applications submitted to UBC departments.
Duration: Fellowships are granted for two years, subject to review at the end of the first year.
Deadline: Mid-October to early November.

ADDRESS INQUIRIES TO:
Diane Tromba, Assistant Dean
(See address above.)

THE UNIVERSITY OF BRITISH COLUMBIA [1898]

Faculty of Graduate Studies
170-6371 Crescent Road
Vancouver BC V6T 1Z2 Canada
(604) 822-0976
Fax: (604) 822-5802

E-MAIL ADDRESS:
graduate.awards@ubc.ca

WEB SITE ADDRESS:
www.grad.ubc.ca/awards

AREAS OF INTEREST:
All areas of advanced study.

NAME(S) OF PROGRAMS:
● **Affiliated Fellowships**

TYPE:
Fellowships. For postgraduate studies leading to a Master's or Doctorate degree at the University of British Columbia.

PURPOSE:
To allow outstanding students to devote full-time to research and study leading to a Master's or Doctorate degree.

LEGAL BASIS:
University.

ELIGIBILITY:
Citizens of any country may apply. Applicants must have outstanding academic records.

FINANCIAL DATA:
Amount of support per award: $8,000 to
$27,500 (CAN) per annum.

Total amount of support: Approximately
$750,000 (CAN) per annum.

NUMBER OF APPLICANTS MOST RECENT YEAR:
Approximately 1,000.

NUMBER OF AWARDS: 50 per year.

APPLICATION INFORMATION:
Fellowships are awarded on the basis of
applications submitted to graduate programs.

Duration: One or two years.

Deadline: Mid- to late September.

STAFF:
Brendan Morey, Graduate Awards Manager

ADDRESS INQUIRIES TO:
Brendan Morey
Graduate Awards Manager
(See address above.)

THE UNIVERSITY OF BRITISH COLUMBIA   [1899]

Faculty of Graduate Studies
170-6371 Crescent Road
Vancouver BC V6T 1Z2 Canada
(604) 822-0976
Fax: (604) 822-5802

E-MAIL ADDRESS:
graduate.awards@ubc.ca

WEB SITE ADDRESS:
www.grad.ubc.ca/awards

AREAS OF INTEREST:
Research-based Master's and doctoral studies.

NAME(S) OF PROGRAMS:
● **Graduate Student Initiative**

TYPE:
Scholarships.

YEAR PROGRAM STARTED: 2008

PURPOSE:
To provide funding for graduate students
through entrance scholarships, multiyear
funding packages, tuition awards, and
scholarship top-ups.

LEGAL BASIS:
University.

ELIGIBILITY:
Citizens of any country may apply.

FINANCIAL DATA:
Amount of support per award: Set by
graduate programs.

Total amount of support: $6,700,000.

APPLICATION INFORMATION:
Student should submit research proposal and
academic record to the graduate department
of interest.

Duration: Up to four years.

Deadline: Inquiry to graduate program of
interest accepted throughout the year. Most
funding decisions are made January to
March.

ADDRESS INQUIRIES TO:
Brendan Morey, Graduate Awards Manager
(See address above.)

THE UNIVERSITY OF BRITISH COLUMBIA   [1900]

Faculty of Graduate Studies
170-6371 Crescent Road
Vancouver BC V6T 1Z2 Canada
(604) 822-0976
Fax: (604) 822-5802

E-MAIL ADDRESS:
graduate.awards@ubc.ca

WEB SITE ADDRESS:
www.grad.ubc.ca/awards

AREAS OF INTEREST:
Doctoral study in all disciplines.

NAME(S) OF PROGRAMS:
● **Four Year Doctoral Fellowships**

TYPE:
Fellowships.

YEAR PROGRAM STARTED: 2009

PURPOSE:
To attract and retain outstanding doctoral
students by offering stable, base-level
funding for the first four years of their Ph.D.
studies and research.

ELIGIBILITY:
Open to doctoral students in any discipline.
Citizens of any country may apply.

FINANCIAL DATA:
Ensures student receives financial support of
at least $16,000 (CAN) per year plus tuition.

Total amount of support: Approximately
$14,000,000.

NUMBER OF AWARDS: 200 new fellowships
offered by graduate programs each year.

APPLICATION INFORMATION:
Applicant must first contact graduate program
of interest. Fellowships are awarded on basis
of nomination made by graduate program.

Duration: Four years.

Deadline: Most funding decisions made in
January to March.

ADDRESS INQUIRIES TO:
Brendan Morey, Graduate Awards Manager
(See address above.)

THE UNIVERSITY OF CALGARY   [1901]

Faculty of Graduate Studies
Earth Sciences Building, Room 720
2500 University Drive, N.W.
Calgary AB T2N 1N4 Canada
(403) 220-4938
Fax: (403) 289-7635

E-MAIL ADDRESS:
gsaward@ucalgary.ca

WEB SITE ADDRESS:
www.grad.ucalgary.ca

FOUNDED: 1966

AREAS OF INTEREST:
Petroleum industry.

NAME(S) OF PROGRAMS:
● **The Archibald Waynne Dingman
Memorial Graduate Scholarship**

TYPE:
Awards/prizes; Scholarships. Graduate
scholarship for study in all areas relevant to
the petroleum industry. Tenable at The
University of Calgary. Award endowed
through a bequest of the late Corinne
Patteson.

ELIGIBILITY:
Open to qualified graduates of any
recognized university who are registered in or
admissible to a program leading to a Master's
or doctoral degree at The University of
Calgary.

FINANCIAL DATA:
Amount of support per award: $2,600
(CAN).

Total amount of support: $2,600 (CAN).

NUMBER OF AWARDS: 1.

APPLICATION INFORMATION:
Students should consult the Graduate Award
Competition Guidelines and Application
available online.

Duration: One year.

Deadline: February 1 to candidate's Graduate
Program Office, unless program has an
earlier deadline.

ADDRESS INQUIRIES TO:
Graduate Scholarship Office
(See address above.)

THE UNIVERSITY OF CALGARY   [1902]

Faculty of Graduate Studies
Earth Sciences Building, Room 720
2500 University Drive, N.W.
Calgary AB T2N 1N4 Canada
(403) 220-4938
Fax: (403) 289-7635

E-MAIL ADDRESS:
gsaward@ucalgary.ca

WEB SITE ADDRESS:
www.grad.ucalgary.ca

FOUNDED: 1966

NAME(S) OF PROGRAMS:
● **Queen Elizabeth II Graduate
Scholarships**

TYPE:
Awards/prizes; Fellowships; Scholarships.
Graduate scholarships and fellowships in all
fields of study tenable at The University of
Calgary.

ELIGIBILITY:
Open to qualified graduate students who are
or will be, at the time of tenure, registered in
a full-time Master's or doctoral program in
the Faculty of Graduate Studies. Candidates
must be either Canadian citizens or
permanent residents and a resident of
Alberta. Students whose awards begin in
May are expected to carry out a full-time
research program during the summer months.

This award cannot be held in addition to
funding from a major award.

FINANCIAL DATA:
Amount of support per award: Master's level:
Up to $10,800 (CAN); Doctoral level: Up to
$15,000 (CAN).

NUMBER OF AWARDS: Varies.

APPLICATION INFORMATION:
Students should consult with their Graduate
Program Office for application information.

Duration: One year.

Deadline: Students should consult with their
Graduate Program Office for deadline
information.

ADDRESS INQUIRIES TO:
Graduate Program Office
(See address above.)

THE UNIVERSITY OF CALGARY   [1903]

Faculty of Graduate Studies
Earth Sciences Building, Room 720
2500 University Drive, N.W.
Calgary AB T2N 1N4 Canada
(403) 220-4938
Fax: (403) 289-7635

E-MAIL ADDRESS:
gsaward@ucalgary.ca

WEB SITE ADDRESS:
www.grad.ucalgary.ca

FOUNDED: 1966

AREAS OF INTEREST:
Medical sciences.

NAME(S) OF PROGRAMS:
- **William H. Davies Medical Research Scholarships**

TYPE:
Awards/prizes; Scholarships. Awards for study in the medical sciences. Tenable at The University of Calgary. Award endowed through a bequest of the late William H. Davies.

ELIGIBILITY:
Open to qualified graduates of any recognized university who will be registered in the Faculty of Graduate Studies at The University of Calgary. Successful candidates must contact their research program within the Faculty of Medicine; others cannot be considered. Awards are made solely on the basis of academic excellence.

FINANCIAL DATA:
Amount of support per award: $3,000 to $11,000 (CAN), depending upon the candidate's qualifications, experience and graduate program.

NUMBER OF AWARDS: Varies.

APPLICATION INFORMATION:
Information is available from the Faculty of Graduate Studies. Candidates should apply to the Associate Dean, Graduate Science Education, Faculty of Medicine. Recommendations from the Faculty of Medicine will be submitted for approval to the Graduate Scholarship Committee.
Duration: One year.
Deadline: June 15.

ADDRESS INQUIRIES TO:
Research Program, Faculty of Medicine
Foothills Hospital
3330 Hospital Drive, N.W.
Calgary, AB T2N 4N1
Canada

THE UNIVERSITY OF CALGARY　　[1904]

Faculty of Graduate Studies
Earth Sciences Building, Room 720
2500 University Drive, N.W.
Calgary AB T2N 1N4 Canada
(403) 220-4938
Fax: (403) 289-7635

E-MAIL ADDRESS:
gsaward@ucalgary.ca

WEB SITE ADDRESS:
www.grad.ucalgary.ca

FOUNDED: 1966

AREAS OF INTEREST:
Cellular, molecular, microbial and biochemical biology.

NAME(S) OF PROGRAMS:
- **Bettina Bahlsen Memorial Graduate Scholarship**

TYPE:
Awards/prizes; Scholarships. Award for study in the fields of cellular, molecular, microbial or biochemical biology. Tenable at The University of Calgary, Department of Biological Sciences.

ELIGIBILITY:
Open to full-time graduate students registered in or eligible to register in the Department of Biological Sciences. Selection will be based on academic excellence. Preference will be accorded to an international student and, if possible, to a student entering the first year of graduate studies.

FINANCIAL DATA:
Total amount of support: $14,600 (CAN).

NUMBER OF AWARDS: 1.

APPLICATION INFORMATION:
Students should consult the Graduate Award Competition Guidelines and Application found at the web site.
Duration: One year. Possible renewal in open competition.
Deadline: February 1, unless the candidate's graduate program office has an earlier deadline.

ADDRESS INQUIRIES TO:
Graduate Scholarship Office
(See address above.)

THE UNIVERSITY OF CALGARY　　[1905]

Faculty of Graduate Studies
Earth Sciences Building, Room 720
2500 University Drive, N.W.
Calgary AB T2N 1N4 Canada
(403) 220-4938
Fax: (403) 289-7635

E-MAIL ADDRESS:
gsaward@ucalgary.ca

WEB SITE ADDRESS:
www.grad.ucalgary.ca

FOUNDED: 1966

AREAS OF INTEREST:
Business and management.

NAME(S) OF PROGRAMS:
- **John Labatt Limited Scholarship**
- **ScotiaMcLeod Scholarship**

TYPE:
Awards/prizes; Scholarships. Awards for study in the fields of business, management and related areas. Tenable at the University of Calgary. Awards are endowed through gifts from John Labatt Limited and ScotiaMcLeod Inc. Matching grants provided from the Province of Alberta's Advanced Education Endowment Fund.

ELIGIBILITY:
Open to qualified graduate students who are registered in or admissible to the MBA program at The University of Calgary. Awardees must be engaged in full-time study during the tenure of the award.

FINANCIAL DATA:
Amount of support per award: Labatt Scholarship: $2,400 (CAN); ScotiaMcLeod Scholarship: $2,600 (CAN).

NUMBER OF AWARDS: 1 per award.

APPLICATION INFORMATION:
No applications are required.
Labatt Scholarship: Recommendations from the Director of the MBA Program, Haskayne School of Business will be forwarded to the Graduate Scholarship Office. The recommendation is subject to final approval of the Graduate Scholarship Committee.
ScotiaMcLeod Scholarship: The Associate Dean, Calgary MBA Program, Faculty of Management, will submit recommendations

to the Graduate Scholarship Office. Recommendation is subject to final approval of the Graduate Scholarship Committee.
Duration: One year.
Deadline: May 15.

ADDRESS INQUIRIES TO:
Haskayne School of Business
2500 University Drive, N.W.
Calgary, AB T2N 1N4
Canada

THE UNIVERSITY OF CALGARY　　[1906]

Faculty of Graduate Studies
Earth Sciences Building, Room 720
2500 University Drive, N.W.
Calgary AB T2N 1N4 Canada
(403) 220-4938
Fax: (403) 289-7635

E-MAIL ADDRESS:
gsaward@ucalgary.ca

WEB SITE ADDRESS:
www.grad.ucalgary.ca

FOUNDED: 1966

NAME(S) OF PROGRAMS:
- **Izaak Walton Killam Predoctoral Scholarships**

TYPE:
Awards/prizes; Scholarships.

YEAR PROGRAM STARTED: 1967

PURPOSE:
To encourage advanced study, to increase the scientific and scholastic attainment of Canadians and to promote sympathetic understanding between Canadians and the peoples of other countries. Those receiving scholarships would likely contribute to the advancement of learning or win distinction in their profession.

ELIGIBILITY:
Scholarships are normally awarded to students who will be in their first, second, third or fourth year of Ph.D. studies during the tenure of the award. The recipients must be registered full-time in a doctoral program at the University of Calgary. Applicants must have completed at least one year of graduate study before taking up an award.

GEOGRAPHIC RESTRICTIONS:
Canada.

FINANCIAL DATA:
$3,000 of this award (a Killam Research Scholarship) is reserved to cover costs associated with special equipment, conferences and/or travel in direct connection with the Ph.D. research.
Amount of support per award: $36,000 (CAN).
Total amount of support: Varies.

NUMBER OF AWARDS: Varies.

APPLICATION INFORMATION:
In order to receive the Killam Research Scholarship portion of the award, the student must submit a letter outlining the proposed use of funds. This statement must be signed by the supervisor approving the use. No receipts are required.
Duration: One year. Renewable once upon presentation of evidence of satisfactory progress.

Deadline: February 1, unless candidate's graduate program office has an earlier deadline.

ADDRESS INQUIRIES TO:
Graduate Scholarship Office
(See address above.)

THE UNIVERSITY OF CALGARY [1907]

Faculty of Graduate Studies
Earth Sciences Building, Room 720
2500 University Drive, N.W.
Calgary AB T2N 1N4 Canada
(403) 220-4938
Fax: (403) 289-7635

E-MAIL ADDRESS:
gsaward@ucalgary.ca

WEB SITE ADDRESS:
www.grad.ucalgary.ca

FOUNDED: 1966

NAME(S) OF PROGRAMS:
● **The University of Calgary Silver Anniversary Graduate Fellowships**

TYPE:
Awards/prizes; Fellowships. Graduate fellowships in all fields of study tenable in The Faculty of Graduate Studies at The University of Calgary. Award endowed by an anonymous donor and matched by the Province of Alberta.

ELIGIBILITY:
Open to qualified graduates of any recognized university who are registered in or admissible to a doctoral program at The University of Calgary. Candidates must be residents of Canada. Awards are granted on the basis of academic standing and demonstrated potential for advanced study and research.

FINANCIAL DATA:
Amount of support per award: $16,000 to $20,000.
Total amount of support: Varies.

NUMBER OF AWARDS: Varies depending on funds.

APPLICATION INFORMATION:
Duration: One year. Renewable once upon presentation of evidence of satisfactory progress.
Deadline: February 1, unless specific program has an earlier deadline.

ADDRESS INQUIRIES TO:
Student's Graduate Program Office
(See address above.)

THE UNIVERSITY OF CALGARY [1908]

Faculty of Graduate Studies
Earth Sciences Building, Room 720
2500 University Drive, N.W.
Calgary AB T2N 1N4 Canada
(403) 220-4938
Fax: (403) 289-7635

E-MAIL ADDRESS:
gsaward@ucalgary.ca

WEB SITE ADDRESS:
www.grad.ucalgary.ca

FOUNDED: 1966

AREAS OF INTEREST:
Creative writing in English, English literature, and related literary fields.

NAME(S) OF PROGRAMS:
● **The A.T.J. Cairns Memorial Scholarship**

TYPE:
Awards/prizes; Scholarships. Graduate scholarship tenable at The University of Calgary. Award endowed through the estate of the late A.T.J. Cairns, with a matching grant provided by the Province of Alberta's Advanced Education Endowment Fund.

ELIGIBILITY:
Candidates must be registered in or admissible to a Master's or doctoral degree program in the Department of English.

FINANCIAL DATA:
Amount of support per award: $1,000 to $5,000.
Total amount of support: Varies.

NUMBER OF AWARDS: Determined annually.

APPLICATION INFORMATION:
Students interested in the award should apply to the Department of English in the first instance. Recommendations from the Department will be considered by the University Graduate Scholarship Committee.
Duration: One year.
Deadline: April 30.

ADDRESS INQUIRIES TO:
Graduate Scholarship Office
(See address above.)

THE UNIVERSITY OF CALGARY [1909]

Faculty of Graduate Studies
Earth Sciences Building, Room 720
2500 University Drive, N.W.
Calgary AB T2N 1N4 Canada
(403) 220-4938
Fax: (403) 289-7635

E-MAIL ADDRESS:
gsaward@ucalgary.ca

WEB SITE ADDRESS:
www.grad.ucalgary.ca

FOUNDED: 1966

NAME(S) OF PROGRAMS:
● **Graduate Faculty Council Scholarship**

TYPE:
Awards/prizes; Scholarships. Graduate scholarship in all fields of study tenable at The University of Calgary. Award endowed by The University of Calgary Graduate Faculty Council.

ELIGIBILITY:
Open to qualified full-time graduate students who are or will be, at the time of tenure, registered in a thesis-based doctoral program in the Faculty of Graduate Studies.

FINANCIAL DATA:
Amount of support per award: $10,000 per annum.
Total amount of support: Varies depending on funds available.

NUMBER OF AWARDS: Varies.

APPLICATION INFORMATION:
Students should consult their Graduate Program Officer for application information.
Duration: One year.

Deadline: February 1.

ADDRESS INQUIRIES TO:
Graduate Scholarship Office
(See address above.)

THE UNIVERSITY OF CALGARY [1910]

Faculty of Graduate Studies
Earth Sciences Building, Room 720
2500 University Drive, N.W.
Calgary AB T2N 1N4 Canada
(403) 220-4938
Fax: (403) 289-7635

E-MAIL ADDRESS:
gsaward@ucalgary.ca

WEB SITE ADDRESS:
www.grad.ucalgary.ca

FOUNDED: 1966

AREAS OF INTEREST:
Humanities.

NAME(S) OF PROGRAMS:
● **Peter C. Craigie Memorial Scholarship**

TYPE:
Awards/prizes; Scholarships. Graduate scholarship tenable at The University of Calgary. Award endowed by friends, family and colleagues of Peter Craigie, who was Vice President (Academic) at the University; matching grant provided from the Province of Alberta's Advanced Education Endowment Fund.

ELIGIBILITY:
Open to full-time registrants who are registered in and have completed one term of study in a program of studies leading to a Master's degree in a department in the Faculty of Humanities. The recipient must have an outstanding scholastic record and have been or be involved in activities contributing to the general welfare of the University community.

FINANCIAL DATA:
Amount of support per award: $4,500.
Total amount of support: $4,500.

NUMBER OF AWARDS: 1.

APPLICATION INFORMATION:
Duration: One year.
Deadline: May 15, or the next business day if deadline falls on a weekend.

ADDRESS INQUIRIES TO:
Graduate Scholarship Office
(See address above.)

THE UNIVERSITY OF CALGARY [1911]

Faculty of Graduate Studies
Earth Sciences Building, Room 720
2500 University Drive, N.W.
Calgary AB T2N 1N4 Canada
(403) 220-4938
Fax: (403) 289-7635

E-MAIL ADDRESS:
gsaward@ucalgary.ca

WEB SITE ADDRESS:
www.grad.ucalgary.ca

FOUNDED: 1966

AREAS OF INTEREST:
Economics, geology and geophysics, engineering and management.

NAME(S) OF PROGRAMS:
- **Canadian Natural Resources Limited Graduate Scholarship**

TYPE:
Awards/prizes; Scholarships. Graduate scholarship tenable at The University of Calgary. Award donated by Sceptre Resources Limited, with a matching grant provided from the Province of Alberta's Advanced Education Endowment Fund.

ELIGIBILITY:
Open to full-time graduate students registered in or eligible to register as a full-time graduate student in one of the above fields of study.

FINANCIAL DATA:
Amount of support per award: Up to $9,000.
Total amount of support: $9,000.

NUMBER OF AWARDS: 1.

APPLICATION INFORMATION:
Duration: One year.
Deadline: May 15, or next business day if deadline falls on weekend.

ADDRESS INQUIRIES TO:
Graduate Scholarship Office
(See address above.)

THE UNIVERSITY OF CALGARY [1912]
Faculty of Graduate Studies
Earth Sciences Building, Room 720
2500 University Drive, N.W.
Calgary AB T2N 1N4 Canada
(403) 220-4938
Fax: (403) 289-7635

E-MAIL ADDRESS:
gsaward@ucalgary.ca

WEB SITE ADDRESS:
www.grad.ucalgary.ca

AREAS OF INTEREST:
Natural resources, energy and environmental law.

NAME(S) OF PROGRAMS:
- **Alberta Law Foundation Graduate Scholarship**
- **Faculty of Law Graduate Scholarship**

TYPE:
Awards/prizes; Fellowships; Scholarships.

ELIGIBILITY:
Open to full-time graduate students registered in or admissible to a program of studies leading to a Master's degree in the Faculty of Law. If, in the opinion of the University Graduate Scholarships Selection Committee, no suitable applications are received, no awards will be made.

FINANCIAL DATA:
Amount of support per award: Faculty of Law Scholarship: Up to $9,700. Alberta Law Scholarship: Up to $17,500 for the L.L.M. program and up to $20,000 for the Ph.D. program.
Total amount of support: Faculty of Law Graduate Scholarship: $9,700.

NUMBER OF AWARDS: Faculty of Law Scholarship: 1; Alberta Law Scholarship: 1 in the Ph.D. program and varies for the L.L.M. program.

APPLICATION INFORMATION:
Application forms available from the Director, Graduate Programme, Faculty of Law. Awards will be recommended to the University Graduate Scholarship Committee by a committee of the Faculty of Law based upon academic excellence.
Duration: One year. Nonrenewable.
Deadline: December 15.

PUBLICATIONS:
Academic calendar.

ADDRESS INQUIRIES TO:
Graduate Scholarship Office
(See address above.)

UNIVERSITY OF CALIFORNIA, LOS ANGELES [1913]
11353 Bunche Hall
Box 951487
Los Angeles, CA 90095-1486
(310) 206-6365
Fax: (310) 206-3555

E-MAIL ADDRESS:
burkle@international.ucla.edu

WEB SITE ADDRESS:
www.international.ucla.edu/burkle

FOUNDED: 1979

AREAS OF INTEREST:
International relations, law, development and globalization.

NAME(S) OF PROGRAMS:
- **Alice Belkin Memorial Scholarship**

TYPE:
Conferences/seminars; Fellowships; Internships; Research grants; Scholarships.

PURPOSE:
To support minority students in the field of international relations who are in financial need.

ELIGIBILITY:
Granted to qualified graduate applicants who, in addition to outstanding leadership skills and academic achievement, demonstrate financial need. Individuals from cultural, racial, linguistic and geographic backgrounds that are currently underrepresented in graduate education are especially encouraged to apply.

Applicants must:
(1) have a minimum grade point average of 3.0 or higher;
(2) maintain a cumulative grade point average of 3.0 or higher during the academic year of award;
(3) be a currently enrolled minority graduate student with studies related to the fields of globalization or international relations at UCLA;
(4) be a citizen or permanent resident of the U.S. and;
(5) be a graduate student pursuing a J.D., M.B.A., Ph.D., LL.M., or M.A.

FINANCIAL DATA:
Amount of support per award: Up to $4,000.

NUMBER OF APPLICANTS MOST RECENT YEAR: 35.

NUMBER OF AWARDS: Up to 4 for the 2010-11 academic year.

APPLICATION INFORMATION:
Application form is available online. Application must include:
(1) statement of interest expressing personal background, career goals and confirming eligibility;
(2) resume or curriculum vitae;
(3) official transcript from UCLA (if this is applicant's first year at UCLA, he or she must include an official transcript from a prior institution);
(4) two letters of recommendation from professors, mentors and/or employers, preferably in a sealed/signed envelope and;
(5) complete list of other sources of financial support (including TAships and GSRs) applied for, pending and received up to the present.
Duration: One year.
Deadline: February 25 at 5 P.M.

ADDRESS INQUIRIES TO:
See e-mail address above.

UNIVERSITY OF SOUTHERN CALIFORNIA [1914]
Stonier Hall, Room 315 (STO 315)
837 Downey Way
Los Angeles, CA 90089
(213) 740-8207
(213) 740-7762
Fax: (213) 740-6070

E-MAIL ADDRESS:
jeri.muniz@usc.edu

WEB SITE ADDRESS:
www.usc.edu/research/dcg

AREAS OF INTEREST:
Art history.

TYPE:
Fellowships; Grants-in-aid.

PURPOSE:
To support graduate education in art history at USC.

ELIGIBILITY:
Admission to Ph.D. program in art history.

GEOGRAPHIC RESTRICTIONS:
California.

APPLICATION INFORMATION:
Applicants must submit the Graduate School Application and the Supplemental Application form along with Graduate Record Exam (GRE) scores and letters of recommendation.
Duration: One year. Renewal possible based on academic progress.
Deadline: January.

ADDRESS INQUIRIES TO:
Contracts and Grants
(See address above.)

UNIVERSITY OF SOUTHERN CALIFORNIA [1915]
USC Graduate School
3601 Watt Way, GFS 315
Los Angeles, CA 90089-1695
(213) 740-9033
Fax: (213) 740-9048

E-MAIL ADDRESS:
gradsch@usc.edu

WEB SITE ADDRESS:
www.usc.edu/schools/GraduateSchool/

NAME(S) OF PROGRAMS:
- **Provost's Ph.D. Fellowship Program**

TYPE:
Fellowships. Merit fellowships. Fellowships will be combined with matching funds from individual schools to provide four or more years of funding toward the Ph.D.

YEAR PROGRAM STARTED: 1982

PURPOSE:
To allow outstanding students to devote full-time to research and study at USC leading to a career in university teaching and research.

LEGAL BASIS:
University.

ELIGIBILITY:
Excellent incoming Ph.D. applicants who show outstanding promise for academic careers in research and training.

FINANCIAL DATA:
Amount of support per award: $30,000 plus tuition and mandatory fees.

NUMBER OF AWARDS: Up to 100 for the 2011-12 academic year.

APPLICATION INFORMATION:
Nomination by department only.
Duration: Two years, awarded annually with at least two years subsequent departmental/school support, based upon continued superior performance.

PUBLICATIONS:
Program announcements.

ADDRESS INQUIRIES TO:
Marti Rood
Administrative Services Coordinator
(See address above.)

VERMONT STUDENT ASSISTANCE CORPORATION   [1916]

10 East Allen Street
Winooski, VT 05404-2601
(800) 642-3177 (continental U.S.)
(802) 655-9602 (Burlington area)
Fax: (802) 654-3765
TDD: (800) 281-3341

E-MAIL ADDRESS:
info@vsac.org

WEB SITE ADDRESS:
www.vsac.org

FOUNDED: 1965

AREAS OF INTEREST:
Students in need.

NAME(S) OF PROGRAMS:
- **Compliance and Quality Assurance**
- **Educational Loan Finance Program**
- **Loan Delivery Services**
- **Vermont Incentive Grants and Scholarships**
- **Vermont Outreach Programs**

TYPE:
Grants-in-aid; Scholarships; Work-study programs. Grants and loans for students enrolled in approved postsecondary institutions.

YEAR PROGRAM STARTED: 1965

PURPOSE:
To ensure that all Vermonters have the necessary financial and informational resources to pursue their educational goals beyond high school.

LEGAL BASIS:
Nonprofit, public corporation.

ELIGIBILITY:
For Incentive Grant, applicant must be a Vermont resident, enrolled full-time at an approved postsecondary institution, and must meet need test.

For Part-time Grant, applicant must be a Vermont resident, taking fewer than 12 credit hours, have not received a Bachelor's degree and must meet need test.

For Non-Degree Grant, applicant must be a Vermont resident, not matriculated, and must meet need test.

GEOGRAPHIC RESTRICTIONS:
Vermont.

FINANCIAL DATA:
Amount of support per award: Incentive Grant: $1,905 average; Part-Time Grant: $499 average; Non-Degree Grant: $1,514 average for academic year 2009-10.

NUMBER OF APPLICANTS MOST RECENT YEAR: 23,653.

NUMBER OF AWARDS: 12,717 grant recipients for academic year 2009-10.

APPLICATION INFORMATION:
Incentive grant application is required.
Duration: One academic year. Renewal possible under annual reapplication.
Deadline: Applications accepted on a rolling basis for all grants.

PUBLICATIONS:
Financial aid programs brochure (for Vermont residents).

ADDRESS INQUIRIES TO:
VSAC Research Department
(See address above.)

VERTICAL FLIGHT FOUNDATION

217 North Washington Street
Alexandria, VA 22314
(703) 684-6777
Fax: (703) 739-9279

E-MAIL ADDRESS:
staff@vtol.org

WEB SITE ADDRESS:
www.vtol.org

TYPE:
Scholarships. Annual scholarships to undergraduate senior, Master's or Ph.D. students interested in pursuing careers in some technical aspect of helicopter or vertical flight engineering.

See entry 2794 for full listing.

WASHINGTON HIGHER EDUCATION COORDINATING BOARD   [1917]

917 Lakeridge Way, S.W.
P.O. Box 43430
Olympia, WA 98504-3430
(360) 753-7847
Fax: (360) 704-6204

E-MAIL ADDRESS:
rochellew@hecb.wa.gov
health@hecb.wa.gov

WEB SITE ADDRESS:
www.hecb.wa.gov/health

AREAS OF INTEREST:
Primary care health care.

NAME(S) OF PROGRAMS:
- **Health Professional Scholarship**

TYPE:
Scholarships; Loan forgiveness programs.

YEAR PROGRAM STARTED: 1991

PURPOSE:
To encourage health professionals to work in rural or underserved urban areas of the state of Washington by providing scholarships.

LEGAL BASIS:
Government agency.

ELIGIBILITY:
Applicants must be accepted in or enrolled in designated health profession training leading to licensure as a health professional in the state of Washington.

GEOGRAPHIC RESTRICTIONS:
Washington state.

FINANCIAL DATA:
Amount of support per award: $1,500 to $12,500.
Total amount of support: $562,500 for the year 2008-09.

NUMBER OF APPLICANTS MOST RECENT YEAR: 51 for the academic year 2008-09.

NUMBER OF AWARDS: 34 for the academic year 2008-09.

APPLICATION INFORMATION:
Application form required.
Duration: Completion of training program. Maximum of five years.
Deadline: Approximately April 30.

PUBLICATIONS:
Application form; brochure.

STAFF:
Chris Wilkins, Program Coordinator
Rochelle Wambach, Program Associate

ADDRESS INQUIRIES TO:
Chris Wilkins, Program Coordinator
(See address above.)

*SPECIAL STIPULATIONS:
Must commit to employment in Washington state.

WASHINGTON HIGHER EDUCATION COORDINATING BOARD   [1918]

917 Lakeridge Way
P.O. Box 43430
Olympia, WA 98504-3430
(360) 753-7861
Fax: (360) 704-6247

E-MAIL ADDRESS:
sws@hecb.wa.gov

WEB SITE ADDRESS:
www.hecb.wa.gov

FOUNDED: 1969

AREAS OF INTEREST:
Postsecondary education planning and policy development, advisory board.

NAME(S) OF PROGRAMS:
- **Washington State Need Grant Program**
- **Washington State Work-Study Program**

TYPE:
Work-study programs. Subsidized employment opportunities.

YEAR PROGRAM STARTED: 1974

PURPOSE:
To provide financial assistance to needy students attending eligible postsecondary institutions in the state of Washington by stimulating and promoting their employment and to provide such needy students, wherever possible, with employment related to their academic pursuits.

LEGAL BASIS:
State agency.

ELIGIBILITY:
Applicants must demonstrate financial need, be enrolled or accepted for enrollment as at least half-time undergraduate, graduate or professional students and be capable, in the opinion of the institution, of maintaining good standing in a course of study while employed under the program.

GEOGRAPHIC RESTRICTIONS:
Washington state.

FINANCIAL DATA:
Amount of support per award: Varies.
Total amount of support: Approximately $21,340,000 for the 2009-10 academic year.

NUMBER OF AWARDS: 9,330 for the academic year 2009-10.

APPLICATION INFORMATION:
There is no separate application for this program. Students are awarded automatically by their school on the basis of their financial need as evidenced from their Free Application for Federal Student Aid (FAFSA) results.
Duration: Renewable.

STAFF:
Marlena Robbins, Program Manager

ADDRESS INQUIRIES TO:
Financial Aid Officer at institution of student's choice, or
Higher Education Coordinating Board
(See address above.)

WASHINGTON UNIVERSITY [1919]

Graduate School of Arts and Sciences
Campus Box 1187
One Brookings Drive
St. Louis, MO 63130
(314) 935-6818
Fax: (314) 935-4887

E-MAIL ADDRESS:
buchanan@wustl.edu

WEB SITE ADDRESS:
olinfellowship.wustl.edu

FOUNDED: 1974

NAME(S) OF PROGRAMS:
● **Mr. and Mrs. Spencer T. Olin Fellowships for Women**

TYPE:
Fellowships. The Olin Fellowships are open to candidates for any of the following graduate and professional schools at Washington University: architecture, art, arts and sciences, business, engineering, medicine, and social work.

YEAR PROGRAM STARTED: 1974

PURPOSE:
To encourage women of exceptional promise to prepare for careers in higher education and the professions; to continue and extend the historically important contributions of Monticello College to the education of women; to extend the influence of Washington University by assisting in the advanced education of outstanding young women who are likely to make significant contributions to higher education and the professions.

LEGAL BASIS:
Joint program of a private foundation (The Monticello College Foundation) and of Washington University in St. Louis.

ELIGIBILITY:
Any female graduate of a Baccalaureate institution in the U.S. who plans to prepare for a career in higher education or the professions by full-time advanced study at Washington University is eligible to apply. Applicants are considered without regard to age, handicap, religious creed, race or national origin and only with regard to the excellence of their qualifications. Applicants must meet the admission requirements of the graduate or professional school of Washington University. Preference will be given to those who wish to study for the highest earned degree in their chosen field.

FINANCIAL DATA:
The Olin Fellowships are tenable only at Washington University. They carry awards which compare favorably in each discipline with the most attractive financial aid offers available in that discipline at Washington University.

NUMBER OF APPLICANTS MOST RECENT YEAR: 415.

NUMBER OF AWARDS: 12.

APPLICATION INFORMATION:
A complete application consists of the following:
(1) an online information form;
(2) an uploaded curriculum vitae;
(3) an uploaded essay;
(4) uploaded transcript(s) and;
(5) three letters of recommendation, to be uploaded by recommenders.

Application materials must be submitted via the web site.
Duration: Given satisfactory academic achievement, awards are renewable for a period of four years or until the completion of the program of academic degree study, whichever is first.
Deadline: Applications, with all supporting documents, are due in the Office of the Graduate School of Arts and Sciences no later than January 25 preceding the academic year for which application has been made.

ADDRESS INQUIRIES TO:
Nancy P. Pope, Director
(See address above.)

WASHINGTON UNIVERSITY [1920]

Graduate School of Arts and Sciences
One Brookings Drive
Campus Box 1186
St. Louis, MO 63130-4899
(314) 935-6821
Fax: (314) 935-4887

E-MAIL ADDRESS:
snotaro@wustl.edu
agassel@wustl.edu

WEB SITE ADDRESS:
cgfp.wustl.edu

FOUNDED: 1853

AREAS OF INTEREST:
Anthropology, architecture, art history, archaeology, biology, biomedical sciences, business administration, chemistry, Chinese/Japanese and comparative literature, earth and planetary sciences, economics, education, engineering, English, fine arts, German, history, mathematics, movement science, music, philosophy, physics, political science, psychology, romance languages and social work.

NAME(S) OF PROGRAMS:
● **The Chancellor's Graduate Fellowship Program at Washington University in St. Louis**

TYPE:
Fellowships; Research grants; Scholarships; Travel grants.

YEAR PROGRAM STARTED: 1991

PURPOSE:
To facilitate training for students interested in becoming college or university professors, and who can contribute to diversity on the Washington University campus.

LEGAL BASIS:
University.

ELIGIBILITY:
Open to students who are admissible into any of Washington University's Ph.D. or D.Sc. programs in Arts and Sciences, Business, Engineering or Social Work. Also eligible are students admissible to other Washington University programs providing final disciplinary training for prospective college professors. Students must be able to contribute to the diversity on the Washington University campus.

FINANCIAL DATA:
Amount of support per award: Doctoral candidates are provided stipends and allowances of $28,000 per year for five years, plus full tuition scholarships, with a total value in excess of $120,000.

COOPERATIVE FUNDING PROGRAMS: Fellows will meet as a community on a regular basis to discuss trends and activities within their various disciplines. Scholars will lead discussions on a multitude of topics and the fellows will participate in an annual conference.

APPLICATION INFORMATION:
Duration: Five years for doctoral candidates, contingent upon satisfactory academic progress.
Deadline: January 15 for application to a degree program. January 25 for application for Chancellor's Program.

PUBLICATIONS:
Program announcement.

ADDRESS INQUIRIES TO:
Dr. Sheri R. Notaro, Associate Dean
Graduate School of Arts and Sciences
(See address above.)

WELLESLEY COLLEGE

Center for Work and Service
Green Hall 442, 106 Central Street
Wellesley, MA 02481-8203
(781) 283-2352
Fax: (781) 283-3674

E-MAIL ADDRESS:
cws-fellowships@wellesley.edu

WEB SITE ADDRESS:
www.wellesley.edu/CWS

TYPE:
Fellowships; Research grants. The Anne Louise Barrett Fellowship is given preferably in music and primarily for study or research in musical theory, composition, or in the history of music, abroad or in the U.S.

The Margaret Freeman Bowers Fellowship is given for first year of study in the fields of social work, law, or policy/public administration, including M.B.A. candidates with plans for a career in the field of social services.

The Eugene L. Cox Fellowship is for graduate study in medieval or renaissance history and culture abroad or in the U.S.

The Professor Elizabeth F. Fisher Fellowship is given for research or further study in geology or geography, including urban, environmental or ecological studies.

The Ruth Ingersoll Goldmark Fellowship is awarded for graduate study in English literature, English composition or in the classics.

The Horton-Hallowell Fellowship is awarded for graduate study in any field, preferably in the last two years of candidacy for the Ph.D. degree, or its equivalent, or for private research of equivalent standard.

The Peggy Howard Fellowship in Economics is given to provide financial aid for Wellesley students or alumnae continuing their study of economics. Administered by the economics faculty who may name one or two recipients depending on the income available.

The Edna V. Moffett Fellowship is given to a young alumna, preferably for a first year of graduate study in history.

The Alice Freeman Palmer Fellowship is awarded for study or research abroad or in the U.S.

The Kathryn Conway Preyer Fellowship is for advanced study in history.

The Vida Dutton Scudder Fellowship is given for study in the field of social science, political science or literature.

The Harriet A. Shaw Fellowship is given for study or research in music and the allied arts, in the U.S. or abroad.

Mary Elvira Stevens Traveling Fellowship is awarded for travel or study outside the U.S.

The Sarah Perry Wood Medical Fellowship is awarded for the study of medicine at an accredited medical school approved by the American Medical Association.

The Fanny Bullock Workman Fellowship is given for graduate study in any field.

See entry 1162 for full listing.

WELLESLEY COLLEGE

Center for Work and Service
Green Hall 442, 106 Central Street
Wellesley, MA 02481-8203
(781) 283-2352
Fax: (781) 283-3674

E-MAIL ADDRESS:
cws-fellowships@wellesley.edu

WEB SITE ADDRESS:
www.wellesley.edu/CWS

TYPE:
Fellowships; Scholarships. Awards are made to female applicants who plan for full-time graduate study for the coming year.

The Mary McEwen Schimke Scholarship is a supplemental award given to afford relief from household and child care expenses while pursuing graduate study.

The M.A. Cartland Shackford Medical Fellowship is given for study of medicine with a view to general practice, not psychiatry.

See entry 1163 for full listing.

WEST VIRGINIA HIGHER EDUCATION POLICY COMMISSION   [1921]

1018 Kanawha Boulevard East, Suite 700
Charleston, WV 25301
(304) 558-4016
Fax: (304) 558-5719

E-MAIL ADDRESS:
kwalthers@hepc.wvnet.edu

WEB SITE ADDRESS:
www.hepc.wvnet.edu

FOUNDED: 1969

AREAS OF INTEREST:
Education.

NAME(S) OF PROGRAMS:
- **West Virginia Higher Education Grant Program**

TYPE:
Grants-in-aid. Monetary grants awarded to undergraduate students attending approved institutions of higher education.

YEAR PROGRAM STARTED: 1968

PURPOSE:
To guarantee that the most able and needy students are given the opportunity to continue their program of self-improvement at the postsecondary level by assisting in the removal of financial barriers through monetary awards.

LEGAL BASIS:
West Virginia Higher Education Grant Program is a government program administered under the authority of West Virginia Code 18-C-5-1.

ELIGIBILITY:
An applicant must be a citizen of the U.S., have been a resident of West Virginia for at least one year immediately preceding the date of application for a grant or renewal of a grant, require financial assistance to pursue a college education, possess academic promise or be making satisfactory progress and enroll as a full-time undergraduate in an approved educational institution.

Grants are restricted to approved educational institutions located in West Virginia and Pennsylvania.

GEOGRAPHIC RESTRICTIONS:
West Virginia and Pennsylvania.

FINANCIAL DATA:
Amount of support per award: Up to $2,100.
Total amount of support: $37,379,801 total funding for student awards for academic year 2010-11 in state-appropriated funds, special fee revenues allocated by the governing Boards, and in federal LEAP/SLEAP funds.
Matching fund requirements: Participation in Federal Matching Program, Leveraging Educational Assistance Partnership (LEAP).

NUMBER OF APPLICANTS MOST RECENT YEAR:
Approximately 60,000 for academic year 2010-11.

NUMBER OF AWARDS: Approximately 23,200 for academic year 2010-11.

APPLICATION INFORMATION:
Applicants must submit the Free Application for Federal Student Aid (FAFSA).
Duration: Total of eight semesters or 12 quarters. The eight semesters do not have to be consecutive. Receipt of a grant in a given year does not guarantee its continuance in a subsequent year even though eligibility may be maintained. Students must reapply each year.

Deadline: April 15. Awards announcement in early to mid-May.

IRS IDENTIFICATION NUMBER: 55-0517092

OFFICERS:
Kevin G. Walthers, Vice Chancellor for Administration
Jack Toney, Director, State Financial Aid Programs

ADDRESS INQUIRIES TO:
Jack Toney, Director
State Financial Aid Programs
(See address above.)

THE WOODROW WILSON NATIONAL FELLOWSHIP FOUNDATION   [1922]

5 Vaughn Drive
Princeton, NJ 08540
(609) 452-7007 ext. 310

E-MAIL ADDRESS:
billmaier@woodrow.org

WEB SITE ADDRESS:
www.woodrow.org

FOUNDED: 1945

AREAS OF INTEREST:
Higher education.

NAME(S) OF PROGRAMS:
- **Charlotte W. Newcombe Doctoral Dissertation Fellowships**

TYPE:
Fellowships. Awards to support and encourage original and significant study of ethical and/or religious values in all areas of human endeavor.

YEAR PROGRAM STARTED: 1981

PURPOSE:
To encourage study of ethical or religious values.

LEGAL BASIS:
Publicly supported charity.

GEOGRAPHIC RESTRICTIONS:
United States.

FINANCIAL DATA:
Amount of support per award: $25,000 for 12 months of dissertation writing.

COOPERATIVE FUNDING PROGRAMS: Program made available by funds from the Charlotte W. Newcombe Foundation.

NUMBER OF APPLICANTS MOST RECENT YEAR:
585.

NUMBER OF AWARDS: Minimum of 20.

APPLICATION INFORMATION:
Applications must be filed electronically. Applications will be accepted starting in early September.
Deadline: Early November.

OFFICERS:
Arthur Levine, President

ADDRESS INQUIRIES TO:
See e-mail address above.

*SPECIAL STIPULATIONS:
Fellowship is for humanities and social sciences. Applicants in highly quantitative fields should not apply.

WINSHIP MEMORIAL SCHOLARSHIP FOUNDATION [1923]

c/o Comerica Bank, Trust Division
49 Michigan Avenue West
Battle Creek, MI 49017-3603
(269) 966-6340
Fax: (269) 966-6356

E-MAIL ADDRESS:
lori_a_hill@comerica.com

AREAS OF INTEREST:
College scholarships.

TYPE:
Scholarships.

PURPOSE:
To further the education of Battle Creek
public high school graduates.

LEGAL BASIS:
Private foundation.

ELIGIBILITY:
Applicants must be graduates of area public
schools.

GEOGRAPHIC RESTRICTIONS:
Battle Creek, Michigan and surrounding area.

FINANCIAL DATA:
Amount of support per award: $800 to
$2,100 per year.
Total amount of support: $130,950 for the
year 2010.

NUMBER OF APPLICANTS MOST RECENT YEAR:
87 for the year 2009.

NUMBER OF AWARDS: 19 for the year 2009.

APPLICATION INFORMATION:
Applications are available through high
school guidance departments at local high
schools.
Duration: One year. Renewable.
Deadline: March 1.

ADDRESS INQUIRIES TO:
Lori Hill, Secretary
(See address above.)

WISCONSIN HIGHER EDUCATIONAL AIDS BOARD [1924]

131 West Wilson Street
Madison, WI 53703
(608) 267-2206
Fax: (608) 267-2808

E-MAIL ADDRESS:
heabmail@wisconsin.gov

WEB SITE ADDRESS:
heab.wi.gov

FOUNDED: 1965

AREAS OF INTEREST:
Student financial aid.

NAME(S) OF PROGRAMS:
- **Academic Excellence Scholarship**
- **Handicapped Student Grant**
- **Indian Student Assistance Grant**
- **Minority Retention Grant**
- **Talent Incentive Program Grant**
- **Wisconsin Higher Education Grant**
- **Wisconsin Tuition Grant**

TYPE:
Grants-in-aid; Scholarships; Loan forgiveness
programs. Student financial aid programs in
Wisconsin.

PURPOSE:
To support students from Wisconsin willing
to pursue higher education at colleges in the
state of Wisconsin.

LEGAL BASIS:
State government agency.

ELIGIBILITY:
The Wisconsin Higher Education Grant
(WHEG) provides an undergraduate grant
program open to Wisconsin residents enrolled
at least half-time at the University of
Wisconsin, Wisconsin Technical College and
Wisconsin Tribal Colleges. Awards are based
on financial need.

Talent Incentive Program (TIP) provides
grants to most needy and educationally
disadvantaged resident students attending
colleges and universities in Wisconsin. The
student must be enrolled at least half-time.

The Wisconsin Tuition Grant provides an
undergraduate grant program open to students
enrolled in independent colleges or
universities throughout Wisconsin. Awards
are based on financial need and are partially
based on that portion of tuition in excess of
UW-Madison tuition. The student must be
enrolled at least half-time.

The Handicapped Student Grant provides
funding for Wisconsin students, enrolled at
an in-state or eligible out-of-state public or
independent institution, which show financial
need and have a severe or profound hearing
or visual impairment.

The Minority Retention Grant provides
awards to resident minority undergraduates,
excluding first-year students, enrolled at least
half-time in independent or Wisconsin
technical college institutions. A minority
student is defined as a student who is an
African American, American Indian,
Hispanic, or Southeast Asian from Laos,
Cambodia or Vietnam admitted to the U.S.
after December 31, 1975. The University of
Wisconsin has a similar program for students
attending those institutions. Students must
attend at least half-time.

The Indian Student Grant provides awards to
Wisconsin residents who are at least 25%
Native American and are undergraduate or
graduate students enrolled in degree or
certificate programs at the University of
Wisconsin, Wisconsin Technical College,
independent colleges and universities or
proprietary institutions throughout Wisconsin.
Awards are based on financial need. Students
may be part-time or full-time.

The Minnesota-Wisconsin Reciprocity
Program provides reciprocity tuition for
Wisconsin residents who enroll in an eligible
Minnesota public program on a
space-available basis. Students who qualify
pay the established reciprocity fee for course
work that is available at public institutions in
Wisconsin. Professional students enrolling in
a Doctor of Medicine, Doctor of Dental
Sciences, or a Doctor of Veterinary Medicine
program are not eligible for tuition
reciprocity under this program.

Academic Excellence Scholarships are
awarded to Wisconsin high school seniors
who have the highest grade point average in
each public and private high school
throughout the state of Wisconsin. The
number of scholarships each high school is
eligible for is based on total student
enrollment. In order to receive a scholarship,
a student must be enrolled on a full-time

basis by September 30 of the academic year
following the academic year in which he or
she was designated a scholar at a
participating University of Wisconsin,
Wisconsin Technical College or independent
institution.

GEOGRAPHIC RESTRICTIONS:
Wisconsin.

FINANCIAL DATA:
Amount of support per award: Academic
Excellence Scholarship: $2,250; Handicapped
Student Grant: $250 to $1,800; Indian
Student Assistance: $250 to $1,100; Minority
Retention Grant: $250 to $2,500; Talent
Incentive Program: $600 to $1,800;
Wisconsin Higher Education Grant: $250 to
$3,000; Wisconsin Tuition Grant: $250
minimum.
Total amount of support: Varies.

NUMBER OF APPLICANTS MOST RECENT YEAR:
Approximately 200,000 Financial Aid
applications processed each year.

APPLICATION INFORMATION:
Contact the Educational Aids Board for
application information. Include program
name.
Duration: Wisconsin Higher Education Grant
and Wisconsin Tuition Grant: Maximum of
10 semesters; Handicapped Student Grant:
Up to five years.

OFFICERS:
Scott Walker, Governor

ADDRESS INQUIRIES TO:
For Wisconsin Higher Education Grant,
Handicapped Student Grant and Indian
Student Grant:
Sandra Thomas
E-mail: sandy.thomas@heab.state.wi.us
Tel: (608) 266-0888

For Talent Incentive Program Grant:
Contact one's school's financial
aid office.

For Wisconsin Tuition Grant, Minority
Retention Grant and Minority Teacher Loan:
Mary Lou Kuzdas
E-mail: mary.kuzdas@heab.state.wi.us
Tel: (608) 267-2212

For Minnesota-Wisconsin Reciprocity
Program:
Cindy Lehrman
E-mail: cindy.lehrman@heab.state.wi.us
Tel: (608) 267-2209

For Academic Excellence Scholarship:
Nancy Wilkison
E-mail: nancy.wilkison@heab.state.wi.us
Tel: (608) 267-2213

YOUNG MUSICIANS FOUNDATION

195 South Beverly Drive
Suite 414
Beverly Hills, CA 90212
(310) 859-7668
Fax: (310) 859-1365

E-MAIL ADDRESS:
info@ymf.org

WEB SITE ADDRESS:
www.ymf.org

TYPE:
Awards/prizes; Internships; Scholarships.
Financial assistance for private study and/or
tuition at recognized musical institutions.
Significant performance opportunity may be
offered.

See entry 843 for full listing.

SCIENCES (multiple disciplines)

Sciences (multiple disciplines)

THE ACADEMY OF NATURAL SCIENCES OF PHILADELPHIA [1925]
1900 Benjamin Franklin Parkway
Philadelphia, PA 19103-1101
(215) 405-5093
Fax: (215) 299-1079

E-MAIL ADDRESS:
kepics@ansp.org

WEB SITE ADDRESS:
www.ansp.org/research

FOUNDED: 1812

AREAS OF INTEREST:
Research, exhibition and education in natural sciences.

NAME(S) OF PROGRAMS:
- **John J. and Anna H. Gallagher Fellowship**

TYPE:
Fellowships; Project/program grants; Research grants; Residencies; Training grants; Visiting scholars. The Gallagher Fellowship provides support for original postdoctoral or sabbatical research on the systematics of microscopic invertebrates, with priority for the study of rotifers.

YEAR PROGRAM STARTED: 1990

LEGAL BASIS:
Private, nonprofit natural science museum.

ELIGIBILITY:
Candidates must have a Ph.D. in zoology or in ecology, evolution and biodiversity from a major university. Applicants must provide a research proposal involving microscopic freshwater invertebrate animals, including development of expertise in one or more taxonomic groups and the names of three references who are acknowledged scholars in the field. Preference will be given to candidates specializing in Rotifera.

Work must take place primarily at the Academy of Natural Sciences of Philadelphia and/or in the field and should emphasize utilization of the Academy's collections of literature and specimens. Projects should be scaled for completion during the one-year duration of the fellowship.

FINANCIAL DATA:
Fellowship includes salary, benefits, travel expenses, field and laboratory supplies.
Total amount of support: $30,000 to $50,000.

NUMBER OF APPLICANTS MOST RECENT YEAR: 9.

NUMBER OF AWARDS: 1.

APPLICATION INFORMATION:
Research proposal should include:
(1) curriculum vitae;
(2) statement of research interests;
(3) a three- to five-page description of the project (including salary request, research project costs and a timeline) and;
(4) names and contact information of three references.
Duration: Up to 12 months.
Deadline: Varies.

ADDRESS INQUIRIES TO:
Kristen Kepics
Assistant Science Administrator
(See e-mail address above.)

ALABAMA ACADEMY OF SCIENCE, INC. [1926]
University of Alabama at Birmingham
Department of Chemistry, CHEM-201
Birmingham, AL 35294
(205) 934-8017
Fax: (205) 934-2543

E-MAIL ADDRESS:
krannich@uab.edu

WEB SITE ADDRESS:
www.alabamaacademyofscience.org

FOUNDED: 1924

AREAS OF INTEREST:
Chemistry, biology, archaeology, earth science, forestry, geography, conservation, physics, industry, economics, mathematics, computer science, anthropology, engineering, psychology, behavioral and social sciences, physical sciences, health sciences and ecology.

CONSULTING OR VOLUNTEER SERVICES:
Visiting Scientist Speaker Program for elementary schools, high schools and colleges.

NAME(S) OF PROGRAMS:
- **Gorgas Scholarship**
- **Mason Science Teaching Fellowships**
- **Student Research Grants**
- **Student Travel Awards**

TYPE:
Assistantships; Awards/prizes; Conferences/seminars; Fellowships; Project/program grants; Research grants; Scholarships; Travel grants; Visiting scholars. Grants to college and university students for small research projects and for travel to scientific meetings to present papers.

Fellowships are for teaching science for Alabama teachers.

The Gorgas Scholarships are awarded to high school senior students who were Alabama Science Scholar Search entrants for any Alabama college or university.

YEAR PROGRAM STARTED: 1924

PURPOSE:
To stimulate student science study and research; to promote the development of interested scientific matter in the state; to render public service in scientific matters.

LEGAL BASIS:
Tax-exempt membership organization.

ELIGIBILITY:
Open to individuals committed to the purpose of the Academy.

GEOGRAPHIC RESTRICTIONS:
Alabama.

FINANCIAL DATA:
Amount of support per award: Typically three or four $250 research grants; four or five $50 travel grants; one $1,000 teacher MAT fellowship and $50 to $100 per award for student research; $10,000 in scholarships to high school seniors.
Total amount of support: Up to $13,000 annually.

COOPERATIVE FUNDING PROGRAMS: Gorgas Scholarship Program is supported by the Alabama Power Foundation, Inc. All other programs are funded by membership dues, meeting registrations, exhibits, contributions and university memberships.

REPRESENTATIVE AWARDS:
$300 to Kay Tipton, Vestavia High School, Vestavia Hills, AL, for top teacher sponsor of Intel Science Talent winner.

APPLICATION INFORMATION:
Duration: One year.
Deadline: Approximately February 1. Award announcement at annual meeting in March.

PUBLICATIONS:
Journal of the Alabama Academy of Sciences.

IRS IDENTIFICATION NUMBER: 063-6050246

OFFICERS:
Dr. D. Brian Thompson, President
Dr. Brian Burnes, President-Elect
Dr. Mickie Powell, Second Vice President
Taba Hamissou, Treasurer
Dr. James Rayburn, Secretary

BOARD OF TRUSTEES:
Dr. James Bradley
Dr. Ellen B. Buckner
Dr. Brian Burns
Dr. Anne Cusic
Dr. Roland Dute
Dr. Richard Hudiburg
Dr. Adriane Ludwick
Dr. Ken Marion
Dr. David Nelson
Dr. Prakash Sharma
Dr. Stephen Watts

ADDRESS INQUIRIES TO:
Larry K. Krannich, Ph.D.
Executive Director
(See address above.)

ALBERTA INNOVATES HEALTH SOLUTIONS
Suite 1500
10104 - 103 Avenue, N.W.
Edmonton AB T5J 4A7 Canada
(780) 423-5727
Fax: (780) 429-3509

E-MAIL ADDRESS:
health@albertainnovates.ca

WEB SITE ADDRESS:
www.ahfmr.ab.ca
www.albertainnovates.ca

TYPE:
Assistantships; Awards/prizes; Block grants; Capital grants; Challenge/matching grants; Conferences/seminars; Development grants; Fellowships; General operating grants; Grants-in-aid; Internships; Matching gifts; Product donations; Professorships; Project/program grants; Research grants; Residencies; Scholarships; Seed money grants; Technical assistance; Training grants; Travel grants; Visiting scholars; Research contracts. Interdisciplinary team grants. Awards for personnel support, equipment purchase, conferences and workshops.

See entry 2359 for full listing.

ALTERNATIVES RESEARCH AND DEVELOPMENT FOUNDATION [1927]
801 Old York Road, Suite 316
Jenkintown, PA 19046
(215) 887-8076
Fax: (215) 887-0771

E-MAIL ADDRESS:
grants08@ardf-online.org

WEB SITE ADDRESS:
www.ardf-online.org

FOUNDED: 1990

AREAS OF INTEREST:
Development and validation of non-animal methods in biomedical research, safety testing and education.

NAME(S) OF PROGRAMS:
- **Alternatives Research Grant Program**
- **William and Eleanor Cave Award**

TYPE:
Awards/prizes; Research grants.

YEAR PROGRAM STARTED: 1991

PURPOSE:
To develop and promote the use of alternatives to traditional uses of animals in biomedical research, testing and education.

ELIGIBILITY:
Details available in Research Grant Application Guidelines. All applicants must utilize the document to prepare proposals. Non-sectarian religious programs may apply. Preference is given to organizations in the U.S. No grants are made to individuals.

FINANCIAL DATA:
Amount of support per award: $5,000 to $40,000.

APPLICATION INFORMATION:
Proposal with no indirect cost is preferred. Primary grant application should be no more than 15 pages, including the Alternatives Research Grant Program Application Form. Send five copies of the primary grant application and supplemental material.

Primary grant application is composed of:
(1) abstract (not to exceed 200 words) that describes the proposed research project and includes an explanation of how the work will contribute to reducing or replacing current uses of laboratory animals in biomedical research, product safety testings, or educational demonstrations;
(2) proposal that presents a clear research plan and includes sections on materials and methods, expected results, and a list of relevant references;
(3) description of how the proposed research will lead to a significant reduction or replacement of laboratory animals;
(4) detailed budget and justification for equipment and supplies;
(5) description of additional sources of funding for the project currently available or applied for. Also supply information about previous grant support in this project area during the past two years and;
(6) curriculum vitae for the principal investigator.

Supplemental material includes previous publications which directly support the current grant application and curriculum vitae (one page each) for up to three personnel involved other than the principal investigator.

Duration: One year.

Deadline: May 2.

ADDRESS INQUIRIES TO:
Sue Leary, President
(See address above.)

AMERICAN ASSOCIATION FOR THE ADVANCEMENT OF SCIENCE

1200 New York Avenue, N.W.
Washington, DC 20005
(202) 326-6441
Fax: (202) 371-9849

E-MAIL ADDRESS:
spasco@aaas.org

WEB SITE ADDRESS:
www.aaas.org/programs/education/MassMedia

TYPE:
Fellowships; Internships. Program to primarily support graduate students in the fields of social and natural sciences, mathematics, and engineering during the summer as intern reporters, researchers or production assistants in mass media organizations nationwide. Fellows will have the opportunity to observe and participate in the process by which events and ideas become news, improve their communication skills by learning to describe complex technical subjects in a manner understandable to the lay public, and increase their understanding of editorial decision making and the way in which information is effectively disseminated.

Each fellow will work for a specific media organization. Some will work for newspapers or magazines on news and feature writing assignments. Others may be involved in television or radio production.

See entry 2044 for full listing.

AMERICAN INSTITUTE OF CHEMICAL ENGINEERS (AICHE)   [1928]

3 Park Avenue, 19th Floor
New York, NY 10016-5991
(203) 702-7660
(646) 495-1331
(800) 242-4363
Fax: (212) 591-8890

E-MAIL ADDRESS:
awards@aiche.org

WEB SITE ADDRESS:
www.aiche.org

AREAS OF INTEREST:
Chemical engineering.

NAME(S) OF PROGRAMS:
- **Food, Pharmaceutical and Bioengineering Division Award in Chemical Engineering**

TYPE:
Awards/prizes.

YEAR PROGRAM STARTED: 1970

PURPOSE:
To recognize an individual's outstanding chemical engineering contribution in the food, pharmaceutical and/or bioengineering industry.

LEGAL BASIS:
Professional association.

ELIGIBILITY:
Grants given to individuals. Contribution may have been made in industry, government, or academic areas, or with other organizations.

FINANCIAL DATA:
Amount of support per award: $4,000.
Total amount of support: $4,000.

NUMBER OF AWARDS: 1 annually.

APPLICATION INFORMATION:
Deadline: February 15.

PUBLICATIONS:
Awards brochure.

ADDRESS INQUIRIES TO:
Dr. Eleftherios Terry Papoutsakis, Director
Eugene DuPont Chair of Chemical Engineering
Delaware Biotechnology Institute
University of Delaware
15 Innovation Way
Newark, DE 19711
Tel: (302) 831-8376

THE AMERICAN MUSEUM OF NATURAL HISTORY   [1929]

Richard Gilder Graduate School
Central Park West at 79th Street
New York, NY 10024-5192
(212) 769-5017
Fax: (212) 769-5257

E-MAIL ADDRESS:
fellowships-rggs@amnh.org
mrios@amnh.org

WEB SITE ADDRESS:
rggs.amnh.org/pages/academics_and_research/fellowship_and_grant_opportunities

FOUNDED: 1869

AREAS OF INTEREST:
Anthropology, paleontology and zoology.

NAME(S) OF PROGRAMS:
- **Collection Study Grants**
- **Lerner-Gray Grants for Marine Research**
- **Theodore Roosevelt Memorial Grants**

TYPE:
Grants-in-aid; Research grants. Collection Study Grants enable predoctoral and recent postdoctoral investigators to study any of the scientific collections at the American Museum in the departments of anthropology, earth and planetary sciences, entomology, herpetology, ichthyology, invertebrates, mammalogy, ornithology, and vertebrate paleontology.

The Lerner-Gray Grants for Marine Research provide support to highly qualified persons starting careers in marine zoology.

The Theodore Roosevelt Memorial Grants support research on North American fauna in wildlife conservation or natural history.

YEAR PROGRAM STARTED: 1976

PURPOSE:
To provide modest short-term awards to advanced graduate students and postdoctoral researchers who are commencing their careers in the fields of zoology, paleontology and anthropology.

ELIGIBILITY:
Applicants should be advanced graduate students and postdoctoral researchers who are beginning their careers in the interest areas listed above. Research projects need not be carried out at the American Museum.

FINANCIAL DATA:
Amount of support per award: $200 to $2,000; $1,400 average.
Total amount of support: Varies.

NUMBER OF AWARDS: Average 45 per program.

APPLICATION INFORMATION:
Duration: One year.
Deadline: Varies by grant.

ADDRESS INQUIRIES TO:
Maria Dickson, Assistant Director
Fellowships and Student Affairs
(See address above.)

THE AMERICAN MUSEUM OF NATURAL HISTORY **[1930]**

Center for Biodiversity and Conservation
Central Park West at 79th Street
New York, NY 10024-5192
(212) 313-7052
Fax: (212) 769-5292

E-MAIL ADDRESS:
alporze@amnh.org

WEB SITE ADDRESS:
cbc.amnh.org

FOUNDED: 1869

NAME(S) OF PROGRAMS:
- **The International Graduate Student Fellowship Program at the Museum's Center for Biodiversity and Conservation**

TYPE:
Fellowships; Visiting scholars. For non-U.S. citizens to study a diversified curriculum in biodiversity, conservation, systematics, and public policy. Students are able to choose among the numerous offerings of four major universities to create a graduate program from which they will bring an interdisciplinary mix of skills and experience to bear on the environmental problems of their countries. Students are part of a joint museum-university program offering the Ph.D. degree. Under the direction of a museum curator or other staff member, students will attend classes at both the museum and their chosen university. Joint programs are with the following universities: (1) Columbia University, providing students opportunities in vertebrate and invertebrate paleontology, astrophysics, earth and planetary sciences, and evolutionary biology; (2) Cornell University in entomology; (3) City University of New York in the evolutionary biology and the biological anthropology programs and; (4) Yale University in molecular biology/systematics.

YEAR PROGRAM STARTED: 1951

PURPOSE:
To affirm and expand the Museum's role in the training of future scientists as part of its total commitment as a scientific institution; to encourage bright and promising students to enter the fields of science in which the Museum participates; to foster a stronger role for the Museum in recruiting and selecting students to train there.

ELIGIBILITY:
U.S. and non-U.S. citizens are eligible to apply. Applicants must have a Bachelor's degree and be able to fulfill university admission requirements which may include TOEFL and Graduate Record Examinations. This program is not open to candidates for the Master's degree.

FINANCIAL DATA:
The fellowship will provide a stipend and health insurance.

APPLICATION INFORMATION:
Students must simultaneously apply to the museum and to one of four cooperating universities depending upon field of study. Application must be submitted to the museum on the prescribed form and include: (1) a resume or curriculum vitae including academic background, work experience, previous awards, grants or fellowships, and a list of any publications; (2) official statement of Graduate Record Examination (GRE) scores; (3) official TOEFL score for foreign students; (4) official undergraduate transcripts from all institutions attended; (5) official graduate transcripts, if beyond first semester of graduate work; (6) statement of research interests (if the applicant has completed less than one year of graduate study) or summary of thesis proposal and progress to date (if the applicant is beyond the first year of graduate study) and; (7) letters of recommendation from three persons (including applicant's major professor) who are familiar with the applicant's academic and research background.

Application to one of the cooperating universities should be made based on field of interest and submitted by the university's deadline. Students should contact the university to request application forms for the Ph.D. program in the appropriate field of study, and to ascertain the university deadline date.
Duration: One year. Renewable annually for four years providing the student remains in good standing.
Deadline: November 30.

ADDRESS INQUIRIES TO:
Office of Grants and Fellowships
(See address above.)

THE AMERICAN MUSEUM OF NATURAL HISTORY **[1931]**

Richard Gilder Graduate School
Central Park West at 79th Street
New York, NY 10024-5192
(212) 769-5017
Fax: (212) 769-5257

E-MAIL ADDRESS:
fellowships-rggs@amnh.org
mrios@amnh.org

WEB SITE ADDRESS:
rggs.amnh.org/pages/academics_and_research/
fellowship_and_grant_opportunities

FOUNDED: 1869

AREAS OF INTEREST:
Vertebrate and invertebrate zoology, paleozoology, anthropology, earth and planetary sciences.

NAME(S) OF PROGRAMS:
- **Postdoctoral Research Fellowship Program**

TYPE:
Fellowships. Provides training to postdoctoral investigators and established scientists to carry out a specific project, which must fit into the Museum's areas of interest. Postdoctoral Fellows are expected to be in residence at the Museum.

YEAR PROGRAM STARTED: 1960

PURPOSE:
To advance the training of recent postdoctoral investigators and established scientists.

LEGAL BASIS:
Nonprofit.

FINANCIAL DATA:
Limited relocation, research, and publication support is provided.

APPLICATION INFORMATION:
Applications require a project description with bibliography, budget, curriculum vitae including a list of publications, and letters of recommendation.
Duration: Up to two years.
Deadline: Postmarked by November 15.

PUBLICATIONS:
Grants and Fellowships of the American Museum of Natural History, booklet.

ADDRESS INQUIRIES TO:
Maria Dickson, Assistant Director
Fellowships and Student Affairs
(See address above.)

AMERICAN SOCIETY FOR ENGINEERING EDUCATION

1818 N Street, N.W., Suite 600
Washington, DC 20036
(202) 331-3552
Fax: (202) 463-1401

E-MAIL ADDRESS:
sffp@asee.org

WEB SITE ADDRESS:
www.asee.org/sffp

TYPE:
Fellowships. Research fellowship.

See entry 2812 for full listing.

AMERICAN TINNITUS ASSOCIATION (ATA) **[1932]**

522 S.W. 5th Avenue
Suite 825
Portland, OR 97204
(503) 248-9985 ext. 211
(800) 634-8978 ext. 218
Fax: (503) 248-0024

E-MAIL ADDRESS:
research@ata.org

WEB SITE ADDRESS:
www.ata.org

FOUNDED: 1971

AREAS OF INTEREST:
Tinnitus.

NAME(S) OF PROGRAMS:
- **ATA Student Research Grant Program**
- **ATA Tinnitus Research Grant Program**

TYPE:
Research grants. Financially supports scientific studies about tinnitus.

YEAR PROGRAM STARTED: 1980

PURPOSE:
To identify the mechanisms of tinnitus or to improve tinnitus treatments.

ELIGIBILITY:
Tinnitus Research Grant: Postdoctorate. Student Grant: Doctorate or medical student. ATA will consider the subject of research, quality of its design, potential for significant advances in basic knowledge or clinical application, available facilities and personnel at the institution and qualifications of investigators. Facility must be nonprofit.

GEOGRAPHIC RESTRICTIONS:
United States.

FINANCIAL DATA:
Amount of support per award: Tinnitus Research Grant: Up to $150,000 ($50,000 per year); Student Grant: $10,000.
Total amount of support: Up to $150,000.

APPLICATION INFORMATION:
In addition to the application form, applicants must submit a concisely written research proposal containing detailed descriptions of the following elements:
(1) introduction, statement of the problem and specific aims of the research;
(2) background and significance of the issue;
(3) relevant preliminary or pilot studies;
(4) the facility that will house the study and/or administer the funds;
(5) discussion of relevant literature and, where appropriate, standardized tinnitus measures;
(6) outline of intended study procedures including study design, sampling and measurement data to be used, and description of analysis and evaluation plan and;
(7) outcomes expected from the study and the study's use.
Duration: Tinnitus Research Grant: Three years. Student Grant: One year.
Deadline: June 30.

STAFF:
Daniel Born, Director, Research and Special Projects

ADDRESS INQUIRIES TO:
Daniel Born, Director, Research and Special Projects
(See address above.)

ARGONNE NATIONAL LABORATORY   [1933]
Division of Educational Programs
9700 South Cass Avenue
Argonne, IL 60439
(630) 252-3376
Fax: (630) 252-3193

E-MAIL ADDRESS:
dsk@anl.gov

WEB SITE ADDRESS:
www.dep.anl.gov

FOUNDED: 1968

AREAS OF INTEREST:
Basic physical and life sciences, mathematics, computer science, engineering, applied research relating to coal, conservation, environmental impact and technology, fission and fusion energy.

NAME(S) OF PROGRAMS:
● **Science Undergraduate Laboratory Internships**

TYPE:
Internships.

PURPOSE:
To encourage the further study of science.

LEGAL BASIS:
Research center of the U.S. Department of Energy.

ELIGIBILITY:
Applicants must be U.S. citizens or permanent resident aliens who are full-time students at accredited U.S. colleges or universities. In addition to their research activities, participants are expected to attend a series of seminars and tours dealing with current topics in science and engineering.

GEOGRAPHIC RESTRICTIONS:
United States.

FINANCIAL DATA:
Amount of support per award: $425 per week.
Total amount of support: $250,000.

NUMBER OF APPLICANTS MOST RECENT YEAR:
100.

APPLICATION INFORMATION:
Apply online.
Duration: 10 weeks during the summer.
Deadline: February 1.

ADDRESS INQUIRIES TO:
Dave Kupperman Ph.D.
Assistant Division Director
See address above.)

ARGONNE NATIONAL LABORATORY   [1934]
Division of Educational Programs
9700 South Cass Avenue
Argonne, IL 60439
(630) 252-3376
Fax: (630) 252-3193

E-MAIL ADDRESS:
dsk@anl.gov

WEB SITE ADDRESS:
www.dep.anl.gov

FOUNDED: 1968

AREAS OF INTEREST:
Basic physical and life sciences, mathematics, computer science and engineering, conservation, environmental science and energy technologies and fission and fusion energy.

NAME(S) OF PROGRAMS:
● **Laboratory-Graduate Program**
● **Thesis Parts Program**

TYPE:
Fellowships. Laboratory Graduate Program provides support for thesis research in residence at Argonne.

Thesis Parts Program provides support for partial dissertation research or to satisfy practicum requirements at Argonne.

YEAR PROGRAM STARTED: 1968

PURPOSE:
To encourage the advanced study of science.

LEGAL BASIS:
Research center of the U.S. Department of Energy.

ELIGIBILITY:
U.S. citizens or permanent residents are eligible. Appointments are made to graduate students who have completed all requirements for their Master's or doctoral degrees except for the dissertation. The research must require resources not available on campus.

GEOGRAPHIC RESTRICTIONS:
United States.

FINANCIAL DATA:
Amount of support per award:
Laboratory-Graduate Program provide stipend, plus up to $5,000 per year tuition. Thesis Parts Program provide per diem amount.
Total amount of support: $1,200,000.

NUMBER OF AWARDS: 30.

APPLICATION INFORMATION:
Applications must be submitted electronically.

Duration: Laboratory-Graduate Programs: Up to one year. Renewable for a total of three years. Thesis Parts Programs: Few days to few months.
Deadline: Application should be submitted two months prior to the proposed starting date.

ADDRESS INQUIRIES TO:
Dave Kupperman, Ph.D.
Assistant Division Director
See address above.)

ASSOCIATION FOR WOMEN IN SCIENCE EDUCATIONAL AWARDS
1321 Duke Street
Suite 210
Alexandria, VA 22314
(703) 894-4490
Fax: (703) 894-4489

E-MAIL ADDRESS:
awis@awis.org

WEB SITE ADDRESS:
www.awis.org

TYPE:
Awards/prizes. (Graduate and Predoctoral): To recognize and honor women and men who have demonstrated exemplary commitment to the achievement of equity for women in science, technology, engineering and mathematics (STEM).

See entry 1138 for full listing.

BAYER USA FOUNDATION [1935]
100 Bayer Road
Pittsburgh, PA 15205
(412) 777-2000
Fax: (412) 778-4430

E-MAIL ADDRESS:
karen.wirth@bayer.com

WEB SITE ADDRESS:
www.bayerus.com/foundation/foundation_home.aspx

FOUNDED: 1953

AREAS OF INTEREST:
Education and workforce development, environment and sustainability, health and human services, arts and culture.

TYPE:
Challenge/matching grants; General operating grants; Grants-in-aid; Project/program grants.

PURPOSE:
To take an active role in business communities; to enhance the quality of life for Bayer employees and neighbors.

LEGAL BASIS:
Corporate giving program.

ELIGIBILITY:
Proposed projects must impact at least one of Bayer Corporation's business locations. No grants to organizations without IRS 501(c)(3) status, United Way affiliated agencies for general operating support, charitable dinners and events, individuals, political organizations, endowment funds, deficit reduction, religious organizations, student trips or exchange programs, community advertising, athletic sponsorships or telephone solicitations.

GEOGRAPHIC RESTRICTIONS:
United States and its territories.

FINANCIAL DATA:
Amount of support per award: Varies depending on needs and nature of the request.

APPLICATION INFORMATION:
Applications may be made by letter and must include:
(1) the organization's name, contact person, title, address, phone number, and federal I.D. number;
(2) United Way information if operating funds are received;
(3) the organization's history and purpose, services it provides and geographic area served;
(4) the purpose for the grant request;
(5) organizational budget with actual revenues and expenses;
(6) copy of the most recent accountant's audit and 990;
(7) copy of IRS 501(c)(3) tax-exempt letter;
(8) a list of the organization's board of directors with names, addresses, and affiliations and;
(9) a list of significant funding sources for the past two years.

Applications should be sent to the nearest Bayer region. A list of the regions is available on the Foundation web site.
Deadline: Varies by location.

PUBLICATIONS:
Guidelines brochure.

*SPECIAL STIPULATIONS:
Applicants should not telephone the Foundation concerning their applications. All questions should be submitted in writing.

BROOKHAVEN WOMEN IN SCIENCE
P.O. Box 183
Upton, NY 11973
(631) 344-2425
Fax: (631) 344-5676

E-MAIL ADDRESS:
bwisawards@bnl.gov

WEB SITE ADDRESS:
www.bnl.gov/bwis/awards.asp

TYPE:
Awards/prizes; Scholarships. These scholarships are offered to encourage women to resume their formal education in the natural sciences, engineering or mathematics.

See entry 1140 for full listing.

CARNEGIE INSTITUTION OF WASHINGTON   [1936]
1530 P Street, N.W.
Washington, DC 20005
(202) 939-1120
Fax: (202) 939-1120

E-MAIL ADDRESS:
tmcdowell@ciw.edu

WEB SITE ADDRESS:
www.carnegiescience.edu

FOUNDED: 1902

AREAS OF INTEREST:
Astronomy, physics, chemistry, earth sciences, materials science, plant biology, developmental biology and global ecology.

NAME(S) OF PROGRAMS:
● **Predoctoral and Postdoctoral Fellowships at the Carnegie Institution**

TYPE:
Fellowships; Internships; Technical assistance; Visiting scholars; Research contracts. Predoctoral and Postdoctoral fellowships for research training in the fields of astronomy, geophysics, physics and related sciences, plant biology, genetics and developmental biology in residence at one of the Carnegie Institution's six operating centers.

YEAR PROGRAM STARTED: 1938

PURPOSE:
To encourage in the broadest and most liberal manner investigation, research and discovery and the application of knowledge to the improvement of mankind.

LEGAL BASIS:
Exempt under Section 501(c)(3) of the Internal Revenue Code.

ELIGIBILITY:
Qualified scientists who have obtained the doctoral degree or are in the process are eligible. Candidates are evaluated on the basis of academic record, recommendations of professors and associates and the complementing nature of their research to work in progress at the Carnegie department. Women and minorities are encouraged to apply.

FINANCIAL DATA:
Fellowships provide direct financial support and the use of the Institution's laboratory and observational facilities, including special equipment when needed. Travel funds may be included where long-distance travel is required to reach the Institution.
Amount of support per award: Varies by department.

NUMBER OF AWARDS: Approximately 150 for the year 2008.

APPLICATION INFORMATION:
Fellowship applications should be made to the Directors of the Departments of Carnegie Institution at the addresses listed below.
Duration: Fellowships are usually awarded for one year with the possibility of renewal for another year.
Deadline: Varies.

PUBLICATIONS:
Newsletter.

OFFICERS:
Richard A. Meserve, President
Gary Kowalczyk, Director of Administration and Finance

DIRECTORS:
Allan Spradling, Director, Department of Embryology
Christopher Field, Director, Department of Global Ecology
Wolf Frommer, Director, Department of Plant Biology
Sean C. Solomon, Director, Department of Terrestrial Magnetism
Russell Hemly, Director, Geophysical Laboratory
Wendy Freedman, Director, Observatories of Carnegie

ADDRESS INQUIRIES TO:
Call first to determine to whom inquiry should be directed.

Allan Spradling
Director, Department of Embryology
115 West University Parkway
Baltimore, MD 21210 or

Christopher Field
Director, Department of Global Ecology
260 Panama Street
Stanford, CA 94305
Tel: (650) 462-1047 or

Wolf Frommer
Director, Department of Plant Biology
290 Panama Street
Stanford, CA 94305 or

Sean C. Solomon
Director, Department of Terrestrial Magnetism
5241 Broad Branch Road, N.W.
Washington, DC 20015 or

Russel Hemley
Director, Geophysical Laboratory
5251 Broad Branch Road
Washington, DC 20015 or

Wendy Freedman
Director, Observatories of Carnegie
813 Santa Barbara Street
Pasadena, California 91101

*SPECIAL STIPULATIONS:
Fellowships are tenable only at one of the Institution's facilities. No extracurricular grants.

EARTHWATCH INSTITUTE   [1937]
114 Western Avenue
Boston, MA 02134
(978) 461-0081
(800) 776-0188
Fax: (978) 461-2332

E-MAIL ADDRESS:
research@earthwatch.org

WEB SITE ADDRESS:
www.earthwatch.org/research

FOUNDED: 1971

AREAS OF INTEREST:
Any significant postdoctoral field research in the sciences, social sciences and humanities that can utilize teams of qualified assistant field volunteers, including animal behavior, archaeology, art and architecture, biodiversity and ecology, birds, coral reefs, culture and tradition, dinosaurs and other fossils, earth dynamics, endangered species, global change, health and nutrition, rain forests, resource management, sustainable development, whales, dolphins and other marine mammals, wildlife management, and climate change.

CONSULTING OR VOLUNTEER SERVICES:
The Research Program receives and reviews applications and recommends awards from EARTHWATCH Institute of funds and volunteer assistance for research expeditions. All funds distributed are derived from donations of qualified participants on the actual research teams, who are recruited by the Program's affiliate organization, EARTHWATCH Institute.

NAME(S) OF PROGRAMS:
● **Earthwatch Education Awards**
● **Earthwatch Funding for Field Research**

TYPE:
Research grants. Both personnel and financial support to field research projects. Volunteers pay to support the project and also work as research assistants to the scholars, usually for two to three-week periods. Teams range in size from four to 20, with the average expedition using three to five teams. Since numbers of dollars vary directly with

numbers of volunteers, applicants are urged to pay close attention to that relationship in their research design.

YEAR PROGRAM STARTED: 1971

PURPOSE:
To fund field research and additionally to promote public appreciation of the world's natural and cultural resources and of their interdependence, through participant-funding of significant research in the sciences and humanities.

LEGAL BASIS:
Incorporated as a nonprofit, tax-exempt organization, 501(c)(3) of the IRS code.

ELIGIBILITY:
Applicants must hold Ph.D. or have had significant research experience as evidenced through publications or other accomplishments.

Proposals may be submitted by researchers of any nationality, covering work in any geographic region. Participation of host-country researchers or staff is strongly encouraged.

Grants vary according to project needs and are determined according to the total number of volunteer-participants that can be constructively utilized in the project.

FINANCIAL DATA:
Amount of support per award: $17,000 to $51,000. Average $850 per volunteer.
Total amount of support: $57,000,000 since 1971.

NUMBER OF APPLICANTS MOST RECENT YEAR: 400.

REPRESENTATIVE AWARDS:
Residence Patterns and Habitat Use of Florida Manatees; Geophysical Structure, Petrology and Geochemistry of the Tonganro Volcano, New Zealand; Excavation of an Etruscan and Roman Farm in Tuscany, Italy.

APPLICATION INFORMATION:
Contact Earthwatch for application details.
Duration: Consider proposals for three or more years.
Deadline: Preliminary proposals are accepted year-round, and should be submitted 18 months in advance of fielding.

PUBLICATIONS:
Earthwatch, magazine; *Project Briefings;* proposal guidelines; grants list.

OFFICERS:
Dr. Marie Studer, Chief Science Officer

ADDRESS INQUIRIES TO:
Research Department
(See address above.)

THE ELECTROCHEMICAL SOCIETY   [1938]
65 South Main Street, Building D
Pennington, NJ 08534-2896
(609) 737-1902
(609) 737-1902 ext. 111
Fax: (609) 737-2743

E-MAIL ADDRESS:
ecs@electrochem.org
colleen.klepser@electrochem.org

WEB SITE ADDRESS:
www.electrochem.org

FOUNDED: 1902

AREAS OF INTEREST:
Advancement of the theory and practice of electrochemistry, electrometallurgy, solid-state science, electrothermics and allied subjects.

NAME(S) OF PROGRAMS:
● **ECS Summer Fellowships**

TYPE:
Awards/prizes; Conferences/seminars; Development grants; Fellowships; Grants-in-aid; Project/program grants; Research grants; Training grants; Travel grants. Five summer fellowships granted annually for study in a college or university.

YEAR PROGRAM STARTED: 1928

PURPOSE:
To stimulate and encourage participation and education in the fields of electrochemical science and technology as well as other interests to the Society.

LEGAL BASIS:
Scientific, educational, nonprofit, tax-exempt organization.

ELIGIBILITY:
For Fellowships, the applicant must be a graduate student (between B.S. and Ph.D.) in a college or university who will continue studies following the summer months the award is given.

No limitations on sex, race, nationality or religion.

FINANCIAL DATA:
Amount of support per award: Varies upon approval from the Board of Directors; usually $5,000 each.
Total amount of support: Varies.

NUMBER OF APPLICANTS MOST RECENT YEAR: 50.

NUMBER OF AWARDS: Up to 5 Summer Fellowships annually.

APPLICATION INFORMATION:
Submit a brief statement of educational objectives, work accomplished on thesis, work planned, transcript of undergraduate and graduate work, two letters of recommendation and a letter of agreement not to hold other appointments or fellowships simultaneously.
Deadline: Fellowships: January 1. Notification for Fellowships will be made on or before June 1.

PUBLICATIONS:
Interface Magazine.

STAFF:
Colleen B. Klepser, Executive Administrator

ADDRESS INQUIRIES TO:
The Electrochemical Society
Awards/ECS
(See address above.)

THE ELECTROCHEMICAL SOCIETY   [1939]
65 South Main Street, Building D
Pennington, NJ 08534-2896
(609) 737-1902
(609) 737-1902 ext. 111
Fax: (609) 737-2743

E-MAIL ADDRESS:
ecs@electrochem.org
colleen.klepser@electrochem.org

WEB SITE ADDRESS:
www.electrochem.org

FOUNDED: 1902

AREAS OF INTEREST:
Advancement of the theory and practice of electrochemistry, electrometallurgy, solid-state science, electrothermics and allied subjects.

NAME(S) OF PROGRAMS:
● **Edward Goodrich Acheson Award**
● **Vittorio de Nora Award**
● **Gordon E. Moore Medal for Outstanding Achievement in Solid State Science and Technology**
● **Olin Palladium Award**

TYPE:
Awards/prizes. Edward Goodrich Acheson Award is for distinguished contributions to the advancement of any of the objects, purposes or activities of The Electrochemical Society.

Vittorio de Nora Award is for contributions to the field of electrochemical engineering and technology.

Olin Palladium Award is for distinguished contributions to the field of electrochemical or corrosion science.

Gordon E. Moore Medal for Outstanding Achievement in Solid State Science and Technology is for distinguished contributions to the field of solid state science.

FINANCIAL DATA:
Amount of support per award: Edward Goodrich Acheson Award: Gold medal, wall plaque, and prize of $10,000. Vittorio de Nora Award: Gold medal, wall plaque and prize of $7,500. Olin Palladium Award: Palladium medal, wall plaque and prize of $7,500. Gordon E. Moore Medal for Outstanding Achievement in Solid State Science and Technology: Silver medal, wall plaque and prize of $7,500.

ADDRESS INQUIRIES TO:
E-mail: awards@electrochem.org

THE EPPLEY FOUNDATION FOR RESEARCH, INC.   [1940]
260 Madison Avenue, 17th Floor
New York, NY 10016
Fax: (212) 448-6260

FOUNDED: 1947

AREAS OF INTEREST:
Support of postdoctoral research in advanced scientific subjects.

TYPE:
Research grants. Grants in support of postdoctoral research projects funded through recognized educational or charitable organizations.

YEAR PROGRAM STARTED: 1972

PURPOSE:
To support significant research projects in the physical and biological sciences, usually where funding elsewhere was not readily available; to provide seed money toward larger undertakings.

LEGAL BASIS:
Privately supported charitable organization exempt under 501(c)(3).

ELIGIBILITY:
Postdoctoral project in the physical and biological sciences sponsored by a recognized educational or research institution. Funds are not issued directly to individuals. Grant proposals from foreign countries are considered only when such applicants are

associated with a U.S. institution which will administer the grant on their behalf. Grants are not awarded to foreign applicants directly.

Under most circumstances, the Foundation will not support DNA research, heart, HIV or cancer research, or other areas where there is considerable existent funding from conventional sources.

The Foundation prefers to fund individuals rather than ongoing programs or equipment purchases. The Board often considers the most effective use of its funds to be research-initiation grants, with the understanding that sufficient work can be accomplished to enable the researcher to apply for greater sums from federal or other sources.

It is important to the Foundation that work proposed for support be original in its insights. Research being pursued in numerous laboratories across the country often does not meet the Board's standards for originality.

All grants have been made to institutions qualifying as Internal Revenue Code Section 501(c)(3) organizations to support the work of individuals engaged in postgraduate research.

GEOGRAPHIC RESTRICTIONS:
United States.

FINANCIAL DATA:
Amount of support per award: Up to $25,000.
Total amount of support: $136,370 in 2010.

NUMBER OF APPLICANTS MOST RECENT YEAR:
7.

NUMBER OF AWARDS: 4.

REPRESENTATIVE AWARDS:
$35,000 to Dr. Karen Maass, NYU Langone Medical Center, "Potential Therapeutic Use of Stem Cells in Heart Failure;" $40,000 to Dr. P. Timon McPhearson, The New School, "Assessing Soil Heterogeneity and its Effect on Afforestation in New York City's Urban Forests;" $25,720 to Dr. Amy Litt, The New York Botanical Garden, "Identifying the Genetic Basis of an Evolutionary Change in Flowering Time;" $35,650 to Dr. Daniel Pouakouyou, Fauna & Flora International, "Biomonitoring Research to Strengthen Environmental Governance and Sustainable Protection of Critically Endangered Cross River Gorillas in Western Cameroon."

APPLICATION INFORMATION:
Candidates must fill out an application form which may be obtained by writing to the Foundation office at the address above. Proposals must be concise and state clearly the methods and goals of the research and, where feasible, be understandable to the layman.
Duration: Commitments are usually made on an annual basis, although support for two-year projects has been made.
Deadline: February 1, May 1, August 1, and November 1. Announcement within three months.

PUBLICATIONS:
Application guidelines.

IRS IDENTIFICATION NUMBER: 05-0258857

*PLEASE NOTE:
Telephone calls are discouraged.

*SPECIAL STIPULATIONS:
A full report is required from a grant recipient after one year. An interim report,

which may be in the form of a letter, should be submitted by December 1 of the year during which the work is in progress.

FATS AND PROTEINS RESEARCH FOUNDATION, INC.   [1941]
801 North Fairfax Street, Suite 205
Alexandria, VA 22314
(703) 683-2914
Fax: (703) 683-2626

E-MAIL ADDRESS:
snates@nationalrenderers.com

WEB SITE ADDRESS:
www.fprf.org

FOUNDED: 1962

AREAS OF INTEREST:
Chemistry, agriculture, animal nutrition, biology, animal fats, animal and protein ingredients, biosecurity-related alternative uses and new use opportunities for animal coproducts.

TYPE:
Demonstration grants; Grants-in-aid; Product donations; Project/program grants; Research grants; Seed money grants; Technical assistance; Research contracts. Research projects pertaining to new and expanded uses for inedible and edible animal and poultry fats and proteins and the processing of animal by-products.

YEAR PROGRAM STARTED: 1962

PURPOSE:
To promote scientific and technological research into new and expanded uses for fats and proteins from animal by-products and processing technology; to encourage cooperative studies.

LEGAL BASIS:
Nonprofit foundation, 501(c)(6).

ELIGIBILITY:
Colleges, universities and research institutes with appropriate interests and capabilities are eligible to apply.

FINANCIAL DATA:
Amount of support per award: $10,000 to $250,000.
Total amount of support: $180,000 for the year 2008.

COOPERATIVE FUNDING PROGRAMS:
Encouraged.

NUMBER OF APPLICANTS MOST RECENT YEAR:
30.

NUMBER OF AWARDS: 4 for the year 2008.

APPLICATION INFORMATION:
Request proposal format from the above address or visit the web site. Prospective applicants should submit a brief outline of the proposed project (including background information, objectives, scope and mode of approach) along with a statement of the required budget and a brief biographical sketch of personnel to be involved in the research.
Duration: Varies.
Deadline: March 15 and September 15 for review of applications.

PUBLICATIONS:
Annual report; contributions policy; application guidelines.

IRS IDENTIFICATION NUMBER: 89-490286

DIRECTORS:
Carl Wintzer, Chairman
David Kirstein, Vice Chairman
Dr. Sergio F. Nates, President
Erika Weltzien, Secretary/Treasurer

ADDRESS INQUIRIES TO:
Dr. Sergio F. Nates, President
(See address above.)

FLORIDA EDUCATION FUND
201 East Kennedy Boulevard
Suite 1525
Tampa, FL 33602
(813) 272-2772 ext. 203
Fax: (813) 272-2784

E-MAIL ADDRESS:
fef.jackson@verizon.net

WEB SITE ADDRESS:
www.fefonline.org

TYPE:
Fellowships.

See entry 1646 for full listing.

THE FOUNDATION FOR AIDS RESEARCH (AMFAR)   [1942]
120 Wall Street, 13th Floor
New York, NY 10005-3908
(212) 806-1600
Fax: (212) 806-1601

E-MAIL ADDRESS:
grants@amfar.org

WEB SITE ADDRESS:
www.amfar.org

FOUNDED: 1985

AREAS OF INTEREST:
Research relevant to HIV/AIDS and projects that extend the benefits of HIV/AIDS research to vulnerable populations.

NAME(S) OF PROGRAMS:
- **Mathilde Krim Fellowships in Basic Biomedical Research**
- **MSM Initiative**
- **Research**
- **Treat Asia**

TYPE:
Awards/prizes; Fellowships; Project/program grants; Research grants. Fellowships are grants designed to attract investigators new to HIV/AIDS and provide salary and limited supplies support to those involved in postdoctoral work for mentored research projects relevant to topic areas delineated in requests for proposals (RFPs).

Mathilde Krim Fellowships in Basic Biomedical Research are grants designed to support outstanding postdoctoral scientists in the transition to an independent research career in a tenure-track faculty-level position.

MSM Initiative Awards provide project support to community-based, grassroots organizations worldwide working to address HIV/AIDS among men who have sex with men (MSM) by increasing access to HIV/AIDS prevention, treatment and care, through outreach, direct services, policy, advocacy and human rights-based projects, or community-based research.

Research Grants provide one year of support for research projects relevant to topic area(s) delineated in current RFPs.

YEAR PROGRAM STARTED: 1985

PURPOSE:
To end the global AIDS epidemic through innovative research; to fund research to explore scientific approaches for preventing and treating HIV infection and enhancing the health and survival of people with HIV/AIDS; to support global initiatives to facilitate the development and implementation of effective research, treatment, prevention and education strategies in developing countries; to support public policy analysis and the advocacy of rational and compassionate policies that promote public health and protect the rights of people threatened by HIV/AIDS; to support public information programs to build awareness of the continued threat HIV/AIDS poses and to provide up-to-date medical, scientific and prevention information to people with HIV/AIDS, health care professionals and the public.

LEGAL BASIS:
Not-for-profit public benefit corporation.

ELIGIBILITY:
Varies by program.

FINANCIAL DATA:
Since 1985, amfAR has invested more than $307,000,000 in its mission and has awarded grants to more than 2,000 research teams worldwide.
Amount of support per award: Fellowships: $113,635 direct costs for two years; Research Grants: $100,000 direct costs for one year, up to $300,000 direct costs for one year for collaborative projects; MSM Initiative Community Awards: Up to $20,000.

APPLICATION INFORMATION:
The Foundation does not accept unsolicited grant applications or requests. Requests for Proposals details and downloadable forms are available at the web site.
Duration: Fellowships: Two years. MSM Community Awards and Research Grants: One year.
Deadline: Varies.

STAFF:
Rowena Johnston, Ph.D., Vice President, Research
Kent Cozad, Director, Grants Administration and Compliance
Kent Klindera, Director, MSM Initiative
Marije Klep, Grants Administrator
Jordan Kramer, Grants Administrator
Russell Ramm, Grants Administrator

ADDRESS INQUIRIES TO:
Grants Administration
(See address above.)

FOUNDATION FOR SCIENCE AND DISABILITY

503 N.W. 89th Street
Gainesville, FL 32607
(352) 374-5774
Fax: (352) 374-5781

E-MAIL ADDRESS:
rmankin@nersp.nerdc.ufl.edu

WEB SITE ADDRESS:
stemd.org

TYPE:
Grants-in-aid; Research grants.

See entry 1047 for full listing.

HARVARD TRAVELLERS CLUB, PERMANENT FUND   [1943]

P.O. Box 162
Lincoln, MA 01773
(781) 259-8665

E-MAIL ADDRESS:
jessepage@comcast.net

WEB SITE ADDRESS:
www.harvardtravellersclub.org

FOUNDED: 1937

AREAS OF INTEREST:
Various scientific fields.

TYPE:
Research grants. Small grants for research projects.

PURPOSE:
To foster research and/or exploration which involves travel.

LEGAL BASIS:
501(c)(3) nonprofit organization.

ELIGIBILITY:
Applicants must have ability to make a competent contribution in the field of research. The Fund does not pay travel expenses unless it is intimately involved with the research and/or exploration. Preference is given to applicants working on advanced degrees.

FINANCIAL DATA:
Amount of support per award: Up to $3,000.
Total amount of support: Varies.

APPLICATION INFORMATION:
Applicants should submit an explanation of goals, an indication of ability, and a resume.
Duration: Usually one-time grant.
Deadline: End of February.

IRS IDENTIFICATION NUMBER: 04-6115589

TRUSTEES:
George P. Bates
Lansing Fair
Jesse R. Page

ADDRESS INQUIRIES TO:
Jesse R. Page, Trustee
(See address above.)

***SPECIAL STIPULATIONS:**
No scholarships for study at educational institutions.

THE HERB SOCIETY OF AMERICA, INC.

9019 Kirtland Chardon Road
Kirtland, OH 44094
(440) 256-0514
Fax: (440) 256-0541

E-MAIL ADDRESS:
herbs@herbsociety.org

WEB SITE ADDRESS:
www.herbsociety.org

TYPE:
Research grants. Cash award for research on herbal projects.

See entry 2254 for full listing.

HILGENFELD FOUNDATION FOR MORTUARY EDUCATION   [1944]

120 East Broadway
Anaheim, CA 92805
(714) 535-4105
Fax: (714) 635-6842

E-MAIL ADDRESS:
becky@hilgenfeldmortuary.com

WEB SITE ADDRESS:
www.hilgenfeldmortuary.com

FOUNDED: 1978

AREAS OF INTEREST:
Funeral service and thanatology.

NAME(S) OF PROGRAMS:
● **Funeral Service and/or Thanatology Grants for Research/Scholarships**

TYPE:
Challenge/matching grants; Conferences/seminars; Demonstration grants; Development grants; Project/program grants; Research grants; Technical assistance; Training grants. Entry-level scholarships; Graduate scholarship awards; Research studies. The Foundation has a broad interest in research which shows a promise of improving the practice of funeral service.

YEAR PROGRAM STARTED: 1978

PURPOSE:
To enrich the instruction of funeral service education at accredited colleges; to encourage an interchange of instructors between accredited colleges, as well as to bring to accredited colleges in southern California qualified guest lecturers for a series of lectures; to assist in the distribution of books, pamphlets and documents to libraries so that the general public will have available objective resource material to promote mental health; to identify and contribute to the solution of problems in funeral service, which will benefit the public at large by assisting graduate students in such research activity; to encourage qualified funeral service investigators, as well as scholars in the health care, psychological and business fields, to write full-length monographs reflecting their knowledge and thought.

LEGAL BASIS:
501(c)(3).

GEOGRAPHIC RESTRICTIONS:
California.

FINANCIAL DATA:
Amount of support per award: Varies.
Matching fund requirements: Varies.

COOPERATIVE FUNDING PROGRAMS: American Board for Funeral Service.

NUMBER OF APPLICANTS MOST RECENT YEAR: Approximately 100.

NUMBER OF AWARDS: Approximately 2.

APPLICATION INFORMATION:
Application forms are available on request.
Duration: Usually one year, although there may be exceptions.
Deadline: Applications may be submitted at any time.

OFFICERS:
Margie Field, President
Becky Field-Areias, Secretary-Treasurer

ADDRESS INQUIRIES TO:
Becky Field-Areias, Secretary-Treasurer
(See address above.)

HISTORY OF SCIENCE SOCIETY

440 Geddes Hall
University of Notre Dame
Notre Dame, IN 46556
(574) 631-1194
Fax: (574) 631-1533

E-MAIL ADDRESS:
info@hssonline.org

WEB SITE ADDRESS:
www.hssonline.org

TYPE:
Awards/prizes. The Davis Prize honors books in the history of science directed to a wide public and was established through a long-term pledge from Miles and Audrey Davis.

The Joseph H. Hazen Education Prize recognizes excellence in teaching in the history of science.

The Levinson Prize is awarded in even-numbered years to an outstanding book in the life sciences and natural history.

The Pfizer Prize honors the best English-language work related to the history of science published in the preceding three years.

The Nathan Reingold Prize is given for an original essay in the history of science and its cultural influences. Essay must be no more than 8,000 words in length and thoroughly documented.

The Margaret W. Rossiter History of Women in Science Prize honors an outstanding book, or in even-numbered years an article, published in the preceding four years.

The Sarton Medal is given to an outstanding historian of science selected from the international scholarly community.

See entry 636 for full listing.

HISTORY OF SCIENCE SOCIETY
440 Geddes Hall
University of Notre Dame
Notre Dame, IN 46556
(574) 631-1194
Fax: (574) 631-1533

E-MAIL ADDRESS:
info@hssonline.org

WEB SITE ADDRESS:
www.hssonline.org

TYPE:
Awards/prizes. Prize for the best scholarly article published in *Isis* during the past three years.

See entry 635 for full listing.

ILLINOIS STATE ACADEMY OF SCIENCE   [1945]
c/o Illinois State Museum
502 South Spring Street
Springfield, IL 62706-5000
(217) 782-6436
Fax: (217) 782-1254

E-MAIL ADDRESS:
rmyers@museum.state.il.us

WEB SITE ADDRESS:
www.il-acad-sci.org

FOUNDED: 1907

AREAS OF INTEREST:
Promotion of science in the state of Illinois.

NAME(S) OF PROGRAMS:
● **Scientific Research Grants/Proposal Writing Contest**

TYPE:
Awards/prizes; Grants-in-aid; Project/program grants; Research grants; Seed money grants. Cash grants and certificates to Illinois college or junior college students for writing a scientific proposal and conducting the proposed research.

YEAR PROGRAM STARTED: 1981

PURPOSE:
To promote science in the state of Illinois.

LEGAL BASIS:
Nonprofit organization.

ELIGIBILITY:
All public or private college or junior college students in the state of Illinois who are sponsored by a signing instructor are eligible. ISAS membership is required. Proposals do not have to be original. They can be a spin-off of a lab experiment from class or something the student is interested in as a hobby.

GEOGRAPHIC RESTRICTIONS:
Illinois.

FINANCIAL DATA:
Amount of support per award: Maximum $200 to undergraduate and $400 to graduate for research supplies.
Total amount of support: Varies.

NUMBER OF AWARDS: Varies.

APPLICATION INFORMATION:
Students must submit application electronically through the Academy's web site.
Duration: One-time award. Renewable.
Deadline: November 1.

PUBLICATIONS:
Transactions of the Illinois State Academy of Science.

IRS IDENTIFICATION NUMBER: 37-6043007

ADDRESS INQUIRIES TO:
Robyn Myers, Executive Secretary
(See address above.)

INSTITUTE OF FOOD TECHNOLOGISTS FOUNDATION
Scholarship Department
525 West Van Buren Street, Suite 1000
Chicago, IL 60607
(312) 604-0284
Fax: (312) 416-7919

E-MAIL ADDRESS:
akproctor@ift.org

WEB SITE ADDRESS:
www.ift.org

TYPE:
Scholarships. Graduate Scholarships support advanced study in the field of food science and technology. Junior/Senior Scholarships and Freshman/Sophomore Scholarships encourage undergraduate enrollment in food science and technology.

See entry 2773 for full listing.

INTERNATIONAL FOUNDATION FOR ETHICAL RESEARCH, INC.   [1946]
53 West Jackson Boulevard, Suite 1552
Chicago, IL 60604
(312) 427-6025
Fax: (312) 427-6524

E-MAIL ADDRESS:
podonovan@navs.org
ifer@navs.org

WEB SITE ADDRESS:
www.ifer.org

FOUNDED: 1985

AREAS OF INTEREST:
Scientifically valid alternatives to the use of animals in research, product testing, and education.

TYPE:
Fellowships. Graduate Fellowships in Animal Welfare support research in, but not limited to, tissue, cell and organ cultures, clinical studies using animals or humans, epidemiological studies, enhanced use of extensive tissue repositories and patient databases, public education, and computer modeling.

YEAR PROGRAM STARTED: 1997

PURPOSE:
To provide monetary assistance to graduate students whose programs of study seem likely to have impact on animal welfare.

LEGAL BASIS:
Nonprofit.

ELIGIBILITY:
Application is open to students enrolled in Master's and Ph.D. programs in the sciences, humanities, psychology, and journalism.

GEOGRAPHIC RESTRICTIONS:
United States.

FINANCIAL DATA:
Amount of support per award: Up to $12,500 stipend, plus up to $2,500 for supplies per year.

APPLICATION INFORMATION:
Information and preproposal guidelines are available from the Foundation.
Duration: The fellowships are renewable for up to three years.
Deadline: March 15. Awards announced October.

PUBLICATIONS:
Newsletter.

IRS IDENTIFICATION NUMBER: 22-2628153

STAFF:
Peter O'Donovan, Executive Director

ADDRESS INQUIRIES TO:
Peter O'Donovan, Executive Director
(See address above.)

INVENT NOW   [1947]
3701 Highland Park, N.W.
North Canton, OH 44720-4535
(330) 849-6887
(800) 968-4332 (option 5)
Fax: (330) 762-6313

E-MAIL ADDRESS:
collegiate@invent.org

WEB SITE ADDRESS:
www.invent.org/collegiate

AREAS OF INTEREST:
Creative invention: science, engineering, mathematics, technology and related fields.

NAME(S) OF PROGRAMS:
● **Collegiate Inventors Competition**

TYPE:
Awards/prizes. National competition in the U.S. and Canada that recognizes and rewards innovations, discoveries, and research by college and university students and their faculty advisors.

YEAR PROGRAM STARTED: 1990

PURPOSE:
To promote exploration in invention, science, engineering, technology, and other creative endeavors and provide a window on the future technologies from which society will benefit in the future.

ELIGIBILITY:
Open to students who are enrolled (or have been enrolled) full-time in any U.S. or Canadian college or university at least part of the 12-month period prior to the date the entry is submitted. In the case of a team (maximum of four students), at least one member must meet the full-time eligibility criteria.

Entry must be the original idea and work product of the student/advisor team, and must not have been:
(1) made available to the public as a commercial product or process or;
(2) patented or published more than one year prior to the date of competition submission.

Entries must be written in English.

GEOGRAPHIC RESTRICTIONS:
United States and Canada.

FINANCIAL DATA:
Up to 12 finalists will win an all-expense paid trip in Fall 2011 to present their work to a panel of expert judges. Academic advisors of each of the top winning teams will also receive a cash award.
Total amount of support: Up to $75,000.

APPLICATION INFORMATION:
All entries must be submitted on the official application form.
Deadline: Postmarked by June 24.

ADDRESS INQUIRIES TO:
Collegiate Inventors Competition
(See address above.)

THE LALOR FOUNDATION, INC.   [1948]
c/o GMA Foundations
77 Summer Street, Eighth Floor
Boston, MA 02110-1006
(617) 426-7080 ext. 323
Fax: (617) 426-7087

E-MAIL ADDRESS:
fellowshipmanager@gmafoundations.com

WEB SITE ADDRESS:
www.lalorfound.org

FOUNDED: 1935

AREAS OF INTEREST:
Basic postdoctoral research in reproductive physiology and biochemistry bearing on sterilization and/or prevention or termination of pregnancy.

NAME(S) OF PROGRAMS:
● **The Lalor Foundation Postdoctoral Fellowship Program**

TYPE:
Fellowships; Project/program grants; Research grants. Grants to institutions for basic postdoctoral research in reproductive biology as related to the regulation of fertility.

YEAR PROGRAM STARTED: 1937

PURPOSE:
To promote intensive research in selected areas and to assist and encourage young

Ph.D. investigators in academic positions to follow research careers in reproductive physiology.

LEGAL BASIS:
Tax-exempt philanthropic foundation.

ELIGIBILITY:
Domestic institutions must be exempt from federal income taxes under Section 501(c)(3) of the Internal Revenue Code. Domestic and foreign institutions must qualify under Section 509(a)(1), (2) or (3). Individuals who are nominated by the applicant institution may be citizens of any country and should have training and experience at least equal to the Ph.D. or M.D. level. Potential fellows should not have held the doctoral degree more than two years.

The applicant institution may make its nomination of a Fellow from among its own personnel or elsewhere, but, qualifications being equal, candidates from other than the proposing institution itself may carry modest preference. The application must name the institution's nominee for fellowship and include his or her performance record.

GEOGRAPHIC RESTRICTIONS:
United States.

FINANCIAL DATA:
Grants for coverage of fellowship stipend and institutional expenses.
Amount of support per award: $35,000.
Total amount of support: $280,000 for fiscal year 2010.

NUMBER OF APPLICANTS MOST RECENT YEAR:
40.

NUMBER OF AWARDS: 8 for fiscal year 2010.

APPLICATION INFORMATION:
One reference letter and two project reviews are requested and IRS determination letter is required.
Duration: One year. Renewable under some circumstances.
Deadline: January 15. Notification by April 15.

PUBLICATIONS:
Annual announcement of program.

IRS IDENTIFICATION NUMBER: 51-6000153

OFFICERS:
Cynthia B. Patterson, President
Sally H. Zeckhauser, Vice President
Lalor Burdick, Secretary and Treasurer

BOARD OF TRUSTEES:
Andrew G. Braun, Sc.D.
Christopher Burdick
Lalor Burdick
Carol Chandler, Esq.
Cynthia B. Patterson
Sally H. Zeckhauser

ADDRESS INQUIRIES TO:
Fellowship Manager
(See address above.)

LOS ALAMOS NATIONAL LABORATORY   [1949]
P.O. Box 1663
MS-P125
Los Alamos, NM 87545
(505) 664-6947 ext. 05004
Fax: (505) 606-5901

E-MAIL ADDRESS:
hrstaffing-postdocs@lanl.gov

WEB SITE ADDRESS:
www.lanl.gov/science/postdocs

FOUNDED: 1943

AREAS OF INTEREST:
Biosciences, chemistry, computing, Earth and space science, engineering, materials science, mathematics and physics.

NAME(S) OF PROGRAMS:
● **Richard P. Feynman Postdoctoral Fellowship in Theory and Computing**
● **J. Robert Oppenheimer Postdoctoral Fellowship**
● **Frederick Reines Postdoctoral Fellowship in Experimental Sciences**

TYPE:
Fellowships. The Distinguished Postdoctoral Fellowships provide the opportunity for the recipients to collaborate with LANL scientists and engineers on staff-initiated research. Candidates for these awards must display extraordinary ability in scientific research and show clear and definite promise of becoming outstanding leaders in the research they pursue.

YEAR PROGRAM STARTED: 1960

LEGAL BASIS:
Los Alamos National Laboratory is operated by Los Alamos National Security, L.L.C. for the U.S. Department of Energy's NNSA.

ELIGIBILITY:
Candidates must have a doctoral degree within the last five years or will have completed all Ph.D. requirements by commencement of their appointment. The Feynman and Reines Fellowships require the ability to obtain a DOE "Q" clearance, which normally requires U.S. citizenship.

Every candidate must be sponsored by a technical staff member before being reviewed by the Postdoctoral Committee.

FINANCIAL DATA:
A generous and comprehensive salary and benefits package is provided, including incoming relocation.
Amount of support per award: Feynman, Oppenheimer and Reines Postdoctoral Fellowships provide a starting salary of $104,900.

NUMBER OF AWARDS: Up to 2 in each fellowship category.

APPLICATION INFORMATION:
Details are available online.
Duration: Appointments are for three years.
Deadline: January.

ADDRESS INQUIRIES TO:
See e-mail address above.

MICHIGAN SOCIETY OF FELLOWS
University of Michigan
0540 Rackham Building
915 East Washington Street
Ann Arbor, MI 48109-1070
(734) 763-1259

E-MAIL ADDRESS:
society.of.fellows@umich.edu

WEB SITE ADDRESS:
www.rackham.umich.edu/sof

TYPE:
Fellowships. Fellows are appointed as Assistant Professors or Research Scientists in appropriate departments and as Postdoctoral

Scholars in the Michigan Society of Fellows. They are expected to be in residence in Ann Arbor during the academic years of the fellowship, to teach for the equivalent of one academic year, to participate in the informal intellectual life of the Society, and to devote time to their independent research or artistic projects.

See entry 412 for full listing.

MICRON TECHNOLOGY FOUNDATION, INC.

8000 South Federal Way
P.O. Box 6
Boise, ID 83707-0006
(208) 363-3675
Fax: (208) 368-4435

E-MAIL ADDRESS:
mtf@micron.com

WEB SITE ADDRESS:
www.micron.com/foundation

TYPE:
Awards/prizes; Matching gifts; Professorships; Project/program grants; Research grants.

See entry 2228 for full listing.

MICROSCOPY SOCIETY OF AMERICA

12100 Sunset Hills Road
Suite 130
Reston, VA 20190
(703) 234-4115
(800) 538-3672
Fax: (703) 435-4390

E-MAIL ADDRESS:
associationmanagement@microscopy.org

WEB SITE ADDRESS:
www.microscopy.org

TYPE:
Awards/prizes; Conferences/seminars. Awards to encourage attendance at the MSA Annual Meeting by microscopists working in developing countries who will travel to the meeting. Several awards include free full registration and attendance to the proceedings.

See entry 2776 for full listing.

MICROSCOPY SOCIETY OF AMERICA   [1950]

12100 Sunset Hills Road
Suite 130
Reston, VA 20190
(703) 234-4115
(800) 538-3672
Fax: (703) 435-4390

E-MAIL ADDRESS:
associationmanagement@microscopy.org

WEB SITE ADDRESS:
www.microscopy.org

FOUNDED: 1942

AREAS OF INTEREST:
Microscopy.

NAME(S) OF PROGRAMS:
● **Undergraduate Research Scholarship Program**

TYPE:
Scholarships.

PURPOSE:
To further educational and research potential in full-time undergraduate students' intent on pursuing microscopy as a career or research tool.

LEGAL BASIS:
Nonprofit society.

ELIGIBILITY:
The applicant must be a full-time undergraduate student and must have achieved junior or senior standing by the time the work is initiated. Research must be completed prior to graduation. Scholarship funds must be expended within one year of award date.

Applicants may receive only one scholarship and may perform research at an institution other than the one in which the applicant is enrolled. Successful applicants must agree to furnish MSA with an abstract for publication in the Society Journal, *Microscopy & Microanalysis*, describing the results and status of their project within two months after the conclusion of the award period, to acknowledge the award in all resulting publications, and to provide reprints of any other resulting publications to the Society.

FINANCIAL DATA:
Amount of support per award: Up to $3,000.
Total amount of support: Varies.

NUMBER OF APPLICANTS MOST RECENT YEAR:
20

NUMBER OF AWARDS: Average 5.

APPLICATION INFORMATION:
Required application form should include:
(1) a research proposal not to exceed three pages in length, including a brief introduction, a short methods section and description and itemized goals of the study;
(2) a budget proposal detailing utilization of awards;
(3) two letters of reference from scientists or university faculty familiar with the applicant's capabilities are required;
(4) a letter from the laboratory supervisor where the proposed research will be performed;
(5) a curriculum vitae detailing previous education and/or training in microscopy and a brief statement of career goals and;
(6) a letter of recommendation from an MSA member.
Duration: One year. No renewals.
Deadline: December 31. Award announcement April 1.

PUBLICATIONS:
Program announcement.

ADDRESS INQUIRIES TO:
Business Office
MSA Undergraduate Research Scholarships
(See address above.)

MICROSCOPY SOCIETY OF AMERICA   [1951]

12100 Sunset Hills Road
Suite 130
Reston, VA 20190
(703) 437-4377
(800) 538-3672
Fax: (703) 435-4390

E-MAIL ADDRESS:
associationmanagement@microscopy.org

WEB SITE ADDRESS:
www.microscopy.org

FOUNDED: 1942

AREAS OF INTEREST:
All phases of microscopy.

NAME(S) OF PROGRAMS:
● **MSA Presidential Student Awards**

TYPE:
Awards/prizes; Conferences/seminars. Awards are given to outstanding students selected on the basis of the quality and originality of their research abstracts submitted for the Annual MSA Scientific Program. The award consists of free registration for the meeting, a copy of *Proceedings*, and an invitation to the Sunday social event.

PURPOSE:
To promote student interest in microscopy and exchange of information.

LEGAL BASIS:
Nonprofit.

ELIGIBILITY:
Applicants must be bona fide students at a recognized college or university at the time of the meeting. Awards are based on the quality of the paper submitted for presentation at the meeting and the applicant must be the submitted paper's first author. The paper may be submitted for platform or poster presentation. Successful applicants must present their papers personally at the meeting in order to receive the award. They are expected to attend and participate in the entire meeting. Candidates should be juniors or seniors at the time the work is initiated. Former winners are ineligible.

GEOGRAPHIC RESTRICTIONS:
United States.

FINANCIAL DATA:
Awardees will be reimbursed for travel (round-trip, lowest-fare, continental U.S.) and lodging ($1,000 reimbursement).
Amount of support per award: Varies.
Total amount of support: Average $10,000.

NUMBER OF APPLICANTS MOST RECENT YEAR:
100 for the year 2010.

NUMBER OF AWARDS: 8.

APPLICATION INFORMATION:
Applications consist of a completed Advanced Reservation Form, payment for student registration, a supporting letter from a member of MSA, preferably a research advisor, attesting to the applicant's status and a scientific paper for presentation accompanied by a completed Data Form.
Deadline: February 15.

PUBLICATIONS:
The MSA Proceedings.

ADDRESS INQUIRIES TO:
Presidential Student Award
(See address above.)

NATIONAL CENTER FOR ATMOSPHERIC RESEARCH   [1952]

1850 Table Mesa Drive
Boulder, CO 80303
(303) 497-1328
Fax: (303) 497-1646

E-MAIL ADDRESS:
paulad@ucar.edu

WEB SITE ADDRESS:
www.asp.ucar.edu

FOUNDED: 1960

AREAS OF INTEREST:
Research in atmospheric sciences, including such topics as atmospheric dynamics (on all scales) and models, climate science, cloud physics, atmospheric chemistry and radiation, turbulence, upper-atmosphere physics, solar and solar-terrestrial physics (including ionospheric studies and aeronomy), oceanography and atmospheric technology. Also included are studies of the interaction of the atmosphere with the oceans, the cryosphere, the Earth's surface and human society and application of biology, ecology, geology, economics and political science skills to atmospheric issues.

NAME(S) OF PROGRAMS:
- **Postdoctoral Fellowships at NCAR**

TYPE:
Fellowships. The fellowships cover a year's appointment, with a likely extension to two years, at NCAR to take advantage of its educational programs and/or research facilities in the broad field of atmospheric sciences.

YEAR PROGRAM STARTED: 1964

PURPOSE:
To provide an opportunity for talented scientists who have recently received their Ph.Ds. to continue to pursue their research interests and to develop expertise in new areas; to enrich the research talent in the atmospheric sciences by offering an opportunity for highly qualified Ph.D. physicists, chemists, applied mathematicians, engineers and specialists from other disciplines such as biology, geology, science education, economics and geography, as well as atmospheric science, to apply their training to research in the atmospheric sciences.

LEGAL BASIS:
Research institution operated by the nonprofit University Corporation for Atmospheric Research (UCAR) under sponsorship of the National Science Foundation (NSF).

ELIGIBILITY:
Interested scientists who have received their Ph.D. (or equivalent) are eligible. NCAR encourages applications from women and minorities. There are no restrictions for foreign applicants.

Primary criteria in selection of postdoctoral appointees are the applicant's scientific capability and potential, originality and independence and the ability to take advantage of the research opportunities at NCAR.

FINANCIAL DATA:
All appointees are eligible for life and health insurance in addition to excellent retirement benefits. Travel expenses to NCAR will be reimbursed for the fellow and his or her family. A small allowance for moving and storage is provided. Scientific travel and conference registration that costs up to $2,000 each year is normally available.

Amount of support per award: Currently, first-year appointments carry a basic stipend of $56,000, and $58,500 in the second year.

NUMBER OF APPLICANTS MOST RECENT YEAR: 122.

NUMBER OF AWARDS: 7 to 9 new positions.

APPLICATION INFORMATION:
Duration: Two years.

Deadline: January 5, to be considered for fellowship awards to begin the following summer or fall. Selections announced in April.

PUBLICATIONS:
Program announcement.

ADDRESS INQUIRIES TO:
Paula Fisher, Coordinator
Advanced Study Program
(See address above.)

*SPECIAL STIPULATIONS:
Appointments are tenable only in residence at the National Center for Atmospheric Research.

NATIONAL OCEANIC AND ATMOSPHERIC ADMINISTRATION   [1953]
NOAA/Sea Grant, R/SG
1315 East-West Highway, SSMC-3, 11th Floor
Silver Spring, MD 20910
(301) 734-1066
(301) 734-1071
Fax: (301) 713-0799

WEB SITE ADDRESS:
www.seagrant.noaa.gov

FOUNDED: 1966

AREAS OF INTEREST:
Marine resource development.

NAME(S) OF PROGRAMS:
- **National Sea Grant College Program**

TYPE:
Research grants. Grants for research, education and outreach in oceanography, fisheries science and environmental studies; marine commerce and engineering and marine biotechnology; economic, legal and sociological considerations related to the management and development of natural resources in the marine environment; and development, conservation and economic utilization of resources in the marine environment.

The grant provides training and advisory service activities in order to increase the understanding, development and wise use of ocean, coastal and Great Lakes resources. The Secretary of Commerce, through NOAA, awards grants on a competitive basis for these purposes.

The program is carried out through a network of 30 Sea Grant programs, located in coastal and Great Lakes states, involving hundreds of universities nationwide.

YEAR PROGRAM STARTED: 1966

PURPOSE:
To promote wise utilization of marine and coastal resources.

LEGAL BASIS:
The National Sea Grant College and Program Act of 1966, Public Law 89-688, as amended. (33 U.S.C. 1121, et seq.)

ELIGIBILITY:
Universities and colleges, junior colleges, technical schools, institutes, laboratories and other public or private agencies with appropriate interests are eligible to apply.

FINANCIAL DATA:
Amount of support per award: Varies.

Total amount of support: Approximately $60,000,000 in grant funds per year.

APPLICATION INFORMATION:
Detailed information available upon request to the Administration.

Duration: Generally two years.

Deadline: Varies.

ADDRESS INQUIRIES TO:
Leon Cammen, Director
(See address above.)

NATIONAL RESEARCH COUNCIL OF CANADA   [1954]
1200 Montreal Road, Building M-58
Ottawa ON K1A 0R6 Canada
(613) 993-1947
Fax: (613) 941-6283

E-MAIL ADDRESS:
info@nrc-cnrc.gc.ca
racoordinator.hrb@nrc-cnrc.gc.ca

WEB SITE ADDRESS:
careers-carrieres.nrc-cnrc.gc.ca
www.nrc-cnrc.gc.ca

FOUNDED: 1916

AREAS OF INTEREST:
Science and engineering.

NAME(S) OF PROGRAMS:
- **National Research Council Laboratories Research Associateships Program**

TYPE:
Assistantships. Research Associates will be appointed to the staff of the National Research Council on a term basis and will be offered salaries and benefits currently available to members of the continuing staff.

YEAR PROGRAM STARTED: 1975

PURPOSE:
To undertake, assist or promote scientific and engineering research to further Canada's economic and social development and to give promising scientists and engineers an opportunity to work on challenging research problems.

LEGAL BASIS:
Federal government agency.

ELIGIBILITY:
Recent graduates (within previous five years) at the Ph.D. level in physical or life science or Master's level in engineering or in a program leading to the acquisition of one of these degrees and having demonstrated the ability to perform original research of a high quality in the chosen field. Open to nationals of all countries, although preference will be given to Canadians.

FINANCIAL DATA:
Amount of support per award: Ph.D. recruiting rate is $49,489 plus allowance of $8,000 per year.

NUMBER OF APPLICANTS MOST RECENT YEAR: 400.

NUMBER OF AWARDS: Varies.

APPLICATION INFORMATION:
Applicants must apply online. All applicants must submit university transcripts, two letters of recommendation, list of publications and resume. Application is valid for one year.

Duration: Two years. Renewal to a maximum of five years.

ADDRESS INQUIRIES TO:
Research Associates Program Coordinator
(See address above.)

NATIONAL SCIENCE FOUNDATION [1955]

Directorate for Education and
Human Resources
Division of Graduate Education
4201 Wilson Boulevard, Suite 875
Arlington, VA 22230
(703) 292-7468
Fax: (703) 292-9048

E-MAIL ADDRESS:
gtmuller@nsf.gov
outreach@nsfgrfp.org (GRFP)

WEB SITE ADDRESS:
www.nsfgrfp.org

FOUNDED: 1950

AREAS OF INTEREST:
Science, math and engineering.

NAME(S) OF PROGRAMS:
● **NSF Graduate Research Fellowships**

TYPE:
Fellowships. Awarded for graduate study
leading to research-based master's and
doctoral degrees in the fields and programs
of science and engineering supported by the
National Science Foundation.

YEAR PROGRAM STARTED: 1952

PURPOSE:
To help ensure the vitality and diversity of
the scientific and engineering workforce in
the United States. The program recognizes
and supports outstanding graduate students
who are pursuing research-based masters and
doctoral degrees in fields within NSF's
mission. The GRFP provides three years of
support for the graduate education of
individuals who have demonstrated their
potential for significant achievements in
science and engineering research. The ranks
of NSF Fellows include individuals who have
made transformative breakthroughs in science
and engineering research and have become
leaders in their chosen careers and Nobel
laureates.

LEGAL BASIS:
Government agency.

ELIGIBILITY:
Open only to applicants who are citizens or
nationals of the U.S. or permanent resident
aliens of the U.S. at the time of application.

The guidelines below should be used to
assess eligibility according to the field of
study criterion.

Categories and programs of study that are
always ineligible:
Practice-oriented professional degree
programs, joint professional degree-science
programs (MD/PhD and JD/PhD), or
medical, dental, law, and public health
programs. Examples of typical ineligible
degree programs include MBA, MPH, MSW,
ED, etc.

Clinical (see below), counseling, business
administration or management programs,
social work, education (except in science and
engineering education in an NSF-supported
discipline), or history (except in history of
science).

Clinical and counseling psychology programs
are not supported in this program. Clinical
study includes patient-oriented research,
epidemiological and behavioral studies,
outcomes research and health services
research. Clinical study includes, for
example, investigations to provide evidence
leading to a scientific basis for consideration
of a change in health policy or standard of
care, and includes pharmacologic,
non-pharmacologic, and behavioral
interventions for disease prevention,
prophylaxis, diagnosis, or therapy.
Community and other population-based
intervention trials are also included.
Applicants in clinical or counseling
psychology graduate programs are ineligible
even if the proposed graduate research may
be classified under one of the NSF-supported
fields of psychology.

Research and programs of study with
disease-related goals, including work of the
etiology, diagnosis or treatment of physical
or mental disease, abnormality, or
malfunction in human beings or animals, are
not supported. Animal models of such
conditions or the development or testing of
drugs or other procedures for their treatment
also are not eligible for support. However,
applicants in eligible programs may conduct
research in bioengineering, with diagnosis or
treatment-related goals that applies
engineering principles to problems in biology
and medicine while advancing engineering
knowledge. Applicants in eligible programs
may also conduct bioengineering research to
aid persons with disabilities.

GEOGRAPHIC RESTRICTIONS:
United States.

FINANCIAL DATA:
Amount of support per award: $40,500
annually, includes $30,000 stipend to the
Fellow and $10,500 cost of education
allowance to the institution.

Total amount of support: $40,500 annually,
for maximum of three years.

NUMBER OF APPLICANTS MOST RECENT YEAR:
12,000.

NUMBER OF AWARDS: 200 for the year 2011.

APPLICATION INFORMATION:
The following material is required from all
applicants:
(1) personal statement essay;
(2) previous research experience essay;
(3) proposed plan of research essay;
(4) three reference letters and;
(5) academic transcripts.

Duration: Normal tenure is 12 months for
each fellowship year. Availability of the
second and third years of a three-year award
is contingent upon certification by the
fellowship institution that progress is being
made and availability of appropriated funds.

Deadline: Applications must be filed early in
November. Notification after mid-March of
the following year.

ADDRESS INQUIRIES TO:
Graduate Research Fellowship Program
(See address above.)

*PLEASE NOTE:
Program eligibility requirements subject to
change each year.

NATIONAL SCIENCE FOUNDATION [1956]

4201 Wilson Boulevard, Room 990
Arlington, VA 22230
(703) 292-7283
Fax: (703) 292-9068

E-MAIL ADDRESS:
fkronz@nsf.gov

WEB SITE ADDRESS:
www.nsf.gov/funding/pgm_summ.
jsp?pims_id=5324&org=ses&from=home

FOUNDED: 1950

AREAS OF INTEREST:
Ethical, value and policy issues in the
interactions of science, technology and
society, management of research and
development.

NAME(S) OF PROGRAMS:
● **Science, Technology and Society**

TYPE:
Conferences/seminars; Fellowships;
Project/program grants; Research grants;
Training grants. Grants support research and
educational projects, national meetings,
dissemination efforts, cross-disciplinary
study, dissertation research, small group
training activities, dissertation improvement
grants for graduate students, and postdoctoral
fellowships. The proposals considered for
support examine ethics, the conduct and
impacts of science, engineering and
technology, or undertake research to improve
approaches and information for decision
making concerning management and
direction of research, science and technology.

YEAR PROGRAM STARTED: 1976

PURPOSE:
To improve knowledge and education about
these issues, abilities to formulate sound
policies and professional and public
discussion.

LEGAL BASIS:
Government agency.

ELIGIBILITY:
Individuals, universities, colleges and other
profit and nonprofit organizations may submit
proposals for consideration.

FINANCIAL DATA:
Amount of support per award: Generally,
$12,000 to $500,000.

Total amount of support: Approximately
$9,000,000.

COOPERATIVE FUNDING PROGRAMS: National
Institutes of Health; Department of
Agriculture.

NUMBER OF APPLICANTS MOST RECENT YEAR:
400.

NUMBER OF AWARDS: 80.

REPRESENTATIVE AWARDS:
"Academic Life Project: Longitudinal
Research on Doctoral Education;" "The Body
as Property: Disputes over the Control of
Human Tissue in a Biotechnological Age;"
"Impacts of Cooperative R&D on
Participating Firms."

APPLICATION INFORMATION:
Proposers should consult the SDEST
Announcement 08-553 and appropriate NSF
brochures such as Grant Proposal Guide,
available from the address above.

Duration: One to four years.

Deadline: August 1 and February 1.

PUBLICATIONS:
*Societal Dimensions of Engineering, Science,
and Technology–Ethics and Value Studies,
Research on Science and Technology* (NSF
01-152); application guidelines.

ADDRESS INQUIRIES TO:
Frederick Kronz, Program Director
(See address above.)

NATIONAL SCIENCE FOUNDATION [1957]

Office of Polar Programs
4201 Wilson Boulevard, Suite 755
Arlington, VA 22230
(703) 292-8014
Fax: 703-292-9082

E-MAIL ADDRESS:
dfriscic@nsf.gov

WEB SITE ADDRESS:
www.nsf.gov/home/grants.htm

FOUNDED: 1950

AREAS OF INTEREST:
Antarctic natural sciences.

NAME(S) OF PROGRAMS:
● U.S. Antarctic Research Program

TYPE:
Fellowships; Project/program grants;
Research grants. Grants for research projects
in all fields of science pertinent to the
Antarctic, including both field work in the
Antarctic and study in the U.S. of already
gathered data and specimens. Support is
provided for research projects in astronomy,
astrophysics, the behavioral sciences, biology,
cartography, geology, glaciology,
meteorology, oceanography, solid earth
geophysics, upper atmospheric physics and
magnetospheric physics. Logistics and
support in Antarctica are arranged by the
Foundation.

YEAR PROGRAM STARTED: 1959

PURPOSE:
To fund, coordinate and arrange for support
of research in all fields of science pertinent
to Antarctica.

LEGAL BASIS:
Federal agency under the National Science
Foundation Act of 1950, Public Law 81-507,
as amended. Also White House memo 6646
dated February 5, 1982.

ELIGIBILITY:
U.S. universities and colleges are the primary
participants in the program. Other eligible
participants include non-academic research
institutions, profit or nonprofit, and
unaffiliated scientists or scientists employed
by other federal agencies.

GEOGRAPHIC RESTRICTIONS:
United States.

FINANCIAL DATA:
Amount of support per award: Varies with
need.
Total amount of support: Approximately
$50,000,000.
Matching fund requirements: Grantee
institutions are generally required to share in
project costs by a contribution to any cost
element in the project, direct or indirect.

NUMBER OF AWARDS: Approximately 50.

APPLICATION INFORMATION:
Applications are submitted in the form of a
proposal with a detailed research plan and
budget. Information concerning proposal
preparation is available in the PAPPG, NSF
11-1, *Grant Proposal Guide, Antarctic
Research Program Announcement and
Proposal Guide* and NSF 11-532, *Antarctic
Conservation Act of 1978.*
Duration: Average of two to four years
depending on the quality of submissions and
the availability of funds.
Deadline: Applications should be submitted
by June 6.

OFFICERS:
Karl A. Erb, Director, Office of Polar
Programs

ADDRESS INQUIRIES TO:
David Friscic, Tech Information Specialist
(See address above.)

NATIONAL SCIENCE FOUNDATION [1958]

Division of Information and
Intelligent Systems
4201 Wilson Boulevard, Suite 1115
Arlington, VA 22230
(703) 292-8930
Fax: (703) 292-9073

E-MAIL ADDRESS:
lbroom@nsf.gov

WEB SITE ADDRESS:
www.cise.nsf.gov/iis/index.html

FOUNDED: 1950

AREAS OF INTEREST:
Basic research in information, robotics and
intelligent systems.

TYPE:
Assistantships; Challenge/matching grants;
Conferences/seminars; Development grants;
Research grants; Seed money grants; Travel
grants. Supplements to existing grants for
"Research Experience for Undergraduates."

Digital Society and Technologies: encourages
and supports research in two broad and
highly interrelated areas: (1) integration,
sustainable use, and impacts of information
technology on groups, organizations,
communities and societies and; (2) theories
and technologies for reasoning, decision
making, interaction and collaboration in
groups, organizations, communities and
societies. The research addresses issues and
technologies at the level of groups,
organizations, communities and societies and
human-centered as well as technological
aspects.

Human Computer Interaction: supports
research fundamental to the design of
systems that mediate between computers and
humans.

Information and Data Management: supports
research fundamental to the design,
implementation, development, management
and use of databases, information retrieval,
and knowledge-based systems.

Knowledge and Cognitive Systems: supports
research fundamental to the development of
machines that behave intelligently.

Robotics and Human Augmentation: supports
research fundamental to the design of
machines and systems that implement some
characteristics of intelligence, so that the
machines can serve effectively to augment
human activities.

Special Projects: supports research activities
that explore new relationships among
computing, communication and digital
content from human-centered perspectives in
order to support communities of users in
scholarly, social and work contexts.

Universal Access: aims primarily to support
research fundamental to empowering people
with disabilities so that they are able to
participate as first-class citizens in the
emerging information society.

YEAR PROGRAM STARTED: 1985

PURPOSE:
To discover and formulate in general terms
the principles governing the generation,
transmission and use of information, as
accomplished through the support of research
to increase understanding of the properties
and structure of information and information
transfer; to contribute to the store of
scientific and technical knowledge that can
be applied in the design of new information
technologies; to improve understanding of the
impact of information and information
technology on the economic and social fabric
of society.

LEGAL BASIS:
Government agency.

ELIGIBILITY:
Proposals may be submitted by academic
institutions, nonprofit and profit making
organizations, or by a combination of them.
Joint proposals that bring a coordinated range
of expertise and research skills to bear on
complex problems are particularly
encouraged. Proposals from graduate students
and unaffiliated investigators may be
submitted but are supported only in special
circumstances.

GEOGRAPHIC RESTRICTIONS:
United States.

FINANCIAL DATA:
Amount of support per award: Varies.
Total amount of support: Varies.

NUMBER OF APPLICANTS MOST RECENT YEAR:
1,000.

NUMBER OF AWARDS: Varies.

REPRESENTATIVE AWARDS:
$120,135 to David McAllester, Massachusetts
Institute of Technology, for "Knowledge
Representation for Mathematics;" $85,521 to
Dana H. Ballard, for "Parameter Networks
and Spatial Cognition;" $109,340 to James S.
Jordan, University of Minnesota, for
"Information Processing in Interactive
Organizations."

APPLICATION INFORMATION:
Potential applicants are encouraged to discuss
their research ideas with Division of
Information, Robotics and Intelligent Systems
staff, either in person, by letter, or by
telephone.
The research proposal should describe:
(1) objectives and scientific significance of
the proposed research;
(2) methods proposed and their suitability;
(3) qualifications of the investigator(s) and
the proposing organization and;
(4) level of support required to perform the
research.

It should be self-contained and written with
the care and thoroughness accorded papers
prepared for publication. The Foundation's
brochure *Grants for Scientific Research*
should be consulted for more detailed
guidance. Consult NSF 94-2.
Duration: Usually one to three years.

PUBLICATIONS:
Summary of Awards.

ADDRESS INQUIRIES TO:
Howard Wactlar, Division Director
(See address above.)

NATIONAL SCIENCE FOUNDATION [1959]

Office of Polar Programs, Room 755
4201 Wilson Boulevard
Arlington, VA 22230
(703) 292-8014
Fax: (703) 292-9082

E-MAIL ADDRESS:
dfriscic@nsf.gov

WEB SITE ADDRESS:
www.nsf.gov/home/grants.htm

FOUNDED: 1950

AREAS OF INTEREST:
Arctic natural sciences and social sciences.

NAME(S) OF PROGRAMS:
● **Arctic Research Program**

TYPE:
Conferences/seminars; Research grants;
Research contracts. Grants and contracts to
support scientific research projects relating to
the Arctic as well as the subsequent analysis
of data. Research may be concerned with
problems of marine research, including the
polar pack ice; terrestrial biology, including
analysis of the ecosystem; meteorology;
solar-terrestrial physics; glaciology, including
permafrost; geology and geophysics; social
sciences; and data and information.

YEAR PROGRAM STARTED: 1971

PURPOSE:
To increase man's knowledge of the Arctic
environment and its dynamic parameters; to
increase cooperation in research with other
agencies and nations having Arctic interests.

LEGAL BASIS:
The National Science Foundation Act of
1950, Public Law 81-507, as amended;
Arctic Research and Policy Act of 1984.

ELIGIBILITY:
Proposals may be submitted by U.S. colleges
and universities and by academically related
nonprofit research organizations. Industry and
other organizations are also eligible for
support.

GEOGRAPHIC RESTRICTIONS:
United States.

FINANCIAL DATA:
Amount of support per award: Varies.
Total amount of support: Approximately
$25,000,000 per year; depending on
availability of funds.
Matching fund requirements: Cost sharing is
not required.

NUMBER OF AWARDS: 75 per year, pending
availability of funds.

APPLICATION INFORMATION:
Application information may be requested
from the address above. Because of
far-reaching scientific, logistic and
international implications of Arctic research
projects, it is essential that scientists specify
all field needs when submitting proposals.
Special procedures and a longer lead time
apply to research proposed for Greenland.
Proposers should also consult the
Foundation's *Proposal and Award Procedures
Guide* (PAPPG) (NSF 11-1).
Duration: Three years or more depending on
the scientific merit and requirements of the
project.
Deadline: October 18, 2011; October 18
annually, thereafter.

ADDRESS INQUIRIES TO:
David Friscic, Tech Information Specialist
(See address above.)

SIGMA DELTA EPSILON/GRADUATE WOMEN IN SCIENCE [1960]

P.O. Box 240607
St. Paul, MN 55124-0607
(952) 236-9112

E-MAIL ADDRESS:
gwised@mac.com

WEB SITE ADDRESS:
www.gwis.org

FOUNDED: 1922

AREAS OF INTEREST:
Science and research.

CONSULTING OR VOLUNTEER SERVICES:
A great deal of volunteering is provided by
16 chapters of the organization (e.g., science
fair judges, girl scout support in science,
etc.).

NAME(S) OF PROGRAMS:
● **SDE Fellowship Program**

TYPE:
Awards/prizes; Fellowships; Travel grants.
Leadership Awards are given to Graduate
Women in Science officers.

YEAR PROGRAM STARTED: 1935

PURPOSE:
To increase knowledge in the fundamental
sciences; to encourage research careers in the
sciences by women.

ELIGIBILITY:
Applicants must be enrolled as a graduate
student or engaged in postdoctoral or
early-stage academic research.

FINANCIAL DATA:
Applications are vetted for scientific expertise
and financial need.
Amount of support per award: $5,000 to
$10,000.
Total amount of support: Varies.

NUMBER OF APPLICANTS MOST RECENT YEAR:
300 for the year 2008-09.

NUMBER OF AWARDS: 15 awards for the year
2007-08.

APPLICATION INFORMATION:
Information about the application process is
available online.
Duration: One year. No renewals.
Deadline: January 15.

PUBLICATIONS:
GWIS Bulletin; *GWIS e-news*, monthly
electronic newsletter.

ADDRESS INQUIRIES TO:
Ms. Dee M. McManus
National Executive Director
(See address above.)

SIGMA XI: THE SCIENTIFIC RESEARCH SOCIETY [1961]

3106 East NC Highway 54
Research Triangle Park, NC 27709
(919) 549-4691
Fax: (919) 549-0090

E-MAIL ADDRESS:
giar@sigmaxi.org

WEB SITE ADDRESS:
www.sigmaxi.org

FOUNDED: 1886

AREAS OF INTEREST:
The sciences, physical sciences, engineering,
social, behavioral and life sciences.

NAME(S) OF PROGRAMS:
● **Grants-in-Aid of Research**

TYPE:
Grants-in-aid; Project/program grants;
Research grants; Travel grants. Grants-in-aid
to support research projects in any field of
scientific investigation. Assistance is available
for such research-related activities as travel to
research location or supplies.

YEAR PROGRAM STARTED: 1921

PURPOSE:
To encourage scientific research.

LEGAL BASIS:
Nonprofit organization.

ELIGIBILITY:
Graduate and undergraduate students with
proposals for specific research projects are
eligible to apply. Student faculty advisor
(first recommender) should be a full, active
member of Sigma Xi to compete for Sigma
Xi funds. NAS funds in the program are
unrestricted and cover the physical, life and
medical sciences (excluding the social
sciences).

Grants do not cover overhead costs. No
grants for publication/presentation costs,
travel to meetings or stipends. Will fund
travel to a research site.

FINANCIAL DATA:
Amount of support per award: Up to $1,000
for all areas of the sciences and engineering;
Up to $5,000 for astronomy; Up to $2,500
for eye/vision research.
Total amount of support: Approximately
$300,000.

COOPERATIVE FUNDING PROGRAMS: National
Academy of Sciences.

APPLICATION INFORMATION:
Duration: Applicants may apply for a second
grant after submitting a report on the
outcome of the project supported by a first
grant.
Deadline: Applications and supporting letters
must be received by March 15 or October 15.
Awards are announced within 12 weeks.

PUBLICATIONS:
Annual report; application guidelines.

ADDRESS INQUIRIES TO:
Kevin Bowen, Manager
(See address above.)

ALFRED P. SLOAN FOUNDATION

630 Fifth Avenue, Suite 2550
New York, NY 10111
(212) 649-1649
Fax: (212) 757-5117

E-MAIL ADDRESS:
boylan@sloan.org

WEB SITE ADDRESS:
www.sloanphds.org

TYPE:
Fellowships; Scholarships. Offers substantial
scholarship support to underrepresented
minority (African American, Hispanic
American or Native American) students who
are U.S. citizens and who are beginning their

doctoral work in engineering, natural science and mathematics in selected departments at selected U.S. universities.

See entry 1077 for full listing.

ALFRED P. SLOAN FOUNDATION

630 Fifth Avenue, Suite 2550
New York, NY 10111
(212) 649-1649
Fax: (212) 757-5117

E-MAIL ADDRESS:
boylan@sloan.org

WEB SITE ADDRESS:
www.sloanphds.org

TYPE:
Fellowships; Scholarships. Offers substantial scholarship support to indigenous students (Native Americans, including American Indians, Native Alaskans and Native Hawaiians) who are beginning their Master's or doctoral work in engineering, natural science and mathematics in selected departments at selected U.S. universities.

See entry 1078 for full listing.

SMITHSONIAN INSTITUTION [1962]

Office of Fellowships and Internships
470 L'Enfant Plaza, S.W., Suite 7102
MRC 902, P.O. Box 37012
Washington, DC 20013-7012
(202) 633-7070
Fax: (202) 633-7069

E-MAIL ADDRESS:
siofg@si.edu

WEB SITE ADDRESS:
www.si.edu/research+study

FOUNDED: 1846

AREAS OF INTEREST:
Animal behavior, ecology and environmental science, including an emphasis on the tropics; anthropology, including archaeology; astrophysics and astronomy; earth sciences and paleobiology; evolutionary and systematic biology; history of science and technology; history of art, especially American, contemporary, African and Asian art; twentieth-century American crafts and decorative arts; social and cultural history of the U.S.; and folklore.

NAME(S) OF PROGRAMS:
- **Smithsonian Graduate Student Fellowships**
- **Smithsonian Postdoctoral Fellowships**
- **Smithsonian Predoctoral Fellowships**
- **Smithsonian Senior Fellowships**

TYPE:
Fellowships. Offered to qualified scholars for research to be conducted in residence at the Smithsonian in association with the staff, using collections and research facilities.

YEAR PROGRAM STARTED: 1964

PURPOSE:
To provide students and scholars in the sciences, arts and humanities with an opportunity for research utilizing the unique collections and facilities of the Smithsonian, while working with the institution's research staff.

LEGAL BASIS:
Act of Congress approved August 10, 1846; 20 U.S.C. 41 et seq.

ELIGIBILITY:
Smithsonian Fellowships are open to both U.S. citizens and foreign nationals. Fluency in English is required.

For the graduate fellowships, students must be formally enrolled and engaged in a graduate program of study at a degree granting institution, have completed at least one semester and have not yet been advanced to candidacy if in a Ph.D. program.

For the predoctoral fellowships, students must be enrolled in a university as candidates for the Ph.D. or equivalent. At the time of appointment, the university must approve the undertaking of dissertation research at the Smithsonian and indicate that requirements for the Doctorate, other than the dissertation, have been met.

For the postdoctoral fellowships, applicants must have received the Ph.D., or equivalent, within seven years of the program deadline and must have completed the degree or certificate at the time the fellowship commences.

For the senior fellowships, applicants must have received the Ph.D., or equivalent, seven or more years before the program deadline.

Research must be conducted while in residence at the Smithsonian.

The Smithsonian Institution does not offer financial assistance for degree-granting programs at academic institutions. All forms of financial assistance are to support research in residence at the Smithsonian and its facilities.

FINANCIAL DATA:
Stipends are offered per calendar year and are prorated for terms of less than one year. Pre, Post and Senior Postdoctoral Fellows also receive research and travel allowances. *Amount of support per award:* Graduate Fellowships: $6,500; Predoctoral Fellowships: $30,000; Postdoctoral and Senior Postdoctoral Fellowships: $45,000; Earth and Planetary Sciences Senior and Postdoctoral Fellowships: $50,000.

APPLICATION INFORMATION:
Official application materials are available upon request. Specify the fellowship corresponding to your academic level. *Duration:* Graduate Fellowships: Ten weeks; Predoctoral, Postdoctoral and Senior Fellowships: Three to 12 months. *Deadline:* January 15. Research appointments with or without fellowships may be conducted at any time during the year.

PUBLICATIONS:
Smithsonian Opportunities for Research and Study.

OFFICER:
Catherine F. Harris, Director

ADDRESS INQUIRIES TO:
Office of Fellowships and Internships
(See address above.)

SOCIETY FOR SCIENCE AND THE PUBLIC [1963]

1719 N Street, N.W.
Washington, DC 20036
(202) 785-2255

E-MAIL ADDRESS:
sciedu@societyforscience.org

WEB SITE ADDRESS:
www.societyforscience.org

FOUNDED: 1942

AREAS OF INTEREST:
Sciences, mathematics, engineering and medicine.

NAME(S) OF PROGRAMS:
- **Intel Science Talent Search**

TYPE:
Awards/prizes. Competition for high school seniors excelling in science, math and engineering.

YEAR PROGRAM STARTED: 1942

PURPOSE:
To discover at the high school senior year level those who have the potential to become the scientists, mathematicians and engineers of the future; to make the public aware of the impact that a quality science, mathematics or engineering education has on our future and the future of our nation.

LEGAL BASIS:
Nonprofit educational institution.

ELIGIBILITY:
Student must be in the last year of secondary school in the U.S., Puerto Rico, Guam, Virgin Islands, American Samoa, Wake and Midway Islands, the Marianas, DOD Schools or American schools abroad or for citizens studying abroad.

FINANCIAL DATA:
Amount of support per award: 10 four-year scholarships: one $100,000 ($25,000/year), one $75,000 ($18,750/year), one $50,000 ($12,500/year), one $40,000 ($10,000/year), one $30,000 ($7,500/year), two $25,000 ($6,250/year), three $20,000 ($5,000/year), and 30 $7,500 scholarships. *Total amount of support:* Over $1,250,000.

APPLICATION INFORMATION:
Official entry materials must be requested. Applicants must submit an entry form and all components, write a report on independent scientific research, and send a project report. *Duration:* Four-year scholarship. *Deadline:* Fall.

ADDRESS INQUIRIES TO:
Program Manager
(See address above.)

THE SOCIETY FOR THE SCIENTIFIC STUDY OF SEXUALITY [1964]

P.O. Box 416
Allentown, PA 18105
(610) 443-3100
Fax: (610) 443-3105

E-MAIL ADDRESS:
thesociety@sexscience.org

WEB SITE ADDRESS:
www.sexscience.org

FOUNDED: 1957

AREAS OF INTEREST:
Sex research, sex therapy and sex education.

NAME(S) OF PROGRAMS:
- **Student Research Grants**

TYPE:
Grants-in-aid; Research grants. Cash award for two graduate student research projects per year.

YEAR PROGRAM STARTED: 1985

PURPOSE:
To assist with the development of quality graduate research projects in the area of sex research.

LEGAL BASIS:
Tax-exempt, private, not-for-profit corporation.

ELIGIBILITY:
Research conducted by Master's or doctoral students is eligible, although the project need not be restricted to thesis or doctoral projects. Students must be or become members of SSSS.

FINANCIAL DATA:
Amount of support per award: $1,000.
Total amount of support: $2,000.

NUMBER OF APPLICANTS MOST RECENT YEAR: 48.

NUMBER OF AWARDS: 2.

APPLICATION INFORMATION:
Students will be asked to submit a 10-page abstract of the proposed research and bibliography, along with proposed budget (one copy submitted electronically). Applications and further information may be obtained on the web site or from Dr. Peter Anderson at the address above.
Deadline: January 1 and June 1.

PUBLICATIONS:
Application guidelines.

IRS IDENTIFICATION NUMBER: 13-2642753

ADDRESS INQUIRIES TO:
Mandy Peters, Office Manager
(See address above.)

TOURETTE SYNDROME ASSOCIATION, INC.
42-40 Bell Boulevard
Suite 205
Bayside, NY 11361-2820
(718) 224-2999
Fax: (718) 279-9596

E-MAIL ADDRESS:
ts@tsa-usa.org

WEB SITE ADDRESS:
www.tsa-usa.org

TYPE:
Demonstration grants; Development grants; Fellowships; General operating grants; Research grants; Seed money grants; Technical assistance. Research and training grants available for Ph.D. and M.D. researchers in the following categories: (1) proposals in basic neuroscience specifically relevant to Tourette Syndrome; (2) clinical studies related to the etiology, pathophysiology and treatment of Tourette Syndrome and; (3) one-year training postdoctoral fellowships.

See entry 2641 for full listing.

U.S. ARMY RESEARCH OFFICE [1965]
4300 South Miami Boulevard
Research Triangle Park, NC 27709-2211
(919) 549-4271
(919) 549-0641
Fax: (919) 549-4388

E-MAIL ADDRESS:
larry.travis@us.army.mil

WEB SITE ADDRESS:
www.arl.army.mil

FOUNDED: 1951

AREAS OF INTEREST:
Biosciences, chemistry, electronics, engineering, environmental sciences, materials sciences, mathematical and computer sciences and physics.

TYPE:
Conferences/seminars; Research grants; Research contracts. Grants and contracts for scientific research in such areas of interest to the U.S. Army as chemistry, engineering, biology, mathematics, metallurgy and materials, physics, electronics and environmental sciences. Support is also provided for symposia on particular aspects of scientific investigation, the results of which further Department of the Army objectives.

YEAR PROGRAM STARTED: 1951

PURPOSE:
To increase knowledge of natural phenomena and environment in an attempt to solve problems in the physical, engineering, environmental and life sciences.

LEGAL BASIS:
Government agency.

ELIGIBILITY:
Organizations with appropriate interests are eligible to apply.

FINANCIAL DATA:
Amount of support per award: Grants and contracts vary in amount, depending upon the needs and nature of the request; $136,000 yearly average.
Total amount of support: $500,000,000 to $550,000,000 including both grants and contracts.

NUMBER OF APPLICANTS MOST RECENT YEAR:
Approximately 1,500.

APPLICATION INFORMATION:
Research awards are predicted upon proposals submitted in response to an open-ended Broad Agency Announcement (BAA). Contractors interested in submitting proposals should contact the Army Research Office and request a copy of the BAA. This publication outlines ARO's current research interests and provides a scientific point of contact for pre-proposal discussion purposes. The BAA also provides necessary instructions and forms for preparation of the proposal.
Duration: One to three years. Continuations possible if work has not been completed.
Deadline: Varies.

ADDRESS INQUIRIES TO:
Larry Travis, Chief
RDECOM Acquisitions Center
(See address above.)

U.S. DEPARTMENT OF ENERGY
P.O. Box 10940, MS-922-273
Pittsburgh, PA 15236
(412) 386-4781
Fax: (412) 386-5917

E-MAIL ADDRESS:
flenory@netl.doe.gov

WEB SITE ADDRESS:
www.grants.gov

TYPE:
Assistantships; Project/program grants; Research grants.

See entry 2831 for full listing.

U.S. DEPARTMENT OF THE NAVY [1966]
Office of Naval Research
One Liberty Center, Suite 1425
875 North Randolph Street
Arlington, VA 22203-1995
(703) 696-5031
Fax: (703) 696-5940

E-MAIL ADDRESS:
onrpao@onr.navy.mil

WEB SITE ADDRESS:
www.onr.navy.mil

FOUNDED: 1946

AREAS OF INTEREST:
Advanced materials, ocean sciences, mathematics, information sciences, physics, electronics, chemistry, mechanics, cognitive and neural sciences.

NAME(S) OF PROGRAMS:
- **Basic Research Challenge Program**
- **University Research Initiative**
- **Young Investor Program**

TYPE:
Research grants; Research contracts. ONR sponsors long-range scientific research, applied research and advanced technology development which offer potential for advancement and improvement of naval operations. Programs include physics, electronic and solid state sciences, mathematics, operations research, statistics and probability, information science, fluid dynamics, physiology, biochemistry, biophysics, microbiology, naval biology, cognitive and neural sciences research, personnel and training research, Arctic research, coastal sciences, earth and environmental physics, atmospheric sciences, metallurgy and ceramics research, chemistry, energy research, structural mechanics, physical and chemical oceanography, marine geology and geophysics, ocean biology, ocean acoustics and ocean engineering.

YEAR PROGRAM STARTED: 1946

PURPOSE:
To support research in various scientific fields including ocean science and physics.

LEGAL BASIS:
Public Law 588, as amended and Public Law 85-934, as amended.

ELIGIBILITY:
Nonprofit institutions of higher education and organizations whose primary purpose is the conduct of scientific research may apply for contracts or grants. Nonprofit and profit-making institutions, organizations or industrial establishments, as well as qualified individuals, are eligible for contract support.

FINANCIAL DATA:
Amount of support per award: Varies, depending upon the needs and nature of the request.
Total amount of support: Varies.

NUMBER OF APPLICANTS MOST RECENT YEAR:
Approximately 4,000 inquiries.

NUMBER OF AWARDS: Approximately 2,500 annually.

APPLICATION INFORMATION:
Before submitting a proposal, interested individuals are encouraged to assess the relevance of their research interests to Navy research priorities by consulting the ONR web page and talking to the relevant ONR Program Manager. Applications are submitted in the form of a proposal which should include:
(1) general statement requesting consideration of the proposal;
(2) brief review of the scientific background of the proposed research;
(3) technical description of the project, including statement of objectives and scientific methods to be employed;
(4) description of available facilities;
(5) background of principal investigator(s) and associates;
(6) bibliography of pertinent publications;
(7) proposed duration of project and annual itemized budget;
(8) other research projects currently undertaken by the principal investigator;
(9) other agencies to whom the proposal is being submitted for possible financial support and;
(10) cost breakdown by year.

UC DISCOVERY GRANT PROGRAM (INDUSTRY-UNIVERSITY COOPERATIVE RESEARCH)

University of California, Office of the President
300 Lakeside Drive, 6th Floor
Oakland, CA 94612
(510) 987-9386

WEB SITE ADDRESS:
www.ucop.edu/ucdiscovery

TYPE:
Challenge/matching grants. UC Discovery Grants form a three-way partnership between the University of California, industry sponsors, and the state of California.

See entry 1020 for full listing.

THE VAN SLYKE FOUNDATION [1967]

1850 K Street, N.W., Suite 625
Washington, DC 20006
(202) 857-0717
(800) 892-1400 ext. 1712
Fax: (202) 887-5093

E-MAIL ADDRESS:
skleinman@aacc.org

WEB SITE ADDRESS:
www.aacc.org

AREAS OF INTEREST:
Clinical laboratory science and study of outcomes of point-of-care testing (POCT).

NAME(S) OF PROGRAMS:
● **AACC Van Slyke Foundation Critical and Point-of-Care Testing Research Grant**

TYPE:
Research grants; Scholarships; Travel grants. Science Fair awards; Poster contest.

The Van Slyke Foundation is the American Association for Clinical Chemistry's philanthropic program.

PURPOSE:
To encourage and support deserving clinical laboratory scientists and students throughout the world.

FINANCIAL DATA:
Amount of support per award: $500.

APPLICATION INFORMATION:
Duration: One year. Renewable.
Deadline: March 15.

ADDRESS INQUIRIES TO:
Stephanie Kleinman, Foundation Coordinator
(See address above.)

WEIZMANN INSTITUTE OF SCIENCE

Feinberg Graduate School of the
Weizmann Institute of Science
P.O. Box 26
Rehovot 76100 Israel
(972-8) 9343843
(972-8) 9342924
Fax: (972-8) 9344114

E-MAIL ADDRESS:
postdoc@weizmann.ac.il

WEB SITE ADDRESS:
www.fgs.org.il

TYPE:
Fellowships. The Feinberg Graduate School of the Weizmann Institute of Science offers a limited number of postdoctoral fellowships in all areas of research in which the Weizmann Institute is engaged. The fellowships are offered in various fields of biology, chemistry, physics, biochemistry-biophysics, mathematics and computer science.

See entry 1004 for full listing.

THE HELEN HAY WHITNEY FOUNDATION [1968]

20 Squadron Boulevard
Suite 630
New City, NY 10956-5247
(845) 639-6799
Fax: (845) 639-6798

E-MAIL ADDRESS:
hhwf@earthlink.net

WEB SITE ADDRESS:
www.hhwf.org

FOUNDED: 1947

AREAS OF INTEREST:
Biomedical sciences.

NAME(S) OF PROGRAMS:
● **Early Postdoctoral Research Fellowship Program in Biomedical Sciences**

TYPE:
Fellowships. Postdoctoral research fellowships.

YEAR PROGRAM STARTED: 1957

PURPOSE:
To provide beginning postdoctoral research training to young M.Ds. and Ph.Ds. to further their careers in research in biomedical sciences.

LEGAL BASIS:
Independent foundation.

ELIGIBILITY:
Candidates living in North America or foreign nationals that pursue their fellowship in the U.S., who hold the M.D., Ph.D. or equivalent degree, who are seeking beginning postdoctoral training in basic biomedical research and have no more than one year postdoctoral experience by July 15 are eligible. U.S. citizenship is not a requirement,

but fellowships to resident non-citizens are awarded only for training in the U.S. Citizens may train abroad.

Applications from established scientists or advanced fellows will not be considered. Applicants who have already had one year's postdoctoral laboratory training at the time of deadline will not be considered for a Whitney Fellowship.

FINANCIAL DATA:
Amount of support per award: Fellowships provide stipends as follows: $43,000 for the first year, $44,000 for the second year and $45,000 for the third year, plus a $2,500 research allowance to the department for each year of tenure, travel to fellowship location and annual meeting of all fellows. Additionally, there is a dependent child allowance of $1,000 per each dependent child.
Total amount of support: $2,488,613 for the year ended December 31, 2008.

NUMBER OF APPLICANTS MOST RECENT YEAR:
400.

NUMBER OF AWARDS: 60 for the year 2008.

APPLICATION INFORMATION:
Application forms are available online. Information solicited includes academic training, bibliography, description of proposed research, transcripts and references.
Duration: Three years. Contingent upon satisfactory performance.
Deadline: Applications accepted online April 15 to July 15. Fellowships begin the following April 1 through December 1.

PUBLICATIONS:
Annual report.

TRUSTEES:
Averil Payson Meyer, President
Stephen C. Harrison, Ph.D., Vice President
Lisa A. Steiner, M.D., Vice President
W. Perry Welch, Treasurer
Jerome Gross, M.D.
Payne W. Middleton
Thomas P. Sakmar, M.D.
Stephen C. Sherrill
Christopher T. Walsh, Ph.D.

ADDRESS INQUIRIES TO:
Robert Weinberger
Administrative Director and Secretary
(See address above.)

WOODS HOLE OCEANOGRAPHIC INSTITUTION [1969]

Clark Laboratory
360 Woods Hole Road
Education Office, MS #31
Woods Hole, MA 02543-1541
(508) 289-2219
Fax: (508) 457-2188

E-MAIL ADDRESS:
education@whoi.edu

WEB SITE ADDRESS:
www.whoi.edu

FOUNDED: 1930

AREAS OF INTEREST:
Research in biological oceanography, marine chemistry and geochemistry, marine geology and geophysics, applied ocean physics and engineering, physical oceanography and marine policy.

NAME(S) OF PROGRAMS:
- **Summer Student Fellowship Program in Oceanography**

TYPE:
Fellowships. Awards for independent research in oceanography/ocean engineering and marine policy projects pursued under the guidance of a member of the research staff of the Woods Hole Oceanographic Institution. Fellowship is for a 10- to 12-week summer study at Woods Hole Oceanographic Institution.

YEAR PROGRAM STARTED: 1954

PURPOSE:
To give a small group of qualified undergraduate science and engineering students experience that will enable them to determine whether they wish to devote lifetime careers to studying the oceans.

LEGAL BASIS:
Charter under the Commonwealth of Massachusetts.

ELIGIBILITY:
Applicant must be an undergraduate (junior or senior) studying at a college or university in any fields of science or engineering with at least a tentative interest in oceanography.

FINANCIAL DATA:
Amount of support per award: Stipend $468 per week and travel allowance and housing allowance for WHOI housing.

Total amount of support: Varies.

APPLICATION INFORMATION:
Applications should be made to the Fellowship Committee at the address above. A complete application should include an application form, transcripts of college and university records, at least three personal references, a concise statement of the applicant's research plans and interests, future education and career plans and reasons for applying to the Institution.

Duration: 10 to 12 weeks.

Deadline: February 15. Notification by March 15.

OFFICERS:
Susan Avery, President and Director
Dr. James A. Yoder, Dean

ADDRESS INQUIRIES TO:
See e-mail address above.

SOCIAL SCIENCES

Social sciences (general)

AGENCY FOR HEALTHCARE RESEARCH AND QUALITY (AHRQ)

Office of Communications
and Knowledge Transfer
540 Gaither Road, 2nd Floor
Rockville, MD 20850
(301) 427-1447
Fax: (301) 427-1562

WEB SITE ADDRESS:
www.ahrq.gov

TYPE:
Conferences/seminars; Development grants;
Fellowships; Project/program grants;
Research grants; Training grants. Dissertation
support highlighting primary care, market
forces, cost containment, managed care, the
cost of treating AIDS, the improvement of
treatment for persons with HIV, rural health
care, infant mortality, medical liability,
malpractice reform, health care of the aged
and disabled and policy studies.

See entry 1511 for full listing.

AMERICAN BAR FOUNDATION

750 North Lake Shore Drive
Fourth Floor
Chicago, IL 60611
(312) 988-6515
Fax: (312) 988-6579

E-MAIL ADDRESS:
fellowships@abfn.org

WEB SITE ADDRESS:
www.americanbarfoundation.org

TYPE:
Fellowships; Internships.

See entry 1022 for full listing.

AMERICAN BAR FOUNDATION

750 North Lake Shore Drive
Fourth Floor
Chicago, IL 60611-4403
(312) 988-6515
Fax: (312) 988-6579

E-MAIL ADDRESS:
kharris@abfn.org

WEB SITE ADDRESS:
www.americanbarfoundation.org

TYPE:
Fellowships. Residential fellowships at the
ABF.

The American Bar Foundation is committed
to developing the next generation of scholars
in the field of law and social science. Since
1987, the Foundation has supported the
dissertation research of a diverse group of
graduate students from all social science
disciplines and, in 1996, added a postdoctoral
component to its fellowship program.

See entry 2098 for full listing.

BRETT FAMILY FOUNDATION   [1970]

1123 Spruce Street
Boulder, CO 80302
(303) 442-1200
Fax: (303) 442-1221

E-MAIL ADDRESS:
mike@brettfoundation.org

WEB SITE ADDRESS:
www.brettfoundation.org

FOUNDED: 2000

AREAS OF INTEREST:
Social justice, equal rights and access to
opportunity for individuals and families.

NAME(S) OF PROGRAMS:
● **Social Justice Grant Program**

TYPE:
General operating grants.

PURPOSE:
To promote caring communities by investing
in organizations throughout Colorado
working for social justice and Boulder
County nonprofits addressing the needs of
underserved communities, primarily
disadvantaged youth and their families.

ELIGIBILITY:
Applicants must be nonprofit 501(c)(3)
organizations within the state of Colorado
working to address the root causes of social,
economic, gender, and racial inequities
through strategies that challenge existing
power structures and provide access to
opportunity for individuals and families. No
grants to individuals.

GEOGRAPHIC RESTRICTIONS:
Colorado.

FINANCIAL DATA:
Amount of support per award: $2,000 to
$25,000.
Total amount of support: $400,000.

NUMBER OF APPLICANTS MOST RECENT YEAR:
98.

NUMBER OF AWARDS: 75.

APPLICATION INFORMATION:
Submit a letter of inquiry (up to three pages),
unless requested to submit a full proposal by
Foundation staff. A copy of current 501(c)(3)
determination letter from the IRS must also
be included.
Duration: One year. Must reapply.
Deadline: Social Justice: Letter of Inquiry,
January 15. Full proposals, March 1; Boulder
County: Letter of Inquiry, July 15. Full
proposals, September 1.

ADDRESS INQUIRIES TO:
Claire Gilbert, Program Officer
(See address above.)

CANADIAN FEDERATION FOR THE HUMANITIES AND SOCIAL SCIENCES   [1971]

275 Bank Street, Suite 300
Ottawa ON K2P 2L6 Canada
(613) 238-6112 ext. 352
Fax: (613) 238-6114

E-MAIL ADDRESS:
secaspp@fedcan.ca

WEB SITE ADDRESS:
www.fedcan.ca/english/aspp/aspp.html

FOUNDED: 1941

AREAS OF INTEREST:
Social sciences and humanities.

NAME(S) OF PROGRAMS:
● **Aid to Scholarly Publications Program**

TYPE:
Grants-in-aid. Grants to aid the publication of
scholarly manuscripts in the social sciences
and humanities.

YEAR PROGRAM STARTED: 1941

PURPOSE:
To assist the publication of works of
advanced scholarship which are unlikely to
be self-supporting.

LEGAL BASIS:
NGO, nonprofit.

ELIGIBILITY:
Manuscripts may be submitted by Canadian
citizens or landed immigrants. The quality of
a manuscript's contribution to scholarship is
the sole basis for assessment. The following
categories are not eligible: textbooks and
anthologies, unrevised theses, fiction, poetry
and incomplete manuscripts. Approved
manuscripts must be published by recognised
Canadian scholarly publishers.

GEOGRAPHIC RESTRICTIONS:
Canada.

FINANCIAL DATA:
Subventions are paid directly to publishers
after an approved work appears in print.
Amount of support per award: $8,000 per
manuscript.

NUMBER OF APPLICANTS MOST RECENT YEAR:
320 each year.

NUMBER OF AWARDS: Approximately 145 per
year.

APPLICATION INFORMATION:
Send two copies of the final and complete
manuscript and a registration form with a
cover letter to the individual listed below.

PUBLICATIONS:
Application guidelines; application form.

OFFICERS:
Dr. Kel Morin-Parsons, Manager

ADDRESS INQUIRIES TO:
Dr. Kel Morin-Parsons, Manager, ASPP
(See address above.)

*SPECIAL STIPULATIONS:
American citizens may be eligible for ASPP
support if their work is on a Canadian
subject and they are publishing with an
eligible Canadian scholarly publisher.

CANADIAN INSTITUTE OF UKRAINIAN STUDIES

University of Alberta
430 Pembina Hall
Edmonton AB T6G 2H8 Canada
(780) 492-2972
Fax: (780) 492-4967

E-MAIL ADDRESS:
cius@ualberta.ca

WEB SITE ADDRESS:
www.cius.ca

TYPE:
Fellowships; Research grants; Scholarships.

See entry 623 for full listing.

COUNCIL FOR EUROPEAN STUDIES AT COLUMBIA UNIVERSITY

420 West 118th Street, MC 3307
New York, NY 10027
(212) 854-4172
Fax: (212) 854-8808

E-MAIL ADDRESS:
ces@columbia.edu

WEB SITE ADDRESS:
www.ces.columbia.edu

TYPE:
Awards/prizes; Fellowships. The CES Book
Award honors talented emerging scholars
with an award for the best first book on any
subject in European studies.

Council for European Studies Pre
Dissertation Research Fellowships are
intended to fund students' first major
research project in Europe.

See entry 887 for full listing.

CROSSROADS FUND   [1972]
3411 West Diversey Avenue, Suite 20
Chicago, IL 60647-1245
(773) 227-7676
Fax: (773) 227-7790

E-MAIL ADDRESS:
info@crossroadsfund.org

WEB SITE ADDRESS:
www.crossroadsfund.org

FOUNDED: 1981

AREAS OF INTEREST:
Social change.

TYPE:
General operating grants; Project/program
grants; Seed money grants; Technical
assistance.

PURPOSE:
To support grassroots organizations working
to alleviate underlying causes of social ills.

LEGAL BASIS:
Public foundation.

ELIGIBILITY:
Projects must be run by community
organizations or nonprofits. No individuals.
The Foundation only funds groups with
annual expenses under $300,000.

GEOGRAPHIC RESTRICTIONS:
Chicago, Illinois metropolitan area and
northwestern Indiana.

FINANCIAL DATA:
Amount of support per award: Up to
$10,000.
Total amount of support: $268,256 for the
year 2010.

NUMBER OF AWARDS: 67 for the year 2008.

APPLICATION INFORMATION:
Duration: One year.
Deadline: March 1.

PUBLICATIONS:
Application guidelines; newsletter; brochure;
annual report.

ADDRESS INQUIRIES TO:
Jane Kimondo, Program Director
(See address above.)

EARHART FOUNDATION   [1973]
2200 Green Road, Suite H
Ann Arbor, MI 48105
(734) 761-8592
Fax: (734) 761-2722

FOUNDED: 1929

AREAS OF INTEREST:
Graduate education and scholarly research,
especially in the social sciences and
humanities.

NAME(S) OF PROGRAMS:
● **Fellowship Research Grants**
● **Grants to Organizations**

TYPE:
Fellowships; Project/program grants.
Fellowship Research Grants allow the
advancement of knowledge through teaching,
lecturing and publication.

ELIGIBILITY:
For Fellowship Research Grants, applicants
must be associated with educational or
research institutions.

For Grants to Organizations, applicants must
be publicly supported educational and
research organizations.

FINANCIAL DATA:
Amount of support per award: Varies.
Total amount of support: Varies.

APPLICATION INFORMATION:
Fellowship Research Grant applications must
include:
(1) a personal history statement;
(2) a full description of the proposed
research;
(3) an abstract of approximately one page,
single-spaced;
(4) the intended end use or publication;
(5) a budget and time schedule;
(6) a list of referrers and;
(7) a statement about applications pending
elsewhere.

Each award is for a specific purpose and
progress is monitored.

For Fellowship Research Grants and Grants
to Organizations, written inquiries are
preferable before a formal submission.
Duration: One year.
Deadline: Fellowship Research Grant
proposals should be submitted no less than
six months before commencement of the
projected work period.

PUBLICATIONS:
Summary report.

OFFICERS:
Dennis L. Bark, Chairman
John H. Moore, Vice Chairman
Ingrid A. Gregg, President
Kathleen B. Mason, Treasurer

ADDRESS INQUIRIES TO:
Montgomery B. Brown
Secretary and Director of Program
(See address above.)

EPILEPSY FOUNDATION OF
AMERICA   [1974]
8301 Professional Place East
Landover, MD 20785-8301
(301) 459-3700
Fax: (301) 577-4941

E-MAIL ADDRESS:
grants@efa.org

WEB SITE ADDRESS:
www.epilepsyfoundation.org

FOUNDED: 1968

AREAS OF INTEREST:
Epilepsy research and training.

NAME(S) OF PROGRAMS:
● **Behavioral Sciences Student
Fellowships**
● **Health Sciences Student Fellowships**

TYPE:
Fellowships. Offers qualified individuals an
opportunity to develop expertise in the area

of epilepsy research relative to the health
sciences through a three-month training
experience with involvement in an epilepsy
research project in either a clinical or
laboratory setting.

YEAR PROGRAM STARTED: 1975

PURPOSE:
To encourage students in vocational
rehabilitation and behavioral sciences to work
in the field of epilepsy.

LEGAL BASIS:
Nonprofit private foundation.

ELIGIBILITY:
The projects must be conducted at an
approved facility at a U.S. institution of the
student's choice and carried out during any
free period of the student's year. A preceptor
must accept responsibility for supervision of
the student and the project. Applications
from women and minorities are encouraged.

For the Behavioral Science Student
Fellowship, applicants must be actively
enrolled in a degree program at the time the
fellowship is to be undertaken. Both
undergraduate and graduate students are
eligible. Appropriate fields of study include
sociology, social work, psychology,
anthropology, nursing, economics, vocational
rehabilitation, counseling, political science
and others relevant to epilepsy research or
practice.

GEOGRAPHIC RESTRICTIONS:
United States.

FINANCIAL DATA:
Amount of support per award: Up to $3,000
depending upon the experience and
qualifications of the applicant and the scope
and duration of the proposed project.

APPLICATION INFORMATION:
Duration: Three months.
Deadline: On or about March 15 for funding
during the same year.

ADDRESS INQUIRIES TO:
Research Department
(See address above.)

EPILEPSY FOUNDATION OF
AMERICA   [1975]
8301 Professional Place East
Landover, MD 20785-8301
(301) 459-3700
Fax: (301) 577-4941

E-MAIL ADDRESS:
grants@efa.org

WEB SITE ADDRESS:
www.epilepsyfoundation.org

FOUNDED: 1968

AREAS OF INTEREST:
Epilepsy research and training.

NAME(S) OF PROGRAMS:
● **Behavioral Sciences Postdoctoral
Fellowship**

TYPE:
Fellowships. Awards for postdoctoral study
through a one-year training experience in the
area of epilepsy research. Appropriate fields
of study for applications in the behavioral
sciences include sociology, social work,
psychology, anthropology, nursing, political
science and others relevant to epilepsy
research or practice.

YEAR PROGRAM STARTED: 1987

PURPOSE:
To offer qualified individuals an opportunity to develop expertise in the area of epilepsy research through a one-year training experience with involvement in an epilepsy research project.

LEGAL BASIS:
Private foundation.

ELIGIBILITY:
Individuals who have received their doctoral degree in a field of the social sciences by the time the fellowship commences and desire additional postdoctoral research experience in epilepsy may apply. Proposed projects must be carried out at an approved facility.

GEOGRAPHIC RESTRICTIONS:
United States.

FINANCIAL DATA:
Amount of support per award: Up to $40,000.

NUMBER OF APPLICANTS MOST RECENT YEAR:
1.

NUMBER OF AWARDS: 1.

APPLICATION INFORMATION:
Duration: One year.
Deadline: On or about March 15 to be considered for funding during the same year.

ADDRESS INQUIRIES TO:
Research Department
(See address above.)

THE HARRY FRANK GUGGENHEIM FOUNDATION [1976]

25 West 53rd Street
16th Floor
New York, NY 10019-5401
(646) 428-0971
Fax: (646) 428-0981

E-MAIL ADDRESS:
info@hfg.org

WEB SITE ADDRESS:
www.hfg.org

FOUNDED: 1929

AREAS OF INTEREST:
Research on dominance, aggression and violence.

NAME(S) OF PROGRAMS:
● **The Harry Frank Guggenheim Foundation Research Grant**

TYPE:
Research grants. Support for projects which seek to advance and coordinate creative breakthroughs in the social and biological sciences relating to the study of dominance, violence and aggression.

YEAR PROGRAM STARTED: 1972

PURPOSE:
To further understanding of human social problems related to dominance, violence and aggression.

LEGAL BASIS:
Private, operating foundation.

ELIGIBILITY:
The Foundation awards research grants to individuals (or a few principal investigators at most) for individual projects and does not award grants to institutions for institutional programs.

Applicants for a research grant may be citizens of any country. While almost all recipients of a Foundation research grant possess a Ph.D., M.D., or equivalent degree, there are no formal degree requirements for the grant. The grant, however, may not be used to support research undertaken as part of the requirements for a graduate degree. Applicants need not be affiliated with an institution of higher learning, although most are college or university professors.

FINANCIAL DATA:
Amount of support per award: Usually $15,000 to $40,000 per year.
Total amount of support: Grants and Fellowships: $400,000-$500,000.

NUMBER OF APPLICANTS MOST RECENT YEAR:
175.

NUMBER OF AWARDS: Approximately 10.

REPRESENTATIVE AWARDS:
Dr. William F. Fisher, "Contesting the Nation: The 'Restoration' of Democracy and the Volatility of Ethnic/State Conflict in Nepal;" Dr. Mark S. Fleisher, "An Ethnographic and Social Network Study of the Onset of Youth Gangs;" Dr. Beatrice Golomb, "Low Serum Cholesterol and Violent Behavior;" Dr. Leonard Weinberg and Dr. Jeffrey Kaplan, "The Emergence of a Violent Euro-American Radical Right."

APPLICATION INFORMATION:
Duration: Usually one-two years. Renewal is possible if requested in original application, but not guaranteed.
Deadline: For new applications, August 1 (received, not postmarked).

PUBLICATIONS:
Guidelines; Annual Report.

OFFICERS:
Josiah Bunting, III, President
Deirdre Hamill, Secretary-Treasurer
Karen Colvard, Program Director
Joel Wallman, Senior Program Officer

ADDRESS INQUIRIES TO:
Research Grants
(See address above.)

THE HARRY FRANK GUGGENHEIM FOUNDATION [1977]

25 West 53rd Street
16th Floor
New York, NY 10019-5401
(646) 428-0971
Fax: (646) 428-0981

E-MAIL ADDRESS:
info@hfg.org

WEB SITE ADDRESS:
www.hfg.org

FOUNDED: 1929

AREAS OF INTEREST:
Scholarly research on dominance, aggression and violence.

NAME(S) OF PROGRAMS:
● **The Harry Frank Guggenheim Foundation Dissertation Fellowship**

TYPE:
Fellowships. Awarded to individuals who will complete the writing of the dissertation within the award year. Support is for projects which seek to advance and coordinate

creative breakthroughs in the social and biological sciences relating to the study of dominance, violence and aggression.

YEAR PROGRAM STARTED: 1990

PURPOSE:
To further understanding of human social problems related to violence, aggression and dominance.

LEGAL BASIS:
Private foundation.

ELIGIBILITY:
Fellowships are for students in the final year of their doctoral programs. They are designed to support the write-up stage of the dissertation. They are available to citizens of any country in the world.

FINANCIAL DATA:
Amount of support per award: One-time awards of $20,000.
Total amount of support: $200,000 each year.

NUMBER OF APPLICANTS MOST RECENT YEAR:
Approximately 225.

NUMBER OF AWARDS: Usually 10 each year.

REPRESENTATIVE AWARDS:
Amy Chasteen for "Constructing Rape;" James Hogue for "Bayonet Rule: Five Street Battles in New Orleans and the Rise and Fall of Radical Reconstruction;" David LeMarquand for "Tryptophan Depletion, Aggression, and Passive Avoidance Learning in Nonalcoholic Young Men with Paternal Family Histories of Alcoholism."

APPLICATION INFORMATION:
Contact the Foundation for comprehensive guidelines.
Duration: Dissertation Fellowships are one-time awards and are not renewable.
Deadline: February 1.

PUBLICATIONS:
Guidelines and Annual Report.

OFFICERS:
Josiah Bunting, III, President
Deirdre Hamill, Treasurer and Secretary
Karen Colvard, Program Director
Joel Wallman, Senior Program Officer

ADDRESS INQUIRIES TO:
Dissertation Fellowship
(See address above.)

*SPECIAL STIPULATIONS:
Recipients of the Dissertation Fellowship must submit a copy of the dissertation, approved and accepted by their institution, within six months after the end of the award year. Any papers, books, articles, or other publications based on the research should also be sent to the Foundation.

THE JOHN RANDOLPH HAYNES AND DORA HAYNES FOUNDATION

888 West Sixth Street, Suite 1150
Los Angeles, CA 90017-2737
(213) 623-9151
Fax: (213) 623-3951

E-MAIL ADDRESS:
info@haynesfoundation.org

WEB SITE ADDRESS:
www.haynesfoundation.org

TYPE:
Fellowships; Research grants.
See entry 1748 for full listing.

THE HOROWITZ FOUNDATION FOR SOCIAL POLICY   [1978]
P.O. Box 7
Rocky Hill, NJ 08553-0007
(732) 445-2280

E-MAIL ADDRESS:
info@horowitz-foundation.org
applications@horowitz-foundation.org

WEB SITE ADDRESS:
www.horowitz-foundation.org

FOUNDED: 1997

AREAS OF INTEREST:
Social sciences, including anthropology, area studies, economics, political science, psychology, sociology, urban studies, as well as newer areas such as evaluation research.

TYPE:
Awards/prizes; Research grants. Grant giving direct assistance to individual scholars who require small grants to further their research with emphasis on policy-oriented studies.

PURPOSE:
To support the advancement of research and understanding in the major fields of the social sciences.

ELIGIBILITY:
Applicants are not required to be U.S. citizens/residents. Candidates may propose new projects, and they may also solicit support for research in progress, including final work on a dissertation, supplementing research in progress, or travel funds. Preference will be given to advanced graduate students and untenured assistant professors and instructors. Preference will also be given to projects that deal with contemporary issues in the social sciences and issues of policy relevance, and to scholars in the initial stages of their career. Awards are not allocated so as to ensure a representative base of disciplines, but are approved solely on merit.

Awards are made to individuals, not institutions, and if processed through an institution, a waiver for overhead is requested.

FINANCIAL DATA:
Amount of support per award: $2,500 to $5,000.

NUMBER OF APPLICANTS MOST RECENT YEAR:
250 for the year 2010.

NUMBER OF AWARDS: Approximately 15 annually.

APPLICATION INFORMATION:
Applications can be obtained via download from Foundation web site.

Applications must be sent via e-mail to applications@horowitz-foundation.org. (Submission via e-mail is recommended for speedy processing.) Regular mail may also be used for supplemental materials. Private delivery services do not deliver to post office box addresses.

All submitted applications, letters and documents must be in English. E-mail letters of support must be sent via the supporter's organizational e-mail account and, if possible, be displayed upon the letterhead with which the supporter is affiliated. Submitted materials become the property of the Foundation and will not be returned. Applicants should not send originals or other materials that cannot be replaced. Incomplete applications cannot be considered or processed.

Duration: One year. Nonrenewable.
Deadline: Applications and all required materials must be postmarked no later than January 31 of each year and received no later than February 10. Early submission is encouraged. Last-minute applicants cannot be advised of errors or omissions. Award winners will be announced in June of each year.

IRS IDENTIFICATION NUMBER: 31-1612153

ADDRESS INQUIRIES TO:
Mary E. Curtis
Vice Chairman and Trustee
(See address above.)

INSTITUT FRANCAIS D'AMERIQUE
Romance Language Department CB 3170
University of North Carolina
Chapel Hill, NC 27599-3170
(919) 929-6919
(919) 962-9824
Fax: (919) 962-1403

E-MAIL ADDRESS:
cmaley@email.unc.edu

WEB SITE ADDRESS:
www.unc.edu/depts/institut

TYPE:
Awards/prizes; Fellowships; Research grants. Fellowships available consist of four annual supporting grants for Ph.D. candidates or assistant professors to pursue research in France.

See entry 407 for full listing.

INSTITUTE FOR ADVANCED STUDY   [1979]
Einstein Drive
Princeton, NJ 08540
(609) 734-8250
Fax: (609) 951-4457

E-MAIL ADDRESS:
donne@ias.edu

WEB SITE ADDRESS:
www.sss.ias.edu

FOUNDED: 1930

AREAS OF INTEREST:
Economics, political science, sociology, education, anthropology and history.

NAME(S) OF PROGRAMS:
• **School of Social Science Fellowships**

TYPE:
Fellowships. Postdoctoral research fellowships at the School of Social Science. In 2012-13, the thematic focus will be "Economics and Politics."

YEAR PROGRAM STARTED: 1970

PURPOSE:
To support fundamental research and scholarship in the social sciences and humanities.

LEGAL BASIS:
Private, nonprofit research center.

ELIGIBILITY:
Scholars of any nationality who have obtained their highest degree and whose work is relevant to any aspect of the social sciences are urged to apply.

FINANCIAL DATA:
Amount of support per award:
Approximately $35,000 to $65,000.
Total amount of support: Varies.
Matching fund requirements: Institute strongly encourages applicants to apply for outside funds as well.

NUMBER OF APPLICANTS MOST RECENT YEAR:
230.

NUMBER OF AWARDS: 24.

APPLICATION INFORMATION:
Applications must be submitted online at www.sss.ias.edu/applications.
Duration: One academic year.
Deadline: November 1.

PUBLICATIONS:
Annual report.

STAFF:
Donne Petito, Administrative Officer

ADDRESS INQUIRIES TO:
School of Social Science
(See address above.)

*SPECIAL STIPULATIONS:
This is a residential (on-site) fellowship.

INSTITUTE FOR QUANTITATIVE SOCIAL SCIENCE, HARVARD UNIVERSITY   [1980]
Henry A. Murray Research Archive
318, CGIS Knafel Building
1737 Cambridge Street
Cambridge, MA 02138
(617) 496-6528
Fax: (617) 496-5149

E-MAIL ADDRESS:
mra_support@help.hmdc.harvard.edu

WEB SITE ADDRESS:
www.murray.harvard.edu

FOUNDED: 1976

AREAS OF INTEREST:
Social sciences, psychology and human development, and education.

NAME(S) OF PROGRAMS:
• **Jeanne Humphrey Block Dissertation Award**

TYPE:
Awards/prizes. The Block Dissertation Award is offered by the Henry A. Murray Research Archive.

YEAR PROGRAM STARTED: 1990

PURPOSE:
To support research that best embodies Henry A. Murray's commitment to the in-depth study of individuals in context, over time and from a variety of perspectives.

LEGAL BASIS:
University or research association.

ELIGIBILITY:
Applicant must be a Harvard Ph.D. candidate in the social sciences.

FINANCIAL DATA:
Amount of support per award: $2,500.
Total amount of support: $2,500.

NUMBER OF AWARDS: 1.

APPLICATION INFORMATION:
Detailed information and application guidelines are available upon request to the Institute.
Deadline: March 15.

PUBLICATIONS:
Program announcement.

IRS IDENTIFICATION NUMBER: 04-2103589

STAFF:
Stephen Coady, Staff Assistant

ADDRESS INQUIRIES TO:
E-mail: funding@lists.iq.harvard.edu

MADDIE'S FUND   [1981]
2223 Santa Clara Avenue
Suite B
Alameda, CA 94501-4416
(510) 337-8989
Fax: (510) 337-8988

E-MAIL ADDRESS:
grants@maddiesfund.org

WEB SITE ADDRESS:
www.maddiesfund.org

AREAS OF INTEREST:
Animal welfare.

NAME(S) OF PROGRAMS:
- **Community Collaborative Grants**
- **Medical Equipment Grants**
- **Shelter Medicine Programs**
- **Starter Grants**

TYPE:
Project/program grants.

PURPOSE:
To revolutionize the status and well-being of companion animals.

ELIGIBILITY:
Grants are made to organizations that have tax-exempt status under Section 501(c)(3) of the Internal Revenue Code, or that are government agencies, and that build coalitions in support of animal welfare and protection.

GEOGRAPHIC RESTRICTIONS:
United States.

APPLICATION INFORMATION:
Duration: Varies by program.

ADDRESS INQUIRIES TO:
Shelly Thompson, Grants Manager or Mary Smith, Vice President of Operations
(See address above.)

THE MCKAY FOUNDATION   [1982]
303 Sacramento Street
4th Floor
San Francisco, CA 94111
(415) 288-1313
Fax: (415) 288-1320

E-MAIL ADDRESS:
fndn@mckayfund.org

WEB SITE ADDRESS:
www.mckayfund.org

FOUNDED: 1992

AREAS OF INTEREST:
Grassroots community organization.

TYPE:
General operating grants.

PURPOSE:
To support long-term, social, political and economic justice.

LEGAL BASIS:
Private foundation.

ELIGIBILITY:
Organizations must be IRS 501(c)(3) tax-exempt. No grants made to individuals.

GEOGRAPHIC RESTRICTIONS:
Primarily California.

FINANCIAL DATA:
Amount of support per award: Average $35,000 to $50,000.

APPLICATION INFORMATION:
The Foundation does not accept unsolicited proposals or letters of inquiry.

PUBLICATIONS:
Annual report; guidelines.

ADDRESS INQUIRIES TO:
Chief Operating Officer
(See address above.)

THE NATIONAL ASSOCIATION OF BLACK SOCIAL WORKERS
2305 Martin Luther King Jr. Avenue, S.E.
Washington, DC 20020
(202) 678-4570
Fax: (202) 678-4572

E-MAIL ADDRESS:
harambee@nabsw.org
office-manager@nabsw.org

WEB SITE ADDRESS:
www.nabsw.org

TYPE:
Scholarships.

See entry 1095 for full listing.

NATIONAL COUNCIL FOR THE SOCIAL STUDIES   [1983]
8555 16th Street, Suite 500
Silver Spring, MD 20910
(301) 588-1800
Fax: (301) 588-2049

E-MAIL ADDRESS:
excellence@ncss.org

WEB SITE ADDRESS:
www.socialstudies.org

FOUNDED: 1921

AREAS OF INTEREST:
Social studies education.

NAME(S) OF PROGRAMS:
- **Exemplary Research in Social Studies**
- **Jean Dresden Grambs Distinguished Career in Social Studies**
- **The Larry Metcalf Exemplary Dissertation Award**
- **Outstanding Social Studies Teacher of the Year Awards**
- **Carter G. Woodson Book Awards**

TYPE:
Awards/prizes; Grants-in-aid.

PURPOSE:
To provide leadership, service and support for all social studies educators.

FINANCIAL DATA:
Amount of support per award: Up to $3,000.
Total amount of support: Varies.

ADDRESS INQUIRIES TO:
Prema Cordeiro, Program Manager
(See address above.)

NATIONAL COUNCIL FOR THE SOCIAL STUDIES   [1984]
8555 16th Street, Suite 500
Silver Spring, MD 20910
(301) 588-1800 ext. 106
Fax: (301) 588-2049

E-MAIL ADDRESS:
excellence@ncss.org

WEB SITE ADDRESS:
www.socialstudies.org

FOUNDED: 1921

AREAS OF INTEREST:
Social studies education.

NAME(S) OF PROGRAMS:
- **Christa McAuliffe Reach for the Stars Award**

TYPE:
Awards/prizes. Annual award for projects representing excellence and innovation in social studies education and having the potential of serving as a model for other teachers.

YEAR PROGRAM STARTED: 1986

PURPOSE:
To help a social studies educator make his or her dream of innovative social studies a reality; to assist classroom teachers in developing and implementing imaginative, innovative, and illustrative social studies teaching strategies; to assist classroom teachers in supporting student implementation of innovative social studies, citizenship projects, field experiences, and community connections.

ELIGIBILITY:
NCSS membership is required. Applicant must be a full-time social studies teacher or social studies teacher educator currently engaged with K-12 students.

GEOGRAPHIC RESTRICTIONS:
Continental United States.

FINANCIAL DATA:
Amount of support per award: Up to $2,500.

NUMBER OF APPLICANTS MOST RECENT YEAR:
10.

NUMBER OF AWARDS: 1.

APPLICATION INFORMATION:
Submit full proposal application via e-mail in a single PDF document. Include subject headers for each Proposal Requirement Outline. No mail-in copies will be allowed. A complete proposal contains the following:
(1) cover page;
(2) 50 to 150-word project proposal abstract;
(3) project proposal and narrative description;
(4) professional resume (including current teaching assignment);
(5) two letters of support from applicant's supervisor acknowledging teaching status and support for the project (one letter may be from state or local social studies council);
(6) publicity outreach, including name, contact name, title and e-mail for a major local/community newspaper (up to two),

district superintendent, and direct supervisor and;

(7) information release statement.

The project proposal and narrative description must include the following information:
(1) clear, concise statement of the project objectives;
(2) brief summary of project activities and timeline for completion;
(3) identification of population served, including relevant demographic information;
(4) budget showing how the funds will be used and if additional funds are being sought from other sources;
(5) brief explanation of how the award can facilitate the project;
(6) brief explanation of how the success of the project will be evaluated;
(7) description of the specific plan for sharing the project with local or state councils and with NCSS and;
(8) brief explanation of how the project can serve as a model for other teachers.

Deadline: May 1.

ADDRESS INQUIRIES TO:
Prema Cordeiro, Program Manager
(See address above.)

NATIONAL COUNCIL FOR THE SOCIAL STUDIES [1985]
8555 16th Street, Suite 500
Silver Spring, MD 20910
(301) 588-1800 ext. 106
Fax: (301) 588-2049

E-MAIL ADDRESS:
excellence@ncss.org

WEB SITE ADDRESS:
www.socialstudies.org

FOUNDED: 1921

AREAS OF INTEREST:
Social studies education.

NAME(S) OF PROGRAMS:
● **Grant for the Enhancement of Geographic Literacy**

TYPE:
Awards/prizes. Annual award honoring the outstanding performance of teachers, researchers, and other worthy individuals and programs.

PURPOSE:
To promote geography education in the schools; to enhance the geographic literacy of students at the classroom, district, or statewide level; to encourage integration of geography into the social studies curriculum/classroom.

ELIGIBILITY:
Programs, not individuals, individual lessons or units, which will enhance the geographic literacy of students at the classroom, district, or statewide levels. Recipients may be individuals or groups in school districts, public institutions, or universities.

GEOGRAPHIC RESTRICTIONS:
Continental United States.

FINANCIAL DATA:
Amount of support per award: $2,500.

NUMBER OF APPLICANTS MOST RECENT YEAR:
10 to 12.

NUMBER OF AWARDS: 1.

APPLICATION INFORMATION:
Materials must be submitted in a single PDF. Include subject headers for each Proposal Requirement. No mail-in copies will be allowed. A complete proposal includes the following:
(1) cover page;
(2) 150 to 200-word, double-spaced program abstract containing a clear and concise statement of the program's objective, a summary of the program activities and identification of the population served;
(3) five-page (maximum), double-spaced proposal;
(4) publicity outreach, including name, contact name, title, and e-mail for a major local/community newspaper (up to two), district superintendent, and direct supervisor and;
(5) information release statement (on cover page).

The project proposal must contain the following elements:
(1) concise rationale statement;
(2) complete program description that highlights specific geography skills and knowledge that will be introduced or reinforced;
(3) number of teachers and students served;
(4) specific criteria for and means of evaluating program effectiveness;
(5) statement of potential program impact after the first year;
(6) specific line-item budget for the program grant and;
(7) curriculum vitae or professional resume for all key persons involved in the implementation of the grant.

Deadline: Approximately March 21.

ADDRESS INQUIRIES TO:
Prema Cordeiro, Program Manager
(See address above.)

NATIONAL COUNCIL FOR THE SOCIAL STUDIES [1986]
8555 16th Street, Suite 500
Silver Spring, MD 20910
(301) 588-1800 ext. 106
Fax: (301) 588-2049

E-MAIL ADDRESS:
excellence@ncss.org

WEB SITE ADDRESS:
www.socialstudies.org

FOUNDED: 1921

AREAS OF INTEREST:
Social studies education.

NAME(S) OF PROGRAMS:
● **Defense of Academic Freedom Award**

TYPE:
Awards/prizes. Annual award recognizing those who have distinguished themselves in defending the principles of academic freedom.

PURPOSE:
To recognize and honor those who have distinguished themselves in defending the principles of academic freedom in specific controversies, in fostering academic freedom through advocacy, and in defending or advocating the freedom to teach and learn.

ELIGIBILITY:
Classroom teachers, professionals in other areas of education, students, parents, community groups, and members of other organizations who have engaged in or are currently engaged in activities that support academic freedom in the face of personal challenge or promote awareness of and support for academic freedom.

GEOGRAPHIC RESTRICTIONS:
Continental United States.

FINANCIAL DATA:
Amount of support per award: $1,500.

APPLICATION INFORMATION:
Complete guidelines is available on the web site.

Deadline: March 21.

ADDRESS INQUIRIES TO:
Prema Cordeiro, Program Manager
(See address above.)

NATIONAL COUNCIL FOR THE SOCIAL STUDIES [1987]
8555 16th Street, Suite 500
Silver Spring, MD 20910
(301) 588-1800 ext. 106
Fax: (301) 588-2049

E-MAIL ADDRESS:
excellence@ncss.org

WEB SITE ADDRESS:
www.socialstudies.org

FOUNDED: 1921

AREAS OF INTEREST:
Social studies education.

NAME(S) OF PROGRAMS:
● **Award for Global Understanding**

TYPE:
Awards/prizes.

PURPOSE:
To recognize a social studies educator (or a team of educators) who has made notable contributions in helping social studies students increase their understanding of the world.

ELIGIBILITY:
NCSS membership is required. Anyone may nominate. Nominees must be social studies educators who are affecting the global understanding of preK-12 students.

GEOGRAPHIC RESTRICTIONS:
Continental United States.

FINANCIAL DATA:
Amount of support per award: $2,000 cash award, up to $700 in transportation/lodging reimbursement, a complimentary NCSS conference registration, publicity for a session to present at the NCSS annual conference, and a commemorative gift.

NUMBER OF APPLICANTS MOST RECENT YEAR:
10.

NUMBER OF AWARDS: 1 annually.

APPLICATION INFORMATION:
Seven sets of all nomination materials are to be submitted, bound and containing subject dividers identifying materials by the requirement headings listed below.
Nomination must include:
(1) cover page;
(2) letter of nomination written by the nominator which highlights the nominee's major strengths and accomplishments in infusing global perspectives and cross-cultural understanding into his or her current work assignment (not to exceed two, single-spaced pages);
(3) curriculum vitae or professional resume prepared by the nominee;
(4) two letters supporting the nomination from two of the following: immediate

supervisor, parents, academic teammates, State Social Studies Council, Local Social Studies Council, or other social studies professionals;

(5) nominee narrative describing in some detail how he or she meets the award criteria (not to exceed seven one-sided, single-spaced 8 1/2 x 11-inch pages of 12-point type);

(6) appendices of documentation for narrative which includes evidence of instructional planning (one lesson/unit plans), actual instruction (video or CD), as well as evidence of student work (sample projects, photos, videos/CDs, web sites, etc.), professional presentations, or publications;

(7) publicity outreach, including name, contact name, title and e-mail for a major local/community newspaper (up to two), district superintendent, and direct supervisor and;

(8) information release statement (on cover page).

Deadline: Approximately May 15.

ADDRESS INQUIRIES TO:
Prema Cordeiro, Program Manager
(See address above.)

NATIONAL COUNCIL ON FAMILY RELATIONS

1201 West River Parkway
Suite 200
Minneapolis, MN 55454
(763) 781-9331
Fax: (763) 781-9348

E-MAIL ADDRESS:
jeannestrand@ncfr.org

WEB SITE ADDRESS:
www.ncfr.org

TYPE:
Awards/prizes. Awards given for contributions to the area of family relations. All of the awards, except the Reuben Hill Award, require NCFR membership. The Ruben Hill Award is a juried award.

See entry 1601 for full listing.

NATIONAL INSTITUTE OF MENTAL HEALTH [1988]

Division of Adult Translational Research and Treatment Development (DATR)
6001 Executive Boulevard, Room 7123, MSC 9632
Bethesda, MD 20892-9632
(301) 443-4863

E-MAIL ADDRESS:
bcuthber@mail.nih.gov

WEB SITE ADDRESS:
www.nimh.nih.gov/about/organization/datr/index.shtml

AREAS OF INTEREST:
Traumatic stress, violence (both perpetrators and victims) and disaster within the scope of the biological, behavioral, clinical, applied and psychosocial sciences.

NAME(S) OF PROGRAMS:
● **Research Training and Career Development Program**
● **Traumatic Stress Research Program**

TYPE:
Fellowships; Internships; Project/program grants; Research grants; Technical assistance; Training grants; Visiting scholars; Research contracts.

YEAR PROGRAM STARTED: 1969

PURPOSE:
To plan, support and administer programs of research, research training and resource development aimed at understanding the pathophysiology of mental illness and hastening the translation of behavioral science and neuroscience advances into innovations in clinical care.

LEGAL BASIS:
Section 301 of the Public Health Service Act, as amended; Public Law 78-410, 42 U.S.C. 241.

ELIGIBILITY:
Applicants can be any public or nonprofit institution such as a university, college, hospital or a community agency, unit of state or local government, an authorized unit of the federal government or a for-profit institution and/or entity.

GEOGRAPHIC RESTRICTIONS:
United States and its territories.

FINANCIAL DATA:
Amount of support per award: Small Grant Awards: $50,000 to $150,000 or more indirect costs per year. Average $120,000 to $160,000.

NUMBER OF APPLICANTS MOST RECENT YEAR: 62.

NUMBER OF AWARDS: 20.

REPRESENTATIVE AWARDS:
"Fluxotine Treatment of Posttraumatic Stress Disorder;" "Female Delinquency: Treatment Processes and Outcomes;" "Identifying Subtypes of Martially Violent Men."

APPLICATION INFORMATION:
Forms and instructions are available online.

Duration: Average three to five years.

Deadline: New research applications: February 1; June 1 and October 1. New research training applications: May 10. Earliest starting date is approximately six to eight months after submission of application.

NATIONAL SCIENCE FOUNDATION

4201 Wilson Boulevard, Room 990
Arlington, VA 22230
(703) 292-7283
Fax: (703) 292-9068

E-MAIL ADDRESS:
fkronz@nsf.gov

WEB SITE ADDRESS:
www.nsf.gov/funding/pgm_summ.jsp?pims_id=5324&org=ses&from=home

TYPE:
Conferences/seminars; Fellowships; Project/program grants; Research grants; Training grants. Grants support research and educational projects, national meetings, dissemination efforts, cross-disciplinary study, dissertation research, small group training activities, dissertation improvement grants for graduate students, and postdoctoral fellowships. The proposals considered for support examine ethics, the conduct and impacts of science, engineering and technology, or undertake research to improve approaches and information for decision making concerning management and direction of research, science and technology.

See entry 1956 for full listing.

NATIONAL SOCIETY DAUGHTERS OF THE AMERICAN REVOLUTION [1989]

1776 D Street, N.W.
Washington, DC 20006-5303
(202) 879-3292
Fax: (202) 879-3348

WEB SITE ADDRESS:
www.dar.org

FOUNDED: 1895

AREAS OF INTEREST:
Political science, history, government and economics.

NAME(S) OF PROGRAMS:
● **Enid Hall Griswold Memorial Scholarship**

TYPE:
Scholarships. Undergraduate scholarships awarded to a deserving junior or senior accepted or enrolled in an accredited college or university in the U.S. who is majoring in either political science, history, government or economics.

YEAR PROGRAM STARTED: 1982

PURPOSE:
To provide ways and means to aid students to attain higher education.

LEGAL BASIS:
Incorporated historical society.

ELIGIBILITY:
Scholarships are awarded without regard to race, religion, sex or national origin. Candidates must be U.S. citizens and must attend an accredited college or university in the U.S. No affiliation or relationship to DAR is required for qualification, but candidate must be sponsored by a local DAR Chapter. Awards are judged on the basis of academic excellence, commitment to field of study, as required, and financial need.

GEOGRAPHIC RESTRICTIONS:
United States.

FINANCIAL DATA:
Amount of support per award: $1,000.

Total amount of support: Varies.

NUMBER OF AWARDS: Varies.

APPLICATION INFORMATION:
To obtain a scholarship application packet, send a self-addressed, stamped #10 business-size envelope to the Office of the Reporter General, DAR Scholarship Committee, at the address listed above.

Included with the application packet is the list of DAR State Scholarship Chairmen. All scholarship applicants are required to have a letter of sponsorship from a chapter. Individuals interested in obtaining a letter of sponsorship from a local chapter are encouraged to contact the DAR State Chairman.

Duration: One academic year. Nonrenewable.

Deadline: February 15.

PUBLICATIONS:
American Spirit, magazine.

ADDRESS INQUIRIES TO:
Office of the Reporter General
DAR Scholarship Committee
(See address above.)

*SPECIAL STIPULATIONS:
Awards are placed on deposit with the college or university. Any unused portion shall be returned to the National Society.

Candidate must major in political science, history, government or economics.

OPEN SOCIETY INSTITUTE - NEW YORK [1990]
400 West 59th Street
New York, NY 10019
(212) 548-0600
Fax: (212) 548-4600

E-MAIL ADDRESS:
grants@sorosny.org
osfellows@sorosny.org

WEB SITE ADDRESS:
www.soros.org

FOUNDED: 1993

AREAS OF INTEREST:
Civil society, education, media, public health, human rights, women's rights and social, legal and economic reform.

TYPE:
Fellowships; Project/program grants; Scholarships; Technical assistance; Training grants.

PURPOSE:
To shape public policy to promote democratic governance, human rights, and economic, legal and social reform; to support, on a local level, the rule of law, education, public health and independent media; to build alliances across borders and continents on issues such as combating corruption and rights abuses.

ELIGIBILITY:
Grants are made to individuals and to organizations that have tax-exempt status under Section 501(c)(3) of the Internal Revenue Code. Faith-based organizations that match the mission of the Open Society Institute may apply.

APPLICATION INFORMATION:
Contact the Organization for application procedures.

PI GAMMA MU, INTERNATIONAL HONOR SOCIETY IN SOCIAL SCIENCE
1001 Millington, Suite B
Winfield, KS 67156
(620) 221-3128
Fax: (620) 221-7124

E-MAIL ADDRESS:
pgm@sckans.edu

WEB SITE ADDRESS:
www.pigammamu.org

TYPE:
Scholarships. Awarded principally for first-year graduate study.

See entry 1866 for full listing.

POVERTY & RACE RESEARCH ACTION COUNCIL [1991]
1200 18th Street, N.W.
Suite 200
Washington, DC 20036
(202) 906-8025
Fax: (202) 842-2885

E-MAIL ADDRESS:
chartman@prrac.org

WEB SITE ADDRESS:
www.prrac.org

FOUNDED: 1991

AREAS OF INTEREST:
Poverty and race.

TYPE:
Research grants. Research grants on the intersection of race and poverty must support an advocacy plan.

PURPOSE:
To generate, gather and disseminate information and resources regarding the intersection of race and poverty in the U.S.; to promote the development and implementation of policies and practices that alleviate conditions caused by the interaction of race and poverty.

LEGAL BASIS:
Nonprofit organization.

ELIGIBILITY:
Must be an advocate or social science researcher and be a tax-exempt 501(c)(3) organization or have a tax-exempt fiscal sponsor.

GEOGRAPHIC RESTRICTIONS:
United States.

FINANCIAL DATA:
Amount of support per award: $10,000 maximum.
Total amount of support: Varies.

APPLICATION INFORMATION:
Applicants must submit a brief letter outlining the purpose of the grant. Further information is available online.
Duration: One-time. Must reapply.

PUBLICATIONS:
Poverty & Race, bimonthly newsletter; journal; annual report; application guidelines.

IRS IDENTIFICATION NUMBER: 52-1705073

ADDRESS INQUIRIES TO:
Chester Hartman, Director of Research
(See address above.)

*SPECIAL STIPULATIONS:
Research must support planned advocacy agenda.

SMITH RICHARDSON FOUNDATION, INC. [1992]
60 Jesup Road
Westport, CT 06880
(203) 222-6222
Fax: (203) 222-6282

E-MAIL ADDRESS:
jhollings@srf.org

WEB SITE ADDRESS:
www.srf.org

FOUNDED: 1935

AREAS OF INTEREST:
Improvement of public policy in the fields of social welfare, economic and regulatory schemes and education issues; improvement of American foreign policy, particularly as it relates to national security.

NAME(S) OF PROGRAMS:
● **Domestic Public Policy Program**
● **International Security and Foreign Policy Program**

TYPE:
Conferences/seminars; Project/program grants; Research grants. The Domestic Policy Program primarily supports research on ways to improve public policy in the fields of social welfare, economic and regulatory schemes and education issues. The program has a particular interest in research that examines the effectiveness of institutions which serve children and families at-risk.

The Foreign Policy Program supports projects in national security and defense policy, in military history and strategy, in the political, military and economic affairs of Eastern Europe and the states of the former Soviet Union, economic and security developments in the Asia Pacific, and also in international economic issues of vital interest to American policymakers. The program aims to define the nature of the post-cold war security environment.

YEAR PROGRAM STARTED: 1935

PURPOSE:
To support and promote a vigorous and free society.

LEGAL BASIS:
Private foundation.

ELIGIBILITY:
Organizations sponsoring projects appropriate to the Foundation's interests are eligible. The Foundation originates many of the grant commitments which are made, and the vast majority of unsolicited requests for funding must be rejected. Because of fund limitations, no grants are available for deficit funding of previously established operations, projects relating to building construction (i.e., "brick and mortar"), programs related to the arts, historic restoration projects, or research in the physical sciences. No grants are made directly to individuals or to advocacy organizations. The Foundation does not provide support for the operating costs of direct service programs or charities. The Foundation rarely provides general support for any organization or funding for conferences and documentaries.

The Foundation awards grants for policy research with national implications. Some small grants are available to support innovative service and educational programs in Connecticut and North Carolina which assist children and families at-risk. Nearly all such local grants are solicited by the staff and the Board of the Foundation. Service programs in states other than Connecticut and North Carolina are ineligible for funding.

GEOGRAPHIC RESTRICTIONS:
Connecticut and North Carolina.

FINANCIAL DATA:
Amount of support per award: Median grant: $120,000.

REPRESENTATIVE AWARDS:
Center for Strategic and Budgetary Assessments to conduct research on how the U.S. should transform its military forces in response to the changing security environment, particularly the challenges posed by the war on terrorism and the revolution in military affairs; The Rand Corporation to undertake a project that will assist the U.S. policy community in thinking through ways to influence young people in the Muslim world by examining the development of opposition among Iranian youth to the fundamentalist regime in their country; U.S. Committee for Human Rights in North Korea to document the nature and extent of North Korea's systematic abuse of its population in order to focus the policy community on the need to include responses to this human rights crisis in U.S. strategy toward developments on the Korean peninsula.

APPLICATION INFORMATION:
The Foundation has a rigorous proposal review process. The first step in the process is the submission of a concept paper (not to exceed five pages).

If the staff determines that a project warrants further consideration under the Foundation's guidelines, an applicant will be asked to submit a full proposal that conforms to a proposal template provided by the Foundation.

Upon receipt of a grant application, the Foundation will either mail or e-mail a confirmation of receipt to the grant applicant. The Foundation will respond to all grant requests in a timely manner. However, given the large number of grant proposals that it receives, it cannot guarantee a response within a specific time frame.

Requests for grants greater than $50,000 and for multiyear grant support are made at one of its regular board meetings. Requests for grants of $50,000 or less are reviewed on an ongoing basis and are handled as promptly as possible.
Duration: Typically one year. Nonrenewable.
Deadline: Grants are reviewed on an ongoing basis.

PUBLICATIONS:
Annual report.

IRS IDENTIFICATION NUMBER: 56-0611550

STAFF:
Dr. Nadia Schadlow, Senior Program Officer
Allan Song, Senior Program Officer
Mark Steinmeyer, Senior Program Officer
Scott Boston, Program Associate
Olga Ramous, Grants Coordinator
Dale Stewart, Records Coordinator

OFFICERS AND TRUSTEES:
Peter L. Richardson, Chairman of the Board
Marin J. Strmecki, Ph.D., Senior Vice President, Director of Programs
Ross F. Hemphill, Vice President and Chief Financial Officer
Arvid R. Nelson, Ph.D., Secretary
Diana B. Washburn, Assistant Secretary
W. Winburne King, III, General Counsel
Adele Richardson Ray
Peter L. Richardson
Stuart S. Richardson

ADDRESS INQUIRIES TO:
Domestic Policy or Foreign Policy Program
(See address above.)

*PLEASE NOTE:
The staff does not meet with grant applicants to discuss proposals.

THE ROYAL TOWN PLANNING INSTITUTE   [1993]
41 Botolph Lane
London EC3R 8DL England
(020) 7929-9473
Fax: (020) 7929-9490

WEB SITE ADDRESS:
www.rtpi.org.uk

FOUNDED: 1914

AREAS OF INTEREST:
Urban and regional planning, land use, transport and housing, industrial strategy on planning, rural planning, conservation and recreational planning.

NAME(S) OF PROGRAMS:
• **George Pepler International Award**

TYPE:
Travel grants. This biennial award is made to individuals under 30 years of age, who wish to visit Britain or, as residents of Britain, desire to visit another country for a short period to study the theory and practice of town and country planning or some particular aspect of planning.

YEAR PROGRAM STARTED: 1964

PURPOSE:
To provide an international travelling award for young people of any nationality who wish to visit another country in order to study town planning or a related subject.

LEGAL BASIS:
Charitable trust.

ELIGIBILITY:
Young people of any nationality under the age of 30 are eligible to apply. Professional qualifications are not necessary. Each applicant is required to complete a prescribed application form and submit to a panel of advisers a statement showing the nature of the study and suggested itinerary.

FINANCIAL DATA:
Amount of support per award: GBP 1,500 paid in two installments.

NUMBER OF APPLICANTS MOST RECENT YEAR:
15.

NUMBER OF AWARDS: 1 for the year 2010.

APPLICATION INFORMATION:
Application forms are available only from the address above.
Deadline: April 26.

ADDRESS INQUIRIES TO:
Awards Events Officer
(See address above.)

RUSSELL SAGE FOUNDATION   [1994]
112 East 64th Street
New York, NY 10065
(212) 750-6000
Fax: (212) 371-4761

E-MAIL ADDRESS:
info@rsage.org

WEB SITE ADDRESS:
www.russellsage.org

FOUNDED: 1907

AREAS OF INTEREST:
Research in the future of work, cultural contact, immigration to the U.S. and social inequality.

TYPE:
Conferences/seminars; Research grants; Visiting scholars. Research awards. The Foundation currently pursues three principal programs:
(1) a program of research on the future of work, concerned principally with the causes and consequences of changes in the quality of low-wage work in the U.S. and other advanced economies;
(2) a program of research on current U.S. immigration focused on the adaptation of the second generation to American society and;
(3) a program on cultural contact that focuses on understanding and improving relations between racial and ethnic groups in schools, workplaces and neighborhood settings.

YEAR PROGRAM STARTED: 1907

PURPOSE:
To improve social and living conditions in the U.S. by conducting and supporting social science research relevant to public policy issues.

LEGAL BASIS:
Private operating foundation.

ELIGIBILITY:
The Foundation supports focused, empirical research projects under the direction of a principal investigator. Under the terms of the contract, the research must be coordinated through a fiscal agency (university, college or 501(c)(3) organization under the Internal Revenue Code).

The Foundation's awards are restricted to support for basic social science research within its announced programs. These currently include research on the future of work, immigration and the social psychology of social contact.

The Foundation conducts a Visiting Scholar program under which persons working in the areas of current interest to the Foundation join the staff for one year to consult and continue their own research and writing.

GEOGRAPHIC RESTRICTIONS:
United States and Britain.

FINANCIAL DATA:
Total amount of support: $6,791,000.

REPRESENTATIVE AWARDS:
$146,538 to Eileen Appelbaum, Economic Policy Institute, Peter Berg, Michigan State University, Ann Frost, University of Western Ontario and Gil Preuss, Case Western Reserve University, for "The Transformation of Low-Skilled Work and Careers in the North American Health Care Industry;" $221,382 to Claude M. Steel, Hazel Markus and Dorothy M. Steele, Stanford University, for "Group Differences Revisited: The Role of Social Identity Threat and Cultural Models in the Experience of Diversity;" $720,762 to Alejandro Portes, Princeton University and Ruben Rumbaut, Michigan State University, for "The Second Generation in Early Childhood: A Decade-Long Panel Study."

APPLICATION INFORMATION:
Applications for awards should be preceded by a letter of inquiry to the Foundation. Guidelines and other details are available on the web site.
Duration: Varies.
Deadline: Eight weeks prior to Board meetings to be held March 15 and August 15.

PUBLICATIONS:
Biennial report; scholarly books.

IRS IDENTIFICATION NUMBER: 13-1635303

OFFICERS:
Eric Wanner, President
Pat Woodford, Director of Administration and Secretary

BOARD OF TRUSTEES:
Thomas D. Cook, Chairman
W. Bowman Cutter
Christopher Edley, Jr.
John A. Ferejohn
Larry V. Hedges
Kathleen Hall Jamieson
Melvin J. Konner
Cora B. Marrett
Nancy Rosenblum
Richard H. Thaler
Eric Wanner
Mary C. Waters

ADDRESS INQUIRIES TO:
Pat Woodford, Director of Administration
(See address above.)

SOCIAL SCIENCES AND HUMANITIES RESEARCH COUNCIL OF CANADA   [1995]
350 Albert Street
Ottawa ON K1P 6G4 Canada
(613) 943-7777
Fax: (613) 943-1329

E-MAIL ADDRESS:
fellowships@sshrc-crsh.gc.ca

WEB SITE ADDRESS:
www.sshrc-crsh.gc.ca

FOUNDED: 1977

AREAS OF INTEREST:
The development and support of research and research training in the social sciences and humanities.

NAME(S) OF PROGRAMS:
• **Doctoral Awards**

TYPE:
Awards/prizes; Fellowships; Scholarships. Through its Doctoral Awards program, SSHRC offers two types of funding for doctoral students:
(1) SSHRC Doctoral Fellowships and;
(2) Joseph-Armand Bombardier (JAB) Canada Graduate Scholarships (CGS) program–Doctoral Scholarships.

YEAR PROGRAM STARTED: 1977

PURPOSE:
To develop research skills and assist in the training of highly qualified personnel by supporting students who demonstrate a high standard of scholarly achievement in undergraduate and graduate studies in the social sciences and humanities.

LEGAL BASIS:
Government agency.

ELIGIBILITY:
Applicants must be Canadian citizens or permanent residents of Canada. SSHRC Doctoral Fellowships are tenable at any recognized university in Canada, or abroad, in which case the award holder has to have at least one previous degree from a Canadian university.

Joseph-Armand Bombardier Canada Graduate Scholarships-Doctoral Scholarships are tenable only at Canadian universities.

FINANCIAL DATA:
Amount of support per award: SSHRC Doctoral Fellowships: $20,000 (CAN) per year; Joseph-Armand Bombardier Canada Graduate Scholarships-Doctoral Scholarships: $35,000 (CAN) per year.

Total amount of support: SSHRC Doctoral Fellowship: Up to $80,000 (CAN; four years); Joseph-Armand Bombardier Canada Graduate Scholarships-Doctoral Scholarships: $105,000 (CAN; three years).

NUMBER OF APPLICANTS MOST RECENT YEAR:
3,624 for the year 2010.

NUMBER OF AWARDS: SSHRC Doctoral Fellowships: 500; Joseph-Armand Bombardier Canada Graduate Scholarships-Doctoral Scholarships: 430.

APPLICATION INFORMATION:
On university campuses, information may be obtained from the Dean or Faculty of Graduate Studies, the Office of Research Administration, the Registrar, or the Student Awards Office. Inquiries may also be addressed directly to the Fellowships Division of the Council at the address above. Detailed program and application information is available online.
Duration: SSHRC Doctoral Fellowships: From six months to four years; Joseph-Armand Bombardier Canada Graduate Scholarships-Doctoral Scholarships: Three years.

Deadline: For applicants registered at a Canadian university, in the fall on the date set by the university; for other applicants, usually in mid-November.

OFFICERS AND STAFF:
Dr. Chad Gaffield, President
Dr. Brent Herbert-Copley, Vice President, Research Capacity
Gordana Krcevinac, Director, Research Training

ADDRESS INQUIRIES TO:
Research Training Portfolio
(See address above.)

SOCIAL SCIENCES AND HUMANITIES RESEARCH COUNCIL OF CANADA   [1996]
350 Albert Street
Ottawa ON K1P 6G4 Canada
(613) 943-7777
Fax: (613) 943-1329

E-MAIL ADDRESS:
fellowships@sshrc-crsh.gc.ca

WEB SITE ADDRESS:
www.sshrc-crsh.gc.ca

FOUNDED: 1977

AREAS OF INTEREST:
The development and support of research training in the social sciences and humanities.

NAME(S) OF PROGRAMS:
• **Queen's Fellowship**

TYPE:
Fellowships; Scholarships. Award is offered to one outstanding successful doctoral award holder who intends to enter a Canadian Studies program at a Canadian university.

YEAR PROGRAM STARTED: 1977

LEGAL BASIS:
Government agency.

ELIGIBILITY:
Applicants must be Canadian citizens or permanent residents of Canada.

GEOGRAPHIC RESTRICTIONS:
Canada.

FINANCIAL DATA:
Tuition fees and travel allowance are provided in addition to the value of the doctoral award.
Amount of support per award: Varies, up to $15,000.
Total amount of support: Varies, up to $15,000.

NUMBER OF APPLICANTS MOST RECENT YEAR:
6.

NUMBER OF AWARDS: 1 per year.

APPLICATION INFORMATION:
On university campuses, information may be obtained from the Dean or Faculty of Graduate Studies, the Officer of Research Administration, the Registrar or the Student Awards Officer. Inquiries may also be addressed directly to the Fellowships Division of the Council at the address above. Detailed program and application information is available online.
Duration: 12 months.

OFFICERS AND STAFF:
Dr. Chad Gaffield, President
Dr. Brent Herbert-Copley, Vice President, Research Capacity
Gordana Krcevinac, Director, Research Training

ADDRESS INQUIRIES TO:
Fellowships Division
(See address above.)

SOCIAL SCIENCES AND HUMANITIES RESEARCH COUNCIL OF CANADA   [1997]
350 Albert Street
Ottawa ON K1P 6G4 Canada
(613) 943-7777
Fax: (613) 943-1329

E-MAIL ADDRESS:
fellowships@sshrc-crsh.gc.ca

WEB SITE ADDRESS:
www.sshrc-crsh.gc.ca

FOUNDED: 1977

AREAS OF INTEREST:
The development and support of research, research training, and scholarly activities in the social sciences and humanities.

NAME(S) OF PROGRAMS:
• **SSHRC Postdoctoral Fellowships**

TYPE:
Fellowships. For Canadian citizens or permanent residents of Canada, to support postdoctoral research in the humanities and social sciences.

YEAR PROGRAM STARTED: 1977

PURPOSE:
To support promising new scholars in the social sciences and humanities and to assist them in establishing a research base at an important time in their research careers.

LEGAL BASIS:
Government agency.

ELIGIBILITY:
Competition is open to persons who have been awarded an earned Doctorate within the three years preceding competition closing date. Applicants must demonstrate that all doctoral requirements will be completed before the proposed starting date of tenure. Awards are for postdoctoral study or research within a university or research institution. Applicants must be Canadian citizens or permanent residents of Canada living in the country at the time of application.

FINANCIAL DATA:
Amount of support per award: $38,000 per year for one or two years, plus a one-time $5,000 research allowance.
Total amount of support: Up to $81,000.

NUMBER OF APPLICANTS MOST RECENT YEAR:
887 for the year 2010.

NUMBER OF AWARDS: 175 for the year 2011.

APPLICATION INFORMATION:
Fellowships are tenable only at universities or other recognized research institutions in Canada or abroad. Applicants must present a significant and feasible program of

postdoctoral research. Fellowships may not be used to obtain a degree. Fellows may be allowed to assume limited teaching duties, equivalent to one course per year. Detailed program and application information is available online.

Duration: Twelve to 24 months.

Deadline: Usually, in early or mid-October. Announcement usually between mid-February and early March.

OFFICERS AND STAFF:
Dr. Chad Gaffield, President
Dr. Brent Herbert-Copley, Vice President, Research Capacity
Gordana Krcevinac, Director, Research Training

ADDRESS INQUIRIES TO:
Fellowships Division
(See address above.)

SOCIAL SCIENCES AND HUMANITIES RESEARCH COUNCIL OF CANADA   [1998]

350 Albert Street, 16th Floor
Ottawa ON K1P 6G4 Canada
(613) 992-3027
Fax: (613) 947-0223

E-MAIL ADDRESS:
strategic@sshrc-crsh.gc.ca

WEB SITE ADDRESS:
www.sshrc.ca

FOUNDED: 1977

AREAS OF INTEREST:
The development and support of research and scholarly activities, such as knowledge mobilization in the social sciences and humanities.

NAME(S) OF PROGRAMS:
● **Strategic Programs**

TYPE:
Research grants. Strategic research grants. Assistance for research or training of researchers in areas of national importance to establish a knowledge base on identified social needs or problems. Grants are available for strategic research, strategic research networks, strategic research workshops and strategic partnership development.

YEAR PROGRAM STARTED: 1979

PURPOSE:
To support research on issues of national importance; to help redress underdevelopment in specific areas in the humanities and social sciences.

LEGAL BASIS:
Government agency.

ELIGIBILITY:
Applications must be submitted by researchers who are affiliated with Canadian universities or other postsecondary institutions. Some programs can accommodate foreign co-applicants or not-for-profit community-based organizations.

GEOGRAPHIC RESTRICTIONS:
Canada.

FINANCIAL DATA:
Direct costs of research. University overhead is not an eligible expense.

Amount of support per award: Varies by program.

APPLICATION INFORMATION:
Duration: Six- to 60-month grant periods.
Deadline: Varies.

OFFICERS AND STAFF:
Dr. Chad Gaffield, President
Carmen Charett, Executive Vice President

SOCIAL SCIENCES AND HUMANITIES RESEARCH COUNCIL OF CANADA   [1999]

350 Albert Street
Ottawa ON K1P 6G4 Canada
(613) 943-7777
Fax: (613) 943-1329

E-MAIL ADDRESS:
fellowships@sshrc-crsh.gc.ca

WEB SITE ADDRESS:
www.vanier.gc.ca

FOUNDED: 1977

AREAS OF INTEREST:
The development and support of research and research training in the social sciences and humanities.

NAME(S) OF PROGRAMS:
● **Vanier Canada Graduate Scholarships (CGS)**

TYPE:
Awards/prizes; Fellowships; Scholarships. For full-time doctoral students in the humanities and social sciences.

YEAR PROGRAM STARTED: 2008

PURPOSE:
To attract and retain world-class doctoral students by supporting students who demonstrate both leadership skills and a high standard of scholarly achievement in graduate studies in social sciences and humanities, natural sciences and engineering, and health.

LEGAL BASIS:
Government agency.

ELIGIBILITY:
Applicants can be citizens or permanent residents of Canada, as well as international students.

GEOGRAPHIC RESTRICTIONS:
Canada.

FINANCIAL DATA:
Amount of support per award: $50,000/year for three years.
Total amount of support: $150,000 (three years).

NUMBER OF APPLICANTS MOST RECENT YEAR:
125 for 2009.

NUMBER OF AWARDS: 55.

APPLICATION INFORMATION:
On university campuses, information may be obtained from the Dean or Faculty of Graduate Studies, the Office of Research Administration, the Registrar, or the Student Awards Office. Inquiries may also be addressed directly to the Fellowships Division of the Council at the address above.

Duration: Two or three years.

Deadline: For applicants registered at a Canadian university, in the fall on the date set by the university; for universities to submit their nominations to SSHRC: Usually early November.

OFFICERS AND STAFF:
Dr. Chad Gaffield, President

Dr. Brent Herbert-Copley, Vice President, Research Capacity
Gordana Krcevinac, Director, Research Training

ADDRESS INQUIRIES TO:
Fellowships Division
(See address above.)

SOCIAL SCIENCES AND HUMANITIES RESEARCH COUNCIL OF CANADA   [2000]

350 Albert Street
Ottawa ON K1P 6G4 Canada
(613) 943-7777
Fax: (613) 943-1329

E-MAIL ADDRESS:
fellowships@sshrc-crsh.gc.ca

WEB SITE ADDRESS:
www.sshrc-crsh.gc.ca

FOUNDED: 1977

AREAS OF INTEREST:
The development and support of research, research training and scholarly activities in the social sciences and humanities.

NAME(S) OF PROGRAMS:
● **Banting Postdoctoral Fellowships**

TYPE:
Fellowships. Banting Postdoctoral Fellowships are for Canadian citizens, permanent residents of Canada and foreign citizens to support postdoctoral research in the humanities and social sciences.

YEAR PROGRAM STARTED: 2010

PURPOSE:
To support promising new scholars in the social sciences and humanities and to assist them in establishing a research base at an important time in their research careers.

LEGAL BASIS:
Government agency.

ELIGIBILITY:
Competition is open to persons who have been awarded an earned Doctorate within the three years preceding competition. Applicants can be citizens or permanent residents of Canada, as well as international students.

Without exception, the Banting Postdoctoral Fellowships:
(1) are tenable only at the institution which supported the original application for the program;
(2) must be taken up no earlier than April 1 and no later than October 1 of the year following the application deadline and;
(3) are for two years from the date of up-take.

FINANCIAL DATA:
Amount of support per award: $70,000 per year for two years.
Total amount of support: $140,000.

NUMBER OF APPLICANTS MOST RECENT YEAR:
137 in November 2010.

NUMBER OF AWARDS: 23 in late March 2011.

APPLICATION INFORMATION:
On university campuses, information may be obtained from the Dean or Faculty of Graduate Studies, the Office of Research Administration, the Registrar, or the Student Awards Office. Inquiries may also be addressed directly to the Fellowships Division of the Council at the address above.

Duration: Period of tenure is 24 months.

Deadline: Usually, in early or mid-November. Announcement usually at end of March.

OFFICERS AND STAFF:
Dr. Chad Gaffield, President
Dr. Brent Herbert-Copley, Vice President, Research Capacity
Gordana Krcevinac, Director, Research Training

ADDRESS INQUIRIES TO:
Fellowships Division
(See address above.)

SOCIAL SCIENCES AND HUMANITIES RESEARCH COUNCIL OF CANADA   [2001]
350 Albert Street
Ottawa ON K1P 6G4 Canada
(613) 943-7777
Fax: (613) 943-1329

E-MAIL ADDRESS:
scholfin@sshrc-crsh.gc.ca

WEB SITE ADDRESS:
www.sshrc-crsh.gc.ca

FOUNDED: 1977

AREAS OF INTEREST:
The development and support of research and research training in the social sciences and humanities.

NAME(S) OF PROGRAMS:
● **Joseph-Armand Bombardier Canada Graduate Scholarships-Master's Scholarships**

TYPE:
Awards/prizes; Fellowships; Scholarships.

YEAR PROGRAM STARTED: 2003

PURPOSE:
To develop research skills and assist in the training of highly qualified personnel by supporting students who demonstrate a high standard of scholarly achievement in undergraduate and graduate studies in the social sciences and humanities.

LEGAL BASIS:
Government agency.

GEOGRAPHIC RESTRICTIONS:
Applicants must be Canadian citizens or permanent residents of Canada. Scholarships are tenable only at Canadian universities.

FINANCIAL DATA:
Amount of support per award: $17,500 (CAN), one year only.
Total amount of support: $17,500 (CAN), one year.

NUMBER OF APPLICANTS MOST RECENT YEAR:
1,300 for the year 2010.

NUMBER OF AWARDS: 1,151.

APPLICATION INFORMATION:
On university campuses, information may be obtained from the Dean or Faculty of Graduate Studies, the Office of Research Administration, the Registrar, or the Student Awards Office. Inquiries may also be addressed directly to the Fellowships Division of the Council at the address above. Detailed program and application information is available online.
Duration: One year.
Deadline: For applicants registered at a Canadian university, in the fall on the date set by the university; for other applicants, usually in mid-November.

OFFICERS AND STAFF:
Dr. Chad Gaffield, President
Dr. Brent Herbert-Copley, Vice President, Research Capacity
Gordana Krcevinac, Director, Research in Training

ADDRESS INQUIRIES TO:
Fellowships Division
(See address above.)

THE SOCIETY FOR THE PSYCHOLOGICAL STUDY OF SOCIAL ISSUES   [2002]
208 I Street, N.E.
Washington, DC 20002-4340
(202) 675-6956
Fax: (202) 675-6902

E-MAIL ADDRESS:
spssi@spssi.org
awards@spssi.org

WEB SITE ADDRESS:
www.spssi.org

FOUNDED: 1936

AREAS OF INTEREST:
Social psychology research.

NAME(S) OF PROGRAMS:
● **SPSSI Grants-in-Aid**

TYPE:
Grants-in-aid.

YEAR PROGRAM STARTED: 1956

PURPOSE:
To support scientific research in social problem areas related to the basic interests and goals of SPSSI and particularly those that are not likely to receive support from traditional sources.

LEGAL BASIS:
Independently incorporated society.

ELIGIBILITY:
Applicant must be a member of SPSSI. Applicants may submit only one application per deadline. If an applicant has applied to the Clara Mayo Grant in the same award year (July 1 to June 30), he or she is not eligible to apply for Grants-in-Aid. Individuals may submit a joint application.

The Committee especially encourages proposals involving:
(1) unique and timely research opportunities;
(2) underrepresented institutions, graduate students and junior scholars;
(3) volunteer research teams and;
(4) actual (not pilot) projects.

FINANCIAL DATA:
Funds are normally not provided for travel to conventions, travel or living expenses while conducting research, stipends of principal investigators, costs associated with manuscript preparation, or the indirect costs of institutions.
Amount of support per award: Usually, up to $2,000 for postdoctoral work and up to $1,000 for predoctoral work.
Total amount of support: Varies.
Matching fund requirements: Varies per award.

NUMBER OF APPLICANTS MOST RECENT YEAR:
35.

NUMBER OF AWARDS: 20.

APPLICATION INFORMATION:
Online submissions are the preferred method. The application should include:

(1) cover sheet with applicant's name, address, phone number, e-mail address and title of the proposal;
(2) abstract of 100 words or less summarizing the proposed research;
(3) project purposes, theoretical rationale, and research methodology and analytical procedures to be employed;
(4) relevance of research to SPSSI goals and Grants-in-Aid criteria;
(5) status of human subjects review process (which must be satisfactorily completed before grant funds can be forwarded);
(6) resume of investigator (a faculty sponsor's recommendation must be provided if the investigator is a graduate student; support is seldom awarded to students who have not yet reached the dissertation stage) and;
(7) specific amount requested, including a budget; for co-authored submissions, please indicate only one name and institution to whom a check should be jointly issued if selected for funding.
Duration: One year.
Deadline: May 15 and October 20.

PUBLICATIONS:
Application guidelines.

ADDRESS INQUIRIES TO:
SPSSI Central Office
(See address above.)

THE SOCIETY FOR THE PSYCHOLOGICAL STUDY OF SOCIAL ISSUES   [2003]
208 I Street, N.E.
Washington, DC 20002-4340
(202) 675-6956
Fax: (202) 675-6902

E-MAIL ADDRESS:
awards@spssi.org

WEB SITE ADDRESS:
www.spssi.org

FOUNDED: 1936

AREAS OF INTEREST:
Social issues and psychology.

NAME(S) OF PROGRAMS:
● **Awards for Outstanding Teaching and Mentoring**

TYPE:
Awards/prizes. One award is given for a teacher/mentor from a program or department that grants Master's or doctoral degrees. Another award will be given to a teacher/mentor from a program or department that is undergraduate-only. The third award will be given to a teacher/mentor from contingent and/or community college faculty.

PURPOSE:
To recognize outstanding teaching in areas related to the psychological study of social issues.

LEGAL BASIS:
Independently incorporated society.

ELIGIBILITY:
Nominees should be persons who have made substantial contributions to students in the psychological study of social issues. To be eligible, an individual must have been teaching and/or mentoring students for at least 10 years. Nominees must be members of SPSSI. Self-nominations are encouraged.

FINANCIAL DATA:
Amount of support per award: $500 plus a plaque.

NUMBER OF AWARDS: 3.

APPLICATION INFORMATION:
Deadline: May 10.

PUBLICATIONS:
Application guidelines.

ADDRESS INQUIRIES TO:
SPSSI Central Office
(See address above.)

THE SOCIETY FOR THE PSYCHOLOGICAL STUDY OF SOCIAL ISSUES [2004]

208 I Street, N.E.
Washington, DC 20002-4340
(202) 675-6956
Fax: (202) 675-6902

E-MAIL ADDRESS:
awards@spssi.org
spssi@spssi.org

WEB SITE ADDRESS:
www.spssi.org/awards

FOUNDED: 1936

AREAS OF INTEREST:
Intergroup relations, social issues and psychology.

NAME(S) OF PROGRAMS:
- **The Applied Social Issues Internship Program**

TYPE:
Internships.

PURPOSE:
To encourage research that is conducted in cooperation with a community or government organization, public interest group or other not-for-profit entity that will benefit directly from the project.

LEGAL BASIS:
Independently incorporated society.

ELIGIBILITY:
College seniors, graduate students and first-year postdoctorates in psychology, applied social science, and related disciplines are eligible. Applicant must be an SPSSI member.

FINANCIAL DATA:
Amount of support per award: $300 to $2,500 to cover research costs, community organizing and, in unusual cases, a stipend for the intern.

COOPERATIVE FUNDING PROGRAMS: Cost sharing by sponsoring department or organization is desirable.

NUMBER OF APPLICANTS MOST RECENT YEAR:
10.

APPLICATION INFORMATION:
Deadline: April 19. Announcement of the awards will be made by May 28.

ADDRESS INQUIRIES TO:
Anila Balkissoon
Administrative Coordinator
(See address above.)

THE SOCIETY FOR THE PSYCHOLOGICAL STUDY OF SOCIAL ISSUES [2005]

208 I Street, N.E.
Washington, DC 20002-4340
(202) 675-6956
Fax: (202) 675-6902

E-MAIL ADDRESS:
awards@spssi.org
spssi@spssi.org

WEB SITE ADDRESS:
www.spssi.org/awards

FOUNDED: 1936

AREAS OF INTEREST:
Intergroup relations, social issues and psychology.

NAME(S) OF PROGRAMS:
- **Clara Mayo Grants**

TYPE:
Research grants. Supports Master's theses and predissertation research on sexism, racism or prejudice, with preference given to students enrolled in a terminal Master's program. Studies of the application of theory or the design of interventions or treatments to address these problems are welcome.

PURPOSE:
To support Master's theses or predissertation research on aspects of sexism, racism or prejudice, with preference given to students enrolled in a terminal Master's program.

LEGAL BASIS:
Independently incorporated society.

ELIGIBILITY:
Individuals who are SPSSI members and who have matriculated in graduate programs in psychology, applied social science and related disciplines are eligible to apply. A student who is applying for the Grants-In-Aid program may not apply for the Clara Mayo award in the same award year. Applicants may submit only one Mayo application per calendar year.

Proposals that include a college or university agreement to match the amount requested will be favored, but proposals without matching funds will also be considered.

FINANCIAL DATA:
Amount of support per award: $1,000.

NUMBER OF APPLICANTS MOST RECENT YEAR:
15.

NUMBER OF AWARDS: Up to 4 annually.

APPLICATION INFORMATION:
Deadline: April 30 and October 18. Winners will be announced by December 1 and July 12. Late applications may be held until the next round.

ADDRESS INQUIRIES TO:
Anila Balkissoon
Administrative Coordinator
(See address above.)

THE SOCIETY FOR THE PSYCHOLOGICAL STUDY OF SOCIAL ISSUES [2006]

208 I Street, N.E.
Washington, DC 20002-4340
(202) 675-6956
Fax: (202) 675-6902

E-MAIL ADDRESS:
spssi@spssi.org
awards@spssi.org

WEB SITE ADDRESS:
www.spssi.org/awards

FOUNDED: 1936

AREAS OF INTEREST:
Interests, intergroup relations, social issues and psychology.

NAME(S) OF PROGRAMS:
- **The SAGES Program**

TYPE:
Research grants. Program to encourage members 60 years of age and over and retired members to apply their knowledge to helping solve social problems or to assist policy makers to solve social problems. Proposals are invited that use social science research findings to address social problems through direct action projects, consulting with not-for-profit groups, or through preparing reviews of existing social science literature that could be used by policy makers.

LEGAL BASIS:
Independently incorporated society.

ELIGIBILITY:
SPSSI members 60 years of age and over and/or retired. Proposals will be evaluated in terms of how well they build on existing social science research and theory, the feasibility of the project, and the importance of the project.

FINANCIAL DATA:
Funding can be submitted for direct costs related to the project. This can be spent over a two-year period. Money can be used for hiring staff (including clerical assistance), computing fees, travel, telephone, or other justifiable expenses. Funding cannot be used as a stipend for the applicant.

Amount of support per award: $1,000 to $10,000.

NUMBER OF APPLICANTS MOST RECENT YEAR:
10.

NUMBER OF AWARDS: 1 award, 2 honorable mentions.

APPLICATION INFORMATION:
Duration: Up to two years.

Deadline: February 15. Announcement by May 5.

ADDRESS INQUIRIES TO:
Anila Balkissoon
Administrative Coordinator
(See address above.)

THE SOCIETY FOR THE PSYCHOLOGICAL STUDY OF SOCIAL ISSUES [2007]

208 I Street, N.E.
Washington, DC 20002-4340
(202) 675-6956
Fax: (202) 675-6902

E-MAIL ADDRESS:
awards@spssi.org
spssi@spssi.org

WEB SITE ADDRESS:
www.spssi.org/awards

FOUNDED: 1936

AREAS OF INTEREST:
Intergroup relations, social issues and psychology.

NAME(S) OF PROGRAMS:
- **The Louise Kidder Early Career Award**

TYPE:
Awards/prizes. This award is named in honor of Louise Kidder for her early career accomplishments and contributions to SPSSI.

PURPOSE:
To recognize social issues researchers who have made substantial contributions to the field early in their careers.

LEGAL BASIS:
Independently incorporated society.

ELIGIBILITY:
Nominees should be investigators who have made substantial contributions to social issues research within five years of receiving a graduate degree and who have demonstrated the potential to continue such contributions. Nominees need not be current Society members.

FINANCIAL DATA:
Amount of support per award: $500 and plaque.

NUMBER OF APPLICANTS MOST RECENT YEAR:
10.

NUMBER OF AWARDS: 1.

APPLICATION INFORMATION:
Deadline: June 15. Announcement by August 1. Late applications will be retained for one year.

ADDRESS INQUIRIES TO:
Anila Balkissoon
Administrative Coordinator
(See address above.)

THE SOCIETY FOR THE PSYCHOLOGICAL STUDY OF SOCIAL ISSUES   [2008]
208 I Street, N.E.
Washington, DC 20002-4340
(202) 675-6956
Fax: (202) 675-6902

E-MAIL ADDRESS:
awards@spssi.org
spssi@spssi.org

WEB SITE ADDRESS:
www.spssi.org

FOUNDED: 1936

AREAS OF INTEREST:
Intergroup relations, social issues and psychology.

NAME(S) OF PROGRAMS:
● **The Gordon Allport Intergroup Relations Prize**
● **The Social Issues Dissertation Award**

TYPE:
Awards/prizes. The Gordon Allport Intergroup Relations Prize is given for the best paper or article of the year on intergroup relations. The research area of intergroup relations includes such dimensions as age, sex and socioeconomic status, as well as race.

The Social Issues Dissertation Award is given for the best psychological dissertation concerned with social issues. It is judged upon scientific excellence and potential application to social problems.

PURPOSE:
The Gordon Allport Intergroup Relations Prize: To award the best paper or article of the year on intergroup relations in areas of study such as age, gender, and socioeconomic status, as well as ethnicity.

The Social Issues Dissertation Award: To award dissertations that best demonstrate scientific excellence and potential application to social problems.

LEGAL BASIS:
Independently incorporated society.

ELIGIBILITY:
For the Allport Prize, entries can be either papers published during the current year or unpublished manuscripts. Entries cannot be returned. The competition is open to non-members, as well as members of SPSSI. Graduate students are especially urged to submit papers. Please note that an individual or group may only submit one paper to SPSSI awards per award year.

Any doctoral dissertation in psychology (or in a social science with psychological subject matter) accepted between March 1, 2010 and March 1, 2011 is eligible for The Social Issues Dissertation Award. An individual or group may only submit to one SPSSI paper award per year.

FINANCIAL DATA:
Amount of support per award: Allport Prize: $1,000; Social Issues Dissertation Award: first prize $750, second prize $500.

APPLICATION INFORMATION:
Contact the SPSSI Central Office for application information.
Deadline: Allport Prize: Submitted applications must be received by October 11; Social Issues Dissertation Award: May 10.

PUBLICATIONS:
Application guidelines.

*SPECIAL STIPULATIONS:
An individual or group may only submit one SPSSI paper award per year.

STIFTELSEN RIKSBANKENS JUBILEUMSFOND
Kungstradgardsg. 18
SE-114 86 Stockholm Sweden
46 08-50 62 64 00
Fax: 46 08-50 62 64 31

E-MAIL ADDRESS:
rj@rj.se

TYPE:
Conferences/seminars; Exchange programs; Fellowships; General operating grants; Project/program grants; Research grants; Travel grants; Visiting scholars.

See entry 427 for full listing.

DR. W.C. SWANSON FAMILY FOUNDATION, INC.   [2009]
2520 North 1500 West
Ogden, UT 84404
(801) 392-0360
Fax: (801) 392-0429

E-MAIL ADDRESS:
sff@swanfound.org

WEB SITE ADDRESS:
www.swanfound.org

AREAS OF INTEREST:
Education, literacy, religion, science and prevention of cruelty to children or animals.

TYPE:
Matching gifts; Product donations; Project/program grants.

YEAR PROGRAM STARTED: 1977

PURPOSE:
To provide support for charitable, religious, literacy, scientific or educational purposes and the prevention of cruelty to children or animals.

LEGAL BASIS:
Private foundation.

ELIGIBILITY:
Grants are made to organizations that have tax-exempt status under Section 501(c)(3) of the Internal Revenue Code. Non-sectarian religious programs may apply. No grants are made to individuals.

GEOGRAPHIC RESTRICTIONS:
Primarily Ogden City, Weber County and northern Utah.

FINANCIAL DATA:
Amount of support per award: Varies.
Total amount of support: Varies.

APPLICATION INFORMATION:
Duration: One year. Renewal possible.
Deadline: October 31, February 28 and June 30.

BOARD OF DIRECTORS:
Michael Fosmark
Jon Greiner
Tom Hanrahan
Annabel Hofer
W. Charles Swanson

ADVISORY BOARD:
Kim Dohrer
Marcy Korgenski
Cindy R. Purcell
Robin Stoddard
Tami Swanson
W. Charles Swanson

ADDRESS INQUIRIES TO:
Bridgett Tasker, Grants Administrator
(See address above.)

U.S. ARMY RESEARCH INSTITUTE FOR BEHAVIORAL AND SOCIAL SCIENCES   [2010]
2511 Jefferson Davis Highway
Arlington, VA 22202-3926
(703) 545-2410
Fax: (703) 602-7710

E-MAIL ADDRESS:
jay.goodwin@us.army.mil

FOUNDED: 1940

AREAS OF INTEREST:
Leadership, interactive simulation training, individual performance and information comprehension, and social structures affecting army performance.

TYPE:
Conferences/seminars; Fellowships; Visiting scholars; Work-study programs; Research contracts.

PURPOSE:
To contribute to the cumulative knowledge base in behavioral science, with an eye to building new technologies capable of improving the effectiveness of Army personnel and their units.

LEGAL BASIS:
Government agency.

ELIGIBILITY:
Both single-investigator and collaborative research efforts will be considered, and multidisciplinary approaches to a central problem are encouraged. Collaborative efforts may involve researchers at a single institution or in cooperating institutions and joint university/industry partnerships are welcomed. Interest is welcomed from the

widest range of institutions, including historically Black colleges and universities and minority institutions.

No consideration will be given to applied research or investigations whose primary focus is on physiological or chemical mechanisms or psychopathology. Another consideration determining support for the research is the judgment that findings have the potential for feeding into development of new behavioral technologies capable of improving the effectiveness of Army personnel and their units.

FINANCIAL DATA:
Amount of support per award: Contract amounts vary according to funds available and Army requirements. Generally $100,000 to $800,000. Average $300,000 per year. *Total amount of support:* $5,000,000 for the year 2010.

APPLICATION INFORMATION:
Interested individuals should seek ARI's Broad Agency Announcement, issued annually between January and June, on www.fedbizopps.gov. Preliminary concept papers (three to five pages) as well as formal proposals may be submitted. Concept papers should describe the problem to be addressed, justify the effort's theoretical significance and uniqueness, briefly describe the approach to the problem and state potential benefits to the Army. An estimated budget and project duration should be included, along with brief vitae of the principal investigators.

Concept papers will be reviewed within ARI for their relevance to Army priorities, theoretical significance and technical merit. Offers of highly rated concept papers will be invited to submit formal proposals.
Duration: Maximum four years. Average three years.
Deadline: August 1.

PUBLICATIONS:
Program announcement.

STAFF:
Dr. Jay Goodwin, Chief of Basic Research Unit

ADDRESS INQUIRIES TO:
Dr. Jay Goodwin, Ph.D.
Chief of Basic Research Unit
(See address above.)

U.S. DEPARTMENT OF EDUCATION
Jacob K. Javits Fellowships Program
1990 K Street, N.W., Suite 6018
Washington, DC 20006-8524
(202) 219-7138
Fax: (202) 502-7859

E-MAIL ADDRESS:
ope_javits_program@ed.gov

WEB SITE ADDRESS:
www.ed.gov/programs/jacobjavits/index.html

TYPE:
Fellowships.

See entry 429 for full listing.

U.S. DEPARTMENT OF JUSTICE
Office of Juvenile Justice and
Delinquency Prevention
810 7th Street, N.W., 5th Floor
Washington, DC 20531
(202) 307-5911
Fax: (202) 307-2093

WEB SITE ADDRESS:
www.ojjdp.ncjrs.gov

TYPE:
Conferences/seminars; Development grants; Fellowships; Internships; Project/program grants; Research grants; Residencies; Visiting scholars; Research contracts. Grants to conduct research, evaluation and development on juvenile justice and delinquency prevention activities, including the development of new or improved approaches, techniques, systems and program models to conduct behavioral research on the causes of juvenile crime, means of, intervention and prevention, and to evaluate juvenile programs and procedures.

See entry 1504 for full listing.

WOODROW WILSON INTERNATIONAL CENTER FOR SCHOLARS
One Woodrow Wilson Plaza
1300 Pennsylvania Avenue, N.W.
Washington, DC 20004-3027
(202) 691-4170
Fax: (202) 691-4001

E-MAIL ADDRESS:
fellowships@wilsoncenter.org

WEB SITE ADDRESS:
www.wilsoncenter.org

TYPE:
Fellowships; Research grants; Residencies; Scholarships; Visiting scholars. The Center seeks to commemorate, through its residential fellowship program of advanced research, both the scholarly depth and the public concerns of Woodrow Wilson. The Center welcomes outstanding project proposals in the social sciences and humanities on national and/or international issues - topics that intersect with questions of public policy or provide the historical framework to illume policy issues of contemporary importance. The Center especially welcomes projects likely to foster communication between the world of ideas and the world of public affairs.

Projects should have relevance to the world of public policy. Fellows should be prepared to interact with policymakers in Washington and with the Center's staff working on similar areas.

Fellowships are tenable in residence only at the Woodrow Wilson International Center for Scholars. The Center will not provide support for research to be carried out elsewhere. Fellows devote their full time to research and writing.

See entry 433 for full listing.

CARTER G. WOODSON INSTITUTE FOR AFRICAN-AMERICAN AND AFRICAN STUDIES
University of Virginia
McCormick Road, 108 Minor Hall
Charlottesville, VA 22903
(434) 924-3109
Fax: (434) 924-8820

E-MAIL ADDRESS:
woodson@virginia.edu

WEB SITE ADDRESS:
www.virginia.edu/~woodson

TYPE:
Fellowships. The Woodson Institute offers residential fellowships to predoctoral and postdoctoral scholars. These fellowships are designed to facilitate the completion of works in progress by providing scholars with unencumbered leave.

Afro-American and African Studies is considered to cover Africa, Africans and peoples of African descent in North, Central and South America and the Caribbean, past and present.

See entry 435 for full listing.

Business and economics

THE ACTUARIAL FOUNDATION
475 North Martingale Road, Suite 600
Schaumburg, IL 60173-2226
(847) 706-3535
Fax: (847) 706-3599

E-MAIL ADDRESS:
Scholarships@ActFnd.org

WEB SITE ADDRESS:
www.actuarialfoundation.org

TYPE:
Scholarships.

See entry 2223 for full listing.

THE ACTUARIAL FOUNDATION
475 North Martingale Road, Suite 600
Schaumburg, IL 60173-2226
(847) 706-3535
Fax: (847) 706-3599

E-MAIL ADDRESS:
Scholarships@ActFnd.org

WEB SITE ADDRESS:
www.actuarialfoundation.org

TYPE:
Scholarships.

See entry 2224 for full listing.

AMERICAN INSTITUTE OF CERTIFIED PUBLIC ACCOUNTANTS (AICPA)   [2011]
Team 331
220 Leigh Farm Road
Durham, NC 27707
(919) 402-4931

E-MAIL ADDRESS:
scholarships@aicpa.org

WEB SITE ADDRESS:
www.aicpa.org/accountemps

AREAS OF INTEREST:
Accounting, finance and information systems.

NAME(S) OF PROGRAMS:
● **AICPA/Accountemps Student Scholarship**

TYPE:
Scholarships. Awarded to accounting majors to encourage them to become a C.P.A.

PURPOSE:
To provide financial assistance to students who are currently majoring in accounting, finance or information systems; to encourage students to consider careers in accounting and business.

ELIGIBILITY:
An applicant must:
(1) studying accounting or a related major;
(2) full-time undergraduate (12 semester hours or equivalent) or a full-time Master's level student (nine semester hours or equivalent) at an accredited college or university in the U.S. for the upcoming Fall and Spring semesters;
(3) have completed at least 30 semester hours (or equivalent) of college coursework, including at least six semester hours (or equivalent) in accounting;
(4) maintained an overall grade point average and a major grade point average of at least 3.0;
(5) U.S. citizen or permanent resident (Green Card holder);
(6) not presently a C.P.A. and;
(7) AICPA student affiliate member (or have recently submitted a new member application).

GEOGRAPHIC RESTRICTIONS:
United States.

FINANCIAL DATA:
Amount of support per award: $2,500.

NUMBER OF AWARDS: 5.

APPLICATION INFORMATION:
Applications are submitted online.
Duration: One year. Nonrenewable.
Deadline: April 1.

ADDRESS INQUIRIES TO:
See e-mail address above.

AMERICAN INSTITUTE OF CERTIFIED PUBLIC ACCOUNTANTS (AICPA)   [2012]

220 Leigh Farm Road
Durham, NC 27707
(919) 402-4931
Fax: (919) 419-4705

E-MAIL ADDRESS:
scholarships@aicpa.org

WEB SITE ADDRESS:
www.aicpa.org

AREAS OF INTEREST:
Accounting.

NAME(S) OF PROGRAMS:
● John L. Carey Scholarship

TYPE:
Scholarships.

PURPOSE:
To provide financial assistance to liberal arts or other non-business related degree holders pursuing graduate studies in accounting and the CPA designation; to encourage students with little or no previous accounting education to consider professional accounting careers.

ELIGIBILITY:
An eligible student must:
(1) have obtained a liberal arts or non-business undergraduate degree prior to enrolling in a graduate accounting program;
(2) have not earned more than 12 credits in accounting or business during their undergraduate program;
(3) have been accepted into, or in the process of applying to, a graduate program in accounting that is accredited by AACSB International or ACBSP;
(4) not already be actively participating in a

graduate accounting program and;
(5) be intending to pursue a C.P.A. certificate.

GEOGRAPHIC RESTRICTIONS:
United States.

FINANCIAL DATA:
Amount of support per award: $5,000.

NUMBER OF AWARDS: Up to 10.

APPLICATION INFORMATION:
Duration: One year. Renewable.
Deadline: April 1.

ADDRESS INQUIRIES TO:
See e-mail address above.

APICS EDUCATIONAL AND RESEARCH FOUNDATION, INC.

8430 West Bryn Mawr Avenue
Suite 1000
Chicago, IL 60631-3439
(800) 444-2742 (customer service)
(773) 867-1777
Fax: (773) 639-3115

E-MAIL ADDRESS:
jstults@apics.org

WEB SITE ADDRESS:
www.apics.org/education/erfoundation

TYPE:
Awards/prizes; Conferences/seminars; Fellowships; Project/program grants; Research grants. Plossl Doctoral Dissertation Competition is in the area of business management.

Grants are also available at the postdoctoral, academic-practitioner level in the field of business.

See entry 2762 for full listing.

APPRAISAL INSTITUTE EDUCATION TRUST   [2013]

550 West Van Buren Street
Suite 1000
Chicago, IL 60607
(312) 335-4100
Fax: (312) 335-4134

E-MAIL ADDRESS:
educationtrust@appraisalinstitute.org

WEB SITE ADDRESS:
www.appraisalinstitute.org

NAME(S) OF PROGRAMS:
● Appraisal Institute Education Trust Scholarship

TYPE:
Scholarships. Graduate and undergraduate scholarships to help worthy and qualified students finance the cost of college work leading to a degree in the fields of real estate appraisal, land economics, real estate and allied fields.

PURPOSE:
To help finance the educational endeavors of individuals concentrating their studies in real estate appraisal, land economics, real estate or allied fields.

ELIGIBILITY:
Applicants must be citizens of the U.S., attending a full-time college, U.S. university or community college, and have the expressed intention of majoring in real estate evaluation and related subjects. Related subjects may include land economics, economics, economic geography, and others

similarly related. Levels of education for the scholarship must be sophomore, junior, senior and graduate year of college.

Preference will be given to those applicants whose previous training and whose future course of study indicate that they intend to follow a field of endeavor which comes within the scope of the objectives of the Appraisal Institute. Applicants must also demonstrate qualities of leadership and scholarly attainments.

GEOGRAPHIC RESTRICTIONS:
United States.

FINANCIAL DATA:
Amount of support per award: Graduate: $2,000; Undergraduate: $1,000.

NUMBER OF AWARDS: Up to approximately 50 per year.

APPLICATION INFORMATION:
The Appraisal Institute will annually send out application forms, instructions and information regarding the scholarship. For further information, contact Elizabeth Kramer, Project Coordinator, at the address, e-mail or telephone listed above.
Duration: One academic year.
Deadline: March 15 for the following academic year.

OFFICERS:
Fred Grubbe, Chief Executive Officer

ADDRESS INQUIRIES TO:
Scholarship Committee
(See address above.)

CONSORTIUM FOR GRADUATE STUDY IN MANAGEMENT [2014]

5585 Pershing Avenue
Suite 240
St. Louis, MO 63112
(314) 877-5500
Fax: (314) 877-5505

E-MAIL ADDRESS:
frontdesk@cgsm.org

WEB SITE ADDRESS:
www.cgsm.org

FOUNDED: 1966

NAME(S) OF PROGRAMS:
● Consortium Fellowship
● Fellowships for Minorities in Management

TYPE:
Fellowships. Graduate fellowships for minority students interested in management careers in business.

YEAR PROGRAM STARTED: 1967

PURPOSE:
To hasten the entry of minorities into management positions in business.

LEGAL BASIS:
Not-for-profit, IRS 501(c)(3) status.

ELIGIBILITY:
U.S. citizenship and permanent residence in the U.S. is required. African Americans, Hispanic Americans and Native Americans with Baccalaureate degrees are eligible to apply. The undergraduate degree need not be in business or economics.

Fellowships are tenable only at Consortium institutions, including University of California-Berkeley, Carnegie-Mellon University, Dartmouth College, Emory University, Indiana University (Bloomington), New York University, University of Michigan (Ann Arbor), University of North Carolina

(Chapel Hill), University of Rochester, University of Southern California, University of Texas (Austin), University of Virginia, University of Wisconsin (Madison) and Washington University (St. Louis).

There are no fellowships awarded for part-time study.

FINANCIAL DATA:
The fellowship includes full tuition and required fees. Loans are also available for students who establish need in excess of the tuition.
Total amount of support: $22,000,000 for fiscal year 2010.

NUMBER OF APPLICANTS MOST RECENT YEAR: 1,000.

APPLICATION INFORMATION:
Apply online only.
Duration: Fellowships are awarded for a maximum of four semesters of full-time study.
Deadline: December 1 and January 5.

IRS IDENTIFICATION NUMBER: 43-0962198

STAFF:
Peter Aranda, Chief Executive Officer
Glenn Wilen, Vice President of Finance and Administration

CRDF GLOBAL [2015]
1530 Wilson Boulevard, Third Floor
Arlington, VA 22209
(703) 526-9720
Fax: (703) 526-9721

E-MAIL ADDRESS:
cgp@crdf.org

WEB SITE ADDRESS:
www.crdf.org

FOUNDED: 1995

AREAS OF INTEREST:
International research collaborations, science education and infrastructure, science and technology commercialization, nonproliferation of WMD expertise, and international research service and support.

CONSULTING OR VOLUNTEER SERVICES:
The Foundation offers a wide range of services facilitating cooperative research between foreign and U.S. researchers.

Grant Assistance Program (GAP) offers a unique set of financial and project management services to organizations in support of their collaborative scientific research, educational or charitable activities in Eurasia.

NAME(S) OF PROGRAMS:
- **Centers & Institution Building**
- **Cooperative Grants Program**
- **Industry Programs**
- **Nonproliferation Initiatives (NPI)**

TYPE:
Block grants; Challenge/matching grants; Conferences/seminars; Development grants; Exchange programs; Fellowships; Grants-in-aid; Product donations; Project/program grants; Research grants; Technical assistance; Training grants. Centers & Institution Building programs build sustainable institutions patterned on successful international analogs that enable international scientists to develop national and global science and technology advances.

Cooperative Grants Program provides up to two years of support for joint U.S. and international research teams in all areas of basic and applied research in the natural sciences.

Industry Programs enable American companies and international scientists, engineers, and organizations to explore new commercial research partnerships, and move the product of their collaborations to the market through a progressive series of grants programs.

Nonproliferation Initiatives (NPI) program develops and implements innovative ways to encourage the participation of former weapons of mass destruction (WMD) scientists in Foundation grant programs.

YEAR PROGRAM STARTED: 1995

PURPOSE:
To promote scientific and technical collaboration between the U.S. and the countries of the former Soviet Union.

LEGAL BASIS:
A nonprofit, charitable organization created by the U.S. Government.

PUBLICATIONS:
Forge; *GAPnotes*; *Access* (all quarterly electronic newsletters).

DECA [2016]
1908 Association Drive
Reston, VA 20191
(703) 860-5000
Fax: (703) 860-4013

E-MAIL ADDRESS:
decainc@aol.com

WEB SITE ADDRESS:
www.deca.org

FOUNDED: 1946

AREAS OF INTEREST:
Marketing education, management and entrepreneurship.

TYPE:
Scholarships.

YEAR PROGRAM STARTED: 1962

PURPOSE:
To further education and careers in marketing education, management and entrepreneurship.

LEGAL BASIS:
Nonprofit association.

ELIGIBILITY:
Applicant must be a current member of DECA.

GEOGRAPHIC RESTRICTIONS:
United States.

FINANCIAL DATA:
Amount of support per award: Varies.
Total amount of support: Varies.

APPLICATION INFORMATION:
Information is available at the web site.
Duration: One year. Renewals are considered. Must reapply.

ADDRESS INQUIRIES TO:
Scholarship Department
(See address above.)

THE DIRECT MARKETING CLUB OF NEW YORK (DMCNY) [2017]
54 Adams Street
Garden City, NY 11530
(516) 746-6700
Fax: (516) 294-8141

E-MAIL ADDRESS:
info@dmcny.org

WEB SITE ADDRESS:
www.dmcny.org

FOUNDED: 1930

CONSULTING OR VOLUNTEER SERVICES:
Team of creative specialists is available for consulting or speaking.

NAME(S) OF PROGRAMS:
- **Silver Apple Award Scholarships**

TYPE:
Conferences/seminars; Grants-in-aid. Non-degree courses and seminars.

YEAR PROGRAM STARTED: 1977

PURPOSE:
To advance and promote the members' charitable, educational, scientific and literary interests, as well as their understanding and application of professional direct marketing practices.

LEGAL BASIS:
New York State not-for-profit corporation.

ELIGIBILITY:
Scholarships to students in direct marketing studies only. Grants made to universities only.

GEOGRAPHIC RESTRICTIONS:
Connecticut, New Jersey and New York.

FINANCIAL DATA:
Amount of support per award: $500 to $1,500.
Total amount of support: Approximately $3,500.

NUMBER OF AWARDS: 7.

APPLICATION INFORMATION:
Duration: One year.

ADDRESS INQUIRIES TO:
Stuart Boysen, Director
(See address above.)

*SPECIAL STIPULATIONS:
The scholarship applicant's course of study must be related to direct marketing.

DIRECT MARKETING EDUCATIONAL FOUNDATION, INC. [2018]
1120 Avenue of the Americas
New York, NY 10036-6700
(212) 768-7277 ext. 1512
Fax: (212) 790-1561

E-MAIL ADDRESS:
dmef@directworks.org

WEB SITE ADDRESS:
www.directworks.org

FOUNDED: 1965

AREAS OF INTEREST:
Investing in the future of the direct/interactive marketing field.

NAME(S) OF PROGRAMS:
- **Direct Marketing Leadership Development Program**
- **DMEF Scholarship Program**

- Robert Kestnbaum Research Program
- Shankar-Spiegel Award for the Best Dissertation Proposal in Direct/Interactive Marketing

TYPE:
Awards/prizes; Conferences/seminars; Exchange programs; Internships; Research grants; Scholarships; Research contracts. Direct Marketing Leadership Development Program offers qualified applicants the opportunity to acquire valuable work experience at a competitive salary during a unique 12-month program.

DMEF Scholarship Program provides education funding support to undergraduate and graduate students nationwide.

Robert Kestnbaum Research Program is intended to generate leading-edge academic research to impact the future of direct/interactive marketing.

Shankar-Spiegel Award for the Best Dissertation Proposal in Direct/Interactive Marketing recognizes doctoral candidates with the best dissertation proposal in direct/interactive marketing. Doctoral students from accredited doctoral programs are eligible to receive this award.

YEAR PROGRAM STARTED: 1965

PURPOSE:
To nurture, maintain and grow talent throughout the direct/interactive marketing field; to educate students today in order to enrich the talent pool in this field tomorrow.

LEGAL BASIS:
Nonprofit, tax-exempt organization.

ELIGIBILITY:
Varies by program.

GEOGRAPHIC RESTRICTIONS:
United States for student programs. Global for academic engagement.

FINANCIAL DATA:
Amount of support per award: $1,000 to $5,000.

APPLICATION INFORMATION:
Form and guidelines available online.

PUBLICATIONS:
Annual report; conference materials; *Journal of Interactive Marketing®.*

IRS IDENTIFICATION NUMBER: 13-6222757

STAFF:
Terri L. Bartlett, President
Marie Adolphe, Vice President, Program Development
Jeanne K. Murphy, Director, Development

ADDRESS INQUIRIES TO:
Terri L. Bartlett, President
(See address above.)

ECONOMIC HISTORY ASSOCIATION   [2019]
Economics Department
Santa Clara University
500 El Camino Real
Santa Clara, CA 95053-0385
(408) 554-4348
Fax: (408) 554-2331

E-MAIL ADDRESS:
afield@scu.edu

WEB SITE ADDRESS:
www.eh.net/eha

FOUNDED: 1940

AREAS OF INTEREST:
Economic history.

NAME(S) OF PROGRAMS:
- Arthur H. Cole Grants-in-Aid

TYPE:
Grants-in-aid. Grants for advanced research in any aspect of economic history.

YEAR PROGRAM STARTED: 1972

PURPOSE:
To support individual research in the field of economic history or to supplement a major fellowship.

LEGAL BASIS:
Nonprofit.

ELIGIBILITY:
Applicants must have completed their Ph.D. and must be members of the Economic History Association. Preference is given to recent Ph.D. recipients.

FINANCIAL DATA:
Amount of support per award: Up to $5,000.

NUMBER OF APPLICANTS MOST RECENT YEAR:
26.

NUMBER OF AWARDS: 4 for the year 2010.

APPLICATION INFORMATION:
Information is available on the Association web site.
Duration: One year.

PUBLICATIONS:
Annual newsletter; *The Journal of Economic History.*

IRS IDENTIFICATION NUMBER: 13-6128711

THE EDUCATIONAL FOUNDATION FOR WOMEN IN ACCOUNTING   [2020]
136 South Keowee Street
Dayton, OH 45402-2241
(937) 424-3391
Fax: (937) 222-5794

E-MAIL ADDRESS:
info@efwa.org

WEB SITE ADDRESS:
www.efwa.org

FOUNDED: 1966

AREAS OF INTEREST:
Women in the accounting field.

NAME(S) OF PROGRAMS:
- Laurels Fund
- Michelle L. McDonald Scholarship
- Moss Adams LLP Scholarship
- Seattle ASWA Chapter Scholarship
- Women in Need Scholarship
- Women in Transition Scholarship

TYPE:
Scholarships. Laurels Fund provides a one-year academic scholarship for women pursuing a Ph.D. in accounting.

Women in Need Scholarship is available to women in their third, fourth or fifth year of academic pursuit who need the financial support to complete their degrees. It is renewable annually upon satisfactory completion of course requirements.

Women in Transition Scholarship is intended for women returning to school as freshmen to earn a Bachelor's degree in accounting. It is renewable annually upon satisfactory completion of course requirements.

YEAR PROGRAM STARTED: 1966

PURPOSE:
To support the advancement of women in the accounting profession through the funding of education, research, career literature, publications and other projects; to encourage and enable women to enter the accounting profession and empower them to achieve equal opportunities and equal rewards.

LEGAL BASIS:
501(c)(3) organization.

ELIGIBILITY:
Women who are pursuing accounting degrees at the undergraduate, graduate and postgraduate levels.

GEOGRAPHIC RESTRICTIONS:
United States.

FINANCIAL DATA:
Amount of support per award: Laurels Fund: $1,000 to $5,000; McDonald and Moss Adams LLP Scholarships: $1,000 each; Seattle ASWA Chapter Scholarship: $2,000; Women in Need Scholarship: $2,000 per year; Women in Transition Scholarship: Up to $4,000 per year.

NUMBER OF APPLICANTS MOST RECENT YEAR:
40.

NUMBER OF AWARDS: Laurels Fund: 3; Michelle L. McDonald, Moss Adams LLP, Seattle ASWA Chapter and Women in Transition Scholarships: 1 each; Women in Need Scholarship: 2.

APPLICATION INFORMATION:
Applications are available on the web site.
Duration: Laurels Fund, Michelle L. McDonald, Moss Adams LLP and Seattle ASWA Chapter Scholarships: One year; Women in Need Scholarship: Two years; Women in Transition Scholarship: Four years.
Deadline: Laurels Fund: May 30. All others: May 1.

ADDRESS INQUIRIES TO:
Kimberly Fantaci, Foundation Administrator
(See address above.)

ERNST & YOUNG FOUNDATION   [2021]
200 Plaza Drive
Secaucus, NJ 07094
(201) 872-5686
Fax: (866) 855-4960

E-MAIL ADDRESS:
ellen.glazerman@ey.com

WEB SITE ADDRESS:
www.ey.com

FOUNDED: 1937

AREAS OF INTEREST:
Higher education, with specific interests in accounting and business.

TYPE:
Fellowships; Matching gifts; Scholarships.

YEAR PROGRAM STARTED: 1937

PURPOSE:
To support higher education.

LEGAL BASIS:
Public charity.

ELIGIBILITY:
No grants to individuals. No cold requests.

GEOGRAPHIC RESTRICTIONS:
United States and its territories.

FINANCIAL DATA:
Amount of support per award: Varies.
Total amount of support: Varies.
Matching fund requirements: Ernst & Young Foundation will only match contributions to an accredited college, junior college, community college, university, graduate school or professional school.

APPLICATION INFORMATION:
Duration: Varies.
Deadline: Grant requests are reviewed continuously.

ADDRESS INQUIRIES TO:
Ellen Glazerman, Executive Director (See address and e-mail above.)

FEDERATION OF AMERICAN CONSUMERS AND TRAVELERS [2022]

318 Hillsboro Avenue
P.O. Box 104
Edwardsville, IL 62025
(618) 656-0454
(800) 872-3228
Fax: (618) 656-5369

E-MAIL ADDRESS:
vrolens@usafact.org

WEB SITE ADDRESS:
www.usafact.org

NAME(S) OF PROGRAMS:
- **Community and Business Project Grants**

TYPE:
Project/program grants; Seed money grants.

PURPOSE:
To support civic club, church, and community projects that are nominated by members.

ELIGIBILITY:
Projects are nominated by members.

GEOGRAPHIC RESTRICTIONS:
United States.

FINANCIAL DATA:
Amount of support per award: $100 to $2,500, based on funding availability and the needs of the specific proposal.

ADDRESS INQUIRIES TO:
Vicki Rolens, Managing Director (See address above.)

4A'S

405 Lexington Avenue, 18th Floor
New York, NY 10174-1801
(800) 676-9333
Fax: (212) 867-8329

E-MAIL ADDRESS:
maip@aaaa.org

WEB SITE ADDRESS:
www.adunity.aaaa.org

TYPE:
Internships.
See entry 1048 for full listing.

HAGLEY MUSEUM AND LIBRARY

Center for the History of
Business, Technology and Society
298 Buck Road
Wilmington, DE 19807
(302) 658-2400
Fax: (302) 655-3188

E-MAIL ADDRESS:
clockman@hagley.org

WEB SITE ADDRESS:
www.hagley.org

TYPE:
Research grants; Travel grants; Visiting scholars. Grants to support short-term research in the imprint, manuscript, pictorial and artifact collections of the Hagley Museum and Library. Holdings include rich manuscript and imprint collections relating to French history, 1760-1820, and to American economic history, 1800-1950, with special emphasis on American business, industrial and technological developments.

The Henry Belin du Pont Dissertation Fellowship in Business, Technology, and Society supports research and writing by candidates for doctoral degrees. Projects should demonstrate superior intellectual quality and make substantial use of Hagley's collections.

Henry Belin du Pont Fellowships support research in the collections of the museum and library.

Hagley Exploratory Research Grant supports a one-week visit by scholars who believe that their project will benefit from Hagley research collections, but need the opportunity to explore them on-site to determine if a Henry Belin du Pont research grant application is warranted.

See entry 632 for full listing.

THE S.S. HUEBNER FOUNDATION FOR INSURANCE EDUCATION [2023]

The Wharton School of the
University of Pennsylvania
3000 SH-DH
3620 Locust Walk
Philadelphia, PA 19104-6302
(215) 898-9631
Fax: (215) 573-2218

E-MAIL ADDRESS:
jiai@wharton.upenn.edu

WEB SITE ADDRESS:
www.huebnergeneva.org

FOUNDED: 1940

AREAS OF INTEREST:
Insurance and risk management.

TYPE:
Fellowships. For study towards a Ph.D. degree in the field of risk and insurance at the Wharton School of the University of Pennsylvania.

YEAR PROGRAM STARTED: 1940

PURPOSE:
To increase the supply of college faculty specializing in risk and insurance by enabling qualified candidates to pursue graduate studies.

ELIGIBILITY:
Candidates must have a B.A. or B.S. degree from an accredited university or college. Candidates must certify that they intend to study for the doctoral degree in managerial sciences and applied economics with a specialization in risk and insurance at the Wharton School of the University of Pennsylvania and plan to pursue careers as college faculty.

Candidates are also required to take the GMAT or GRE and be admitted to the Doctoral Program at the Wharton School of the University of Pennsylvania. Information regarding the examinations can be obtained directly from the Educational Testing Service, 20 Nassau Street, Princeton, NJ 08540.

FINANCIAL DATA:
Yearly stipend plus tuition, fees and various expenses.
Amount of support per award: Up to $25,750 per year.
Total amount of support: $62,500 for the year 2010.

NUMBER OF APPLICANTS MOST RECENT YEAR: 20.

NUMBER OF AWARDS: 1.

APPLICATION INFORMATION:
Duration: Renewable for up to four years, contingent upon satisfactory progress in the program.
Deadline: December 15.

PUBLICATIONS:
Annual report.

IRS IDENTIFICATION NUMBER: 23-6297325

ADDRESS INQUIRIES TO:
Jing Ai, Associate Director (See address above.)

ILLINOIS RESTAURANT ASSOCIATION EDUCATIONAL FOUNDATION, INC.

33 West Monroe, Suite 250
Chicago, IL 60603
(312) 787-4000
Fax: (312) 845-1956

E-MAIL ADDRESS:
edfound@illinoisrestaurants.org

WEB SITE ADDRESS:
www.illinoisrestaurants.org

TYPE:
Scholarships.
See entry 1818 for full listing.

INSTITUTE FOR SUPPLY MANAGEMENT [2024]

2055 East Centennial Circle
Tempe, AZ 85284
(480) 752-6276
Fax: (480) 752-7890

E-MAIL ADDRESS:
kempr@mchsi.com

WEB SITE ADDRESS:
www.ism.ws

FOUNDED: 1915

AREAS OF INTEREST:
Purchasing/supply management.

NAME(S) OF PROGRAMS:
- **ISM Dissertation Research Grant - Phase 1 (Doctoral)**

TYPE:
Research grants. A limited number of grants are available to doctoral candidates interested in pursuing advanced study in industrial and/or institutional purchasing, supply management and closely related fields.

YEAR PROGRAM STARTED: 1984

PURPOSE:
To produce useful research that can be applied to purchasing and supply management; to help develop high-potential academicians who will teach and conduct research in purchasing and supply management.

LEGAL BASIS:
501(c)(3) nonprofit educational and research organization.

ELIGIBILITY:
Applicants must be doctoral candidates who are pursuing a Ph.D. or D.B.A. in purchasing, business, logistics, management, economics, industrial engineering, or related fields. Applicants must be enrolled full-time in accredited U.S. universities.

GEOGRAPHIC RESTRICTIONS:
United States.

FINANCIAL DATA:
The stipend is allocated to the student for support in conducting the research project and related academic work. Payment is made in two installments; one-half upon receipt of a written statement from the dissertation committee chairperson verifying that the research project is approximately 50% completed and one-half upon receipt of a signed copy, by the dissertation committee, of the dissertation.
Amount of support per award: Up to $12,000 per grant.
Total amount of support: $20,000 for the year 2009-10.

NUMBER OF APPLICANTS MOST RECENT YEAR:
15.

APPLICATION INFORMATION:
Application forms are available online. Detailed guidelines may be obtained from the Institute.
Duration: Must be complete within three years.
Deadline: January 31. Announcement on or about May 31.

PUBLICATIONS:
Brochure.

ADDRESS INQUIRIES TO:
Scott R. Sturzl, Vice President
Doctoral Grant Committee
P.O. Box 22160
Tempe, AZ 85285-2160

THE CALVIN K. KAZANJIAN ECONOMICS FOUNDATION, INC.   [2025]
P.O. Box 300
Dallas, PA 18612-0300
(570) 675-7074
Fax: (570) 675-8436

E-MAIL ADDRESS:
director@kazanjian.org

WEB SITE ADDRESS:
www.kazanjian.org

FOUNDED: 1947

AREAS OF INTEREST:
Promoting the understanding of economics and addressing the issue of economic illiteracy.

TYPE:
Grants-in-aid. Grants for economic education.

PURPOSE:
To aid in bringing greater happiness and prosperity to all through a better understanding of economics.

ELIGIBILITY:
The Foundation will only give serious consideration to those projects which directly advance its immediate purposes and meet its guidelines.

FINANCIAL DATA:
Amount of support per award: $5,000 to $50,000 per year.
Total amount of support: $350,000.

APPLICATION INFORMATION:
Applicants must include:
(1) copy of an IRS nonprofit determination letter;
(2) latest audited financial statement;
(3) list of board of trustees;
(4) annual budget and;
(5) project budget.
Deadline: September 15 for December review. February 15 for June review.

ADDRESS INQUIRIES TO:
Michael MacDowell, Managing Director
(See address above.)

KPMG FOUNDATION   [2026]
3 Chestnut Ridge Road
Montvale, NJ 07645-0435
(201) 307-7932
Fax: (201) 624-7763

E-MAIL ADDRESS:
tperino@kpmg.com

WEB SITE ADDRESS:
www.kpmgfoundation.org

FOUNDED: 1968

AREAS OF INTEREST:
Academic research, education and professional development in the area of business.

NAME(S) OF PROGRAMS:
- **KPMG Professorships**
- **Minority Accounting Doctoral Scholarships**
- **The PhD Project**

TYPE:
Conferences/seminars; Matching gifts; Professorships; Project/program grants; Research grants. Special grants, made on the recommendations of the Firm's college relations partners, are for specific projects that create new educational opportunities.

YEAR PROGRAM STARTED: 1968

PURPOSE:
To recognize outstanding achievement in accounting education and research; to recognize academic excellence and community achievement; to help minority students obtain careers in business and industry; to promote research that will benefit the profession now and in the future.

LEGAL BASIS:
Private foundation.

ELIGIBILITY:
The Foundation restricts grants to educational purposes related to its firm's functional areas, including accounting and auditing and tax.

GEOGRAPHIC RESTRICTIONS:
United States.

FINANCIAL DATA:
Amount of support per award: Minority Accounting Doctoral Scholarships: $10,000.

Matching fund requirements: The Matching Gift Program matches employee/partner gifts to colleges and universities from which the donors are alumni or where KPMG recruits. Minimum $50 for employees and maximum $5,000 per institution per fiscal year.

NUMBER OF APPLICANTS MOST RECENT YEAR:
15.

NUMBER OF AWARDS: 10.

APPLICATION INFORMATION:
Details available on the web site.
Duration: One year. Renewable for a total of five years.
Deadline: Doctoral Scholarships: May 1.

PUBLICATIONS:
Annual report.

IRS IDENTIFICATION NUMBER: 13-6262199

ADDRESS INQUIRIES TO:
Tara Perino, Associate Director
(See address above.)

LIBRA FUTURE FUND   [2027]
3 Canal Plaza, Suite 500
Portland, ME 04101
(207) 879-6280
Fax: (207) 879-6281

E-MAIL ADDRESS:
erik@librafuturefund.org

WEB SITE ADDRESS:
www.librafoundation.org/libra-future-fund

FOUNDED: 2005

AREAS OF INTEREST:
Economic development and job opportunities in Maine.

NAME(S) OF PROGRAMS:
- **Libra Future Fund Youth Grant Program**

TYPE:
Project/program grants. To promote economic development and create job opportunities in Maine.

YEAR PROGRAM STARTED: 2005

PURPOSE:
To capitalize upon the energy and creativity that Maine's young people embody; to combat youth out-migration by supporting initiatives that increase the number of Maine-based professional opportunities.

ELIGIBILITY:
Applicants must be 18 to 29 years of age, reside in Maine at least eight months per year, or be originally from Maine, but attending school out of state.

GEOGRAPHIC RESTRICTIONS:
Maine.

FINANCIAL DATA:
Amount of support per award: $3,000 to $5,000.

Total amount of support: Approximately $40,000 for the year 2010.

APPLICATION INFORMATION:
Deadline: April 1, July 1 and November 1.

ADDRESS INQUIRIES TO:
Erik Hayward, President
(See address above.)

THE GERALD LOEB AWARDS

UCLA Anderson School of Management
110 Westwood Plaza
Gold Hall, Suite B307
Los Angeles, CA 90095-1481
(310) 825-4478
Fax: (310) 825-4479

E-MAIL ADDRESS:
loeb@anderson.ucla.edu

WEB SITE ADDRESS:
www.loeb.anderson.ucla.edu

TYPE:
Awards/prizes. Awards to recognize business and financial journalists for important contributions to the understanding of business, finance and the economy.

See entry 2070 for full listing.

THE MCGRAW-HILL COMPANIES CORPORATE CONTRIBUTIONS AND COMMUNITY RELATIONS [2028]

1221 Avenue of the Americas, 47th Floor
New York, NY 10020-1095
(212) 512-6480
Fax: (212) 512-3611

E-MAIL ADDRESS:
susan_wallman@mcgraw-hill.com

WEB SITE ADDRESS:
www.mcgraw-hill.com

FOUNDED: 1979

AREAS OF INTEREST:
Corporate giving program: Financial literacy/economic empowerment.

CONSULTING OR VOLUNTEER SERVICES:
Employee Volunteer Grants and Global Volunteer Day Grants.

TYPE:
Matching gifts; Project/program grants. Matching gift program for McGraw-Hill employees and retirees.

The grants program places its strongest emphasis on financial literacy and economic empowerment. Contributions through matching gifts are to colleges and universities, to financial literacy, to adult literacy organizations whose sole purpose is the delivery or advancement of adult basic skills instruction, and to arts and cultural organizations providing matching gifts on a 1:1 basis.

YEAR PROGRAM STARTED: 1979

PURPOSE:
To contribute to the vitality and well-being of the communities in which it is involved.

LEGAL BASIS:
Corporate giving program.

ELIGIBILITY:
Applicants must be organizations that qualify as public charities under the Internal Revenue Code 501(c)(3). Preference given to areas

containing an employee base. Grants are not made to individual schools or school districts.

FINANCIAL DATA:
Amount of support per award: $5,000 to $25,000. Average grant $10,000.
Total amount of support: $5,600,000 for the year 2010.

APPLICATION INFORMATION:
Duration: One year unless multiyear pledge. Reapply each year.

PUBLICATIONS:
Corporate annual report.

BOARD OF DIRECTORS:
Harold McGraw, III, Chairman
Pedro Aspe
Sir Winfried F.W. Bischoff
Douglas N. Daft
William D. Green
Linda Koch Lorimer
Robert P. McGraw
Hilda Ochoa-Brillembourg
Sir Michael Rake
Edward B. Rust, Jr.
Kurt L. Schmoke, Esq.
Sidney Taurel

ADDRESS INQUIRIES TO:
Susan A. Wallman
Manager, Corporate Contributions
(See address above.)

THE BURTON D. MORGAN FOUNDATION [2029]

22 Aurora Street
Hudson, OH 44236
(330) 655-1660
Fax: (330) 655-1673

E-MAIL ADDRESS:
dhoover@bdmorganfdn.org

WEB SITE ADDRESS:
www.bdmorganfdn.org

FOUNDED: 1967

AREAS OF INTEREST:
Free enterprise system, economics and entrepreneurship education.

TYPE:
Awards/prizes; Capital grants; Challenge/matching grants; Conferences/seminars; Endowments; General operating grants; Internships; Professorships; Project/program grants; Seed money grants; Training grants.

YEAR PROGRAM STARTED: 1967

PURPOSE:
To strengthen the free enterprise system by investing in organizations and institutions that foster the entrepreneurial spirit.

LEGAL BASIS:
Private foundation.

ELIGIBILITY:
Grants are made to organizations recognized as public charities under the Internal Revenue Code Section 501(c)(3). The Foundation does not usually make multiyear grants and does not ordinarily consider grants to annual fund drives, units of government, or organizations and institutions which are primarily tax-supported, including state universities. The Foundation no longer makes grants to arts, mental health and social service organizations or programs.

GEOGRAPHIC RESTRICTIONS:
Primarily northeastern Ohio.

FINANCIAL DATA:
Amount of support per award: Varies.

COOPERATIVE FUNDING PROGRAMS: Northeast Ohio Collegiate Entrepreneurship Program.

NUMBER OF APPLICANTS MOST RECENT YEAR:
157 for the year 2010.

NUMBER OF AWARDS: 71.

REPRESENTATIVE AWARDS:
$35,500 to E City; $75,000 to Junior Achievement of North Central Ohio; $83,500 to Entrepreneurship Education Consortium; $5,000 to Canton Regional SCORE; $36,000 to Northeast Ohio Council on Higher Education.

APPLICATION INFORMATION:
Before submitting a full proposal, organizations should send a letter of inquiry to the Foundation regarding the request. All letters of inquiry and applications must be submitted online through the Foundation's web site.
Duration: One year.
Deadline: Letter of Inquiry: February 1, May 1 and September 1. Full Proposal: March 1, June 1 and October 1.

PUBLICATIONS:
E-Spirit newsletter; Foundation newsletter; *Venture Adventure,* newsletter.

IRS IDENTIFICATION NUMBER: 34-6598971

OFFICER:
Deborah D. Hoover, President

ADDRESS INQUIRIES TO:
Deborah D. Hoover, President
(See address above.)

THE NASDAQ OMX EDUCATIONAL FOUNDATION, INC. [2030]

9600 Blackwell Road
Rockville, MD 20850
(301) 978-8738
(800) 842-0356
Fax: (301) 978-5055

E-MAIL ADDRESS:
foundation@nasdaq.com

WEB SITE ADDRESS:
www.nasdaqomx.com

FOUNDED: 1994

AREAS OF INTEREST:
Financial markets literacy.

TYPE:
Development grants; Fellowships; Project/program grants; Research grants; Seed money grants. The Foundation offers grants in the following areas:
(1) academic study or research;
(2) Ph.D. dissertation fellowships;
(3) curriculum development and;
(4) educational projects or programs.

PURPOSE:
To promote learning about capital formation, financial markets and entrepreneurship through innovative educational programs.

ELIGIBILITY:
The Foundation will accept proposals from educational institutions and organizations designated as tax-exempt according to Section 501(c)(3) of the Internal Revenue Code.

In limited cases, proposals from highly and specifically qualified individuals, only for the purpose of conducting independent academic study or research on financial markets, are accepted.

FINANCIAL DATA:
Amount of support per award: Varies.
Total amount of support: Varies.

APPLICATION INFORMATION:
Applicants must submit a letter of inquiry and be invited to submit a proposal.
Duration: One year, unless otherwise specified.
Deadline: Varies.

ADDRESS INQUIRIES TO:
Joan C. Conley, Senior Vice President and Corporate Secretary
(See address above.)

NATIONAL ENDOWMENT FOR FINANCIAL EDUCATION (NEFE)   [2031]
1331 17th Street, Suite 1200
Greenwood Village, CO 80202
(303) 741-6333
Fax: (303) 220-0838

E-MAIL ADDRESS:
ldj@nefe.org

WEB SITE ADDRESS:
www.nefe.org

FOUNDED: 1997

AREAS OF INTEREST:
Financial education for the American public.

NAME(S) OF PROGRAMS:
- **NEFE Fellows Program**
- **NEFE Grants Program**

TYPE:
Fellowships; Grants-in-aid; Research grants. NEFE Fellows Program recruits qualified individuals from diverse backgrounds who share a common interest in working on projects within NEFE's broad scope of activities and in gaining nonprofit operations and management experience.

NEFE Grants Program awards grants for research projects that will expand the body of knowledge in the field of financial literacy.

YEAR PROGRAM STARTED: 1998

PURPOSE:
To help all Americans acquire the information and gain the skills necessary to take control of their personal finances.

ELIGIBILITY:
To be considered for a fellowship opportunity, candidates must be:
(1) in good standing with their academic institution and;
(2) a currently registered Master's degree-seeking student.

Grants are awarded to organizations that have been designated tax-exempt status according to Internal Revenue Code Section 501(c)(3) or its equivalent for colleges and universities. Grants are not awarded to:
(1) individuals;
(2) organizations that have not been designated tax-exempt under Section 501(c)(3) or its equivalent;
(3) organizations that discriminate on the basis of age, color, disability, marital status, nationality, race, religion, sex, sexual orientation, or veteran status;
(4) organizations and/or project principals

and team members who fail to meet NEFE's Strategy Statement and Procedures requirements concerning the U.S.A. Patriot Act and related regulations;
(5) foreign organizations;
(6) international programs or projects or;
(7) organizations whose projects include re-grant of NEFE funding.

GEOGRAPHIC RESTRICTIONS:
United States.

FINANCIAL DATA:
Amount of support per award: NEFE Grants Program: Generally $100,000 up.
Total amount of support: Varies.

NUMBER OF APPLICANTS MOST RECENT YEAR:
NEFE Grants Program: 47.

NUMBER OF AWARDS: NEFE Grants Program: 6.

APPLICATION INFORMATION:
Fellowship Program does not accept unsolicited applications. Applicants to the Grant Program must first submit a Concept Inquiry Form. Those projects appearing to have strong potential will move to a proposal phase; applicants for those selected projects will be given further instruction at that time.
Deadline: NEFE Grants Program: First Tuesday in June and first Tuesday in December.

PUBLICATIONS:
NEFE Digest.

IRS IDENTIFICATION NUMBER: 84-0632115

THE NATIONAL RESTAURANT ASSOCIATION EDUCATIONAL FOUNDATION   [2032]
175 West Jackson Boulevard
Suite 1500
Chicago, IL 60604-2814
(312) 715-6744

E-MAIL ADDRESS:
scholars@nraef.org

WEB SITE ADDRESS:
www.nraef.org/scholarships

FOUNDED: 1987

AREAS OF INTEREST:
Foodservice education and training.

NAME(S) OF PROGRAMS:
- **Professional Development for Educators Scholarship**

TYPE:
Training grants; Travel grants.

PURPOSE:
To support foodservice educators earning their Certified Secondary Educators Foodservice certification; to provide financial support to attend an NRA Summer Institute or participate in a "hands-on" industry work experience.

ELIGIBILITY:
Must be an educator of a restaurant and/or foodservice-related program in a secondary school and submit a signed letter of recommendation on school letterhead that also verifies employment by an immediate supervisor or program director. Applicants must be U.S. citizens/residents.

GEOGRAPHIC RESTRICTIONS:
United States.

FINANCIAL DATA:
Amount of support per award: $1,750.

NUMBER OF AWARDS: Varies.

ADDRESS INQUIRIES TO:
Scholarships
(See address above.)

THE NATIONAL RESTAURANT ASSOCIATION EDUCATIONAL FOUNDATION
175 West Jackson Boulevard
Suite 1500
Chicago, IL 60604-2702
(800) 765-2122 ext. 6738
Fax: (312) 566-9733

E-MAIL ADDRESS:
scholars@nraef.org

WEB SITE ADDRESS:
www.nraef.org/scholarships

TYPE:
Scholarships. Provides scholarships for students who are pursuing an education and career in the foodservice industry.

See entry 2844 for full listing.

NATIONAL SOCIETY OF HISPANIC MBAS (NSHMBA)
1303 Walnut Hill Lane, Suite 100
Irving, TX 75038
(214) 596-9338
(877) 467-4622
Fax: (214) 596-9325

E-MAIL ADDRESS:
scholarships@nshmba.org

WEB SITE ADDRESS:
www.nshmba.org

TYPE:
Scholarships.

See entry 1070 for full listing.

PHI CHI THETA EDUCATIONAL FOUNDATION   [2033]
1508 East Beltline Road, Suite 104
Carrollton, TX 75006
(972) 245-7202

E-MAIL ADDRESS:
foundationinfo@phichitheta.org

WEB SITE ADDRESS:
www.phichitheta.org/foundation

FOUNDED: 1999

AREAS OF INTEREST:
Business and economics.

NAME(S) OF PROGRAMS:
- **Educational and Scholastic Advancement Programs**

TYPE:
Project/program grants; Scholarships.

YEAR PROGRAM STARTED: 2000

PURPOSE:
To promote the cause of higher business education for all people.

LEGAL BASIS:
Public charity, 501(c)(3) corporation.

ELIGIBILITY:
Open to students who are members of Phi Chi Theta in approved courses in colleges and universities in the U.S. leading to Bachelor's, Master's or doctoral degrees in the fields of business administration and/or economics. Applicants must have completed at least one semester of college-level study.

Selection is based on scholastic achievement, motivation, leadership potential and financial need.

GEOGRAPHIC RESTRICTIONS:
United States.

FINANCIAL DATA:
Amount of support per award: $500 to $1,000.
Total amount of support: Varies.

NUMBER OF APPLICANTS MOST RECENT YEAR:
Over 20.

NUMBER OF AWARDS: Varies.

APPLICATION INFORMATION:
Applicants must submit an official transcript and two letters of recommendation.
Duration: One year. Nonrenewable.
Deadline: May 1.

PUBLICATIONS:
Application guidelines.

IRS IDENTIFICATION NUMBER: 31-1672618

OFFICERS:
Greg Holden, President
Mary Ellen Lewis, Treasurer
Frances Spencer, Secretary

CHARLES SCHWAB FOUNDATION [2034]

211 Main Street, 16th Floor
San Francisco, CA 94105
(877) 408-5438
Fax: (415) 667-1593

E-MAIL ADDRESS:
charlesschwabfoundation@schwab.com

WEB SITE ADDRESS:
www.charlesschwabfoundation.org

FOUNDED: 1993

AREAS OF INTEREST:
Financial education.

NAME(S) OF PROGRAMS:
● **Schwab Moneywise™**

TYPE:
General operating grants; Matching gifts; Project/program grants. The Charles Schwab Foundation awards strategic financial support through direct grants to selected nonprofit organizations that respond to local cultural and social needs or support Schwab's commitment to financial literacy. These grants provide employees with a voice and role in supporting the community groups they care about most.

YEAR PROGRAM STARTED: 1993

PURPOSE:
To give back to communities by supporting employee-selected causes and fostering financial literacy through funding, involvement and expertise.

LEGAL BASIS:
Corporate foundation.

ELIGIBILITY:
Applicants must meet at least one of the following selection criteria:
(1) be recommended by an employee who is an active volunteer in the organization;
(2) be performing community work that corresponds to the Foundation's initiatives or;
(3) promote financial literacy.

Greater consideration will be given to those organizations that already have Schwab employee volunteer involvement. The more

employees involved, the greater the opportunity to be considered for a direct grant.

GEOGRAPHIC RESTRICTIONS:
United States.

FINANCIAL DATA:
Amount of support per award: $2,500 to $25,000.
Total amount of support: $3,946,895 for the year 2010.
Matching fund requirements: Approximately 37% of Foundation's charitable contributions are awarded as dollar-for-dollar matches to employee charitable gifts. Matching gifts must be initiated by employees.

NUMBER OF APPLICANTS MOST RECENT YEAR:
3,052.

NUMBER OF AWARDS: 2,454 including matching grants for employee contributions.

APPLICATION INFORMATION:
Duration: No multiyear grants.
Deadline: Proposals are reviewed on a quarterly basis.

PUBLICATIONS:
Program brochure with application guidelines.

IRS IDENTIFICATION NUMBER: 94-1737782

ADDRESS INQUIRIES TO:
Direct Grant Program
(See address above.)

SIMON FRASER UNIVERSITY [2035]

Maggie Benston Student
Services Centre 1100
8888 University Drive
Burnaby BC V5A 1S6 Canada
(778) 782-3042
Fax: (778) 782-3080

E-MAIL ADDRESS:
dgs-sfu@sfu.ca

WEB SITE ADDRESS:
www.sfu.ca/dean-gradstudies

NAME(S) OF PROGRAMS:
● **SFU Teaching Assistantships**

TYPE:
Assistantships.

PURPOSE:
To provide financial support to the University's students enrolled in a Master's or Ph.D. program.

ELIGIBILITY:
Applicants must have already been accepted into Master's or Ph.D. program. Most teaching assistantships are available to visa students, as well as Canadian citizens and residents.

FINANCIAL DATA:
Amount of support per award: $2,500 to $4,500 (CAN).

APPLICATION INFORMATION:
Duration: One to two semesters.

ADDRESS INQUIRIES TO:
Specific Department of Enrollment
Simon Fraser University
(See address above.)

SIMON FRASER UNIVERSITY [2036]

Maggie Benston Student
Services Centre 1100
8888 University Drive
Burnaby BC V5A 1S6 Canada
(778) 782-3042
Fax: (778) 782-3080

E-MAIL ADDRESS:
dgs-sfu@sfu.ca

WEB SITE ADDRESS:
www.sfu.ca/dean-gradstudies

NAME(S) OF PROGRAMS:
● **SFU Graduate Fellowships**

TYPE:
Fellowships.

PURPOSE:
To offer financial support to the University's students enrolled in a Master's or Ph.D. program.

ELIGIBILITY:
Open to current or entering Master's or Ph.D. program students with a grade point average of 3.5 or above.

FINANCIAL DATA:
Amount of support per award: $6,250 (CAN).

APPLICATION INFORMATION:
Duration: One semester.
Deadline: April 15.

ADDRESS INQUIRIES TO:
Dean of Graduate Studies
(See address above.)

SOCIETY OF ACTUARIES (SOA)

475 North Martingale Road
Suite 600
Schaumburg, IL 60173-2226
(847) 706-3509
Fax: (847) 273-8605

E-MAIL ADDRESS:
acoffelt@soa.org

WEB SITE ADDRESS:
www.soa.org/education/resources/academic-initiatives/soa-doc-stipend.aspx

TYPE:
Awards/prizes; Scholarships. Society of Actuaries' James C. Hickman Scholar Doctoral Stipend Program is designed to provide stipends to doctoral students who will, through their studies, address research and education needs of the profession, including both the theoretical and practical aspects.

See entry 2229 for full listing.

SOCIETY OF ACTUARIES (SOA)

475 North Martingale Road
Suite 600
Schaumburg, IL 60173-2226
(847) 706-3509
Fax: (847) 273-8605

E-MAIL ADDRESS:
acoffelt@soa.org

WEB SITE ADDRESS:
www.soa.org/education/resources/academic-initiatives/soa-doc-stipend.aspx

TYPE:
Awards/prizes; Development grants; General operating grants; Project/program grants; Research grants; Scholarships; Travel grants. Grants to educational institutions.

See entry 2230 for full listing.

THE ROBERT A. TOIGO FOUNDATION [2037]

180 Grand Avenue, Suite 900
Oakland, CA 94612
(510) 763-5771
Fax: (510) 763-5778

E-MAIL ADDRESS:
ligia.gomez@toigofoundation.org

WEB SITE ADDRESS:
www.toigofoundation.org

AREAS OF INTEREST:
Minority participation in the investment community.

NAME(S) OF PROGRAMS:
● **Robert A. Toigo Foundation Fellowship**

TYPE:
Fellowships.

PURPOSE:
To increase minority representation in the investment community.

ELIGIBILITY:
Open to minority students of outstanding academic record who show a dedication to furthering the goals of the finance industry. The level of study is M.B.A.

FINANCIAL DATA:
Amount of support per award: $5,000.

APPLICATION INFORMATION:
Apply online.
Deadline: April 16.

TRANSPORTATION CLUBS INTERNATIONAL SCHOLARSHIPS [2038]

c/o AB Plant Shipping USA LLC
14614 Falling Creek, Suite 132
Houston, TX 77068
(281) 781-7437
Fax: (281) 781-7757

E-MAIL ADDRESS:
bblair@abplantusa.com

WEB SITE ADDRESS:
www.transportationclubsinternational.com

FOUNDED: 1922

AREAS OF INTEREST:
Traffic, transportation and all other aspects of physical distribution.

NAME(S) OF PROGRAMS:
● **Fred Deines Canadian Scholarship**
● **Fred Deines Mexican Scholarship**
● **Hooper Memorial Scholarship**
● **Denny Lydic Scholarship**
● **Texas Transportation Scholarship**
● **Alice Glaisyer Warfield Memorial Scholarship**
● **Charlotte Woods Memorial Scholarship**

TYPE:
Scholarships. Fred Deines Canadian Scholarship is awarded to a student of Canadian nationality who is enrolled in a college/university in Canada or the U.S.

Fred Deines Mexico Scholarship is awarded to a student of Mexican nationality who is enrolled in a college/university in Mexico or the U.S.

The Hooper Memorial and Denny Lydic Scholarships are awarded to any student enrolled in an accredited institution of higher learning in a vocational or degree program.

Texas Transportation Scholarship is awarded to a student who has been enrolled in a Texas school during some phase of their education.

Charlotte Woods Memorial Scholarship is awarded to a student who is a TCI member or a dependent of a member.

PURPOSE:
To encourage advanced vocational, undergraduate and graduate study in the field of transportation and traffic management.

LEGAL BASIS:
Nonprofit association comprised of more than 200 affiliated clubs in the U.S., Canada and Mexico.

ELIGIBILITY:
Offered to any student enrolled in an educational program in an accredited institution of higher learning in the U.S., Canada or Mexico offering courses in transportation, traffic management and related fields, i.e., marketing, economics, accounting, etc., who intends to prepare for a career in logistics, transportation, transportation management or related field. The awards will be based upon scholastic ability and potential, professional interest and character. Financial need will also be given consideration.

FINANCIAL DATA:
Amount of support per award: Varies.
Total amount of support: $12,000.

NUMBER OF APPLICANTS MOST RECENT YEAR:
25.

NUMBER OF AWARDS: 7.

APPLICATION INFORMATION:
In addition to a completed application form, supporting documents include:
(1) certified transcript directly from applicant's college/university;
(2) three letters of recommendation;
(3) small, current photograph (to be used for publication) and;
(4) 500-word essay explaining why the applicant has chosen transportation or an allied field as a career path, and outlining the objectives. Essay should be composed separately in Microsoft Word file only.
Deadline: May 30.

ADDRESS INQUIRIES TO:
Bill Blair, Trustee
(See address above.)

*SPECIAL STIPULATIONS:
All scholarship awards students must major in some field of transportation study.

Requests will not be answered unless self-addressed, stamped return envelope is enclosed.

U.S. DEPARTMENT OF EDUCATION [2039]

International Education Programs Service
1990 K Street, N.W.
Washington, DC 20006
(202) 502-7626
Fax: (202) 502-7859

E-MAIL ADDRESS:
tanyelle.richardson@ed.gov

WEB SITE ADDRESS:
www.ed.gov

AREAS OF INTEREST:
International business education.

CONSULTING OR VOLUNTEER SERVICES:
Offers technical assistance.

NAME(S) OF PROGRAMS:
● **Business and International Education Program**

TYPE:
Conferences/seminars; Demonstration grants; Development grants; Project/program grants; Research grants; Seed money grants; Training grants; Travel grants. The program assists institutions of higher learning in:
(1) innovation and improvement of international education curricula to serve the needs of the business community, including the development of new programs for nontraditional, midcareer or part-time students;
(2) development of programs to inform the public of increasing international economic interdependence and the role of U.S. business within the international economic system;
(3) internationalization of curricula at junior and community colleges, and at undergraduate and graduate schools of business;
(4) development of area studies programs and interdisciplinary international programs;
(5) establishment of export education programs through cooperative arrangements with regional and world trade centers and councils and with bilateral and multilateral trade associations;
(6) research for and development of teaching materials relating to international education, including language materials and facilities appropriate to business-oriented students;
(7) establishment of student and faculty fellowships and internships for training and education in international business activities;
(8) development of opportunities for business and other professional school junior faculty to acquire or strengthen international skills and perspectives and;
(9) development of research programs on issues of common interest to institutions of higher education and private- sector organizations and associations engaged in promoting international economic activity.

YEAR PROGRAM STARTED: 1983

PURPOSE:
To improve the academic teaching and business curriculum at U.S. institutions of higher education; to conduct outreach activities that assist the U.S. business community to engage in international commerce.

LEGAL BASIS:
Government agency.

ELIGIBILITY:
U.S. institutions of higher education that have entered into agreements with U.S. business enterprises, trade organizations or associations engaged in international economic activity.

FINANCIAL DATA:
Amount of support per award: Average $80,000.
Matching fund requirements: 1:1.

COOPERATIVE FUNDING PROGRAMS: Assistance from parties to required "Agreement."

NUMBER OF APPLICANTS MOST RECENT YEAR:
60 for the year 2010.

NUMBER OF AWARDS: 25.

APPLICATION INFORMATION:
Applications for grants under this program are required to be submitted electronically using the Department's e-Grants system.

Duration: Two years.

Deadline: Varies.

STAFF:
Tanyelle Hawkins Richardson, Program Officer

ADDRESS INQUIRIES TO:
Tanyelle Hawkins Richardson
Program Officer
International Education Programs Service
(See address above.)

U.S. DEPARTMENT OF EDUCATION [2040]

Centers for International Business Education
1990 K Street, N.W., 6th Floor
Washington, DC 20006-8521
(202) 502-7628

E-MAIL ADDRESS:
susanna.easton@ed.gov

WEB SITE ADDRESS:
www.ed.gov/about/offices/list/ope/iegps/index.html

AREAS OF INTEREST:
International business education.

CONSULTING OR VOLUNTEER SERVICES:
Offers technical assistance.

NAME(S) OF PROGRAMS:
● **Centers for International Business Education Program**

TYPE:
Project/program grants. The program provides grants to eligible institutions of higher education or combinations of these institutions for planning, establishing and operating Centers for International Business Education.

YEAR PROGRAM STARTED: 1989

PURPOSE:
To provide funding to schools of business for curriculum development, research, and training on issues of importance to U.S. trade and competitiveness.

LEGAL BASIS:
Government agency.

ELIGIBILITY:
An applicant must be an institution of higher education or a combination of such institutions that establishes a Center Advisory Council prior to the date that federal assistance is received. The Center Advisory Council shall conduct extensive planning prior to the establishment of the Center for International Business Education concerning the scope of the Center's activities and the design of its programs. Programs and activities to be conducted by Centers for International Business Education must meet the programmatic requirements listed above.

FINANCIAL DATA:
Grant funds may be used to pay the federal share of costs of faculty and staff travel in foreign areas, regions or countries, teaching and research materials, curriculum planning and development, bringing visiting scholars and faculty to the center to teach or to conduct research, training and improvement of the staff for the purpose of and subject to such conditions as the Secretary finds necessary for carrying out the objectives of this program and other costs consistent with planning, establishing or operating a center.

Amount of support per award: $300,000 for the year 2010.

Total amount of support: $11,800,000 for the year 2010.

NUMBER OF APPLICANTS MOST RECENT YEAR: 65.

NUMBER OF AWARDS: 36 for fiscal year 2010.

APPLICATION INFORMATION:
The Department of Education provides an application package upon request to the Office of Postsecondary Education.

Duration: Four years.

Deadline: Competition held every four years.

PUBLICATIONS:
Application guidelines; abstracts of grantees.

STAFF:
Susanna Easton, Senior Specialist, Centers for International Business Education Program

ADDRESS INQUIRIES TO:
Susanna C. Easton,
Program Specialist-IEPS
(See address above.)

THE UNIVERSITY OF CALGARY

Faculty of Graduate Studies
Earth Sciences Building, Room 720
2500 University Drive, N.W.
Calgary AB T2N 1N4 Canada
(403) 220-4938
Fax: (403) 289-7635

E-MAIL ADDRESS:
gsaward@ucalgary.ca

WEB SITE ADDRESS:
www.grad.ucalgary.ca

TYPE:
Awards/prizes; Scholarships. Awards for study in the fields of business, management and related areas. Tenable at the University of Calgary. Awards are endowed through gifts from John Labatt Limited and ScotiaMcLeod Inc. Matching grants provided from the Province of Alberta's Advanced Education Endowment Fund.

See entry 1905 for full listing.

UNIVERSITY OF NEBRASKA AT OMAHA [2041]

Mammel Hall, Room 300
6708 Pine Street
Omaha, NE 68182-0048
(402) 554-2303
Fax: (402) 554-3747

E-MAIL ADDRESS:
mba@unomaha.edu

WEB SITE ADDRESS:
cba.unomaha.edu/mba

AREAS OF INTEREST:
UNO Master's program.

NAME(S) OF PROGRAMS:
● **UNO Graduate Assistantships**

TYPE:
Assistantships; Scholarships. Graduate, M.B.A. scholarships in all subjects.

ELIGIBILITY:
Graduate assistantships are available for qualified students who are enrolled in a graduate degree program in the College of Business Administration.

FINANCIAL DATA:
Amount of support per award: Waiver of tuition costs up to 12 hours of graduate credit per semester.

NUMBER OF APPLICANTS MOST RECENT YEAR: 25.

NUMBER OF AWARDS: 9.

APPLICATION INFORMATION:
Applicants should complete the Graduate Assistantship application that is available on the web site and submit it with a resume and letters of recommendation prior to the application deadline.

Deadline: July 1.

THE DEAN WITTER FOUNDATION [2042]

57 Post Street, Suite 510
San Francisco, CA 94104
(415) 981-2966
Fax: (415) 981-5218

E-MAIL ADDRESS:
admin@deanwitterfoundation.org

WEB SITE ADDRESS:
www.deanwitterfoundation.org

FOUNDED: 1952

AREAS OF INTEREST:
Research and higher education in finance, wildlife research and conservation projects, and K-12 education.

TYPE:
Challenge/matching grants; Fellowships; General operating grants; Internships; Matching gifts; Professorships; Project/program grants; Research grants; Scholarships; Seed money grants.

YEAR PROGRAM STARTED: 1952

PURPOSE:
To help fund research and higher education in areas of special interest to the Foundation, as well as K-12 education.

LEGAL BASIS:
Private foundation.

ELIGIBILITY:
Grants are made to tax-exempt 501(c)(3) institutions. No grants are made to individuals.

GEOGRAPHIC RESTRICTIONS:
Northern California.

FINANCIAL DATA:
Amount of support per award: $5,000 to $25,000.

Total amount of support: $571,000 for fiscal year ended June 30, 2009.

NUMBER OF APPLICANTS MOST RECENT YEAR: 100 for fiscal year ended June 30, 2009.

NUMBER OF AWARDS: 40 for fiscal year ended June 30, 2009.

APPLICATION INFORMATION:
Applicants should first submit a brief letter to the Consultant, explaining their program and its merits with estimated budget, personnel, time required to carry out the proposal, evidence of tax-exempt status, and a brief explanation of any other sources of support for the project, such as volunteer workers and matching funds commitments. If the project, program or institution falls within the priorities, interests and available funds of the Foundation, a more detailed proposal will be requested.

Duration: One year. Renewal possible.

OFFICERS AND TRUSTEES:
Dean Witter, III, President
Stephen Nessier, Vice President and Chief Financial Officer

ADDRESS INQUIRIES TO:
Kenneth J. Blum, Administrative Director
(See address above.)

ZONTA INTERNATIONAL FOUNDATION [2043]

1211 West 22nd Street, Suite 900
Oak Brook, IL 60523-3384
(630) 928-1400
Fax: (630) 928-1559

E-MAIL ADDRESS:
programs@zonta.org

WEB SITE ADDRESS:
www.zonta.org

FOUNDED: 1919

AREAS OF INTEREST:
Financial support for women of any
nationality pursuing degrees in business
leading to a business management career.

NAME(S) OF PROGRAMS:
● **Jane M. Klausman Women in Business
Scholarships**

TYPE:
Scholarships. For women of any nationality
pursuing degrees in business who
demonstrate outstanding potential in the field
of business.

PURPOSE:
To provide financial support for women of
any nationality pursuing degrees in business
leading to a business management career.

LEGAL BASIS:
Incorporated in the state of Illinois as a
nonprofit organization.

ELIGIBILITY:
Applicant must meet the following minimum
requirements:
(1) be eligible to enter the third or fourth
year of an undergraduate degree program at
an accredited university/college/institute
program at the time funds are received;
(2) have achieved an outstanding academic
record during the first two to three years of
academic studies and;
(3) demonstrate intent to complete a program
in business and show outstanding
achievement in business-related subjects, as
recorded on the official
university/college/institute transcript.

FINANCIAL DATA:
The scholarship award may be used for
tuition, books or living expenses at any
university, college or institution offering
accredited business courses and degrees.
Amount of support per award: $1,000 at the
District Level and 12 scholarships for $5,000.

APPLICATION INFORMATION:
Applications must be completed in English.
English translations must accompany all
non-English documents. The Jane M.
Klausman Women in Business Scholarship
program operates at the club, district and
international levels of Zonta International. To
apply, contact the Zonta Club within the
applicant's district/region for deadlines and
an address to mail application or e-mail one's
name and contact information to Zonta
International Headquarters. Applicants must
be nominated by a local Zonta Club.

ADDRESS INQUIRIES TO:
Ana Ubides, Programs Manager
(See address above.)

Communications

AMERICAN ASSOCIATION FOR THE ADVANCEMENT OF SCIENCE [2044]

1200 New York Avenue, N.W.
Washington, DC 20005
(202) 326-6441
Fax: (202) 371-9849

E-MAIL ADDRESS:
spasco@aaas.org

WEB SITE ADDRESS:
www.aaas.org/programs/education/MassMedia

FOUNDED: 1848

AREAS OF INTEREST:
Science-related issues in the media and
public understanding and appreciation of
science technology.

NAME(S) OF PROGRAMS:
● **Mass Media Science and Engineering
Fellows Program**

TYPE:
Fellowships; Internships. Program to
primarily support graduate students in the
fields of social and natural sciences,
mathematics, and engineering during the
summer as intern reporters, researchers or
production assistants in mass media
organizations nationwide. Fellows will have
the opportunity to observe and participate in
the process by which events and ideas
become news, improve their communication
skills by learning to describe complex
technical subjects in a manner understandable
to the lay public, and increase their
understanding of editorial decision making
and the way in which information is
effectively disseminated.

Each fellow will work for a specific media
organization. Some will work for newspapers
or magazines on news and feature writing
assignments. Others may be involved in
television or radio production.

YEAR PROGRAM STARTED: 1974

PURPOSE:
To strengthen the relationship between
science and technology and the media and to
enhance coverage of science-related issues in
the media in order to improve public
understanding and appreciation of science
and technology.

LEGAL BASIS:
Nonprofit association.

ELIGIBILITY:
Priority is given to graduate students in the
natural and social sciences, mathematics, and
engineering. Applications from outstanding
undergraduate and postdoctoral students also
will be considered. Minorities, women and
disabled persons are especially encouraged to
apply.

Non-U.S. citizens must have a valid work
visa.

Students pursuing graduate degrees in
English, journalism or other nontechnical
fields are not eligible for these fellowships.

FINANCIAL DATA:
Fellowships include a weekly stipend, travel
costs to and from the media site, and travel
and expenses to attend a pre-summer
orientation in Washington, DC, along with a
wrap-up session.
Amount of support per award: $4,500 for a
10-week report.

NUMBER OF APPLICANTS MOST RECENT YEAR:
Over 100.

NUMBER OF AWARDS: Typically 20.

APPLICATION INFORMATION:
In addition to the completed application
form, candidates must submit a current
resume, two writing samples, transcripts of
undergraduate and graduate work, and three
letters of recommendation. Transcripts and
letters of recommendation must be submitted
directly to the program. Applicants should be
available for a telephone interview in March
and be able to accept assignments anywhere
in the U.S.
Duration: 10 weeks in the summer.
Deadline: January 15. Announcement in
April.

STAFF:
Stacey Pasco, Manager, Mass Media Science
and Engineering Fellows Program

ADDRESS INQUIRIES TO:
Stacey Pasco, Manager
(See address above.)

AMERICAN ASSOCIATION FOR THE ADVANCEMENT OF SCIENCE [2045]

1200 New York Avenue, N.W.
Washington, DC 20005
(202) 326-6431
Fax: (202) 789-0455

E-MAIL ADDRESS:
elane@aaas.org

WEB SITE ADDRESS:
www.aaas.org

FOUNDED: 1848

AREAS OF INTEREST:
Science and engineering.

NAME(S) OF PROGRAMS:
● **AAAS Kavli Science Journalism
Awards**

TYPE:
Awards/prizes. U.S. awards for stories of life,
physical and social sciences, engineering and
mathematics, excluding the field of medicine,
published in newspapers, general magazines,
aired on radio and television, and online.
Entries should be intended for general,
non-technical audiences. There is also an
award open to journalists worldwide,
recognizing excellence in science news
reporting for children.

YEAR PROGRAM STARTED: 1945

PURPOSE:
To encourage newspaper, magazine, radio,
television and online science writing.

LEGAL BASIS:
Nonprofit scientific organization.

ELIGIBILITY:
Qualified individuals may apply with
appropriate single stories or series published
in U.S. newspapers or general circulation
magazines, or aired on radio and television.
Reporters for international media outlets are
eligible for the award for reporting on
science for children. Awards may not be

presented to the same entrant in any two consecutive years, and individuals who have already won three of the annual awards are no longer eligible to apply.

Must be published by a U.S.-based news outlet, with the exception of the international award for reporting on science for children.

FINANCIAL DATA:
Amount of support per award: $3,000.
Total amount of support: $24,000.

COOPERATIVE FUNDING PROGRAMS: Sponsored by The Kavli Foundation.

NUMBER OF APPLICANTS MOST RECENT YEAR: 450.

NUMBER OF AWARDS: 8 for the year 2010. Seven awards in the U.S., one each for outstanding science writing in a newspaper with less than 100,000 circulation, a newspaper with over 100,000 daily circulation, in a general circulation magazine, on radio, television (two awards), and online. In addition, an international award for excellence in science news reporting for children, across all news media.

APPLICATION INFORMATION:
Completed materials in the print categories must be accompanied by nine copies of the entry showing name and date of publication. An entry may be submitted by an author or by another person on his or her behalf. Entries should not be elaborate. Radio and television scripts must be submitted, plus CD for radio or a DVD for television.
Deadline: August 1.

PUBLICATIONS:
Application guidelines.

OFFICERS:
Dr. Alan I. Leshner, Chief Executive Officer

ADDRESS INQUIRIES TO:
Earl Lane, AAAS Kavli Science Journalism Awards Administrator
(See address above.)

AMERICAN POLITICAL SCIENCE ASSOCIATION
1527 New Hampshire Avenue, N.W.
Washington, DC 20036
(202) 483-2512
Fax: (202) 483-2657

E-MAIL ADDRESS:
cfp@apsanet.org

WEB SITE ADDRESS:
www.apsanet.org/cfp

TYPE:
Fellowships. Awards to political science professors and journalists in early to mid-careers providing an opportunity for support as a full-time aide to a member of the House or Senate or as a staff member for a Congressional committee.

See entry 2113 for full listing.

ART DIRECTORS CLUB, INC.   [2046]
106 West 29th Street
New York, NY 10001
(212) 643-1440
Fax: (212) 643-4266

E-MAIL ADDRESS:
info@adcglobal.org

WEB SITE ADDRESS:
www.adcglobal.org

FOUNDED: 1920

AREAS OF INTEREST:
Art and graphic design, advertising, visual communications and media arts, art direction, creative arts, computer graphics, art and design education, industrial and environmental design and publication planning.

NAME(S) OF PROGRAMS:
● **ADC National Scholarships**

TYPE:
Awards/prizes; Conferences/seminars; Scholarships. Programs include the annual competition, exhibitions, publications, symposia, workshops, scholarships and other special events.

PURPOSE:
To promote excellence in the fields of visual communications through the support of young and aspiring talent nationwide.

LEGAL BASIS:
Not-for-profit association with an international membership.

ELIGIBILITY:
Applicants must be students at their sophomore or junior level enrolled in an accredited undergraduate program or in their last semester or quarter in a portfolio program and must be enrolled in schools in the U.S.

FINANCIAL DATA:
Amount of support per award: $2,500 to $3,500.
Total amount of support: Varies.

NUMBER OF AWARDS: Varies.

APPLICATION INFORMATION:
Students are required to submit:
(1) five PDF images of recent work on CD;
(2) statement of purpose;
(3) resume;
(4) letter of recommendation from professor and;
(5) application.
Duration: One year.
Deadline: Late June to early July.

ADDRESS INQUIRIES TO:
Flora Moir, Director of Education
(See address above.)

BENTON FOUNDATION   [2047]
1250 Connecticut Avenue, N.W.
Suite 200
Washington, DC 20036
(202) 638-5770
Fax: (240) 235-5024

E-MAIL ADDRESS:
cgarcia@benton.org

WEB SITE ADDRESS:
www.benton.org

FOUNDED: 1948

AREAS OF INTEREST:
The use of media and information technology in solving social problems and strengthening communities.

NAME(S) OF PROGRAMS:
● **Media Policy and Public Service Media**

TYPE:
Technical assistance. Program is funded for preserving, protecting and strengthening the public benefits in America's media environment.

PURPOSE:
To articulate a public-interest vision for the digital age and to demonstrate the value of communications for solving social problems; to leverage media and technology in innovative ways as a means to strengthen communities.

LEGAL BASIS:
501(c)(3) private foundation.

FINANCIAL DATA:
Amount of support per award: $500 to $5,000.
Total amount of support: $250,000 for the year 2010.

APPLICATION INFORMATION:
By invitation only. The Foundation does not accept unsolicited grant applications.
Deadline: Varies.

ADDRESS INQUIRIES TO:
Cecilia Garcia, Executive Director
(See address above.)

BROADCAST EDUCATION ASSOCIATION   [2048]
1771 N Street, N.W.
Washington, DC 20036-2891
(888) 380-7222
(202) 429-3935
Fax: (202) 775-2981

E-MAIL ADDRESS:
beamemberservices@nab.org

WEB SITE ADDRESS:
www.beaweb.org

FOUNDED: 1923

AREAS OF INTEREST:
Electronic media.

NAME(S) OF PROGRAMS:
● **Walter S. Patterson Scholarship**
● **Helen J. Sioussat/Fay Wells Scholarship**
● **Alexander M. Tanger Scholarship**
● **Two Year/Community College BEA Award**
● **Vision Award**
● **Abe Voron Scholarship**
● **Vincent T. Wasilewski Scholarship**

TYPE:
Scholarships. BEA is the professional development association for professors, industry professionals and students involved in teaching and research related to radio, television and other electronic media. BEA administers 14 scholarships annually, to honor broadcasters and the electronic media profession.

The BEA Two Year Award is for study at member schools offering only freshman and sophomore instruction, or for use at a four-year member school by a graduate of a BEA two-year campus. All other scholarships are awarded to juniors, seniors and graduate students at BEA Member institutions.

Helen J. Sioussat/Fay Wells, Alexander M. Tanger, and Vincent T. Wasilewski Scholarships: Study in any area of broadcasting.

Walter S. Patterson and Abe Voron Scholarships: Study toward a career in radio.

YEAR PROGRAM STARTED: 1962

PURPOSE:
To secure mutual advantages that flow from a continuing relationship between broadcasters and institutions of higher learning which

offer a high standard of training and guidance for those who plan to enter the electronic media.

LEGAL BASIS:
Private association.

ELIGIBILITY:
Scholarships will be awarded for full-time degree work for the full academic year. Scholarships must be used exclusively for tuition, student fees, university bookstore course purchases, dormitory and related items eligible to be charged to a student's official campus account. Current scholarship holders are not eligible for reappointment in the year following their award. In no case will any individual receive an award for more than two scholastic years. Winners must be full-time students for the entire academic year of the award. All scholarships must be applied to study at a campus where at least one department is a BEA institutional member.

The applicant should be able to show substantial evidence of superior academic performance and potential to be an outstanding electronic media professional. There should be compelling evidence that the applicant possesses high integrity and a well-articulated sense of personal and professional responsibility.

The Wasilewski Scholarship is intended for graduate students only.

FINANCIAL DATA:
Amount of support per award: Two Year/Community College BEA and Vision, Awards: $1,500 each; Sioussat/Wells Scholarship: $1,250; Patterson Scholarship: $2,750; Tanger and Voron Scholarships: $5,000 each; Wasilewski Scholarship: $2,500.
Total amount of support: Varies.

NUMBER OF AWARDS: Two Year/Community College BEA Award, Patterson and Sioussat/Wells Scholarships: 2 each; Tanger, Voron and Wasilewski Scholarships: 1 each.

APPLICATION INFORMATION:
Scholarship applicants can obtain the official application forms from their campus faculty or download them from the Association web site. The forms ask for personal and academic data and transcripts, broadcast and other experience, a written statement of goals and supportive statements from three references, one of which must be an electronic media faculty member. The completed application should contain:
(1) four completed and collated copies of the main application form;
(2) waiver sheet (four copies);
(3) three letters of reference;
(4) college transcripts (one from each institution attended) and;
(5) NAB station employment/internship affidavit.
Do not send tapes, resumes, photos, etc. No faxed or e-mailed material will be accepted.

Completed applications should be sent to:
Dr. Peter B. Orlik, Scholarships, BEA
344 Moore Hall
Central Michigan University
Mount Pleasant, MI 48859
E-mail: orlik1pb@cmich.edu.
Duration: One academic year.

PUBLICATIONS:
Journal of Broadcasting & Electronic Media; Journal of Radio Studies.

*SPECIAL STIPULATIONS:
All scholarships must be applied to study at a campus where at least one department is a BEA institutional member. Applications listing ineligible schools will be disqualified.

COLUMBIA UNIVERSITY [2049]
Graduate School of Journalism
2950 Broadway, Mail Code 3850
New York, NY 10027
(212) 854-2711
Fax: (212) 854-3900
E-MAIL ADDRESS:
tat5@columbia.edu
WEB SITE ADDRESS:
www.jrn.columbia.edu/knight-bagehot
FOUNDED: 1975
AREAS OF INTEREST:
Economics and business journalism for midcareer journalists.
NAME(S) OF PROGRAMS:
● **Knight-Bagehot Fellowship in Economics and Business Journalism**
TYPE:
Awards/prizes; Fellowships. Awarded to midcareer professional journalists to study business and economics at Columbia University.
YEAR PROGRAM STARTED: 1975
PURPOSE:
To improve the quality of business and economics journalism.
LEGAL BASIS:
University-affiliated fellowship program.
ELIGIBILITY:
Applicants must have at least four years' experience in journalism. Program is limited to journalists whose work regularly appears in the U.S. and Canada.
FINANCIAL DATA:
The Fellowship includes free tuition plus a stipend to cover living expenses.
Amount of support per award: $50,000.
NUMBER OF APPLICANTS MOST RECENT YEAR: 90.
NUMBER OF AWARDS: 10 for the year 2010.
APPLICATION INFORMATION:
Submit two 1,000-word essays, one on the applicant's professional career and his or her interest in business and economics writing, and the other on a major business or economics trend. At least three letters of reference from individuals in a position to comment on the applicant's professional performance and at least five work samples must also be provided.
Duration: One academic year.
Deadline: Mid-August.
PUBLICATIONS:
Annual report.
ADDRESS INQUIRIES TO:
Terri Thompson, Director
Knight-Bagehot Fellowship
(See address above.)

COLUMBIA UNIVERSITY [2050]
709 Journalism Building
2950 Broadway
New York, NY 10027
(212) 854-3841
Fax: (212) 854-3342

E-MAIL ADDRESS:
pulitzer@pulitzer.org
WEB SITE ADDRESS:
www.pulitzer.org
FOUNDED: 1917
AREAS OF INTEREST:
Excellence in journalism, books, drama and music.
NAME(S) OF PROGRAMS:
● **Pulitzer Fellowships**
● **Pulitzer Prizes**
TYPE:
Awards/prizes; Fellowships. Awards in journalism, books and music.

Pulitzer Prizes in Journalism are awarded based on material appearing in a text-based U.S. newspaper or news site that publishes at least once a week during the year. Awards given for:
(1) meritorious public service by a newspaper through the use of its journalistic resources which may include editorials, cartoons, photographs, graphics and online material;
(2) local reporting of breaking news;
(3) investigative reporting by an individual or team, presented as a single article or series;
(4) explanatory journalism that illuminates a significant or complex subject, demonstrating mastery of the subject, lucid writing and clear presentation;
(5) local reporting;
(6) reporting on national affairs;
(7) reporting on international affairs, including United Nations correspondence;
(8) feature writing giving prime consideration to high literary quality and originality;
(9) commentary;
(10) criticism;
(11) editorial writing;
(12) cartoon or portfolio of cartoons;
(13) breaking news photography in black and white or color, which may consist of a photograph or photographs, a sequence or an album and;
(14) feature photography in black and white or color with the same stipulations as above.

Prizes in Letters are restricted to works first published in the U.S. during the year in book form and available for purchase by the general public. Awards given for:
(1) fiction by an American author, preferably dealing with American life;
(2) a play by an American author, preferably original in its source and dealing with American life, produced in the U.S. January 1 to December 31;
(3) appropriately documented book on the history of the U.S.;
(4) appropriately documented biography or autobiography by an American author;
(5) volume of original verse by an American author and;
(6) appropriately documented book of nonfiction by an American author that is not eligible for consideration in any other category.

A prize in music is given for distinguished musical composition by an American that has had its first performance in the U.S. during the year.

Four fellowships enable outstanding graduates to travel, report and study abroad. One fellowship is given to an outstanding graduate who wishes to specialize in drama, music, literary, film or television criticism.

YEAR PROGRAM STARTED: 1917

PURPOSE:
To recognize excellence in journalism, letters and music.

LEGAL BASIS:
University.

ELIGIBILITY:
Competition for prizes is limited to work done during the calendar year ending December 31.

FINANCIAL DATA:
Amount of support per award: $10,000.
Total amount of support: $210,000.

NUMBER OF APPLICANTS MOST RECENT YEAR:
Books: 1,159; Journalism: 1,103.

NUMBER OF AWARDS: Fellowships: 5; Prize in Drama: 1; Prizes in Journalism: 14; Prize in Music: 1.

APPLICATION INFORMATION:
Application form and $50 handling fee required with entries.
Duration: One-time awards. Previous winners are eligible for consideration each year for any award.
Deadline: Prizes in Books: June 15 and October 1; Prizes in Drama and Prize in Music: December 31; Prizes in Journalism: February 1.

PUBLICATIONS:
Award announcement; brochure.

BOARD:
Danielle Allen
Jim Amoss
Randell Beck
Lee C. Bollinger
Kathleen Carroll
Joyce Dehli
Junot Diaz
Thomas L. Friedman
Paul A. Gigot
Sig Gissler
Nicholas Lemann
Ann Marie Lipinski
Gregory L. Moore
Eugene Robinson
Paul Tash
Jim VandeHei
Keven Ann Willey

ADDRESS INQUIRIES TO:
The Pulitzer Prize Board
(See address above.)

COLUMBIA UNIVERSITY [2051]

Graduate School of Journalism
2950 Broadway, Room 709-A
New York, NY 10027-7004
(212) 854-6468
Fax: (212) 854-3148

E-MAIL ADDRESS:
lsr21@columbia.edu

WEB SITE ADDRESS:
www.jrn.columbia.edu/events/berger

FOUNDED: 1960

NAME(S) OF PROGRAMS:
● **Mike Berger Award**

TYPE:
Awards/prizes. A newspaper competition, covering the previous calendar year, open to reporters nationwide.

YEAR PROGRAM STARTED: 1960

PURPOSE:
To honor distinguished newspaper reporting in the tradition of the late Meyer Berger of the New York Times.

LEGAL BASIS:
University.

ELIGIBILITY:
All newspaper reporters across the country are eligible whether they report for dailies, weeklies or monthlies or newspaper magazines. Members of the ethnic press should submit copies of original stories with an English translation.

FINANCIAL DATA:
Winners receive a cash award along with a certificate and hotel and travel expenses to New York.
Amount of support per award: $1,500.

NUMBER OF AWARDS: 1 annually.

APPLICATION INFORMATION:
Nominations are solicited from the editors of all daily newspapers across the country, as well as ethnic and weekly publications. Judges request that a nominating exhibit include two copies of a letter from the editor, a brief biographical resume of the reporter, and two copies of not more than five clippings.
Deadline: Early March. Notification in the spring. Presented at Columbia University in May.

ADDRESS INQUIRIES TO:
Lisa S. Redd
Program Manager, Professional Prizes
(See address above.)

COLUMBIA UNIVERSITY [2052]

Graduate School of Journalism
2950 Broadway, Room 709-A
New York, NY 10027-7004
(212) 854-6468
Fax: (212) 854-3148

E-MAIL ADDRESS:
lsr21@columbia.edu

WEB SITE ADDRESS:
www.jrn.columbia.edu

FOUNDED: 1939

AREAS OF INTEREST:
Journalism and inter-American relations.

NAME(S) OF PROGRAMS:
● **Maria Moors Cabot Prizes**

TYPE:
Awards/prizes. The prize program recognizes distinguished journalistic contributions to inter-American understanding. Prizes are awarded annually by the Trustees of Columbia University on recommendations made by the Dean of the Graduate School of Journalism and the Cabot Board.

YEAR PROGRAM STARTED: 1938

PURPOSE:
To recognize sustained and distinguished contributions of journalists to the advancement of understanding among the peoples of the Western Hemisphere.

LEGAL BASIS:
University.

ELIGIBILITY:
Although awards have been made to publishers or others in managerial positions, the board is particularly interested in working journalists throughout the Americas whose writings or broadcasts have contributed to mutual understanding and freedom of the press over a period of time.

GEOGRAPHIC RESTRICTIONS:
Western Hemisphere.

FINANCIAL DATA:
Amount of support per award: $5,000 and a Cabot medal, plus round-trip transportation to Columbia University for the award ceremonies.

NUMBER OF AWARDS: Approximately 4.

APPLICATION INFORMATION:
The Committee appreciates the submission of two copies of all representative clippings, copies of broadcasts, books and of letters explaining why the nominee is especially deserving.
Deadline: February 15.

ADDRESS INQUIRIES TO:
Lisa S. Redd, Program Manager
Professional Prizes
The Cabot Prize Program
(See address above.)

COLUMBIA UNIVERSITY [2053]

Graduate School of Journalism
2950 Broadway
New York, NY 10027-7004
(212) 854-6468
Fax: (212) 854-3148

E-MAIL ADDRESS:
lsr21@columbia.edu

WEB SITE ADDRESS:
www.jrn.columbia.edu

FOUNDED: 1960

AREAS OF INTEREST:
Environmental journalism.

NAME(S) OF PROGRAMS:
● **John B. Oakes Award**

TYPE:
Awards/prizes. Awarded for distinguished excellence in environmental journalism.

ELIGIBILITY:
To be considered for this Award, submitted articles must have been written between October 1, 2010 and October 4, 2011. The article must have been published in a U.S.-based publication. (It can be an online publication.)

FINANCIAL DATA:
Amount of support per award: $5,000 prize, plus travel expenses to New York, NY, for the Awards luncheon at the Journalism School at Columbia University.

NUMBER OF AWARDS: 1 award yearly.

APPLICATION INFORMATION:
Application is available online.
Duration: Recipients of the Oakes Award can win it a second time.
Deadline: November 20.

ADDRESS INQUIRIES TO:
Lisa S. Redd
Program Manager, Professional Prizes
(See address above.)

COUNCIL FOR THE ADVANCEMENT OF SCIENCE WRITING, INC. [2054]

P.O. Box 910
Hedgesville, WV 25427
(304) 754-6786

E-MAIL ADDRESS:
diane@casw.org

WEB SITE ADDRESS:
www.casw.org

FOUNDED: 1959

AREAS OF INTEREST:
Writing about science, medicine, health, technology, energy, the environment, etc., for the general public via the mass media (distinct from technical writing or technical journalism).

NAME(S) OF PROGRAMS:
- **The Victor Cohn Prize for Excellence in Medical Science Reporting**
- **Rennie Taylor/Alton Blakeslee Fellowships for Graduate Study in Science Writing**

TYPE:
Awards/prizes; Fellowships. The Victor Cohn Prize salutes general excellence in medical science writing for the mass media. The prize, to be given annually, seeks to honor a writer for a body of work published or broadcast within the last five years which, for reasons of uncommon clarity, accuracy, breadth of coverage, enterprise, originality, insight and narrative power, has made a profound and lasting contribution to public awareness and understanding of critical advances in medical science and their impact on human health and well-being.

Rennie Taylor/Alton Blakeslee Fellowships support graduate students in science journalism and experienced reporters who wish to study science writing at the graduate level.

PURPOSE:
To increase public understanding of science by upgrading the quality and quantity of science and medical writing and by improving relationships between scientists and the press.

LEGAL BASIS:
Nonprofit 501(c)(3).

ELIGIBILITY:
The Victor Cohn Prize: Editors, colleagues, scientists and others familiar with the candidate's body of work may proffer nominations. Individuals may nominate themselves. The nominator should submit no more than five examples of the candidate's journalistic efforts, all published or aired since January 1998. Books are not eligible. The letter of nomination should include an in-depth evaluation of the stories being submitted that, in the eyes of the nominator, make the candidate worthy of the prize and a biographical sketch of the candidate. Provide five copies of the published work, or standard audio or videocassettes (accompanied by typed or printed scripts). Send the nomination package to The Victor Cohn Prize, CASW, at the address listed above.

Rennie Taylor/Alton Blakeslee Fellowships: Journalists with two years of experience who wish to specialize in science writing will receive priority selection. Such applicants should be employed by daily newspapers, wire services, news magazines, radio stations, or television stations or networks. Students must have undergraduate degrees in science or journalism and prove to the satisfaction of a selection committee that they have the motivation and ability to pursue a career in science writing. Fellows may attend school full- or part-time.

Fellowships are not available to those who are pursuing or plan to pursue careers in public relations or public information work.

FINANCIAL DATA:
Amount of support per award: The Victor Cohn Prize: $3,000 and a framed certificate; Rennie Taylor/Alton Blakeslee Fellowships: $2,000 to $5,000.

NUMBER OF APPLICANTS MOST RECENT YEAR:
Rennie Taylor/Alton Blakeslee Fellowships: 12 to 18.

NUMBER OF AWARDS: The Victor Cohn Prize: 1; Rennie Taylor/Alton Blakeslee Fellowships: 4.

APPLICATION INFORMATION:
Applications can be obtained from the address above and must be submitted with the following:
(1) a complete resume;
(2) undergraduate transcript;
(3) three recommendations;
(4) three writing samples;
(5) short statement on career goals and why applicant wants to study science writing;
(6) specific information on resources available at journalism school or university for study of science or science writing and;
(7) specific information on program and courses applicant plans to pursue.

Duration: One academic year. Nonrenewable.

Deadline: The Victor Cohn Prize: July 31. Rennie Taylor/Alton Blakeslee Fellowships: July 1. Various announcement dates.

PUBLICATIONS:
Guide to Careers in Science Writing.

IRS IDENTIFICATION NUMBER: 13-1953314

OFFICERS AND DIRECTORS:
Cristine Russell, President
Charles Petit, Vice President
Alan Boyle, Treasurer
Thomas Siegfried, Secretary
Ben Patrusky, Executive Director
Philip M. Boffey
Lewis Cope
Barbara J. Culliton
Warren E. Leary
Miles O'Brien
David Perlman
Rosalind Reid

ADDRESS INQUIRIES TO:
Ben Patrusky, Executive Director
(See address above.)

*SPECIAL STIPULATIONS:
United States citizens only.

COUNCIL ON FOREIGN RELATIONS   [2055]
58 East 68th Street
New York, NY 10065
(212) 434-9489
Fax: (212) 434-9870

E-MAIL ADDRESS:
fellowships@cfr.org

WEB SITE ADDRESS:
www.cfr.org

FOUNDED: 1921

AREAS OF INTEREST:
International relations and journalism/media.

NAME(S) OF PROGRAMS:
- **Edward R. Murrow Fellowship**

TYPE:
Fellowships; Research grants. The Edward R. Murrow Press Fellow spends nine months at CFR's headquarters in New York. The program gives the Fellow an opportunity to broaden his or her perspective of international affairs and to pursue proposed research using CFR resources, which include: participating in events sponsored by the CFR Meetings and Studies departments; speaking for and moderating study groups; and sharing expertise and advising on other CFR projects. The Fellow will be part of the David Rockefeller Studies Program, CFR's think tank, alongside the program's full-time, adjunct and visiting fellows, whose expertise extends across the broad range of significant foreign policy issues facing the U.S. and the international community.

One resident fellowship is awarded each year to a distinguished foreign correspondent or editor. The program enables the Fellow to engage in sustained analysis and writing and expand his or her intellectual and professional horizons.

YEAR PROGRAM STARTED: 1949

PURPOSE:
To promote the quality of responsible and discerning journalism that exemplified the work of Edward R. Murrow.

LEGAL BASIS:
Not-for-profit institution.

ELIGIBILITY:
An applicant must have distinguished credentials in the field of journalism and covered international news as a working journalist for print, broadcast or online media widely available in the U.S. Applicants are limited to those individuals who are authorized to work in the U.S. and who will continue to be authorized for the duration of the Fellowship. CFR does not sponsor for visas.

FINANCIAL DATA:
The duration of the Fellowship typically coincides with the CFR program year beginning in September and extending into May. The program awards a stipend of $65,000 for nine months. The Fellow is considered an independent contractor rather than an employee of CFR, and is not eligible for employment benefits including health insurance.

Amount of support per award: $65,000.

Total amount of support: $65,000.

NUMBER OF AWARDS: 1 award per year.

APPLICATION INFORMATION:
Applications are primarily by invitation on the recommendation of a CFR member, a former or current Murrow Fellow, or the candidate's employer. Candidates may self-nominate. The nomination letter should provide a brief description of the candidate's background and state why the candidate is an appropriate prospect for the Fellowship. Nominees who meet the criteria of the program will then be forwarded an application requesting:
(1) a statement of no more than 2,500 words summarizing and appraising his or her experience as a foreign correspondent;
(2) an overall plan for the Fellowship year, including the applicant's proposed writing and how it relates to long-term career goals;
(3) at least one and no more than three written samples of work and;
(4) any additional information the candidate would like to bring to the selection committee's attention.

Duration: Nine months.

Deadline: Nomination deadline is the first week of February each year. Announcements are made in May of each year.

STAFF:
Janine W. Hill, Director for Fellowship Affairs and Studies Strategic Planning
Victoria Alekhine, Associate Director, Fellowship Affairs

ADDRESS INQUIRIES TO:
See e-mail address above.

DISNEY/ABC TELEVISION GROUP [2056]

500 South Buena Vista Street
Burbank, CA 91521-4016

E-MAIL ADDRESS:
abcwritingfellowship@disney.com

WEB SITE ADDRESS:
www.disneyabctalentdevelopment.com

FOUNDED: 1989

AREAS OF INTEREST:
Motion pictures, television and screenwriting.

NAME(S) OF PROGRAMS:
● **Television Writing Fellowship Program**

TYPE:
Fellowships. Annual opportunities for up to 8 writers to work full-time developing their craft at Walt Disney Studios and ABC Entertainment. Fellows may work in feature film or television divisions. The Program offers fellowships in the feature film and television areas.

PURPOSE:
To discover creative talent; to employ culturally and ethnically diverse new writers.

LEGAL BASIS:
Corporation.

FINANCIAL DATA:
Support includes salary. Fellows chosen outside of the Los Angeles (CA) area will be provided with coach round-trip airfare and one month's accommodations.
Amount of support per award: $50,000.
Total amount of support: Varies.

APPLICATION INFORMATION:
Guidelines and application form can be obtained at the web site.
Duration: One year, beginning in February.

THE DOW JONES NEWSPAPER FUND [2057]

4300 Route One North
South Brunswick, NJ 08852
(609) 452-2820
Fax: (609) 520-5804

E-MAIL ADDRESS:
newsfund@wsj.dowjones.com

WEB SITE ADDRESS:
www.newsfund.org

FOUNDED: 1958

AREAS OF INTEREST:
Print journalism.

NAME(S) OF PROGRAMS:
● **Business Reporting Interns, Sophomore and Junior Students**
● **Editing Intern Program for College Juniors, Seniors and Graduate Students**

TYPE:
Internships. Editing intern program for juniors, seniors and graduate college students who successfully complete a summer of work as beginning copy editors at newspapers.

PURPOSE:
To encourage students to consider careers in copy-editing.

LEGAL BASIS:
Nonprofit foundation.

ELIGIBILITY:
Applicants must be juniors, seniors or graduate students at any college who have a sincere interest in professional copy-editing news work. Working on a school publication is not a stated requirement, but highly recommended. Applicants must also be U.S. citizens.

GEOGRAPHIC RESTRICTIONS:
United States.

FINANCIAL DATA:
Interns will receive regular wages (minimum $350 per week) from the newspapers for which they work. After the summer of work, a $1,000 scholarship check is awarded to the intern's college, but only if that intern returns to school following the internship.
Amount of support per award: $1,000.
Total amount of support: $200,000 to $300,000. Depends on number of interns selected and cost of pre-training course.

NUMBER OF APPLICANTS MOST RECENT YEAR: 700.

NUMBER OF AWARDS: Up to 125.

APPLICATION INFORMATION:
Applications available July 15 to October 25.
Duration: Full summer.
Deadline: November 1.

OFFICERS:
Richard J. Levine, President
Ken Herts, Treasurer
Barbara Martinez, Secretary

STAFF:
Richard S. Holden, Executive Director
Linda Waller-Shockley, Deputy Director
Diane Cohn, Director of Finance

DIRECTORS:
Thomas E. Engleman
Gregory Giangrande
Les Hinton
Peter Kann
Melanie Kirkpatrick
Richard J. Levine
Neal Lipschutz
Barbara Martinez
Diana Mitsu-Klos
Laurence O'Donnell
Reginald Owens
Cathy Pangoulias
Robyn Sawyer
Russell Todd

ADDRESS INQUIRIES TO:
Internship Coordinator
Editing Intern Programs
(See address above.)

FUND FOR INVESTIGATIVE JOURNALISM [2058]

1331 H Street, N.W.
Suite 701
Washington, DC 20005
(202) 391-0206

E-MAIL ADDRESS:
fundfij@gmail.com

WEB SITE ADDRESS:
www.fij.org

FOUNDED: 1969

AREAS OF INTEREST:
Promoting the work of investigative journalism.

TYPE:
Awards/prizes; Grants-in-aid. The Fund gives grants to investigative reporters working outside the protection and backing of major news organizations.

PURPOSE:
To provide funding for reporters engaged in investigative journalism.

FINANCIAL DATA:
Amount of support per award: Average grant: $5,000.
Total amount of support: Varies.

APPLICATION INFORMATION:
Applications are to be submitted online. Applicant must write a proposal letter outlining the story, what he or she expects to prove, how this will be done, and the sources for the proof. For projects, include the anticipated completion date.

The letter must be supported by a resume, a detailed budget to justify the size of the grant, no more than two writing samples or one sample chapter in the case of a book applicant, and a letter of commitment from an editor or publisher or an executive of a broadcast news operation or online news outlet stating that the project will be considered for publication or broadcast if completed according to the proposal.

A letter of commitment is required for all applicants and is a non-negotiable requirement. In the case of individuals seeking grants for books, a signed copy of a contract with a publisher is required and should be substituted for the commitment letter.
Deadline: Varies.

ADDRESS INQUIRIES TO:
Sandy Bergo, Executive Director
(See address above.)

FUNDING EXCHANGE [2059]

666 Broadway, Suite 500
New York, NY 10012
(212) 529-5300 ext. 320
Fax: (212) 982-9272

E-MAIL ADDRESS:
grants@fex.org

WEB SITE ADDRESS:
www.fex.org

AREAS OF INTEREST:
Social issue media.

NAME(S) OF PROGRAMS:
● **The Paul Robeson Fund for Independent Media**

TYPE:
Grants-in-aid.

YEAR PROGRAM STARTED: 1987

PURPOSE:
To support the work of independent film and video makers who are producing film, television or video projects for social change, including preproduction or distribution stages only or radio projects in any stage of development.

ELIGIBILITY:
Media artists whose works reflect and comment on the ills of our society while emphasizing the struggles to overcome them.

FINANCIAL DATA:
Amount of support per award: Typically $5,000 to $20,000.

APPLICATION INFORMATION:
Contact the Organization for guidelines and application procedures.
Deadline: Letters of Inquiry: September 1. Proposals: October 30.

RUTH HANCOCK SCHOLARSHIP FOUNDATION [2060]

95 St. Clair Avenue West
Suite 1103
Toronto ON M4V 1N6 Canada
(416) 729-1950
Fax: (416) 964-0771

E-MAIL ADDRESS:
bob.reaume@gmail.com

WEB SITE ADDRESS:
www.bes.ca

FOUNDED: 1926

AREAS OF INTEREST:
Communications and marketing.

NAME(S) OF PROGRAMS:
• **Ruth Hancock Scholarships**

TYPE:
Scholarships. Scholarships to encourage talented, hard-working students to pursue careers in Canadian broadcasting.

PURPOSE:
To assist students in broadcast communication studies at community colleges and universities.

LEGAL BASIS:
Private.

ELIGIBILITY:
Open to Canadian citizens enrolled in a recognized communications course at a Canadian college or university.

GEOGRAPHIC RESTRICTIONS:
Canada.

FINANCIAL DATA:
Amount of support per award: $1,500.
Total amount of support: $6,000.

NUMBER OF AWARDS: 4.

APPLICATION INFORMATION:
Signed recommendation from course director or professor and a 500-word essay must be submitted with the application form.
Duration: One year. Recipients can reapply.
Deadline: June 30. Announcement in the fall.

ADDRESS INQUIRIES TO:
Bob Reaume, Vice President
Policy and Research
(See address above.)

WILLIAM RANDOLPH HEARST FOUNDATION [2061]

90 New Montgomery Street, Suite 1212
San Francisco, CA 94105
(415) 908-4560
Fax: (415) 243-0760

E-MAIL ADDRESS:
jwatten@hearstfdn.org

WEB SITE ADDRESS:
www.hearstawards.org

FOUNDED: 1948

AREAS OF INTEREST:
Writing, photojournalism and broadcast journalism.

NAME(S) OF PROGRAMS:
• **Journalism Awards Program**

TYPE:
Awards/prizes; Scholarships. Awards to the top 10 winners of 13 monthly competitions: six writing, three photo, two broadcast (TV and radio) and multi-media. Entrants must be journalism majors attending one of the 105 accredited schools of journalism. The schools receive a matching grant.

YEAR PROGRAM STARTED: 1960

PURPOSE:
To provide support, encouragement and assistance to education in journalism at the undergraduate college level.

LEGAL BASIS:
Nonprofit foundation.

ELIGIBILITY:
Participation in the program is open only to journalism majors who are undergraduates at the colleges and universities that are members of the Association of Schools of Journalism and Mass Communication.

GEOGRAPHIC RESTRICTIONS:
United States.

FINANCIAL DATA:
Amount of support per award: $1,000 to $2,600, depending upon placement of winners.
Total amount of support: Over $500,000 for the year 2010-11.

NUMBER OF APPLICANTS MOST RECENT YEAR:
1,050 for the year 2010-11.

NUMBER OF AWARDS: 150 scholarships and grants.

APPLICATION INFORMATION:
Full application information may be obtained through individual departments of journalism at participating schools. A list of accredited schools is available at Hearst Foundation's San Francisco address.
Duration: Varies.
Deadline: Monthly during academic year.

STAFF:
Dino Dinovitz, Executive Director
Jan C. Watten, Program Director
Yasi Haerizadeh, Program Assistant

BOARD OF DIRECTORS:
William R. Hearst, III, President
James Asher
Annissa Balson
David Barrett
Frank A. Bennack, Jr.
John G. Conomikes
Ron Doerfler
George R. Hearst, Jr.
John R. Hearst, Jr.
Harvey Lipton
Gilbert C. Maurer
Mark Miller
Virginia Randt

ADDRESS INQUIRIES TO:
Jan C. Watten, Program Director
(See address above.)

THE SIDNEY HILLMAN FOUNDATION, INC. [2062]

49 West 27th Street
Third Floor
New York, NY 10001
(917) 696-2494

E-MAIL ADDRESS:
alex@hillmanfoundation.org

WEB SITE ADDRESS:
www.hillmanfoundation.org

FOUNDED: 1950

AREAS OF INTEREST:
Civil liberties, race relations, labor movement, social welfare, housing, economic security and international understanding.

NAME(S) OF PROGRAMS:
• **Hillman Prizes in Journalism**
• **Sidney Awards**

TYPE:
Awards/prizes. Monetary awards presented annually for outstanding contributions in the fields of daily or periodical journalism, photojournalism, nonfiction, radio and television, and blogs.

YEAR PROGRAM STARTED: 1950

PURPOSE:
To recognize outstanding contributions to the field of journalism dealing with themes relating to the ideals which Sidney Hillman held throughout his life, including the protection of individual civil liberties, improved race relations, a strengthened labor movement, the advancement of social welfare, housing and economic security, greater world understanding and related problems.

LEGAL BASIS:
Private foundation.

ELIGIBILITY:
Only work published in English in the previous calendar year and distributed in the U.S. and Canada is eligible for consideration. Radio and television contributions must have been produced under professional auspices in the previous calendar year.

GEOGRAPHIC RESTRICTIONS:
United States and Canada.

FINANCIAL DATA:
Amount of support per award: Hillman Prize: $5,000; Sidney Award: $500.

NUMBER OF APPLICANTS MOST RECENT YEAR:
300.

NUMBER OF AWARDS: 6.

APPLICATION INFORMATION:
Material may be submitted by the author, his or her publication or publisher, or by anyone connected with it. The submission must be accompanied by a brief letter. The Foundation will endeavor to return submissions if requested.
Deadline: January 31.

ADDRESS INQUIRIES TO:
Alexandra Lescaze, Executive Director
(See address above.)

INSTITUTE FOR WAR AND PEACE REPORTING (IWPR) [2063]

48 Gray's Inn Road
London WC1X 8LT England
44 (0)20 7831 1030
Fax: 44 (0)20 7831 1050

E-MAIL ADDRESS:
schorkawards@iwpr.net

WEB SITE ADDRESS:
www.iwpr.net

FOUNDED: 2002

AREAS OF INTEREST:
International journalism.

NAME(S) OF PROGRAMS:
- **Kurt Schork Awards in International Journalism**

TYPE:
Awards/prizes. Awards for print reporters whose stories shed new light on controversial issues. Two prizes are awarded each year, one to a local reporter in a developing country or nation in transition, and the other to a freelance journalist covering international news.

The awards are underwritten by the Kurt Schork Memorial Fund and Reuters, and administered by the Columbia University Graduate School of Journalism.

YEAR PROGRAM STARTED: 2002

PURPOSE:
To honor Kurt Schork, an American freelance journalist, killed in a military ambush while on assignment for Reuters on May 24, 2000 in Sierra Leone.

LEGAL BASIS:
Registered charity in the U.K.

ELIGIBILITY:
Local Reporter: Print journalists employed by a local news outlet and residing in a developing country or nation in transition (non-OECD or EU countries), whose work has been published in a local publication, are eligible.

Freelance Journalist: All freelance print journalists and those contracted by news organizations are eligible.

Eligible Media: Entries are welcomed from all types of print-based media including newspapers and magazines and established online publications.

FINANCIAL DATA:
Amount of support per award: $5,000.
Total amount of support: $10,000 annually.

APPLICATION INFORMATION:
Deadline: July 13.

ADDRESS INQUIRIES TO:
Alan Davis
Special Projects Director
(See address above.)

INTER AMERICAN PRESS ASSOCIATION   [2064]

Jules Dubois Building
1801 S.W. 3rd Avenue
Miami, FL 33129
(305) 634-2465
Fax: (305) 635-2272

E-MAIL ADDRESS:
zchirinos@sipiapa.org

WEB SITE ADDRESS:
www.sipiapa.org

FOUNDED: 1954

AREAS OF INTEREST:
Press freedom.

NAME(S) OF PROGRAMS:
- **IAPA Scholarship Fund**

TYPE:
Exchange programs; Fellowships; Scholarships. Scholarships for American and Canadian working journalists, journalism graduates or journalism students to study in Latin America and for journalists who are citizens or residents of countries outside the U.S. or Canada to study in the U.S. or Canada.

YEAR PROGRAM STARTED: 1954

PURPOSE:
To support the exchange of journalists and journalism students between countries of the Western Hemisphere.

LEGAL BASIS:
Nonprofit association, tax-exempt under Internal Revenue Code 501(c)(3).

ELIGIBILITY:
Journalists or journalism school seniors or graduates between 21 and 35 years of age with a good command of the language they are to use. Students must have completed their degree before beginning the scholarship year.

Language ability for U.S. and Canadian candidates must be confirm by a recognize authority in Spanish or Portuguese. Latin American candidates must take a TOEFL (Test of English as a Foreign Language).

FINANCIAL DATA:
U.S. and Canadian scholars will receive $20,000 for the duration of their stay abroad. Latin American and Caribbean scholars will receive $20,000 and a one-time round-trip airfare for the year.

APPLICATION INFORMATION:
Online application is available at the Association web site or write to the Association, for an application.
Duration: One academic year.
Deadline: March 1.

OFFICERS:
Jorge Andres Saieh, President
Alfredo Jimenez de Sandi, Vice President
Carlos Salinas, Vice President
Silvia Miro Quesada, Treasurer
Nelida Rajneri, Secretary
Mauricio J. Montaldo, Coordinator of Scholarship Fund

ADDRESS INQUIRIES TO:
Mauricio J. Montaldo
Coordinator of Scholarship Fund
(See address above.)

INTERNATIONAL DOCUMENTARY ASSOCIATION

1201 West 5th Street
Suite M270
Los Angeles, CA 90017-1461
(213) 534-3600
Fax: (213) 534-3610

E-MAIL ADDRESS:
info@documentary.org

WEB SITE ADDRESS:
www.documentary.org

TYPE:
Awards/prizes; Internships. IDA Music Documentary Award is given to a filmmaker for an outstanding documentary communicating the cultural importance of music and its power to enrich the human spirit.

IDA/ABC News Videosource Award is awarded for the best use of news footage as an integral component in a documentary.

IDA/David L. Wolper Student Documentary Achievement Award recognizes exceptional achievement in non-fiction film and video production at the university level and brings greater public and industry awareness to the work of students in the documentary field.

The Pare Lorentz Award winner will demonstrate one or more of Lorentz's central concerns: the appropriate use of the natural environment, justice for all and the illumination of pressing social problems, presented as a compelling story by skillful filmmaking.

See entry 494 for full listing.

INTERNATIONAL READING ASSOCIATION   [2065]

800 Barksdale Road
Newark, DE 19714
(302) 731-1600
Fax: (302) 731-1057

E-MAIL ADDRESS:
pubinfo@reading.org

WEB SITE ADDRESS:
www.reading.org

FOUNDED: 1956

NAME(S) OF PROGRAMS:
- **Annual Print Media Award**
- **Broadcast Media Awards for Television**

TYPE:
Awards/prizes. The Annual Print Media Award is given to recognize outstanding reporting in newspapers, magazines and wire services which deals with reading and literacy.

The Broadcast Media Award is given to recognize outstanding reporting and programming on television and cable television that deal with reading and literacy, recognize the value of reading in today's society and/or promote reading as a lifetime habit.

PURPOSE:
To recognize outstanding journalism.

ELIGIBILITY:
The Print Media Award Contest is limited to professional journalists. Entries may include in-depth studies of reading instruction, discussion of research, or ongoing coverage of reading programs in the community. Entries must be oriented toward the general public rather than the reading profession.

The Broadcast Media Awards are open to broadcast media personnel. Entries must be oriented toward the general public rather than the reading profession and should be informational, critical, or motivational rather than instructional.

NUMBER OF AWARDS: 1 for each category.

APPLICATION INFORMATION:
For information or applications, write to the Public Information Office of the International Reading Association at the address above or download application form at the Association's web site.
Deadline: January 8.

ADDRESS INQUIRIES TO:
Laveria F. Hutchison
University of Houston
College of Education, 256 Farish Hall
Houston, TX 77204
Tel: (713) 743-4958
E-mail: lhutchison@uh.edu

INVESTIGATIVE REPORTERS AND EDITORS [2066]

141 Neff Annex
Missouri School of Journalism
Columbia, MO 65211
(573) 882-6668
Fax: (573) 884-5544

E-MAIL ADDRESS:
rescntr@ire.org

WEB SITE ADDRESS:
www.ire.org

FOUNDED: 1975

AREAS OF INTEREST:
Journalism across all media.

NAME(S) OF PROGRAMS:
- **Investigative Reporters and Editors Contest**

TYPE:
Awards/prizes; Fellowships. Investigative Reporters and Editors Contest is an annual investigative reporting contest. The Tom Renner Award (one of the 18 categories of this Contest) is given to the best investigative reporting in print, broadcast or book form, covering crime and its impact on society.

IRE also offers fellowships to minority journalism students and professionals to attend IRE national or regional conferences. There are also fellowships available for small newspaper staffers and for journalism students.

PURPOSE:
To promote high-quality, in-depth journalism.

LEGAL BASIS:
University.

ELIGIBILITY:
Individual journalists and news organizations may submit entries for the Renner Award. No more than 10 stories can be entered. Entries that disregard the rules will be disqualified. Qualifications for IRE minority fellowships include financial need, references and answers to essay questions.

FINANCIAL DATA:
Amount of support per award: Renner Award: $500; Student Award: $250.

Total amount of support: Varies.

NUMBER OF APPLICANTS MOST RECENT YEAR:
450.

NUMBER OF AWARDS: 18.

APPLICATION INFORMATION:
Entry form required. Entrants must include three copies of the story or script cut and pasted or photocopied onto 8 1/2 x 11 inch paper with no foldovers. In addition, radio entries must be on audio CD and television entries on a DVD. Television and radio entries must include three copies of a transcript. For book entries, entrants must send three copies of the published book. There is no limit on the number of entries allowed from individual journalists.

Deadline: Mid-January. Deadline for fellowships depends on conference dates.

PUBLICATIONS:
Program announcement; entry form.

IRS IDENTIFICATION NUMBER: 51-0166741

ADDRESS INQUIRIES TO:
Contest Coordinator
(See address above.)

JOURNAL OF THE AMERICAN MEDICAL ASSOCIATION [2067]

515 North State Street
Chicago, IL 60654
(312) 464-4334
Fax: (312) 464-5824

E-MAIL ADDRESS:
robert.golub@jama-archives.org

WEB SITE ADDRESS:
www.jama.com

FOUNDED: 1847

AREAS OF INTEREST:
Public health, physician and health care personnel education and medical publications.

NAME(S) OF PROGRAMS:
- **Morris Fishbein Fellowship in Medical Editing**

TYPE:
Fellowships. Award granted to physicians exclusively as a one-year, full-time editorial fellowship with *The Journal of the American Medical Association.* The successful candidate will work with the editorial and production staff in all facets of editing and publishing a major weekly medical journal. At the completion of the program, it is expected that the candidate will be proficient in all aspects of manuscript selection, peer review, issue makeup, copy editing and styling, issue planning and managing, in addition to the many other elements of medical journal publication.

YEAR PROGRAM STARTED: 1978

PURPOSE:
To provide physicians with an opportunity to learn the editorial functions of a major medical journal.

LEGAL BASIS:
Not-for-profit organization serving members in the medical profession.

ELIGIBILITY:
Applicants must be physicians. Candidates also must have proven writing ability at the time of application because they will be required during the course of the year to prepare articles for publication. Although the fellow will work under the supervision of a physician-editor, ability to work independently is a must. Ability to use a resource library is a strong plus.

Fellow must live in Chicago during the 12-month full-time fellowship (July to June).

FINANCIAL DATA:
Amount of support per award: $51,500 stipend.

Total amount of support: $51,500 annually.

NUMBER OF APPLICANTS MOST RECENT YEAR:
12.

NUMBER OF AWARDS: 1 annually.

APPLICATION INFORMATION:
Application forms may be obtained from the address or e-mail listed above.

Duration: One year.

Deadline: January 8.

ADDRESS INQUIRIES TO:
Robert Golub, M.D., Deputy Editor
(See e-mail and address above.)

KAPPA TAU ALPHA [2068]

76 Gannett Hall
School of Journalism
University of Missouri
Columbia, MO 65211-1200
(573) 882-7685
Fax: (573) 884-1720

E-MAIL ADDRESS:
umcjourkta@missouri.edu

WEB SITE ADDRESS:
www.kappataualpha.org

FOUNDED: 1910

AREAS OF INTEREST:
Journalism research and mass communication.

NAME(S) OF PROGRAMS:
- **Frank Luther Mott KTA Research/Book Award**

TYPE:
Awards/prizes. Annual award for a published book concerned with journalism and mass communications research.

YEAR PROGRAM STARTED: 1944

PURPOSE:
To recognize the top book published in the field of journalism and mass communications research; to promote interest in Kappa Tau Alpha among students and faculty.

LEGAL BASIS:
National society honoring scholarship in journalism and mass communication.

ELIGIBILITY:
Qualified individuals may apply for the award with an appropriate book published during the year.

FINANCIAL DATA:
Amount of support per award: $1,000 and a plaque.

NUMBER OF APPLICANTS MOST RECENT YEAR:
21.

NUMBER OF AWARDS: 1 annually.

APPLICATION INFORMATION:
Interested applicants should submit six copies of the published work to be considered.
Deadline: Typically first Monday in December.

OFFICERS:
W. Joseph Campbell, President
Peter J. Gade, Vice President
Dr. Keith P. Sanders, Executive Director

JUDGES:
W. Joseph Campbell
Peter J. Gade
Keith P. Sanders

ADDRESS INQUIRIES TO:
Dr. Keith P. Sanders, Executive Director
(See address above.)

LIVINGSTON AWARDS [2069]

Wallace House, University of Michigan
620 Oxford Road
Ann Arbor, MI 48104
(734) 998-7575
Fax: (734) 998-7979

E-MAIL ADDRESS:
livingstonawards@umich.edu

WEB SITE ADDRESS:
www.livawards.org

AREAS OF INTEREST:
Broadcast, print and online journalism.

NAME(S) OF PROGRAMS:
- **Livingston Awards for Young Journalists**

TYPE:
Awards/prizes.

LEGAL BASIS:
Foundation.

ELIGIBILITY:
Entries must be directly related to current events or include new information about old events. Features and commentary are eligible. There are no awards for still photography.

Journalists who are 34 years old or younger as of December 31 and whose work appears in print, broadcast or online media may apply.

Submissions must consist of materials prepared in the ordinary course of the journalist's professional production. One entry per individual. Individuals may apply on their own, or be entered by their organization. Multiple by-lines are eligible, but all must meet age criteria. Materials prepared by journalists specifically for submission to the Livingston Awards will not qualify and may not be considered. Student media are not eligible.

All entries will be judged on the basis of either a single piece, or in the case of series, a maximum of three related pieces.

FINANCIAL DATA:
Amount of support per award: $10,000.
Total amount of support: $30,000.

NUMBER OF AWARDS: 3.

APPLICATION INFORMATION:
Detailed information is available online.
Deadline: February 1. Announcement in June.

PUBLICATIONS:
Program brochure.

ADDRESS INQUIRIES TO:
See e-mail address above.

THE GERALD LOEB AWARDS   [2070]
UCLA Anderson School of Management
110 Westwood Plaza
Gold Hall, Suite B307
Los Angeles, CA 90095-1481
(310) 825-4478
Fax: (310) 825-4479

E-MAIL ADDRESS:
loeb@anderson.ucla.edu

WEB SITE ADDRESS:
www.loeb.anderson.ucla.edu

FOUNDED: 1957

AREAS OF INTEREST:
Business, economic and financial news writing and journalism.

TYPE:
Awards/prizes. Awards to recognize business and financial journalists for important contributions to the understanding of business, finance and the economy.

YEAR PROGRAM STARTED: 1957

PURPOSE:
To recognize journalists who make significant contributions to the understanding of business and finance.

LEGAL BASIS:
University.

ELIGIBILITY:
Entries submitted must have been published or broadcast for the first time during the previous calendar year in the U.S.

FINANCIAL DATA:
Amount of support per award: $2,000; $500 Honorable Mention.
Total amount of support: $24,000 annually.

APPLICATION INFORMATION:
Application must be submitted online. Each entry must be accompanied by an entry fee of $100, payable online.

PUBLICATIONS:
Entry brochure.

ADDRESS INQUIRIES TO:
Jonathan Daillak, Program Manager
(See address above.)

MASSACHUSETTS INSTITUTE OF TECHNOLOGY   [2071]
MIT E19-623
77 Massachusetts Avenue
Cambridge, MA 02139-4307
(617) 253-3442
Fax: (617) 258-8100

E-MAIL ADDRESS:
knight-info@mit.edu

WEB SITE ADDRESS:
web.mit.edu/knight-science

AREAS OF INTEREST:
Science journalism.

NAME(S) OF PROGRAMS:
- **Knight Science Journalism Fellowships**

TYPE:
Fellowships. Nine months access to courses, laboratories and researchers.

YEAR PROGRAM STARTED: 1983

PURPOSE:
To recognize excellence in explaining science, medicine, technology and the environment to the public; to provide a deeper familiarity with the processes of research and development to widen the fellows' acquaintance with leading engineers, scientists and medical researchers experienced in explaining complex issues.

LEGAL BASIS:
University.

ELIGIBILITY:
Must have at least three years full-time experience covering science techology, medicine or environment. Also consider journalists who wish to gain expertise in these fields and who have at least five years of full-time experience.

FINANCIAL DATA:
Fellowship includes stipend. During their residence, fellows may join an MIT affiliates health plan.
Amount of support per award: $65,000 stipend.

COOPERATIVE FUNDING PROGRAMS: Sponsored by the John S. and James L. Knight Foundation.

NUMBER OF AWARDS: 10 to 12 annually.

APPLICATION INFORMATION:
Online submission only.
Duration: August 1 to May 31.
Deadline: March 1. Interviews will begin in April with public announcement in early May.

ADDRESS INQUIRIES TO:
Phil Hilts, Director
Knight Science Journalism Fellowships
(See address above.)

NATIONAL ASSOCIATION OF BROADCASTERS   [2072]
1771 N Street, N.W.
Washington, DC 20036-2800
(202) 429-5479
Fax: (202) 429-4199

E-MAIL ADDRESS:
irc@nab.org

WEB SITE ADDRESS:
www.nab.org

NAME(S) OF PROGRAMS:
- **Grants for Research in Broadcasting**

TYPE:
Research grants. Grants are intended to stimulate interest in broadcast research, especially research on economic, business, social or policy issues of importance to the U.S. commercial broadcast industry.

YEAR PROGRAM STARTED: 1967

PURPOSE:
To attract qualified personnel into the field of broadcast research; to facilitate the training of broadcast researchers; to assist individuals already working in this area; to make high quality academic research available to industry practitioners as well as other academics.

LEGAL BASIS:
Nonprofit association.

ELIGIBILITY:
The competition is open to all academic personnel and graduate students. Senior undergraduates are invited to submit proposals.

FINANCIAL DATA:
Monies are not to be used for overhead or benefits.
Amount of support per award: Average $5,000. More can be awarded if the project merits additional funds.
Total amount of support: Up to $10,000.

NUMBER OF APPLICANTS MOST RECENT YEAR: 50.

NUMBER OF AWARDS: 4 to 6 annually.

APPLICATION INFORMATION:
Official application materials are available upon request.
Duration: One year.
Deadline: Late January. Award notification by April 1.

ADDRESS INQUIRIES TO:
Vice President
Research and Information
(See address above.)

NATIONAL ASSOCIATION OF FARM BROADCASTING FOUNDATION   [2073]
700 Branch Street, Suite 8
Platte City, MO 64079
(816) 431-4032
Fax: (816) 431-4087

E-MAIL ADDRESS:
info@nafb.com

WEB SITE ADDRESS:
www.nafb.com

AREAS OF INTEREST:
Agricultural journalism and communications.

NAME(S) OF PROGRAMS:
● **Ag Broadcast Scholarships**

TYPE:
Scholarships. Ag Broadcast Scholarships consist of two scholarship funds, the Glenn Kummerow Memorial Scholarship and the NAFB College Scholarships, for college students actively interested in becoming agricultural broadcasters.

YEAR PROGRAM STARTED: 1975

PURPOSE:
To provide financial support and educational opportunities for students in pursuit of careers in agricultural communications.

ELIGIBILITY:
Must be at least junior-year college students or in graduate school, enrolled in an agricultural journalism/agricultural communications curriculum, or plan to transfer to a university which offers a designated professional program of study in agricultural radio-television broadcasting. Selection is by application and is based on agricultural communications aptitude and leadership achievements, academic record and career plans.

FINANCIAL DATA:
Amount of support per award: $4,000 to $5,000.
Total amount of support: $13,000.

NUMBER OF APPLICANTS MOST RECENT YEAR:
5.

NUMBER OF AWARDS: 3.

APPLICATION INFORMATION:
Applications are available in Spring.
Duration: One school year.
Deadline: May 27.

STAFF:
Jennifer Saylor, NAFB Member Services Manager

ADDRESS INQUIRIES TO:
NAFB Foundation Scholarship Committee
P.O. Box 500
Platte City, MO 64079

NATIONAL ASSOCIATION OF HISPANIC JOURNALISTS

National Press Building
529 14th Street, N.W., Suite 1000
Washington, DC 20045-2001
(202) 662-7145
Fax: (202) 662-7144

E-MAIL ADDRESS:
iroman@nahj.org

WEB SITE ADDRESS:
www.nahj.org

TYPE:
Awards/prizes; Internships; Scholarships.

See entry 1064 for full listing.

NATIONAL ASSOCIATION OF SCIENCE WRITERS, INC.   [2074]

P.O. Box 7905
Berkeley, CA 94707
(510) 547-9500

E-MAIL ADDRESS:
director@nasw.org

WEB SITE ADDRESS:
www.nasw.org

FOUNDED: 1934

AREAS OF INTEREST:
Dissemination of scientific and medical information to a general lay audience.

NAME(S) OF PROGRAMS:
● **Science in Society Awards**

TYPE:
Awards/prizes. Separate monetary prizes and Certificates of Recognition awards for writers in four categories:
(1) books;
(2) commentary or opinion;
(3) science reporting and;
(4) science reporting for a local or regional audience.

YEAR PROGRAM STARTED: 1972

PURPOSE:
To recognize investigative or interpretive reporting about the sciences and their impact on society.

LEGAL BASIS:
Professional membership organization.

ELIGIBILITY:
Any writer (or team) is eligible to submit not more than three entries in each category. Material may be single article or broadcast or a series. Books with a copyright date of 2011 are eligible. Works must be written or spoken, in English, intended for the layperson and published or broadcast in North America between January 1, 2011 and December 31, 2011.

GEOGRAPHIC RESTRICTIONS:
North America.

FINANCIAL DATA:
Amount of support per award: $2,500 and Certificates of Recognition in each category.

NUMBER OF APPLICANTS MOST RECENT YEAR:
150.

NUMBER OF AWARDS: 4 annually.

APPLICATION INFORMATION:
Details are available online.
Duration: One year.
Deadline: February 1, 2012.

ADDRESS INQUIRIES TO:
Tinsley Davis, Executive Director
(See address above.)

NATIONAL ENDOWMENT FOR THE HUMANITIES   [2075]

1100 Pennsylvania Avenue, N.W.
Washington, DC 20506
(202) 606-8269
Fax: (202) 606-8557

E-MAIL ADDRESS:
publicpgms@neh.gov

WEB SITE ADDRESS:
www.neh.gov

FOUNDED: 1965

AREAS OF INTEREST:
Scholarship, research, education and public programs in the humanities. In the act that established the Endowment, the term humanities includes, but is not limited to, the study of history, philosophy, languages, linguistics, literature, archaeology, jurisprudence, the history, theory and criticism of the arts, ethics, comparative religion and those aspects of the social sciences that employ historical or philosophical approaches.

NAME(S) OF PROGRAMS:
● **Public Programs**

TYPE:
Project/program grants. Grants support the planning and production of television and radio programs in the humanities intended for general audiences; the planning and implementation of exhibitions, the interpretation of historic sites and the production of related publications; multimedia components and educational programs and the planning and implementation of projects through the use of books, new technologies and other resources in the collections of libraries and archives in formats such as reading and discussion programs, lectures, symposia and interpretive exhibitions.

YEAR PROGRAM STARTED: 1969

PURPOSE:
To create an understanding and appreciation of the humanities among the general public.

LEGAL BASIS:
The National Foundation on the Arts and Humanities Act of 1965, Public Law 89-209, as amended.

ELIGIBILITY:
Nonprofit institutions, organizations and groups, including public television and radio stations and state humanities councils, are eligible for support.

GEOGRAPHIC RESTRICTIONS:
United States.

FINANCIAL DATA:
Amount of support per award: Varies.
Total amount of support: Varies.

NUMBER OF APPLICANTS MOST RECENT YEAR:
350.

NUMBER OF AWARDS: 63.

APPLICATION INFORMATION:
Prospective applicants are urged to submit a letter of inquiry which indicates an interest in the program and explains the general nature of the proposed project as well as its approximate cost. If appropriate, the applicant may then file a formal application for support.
Deadline: January, June and August.

PUBLICATIONS:
Annual report; *Grant Programs*; *Humanities Magazine*.

IRS IDENTIFICATION NUMBER: 52-1098584

ADDRESS INQUIRIES TO:
Division of Public Programs
(See address above.)

NATIONAL INSTITUTE FOR LABOR RELATIONS RESEARCH   [2076]

5211 Port Royal Road
Suite 510
Springfield, VA 22151
(703) 321-9606 ext. 2231
Fax: (703) 321-7143

E-MAIL ADDRESS:
research@nilrr.org

WEB SITE ADDRESS:
www.nilrr.org

FOUNDED: 1985

AREAS OF INTEREST:
Research and analysis exposing the economic and social inequities of compulsory unionism.

NAME(S) OF PROGRAMS:
- **The William B. Ruggles Journalism Scholarship**

TYPE:
Scholarships. Unrestricted scholarship awarded annually to the student who exemplifies the dedication to principle and high journalistic standards of the late William B. Ruggles, the well-known and respected Texas journalist who contributed significantly to the Right to Work movement.

YEAR PROGRAM STARTED: 1974

PURPOSE:
To honor the late William B. Ruggles, former editorial page editor of *The Dallas Morning News.*

LEGAL BASIS:
Nonpartisan coalition of citizens.

ELIGIBILITY:
Applicants are limited to graduate or undergraduate students majoring in journalism in institutions of higher learning throughout the U.S. Graduating high school seniors may apply, if accepted to a journalism or communications school. To be considered, applicants must demonstrate the potential for a successful completion of educational requirements in an accredited journalism program and an understanding of voluntarism and of the problems of compulsory unionism.

GEOGRAPHIC RESTRICTIONS:
United States.

FINANCIAL DATA:
Amount of support per award: $2,000.
Total amount of support: $2,000 each year.

NUMBER OF APPLICANTS MOST RECENT YEAR:
350.

NUMBER OF AWARDS: 1 annually.

APPLICATION INFORMATION:
A total application will consist of a completed formal application form, available from the address above, an official grade transcript from essay finalists and a typewritten essay of approximately 500 words clearly demonstrating an interest in and a knowledge of the Right to Work principle. Electronic application available on web site, or download application and send by mail.
Deadline: Postmark by December 31. Announcement in April.

OFFICERS:
Mark Mix, President

ADDRESS INQUIRIES TO:
Cathy Jones
Journalism Scholarship Administrator
(See address above.)

NATIONAL PRESS FOUNDATION   [2077]
1211 Connecticut Avenue, N.W.
Suite 310
Washington, DC 20036
(202) 663-7280
Fax: (202) 530-2855

E-MAIL ADDRESS:
npf@nationalpress.org

WEB SITE ADDRESS:
www.nationalpress.org

AREAS OF INTEREST:
Journalism.

NAME(S) OF PROGRAMS:
- **Clifford K. and James T. Berryman Award for Editorial Cartoons**
- **Capitol Hill Issues Briefings**
- **The Feddie Award**
- **Paul Miller Washington Reporting Fellowship**
- **National Issues Programs**
- **Thomas L. Stokes Award**

TYPE:
Awards/prizes; Fellowships. International programs. The Feddie Award recognizes coverage of the impact of federal laws on local communities.

Paul Miller Washington Reporting Fellowship provides free professional development opportunities to nine, day-long monthly seminars to reporters new to covering Washington. Agency visits, briefings from officials and presentations by experts enable journalists to add depth and insight to topics they cover.

National Issues Programs offer free, all-expenses-paid fellowships to one- to four-day seminars on a variety of topics including Alzheimer's disease, cancer, and retirement.

PURPOSE:
To help journalists better understand the issues about which they write and broadcast.

ELIGIBILITY:
Clifford K. and James T. Berryman Award for Editorial Cartoons is open to editorial cartoonists of newspapers and magazines for work that exhibits power to influence public opinion, plus good drawing and striking effect.

Thomas L. Stokes Award is for the best writing in a daily newspaper on the subject of energy. The subject may be any form of energy–oil, gas, coal, nuclear, water, solar, etc. The writing may be reporting, analysis or comment. The work must have been published in a daily newspaper in the U.S. between January 1 and December 31.

FINANCIAL DATA:
Amount of support per award: Berryman Award: $2,500; Stokes Award: $1,000 and citation.

APPLICATION INFORMATION:
For the Berryman Award, applicants must submit three complete packets containing five cartoons (copies are acceptable), a supporting letter from an editor or supervisor and a brief biography.
Deadline: Berryman Award: October 1; Stokes Award: January 31.

STAFF:
Bob Meyers, President

NEW YORK STATE SENATE
Student Programs Office
80 South Swan Street, Suite 1426
Albany, NY 12210
(518) 455-2611
Fax: (518) 426-6827

E-MAIL ADDRESS:
students@nysenate.gov

WEB SITE ADDRESS:
www.nysenate.gov/department/student-programs

TYPE:
Fellowships. These fellowships are intended for the graduate/postgraduate/midcareer level. Stipends which allow for bipartisan opportunities to train in government while on-site in Albany, NY. Fellows spend almost a year immersed in the work of the Senate, learning techniques associated with policymaking and legislative process. Placement is usually to the office of an elected Senate member. The Senate Legislative Fellows Program, Biggane Fellowship, Roth Journalism Fellowship and Wiebe Public Service Fellowship constitute the Senate Graduate/Post-Graduate/Mid-Career Fellowships.

See entry 2133 for full listing.

THE NEWSPAPER GUILD-CWA   [2078]
501 Third Street, N.W.
6th Floor
Washington, DC 20001-2797
(202) 434-7177
Fax: (202) 434-1472

E-MAIL ADDRESS:
azipser@cwa-union.org

WEB SITE ADDRESS:
www.newsguild.org

FOUNDED: 1933

AREAS OF INTEREST:
News industry, labor and free press.

NAME(S) OF PROGRAMS:
- **Heywood Broun Award**

TYPE:
Awards/prizes. Cash award and citation for outstanding journalistic achievement "in the spirit of Heywood Broun," the great newspaper columnist who founded The Newspaper Guild.

YEAR PROGRAM STARTED: 1941

PURPOSE:
To encourage and recognize individual journalistic achievement in this spirit by members of the working press, particularly if it helps right a wrong or correct an injustice, or shows an "abiding concern for the underdog and the underprivileged."

LEGAL BASIS:
Labor union.

ELIGIBILITY:
Journalistic work completed within the calendar year is eligible. Journalists working on behalf of newspapers, news services, news magazines, and radio and TV stations in the U.S., Canada and Puerto Rico are eligible. Managerial employees are not eligible, nor are publications and other employers as such, or entries on behalf of entire staffs that, in effect, constitute entries on behalf of a publication or employer.

Applicants may submit entries on their own or others' behalf. First consideration is given to entries on behalf of individuals or teams of no more than two persons.

GEOGRAPHIC RESTRICTIONS:
United States, Puerto Rico and Canada.

FINANCIAL DATA:
Amount of support per award: $5,000 plus a Guild citation; two awards of $1,000 for

entries of substantial distinction, including one such award reserved specifically for a broadcast (radio or television) entry.

Total amount of support: $7,000.

NUMBER OF APPLICANTS MOST RECENT YEAR: 125.

NUMBER OF AWARDS: 1 annually.

APPLICATION INFORMATION:
Submit entries to the Broun Award Committee at the address above. There are no application forms, but each entry should be accompanied by a letter describing the circumstances under which the work was done and its results. To facilitate judging, entries and cover letters should be submitted in triplicate.

Deadline: Last Friday in January.

OFFICERS:
Bernard J. Lunzer, President
Carol Rothman, Secretary and Treasurer

ADDRESS INQUIRIES TO:
Broun Award Committee
(See address above.)

THE NEWSPAPER GUILD-CWA   [2079]

501 Third Street, N.W.
6th Floor
Washington, DC 20001-2797
(202) 434-7177
Fax: (202) 434-1472

E-MAIL ADDRESS:
dedmondson@cwa-union.org

WEB SITE ADDRESS:
www.newsguild.org

FOUNDED: 1933

AREAS OF INTEREST:
Union for journalists and related occupations in the newspaper industry.

NAME(S) OF PROGRAMS:
- **David S. Barr Award**

TYPE:
Awards/prizes; Scholarships. For student journalists.

YEAR PROGRAM STARTED: 2001

PURPOSE:
To recognize and encourage student journalists.

ELIGIBILITY:
The Award is open to all high school and college students. The journalistic work must have been published or broadcast in prior year and should focus on social justice.

FINANCIAL DATA:
Amount of support per award: High School Students: $500; College Students: $1,500.

NUMBER OF APPLICANTS MOST RECENT YEAR: 180.

NUMBER OF AWARDS: High School and College: 1 each.

APPLICATION INFORMATION:
Application form is available at the Guild web site. Entry must be mailed to TNG-CWA, along with four copies and the application form.

Duration: One-time award.

Deadline: Last Friday of January (postmark).

ADDRESS INQUIRIES TO:
Dominique Edmondson, Secretary to Collective Bargaining Department
David S. Barr Award
(See address above.)

NIEMAN FOUNDATION FOR JOURNALISM AT HARVARD   [2080]

Walter Lippmann House
One Francis Avenue
Cambridge, MA 02138
(617) 495-2342
Fax: (617) 495-8976

E-MAIL ADDRESS:
ellen_tuttle@harvard.edu

WEB SITE ADDRESS:
www.nieman.harvard.edu

FOUNDED: 1938

AREAS OF INTEREST:
Journalism and investigative reporting.

NAME(S) OF PROGRAMS:
- **Worth Bingham Prize for Investigative Journalism**

TYPE:
Awards/prizes. Honors investigative reporting of stories of national significance where the public interest is being ill-served. These stories may involve state, local or national government, lobbyists or the press itself wherever there exists an "atmosphere of easy tolerance" that journalist Worth Bingham himself once described in his reporting on the nation's capital. The investigative reporting may cover actual violations of the law, rule or code; lax or ineffective administration or enforcement; or activities which create conflicts of interest, entail excessive secrecy or otherwise raise questions of propriety.

YEAR PROGRAM STARTED: 1967

PURPOSE:
To honor exceptional investigative reporting of stories of national significance where the public interest is being ill-served.

ELIGIBILITY:
All submissions must have been published in a U.S. newspaper or magazine or on the newspaper or magazine's web site during the calendar year. Web-based news organizations that follow a strict code of journalistic ethics and publish original reporting on a regular basis may also submit entires. No broadcast-only entries are allowed.

Entries may include a single story, a related series of stories, or up to three unrelated stories. Columns and editorials are eligible. Individuals are encouraged to submit their own entries. In case of a series, at least half the individual stories must have been published during the contest year.

Winners in any one year will be eligible for future awards without restriction.

GEOGRAPHIC RESTRICTIONS:
United States.

FINANCIAL DATA:
Amount of support per award: $20,000 annually.

APPLICATION INFORMATION:
Entries should be submitted in five copies, each with a completed entry blank. All entries must be accompanied by a $50 entry fee made payable to the Worth Bingham Memorial Fund.

Deadline: January for reports published the previous calendar year.

NIEMAN FOUNDATION FOR JOURNALISM AT HARVARD   [2081]

Walter Lippmann House
One Francis Avenue
Cambridge, MA 02138
(617) 495-2342
Fax: (617) 495-8976

E-MAIL ADDRESS:
ellen_tuttle@harvard.edu

WEB SITE ADDRESS:
www.nieman.harvard.edu

FOUNDED: 1938

AREAS OF INTEREST:
Newspaper journalism.

NAME(S) OF PROGRAMS:
- **Taylor Family Award for Fairness in Newspapers**

TYPE:
Awards/prizes. Established through gifts for an endowment by members of the Taylor family, which published *The Boston Globe* from 1872 to 1999.

PURPOSE:
To encourage fairness in news coverage by America's daily newspapers.

ELIGIBILITY:
Nominations are for a single article, editorial, commentary, photograph; series of stories, photographs, editorials, commentaries; or a body of work by an individual journalist. The work must have been published in a U.S. daily newspaper between January 1, 2011, and December 31, 2011.

FINANCIAL DATA:
Amount of support per award: First Place: $10,000; Top two finalists: $1,000 each.

Total amount of support: $12,000.

APPLICATION INFORMATION:
Anyone may submit a nomination. A completed application includes the application form, five copies of the work and a letter explaining why the entry is an exemplary example of fairness in newspapers. The letter must also explain how the work was developed, reported and presented to readers in the context of fairness.

Deadline: Mid to late January.

ADDRESS INQUIRIES TO:
Communications Department
(See address above.)

NIEMAN FOUNDATION FOR JOURNALISM AT HARVARD   [2082]

Walter Lippmann House
One Francis Avenue
Cambridge, MA 02138
(617) 495-2237
Fax: (617) 495-8976

E-MAIL ADDRESS:
nieman_applications@harvard.edu

WEB SITE ADDRESS:
www.nieman.harvard.edu

FOUNDED: 1938

AREAS OF INTEREST:
To provide an opportunity for midcareer journalists to spend a year at Harvard University.

NAME(S) OF PROGRAMS:
- **Nieman Fellowships in Journalism**

TYPE:
Fellowships. Provides midcareer journalists with the opportunity to spend a year of study at Harvard University. Awards are for U.S. and international journalists. Some Fellowships are designed for journalists from the U.S., Europe, and the developing world who want to concentrate on global health issues. Nieman Fellowships in global health reporting include four months of journalistic fieldwork in a developing country following the academic year.

YEAR PROGRAM STARTED: 1938

PURPOSE:
To provide an opportunity for journalists to deepen their knowledge in a field of specialty, broaden their knowledge in several areas, or prepare for a new journalistic assignment.

LEGAL BASIS:
A foundation of Harvard University.

ELIGIBILITY:
Print, broadcast and online reporters, editors, photographers, producers, editorial writers and cartoonists with at least five years of full-time, professional experience in the news media are invited to apply.

FINANCIAL DATA:
Nieman Fellows receive a stipend plus housing, child care and health insurance allowance, if appropriate.
Amount of support per award: $60,000 stipend.

NUMBER OF APPLICANTS MOST RECENT YEAR: Approximately 300 for the year 2009-10.

NUMBER OF AWARDS: Approximately 24 annually (12 to journalists from the U.S. and 12 to journalists from other countries).

APPLICATION INFORMATION:
Duration: 10 months, except for the Nieman Fellowships in global health reporting, which are 14 months.
Deadline: U.S. applications and all applications for the Nieman Fellowships in global health reporting are due January 31 for the academic year beginning in August. International applications, other than those for global health reporting fellowships, are due December 15 for the academic year beginning the following August.

PUBLICATIONS:
Nieman Reports.

STAFF:
John Breen, Fellowship Administrator

ADDRESS INQUIRIES TO:
John Breen, Fellowship Administrator
(See address above.)

*SPECIAL STIPULATIONS:
Once candidates have been chosen and before their confirmation as Nieman Fellows by the Harvard Corporation, they must agree in writing to return at the end of the sabbatical year to the employer who granted the leave of absence; to refrain from professional work during the period of the Fellowship; to complete all the work in one academic course of their choice each semester, and to remain in residence in the Cambridge area each term while classes are in session.

THE ALICIA PATTERSON FOUNDATION [2083]
1090 Vermont Avenue, N.W.
Suite 1000
Washington, DC 20005
(202) 393-5995
Fax: (301) 951-8512
E-MAIL ADDRESS:
info@aliciapatterson.org
WEB SITE ADDRESS:
www.aliciapatterson.org
FOUNDED: 1961
AREAS OF INTEREST:
Journalism.
NAME(S) OF PROGRAMS:
● **Fellowship Program for Journalists**
TYPE:
Fellowships. Awarded to a small number of working print journalists for a year of travel and inquiry. On leave from their normal writing, editing or photographing duties, Fellows examine their chosen subjects (areas or problems of significant interest, foreign or domestic) and write quarterly articles for the *APF Reporter.* These articles may be reprinted.

YEAR PROGRAM STARTED: 1965

PURPOSE:
To provide a few talented and promising American journalists with the opportunity to pursue independent projects.

LEGAL BASIS:
Section 501(c)(3) of the IRS Code and Not For Profits Corporation Law: New York State.

ELIGIBILITY:
The program is open to U.S. citizens who are full-time print journalists or to non-U.S. citizens who work full-time for U.S. print publication, either in America or abroad.

GEOGRAPHIC RESTRICTIONS:
United States.

FINANCIAL DATA:
Amount of support per award: $20,000 stipend for six months or $40,000 stipend for the year.
Total amount of support: Varies.

APPLICATION INFORMATION:
Application forms are available in June. Information may be requested from the address above throughout the year.
Duration: Fellowships support a one-year or six-month leave of absence. The fellowship begins within the first three months of the calendar year.
Deadline: October 1 (postmark).

PUBLICATIONS:
APF Reporter, quarterly magazine.

IRS IDENTIFICATION NUMBER: 13-6092124

ADDRESS INQUIRIES TO:
Margaret Engel
(See address above.)

THE PRESS CLUB OF METROPOLITAN ST. LOUIS AND JOURNALISM FOUNDATION OF METROPOLITAN ST. LOUIS
c/o The Press Club of Metropolitan St. Louis
P.O. Box 410522
St. Louis, MO 63141
(636) 230-1973
Fax: (636) 203-2441

E-MAIL ADDRESS:
info@stlpressclub.org
WEB SITE ADDRESS:
stlpressclub.org
TYPE:
Awards/prizes; Conferences/seminars; Fellowships; Internships; Scholarships; Seed money grants.
See entry 1871 for full listing.

PULLIAM JOURNALISM FELLOWSHIP [2084]
P.O. Box 145
Indianapolis, IN 46206-0145
(317) 444-6001
E-MAIL ADDRESS:
russell.pulliam@indystar.com
WEB SITE ADDRESS:
www.indystar.com/pjf
FOUNDED: 1974
AREAS OF INTEREST:
Journalism awards.
TYPE:
Fellowships. Cash awards and on-the-job study at *The Indianapolis Star* or *The Arizona Republic,* which are owned by Gannett Co.

YEAR PROGRAM STARTED: 1974

PURPOSE:
To offer on-the-job experience, plus seminars and writing criticism, to college students seriously pursuing a newspaper journalism career.

LEGAL BASIS:
Corporate-sponsored.

ELIGIBILITY:
Applicants are generally college journalism majors or liberal arts majors with part-time newspaper experience, outstanding character references, proven writing ability and a solid academic record.

GEOGRAPHIC RESTRICTIONS:
United States.

FINANCIAL DATA:
Amount of support per award: $6,500 ($650 per week for 10-week program).

NUMBER OF APPLICANTS MOST RECENT YEAR: 175.

NUMBER OF AWARDS: 25.

APPLICATION INFORMATION:
Brochures are available from the address above. View the instructions and download the application at the web site.
Duration: 10 weeks, June to August. No renewals.
Deadline: November 1.

PUBLICATIONS:
Brochure.

ADDRESS INQUIRIES TO:
Russ Pulliam, Director
(See address above.)

QUILL AND SCROLL FOUNDATION [2085]
School of Journalism and
Mass Communication
The University of Iowa
100 Adler Journalism Building, Room E346
Iowa City, IA 52242-2004
(319) 335-3321
(319) 335-3457
Fax: (319) 335-3989

E-MAIL ADDRESS:
quill-scroll@uiowa.edu

WEB SITE ADDRESS:
www.uiowa.edu/~quill-sc

FOUNDED: 1926

AREAS OF INTEREST:
Journalism, high school media, media law and ethics, and scholastic journalism education.

TYPE:
Awards/prizes; Project/program grants; Research grants; Scholarships. Grants for research projects in the field of high school journalism and school media.

YEAR PROGRAM STARTED: 1964

PURPOSE:
To improve the quality of secondary school journalism.

LEGAL BASIS:
Nonprofit special-interest foundation.

ELIGIBILITY:
Qualified scholars or educational departments with appropriate interests are eligible to apply.

GEOGRAPHIC RESTRICTIONS:
Primarily United States.

FINANCIAL DATA:
Support may be provided to cover partial or complete project costs.
Amount of support per award: $500 to $1,000.
Total amount of support: $6,000 for the year 2010-11.

NUMBER OF APPLICANTS MOST RECENT YEAR:
30 for the year 2010-11.

NUMBER OF AWARDS: 6 for the year 2010-11.

APPLICATION INFORMATION:
No official application forms are issued. Prospective applicants should submit a letter describing the proposed project in terms of scope, objectives and financial need. Also include a letter of support from project, thesis adviser.
Duration: One-time award.
Deadline: May 10.

PUBLICATIONS:
Application guidelines.

IRS IDENTIFICATION NUMBER: 42-0795095

TRUSTEES:
Richard P. Johns, Chairperson
Julie Dodd, Vice Chairperson
Jack Dvorak
Thomas Eveslage
H.L. Hall
John Humenik
Lydia Ramos
George Rede
Vanessa Shelton
Sara Van Allen
Ann Visser

OFFICER:
Vanessa Shelton, Executive Director

ADDRESS INQUIRIES TO:
Vanessa Shelton, Executive Director
(See address above.)

RADIO AND TELEVISION DIGITAL NEWS FOUNDATION   [2086]
4121 Plank Road, No. 512
Fredericksburg, VA 22407
(202) 659-6510

E-MAIL ADDRESS:
katies@rtdna.org

WEB SITE ADDRESS:
www.rtdna.org

FOUNDED: 1946

AREAS OF INTEREST:
Electronic journalism.

NAME(S) OF PROGRAMS:
- **N.S. Biestock Fellowship**
- **Ed Bradley Scholarship**
- **Broadcast Journalism Undergraduate Scholarships**
- **Michele Clark Fellowship**
- **George Foreman Tribute to Lyndon B. Johnson**
- **Ken Kashiwahara Scholarship**
- **Jacque I. Mimmotte Fellowship**
- **Vada and Barney Oldfield Fellowship for National Security Reporting**
- **Lou and Carole Prato Sports Reporting Scholarship**
- **The President's Scholarships**
- **Abe Schecter Graduate Scholarship**
- **Carole Simpson Scholarship**
- **Pete Wilson Scholarship**

TYPE:
Fellowships; Internships; Scholarships. Awards for one year of undergraduate and/or graduate study in broadcast journalism.

YEAR PROGRAM STARTED: 1967

PURPOSE:
To aid in advanced learning of electronic journalism.

LEGAL BASIS:
Incorporated.

ELIGIBILITY:
For scholarships, applicants must be officially enrolled in college and have at least one full academic year remaining, must be a fully enrolled college sophomore or higher, may apply for only one scholarship, and may be enrolled in any major so long as their career intent is television or radio news. The fellowships are available to present electronic journalists who wish to continue studying the field without leaving their job. U.S. citizens and international applicants are eligible.

FINANCIAL DATA:
Amount of support per award: Scholarships: $1,000 to $10,000; Fellowships: $1,000 and $2,500.

NUMBER OF APPLICANTS MOST RECENT YEAR:
200.

NUMBER OF AWARDS: Scholarships: 12; Fellowships and Internships: 1 each.

APPLICATION INFORMATION:
Contact the Foundation for application information.
Duration: Scholarships: One year.

PUBLICATIONS:
Annual report.

IRS IDENTIFICATION NUMBER: 38-1860090

ADDRESS INQUIRIES TO:
Katie Switchenko, Program Coordinator
(See address above.)

REPORTERS COMMITTEE FOR FREEDOM OF THE PRESS [2087]
1101 Wilson Boulevard
Suite 1100
Arlington, VA 22209-2275
(703) 807-2100
Fax: (703) 807-2109

E-MAIL ADDRESS:
rcfp@rcfp.org

WEB SITE ADDRESS:
www.rcfp.org

AREAS OF INTEREST:
First Amendment interests of the news media.

NAME(S) OF PROGRAMS:
- **The Reporters Committee Legal Fellowship**

TYPE:
Fellowships. Legal fellows monitor significant developments in First Amendment media law, assist with legal defense requests from reporters, prepare legal memoranda, amicus briefs and other special projects. The Fellowship focuses on media law.

YEAR PROGRAM STARTED: 1987

PURPOSE:
To promote legal research that helps protect the First Amendment interests of the news media.

ELIGIBILITY:
Candidates must have received a law degree by August of the year the Fellowship begins. Strong legal research and writing skills are required, and a background in news reporting is very strongly preferred.

FINANCIAL DATA:
Fellowship includes fully paid health benefits.
Amount of support per award: $35,000.

APPLICATION INFORMATION:
Duration: One year, September to August.
Deadline: February 1.

PUBLICATIONS:
News Media & the Law.

ADDRESS INQUIRIES TO:
Lucy Dalglish, Executive Director
(See address above.)

TECHFOUNDATION
30 Brattle Street, Third Floor
Cambridge, MA 02138
(617) 354-7500
Fax: (617) 354-7510

E-MAIL ADDRESS:
info@techfoundation.org

WEB SITE ADDRESS:
www.techfoundation.org

TYPE:
Conferences/seminars; Fellowships; Grants-in-aid; Product donations.
TechConnect: A series of educational seminars designed to bring needed technology expertise to the nonprofit community.

TechGrants: A newsletter and a grant program that provides nonprofit organizations with access to capital to help fulfill their technology needs.

TechMarketplace: A business-to-nonprofit program that provides discounted and donated technology hardware, software and services to nonprofit organizations.

See entry 1477 for full listing.

UNITED METHODIST COMMUNICATIONS [2088]

810 12th Avenue South
Nashville, TN 37203-4704
(888) 278-4862
Fax: (615) 742-5777

E-MAIL ADDRESS:
scholarships@umcom.org

WEB SITE ADDRESS:
www.umcom.org/specialinitiatives

FOUNDED: 1948

AREAS OF INTEREST:
Religion communications.

NAME(S) OF PROGRAMS:
● **The Stoody-West Fellowship**

TYPE:
Fellowships. Assists one United Methodist student in graduate study at an accredited U.S. college or university who intends to pursue a career in religious journalism.

YEAR PROGRAM STARTED: 1964

PURPOSE:
To enable the recipient to continue graduate studies in religion journalism and to promote a level of excellence in communication at the graduate level.

LEGAL BASIS:
Nonprofit.

ELIGIBILITY:
Applicant must be a member of The United Methodist Church who intends to pursue a career in religion journalism and is enrolled in graduate study at an accredited U.S. college or university (includes electronic and broadcast media as well as print). Employees of United Methodist Communications and members of the General Commission on Communication are not eligible for the Fellowship.

FINANCIAL DATA:
Amount of support per award: $6,000.
Total amount of support: $6,000.

NUMBER OF AWARDS: 1 annually.

APPLICATION INFORMATION:
Application forms are available online.

Applicant must submit:
(1) completed application form;
(2) official transcripts of schools attended, including evidence of enrollment as a graduate student in the journalism or communications department of a duly accredited college or university in the U.S.;
(3) three letters of recommendation;
(4) statement of interest and plans;
(5) three writing samples and;
(6) recent personal photograph.

If materials must be mailed, use the following address:
Stoody-West Fellowship Committee
United Methodist Communications
P.O. Box 320
Nashville, TN 37202-0320.

If submitting by FedEx or UPS, send to:
Stoody-West Fellowship Committee, United Methodist Communications, at the street address above.
Duration: One academic year.
Deadline: March 15 (postmark).

PUBLICATIONS:
Application guidelines.

ADDRESS INQUIRIES TO:
Communications Ministry
(See address above.)

---

*PLEASE NOTE:
Religious journalism is interpreted to include news writing for secular press, church press and for church institutions. Appropriate news and journalism forms will be considered, including electronic and broadcast media, as well as print.

UNITED METHODIST COMMUNICATIONS

810 12th Avenue South
Nashville, TN 37203-4704
(888) 278-4862
Fax: (615) 742-5485

E-MAIL ADDRESS:
scholarships@umcom.org

WEB SITE ADDRESS:
www.umcom.org/specialinitiatives

TYPE:
Fellowships; Scholarships. Award for junior or senior undergraduate study in religion journalism or mass communications. The term *communications* is meant to cover various media as audio-visual, electronic and print journalism.

See entry 1083 for full listing.

UNIVERSITY FILM AND VIDEO ASSOCIATION [2089]

Rochester Institute of Technology
Building 7B, Room 2270
70 Lomb Memorial Drive
Rochester, NY 14623-5604

E-MAIL ADDRESS:
axcpph@rit.edu

WEB SITE ADDRESS:
www.ufva.org

AREAS OF INTEREST:
Film, video and multi-media production.

NAME(S) OF PROGRAMS:
● **Carole Fielding Student Grants**

TYPE:
Block grants; Capital grants; Development grants; General operating grants; Project/program grants. Annual support for student projects in film, video and multi-media productions or research activities in historical, critical, theoretical or experimental studies in film or video.

YEAR PROGRAM STARTED: 1993

PURPOSE:
To support and promote student film and video makers.

LEGAL BASIS:
UFVA membership funded.

ELIGIBILITY:
An applicant must be a graduate or undergraduate student at the time the application is made, be sponsored by a faculty member who is an active member of the University Film and Video Association and agree to present, or have presented by his or her representative, a report on the project or production at the next annual meeting of the Association.

The judges reserve the right not to make an award if quality or quantity of submissions so justify.

FINANCIAL DATA:
Amount of support per award: Varies.
Total amount of support: $5,000 per year.

NUMBER OF APPLICANTS MOST RECENT YEAR: 90.

APPLICATION INFORMATION:
Applicants should submit six stapled and collated copies of their proposal to the Scholarship and Grants Office. The proposal must include a one-page description of the production or project which includes a statement of purpose, an indication of the resources available to complete the work and a summary of the proposed film, video production or study. If a narrative film is proposed, submit a copy of the script. A documentary proposal should include a short treatment. An experimental or animated film proposal should include a treatment (or script) and/or story boards. Also include a one-page budget, indicating what portion of the total project will be supported by this grant and a statement by a faculty member who is an active member of the University Film and Video Association assessing the feasibility of the project or production and indicating his or her willingness to serve as faculty supervisor or consultant.
Deadline: December 15. Announcements by March 31.

OFFICERS:
Rob Sabal, President
Adrianne Carageorge, Executive Vice President
Steve Lipkin, Editorial Vice President

ADDRESS INQUIRIES TO:
Adrianne Carageorge, Executive Vice President
(See e-mail address above.)

THE UNIVERSITY OF CALGARY [2090]

Faculty of Graduate Studies
Earth Sciences Building, Room 720
2500 University Drive, N.W.
Calgary AB T2N 1N4 Canada
(403) 220-4938
Fax: (403) 289-7635

E-MAIL ADDRESS:
gsaward@ucalgary.ca

WEB SITE ADDRESS:
www.grad.ucalgary.ca

FOUNDED: 1966

AREAS OF INTEREST:
Communications studies.

NAME(S) OF PROGRAMS:
● **Cogeco Inc. Graduate Scholarship**

TYPE:
Awards/prizes; Scholarships.

LEGAL BASIS:
University scholarship program.

ELIGIBILITY:
Applicants must be students admissible to or registered in a Master's program (either thesis-based or course-based) in the Communications Studies Programme at the University of Calgary. Awards will be made on the basis of academic excellence.

FINANCIAL DATA:
Amount of support per award: $7,500.
Total amount of support: $7,500.

COOPERATIVE FUNDING PROGRAMS: Scholarship is financed by Cogeco Inc.

NUMBER OF AWARDS: 1 each year.

APPLICATION INFORMATION:
Candidates should apply to the Master of Communications Studies Programme in the first instance. Recommendations from the Programme will be submitted to the University of Calgary Graduate Scholarship Office for approval.

Duration: One year.

Deadline: February 1.

ADDRESS INQUIRIES TO:
Graduate Scholarship Office
(See address above.)

UNIVERSITY OF MICHIGAN [2091]

Knight-Wallace Fellows
Wallace House
620 Oxford Road
Ann Arbor, MI 48104-2635
(734) 998-7666
Fax: (734) 998-7979

E-MAIL ADDRESS:
kwfellows@umich.edu

WEB SITE ADDRESS:
www.kwfellows.org

AREAS OF INTEREST:
Arts, sciences and professions.

NAME(S) OF PROGRAMS:
● **Knight-Wallace Fellows**

TYPE:
Fellowships.

YEAR PROGRAM STARTED: 1973

PURPOSE:
To offer a full academic year in any field or fields at the University of Michigan.

LEGAL BASIS:
A unit of the School of Graduate Studies, University of Michigan.

ELIGIBILITY:
Eligibility extends to all full-time print, broadcast, photo and film journalists with five years' experience whose work appears regularly in U.S.-controlled news organizations. Freelancers are included. Work may be related or unrelated to professional objectives.

FINANCIAL DATA:
Fellowship also includes tuition and fees.
Amount of support per award: $70,000 stipend.

NUMBER OF APPLICANTS MOST RECENT YEAR: 96.

NUMBER OF AWARDS: 12 National.

APPLICATION INFORMATION:
Application form, a leave of absence for the period of the Fellowship, and a support letter from direct supervisor is required. Two statements, an intellectual autobiography, and a proposed program of study must be included. Do not submit more than five examples of applicant's work.

Duration: Eight-month academic year, September to April.

Deadline: February 1. Announcement in May.

PUBLICATIONS:
The Journal of Knight-Wallace Fellows.

ADDRESS INQUIRIES TO:
Birgit Rieck, Assistant Director
(See address above.)

Labor

CENTERS FOR DISEASE CONTROL AND PREVENTION (CDC) [2092]

National Institute for Occupational Safety and Health (NIOSH)
626 Cochrans Mill Road
Pittsburgh, PA 15236
(412) 386-6826
Fax: (412) 386-6429

E-MAIL ADDRESS:
lguess@cdc.gov

WEB SITE ADDRESS:
www.cdc.gov/niosh

FOUNDED: 1970

AREAS OF INTEREST:
The program priorities, listed below, are applicable to all grants supported by NIOSH. These priority areas were developed into the National Occupational Research Agenda, which identifies 21 research priorities, to guide occupational safety and health research in the next decade.

Disease and Injury:
Allergic and Irritant Dermatitis, Asthma and Chronic Obstructive Pulmonary Disease, Fertility and Pregnancy Abnormalities, Hearing Loss, Infectious Diseases, Low Back Disorders, Musculoskeletal Disorders of the Upper Extremities, and Traumatic Injuries;

Work Environment and Workforce:
Emerging Technologies, Indoor Environment, Mixed Exposures, Organization of Work, and Special Populations at Risk;

Research Tools and Approaches:
Cancer Research Methods, Control Technology and Personal Protective Equipment, Exposure Assessment Methods, Health Services Research, Intervention Effectiveness Research, Risk Assessment Methods, Social and Economic Consequences of Workplace Illness and Injury, and Surveillance Research Methods.

NAME(S) OF PROGRAMS:
● **First Independent Research Support and Transition (FIRST) Grants**
● **Small Grants**
● **Special Emphasis Research Career Award (SERCA)**

TYPE:
Demonstration grants; Project/program grants; Research grants. Research and demonstrations relating to occupational safety and health (Catalog of Federal Domestic Assistance number 13.262).

First Independent Research Support and Transition (FIRST) Grants (R29) provides support for newly independent investigators to initiate their own research and demonstrate the merit of their own research ideas.

Special Emphasis Research Career Award (SERCA) grants support individuals in the formative stages of their careers who have demonstrated outstanding potential for contributing as independent investigators to health-related research.

Small Grants provide financial support to carry out exploratory or pilot studies, to develop or test new techniques or methods, or to analyze data previously collected. This grant is intended for predoctoral graduate students, postdoctoral researchers and junior faculty members.

YEAR PROGRAM STARTED: 1970

PURPOSE:
To develop knowledge that can be used in preventing occupational diseases and injuries.

LEGAL BASIS:
Public Health Service Act, as amended, Section 301 (42 U.S.C. 241); Occupational Safety and Health Act of 1970, Section 20(a) (29 U.S.C. 669[a]); Federal Mine Safety and Health Amendments Act of 1977, as amended, Section 501 (30 U.S.C. 951).

ELIGIBILITY:
Eligible applicants include nonprofit and for-profit organizations. Thus, universities, colleges, research institutions and other public and private organizations, including state and local governments and small, minority and/or female-owned businesses, are eligible to apply.

A research project grant application should be designed to establish, discover, develop, elucidate or confirm information relating to occupational safety and health, including innovative methods, techniques and approaches for dealing with occupational safety and health problems. These studies may generate information that is readily available to solve problems or contribute to a better understanding of underlying causes and mechanisms. A demonstration project grant application should address, either on a pilot or full-scale basis, the technical or economic feasibility or application of a new or improved procedure, method, technique or system, or an innovative method, technique or approach for preventing occupational safety or health problems.

FINANCIAL DATA:
Amount of support per award: Research Project Demonstration Grants: Average $180,000; SERCA Grants: $54,000; Small Grants: $37,500.

APPLICATION INFORMATION:
Application forms are mailed upon request from the office at the address above.

Duration: Research Project Demonstration Grants: Up to five years; SERCA Grants: Three years; Small Grants: Two years. Continuation within project period based on satisfactory progress and availability of funds.

Deadline: New applications: February 1, June 1 and October 1; SERCA and Small Grants, competing renewal and revised applications: March 1, July 1 and November 1.

IMAGINE AMERICA FOUNDATION [2093]

1101 Connecticut Avenue, N.W.
Suite 901
Washington, DC 20036
(202) 336-6800
Fax: (202) 408-8102

E-MAIL ADDRESS:
scholarships@imagine-america.org

WEB SITE ADDRESS:
www.imagine-america.org

FOUNDED: 1982

AREAS OF INTEREST:
Private career education.

NAME(S) OF PROGRAMS:
- **Imagine America Adult Skills Education Program (ASEP)**
- **Imagine America High School Scholarship Program**
- **Imagine America LDRSHIP Award**
- **Imagine America Military Award Program (MAP)**
- **Imagine America Promise Scholarship Program**

TYPE:
Awards/prizes; Scholarships; Research contracts. Sponsorships. Three scholarships are given to each high school listed on the Foundation web site above.

YEAR PROGRAM STARTED: 1982

PURPOSE:
To provide research, scholarship and training for America's career colleges.

LEGAL BASIS:
501(c)(3) nonprofit organization.

ELIGIBILITY:
Applicants must be graduating high school seniors. Applicants for Imagine America MAP must be honorably discharged, active duty, reservist or retired military.

GEOGRAPHIC RESTRICTIONS:
United States and Puerto Rico.

FINANCIAL DATA:
Amount of support per award: Varies.
Total amount of support: $8,000,000.

NUMBER OF AWARDS: More than 35,000.

PUBLICATIONS:
Imagine America's Guide to Career Colleges; Imagine America's Student's Guide; A Profile of Career Colleges and Universities.

ADDRESS INQUIRIES TO:
Torian Brown, Director of Operations
(See address above.)

NATIONAL INSTITUTE OF STANDARDS AND TECHNOLOGY   [2094]
U.S. Department of Commerce, NIST
100 Bureau Drive, Mail Stop 1650
Gaithersburg, MD 20899-1650
(301) 975-8006
Fax: (301) 840-5976

E-MAIL ADDRESS:
usha.ganti@nist.gov

WEB SITE ADDRESS:
www.nist.gov

FOUNDED: 1901

AREAS OF INTEREST:
Advanced manufacturing technology.

NAME(S) OF PROGRAMS:
- **Manufacturing Extension Partnership**

TYPE:
Project/program grants.

YEAR PROGRAM STARTED: 1988

PURPOSE:
To establish, maintain and support manufacturing extension centers and services, the functions of which are to accelerate the usage of appropriate manufacturing technology by smaller U.S.-based manufacturing firms, and partner with the states in developing such technical assistance programs and services for their manufacturing base.

LEGAL BASIS:
Ominibus Trade and Competitiveness Act of 1988, Public Law 100-148, American Technology Preeminence Act of 1991.

ELIGIBILITY:
For extension services, eligible applicants should be U.S.-based nonprofit institutions or organizations or groups thereof. For extension service planning and pilot services agreements, eligible applicants shall be state governments and state-affiliated nonprofit organizations. For multi-state regional planning and pilot services agreements, eligible applicants shall be state and local governments, representing either themselves or a consortium of states, and appropriate private or public nonprofit organizations, operating on behalf of a consortium of states or as a representative of states. Beneficiary shall be U.S.-based manufacturing firms, especially smaller companies.

FINANCIAL DATA:
Amount of support per award: Awards for manufacturing extension centers: $7,000,000 annually. Individual awards for extension service planning and pilot testing agreements: $25,000 to $100,000.

Total amount of support: Varies.

Matching fund requirements: Applicants must provide at least 50% of the capital, annual operating and maintenance funds required to create and maintain the center. Funds may be provided by any non-federal source. A minimum of 50% of the applicant's share must be as cash of full-time personnel.

REPRESENTATIVE AWARDS:
NIST Mid-American Manufacturing Technology Center, Overland Park, KS, and hosted by the Kansas Technology Enterprise Corporation; NIST Minnesota Manufacturing Technology Center, Minneapolis, MN, and hosted by Minnesota Technology, Inc.; NIST California Manufacturing Technology Center, Hawthorne, CA.

APPLICATION INFORMATION:
An applicant should consult the office or official designated as the single point of contact in his or her state for information on the process the state requires to be followed in applying for assistance, if the state has selected the program for review. For manufacturing extension centers, no formal preapplication is required, although applicants are advised to discuss their proposal during the early stages of development with NIST MEP regional managers. This portion of the program is excluded from coverage under E.O. 12372.

A *Federal Register* notice announcing the request for proposals from qualified organizations will be published when funds are available.

Duration: One year for extension service planning and pilot-testing agreements. Six years maximum for manufacturing extension centers. Agreements are renewed annually based upon positive evaluation and availabilty of funds.

Deadline: Notice of availability of funds and deadlines are published on cfda.gov.

ADDRESS INQUIRIES TO:
Usha Ganti, Chief, Grants and Agreements Management Division
Tel: (301) 975-5020
(See address above.)

U.S. DEPARTMENT OF HEALTH AND HUMAN SERVICES   [2095]
Administration for Children and Families
Office of Family Assistance
370 L'Enfant Promenade S.W.
5th Floor East
Washington, DC 20447
(202) 401-9275
Fax: (202) 205-5887

E-MAIL ADDRESS:
ann.barbagallo@acf.hhs.gov

WEB SITE ADDRESS:
www.acf.hhs.gov

FOUNDED: 1996

AREAS OF INTEREST:
Education, employment and support services, and financial assistance.

NAME(S) OF PROGRAMS:
- **Temporary Assistance for Needy Families (TANF)**

TYPE:
Block grants; Internships; Technical assistance. Grants and assistance payments to State IV-A (Welfare) agencies for education, employment, and training and supportive services to help persons receiving temporary assistance for needy families, to move to work and self-sufficiency.

YEAR PROGRAM STARTED: 1996

PURPOSE:
To help needy families achieve self-sufficiency.

LEGAL BASIS:
Social Security Act, Title IV-A and Title IV-F, as amended (42 USC 602-603, 681-687 and 1302) and Public Law 100-485.

ELIGIBILITY:
Grants are awarded to state welfare agencies, Indian Tribes and Alaska Native Organizations based on a complete TANF plan. Statute precludes any grantees other than those stated above.

FINANCIAL DATA:
Amount of support per award: Calculated share of federal block grant.
Total amount of support: $16.5 billion.

PUBLICATIONS:
TANF Annual Report to Congress; policy announcements; program instructions; information memoranda.

ADDRESS INQUIRIES TO:
Ann Barbagallo, Senior Policy Advisor
Office of the Director
(See address above.)

U.S. DEPARTMENT OF LABOR   [2096]
Office of Apprenticeship
Room N-5311
200 Constitution Avenue, N.W.
Washington, DC 20210
(202) 693-2796
Fax: (202) 692-3799

E-MAIL ADDRESS:
ladd.john@dol.gov

WEB SITE ADDRESS:
www.doleta.gov/grants

FOUNDED: 1937

AREAS OF INTEREST:
Apprenticeship, skill and technical training.

CONSULTING OR VOLUNTEER SERVICES:
Provides technical assistance at no cost.

NAME(S) OF PROGRAMS:
- **National Apprenticeship System**

TYPE:
Technical assistance. Management and labor, along with government and the education system, work together at the national, state and local levels to formulate and promote effective apprenticeship programs. The program must be an organized, written plan embodying training and supervision of one or more apprentices in an apprenticeable occupation, as defined in 29 CFR 29.4 and subscribed to by a sponsor who has undertaken to carry out the apprenticeship program.

YEAR PROGRAM STARTED: 1937

PURPOSE:
To formulate, promote and publish labor standards necessary to safeguard the welfare of apprentices, encourage the inclusion of such standards in apprenticeship contracts, bring together employers and labor to create apprenticeship programs, cooperate with state agencies in formulating and promoting apprenticeship standards, and cooperate with the U.S. Department of Education on vocational education and related instruction in apprenticeship.

LEGAL BASIS:
National Apprenticeship Act of 1937 (P.L. 308-75); Title 29, CFR Part 30; Title 29, CFR Part 29.

ELIGIBILITY:
To be eligible as a sponsor, apprenticeship programs must meet the basic standards and established criteria set forth by the Secretary of Labor and may be registered upon request of the program sponsor. Registration of programs and apprentices in states having apprenticeship agencies recognized by the U.S. Department of Labor is performed by the state apprenticeship agencies. Programs in states not having recognized apprenticeship agencies will be registered by the Bureau of Apprenticeship and Training.

To be eligible as a beneficiary, applicants for apprenticeship must be at least 16 years of age. They must have the ability and aptitude to master the occupations and sufficient education to complete satisfactorily the required hours of related theoretical instruction.

GEOGRAPHIC RESTRICTIONS:
United States.

FINANCIAL DATA:
The Department of Labor does not finance apprenticeships. Program sponsors bear the expenses of the program.

NUMBER OF APPLICANTS MOST RECENT YEAR: 100,000.

APPLICATION INFORMATION:
Notices for accepting applications are published locally by apprenticeship program sponsors. Information may be obtained from local One Stop Centers or may be requested by contacting regional, state or area offices of the Office of Apprenticeship, U.S. Department of Labor, or the ETA Grants Office.

PUBLICATIONS:
Apprenticeship Past and Present; *National Apprenticeship Program*.

ADDRESS INQUIRIES TO:
Grants Department
Division of Grants and Contracts
(See address above.)

W.E. UPJOHN INSTITUTE FOR EMPLOYMENT RESEARCH [2097]
300 South Westnedge Avenue
Kalamazoo, MI 49007-4686
(269) 343-5541
Fax: (269) 343-3308

E-MAIL ADDRESS:
communications@upjohn.org

WEB SITE ADDRESS:
www.upjohn.org

FOUNDED: 1945

AREAS OF INTEREST:
Policy-relevant research on employment and unemployment at the international, national, state and local levels. The Institute is also receptive to international studies for the purpose of drawing lessons for U.S. policy. Topics of interest include job creation, job stabilization, matching of jobs and people, alleviation of unemployment hazards, the political science of manpower programs and the quality of work life.

CONSULTING OR VOLUNTEER SERVICES:
Both consulting and volunteer services are available, though the latter are limited.

NAME(S) OF PROGRAMS:
- **Mini-Grants**
- **Policy Research Grants**

TYPE:
Research grants. Mini-Grants are especially targeted on untenured junior faculty within six years of earning their Ph.D. degree, and are intended to provide flexibility to meet special funding needs that, without support, would prevent researchers from pursuing the project.

Through its Policy Research Grants program, the Institute invites submission of proposals to conduct original, policy-relevant research on labor market and regional economic development issues. This program focuses on article-length Research Papers, accompanied by a Policy Brief. The Institute expects its grantees to produce two distinct products: (1) a Research Paper and (2) a Policy Brief. The Research Paper is expected to be suitable for publication in a peer-reviewed journal, and acceptable papers will be published in the Upjohn Institute Working Paper series. The Policy Brief expands upon the policy implications of the analysis presented in the Research Paper, and its 12-page format is intended to be accessible to practitioners and policymakers.

YEAR PROGRAM STARTED: 1976

PURPOSE:
To conduct research into the causes and effects of unemployment and measures for the alleviation of unemployment at the national, state and local levels.

LEGAL BASIS:
Public nonprofit organization.

ELIGIBILITY:
Proposals for Mini-Grants will be evaluated according to the following criteria:
(1) contribution to important labor market policy issues and to the professional literature;
(2) technical merit and;
(3) professional qualifications.

For Policy Research Grants, proposals will be evaluated according to the following criteria:
(1) extent to which the research is likely to influence employment policy discourse;
(2) extent to which the proposed analysis will contribute to a better understanding of the policy issues;
(3) appropriateness of the methodology for doing the analysis;
(4) professional qualifications and;
(5) cost effectiveness.

The Institute does not fund dissertation research.

The Institute expects the research to be completed within a year.

FINANCIAL DATA:
The Institute does not pay indirect costs but will entertain any legitimate research expense as part of the budget. Acceptable items include costs for professional, technical, and support personnel, data acquisition, materials and supplies, computer services, and travel.

Amount of support per award: Mini-Grants: Up to $5,000; Policy Research Grants: Up to $10,000.

NUMBER OF APPLICANTS MOST RECENT YEAR: 35.

NUMBER OF AWARDS: 10.

APPLICATION INFORMATION:
Applicants for a Research Policy Grant should submit a proposal of up to five double-spaced pages. The proposal should outline their proposed research and its policy relevance and include a budget.

Applicants for a Mini-Grant should submit a proposal of up to three double-spaced pages; it should outline their proposed research and its policy relevance and include a budget.

All applicants must submit a vita that describes their professional qualifications.

Submissions by e-mail are accepted. (Send to e-mail address above.)

Duration: Ordinarily, one year for research, plus one year for monograph publication.

Deadline: Applications: February 1. Announcement: February 22.

PUBLICATIONS:
Program announcement; proposal guidelines.

IRS IDENTIFICATION NUMBER: 38-1360419

TRUSTEES:
Donald R. Parfet, Chairman
Marilyn Schlack, Vice Chairman
Thomas W. Lambert, Secretary-Treasurer
John M. Dunn
William C. Richardson
Frank J. Sardone
Paul H. Todd
Amanda Van Dusen
B. Joseph White
Dr. Eileen Wilson-Oyelaran

ADDRESS INQUIRIES TO:
Randall W. Eberts, President
(See address above.)

*PLEASE NOTE:
Grant awards are essentially performance-based contracts. Applications for grants and all work submitted under grants become the property of the Institute.

Law

AMERICAN ASSOCIATION OF LAW LIBRARIES

105 West Adams Street
Suite 3300
Chicago, IL 60603
(312) 939-4764
Fax: (312) 431-1097

E-MAIL ADDRESS:
membership@aall.org

WEB SITE ADDRESS:
www.aallnet.org

TYPE:
Scholarships. For study of law or librarianship, with support intended for prospective law librarians.

See entry 751 for full listing.

AMERICAN BAR FOUNDATION [2098]

750 North Lake Shore Drive
Fourth Floor
Chicago, IL 60611-4403
(312) 988-6515
Fax: (312) 988-6579

E-MAIL ADDRESS:
kharris@abfn.org

WEB SITE ADDRESS:
www.americanbarfoundation.org

FOUNDED: 1952

AREAS OF INTEREST:
Socio-legal research. Current research interests include: professionalism and the transformation of the legal profession in the U.S. and abroad, the impact of civil rights law on the economic progress of minorities, hate speech and its regulation, the influence of family and environmental factors on juvenile delinquency, the impact of public policy on the spread of the Internet, jury decision-making, historical analyses of labor and regulatory law, public interest lawyering and social reform, and sentencing judgement and the effect of victim impact evidence.

NAME(S) OF PROGRAMS:
● **ABF Fellowships in Law and Social Science**

TYPE:
Fellowships. Residential fellowships at the ABF.

The American Bar Foundation is committed to developing the next generation of scholars in the field of law and social science. Since 1987, the Foundation has supported the dissertation research of a diverse group of graduate students from all social science disciplines and, in 1996, added a postdoctoral component to its fellowship program.

YEAR PROGRAM STARTED: 1987

PURPOSE:
To encourage original and significant research on law, the legal profession and legal institutions.

LEGAL BASIS:
Private foundation.

ELIGIBILITY:
Applications are invited from outstanding students who are candidates for Ph.D. degrees in the social sciences, or who have completed their Ph.D. within the past two years. Proposed research must be in the general area of sociolegal studies or in social scientific approaches to law, the legal profession or legal institutions. The research must address significant issues in the field and show promise of a major contribution to social scientific understanding of law and legal processes. Applicants must, at a minimum, have been admitted to candidacy for the Ph.D. before the commencement of the fellowship.

Minority applicants are especially encouraged.

In exceptional circumstances, candidates with a J.D. who have substantial social science training may also be considered.

GEOGRAPHIC RESTRICTIONS:
United States.

FINANCIAL DATA:
Fellows will receive a stipend with fringe benefits for 12 months. Fellows may also request up to $3,500 each fellowship year for research support, including travel to conferences at which papers are presented. Relocation expenses of up to $1,000 may be reimbursed upon application.
Amount of support per award: $25,000 stipend.

NUMBER OF APPLICANTS MOST RECENT YEAR:
66.

NUMBER OF AWARDS: Varies.

APPLICATION INFORMATION:
Applications must include:
(1) letter of application;
(2) statement describing research interests and achievements to date and plans for the fellowship period;
(3) two letters of reference;
(4) curriculum vitae;
(5) transcript of graduate record;
(6) sample of written work (conference paper, dissertation chapter or published article) and;
(7) Ph.D. candidates should include a copy of their dissertation proposal.
Duration: One year. Renewable for a second year subject to satisfactory progress and participation.
Deadline: December.

*PLEASE NOTE:
Fellowships are held in residence at the American Bar Foundation. Appointments to fellowships are full-time. Fellows are expected to participate fully in the academic life of the ABF so that they may develop close collegial ties with other scholars in residence.

AMERICAN COLLEGE OF LEGAL MEDICINE

1100 East Woodfield Road
Suite 520
Schaumburg, IL 60173-5125
(847) 969-0283
Fax: (847) 517-7229

E-MAIL ADDRESS:
info@aclm.org

WEB SITE ADDRESS:
www.aclm.org

TYPE:
Awards/prizes. The Hirsh Award is awarded to a law, dentistry, podiatry, nursing, pharmacy, health science, health care administration, or public health student.

See entry 2368 for full listing.

THE CANADIAN BAR ASSOCIATION [2099]

500-865 Carling Avenue
Ottawa ON K1S 5S8 Canada
(613) 237-2925
(800) 267-8860
Fax: (613) 237-0185

E-MAIL ADDRESS:
info@cba.org

WEB SITE ADDRESS:
www.cba.org

FOUNDED: 1914

AREAS OF INTEREST:
Law and the administration of justice, promoting access to justice and promotion of equality in the professional justice system.

NAME(S) OF PROGRAMS:
● **Viscount Bennett Fellowship**

TYPE:
Awards/prizes; Fellowships. Award is paid to one law student for legally oriented graduate study in an institution of higher learning anywhere, to be approved by selection committee.

YEAR PROGRAM STARTED: 1946

PURPOSE:
To encourage a high standard of legal education, training and ethics.

ELIGIBILITY:
Canadian citizens who have graduated from an approved law school in Canada or who, at the time of application, are pursuing final-year studies as undergraduate students at such approved law school.

GEOGRAPHIC RESTRICTIONS:
Canada.

FINANCIAL DATA:
Amount of support per award: $40,000 (CAN) paid in two equal installments.
Total amount of support: $40,000 (CAN).

NUMBER OF APPLICANTS MOST RECENT YEAR:
44.

NUMBER OF AWARDS: 1 for the year 2011-12.

APPLICATION INFORMATION:
Applications may be secured from the address or web site above. Completed applications should be in writing, to the Senior Director of Communications of The Canadian Bar Association.

Applications and the accompanying documents should be forwarded in a sealed envelope, addressed to:
Viscount Bennett Fellowship
c/o Stephen Hanson
Senior Director of Communications
The Canadian Bar Association
(See address above.)
Duration: One year. Nonrenewable.
Deadline: November 15 (postmark).

ADDRESS INQUIRIES TO:
Stephen Hanson
Senior Director of Communications
(See address above.)

*SPECIAL STIPULATIONS:
As a condition of the Fellowship, recipient(s) of the Viscount Bennett Fellowship must submit a written report at midterm and at the end of the year of graduate study, and must submit a copy of their final thesis at year end.

CANADIAN INSTITUTE FOR ADVANCED LEGAL STUDIES [2100]

P.O. Box 43538, Leaside Post Office
1531 Bayview Avenue
Toronto ON M4G 4G8 Canada
(416) 429-3292
Fax: (416) 429-9805

E-MAIL ADDRESS:
info@canadian-institute.com

WEB SITE ADDRESS:
www.canadian-institute.com

FOUNDED: 1979

AREAS OF INTEREST:
Law.

NAME(S) OF PROGRAMS:
● **The Right Honourable Paul Martin, Sr. Scholarship**

TYPE:
Scholarships.

YEAR PROGRAM STARTED: 1983

PURPOSE:
To study for an L.L.M. at the University of Cambridge.

ELIGIBILITY:
At the time of application, applicants must be graduates of Canadian Faculty of Law, law students in their articling year, or students registered in their Bar Admission course.

FINANCIAL DATA:
Scholarships include tuition and college fees.
Total amount of support: Approximately $25,000 (CAN).

NUMBER OF APPLICANTS MOST RECENT YEAR: 25.

NUMBER OF AWARDS: 2.

APPLICATION INFORMATION:
Applicants must complete an application consisting of a letter of application, undergraduate and faculty of law transcripts and no more than three letters of recommendation. There is no application form.
Duration: One year.
Deadline: December 31.

CIVIL JUSTICE FOUNDATION [2101]

777 6th Street, N.W.
Suite 200
Washington, DC 20001
(202) 965-3500
Fax: (866) 452-5269

E-MAIL ADDRESS:
civiljusticefoundation@yahoo.com

WEB SITE ADDRESS:
www.civiljusticefoundation.org

FOUNDED: 1986

AREAS OF INTEREST:
Advocacy for injury prevention.

TYPE:
Development grants; General operating grants; Project/program grants. Funding for progressive grassroots organizations focused on models which seek to prevent consumer injury and defend a consumer's access to justice.

YEAR PROGRAM STARTED: 1986

PURPOSE:
To prevent harm to individuals by supporting both organizations of injured consumers and injury prevention research.

LEGAL BASIS:
501(c)(3) not-for-profit foundation.

ELIGIBILITY:
Applicants must be nonprofit organizations and must provide a letter of tax-exempt determination from the IRS. The Foundation is committed to preventing consumer injury and defending a consumer's access to justice through grants to progressive grassroots organizations seeking systemic change. The Foundation is especially interested in organizations or projects that find it difficult to obtain funding from more traditional sources because they are newly organized and/or address a controversial problem. The Foundation will not support organizations with a current annual operating budget over $500,000.

GEOGRAPHIC RESTRICTIONS:
United States and Canada.

FINANCIAL DATA:
Amount of support per award: Average: $5,000 to $20,000.

NUMBER OF APPLICANTS MOST RECENT YEAR: 3 grant applications; 12 Letters of Proposal.

NUMBER OF AWARDS: 3 grants.

REPRESENTATIVE AWARDS:
$15,000 to Childhood Lead Action Project to eliminate childhood lead poisoning in Rhode Island through education, parent support and advocacy; $10,000 to Kids in Danger to advocate, promote and educate people about children's product safety; $10,000 to Lead Safe Bellows Falls: Parks Place Community Center for lead poisoning prevention, outreach and education program.

APPLICATION INFORMATION:
Applicants must submit a brief one- or two-page letter to the Foundation, outlining the intended project and supplying an estimate of the funds involved. The Foundation will select those to invite to submit a full proposal. Unsolicited full proposals will not be accepted or considered for review.
Duration: Generally one to three years.
Deadline: February 15.

PUBLICATIONS:
Annual report; guidelines; fact sheet; *Branching Out*, newsletter.

ADDRESS INQUIRIES TO:
Edward L. Chester, Executive Director
(See address above.)

ENVIRONMENTAL LAW INSTITUTE [2102]

2000 L Street, N.W.
Suite 620
Washington, DC 20036-4919
(202) 939-3800
Fax: (202) 939-3868

E-MAIL ADDRESS:
law@eli.org

WEB SITE ADDRESS:
www.eli.org

FOUNDED: 1969

AREAS OF INTEREST:
Environmental law, management, and policy, including economic and scientific aspects and protection of natural areas.

CONSULTING OR VOLUNTEER SERVICES:
Variety of services including tuition scholarships to continuing legal education programs, consulting services and technical assistance.

NAME(S) OF PROGRAMS:
● **Continuing Legal Education Scholarship Program**

TYPE:
Scholarships. Tuition scholarships to annual Environmental Law Course.

YEAR PROGRAM STARTED: 1970

PURPOSE:
To provide access to education on environmental law and policy; to improve the level of practice and raise the quality of debate on key legal/policy questions.

LEGAL BASIS:
Nonprofit corporation, 501(c)(3).

ELIGIBILITY:
For annual Environmental Law Course/CLE Scholarship Program, send letter of application from public interest lawyers, attorneys doing substantial pro bono work, state and local government attorneys involved in environmental law stating need and expected benefit.

FINANCIAL DATA:
Amount of support per award: Approximately $800 to $900 per scholarship applicant approved.
Total amount of support: Approximately $25,000 for the year 2011.

COOPERATIVE FUNDING PROGRAMS:
Environmental Law Conference with ALI-ABA.

NUMBER OF APPLICANTS MOST RECENT YEAR: Approximately 25.

NUMBER OF AWARDS: Approximately 25.

PUBLICATIONS:
Annual report; *Environmental Law Reporter*; *The Environmental Forum*; *National Wetlands Newsletter*; *Deskbooks*, series; *Monograph*, series.

IRS IDENTIFICATION NUMBER: 52-0901863

OFFICERS:
Leslie Carothers, President
William Eichbaum, Chairman of the Board
Wayne Balta, Vice Chairman and Treasurer
Lisa Goldman, Assistant Corporate Secretary, Vice President/General Counsel

ADDRESS INQUIRIES TO:
See e-mail address above.

For Conference Scholarship Support:
Director of Seminars
(See address above.)

FOOD AND DRUG LAW INSTITUTE (FDLI) [2103]

1155 15th Street, N.W., Suite 800
Washington, DC 20005-2706
(202) 371-1420
Fax: (202) 371-0649

E-MAIL ADDRESS:
pubsdept@fdli.org

WEB SITE ADDRESS:
www.fdli.org

FOUNDED: 1949

AREAS OF INTEREST:
Food and drug law issues.

NAME(S) OF PROGRAMS:
- **H. Thomas Austern Memorial Writing Competition-Food and Drug Law**

TYPE:
Awards/prizes. The subject matter of the competition is an in-depth analysis of a current issue relevant to the food and drug field, including a relevant case law, legislative history and other authorities, particularly where the U.S. Food and Drug Administration is involved.

There are two categories of prizes:
(1) papers of 40 pages or less (including appendices and footnotes) and;
(2) papers of more than 40 pages, but less than 101 pages.

YEAR PROGRAM STARTED: 1978

PURPOSE:
To encourage law students interested in the areas of law affecting foods, drugs, devices, cosmetics and biologics; to provide a marketplace for discussing food and drug law issues.

LEGAL BASIS:
Nonprofit educational association.

ELIGIBILITY:
The level of study is postgraduate. Entrants must currently be enrolled in a J.D. program at any of the U.S. law schools.

FINANCIAL DATA:
Amount of support per award: Both categories: $4,000 first prize; $1,000 second prize.
Total amount of support: $10,000.

NUMBER OF APPLICANTS MOST RECENT YEAR:
50.

NUMBER OF AWARDS: 4.

APPLICATION INFORMATION:
Contact the Institute for complete details. Applicants can submit their materials electronically.
Deadline: May 31.

PUBLICATIONS:
Food and Drug Law Journal.

THE HAGUE ACADEMY OF INTERNATIONAL LAW [2104]
Peace Palace
Carnegieplein 2
2517 KJ The Hague The Netherlands
(31-70) 302-4242
Fax: (31-70) 302-4153

E-MAIL ADDRESS:
registration@hagueacademy.nl

WEB SITE ADDRESS:
www.hagueacademy.nl

FOUNDED: 1923

AREAS OF INTEREST:
Private and public international law.

NAME(S) OF PROGRAMS:
- **Doctoral Scholarships in International Law**

TYPE:
Project/program grants. Study programs. Residential scholarships for doctoral candidates from developing countries whose thesis, in private international law or public international law, is in an advanced stage of preparation, who reside in their home country and who do not have access to scientific sources.

YEAR PROGRAM STARTED: 1923

PURPOSE:
To facilitate the completion of the theses through the use of the Academy, especially from the directors of studies and the use of the resources of the Library of the Peace Palace.

LEGAL BASIS:
Government agency.

ELIGIBILITY:
Each candidate must show proof that they are at the postgraduate level and that their thesis is necessary to obtain the doctoral degree.

FINANCIAL DATA:
Financial help in the form of a contribution towards travelling expenses may be granted to participants, taking into account the distance of their country of normal residence.
Amount of support per award: EUR 35 per day.

NUMBER OF APPLICANTS MOST RECENT YEAR:
30.

NUMBER OF AWARDS: 4.

APPLICATION INFORMATION:
Applications should be accompanied by a recommendation from the professor under whose direction the thesis is being written which mentions the title of the thesis. Candidates must possess a satisfactory knowledge of either French or English, the working languages of the Academy.
Duration: Two months from July 1 onward.
Deadline: March 1.

PUBLICATIONS:
Programme de la Session; *Collected Courses*, series of published lectures.

ADDRESS INQUIRIES TO:
Registration Office
(See address above.)

THE HAGUE ACADEMY OF INTERNATIONAL LAW [2105]
Peace Palace
Carnegieplein 2
2517 KJ The Hague The Netherlands
(31-70) 302-4242
Fax: (31-70) 302-4153

E-MAIL ADDRESS:
registration@hagueacademy.nl

WEB SITE ADDRESS:
www.hagueacademy.nl

FOUNDED: 1923

AREAS OF INTEREST:
Private and public international law.

NAME(S) OF PROGRAMS:
- **Hague Academy of International Law Summer Courses**

TYPE:
Project/program grants; Scholarships. Study programs. A limited number of scholarships are given to cover tuition and living expenses while studying at the three-week summer session of the Hague Academy of International Law. Because of the limited number, granting of scholarships to attendees from every country is not possible.

YEAR PROGRAM STARTED: 1923

PURPOSE:
To support personal and effective participation of members in scientific work related to international law and international affairs.

ELIGIBILITY:
Those wishing to apply for admission should have studied law for at least four years.

FINANCIAL DATA:
Amount of support per award: EUR 1,150 (including registration fees) covering general expenses incurred during the three weeks of one of the teaching periods. Travelling expenses will not be refunded.

NUMBER OF APPLICANTS MOST RECENT YEAR:
680.

NUMBER OF AWARDS: 110.

APPLICATION INFORMATION:
Application for scholarship must be made by the applicant and submitted directly by normal mail to the Secretariat of the Academy at the address above. The application must contain a statement of surname, first names, qualities, profession, nationality, place and date of birth, photograph and a statement of the evidence which the applicant considers to be of value in support of his or her candidacy. Every application must be typewritten and should be accompanied by a recommendation from a professor of international law.
Duration: Three weeks.
Deadline: Complete files of scholarship candidates should be in the possession of the Secretariat before March 1.

PUBLICATIONS:
Collected Courses, series of published lectures.

OFFICERS:
Prof. Y. Daudet, Secretary-General of the Academy

ADDRESS INQUIRIES TO:
Registration Office
(See address above.)

THE HISPANIC BAR ASSOCIATION OF D.C. FOUNDATION [2106]
1640 Rhode Island Avenue, N.W.
Suite 600
Washington, DC 20036
(202) 466-8585
Fax: (202) 463-4803

E-MAIL ADDRESS:
info@hbadc.org

WEB SITE ADDRESS:
www.hbadc.org

FOUNDED: 1995

AREAS OF INTEREST:
Law and public interest.

NAME(S) OF PROGRAMS:
- **The HBA-DC Foundation Fellowship**

TYPE:
Fellowships.

PURPOSE:
To provide students with valuable work experience and exposure to an area of public interest law.

ELIGIBILITY:
Eligible students are first- and second-year law students of law schools in the District of Columbia.

GEOGRAPHIC RESTRICTIONS:
District of Columbia and the metropolitan area.

FINANCIAL DATA:
Amount of support per award: $5,000.
Total amount of support: Varies.

NUMBER OF AWARDS: 3 for the year 2010.

APPLICATION INFORMATION:
Deadline: April 7.

ADDRESS INQUIRIES TO:
E-mail: foundation@hbadc.org

HISPANIC NATIONAL BAR FOUNDATION   [2107]

1900 K Street, N.W.
Suite 100
Washington, DC 20006
(202) 496-7206
Fax: (202) 496-7756

E-MAIL ADDRESS:
mprego@hnbf.org

WEB SITE ADDRESS:
www.hnbf.org

FOUNDED: 1987

AREAS OF INTEREST:
Promoting the legal education of persons of
Hispanic heritage throughout the U.S. and
Puerto Rico.

NAME(S) OF PROGRAMS:
● **Future Latino Leaders Law Camp**

TYPE:
Conferences/seminars; Training grants.
Week-long program held by the Foundation
in Washington, DC which provides 25 Latino
high school students with the opportunity to
learn more about the legal profession. The
Law Camp offers students the chance to
come to the nation's capital and learn more
about the college application process, meet
influential Latino leaders, and tour national
monuments and various government agencies.

PURPOSE:
To provide tools and resources necessary to
ensure full and equal opportunity for
Hispanics to become leaders in the global
community, thereby ensuring a brighter
future for all.

LEGAL BASIS:
Section 501(c)(3) organization dedicated to
charitable and educational purposes.

ELIGIBILITY:
Applicants must meet the following criteria:
(1) be a high school student entering the
sophomore, junior or senior year, or be a
recent graduate;
(2) have an interest in learning about law
school and becoming a lawyer;
(3) be a U.S. citizen, legal permanent
resident or be a legal U.S. visitor with a
valid visa and passport and;
(4) have a demonstrated interest in helping
one's community and building one's
leadership skills.

FINANCIAL DATA:
There is no cost to participate in the Law
Camp. However, accepted students must pay
a $50 application fee, unless a waiver of this
fee is requested and granted. Students are
also responsible for arranging transportation
to Washington, DC. The cost of
transportation should not deter one from
applying. Upon acceptance to the program,
the Foundation is committed to working with
the attendee and his or her family in order to
ensure that person's ability to attend.
Amount of support per award: Valued at over
$3,000 per person.

NUMBER OF AWARDS: 25.

APPLICATION INFORMATION:
Application can be completed online or sent
by mail and must include:
(1) Applicant Information Form;
(2) Rules and Regulations Form;
(3) essays;
(4) two letters of recommendation (from
teachers, counselors or employers);
(5) resume (may include community service,
leadership positions or civic activities);
(6) certified copy of academic record from
high school and;
(7) $50 application fee or fee waiver
approval.
Duration: One week.
Deadline: Late April. Notification in early
May.

ADDRESS INQUIRIES TO:
Program Coordinator
E-mail: info@hnbf.org

THURGOOD MARSHALL COLLEGE FUND/AMERICAN INTELLECTUAL PROPERTY LAW EDUCATION FOUNDATION   [2108]

80 Maiden Lane, Suite 2204
New York, NY 10038
(212) 573-8888
Fax: (212) 573-8497

E-MAIL ADDRESS:
tamekia.jackson@tmcfund.org

WEB SITE ADDRESS:
www.thurgoodmarshallfund.org
www.aiplef.org

AREAS OF INTEREST:
American intellectual property law.

NAME(S) OF PROGRAMS:
● **The Sidney B. Williams, Jr. Intellectual
Property Law Scholarship**

TYPE:
Scholarships. Program for underrepresented
minority students who intend to enter the
intellectual property law field, to attend law
school.

PURPOSE:
To significantly increase the number of
underrepresented minorities working as
intellectual property law lawyers in both
private and corporate practice.

ELIGIBILITY:
Applicant must:
(1) be a U.S. citizen;
(2) be a member of an underrepresented
minority group;
(3) be currently enrolled in or have been
accepted to an ABA accredited law school;
(4) have a demonstrated commitment to
developing a career in intellectual property
law and;
(5) be in need of financial assistance.

FINANCIAL DATA:
Amount of support per award: $10,000 per
school year.

ADDRESS INQUIRIES TO:
Tamekia Jackson, Scholarship Manager
(See address above.)

MCGILL UNIVERSITY   [2109]

Chancellor Day Hall
3644 Peel Street
Montreal QC H3A 1W9 Canada
(514) 398-6666
Fax: (514) 398-4659

WEB SITE ADDRESS:
www.mcgill.ca/law

AREAS OF INTEREST:
Law, especially pertaining to the Canadian
legal system and legal community.

NAME(S) OF PROGRAMS:
● **Maxwell Boulton Q.C. Fellowship**

TYPE:
Fellowships.

PURPOSE:
To provide younger scholars with an
opportunity to pursue a major research
project or to complete the research
requirement for a higher degree.

ELIGIBILITY:
Open to candidates who have completed
residency requirements for a doctoral degree
in law.

FINANCIAL DATA:
Amount of support per award: $30,000 to
$35,000 (CAN) per year.

NUMBER OF APPLICANTS MOST RECENT YEAR:
13.

NUMBER OF AWARDS: 1.

APPLICATION INFORMATION:
Application available on the web site.
Duration: One year.
Deadline: February 1.

ADDRESS INQUIRIES TO:
Office of the Dean
(See address above.)

MEXICAN AMERICAN LEGAL DEFENSE AND EDUCATIONAL FUND   [2110]

634 South Spring Street, 11th Floor
Los Angeles, CA 90014
(213) 629-2512
Fax: (213) 629-0266

WEB SITE ADDRESS:
www.maldef.org

FOUNDED: 1968

AREAS OF INTEREST:
Law students.

NAME(S) OF PROGRAMS:
● **MALDEF Law School Scholarship**

TYPE:
Awards/prizes; Internships; Scholarships.
Awarded annually to law students who have
a demonstrated commitment to serving the
Latino community with their law degree.

YEAR PROGRAM STARTED: 1968

PURPOSE:
National nonprofit civil rights organization.

LEGAL BASIS:
Private nonprofit.

ELIGIBILITY:
All full-time law students with demonstrated
commitment to serving the Latino community
with their law degrees.

FINANCIAL DATA:
Amount of support per award: Varies;
typically $5,000.
Total amount of support: The number of
awards and amounts are dependent on
contributions received.

NUMBER OF APPLICANTS MOST RECENT YEAR: 80.

NUMBER OF AWARDS: 5 to 10.

APPLICATION INFORMATION:
Application forms are available on the web site.

THE PLAYBOY FOUNDATION [2111]

680 North Lake Shore Drive
Chicago, IL 60611
(312) 751-8000 ext. 2435
Fax: (312) 266-8506

WEB SITE ADDRESS:
www.playboyenterprises.com/foundation

FOUNDED: 1965

AREAS OF INTEREST:
First amendment freedoms, reproductive rights and reproductive health, civil rights and civil liberties, AIDS and AIDS-related public policy and legal issues.

NAME(S) OF PROGRAMS:
● **Social Change Documentary Film Grant Program**

TYPE:
Matching gifts; Project/program grants. Employee-initiated matching gifts.

YEAR PROGRAM STARTED: 1965

PURPOSE:
To protect and promote the American principles of personal freedom and social justice.

LEGAL BASIS:
Corporate giving department of Playboy Enterprises, Inc.

ELIGIBILITY:
Organizations throughout the U.S. are eligible to apply. Grants are not made to individual filmmakers. No grants are awarded for scholarships, capital campaigns for endowments or religious purposes.

GEOGRAPHIC RESTRICTIONS:
United States.

FINANCIAL DATA:
Amount of support per award: Up to $5,000.

APPLICATION INFORMATION:
Organizations should first submit a letter of inquiry. Applicant organizations are required to submit the following:
(1) brief summary of background and purposes of organization;
(2) description of problem addressed by proposal with explanation of how the project will address the problem;
(3) history of the applicant organization and individuals;
(4) list of donors and;
(5) IRS ruling.

Filmmakers applying for Social Change Documentary Film Grants should submit a full proposal which includes the following:
(1) description of the project, including a film summary, distribution plan and experience in filmmaking;
(2) itemized project budget and proposed funding sources, amount of funds requested, their proposed use and over what time period, and project income and expenses;
(3) names and qualifications of people involved with the project, titles, outside affiliations and phone numbers and;
(4) IRS verification from the sponsoring organization that states the organization is not a private foundation and is exempt from taxation under IRS Sections 509(a) and 501(c)(3).

Plan to send a copy of the film or rough-cut on DVD. DVDs will not be returned.

Duration: One year. Renewal possible.

Deadline: Letters of inquiry continuously accepted.

OFFICERS:
Matthew Pakula, Director

ADDRESS INQUIRIES TO:
Matthew Pakula, Director
(See address above.)

*PLEASE NOTE:
No new grants in 2011, except in Social Change Documentary Film Grant Program.

*SPECIAL STIPULATIONS:
Letters of inquiry preferred. Do not send full application unless applying for Social Change Documentary Film Grant.

REPORTERS COMMITTEE FOR FREEDOM OF THE PRESS

1101 Wilson Boulevard
Suite 1100
Arlington, VA 22209-2275
(703) 807-2100
Fax: (703) 807-2109

E-MAIL ADDRESS:
rcfp@rcfp.org

WEB SITE ADDRESS:
www.rcfp.org

TYPE:
Fellowships. Legal fellows monitor significant developments in First Amendment media law, assist with legal defense requests from reporters, prepare legal memoranda, amicus briefs and other special projects. The Fellowship focuses on media law.

See entry 2087 for full listing.

STATE OF RHODE ISLAND

Commission on State Government Internships
State House, Room 8AA
Providence, RI 02903
(401) 222-6782
Fax: (401) 222-4447

E-MAIL ADDRESS:
rgemma@rilin.state.ri.us

WEB SITE ADDRESS:
www.rilin.state.ri.us

TYPE:
Internships; Work-study programs. Funding through General Assembly is also available. Internship opportunities for graduate and undergraduate students in the state government operation. Students are involved in executive, legislative and judicial assignments. The internship is viewed as an extension of the classroom and is seen as complementing and building upon the educational opportunities available on campuses.

This program has established a Summer Internship section, open to Rhode Island residents only, that begins in late June and concludes in August.

See entry 2140 for full listing.

THE SUPREME COURT OF THE U.S.

One First Street, N.E.
Room 5
Washington, DC 20543
(202) 479-3415
Fax: (202) 479-3484

E-MAIL ADDRESS:
fellowsprogram@supremecourt.gov

WEB SITE ADDRESS:
www.fellows.supremecourtus.gov

TYPE:
Fellowships. Fellows serve in the Supreme Court, the Federal Judicial Center, the U.S. Sentencing Commission, and the Administrative Office of the U.S. Courts.

See entry 2142 for full listing.

THE UNIVERSITY OF CALGARY [2112]

Faculty of Graduate Studies
Earth Sciences Building, Room 720
2500 University Drive, N.W.
Calgary AB T2N 1N4 Canada
(403) 220-4938
Fax: (403) 289-7635

E-MAIL ADDRESS:
gsaward@ucalgary.ca

WEB SITE ADDRESS:
www.grad.ucalgary.ca

FOUNDED: 1966

AREAS OF INTEREST:
Law.

NAME(S) OF PROGRAMS:
● **The Honourable N.D. McDermid Graduate Scholarship in Law**

TYPE:
Awards/prizes; Scholarships. Graduate scholarships in law tenable at The University of Calgary. Awards endowed by the McDermid Law Fund in memory of the late Honourable Neil Douglas McDermid, Q.C., who was a prominent member of the legal profession of Alberta and the Calgary community for many years.

PURPOSE:
To financially assist students who want to study law at the university.

LEGAL BASIS:
University.

ELIGIBILITY:
Graduate students enrolled on a full-time basis in the LL.M. program in the Faculty of Law at The University of Calgary. Awards will be recommended by a Committee of the Faculty of Law based upon academic excellence and are subject to the approval of The University of Calgary Graduate Scholarships Committee.

GEOGRAPHIC RESTRICTIONS:
Canada.

FINANCIAL DATA:
Amount of support per award: $12,000.
Total amount of support: $24,000.

NUMBER OF AWARDS: Maximum of 2 annually.

APPLICATION INFORMATION:
Application forms are available from the Dean's Office, Faculty of Law.

Duration: One year. Nonrenewable.

Deadline: December 15.

ADDRESS INQUIRIES TO:
Graduate Scholarship Office
(See address above.)

THE UNIVERSITY OF CALGARY
Faculty of Graduate Studies
Earth Sciences Building, Room 720
2500 University Drive, N.W.
Calgary AB T2N 1N4 Canada
(403) 220-4938
Fax: (403) 289-7635

E-MAIL ADDRESS:
gsaward@ucalgary.ca

WEB SITE ADDRESS:
www.grad.ucalgary.ca

TYPE:
Awards/prizes; Fellowships; Scholarships.

See entry 1912 for full listing.

Political science

AMERICAN POLITICAL
SCIENCE ASSOCIATION   [2113]
1527 New Hampshire Avenue, N.W.
Washington, DC 20036
(202) 483-2512
Fax: (202) 483-2657

E-MAIL ADDRESS:
cfp@apsanet.org

WEB SITE ADDRESS:
www.apsanet.org/cfp

FOUNDED: 1903

AREAS OF INTEREST:
Political science.

NAME(S) OF PROGRAMS:
● **Congressional Fellowship Program**

TYPE:
Fellowships. Awards to political science
professors and journalists in early to
mid-careers providing an opportunity for
support as a full-time aide to a member of
the House or Senate or as a staff member for
a Congressional committee.

YEAR PROGRAM STARTED: 1953

PURPOSE:
To equip outstanding young political
scientists and journalists with a better
understanding of the national legislative
process.

LEGAL BASIS:
Nonprofit association.

ELIGIBILITY:
Open to U.S. political scientists and
journalists. Political scientists must have
completed their Ph.D. within the last 15
years or are near completion. Applicant
journalists must have a Bachelor's degree and
between two and 10 years of full-time
professional experience in newspaper,
magazine, radio or television work. Special
fellowships are available for Ph.D.-level
scholars of any discipline or journalists with
demonstrated professional interest in
telecommunications.

Candidates who are not current residents of
the U.S. must fund their own transportation
to Washington to be interviewed should they
be selected as finalists.

FINANCIAL DATA:
Amount of support per award: $38,000
stipend plus travel for the year 2011-12.
Total amount of support: $380,000.

NUMBER OF APPLICANTS MOST RECENT YEAR:
50 in political science and journalism.

NUMBER OF AWARDS: 10 for the year 2010-11.

APPLICATION INFORMATION:
Official application materials are available
upon request to the Association or on the
web site.
Duration: 10 months, November to August.
Nonrenewable.
Deadline: December 1.

ADDRESS INQUIRIES TO:
Jeffrey Biggs, Program Director or
Veronica Jones, Program Associate
(See address above.)

AMERICAN POLITICAL
SCIENCE ASSOCIATION   [2114]
1527 New Hampshire Avenue, N.W.
Washington, DC 20036
(202) 483-2512
Fax: (202) 483-2657

E-MAIL ADDRESS:
minority@apsanet.org

WEB SITE ADDRESS:
www.apsanet.org

FOUNDED: 1903

AREAS OF INTEREST:
Political science.

NAME(S) OF PROGRAMS:
● **APSA Minority Fellows Program**

TYPE:
Fellowships; Grants-in-aid; Scholarships.
Awards to aid prospective African American,
Asian Pacific, Latino/Latina and Native
American political science students beginning
the doctoral study of political science.

YEAR PROGRAM STARTED: 1969

PURPOSE:
To increase the number of minority scholars
in the discipline; to assist minority students
in completing their doctorates by
concentrating not only on the recruitment of
minorities, but also on the retention of these
groups within the profession.

LEGAL BASIS:
Nonprofit association.

ELIGIBILITY:
Applicants must:
(1) be minority students applying to enter a
doctoral program in political science for the
first time;
(2) be members of one of the following
racial/ethnic minority groups: African
Americans, Asian Pacific Americans,
Latinos/Latinas, and Native Americans
(federal and state recognized tribes);
(3) demonstrate an interest in teaching and
potential for research in political science;
(4) be a U.S. citizen at time of award and;
(5) demonstrate financial need.

FINANCIAL DATA:
Amount of support per award: $4,000,
disbursed in two $2,000 payments, one at the
end of their first graduate year and one at the
end of their second, provided that they
remain in good academic standing.
Total amount of support: $48,000.

NUMBER OF APPLICANTS MOST RECENT YEAR:
30.

NUMBER OF AWARDS: 12.

APPLICATION INFORMATION:
Forms can be downloaded from the web site.

Duration: One year.

ADDRESS INQUIRIES TO:
Kimberly Mealy, Program Director
(See address above.)

ASHBURN INSTITUTE INC.
198 Okatie Village Drive
Suite 103, PMB 301
Bluffton, SC 29909
(843) 705-7643
Fax: (843) 705-7643

E-MAIL ADDRESS:
info@ashburninstitute.org

WEB SITE ADDRESS:
www.ashburninstitute.org

TYPE:
Research grants; Scholarships.

See entry 877 for full listing.

ASSOCIATION OF
UNIVERSITIES AND COLLEGES
OF CANADA   [2115]
350 Albert Street, Suite 600
Ottawa ON K1R 1B1 Canada
(613) 563-1236
Fax: (613) 563-9745

E-MAIL ADDRESS:
awards@aucc.ca

WEB SITE ADDRESS:
www.aucc.ca

FOUNDED: 1911

AREAS OF INTEREST:
Canadian national security problems,
including their political, international,
historical, social, military, industrial and
economic dimensions.

NAME(S) OF PROGRAMS:
● **Security and Defence Forum Internship
Program**

TYPE:
Awards/prizes; Internships. The internship
provides for a year-long placement in a
research or related position in a Canadian
organization, excluding universities and
government. Placement in Canadian
government offices outside Canada
(embassies, NATO and international
organizations) may also be considered.

YEAR PROGRAM STARTED: 1971

PURPOSE:
To promote relevant work experience
opportunities for recent M.A. graduates with
a background in security and defense, which
will complement their studies.

LEGAL BASIS:
Nonprofit association.

ELIGIBILITY:
Applicants must be Canadian citizens or
permanent residents at the time of application
and hold a Master's degree before taking up
the award. Internships are tenable within a
wide spectrum of security and defense-related
institutions. Internships related to current and
future Canadian security and defense issues
and their political, international, historical,
social, military, industrial and economic
dimensions are encouraged. Applicants must
clearly explain in their proposal the
relationship between their work plans and
Canadian security and defense issues.

Placements in Canadian government offices outside Canada (i.e. embassies, NATO and other international organizations) may be considered. Universities and governmental departments or agencies in Canada are excluded.

GEOGRAPHIC RESTRICTIONS:
Canada.

FINANCIAL DATA:
Amount of support per award: Varies.

COOPERATIVE FUNDING PROGRAMS:
Participating organizations are encouraged to supplement the award with additional funds.

NUMBER OF AWARDS: Up to 4.

APPLICATION INFORMATION:
Duration: Up to one year. Nonrenewable.
Deadline: February 8 (postmark).

PUBLICATIONS:
Program announcement; *Annex A,* list of potential organizations for internships.

ADDRESS INQUIRIES TO:
Customer Relations Officer
Higher Education Scholarships
(See address above.)

*SPECIAL STIPULATIONS:
Upon completion of the internship, one copy of the thesis, or a reasonably detailed account of the research undertaken, must be submitted to the Directorate of Public Policy, Department of National Defence, no later than October 1 of the following year.

CENTER FOR CALIFORNIA STUDIES, CAPITAL FELLOWS PROGRAMS [2116]

California State University, Sacramento
6000 J Street
Sacramento, CA 95819-6081
(916) 278-6906
Fax: (916) 278-5199

E-MAIL ADDRESS:
calstudies@csus.edu

WEB SITE ADDRESS:
www.csus.
edu/calst/assembly_fellowship_program

FOUNDED: 1982

AREAS OF INTEREST:
California state government.

NAME(S) OF PROGRAMS:
● **Jesse M. Unruh Assembly Fellowship Program**

TYPE:
Fellowships. Jointly sponsored by the Center for California Studies at California State University, Sacramento and the California State Assembly. Full-time fellowships for 18 fellows, 11 months and units of graduate study through California State University, Sacramento.

PURPOSE:
To provide educational and governmental experience and assistance for legislators.

LEGAL BASIS:
University/government program funded by State Budget-General Budget Fund.

ELIGIBILITY:
Must be 20 years of age by September 1 of applying year and have a minimum four-year Bachelor's degree with graduation by August of applying year. Graduate, postgraduate and midcareer applicants are welcome.

FINANCIAL DATA:
In addition to the stipend, full medical, vision and dental benefits are provided.
Amount of support per award: $1,972 per month stipend.

NUMBER OF APPLICANTS MOST RECENT YEAR:
300.

NUMBER OF AWARDS: 18 annually.

APPLICATION INFORMATION:
Applicants must submit all transcripts, three letters of recommendation and two essays.
Duration: 11 months.
Deadline: Late February. Interviews in Los Angeles and Sacramento in May. Fellowship announcement in May.

ADDRESS INQUIRIES TO:
Pam Chueh, Program Director
(See address above.)

*SPECIAL STIPULATIONS:
International fellows must have a valid work visa.

CENTER FOR CALIFORNIA STUDIES, CAPITAL FELLOWS PROGRAMS [2117]

California State University, Sacramento
6000 J Street
Sacramento, CA 95819-6081
(916) 278-6906
(916) 278-4487

E-MAIL ADDRESS:
calstudies@csus.edu
hoenigco@csus.edu

WEB SITE ADDRESS:
www.csus.edu/calst/judicial

FOUNDED: 1982

AREAS OF INTEREST:
California judicial system.

NAME(S) OF PROGRAMS:
● **Judicial Administration Fellowship Program**

TYPE:
Fellowships. Jointly sponsored by the Center for California Studies at California State University, Sacramento and the California Judicial Council. Full-time fellowships for 10 fellows, 10 months and graduate units earned from California State University, Sacramento.

YEAR PROGRAM STARTED: 1997

PURPOSE:
To enable fellows to conduct research, advocate on behalf of the judiciary, develop and implement programs, seek grants, and engage in educational outreach, strategic planning, and policy analysis.

ELIGIBILITY:
Must be 20 years of age by September 1 of applying year and have a minimum four-year Bachelor's degree with graduation by August of applying year. Graduate, postgraduate and midcareer applicants are welcome.

FINANCIAL DATA:
Fellowship includes monthly stipend plus health, vision and dental benefits.
Amount of support per award: $1,972 monthly stipend.

NUMBER OF APPLICANTS MOST RECENT YEAR:
150.

NUMBER OF AWARDS: 10 annually.

APPLICATION INFORMATION:
Applications will only be accepted if sent via regular mail or delivered. Applicants must submit all transcripts, letters of recommendation and two essays.
Duration: 10 months.
Deadline: Late February. Interviews in Los Angeles and Sacramento in May. Fellowship announcement in May.

ADDRESS INQUIRIES TO:
Donna Hoenig-Couch, Program Director
(See address above.)

*SPECIAL STIPULATIONS:
International fellows must have a valid work visa.

CENTER FOR CALIFORNIA STUDIES, CAPITAL FELLOWS PROGRAMS [2118]

California State University, Sacramento
6000 J Street
Sacramento, CA 95819-6081
(916) 278-6906

E-MAIL ADDRESS:
calstudies@csus.edu

WEB SITE ADDRESS:
www.csus.edu/calst/senate

FOUNDED: 1982

AREAS OF INTEREST:
California state government.

NAME(S) OF PROGRAMS:
● **California Senate Fellows Program**

TYPE:
Fellowships. Jointly sponsored by the Center for California Studies at California State University, Sacramento and the California State Senate. Full-time fellowships for 18 fellows, 11 months and graduate units earned from California State University, Sacramento.

PURPOSE:
To provide participants with insight into the legislative process, including exposing people with diverse life experiences and backgrounds to the legislative process and providing research and other professional staff assistance to the Senate.

ELIGIBILITY:
Must be 20 years of age by September 1 of applying year and have a minimum four-year Bachelor's degree with graduation by August of applying year. Graduate, postgraduate and midcareer applicants are welcome. Applicants need not be California residents; however, preference will be given to candidates who demonstrate knowledge of and commitment to the state.

FINANCIAL DATA:
Fellowship includes monthly stipend plus full health, vision and dental benefits.
Amount of support per award: $1,972 monthly stipend.

NUMBER OF APPLICANTS MOST RECENT YEAR:
400.

NUMBER OF AWARDS: 18 annually.

APPLICATION INFORMATION:
Applications will only be accepted if sent via regular mail or delivered. Applicants must submit all transcripts, letters of recommendation and essay.
Duration: 11 months.
Deadline: Late February. Interviews in Los Angeles and Sacramento in May. Fellowship announcement in May.

ADDRESS INQUIRIES TO:
David Pacheco, Program Director
(See address above.)

*SPECIAL STIPULATIONS:
International fellows must have a valid work visa.

CENTER FOR CALIFORNIA STUDIES, CAPITAL FELLOWS PROGRAMS [2119]

California State University, Sacramento
6000 J Street
Sacramento, CA 95819-6081
(916) 278-6906

E-MAIL ADDRESS:
calstudies@csus.edu

WEB SITE ADDRESS:
www.csus.edu/calst/executive

FOUNDED: 1982

AREAS OF INTEREST:
California state government.

NAME(S) OF PROGRAMS:
● **Executive Fellowship Program**

TYPE:
Fellowships. Jointly sponsored by the Center for California Studies at California State University, Sacramento and the California governor. Full-time fellowships for 18 fellows, 10 months and six units of graduate study through California State University, Sacramento.

YEAR PROGRAM STARTED: 1982

PURPOSE:
To provide an experiential learning opportunity in California state government. Fellows gain valuable insights and experiences in the realm of public policy and politics.

ELIGIBILITY:
Must be 20 years of age by September 1 of applying year and have a minimum four-year Bachelor's degree with graduation by August of applying year. Graduate, postgraduate and midcareer applicants are welcome.

FINANCIAL DATA:
Fellowship includes monthly stipend plus medical, vision and dental benefits. Recipients also earn units of graduate credit.
Amount of support per award: $1,972 per month stipend.

NUMBER OF APPLICANTS MOST RECENT YEAR: 340.

NUMBER OF AWARDS: 18 annually.

APPLICATION INFORMATION:
Applications will only be accepted if sent via regular mail or delivered. Applicants must submit all transcripts, letters of recommendation and two essays.
Duration: 10 months.
Deadline: Late February. Interviews in Los Angeles and Sacramento, CA in May. Fellowship announced in May.

ADDRESS INQUIRIES TO:
Mark Grisby, Program Director
(See address above.)

*SPECIAL STIPULATIONS:
International fellows must have a valid work visa.

CITY OF NEW YORK [2120]

Department of Citywide Administrative Services
One Centre Street, Room 2425
New York, NY 10007
(212) 669-3695
Fax: (212) 669-3688

E-MAIL ADDRESS:
bsimmons@dcas.nyc.gov

WEB SITE ADDRESS:
www.nyc.gov/fellowships

FOUNDED: 1969

AREAS OF INTEREST:
City government and New York City government.

NAME(S) OF PROGRAMS:
● **New York City Urban Fellows Program**

TYPE:
Fellowships. Stipend for full-time work in New York City government agencies. Fellows work closely with city officials on long- and short-term projects and attend weekly seminars to get an academic perspective on the workings and problems of local government. Assignments range over fields such as urban planning, housing, health and social sciences, economic and financial administration, youth service, intergovernmental relations, criminal justice, cultural affairs and innumerable others. Positions are at relatively high levels as assistants to administrators and staff within the various city agencies.

YEAR PROGRAM STARTED: 1969

PURPOSE:
To attract qualified college graduates to participate in a management training program in New York City government.

LEGAL BASIS:
City Government agency.

ELIGIBILITY:
As of September of the program year, applicants must be recent college graduates (no more than two full years out of college). Fellows participate on a full-time basis. A political science major is not required. Demonstrated interest in government is required. All students who are interested in pursuing a career in municipal government are encouraged to apply regardless of academic major or previous field of training.

FINANCIAL DATA:
A choice of paid health insurance plans is provided.
Amount of support per award: Currently $30,000 for nine-month duration (annualized to $40,000).

NUMBER OF APPLICANTS MOST RECENT YEAR: Approximately 350.

NUMBER OF AWARDS: 25 to 30.

APPLICATION INFORMATION:
Duration: Nine months, September to May.
Deadline: First Friday in January.

PUBLICATIONS:
Application guidelines.

ADDRESS INQUIRIES TO:
Barbara Simmons, Director
New York City Urban Fellows Program
(See address above.)

CONGRESSIONAL BLACK CAUCUS FOUNDATION, INC.

1720 Massachusetts Avenue, N.W.
Washington, DC 20036
(202) 263-2800
Fax: (202) 263-0846

E-MAIL ADDRESS:
info@cbcfinc.org

WEB SITE ADDRESS:
www.cbcfinc.org

TYPE:
Fellowships; Internships; Scholarships. The Congressional Black Caucus Foundation Congressional Fellows Program helps participants gain invaluable experience as they assist in the development of legislative and public policy initiatives while working as congressional staff for a year. This program targets early career policy professionals who have completed a professional and/or graduate degree and have demonstrated commitment to improving the lives and services for individuals living in underserved communities. Fellows work on Capitol Hill in the office of a Congressional Black Caucus member.

The Congressional Internship Program provides undergraduate students with an in-depth orientation to Capitol Hill and the legislative process through actual work experience in the offices of Congressional Black Caucus Members. In this way interns prepare to become decision makers in the policymaking process.

The Congressional Black Caucus Spouses Education Scholarship Fund is a national program that awards scholarships to academically talented and highly motivated students who intend to pursue full-time undergraduate, graduate or doctoral degrees.

CBC Spouses Cheerios Brand Health Initiative Scholarship is intended to increase the number of minority students pursuing degrees in the fields of medicine, engineering, technology, nutrition and other health-related professions.

See entry 1089 for full listing.

THE DIRKSEN CONGRESSIONAL CENTER [2121]

2815 Broadway
Pekin, IL 61554
(309) 347-7113
Fax: (309) 347-6432

E-MAIL ADDRESS:
fmackaman@dirksencenter.org

WEB SITE ADDRESS:
www.dirksencongressionalcenter.org

FOUNDED: 1963

AREAS OF INTEREST:
U.S. Congress and its leaders.

NAME(S) OF PROGRAMS:
● **Congressional Research Awards**

TYPE:
Project/program grants; Research grants; Seed money grants; Travel grants. Financial awards to individuals conducting research about the U.S. Congress and its leaders.

YEAR PROGRAM STARTED: 1978

PURPOSE:
To foster study of Congress in order to enhance public understanding and appreciation of the legislative branch of the federal government.

LEGAL BASIS:
Independent, nonpartisan, not-for-profit research and educational organization.

ELIGIBILITY:
Open to anyone with a serious interest in studying Congress. The Center seeks applications specifically from political scientists, historians, biographers, scholars of public administration or American studies or journalists. Graduate students may also apply.

The program does not fund undergraduates or pre-Ph.D. study. Organizations are not eligible. No institutional overhead or indirect costs will be covered.

FINANCIAL DATA:
Amount of support per award: Up to $3,500.
Total amount of support: Up to $35,000 annually.

NUMBER OF AWARDS: Approximately 12 per year.

APPLICATION INFORMATION:
There is no standard application form. Applicants are responsible for showing the relationship between their work and the awards program guidelines. Applicants must submit the original and five copies of:
(1) Application Summary Sheet listing name, address (including e-mail address) and telephone numbers for work and home, Social Security number, institutional affiliation when appropriate, project title, project abstract (not to exceed 100 words), and total amount requested;
(2) description of the project's goals, methods, and intended results, demonstrating clearly its importance to the awards program priorities. This is the most essential element of the application. Be sure to explain the project's significance and relationship to existing scholarship;
(3) curriculum vitae, including a list of publications;
(4) budget indicating how funds will be spent and the extent of matching funds available, if any;
(5) graduate students must include in their submission the original and five copies of a letter of reference from the person directing their dissertation work. This letter and the copies should be sealed in a separate envelope and;
(6) if potential recipients prefer to have payments made to an institutional entity on their behalf, they must submit with their proposal a letter from the responsible official stipulating that no indirect or overhead costs will be charged against the grant. In other words, the entire amount must be paid out to the individual.

The complete application should not exceed nine pages, excluding letters of reference, the application summary sheet, and institutional support letters. Applications which exceed the page limit and incomplete applications will not be forwarded to the screening committee for consideration.
Duration: Usually one year.
Deadline: March 1 postmark. Late-March announcement.

IRS IDENTIFICATION NUMBER: 36-6132816

BOARD OF DIRECTORS:
Hon. Robert H. Michel, Senior Advisor

Frank H. Mackaman, Staff Member
Janet M. Box-Steffensmeier
Paula Davis
Jim Deverman
Timothy Elder
John Gilligan
Buster Hanley
Brian K. Lee
Jim McConoughey
Rich McCoy
Peggy Meisinger
Stephanie Vance
James Wolf
Don Wolfensberger
Julian Zelizer

ADDRESS INQUIRIES TO:
Frank H. Mackaman
(See address above.)

*SPECIAL STIPULATIONS:
This program does not fund tuition.

DONNER CANADIAN FOUNDATION　[2122]

8 Prince Arthur Avenue, 3rd Floor
Toronto ON M5R 1A9 Canada
(416) 920-6400

E-MAIL ADDRESS:
mclean@donner.ca

WEB SITE ADDRESS:
www.donnerfoundation.org

FOUNDED: 1950

AREAS OF INTEREST:
Local and municipal government, school reform, environmental education and provincial fiscal policy.

TYPE:
Project/program grants.

PURPOSE:
To determine how government handles public assets in delivering public services.

LEGAL BASIS:
Private foundation.

ELIGIBILITY:
The Foundation only makes grants to charitable organizations under the Income Tax Act of Canada. Grants are usually made for specific projects. The Foundation does not make grants for ongoing expenses, the acquisition of capital (equipment, buildings, land, etc.), endowments, fund-raising drives or to cover budget deficits. The Foundation does not accept unsolicited proposals.

GEOGRAPHIC RESTRICTIONS:
Canada.

FINANCIAL DATA:
Amount of support per award: Varies.
Total amount of support: Approximately $3,000,000.

APPLICATION INFORMATION:
The Foundation does not regularly respond to letters of inquiry or unsolicited requests for funding. Charitable organizations may send the Foundation's Executive Director a two- to three-page description of their goals and programs and if there is a potential match between this work and the interests of the Foundation, staff will contact the charity for more information.
Duration: One year.

EXECUTIVE DIRECTOR:
Helen McLean

ADDRESS INQUIRIES TO:
Helen McLean, Executive Director
(See address above.)

GERALD R. FORD PRESIDENTIAL LIBRARY　[2123]

1000 Beal Avenue
Ann Arbor, MI 48109
(734) 205-0557
Fax: (734) 205-0571

E-MAIL ADDRESS:
ford.library@nara.gov

WEB SITE ADDRESS:
www.fordlibrarymuseum.gov

AREAS OF INTEREST:
Domestic issues, foreign policy and politics of the 1970s.

NAME(S) OF PROGRAMS:
● **Research Travel Grant Program**

TYPE:
Research grants; Travel grants. Research Travel Grants are awarded biannually to scholars to help defray the expenses of travel to conduct archival research in the collections of the Ford Library. Library collections focus on federal policies, foreign relations, and politics in the 1970s.

PURPOSE:
To promote research in the holdings of the Ford Library.

ELIGIBILITY:
Overseas applicants are welcome to apply, but they are responsible for costs of travel from their home country to North America.

FINANCIAL DATA:
Amount of support per award: Up to $2,000.
Total amount of support: Approximately $35,000 annually.

NUMBER OF AWARDS: Varies.

APPLICATION INFORMATION:
Before applying, contact the Library for information about holdings related to your project. Applicants should submit the application form, a curriculum vitae, and a two- or three-page project proposal to the Library by mail, fax or e-mail. The proposal should provide both a description of the project and the ways in which Ford Library resources can advance the research. Three professional references must submit supporting letters of recommendation by mail, fax or e-mail.
Duration: Research to be conducted within one year of acceptance of grant.
Deadline: March 15 and September 15 (postmark).

ADDRESS INQUIRIES TO:
William H. McNitt, Grants Coordinator
(See address above.)

*SPECIAL STIPULATIONS:
The Gerald R. Ford Foundation expects acknowledgment of its support in resulting publication(s) and a donated copy of same to the Gerald R. Ford Presidential Library.

GERALD R. FORD PRESIDENTIAL LIBRARY　[2124]

1000 Beal Avenue
Ann Arbor, MI 48109
(734) 205-0555
Fax: (734) 205-0571

E-MAIL ADDRESS:
ford.library@nara.gov

WEB SITE ADDRESS:
www.fordlibrarymuseum.gov

FOUNDED: 1981

AREAS OF INTEREST:
The U.S. political process, broadly defined, since circa 1970. Of special interest is the role and analysis of public opinion in that process.

NAME(S) OF PROGRAMS:
● **Gerald R. Ford Scholar Award (Dissertation Award) in Honor of Robert M. Teeter**

TYPE:
Awards/prizes; Research grants. Annual award to a doctoral student doing dissertation research and writing on an aspect of the U.S. political process during the latter part of the 20th century. Robert Teeter spent over 30 years as a leader in public opinion analysis and campaign strategy, including the 1976 campaign of President Gerald R. Ford. The majority of written materials from Teeter's career are part of the Gerald R. Ford Presidential Library collections. The Robert M. Teeter Papers document public opinion analysis and political campaign strategy from 1972 to 2004. They also include NBC News and *Wall Street Journal* National Public Opinion Surveys from 1989 to 2004.

PURPOSE:
To promote research regarding the U.S. political process during the latter part of the 20th century.

ELIGIBILITY:
Applicants must have completed all requirements for the Ph.D. program (coursework and examinations) by the application deadline, except for the dissertation.

FINANCIAL DATA:
The Library will present the award when the recipient arrives at the Library to conduct research. The recipient determines use of the award money, including, but not limited to, travel, paper and audiovisual reproductions and administrative costs, and other research and writing expenses.
Amount of support per award: $5,000.

COOPERATIVE FUNDING PROGRAMS: The Award has been made possible by the generous support of the Teeter family and friends, and the United Parcel Service.

APPLICATION INFORMATION:
Applicants must submit each of the following:
(1) an abstract describing the dissertation (no longer than 150 words);
(2) a five- to 10-page proposed plan of research;
(3) three letters of recommendation from individuals who can attest to the applicant's qualifications for the Award (one must be from their academic director that includes a statement approving the dissertation topic);
(4) unofficial transcripts from all graduate schools attended and;
(5) a curriculum vitae.
Deadline: May 1 annually. Awards are made each spring. Applications may be submitted at any time, but those received after the deadline will automatically be entered for the following year's award.

ADDRESS INQUIRIES TO:
Gerald R. Ford Scholar Award in Honor of Robert M. Teeter
(See address above.)

HERBERT HOOVER PRESIDENTIAL LIBRARY ASSOCIATION, INC. [2125]
302 Parkside Drive
West Branch, IA 52358
(319) 643-5327
Fax: (319) 643-2391

E-MAIL ADDRESS:
info@hooverassociation.org

WEB SITE ADDRESS:
www.hooverassociation.org

FOUNDED: 1954

NAME(S) OF PROGRAMS:
● **Herbert Hoover Presidential Travel Grant Program**

TYPE:
Travel grants. Money is only available for travel to the Hoover Presidential Library in West Branch, IA. The program seeks to encourage scholarly use of the holdings of the Herbert Hoover Presidential Library. It is specifically intended to promote the study of subjects of interest and concern to Herbert Hoover, Lou Henry Hoover, their associates and other public figures as reflected in the Library's 150 manuscript collections.

YEAR PROGRAM STARTED: 1978

PURPOSE:
To encourage graduate and postdoctoral scholarship consistent with Program objectives.

LEGAL BASIS:
Tax-exempt, privately supported educational foundation.

ELIGIBILITY:
Open on a competitive basis to all scholars whose research projects are consistent with Program objectives. Qualified nonacademic researchers are also encouraged to apply. The program is also open to qualified undergraduates and independent scholars/researchers.

FINANCIAL DATA:
Amount of support per award: Up to $1,500. The Association will consider larger requests for extended graduate and postgraduate research at the Library.
Total amount of support: Varies.

NUMBER OF APPLICANTS MOST RECENT YEAR: 10.

NUMBER OF AWARDS: 9.

APPLICATION INFORMATION:
Application materials are available on the web site or upon request from the Hoover Presidential Library Association, P.O. Box 696, West Branch, IA 52358. Applicants must consult with the archival staff concerning their topic prior to submitting a request for funding. Tel: (319) 643-5301.
Duration: No grants made on a continuing basis. Reapplications for consecutive support periods are accepted. No more than two grants are allowed within a five-year period.
Deadline: March 1. Announcement April 30.

PUBLICATIONS:
Historical Materials in the Herbert Hoover Presidential Library.

OFFICERS:
Ruby Triplett, President

ADDRESS INQUIRIES TO:
Delene W. McConnaha
Academic Programs Manager
(See address above.)

INSTITUTE FOR HUMANE STUDIES (IHS) [2126]
3301 North Fairfax Drive, Suite 440
Arlington, VA 22201-4432
(703) 993-4880
Fax: (703) 993-4890

E-MAIL ADDRESS:
ihs@ihs.gmu.edu

WEB SITE ADDRESS:
www.theihs.org

AREAS OF INTEREST:
Individual liberty.

NAME(S) OF PROGRAMS:
● **Humane Studies Fellowships**
● **Charles G. Koch Summer Fellowship**

TYPE:
Awards/prizes; Fellowships. Humane Studies Fellowships cover the fields of arts and humanities, fine and applied art, law, mass communication and information, religion and theology, or social and behavioral science.

Charles G. Koch Summer Fellowship deals with current public policy issues, career development workshops, writing projects with a professional editor, and the experience of spending a summer in a Washington, DC, or state-based policy community.

PURPOSE:
To assist graduate students worldwide with a special interest in individual liberty.

ELIGIBILITY:
Humane Studies Fellowships: Open to graduate students or undergraduate students with junior or senior standing in the next academic year at accredited colleges and universities.

Charles G. Koch Summer Fellowship: Undergraduates or recent graduates.

FINANCIAL DATA:
Amount of support per award: Humane Studies Fellowships: Up to $15,000; Charles G. Koch Summer Fellowship: $1,500 stipend plus housing assistance.
Total amount of support: Approximately $850,000 for the year 2010.

APPLICATION INFORMATION:
Deadline: Humane Studies Fellowships: December 31; Charles G. Koch Summer Fellowship: January 31.

ADDRESS INQUIRIES TO:
See e-mail address above.

THE INTERCOLLEGIATE STUDIES INSTITUTE [2127]
3901 Centerville Road
Wilmington, DE 19807
(302) 652-4600
(800) 526-7022
Fax: (302) 652-1760

E-MAIL ADDRESS:
awards@isi.org
simon@isi.org

WEB SITE ADDRESS:
www.simonfellowship.org
www.isifellowships.org

FOUNDED: 1953

AREAS OF INTEREST:
Education.

NAME(S) OF PROGRAMS:
- **Salvatori Fellowship**
- **William E. Simon Fellowship for Noble Purpose**
- **Richard M. Weaver Fellowship**
- **Western Civilization Fellowship**

TYPE:
Awards/prizes; Fellowships; Scholarships.

PURPOSE:
To convey to successive generations of college students a better understanding of the values and institutions that sustain a free society.

LEGAL BASIS:
A nonprofit, nonpartisan, tax-exempt educational organization.

ELIGIBILITY:
Salvatori, Richard M. Weaver and Western Civilization Fellowships: An applicant must engage in graduate studies for the purpose of teaching at the college level. Those attending professional schools (such as law, business, medicine and divinity) are ineligible. Applicants must be U.S. citizens and college seniors or graduate students who are familiar with the Institute's mission and principles. Applicants may apply for more than one fellowship, but an applicant may receive only one during his or her academic career.

William E. Simon Fellowship for Noble Purpose: Applicants must be graduating college seniors.

Recipients must be citizens of the U.S., but may study abroad.

FINANCIAL DATA:
Amount of support per award: Salvatori Fellowship: $10,000 grant; Simon Fellowship: $40,000; Weaver Fellowship: $1,000 book stipend, $5,000 stipend and payment of tuition at the school of his or her choice (either in the U.S. or abroad); Western Civilization Fellowship: $20,000 grant to pursue studies at the school of his or her choice.

Total amount of support: Varies.

NUMBER OF AWARDS: Salvatori Fellowship: 2; Richard M. Weaver Fellowship: 10 to 12; Western Civilization Fellowship and William E. Simon Fellowship for Noble Purpose: 3 each.

APPLICATION INFORMATION:
Deadline: February 15.

ADDRESS INQUIRIES TO:
Director of Honors
Program and Fellowships
(See address above.)

THE JAPANESE AMERICAN CITIZENS LEAGUE (JACL) [2128]

1850 M Street, N.W.
Suite 1100
Washington, DC 20036
(202) 223-1240
Fax: (202) 296-8082

E-MAIL ADDRESS:
dc@jacl.org

WEB SITE ADDRESS:
www.jacl.org

FOUNDED: 1929

AREAS OF INTEREST:
Public service leadership development.

NAME(S) OF PROGRAMS:
- **Mike M. Masaoka Fellowship Fund Congressional Program**

TYPE:
Fellowships. Congressional fellowship established to help understand the importance of public service at the national level. The Masaoka fellow serves in the Washington, DC office of a member of Congress in either the U.S. House of Representatives or the U.S. Senate.

YEAR PROGRAM STARTED: 1988

PURPOSE:
To develop leaders for public service.

ELIGIBILITY:
Candidates must be U.S. citizens who are graduating college seniors or students in graduate or professional programs. Preference will be given to those who have demonstrated commitment to Asian American and Pacific Islander (AAPI) issues, particularly those affecting the Japanese American community. Membership in the JACL is required. Communication skills, especially in writing, are important.

GEOGRAPHIC RESTRICTIONS:
United States.

FINANCIAL DATA:
Fellowship includes round-trip airfare from fellow's home to Washington, DC.

Amount of support per award: $2,200 to $2,500 monthly stipend.

Total amount of support: $10,000.

NUMBER OF AWARDS: 1 annually.

APPLICATION INFORMATION:
Completed application materials may be sent via e-mail to policy@jacl.org or by fax to the number listed above.

Duration: Six to eight months.

Deadline: April 15. Announcement by June 1.

ADDRESS INQUIRIES TO:
Floyd Mori, National Director
(See address above.)

THE LYNDON BAINES JOHNSON FOUNDATION [2129]

2313 Red River Street
Austin, TX 78705-5702
(512) 232-2266
Fax: (512) 232-2285

E-MAIL ADDRESS:
johnson.grants@nara.gov

WEB SITE ADDRESS:
www.lbjlib.utexas.edu
www.lbjfoundation.org

FOUNDED: 1969

AREAS OF INTEREST:
Financial support for special programs of the Lyndon B. Johnson Library.

TYPE:
Grants-in-aid.

YEAR PROGRAM STARTED: 1972

PURPOSE:
To defray living, travel and related expenses incurred while conducting research at the LBJ Library during the period for which the grant is awarded.

LEGAL BASIS:
Operating, public foundation.

ELIGIBILITY:
In accepting a grant, an applicant must agree to the following conditions:
(1) that the product of the research which is made possible through these funds will not be used for any political purpose;
(2) that the funds are for the purpose of helping to defray expenses incurred while conducting research at the Johnson Library;
(3) that the grant must be used in the grant period in which it is awarded and;
(4) that the LBJ Foundation will be promptly provided with a copy of any publication, paper, article or book resulting from research made possible by this grant.

FINANCIAL DATA:
Amount of support per award: Maximum $2,500.

Total amount of support: Approximately $50,000 annually.

NUMBER OF APPLICANTS MOST RECENT YEAR:
44 for the year 2009-10.

NUMBER OF AWARDS: 28 for the year 2009-10.

APPLICATION INFORMATION:
Application forms must be accompanied by a written proposal. Candidates should state clearly and precisely how the holdings of the LBJ Library will contribute to the completion of the project. General and vague requests for assistance or those written in haste will be less competitive.

Duration: Six months.

Deadline: September 15 for January to August grant period. Announcement in October. March 15 for June to December grant period. Announcement in April.

STAFF:
Elizabeth Boone, Deputy Director

ADDRESS INQUIRIES TO:
Elizabeth Boone, Deputy Director
E-mail: elizabeth@lbjfoundation.org
(See address above.)

NATIONAL ENDOWMENT FOR DEMOCRACY [2130]

1025 F Street, N.W.
Suite 800
Washington, DC 20004
(202) 378-9700
Fax: (202) 378-9407

E-MAIL ADDRESS:
info@ned.org

WEB SITE ADDRESS:
www.ned.org/grants/grants.html

FOUNDED: 1983

AREAS OF INTEREST:
Democracy throughout the world.

NAME(S) OF PROGRAMS:
- **National Endowment for Democracy Grants**

TYPE:
Project/program grants.

PURPOSE:
To strengthen democratic institutions throughout the world.

ELIGIBILITY:
Individuals and religious organizations are ineligible.

FINANCIAL DATA:
Amount of support per award: $25,000.
Total amount of support: Varies.

APPLICATION INFORMATION:
Duration: Annual. Renewable.

Deadline: Seven weeks prior to board meetings held in January, March, June and September.

NATIONAL FEDERATION OF REPUBLICAN WOMEN

124 North Alfred Street
Alexandria, VA 22314
(703) 548-9688
Fax: (703) 548-9836

E-MAIL ADDRESS:
mail@nfrw.org

WEB SITE ADDRESS:
www.nfrw.org

TYPE:
Internships; Scholarships. Dorothy Kabis Internship includes a six-week internship in Washington, DC, housing, travel and stipend.

National Pathfinder's Scholarships are given to the best nominated candidates.

Betty Rendel Scholarships are given to undergraduate women who are majoring in political science, government or economics.

See entry 1155 for full listing.

NEW YORK STATE ASSEMBLY INTERN COMMITTEE   [2131]

Legislative Office Building, Room 104A
Albany, NY 12248
(518) 455-4704
Fax: (518) 455-4705

E-MAIL ADDRESS:
intern@assembly.state.ny.us

WEB SITE ADDRESS:
www.assembly.state.ny.us/internship

FOUNDED: 1971

AREAS OF INTEREST:
Government.

NAME(S) OF PROGRAMS:
● **Assembly Session Internships**

TYPE:
Internships. Program provides first-hand knowledge of the legislative process and functions. The interns are assigned research and administrative responsibilities in an Assembly office. They receive a practical educational experience and attend weekly classes. The Assembly benefits from the new ideas and fresh perspectives of the interns. All Intern placements are in Albany, NY.

YEAR PROGRAM STARTED: 1971

PURPOSE:
To encourage talented students from all fields to learn about and get involved in state government.

LEGAL BASIS:
Government legislature.

ELIGIBILITY:
Applicants must be matriculated in a U.S. college or university degree program as juniors or seniors. Applications are welcome from students in any academic field. Colleges generally award a full semester of credit for participation. International students should have academic requirements in the U.S. to be eligible.

FINANCIAL DATA:
Session interns receive a stipend and semester of college credit.
Amount of support per award: $4,140 session term.

NUMBER OF APPLICANTS MOST RECENT YEAR:
200.

NUMBER OF AWARDS: 150.

APPLICATION INFORMATION:
Applications are available from an Intern Program liaison officer on college campuses. Applications and all supporting documents must be submitted to the Intern Committee in a complete package.

The following documents must be included with the application:
(1) personal statement;
(2) official transcripts of all college courses completed and in progress;
(3) two letters of recommendation;
(4) a letter from an appropriate college official endorsing the student's participation and indicating the amount of credit to be granted by the college and;
(5) a concise writing sample.
Duration: January to mid-May.
Deadline: Mid-October.

STAFF:
Kathleen McCarty, Director, Assembly Intern Committee

ADDRESS INQUIRIES TO:
Kathleen McCarty, Director
Assembly Intern Committee
(See address above.)

NEW YORK STATE ASSEMBLY INTERN COMMITTEE   [2132]

Legislative Office Building, Room 104A
Albany, NY 12248
(518) 455-4704
Fax: (518) 455-4705

E-MAIL ADDRESS:
intern@assembly.state.ny.us

WEB SITE ADDRESS:
www.assembly.state.ny.us/internship

FOUNDED: 1971

AREAS OF INTEREST:
Government.

TYPE:
Internships. Assignments designed to provide up to 10 graduate students with full-time work placements as Assembly researchers and policy analysts with all the responsibilities and expectations of such positions. The work placements are with Assembly leaders. The interns will have the opportunity to develop a better understanding of the legislative process while contributing new ideas and fresh perspectives to the legislative decision making process.

YEAR PROGRAM STARTED: 1976

PURPOSE:
To bring the expertise and thinking of the state's best graduate students into the legislative process.

LEGAL BASIS:
Government.

ELIGIBILITY:
All students matriculated in or who have recently completed a graduate degree program may apply. Students with expertise in a variety of public policy issues are being sought. Issues include public finance, education, environmental conservation, etc. Students must work full-time in the Assembly. International students should have

academic requirements in the U.S. to be eligible. Credit can often be arranged by the school.

GEOGRAPHIC RESTRICTIONS:
New York state.

FINANCIAL DATA:
Amount of support per award: $11,500 per year.

NUMBER OF APPLICANTS MOST RECENT YEAR:
50.

NUMBER OF AWARDS: Up to 10 each year.

APPLICATION INFORMATION:
Applications are available from graduate schools, directly from the Assembly Intern Committee, or on the web site. Applications must include two letters of recommendation, a letter from graduate program dean or director, official transcripts, a writing sample and a personal statement.
Duration: Six months (January to June). Nonrenewable.
Deadline: November 1. Selection by December 1.

STAFF:
Kathleen McCarty, Director

ADDRESS INQUIRIES TO:
Kathleen McCarty, Director
(See address above.)

NEW YORK STATE SENATE   [2133]

Student Programs Office
80 South Swan Street, Suite 1426
Albany, NY 12210
(518) 455-2611
Fax: (518) 426-6827

E-MAIL ADDRESS:
students@nysenate.gov

WEB SITE ADDRESS:
www.nysenate.gov/department/student-programs

FOUNDED: 1965

AREAS OF INTEREST:
New York state government and education which includes improved public access to and understanding of government, resulting in enhanced citizenship, career staffing, government administration and leadership.

CONSULTING OR VOLUNTEER SERVICES:
Placement in staff support roles in senate offices, ordinarily in the office of a senator. Also, host or travel to inform interested citizens, students and faculty; host or travel to government offices responsible for development or administration of similar programs.

NAME(S) OF PROGRAMS:
● **James L. Biggane Fellowship in Finance**
● **New York State Senate Legislative Fellows Program**
● **Richard J. Roth Journalism Fellowship**
● **Richard A. Wiebe Public Service Fellowship**

TYPE:
Fellowships. These fellowships are intended for the graduate/postgraduate/midcareer level. Stipends which allow for bipartisan opportunities to train in government while on-site in Albany, NY. Fellows spend almost a year immersed in the work of the Senate, learning techniques associated with policymaking and legislative process. Placement is usually to the office of an elected Senate member. The Senate

Legislative Fellows Program, Biggane Fellowship, Roth Journalism Fellowship and Wiebe Public Service Fellowship constitute the Senate Graduate/Post-Graduate/Mid-Career Fellowships.

YEAR PROGRAM STARTED: 1965

PURPOSE:
To provide an opportunity for career experience and correction for undergraduate assistants, career recruitment among superior fellows, and citizenship training in general.

LEGAL BASIS:
Legislative authority.

ELIGIBILITY:
Graduate/Postgraduate/Midcareer Fellowships: All applicants must be U.S. citizens (except in the case of the International Fellowship Program). In most cases, Fellows must be full-time matriculating graduate students in an accredited university during the immediately previous spring and fall semesters. Fellowships are open to all majors. Training in the history/politics/government of New York state is not required.

The Biggane Fellow will be a person in midcareer, not less than 35 years of age at the time of application. Biggane applicants need not be currently enrolled in graduate-level study, but must have previous graduate-level experience. Legislative Fellows will be talented and skilled graduate/postgraduate students from a variety of academic disciplines.

The Roth Fellow may be a student with experience and/or intentions in the fields of communications, journalism and/or public relations.

Wiebe Fellow may be a student with legal training and a variety of other backgrounds.

Students are not required to presently reside in New York state or attend school in New York state.

GEOGRAPHIC RESTRICTIONS:
New York.

FINANCIAL DATA:
The stipend is distributed in biweekly installments prorated from the first day to the last day of enrollment. Some benefit options are available (health, dental, vision, life insurance, and the retirement program). Fellows are not Senate employees; they do not earn vacation or personal leave.

All Senate Fellowships are on-site in Albany, NY. Fellowships are not financial aid for academic work, on-campus or classroom study. Housing in Albany is the responsibility of the Fellow.

Amount of support per award:
Grant-in-Study stipend of $32,000 for the year 2011-12.

NUMBER OF APPLICANTS MOST RECENT YEAR: 50.

NUMBER OF AWARDS: Approximately 14 fellowships each year. Legislative Fellows Program: Up to 11; Biggane, Roth and Wiebe Fellowships: 1 each.

APPLICATION INFORMATION:
Applications must include the following:
(1) course work-in-progress list signed by campus official (if not on transcript);
(2) calling of Office of Student Programs to indicate one's intent to apply;
(3) policy proposal;

(4) rebuttal of policy proposal;
(5) statement of purpose;
(6) writing sample essay;
(7) resume or curriculum vitae;
(8) all official transcripts (graduate and undergraduate) and;
(9) three letters of reference from persons familiar with the applicant's character, academic and/or professional abilities (at least two from faculty members).

Duration: Approximately one year, September through mid-July. No renewals.

Deadline: April 15.

PUBLICATIONS:
Program announcement.

ADDRESS INQUIRIES TO:
Director, Office of Student Programs
New York State Senate
Legislative Office Building, Suite 1426
Albany, NY 12247

NEW YORK STATE SENATE [2134]

80 South Swan Street, Suite 1426
Albany, NY 12247
(518) 455-2611
Fax: (518) 426-6827

E-MAIL ADDRESS:
students@nysenate.gov

WEB SITE ADDRESS:
www.nysenate.gov/department/student-programs

FOUNDED: 1978

AREAS OF INTEREST:
State government internships for undergraduates.

NAME(S) OF PROGRAMS:
● **Undergraduate Session Assistants Program**

TYPE:
Internships. Annual undergraduate internship running second Thursday in January to third Wednesday in April.

YEAR PROGRAM STARTED: 1978

PURPOSE:
To provide on-site experience at the New York State Senate, Albany, NY.

ELIGIBILITY:
Each applicant must be a U.S. citizen matriculating full-time in an accredited, undergraduate degree program on a campus in New York State. The program is intended and designed for college juniors and seniors; exceptional sophomores may occasionally be selected. Freshmen are ineligible.

The Senate welcomes majors in all accredited disciplines. Training in the history/politics/government of New York is neither a prerequisite of nor an advantage to selection. Skill and ability, initiative, eagerness to learn, discretion and mature flexibility are essential for success.

Each student should demonstrate a 3.0 grade point average, and meet the campus/departmental standard for off-campus study; full-time enrollment in the immediately previous spring (not summer) and current fall semester/previous two trimesters. Each standard is to be certified by the Campus Liaison Officer (CLO), student's academic advisor, chairman, dean, or other duly authorized campus official.

Placements are ordinarily to the offices of individual senators. Students may observe, participate in, and/or acquire experience with state government procedures. Combined participation in the program and legislative placement is for a minimum of 35 hours per week. Longer hours are possible and should be expected.

Each applicant must be able to earn campus-awarded credit for participation in the program to be eligible. On-campus faculty is responsible for academic advisement, evaluation, grading and granting of credit for their student participant(s) enrolled in this Senate program.

GEOGRAPHIC RESTRICTIONS:
New York state.

FINANCIAL DATA:
Arrangement of housing in Albany is the responsibility of the individual enrollee.

Amount of support per award: A stipend of $4,140 to offset costs of moving to and living in Albany.

NUMBER OF AWARDS: Approximately 30.

APPLICATION INFORMATION:
Enrollment is on-site at the New York State Senate in Albany, NY. Applications are available on campus, from the Student Programs Office, or at the web site.

If there is no CLO on campus, contact Nicholas J. Parrella, Director Programs, at the address listed above.

Duration: Approximately four months.

Deadline: The last Friday in October. Expect an earlier on-campus deadline if one's school has a Campus Liaison Officer (CLO). Announcement of selections is approximately mid-November.

STAFF:
Nicholas J. Parrella, Director of Student Programs
Kimberly Drofitz, Confidential Assistant

ADDRESS INQUIRIES TO:
Nicholas J. Parrella
Director of Student Programs
New York State Senate
Legislative Office Building, Suite 1426
Albany, NY 12247

THE PHILLIPS FOUNDATION [2135]

One Massachusetts Avenue, N.W.
Suite 620
Washington, DC 20001
(202) 250-3887 ext. 609
Fax: (202) 216-9188

E-MAIL ADDRESS:
jfarley@thephillipsfoundation.org

WEB SITE ADDRESS:
www.thephillipsfoundation.org

FOUNDED: 1990

AREAS OF INTEREST:
Advancement of constitutional principles, a democratic society and a vibrant free enterprise system.

NAME(S) OF PROGRAMS:
● **The Robert Novak Journalism Fellowship Program**

TYPE:
Fellowships. One-year writing project on a topic of applicant's choosing, focusing on journalism supportive of American culture and a free society.

YEAR PROGRAM STARTED: 1994

PURPOSE:
To award grants to working print and online journalists who share the Foundation's mission.

ELIGIBILITY:
Applicants must be U.S. citizens and working journalists with less than 10 years of professional experience in print and online journalism and who share the mission to advance constitutional principles, a democratic society and a vibrant free enterprise system.

FINANCIAL DATA:
Amounts include funds for reimbursement of fellowship-related expenses.

Amount of support per award: $50,000 full-time gold fellowship and $25,000 part-time silver fellowship.

NUMBER OF AWARDS: Varies, depending upon funding available and the number of qualified applicants.

APPLICATION INFORMATION:
Duration: One year.
Deadline: February 22.

TRUSTEES AND OFFICERS:
Thomas L. Phillips, Chairman
Jon A. Heimerman, Treasurer
D. Jeffrey Hollingsworth, Assistant Secretary
Kellyanne E. Conway
Becky Norton Dunlop
Thomas A. Fuentes
Alfred S. Regnery
Ronald E. Robinson

EXECUTIVE DIRECTOR:
John W. Farley

ADDRESS INQUIRIES TO:
John W. Farley, Executive Director
(See address above.)

PIPER FUND   [2136]

101 University Drive
Suite A2
Amherst, MA 01002-2376
(413) 256-0349
Fax: (413) 256-3536

E-MAIL ADDRESS:
grantsmanager@proteusfund.org

WEB SITE ADDRESS:
www.proteusfund.org

AREAS OF INTEREST:
Campaign finance reform in the American political system.

TYPE:
General operating grants; Project/program grants.

PURPOSE:
To help meet the needs of the growing movement for campaign finance reform in America.

FINANCIAL DATA:
Amount of support per award: $10,000 to $50,000.

Total amount of support: Approximately $12,000,000 since inception. $1,000,000 for the year 2010.

APPLICATION INFORMATION:
Guidelines available on the web site.
Duration: One year.

ADDRESS INQUIRIES TO:
Beery Adams, Grants Manager
(See address above.)

PRESIDENT'S COMMISSION ON WHITE HOUSE FELLOWSHIPS   [2137]

712 Jackson Place, N.W.
Washington, DC 20503
(202) 395-4522
Fax: (202) 395-6179

E-MAIL ADDRESS:
whitehousefellows@whf.eop.gov

WEB SITE ADDRESS:
www.whitehouse.gov/fellows

FOUNDED: 1964

AREAS OF INTEREST:
Leadership and public service for young professionals.

NAME(S) OF PROGRAMS:
● **White House Fellowships**

TYPE:
Fellowships. The White House Fellows program is America's most prestigious program for leadership and public service. White House Fellowships offer exceptional young men and women firsthand experience working at the highest levels of the federal government.

White House Fellows typically spend a year working as full-time, paid special assistants to senior White House staff, the Vice President, cabinet secretaries and other top-ranking government officials. Fellows also participate in an education program consisting of roundtable discussions with renowned leaders from the private and public sectors, and trips to study U.S. policy in action both domestically and internationally. Fellowships are awarded on a strictly nonpartisan basis.

PURPOSE:
To give those who participate in the program firsthand, high-level experience with the workings of the federal government and to increase their sense of participation in national affairs.

ELIGIBILITY:
The following criteria apply:
(1) applicants must be U.S. citizens and not hold any foreign citizenships;
(2) employees of the federal government are not eligible unless they are career military personnel;
(3) applicants should be finished with their undergraduate education and working in their chosen professions and;
(4) there are no formal age restrictions; however, the fellowship program was created to give selected Americans the experience of government service early in their careers.

The Commission awards fellowships on a strict nonpartisan basis and encourages balance and diversity in all aspects of the program.

GEOGRAPHIC RESTRICTIONS:
United States.

FINANCIAL DATA:
Fellows are eligible to purchase health insurance through the Federal Employee Health Benefit Plans.

Total amount of support: Fellows are considered federal employees, with the rank of GS-14, step 3. With this comes a salary of approximately $100,000 for the year 2010-11. Military personnel, however, maintain their current salary and benefits.

NUMBER OF APPLICANTS MOST RECENT YEAR:
Up to 1,000.

NUMBER OF AWARDS: 11 to 19 fellowships per year.

APPLICATION INFORMATION:
Application must be submitted online and is available beginning in the Fall.
Deadline: Mid-January.

STAFF:
Erika Henderson, Deputy Director
Natalie Bookey Baker, Program Director

SARAH SCAIFE FOUNDATION, INC.   [2138]

One Oxford Centre, Suite 3900
301 Grant Street
Pittsburgh, PA 15219-6401
(412) 392-2900

WEB SITE ADDRESS:
www.scaife.com

FOUNDED: 1941

AREAS OF INTEREST:
Domestic and international public policy issues.

TYPE:
Challenge/matching grants; Fellowships; General operating grants; Project/program grants; Seed money grants.

YEAR PROGRAM STARTED: 1941

PURPOSE:
To direct money to programs that address major domestic and international issues.

LEGAL BASIS:
Private foundation.

ELIGIBILITY:
The Foundation's grant program is directed primarily toward public policy programs that address major domestic and international issues. The Foundation does not make grants to individuals for any purpose or to nationally organized fund-raising groups.

FINANCIAL DATA:
Amount of support per award: Average $25,000 to $200,000.

REPRESENTATIVE AWARDS:
$200,000 to American Civil Rights Institute; $125,000 to Foundation for Individual Rights in Education, Inc.; $60,000 to New England Legal Foundation.

APPLICATION INFORMATION:
Initial inquiries to the Foundation should be in letter form signed by the organization's chief executive officer or authorized representative and have the approval of the organization's Board of Directors. The letter should include a concise description of the purpose for which funds are requested, along with the related budget.

Applicant must also provide:
(1) latest audited financial statements and annual report;
(2) current annual budget;
(3) list of officers and directors and their major affiliations and;
(4) copy of current determination letter from the IRS evidencing tax-exempt status under Section 501(c)(3).

Duration: One year.

Deadline: Board meets quarterly in February, May, September and November. Notification within two to four weeks.

PUBLICATIONS:
Annual report.

OFFICERS:
Richard M. Scaife, Chairman
Michael W. Gleba, President
Barbara L. Slaney, Vice President and
Treasurer
R. Daniel McMichael, Secretary

ADDRESS INQUIRIES TO:
Michael W. Gleba, President
(See address above.)

THE SOCIETY FOR THE PSYCHOLOGICAL STUDY OF SOCIAL ISSUES [2139]

208 I Street, N.E.
Washington, DC 20002-4340
(202) 675-6956
Fax: (202) 675-6902

E-MAIL ADDRESS:
awards@spssi.org
spssi@spssi.org

WEB SITE ADDRESS:
www.spssi.org

FOUNDED: 1936

AREAS OF INTEREST:
Public policy, social issues, psychology and
international relations.

NAME(S) OF PROGRAMS:
● **Otto Klineberg Intercultural and International Relations Award**

TYPE:
Awards/prizes. The Klineberg Award is given
for the best paper or article of the year on
intercultural or international relations.

PURPOSE:
To award the best paper or article of the year
on intercultural or international relations.

LEGAL BASIS:
Independently incorporated society.

ELIGIBILITY:
Entries can be either unpublished
manuscripts, in press papers or books, or
papers or books published no more than 18
months prior to the submission date. Entries
cannot be returned. The competition is open
to nonmembers and members of SPSSI.
Graduate students are especially urged to
submit papers.

FINANCIAL DATA:
Amount of support per award: $1,000.

NUMBER OF APPLICANTS MOST RECENT YEAR:
30.

NUMBER OF AWARDS: 1.

APPLICATION INFORMATION:
Online submissions are the preferred method.
Please limit the number and size of files
uploaded when applying online. For
hard-copy submissions, send five (5) copies
to the address listed above, "Attn: Klineberg
Award."
Deadline: February 22.

PUBLICATIONS:
Program announcement; application
guidelines.

STATE OF RHODE ISLAND [2140]

Commission on State Government Internships
State House, Room 8AA
Providence, RI 02903
(401) 222-6782
Fax: (401) 222-4447

E-MAIL ADDRESS:
rgemma@rilin.state.ri.us

WEB SITE ADDRESS:
www.rilin.state.ri.us

FOUNDED: 1969

NAME(S) OF PROGRAMS:
● **State Government Intern Program (Spring Semester Program)**
● **State Intern Summer Program**

TYPE:
Internships; Work-study programs. Funding
through General Assembly is also available.
Internship opportunities for graduate and
undergraduate students in the state
government operation. Students are involved
in executive, legislative and judicial
assignments. The internship is viewed as an
extension of the classroom and is seen as
complementing and building upon the
educational opportunities available on
campuses.

This program has established a Summer
Internship section, open to Rhode Island
residents only, that begins in late June and
concludes in August.

YEAR PROGRAM STARTED: 1969

PURPOSE:
To provide a link between the public and
state government; to open a channel for the
potential recruitment of personnel for state
government internship; to supplement college
and university course offerings in state and
local government; to enable students to
develop a knowledge of the structure and
procedure of state government.

LEGAL BASIS:
Chapter 47, General Laws, state of Rhode
Island.

ELIGIBILITY:
Spring semester interns are chosen by
members of the faculties of 11 participating
Rhode Island colleges and universities.
Students must have junior or senior status.
Summer applicants must be Rhode Island
residents attending an out-of-state college or
university.

FINANCIAL DATA:
Academic credit, up to a maximum of six
credits, is available. For the Summer
Internship, a student is required to work 35
hours per week and receives a monthly
stipend.

Amount of support per award: $100 per
week for eight weeks.

APPLICATION INFORMATION:
Interns are selected by the academic
committee and referred to Intern Staff.

Duration: 12 weeks in the spring (one school
semester) and eight weeks (July and August)
for Summer Internship.

Deadline: November 15. May 15 for Summer
Internship. Announcement by the end of
May.

ADDRESS INQUIRIES TO:
Robert W. Gemma, Executive Director
(See address above.)

*PLEASE NOTE:
The Summer Program is for Rhode Island
residents only.

HATTON W. SUMNERS FOUNDATION [2141]

325 North St. Paul Street
Suite 3920
Dallas, TX 75201
(214) 220-2128
Fax: (214) 953-0737

E-MAIL ADDRESS:
info@hattonsumners.org

WEB SITE ADDRESS:
www.hattonsumners.org

FOUNDED: 1949

AREAS OF INTEREST:
Self-government, political science and
democracy.

TYPE:
Challenge/matching grants;
Conferences/seminars; Endowments;
Fellowships; Internships; Project/program
grants; Scholarships. Scholarship programs at
selected universities and grants to support
other educational activities for both students
and adults, which are designed to create an
appreciation and understanding for the U.S.
executive, legislative and judicial processes.

YEAR PROGRAM STARTED: 1949

PURPOSE:
To encourage the study, teaching and
research into the science and art of
self-government so that the American people
may understand the fundamental principles of
democracy and be guided thereby in shaping
governmental policies.

LEGAL BASIS:
Private charitable foundation.

GEOGRAPHIC RESTRICTIONS:
Arkansas, Kansas, Louisiana, Missouri,
Nebraska, New Mexico, Oklahoma and
Texas.

FINANCIAL DATA:
Amount of support per award: Varies.
Total amount of support: $2,500,000 for the
year 2010.

NUMBER OF AWARDS: 49.

REPRESENTATIVE AWARDS:
$25,000 to Bill of Rights Institute, Arlington,
VA, for constitutional seminars in Oklahoma
and New Mexico; $35,000 to Project Vote
Smart, Philipsburg, MT, for National Key
Votes Database Project; $45,000 to Law
Focused Education, Austin, TX, for Texas
Citizen Bee Competition.

APPLICATION INFORMATION:
Grant applications must be in writing, but do
not need to be formal. The Foundation does
not accept applications via fax or e-mail.
Duration: One year. Occasional multiyear
funding.
Deadline: August 1. Decision in October.

PUBLICATIONS:
Annual report.

STAFF:
Hugh C. Akin, Executive Director

ADDRESS INQUIRIES TO:
Hugh C. Akin, Executive Director
(See address above.)

THE SUPREME COURT OF THE U.S. [2142]

One First Street, N.E.
Room 5
Washington, DC 20543
(202) 479-3415
Fax: (202) 479-3484

E-MAIL ADDRESS:
fellowsprogram@supremecourt.gov

WEB SITE ADDRESS:
www.fellows.supremecourtus.gov

FOUNDED: 1789

AREAS OF INTEREST:
Judicial administration, judicial planning and management, public administration, behavioral sciences, business management, operations research and systems analysis, as well as law.

NAME(S) OF PROGRAMS:
● **Supreme Court Fellows Program**

TYPE:
Fellowships. Fellows serve in the Supreme Court, the Federal Judicial Center, the U.S. Sentencing Commission, and the Administrative Office of the U.S. Courts.

YEAR PROGRAM STARTED: 1973

PURPOSE:
To offer a unique opportunity to a select group of talented professionals for creative work and broad firsthand experience in judicial administration.

LEGAL BASIS:
Judicial Branch of the U.S. Government.

ELIGIBILITY:
Program is designed for professionals in the formative period of their career development who will receive long-term benefits from the experience and who will contribute to judicial modernization both during and after their Fellowship. Candidates should have one or more postgraduate degrees and at least two years of professional experience with a record of high performance.
Multi-disciplinary training and experience is highly desirable.

Fellows must relocate to Washington, DC.

FINANCIAL DATA:
Amount of support per award: Salary is the prevailing rate of pay for a GS-15, Step 3, which is equivalent to $132,009 per year.

COOPERATIVE FUNDING PROGRAMS: The Program is administered by the Office of the Counselor to the Chief Justice, in cooperation with the Federal Judicial Center, the Administrative Office of the U.S. Courts, the U.S. Sentencing Commission and the Supreme Court Historical Society.

NUMBER OF APPLICANTS MOST RECENT YEAR:
Approximately 100.

NUMBER OF AWARDS: 4.

APPLICATION INFORMATION:
Applications must include:
(1) a candidate information form;
(2) a resume highlighting academic, professional and personal achievements;
(3) copies of no more than two writing samples on 8 1/2 x 11-inch paper in a format that is easily reproduced;
(4) a candidate statement of 700 words or less describing why the applicant is applying for the fellowship, what the applicant considers their major strengths and qualifications for the program, and what benefits the applicant feels are likely to result from their participation and;
(5) three candidate evaluations.
Duration: One year, beginning in August or September. Duration subject to mutual agreement between fellow and Executive Director.
Deadline: November. Notification the following February or March.

PUBLICATIONS:
Supreme Court Fellows Program brochure.

EXECUTIVE DIRECTOR:
Vanessa M. Yarnall

ADDRESS INQUIRIES TO:
Vanessa M. Yarnall, Administrative Director
Supreme Court Fellows Program
(See address above.)

THE ROBERT A. TAFT INSTITUTE OF GOVERNMENT   [2143]

Taft Institute at Queen's College
Powdermaker Hall, Room 150
65-30 Kissena Boulevard
Flushing, NY 11367-1597
(718) 997-5164
(718) 997-5000
Fax: (718) 997-5333

E-MAIL ADDRESS:
jack.zevin@gmail.com

WEB SITE ADDRESS:
taftinstitute.org

FOUNDED: 1961

AREAS OF INTEREST:
Education to stimulate citizen participation through understanding of the U.S. Constitution and the principles and processes of American government.

CONSULTING OR VOLUNTEER SERVICES:
Graduate credit seminars on politics and government for elementary and secondary school teachers, administrators, librarians and community college instructors, or other programs.

NAME(S) OF PROGRAMS:
● **Community Leadership Training**
● **Taft Seminars for Teachers**

TYPE:
Conferences/seminars; Demonstration grants; Development grants; Endowments; Fellowships; Project/program grants; Scholarships; Seed money grants; Training grants. Grants are given to colleges and universities to conduct Taft Seminars for Teachers.

Scholarships are awarded to elementary and secondary school teachers, administrators, librarians, community college instructors, graduate students in social studies education, and ESL teachers to participate for graduate credit for two to three weeks.

YEAR PROGRAM STARTED: 1963

PURPOSE:
To help teachers increase their knowledge of government and politics; to improve teaching of the American political system in elementary and secondary schools and in community colleges.

LEGAL BASIS:
Nonpartisan, nonprofit, educational tax-exempt organization designated by IRS as a publicly supported organization.

ELIGIBILITY:
Universities which offer Master's degree credit in political science and/or education apply for sponsorship of Taft Seminars. Elementary or secondary teachers, administrators, librarians, community college instructors, graduate students in social studies education and ESL teachers apply for scholarships to participate in the Seminars.

FINANCIAL DATA:
University sponsors receive financial support for conducting seminars.
Amount of support per award: $1,000 to $1,500.

APPLICATION INFORMATION:
Duration: Varies.
Deadline: Varies.

PUBLICATIONS:
Annual report.

ADDRESS INQUIRIES TO:
Dr. Jack Zevin, Co-Director
(See address above.)

HARRY S. TRUMAN LIBRARY INSTITUTE   [2144]

500 West U.S. Highway 24
Independence, MO 64050
(816) 268-8248
Fax: (816) 268-8299

E-MAIL ADDRESS:
lisa.sullivan@truman.nara.gov

WEB SITE ADDRESS:
www.trumanlibrary.org

FOUNDED: 1957

AREAS OF INTEREST:
Harry S. Truman and the Truman administration.

NAME(S) OF PROGRAMS:
● **Dissertation Year Fellowships**
● **Research Grant**
● **Scholar's Award**
● **Harry S. Truman Book Award**

TYPE:
Awards/prizes; Fellowships; Grants-in-aid; Research grants; Travel grants. The Dissertation Year Fellowships are given to encourage historical scholarship of the public career of Harry S. Truman or the Truman era. Support is given annually to one or two graduate students who have completed the dissertation research and are in the writing stage. Preference will be given to projects based on extensive research at the Truman Library. Successful applicants will be expected to deposit one copy of their completed dissertation, or any publication resulting therefrom, with the Truman Library.

Research Grants are intended to enable graduate students as well as postdoctoral scholars to come to the Library for one to three weeks to use its archival facilities.

The Scholar's Award is given every other year, even-numbered years only, to a scholar engaged in a study of either the public career of Harry S. Truman or some aspect of the history of the Truman administration or of the U.S. during that administration. The scholar's work must be based on extensive research at the Truman Library and must be designed to result in the publication of a book-length manuscript. One copy of such book (and/or any other publication resulting from work done under this award) shall be deposited by the author with the Harry S. Truman Library.

The Harry S. Truman Book Award is given in even years for the best book dealing with some aspect of history of the U.S. between April 12, 1945 and January 20, 1953 or with the public career of Harry S. Truman.

YEAR PROGRAM STARTED: 1959

PURPOSE:
To encourage study of the history of the Truman administration and the public career of Harry S. Truman; to promote the use of the Truman Library as a national center for historical scholarship.

ELIGIBILITY:
Undergraduate students, doctoral candidates and postdoctoral scholars with appropriate interests are eligible for support. Applicants must be competent researchers with viable topics for which pertinent materials are available at the Truman Library.

FINANCIAL DATA:
Amount of support per award: Dissertation Year Fellowships: $16,000 payable in two installments; Research Grants: Up to $2,500; Scholar's Award: Up to $30,000; Truman Book Award: $2,500.

REPRESENTATIVE AWARDS:
Alonzo Hamby for "Man of the People: A Life of Harry S. Truman;" Richard B. Frank for "Downfall: The End of the Japanese Imperial Empire;" Kari Frederickson for "The Dixiecrat Revolt and the End of Solid South, 1932-1968;" Stephen C. Schlesinger for "Act of Creation: The Founding of the United Nations;" John Lewis Gaddis for "The Cold War: A New History."

APPLICATION INFORMATION:
Applicants for the Scholar's Award should submit an application and proposal for preliminary screening. If selected, applicants must submit further information including a list of Truman files already utilized or planned to be utilized, a projected timeline for completion, and projected income for the academic year in which the award will be announced. Applicants for Research Grants may receive no more than two grants in this category in any one five-year period.

For the Harry S. Truman Book Award, five copies of each book entered must be submitted to the Book Award Administrator.
Duration: Research Grants: One to three weeks.
Deadline: Dissertation Year Fellowships: February 1. Announcement first week of April. Research Grants: April 1 and October 1. Results announced six weeks later. Scholar's Award: December 15 for preliminary screening. Decision by February 1. If selected, further information will be requested with announcement by April 15. Harry S. Truman Book Award: Books must be received by January 20 in even-numbered years.

PUBLICATIONS:
Program announcement; *Whistle Stop*, newsletter.

OFFICERS:
Mary E. Hunkeler, Chairman of the Board
John J. Sherman, Vice Chairperson
Roger A. Novak, Treasurer
Herb M. Kohn, Secretary

BOARD OF DIRECTORS:
Clifton Truman Daniel, Honorary Chairperson
Carol Anderson
Alan Atterbury
Kirk Carpenter
Michael J. Devine
John A. Dillingham
Charles M. Foudree
Sam F. Hamra
Mary Ann Heiss
Allen L. Lefko

Thomas R. McGee, Jr.
John P. McMeel
Larry L. McMullen
James B. Nutter, Jr.
Carol P. Powell
Page Branton Reed
Beth K. Smith
Elizabeth T. Solberg
Charles S. Sosland
James W. Symington
Maurice A. Watson

ADDRESS INQUIRIES TO:
Grants Administrator
(See address above.)

THE HARRY S. TRUMAN SCHOLARSHIP FOUNDATION [2145]

712 Jackson Place, N.W.
Washington, DC 20006-4901
(202) 395-4831
Fax: (202) 395-6995

E-MAIL ADDRESS:
office@truman.gov

WEB SITE ADDRESS:
www.truman.gov

FOUNDED: 1975

AREAS OF INTEREST:
Local, state and national government service.

NAME(S) OF PROGRAMS:
● **Harry S. Truman Scholarship Program**

TYPE:
Awards/prizes. Awards for undergraduate students who demonstrate outstanding leadership potential, plan to pursue careers in government or elsewhere in public service and wish to attend graduate school to help prepare for their careers. At least one Truman Scholar is selected each year from each state, the District of Columbia, Puerto Rico and, considered as a single entity, Guam, the Virgin Islands, American Samoa and the Commonwealth of the Northern Mariana Islands. Scholars may attend graduate schools in the U.S. or in foreign countries.

YEAR PROGRAM STARTED: 1975

PURPOSE:
To develop increased opportunities for young Americans to prepare for and pursue careers in public service, whether it be at the local, county, state or national level, through an educational scholarship program. The Foundation defines public service as employment in government at any level, including uniformed services, public-interest organizations, non-governmental research and/or educational organizations and public-service oriented nonprofit organizations such as those whose primary purposes are to help needy or disadvantaged persons or to protect the environment.

LEGAL BASIS:
Authorized by Congress in 1975; the sole Federal memorial to President Harry S. Truman.

ELIGIBILITY:
To be considered for nomination as a Truman Scholar, a student must be:
(1) a full-time student as a junior at a four-year institution pursuing a Bachelor's degree;
(2) enrolled in a four-year accredited institution of higher education;
(3) committed to a career in government or in public service as defined above;

(4) in the upper quarter of his or her class and;
(5) a U.S. citizen or, in the case of nominees from American Samoa or the Commonwealth of the Northern Mariana Islands, a U.S. national.

FINANCIAL DATA:
The award may only be used for tuition, fees, books, room and board and other specifically approved expenses in graduate school.
Amount of support per award: Up to $30,000.

NUMBER OF APPLICANTS MOST RECENT YEAR:
600.

NUMBER OF AWARDS: 60 for the year 2010.

APPLICATION INFORMATION:
All candidates for scholarships are nominated by their institutions of higher education. The Foundation neither solicits nor accepts direct candidate applications. Each participating institution must appoint a faculty representative to serve as liaison between the institution and the Foundation. The Foundation's nomination and supporting information forms are available from faculty representatives.
Duration: Up to four years.
Deadline: February 17.

THE MORRIS K. UDALL AND STEWART L. UDALL FOUNDATION

130 South Scott Avenue
Tucson, AZ 85701
(520) 342-6566
Fax: (520) 901-8570

E-MAIL ADDRESS:
halpern@udall.gov

WEB SITE ADDRESS:
www.udall.gov

TYPE:
Internships. Congressional Internships: Native American college students work in congressional offices and the White House to gain a firsthand understanding of the federal government. They also take field trips and meet with congressional members, agency heads and cabinet secretaries.

See entry 1125 for full listing.

WOMEN'S RESEARCH AND EDUCATION INSTITUTE (WREI)

714 G Street, S.E.
Suite 200
Washington, DC 20003
(202) 280-2720
Fax: (202) 293-4507

E-MAIL ADDRESS:
wrei@wrei.org

WEB SITE ADDRESS:
www.wrei.org

TYPE:
Fellowships.

See entry 1168 for full listing.

Sociology and anthropology

AMERICAN SOCIOLOGICAL ASSOCIATION
1430 K Street, N.W.
Suite 600
Washington, DC 20005
(202) 383-9005 ext. 321
TDD: (202) 638-0981
Fax: (202) 638-0882

E-MAIL ADDRESS:
minority.affairs@asanet.org

WEB SITE ADDRESS:
www.asanet.org

TYPE:
Fellowships. Predoctoral training fellowships for minority-group members studying sociology.

See entry 1027 for full listing.

L.S.B. LEAKEY FOUNDATION   [2146]
1003B O'Reilly Avenue
San Francisco, CA 94129-1359
(415) 561-4646
Fax: (415) 561-4647

E-MAIL ADDRESS:
grants@leakeyfoundation.org

WEB SITE ADDRESS:
www.leakeyfoundation.org

FOUNDED: 1968

AREAS OF INTEREST:
Human evolution, including research into the environments, archaeology and human paleontology of the Miocene, Pliocene and Pleistocene, into the behavior, morphology and ecology of the great apes and other primate species when it contributes to the development or testing of models of human evolution and into the ecology and adaptations of living hunter-gatherer peoples.

NAME(S) OF PROGRAMS:
• Leakey Foundation Grants

TYPE:
Research grants. The General Research Grants priority is normally given to the exploratory phase of promising new projects that most closely meet the stated purpose of the Foundation.

YEAR PROGRAM STARTED: 1968

PURPOSE:
To conduct research related to human origins.

LEGAL BASIS:
Public foundation 501(c)(3).

ELIGIBILITY:
Grants are made to senior scientists and postdoctoral students with professional qualifications and demonstrated capability in the area of human evolution. Applications from graduate students working for an advanced degree will be considered if supported by their faculty advisor.

FINANCIAL DATA:
Amount of support per award: General Research Grants are awarded up to $13,500 for Ph.D. candidate students (ABD), and up to $22,000 for senior scientists and postdoctoral.
Total amount of support: Approximately $600,000 per year.

NUMBER OF AWARDS: Approximately 40 to 60 per year.

APPLICATION INFORMATION:
Guidelines and application forms are available from the Foundation.

All applications must be for research projects related to understanding human evolution.
Duration: One year. Renewal possible for general research grants.
Deadline: Session One (Fall): July 15, with notification in mid-December. Session Two (Spring): January 5, with notification in May.

PUBLICATIONS:
Application guidelines; newsletter.

IRS IDENTIFICATION NUMBER: 95-2536475

ADDRESS INQUIRIES TO:
Paddy Moore, Grants Officer
E-mail: paddy@leakeyfoundation.org

NATIONAL SCIENCE FOUNDATION   [2147]
4201 Wilson Boulevard
Arlington, VA 22230
(703) 292-7315
Fax: (703) 292-9068

E-MAIL ADDRESS:
dwinslow@nsf.gov

WEB SITE ADDRESS:
www.nsf.gov

FOUNDED: 1950

AREAS OF INTEREST:
Scientific research on the causes and consequences of human social and cultural variability.

NAME(S) OF PROGRAMS:
• Cultural Anthropology Program

TYPE:
Conferences/seminars; Grants-in-aid; Project/program grants; Research grants. The program supports a broad portfolio of research by both senior scholars and by graduate students.

YEAR PROGRAM STARTED: 1952

PURPOSE:
The primary objective of the program is to support basic scientific research on the causes, consequences, and complexities of human social and cultural variability.

LEGAL BASIS:
National Science Foundation Act of 1950.

ELIGIBILITY:
The program does not fund research that takes as its primary goal improved clinical practice or applied policy.

Applicants may be colleges and universities on behalf of their staff members, nonprofit, U.S. nonacademic research institutions, such as independent museums, observatories, research laboratories, stock centers and similar organizations, private profit organizations, in exceptional circumstances, rarely, foreign institutions utilizing U.S. currency, and under special circumstances, unaffiliated U.S. scientists.

FINANCIAL DATA:
Support may cover salaries, research assistantships, staff benefits related directly to purpose, permanent equipment, travel, publication costs, computer costs and certain other direct and indirect costs.

Amount of support per award: $5,000 to $300,000; average $150,000.

Total amount of support: Approximately $8,000,000 for fiscal year 2010.

APPLICATION INFORMATION:
Application must be submitted online at FastLane or Grants.gov.
Duration: 12 to 60 months, depending on the scientific merit and requirements of the project.
Deadline: August 15.

STAFF:
Deborah Winslow, Ph.D., Program Director

ADDRESS INQUIRIES TO:
Deborah Winslow
Program Director
(See address above.)

*PLEASE NOTE:
All proposals must be submitted online at FastLane or Grants.gov.

NATIONAL SCIENCE FOUNDATION   [2148]
Division of Behavioral and Cognitive Sciences
4201 Wilson Boulevard
Arlington, VA 22230
(703) 292-7315
Fax: (703) 292-9068

E-MAIL ADDRESS:
kreed@nsf.gov

WEB SITE ADDRESS:
www.nsf.gov

NAME(S) OF PROGRAMS:
• Physical Anthropology Program

TYPE:
Conferences/seminars; Grants-in-aid; Project/program grants; Research grants. The program supports basic research in areas related to human evolution and contemporary human biological variation. Research areas supported by the program include, but are limited to, human genetic variation, human adaptation, human osteology and bone biology, human and nonhuman primate paleontology, functional anatomy, and primate socioecology.

PURPOSE:
To support research in areas related to human evolution.

ELIGIBILITY:
Colleges and universities on behalf of their staff members, nonprofit, U.S. nonacademic research institutions and private profit organizations.

APPLICATION INFORMATION:
Preparation and submission of NSF application is available online at Grants.gov.
Deadline: July 1 and December 1.

STAFF:
Kaye Reed, Program Director

ADDRESS INQUIRIES TO:
Kaye Reed, Program Director
(See address above.)

*PLEASE NOTE:
All proposals must be submitted online at Grants.gov or FastLane.

NATIONAL SCIENCE FOUNDATION   [2149]
Division of Behavioral and Cognitive Sciences
4201 Wilson Boulevard
Arlington, VA 22230
(703) 292-7315
Fax: (703) 292-9068

E-MAIL ADDRESS:
jyellen@nsf.gov

WEB SITE ADDRESS:
www.nsf.gov

NAME(S) OF PROGRAMS:
- **Archaeology Program**
- **Archaeometry Program**

TYPE:
Conferences/seminars; Grants-in-aid; Project/program grants; Research grants. The programs provide support for anthropologically relevant archaeological research at both a "senior" and doctoral-dissertation level. It also funds anthropologically significant archaeometric research and high-risk exploratory research proposals.

FINANCIAL DATA:
Maximum of $20,000 to meet expenses associated with doctoral dissertation research.

APPLICATION INFORMATION:
Complete details and application form is available online at Grant.gov or FastLane.

Deadline: Archaeology: July 1 and December 1; Archaeometry: October 31.

STAFF:
Dr. John E. Yellen, Program Director
Janine N. Powell, Program Assistant

ADDRESS INQUIRIES TO:
Dr. John E. Yellen, Program Director
(See address above.)

*PLEASE NOTE:
All proposals must be submitted online at Grants.gov or FastLane.

SCHOOL FOR ADVANCED RESEARCH [2150]
P.O. Box 2188
Santa Fe, NM 87504-2188
(505) 954-7201
Fax: (505) 954-7214

E-MAIL ADDRESS:
scholar@sarsf.org
seminar@sarsf.org

WEB SITE ADDRESS:
www.sarweb.org

FOUNDED: 1907

AREAS OF INTEREST:
Anthropology and allied disciplines in the humanities and social sciences.

NAME(S) OF PROGRAMS:
- **Advanced Seminar Program**
- **Resident Scholar Fellowships**

TYPE:
Conferences/seminars; Fellowships; Residencies. Advanced Seminars promote in-depth communication among scholars who are at a critical stage of research on a common topic and whose interaction has the potential to move the discipline of anthropology forward with new insights into human evolution, behavior, culture or society, including critical contemporary issues. Each consists of 10 scholars who meet at SAR's Santa Fe campus for five days of intense discussion. Participants appraise ongoing research, assess recent innovations in theory and methods, and share data relevant to broad problems in anthropology and related disciplines.

Resident Scholar Fellowships are awarded each year to scholars who have completed their research and who need time to prepare manuscripts on topics important to the understanding of humankind.

YEAR PROGRAM STARTED: 1973

PURPOSE:
To support advanced research in anthropology and related disciplines.

LEGAL BASIS:
Private, nonprofit.

ELIGIBILITY:
Resident Scholar Program: Applications are evaluated on the basis of the overall excellence and significance of the proposed project, clarity of presentation and the applicant's academic accomplishments relative to subdiscipline and career stage. The program supports scholars whose work is broad, synthetic and interdisciplinary and promises to yield significant advances in understanding human culture, behavior, evolution or critical contemporary issues. Projects that are narrowly focused geographically and theoretically or that are primarily methodological seldom receive strong consideration. Each year the program supports a mix of scholars with scientific and humanistic orientations. Preference is given to applicants whose research and analysis are complete and who need time to prepare manuscripts. The fellowships are not intended as immediate postdoctoral positions, and dissertation rewrites are not encouraged.

FINANCIAL DATA:
Advanced Seminars: SAR provides round-trip coach airfare within the U.S., lodging and all meals. Overseas airfare for up to two participants may also be offered.

Resident scholars are provided with an office, low-cost housing, a stipend, library assistance and other benefits during a nine-month tenure, from September through the following May. Books written by scholars may be considered for publication by SAR Press.

Amount of support per award: Resident Scholar Program: Maximum stipend of $40,000.

COOPERATIVE FUNDING PROGRAMS: Funding for the Resident Scholar Program is provided by the Weatherhead Foundation, the Katrin H. Lamon Endowment for Native American Art and Education, the Anne Ray Charitable Trust, the Henry Luce Foundation and the National Endowment for the Humanities (NEH).

NUMBER OF APPLICANTS MOST RECENT YEAR: 235.

NUMBER OF AWARDS: Advanced Seminars: 2 to 3 seminars annually (10 per seminar); Resident Scholar Fellowships: Approximately 6 annually.

APPLICATION INFORMATION:
Detailed information is available from SAR Director of Scholar Programs.
Duration: Advanced Seminars: Five days; Resident Scholar Fellowships: Mostly, nine months, September 1 through May 31.
Deadline: Advanced Seminars: April 1. Announcement within three months. Resident Scholar Program: November 1. Announcement in March.

PUBLICATIONS:
Application guidelines.

OFFICERS:
James F. Brooks, President and Chief Executive Officer
Nancy Owen Lewis, Director of Scholar Programs

ADDRESS INQUIRIES TO:
Nancy Owen Lewis
Director of Scholar Programs
(See address above.)

For overnight delivery:
660 Garcia Street
Santa Fe, NM 87505

SCHOOL FOR ADVANCED RESEARCH [2151]
P.O. Box 2188
Santa Fe, NM 87504-2188
(505) 954-7201
Fax: (505) 954-7214

E-MAIL ADDRESS:
staley@sarsf.org

WEB SITE ADDRESS:
www.sarweb.org

FOUNDED: 1907

AREAS OF INTEREST:
Anthropology and related disciplines in the humanities and social sciences.

NAME(S) OF PROGRAMS:
- **J.I. Staley Prize**

TYPE:
Awards/prizes. Prize awarded annually to a living author of a ground-breaking book that exemplifies outstanding scholarship and writing in anthropology. The award recognizes innovative works that add new dimensions to the understanding of the human species.

YEAR PROGRAM STARTED: 1988

PURPOSE:
To acknowledge those innovative works that have gone beyond traditional frontiers and dominant schools of thought in anthropology and given new dimensions to our understanding of the human species; to honor books that cross subdisciplinary boundaries within anthropology and reach out in new and expanded interdisciplinary directions.

LEGAL BASIS:
Private, nonprofit.

ELIGIBILITY:
To be considered, a book must be currently in print and must have been in publication at least two years, but not more than eight years. Co-authored books may be nominated, but edited volumes may not. The nomination must clearly be for a single book. The award is for one outstanding and influential publication, not for an author's lifetime achievement.

Nominated books are evaluated according to the following criteria:
(1) significant contribution to our understanding of humankind;
(2) innovative and rigorous thinking in terms of theory, research methods and/or application of findings;
(3) superior integration of subdisciplinary and/or interdisciplinary perspectives;
(4) exemplary writing and clarity of expression and;
(5) demonstrated or anticipated impact on the field of anthropology.

FINANCIAL DATA:
Amount of support per award: Cash award of $10,000.
Total amount of support: $10,000.

NUMBER OF APPLICANTS MOST RECENT YEAR:
45 for the year 2008.

NUMBER OF AWARDS: 1 annually.

REPRESENTATIVE AWARDS:
2008: Fred R. Myers, "Painting Culture: The Making of an Aboriginal High Art;" 2009: Jonathan Marks, "What It Means To Be 98% Chimpanzee: Apes, People, and Their Genes;" 2010: Sally Engle Merry, "Human Rights and Gender Violence: Translating International Law into Local Justice."

APPLICATION INFORMATION:
Detailed information is available on the web site.
Duration: One-time award.
Deadline: Nominations may be submitted at any time throughout the year. Nominations received by October 1 will be considered for next year's prize.

OFFICERS:
James F. Brooks, President and Chief Executive Officer
Nancy Owen Lewis, Director of Scholar Programs

ADDRESS INQUIRIES TO:
Nancy Owen Lewis
Director of Scholar Programs
(See address above.)

THE AMAURY TALBOT FUND [2152]

Barclays Bank Trust Company Ltd.
Executorship and Trustee Service
P.O. Box 15, Osborne Court
Gadbrook Park, Northwich
Cheshire CW9 7UE England
(01606) 313188
Fax: (01606) 313005; (01606) 313006
TELEX: 667020

FOUNDED: 1948

AREAS OF INTEREST:
Nigeria or West Africa.

NAME(S) OF PROGRAMS:
● **Amaury Talbot Prize for African Anthropology**

TYPE:
Awards/prizes. Prize for a significant book, article or work of anthropological research relating to West Africa.

YEAR PROGRAM STARTED: 1948

PURPOSE:
To recognize and support valuable works dealing with African anthropological research.

LEGAL BASIS:
Created under the terms of the will of Mrs. Miriam Winifred Florence Talbot.

ELIGIBILITY:
Works of anthropological research concerning Africa which were published during a calendar year, to be received no later than January 31 in succeeding year, are eligible for the prize. Although works relating to any region of Africa may be submitted, preference is given first to works focusing on Nigeria, then to those dealing with any other section of West Africa or to publications relating to West Africa in general.

GEOGRAPHIC RESTRICTIONS:
Africa.

FINANCIAL DATA:
The amount of the prize is determined by income from investments and is therefore not constant.
Amount of support per award: Approximately GBP 500 per annum.

NUMBER OF APPLICANTS MOST RECENT YEAR:
10.

APPLICATION INFORMATION:
No official application form is required, but copies of the prospectus are available upon request to the Coordinator at the address below. Entries must be accompanied by two copies of the book, article or work in question. Entries will not be returned.
Deadline: January 31 in the year following publication.

ADDRESS INQUIRIES TO:
Amaury Talbot Prize Coordinator
Royal Anthropological Institute
50 Fitzroy Street
London, England W1P 5HS

WENNER-GREN FOUNDATION FOR ANTHROPOLOGICAL RESEARCH, INC. [2153]

470 Park Avenue South
8th Floor
New York, NY 10016-6819
(212) 683-5000
Fax: (212) 683-9151

E-MAIL ADDRESS:
inquiries@wennergren.org

WEB SITE ADDRESS:
www.wennergren.org

FOUNDED: 1941

AREAS OF INTEREST:
All branches of anthropology, including cultural/social anthropology, ethnology, biological/physical anthropology, archaeology and anthropological linguistics, and closely related disciplines concerned with human origins, development and variation.

NAME(S) OF PROGRAMS:
● **Individual Research Grants**

TYPE:
Awards/prizes; Research grants. The Foundation offers Dissertation Fieldwork Grants, Post-Ph.D. Research Grants, and Hunt Postdoctoral Fellowships. Awards are available for basic research in all branches of anthropology. Grants are made to cover specific expenses or phases of a project. The Foundation particularly invites projects employing comparative perspectives or integrating two or more subfields of anthropology.

The Hunt Postdoctoral Fellowship is awarded to scholars within 10 years of receipt of the Doctorate to aid the write-up of research results for publication.

Predoctoral grants are awarded to individuals to aid doctoral dissertation or thesis research.

Post-Ph.D. Research Grants are awarded to individual scholars holding the Doctorate or equivalent qualification in anthropology or a related discipline.

YEAR PROGRAM STARTED: 1941

PURPOSE:
To support anthropological research.

LEGAL BASIS:
Private operating foundation.

ELIGIBILITY:
Qualified scholars are eligible without regard to nationality or institutional affiliation for Dissertation Fieldwork, Post-Ph.D. Research Grants and Hunt Postdoctoral Fellowships.

Application for Regular Grants may be made by the scholar. Predoctoral grants application must be made jointly with a thesis advisor.

Applicants must be enrolled for a doctoral degree for Dissertation Fieldwork Grants. These grants are contingent upon the applicant's successful completion of all requirements for the degree other than the dissertation/thesis.

Post-Ph.D. Research Grants are for individual scholars holding the Doctorate or equivalent qualification in anthropology or a related discipline.

Hunt Postdoctoral Fellowships are available to all scholars regardless of institutional affiliation and nationality. Applicants must have their Ph.D. in hand to apply and be within 10 years of receipt of their Doctorate.

FINANCIAL DATA:
Individual Research Grants are primarily for basic research. Grants cover research expenses directly related and essential to the project (i.e., travel, living expenses during fieldwork, equipment, supplies, research assistance and other relevant expenditures). Aid is not provided for salary and/or fringe benefits of applicant, tuition, non-project personnel, travel to meetings, institutional overhead or institutional support. Expenses incurred prior to the effective date of an award will not be covered.
Amount of support per award: Dissertation Fieldwork Grants and Post Ph.D. Research Grants: Up to $15,000; May apply for a supplementary award, maximum $5,000. Hunt Fellowship: $40,000.
Total amount of support: Approximately $8,000,000 for the year 2010.

NUMBER OF AWARDS: 125 for the year 2010.

APPLICATION INFORMATION:
Applicants are required to submit a formal application. Application forms must be submitted online through the Foundation's web site beginning three months prior to the application deadline.
Duration: Hunt Postdoctoral Fellowship: Up to one year (12 continuous months of full-time writing). Nonrenewable. Research Grants: Duration of the project.
Deadline: May 1 for funding during first half of the year. November 1 for projects scheduled to begin July or later. Announcement within six to eight months.

PUBLICATIONS:
Program announcement.

IRS IDENTIFICATION NUMBER: 13-1813827

OFFICERS:
Seth Masters, Chairman of the Board
Dr. Leslie Aiello, President

TRUSTEES:
Dr. Leslie Aiello
David Alexander
Beverly Chase
William L. Cobb, Jr.
Joan Girgus
John Immerwahr
Ruth H. Kennedy
Seth Masters
Ellen Mickiewicz

David Patterson
William B. Peterson
Lorraine Sciarra
Deborah Wadsworth

WENNER-GREN FOUNDATION FOR ANTHROPOLOGICAL RESEARCH, INC. [2154]

470 Park Avenue South, 8th Floor
New York, NY 10016-6819
(212) 683-5000
Fax: (212) 683-9151

E-MAIL ADDRESS:
internationalprograms@wennergren.org

WEB SITE ADDRESS:
www.wennergren.org

FOUNDED: 1941

AREAS OF INTEREST:
All branches of anthropology, including cultural/social anthropology, ethnology, biological/physical anthropology, archaeology and anthropological linguistics, and closely related disciplines concerned with human origins, development and variation.

NAME(S) OF PROGRAMS:
● **Wadsworth International Fellowships**

TYPE:
Fellowships; Scholarships; Training grants. Wadsworth International Fellowship is for scholars and advanced students from developing countries who need to leave their country in order to obtain advanced training in anthropology and its related subdisciplines. The proposed course of study must enhance their skills or expand their area of expertise.

The program offers a Predoctoral Fellowship for study leading to a Ph.D.

YEAR PROGRAM STARTED: 1980

PURPOSE:
To support anthropological research.

LEGAL BASIS:
Private operating foundation.

ELIGIBILITY:
Applicants must be scholars/students from developing countries. Applicants may pursue either a course of studies leading to a degree or a specific non-degree plan for obtaining advanced training in any qualified institution in the world where appropriate training is available. Applicants must be prepared to demonstrate the unavailability of such training in their home country, their provisional acceptance by a host institution that will provide such training, and their intention to return and work in their home country upon completion of their training.

The applicant must have a Home Sponsor who is a member of the institution with which he or she is affiliated in the home country and a Host Sponsor who is a member of the institution in which the candidate plans to pursue training. The Host Sponsor must be willing to assume responsibility for overseeing the candidate's training.

FINANCIAL DATA:
Fellowships may be used to cover travel, living expenses, tuition, student fees, insurance, books and any other relevant categories of expenditure. Aid is not provided for salary and/or fringe benefits of applicant, family expenses or institutional overhead.
Amount of support per award: Up to $17,500 per year.

Total amount of support: Varies.
Matching fund requirements: Because the fellowship is intended as a partnership with the host institution in providing the fellow's training, it is expected that candidates will also be offered support by the institution.

NUMBER OF AWARDS: Approximately 5 per year.

APPLICATION INFORMATION:
The Foundation operates an online application submission procedure. Application forms and guidelines for completing these forms are available three months before each application deadline. Two printed copies of the application materials must also be mailed to the Foundation. Applications and supporting materials must be in English. The application asks for the following categories of information:
(1) general information about the applicant, the home institution and sponsor, and the host institution and sponsor;
(2) answers to three questions about the proposed plan of study, research interests, and professional goals and plans;
(3) a detailed budget;
(4) copies of official transcripts from the home institution (provide a translation if they are not in English);
(5) where applicable, the applicant must provide evidence of competency in the language of the country in which he/she will be pursuing training;
(6) curriculum vitae of the applicant and host sponsor and;
(7) the applicant should request letters from both the home sponsor and the host sponsor, to be sent directly to the Foundation. These letters must clearly identify the applicant by their full legal name. Applications cannot be processed unless both letters of recommendation are received by the application deadline.
Duration: Renewable up to three years.
Deadline: March 1.

PUBLICATIONS:
Program announcement.

IRS IDENTIFICATION NUMBER: 13-1813827

OFFICERS:
Seth Masters, Chairman of the Board
Dr. Leslie Aiello, President

ADDRESS INQUIRIES TO:
International Program Office
(See address and e-mail above.)

WENNER-GREN FOUNDATION FOR ANTHROPOLOGICAL RESEARCH, INC. [2155]

470 Park Avenue South, 8th Floor North
New York, NY 10016-6819
(212) 683-5000
Fax: (212) 683-9151

E-MAIL ADDRESS:
inquiries@wennergren.org

WEB SITE ADDRESS:
www.wennergren.org

FOUNDED: 1941

AREAS OF INTEREST:
All branches of anthropology, including cultural/social anthropology, ethnology, biological/physical anthropology, archaeology, anthropological linguistics, and closely related disciplines concerned with human origins, development and variation.

NAME(S) OF PROGRAMS:
● **Conference Grants**

TYPE:
Conferences/seminars. Workshops.

PURPOSE:
To support anthropological research.

LEGAL BASIS:
Private operating foundation.

ELIGIBILITY:
The Foundation provides conference support in two forms. Conference and workshop grants are made to the organizer(s). Priority is given to public conferences sponsored by international scholarly organizations (e.g., the IUAES and EASA) that serve as their annual or periodic meetings and to working conferences that address broad research issues in anthropology and provide for intensive interaction among participants. Symposia and panels within larger professional meetings, lectures, and public events are not normally supported. However, organizers of international congresses or professional meetings may apply for grants specifically to aid the participation of scholars from the developing world.

The Foundation also sponsors and directly administers a limited number of conferences each year under the Wenner-Gren Symposium Program. These symposia are intended for topics of broad significance for anthropology. They are planned jointly by the organizer and the president and follow a specific format developed by the Foundation.

Requests by individuals to support their own travel to meetings are not accepted.

FINANCIAL DATA:
The Foundation pays all costs related to the symposium and actively manages it, including sending out invitations and making travel arrangements.
Amount of support per award: Up to $15,000.
Total amount of support: Varies.

NUMBER OF APPLICANTS MOST RECENT YEAR: 49.

NUMBER OF AWARDS: 10 to 20.

APPLICATION INFORMATION:
All suggestions for Wenner-Gren Symposia should be sent in the form of a letter to the Foundation's president. Anthropologists who wish to propose a symposium to the Foundation should take note of the following guidelines:
(1) Proposals for symposia should be received by the Foundation no less than two years before the proposed date for the symposium;
(2) Symposia must aim to make major theoretical or methodological interventions in current issues within anthropology, broadly construed;
(3) Symposia must also advance the Foundation's goal of fostering an international community of anthropologists by drawing participants from around the world;
(4) The Foundation prefers two organizers for the symposium, ideally from two different countries;
(5) The objectives of the symposium should be to coalesce and advance knowledge on the issue, to present and address divergent viewpoints, and to mark out directions for future research;
(6) Symposia should show the relevance of

basic research in anthropology to analyzing the human condition, past and/or present and; (7) Organizers choose the location from a list of suggested sites provided by the Foundation.

Duration: Length of particular conference.

Deadline: June 1 and December 1.

PUBLICATIONS:
Program announcement.

IRS IDENTIFICATION NUMBER: 13-1813827

OFFICERS:
Seth Masters, Chairman
Dr. Leslie Aiello, President

ADDRESS INQUIRIES TO:
Laurie Obbink
Conference Program Associate
(See address above.)

*PLEASE NOTE:
Grants currently approved to 2013. New grants will be approved for later dates.

WENNER-GREN FOUNDATION FOR ANTHROPOLOGICAL RESEARCH, INC. [2156]
470 Park Avenue South, 8th Floor
New York, NY 10016-6819
(212) 683-5000
Fax: (212) 683-9151

E-MAIL ADDRESS:
inquiries@wennergren.org

WEB SITE ADDRESS:
www.wennergren.org

AREAS OF INTEREST:
All branches of anthropology, including cultural/social anthropology, ethnology, biological/physical anthropology, archaeology and anthropological linguistics, and closely related disciplines concerned with human origins, development and variation.

NAME(S) OF PROGRAMS:
● **International Collaborative Research Grants**

TYPE:
Research grants. Projects normally should include one principal investigator from outside North America, Western Europe and Australia.

Grants are awarded to cover expenses of a specific research project. Applications are evaluated by two main criteria: the quality of

the proposed research, and the potential benefits of the collaboration for international anthropology.

PURPOSE:
To encourage collaborations in which the principal investigators bring different and complementary perspectives, knowledge and/or skills.

ELIGIBILITY:
Individual scholars who hold the Doctorate or equivalent qualification in anthropology or a related discipline. The projects should contribute to anthropology as a discipline and provide new perspectives. Priority is given to new collaborations which create new partnerships between researchers.

FINANCIAL DATA:
Grants cover research expenses directly related and essential to the project (i.e., travel, living expenses during fieldwork, equipment, supplies, research assistance, expenses of communication between the investigators, and other relevant expenditures). Aid is not provided for salary and/or fringe benefits of applicants, tuition, non-project personnel, institutional overhead, or institutional support.

Amount of support per award: $35,000.

Total amount of support: Varies.

NUMBER OF AWARDS: 6.

APPLICATION INFORMATION:
Applications are available on the web site.

Deadline: June 1 and December 1.

OFFICERS:
Seth Masters, Chairman
Dr. Leslie Aiello, President

ADDRESS INQUIRIES TO:
International Program Office
E-mail:
internationalprograms@wennergren.org

*SPECIAL STIPULATIONS:
Application forms must be downloaded from the Foundation web site.

WHATCOM MUSEUM [2157]
121 Prospect Street
Bellingham, WA 98225
(360) 778-8968
Fax: (360) 778-8931

E-MAIL ADDRESS:
jgrant@cob.org

WEB SITE ADDRESS:
www.whatcommuseum.org

FOUNDED: 1973

AREAS OF INTEREST:
Linguistics.

NAME(S) OF PROGRAMS:
● **Jacobs Research Funds Small Grants Program**

TYPE:
Research grants. Grants are given for work on problems in language, social organization, political organization, religion, mythology, music and other arts, psychology and folk science.

YEAR PROGRAM STARTED: 1973

PURPOSE:
To support anthropological and linguistics research on the indigenous peoples of Canada, mainland U.S. and Mexico, with a focus on the Pacific Northwest.

ELIGIBILITY:
Formal academic credentials are not required. Applicants who are inexperienced in research should arrange for the collaboration or supervision of an appropriate and experienced research scholar.

GEOGRAPHIC RESTRICTIONS:
Canada, Mexico, United States and Pacific Northwest.

FINANCIAL DATA:
Amount of support per award: Individuals: $3,000; Group Grant: $6,000; Kinkade Grant: $9,000.

NUMBER OF APPLICANTS MOST RECENT YEAR: 35.

NUMBER OF AWARDS: 20.

APPLICATION INFORMATION:
Two letters in support of the applicant and the project are required. Applications are also accepted online.

Duration: One year. Must reapply for renewal.

Deadline: February 15 (postmark).

ADDRESS INQUIRIES TO:
Amy Geise, Museum Representative
(See address above.)

PHYSICAL SCIENCES

Physical sciences (general)

AMERICAN CHEMICAL SOCIETY [2158]
1155 16th Street, N.W.
Washington, DC 20036
(202) 872-4481
(800) 227-5558
Fax: (202) 872-6319

E-MAIL ADDRESS:
prfinfo@acs.org

WEB SITE ADDRESS:
www.acsprf.org

FOUNDED: 1944

AREAS OF INTEREST:
Fundamental research in chemistry, engineering and earth sciences which may impact the petroleum field.

NAME(S) OF PROGRAMS:
- **The Petroleum Research Fund**

TYPE:
Grants-in-aid; Research grants. Grants-in-aid in support of advanced scientific education and fundamental research projects in the petroleum field. The project may be in any field of pure science which may afford a basis for subsequent research directly connected with the petroleum field.

YEAR PROGRAM STARTED: 1944

PURPOSE:
To support advanced scientific education and fundamental research in the petroleum field.

LEGAL BASIS:
Private trust established in 1944 with contributions of seven petroleum companies.

ELIGIBILITY:
Grants are made to nonprofit scientific or educational institutions, such as universities, on behalf of projects of their regularly appointed faculty.

FINANCIAL DATA:
Amount of support per award: Up to $50,000 per year, depending upon the grant program.
Total amount of support: $22,800,000 for the year 2009.
Matching fund requirements: Varies.

APPLICATION INFORMATION:
Duration: Up to two years.
Deadline: Five months prior to each scheduled meeting held in February, May, and October.

PUBLICATIONS:
Annual report.

ADDRESS INQUIRIES TO:
Ronald Siatkowski, Director
(See address above.)

AMERICAN INDIAN SCIENCE AND ENGINEERING SOCIETY (AISES)
P.O. Box 9828
Albuquerque, NM 87119-9828
(505) 765-1052

E-MAIL ADDRESS:
info@aises.org

WEB SITE ADDRESS:
www.aises.org/Programs/ScholarshipsandInternships/Scholarships

TYPE:
Scholarships.
See entry 1102 for full listing.

AMERICAN SOCIETY FOR MASS SPECTROMETRY [2159]
2019 Galisteo Street
Building I-1
Santa Fe, NM 87505
(505) 989-4517
Fax: (505) 989-1073

E-MAIL ADDRESS:
office@asms.org

WEB SITE ADDRESS:
www.asms.org

FOUNDED: 1969

AREAS OF INTEREST:
Mass spectrometry.

NAME(S) OF PROGRAMS:
- **ASMS Research Awards in Mass Spectrometry**

TYPE:
Project/program grants; Research grants.

YEAR PROGRAM STARTED: 1988

PURPOSE:
To promote academic research in mass spectrometry by young scientists.

LEGAL BASIS:
Nonprofit corporation.

ELIGIBILITY:
Grant applicants must be academic scientists within four years of joining the tenure track or research faculty of a North American university for research in mass spectrometry.

Applicants can be from any country, but must be on the faculty of a North American university when the award is made.

GEOGRAPHIC RESTRICTIONS:
North America.

FINANCIAL DATA:
Grants are made to the university in the name of the selected individual.
Amount of support per award: $25,000.
Total amount of support: $50,000 annually.

NUMBER OF APPLICANTS MOST RECENT YEAR: 15.

NUMBER OF AWARDS: 2.

APPLICATION INFORMATION:
Applicants should submit seven collated sets including a curriculum vitae, list of current research support, three-page proposal, one-page fiscal proposal and justification, and two letters of recommendation. Proposals are ranked primarily on scientific merit and secondarily on effectiveness of proposed use of funds.
Duration: Varies.
Deadline: November 30.

IRS IDENTIFICATION NUMBER: 23-7050068

ADDRESS INQUIRIES TO:
Judith A. Sjoberg, Executive Director
Research Awards
(See address above.)

AMERICAN SOCIETY OF NAVAL ENGINEERS (ASNE)
1452 Duke Street
Alexandria, VA 22314-3458
(703) 836-6727
Fax: (703) 836-7491

E-MAIL ADDRESS:
mobrien@navalengineers.org

WEB SITE ADDRESS:
www.navalengineers.org

TYPE:
Scholarships. Stipend for tuition, fees and expenses to follow a full-time or co-op program of study that applies to naval engineering, such as naval architecture, marine engineering, ocean engineering, mechanical engineering, structural engineering, electrical engineering, electronic engineering and the physical sciences, as well as other programs leading to careers with civilian and military maritime organizations supporting and developing work and life at sea.

See entry 2819 for full listing.

ASPRS - THE IMAGING AND GEOSPATIAL INFORMATION SOCIETY [2160]
5410 Grosvenor Lane
Suite 210
Bethesda, MD 20814-2160
(301) 493-0290 ext. 101
Fax: (301) 493-0208

E-MAIL ADDRESS:
scholarships@asprs.org

WEB SITE ADDRESS:
www.asprs.org

FOUNDED: 1934

AREAS OF INTEREST:
Geospatial sciences, photogrammetry, remote sensing, geographic information systems (GIS) and supporting technologies.

NAME(S) OF PROGRAMS:
- **Robert E. Altenhofen Memorial Scholarship**
- **ERDAS Internship**
- **William A. Fischer Memorial Scholarship**
- **GeoEye Award**
- **Ta Liang Memorial Award**
- **Paul R. Wolf Memorial Scholarship**
- **Z/I Imaging Award**

TYPE:
Awards/prizes; Internships; Scholarships; Travel grants. Robert E. Altenhofen Memorial Scholarship is for undergraduate or graduate study in photogrammetry.

ERDAS Internship is an eight-week internship for graduate students in photogrammetry and remote sensing at the ERDAS facilities in Atlanta or elsewhere. The internship stipend includes an allowance for travel and living expenses.

William A. Fischer Memorial Scholarship is open to students pursuing graduate-level studies in remote sensing at an accredited institution.

GeoEye Award is open to full-time undergraduate or graduate students at an accredited college or university in the U.S. or Canada with image processing facilities appropriate for conducting the proposed work.

Ta Liang Memorial Award is awarded to a graduate student in remote sensing to be used for research-related travel.

The Paul R. Wolf Memorial Scholarship is designed for prospective teachers in the general area of surveying, mapping or photogrammetry.

Z/I Imaging Award is for a student who is currently pursuing graduate-level studies or who plans to enroll for graduate studies in a recognized college or university in the U.S. or elsewhere.

YEAR PROGRAM STARTED: 1960

PURPOSE:
To advance knowledge and improve understanding of mapping sciences; to promote the responsible applications of photogrammetry, remote sensing, geographic information systems (GIS) and supporting technologies.

LEGAL BASIS:
501(c)(3) organization.

ELIGIBILITY:
Applicant must be enrolled in an accredited college or university and in some cases be a member of ASPRS.

GEOGRAPHIC RESTRICTIONS:
Some awards are for students in United States universities only.

FINANCIAL DATA:
Amount of support per award: Robert E. Altenhofen Memorial Scholarship, William A. Fischer Memorial Scholarship and Z/I Imaging Award: $2,000; ERDAS Internship: $2,500, plus expenses; GeoEye Awards: Potential value of up to $20,000; Ta Liang Memorial Award: $1,500; Paul R. Wolf Memorial Scholarship: $3,000.

COOPERATIVE FUNDING PROGRAMS: All awards are offered through the ASPRS Foundation.

NUMBER OF APPLICANTS MOST RECENT YEAR: 161 for the year 2010.

NUMBER OF AWARDS: At least one of each.

APPLICATION INFORMATION:
Applications for ASPRS scholarships and awards must be made on the ASPRS online application form.
Duration: One year.
Deadline: Approximately December 1.

PUBLICATIONS:
ASPRS Foundation Awards & Scholarships booklet.

STAFF:
James R. Plasker, Executive Director
Jesse Winch, Scholarship Administrator

ADDRESS INQUIRIES TO:
Awards and Scholarships
(See street or e-mail address above.)

ASPRS - THE IMAGING AND GEOSPATIAL INFORMATION SOCIETY   [2161]

5410 Grosvenor Lane
Suite 210
Bethesda, MD 20814-2160
(301) 493-0290 ext. 101
Fax: (301) 493-0208

E-MAIL ADDRESS:
scholarships@asprs.org

WEB SITE ADDRESS:
www.asprs.org

FOUNDED: 1934

AREAS OF INTEREST:
Geospatial sciences, photogrammetry, remote sensing, geographic information systems (GIS) and supporting technologies.

NAME(S) OF PROGRAMS:
● **The Abraham Anson Memorial Scholarship**
● **BAE Systems Award**
● **The John O. Behrens Institute for Land Information (ILI) Memorial Scholarship**
● **Robert N. Colwell Memorial Fellowship**
● **Francis H. Moffitt Memorial Scholarship**
● **The Kenneth J. Osborn Memorial Scholarship**

TYPE:
Fellowships; Scholarships; Travel grants. The Abraham Anson Memorial Scholarship is designed to encourage undergraduate students who have an exceptional interest in pursuing scientific research or education in geospatial science or technology related to photogrammetry, remote sensing, surveying and mapping, to enter a professional field where they can use the knowledge of their discipline to excel in their profession.

BAE Systems Award is limited to papers describing civil (nonmilitary) applications of photogrammetry or remote sensing.

The John O. Behrens Institute for Land Information (ILI) Memorial Scholarship is an undergraduate award established by the Institute for Land Information as a tribute to the many contributions of Mr. Behrens to the field of geographic and land-related information and technology.

Robert N. Colwell Memorial Fellowship is made to a graduate student (Master's or Ph.D. level) currently enrolled or intending to enroll in a college or university in the U.S. or Canada, or a recently graduated (within three years of graduation) postdoctoral researcher, who is pursuing a program of study aimed at starting a professional career where expertise is required in remote sensing or other related geospatial information technologies.

Francis H. Moffitt Memorial Scholarship is for students currently enrolled or intending to enroll in a college or university in the U.S. or Canada, who are pursuing a program of study in surveying or photogrammetry leading to a career in the geospatial mapping profession.

Kenneth J. Osborn Memorial Scholarship is made to an undergraduate student currently enrolled or intending to enroll in a college or university in the U.S., who is pursuing a program of study in preparation for entering the profession in the general area of surveying, mapping, photogrammetry or geospatial information and technology.

PURPOSE:
To advance knowledge and improve understanding of mapping sciences; to promote the responsible applications of photogrammetry, remote sensing, geographic information systems (GIS) and supporting technologies.

LEGAL BASIS:
501(c)(3) organization.

ELIGIBILITY:
Applicant must be enrolled in an accredited college or university and be a member of ASPRS.

FINANCIAL DATA:
Amount of support per award: Anson Memorial Scholarship and Behrens Memorial Scholarship: $1,000; BAE Systems Award and Kenneth J. Osborn Memorial Scholarship: $2,000; Robert N. Colwell Memorial Fellowship: $5,000; Francis H. Moffitt Memorial Scholarship: $3,000.

COOPERATIVE FUNDING PROGRAMS: All awards are offered through the ASPRS Foundation.

NUMBER OF APPLICANTS MOST RECENT YEAR: 100.

NUMBER OF AWARDS: 1 for each award.

APPLICATION INFORMATION:
Applications for ASPRS scholarships and awards must be made on the ASPRS application form. Electronic submissions of all applications are encouraged.
Duration: One year.
Deadline: December 3.

PUBLICATIONS:
ASPRS Awards and Scholarships booklet (including application form).

STAFF:
James R. Plasker, Executive Director

ADDRESS INQUIRIES TO:
Awards and Scholarships
(See address above.)

BUILDING AND FIRE RESEARCH LABORATORY   [2162]

National Institute of Standards and Technology
100 Bureau Drive, Stop 8600
Gaithersburg, MD 20899-8600
(301) 975-6850
Fax: (301) 975-4032

WEB SITE ADDRESS:
www.bfrl.nist.
gov/866/grants/extramuralprogram.htm

FOUNDED: 1974

AREAS OF INTEREST:
Exploratory fire research, furnishing flammability, fire performance and validation, smoke hazard calculation, fire growth and extinction, compartment fire models and fire safety performance.

NAME(S) OF PROGRAMS:
● **Fire Research Grants Program**

TYPE:
Research grants. The program includes the following: Fire Model and Application, Large Fire Research, Advanced Fire Measurement, Materials Fire Research, and Fire Sensing Equipment.

YEAR PROGRAM STARTED: 1981

PURPOSE:
To conduct research in the areas of fire analysis and prediction, fire metrology, fire fighting technology, integrated performance assessment, and materials and products.

LEGAL BASIS:
Public Law 93-498; Section 18.

ELIGIBILITY:
Institutions of higher education, hospitals, nonprofit organizations, commercial organizations, state, local, and Indian tribal governments, foreign governments, organizations under the jurisdiction of foreign governments, and international organizations are eligible. Joint programs with participation by more than one eligible entity are possible.

GEOGRAPHIC RESTRICTIONS:
United States.

FINANCIAL DATA:
Amount of support per award: Average $10,000 to $100,000 per award.

NUMBER OF APPLICANTS MOST RECENT YEAR:
30.

NUMBER OF AWARDS: 12 for the year 2010.

APPLICATION INFORMATION:
Duration: One year. Renewals possible.
Deadline: As listed in *Federal Register* notice.

COOPERATIVE INSTITUTE FOR RESEARCH IN ENVIRONMENTAL SCIENCES (CIRES)

CIRES Building, Room 318
University of Colorado
Boulder, CO 80309-0216
(303) 492-1143
Fax: (303) 492-1149

E-MAIL ADDRESS:
info@cires.colorado.edu
dempsey@cires.colorado.edu

WEB SITE ADDRESS:
cires.colorado.edu/collaboration/fellowships

TYPE:
Fellowships. The program provides opportunities for interactions between CIRES scientists and visiting fellows to pursue common research interests. CIRES research includes theoretical studies, laboratory experimentation, and field investigations which may affect the enhancement of air and water quality and prediction of weather climate fluctuations.

See entry 2314 for full listing.

INTERNATIONAL UNION FOR VACUUM SCIENCE, TECHNIQUE AND APPLICATIONS (IUVSTA) [2163]

84 Oldfield Drive, Vicars Cross
Chester CH3 5LW England
44 1244 342675
Fax: 44 700 596 3675

E-MAIL ADDRESS:
iuvsta.secretary.general@ronreid.me.uk

WEB SITE ADDRESS:
www.iuvsta.org

FOUNDED: 1958

AREAS OF INTEREST:
Scientific and technological fields of study or applications using vacuum.

NAME(S) OF PROGRAMS:
• **M.W. Welch International Scholarship**

TYPE:
Scholarships. Support for a scholar for one year working in a research laboratory abroad.

YEAR PROGRAM STARTED: 1968

PURPOSE:
To support younger scientists working abroad in vacuum science and technology.

LEGAL BASIS:
Scientific association.

ELIGIBILITY:
Applicants must make arrangements for the proposed research program with a laboratory

of their choice. The laboratory must be outside the applicant's native country. Strong preference will be given to applicants who propose to study in a foreign lab in which they have not yet studied. The research must be on a topic of vacuum science, technique or application. It is expected that the successful applicant will be encouraged to publish most of the results in scientific and technical journals. Candidates for the scholarship should have at least a Bachelor's degree; a doctoral degree is preferred.

FINANCIAL DATA:
Award does not automatically include travel expenses. In principle, the successful applicant makes his or her own arrangements.
Amount of support per award: Approximately $15,000 (U.S.).
Total amount of support: Approximately $15,000 (U.S.).

NUMBER OF APPLICANTS MOST RECENT YEAR:
14.

NUMBER OF AWARDS: 1 annually.

APPLICATION INFORMATION:
Application information is available online, or contact Dr. F.R. Shepherd, Administrator
3 Grierson Lane
Ottawa, ON K2W 1A6
Canada
E-mail: frank_shepherd@avs.org.
Duration: One year. Nonrenewable.
Deadline: April 15.

PUBLICATIONS:
Application guidelines.

ADDRESS INQUIRIES TO:
Dr. R.J. Reid, Secretary General
(See address above.)

*SPECIAL STIPULATIONS:
Applicants must submit a form outlining the research program and signed by the supervisor in the laboratory where the research is to be carried out to indicate the agreement of the laboratory and the proposed supervisor to the proposed studies.

JILA [2164]

440 UCB
University of Colorado at Boulder
Boulder, CO 80309-0440
(303) 492-7789
Fax: (303) 492-5235

E-MAIL ADDRESS:
jilavf@jilau1.colorado.edu

WEB SITE ADDRESS:
jila.colorado.edu

FOUNDED: 1962

AREAS OF INTEREST:
Atomic and molecular physics, chemical physics, laser physics, astrophysics, precision measurements, geophysical measurement and other closely related areas.

NAME(S) OF PROGRAMS:
• **Postdoctoral Research Associateships**
• **Visiting Fellowships**

TYPE:
Assistantships; Fellowships. Visiting Fellowships support research and study for experienced scientists. Postdoctoral Research Associateships provide advanced research experience in the years immediately after the Ph.D. degree.

YEAR PROGRAM STARTED: 1963

PURPOSE:
To further scientific exchange.

LEGAL BASIS:
Jointly sponsored by the University of Colorado at Boulder and the National Institute of Standards and Technology.

ELIGIBILITY:
Visiting Fellowships are available to scientists with extensive research experience beyond the doctoral degree, although younger persons with significant scientific achievements are also encouraged to apply. Awards are based on the fields of scientific interest and the scholarly achievements or promise of the applicants. There are no restrictions as to citizenship.

Postdoctoral Research Associateships are awarded on the basis of the applicants' scholarly qualifications, promise as research scientists, and research interests and experience in relation to those specific ongoing research programs for which financial support is available. There are no restrictions as to citizenship except as may be imposed by conditions of individual contracts. Ph.D. required.

FINANCIAL DATA:
Visiting Fellowships include round-trip transportation costs for the recipients.

Postdoctoral Research Associateships include a salary, plus transportation for the appointee and his or her spouse and minor children, a small allowance for shipment of personal effects and an allowance for appropriate professional travel within the U.S. during the period of the appointment.
Amount of support per award: Visiting Fellowships: $4,000 stipend per month for longer-term visitors; Postdoctoral Research Associateships: Salaries $35,000 to $49,000.

NUMBER OF APPLICANTS MOST RECENT YEAR:
Varies.

NUMBER OF AWARDS: Varies.

APPLICATION INFORMATION:
Duration: Postdoctoral Research Associateships: One year. Renewal possible for a second year.
Deadline: Visiting Fellowships, November 1. Postdoctoral Research Associateships, appointments are offered throughout the year, with many appointments commencing in September. Applicants should apply early in the year.

ADDRESS INQUIRIES TO:
Kim Monteleone, Coordinator
Visiting Scientists Program
(See address above.)

LINK FOUNDATION [2165]

c/o Binghamton University Foundation
P.O. Box 6005
Binghamton, NY 13902-6005
(607) 777-2210
Fax: (607) 777-2533

WEB SITE ADDRESS:
www.linkfoundation.org

FOUNDED: 1953

AREAS OF INTEREST:
Energy, oceanographic, aerospace simulation research and fellowships.

NAME(S) OF PROGRAMS:
• **Energy Fellowship Program**
• **Oceanography Engineering Fellowship Program**
• **Simulation Fellowship Program**

TYPE:
Development grants; Fellowships; Internships; Research grants. Grants for research, development and training related to the mastery of air, sea and energy resources.

YEAR PROGRAM STARTED: 1954

PURPOSE:
To promote the general welfare through the advancement of scientific, technological and general educational projects.

ELIGIBILITY:
Nonprofit educational institutions and organizations with appropriate interests are eligible to apply. Grants are not awarded directly to individuals.

FINANCIAL DATA:
Amount of support per award: $3,700 to $25,000.

APPLICATION INFORMATION:
Information on applying for fellowships may be obtained from the administrators for the individual programs. Proof of an organization's tax-exempt status must accompany the application if not listed in the publication Cumulative List of Organizations described in Section 170(c) of the Internal Revenue Code.

The following documents must be submitted in the order indicated or they will not be accepted:
(1) cover sheet specific to the individual program;
(2) 500-word description of the project that places the research in the context of current activities in the field;
(3) two letters of recommendation, as specified for the individual program;
(4) two additional letters of reference (professional or educational);
(5) project objectives, timeline and projected budget (projected budget only for Energy Program) and;
(6) current resume.
Duration: Subject to annual review.
Deadline: January.

TRUSTEES:
Dr. Thomas F. Kelly, Chairman
Douglas R. Johnson, Treasurer
Jimmie Anne Haisley, Special Advisor/Secretary
Andrew Clark
Jon Forbes
Lee Lynd

ADDRESS INQUIRIES TO:
Dr. Thomas F. Kelly, Chairman
(See address above.)

NATIONAL RESEARCH COUNCIL OF THE NATIONAL ACADEMIES   [2166]

Research Associateship Programs
500 Fifth Street, N.W. (Keck 568)
Washington, DC 20001
(202) 334-2760
Fax: (202) 334-2759

E-MAIL ADDRESS:
rap@nas.edu

WEB SITE ADDRESS:
www.national-academies.org/rap

AREAS OF INTEREST:
All fields in science and engineering.

NAME(S) OF PROGRAMS:
● **National Research Council Graduate, Postdoctoral and Senior Research Associateship Programs**

TYPE:
Fellowships. Research awards. For research-in-residence at U.S. federal laboratories and affiliated institutions.

YEAR PROGRAM STARTED: 1954

PURPOSE:
To provide research opportunities for qualified personnel.

LEGAL BASIS:
Not-for-profit agency.

ELIGIBILITY:
Citizens of the U.S. and foreign nationals may apply. Must have or expect to receive Ph.D., Sc.D. or other earned equivalent research Doctorate. Program also available for graduate-level applicants.

Awards are tenable only at participating U.S. federal laboratories and affiliated institutions.

FINANCIAL DATA:
Research Associateship awards include stipend, support for relocation and professional travel and health insurance.
Amount of support per award: Annual stipend for recent Ph.D. recipients: $42,000 to $75,000; stipend is higher for additional experience. Annual entry-level stipend for graduate awards: $30,000; stipend is higher for additional experience.
Total amount of support: Varies.

NUMBER OF APPLICANTS MOST RECENT YEAR:
800.

NUMBER OF AWARDS: 250.

APPLICATION INFORMATION:
Duration: One to three years.
Deadline: February 1, May 1, August 1 and November 1.

STAFF:
Dr. H. Ray Gamble, Director of Fellowships and Associateships

ADDRESS INQUIRIES TO:
Research Associateship Programs
(See address above.)

NATIONAL SCIENCE FOUNDATION   [2167]

Division of Atmospheric and Geospace Sciences
4201 Wilson Boulevard, Room 775S
Arlington, VA 22230
(703) 292-8520
Fax: (703) 292-9022

WEB SITE ADDRESS:
www.geo.nsf.gov

FOUNDED: 1950

AREAS OF INTEREST:
The Atmospheric Sciences program supports research to add new understanding of the behavior of the Earth's atmosphere and its interactions with the Sun. Included are studies of the physics, chemistry and dynamics of the Earth's upper and lower atmosphere and its space environment, research on climate processes and variations and studies to understand the natural global cycles of gases and particles in the Earth's atmosphere.

NSF also provides support to operate the National Center for Atmospheric Research (NCAR), the Upper Atmospheric Facilities (UAF) and the Lower Atmospheric Facilities (LAF).

TYPE:
Conferences/seminars; Research grants. Basic research support provided under the programs listed below.

In the area of aeronomy, the Foundation supports research that studies the upper and middle atmosphere phenomena of ionization, recombination, chemical reaction, photoemission and transport, the transport of energy, momentum and mass in the mesosphere-thermosphere-ionosphere system (includes the processes involved and the coupling of this global system to the stratosphere below and magnetosphere above), and the plasma physics of phenomena manifested in the upper atmosphere-ionosphere system, including magnetospheric coupling efforts.

In the area of atmospheric chemistry, the Foundation supports research that studies the measurement and modeling of concentration and distribution of gases and aerosols in the lower and middle atmosphere, chemical reactions among atmospheric species, sources and sinks of important trace gases and aerosols, aqueous phase atmospheric chemistry, transport of gases and aerosols throughout the atmosphere and improved methods for measuring the concentrations of trace species and their fluxes into and out of the atmosphere.

In the area of climate dynamics, the Foundation supports research on processes that govern climate and the causes of climate variability and change, methods to predict climate variations and assess their impact on human activities, assembly and analysis of both paleoclimatic and modern climatic data, and development and use of climate models to diagnose and simulate climate and its variations.

In the area of large-scale dynamic meteorology, the Foundation supports basic research to improve the understanding and prediction of atmospheric motion on synoptic to planetary scales. Research topics include the general circulation, synoptic scale weather phenomena, atmospheric predictability and improved parameterization of physical processes and numerical methods for use in large-scale models.

In the area of magnetospheric physics, the Foundation supports research into the magnetized plasma envelope of the outer atmosphere. It is concerned with energization by the solar wind, the origin of geomagnetic storms and substorms, the population by solar and ionospheric sources, the origin of electric fields, the coupling between the magnetosphere, ionosphere and atmosphere and waves and instabilities in the natural plasma. Observational programs mainly concern the aurora. Theory programs quite often include numerical simulations/modeling using nonlinear, three-dimensional plasma physics. The analysis of data from all sources, whether ground-based or from spacecraft, is also supported.

In the area of mesoscale dynamic meteorology, the Foundation supports research on all aspects of mesoscale meteorological phenomena. Sponsored research includes studies of morphological, thermodynamic and kinematic structure of mesoscale systems, development of mesoscale systems and precipitation processes and energy transfer between scales.

In the area of paleoclimate data, the Foundation supports the retrieval, analysis and interpretation of high-quality paleoclimate data sets and the development of numerical models of the Earth's paleoclimate system. Research is designed to establish the history of the Earth's climate and to understand the processes that govern natural climate variability.

In the area of physical meteorology, the Foundation supports basic research devoted to the physics of the atmosphere with special emphasis on cloud physics, atmospheric electricity, radiation, boundary layer and turbulence and the initiation, growth and propagation of gravity waves. The program also sponsors the development of new techniques and devices for atmospheric measurements.

In the area of solar terrestrial, the Foundation supports research into processes by which energy in diverse forms is generated by the Sun, transported to Earth and ultimately deposited in the terrestrial environment. Major topics include helioseismology, the solar dynamo, the 11-year variation, magnetic flux emergence, solar flares and activity, coronal mass ejections, solar wind heating, interactions with cosmic rays and solar wind/magnetosphere boundary problems. Atmospheric topics include photochemistry/solar UV changes, solar constant changes and climatic impacts, C14 and Sun/climate connections, solar activity/climate variability and Sun/weather variations on various time scales.

YEAR PROGRAM STARTED: 1962

PURPOSE:
To continue to build a base of fundamental knowledge of the atmospheres of the Earth and other planets and of the Sun.

LEGAL BASIS:
Government agency.

ELIGIBILITY:
Proposals may be submitted by academic institutions, nonacademic and nonprofit research organizations, profitmaking and private research organizations and individuals. Occasionally, NSF sponsors efforts by other government agencies, particularly for field programs.

GEOGRAPHIC RESTRICTIONS:
United States and its territories. Some international awards given.

FINANCIAL DATA:
Amount of support per award: Varies.
Total amount of support: Varies.

APPLICATION INFORMATION:
Duration: Varies.
Deadline: Varies.

PUBLICATIONS:
NSF Guide to Programs.

ADDRESS INQUIRIES TO:
Tracy L. Rozell, Program Support Manager
(See address above.)

OAK RIDGE INSTITUTE FOR SCIENCE AND EDUCATION [2168]

Science and Engineering Education
P.O. Box 117, MS 36
Oak Ridge, TN 37831-0117
(865) 574-7798
(865) 576-3000
Fax: (865) 576-1609

E-MAIL ADDRESS:
ruth.keller@orau.org

WEB SITE ADDRESS:
orise.orau.gov/index.htm

FOUNDED: 1946

AREAS OF INTEREST:
Education and research in areas related to energy, health and the environment.

NAME(S) OF PROGRAMS:
- **Faculty Research Participation Program**
- **Postdoctoral Fellowship**
- **Postgraduate Fellowship**

TYPE:
Fellowships; Internships; Research grants; Scholarships; Visiting scholars. Opportunities for faculty participation in research and development projects at major installations of the Department of Energy and other federal agencies to work with the scientific personnel and utilize specialized equipment at these installations in the areas of computer sciences, engineering, environmental and life sciences, mathematics/statistics, medical and health sciences and physical and earth sciences.

YEAR PROGRAM STARTED: 1946

PURPOSE:
To enable college and university faculty members to participate in advanced, mission-oriented research at DOE and other participating research and development facilities; to provide the opportunity to gain experience and knowledge that can be incorporated into the curriculum at the participant's college or university.

LEGAL BASIS:
Federally funded research and development center. University consortium.

ELIGIBILITY:
Applicants must be full-time permanent faculty members at accredited colleges or universities and must be U.S. citizens or permanent resident aliens. Eligibility may also be affected by past participation depending on the research center applied for.

GEOGRAPHIC RESTRICTIONS:
United States.

FINANCIAL DATA:
Faculty members are paid a monthly stipend commensurate with their academic salaries. Participants with sabbatical leave appointments are expected to have at least one-half of their salary and one-half benefits paid by their home institution. Cost of travel for one round-trip between home or academic institution and assigned faculty members will be reimbursed if the distance is greater than 60 miles one way.
Total amount of support: $1,000,000 for the year 2010.
Matching fund requirements: 50% matching funds on sabbatical leaves.

NUMBER OF APPLICANTS MOST RECENT YEAR:
50 for the year 2010.

APPLICATION INFORMATION:
Duration: Appointments are generally for 10 to 12 weeks (normally during the summer) and a maximum of 12 months.

DIRECTORS:
Andy Page, Director of ORAU

ADDRESS INQUIRIES TO:
Ruth Keller, Project Manager
Faculty Research Participation Program
(See address above.)

OAK RIDGE INSTITUTE FOR SCIENCE AND EDUCATION

P.O. Box 117
Oak Ridge, TN 37831-0117
(865) 574-7798
Fax: (865) 576-1609

E-MAIL ADDRESS:
ruth.keller@orau.org
science.education@orau.org

WEB SITE ADDRESS:
orise.orau.gov/sep/catalog.htm
see.orau.org

TYPE:
Internships. Full- and part-time appointments are available for a period of three to 12 months. Assignments afford students the opportunity to apply and practice theories and methods learned in the classroom. Program participants are assigned individual projects that relate to their academic majors, career goals, and the ongoing research and development missions of the facility. They make recommendations or reports regarding their findings or solutions to a staff member of the facility who provides guidance and advice, serves as their research advisor, and reviews their findings.

See entry 2826 for full listing.

RESEARCH CORPORATION FOR SCIENCE ADVANCEMENT [2169]

4703 East Camp Lowell Drive
Suite 201
Tucson, AZ 85712-1281
(520) 571-1111
Fax: (520) 571-1119

E-MAIL ADDRESS:
awards@rescorp.org

WEB SITE ADDRESS:
www.rescorp.org

FOUNDED: 1912

AREAS OF INTEREST:
University research and education in physics, chemistry and astronomy.

NAME(S) OF PROGRAMS:
- **Cottrell Scholar Awards**
- **Multi-Investigator Cottrell College Science Awards**
- **Scialog: Solar Energy Conversion**
- **Single Investigator Cottrell College Science Awards**

TYPE:
Awards/prizes. Cottrell Scholar Awards recognize beginning faculty members who excel at teaching and research.

Multi-Investigator Cottrell College Science Awards fund cross-disciplinary teams of early career scientists in primarily undergraduate institutions to initiate a new program in collaborative research.

Scialog: Solar Energy Conversion funds transformative research in solar energy conversion at colleges and universities.

Single Investigator Cottrell College Science Awards help early career faculty in primarily undergraduate institutions start a program of research.

PURPOSE:
To promote excellence in both research and teaching in science departments granting Ph.Ds.

LEGAL BASIS:
Operating foundation.

ELIGIBILITY:
Cottrell Scholar Awards: Applicants must be tenure-track assistant professors in a Ph.D.-granting department of astronomy, chemistry or physics who are in, or who will begin, their third academic year during the calendar year of application.

Multi-Investigator Cottrell College Science Awards: Science faculty in primarily undergraduate institutions.

Scialog: Solar Energy Conversion: Faculty in U.S. colleges and universities.

Single Investigator Cottrell College Science Awards: Faculty in the first three years of first tenure-track appointment in a primarily undergraduate institution.

The Corporation does not make awards to individuals or businesses. Proposals are only accepted from U.S. academic institutions.

GEOGRAPHIC RESTRICTIONS:
United States.

FINANCIAL DATA:
Grant awards can be used at discretion of awardee for most direct costs.
Amount of support per award: Cottrell Scholar Awards: $75,000; Multi-Investigator Cottrell College Science Awards: $75,000; Scialog: Solar Energy Conversion: $100,000 to $250,000; Single Investigator Cottrell College Science Awards: $35,000.
Matching fund requirements: Multi-Investigator Cottrell College Science Awards: $25,000. Single Investigator Cottrell College Science Awards: 20%.

APPLICATION INFORMATION:
Duration: Two years with a possible one-year no-cost extension.
Deadline: Cottrell College Science Awards: Preliminary proposal due September 15, with target date of November 15 for completed application. Cottrell Scholar Awards: August 1 for proposals.

PUBLICATIONS:
Annual report; newsletter; occasional publications and guidelines.

IRS IDENTIFICATION NUMBER: 13-1963407

OFFICERS:
James M. Gentile, Ph.D., President
Martha Gilliland, Ph.D., Vice President

BOARD OF DIRECTORS:
Patricia C. Barron
G. Scott Clemons
Peter K. Dorhout
Robert B. Hallock
Robert Holland, Jr.
Brent Iverson
Gayle P.W. Jackson
Suzanne D. Jaffe
Seth Lederman
Patrick S. Osmer

ADDRESS INQUIRIES TO:
Science Advancement Program
(See address above.)

*SPECIAL STIPULATIONS:
Applicants must be in the third calendar year of their first tenure-track position, and provide both research and teaching proposals for peer review.

ALFRED P. SLOAN FOUNDATION [2170]
630 Fifth Avenue
Suite 2550
New York, NY 10111-0242
(212) 649-1649
Fax: (212) 757-5117

E-MAIL ADDRESS:
stella@sloan.org

WEB SITE ADDRESS:
www.sloan.org

FOUNDED: 1934

AREAS OF INTEREST:
Science, technology, mathematics, computer science, economics and ocean sciences.

NAME(S) OF PROGRAMS:
● **Sloan Research Fellowships**

TYPE:
Fellowships. Research fellowships are awarded to young scholars in chemistry, computational and evolutionary molecular biology, computer science, economics, mathematics, neuroscience, physics, and ocean sciences. The Fellow need not pursue a specified research project and is free to change the direction of his or her research at any time.

YEAR PROGRAM STARTED: 1955

PURPOSE:
To identify and support promising young scientists at an early stage.

LEGAL BASIS:
Private foundation.

ELIGIBILITY:
Candidates are required to hold a Ph.D. (or equivalent) in chemistry, physics, mathematics, computer science, economics, computational and evolutionary molecular biology, neuroscience, or ocean sciences, and must be members of the regular faculty of a U.S. or Canadian college or university. They may be no more than six years from completion of the most recent Ph.D. or equivalent as of the year of their nomination, unless special circumstances are involved such as military service, a change of field, child rearing or for less than two years they have held a faculty appointment.

FINANCIAL DATA:
Each fellowship is administered by the Fellow's institution and is designed to allow the greatest possible freedom and flexibility in its use. The award may be used for equipment, technical assistance, professional travel, or any other activity directly related to the Fellow's research.
Amount of support per award: $50,000 over a two-year term.
Total amount of support: $5,310,000.

NUMBER OF APPLICANTS MOST RECENT YEAR:
700.

NUMBER OF AWARDS: 118 fellowships: 23 for physics, 23 for chemistry, 20 for mathematics, 16 for neuroscience, 16 for computer science, 8 for economics, and 12 for computational and evolutionary molecular biology.

APPLICATION INFORMATION:
Candidates may not apply directly, but must be nominated by a department head or other senior scholar. The nominator should submit a letter describing the candidate's qualifications and must see that the Foundation receives three supporting letters

directly from other scholars, preferably not at the same institution. A curriculum vitae, a list of scientific publications plus one copy of no more than two representative publications, and a one-page statement by the nominee describing his or her significant scientific work and immediate research plans should accompany the nomination form and letter. Strong evidence in submitted publications and supporting letters of the nominee's independent creativity is one of the most important considerations in the review process.
Duration: Two years. One two-year extension is permitted on request.
Deadline: Selections are made in February. Nominations must be received no later than September 15 for awards to begin the following September.

PUBLICATIONS:
Brochure; annual report.

ADMINISTRATIVE OFFICERS AND STAFF:
Paul L. Jaskow, President
Leisle Lin, Financial Vice President and Secretary
Christopher T. Sia, Controller
Erica Stella, Fellowship Administrator

SOCIETY FOR THE STUDY OF AMPHIBIANS AND REPTILES [2171]
Department of Environmental Studies and Biology
Elon University, Campus Box 2015
Elon, NC 27244
(336) 278-6229

E-MAIL ADDRESS:
jkapfer@elon.edu

WEB SITE ADDRESS:
www.ssarherps.org/pages/GIH.php

AREAS OF INTEREST:
Herpetology.

NAME(S) OF PROGRAMS:
● **Grants in Herpetology**

TYPE:
Awards/prizes; Research grants. Awards are given in six categories: Conservation of Amphibians and/or Reptiles, Field Research, Laboratory Research, Herpetological Education, Travel and International Research.

PURPOSE:
To advance research, conservation, and education concerning amphibians and reptiles; to provide financial support for deserving individuals or organizations involved in herpetological research, education, or conservation.

ELIGIBILITY:
Applicants must be students and members of the SSAR with the exception of those applying for support of regional herpetological society projects.

FINANCIAL DATA:
Amount of support per award: $500.
Total amount of support: $3,000.

NUMBER OF AWARDS: 6.

APPLICATION INFORMATION:
Applicants may only apply for one category and must designate to which of the six their proposal is submitted. Each proposal must include the following:
(1) title page;

(2) background and objects of the proposed project;
(3) methods of carrying out the project;
(4) complete project budget;
(5) brief resume or curriculum vitae of the applicant or project coordinator and;
(6) letter of support.

Deadline: December 15.

ADDRESS INQUIRIES TO:
Dr. Joshua M. Kapfer, Chairperson
(See address above.)

TUSKEGEE UNIVERSITY [2172]

1200 West Montgomery Road
Tuskegee, AL 36088
(334) 727-8375
Fax: (334) 724-4224

E-MAIL ADDRESS:
bufford@tuskegee.edu

WEB SITE ADDRESS:
www.tuskegee.edu

FOUNDED: 1881

AREAS OF INTEREST:
Postgraduate education in the sciences.

NAME(S) OF PROGRAMS:
● **Ph.D. Program in Material Science and Engineering**

TYPE:
Fellowships.

YEAR PROGRAM STARTED: 1944

PURPOSE:
To enable students who might otherwise be unable to pursue a Master's degree at Tuskegee University.

LEGAL BASIS:
University.

ELIGIBILITY:
Applicants must be U.S. citizens.

FINANCIAL DATA:
Amount of support per award: $54,000 per year ($36,000 stipend plus tuition and other fees up to $18,000).

NUMBER OF AWARDS: Varies.

APPLICATION INFORMATION:
Application form is available online.
Duration: Three to five years, depending upon student's performance.

ADDRESS INQUIRIES TO:
Lisa McMullin, Manager, Research and Sponsored Programs
(See address above.)

WILLIAM P. WHARTON TRUST [2173]

c/o Choate, Hall & Stewart
2 International Place
Boston, MA 02110
(617) 248-5000
Fax: (617) 248-4000

E-MAIL ADDRESS:
williamwhartontrust@choate.com

WEB SITE ADDRESS:
williamwharton.org

AREAS OF INTEREST:
Conservation and nature.

TYPE:
Project/program grants.

YEAR PROGRAM STARTED: 1976

PURPOSE:
To support projects that directly promote the study, conservation and appreciation of nature.

ELIGIBILITY:
Organizations must be 501(c)(3) tax-exempt. No funding for individuals.

FINANCIAL DATA:
Amount of support per award: $2,500 to $10,000.
Total amount of support: Approximately $200,000 annually.

NUMBER OF AWARDS: Approximately 30.

APPLICATION INFORMATION:
Applicants must provide proof of IRS 501(c)(3) tax-exempt status.

ADDRESS INQUIRIES TO:
John M. Cornish, Trustee
(See address above.)

Astronomy and aerospace science

AMERICAN ASTRONOMICAL SOCIETY [2174]

2000 Florida Avenue, N.W.
Suite 400
Washington, DC 20009-1231
(202) 328-2010
Fax: (202) 234-2560

E-MAIL ADDRESS:
marvel@aas.org

WEB SITE ADDRESS:
www.aas.org

FOUNDED: 1899

AREAS OF INTEREST:
The advancement of astronomy and closely related branches of science.

NAME(S) OF PROGRAMS:
● **Chrétien International Research Grant**

TYPE:
Research grants. Research grant(s) with preference given to individuals of high promise who are otherwise unfunded.

YEAR PROGRAM STARTED: 1982

PURPOSE:
To further international collaborative projects in observational astronomy, with emphasis on long-term international visits and the development of close working relationship with astronomers in other countries.

LEGAL BASIS:
Nonprofit, scientific corporation.

ELIGIBILITY:
Astronomers with a Ph.D. or equivalent are eligible. Graduate students are not eligible.

Open to astronomers throughout the world. Decisions will be made on the basis of quality of research, importance of the proposed research to international astronomy, the ability of the applicant to carry out the research and reasonableness of the budget estimates. Preference will be given to individuals of high promise who are otherwise unfunded. Innovative technical approaches including the development and use of new optics, new devices and new techniques will count heavily in the applicant's favor. The awards will normally

not be given to supplement a major research project which is funded elsewhere. Letters of reference will be given high weight.

FINANCIAL DATA:
Amount of support per award: Up to $20,000.
Total amount of support: $20,000 each year.

NUMBER OF APPLICANTS MOST RECENT YEAR:
20.

APPLICATION INFORMATION:
Applications should include:
(1) a description of the research project (less than three pages in length), including an assessment of its importance to that particular subfield of astronomy and a statement enumerating all the aspects of international collaboration;
(2) a statement of the candidate's ability to do the proposed research, with special emphasis on international collaboration and foreign visits which have been arranged, including facilities available and observing time allocations, if any;
(3) the proposed budget, with brief justification for the amount requested;
(4) a description of other financial resources available;
(5) the candidate's curriculum vitae and bibliography of recent papers;
(6) two letters of reference from astronomers who know the candidate's work and;
(7) any special circumstances which might help in the decision process.
Duration: One year.
Deadline: Application due April 1. Announcement the following September.

ADDRESS INQUIRIES TO:
Chrétien International Research Grant Committee
(See address above.)

AMERICAN ASTRONOMICAL SOCIETY [2175]

2000 Florida Avenue, N.W.
Suite 400
Washington, DC 20009-1231
(202) 328-2010
Fax: (202) 234-2560

E-MAIL ADDRESS:
marvel@aas.org

WEB SITE ADDRESS:
www.aas.org/grants/awards.html

FOUNDED: 1899

AREAS OF INTEREST:
Astronomy and closely related branches of science.

NAME(S) OF PROGRAMS:
● **Newton Lacy Pierce Prize in Astronomy**

TYPE:
Awards/prizes. Given to recognize outstanding achievement during the five years preceding the award in observational astronomical research based on measurements of radiation from an astronomical object. A monetary prize and certificate are awarded annually.

YEAR PROGRAM STARTED: 1974

LEGAL BASIS:
Nonprofit, scientific corporation.

ELIGIBILITY:
Applicants must be residents of North America (including Hawaii or Puerto Rico)

or a member of a North American institution stationed abroad. Applicants should also be under 36 years of age.

FINANCIAL DATA:
Award may include certificate, honorarium and/or citation.
Amount of support per award: $1,500.
Total amount of support: $1,500.

NUMBER OF AWARDS: 1.

APPLICATION INFORMATION:
Contact the Society regarding application materials and requirements.
Deadline: Contact Society for specific dates.

PUBLICATIONS:
Program announcement.

ADDRESS INQUIRIES TO:
Dr. G. Fritz Benedict
American Astronomical Society
University of Texas-Austin
McDonald Observatory
Austin, TX 78712-1083

ASTRONOMICAL SOCIETY OF THE PACIFIC [2176]
390 Ashton Avenue
San Francisco, CA 94112
(415) 337-1100
Fax: (415) 337-5205

E-MAIL ADDRESS:
jmanning@astrosociety.org

WEB SITE ADDRESS:
www.astrosociety.org

FOUNDED: 1889

AREAS OF INTEREST:
Astronomy and science education.

NAME(S) OF PROGRAMS:
● **Muhlmann Award**

TYPE:
Awards/prizes.

YEAR PROGRAM STARTED: 1995

PURPOSE:
To improve significant observational research, possibly through advances in astronomical instrumentation, software or support infrastructure.

ELIGIBILITY:
Award is available to individuals. Applicants do not have to be U.S. citizens or residents.

FINANCIAL DATA:
Amount of support per award: $500 and plaque.
Total amount of support: $500 each year.

APPLICATION INFORMATION:
Sponsors should submit a two-page nomination giving strong support to the choice.
Duration: One year.
Deadline: January 15.

ADDRESS INQUIRIES TO:
James G. Manning
(See address above.)

ASTRONOMICAL SOCIETY OF THE PACIFIC [2177]
390 Ashton Avenue
San Francisco, CA 94112
(415) 337-1100
Fax: (415) 337-5205

E-MAIL ADDRESS:
jmanning@astrosociety.org

WEB SITE ADDRESS:
www.astrosociety.org

AREAS OF INTEREST:
Astronomy.

NAME(S) OF PROGRAMS:
● **Robert J. Trumpler Award for an Outstanding Ph.D. Thesis**

TYPE:
Awards/prizes.

PURPOSE:
To honor a recent recipient of the Ph.D. degree in North America whose research is considered unusually important to astronomy.

ELIGIBILITY:
Nominee's Ph.D. must have been awarded within two years of the time of the nomination and most or all of the thesis must have been published in a recognized journal with an issue date prior to January 1, 2012.

FINANCIAL DATA:
Award includes travel reimbursement and hotel accommodation to annual meeting.
Amount of support per award: $500 and plaque.

APPLICATION INFORMATION:
Nominations are solicited from chairpersons of astronomy and physics departments in North America. The department chairman should submit an electronic letter of nomination supporting the selection and discussing the extent of independence exhibited by the nominee in the choice and execution of the thesis research. Electronic copies of the published articles must accompany the nomination. Only one nomination will be accepted from each institution per year. Only under exceptional conditions will two submissions be accepted.
Deadline: January 1. Announcement in spring.

ADDRESS INQUIRIES TO:
James G. Manning
(See address above.)

ASTRONOMICAL SOCIETY OF THE PACIFIC [2178]
390 Ashton Avenue
San Francisco, CA 94112
(415) 337-1100
Fax: (415) 337-5205

E-MAIL ADDRESS:
jmanning@astrosociety.org

WEB SITE ADDRESS:
www.astrosociety.org

AREAS OF INTEREST:
Astronomy.

NAME(S) OF PROGRAMS:
● **Klumpke-Roberts Award**

TYPE:
Awards/prizes.

PURPOSE:
To recognize outstanding contributions to the public understanding and appreciation of astronomy.

ELIGIBILITY:
There are no restrictions on nominations for this award. The contributions may be in the form of popular books and articles; lectures; radio, TV or movie productions; or service to public education in astronomy of any other nature.

FINANCIAL DATA:
Amount of support per award: $500 and plaque.

NUMBER OF APPLICANTS MOST RECENT YEAR: 12.

NUMBER OF AWARDS: 1.

APPLICATION INFORMATION:
Nominations only. Self-nominations are not accepted.
Deadline: December 15.

ADDRESS INQUIRIES TO:
James G. Manning
(See e-mail address above.)

ASTRONOMICAL SOCIETY OF THE PACIFIC [2179]
390 Ashton Avenue
San Francisco, CA 94112
(415) 337-1100
Fax: (415) 337-5205

E-MAIL ADDRESS:
jmanning@astrosociety.org

WEB SITE ADDRESS:
www.astrosociety.org

AREAS OF INTEREST:
Astronomy.

NAME(S) OF PROGRAMS:
● **Thomas Brennan Award for Outstanding Contributions to the Teaching of Astronomy in Grades 9-12**

TYPE:
Awards/prizes.

PURPOSE:
To recognize exceptional achievement related to the teaching of astronomy at the high school level.

ELIGIBILITY:
Nominees must reside in North America.

GEOGRAPHIC RESTRICTIONS:
North America.

FINANCIAL DATA:
Amount of support per award: $500 and plaque.

NUMBER OF APPLICANTS MOST RECENT YEAR: 8.

NUMBER OF AWARDS: 1.

APPLICATION INFORMATION:
Nominations must be made on the Brennan Award form, available on the web site. Neither self-nominations nor nomination by a family member will be accepted.
Deadline: December 15.

ADDRESS INQUIRIES TO:
James G. Manning
(See e-mail address above.)

ASTRONOMICAL SOCIETY OF THE PACIFIC [2180]
390 Ashton Avenue
San Francisco, CA 94112
(415) 337-1100
Fax: (415) 337-5205

E-MAIL ADDRESS:
jmanning@astrosociety.org

WEB SITE ADDRESS:
www.astrosociety.org

AREAS OF INTEREST:
Astronomy and amateur astronomy.

NAME(S) OF PROGRAMS:
- **Amateur Achievement Award**
- **Las Cumbres Amateur Outreach Award**

TYPE:
Awards/prizes. Amateur Achievement Award recognizes significant observational or technological contributions to astronomy or amateur astronomy.

Las Cumbres Amateur Outreach Award honors outstanding educational outreach by an amateur astronomer to K-12 children and the interested lay public.

PURPOSE:
To award outstanding contribution or educational outreach in the field of astronomy or amateur astronomy.

ELIGIBILITY:
"Amateur" is understood to mean someone who does not receive compensation (other than expenses) for their activity and does not receive the majority of their income from a profession in astronomy.

FINANCIAL DATA:
Amount of support per award: $500 and plaque.

NUMBER OF APPLICANTS MOST RECENT YEAR:
11.

NUMBER OF AWARDS: 1 per award.

APPLICATION INFORMATION:
Nominations are made from the ASP Amateur Advisory Committee and by members of the astronomical community. Self-nominations or nomination by a family member will not be accepted. Letters of support are required.
Deadline: December 15. Announcements in spring.

ADDRESS INQUIRIES TO:
James G. Manning
(See e-mail address above.)

HARVARD-SMITHSONIAN CENTER FOR ASTROPHYSICS [2181]

Mail Stop 67
60 Garden Street
Cambridge, MA 02138
(617) 495-7103
Fax: (617) 496-7589

E-MAIL ADDRESS:
postdoc@cfa.harvard.edu

WEB SITE ADDRESS:
www.cfa.harvard.edu/opportunities/postdocs.html

FOUNDED: 1973

AREAS OF INTEREST:
Astrophysics, including the areas of theory, observation, instrumentation and/or laboratory research. Research programs at the Center are organized into seven divisions including atomic and molecular physics, high energy astrophysics, optical and infrared astronomy, radio and geoastronomy, solar, stellar and planetary sciences, theoretical astrophysics, and science education.

NAME(S) OF PROGRAMS:
- **Postdoctoral Fellowship**

TYPE:
Fellowships. Postdoctoral fellowships for research in the Center's areas of interest.

YEAR PROGRAM STARTED: 1974

ELIGIBILITY:
Open to recent Ph.D. recipients with interests in any of the areas above.

FINANCIAL DATA:
Amount of support per award: Stipends of approximately $63,500; annual research budget of approximately $16,000 per appointee for the year 2011-12.

NUMBER OF APPLICANTS MOST RECENT YEAR:
176.

NUMBER OF AWARDS: 1 for the year 2010.

APPLICATION INFORMATION:
Application forms are available online.
Duration: Two years. Renewal possible for a third year.
Deadline: October 30.

PUBLICATIONS:
Observatory reports issue of the *Bulletin of the American Astronomical Society.*

STAFF:
Charles R. Alcock, Director

LUNAR AND PLANETARY INSTITUTE [2182]

3600 Bay Area Boulevard
Houston, TX 77058-1113
(281) 486-2180
Fax: (281) 486-2127

E-MAIL ADDRESS:
webmaster@lpi.usra.edu

WEB SITE ADDRESS:
www.lpi.usra.edu

FOUNDED: 1968

AREAS OF INTEREST:
Study of lunar exploration, planetary remote sensing and spectroscopy, image processing, planetary geology and surface processes, impact studies, geophysical data analysis and modeling, physics and chemistry of planetary atmospheres, meteorites and sample analysis, interplanetary dust and presolar grains, minerology/petrology and astrobiology.

NAME(S) OF PROGRAMS:
- **Postdoctoral Fellow Programs**
- **Summer Intern Program**
- **Visiting Scientist Program**

TYPE:
Conferences/seminars; Fellowships; Internships; Scholarships; Travel grants; Visiting scholars. Postdoctoral and Visiting Scientist Programs: Several positions are available in planetary science research at the Postdoctoral and Visiting Scientist levels. Applicants may propose to work in any area of the planetary sciences, with preference given to topics that enhance the interactions between the Institute and the Astromaterials Research Group at the NASA Johnson Space Center.

Summer Intern Program: LPI invites undergraduates to experience cutting-edge research in the planetary sciences through this program. Interns complete a research project of current interest in planetary science, working one-on-one with a scientist at the Institute or at Johnson Space Center.

YEAR PROGRAM STARTED: 1969

PURPOSE:
To promote and assist in the analysis and interpretation of lunar and planetary data.

LEGAL BASIS:
Operated by the Universities Space Research Association with a NASA contract.

ELIGIBILITY:
Postdoctoral and Visiting Scientist Programs: Applicants for both types of position should have a Ph.D. in planetary sciences or a geosciences-related field. Visiting Scientist positions are available for scientists with established records of research productivity.

Summer Intern Program: College undergraduates with at least 50 semester-hours of credit who are interested in pursuing a career in the sciences are eligible. Relevant disciplines include the natural sciences, engineering, computer sciences and mathematics. Applicants will be considered for appointment without regard to race, creed, color, sex, national origin, age, handicap status or other nonmerit factors. Selection is based on the following criteria: (1) scholarship, curriculum and experience; (2) career objectives and scientific interest and; (3) match of interest of applicant with available research projects.

FINANCIAL DATA:
Amount of support per award: Summer Intern Program: $3,500 plus housing and up to $1,000 maximum for travel expenses.

APPLICATION INFORMATION:
Postdoctoral and Visiting Scientist Programs: Applicants should send a letter of interest, a curriculum vitae with a list of relevant publications, a brief (three pages maximum) statement of proposed research, and a list of three references. Application materials should be sent to Dr. Stephen Mackwell at the address above.

For the Summer Intern Program, applications must be submitted using the electronic application form found at the Summer Intern Program web site. Paper applications will not be accepted.
Duration: Postdoctoral Program: Initial period of up to two years, with possible extension to a maximum of three years; Summer Intern Program: 10 weeks; Visiting Scientist Program: Generally one to 12 months.
Deadline: Postdoctoral and Visiting Scientist Programs: Applications are considered throughout the year; Summer Intern Program: January 20.

STAFF:
Dr. Stephen Mackwell, Director

ADDRESS INQUIRIES TO:
Dr. Stephen Mackwell, Director
(See address above.)

MCDONNELL CENTER FOR THE SPACE SCIENCES

Washington University, Campus Box 1105
One Brookings Drive
St. Louis, MO 63130-4899
(314) 935-5332
Fax: (314) 935-4134

E-MAIL ADDRESS:
trecia@physics.wustl.edu

WEB SITE ADDRESS:
mcss.wustl.edu

TYPE:
Fellowships. These fellowships are funded by a gift from the McDonnell Douglas Foundation to Washington University and provide tuition remission plus stipend for graduate students interested in pursuing

research in the space sciences who are enrolled in the Washington University Departments of Physics or Earth and Planetary Sciences.

See entry 2787 for full listing.

NATIONAL CENTER FOR ATMOSPHERIC RESEARCH [2183]

High Altitude Observatory
P.O. Box 3000
Boulder, CO 80307-3000
(303) 497-1598
Fax: (303) 497-1589

E-MAIL ADDRESS:
knack@ucar.edu

WEB SITE ADDRESS:
www.hao.ucar.edu/people/visitors/newkirk.php

FOUNDED: 1940

AREAS OF INTEREST:
Solar physics, solar-terrestrial physics and related astrophysics. Specific research interests include coronal and interplanetary physics, solar activity and magnetic fields, the solar interior and terrestrial interactions.

NAME(S) OF PROGRAMS:
● **Newkirk Graduate Research Assistantships**

TYPE:
Assistantships.

PURPOSE:
To promote cooperative research between HAO and academic institutions by providing support for aspiring young scientists at formative stages in their careers.

ELIGIBILITY:
Applicants must be full-time graduate students enrolled in a university program leading to the Ph.D. Students must declare their intention of working on their thesis in cooperation with an HAO staff member and should expect to spend a significant fraction of their time in residence at HAO.

FINANCIAL DATA:
Total amount of support: $42,000.

APPLICATION INFORMATION:
Application includes transcripts of undergraduate and graduate courses, brief statement of goals and three letters of recommendation.
Duration: One-year term with possibility of renewals until completion of the Ph.D. degree.

PUBLICATIONS:
Brochure.

ADDRESS INQUIRIES TO:
Amy Knack
(See address above.)

NATIONAL RADIO ASTRONOMY OBSERVATORY [2184]

520 Edgemont Road
Charlottesville, VA 22903-2475
(434) 296-0221
Fax: (434) 296-0385

E-MAIL ADDRESS:
jutley@nrao.edu

WEB SITE ADDRESS:
www.nrao.edu

FOUNDED: 1957

AREAS OF INTEREST:
Ground-based radio astronomy. Current areas of research include cosmology, theoretical and observational studies of radio sources, the interstellar and intergalactic medium, structure and dynamics of galactic and extragalactic sources, physics of HII regions, stars, solar system objects and astrometry. Research staff is also involved in instrumentation development and image processing.

NAME(S) OF PROGRAMS:
● **Jansky Fellowships at the NRAO**

TYPE:
Fellowships. Research appointments. Postdoctoral appointments with liberal support for research travel, data reduction and publication. Jansky Fellows may or may not be residents at NRAO sites.

YEAR PROGRAM STARTED: 1960

LEGAL BASIS:
Federally funded research organization.

ELIGIBILITY:
Fellows must have received their Ph.D. prior to beginning the appointment. Preference is given to recent Ph.D. recipients.

FINANCIAL DATA:
10% contribution to TIAA/CREF in addition to salary, travel budget and scientific page charge support. Vacation allowance, health insurance, a moving allowance and other benefits available.
Amount of support per award: Annual salary $60,000 for the year 2011.

NUMBER OF APPLICANTS MOST RECENT YEAR: 70.

NUMBER OF AWARDS: 4 for the academic year 2010-11.

APPLICATION INFORMATION:
Application should include a curriculum vitae and a statement of the type of research activity to be undertaken at the NRAO. The applicant should request letters of recommendation from three references. These letters should be sent directly to the NRAO.
Duration: Two years. Possibility of renewal for a third year if mutually agreeable.
Deadline: Fall.

PUBLICATIONS:
Program announcement.

STAFF:
Fred K.Y. Lo, Observatory Director

ADDRESS INQUIRIES TO:
Jessica Utley
Science and Academic Affairs
(See address above.)

NATIONAL SCIENCE FOUNDATION [2185]

Division of Astronomical Sciences
4201 Wilson Boulevard, Room 1045
Arlington, VA 22230
(703) 292-8820
Fax: (703) 292-9034

E-MAIL ADDRESS:
nsharp@nsf.gov

WEB SITE ADDRESS:
www.nsf.gov

FOUNDED: 1950

NAME(S) OF PROGRAMS:
● **Astronomy and Astrophysics Research Grants**

TYPE:
Awards/prizes; Challenge/matching grants; Conferences/seminars; Fellowships; Project/program grants; Research grants; Seed money grants; Travel grants; Research contracts. Broad base of support for fundamental research directed at explaining celestial objects and the cosmos in terms of physical principles.

Basic research support is provided under the following grant programs:

Planetary Astronomy - Objects studied in this program include the planets and their satellites, the asteroids and the comets. Ground-based observations are indispensable to the complete understanding of their structure, composition and origin.

Stellar Astronomy and Astrophysics - This program supports studies of the physical and chemical characteristics of the Sun and other stars, especially as they relate to the stars' past and future evolution. These studies make use of observations at many wavelengths, as well as laboratory measurements and theoretical modeling.

Galactic Astronomy - The topics studied in this program are the spatial and kinematics characteristics of the stars in our galaxy and the properties and distribution of the interstellar medium.

Extragalactic Astronomy and Cosmology - The objective of this program is the description of the nature, structure and evolution of external galaxies and quasars, as well as the implications of these data for the birth, expansion rate and future of the universe.

Advanced Technologies and Instrumentation - This program provides support for development of astronomical equipment at universities. In addition to supporting the acquisition of telescopes and auxiliary instrumentation, this program also supports the reduction of astronomical data by providing funds for minicomputers. Particular emphasis is being placed on the use of advanced technology detectors at radio, infrared and optical wavelengths.

PURPOSE:
To increase man's knowledge of the universe.

LEGAL BASIS:
Government agency.

ELIGIBILITY:
Applicant should be a scientist at a university or college.

GEOGRAPHIC RESTRICTIONS:
United States.

FINANCIAL DATA:
Amount of support per award: Varies.
Total amount of support: $45,000,000 for fiscal year 2010.

APPLICATION INFORMATION:
Application information can be obtained from the address above.
Duration: Varies.
Deadline: November 15 for all Planetary, Stellar, Galactic and Extragalactic.

PUBLICATIONS:
Guide to Programs; Grants for Scientific and Engineering Research.

OFFICERS:
G. Wayne Van Citters, Jr., Chief Advisor
Vernon Pankonin, Program Director
Nigel Sharp, Program Director

ADDRESS INQUIRIES TO:
Nigel Sharp, Grants Coordinator
(See address and e-mail above.)

SMITHSONIAN ASTROPHYSICAL OBSERVATORY [2186]

60 Garden Street
Mail Stop 67
Cambridge, MA 02138
(617) 495-7103
Fax: (617) 496-7589

E-MAIL ADDRESS:
predoc@cfa.harvard.edu

WEB SITE ADDRESS:
www.cfa.harvard.
edu/opportunities/fellowships/predoc

FOUNDED: 1890

AREAS OF INTEREST:
Astrophysical research, including the fields of astronomy, astrophysics and planetary sciences.

NAME(S) OF PROGRAMS:
● **Predoctoral Research Fellowships**

TYPE:
Exchange programs; Fellowships; Internships. Predoctoral fellowships for thesis research. Fellowships are designed to allow students from other institutions throughout the world to do all or part of their thesis research at the Observatory. A wide variety of research projects may be proposed. About 300 scientific staff conduct research in observation, theory and instrumentation, and in nearly all areas related to astronomy.

YEAR PROGRAM STARTED: 1985

ELIGIBILITY:
Applicants must have completed preliminary course work and examinations and be ready to begin dissertation research at the time of the award. They must have the approval of their department head at their home institution to conduct their thesis research at the Observatory. Students from any country are eligible.

FINANCIAL DATA:
Some funds may also be available for relocation, travel and other expenses.
Amount of support per award: $29,352 for the year 2011.

NUMBER OF APPLICANTS MOST RECENT YEAR:
14 for the year 2010.

NUMBER OF AWARDS: 6 for the year 2010.

APPLICATION INFORMATION:
Application forms are available on the web site.
Duration: One year. Renewable up to three years.
Deadline: April 15.

STAFF:
Charles R. Alcock, Director

ADDRESS INQUIRIES TO:
Fellowship Program Coordinator
(See address above.)

*SPECIAL STIPULATIONS:
Applicants must be enrolled in a Ph.D. program in appropriate fields (i.e., astronomy or astrophysics) and have completed all course work and examinations.

SPACE TELESCOPE SCIENCE INSTITUTE [2187]

3700 San Martin Drive
Baltimore, MD 21218
(410) 338-4574
Fax: (410) 338-4976

E-MAIL ADDRESS:
hfinquiry@stsci.edu

WEB SITE ADDRESS:
www.stsci.edu

FOUNDED: 1990

AREAS OF INTEREST:
Astronomy, astrophysics and related disciplines.

NAME(S) OF PROGRAMS:
● **Hubble Fellowship Program**

TYPE:
Fellowships. Provides a limited number of recent postdoctoral scientists of unusual promise and ability with the opportunity to pursue research of their choice at a participating U.S. astronomical institution designated as host institution by the scientist.

YEAR PROGRAM STARTED: 1990

PURPOSE:
To expand and strengthen the research work of the astronomical community.

ELIGIBILITY:
Applicants must have earned a Doctorate degree, three years prior to application, in physics, astronomy or a related discipline. Applicants can be any nationality. Candidates are selected on the basis of their research proposal, publications and academic achievement. No more than one fellow per year is approved for any one academic location.

Fellowships must be held at U.S. institutions.

FINANCIAL DATA:
Amount of support per award: Annual stipend of approximately $60,000, plus $16,000 per year for research expenses.
Total amount of support: Varies.

COOPERATIVE FUNDING PROGRAMS: Funded by the National Aeronautics and Space Administration (NASA).

NUMBER OF APPLICANTS MOST RECENT YEAR:
269 for the year 2011.

NUMBER OF AWARDS: 17.

APPLICATION INFORMATION:
Duration: One year and two annual renewals contingent on satisfactory performance and availability of NASA funds.
Deadline: First week in November.

ADDRESS INQUIRIES TO:
Dr. Ron Allen, Program Director
Hubble Fellowship Program
(See address above.)

ZONTA INTERNATIONAL FOUNDATION [2188]

1211 West 22nd Street, Suite 900
Oak Brook, IL 60523-3384
(630) 928-1400
Fax: (630) 928-1559

E-MAIL ADDRESS:
programs@zonta.org

WEB SITE ADDRESS:
www.zonta.org

FOUNDED: 1919

AREAS OF INTEREST:
Fellowships to women pursuing graduate study in aerospace-related sciences and engineering.

NAME(S) OF PROGRAMS:
● **Amelia Earhart Fellowship**

TYPE:
Fellowships. Awarded annually to women for graduate study in aerospace-related sciences and aerospace-related engineering at any university or college offering accredited graduate courses and degrees.

YEAR PROGRAM STARTED: 1938

PURPOSE:
To encourage and support the study and research of women scientists and engineers throughout the world and to improve the status of women.

LEGAL BASIS:
Incorporated in the state of Illinois as a nonprofit organization.

ELIGIBILITY:
Women of any nationality who must meet the following minimum requirements:
(1) be registered in an accredited Ph.D./doctoral program in a qualifying area of science or engineering closely related to advanced studies in aerospace-related science or aerospace-related engineering; a letter of acceptance or verification of enrollment must be submitted with the application;
(2) demonstrate a superior academic record at a recognized university or college with accredited courses in aerospace-related studies as verified by transcripts and recommendations;
(3) provide evidence of a well-defined research program in aerospace-related science or aerospace-related engineering as described in the application essay, research and publications;
(4) clearly demonstrate the relationship of their research to aerospace and furnish verification of their research program through at least one of the reference letters required with the application (i.e., research supervisor or advisor must be one of the referees) and;
(5) be registered in a Ph.D./Doctorate program by the time the Fellowship is awarded.

The award may be used at any university or college offering accredited graduate courses and degrees in aerospace studies. Awards may be renewed for an additional year by a current Fellow and will undergo the same application and evaluation procedures as first-time applicants. Fellows may accept additional grants and scholarships from other sources.

Defense-related and postdoctoral research programs are not eligible for the Fellowship. Members and employees of Zonta International or the Zonta International Foundation are also not eligible to apply for the Fellowships.

FINANCIAL DATA:
Fellowship awards may be used for tuition, books, fees or living expenses.
Amount of support per award: $10,000 annually.

NUMBER OF AWARDS: 35 per year.

APPLICATION INFORMATION:
Applications can be secured from the web site above. Elements to be included are biographical information, list of schools attended and degrees received, transcripts of

grades and school verification form (on Foundation web site), employment history, plans for intended study, essay on academic and professional goals, and three recommendations from teachers or supervisors. Information other than transcripts and recommendations must be limited to the space provided. Attachments will not be considered.

The application must be completed in English. In addition, international applicants must provide English translations for all non-English documents.

Duration: One academic year. Recipient may reapply.

Deadline: November 15.

AWARDS COMMITTEE:
Sharon Langenbeck, Chairman

ADDRESS INQUIRIES TO:
Ana Ubides, Programs Manager
(See address above.)

Chemistry

AMERICAN CHEMICAL SOCIETY   [2189]
1155 16th Street, N.W.
Washington, DC 20036-4800
(202) 872-6283
Fax: (202) 776-8008

E-MAIL ADDRESS:
awards@acs.org

WEB SITE ADDRESS:
www.acs.org/nationalawards

FOUNDED: 1876

AREAS OF INTEREST:
Chemical.

CONSULTING OR VOLUNTEER SERVICES:
Volunteer services.

NAME(S) OF PROGRAMS:
● **Nakanishi Prize**

TYPE:
Awards/prizes. Award presented in the U.S. in odd years and Japan in even years.

YEAR PROGRAM STARTED: 1995

PURPOSE:
To recognize and stimulate significant work that extends chemical and spectroscopic methods to the study of important biological phenomena.

LEGAL BASIS:
Nonprofit association.

ELIGIBILITY:
Individuals can apply. There are no limits on age or nationality.

FINANCIAL DATA:
Amount of support per award: $3,000 plus travel allowance, medallion with presentation box and certificate.

NUMBER OF APPLICANTS MOST RECENT YEAR:
13.

NUMBER OF AWARDS: 1.

APPLICATION INFORMATION:
Application procedures are available online.
Duration: Nomination renewable.
Deadline: November 1.

ADDRESS INQUIRIES TO:
Office of Awards
(See address above.)

*SPECIAL STIPULATIONS:
Special consideration will be given for work that has contributed broadly on an international scope.

AMERICAN CHEMICAL SOCIETY   [2190]
1155 16th Street, N.W.
Washington, DC 20036-4800
(202) 872-6283
Fax: (202) 776-8008

E-MAIL ADDRESS:
awards@acs.org

WEB SITE ADDRESS:
www.acs.org/awards

FOUNDED: 1876

AREAS OF INTEREST:
Research in industrial and engineering chemistry and chemical engineering principles.

NAME(S) OF PROGRAMS:
● **E.V. Murphree Award in Industrial and Engineering Chemistry**

TYPE:
Awards/prizes.

YEAR PROGRAM STARTED: 1955

PURPOSE:
To stimulate fundamental research in industrial and engineering chemistry, the development of chemical engineering principles and their application to industrial processes.

LEGAL BASIS:
Nonprofit association.

ELIGIBILITY:
Individuals can apply. Nominee must have accomplished outstanding research of theoretical or experimental nature in fields of industrial chemistry or chemical engineering. There are no limits on age or nationality.

FINANCIAL DATA:
Amount of support per award: $5,000, certificate, and up to $1,000 travel expenses.

NUMBER OF APPLICANTS MOST RECENT YEAR:
17.

NUMBER OF AWARDS: 1 for the year 2011.

APPLICATION INFORMATION:
Contact the Society for application procedures.
Duration: One year. Nominations renewable.
Deadline: November 1.

ADDRESS INQUIRIES TO:
Office of Awards
(See address above.)

AMERICAN INSTITUTE OF CHEMICAL ENGINEERS (AICHE)
3 Park Avenue, 19th Floor
New York, NY 10016
(203) 702-7660
Fax: (203) 775-5177

E-MAIL ADDRESS:
awards@aiche.org

WEB SITE ADDRESS:
www.aiche.org

TYPE:
Awards/prizes.

See entry 2802 for full listing.

AMERICAN NUCLEAR SOCIETY (ANS)   [2191]
555 North Kensington Avenue
LaGrange Park, IL 60526
(708) 352-6611
Fax: (708) 352-0499

E-MAIL ADDRESS:
outreach@ans.org

WEB SITE ADDRESS:
www.ans.org

FOUNDED: 1954

AREAS OF INTEREST:
Radioanalytical chemistry or analytical applications of nuclear science.

NAME(S) OF PROGRAMS:
● **James R. Vogt Radiochemistry Scholarship**

TYPE:
Scholarships. Scholarship award to recognize one outstanding undergraduate student or one graduate student pursuing a career in radioanalytical chemistry or analytical applications of nuclear science.

YEAR PROGRAM STARTED: 1987

ELIGIBILITY:
Applicants must have completed a minimum of two years in an accredited undergraduate program and be enrolled in a four-year college or university in the U.S. and must be U.S. citizens or possess a permanent resident visa. Also open to first-year graduate students. Academic accomplishments must be substantiated by transcript. Graduate students must have completed their first year of graduate studies to be eligible. Applicants must be sponsored by an ANS local section, division, student branch, committee, member or organization member.

FINANCIAL DATA:
Scholarship funds may be used by the student to defray any bona fide education costs including tuition, fees, books, room and board.
Amount of support per award:
Undergraduate: $2,000; Graduate: $3,000.

NUMBER OF AWARDS: 1 annually.

APPLICATION INFORMATION:
Nominations are made on a form available from ANS headquarters at the address above. The applicant must check the "Vogt" box on the scholarship form to be considered for this scholarship. Please provide a self-addressed, stamped envelope. In addition, applicant must include year in school, major and the school he or she will be attending. Application is available online.
Duration: One year. Nonrenewable.
Deadline: February 1.

ADDRESS INQUIRIES TO:
Scholarship Coordinator
(See address above.)

AMERICAN OIL CHEMISTS SOCIETY   [2192]
2710 South Boulder Drive
Urbana, IL 61802-6996
(217) 359-2344
Fax: (217) 351-8091

E-MAIL ADDRESS:
awards@aocs.org

WEB SITE ADDRESS:
www.aocs.org

FOUNDED: 1909

AREAS OF INTEREST:
Lipid chemistry, biochemistry, fats, oils and related materials, surfactants and detergents, and personal care products.

NAME(S) OF PROGRAMS:
- **Stephen S. Chang Award**
- **Schroepfer Medal Award**
- **Supelco AOCS Research Award**

TYPE:
Awards/prizes.

YEAR PROGRAM STARTED: 1982

PURPOSE:
To annually recognize scientists, technologists or engineers who have made substantial accomplishments in lipid chemistry, either by one major breakthrough or by an accumulation of publications.

LEGAL BASIS:
Professional society.

ELIGIBILITY:
Nominations are accepted. Preference shall be given to individuals who are actively associated with research and who have made discoveries that have influenced their fields of endeavor.

FINANCIAL DATA:
Amount of support per award: Varies.
Total amount of support: $20,000 for the year 2010.

NUMBER OF APPLICANTS MOST RECENT YEAR:
10.

NUMBER OF AWARDS: Chang Award and Supelco Award: 1 of each annually. Schroepfer Medal: 1 biennially in even-numbered years.

APPLICATION INFORMATION:
Nominations for the Chang Award must include a letter from the nominator describing the nominee's distinguished accomplishments in basic research and how they have been utilized by industry to help improve or develop products related to lipids. The nomination must include at least three letters of recommendation and biographical information, including the curriculum vitae. Nominations for the Supelco Award consist of the same supporting documentation as the Chang Award. Nominations for the Schroepfer Medal should include a 300- to 1,000-word summary describing the significance of the nominee's accomplishments in the steriod field, a current curriculum vitae including a full list of publications, and two supporting letters.
Duration: One-time awards.
Deadline: October 15 for the Chang Award and Schroepfer Medal; November 1 for the Supelco Award.

PUBLICATIONS:
INFORM: International News on Fats, Oils, and Related Materials; *JAOCS: Journal of the American Oil Chemists' Society*; *Lipids*; *Journal of Surfactants and Detergents*.

ADDRESS INQUIRIES TO:
Membership Department
(See address above.)

CANADIAN SOCIETY FOR CHEMICAL TECHNOLOGY [2193]

130 Slater Street
Suite 550
Ottawa ON K1P 6E2 Canada
(613) 232-6252 ext. 223
Fax: (613) 232-5862

E-MAIL ADDRESS:
awards@cheminst.ca

WEB SITE ADDRESS:
www.chem-tech.ca

AREAS OF INTEREST:
Chemistry, biochemistry, chemical engineering technology or chemical technology.

NAME(S) OF PROGRAMS:
- **Norman and Marion Bright Memorial Award**

TYPE:
Awards/prizes.

YEAR PROGRAM STARTED: 1980

PURPOSE:
To reward an individual who has made an outstanding contribution in Canada to the furtherance of chemical technology.

ELIGIBILITY:
The person honored must be either a chemical sciences technologist or a person from outside the field who had made a significant or noteworthy contribution to its advancement.

NUMBER OF AWARDS: 1.

APPLICATION INFORMATION:
Applicants must complete a nomination form.
Deadline: December 1.

ADDRESS INQUIRIES TO:
Gale Thirlwall, Awards Manager
(See address above.)

CANADIAN SOCIETY FOR CHEMISTRY [2194]

130 Slater Street
Suite 550
Ottawa ON K1P 6E2 Canada
(613) 232-6252 ext. 223
Fax: (613) 232-5862

E-MAIL ADDRESS:
awards@cheminst.ca

WEB SITE ADDRESS:
www.chemistry.ca

AREAS OF INTEREST:
Biochemistry, organic and bioorganic chemistry.

NAME(S) OF PROGRAMS:
- **The Alfred Bader Scholarship**
- **Boehringer Ingelheim (Canada) Doctoral Research Award**
- **CCUCC Chemistry Doctoral Award**
- **The Ichikizaki Fund for Young Chemists**

TYPE:
Awards/prizes; Scholarships. The Alfred Bader Scholarship is awarded as a mark of excellence for achievement in organic chemistry or biochemistry by undergraduate students completing their final year of study in an honors program.

Boehringer Ingelheim (Canada) Doctoral Research Award is given to a Canadian citizen or landed immigrant whose Ph.D. thesis is in the field of organic or bioorganic chemistry and is judged to be of outstanding quality.

CCUCC Chemistry Doctoral Award recognizes outstanding achievement and potential in research by a graduate student.

The Ichikizaki Fund for Young Chemists is awarded to provide financial assistance to young chemists who are showing unique achievements in basic research by facilitating their participation in international conferences or symposia.

PURPOSE:
To recognize outstanding contributions by chemists for their research in a wide variety of fields.

ELIGIBILITY:
Nominees for the Bader Scholarship must be members of the CSC and be continuing in a graduate program in chemistry or biochemistry at a Canadian university.

The Boehringer Ingelheim (Canada) Doctoral Research Award shall be awarded to a Canadian citizen or landed immigrant whose Ph.D. thesis is in the field of organic or bioorganic chemistry. They must have been formally accepted by a Canadian university in the 12-month period preceding the nomination deadline and their doctoral research judged to be of outstanding quality.

CCUCC Chemistry Doctoral Award is intended to recognize outstanding achievement and potential in research by a graduate student whose Ph.D. thesis in chemistry was formally accepted by a Canadian university in the 12-month period preceding the nomination deadline of September 15.

To be eligible for the Ichikizaki Fund for Young Chemists, an applicant must be a member of the CSC or the Chemical Society of Japan, not have passed his or her 34th birthday as of December 31st of the year in which the application is submitted, have a research specialty in synthetic organic chemistry and be scheduled to attend, within one year, an international conference or symposium directly related to synthetic organic chemistry.

FINANCIAL DATA:
Amount of support per award: Bader Scholarship: $1,000; Boehringer Ingelheim (Canada) Doctoral Research Award and CCUCC Chemistry Doctoral Award: $2,000; Ichikizaki Fund: Up to $10,000. (Applicants may reapply in subsequent years, in which case the cumulative award total must not exceed $15,000.)
Total amount of support: Varies.

NUMBER OF AWARDS: Bader Scholarship: Maximum 3; Boehringer Ingelheim (Canada) Doctoral Award and CCUCC Chemistry Doctoral Award: 1 of each; Ichikizaki Fund: Varies.

APPLICATION INFORMATION:
Applications for the Alfred Bader Scholarship should include four copies of the following information:
(1) honors research project report;
(2) a statement from the research supervisor describing the student's contribution at the academic and extracurricular levels;
(3) a second letter of reference and;
(4) an official transcript of the student's academic record.

Nominations for the Boehringer Ingelheim (Canada) Doctoral Research Award shall be made in writing through the Awards Manager of the Canadian Society for Chemistry. Nominations shall be accompanied by five copies of:
(1) a curriculum vitae of the nominee;
(2) a synopsis (no longer than 10 double-spaced typewritten pages) of the doctoral thesis and;
(3) two letters from independent experts in the field assessing the significance of the thesis.

Nominations for the CCUCC Chemistry Doctoral Award should include:
(1) letter of support by nominator;
(2) curriculum vitae (using NSERC guidelines);
(3) brief synopsis of doctoral thesis (10 pages double-spaced maximum) and;
(4) copy of the official thesis appraisal.

Applications for the Ichikizaki Fund for Young Chemists should include four copies of the following:
(1) a resume (including date of birth);
(2) copies of recent research papers;
(3) the title and brief description of the conference the applicant wishes to attend;
(4) the title (and abstract, if available) of the research paper the applicant intends to present;
(5) a proposed budget and;
(6) an accompanying letter of reference from the research supervisor (if application is from a graduate student).

Deadline: Bader Scholarship: May 15; Boehringer Ingelheim (Canada) Doctoral Research Award: July 2; CCUCC Chemistry Doctoral Award: September 15; Ichikizaki Fund: December 31.

PUBLICATIONS:
Program announcement.

ADDRESS INQUIRIES TO:
Gale Thirlwall, Awards Manager
(See address above.)

THE CAMILLE AND HENRY DREYFUS FOUNDATION [2195]

555 Madison Avenue, 20th Floor
New York, NY 10022
(212) 753-1760

E-MAIL ADDRESS:
admin@dreyfus.org

WEB SITE ADDRESS:
www.dreyfus.org

FOUNDED: 1946

AREAS OF INTEREST:
Chemical science.

NAME(S) OF PROGRAMS:
● **Jean Dreyfus Boissevain Lectureship for Undergraduate Institutions**
● **Camille Dreyfus Teacher-Scholar Awards Program**
● **Henry Dreyfus Teacher-Scholar Awards Program**
● **Special Grant Program in the Chemical Sciences**

TYPE:
Awards/prizes; Research grants; Scholarships.

PURPOSE:
To advance the science of chemistry, chemical engineering and related sciences as a means of improving human relations and circumstances around the world.

LEGAL BASIS:
Not-for-profit corporation.

ELIGIBILITY:
Awards are made to institutions within the U.S.

The Foundation occasionally may make unsolicited grants at its discretion within its general area of interest.

GEOGRAPHIC RESTRICTIONS:
United States.

FINANCIAL DATA:
Amount of support per award: $20,000 to $75,000 depending on program.

APPLICATION INFORMATION:
Contact the Foundation for application procedures.
Duration: Varies.
Deadline: Varies according to grant.

BOARD OF DIRECTORS AND OFFICERS:
Henry C. Walter, President
Dorothy Dinsmoor, Vice President and Secretary
John R.H. Blum, Treasurer

ADDRESS INQUIRIES TO:
Gerard Brandenstein, Grant Administrator
(See address above.)

THE ELECTROCHEMICAL SOCIETY [2196]

65 South Main Street
Building D
Pennington, NJ 08534-2839
(609) 737-1902
Fax: (609) 737-2743

E-MAIL ADDRESS:
ecs@electrochem.org
colleen.klepser@electrochem.org

WEB SITE ADDRESS:
www.electrochem.org

FOUNDED: 1902

AREAS OF INTEREST:
Industrial electrochemistry.

NAME(S) OF PROGRAMS:
● **Oronzio de Nora Industrial Electrochemistry Fellowship of The Electrochemical Society**

TYPE:
Awards/prizes; Conferences/seminars; Fellowships; Research grants; Travel grants. Awarded to a postdoctoral scientist or engineer for research in the field of industrial electrochemistry.

PURPOSE:
To promote the continuation of research in industrial electrochemistry.

ELIGIBILITY:
Fellow is required to not hold other named fellowships. Nominee's 35th birthday may not precede January 1 of the year in which fellowship is made.

FINANCIAL DATA:
Amount of support per award: $25,000.

APPLICATION INFORMATION:
Online nomination only.
Duration: One year. Fellowship is renewable; must reapply.
Deadline: January 1.

ADDRESS INQUIRIES TO:
E-mail: awards@electrochem.org

GEORGETOWN UNIVERSITY [2197]

Department of Chemistry
Box 571227
Washington, DC 20057-1227
(202) 687-6073
Fax: (202) 687-6209

E-MAIL ADDRESS:
chemad@georgetown.edu

WEB SITE ADDRESS:
chemistry.georgetown.edu

FOUNDED: 1789

AREAS OF INTEREST:
Graduate education in chemistry.

NAME(S) OF PROGRAMS:
● **Doctoral Program in Chemistry**

TYPE:
Assistantships; Awards/prizes; Conferences/seminars; Exchange programs; Fellowships; General operating grants; Professorships; Research grants; Scholarships; Visiting scholars; Work-study programs.

YEAR PROGRAM STARTED: 1924

PURPOSE:
To enable graduate students to earn a Ph.D. degree in chemistry, inorganic, organic, analytical, physical or theoretical chemistry, organometallic, synthetic, or nano-chemistry, biochemistry, or structural crystallography.

LEGAL BASIS:
University.

ELIGIBILITY:
Fellowships are open to nationals of any country and a Bachelor's degree or the equivalent is required.

FINANCIAL DATA:
Amount of support per award: $26,650 plus $1,750 health insurance and $1,623 per credit tuition for the year 2011-12. Maximum $54,205 for the first year; $41,221 for the second year and $33,895 for the remaining years.

NUMBER OF APPLICANTS MOST RECENT YEAR:
95.

NUMBER OF AWARDS: 12 for the year 2009-10; 10 for the year 2010-11.

APPLICATION INFORMATION:
Duration: Nine months to one year. Renewable for as long as student continues good progress toward the degree.
Deadline: Although applications will be accepted at any time, priority deadline is January 15.

PUBLICATIONS:
Graduate Studies in Chemistry, booklet.

DIRECTORS:
Dr. YuYe J. Tong, Professor and Chairperson
Dr. Diana Glick, Professor
Dr. Steven Metallo, Professor

ADDRESS INQUIRIES TO:
Dr. YuYe J. Tong
Professor and Chairperson
(See address above.)

THE HAMNER INSTITUTES FOR HEALTH SCIENCES [2198]

6 Davis Drive
Research Triangle Park, NC 27709
(919) 558-1331
Fax: (919) 558-1430

E-MAIL ADDRESS:
koverman@thehamner.org

WEB SITE ADDRESS:
www.thehamner.org

FOUNDED: 1974

AREAS OF INTEREST:
All areas of human health and related risk assessment.

NAME(S) OF PROGRAMS:
● **Postdoctoral Fellowship at The Hamner Institutes for Health Sciences**

TYPE:
Conferences/seminars; Fellowships; Internships; Visiting scholars.

YEAR PROGRAM STARTED: 1976

PURPOSE:
To train toxicologists and computational biologists.

LEGAL BASIS:
Nonprofit, 501(c)(3) organization.

ELIGIBILITY:
Candidate must have completed a doctoral degree in a bioscience or related field.

FINANCIAL DATA:
Amount of support per award: $40,000 to $44,000.

NUMBER OF APPLICANTS MOST RECENT YEAR:
Over 30.

NUMBER OF AWARDS: 20 ongoing awards.

APPLICATION INFORMATION:
Duration: One to three years. Renewal for second and third year contingent on satisfactory performance the first year.
Deadline: Information on deadline can be obtained from the address above.

PUBLICATIONS:
Annual report; *The Hamner Activities,* monthly; Index of The Hamner publications available on request.

BOARD OF DIRECTORS:
Charles Hamner, Chairman

ADDRESS INQUIRIES TO:
Human Resources Department
(See address above.)

NATIONAL MOLE DAY FOUNDATION [2199]

P.O. Box 602
Millersport, OH 43046
(740) 928-8455
Fax: (740) 928-8455

E-MAIL ADDRESS:
mole@avolve.net

WEB SITE ADDRESS:
www.moleday.org

FOUNDED: 1991

AREAS OF INTEREST:
Chemistry education.

NAME(S) OF PROGRAMS:
● **The George Hague Memorial Travel Award**
● **The Maury Award**
● **National Mole of the Year Award (MOTY)**

TYPE:
Grants-in-aid. The George Hague Memorial Travel Award is given to financially support a young chemistry instructor (with two to five years of chemistry experience) in attending a biennial ChemEd conference.

The Maury Award is given to teachers to support student-centered Mole Day activities (promoting chemistry education).

The National Mole of the Year Award (MOTY) is given to a member of the National Mole Day Foundation who has contributed the most to furthering the cause of Mole Day and chemistry education.

PURPOSE:
To support Mole Day activities in classrooms, schools or communities.

ELIGIBILITY:
Must be a member of the National Mole Day Foundation and be involved with chemical education. Those receiving grants are not eligible again for the following three years.

FINANCIAL DATA:
Amount of support per award: The George Hague Memorial Travel Award: Up to $750; The Maury Award: Up to $200; National Mole of the Year Award (MOTY): $250.

APPLICATION INFORMATION:
Deadline: Hague and Maury Awards: March 1. National Mole of the Year Award: May 1 of odd-numbered years.

ADDRESS INQUIRIES TO:
Tom Tweedle, Executive Director
(See address above.)

THE UNIVERSITY OF SYDNEY [2200]

Scholarships Office
Level 5, Jane Foss Russell Building G02
The University of Sydney N.S.W. 2006
Australia
(02) 8627 8112
Fax: (02) 8627 8145

E-MAIL ADDRESS:
research.training@sydney.edu.au

WEB SITE ADDRESS:
www.sydney.edu.au/scholarships/research

FOUNDED: 1850

AREAS OF INTEREST:
Chemistry in relation to agriculture and industry.

NAME(S) OF PROGRAMS:
● **Henry Bertie and Florence Mabel Gritton Postgraduate Research Scholarships/Fellowships**

TYPE:
Fellowships; Scholarships. Scholarships are awarded for research leading to a higher degree. Fellowships are available for postdoctoral research.

PURPOSE:
To promote the knowledge and study of chemistry in relation to industry and agriculture, including chemistry connected with electrical engineering, metallurgical chemistry and chemistry in its application to mining and the winning and treatment of minerals and natural products of the soil.

LEGAL BASIS:
University.

ELIGIBILITY:
Open to graduates of universities which are members of the Association of Commonwealth Universities or to graduates of any university who are either citizens of a Commonwealth country or who are permanent residents of Australia. Candidates

for scholarships must hold at least a first class honours degree. Candidates for Fellowships must hold a Ph.D. degree.

Tenable at the University of Sydney.

FINANCIAL DATA:
Scholarship does not cover tuition fees payable by international students.
Amount of support per award: Scholarships: $22,860 (AUD) per annum for the year 2011; Fellowships: $74,481 to $79,950 (AUD) per annum.

NUMBER OF AWARDS: 7 scholarships for the year 2011.

APPLICATION INFORMATION:
Duration: Scholarships: Two years for a Master's research degree and three years for a Ph.D.; Fellowships: Tenable for two years.
Deadline: Scholarships: First week in January and first week in July. Fellowships: As vacancy occurs.

THE ROBERT A. WELCH FOUNDATION [2201]

5555 San Felipe
Suite 1900
Houston, TX 77056-2730
(713) 961-9884
Fax: (713) 961-5168

WEB SITE ADDRESS:
www.welch1.org

FOUNDED: 1954

AREAS OF INTEREST:
Basic research in chemistry.

NAME(S) OF PROGRAMS:
● **Departmental Grants**
● **Research Grants**
● **Welch Summer Scholar Program**

TYPE:
Research grants. Grants to support long-range fundamental research in the broad domain of chemistry.

The Welch Foundation supports chemical research at educational institutions within the state of Texas.

LEGAL BASIS:
Corporate.

ELIGIBILITY:
Full-time regular faculty members at Texas colleges or universities, who are tenured or on the tenured track, are eligible to apply for research grants.

GEOGRAPHIC RESTRICTIONS:
Texas.

FINANCIAL DATA:
Amount of support per award: Minimum $50,000 per year.
Total amount of support: Varies.

NUMBER OF AWARDS: Varies.

APPLICATION INFORMATION:
Duration: Two years. Renewable.
Deadline: February 1.

IRS IDENTIFICATION NUMBER: 76-0343128

Earth sciences

AMERICAN ASSOCIATION OF PETROLEUM GEOLOGISTS FOUNDATION   [2202]

1444 South Boulder
Tulsa, OK 74119
(918) 560-2644
Fax: (918) 560-2642

E-MAIL ADDRESS:
    foundation@aapg.org

WEB SITE ADDRESS:
    foundation.aapg.org

FOUNDED: 1917

AREAS OF INTEREST:
    The science of geology, especially as it
    relates to the search and development of
    hydrocarbons and economic sedimentary
    minerals and/or to environmental geology as
    it pertains to the petroleum industry.

NAME(S) OF PROGRAMS:
    • **AAPG Foundation Grants-in-Aid**

TYPE:
    Grants-in-aid. One-time support for Master's
    and Ph.D. thesis work.

YEAR PROGRAM STARTED: 1956

PURPOSE:
    To foster research in the geosciences by
    providing support to graduate students in the
    earth sciences whose research has application
    to the search for and development of
    petroleum and energy mineral resources, and
    to related environmental geology issues.

LEGAL BASIS:
    Special-interest foundation.

ELIGIBILITY:
    Graduate students in the geological sciences
    are eligible to apply. Factors weighed in
    selection of successful applicants include
    qualifications of the applicant as indicated by
    past performance, originality and imagination
    of the proposed project, support of the
    department in which the work is being done
    and perceived significance of the project to
    science and industry. The program focuses on
    support of qualified Master's candidates.
    Qualified doctoral candidates with expenses
    outside the usual scope of funding by other
    agencies are also encouraged to apply.

    Grants are based on merit and, in part, on the
    financial needs of the applicant.

FINANCIAL DATA:
    Grants are to be applied to selected expenses
    of graduate study such as a summer of field
    work, etc. Funds may not be used for tuition,
    room and board, capital expenses, to pay
    salaries or attend conferences.
    Amount of support per award: Grants not to
    exceed $3,000.
    Total amount of support: $203,000 for the
    year 2010.

NUMBER OF APPLICANTS MOST RECENT YEAR:
    350 for the year 2010.

NUMBER OF AWARDS: 86 for the year 2010.

APPLICATION INFORMATION:
    Applications must be submitted
    electronically. A completed application
    includes:
    (1) applicant name and contact information;
    (2) academic and employment history;
    (3) a project summary;
    (4) description of the research project
    (limited to 300 words);

(5) project budget and funding request;
(6) disclose if applicant has been a previous
    recipient of an AAPG Foundation grant;
(7) name and e-mail address for two separate
    references qualified to endorse the applicant
    and project and;
(8) official academic transcripts from the last
    two years (or equivalent).

The transcript cannot be submitted online. It
must be mailed to the Grants-in-Aid Program
at the address listed above. Xerographic
copies, facsimile copies and
computer-generated transcripts are
unacceptable.
Deadline: January 31. Announcement in
early April.

PUBLICATIONS:
    Annual report; application guidelines.

OFFICER:
    Richard D. Fritz, Executive Director

ADDRESS INQUIRIES TO:
    Chairman, AAPG Grants-in-Aid Committee
    (See address above.)

*PLEASE NOTE:
    This program is intended for support of
    individuals only in earth sciences related to
    the petroleum industry.

AMERICAN CONGRESS ON SURVEYING AND MAPPING (ACSM)

6 Montgomery Village Avenue
Suite 403
Gaithersburg, MD 20879
(240) 632-9716 ext. 109
Fax: (240) 632-1321

E-MAIL ADDRESS:
    ilse.genovese@acsm.net

WEB SITE ADDRESS:
    www.acsm.net

TYPE:
    Fellowships. Annual fellowship award to
    support graduate study in a program with a
    significant focus on geodetic surveying or
    geodesy at a school of the recipient's choice.

See entry 2797 for full listing.

AMERICAN CONGRESS ON SURVEYING AND MAPPING (ACSM)

6 Montgomery Village Avenue
Suite 403
Gaithersburg, MD 20879
(240) 632-9716 ext. 109
Fax: (240) 632-1321

E-MAIL ADDRESS:
    ilse.genovese@acsm.net

WEB SITE ADDRESS:
    www.acsm.net

TYPE:
    Scholarships. The award is intended for
    students enrolled in four-year degree
    programs in surveying or in closely related
    degree programs.

See entry 2798 for full listing.

AMERICAN CONGRESS ON SURVEYING AND MAPPING (ACSM)

6 Montgomery Village Avenue
Suite 403
Gaithersburg, MD 20879
(240) 632-9716 ext. 109
Fax: (240) 632-1321

E-MAIL ADDRESS:
    ilse.genovese@acsm.net

WEB SITE ADDRESS:
    www.acsm.net

TYPE:
    Scholarships. Berntsen International
    Scholarship in Surveying: Annual scholarship
    award for undergraduate study in four-year
    degree programs in surveying or in closely
    related degree programs such as geomatics or
    surveying engineering.

    Berntsen International Scholarship in
    Surveying Technology: For students enrolled
    in two-year degree programs in surveying
    technology.

See entry 2799 for full listing.

AMERICAN CONGRESS ON SURVEYING AND MAPPING (ACSM)

6 Montgomery Village Avenue
Suite 403
Gaithersburg, MD 20879
(240) 632-9716 ext. 109
Fax: (240) 632-1321

E-MAIL ADDRESS:
    ilse.genovese@acsm.net

WEB SITE ADDRESS:
    www.acsm.net

TYPE:
    Scholarships. For students enrolled in
    four-year degree programs in surveying or in
    closely related degree programs such as
    geomatics or surveying engineering.

See entry 2800 for full listing.

AMERICAN CONGRESS ON SURVEYING AND MAPPING (ACSM)

6 Montgomery Village Avenue
Suite 403
Gaithersburg, MD 20879
(240) 632-9716 ext. 113
Fax: (240) 632-1321

E-MAIL ADDRESS:
    ilse.genovese@acsm.net

WEB SITE ADDRESS:
    www.acsm.net

TYPE:
    Scholarships.

See entry 2801 for full listing.

AMERICAN GEOLOGICAL INSTITUTE   [2203]

4220 King Street
Alexandria, VA 22302-1502
(703) 379-2480 ext. 227
Fax: (703) 379-7563

E-MAIL ADDRESS:
    cmm@agiweb.org
    mpp@agiweb.org

WEB SITE ADDRESS:
www.agiweb.org/mpp

FOUNDED: 1948

AREAS OF INTEREST:
Major study in the fields of geology, geophysics, geochemistry, hydrology, meteorology, physical oceanography, planetary geology and earth-science education.

NAME(S) OF PROGRAMS:
- **AGI Minority Geoscience Scholarships**

TYPE:
Scholarships. Awards to expand the role of underrepresented minorities in the earth sciences.

YEAR PROGRAM STARTED: 1971

PURPOSE:
To increase the participation of ethnic minorities in the geosciences by providing financial support and advisory counseling.

LEGAL BASIS:
Nonprofit, tax-exempt scientific federation.

ELIGIBILITY:
Eligible applicants must be:
(1) a geoscience major, including the geoscience subdisciplines of geophysics, geochemistry, hydrology, meteorology, physical oceanography, planetary geology or earth-science education. This program does not support students in other natural sciences, mathematics or engineering;
(2) U.S. citizens who are full-time undergraduates (beginning their sophomore year) or graduate students (M.A., M.S., Ph.D.);
(3) those in demonstrated financial need and;
(4) verifiable members of one of the following ethnic minority groups: Black, Hispanic or Native American (American Indian, Eskimo, Hawaiian or Samoan).

The selection criteria is based on academic performance, financial need, recommendations and personal statement.

The scholarships are valid at any accredited college or university in the U.S.

GEOGRAPHIC RESTRICTIONS:
United States.

FINANCIAL DATA:
Amount of support per award: $250 to $3,000.
Total amount of support: Varies.

COOPERATIVE FUNDING PROGRAMS: Funding provided by contributions from geoscience industries, professional societies and individuals.

APPLICATION INFORMATION:
Those interested can print the application from the Institute web site, posted in January. Application must be completed using dark-colored ink, or typed.

Applicants must submit completed and signed application (four pages) along with the following:
(1) official transcripts;
(2) SAT, ACT and/or GRE scores and;
(3) three letters of recommendation from persons qualified to judge the applicant's recent academic performance and character (geoscience faculty/employers preferred, but other science/mathematics faculty are acceptable) by the posted deadline.

Current recipients must reapply for renewal of scholarship. Renewal applications should include completed application, transcripts for current institution and three letters of recommendation, including at least one not included in the previous application(s). The "Statement of Purpose" should be used to describe current academic progress and plans.
Duration: Until graduation. Renewal contingent upon satisfactory performance and reapplication. Scholarships are not automatically renewed.
Deadline: March 15, 2012.

PUBLICATIONS:
Applications guidelines; posters; AGI annual report; *Geotimes* monthly magazine.

ADDRESS INQUIRIES TO:
Minority Geoscience Student Scholarship Coordinator
AGI Minority Geoscience Scholarship Program
(See address above.)

AMERICAN METEOROLOGICAL SOCIETY

45 Beacon Street
Boston, MA 02108-3693
(617) 226-3907
Fax: (617) 742-8718

E-MAIL ADDRESS:
dfernandez@ametsoc.org

WEB SITE ADDRESS:
www.ametsoc.org

TYPE:
Fellowships; Scholarships. AMS Freshman Undergraduate Scholarship Program awards funding to high school seniors entering their freshman year of undergraduate study in the fall.

AMS Graduate Fellowship in the History of Science is awarded to a student wishing to complete a dissertation on the history of the atmospheric and related oceanic or hydrologic sciences.

AMS Graduate Fellowships are designed to attract students entering their first year of graduate study in the fall who wish to pursue advanced degrees in the atmospheric and related oceanic and hydrologic sciences.

AMS/Industry Minority Scholarships award funding to high school minority students who have been traditionally underrepresented in the sciences, especially Hispanic, Native American and Black/African American students.

AMS Undergraduate Named Scholarships are directed to students entering their final year of undergraduate study in the fall.

The Father James B. Macelwane Annual Awards in Meteorology are intended to stimulate interest in meteorology among college students through the submission of original student papers concerned with some phase of the atmospheric sciences.

See entry 2784 for full listing.

THE ASSOCIATION OF AMERICAN GEOGRAPHERS (AAG)   [2204]

1710 16th Street, N.W.
Washington, DC 20009
(202) 234-1450
Fax: (202) 234-2744

E-MAIL ADDRESS:
grantsawards@aag.org

WEB SITE ADDRESS:
www.aag.org

FOUNDED: 1904

NAME(S) OF PROGRAMS:
- **AAG-IGIF Graduate Research Awards**
- **AAG-IGIF Student Paper Awards**
- **AAG-IGIF Student Travel Grants**

TYPE:
Research grants; Travel grants. AAG International Geographic Information Fund offers three types of awards:

Graduate Research Awards support research in any area of spatial analysis or geographic information science or systems.

Student Paper Awards are given in recognition of outstanding papers in any area of spatial analysis or geographic information science or systems that were given at a national and international conference or specialized meeting sponsored by recognized professional organizations.

Student Travel Grant supports travel to national and international symposia or specialized meetings sponsored by recognized professional organizations.

PURPOSE:
To support college and university student career development in the academic areas of applied spatial data analysis or geographic information systems (GIS).

ELIGIBILITY:
Full-time students currently registered in undergraduate or graduate degree programs providing a degree or explicit specialization in some area of applied spatial data analysis or GIS study at a duly accredited and recognized college, university or other educational institution located within the U.S.

FINANCIAL DATA:
Amount of support per award: Graduate Research Award: Up to $500; Student Paper Award: Up to $200; Student Travel Grant: Approximately $500.

APPLICATION INFORMATION:
Digital submissions are required for all applications.

For the Graduate Research Award, applicant must submit a proposal of no more than five pages which includes:
(1) an abstract of research intent;
(2) statement of problem and relevancy;
(3) context of proposed research in the literature;
(4) methodology/research design;
(5) anticipated results and significance of such results;
(6) schedule of research;
(7) budget and;
(8) a letter of recommendation from a faculty member.

For the Student Paper Award, applicant must submit:
(1) a copy of the full paper presented at the conference or event;
(2) a letter requesting consideration for the award and indicating the applicant's present status as a student and;
(3) in the case of papers already presented, evidence of the presentation of the paper or, in the case of papers yet to be presented, evidence of acceptance of the paper to the specific event selected by the applicant for presentation of the paper, clearly identifying the name and dates of the conference.

For the Student Travel Grant, applicants must submit:
(1) a letter of no more than three pages in length specifically addressing how the grant funds will be used, the career goals of the student and how these funds will assist in meeting those goals. This may be supplemented, if necessary, by no more than two pages of supporting illustrations;
(2) a letter from the student's faculty advisor including an endorsement from the chairperson of the applicable department or program;
(3) a brief curriculum vitae of the applicant and;
(4) a copy of the applicant's most recent transcript.

Deadline: December 31.

ADDRESS INQUIRIES TO:
See e-mail address above.

THE ASSOCIATION OF AMERICAN GEOGRAPHERS (AAG) [2205]

1710 16th Street, N.W.
Washington, DC 20009
(202) 234-1450
Fax: (202) 234-2744

E-MAIL ADDRESS:
grantsawards@aag.org

WEB SITE ADDRESS:
www.aag.org

FOUNDED: 1904

NAME(S) OF PROGRAMS:
● **AAG Research Grant**

TYPE:
Research grants. Small grant to support research and fieldwork.

PURPOSE:
To support research and fieldwork proposals which offer the prospect of obtaining substantial subsequent support from private foundations or federal agencies and that address questions of major importance to the discipline.

ELIGIBILITY:
Must be an AAG member for at least two years at the time of application. Grants can be used only for direct expenses of research; salary and overhead costs are not allowed. The committee will not approve awards for Master's or doctoral dissertation research.

FINANCIAL DATA:
Amount of support per award: Up to $1,000.

APPLICATION INFORMATION:
Digital submissions are required.
Deadline: December 31.

ADDRESS INQUIRIES TO:
See e-mail address above.

THE ASSOCIATION OF AMERICAN GEOGRAPHERS (AAG) [2206]

1710 16th Street, N.W.
Washington, DC 20009
(202) 234-1450
Fax: (202) 234-2744

E-MAIL ADDRESS:
grantsawards@aag.org

WEB SITE ADDRESS:
www.aag.org

FOUNDED: 1904

NAME(S) OF PROGRAMS:
● **AAG Dissertation Research Grants**

TYPE:
Research grants.

PURPOSE:
To provide financial assistance to candidates preparing doctoral dissertations in geography.

ELIGIBILITY:
Must be an AAG member for at least one year at the time of application, must not have a doctorate at the time of the award, and have completed all Ph.D. requirements except the dissertation by the end of the semester or term following approval of the award. Dissertation supervisor must certify eligibility. The Paul Vouras Fund gives preference to minority student applicants.

FINANCIAL DATA:
Amount of support per award: Up to $500.

APPLICATION INFORMATION:
Digital submissions are required.
Deadline: December 31.

THE ASSOCIATION OF AMERICAN GEOGRAPHERS (AAG) [2207]

1710 16th Street, N.W.
Washington, DC 20009
(202) 234-1450
Fax: (202) 234-2744

E-MAIL ADDRESS:
grantsawards@aag.org

WEB SITE ADDRESS:
www.aag.org

FOUNDED: 1904

NAME(S) OF PROGRAMS:
● **AAG Globe Book Award for Public Understanding of Geography**
● **AAG Meridian Book Award for the Outstanding Scholarly Work in Geography**

TYPE:
Awards/prizes. AAG Globe Book Award is awarded annually to a book that conveys most powerfully the nature and importance of geography to the non-academic world.

AAG Meridian Book Award is awarded annually to a book that makes an unusually important contribution to advancing the science and art of geography.

PURPOSE:
To award outstanding geographic authors.

ELIGIBILITY:
Books must be written or co-authored by a geographer. Books published in the previous calendar year are eligible.

FINANCIAL DATA:
Amount of support per award: $1,000.

APPLICATION INFORMATION:
Nomination statements (two-page maximum) should provide full contact information for the author(s) and the nominator(s), including e-mail addresses, and should document the ways the nominated work conveys the nature and importance of geography to the non-academic world (Globe Book Award) or contributes to advancing the science and art of geography (Meridian Book Award). Nomination statements and four copies of each nominated book should be submitted.
Deadline: December 31.

ADDRESS INQUIRIES TO:
Attn: Globe Book Award or
Attn: Meridian Book Award
(See address and e-mail above.)

THE GEOLOGICAL SOCIETY OF AMERICA, INC. [2208]

P.O. Box 9140
Boulder, CO 80301-9140
(303) 357-1028
Fax: (303) 357-1070

E-MAIL ADDRESS:
dlorenz@geosociety.org
awards@geosociety.org

WEB SITE ADDRESS:
www.geosociety.org

FOUNDED: 1888

AREAS OF INTEREST:
Geoscience.

NAME(S) OF PROGRAMS:
● **GSA Research Grants**

TYPE:
Grants-in-aid; Project/program grants; Research grants; Seed money grants. Grants for projects contributing to the science of geology.

YEAR PROGRAM STARTED: 1933

PURPOSE:
To provide partial support of Master's and doctoral thesis research in earth science for graduate students.

LEGAL BASIS:
Private membership association.

ELIGIBILITY:
Qualified investigators with appropriate interests are eligible to apply. Graduate students apply for support of Master's or doctoral thesis work. The GSA strongly encourages women, minorities and persons with disabilities to participate in this grants program.

Applicants must be members of GSA.

GEOGRAPHIC RESTRICTIONS:
North and Central America.

FINANCIAL DATA:
Funds are intended as an aid to the research project and not to sustain entire research costs.
Amount of support per award: Grants vary in amount, depending upon the needs and nature of the request.
Total amount of support: $4,000.

NUMBER OF APPLICANTS MOST RECENT YEAR:
592.

NUMBER OF AWARDS: 250.

APPLICATION INFORMATION:
Official application materials are available upon request to the Grants, Awards and Recognition Program Officer at the address above. They are also available in geology departments of all graduate degree-granting colleges and universities in the U.S.
Duration: One year.
Deadline: Applications must be postmarked by February 1 for consideration at the spring review meeting.

PUBLICATIONS:
Annual report; application guidelines.

OFFICERS:
Jack Hess, Executive Officer

ADDRESS INQUIRIES TO:
Program Officer
Grants, Awards and Recognition
(See address above.)

INTERNATIONAL WOMEN'S FISHING ASSOCIATION   [2209]
P.O. Box 21066
Fort Lauderdale, FL 33335-1066

E-MAIL ADDRESS:
scholarship@iwfa.org

WEB SITE ADDRESS:
www.iwfa.org

FOUNDED: 1965

AREAS OF INTEREST:
Marine science.

NAME(S) OF PROGRAMS:
● **IWFA Scholarship Trust**

TYPE:
Scholarships. Scholarships for postgraduate
educational expense including tuition,
supplies and books.

YEAR PROGRAM STARTED: 1965

PURPOSE:
To aid needy students who are seeking
postgraduate degrees in marine science.

ELIGIBILITY:
Graduate students in marine science. Student
must be matriculated at a school in the U.S.

FINANCIAL DATA:
Amount of support per award:
Approximately $500 per award.
Total amount of support: $15,000 for the
year 2010.

NUMBER OF APPLICANTS MOST RECENT YEAR:
25.

NUMBER OF AWARDS: 16.

APPLICATION INFORMATION:
Application form will be sent on request.
Duration: One year.
Deadline: March 1. Announcement after
April 1.

ADDRESS INQUIRIES TO:
IWFA Scholarship Trustees
(See address above.)

*SPECIAL STIPULATIONS:
For graduate students in the Marine Science
field only.

LUNAR AND PLANETARY INSTITUTE
3600 Bay Area Boulevard
Houston, TX 77058-1113
(281) 486-2180
Fax: (281) 486-2127

E-MAIL ADDRESS:
webmaster@lpi.usra.edu

WEB SITE ADDRESS:
www.lpi.usra.edu

TYPE:
Conferences/seminars; Fellowships;
Internships; Scholarships; Travel grants;
Visiting scholars. Postdoctoral and Visiting
Scientist Programs: Several positions are
available in planetary science research at the
Postdoctoral and Visiting Scientist levels.
Applicants may propose to work in any area
of the planetary sciences, with preference
given to topics that enhance the interactions

between the Institute and the Astromaterials
Research Group at the NASA Johnson Space
Center.

Summer Intern Program: LPI invites
undergraduates to experience cutting-edge
research in the planetary sciences through
this program. Interns complete a research
project of current interest in planetary
science, working one-on-one with a scientist
at the Institute or at Johnson Space Center.

See entry 2182 for full listing.

THE MINERALOGICAL SOCIETY OF AMERICA   [2210]
3635 Concorde Parkway, Suite 500
Chantilly, VA 20151-1110
(703) 652-9950
Fax: (703) 652-9951

E-MAIL ADDRESS:
business@minsocam.org

WEB SITE ADDRESS:
www.minsocam.org

FOUNDED: 1919

AREAS OF INTEREST:
Crystallography, mineralogy and petrology.

NAME(S) OF PROGRAMS:
● **Research Grant in Crystallography, Mineral Physics or Chemistry and Mineralogy**
● **Student Research Grant in Mineralogy and Petrology**

TYPE:
Research grants.

YEAR PROGRAM STARTED: 1973

PURPOSE:
To encourage research in mineralogy,
crystallography, geochemistry, and petrology.

ELIGIBILITY:
For the crystallography grant, applicant must
have reached his or her 25th birthday, but not
yet have reached his or her 36th birthday, in
the year the grant proposal is submitted, and
must be an MSA Counselor. The
mineralogy/petrology grant is limited to
students.

FINANCIAL DATA:
The grant is for research-related expenses
only. Travel to meetings, conferences, short
courses, nonresearch field trips, tuition,
nonresearch living (room and board)
expenses, etc., are not suitable uses of the
money. Neither should the money be used for
salary or wages for the researcher.
Amount of support per award: $5,000.
Total amount of support: $15,000.

NUMBER OF APPLICANTS MOST RECENT YEAR:
56.

NUMBER OF AWARDS: 3.

APPLICATION INFORMATION:
Proposal submissions are to be made online.
Duration: One year.
Deadline: June 1.

ADDRESS INQUIRIES TO:
Dr. J. Alex Speer, Executive Director
(See address above.)

NATIONAL ASSOCIATION OF GEOSCIENCE TEACHERS   [2211]
c/o Science Education Resource Center
200 Division Street, Suite 210
Northfield, MN 55057
(507) 222-5634
Fax: (507) 222-5175

E-MAIL ADDRESS:
cmanduca@carleton.edu

WEB SITE ADDRESS:
www.nagt.org

FOUNDED: 1938

AREAS OF INTEREST:
Earth sciences.

NAME(S) OF PROGRAMS:
● **Dottie Stout Professional Development Grants**
● **Summer Field Course Scholarship**

TYPE:
Development grants; Scholarships. Dottie
Stout Professional Development Grants will
be awarded in support of the following
activities:
(1) participation in earth science classes or
workshops;
(2) attendance at professional scientific or
science education meetings;
(3) participation in earth science field trips
and;
(4) purchase of earth science materials for
classroom use.
Summer Field Course Scholarship: Cash
award for a summer field course in geology.

YEAR PROGRAM STARTED: 1970

PURPOSE:
To further geological education at the
undergraduate level.

LEGAL BASIS:
Tax-exempt corporation.

ELIGIBILITY:
Dottie Stout Professional Development
Grants: Community college faculty and
K-12th grade teachers who teach one or more
earth science courses and community college
students actively pursuing a career in the
earth sciences are encouraged to apply for
these awards.

Summer Field Course Scholarship:
Applicants must be full-time students with a
geology major. The chief criterion for
selection is advanced students with
distinguished academic records within the
major.

FINANCIAL DATA:
Amount of support per award: Dottie Stout
Professional Development Grants: $750 each
to a community college faculty member, a
community college student and a K-12th
grade educator; Summer Field Course
Scholarship: $500.
Total amount of support: Varies.

APPLICATION INFORMATION:
Application information is available at the
web site.
Deadline: Dottie Stout Professional
Development Grants: April 15. Summer Field
Course Scholarship: February 16.

PUBLICATIONS:
Journal of Geoscience Education.

IRS IDENTIFICATION NUMBER: 74-6068050

OFFICERS:
Janis Treworgy, President
Cathy Manduca, Executive Director

*PLEASE NOTE:
Undergraduate students are given special consideration.

NATIONAL CENTER FOR ATMOSPHERIC RESEARCH

1850 Table Mesa Drive
Boulder, CO 80303
(303) 497-1328
Fax: (303) 497-1646

E-MAIL ADDRESS:
paulad@ucar.edu

WEB SITE ADDRESS:
www.asp.ucar.edu

TYPE:
Fellowships. The fellowships cover a year's appointment, with a likely extension to two years, at NCAR to take advantage of its educational programs and/or research facilities in the broad field of atmospheric sciences.

See entry 1952 for full listing.

NATIONAL GEOGRAPHIC SOCIETY [2212]

1145 17th Street, N.W.
Washington, DC 20036-4688
Fax: (202) 429-5729

E-MAIL ADDRESS:
cre@ngs.org

WEB SITE ADDRESS:
www.nationalgeographic.com/field/grants-programs

FOUNDED: 1888

AREAS OF INTEREST:
Sciences pertinent to geography, including anthropology, archeology, astronomy, biology, botany, geography, geology, oceanography, paleontology and zoology.

NAME(S) OF PROGRAMS:
● **National Geographic Society Committee for Research and Exploration**

TYPE:
Grants-in-aid; Research grants; Seed money grants. Grants-in-aid for basic research in the sciences pertinent to geography (including, but not limited to, projects in geography). Support may also be provided for projects in these fields that depend on exploration. The Society is currently emphasizing multidisciplinary projects that address environmental issues.

YEAR PROGRAM STARTED: 1890

PURPOSE:
To support scientific field research and exploration through its Committee for Research and Exploration.

LEGAL BASIS:
Nonprofit.

ELIGIBILITY:
Applicants are expected to have advanced degrees (Ph.D. or equivalent) and be associated with an educational organization or institution. Independent researchers or those pursuing a Ph.D.-level degree may apply, but competition is keen and awards to non-Ph.D. applicants are rare. As a general rule, all applicants are expected to have published a minimum of three articles in peer-reviewed scientific journals. Individuals between the ages of 18 and 25 are invited to

apply to the Young Explorers Program. These applicants are not expected to have advanced degrees but should have a record of prior experience as it pertains to their proposed project. Citizens of any country are eligible.

Grants normally are made only for field research. Laboratory work is supported only to the extent that it may be a necessary follow-up to Society-funded field research.

Grants are awarded on the basis of the project's scientific merit. All proposed projects must have both a geographical dimension and relevance to other scientific fields and be of broad scientific interest. The Committee pays special attention to the significance of the research proposal in terms of its relationship to major scientific questions or problems. The Committee's priorities favor research that relates to environmental concerns and has relevance to global geographic issues.

FINANCIAL DATA:
Society funds may be used for transportation, supplies, and daily subsistence. Capital equipment (generally defined as any item costing more than U.S. $500) must be individually justified. Laboratory expenses are acceptable, provided the laboratory work is a logical extension of the field research.
Amount of support per award: $15,000 to $20,000 per year.
Total amount of support: $3,000,000 budgeted for research program annually.
Matching fund requirements: National Geographic Society funds are intended to function as complementary support. The committee strongly encourages applicants to seek additional, concurrent funding from other agencies.

NUMBER OF APPLICANTS MOST RECENT YEAR: 976.

NUMBER OF AWARDS: Approximately 250 per year.

APPLICATION INFORMATION:
Prior to applying for a grant, each potential investigator must submit a preapplication, available on the web site, with a 500-word maximum length outlining the significance of the research and describing who will conduct the research and where it will occur. Also, a fieldwork schedule should be projected. Anticipated budgetary expenses must be itemized and, if necessary, justified. A curriculum vitae for each principal investigator, along with a list of his or her scholarly publications, should also be included.

A link to the full application will be e-mailed to those individuals whose project(s) are deemed appropriate for further formal review. Previous Society research grant recipients must comply with all grant obligations from past awards and must be up-to-date with any outstanding reports and/or financial accounting requirements before submitting applications for additional support.
Duration: One year.
Deadline: Applications may be submitted at any time.

PUBLICATIONS:
Program description; National Geographic Index 1888-1988.

*SPECIAL STIPULATIONS:
Society policy does not permit the payment of overhead to any individual or institution or to those with faculty status or any paid

professional affiliation. The Society does not provide scholarships or fellowships or pay tuition at any level, funds for publication of research results, or funds for travel to scientific meetings or conferences. Only in unusual cases is funding allowed for computer equipment or vehicles. Salaries are not allowable.

NATIONAL OCEANIC AND ATMOSPHERIC ADMINISTRATION [2213]

1315 East West Highway, 12th Floor
Silver Spring, MD 20910-5603
(301) 734-1206
Fax: (301) 713-0518

E-MAIL ADDRESS:
cpograms@noaa.gov

WEB SITE ADDRESS:
www.climate.noaa.gov

FOUNDED: 1966

AREAS OF INTEREST:
Climate and atmospheric research.

NAME(S) OF PROGRAMS:
● **Climate and Global Change Program**

TYPE:
Challenge/matching grants; Conferences/seminars; Formula grants.

PURPOSE:
To develop the knowledge required to establish a predictive capability for short- and long-term climate fluctuations and trends.

LEGAL BASIS:
Government agency.

ELIGIBILITY:
Applicants may be institutions of higher education, other nonprofits, commercial organizations, international organizations, state, local and Indian tribal governments. Federal agencies or institutions are ineligible.

FINANCIAL DATA:
Grants may be used for research and development, advisory services and operational systems as they relate to specific programs.
Amount of support per award: Up to $200,000.
Total amount of support: Approximately $56,000,000 in total funding annually.

NUMBER OF AWARDS: Estimated 70 annually.

APPLICATION INFORMATION:
Applications are to be submitted through grants.gov.
Duration: One to three years.

ADDRESS INQUIRIES TO:
Diane Brown
Grants Administration Team Leader
Climate Program Office
(See address above.)

NATIONAL OCEANIC AND ATMOSPHERIC ADMINISTRATION [2214]

National Marine Fisheries Service
263 13th Avenue South
St. Petersburg, FL 33701
(727) 824-5324
Fax: (727) 824-5364

E-MAIL ADDRESS:
ellie.roche@noaa.gov

WEB SITE ADDRESS:
sero.nmfs.noaa.gov/grants/grants.htm

AREAS OF INTEREST:
Southeast region.

NAME(S) OF PROGRAMS:
- **Cooperative Research Program Grants**
- **Marine Fisheries Initiative Grants**

TYPE:
Development grants; Research grants. The organization also offers a Project Grant.

YEAR PROGRAM STARTED: 2003

PURPOSE:
To support research and development.

ELIGIBILITY:
Cooperative Research Program Grants: Applicants who are not commercial or recreational fishermen must have commercial or recreational fishermen participating in their project. There must be a written agreement with a fisherman describing the involvement in the project activity. Eligible applicants include institutions of higher education, other nonprofits, commercial organizations, state, local and Indian tribal governments and individuals. Federal agencies or institutions are not eligible. Foreign governments, organizations under the jurisdiction of foreign governments, and international organizations are excluded for purposes of this solicitation since the objective of the CRP is to optimize research and development benefits from U.S. marine fishery resources.

Marine Fisheries Initiative Grants are available to institutions of higher education, other nonprofits, commercial organizations, state, local and Indian tribal governments. Federal agencies or institutions are not eligible. Foreign governments, organizations under the jurisdiction of foreign governments, and international organizations are excluded for purposes of this solicitation since the objective of the MARFIN program is to optimize research and development benefits from U.S. marine fishery resources.

FINANCIAL DATA:
Amount of support per award: $25,000 to $400,000.
Total amount of support: $2,000,000 for the year 2008.
Matching fund requirements: Cost sharing is not required.

NUMBER OF AWARDS: 8 to 10.

APPLICATION INFORMATION:
Applications are available on grants.gov. New applicants should include IRS documentation.
Deadline: Announced in NOAA solicitation and grant opportunities index.

PUBLICATIONS:
Annual report.

ADDRESS INQUIRIES TO:
Ellie Roche
Supervisory Grants Management Specialist
(See address above.)

NATIONAL OCEANIC AND ATMOSPHERIC ADMINISTRATION [2215]

National Undersea Research Program
SSMC3, R/NURP, Room 10322
1315 East-West Highway
Silver Spring, MD 20910
(301) 734-1006
Fax: (301) 713-1967

E-MAIL ADDRESS:
karen.kohanowich@noaa.gov

WEB SITE ADDRESS:
www.nurp.noaa.gov

AREAS OF INTEREST:
Marine research.

NAME(S) OF PROGRAMS:
- **Undersea Research Program**

TYPE:
Project/program grants; Research grants.

ELIGIBILITY:
Eligible applicants are U.S. institutions of higher education, not-for-profit institutions, and federal, state, and local governments. Federal agencies may not charge salary or overhead.

GEOGRAPHIC RESTRICTIONS:
United States.

FINANCIAL DATA:
Amount of support per award: Varies by center.
Total amount of support: Varies.

APPLICATION INFORMATION:
Each National Undersea Research Center has its own proposal forms and guidelines. Specific locations and instructions are available online.
Duration: One year.
Deadline: Varies by center.

ADDRESS INQUIRIES TO:
Karen Kohanowich, Acting Director
(See address above.)

NATIONAL OCEANIC AND ATMOSPHERIC ADMINISTRATION [2216]

Office of Research and Applications
National Environmental Satellite Data and Information Services
5200 Auth Road, Room 701
Camp Springs, MD 20746
(301) 763-8127
Fax: (301) 763-8108

E-MAIL ADDRESS:
heather.hay@noaa.gov

WEB SITE ADDRESS:
www.nesdis.noaa.gov

AREAS OF INTEREST:
Environmental sciences, application, data and education.

NAME(S) OF PROGRAMS:
- **Research in Remote Sensing of the Earth and Environment Grants**

TYPE:
Research grants.

PURPOSE:
To advance and promote applied research and technology development in satellite remote sensing of the earth and the atmosphere in support of national operational needs.

ELIGIBILITY:
Applicant must be any state university, college, institute or laboratory, public or private nonprofit, tax-exempt institution or consortium. No grants to individuals.

GEOGRAPHIC RESTRICTIONS:
United States.

FINANCIAL DATA:
Amount of support per award: $25,000 to $300,000.

Matching fund requirements: Varies.

APPLICATION INFORMATION:
Applications are available on grants.gov (keyword search NESDIS, JCSDA or NOAA BAA).
Duration: One to three years. Renewals possible.
Deadline: Posted online or published in *Federal Register*.

ADDRESS INQUIRIES TO:
Heather Hay, Administrator
(See address above.)

NATIONAL SCIENCE FOUNDATION [2217]

Division of Earth Sciences, Room 785
4201 Wilson Boulevard
Arlington, VA 22230
(703) 292-8550
Fax: (703) 292-9025

E-MAIL ADDRESS:
pbrookin@nsf.gov

WEB SITE ADDRESS:
www.nsf.gov

FOUNDED: 1950

AREAS OF INTEREST:
Earth sciences.

TYPE:
Research grants. The Division of Earth Sciences supports proposals for research geared toward improving the understanding of the structure, composition, and evolution of the Earth and the processes that govern the formation and behavior of the Earth's materials.

YEAR PROGRAM STARTED: 1950

PURPOSE:
To create a better understanding of the Earth's changing environments and the natural distribution of its mineral, water and energy resources; to provide methods for predicting and mitigating the effects of geologic hazards such as earthquakes, volcanic eruptions, floods and landslides.

LEGAL BASIS:
Federal agency.

ELIGIBILITY:
Scientists and engineers, especially college and university faculty members, are eligible to apply.

GEOGRAPHIC RESTRICTIONS:
United States and its territories.

NUMBER OF APPLICANTS MOST RECENT YEAR: 1,600.

NUMBER OF AWARDS: 500.

APPLICATION INFORMATION:
Duration: One to five years.
Deadline: Two or three deadlines per year as announced in the *National Science Foundation Bulletin*. At least six months should be allowed for review and processing of a proposal.

PUBLICATIONS:
Grant proposal guide (NSF 04-23).

DIRECTORS:
Dr. Robert Detrick, Division Director

ADDRESS INQUIRIES TO:
Division Director
(See address above.)

NATIONAL SCIENCE FOUNDATION   [2218]

Division of Ocean Sciences, Room 725
4201 Wilson Boulevard
Arlington, VA 22230
(703) 292-8580
Fax: (703) 292-9085

WEB SITE ADDRESS:
www.geo.nsf.gov/oce

FOUNDED: 1950

NAME(S) OF PROGRAMS:
- **Ocean Section**

TYPE:
Research grants. Support for fundamental research in marine science, including physical oceanography and limnology, chemical oceanography, biological oceanography and marine geology, geophysics and ocean technology, with the objective of increasing knowledge and enhancing our understanding of the marine environment.

Most of the research supported is basic in character, although some applied research is also supported. This program also supports research workshops, symposia and conferences and purchases of scientific equipment related to projects supported.

YEAR PROGRAM STARTED: 1980

PURPOSE:
To improve understanding of the nature of the ocean and its influence on human activities and of human impacts on the marine environment.

LEGAL BASIS:
Government agency.

ELIGIBILITY:
Program is primarily for support of scientists in basic research in ocean sciences and instrumentation and the facilities to support it.

FINANCIAL DATA:
Amount of support per award: Varies.
Total amount of support: Varies.

NUMBER OF APPLICANTS MOST RECENT YEAR:
1,113 competitive proposal actions.

APPLICATION INFORMATION:
Duration: Varies.
Deadline: Proposals may be submitted at any time. Approximately six months are required for review and processing. Target dates are February 15 and August 15.

PUBLICATIONS:
Grants for Scientific and Engineering Research.

OFFICERS:
P. Taylor, Head, Ocean Section
Bilal Haq, Marine Geology and Geophysics
Eric Itsweire, Physical Oceanography
Don Rice, Chemical Oceanography

ADDRESS INQUIRIES TO:
P. Taylor, Head, Ocean Section
(See address above.)

V. KANN RASMUSSEN FOUNDATION   [2219]

c/o Rockefeller Brothers Fund
475 Riverside Drive, Suite 900
New York, NY 10115
(212) 812-4268
Fax: (212) 812-4299

E-MAIL ADDRESS:
info@vkrf.org

WEB SITE ADDRESS:
www.vkrf.org

FOUNDED: 1991

AREAS OF INTEREST:
Environment, eye research and grants in Greenwood, SC.

TYPE:
Challenge/matching grants; General operating grants; Project/program grants.

PURPOSE:
To emphasize environmental grantmaking, with special focus on collaboration across disciplines and among institutions.

LEGAL BASIS:
Private foundation.

ELIGIBILITY:
Eligible organizations must be IRS 501(c)(3) tax-exempt.

GEOGRAPHIC RESTRICTIONS:
United States.

FINANCIAL DATA:
Amount of support per award: Varies.
Total amount of support: Approximately $3,000,000 for the year ended June 30, 2010.

APPLICATION INFORMATION:
Application procedures can be found on the Foundation web site.

IRS IDENTIFICATION NUMBER: 22-3101266.

STAFF:
Dr. Lois E.H. Smith, Managing Director and Trustee
Irene Krarup, Associate Director and Head of Programs

ADDRESS INQUIRIES TO:
Irene Krarup, Associate Director and Head of Programs
(See address above.)

*PLEASE NOTE:
All correspondence should use full name of the Foundation (V. Kann Rasmussen Foundation) or the initials VKRF.

THE PERCY SLADEN MEMORIAL FUND

c/o The Linnean Society of London
Burlington House, Piccadilly
London W1J 0BF England
44 (0)20 7434 4479
Fax: 44 (0)20 7287 9364

E-MAIL ADDRESS:
info@linnean.org; gina@linnean.org

WEB SITE ADDRESS:
www.linnean.org

TYPE:
Awards/prizes; Project/program grants; Research grants; Travel grants. Field work grants in life and earth sciences (excludes any projects which are part of further education, e.g., a Doctorate or a Master's course).

See entry 2243 for full listing.

SOCIETY OF EXPLORATION GEOPHYSICISTS   [2220]

8801 South Yale Avenue
Suite 500
Tulsa, OK 74137
(918) 497-5500
Fax: (918) 497-5560

E-MAIL ADDRESS:
scholarships@seg.org

WEB SITE ADDRESS:
www.seg.org/foundation
www.seg.org/scholarships

FOUNDED: 1956

AREAS OF INTEREST:
Applied geophysics.

NAME(S) OF PROGRAMS:
- **SEG Scholarship Program**

TYPE:
Scholarships. Undergraduate and graduate scholarships for the study of geophysics.

YEAR PROGRAM STARTED: 1956

PURPOSE:
To assist young people in pursuing careers in the field of applied geophysics.

LEGAL BASIS:
Nonprofit society.

ELIGIBILITY:
Applicant must intend to pursue a college course directed toward a career in applied geophysics and must have an interest in and aptitude for physics, mathematics, and geology. Applicants must be:
(1) a high school student with above average grades planning to enter college the next fall term;
(2) an undergraduate college student whose grades are above average or;
(3) a graduate college student whose studies are directed toward a career in applied geophysics in operations, teaching, or research.

FINANCIAL DATA:
Amount of support per award: $500 to $14,000 per academic year, averaging $2,500 per academic year.
Total amount of support: $484,000 for the academic year 2010-11.

NUMBER OF AWARDS: 175 for the academic year 2010-11.

APPLICATION INFORMATION:
Application must be submitted electronically. Transcripts and letters of recommendation may be submitted online or sent via regular mail. Results of aptitude tests are not required but should be included if taken.
Duration: One year. Renewable at the discretion of the SEG Scholarship Committee, subject to student's maintenance of satisfactory grades, funds available and continued study leading to a career in geophysics.
Deadline: March 1.

ADDRESS INQUIRIES TO:
Scholarship Coordinator
(See address above.)

*SPECIAL STIPULATIONS:
Certain scholarships carry additional qualifications specified by the scholarships' donors.

THE UNIVERSITY OF CALGARY   [2221]

Earth Sciences Building, Room 720
2500 University Drive, N.W.
Calgary AB T2N 1N4 Canada
(403) 220-4938
Fax: (403) 289-7635

E-MAIL ADDRESS:
gsaward@ucalgary.ca

WEB SITE ADDRESS:
www.grad.ucalgary.ca

NAME(S) OF PROGRAMS:
- **Harry and Laura Jacques Bursary Scholarship**

TYPE:
Scholarships. Award is given to graduate students working or studying in field related to the petroleum industry.

ELIGIBILITY:
Open to candidates who at the time of tenure will be registered full-time in a thesis-based graduate program at the University of Calgary.

FINANCIAL DATA:
Amount of support per award: $4,000.
Total amount of support: $4,000.

NUMBER OF AWARDS: 1.

APPLICATION INFORMATION:
Duration: One year.
Deadline: May 15, or next business day if deadline falls on weekend.

ADDRESS INQUIRIES TO:
Graduate Scholarship Office
(See address above.)

Mathematics

THE ACTUARIAL FOUNDATION   [2222]

475 North Martingale Road
Suite 600
Schaumburg, IL 60173-2226
(847) 706-3500
Fax: (847) 706-3599

E-MAIL ADDRESS:
Scholarships@ActFnd.org

WEB SITE ADDRESS:
www.actuarialfoundation.org

FOUNDED: 1949

AREAS OF INTEREST:
Actuarial science, a branch of mathematics based on calculus, probability and statistics, as well as business economics.

NAME(S) OF PROGRAMS:
- **Actuarial Diversity Scholarship**

TYPE:
Scholarships. The scholarship promotes diversity through an annual scholarship program for Black/African American, Hispanic and Native North American students recognizing and encouraging academic achievements by awarding scholarships to full-time undergraduate and graduate students pursuing a degree that may lead to a career in the actuarial profession.

YEAR PROGRAM STARTED: 1977

LEGAL BASIS:
Private and corporate funded.

ELIGIBILITY:
Applicants must be Black/African American, Hispanic and Native North American full-time undergraduate and graduate students.

FINANCIAL DATA:
Amount of support per award: Varies by need.
Total amount of support: $50,000 for the year 2010.

NUMBER OF APPLICANTS MOST RECENT YEAR:
30 for the year 2010.

NUMBER OF AWARDS: 23 for the year 2010.

APPLICATION INFORMATION:
Application guidelines and form are available online.
Duration: One academic year. Renewable based on academic performance.
Deadline: May 4, 2012.

IRS IDENTIFICATION NUMBER: 36-2136422

ADDRESS INQUIRIES TO:
Debbie McCormac
Scholarship Coordinator
(See address above.)

THE ACTUARIAL FOUNDATION   [2223]

475 North Martingale Road, Suite 600
Schaumburg, IL 60173-2226
(847) 706-3535
Fax: (847) 706-3599

E-MAIL ADDRESS:
Scholarships@ActFnd.org

WEB SITE ADDRESS:
www.actuarialfoundation.org

AREAS OF INTEREST:
Actuarial science.

NAME(S) OF PROGRAMS:
- **John Culver Wooddy Scholarship**

TYPE:
Scholarships.

YEAR PROGRAM STARTED: 1996

PURPOSE:
To provide scholarships to actuarial students.

ELIGIBILITY:
College seniors who will receive their undergraduate degree no later than August 31 of the following year. Students must rank in the top quartile of their class and have successfully completed one actuarial examination. Students must be recommended by a professor from their school.

Preference will be given to candidates who have demonstrated leadership potential through extracurricular activities.

FINANCIAL DATA:
Amount of support per award: $2,000.
Total amount of support: Approximately $26,000.

NUMBER OF AWARDS: 13.

APPLICATION INFORMATION:
Students must complete the application and write a brief essay as part of the application process. The student should then submit the completed application and essay to a professor at the student's school. The professor should verify the student's class ranking and senior status, and prepare a letter of recommendation. Mail the completed application form, recommendation letter and required essay to the Foundation.
Duration: One year.
Deadline: April 24. Notification by August 26.

ADDRESS INQUIRIES TO:
Debbie McCormac, Project Specialist
(See address above.)

THE ACTUARIAL FOUNDATION   [2224]

475 North Martingale Road, Suite 600
Schaumburg, IL 60173-2226
(847) 706-3535
Fax: (847) 706-3599

E-MAIL ADDRESS:
Scholarships@ActFnd.org

WEB SITE ADDRESS:
www.actuarialfoundation.org

FOUNDED: 2006

AREAS OF INTEREST:
Actuarial science.

NAME(S) OF PROGRAMS:
- **Actuary of Tomorrow - The Stuart A. Robertson Memorial Scholarship**

TYPE:
Scholarships.

YEAR PROGRAM STARTED: 2006

PURPOSE:
To recognize and encourage the academic achievements of undergraduate students pursuing a career in actuarial science.

ELIGIBILITY:
Applicant must:
(1) be a full-time undergraduate student entering as a sophomore, junior or senior in the fall term;
(2) have a minimum cumulative grade point average of 3.0 (on a 4.0 scale);
(3) have successfully completed two actuarial exams;
(4) attach a current official copy of transcripts (sealed) from attending college/university;
(5) provide a letter of recommendation supporting academic achievement, leadership and communication skills from professor or advisor;
(6) provide a letter of recommendation from an employer or previous employer and;
(7) submit a personal essay of approximately 500 words, focusing on why you want to be an actuary.

GEOGRAPHIC RESTRICTIONS:
United States.

FINANCIAL DATA:
Amount of support per award: $7,500.

APPLICATION INFORMATION:
Applicant should meet the eligibility requirements and mail the completed and signed application, sealed transcripts, personal essay, and a letter of recommendation to the Foundation at the address above.
Deadline: June 1. Notification by mail after August 1.

ADDRESS INQUIRIES TO:
Ellie Vogel
Foundation Administration Assistant
(See e-mail and address above.)

*SPECIAL STIPULATIONS:
Scholarships are awarded directly to the college/university of choice in the recipients' name.

AMERICAN MATHEMATICAL SOCIETY   [2225]

201 Charles Street
Providence, RI 02904-2294
(800) 321-4267 ext. 4101
(401) 455-4101
Fax: (401) 455-4004

E-MAIL ADDRESS:
prof-serv@ams.org

WEB SITE ADDRESS:
www.ams.org

FOUNDED: 1888

AREAS OF INTEREST:
Research mathematics.

NAME(S) OF PROGRAMS:
- **American Mathematical Society Centennial Fellowship**

TYPE:
Fellowships. The AMS Centennial Research Fellowship Program makes awards annually to outstanding mathematicians to help further their careers in research.

PURPOSE:
To help outstanding mathematicians further their careers in research.

LEGAL BASIS:
Nonprofit corporation.

ELIGIBILITY:
The primary selection criterion for the Centennial Fellowship is the excellence of the candidate's research. Preference will be given to candidates who have not had extensive fellowship support in the past. Recipients may not hold the Centennial Fellowship concurrently with another research fellowship such as a Sloan or NSF Postdoctoral fellowship. Under normal circumstances, the fellowship cannot be deferred. A recipient of the fellowship shall have held his or her doctoral degree for at least three years and not more than 12 years at the inception of the award. Applications will be accepted from those currently holding a tenured, tenure-track, postdoctoral, or comparable (at the discretion of the selection committee) position at an institution in North America.

GEOGRAPHIC RESTRICTIONS:
North America.

FINANCIAL DATA:
Amount of support per award:
Approximately $79,000, plus about $7,900 for expenses.
Total amount of support: Varies.

COOPERATIVE FUNDING PROGRAMS: The Society has a matching program so that funds for at least one fellowship are guaranteed.

NUMBER OF AWARDS: 1 fellowship for the 2011-12 academic year.

APPLICATION INFORMATION:
Applications should include a cogent plan indicating how the fellowship will be used. The plan should include travel to at least one other institution and should demonstrate that the fellowship will be used for more than reduction of teaching at the candidate's home institution. The selection committee will consider the plan in addition to the quality of the candidate's research, and will try to award the fellowship to those for whom the award would make a real difference in the development of their research careers. Work in all areas of mathematics, including interdisciplinary work, is eligible.

Application forms can be accessed at the web site. For paper copies of the form, contact the Membership & Programs Department, American Mathematical Society, at the address or e-mail above, or phone (401) 455-4105.
Duration: One year. Nonrenewable.

Deadline: December 1. Announcement in February, or earlier if possible.

PUBLICATIONS:
Application guidelines.

OFFICERS:
Eric Friedlander, President
Jane Hawkins, Treasurer
John Franks, Associate Treasurer

ADDRESS INQUIRIES TO:
Associate Executive Director
(See address above.)

*SPECIAL STIPULATIONS:
Acceptance of the Fellowship cannot be postponed.

CONFERENCE BOARD OF THE MATHEMATICAL SCIENCES   [2226]
1529 18th Street, N.W.
Washington, DC 20036
(202) 293-1170
Fax: (202) 293-3412

E-MAIL ADDRESS:
rosier@georgetown.edu

WEB SITE ADDRESS:
www.cbmsweb.org

FOUNDED: 1960

AREAS OF INTEREST:
Mathematical sciences.

NAME(S) OF PROGRAMS:
- **NSF-CBMS Regional Conferences in the Mathematical Sciences**

TYPE:
Conferences/seminars. Grants given jointly by NSF and the Conference Board for five-day conferences in the mathematical sciences.

YEAR PROGRAM STARTED: 1969

PURPOSE:
To stimulate interest and activity in mathematical research.

LEGAL BASIS:
A nonprofit professional society.

ELIGIBILITY:
Colleges or universities with at least some research competence in the field of the proposal are eligible to apply. Since a major goal of these conferences is to attract new researchers into the field of the conference and to stimulate new research activity, institutions that are interested in upgrading or improving their research efforts are especially encouraged to apply.

FINANCIAL DATA:
Grants for approximately 25 to 30 participants may include travel and lodging costs, director's and secretary's salaries, announcement costs and other miscellaneous expenses.
Amount of support per award: $33,000 to $35,000.

COOPERATIVE FUNDING PROGRAMS: Grants are given jointly with NSF.

NUMBER OF AWARDS: Up to 7 for the year 2010.

APPLICATION INFORMATION:
Proposals must be submitted electronically via Fastlane to the Division of Mathematical Sciences (DMS) at NSF.
Duration: Five days during the summer or during a recess in the academic year.

Deadline: Mid- to late April. Announcement in October.

PUBLICATIONS:
Monographs of the conferences are available from the American Mathematical Society, the Society for Industrial and Applied Mathematics, the Institute of Mathematical Statistics and the American Statistical Association.

IBM THOMAS J. WATSON RESEARCH CENTER   [2227]
Department of Mathematical Sciences
1101 Kitchawan Road, Route 134
Yorktown Heights, NY 10598
(914) 945-1588
Fax: (914) 945-3434

E-MAIL ADDRESS:
goldpost@watson.ibm.com

WEB SITE ADDRESS:
www.research.ibm.com/math/goldstine.html

AREAS OF INTEREST:
Research in pure and applied mathematics and in theoretical and exploratory computer science.

NAME(S) OF PROGRAMS:
- **IBM Herman Goldstine Memorial Postdoctoral Fellowship for Research in Mathematical and Computer Sciences**

TYPE:
Fellowships.

YEAR PROGRAM STARTED: 1972

PURPOSE:
To provide scientists of outstanding ability an opportunity to advance their scholarship as resident department members at the IBM Thomas J. Watson Research Center.

ELIGIBILITY:
Applicant must have a Ph.D. in science, engineering or mathematics received within the last five years.

FINANCIAL DATA:
Allowance provided for moving expenses.
Amount of support per award: $95,000 to $115,000 per year, depending on the area and length of experience.

NUMBER OF APPLICANTS MOST RECENT YEAR: 70.

NUMBER OF AWARDS: 1 annually.

APPLICATION INFORMATION:
Applications accepted via e-mail only.

Applicants are also responsible for arranging for three or more letters of recommendation, including one from the thesis advisor, that must also be e-mailed to the address above.
Duration: One year. Renewable for a second year if of mutual interest.
Deadline: Applications accepted October 26 to January 6.

ADDRESS INQUIRIES TO:
Dharmashankar Subramanian
Research Staff Member
(See address above.)

MICRON TECHNOLOGY FOUNDATION, INC.   [2228]
8000 South Federal Way
P.O. Box 6
Boise, ID 83707-0006
(208) 363-3675
Fax: (208) 368-4435

E-MAIL ADDRESS:
mtf@micron.com

WEB SITE ADDRESS:
www.micron.com/foundation

FOUNDED: 1999

AREAS OF INTEREST:
Education with an emphasis on math, science and technology.

TYPE:
Awards/prizes; Matching gifts; Professorships; Project/program grants; Research grants.

YEAR PROGRAM STARTED: 2000

PURPOSE:
To support a wide range of projects and programs which promote the growth and enhance the quality of the community, with primary emphasis on youth and educational programs related to math and science.

LEGAL BASIS:
Private corporate foundation.

ELIGIBILITY:
Micron will consider projects or programs:
(1) which address an educational need, especially those which advance math and science;
(2) which impact a large number of people;
(3) which have long-term benefits and;
(4) which are in a geographic area where Micron has operations.

Micron generally does not address individual sponsorships or donations, requests for assistance with travel or lodging expenses, religious organizations requesting funds for purposes other than nondenominational education or organizations located in areas where Micron has no operations.

GEOGRAPHIC RESTRICTIONS:
Boise, Idaho and Manassas, Virginia.

FINANCIAL DATA:
Amount of support per award: Varies.
Total amount of support: Varies.
Matching fund requirements: Micron may match employee donations at a 1:1 ratio, K-12 up to $100 and higher education grants up to $1,000 per employee per calendar year to qualified educational institutions.

NUMBER OF AWARDS: Varies.

REPRESENTATIVE AWARDS:
Boise School District Educational Foundation; Boise State University; University of Idaho; University of Washington; Virginia Tech.

APPLICATION INFORMATION:
Supporting materials can be included with the application form, but may not be reviewed in their entirety.

Higher education grants by invitation only.
Duration: Varies.

IRS IDENTIFICATION NUMBER: 82-0516178

ADDRESS INQUIRIES TO:
Micron Technology Foundation, M/S 407
Community and Academic Relations
8000 South Federal Way, P.O. Box 6
Boise, ID 83707-0006

SOCIETY OF ACTUARIES (SOA) [2229]

475 North Martingale Road
Suite 600
Schaumburg, IL 60173-2226
(847) 706-3509
Fax: (847) 273-8605

E-MAIL ADDRESS:
acoffelt@soa.org

WEB SITE ADDRESS:
www.soa.org/education/resources/academic-initiatives/soa-doc-stipend.aspx

FOUNDED: 1949

AREAS OF INTEREST:
Actuarial science, a branch of mathematics based on calculus, probability and statistics, as well as business economics.

NAME(S) OF PROGRAMS:
• **Society of Actuaries' James C. Hickman Scholar Doctoral Stipend Program**

TYPE:
Awards/prizes; Scholarships. Society of Actuaries' James C. Hickman Scholar Doctoral Stipend Program is designed to provide stipends to doctoral students who will, through their studies, address research and education needs of the profession, including both the theoretical and practical aspects.

YEAR PROGRAM STARTED: 2009

PURPOSE:
To increase the number of academic actuaries who hold a Ph.D. and an actuarial designation, and who intend to pursue academic careers in the U.S. or Canada.

LEGAL BASIS:
Society funded.

ELIGIBILITY:
Individuals who meet the following requirements may apply:
(1) enrolled full-time, have recently been admitted or are currently applying to a qualifying doctoral program in the U.S. or Canada; a qualifying doctoral program is one in actuarial science or a field related to actuarial science (e.g., business, demography, economics, financial economics, insurance, mathematics, risk management, statistics); applicants may apply at the same time they are applying for a doctoral program; if selected, these applicants will be awarded the stipend conditional upon enrollment in a qualifying doctoral program;
(2) hold a fellowship-level actuarial credential or are pursuing Associateship or Fellowship membership of an accrediting actuarial organization (i.e., CAS, CIA, FA, IA, IAA, SOA); applicants who are already Associate members (including those awarded the CERA designation) will be expected to pursue a Fellowship credential and;
(3) all applicants must have at least two actuarial exams passed.

While U.S. or Canadian citizenship is not expressly required, the applicant will attest to citizenship status on the application. An applicant's citizenship status may be used to evaluate the likelihood that the applicant will pursue an academic career in the U.S. or Canada.

FINANCIAL DATA:
The stipend is to be used at the discretion of the Ph.D. candidate for appropriate expenses related to the completion of the Ph.D. and the actuarial credential if not yet attained. Applicants should be aware that stipend funds are provided for qualified expenses (tuition, books, fees, etc.). Qualified expenses do not include room and board. Stipend funds not used for qualified expenses may be taxable. Please consult one's tax advisor if one has any questions.

Amount of support per award: Generally $20,000 per academic year.
Total amount of support: Varies.

NUMBER OF APPLICANTS MOST RECENT YEAR:
50.

NUMBER OF AWARDS: Varies.

APPLICATION INFORMATION:
Applicants must submit an application and supporting documentation that includes the following:
(1) Applicants currently applying to doctoral programs must provide the names of the schools/programs to which they have applied, and the intended field of study in each school/program. (If a stipend is awarded, it will be conditional on enrollment in the specified program and for the field of study proposed in the application.);
(2) Applicants already enrolled in a doctoral program will indicate how many years they have been studying, and approximately how many more years they believe they need to complete their Doctorate. They will also provide a statement from their supervisor or program director attesting to progess in their doctoral program and;
(3) Applicant must submit a Statement of Interest. This may be the same statement submitted for the doctoral program, but additional language should be added for this application to clearly explain their goals regarding teaching, research and contributions to the actuarial profession.

Duration: One academic year. Renewable up to four times based on satisfactory progress.
Deadline: Completed application forms and supporting materials must be received at the Society no later than February 15. Recipients will be announced April 15. Recipients must notify the Society of acceptance of the stipend by May 15.

PUBLICATIONS:
Application guidelines.

OFFICERS:
S. Michael McLaughlin, President

ADDRESS INQUIRIES TO:
Doctoral Stipends Program
(See address above.)

SOCIETY OF ACTUARIES (SOA) [2230]

475 North Martingale Road
Suite 600
Schaumburg, IL 60173-2226
(847) 706-3509
Fax: (847) 273-8605

E-MAIL ADDRESS:
acoffelt@soa.org

WEB SITE ADDRESS:
www.soa.org/education/resources/academic-initiatives/soa-doc-stipend.aspx

FOUNDED: 1949

AREAS OF INTEREST:
Actuarial science, a branch of mathematics based on calculus, probability and statistics, as well as business economics.

NAME(S) OF PROGRAMS:
• **Society of Actuaries Educational Institution Grant**

TYPE:
Awards/prizes; Development grants; General operating grants; Project/program grants; Research grants; Scholarships; Travel grants. Grants to educational institutions.

YEAR PROGRAM STARTED: 1991

PURPOSE:
To provide financial support for the promotion and development of educational and research programs in actuarial science; to recognize the added value professional actuarial qualifications offer to actuarial teaching and research.

LEGAL BASIS:
Society funded.

ELIGIBILITY:
A full-time faculty member at the applying institution must attain Associateship (ASA) status or Fellowship (FSA) status to qualify the institution for a grant.

Full-time faculty are defined as individuals employed by a college or university who are considered to be full-time members of the regular faculty by their employer. This does not include visiting faculty, adjuncts, graduate students or teaching assistants.

FINANCIAL DATA:
Amount of support per award: $5,000 (U.S.) one-time grant to an educational institution when a full-time faculty member attains ASA status; $7,500 (U.S.) one-time grant to an educational institution when a full-time faculty member attains FSA status.
Total amount of support: Varies.

NUMBER OF APPLICANTS MOST RECENT YEAR:
3.

NUMBER OF AWARDS: Varies.

APPLICATION INFORMATION:
Application form and details are available online.
Deadline: Applications for institution grants must be received within three years of the date the faculty member attains FSA or ASA status as indicated on the FSA or ASA diploma.

PUBLICATIONS:
Application guidelines.

OFFICERS:
Donald J. Segal, President

ADDRESS INQUIRIES TO:
ASA/FSA Grant Program
(See address above.)

Physics

AMERICAN INSTITUTE OF PHYSICS   [2231]
One Physics Ellipse
College Park, MD 20740-3843
(301) 209-3090
(301) 209-3096
Fax: (301) 209-0846

E-MAIL ADDRESS:
pubinfo@aip.org

WEB SITE ADDRESS:
www.aip.org/aip/writing

FOUNDED: 1931

AREAS OF INTEREST:
The advancement and diffusion of the knowledge of physics and its application to human welfare.

NAME(S) OF PROGRAMS:
- **American Institute of Physics Science Writing Award in Physics and Astronomy**

TYPE:
Awards/prizes. Four writing awards, one to a physicist, astronomer or member of an AIP society, one to a journalist for noteworthy writing about physics and astronomy in the print media, one to a journalist for noteworthy writing about physics and astronomy for broadcast media, and one for science writing aimed at children.

PURPOSE:
To stimulate distinguished reporting and writing that will improve public understanding of physics and astronomy.

ELIGIBILITY:
Entries must have been printed in any recognized international, national or local medium of communication such as newspapers, magazines or books. The media should normally be available to and intended for the general public. Purely scientific, technical and trade publications are excluded.

Entries must have been published or translated into English during the period one year immediately prior to the deadline date. No more than three entries may be submitted by any one individual. Persons other than the author may submit entries on behalf of an author in accordance with the rules.

FINANCIAL DATA:
Amount of support per award: $3,000.
Total amount of support: $9,000.

NUMBER OF APPLICANTS MOST RECENT YEAR:
75.

NUMBER OF AWARDS: 3 for the year 2010.

APPLICATION INFORMATION:
Deadline: March 2.

OFFICERS:
H. Frederick Dylia, Executive Director and Chief Executive Officer
Richard Baccante, Treasurer and Chief Financial Officer
Benjamin Snavely, Secretary
Darlene Walters, Senior Vice President, Publishing
Theresa C. Braun, Vice President, Human Resources
Catherine O'Riordan, Vice President, Physics Resource Center

ADDRESS INQUIRIES TO:
Tatiana Bonilla, Programs Coordinator
(See address above.)

AMERICAN VACUUM SOCIETY (AVS)   [2232]
125 Maiden Lane, Room 1501
New York, NY 10038-4714
(212) 248-0200
Fax: (212) 248-0245

E-MAIL ADDRESS:
avsnyc@avs.org

WEB SITE ADDRESS:
www.avs.org

FOUNDED: 1953

AREAS OF INTEREST:
Vacuum science and technology, thin film research, vacuum metallurgy, surface physics, electronic materials and processing, plasma science and technology and applied surface science.

NAME(S) OF PROGRAMS:
- **Graduate Research Awards**
- **Russell and Sigurd Varian Award**
- **Nellie Yeoh Whetten Award**

TYPE:
Awards/prizes; Fellowships. Cash awards and a one-year fellowship in recognition of scientific promise or excellence in graduate studies in vacuum science.

The Whetten Award is offered to encourage and recognize participation by women in science and engineering.

PURPOSE:
To recognize and encourage excellence in graduate studies in the sciences and technologies of interest to the Society.

LEGAL BASIS:
Nonprofit 501(c)(3) organization.

ELIGIBILITY:
All awards are open to students engaged in graduate studies in major fields of the organization's interest at accredited graduate schools in North America.

For the Whetten Award, the nominee must be a registered female graduate student in an accredited academic institution at the time when the applications are due. Criteria for selection of the awardee are research and academic excellence.

FINANCIAL DATA:
Amount of support per award: Graduate Research Awards: $1,000 per award; $1,500 each for the Whetten Award and for the Varian Award, plus reimbursed travel support (up to $750 maximum) to attend the International Symposium.
Total amount of support: Usually $8,000 to $10,000 each year.

NUMBER OF APPLICANTS MOST RECENT YEAR:
19.

NUMBER OF AWARDS: Graduate Research Awards: Approximately 10 annually; Varian Award and Whetten Award: 1 each per year.

ADDRESS INQUIRIES TO:
Angela Klink
Program Administrator
(See address above.)
E-mail: angela@avs.org

MCDONNELL CENTER FOR THE SPACE SCIENCES
Washington University, Campus Box 1105
One Brookings Drive
St. Louis, MO 63130-4899
(314) 935-5332
Fax: (314) 935-4134

E-MAIL ADDRESS:
trecia@physics.wustl.edu

WEB SITE ADDRESS:
mcss.wustl.edu

TYPE:
Fellowships. These fellowships are funded by a gift from the McDonnell Douglas Foundation to Washington University and provide tuition remission plus stipend for graduate students interested in pursuing research in the space sciences who are

enrolled in the Washington University Departments of Physics or Earth and Planetary Sciences.

See entry 2787 for full listing.

NATIONAL SCIENCE FOUNDATION [2233]

Division of Physics
4201 Wilson Boulevard
Arlington, VA 22230
(703) 292-8890
Fax: (703) 292-9078

E-MAIL ADDRESS:
jdehmer@nsf.gov

WEB SITE ADDRESS:
www.nsf.gov

AREAS OF INTEREST:
Nuclear, theoretical, atomic and molecular, gravitational, and elementary particles, education and interdisciplinary research, physics of living systems, particle and nuclear astrophysics.

NAME(S) OF PROGRAMS:
● **Physics Research Grants**

TYPE:
Research grants.

ELIGIBILITY:
Candidates must be U.S. citizens and enrolled at an eligible U.S. institution.

GEOGRAPHIC RESTRICTIONS:
United States and its territories.

FINANCIAL DATA:
Amount of support per award: Varies.
Total amount of support: $3,000,000 budgeted annually.

APPLICATION INFORMATION:
Duration: Typically one to five years. Renewals by reapplication.
Deadline: Varies according to program; majority by end of September.

STAFF:
Steven J. Gitomer, Program Director, Atomic, Molecular, Optical and Plasma Physics
Wendell T. Hill, Program Director, Atomic, Molecular, Optical and Plasma Physics
Kathleen McCloud, Program Director, Education and Interdisciplinary Research Program
Marvin Goldberg, Program Director, Elementary Particle Physics
Moishe Pripstein, Program Director, Elementary Particle Physics
James J. Reidy, Program Director, Elementary Particle Physics
Beverly Berger, Program Director, Gravitational Physics
Tom Carruthers, Program Director, Gravitational Physics
Bradley D. Keister, Program Director, Nuclear Astrophysics, Nuclear Physics and Theoretical Physics
Kyungseon Joo, Program Director, Nuclear Physics
Jonathan Kotcher, Program Director, Particle Astrophysics Program
James Whitmore, Program Director, Particle Astrophysics Program

C. Denise Caldwell, Program Director, Physics Frontiers Centers Program
Krastan B. Blagoev, Program Director, Physics of Living Systems
Keith R. Dienes, Program Director, Theoretical Physics
Earle Lomon, Program Director, Theoretical Physics
Richard H. Pratt, Program Director, Theoretical Physics

ADDRESS INQUIRIES TO:
Joseph Dehmer, Division Director
Division of Physics
(See address above.)

SOCIETY OF PHYSICS STUDENTS [2234]

American Institute of Physics
One Physics Ellipse
College Park, MD 20740
(301) 209-3007
Fax: (301) 209-0839

E-MAIL ADDRESS:
sps@aip.org

WEB SITE ADDRESS:
www.spsnational.
org/programs/awards/research.htm

AREAS OF INTEREST:
Physics.

NAME(S) OF PROGRAMS:
● **Sigma Pi Sigma Undergraduate Research Awards**

TYPE:
Awards/prizes.

PURPOSE:
To promote interest in physics among students and the general public.

LEGAL BASIS:
Nonprofit.

ELIGIBILITY:
Must participate in annual competition and must be SPS member.

FINANCIAL DATA:
Amount of support per award: Up to $2,000.
Total amount of support: Varies.

COOPERATIVE FUNDING PROGRAMS: Funded through income from the Sigma Pi Sigma Trust Endowment Fund.

NUMBER OF AWARDS: Typically 6 to 10.

APPLICATION INFORMATION:
Submit a proposal to the Society which:
(1) contains a precise statement of the proposed Chapter activity;
(2) shows evidence of imaginative and thoughtful appraisal of the objectives of the SPS program and the ways in which the proposed activity would contribute towards those objectives;
(3) is written clearly and concisely in correct English;
(4) includes bibliographical references;
(5) contains a realistic budget totaling not more than $2,000 and;
(6) is signed by the advisor and officers of the Chapter.
Duration: One year.

Deadline: November 15.

STAFF:
Dr. Gary White, Director

SOCIETY OF PHYSICS STUDENTS [2235]

One Physics Ellipse
College Park, MD 20740
(301) 209-3009
Fax: (301) 209-0839

E-MAIL ADDRESS:
sps@aip.org

WEB SITE ADDRESS:
www.spsnational.org

FOUNDED: 1968

AREAS OF INTEREST:
Physics.

NAME(S) OF PROGRAMS:
● **Marsh W. White Awards**

TYPE:
Awards/prizes.

YEAR PROGRAM STARTED: 1974

PURPOSE:
To promote interest in physics.

LEGAL BASIS:
Not-for-profit, 501(c)(3).

ELIGIBILITY:
Applicant must be a Society of Physics Students member.

FINANCIAL DATA:
Amount of support per award: Up to $300.
Total amount of support: Approximately $2,700 per year.

NUMBER OF APPLICANTS MOST RECENT YEAR:
20.

APPLICATION INFORMATION:
Duration: One year.
Deadline: November 15. Announcement January 1.

STAFF:
Dr. Gary White, Director

ADDRESS INQUIRIES TO:
See e-mail address above.

*SPECIAL STIPULATIONS:
Only one proposal may be submitted by an SPS chapter.

SOCIETY OF PHYSICS STUDENTS

One Physics Ellipse
College Park, MD 20740-3843
(301) 209-3007
Fax: (301) 209-0839

E-MAIL ADDRESS:
sps@aip.org

WEB SITE ADDRESS:
www.spsnational.org

TYPE:
Scholarships.

See entry 1879 for full listing.

LIFE SCIENCES

Life sciences (general)

THE ANXIETY DISORDERS ASSOCIATION OF AMERICA

8730 Georgia Avenue, Suite 600
Silver Spring, MD 20910
(240) 485-1001
Fax: (240) 485-1035

E-MAIL ADDRESS:
  smenase@adaa.org

WEB SITE ADDRESS:
  www.adaa.org

TYPE:
  Conferences/seminars; Project/program grants; Research grants; Seed money grants; Travel grants.

See entry 2730 for full listing.

DELTA SOCIETY [2236]

875 124th Avenue, N.E.
Suite 101
Bellevue, WA 98005
(425) 679-5500
Fax: (425) 679-5539

E-MAIL ADDRESS:
  info@deltasociety.org

WEB SITE ADDRESS:
  www.deltasociety.org

FOUNDED: 1977

AREAS OF INTEREST:
  People and animals.

CONSULTING OR VOLUNTEER SERVICES:
  The Pet Partners Program trains volunteers and screens their pets for visiting animal programs in hospitals, nursing homes and schools.

NAME(S) OF PROGRAMS:
  ● **James M. Harris/Sarah W. Sweatt Student Travel Grant**

TYPE:
  Awards/prizes; Travel grants. An annual grant for transportation costs for a student to attend the Delta Society Training Conference.

YEAR PROGRAM STARTED: 1984

PURPOSE:
  To support transportation costs for a student to attend the Delta Society Training Conference.

LEGAL BASIS:
  Nonprofit, 501(c)(3) organization.

ELIGIBILITY:
  Students must be enrolled full-time in a veterinary or human health professional training program, pursuing a Master's or doctoral degree.

GEOGRAPHIC RESTRICTIONS:
  United States.

FINANCIAL DATA:
  Amount of support per award: Varies.
  Total amount of support: Varies.

NUMBER OF AWARDS: 1.

PUBLICATIONS:
  InterActions.

IRS IDENTIFICATION NUMBER: 91-1158281

BOARD OF DIRECTORS:
  Gregg K. Takashima, D.V.M., Chairman

ADDRESS INQUIRIES TO:
  Research Support Coordinator
  (See address above.)

*PLEASE NOTE:
  Grant will not be offered until Society has a conference within the next five years.

DJ & T FOUNDATION [2237]

9201 Wilshire Boulevard, Suite 204
Beverly Hills, CA 90210
(310) 278-1160
Fax: (310) 275-6202

E-MAIL ADDRESS:
  will@prappascompany.com

WEB SITE ADDRESS:
  www.djtfoundation.org

FOUNDED: 1995

AREAS OF INTEREST:
  Animal population control.

TYPE:
  Grants-in-aid. Fund grants to organizations that operate low-cost spay/neuter clinics or offer free or low-cost spay/neuter voucher programs.

YEAR PROGRAM STARTED: 1995

PURPOSE:
  To fund nonprofit, low-cost spay and neuter clinics.

LEGAL BASIS:
  Private foundation.

ELIGIBILITY:
  Eligible organizations must be IRS 501(c)(3) tax-exempt.

GEOGRAPHIC RESTRICTIONS:
  United States.

FINANCIAL DATA:
  Amount of support per award: Varies.
  Total amount of support: Varies.

NUMBER OF APPLICANTS MOST RECENT YEAR:
  More than 200.

NUMBER OF AWARDS: 75 to 100.

APPLICATION INFORMATION:
  Applications are available at the web site and must include a copy of the IRS tax determination letter.

ADDRESS INQUIRIES TO:
  William Prappas, Business Manager
  (See address above.)

THE ELLISON MEDICAL FOUNDATION [2238]

4710 Bethesda Avenue
Suite 204
Bethesda, MD 20814-5226
(301) 657-1830
Fax: (301) 657-1828

E-MAIL ADDRESS:
  rsprott@ellisonfoundation.org

WEB SITE ADDRESS:
  www.ellisonfoundation.org

FOUNDED: 1997

AREAS OF INTEREST:
  Basic biomedical research on aging relevant to understanding lifespan development processes and age-related diseases and disabilities, including structural biology, molecular genetics, studies with model systems ranging from lower eukaryotes to humans, inquiries testing the relevance of simpler models to human aging, genetic epidemiology of aging, candidate longevity genes, aging in the immune system, host defense molecules in aging systems, mechanisms of free radical-induced cell aging, mechanisms of aging in various differentiated cell populations, gene/environment and gene/gene interactions, integrative physiology, and new approaches to age-modulated disease mechanisms such as those leading to dementias.

NAME(S) OF PROGRAMS:
  ● **New Scholar Award**
  ● **Senior Scholar Award**

TYPE:
  Awards/prizes; Conferences/seminars; Research grants; Training grants. New Scholar Awards are intended to support newly independent investigators of outstanding promise in the field of aging research. The award is intended to provide new faculty with the support needed to permit them to become established.

  Senior Scholar Awards are designed to support established investigators, working at nonprofit institutions in the U.S., to conduct research in the basic biological sciences relevant to understanding lifespan development processes and age-related diseases and disabilities.

YEAR PROGRAM STARTED: 1998

PURPOSE:
  To stimulate innovative research which has rigorous scientific foundations, but which currently may not be funded adequately because of its perceived novelty or high risk, or because the investigator is moving into a new research area.

LEGAL BASIS:
  Nonprofit corporation.

ELIGIBILITY:
  New Scholar applications are solicited by invitation only to U.S. institutions with substantial research programs in areas relevant to aging.

GEOGRAPHIC RESTRICTIONS:
  United States.

FINANCIAL DATA:
  Acceptable uses for the award funds include salary, other personnel, equipment, supplies, resource acquisition and travel.

  Amount of support per award: New Scholar Award: Up to $100,000 per year for up to four years; Senior Scholar Award: Up to $150,000 per year for direct costs plus indirect costs for up to four years.

  Total amount of support: $38,964,726 for the year 2010. New Scholars: $8,539,375; Senior Scholars: $22,921,915; other awards: $7,503,436.

NUMBER OF APPLICANTS MOST RECENT YEAR:
  For the year 2010: New Scholars, 112; Senior Scholars, 190; other applicants, 28.

NUMBER OF AWARDS: For the year 2010: New Scholars, 25; Senior Scholars, 26; other awards, 25.

APPLICATION INFORMATION:
  Guidelines and instructions are available from the Foundation.

  Duration: Up to four years.

PUBLICATIONS:
  Philanthropy for Basic Science: The Ellison Medical Foundation's First Five Years; Philanthropy for Basic Biomedical Sciences.

IRS IDENTIFICATION NUMBER: 94-3269827

STAFF:
  Richard L. Sprott, Ph.D., Executive Director

Kevin Lee, Ph.D, Deputy Executive Director
Esther Paul, Grants Program Manager
Margaret Sprott, Budget Analyst
Lisa Glazier, Office Administrator

ADDRESS INQUIRIES TO:
Richard L. Sprott, Ph.D.
Executive Director
(See address above.)

*SPECIAL STIPULATIONS:
New Scholar applications are solicited by
invitation only.

THE HAMNER INSTITUTES FOR HEALTH SCIENCES

6 Davis Drive
Research Triangle Park, NC 27709
(919) 558-1331
Fax: (919) 558-1430

E-MAIL ADDRESS:
koverman@thehamner.org

WEB SITE ADDRESS:
www.thehamner.org

TYPE:
Conferences/seminars; Fellowships;
Internships; Visiting scholars.

See entry 2198 for full listing.

THE HASTINGS CENTER   [2239]

21 Malcolm Gordon Road
Garrison, NY 10524
(845) 424-4040
Fax: (845) 424-4545

E-MAIL ADDRESS:
visitors@thehastingscenter.org

WEB SITE ADDRESS:
www.thehastingscenter.org

FOUNDED: 1969

AREAS OF INTEREST:
Ethical issues in medicine, health care and
the life sciences. Recent research topics
include biotechnology, death and dying,
aging, neonatal care, allocation of resources,
occupational health, health
professional-patient relationships, chronic
illness, rehabilitation medicine, AIDS,
surrogate motherhood and artificial
reproduction, organ transplantation,
prospective payment systems,
deinstitutionalization, nursing homes, animal
experimentation, environmental protection,
civic education and the professions and the
public good.

NAME(S) OF PROGRAMS:
● **Internships**
● **Visiting Scholars Program**

TYPE:
Internships; Residencies; Visiting scholars.
Independent study. Some financial aid is
available.

YEAR PROGRAM STARTED: 1969

PURPOSE:
To permit scholars and practitioners in the
humanities or the sciences to conduct
productive research on ethical issues in
medicine, the life sciences and the
professions.

LEGAL BASIS:
Nonprofit independent research association.

ELIGIBILITY:
Visiting Scholars Program is open to persons
with a degree in the humanities, sciences,
law or medicine and that are prepared to
pursue their own independent research
project in the Center's areas of interest.

Student Internship is open to undergraduate
and graduate students. Intern work with
researchers on a project or
project-in-development.

FINANCIAL DATA:
Amount of support per award: Waiver of cost
of apartment rental up to $600.
Total amount of support: Up to $600.

NUMBER OF APPLICANTS MOST RECENT YEAR:
21.

NUMBER OF AWARDS: 4.

APPLICATION INFORMATION:
Duration: Two to eight weeks.

PUBLICATIONS:
Annual report; application guidelines;
*Hastings Center Report; Hastings Center
Books in Print; IRB: Ethics and Human
Research; Bioethics Forum.*

ADDRESS INQUIRIES TO:
Visiting Scholars Program or
Interns Program (as appropriate)
(See address above.)

THOMAS F. AND KATE MILLER JEFFRESS MEMORIAL TRUST   [2240]

Bank of America
Philanthropic Management
P.O. Box 26688
Richmond, VA 23261-6688
(804) 788-3698
Fax: (804) 788-2700

FOUNDED: 1982

AREAS OF INTEREST:
Natural sciences, chemistry, physics, biology,
medical sciences, biochemistry and
microbiology.

NAME(S) OF PROGRAMS:
● **Jeffress Research Grants**

TYPE:
Research grants.

YEAR PROGRAM STARTED: 1982

PURPOSE:
To support basic research in chemical,
medical, or other scientific fields at
educational and research institutions in the
Commonwealth of Virginia.

LEGAL BASIS:
Trust.

ELIGIBILITY:
Grants are made to tax-exempt institutions
and organizations which are operated
exclusively for charitable, scientific purposes.
Grants are not made to private foundations.

GEOGRAPHIC RESTRICTIONS:
Virginia.

FINANCIAL DATA:
Grants cover up to $1,000 for national travel.
Grants will not cover indirect costs,
secretarial assistance, academic year salaries
or stipends. Fringe benefits are not included.
Amount of support per award: Maximum
$30,000 for the first year; maximum $10,000
renewal per year for two years by
reapplication.
Total amount of support: $1,300,000.

NUMBER OF APPLICANTS MOST RECENT YEAR:
74.

NUMBER OF AWARDS: 32.

APPLICATION INFORMATION:
Grant applications should include:
(1) a cover letter from the official authorized
to commit the organization in business and
financial affairs, indicating the approval of
the organization for the proposed project;
(2) a statement of the problem to be
investigated;
(3) a review of the literature placing the
problem in context;
(4) a description of experimental procedures;
(5) a detailed budget;
(6) current, anticipated or requested support
from other sources;
(7) a biographical sketch of the principal
investigator and any other senior scientists
involved in the project, including a list of
publications during the past five years and;
(8) the names and addresses of five
references knowledgeable in the field of the
proposed project, three of whom are not
known personally by the applicant.
Duration: Up to a maximum of three years.
Deadline: March 1 and September 1.

PUBLICATIONS:
Guidelines.

ADDRESS INQUIRIES TO:
Richard B. Brandt, Ph.D., Advisor
(See address above.)

*SPECIAL STIPULATIONS:
Items of direct expense essential to the
proposed project will be provided, including
undergraduate, graduate, summer student and
principal investigator summer stipends,
supplies, special equipment, travel to use
specific facilities, other necessary expenses,
and page charges for publications not to be
included in the budget but by invoice.

NATIONAL DAIRY COUNCIL

10255 West Higgins Road
Suite 900
Rosemont, IL 60018-5616
(847) 803-2000
Fax: (847) 803-2077

E-MAIL ADDRESS:
chris.cifelli@rosedmi.com

WEB SITE ADDRESS:
www.nationaldairycouncil.org

TYPE:
Research contracts. The National Dairy
Council is the nutrition research, education
and communications arm of Dairy
Management Inc. On behalf of U.S. dairy
farmers, the National Dairy Council provides
science-based nutrition information to, and in
collaboration with, a variety of stakeholders
committed to fostering a healthier society,
including health professionals, educators,
school nutrition directors, academia, industry,
consumers and media. The National Dairy
Council comprises a staff of nutrition science
researchers, registered dietitians and
communications experts dedicated to
educating the public on the health benefits of
consuming milk and milk products
throughout a person's lifespan.

See entry 2843 for full listing.

NATIONAL EYE INSTITUTE

National Institutes of Health
5635 Fishers Lane, Suite 1300
MSC 9300
Bethesda, MD 20892
(301) 451-2020
Fax: (301) 402-0528

E-MAIL ADDRESS:
2020@nei.nih.gov

WEB SITE ADDRESS:
www.nei.nih.gov

TYPE:
Conferences/seminars; Development grants;
Fellowships; Research grants; Training
grants; Research contracts. Research Project
Grants support individual investigators whose
work is aimed at discovering means of
improving the prevention, diagnosis and
treatment of blinding and disabling eye and
vision disorders.

Small Business Innovation Research Awards
aim to stimulate technological innovations, to
use small business to meet federal
research-development needs that may
ultimately lead to commercial products or
services and to foster and encourage
participation by minority and disadvantaged
persons in technological innovations.

Areas of study include vision research,
retinal diseases, corneal diseases, cataract,
glaucoma, visual impairment and its
rehabilitation, strabismus, amblyopic and
visual processing.

See entry 2676 for full listing.

NATIONAL EYE INSTITUTE

5635 Fishers Lane, Suite 1300
Bethesda, MD 20892
(301) 451-2020
Fax: (301) 496-9997

E-MAIL ADDRESS:
wwd@nei.nih.gov

WEB SITE ADDRESS:
www.nei.nih.gov

TYPE:
Research grants; Research contracts.

See entry 2677 for full listing.

NATIONAL RESEARCH COUNCIL OF THE NATIONAL ACADEMIES

Research Associateship Programs
500 Fifth Street, N.W. (Keck 568)
Washington, DC 20001
(202) 334-2760
Fax: (202) 334-2759

E-MAIL ADDRESS:
rap@nas.edu

WEB SITE ADDRESS:
www.national-academies.org/rap

TYPE:
Fellowships. Research awards. For
research-in-residence at U.S. federal
laboratories and affiliated institutions.

See entry 2166 for full listing.

THE PAUL RAPOPORT FOUNDATION, INC.   [2241]

220 East 60th Street, Suite 3-H
New York, NY 10022
(212) 888-6578
Fax: (212) 980-0867

WEB SITE ADDRESS:
www.paulrapoportfoundation.org

FOUNDED: 1987

AREAS OF INTEREST:
Concerns and needs of the lesbian, gay,
bisexual and transgender communities in the
greater New York area.

TYPE:
Challenge/matching grants; General operating
grants; Project/program grants; Seed money
grants; Technical assistance.

YEAR PROGRAM STARTED: 1987

PURPOSE:
To develop and strengthen institutions within
the lesbian and gay community; to support a
broad range of HIV/AIDS-related activities
(excluding medical research) with significant
focus on the needs of the lesbian, gay,
bisexual and transgender communities.

LEGAL BASIS:
Nonprofit foundation.

ELIGIBILITY:
Nonprofit organizations and/or projects
whose undertakings are in the areas of social
services, health care, legal rights, or
educational endeavors that promote the
development, identity and well-being of the
lesbian, gay, bisexual and transgender
communities in a positive way and efforts to
counter homophobia are eligible. The
Foundation does not support basic medical
research, political or legislative activities,
cultural and artistic activities, endowments,
deficit budgets, scholarships or grants to
individuals or other foundations, or major
building campaigns. The Foundation funds
only nonprofit, charitable organizations as
defined by the IRS Section 509(a).

GEOGRAPHIC RESTRICTIONS:
New York, New York.

FINANCIAL DATA:
Amount of support per award: $50,000 and
up.
Total amount of support: $575,500 for the
year 2007-08.

REPRESENTATIVE AWARDS:
$30,000 to CitiWide Harm Reduction
Program, Inc. for Out of the Shadows
LGBTQ Programming; $35,000 to FIERCE
for general operating support; $42,000 to
Queers for Economic Justice, Inc. for shelter
organizing project.

APPLICATION INFORMATION:
Applicants must first call the Foundation to
see if their project fits current Foundation
guidelines.
Duration: Varies with project.
Deadline: April 1 and October 1, or previous
Friday if the first falls on a weekend.

STAFF:
Ona Winet, Program Officer

ADDRESS INQUIRIES TO:
Jane D. Schwartz, Executive Director
(See address above.)

THE ROCHE FOUNDATION

340 Kingsland Street
Nutley, NJ 07110-1199
(973) 562-2055
Fax: (973) 562-2999

WEB SITE ADDRESS:
www.rocheusa.com

See entry 1720 for full listing.

KENNETH A. SCOTT CHARITABLE TRUST   [2242]

c/o KeyBank Nonprofit Services
127 Public Square, 16th Floor
Cleveland, OH 44114-1306
(216) 752-3301
Fax: (216) 752-3308

E-MAIL ADDRESS:
obermanns@aol.com

FOUNDED: 1995

AREAS OF INTEREST:
Animal welfare.

TYPE:
Project/program grants. Grants are available
for animal welfare research and humane
education projects of national scope or
significance anywhere in the U.S. Grants are
available for localized projects of shelters
and humane groups in Ohio and other Great
Lakes states (only).

YEAR PROGRAM STARTED: 1995

PURPOSE:
To prevent cruelty to animals and promote
the humane treatment of animals, particularly
companion animals (dogs, cats) and other
species commonly kept as household pets.
Requests related to wildlife and animals in
other settings may also be considered.

LEGAL BASIS:
Private foundation.

ELIGIBILITY:
Eligible organizations must be IRS 501(c)(3)
tax-exempt. No grants to individuals.

GEOGRAPHIC RESTRICTIONS:
Ohio. Some grants in other Great Lake states.

FINANCIAL DATA:
Amount of support per award: $15,000
average.

APPLICATION INFORMATION:
A query letter, e-mail or phone call to the
Trust is required before submitting the
application.
Duration: One year.
Deadline: March 15 and September 15 for
Ohio proposals. December 15 and June 15
for National and Great Lakes proposals.

IRS IDENTIFICATION NUMBER: 34-7034544

ADDRESS INQUIRIES TO:
Dr. H. Richard Obermanns
Executive Director
(See address above.)

THE PERCY SLADEN MEMORIAL FUND   [2243]

c/o The Linnean Society of London
Burlington House, Piccadilly
London W1J 0BF England
44 (0)20 7434 4479
Fax: 44 (0)20 7287 9364

E-MAIL ADDRESS:
info@linnean.org; gina@linnean.org

WEB SITE ADDRESS:
www.linnean.org

FOUNDED: 1904

AREAS OF INTEREST:
Natural sciences, with a focus of support on field work in the life and earth sciences, both through expeditions and individual research projects overseas.

NAME(S) OF PROGRAMS:
• **Percy Sladen Memorial Fund Grants**

TYPE:
Awards/prizes; Project/program grants; Research grants; Travel grants. Field work grants in life and earth sciences (excludes any projects which are part of further education, e.g., a Doctorate or a Master's course).

YEAR PROGRAM STARTED: 1904

PURPOSE:
To support field work away from usual country of residence.

LEGAL BASIS:
Registered charity.

ELIGIBILITY:
There are no restrictions in award of grants based on nationality, age, sex or prior qualifications. No grants for field work undertaken as part of a higher degree or general support for undergraduate expeditions.

FINANCIAL DATA:
Grants may be used toward a portion of total costs or for specific items of equipment.
Amount of support per award: Generally, less than GBP 750.
Total amount of support: Approximately GBP 10,000 per year.

NUMBER OF APPLICANTS MOST RECENT YEAR: 100.

NUMBER OF AWARDS: 30.

APPLICATION INFORMATION:
Application form and referees reports are available from the Secretary to the Trustees at the address above.
Duration: Grant must be taken up within one year of receipt.
Deadline: January 30 and September 30.

ADDRESS INQUIRIES TO:
Gina Douglas, Secretary
(See address above.)

*SPECIAL STIPULATIONS:
No support for course work. No undergraduate expeditions. No grants for field work for completion of dissertations or higher degrees.

SOCIETY FOR THE STUDY OF AMPHIBIANS AND REPTILES
Department of Environmental Studies and Biology
Elon University, Campus Box 2015
Elon, NC 27244
(336) 278-6229

E-MAIL ADDRESS:
jkapfer@elon.edu

WEB SITE ADDRESS:
www.ssarherps.org/pages/GIH.php

TYPE:
Awards/prizes; Research grants. Awards are given in six categories: Conservation of Amphibians and/or Reptiles, Field Research, Laboratory Research, Herpetological Education, Travel and International Research.

See entry 2171 for full listing.

ROB AND BESSIE WELDER WILDLIFE FOUNDATION   [2244]
10260 Welder Wildlife
Sinton, TX 78387
(361) 364-2643
Fax: (361) 364-2650

E-MAIL ADDRESS:
welderfoundation@welderwildlife.org

WEB SITE ADDRESS:
www.welderwildlife.org

FOUNDED: 1954

AREAS OF INTEREST:
Wildlife conservation, wildlife ecology, wildlife science and higher education (graduate level only).

TYPE:
Fellowships. Graduate research fellowships only in fields of wildlife ecology and management.

YEAR PROGRAM STARTED: 1956

PURPOSE:
To encourage and sponsor wildlife research and education.

LEGAL BASIS:
Private, nonprofit foundation.

ELIGIBILITY:
Graduate students at accredited universities seeking advanced degrees in the above-designated fields are eligible to apply. Undergraduates need not apply.

GEOGRAPHIC RESTRICTIONS:
Continental United States.

FINANCIAL DATA:
Fellowships are generally $1,400 (M.S.) to $1,600 (Ph.D.) per month, plus some funds for field supplies and travel. Living quarters are available for students doing research on the Foundation's refuge area near Sinton, TX, including utilities.
Amount of support per award: Normally $19,000 per calendar year.
Total amount of support: $85,000 available for the year 2011.

COOPERATIVE FUNDING PROGRAMS: The Foundation participates in cooperative funding for approvable proposals not adequately financed through other sources, if and when surplus funds are available.

NUMBER OF APPLICANTS MOST RECENT YEAR: Over 20.

NUMBER OF AWARDS: 10.

APPLICATION INFORMATION:
Initial contact with the Foundation may be submitted in an abbreviated outline of the research problem, a preliminary estimate of expenses, and letter signed by a qualified member of the faculty at the parent university. If the Foundation staff thereafter entertains the matter further, a more complete proposal will be requested along with material concerning the proposed fellowship recipient.
Duration: One year. May be renewed if progress is satisfactory.
Deadline: October 1; however, preferably earlier.

PUBLICATIONS:
Biennial report of staff and student activities.

IRS IDENTIFICATION NUMBER: 74-1381321

OFFICERS:
Terry Blankenship, Ph.D., Director
Selma Glasscock, Ph.D., Assistant Director

TRUSTEES:
Hughes C. Thomas
H.C. Weil
John J. Welder, V

ADDRESS INQUIRIES TO:
Terry Blankenship, Ph.D., Director
(See address above.)

*SPECIAL STIPULATIONS:
Priority will be given to research proposals involving studies on the Foundation's refuge area and/or in south Texas.

Agriculture, land resources, rural development

AGRICULTURAL HISTORY SOCIETY
MSU History Department
P.O. Box H
Mississippi State, MS 39762
(662) 268-2247

E-MAIL ADDRESS:
jgiesen@history.msstate.edu

WEB SITE ADDRESS:
www.aghistorysociety.org

TYPE:
Awards/prizes. The Everett E. Edwards Award is presented to the graduate student who submits the best manuscript on any aspect of agricultural history and rural studies during the current calendar year.

The Gilbert C. Fite Dissertation Award will be presented to the author of the best dissertation on any aspect of agricultural history completed during the current calendar year.

The Wayne D. Rasmussen Award is given to the author of the best article on agricultural history published by a journal other than *Agricultural History* during the current calendar year.

The Theodore Saloutos Book Award is presented to the author of a book on any aspect of agricultural history in the U.S. within the current year, broadly interpreted.

See entry 612 for full listing.

THE AMERICAN CHESTNUT FOUNDATION   [2245]
160 Zillicoa Street, Suite D
Asheville, NC 28801
(828) 281-0047
Fax: (828) 253-5373

E-MAIL ADDRESS:
bryan@acf.org

WEB SITE ADDRESS:
www.acf.org

FOUNDED: 1983

AREAS OF INTEREST:
Chestnut research.

TYPE:
Research grants.

PURPOSE:
To restore the American chestnut to Eastern forests.

ELIGIBILITY:
Grants are reviewed on a case-by-case basis.

FINANCIAL DATA:
Amount of support per award: $2,000 to $20,000.
Total amount of support: Approximately $50,000 for the year 2010.

APPLICATION INFORMATION:
Send a letter of inquiry letter form, outlining the goal and purpose, the intended use, and amount of the grant requested.
Duration: Up to three years.
Deadline: January 15.

ADDRESS INQUIRIES TO:
Bryan Burhans, President
(See address above.)

AMERICAN FARM BUREAU FOUNDATION FOR AGRICULTURE [2246]
600 Maryland Avenue, S.W.
Suite 1000 West
Washington, DC 20024
(800) 443-8456
Fax: (202) 406-3756

E-MAIL ADDRESS:
foundation@fb.org

WEB SITE ADDRESS:
www.agfoundation.org

AREAS OF INTEREST:
Agricultural, consumer education, classroom, consumer and farm safety programs.

NAME(S) OF PROGRAMS:
• **White-Reinhardt Fund for Education**

TYPE:
Conferences/seminars; Project/program grants; Research contracts. Teacher Scholarships to National Conference.

YEAR PROGRAM STARTED: 1967

PURPOSE:
To initiate and finance education programs and projects.

FINANCIAL DATA:
Amount of support per award: Teacher Scholarships: $1,000; Mini-grants: Up to $500.
Total amount of support: Varies.

APPLICATION INFORMATION:
Mini-grant applications must be completed and submitted to the State Farm Bureau president, Agriculture in the Classroom coordinator or administrator for signature. All applications will be pre-screened for compliance with grant proposal guidelines. Any grant not meeting guidelines will be eliminated from the judging process prior to examination by judges.
Duration: One year.
Deadline: November 2.

ADDRESS INQUIRIES TO:
Julia DeCaro, Program Assistant
(See address above.)

AMERICAN FLORAL ENDOWMENT [2247]
1601 Duke Street
Alexandria, VA 22314
(703) 838-5211
Fax: (703) 838-5212

E-MAIL ADDRESS:
afe@endowment.org

WEB SITE ADDRESS:
www.endowment.org

FOUNDED: 1961

AREAS OF INTEREST:
Floricultural/environmental horticulture research and development funding in the U.S.

TYPE:
Internships; Project/program grants; Research grants; Scholarships. The Endowment funds research and educational development in floriculture and environmental horticulture designed to produce solutions to industry needs and promote the growth and improvement of the floral industry for the benefit of the grower, wholesale, retail, allied segments and the general public.

The Endowment supports educational programs focused on attracting young people to the industry, and educational endeavors to identify and solve industry needs and/or challenges. The programs are divided into two major areas:
(1) paid floriculture internships/scholarships for full-time college students and;
(2) general educational grants to national programs.

YEAR PROGRAM STARTED: 1961

PURPOSE:
To further the advancement of education and science in the field of floriculture through funding research and studies in the floriculture field, the results of which will be published; to finance scholarships and internships to students interested in floriculture.

LEGAL BASIS:
Not-for-profit, nongovernmental organization.

FINANCIAL DATA:
Amount of support per award: Varies.

APPLICATION INFORMATION:
Duration: Grant pre-proposal packet: June 1; Full proposal packet: November 30.
Deadline: Varies.

PUBLICATIONS:
Update, quarterly newsletter; annual report.

AMERICAN SOCIETY FOR ENOLOGY AND VITICULTURE [2248]
1784 Picasso Avenue, Suite D
Davis, CA 95618-0551
(530) 753-3142
Fax: (530) 753-3318

E-MAIL ADDRESS:
society@asev.org

WEB SITE ADDRESS:
www.asev.org

FOUNDED: 1951

AREAS OF INTEREST:
A scientific society of enologists, viticulturists and others in the fields of wine and grape production, promoting technical advancement and integrated research in science and industry.

TYPE:
Scholarships. Awards for undergraduate or graduate students enrolled in enology or viticulture or in a curriculum which emphasizes a science basic to the wine and grape industry and who intend to pursue a career in research for the wine or grape industry after graduation from college or university.

PURPOSE:
To support education and research in enology, viticulture or related fields.

LEGAL BASIS:
Professional, scientific association.

ELIGIBILITY:
Undergraduate and graduate students may apply who have been accepted at an accredited college or university in North America, are enrolled in an appropriate field of study and reside in North America. Applicants must be at least junior level in academic status (60 quarter units or 45 semester units). Undergraduate students must have a minimum 3.0 overall grade point average on a scale of 4.0. Graduate students must have a minimum 3.2 overall grade point average on a scale of 4.0.

FINANCIAL DATA:
Amount of support per award: Varies each academic year.
Total amount of support: $60,000 per year.

APPLICATION INFORMATION:
Applications can be downloaded from the web site.
Duration: One academic year. Renewable in open competition.
Deadline: All completed forms, letters, and transcripts must be received by March 1.

STAFF:
Lyndie M. Boulton, Executive Director

ADDRESS INQUIRIES TO:
Scholarship Committee
P.O. Box 1855
Davis, CA 95617-1855

CENTER FOR PLANT CONSERVATION [2249]
Missouri Botanical Garden
P.O. Box 299
St. Louis, MO 63166-0299
(314) 577-9450
(314) 577-9451
Fax: (314) 577-9456

E-MAIL ADDRESS:
cpc.temp@mobot.org

WEB SITE ADDRESS:
www.centerforplantconservation.org

FOUNDED: 1984

AREAS OF INTEREST:
Education.

NAME(S) OF PROGRAMS:
• **Catherine H. Beattie Fellowship for Conservation Horticulture**

TYPE:
Fellowships.

YEAR PROGRAM STARTED: 1984

PURPOSE:
To aid students who pursue research in the area of rare plant conservation.

ELIGIBILITY:
Must be a graduate student in biology, horticulture, or a related field conducting research on a rare or endangered U.S. plant. Preference is given to students focusing on the endangered flora of the Carolinas or the southeastern U.S.

FINANCIAL DATA:
Amount of support per award: $1,000 to $4,000.

NUMBER OF APPLICANTS MOST RECENT YEAR:
6.

NUMBER OF AWARDS: 1 to 2.

APPLICATION INFORMATION:
Applicants should submit the following:
(1) a two- to three-page proposal, which
includes a description of the research project
and how it relates to the student's academic
and professional development;
(2) an itemized budget for the funds
requested;
(3) a current resume;
(4) a letter of endorsement by an academic
advisor from the institution where the student
is pursuing graduate studies;
(5) the names of three additional persons
qualified to describe the student's character
and ability and;
(6) official transcripts for both undergraduate
and graduate academic records.

Applicant should be prepared to write an
article for CPC Newsletter, *Plant
Conservation*.

Deadline: November 30. Notification by
March 31.

PUBLICATIONS:
Plant Conservation, newsletter.

THE CH FOUNDATION   [2250]
P.O. Box 94038
Lubbock, TX 79493-4038
(806) 792-0448
Fax: (806) 792-7824

E-MAIL ADDRESS:
ksanford@chfoundation.com

WEB SITE ADDRESS:
www.chfoundationlubbock.com

FOUNDED: 1976

AREAS OF INTEREST:
Agriculture, community development, culture
education, health, ranching, research, social
services and youth.

TYPE:
Capital grants; Project/program grants.

YEAR PROGRAM STARTED: 1991

PURPOSE:
To support programs that meet the needs of
and improve the quality of life.

ELIGIBILITY:
Grants are limited to organizations whose
services benefit the Lubbock area of Texas.
Grants are made to organizations that have
tax-exempt status under Section 501(c)(3) of
the Internal Revenue Code. No grants are
made to individuals or political organizations.

GEOGRAPHIC RESTRICTIONS:
Lubbock, Texas and surrounding counties.

APPLICATION INFORMATION:
Contact the Foundation to determine the
interest and appropriateness of a full
proposal.
Duration: One year. Renewal possible.
Deadline: May 1. Disbursements are made in
December.

PUBLICATIONS:
Application guidelines.

IRS IDENTIFICATION NUMBER: 75-1534816

ADDRESS INQUIRIES TO:
Kay Sanford, Grants Administrator
(See address above.)

FARM AID   [2251]
501 Cambridge Street
Third Floor
Cambridge, MA 02141
(617) 354-2922
Fax: (617) 354-6992

E-MAIL ADDRESS:
grants@farmaid.org

WEB SITE ADDRESS:
www.farmaid.org

FOUNDED: 1985

AREAS OF INTEREST:
Helping U.S. farmers with legal assistance,
financial counseling, emergency assistance
and marketing projects.

TYPE:
General operating grants; Project/program
grants; Technical assistance. Grants fall
within three broad categories which make it
possible for organizations to build long-term
solutions to the problems farmers face.

In the area of education, workshops offer
farmers information about credit issues, legal
rights, organizing and sustainable farming
techniques.

In the area of hotlines, telephone staffers
provide advice and referrals to farmers who
are struggling in the midst of financial and
emotional crisis.

In the area of land stewardship, farmers learn
to protect and preserve our nonrenewable
natural resources. They share innovations
with one another in order to stop the
degradation of soil, water and land.

In the area of outreach, farm and rural
advocates develop contacts among farmers
who are confronting similar problems and
they help farmers to push for fair prices and
policies.

Grant Categories:
(1) Growing the Good Food Movement:
funding organizations or projects that seek to
strengthen what Farm Aid calls the Good
Food Movement, the growing number of
Americans reaching for and demanding
family farm-identified, local, organic or
humanely raised food. These grants build
connections between farmers and consumers,
creating new markets for family farmers.
(2) Helping Farmers Thrive: funding
organizations or projects that assist farmers
transition to more sustainable and profitable
farming practices, find alternative markets, or
start a new farming operation as well as
provide support services to farm families in
crisis. These organizations are the core of the
Farm Aid Resource Network which responds
to individual farmers as well as regional
events such as natural disasters.
(3) Taking Action to Change the System:
funding organizations or projects that
promote fair farm policies and grassroots
organizing campaigns to defend and bolster
family farm-centered agriculture. These
grants enable advocates to strengthen the
voices of family farmers and promote their
interests on a local, regional and national
level.

YEAR PROGRAM STARTED: 1985

LEGAL BASIS:
Tax-exempt, charitable and educational
organization.

ELIGIBILITY:
The following types of projects are not
eligible for Farm Aid funding:

(1) grants or loans to individuals;
(2) grants or loans to support commercial
operation of a farming enterprise;
(3) production of book, film, television or
radio projects;
(4) projects outside the U.S.;
(5) projects directed or substantially funded
by government bodies (federal, state or
local);
(6) legal defense funds;
(7) capital campaigns, equipment purchases,
endowments or deficit financing;
(8) historic preservation of farmland or
buildings;
(9) lobbying to influence elections or
legislation and;
(10) conferences, publications or research
projects unless they are directly connected to
ongoing program activities.

GEOGRAPHIC RESTRICTIONS:
United States.

FINANCIAL DATA:
Amount of support per award: $1,000 to
$20,000; mostly $5,000 to $7,500.
Total amount of support: Varies.

NUMBER OF APPLICANTS MOST RECENT YEAR:
150.

NUMBER OF AWARDS: 60.

APPLICATION INFORMATION:
Applications must include
(1) basic contact information;
(2) introduction;
(3) body of the proposal (very important);
(4) budget information;
(5) supplemental information and;
(6) organizational impact.
Do not submit proposals in binders, folders
or booklets.
Deadline: Proposals: August 1. Grants are
awarded in December.

PUBLICATIONS:
Newsletter.

IRS IDENTIFICATION NUMBER: 36-3383233

ADDRESS INQUIRIES TO:
Alicia Harvie, Program Manager
Tel: (800) 327-6243
(See address and e-mail above.)

THE GARDEN CLUB OF
AMERICA   [2252]
14 East 60th Street
New York, NY 10022
(212) 753-8287
Fax: (212) 753-0134

E-MAIL ADDRESS:
scholarships@gcamerica.org

WEB SITE ADDRESS:
www.gcamerica.org

FOUNDED: 1913

AREAS OF INTEREST:
Horticulture or related field, or any endeavor
in the field of gardening including
conservation, historic preservation and plant
conservation.

NAME(S) OF PROGRAMS:
● **Katharine M. Grosscup Scholarships**

TYPE:
Scholarships.

YEAR PROGRAM STARTED: 1981

PURPOSE:
To encourage the study of horticulture and
related fields.

LEGAL BASIS:
Nonprofit national organization.

ELIGIBILITY:
Applicants must be college juniors, seniors, or graduate students who wish to pursue the study of horticulture and related fields.

GEOGRAPHIC RESTRICTIONS:
Indiana, Kentucky, Michigan, Ohio, Pennsylvania and West Virginia.

FINANCIAL DATA:
Amount of support per award: Up to $3,000.

NUMBER OF AWARDS: 2 or more.

APPLICATION INFORMATION:
Application available online. The Committee does not accept telephone inquiries.
Duration: One year.
Deadline: February 1.

PUBLICATIONS:
Program announcement.

ADDRESS INQUIRIES TO:
Grosscup Scholarship Committee
Cleveland Botanical Garden
11030 East Boulevard
Cleveland, OH 44106
Fax: (216) 721-2056

THE FRED C. GLOECKNER FOUNDATION, INC. [2253]
600 Mamaroneck Avenue
Harrison, NY 10528
(914) 698-2300
Fax: (914) 698-0848

E-MAIL ADDRESS:
jsimone@fredgloeckner.com

WEB SITE ADDRESS:
www.gloecknerfoundation.org

FOUNDED: 1960

AREAS OF INTEREST:
Floriculture and related fields such as plant pathology, plant breeding, agricultural engineering, agricultural economics, entomology and plant physiology related to floriculture.

TYPE:
Assistantships; Project/program grants; Research grants.

YEAR PROGRAM STARTED: 1961

PURPOSE:
To support floriculture research and education.

LEGAL BASIS:
Nonprofit educational corporation.

ELIGIBILITY:
Grants are awarded to nonprofit institutions, primarily colleges and universities, for research and education projects in the above fields. Research in basic plant physiology unrelated to floriculture is not considered. Grants may include assistantships for qualified graduate students seeking an M.S. or Ph.D. in the above fields. Grants are not made directly to students.

GEOGRAPHIC RESTRICTIONS:
United States.

FINANCIAL DATA:
Amount of support per award: $2,000 to $12,000.
Total amount of support: $160,000.

NUMBER OF APPLICANTS MOST RECENT YEAR: 60.

NUMBER OF AWARDS: 35.

REPRESENTATIVE AWARDS:
$8,000 to Miller B. McDonald, Ohio State University, for the development of seed quality tests for monitoring flower seed vigor and deterioration; $6,000 to Merriam Karlsson, University of Alaska, Fairbanks, for day and night temperature requirements for flowering and development of cyclamen; $9,700 to Bernard Rubinstein, University of Massachusetts, Amherst, for use of heat shock to preserve flowers not affected by ethylene; $2,000 to Andrew Senesac, Cornell University, for preemergent weed control for transplanted field-grown cutflowers.

APPLICATION INFORMATION:
Applications are available from the Foundation office, or can be downloaded from the web site.
Duration: One year. Renewals possible.
Deadline: April 1.

PUBLICATIONS:
Annual report; application guidelines.

OFFICERS:
Paul L. Daum, President
Dr. Richard Craig, Vice President
Martin D. Kortjohn, Treasurer
Joseph A. Simone, Secretary

DIRECTORS:
Dr. Richard Craig
Paul L. Daum
Douglas K. Dillon
Dr. Paul Allen Hammer
J. Michael Klesa
Martin D. Kortjohn
Philip J. Kurlich
Dr. John G. Seeley
Joseph A. Simone

ADDRESS INQUIRIES TO:
Joseph A. Simone, Secretary
(See address above.)

THE HERB SOCIETY OF AMERICA, INC. [2254]
9019 Kirtland Chardon Road
Kirtland, OH 44094
(440) 256-0514
Fax: (440) 256-0541

E-MAIL ADDRESS:
herbs@herbsociety.org

WEB SITE ADDRESS:
www.herbsociety.org

FOUNDED: 1933

AREAS OF INTEREST:
Furthering the knowledge and use of herbs and contributing the results of the experience and research of its members to the records of horticulture, science, literature, history, art or economics.

CONSULTING OR VOLUNTEER SERVICES:
Volunteer services including maintenance of public gardens and workshops.

TYPE:
Research grants. Cash award for research on herbal projects.

YEAR PROGRAM STARTED: 1971

PURPOSE:
To promote the knowledge, use and delight of herbs through educational programs, research, and sharing the experiences of its members with the community.

LEGAL BASIS:
Tax-exempt, nonprofit corporation under IRS 501(c)(3).

ELIGIBILITY:
Students, professionals and individuals engaged in research on the horticultural, scientific and/or social applications or use of herbs throughout history.

Funding does not cover indirect costs, purchase or maintenance of durable computer, laboratory or office equipment, expenses related to tuition, textbooks, or conference attendance, private garden development, or travel to/from research site.

FINANCIAL DATA:
Total amount of support: Up to $5,000.

NUMBER OF APPLICANTS MOST RECENT YEAR: 30.

NUMBER OF AWARDS: Varies.

APPLICATION INFORMATION:
Applications should include the following:
(1) application form;
(2) professional vita, not to exceed two pages, listing qualifications for the project, academic degrees and honors;
(3) explanation, not to exceed 500 words, describing how the project will be completed, where the work will be done, and what facilities and equipment are available;
(4) detailed listing of all anticipated costs and;
(5) specific timeline for the project.

Successful applicants will be required to sign a Grant Acceptance Form prior to the award of a grant.
Duration: One year. No renewals.
Deadline: January 31. Announcement May 1.

PUBLICATIONS:
The Herbarist; newsletter; grant guidelines.

IRS IDENTIFICATION NUMBER: 34-1596261

ADDRESS INQUIRIES TO:
Research Grant
(See address above.)

*SPECIAL STIPULATIONS:
Under the terms of the grant, periodic progress reports are to be sent to the Research Grant Chairman. At the termination of the project, The Herb Society expects a complete copy of the finished product for the Herb Society Library and a summary of the work for publication in the Society's publication, *The Herbarist*. The Society reserves the right to reject or accept credit in any publication resulting from the grant.

HORTICULTURAL RESEARCH INSTITUTE, INC. [2255]
1000 Vermont Avenue, N.W.
Suite 300
Washington, DC 20005
(202) 741-4852
Fax: (202) 478-7288

E-MAIL ADDRESS:
grants@hriresearch.org

WEB SITE ADDRESS:
www.hriresearch.org

FOUNDED: 1962

AREAS OF INTEREST:
Nursery and landscape research.

NAME(S) OF PROGRAMS:
● **HRI Competitive Grants Program**

TYPE:
Grants-in-aid; Research grants; Scholarships; Seed money grants; Research contracts.

YEAR PROGRAM STARTED: 1974

PURPOSE:
To direct, fund, promote and communicate research which increases the quality and value of plants, improves the productivity and profitability of the nursery and landscape industry and protects and enhances the environment.

LEGAL BASIS:
501(c)(3).

ELIGIBILITY:
Proposals are evaluated on the basis of their relevance to the nursery industry.

FINANCIAL DATA:
Amount of support per award: $5,000 to $35,000 for the year 2009.
Total amount of support: $200,000 for the year 2009.

NUMBER OF APPLICANTS MOST RECENT YEAR: 100.

NUMBER OF AWARDS: 10 to 25 grants.

APPLICATION INFORMATION:
Completed proposals must be submitted using HRI's online application process. No hard copies or e-mailed applications will be accepted.
Deadline: May 15. Announcement in December.

PUBLICATIONS:
Application guidelines.

IRS IDENTIFICATION NUMBER: 52-1052547

ADDRESS INQUIRIES TO:
Teresa Jodon, Executive Director
(See address above.)

HORTICULTURAL RESEARCH INSTITUTE, INC.
1000 Vermont Avenue, N.W.
Suite 300
Washington, DC 20005
(202) 741-4852
Fax: (202) 478-7288

WEB SITE ADDRESS:
www.hriresearch.org

TYPE:
Scholarships. The Carville M. Akehurst Memorial Scholarship was established by the Mid-Atlantic Nursery Trade Show, Inc. (MANTS) to provide scholarship opportunity to qualified students from Maryland, Virginia or West Virginia to help ensure the continuity of the nursery and landscape profession.

The Bigelow Scholarships provide aid to students from New England.

The Muggets Scholarship and the Spring Meadow Nursery Scholarship are intended to help aspiring students from across the U.S. obtain a degree in horticulture (nursery industry).

See entry 1817 for full listing.

INTERNATIONAL DEVELOPMENT RESEARCH CENTRE (IDRC)   [2256]
150 Kent Street
Ottawa ON K1P 0B2 Canada
(613) 236-6163 ext. 2098
Fax: (613) 236-4026

E-MAIL ADDRESS:
cta@idrc.ca

WEB SITE ADDRESS:
www.idrc.ca/awards

FOUNDED: 1970

AREAS OF INTEREST:
Forestry.

NAME(S) OF PROGRAMS:
- **John G. Bene Fellowship in Community Forestry: Trees and People**

TYPE:
Awards/prizes; Endowments; Fellowships. Fellowship provides assistance to Canadian graduate students undertaking research on the relationship of forest resources to the social, economic, cultural and environmental welfare of people in developing countries.

PURPOSE:
To provide assistance to Canadian graduate students undertaking research on the relationship of forest resources to the social, economic, cultural and environmental welfare of people in developing countries.

LEGAL BASIS:
Public corporation.

ELIGIBILITY:
The successful candidate will be the one whose work most benefits the lives of the less privileged people in the developing country. Applicants must:
(1) be Canadian citizens or hold permanent residency status;
(2) be registered at a Canadian university at the Master's or doctoral level;
(3) have an academic background that combines forestry or agroforestry with social sciences; applicants from interdisciplinary programs may also be eligible, provided their programs contain the specified elements;
(4) research proposal must be approved by the research/thesis committee;
(5) provide evidence of affiliation with an institution or organization in the region in which the research will take place and;
(6) have completed course work and passed comprehensive examinations by the time of award tenure.

FINANCIAL DATA:
Amount of support per award: Up to $15,000 per year.
Total amount of support: Up to $15,000.

NUMBER OF APPLICANTS MOST RECENT YEAR: Varies.

NUMBER OF AWARDS: 1 per year.

APPLICATION INFORMATION:
Duration: Generally, three to 12 months. Candidates may apply for renewal of funding for a second year of field work. Renewals are an exception.
Deadline: March 1.

PUBLICATIONS:
Program announcement.

ADDRESS INQUIRIES TO:
Fellowships and Awards
(See address above.)

*PLEASE NOTE:
Proposed field research must take place in a developing country.

LAND O'LAKES FOUNDATION
4001 Lexington Avenue North
Arden Hills, MN 55126
(651) 481-2123
Fax: (651) 481-2000

E-MAIL ADDRESS:
lrbotham@landolakes.com

WEB SITE ADDRESS:
www.foundation.landolakes.com

TYPE:
Scholarships. John Brandt Memorial Scholarship Program is a $25,000 scholarship available to graduate students pursuing dairy-related degrees at Iowa State University, South Dakota State University, the University of Minnesota, Twin Cities, or the University of Wisconsin, Madison. One or two scholarships are awarded annually to deserving candidates who have demonstrated exceptional commitment and aptitude toward their field of study.

See entry 224 for full listing.

MONSANTO COMPANY/NATIONAL ASSOCIATION OF FARM BROADCASTERS
c/o National FFA Organization
Scholarship Office
P.O. Box 68960
Indianapolis, IN 46268-0960

E-MAIL ADDRESS:
scholarships@ffa.org

WEB SITE ADDRESS:
www.monsanto.com
www.ffa.org

TYPE:
Scholarships. Open to high school seniors who have long-term interests in agriculture.

See entry 1840 for full listing.

NATIONAL ASSOCIATION OF FARM BROADCASTING FOUNDATION
700 Branch Street, Suite 8
Platte City, MO 64079
(816) 431-4032
Fax: (816) 431-4087

E-MAIL ADDRESS:
info@nafb.com

WEB SITE ADDRESS:
www.nafb.com

TYPE:
Scholarships. Ag Broadcast Scholarships consist of two scholarship funds, the Glenn Kummerow Memorial Scholarship and the NAFB College Scholarships, for college students actively interested in becoming agricultural broadcasters.

See entry 2073 for full listing.

NATIONAL CATTLEMAN'S BEEF ASSOCIATION
9110 East Nichols Avenue
Centennial, CO 80112-3450
(830) 569-0046
Fax: (303) 770-6921

E-MAIL ADDRESS:
smcneill@beef.org

WEB SITE ADDRESS:
www.beefresearch.org

TYPE:
Grants-in-aid; Research grants; Research contracts. Research contracts and grants-in-aid for experimental projects in the areas of:
(1) beef as part of a balanced diet;

(2) parity studies;
(3) health benefits of beef lipids and;
(4) contribution of beef nutrients to total diet.

Proposals solicited via specific RFPs (request for proposals).

See entry 2842 for full listing.

NATIONAL DAIRY SHRINE   [2257]

P.O. Box 725
Denmark, WI 54208
(920) 863-6333
Fax: (920) 863-6333

E-MAIL ADDRESS:
info@dairyshrine.org

WEB SITE ADDRESS:
www.dairyshrine.org

FOUNDED: 1949

AREAS OF INTEREST:
Dairy production, research, milk products, milk marketing, genetics and education.

NAME(S) OF PROGRAMS:
- **National Dairy Shrine Student Recognition Program**
- **NDS Graduate Production Award**
- **NDS Progressive Dairy Producers Awards**
- **NDS/Core Scholarship**
- **NDS/DMI Milk Marketing Scholarships**
- **NDS/Iager Scholarship**
- **NDS/Kildee Scholarships**
- **NDS/Klussendorf Scholarship**
- **NDS/McCullough Scholarships**
- **NDS/McKown Scholarship**

TYPE:
Awards/prizes; Scholarships. Awards made annually to students interested in careers in the dairy industry. Majors can include dairy science, animal science, agricultural economics, agricultural communications, agriculture education, food and nutrition.

YEAR PROGRAM STARTED: 1951

PURPOSE:
To encourage students to pursue careers in the dairy industry.

LEGAL BASIS:
Nonprofit corporation.

ELIGIBILITY:
National Dairy Shrine Student Recognition Program: Graduating seniors planning a career related to dairy-production agriculture who have demonstrated leadership skills, academic ability and interest in dairy cattle.

NDS/Core Scholarship: Applicants must be outstanding freshman college students at a four-year agricultural college.

NDS/DMI Milk Marketing Scholarships: Available to undergraduate students (except previous winners) during his or her sophomore or junior year with an explicit interest in dairy products marketing. The applicants must have at least a cumulative 2.5 grade point average on a 4.0 scale.

NDS Graduate Production Award: Available to a two- or four-year college graduate to finance replacement animals. Must have graduated four years prior.

NDS/Iager Scholarship: Open to outstanding second-year college dairy students in a two-year agricultural college.

NDS/Kildee Scholarships: Applicants must have placed in Top 25 at National Intercollegiate or National 4-H Dairy Judging Contests. Platinum winners in 2009 National Intercollegiate Dairy Challenge contest may apply for Kildee Graduate Study Scholarships.

NDS/Klussendorf Scholarship: Open to students successfully completing their first, second or third years at a two- or four-year college or university in Dairy/Animal Science.

NDS/McCullough Scholarships: The applicant must be a high school graduating senior planning to enter a four-year college or university with intent to major in Dairy/Animal Science with a Communications emphasis or Agricultural Journalism with a Dairy/Animal Science emphasis and be a U.S. citizen.

NDS/McKown Scholarship: Open to students successfully completing their first, second or third year at a four-year college or university in Dairy/Animal Science.

NDS Progressive Dairy Producers: Must be 21 to 45 years of age. Two divisions: Small Herd Division (300 or less milking cows) and Large Herd Division (301 or more milking cows).

GEOGRAPHIC RESTRICTIONS:
United States.

FINANCIAL DATA:
Amount of support per award: National Dairy Shrine Student Recognition Program: $5,000 to $7,500; NDS/Core Scholarship and NDS/Iager Scholarship: $1,000; NDS/DMI Milk Marketing Scholarships: $1,500 and $1,000; NDS Graduate Production Award: $2,500; NDS/Kildee Scholarships: $6,000 graduate and $2,000 undergraduate; NDS/Klussendorf Scholarships: $8,000; NDS/McCullough Scholarships: $2,500 and $1,000; NDS/McKown Scholarship: $4,000; NDS Progressive Dairy Producers Awards: $2,000 each for educational travel.
Total amount of support: Over $35,000.

NUMBER OF APPLICANTS MOST RECENT YEAR:
130.

NUMBER OF AWARDS: National Dairy Shrine Student Recognition Program: 7 to 10; NDS/Core Scholarship and NDS Graduate Production Award: 1; NDS/DMI Milk Marketing Scholarships: 5 or 8 awards of $1,000 and 1 award of $1,500; NDS/Iager Scholarship: 1 or more; NDS/Kildee Scholarships: 2 graduate and 1 undergraduate; NDS/Klussendorf Scholarships and NDS/McKown Scholarship: 6; NDS/McCullough Scholarships: 1 award of $2,500 and 1 award of $1,000; NDS Progressive Dairy Producers Awards: 2.

APPLICATION INFORMATION:
NDS/DMI Milk Marketing Scholarship: Application form is required. Each application must be accompanied by two letters of recommendation with one being from a faculty member in the applicant's major department. All application information must be typed on the application form and submitted via e-mail.

NDS/McCullough Scholarship: Application form is required. Each must be accompanied by a letter of recommendation and must be mailed to the Executive Director, National Dairy Shrine.

Duration: One year.

Deadline: Applications accepted March 1 to April 15 (postmarked). Announcements by July 1.

PUBLICATIONS:
Application form.

EXECUTIVE DIRECTOR:
David Selner

ADDRESS INQUIRIES TO:
David Selner, Executive Director
(See address above.)

*SPECIAL STIPULATIONS:
The second half of each scholarship will be awarded after successful completion of next year. Recipients will be asked to submit their most recent grade transcript and proof of enrollment in the first term of the following year.

NATIONAL FARMER'S ORGANIZATION   [2258]

528 Billy Sunday Road
Suite 100
Ames, IA 50010
(515) 292-2000
Fax: (866) 629-4853

E-MAIL ADDRESS:
nfo@nfo.org

WEB SITE ADDRESS:
www.nfo.org

AREAS OF INTEREST:
Agricultural careers.

NAME(S) OF PROGRAMS:
- **Farm Kids for College Scholarships**

TYPE:
Scholarships.

PURPOSE:
To assist students planning careers in agriculture and farming.

ELIGIBILITY:
Must be a high school senior that will major in an agricultural field at an accredited college or university.

FINANCIAL DATA:
Amount of support per award: $1,000.
Total amount of support: $3,000.

NUMBER OF AWARDS: 3.

APPLICATION INFORMATION:
Deadline: February.

ADDRESS INQUIRIES TO:
Perry Garner
Director of Communications
(See address above.)

NATIONAL PARK FOUNDATION

1201 Eye Street, N.W.
Suite 550B
Washington, DC 20005
(202) 354-6460
Fax: (202) 371-2066

E-MAIL ADDRESS:
ask-nps@nationalparks.org

WEB SITE ADDRESS:
www.nationalparks.org

TYPE:
Block grants; Challenge/matching grants; Research grants; Scholarships. Grants range from small seed or start-up programs to larger ones which continue successful projects. Grants enable the parks to obtain additional cash and in-kind contributions, such as products, service or volunteer time.

The Albright-Wirth Employee Development Fund underwrites advanced skills training, graduate education and other professional development programs for Park Service employees.

The Harry Yount National Park Ranger Award recognizes a Ranger for leadership, exemplary skills and dedication to the Park Ranger profession.

See entry 2333 for full listing.

NORTHEAST AGRICULTURAL EDUCATION FOUNDATION   [2259]

101 South Salina Street
Suite 400
Syracuse, NY 13202
(315) 671-0588
Fax: (315) 671-0589

E-MAIL ADDRESS:
mhabib@rockbridgeinvest.com

FOUNDED: 1966

AREAS OF INTEREST:
Agriculture, civic and community.

TYPE:
Project/program grants.

PURPOSE:
To support nonprofit organizations dedicated to serving the interests of farmers and rural communities in the Northeast.

LEGAL BASIS:
Private foundation.

ELIGIBILITY:
Grants are made to nonprofit organizations that have tax-exempt status under Section 501(c)(3) of the Internal Revenue Code. No grants are made to individuals.

GEOGRAPHIC RESTRICTIONS:
Primarily northeastern United States.

FINANCIAL DATA:
Amount of support per award: Varies.

APPLICATION INFORMATION:
Send letter, no longer than two pages, describing the organization, the proposed program or activity, the requested funds amount and an evaluation methodology.
Duration: Varies.

PUBLICATIONS:
Background and application guidelines; application requirements; grant request summary.

ADDRESS INQUIRIES TO:
Mary Habib, Administrator
(See address above.)

NORTHEASTERN LOGGERS' ASSOCIATION, INC.   [2260]

3311 State Route 28
Old Forge, NY 13420-0069
(315) 369-3078
Fax: (315) 369-3736

E-MAIL ADDRESS:
mona@northernlogger.com

WEB SITE ADDRESS:
www.northernlogger.com

FOUNDED: 1952

AREAS OF INTEREST:
Forestry, wood science and technology.

NAME(S) OF PROGRAMS:
• **NELA Annual Scholarship Contest**

TYPE:
Scholarships. Essay scholarship contest.

YEAR PROGRAM STARTED: 1975

PURPOSE:
To provide support for students and employees of members.

LEGAL BASIS:
501(c)(6) giving program.

ELIGIBILITY:
Scholarships are available to the immediate families of individual members, or the immediate families of employees of Industrial and Associate Members of the Northeastern Loggers' Association. Applicants must be bound for or engaged in post-high school education and must be either seniors in high school graduating in the current year, students in two-year Associate's degree or technical school programs or juniors/seniors in four-year Bachelor's degree programs.

GEOGRAPHIC RESTRICTIONS:
United States.

FINANCIAL DATA:
Amount of support per award: $500 to $1,000.
Total amount of support: $6,000.

NUMBER OF APPLICANTS MOST RECENT YEAR:
17.

NUMBER OF AWARDS: Up to 8 annually.

APPLICATION INFORMATION:
Application forms and further information are available from the address above. Applicants must prepare a 1,000-word essay (about four pages double-spaced) on the topic: "What It Means to Grow Up in the Forest Industry." The essay must be typed and the quality of the essay will be the primary determining factor for the award. Applicant must submit with the essay a completed application form, grade transcript, and report card information before the application deadline.
Duration: One year.
Deadline: March 31. Notification in May.

ADDRESS INQUIRIES TO:
Mona Lincoln
Director, Safety and Training
(See address above.)

JESSIE SMITH NOYES FOUNDATION

6 East 39th Street
12th Floor
New York, NY 10016
(212) 684-6577
Fax: (212) 689-6549

E-MAIL ADDRESS:
noyes@noyes.org

WEB SITE ADDRESS:
www.noyes.org

TYPE:
General operating grants; Project/program grants. Grants to tax-exempt institutions in the connected and overlapping areas of sustainable agriculture, toxics, reproductive rights, and New York City environment in order to achieve the Foundation's overall goal, which is to promote a sustainable and just social and natural system by supporting grassroots organizations and movements committed to this goal.

See entry 2337 for full listing.

RURAL HOUSING SERVICE   [2261]

1400 Independence Avenue, S.W.
Room 2214
Washington, DC 20250
(202) 720-1474
Fax: (202) 720-6895

WEB SITE ADDRESS:
www.usda.gov

FOUNDED: 1949

AREAS OF INTEREST:
Rural development.

NAME(S) OF PROGRAMS:
• **Rural Housing Grants (Section 504)**

TYPE:
Grants-in-aid; Project/program grants. Grants to assist elderly, very low-income owner-occupants in rural areas to repair or improve their dwellings to make such dwellings safe and sanitary and remove hazards.

RHS is the credit agency for rural development in USDA. RHS has offices at the state, district and county levels which serve every county or parish in the 50 states, plus the western Pacific areas, Guam, Puerto Rico and the Virgin Islands.

YEAR PROGRAM STARTED: 1961

PURPOSE:
To assist applicants who are unable to repay a loan amortized at one percent over 20 years.

LEGAL BASIS:
42 U.S.C. 1474.

ELIGIBILITY:
Open to counties and towns or places of 10,000 or less within SMA's and towns or places of up to 20,000 outside SMA's. Areas classified as rural prior to October 1, 1990, with a population in excess of 10,000 are eligible if the area population is 25,000 or less.

Applicants must own and occupy houses in rural areas that need repair to remove health or safety hazards. Grant recipients must be 62 years of age or older, very low income households (under 50% of median income) owner-occupants, and unable to pay for that cost of repair with a loan.

FINANCIAL DATA:
Amount of support per award: Lifetime assistance cannot exceed $7,500.

APPLICATION INFORMATION:
Applicants must apply at the local county Rural Development (RD) office. Awards are approved by Community Development Manager.

STAFF:
Gloria Denson, Senior Loan Specialist

TREE RESEARCH & EDUCATION ENDOWMENT FUND   [2262]

552 South Washington Street
Suite 109
Naperville, IL 60540
(630) 369-8300
Fax: (630) 369-8382

E-MAIL ADDRESS:
treefund@treefund.org

WEB SITE ADDRESS:
www.treefund.org

FOUNDED: 1975

AREAS OF INTEREST:
Research in areas of urban tree care, preservation and arboriculture education.

NAME(S) OF PROGRAMS:
- **Arborculture Education Grant**
- **John Duling Grant**
- **Robert Felix Memorial Scholarship**
- **Hyland Johns Grant**
- **Jack Kimmel International Grant**
- **Mark S. McClure Research Fund**
- **John Wright Memorial Scholarship**

TYPE:
Research grants; Scholarships; Seed money grants. Grants to further research relating to arboriculture. Scholarships are for arboriculture and horticulture students.

YEAR PROGRAM STARTED: 1976

PURPOSE:
To initiate and foster scientific investigation of problems concerned with the practice of arboriculture.

LEGAL BASIS:
Tax-exempt public supported corporation, 501(c)(3) classification.

ELIGIBILITY:
Qualified persons who have a B.S. degree and are planning on graduate study for a Master's or Doctorate in a related field are eligible to apply for scholarship program. Scholarships available for undergraduate study focusing on arboriculture or horticulture.

GEOGRAPHIC RESTRICTIONS:
Scholarships: United States.

FINANCIAL DATA:
Grants do not pay for overhead expenses.
Amount of support per award: Scholarships: Up to $3,000; Grant awards: $10,000 (Duling and Kimmel) to $25,000 (Johns).
Total amount of support: $250,000.

NUMBER OF APPLICANTS MOST RECENT YEAR:
85.

NUMBER OF AWARDS: 14 grants and 4 scholarships for the year 2010.

APPLICATION INFORMATION:
Applications are to be completed online. Before applying for a grant, carefully read the Grant Guidelines. Applications that do not contain all the requested information may be denied.
Duration: John Duling Grant: One year. Hyland Johns and Jack Kimmel Grants: Multiyear.
Deadline: John Duling and Jack Kimmel Grants: November 1. Hyland Johns Grant: May 1.

PUBLICATIONS:
Application guidelines.

IRS IDENTIFICATION NUMBER: 37-1018692

STAFF:
M. Janet Bornancin, Executive Director
Mary DiCarlo, Fund Development Specialist

ADDRESS INQUIRIES TO:
Barbara Duke, Office Manager
E-Mail: bduke@treefund.org

*SPECIAL STIPULATIONS:
No part of grant can be used for overhead expenses.

U.S. DEPARTMENT OF AGRICULTURE
1400 Independence Avenue, S.W.
Stop 0513
Washington, DC 20250-0510
(202) 720-6221
Fax: (202) 720-4619

E-MAIL ADDRESS:
robertstephenson@wdc.usda.gov

WEB SITE ADDRESS:
www.fsa.usda.gov

TYPE:
Grants-in-aid. Cost-share assistance with agricultural producers to rehabilitate agricultural lands damaged by natural disasters. Assistance may also be provided for carrying out emergency water conservation measures during periods of severe drought.

See entry 2350 for full listing.

U.S.-ISRAEL BINATIONAL AGRICULTURE RESEARCH AND DEVELOPMENT FUND (BARD) [2263]
P.O. Box 6
Bet Dagan 50250 Israel
(972)-3-9683366
Fax: (972)-3-9662506

WEB SITE ADDRESS:
www.bard-isus.com

FOUNDED: 1977

AREAS OF INTEREST:
Agriculture.

NAME(S) OF PROGRAMS:
- **Graduate Student Fellowship Program**
- **Senior Research Fellowship Program**
- **Vaadia-BARD Postdoctoral Fellowship Program**

TYPE:
Fellowships; Research grants; Visiting scholars.

YEAR PROGRAM STARTED: 1977

PURPOSE:
To promote cooperative agriculture research between the U.S. and Israel; to provide BARD with input into new research areas; to enhance scientific competence in these areas.

LEGAL BASIS:
Nonprofit organization. Governmental Associations in U.S. and Israel.

ELIGIBILITY:
Citizens of the U.S. or Israel who are established research scientists, Ph.D. students and young scientists from American or Israeli nonprofit research institutions, universities, or federal or state agencies are eligible.

GEOGRAPHIC RESTRICTIONS:
United States and Israel.

FINANCIAL DATA:
Fellowship includes round-trip airfare and modest living expenses.
Amount of support per award: Postdoctoral Fellowship: $37,000, plus $8,000 for fellows with dependents. Research Grant: Approximately $320,000 over three years.
Total amount of support: $8,000,000 per year.

NUMBER OF APPLICANTS MOST RECENT YEAR:
100.

NUMBER OF AWARDS: 25.

APPLICATION INFORMATION:
For application information, consult with BARD office in Israel.
Duration: Research awards: Three years. Fellowships: Two to 12 months.
Deadline: Research awards: September. Postdoctoral Fellowship, Senior Fellowship Program, and Graduate Student Fellowship Program: January 15.

PUBLICATIONS:
Application guidelines.

OFFICERS:
Edo Chalutz, Executive Director
Miriam Green, Controller

THE UNIVERSITY OF SYDNEY [2264]
Scholarships Office
Level 5, Jane Foss Russell Building G02
The University of Sydney N.S.W. 2006
Australia
(02) 8627 8112
Fax: (02) 8627 8145

E-MAIL ADDRESS:
research.training@sydney.edu.au

WEB SITE ADDRESS:
www.sydney.edu.au/scholarships/research

FOUNDED: 1850

AREAS OF INTEREST:
Agriculture and veterinary science or chemical engineering.

NAME(S) OF PROGRAMS:
- **F.H. Loxton Postgraduate Studentships**

TYPE:
Scholarships. Awarded for research leading to a higher degree. Tenable at the University of Sydney.

PURPOSE:
To enable a male graduate of any university to engage in postgraduate research at the University of Sydney, within the Faculties of Veterinary Science and Agriculture, Food and Natural Resources, and the School of Chemical and Biomolecular Engineering.

LEGAL BASIS:
University.

ELIGIBILITY:
Open only to male graduates of any university enrolled in a higher degree by research in the Faculties of Veterinary Science or Agriculture, Food and Natural Resources, or the School of Chemical and Biomolecular Engineering at the University of Sydney.

FINANCIAL DATA:
Award does not cover tuition fees payable by international students. Relocation allowance within Australia and thesis allowance available.
Amount of support per award: $22,860 AUD per annum for the year 2011.

NUMBER OF AWARDS: Offered as vacancies occur.

APPLICATION INFORMATION:
Particulars are available from the Faculties of Agriculture, Food and Natural Resources, Veterinary Science, or School of Chemical and Biomolecular Engineering, The University of Sydney.
Duration: Master's research degree: Two years; Ph.D. degree: Three years.
Deadline: Varies.

ADDRESS INQUIRIES TO:
The Faculty of Agriculture, Food
and Natural Resources
E-mail: pamela.stern@sydney.edu.au
The Faculty of Veterinary Science
E-mail: pgvetsci@vetsci.usyd.edu.au
School of Chemical and
Biomolecular Engineering
E-mail: timothy.langrish@sydney.edu.au
The University of Sydney
N.S.W. 2006 Australia

THE UNIVERSITY OF
SYDNEY   [2265]
Scholarships Office
Level 5, Jane Foss Russell Building G02
The University of Sydney N.S.W. 2006
Australia
(02) 8627 8112
Fax: (02) 8627 8145

E-MAIL ADDRESS:
research.training@sydney.edu.au

WEB SITE ADDRESS:
www.sydney.edu.au/scholarships/research

FOUNDED: 1850

AREAS OF INTEREST:
Any subject in the Faculty of Agriculture.

NAME(S) OF PROGRAMS:
● **Thomas Lawrance Pawlett Scholarship**
● **Christian Rowe Thornett Scholarship**
● **Alexander Hugh Thurburn Scholarship**

TYPE:
Scholarships. Awarded for postgraduate
research. Tenable at the University of
Sydney.

PURPOSE:
To encourage and promote scientific study in
agriculture at the University of Sydney.

LEGAL BASIS:
University.

ELIGIBILITY:
Open to University of Sydney graduates,
graduands, or persons holding equivalent
qualification who are eligible for admission
to candidature for a higher degree by
research and thesis and who enroll as
full-time candidates in the Faculty of
Agriculture, Food and Natural Resources.

Scholarships may not be held concurrently
with other awards or salaried position, except
with the approval of the Faculty of
Agriculture, Food and Natural Resources.

FINANCIAL DATA:
No assistance with travel costs of scholars
taking up award from outside Australia.
Award does not cover tuition fees payable by
international students.
Amount of support per award: $22,860 AUD
per annum for the year 2011.

NUMBER OF AWARDS: Offered as funds
available.

APPLICATION INFORMATION:
Duration: Tenable for two years for Master's
candidate. Tenable for three years with the
possibility of a six-month extension for Ph.D.
candidate.
Deadline: October 31.

ADDRESS INQUIRIES TO:
The Faculty of Agriculture, Food
and Natural Resources
The University of Sydney

N.S.W. 2006 Australia
Tel: (02) 8627 1002
E-mail: pamela.stern@sydney.edu.au

USDA - RURAL UTILITIES
SERVICE   [2266]
1400 Independence Avenue, S.W.
Stop 1548
Washington, DC 20250
(202) 690-2670
Fax: (202) 720-0718

WEB SITE ADDRESS:
www.usda.gov/rus/water

FOUNDED: 1935

AREAS OF INTEREST:
Rural areas and towns that have a population
of up to 10,000.

NAME(S) OF PROGRAMS:
● **Water and Waste Disposal Systems for
Rural Communities**

TYPE:
Capital grants; Development grants;
Project/program grants. Loans.

YEAR PROGRAM STARTED: 1965

PURPOSE:
To provide financial assistance for water and
waste disposal facilities in rural areas and
towns.

LEGAL BASIS:
Government agency.

ELIGIBILITY:
Only rural areas and cities and towns with
populations under 10,000 are eligible.

Applicants must:
(1) be a public entity, nonprofit corporation
or Indian tribe;
(2) be unable to obtain needed funds from
other sources at reasonable rates and terms;
(3) have legal capacity and;
(4) have adequate security for loans.

FINANCIAL DATA:
Amount of support per award: Varies.
Total amount of support: Approximately
$471,000,000 in grants and $1 billion in
loans for fiscal year 2009.

COOPERATIVE FUNDING PROGRAMS: Can
cooperate with any other federal, state, local
or private credit source.

APPLICATION INFORMATION:
Applicants must submit Form SF-424,
application for federal assistance and state
intergovernmental review comments and
recommendations.
Deadline: Applications accepted throughout
the year.

ADDRESS INQUIRIES TO:
Jacqueline M. Ponti-Lazaruk
Assistant Administrator
Water and Environmental Programs
(See address above.)

THE WOMAN'S NATIONAL
FARM AND GARDEN
ASSOCIATION   [2267]
P.O. Box 1175
Midland, MI 48641-1175
(734) 995-8441

E-MAIL ADDRESS:
mayflowerfg@msn.com

WEB SITE ADDRESS:
www.wnfga.org

FOUNDED: 1914

NAME(S) OF PROGRAMS:
● **Sarah Bradley Tyson Memorial
Fellowship**

TYPE:
Exchange programs; Fellowships; Internships;
Scholarships. Awards for advanced study in
the fields of horticulture, agriculture and
allied subjects.

YEAR PROGRAM STARTED: 1928

PURPOSE:
To encourage better living around the world.

ELIGIBILITY:
Open to properly qualified young women
who have proven their ability by several
years of experience. Awards have been made
in recognition of leadership in cooperative
extension work and initiative in scientific
research. Applicants must be college
graduates. Special consideration will be given
to financial need and an excellent scholastic
record.

The Fellowship is to be used for advanced
study at an educational institution of
recognized standing within the U.S. It is to
be chosen by the candidate and with the
approval of the Fellowship Committee.

FINANCIAL DATA:
Amount of support per award: $1,000 up.

APPLICATION INFORMATION:
There are no application forms. A letter of
application should be sent to the Chairman of
the Committee with a SASE. The letter of
application should contain:
(1) an account of the applicant's educational
training;
(2) a statement in full of the object in view
and the plan of study;
(3) a certificate from the registrar of the
school, college or university awarding the
degree or degrees received by the applicant;
(4) testimonials as to character, ability,
personality and scholarship and;
(5) theses, papers or reports of investigations,
published or unpublished, if available. These
will be returned if postage is sent for that
purpose. Confidential letters sent to the
Committee are retained.

Duration: One year.

Deadline: April 15.

IRS IDENTIFICATION NUMBER: 52-6073829

OFFICERS:
Barbara Hochstettler, President
Marla Diamond, Vice President
Sylvia Anderson, National Advisor
Carol Leonard, Treasurer
Jane Shattuck, Treasurer
Mary Merten, Corresponding Secretary
Kay Engelhart, Advisor

ADDRESS INQUIRIES TO:
Claudia Scioly, Executive Director
1634 East Stadium
Ann Arbor, MI 48104
E-mail: cscioly@hotmail.com

Biology

THE ACADEMY OF NATURAL SCIENCES OF PHILADELPHIA [2268]

1900 Benjamin Franklin Parkway
Philadelphia, PA 19103-1195
(215) 405-5093
Fax: (215) 299-1079

E-MAIL ADDRESS:
kepics@ansp.org

WEB SITE ADDRESS:
www.ansp.org/research/jessupinfo.html

FOUNDED: 1812

AREAS OF INTEREST:
Research, exhibition and education in natural sciences.

NAME(S) OF PROGRAMS:
- **Jessup Fellowship**
- **McHenry Fellowship**

TYPE:
Fellowships. The Jessup Fellowship is for research support in any specialty in which the curatorial staff of the Academy have expertise. The McHenry Fellowship is for botanical research support.

PURPOSE:
To promote research in the natural sciences.

ELIGIBILITY:
The Jessup Fellowships are awarded competitively to students wishing to conduct studies at the postgraduate, doctoral and postdoctoral levels under the supervision or sponsorship of a member of the curatorial staff of the Academy. The Fellowships are not available for undergraduate study. These Fellowships are restricted to those who wish to conduct their study at the Academy and are intended to assist predoctoral and postdoctoral students within several years of receiving their Ph.Ds.

FINANCIAL DATA:
Round-trip travel costs up to a total of $500 for North American (including Mexico and the Caribbean) applicants and $1,000 for applicants from other parts of the world may be available, but cannot be guaranteed. The provision of scientific supplies and equipment is the responsibility of the student and the sponsoring curator.
Amount of support per award: Stipend for subsistence of $375 per week.

APPLICATION INFORMATION:
Applicant is responsible to submit his or her application in time and to be sure that the three letters of recommendation also reach the Fund Chairman in time. One of these letters of recommendation must be from the Academy curator overseeing or sponsoring the student.

Application form and supporting information should be sent to Dr. Edward Daeschler, Jessup-McHenry Fund Committee, using the address above.
Duration: Two to 16 weeks.
Deadline: Applications for grants will be considered in March and October of each year. Applicants wishing to do their research between April 1 and October 31 should apply by March 1; those wishing to work between November 1 and March 31 should apply by October 1.

*SPECIAL STIPULATIONS:
Fellowship awardees are expected to give a seminar after their arrival and are encouraged to publish at least some of their work accomplished at the Academy.

AMERICAN ASSOCIATION OF ZOO KEEPERS [2269]

3601 S.W. 29th Street
Suite 133
Topeka, KS 66614-2054
(785) 273-9149
Fax: (785) 273-1980

E-MAIL ADDRESS:
aazkoffice@zk.kscoxmail.com

WEB SITE ADDRESS:
www.aazk.org

FOUNDED: 1968

AREAS OF INTEREST:
Animal care and the promotion of animal keeping as a profession.

NAME(S) OF PROGRAMS:
- **Zoo Keeper Grants in Zoology**

TYPE:
Project/program grants; Research grants. Grants in the area of zoology, with emphasis on contributions to improving animal management.

YEAR PROGRAM STARTED: 1980

PURPOSE:
To provide funds for original keeper-initiated research of behavioral and/or biomedical topics and general zoological park management principles.

LEGAL BASIS:
Nonprofit corporation.

ELIGIBILITY:
Candidates must be full-time, permanent keepers in the zoo and aquarium profession and must be AAZK professional members in good standing.

GEOGRAPHIC RESTRICTIONS:
United States and Canada.

FINANCIAL DATA:
Amount of support per award: Up to $1,000.
Total amount of support: $2,000 per year.

NUMBER OF AWARDS: 2 annually.

APPLICATION INFORMATION:
Applications consist of an application form, brief research proposal and resume. Application materials and further information are available from the Committee chairperson or can be downloaded from the web site.
Duration: One year. One-year extension is possible with status report and Committee approval.
Deadline: March 1. Successful applicants are notified within three months of the deadline.

PUBLICATIONS:
Application guidelines.

BOARD OF DIRECTORS:
Shane Good, President
Bob Cisneros, Vice President
Ed Hansen, Executive Director
Penny Jolly
Tammy Root
Gisela Wiggins

ADDRESS INQUIRIES TO:
Barbara Manspeaker
Administrative Secretary
(See address above.)

*SPECIAL STIPULATIONS:
Research results must be presented to the AAZK membership by either an oral presentation at an AAZK conference, a paper published in *Animal Keepers' Forum* or a research summary report published in *Animal Keepers' Forum.*

THE AMERICAN MUSEUM OF NATURAL HISTORY [2270]

Richard Gilder Graduate School
Central Park West at 79th Street
New York, NY 10024-5192
(212) 769-5017
Fax: (212) 769-5257

E-MAIL ADDRESS:
mrios@amnh.org

WEB SITE ADDRESS:
rggs.amnh.org

FOUNDED: 1869

AREAS OF INTEREST:
Education of Ph.D. candidates in scientific disciplines.

NAME(S) OF PROGRAMS:
- **Graduate Student Fellowship Program**

TYPE:
Fellowships. An educational partnership with selected universities dedicated to the training of Ph.D. candidates. The university exercises educational jurisdiction over the program and awards the degree. The museum curator serves as a graduate advisor, co-major professor, or major professor. The student benefits by having the staff and facilities of both the university and the museum in order to carry on his or her training and research programs. Joint programs are with the following universities:
(1) Columbia University in vertebrate and invertebrate paleontology, earth and planetary sciences, and evolutionary biology;
(2) Cornell University in entomology and;
(3) City University of New York in evolutionary biology and the biological anthropology programs.

PURPOSE:
To encourage bright and promising students to enter the fields of science in which the museum participates.

ELIGIBILITY:
Applicants must have a Bachelor's degree and be able to fulfill university admission requirements, including TOEFL and Graduate Record Examinations. The program is not open to candidates for the Master's degree.

FINANCIAL DATA:
Fellowships cover stipend, tuition and health insurance.
Amount of support per award: Varies.
Total amount of support: Varies.

NUMBER OF AWARDS: 3 for the year 2010.

APPLICATION INFORMATION:
Students must simultaneously apply to the museum and to one of four cooperating universities depending upon field of study. Application to the museum on prescribed forms and includes:
(1) a resume or curriculum vitae including academic background, work experience, previous awards, grants or fellowships, and a list of any publications;
(2) official statement of Graduate Record Examination (GRE) scores;
(3) official TOEFL score for foreign students;

(4) official undergraduate transcripts from all institutions attended;
(5) official graduate transcripts, if beyond first semester of graduate work;
(6) statement of research interests, if the applicant has completed less than one year of graduate study, or summary thesis proposal and progress to date, if the applicant is beyond the first year of graduate study and;
(7) letters of recommendation from three persons (including applicant's major professor) who are familiar with the applicant's academic and research background.

Students should contact the university to request application forms for the Ph.D. program in the appropriate field of study.
Duration: One year. Renewable annually for up to four years.
Deadline: December 15.

PUBLICATIONS:
Program announcement; application.

ADDRESS INQUIRIES TO:
Maria Rios, Assistant Director
Fellowships and Student Affairs
(See address above.)

AMERICAN ORCHID SOCIETY [2271]
16700 AOS Lane
Delray Beach, FL 33446
(561) 404-2050
Fax: (561) 404-2045

E-MAIL ADDRESS:
theaos@aos.org

WEB SITE ADDRESS:
www.aos.org

FOUNDED: 1921

AREAS OF INTEREST:
Orchid research.

NAME(S) OF PROGRAMS:
● **American Orchid Society Grants for Orchid Research**

TYPE:
Awards/prizes; Block grants; Capital grants; Development grants; Grants-in-aid; Research grants. Grants and research contracts for experimental projects and applied and fundamental research pertaining to orchids and grants-in-aid to graduate students engaged in research on orchids. Support is given in such areas relevant to orchids as biological research (including taxonomy, anatomy, genetics, physiology development, tissue culture and pathology), conservation and education.

YEAR PROGRAM STARTED: 1966

PURPOSE:
To advance the scientific study of orchids in every aspect; to assist in the publication of scholarly and popular scientific literature on orchids.

LEGAL BASIS:
Corporation.

ELIGIBILITY:
Qualified research personnel associated with accredited institutions of higher learning or appropriate research institutes may apply for research grants. Support is not restricted to individuals or institutions within the U.S. The salary of established scientists is not supported. Qualified graduate students with

appropriate interests may apply for grants in support of their research. If justified, their salary may be supported.

In general, travel to collect orchids is not supported. Other types of travel may be supported on a case-by-case basis.

FINANCIAL DATA:
Grants and research contracts vary in amount, depending upon the needs and nature of the request and the potential for securing additional funds from other sources.
Amount of support per award: $500 to $12,000 per year.

APPLICATION INFORMATION:
As a first step, prospective applicants should submit a brief letter outlining the objectives and general plans of the project. If appropriate, an application form and project outline for request of a grant will then be supplied to provide the applicant with further detailed information.
Duration: Although the duration of each grant depends upon the particular project, most grants are awarded for one year with the possibility of renewal. In all cases, the maximum grant period is three years.
Deadline: February 1.

PUBLICATIONS:
Application guidelines.

ADDRESS INQUIRIES TO:
Pamela Giust, Awards Registrar
(See address above.)

*SPECIAL STIPULATIONS:
Research application must involve orchids.

AMERICAN SOCIETY FOR MICROBIOLOGY [2272]
Education Department
1752 N Street, N.W.
Washington, DC 20036
(202) 942-9295
(202) 942-9283
Fax: (202) 942-9329

E-MAIL ADDRESS:
fellowships@asmusa.org

WEB SITE ADDRESS:
www.asm.org/education

FOUNDED: 1899

AREAS OF INTEREST:
Biological research.

NAME(S) OF PROGRAMS:
● **ASM/CDC Postdoctoral Research Fellowship Program**
● **Undergraduate Research Fellowship (URF)**

TYPE:
Fellowships. ASM/CDC Postdoctoral Research Fellowship Program: The American Society for Microbiology and Centers for Disease Control and Prevention (ASM/CDC) Postdoctoral Research Fellowship Program is a comprehensive training program which provides opportunities to participate in interdisciplinary training on global public health issues. Fellows will perform research at one of the Centers for Disease Control and Prevention (CDC) locations.

Undergraduate Research Fellowship: This fellowship encourages students to pursue careers or advanced degrees in the microbiological sciences by providing an opportunity to participate in a research project at their institution and gain

experience in presenting their results. The fellowship allows students to conduct research in the summer with an ASM member faculty mentor and present the results at the ASM General Meeting the following year.

PURPOSE:
To promote study and research in microbiology; to increase the number of underrepresented and historically excluded undergraduate students completing doctoral degrees in microbiology.

LEGAL BASIS:
Private, nonprofit science organization.

ELIGIBILITY:
ASM/CDC Postdoctoral Research Fellowship Program: Must be U.S. citizens or permanent U.S. residents.

FINANCIAL DATA:
Amount of support per award: ASM Undergraduate Research Fellowship: Up to $4,000 for student stipend, a two-year ASM student membership, and up to $1,000 travel support to attend the ASM General Meeting; ASM/CDC Postdoctoral Research Fellowship Program: Up to $46,000 annual stipend, up to $3,000 annually in health benefits for a maximum of two years, up to $500 for relocation benefits, and up to $2,000 annually for professional development for a maximum of two years.

APPLICATION INFORMATION:
Duration: ASM/CDC Postdoctoral Research Fellowship Program: Two years; Undergraduate Research Fellowship: Minimum 12 weeks.
Deadline: ASM/CDC Postdoctoral Research Fellowship Program: January 15; Undergraduate Research Fellowship: February 1.

PUBLICATIONS:
Application guidelines.

ADDRESS INQUIRIES TO:
Manager, Student Programs
(See address above.)

AMERICAN SOCIETY FOR MICROBIOLOGY [2273]
Education Department
1752 N Street, N.W.
Washington, DC 20036
(202) 942-9283
Fax: (202) 942-9329

E-MAIL ADDRESS:
fellowships-careerinformation@asmusa.org
fellowships@asmusa.org

WEB SITE ADDRESS:
www.asm.org/students

FOUNDED: 1899

AREAS OF INTEREST:
Microbiology.

NAME(S) OF PROGRAMS:
● **ASM Robert D. Watkins Graduate Research Fellowships**

TYPE:
Fellowships. Graduate fellowships. This fellowship encourages underrepresented and historically excluded graduate students to conduct research in the microbiological sciences.

YEAR PROGRAM STARTED: 1980

PURPOSE:
To help increase the number of underrepresented and historically excluded groups completing doctoral degrees in microbiology.

LEGAL BASIS:
Private, nonprofit science organization.

ELIGIBILITY:
Fellowships are available to graduate students enrolled in a full-time Ph.D. program in microbiology at an accredited U.S. institution of higher learning who are from an underrepresented and historically excluded group. Applicants must be U.S. citizens or permanent residents, ASM student members, been formally admitted and have successfully completed the first year as a doctoral candidate.

FINANCIAL DATA:
Funds cannot be used for tuition and fees.
Amount of support per award: $63,000 ($21,000 annual stipend).

APPLICATION INFORMATION:
Applications are available online. Students must apply electronically.
Duration: Up to three years.
Deadline: May 1.

PUBLICATIONS:
Application guidelines.

ADDRESS INQUIRIES TO:
Fellowships Program Coordinator
(See address above.)

ATLANTIC SALMON FEDERATION   [2274]
P.O. Box 5200
St. Andrews NB E5B 3S8 Canada
(506) 529-1385
Fax: (506) 529-4985

E-MAIL ADDRESS:
jcarr@asf.ca

WEB SITE ADDRESS:
www.asf.ca

FOUNDED: 1948

AREAS OF INTEREST:
Conservation of Atlantic salmon and its habitat through programs in education, research, enhancement, restoration and international cooperation.

NAME(S) OF PROGRAMS:
● **Olin Fellowships**

TYPE:
Awards/prizes; Block grants; Capital grants; Demonstration grants; Fellowships; General operating grants; Grants-in-aid; Internships; Project/program grants; Research grants; Scholarships; Training grants; Travel grants; Visiting scholars; Work-study programs. Fellowships are offered to individuals seeking to improve their knowledge or skills in advanced fields while looking for solutions to current problems in Atlantic salmon biology, management or conservation.

YEAR PROGRAM STARTED: 1971

PURPOSE:
To further salmon conservation.

LEGAL BASIS:
Tax-exempt, nonprofit organization.

ELIGIBILITY:
Applicants must be legal residents of the U.S. or Canada. The Fellowships are tenable at any accredited university or research

laboratory or in an active management program and may be applied toward a wide range of endeavors including salmon management, graduate study and research. Applicants need not be enrolled in a degree program.

FINANCIAL DATA:
Amount of support per award: $1,000 to $3,000.
Total amount of support: $4,000 for the year 2010.

NUMBER OF APPLICANTS MOST RECENT YEAR: 2.

NUMBER OF AWARDS: 2 for the year 2010.

APPLICATION INFORMATION:
Further information and application forms may be obtained from the Canadian address above, from Atlantic Salmon Federation, P.O. Box 807, Calais, ME 04619 or from the web site.
Duration: One year.
Deadline: Applications must be received at the St. Andrews office by March 15. Applicants will be advised of awards by May 15.

PUBLICATIONS:
Atlantic Salmon Journal; annual report.

OFFICERS:
Bill Taylor, President
Hon. M.A. Meighen, Q.C., Chairman, ASF (Canada)
R.J. Warren, Chairman, ASF (U.S.)

ADDRESS INQUIRIES TO:
Ellen Merrill, Executive Assistant
Research and Environment
(See address above.)

BIOMEDICAL ENGINEERING SOCIETY   [2275]
8201 Corporate Drive, Suite 1125
Landover, MD 20785-2224
(301) 459-1999
Fax: (301) 459-2444

E-MAIL ADDRESS:
info@bmes.org

WEB SITE ADDRESS:
www.bmes.org

FOUNDED: 1968

AREAS OF INTEREST:
Biomedical engineering.

NAME(S) OF PROGRAMS:
● **BMES Achievement Award**
● **BMES Distinguished Lecture Award**
● **BMES Diversity Award**
● **Graduate Student Awards**
● **Robert A. Pritzker Distinguished Lecturer Award**
● **Rita Schaffer Young Investigator Award**
● **Undergraduate Student Awards**

TYPE:
Awards/prizes; Conferences/seminars; Travel grants. BMES Achievement Award is to be awarded each year by the Biomedical Engineering Society to an individual in a university, industry, or government to recognize his/her contributions to the advancement of biomedical engineering.

The BMES Distinguished Lecture Award is awarded each year by the Biomedical Engineering Society to individuals to

recognize outstanding achievements and leadership in the science and practice of biomedical engineering.

The BMES Diversity Award honors an individual, project, organization or institution for outstanding contributions to improving gender and racial diversity in biomedical engineering.

Graduate and Undergraduate Student Awards are given for outstanding biomedical engineering research and/or design project.

Robert A. Pritzker Distinguished Lecturer Award is given in recognition of an individual's outstanding achievements and leadership in the science and practice of biomedical engineering.

Rita Schaffer Young Investigator Award is offered each year by the Biomedical Engineering Society to stimulate research careers in biomedical engineering.

YEAR PROGRAM STARTED: 2007

PURPOSE:
To stimulate research careers in biomedical engineering.

ELIGIBILITY:
Pritzker Distinguished Lecturer Award: The awardee is expected to deliver a plenary lecture at the BMES Annual Fall Meeting and to publish the text of the lecture in the *Annals of Biomedical Engineering.* A very important purpose of the lecture is to critically review a field of biomedical engineering and to offer a vision of its future. The Award is intended to recognize a high level of originality and leadership in an area of biomedical engineering. The awardee may have achieved excellence in biomedical engineering by contributions within the setting of the university, industry or government. The contributions of the awardees do not need to precede the award date by any specific period of time.

Rita Schaffer Young Investigator Award: The Award is in recognition of a high level of originality and ingenuity in a scientific work in biomedical engineering. The awardee must be within five years of receiving his or her highest degree. Since selection of the awardee will largely be based on the review of a published paper describing original work, if the candidate is not the sole author of the manuscript, he or she must be the first author and the manuscript must be accompanied by a letter from the co-authors attesting to the significance of the investigation described in the manuscript. Manuscripts must have been published, or accepted for publication, in a peer-reviewed journal not more than two years prior to the date of nomination. The awardee is expected to be present to accept the Award at the Annual Fall Meeting.

FINANCIAL DATA:
Amount of support per award: BMES Distinguished Lecture Award: $1,000, a plaque and travel expenses up to $1,000; BMES Diversity Award: $1,000 and a plaque; Graduate Student Awards: Certificate, $500 stipend and registration for the BMES Annual Fall Meeting. If there is more than one author/winner, the award is to be shared amongst the winners; Pritzker Distinguished Lecturer Award: $2,000, a plaque and travel expenses up to $1,000; Rita Schaffer Young Investigator Award: $1,000 award and plaque are presented at the BMES Annual Fall Meeting. Travel expenses up to $1,250 and

meeting registration fee will be provided; Undergraduate Student Awards: Certificate, $400 stipend and registration for the BMES Annual Fall Meeting. If there is more than one author/winner, the award is to be shared amongst the winners.

NUMBER OF APPLICANTS MOST RECENT YEAR: 350.

NUMBER OF AWARDS: Distinguished Lectureship Award: 1; Graduate Student Awards: Up to 10; Rita Schaffer Young Investigator Award: 1; Undergraduate Student Awards: Up to 5.

APPLICATION INFORMATION:
Graduate and Undergraduate Student Awards: Competing students will submit extended abstracts (three to four pages for graduate students, and one to two pages for undergraduates) at the time of the official abstract submission deadline for the Annual Fall Meeting. Awardees will be chosen on the basis of the abstract's scientific merit, originality, and quality of presentation. Each student submission requires a letter of support from the scientific advisor or department chair certifying the originality of the student effort. Awardees are expected to participate in the Annual Fall Meeting and present their work.

Rita Schaffer Young Investigator Award: Applications must include the candidate's curriculum vitae and confidential letters by two recognized authorities in the field of the work, neither of whom is associated with the institution at which the work was completed nor a co-author on the paper, attesting to the significance of the investigation described in the manuscript. Submit four copies of manuscripts, curriculum vitae and the verifying letters.

Deadline: Distinguished Lecture Awards and Rita Schaffer Young Investigator Award: May 31; Graduate and Undergraduate Student Awards: Extended abstracts and letter of support by June 1.

PUBLICATIONS:
Program announcement.

IRS IDENTIFICATION NUMBER: 36-6212451

ADDRESS INQUIRIES TO:
Awards Chairperson
(See address above.)

CALIFORNIA ACADEMY OF SCIENCES   [2276]
Department of Invertebrate Zoology and Geology
55 Music Concourse Drive
San Francisco, CA 94118
(415) 379-5270

E-MAIL ADDRESS:
rmooi@calacademy.org

WEB SITE ADDRESS:
www.calacademy.org
research.calacademy.org/opportunities/ssi

FOUNDED: 1853

AREAS OF INTEREST:
Biology, anthropology, aquatic biology, botany, entomology, geology, herpetology, ichthyology, invertebrate zoology, mammalogy, ornithology and paleontology.

NAME(S) OF PROGRAMS:
● **Summer Systematics Institute**

TYPE:
Internships. Matches students with Academy scientists to work on specific research projects. May include laboratory and molecular components.

YEAR PROGRAM STARTED: 1995

PURPOSE:
To allow students to gain hands-on experience in the labs and collections archive.

ELIGIBILITY:
Applicants must be junior- or senior-level undergraduates who are U.S. citizens, with a "B" average or better and demonstrated participation in a wide range of campus activities.

FINANCIAL DATA:
Travel costs up to $500 to San Francisco will be reimbursed and a subsistence allowance of $2,100 is given for housing and food. Research costs, publication costs, and travel to return to CAS or to a conference are supported.

Amount of support per award: $3,600 stipend for the internship period.

Total amount of support: Varies.

NUMBER OF APPLICANTS MOST RECENT YEAR: 150.

NUMBER OF AWARDS: 7 to 10.

APPLICATION INFORMATION:
Duration: Full-time (40 hours per week) for eight weeks (mid-June to mid-August).
Deadline: Mid-February.

PUBLICATIONS:
Program announcement.

IRS IDENTIFICATION NUMBER: 94-1156258

STAFF:
Dr. Rich Mooi, RU Site Director

ADDRESS INQUIRIES TO:
Dr. Rich Mooi, RU Site Director
(See address above.)

COLUMBIA UNIVERSITY   [2277]
College of Physicians and Surgeons
630 West 168th Street, P & S 2-401
New York, NY 10032
(212) 305-7970

E-MAIL ADDRESS:
horwitzprize@columbia.edu

WEB SITE ADDRESS:
www.cumc.columbia.edu/horwitz/index.html

FOUNDED: 1754

NAME(S) OF PROGRAMS:
● **The Louisa Gross Horwitz Prize**

TYPE:
Awards/prizes. An annual prize designed to honor a major scientific contribution in basic research to the fields of biology or biochemistry.

YEAR PROGRAM STARTED: 1967

PURPOSE:
To honor a scientific investigator, or group of investigators, whose contributions to knowledge in either of these fields are deemed worthy of special recognition.

ELIGIBILITY:
The prize is open to scientists for outstanding basic research in the fields of biology or biochemistry.

FINANCIAL DATA:
Prize consists of an honorarium and a citation.

NUMBER OF AWARDS: 2.

REPRESENTATIVE AWARDS:
Arthur L. Horwich, Yale University School of Medicine, New Haven, CT; F. Ulrich Hartl, The Max-Planck Institute of Biochemistry, Martinsfried, Germany.

APPLICATION INFORMATION:
Nomination must include the name, title, mailing address and e-mail address of the nominee and nominator, along with the following supporting documents:
(1) curriculum vitae;
(2) biographical sketch;
(3) 500-word research summary;
(4) 500-word research significance and;
(5) key publications list.
Deadline: January 31.

ADDRESS INQUIRIES TO:
See e-mail address above.

CONSERVATION AND RESEARCH FOUNDATION
P.O. Box 909
Shelburne, VT 05482-0909
(802) 985-4106

WEB SITE ADDRESS:
conservationresearch.wordpress.com

TYPE:
Challenge/matching grants; General operating grants. Grants to organizations and individuals engaged either in biological research or in conservation activities that might have a beneficial effect on environmental quality.

See entry 2313 for full listing.

THE ENTOMOLOGICAL FOUNDATION   [2278]
9332 Annapolis Road
Suite 210
Lanham, MD 20706
(301) 459-9082
Fax: (301) 459-9084

E-MAIL ADDRESS:
melodie@entfdn.org

WEB SITE ADDRESS:
www.entfdn.org

FOUNDED: 1991

AREAS OF INTEREST:
Entomology.

NAME(S) OF PROGRAMS:
● **Stan Beck Fellowship**

TYPE:
Fellowships. Awarded annually to assist needy students at the graduate or undergraduate level of their education. The need may be based on physical limitations or economic, minority, or environmental conditions.

YEAR PROGRAM STARTED: 1996

PURPOSE:
To assist needy students at graduate or undergraduate level of education in entomology and related disciplines.

ELIGIBILITY:
Applicant must have a need based on physical limitations, economic, minority, or environmental conditions.

GEOGRAPHIC RESTRICTIONS:
Canada, Mexico and United States.

FINANCIAL DATA:
Amount of support per award: Varies. The amount is based on the earnings from the investment.

NUMBER OF AWARDS: 1.

APPLICATION INFORMATION:
Nomination package must be submitted electronically. Paper applications will not be accepted.

Deadline: July 1 (i.e., the submission of a complete document in a readable format).

ADDRESS INQUIRIES TO:
Melodie Dziduch, Awards Coordinator (See address above.)

THE ENTOMOLOGICAL FOUNDATION [2279]
9332 Annapolis Road
Suite 210
Lanham, MD 20706
(301) 459-9082
Fax: (301) 459-9084

E-MAIL ADDRESS:
melodie@entfdn.org

WEB SITE ADDRESS:
www.entfdn.org

FOUNDED: 1991

AREAS OF INTEREST:
Entomology.

NAME(S) OF PROGRAMS:
● **Henry and Sylvia Richardson Research Grant**

TYPE:
Research grants.

YEAR PROGRAM STARTED: 1989

PURPOSE:
To provide research funds to postdoctoral members who have at least one year of promising work experience, who are undertaking research in selected areas of entomology and have demonstrated a high level of scholarship.

ELIGIBILITY:
Candidates must be members of Entomological Society of America (ESA), postdoctoral students and working in insect control by attractants, repellents, biological controls, thermo controls, or chemical controls. Second priority is given to those students working in insect control of medical or veterinary importance. When there are no suitable candidates in the above, candidates working in areas of physiology or toxicology may be considered. Candidates must have an overall grade point average equivalent to 3.0 on a 4.0 scale.

FINANCIAL DATA:
Amount of support per award: Varies.
Total amount of support: Varies.

COOPERATIVE FUNDING PROGRAMS: Research grant is funded by interest earned from the Richardson Endowment Fund.

NUMBER OF AWARDS: 1 annually.

APPLICATION INFORMATION:
The entire nomination package, not to exceed 20 pages, must be submitted electronically. Paper nominations will not be accepted. Nominators must provide:
(1) CV-related items, as outlined on the Foundation's web site;
(2) letter of nomination;
(3) letter of application describing eligibility;

(4) two-page description of research in one of the areas defined above;
(5) two letters of recommendation, one from a major professor and one from a previous instructor and;
(6) official graduate-level and postgraduate transcripts. Mail transcripts to the address listed above.

Duration: One academic year.

Deadline: July 1 (i.e., the submission of a complete document in a readable format).

PUBLICATIONS:
Guidelines.

ADDRESS INQUIRIES TO:
Melodie Dziduch, Awards Coordinator (See address above.)

THE ENTOMOLOGICAL FOUNDATION [2280]
9332 Annapolis Road
Suite 210
Lanham, MD 20706-9322
(301) 459-9082
Fax: (301) 459-9084

E-MAIL ADDRESS:
melodie@entfdn.org

WEB SITE ADDRESS:
www.entfdn.org

FOUNDED: 1991

AREAS OF INTEREST:
Entomology.

NAME(S) OF PROGRAMS:
● **Jeffery P. LaFage Graduate Student Research Award**

TYPE:
Awards/prizes; Research grants.

YEAR PROGRAM STARTED: 1992

PURPOSE:
To encourage research by graduate students in the field of the biology and control of termites and other insect pests of the urban environment.

ELIGIBILITY:
The grant is awarded to a graduate student who proposes innovative research to significantly advance or contribute to the knowledge of the biology or control of pests of the urban environment, especially termites or other wood-destroying organisms. The applicant must be a candidate for a Master's or Ph.D. degree at an accredited university. The grant is open to students throughout the world.

Priority will be given to proposals demonstrating a creative and realistic approach to the fields of interest. The recipient is encouraged to present the research results at an ESA meeting and is required to acknowledge the grant award in any publications resulting from these funds.

FINANCIAL DATA:
This grant may be used for salaries, equipment, supplies or travel to initiate, accelerate, augment, or expand a research project.

Amount of support per award: Varies.
Total amount of support: Varies.

NUMBER OF AWARDS: 1.

APPLICATION INFORMATION:
All nomination packages must be submitted electronically. The entire nomination package must not exceed 20 pages, including letters

of nomination or recommendation and publication lists. Paper nominations and printed letters sent in lieu of electronic versions will not be accepted.

Duration: Grant is renewable.

Deadline: July 1 (i.e., the submission of a complete document in a readable format).

PUBLICATIONS:
Guidelines.

ADDRESS INQUIRIES TO:
Melodie Dziduch, Awards Coordinator (See address above.)

*SPECIAL STIPULATIONS:
Science must be related to entomology.

THE ENTOMOLOGICAL FOUNDATION [2281]
9332 Annapolis Road
Suite 210
Lanham, MD 20706
(301) 459-9082
Fax: (301) 459-9084

E-MAIL ADDRESS:
melodie@entfdn.org

WEB SITE ADDRESS:
www.entfdn.org

FOUNDED: 1991

AREAS OF INTEREST:
Entomology.

NAME(S) OF PROGRAMS:
● **Undergraduate Scholarship Program**

TYPE:
Scholarships.

YEAR PROGRAM STARTED: 1992

PURPOSE:
To promote and encourage student interest in the science of entomology.

ELIGIBILITY:
Applicants must be enrolled as undergraduate students majoring in entomology at a recognized university or college in the U.S., Mexico or Canada. The student must also have accumulated a minimum of 90 college credit hours by September 1 following the application deadline, and either completed two junior-level entomology courses or have a research project in entomology. Applicants will be evaluated primarily on their demonstrated enthusiasm, interest and achievement in entomology and on academic credentials.

Preference is given based on financial need.

GEOGRAPHIC RESTRICTIONS:
Canada, Mexico and United States.

FINANCIAL DATA:
Amount of support per award: $2,000.
Total amount of support: $2,000.

COOPERATIVE FUNDING PROGRAMS: Scholarship is funded by BioQuip Products.

NUMBER OF AWARDS: 1.

APPLICATION INFORMATION:
All nomination packages, not to exceed 20 pages, must be submitted electronically. Paper nominations will not be accepted. Nominators must provide:
(1) CV-related items as outlined on the Foundation's web site;
(2) application;
(3) letter of nomination (student can write letter of nomination to request consideration);
(4) statement of no more than two pages in length from the student concerning his/her

interest in entomology, career goals, financial need, and other pertinent factors which illustrate qualifications for the scholarship; (5) three statements from school officials or other knowledgeable individuals attesting to entomological interests, character, aptitude, and financial need and; (6) current official transcript of college grades. Mail transcripts to the address listed above.

Duration: One academic year.

Deadline: July 1 (i.e., the submission of a complete document in a readable format).

PUBLICATIONS:
Guidelines.

ADDRESS INQUIRIES TO:
Melodie Dziduch, Awards Coordinator
(See address above.)

JOHN E. FOGARTY INTERNATIONAL CENTER   [2282]
Division of International Training and Research
Building 31, B2C39
31 Center Drive, MSC 2220
Bethesda, MD 20892-2220
(301) 496-1653
Fax: (301) 402-0779

WEB SITE ADDRESS:
www.fic.nih.gov

AREAS OF INTEREST:
International biomedical, behavioral and social sciences health research and collaboration.

NAME(S) OF PROGRAMS:
• **Fogarty International Research Collaboration Award (FIRCA)**

TYPE:
Research grants. A small grants program to support biomedical, behavioral and social sciences health research.

PURPOSE:
To facilitate collaborative research efforts between U.S. and foreign scientists and their colleagues in low- and middle-income countries.

ELIGIBILITY:
Applications are encouraged for research collaboration with investigators in sub-Saharan African countries.

FINANCIAL DATA:
These small grants will provide funds to the foreign collaborator, through the U.S. grantee institution, for equipment, supplies and research support at his or her home institution and for travel expenses for both the U.S. Principal Investigator and the foreign collaborator.
Amount of support per award: $50,000 in direct costs for up to three years.

NUMBER OF APPLICANTS MOST RECENT YEAR:
Approximately 100 per year.

NUMBER OF AWARDS: Approximately 50 to 60 per year.

APPLICATION INFORMATION:
Detailed information is available online.
Duration: Up to three years.
Deadline: Varies.

PUBLICATIONS:
Program announcement.

ADDRESS INQUIRIES TO:
Xinghzhu Liu, Program Director
(See address above.)

THE HARRY FRANK GUGGENHEIM FOUNDATION
25 West 53rd Street
16th Floor
New York, NY 10019-5401
(646) 428-0971
Fax: (646) 428-0981

E-MAIL ADDRESS:
info@hfg.org

WEB SITE ADDRESS:
www.hfg.org

TYPE:
Fellowships. Awarded to individuals who will complete the writing of the dissertation within the award year. Support is for projects which seek to advance and coordinate creative breakthroughs in the social and biological sciences relating to the study of dominance, violence and aggression.

See entry 1977 for full listing.

THE HARRY FRANK GUGGENHEIM FOUNDATION
25 West 53rd Street
16th Floor
New York, NY 10019-5401
(646) 428-0971
Fax: (646) 428-0981

E-MAIL ADDRESS:
info@hfg.org

WEB SITE ADDRESS:
www.hfg.org

TYPE:
Research grants. Support for projects which seek to advance and coordinate creative breakthroughs in the social and biological sciences relating to the study of dominance, violence and aggression.

See entry 1976 for full listing.

HOWARD HUGHES MEDICAL INSTITUTE   [2283]
Office of Grants and Special Programs
4000 Jones Bridge Road
Chevy Chase, MD 20815
(301) 215-8895
Fax: (301) 347-3053

E-MAIL ADDRESS:
biederma@hhmi.org

WEB SITE ADDRESS:
www.hhmi.org/grants

FOUNDED: 1953

AREAS OF INTEREST:
Fundamental biomedical research and science education.

NAME(S) OF PROGRAMS:
• **Undergraduate Science Education Program**

TYPE:
Project/program grants.

YEAR PROGRAM STARTED: 1988

PURPOSE:
To strengthen the national quality of college-level programs in the biological sciences and other scientific disciplines as they relate to biology; to attract and retain students in scientific research and education careers.

LEGAL BASIS:
Medical research organization.

ELIGIBILITY:
There are three competitions: colleges, universities and HHMI Professors. Colleges and universities are invited to participate on the basis of their recent 10-year records of graduating students who go on to medical school or obtain Ph.Ds. in the sciences. Institutions are invited to participate in the HHMI Professors competition on the basis of their classifications by the Carnegie Foundation for the Advancement of Teaching as doctoral or research universities and their records of postbaccalaureate student achievement in the sciences.

GEOGRAPHIC RESTRICTIONS:
United States and its territories.

FINANCIAL DATA:
Amount of support per award: $800,000 to $1,600,000.

NUMBER OF APPLICANTS MOST RECENT YEAR:
158 (universities).

NUMBER OF AWARDS: 50 (universities).

REPRESENTATIVE AWARDS:
$1,500,000 to Dartmouth College; $1,900,000 to University of Colorado Boulder; $2,200,000 to the University of Maryland Baltimore County.

APPLICATION INFORMATION:
Application for this competition is by invitation only. Required forms are issued by the Institute.

Duration: Four years.

PUBLICATIONS:
Program announcement.

IRS IDENTIFICATION NUMBER: 59-0735717

OFFICERS:
Robert Tjian, Ph.D., President
Craig A. Alexander, Vice President and General Counsel
Sean Carroll, Ph.D., Vice President for Grants and Special Programs
Jack E. Dixon, Ph.D., Vice President and Chief Scientific Officer
Mohamoud Jibrell, Vice President for Information Technology
Avice A. Meehan, Vice President for Communications and Public Affairs
Edward J. Palmerino, Vice President for Finance and Treasurer
Gerald M. Rubin, Ph.D., Vice President and Director, Janiela Farm Research Campus
Landis P. Zimmerman, Vice President and Chief Investment Officer

ADDRESS INQUIRIES TO:
David Asai, Ph.D.
Director, Precollege and Undergraduate Science Education
(See address above.)

*SPECIAL STIPULATIONS:
The Institute does not provide scholarships or other forms of financial assistance directly to undergraduates. The colleges and universities receiving undergraduate grants are responsible for selecting students or teachers and awarding them Institute support for laboratory research and other activities.

HUMAN FRONTIER SCIENCE PROGRAM ORGANIZATION [2284]

12 Quai St. Jean
BP 10034
67080 Strasbourg Cedex France
(33) 3-88-21-51-26 (Grants)
(33) 3-88-21-51-27 (Fellowships)
Fax: (33) 3-88-32-88-97

E-MAIL ADDRESS:
grant@hfsp.org
fellow@hfsp.org

WEB SITE ADDRESS:
www.hfsp.org

AREAS OF INTEREST:
Interdisciplinary research into the complex mechanisms of biological functions.

NAME(S) OF PROGRAMS:
● **Cross-Disciplinary Fellowships**
● **Long-Term Fellowships**
● **Program Grants**
● **Young Investigator Grants**

TYPE:
Fellowships; Project/program grants; Research grants. Grants are awarded to teams of scientists from different continents.

ELIGIBILITY:
Scientists from all countries can apply, but with some restrictions. The principal investigator of grants must be from a member country. Fellowship candidates from nonmember countries can only apply to work in a member country.

FINANCIAL DATA:
Amount of support per award: Varies depending upon the nature of the research.

APPLICATION INFORMATION:
Duration: Up to three years.

PUBLICATIONS:
Program announcement.

ADDRESS INQUIRIES TO:
Dr. Martin Reddington, Director of Scientific Affairs and Communications
For fellowships: fellow@hfsp.org
For grants: grant@hfsp.org

THE EDMUND NILES HUYCK PRESERVE, INC. [2285]

P.O. Box 189
Rensselaerville, NY 12147
(518) 797-3440
Fax: (518) 797-3440

E-MAIL ADDRESS:
huyckpreserve@wildblue.net

WEB SITE ADDRESS:
www.huyckpreserve.org

FOUNDED: 1931

AREAS OF INTEREST:
Ecology, behavior, biology and earth science.

CONSULTING OR VOLUNTEER SERVICES:
Volunteer support is welcome.

NAME(S) OF PROGRAMS:
● **Huyck Grants for Graduate and Postgraduate Research**

TYPE:
Research grants. Stipends, housing and laboratory space for predoctoral and postdoctoral scientists conducting research on and utilizing the natural resources of The E.N. Huyck Preserve.

YEAR PROGRAM STARTED: 1937

PURPOSE:
To promote research and education on the ecology of the Catskill Mountain Region and its environs.

LEGAL BASIS:
Private operating foundation.

ELIGIBILITY:
Applicants must be predoctoral and postdoctoral scientists whose research utilizes the natural resources of The E.N. Huyck Preserve.

FINANCIAL DATA:
Grants include free housing and laboratory space. Research support including funds for support of research associates, some equipment, or equipment and supplies not available on the Preserve.
Amount of support per award: Stipend $2,500 maximum for graduate students and $3,500 for senior scientists, lodging and laboratory.
Total amount of support: $12,000.

COOPERATIVE FUNDING PROGRAMS: Full cooperation will be extended to those organizations whose educational or research programs further the objectives of the E.N. Huyck Preserve.

NUMBER OF APPLICANTS MOST RECENT YEAR: 15.

NUMBER OF AWARDS: Approximately 6 per year.

APPLICATION INFORMATION:
The grant proposal must contain an abstract of not more than 200 words, a section describing the background and significance of the project, a section stating the main objectives of the study, and a methods section. There should also be a section describing other projects that the principal investigator has under way. If the researcher has previously conducted research at the Preserve, please indicate the extent of the research and the resulting publication(s). A literature-cited section should be included. Each investigator must provide an up-to-date curriculum vitae. The budget section must give a detailed breakdown of the proposed budget. The researcher should have three colleagues submit references that deal specifically with the work proposed to be done at the Preserve.
Duration: Up to one year. May be renewed on competitive basis.
Deadline: March 8.

PUBLICATIONS:
Annual scientist reports; occasional papers; newsletters (seasonally).

EXECUTIVE DIRECTOR:
Chad Jemison

ADDRESS INQUIRIES TO:
Chad Jemison, Executive Director
(See address above.)

INTERNATIONAL CRANE FOUNDATION, INC. [2286]

E-11376 Shady Lane Road
Baraboo, WI 53913
(608) 356-9462
Fax: (608) 356-9465

E-MAIL ADDRESS:
cranes@savingcranes.org

WEB SITE ADDRESS:
www.savingcranes.org

FOUNDED: 1973

AREAS OF INTEREST:
Aviculture, crane ecology and conservation education.

CONSULTING OR VOLUNTEER SERVICES:
Work with individuals who have specific questions regarding crane propagation, restoration of natural habitats, or conservation education on an informal basis and as the need arises.

TYPE:
Internships. Formal stipended internship programs in the fields of aviculture, crane ecology and conservation education.

YEAR PROGRAM STARTED: 1980

PURPOSE:
To act as the world center for the study and preservation of cranes and their natural habitats.

LEGAL BASIS:
Nonprofit corporation.

ELIGIBILITY:
College sophomores through recent college graduates in biology, zoology, botany or education who have a willingness to work at a variety of tasks and can work in a self-directed manner. Staff makes all decisions regarding internships at the Foundation.

FINANCIAL DATA:
Amount of support per award: $550 stipend per month, plus housing.

NUMBER OF APPLICANTS MOST RECENT YEAR:
Approximately 80.

NUMBER OF AWARDS: 11.

APPLICATION INFORMATION:
Letter of application indicating interest, relevant coursework and experience, plus three references. An interview will be required, although a phone interview may suffice.
Duration: Three to nine months. Must submit additional application for renewal.

IRS IDENTIFICATION NUMBER: 39-1187711

ADDRESS INQUIRIES TO:
See e-mail address above.

THE JACKSON LABORATORY [2287]

600 Main Street
Bar Harbor, ME 04609
(207) 288-6420
Fax: (207) 288-6697

E-MAIL ADDRESS:
training@jax.org

WEB SITE ADDRESS:
www.jax.org

FOUNDED: 1929

AREAS OF INTEREST:
Mammalian genetics.

NAME(S) OF PROGRAMS:
● **Postdoctoral Program at the Jackson Laboratory**

TYPE:
Fellowships. Research participation at the postdoctoral level in cancer genetics, developmental genetics, hematology and immunology and other fields of mammalian biology. Support is for research training at the Jackson Laboratory.

PURPOSE:
To support postdoctoral research training in mammalian genetics.

LEGAL BASIS:
Private institution.

ELIGIBILITY:
An applicant must be a recent recipient of the Ph.D., M.D., D.V.M. or equivalent degree. An applicant for a training grant appointment must be either a citizen of the U.S. or a foreign national holding a visa permitting permanent residence in the U.S.

FINANCIAL DATA:
Program includes full benefits.
Amount of support per award: $37,740 to $52,068 in stipends, depending upon years of postdoctoral experience.
Total amount of support: Varies.

NUMBER OF AWARDS: Several new awards annually.

APPLICATION INFORMATION:
Applications must include a curriculum vitae and three letters of recommendation.
Duration: Appointments are for one year. Renewable for up to two years.
Deadline: Applications accepted throughout the year.

ADMINISTRATIVE OFFICERS:
Dr. Robert Braun, Associate Director

ADDRESS INQUIRIES TO:
Suzanne Serreze, Manager
(See address above.)

*SPECIAL STIPULATIONS:
Appointments tenable only at the Jackson Laboratory.

LIFE SCIENCES RESEARCH FOUNDATION (LSRF)   [2288]
Lewis Thomas Laboratories
Washington Road
Princeton University
Princeton, NJ 08544
(609) 258-3551
Fax: (609) 258-2957

E-MAIL ADDRESS:
sdirenzo@princeton.edu

WEB SITE ADDRESS:
www.lsrf.org

FOUNDED: 1984

AREAS OF INTEREST:
Biological sciences.

NAME(S) OF PROGRAMS:
● **Three-Year Postdoctoral Fellowships**

TYPE:
Fellowships.

YEAR PROGRAM STARTED: 1984

PURPOSE:
To offer research support for aspiring scientists.

LEGAL BASIS:
Private organization.

ELIGIBILITY:
Fellowship applicants must be graduates with M.D. or Ph.D. degrees in any field of the biological sciences. Awards are based solely on the quality of the individual applicant's previous accomplishments and on the merit of his or her proposal for postdoctoral research. All U.S. citizens are eligible to

apply with no restrictions on the laboratory of their choice. (Foreign applicants will be eligible for study in U.S. laboratories.)

No applicant with a contracted, salaried position (such as assistant professor) is eligible to apply.

FINANCIAL DATA:
Stipend includes salary, fringe benefits, travel to the host institution and to the annual meeting and research expenses.
Amount of support per award: $57,000 per year.
Total amount of support: $2,736,000 to $3,078,000.

NUMBER OF APPLICANTS MOST RECENT YEAR: 790.

NUMBER OF AWARDS: 16 to 18.

APPLICATION INFORMATION:
Application should include the following:
(1) abstract of the proposal (200 words or less);
(2) curriculum vitae (three-page maximum);
(3) research proposal (five-page maximum);
(4) letter from supervisor and;
(5) three letters of reference.

All documents are to be uploaded online as either Microsoft Word or PDF files. Further details can be found on the Foundation's web site.
Duration: Three years.
Deadline: October 1.

ADDRESS INQUIRIES TO:
Susan DiRenzo, Assistant Director
(See address above.)

MARINE BIOLOGICAL LABORATORY   [2289]
Education Office
7 MBL Street
Woods Hole, MA 02543
(508) 289-7173
Fax: (508) 289-7934

E-MAIL ADDRESS:
fellows@mbl.edu

WEB SITE ADDRESS:
www.mbl.edu

FOUNDED: 1888

AREAS OF INTEREST:
Cellular and molecular physiology, molecular biology, developmental biology, neurobiology, innate immunity, ecology, parasitology, microbiology, pharmacology, toxicology, cancer biology, regenerative biology, aging, molecular evolution, microbial biology, sensory physiology, aquaculture, metabolic diseases, environmental science, climate change, and plant physiology.

NAME(S) OF PROGRAMS:
● **Marine Biological Laboratory Research Awards**

TYPE:
Research grants.

PURPOSE:
To provide funding to scientists interested in conducting research projects in various scientific areas.

LEGAL BASIS:
Nonprofit organization.

ELIGIBILITY:
Applicants must be independent investigators. Working scientists must be willing to come

to the Laboratory for a minimum six-week stay to conduct independent research in areas of interest to the Laboratory. Sabbaticals are encouraged.

FINANCIAL DATA:
Amount of support per award: Varies.
Total amount of support: Varies.
Matching fund requirements: Strongly encouraged from home institution.

COOPERATIVE FUNDING PROGRAMS: APA, ASCB and HHMI.

NUMBER OF APPLICANTS MOST RECENT YEAR: 75.

NUMBER OF AWARDS: Varies.

APPLICATION INFORMATION:
Duration: Varies.
Deadline: January 15.

IRS IDENTIFICATION NUMBER: 04-2104690

STAFF:
Joshua Hamilton, Chief Academic and Scientific Officer

ADDRESS INQUIRIES TO:
Research Awards Coordinator
(See address above.)

MICROSCOPY SOCIETY OF AMERICA   [2290]
12100 Sunset Hills Road, Suite 130
Reston, VA 20190-3221
(703) 234-4115
(800) 538-3672
Fax: (703) 435-4390

E-MAIL ADDRESS:
associationmanagement@microscopy.org

WEB SITE ADDRESS:
www.microscopy.org

FOUNDED: 1942

AREAS OF INTEREST:
Microscopy.

NAME(S) OF PROGRAMS:
● **MSA Professional Technical Staff Awards**

TYPE:
Awards/prizes; Conferences/seminars.

PURPOSE:
To stimulate attendance for those who ordinarily might not participate; to encourage employers to support their staff in professional activities.

LEGAL BASIS:
Special interest society.

ELIGIBILITY:
Applicants must have been current members of MSA for three years prior to the time of the annual meeting. Awards are based on the quality of the paper submitted for presentation at the meeting. Abstracts will be judged by the MSA Technologist's Forum. The applicant must be the first author of the submitted paper.

Successful applicants must present their papers personally at the meeting in order to receive the award. They are expected to attend and participate in the entire meeting. Former winners will not be eligible for another award.

FINANCIAL DATA:
Amount of support per award: The award consists of complimentary full registration for the annual meeting including a copy of *Proceedings* and the Sunday evening social

event. In addition, MSA will reimburse awardees up to $600 for travel, lodging and other expenses.

Total amount of support: Varies.

NUMBER OF AWARDS: 4; 2 in biological sciences and 2 in physical sciences.

APPLICATION INFORMATION:
Applications shall consist of a copy of the abstract and data form to be sent to the Technologist's Forum Committee and a supporting letter from the applicant's employer, manager or supervisor, attesting to the applicant's status as a full-time, professional staff member.

Duration: One-time award.

Deadline: February 15.

STAFF:
Peter Doherty, Managing Director
Jean Heavrin, Program Manager

ADDRESS INQUIRIES TO:
Peter Doherty, Managing Director
(See address above.)

MOUNT DESERT ISLAND BIOLOGICAL LABORATORY [2291]

P.O. Box 35
Salsbury Cove, ME 04672
(207) 288-3605
Fax: (207) 288-2130

E-MAIL ADDRESS:
mmckernan@mdibl.org

WEB SITE ADDRESS:
www.mdibl.org

FOUNDED: 1898

AREAS OF INTEREST:
Biological, toxicological and biomedical sciences.

NAME(S) OF PROGRAMS:
● **Summer Research Fellowships for Undergraduate Faculty and Students**

TYPE:
Fellowships; Internships. Faculty fellowship awards are made to teacher scientists with primary responsibilities at the undergraduate level. Summer research awards are given to scientists through a New Investigator Award (NIA) program. Undergraduate fellowships are available to student trainees.

YEAR PROGRAM STARTED: 1898

PURPOSE:
To enhance scientific training in the biological sciences.

LEGAL BASIS:
Nonprofit research institute.

ELIGIBILITY:
Applicants for faculty fellowships must have an earned Doctorate and be actively engaged in biological research. Applicants for undergraduate fellowships must have had a minimum of one year of biology and one year of chemistry. Undergraduate minorities are encouraged to apply.

FINANCIAL DATA:
Fellowships cover housing, travel and research costs in addition to a summer stipend.

Amount of support per award: Faculty Fellowships: Up to $12,000; Undergraduate Fellowships: Up to $4,750.

COOPERATIVE FUNDING PROGRAMS: Grants are made possible with support from private sources, the National Science Foundation and the National Institutes of Health.

APPLICATION INFORMATION:
Duration: One to four months during the summer.

Deadline: January 16.

IRS IDENTIFICATION NUMBER: 01-0202467

ADDRESS INQUIRIES TO:
Dr. Patricia Hand
Administrative Director
(See address above.)

MOUNTAIN LAKE BIOLOGICAL STATION [2292]

University of Virginia
P.O. Box 400327
Charlottesville, VA 22904-4327
(434) 982-5486
Fax: (434) 982-5626

E-MAIL ADDRESS:
mlbs@virginia.edu

WEB SITE ADDRESS:
www.mlbs.org

FOUNDED: 1929

AREAS OF INTEREST:
Ecological and evolutionary studies.

NAME(S) OF PROGRAMS:
● **Postdoctoral Fellowships for Summer Research in Field Biology**

TYPE:
Assistantships; Conferences/seminars; Endowments; Exchange programs; Fellowships; General operating grants; Grants-in-aid; Internships; Research grants; Residencies; Scholarships; Seed money grants; Technical assistance; Visiting scholars; Work-study programs.

YEAR PROGRAM STARTED: 1993

PURPOSE:
To provide support for biological field research.

LEGAL BASIS:
University of Virginia.

ELIGIBILITY:
Priority is given to candidates in the early stages of their scientific careers and to those whose interests show potential for long-term studies at Mountain Lake.

GEOGRAPHIC RESTRICTIONS:
Southern Appalachians.

FINANCIAL DATA:
Amount of support per award: Up to $2,000.
Total amount of support: Varies.

NUMBER OF APPLICANTS MOST RECENT YEAR:
150.

NUMBER OF AWARDS: 25.

APPLICATION INFORMATION:
A letter of application and MLBS application forms are required.

Duration: Up to 12 weeks during the summer.

Deadline: Contact Mountain Lake for exact dates.

PUBLICATIONS:
Brochure.

STAFF:
Dr. Eric Nagy, Associate Director

ADDRESS INQUIRIES TO:
Fellowships:
Dr. Edmund Brodie, Jr., Director
Undergraduate Research Program:
Dr. Eric Nagy, Associate Director
(See address above.)

*SPECIAL STIPULATIONS:
Must be in residence at station to apply for award, fellowships and other funding.

MUSEUM OF COMPARATIVE ZOOLOGY [2293]

Harvard University, OEB Administration
26 Oxford Street, Room 108
Cambridge, MA 02138
(617) 495-2460
Fax: (617) 496-8308

E-MAIL ADDRESS:
grants@oeb.harvard.edu

WEB SITE ADDRESS:
www.mcz.harvard.
edu/grants_and_funding/ernst-mayr-travel.html

FOUNDED: 1858

AREAS OF INTEREST:
Comparative zoology.

NAME(S) OF PROGRAMS:
● **Ernst Mayr Grants in Animal Systematics**

TYPE:
Awards/prizes; Research grants; Travel grants.

YEAR PROGRAM STARTED: 1984

PURPOSE:
To enable animal systematists to make short visits to museums for research needed to complete taxonomic revisions and monographs; to stimulate taxonomic work on neglected taxa, including those with numerous poorly described species, genera and families known to have many undescribed species in institutional collections, taxa for which it is unknown what proportion of the nominal species are synonyms, and difficult genera without keys.

ELIGIBILITY:
Preference is given to studies that use the Museum of Comparative Zoology collections, although applications to work at other museums also will be considered.

FINANCIAL DATA:
Grants may cover travel, lodging and meals for up to a few months while conducting research at the museums, services purchased from the host institution, research supplies, etc.

Amount of support per award: $1,000 average.

Total amount of support: Varies.

NUMBER OF APPLICANTS MOST RECENT YEAR:
42.

NUMBER OF AWARDS: 24.

APPLICATION INFORMATION:
Proposals should consist of an application form which includes a short project description and explicit statement of the goals of the research, itinerary, and budget, a curriculum vitae, and three letters of support. All applications should be written in English. Proposals may be submitted through standard mail to the address above or electronically to the e-mail listed above. Submissions through standard mail must include five copies of the proposal materials and must be received by the deadline.

Duration: Must be used within one year.

Deadline: April 1 and October 15.
Announcements typically within two months
following the application deadline.

STAFF:
Catherine Weisel, Museum Projects
Coordinator

ADDRESS INQUIRIES TO:
Catherine Weisel
Museum Projects Coordinator
(See address and e-mail above.)

*SPECIAL STIPULATIONS:
Each grantee is required to submit a written
report summarizing the scientific
accomplishments achieved with the award
within one month of travel completion.

MYCOLOGICAL SOCIETY OF AMERICA   [2294]

One Gifford Pinchot Drive
Madison, WI 53726
(225) 578-1383
Fax: (225) 578- 1415

E-MAIL ADDRESS:
msasec1@yahoo.com

WEB SITE ADDRESS:
msafungi.org

FOUNDED: 1931

AREAS OF INTEREST:
The study of fungi.

NAME(S) OF PROGRAMS:
- **Myron P. Backus Award**
- **Forest Fungal Ecology Award**
- **Martin-Baker Research Awards**
- **Mentor Student Travel Awards**
- **MSA Graduate Fellowship**
- **NAMA Memorial Graduate Fellowship**
- **John W. Rippon Research Award**
- **Clark T. Rogerson Research Award**
- **Alexander H. and Helen V. Smith Research Fund**

TYPE:
Awards/prizes; Conferences/seminars;
Fellowships; Travel grants. Supplementary
grant for an outstanding candidate awarded in
addition to any fellowship, scholarship or
assistantship support from other sources to
further graduate studies in the field of
mycology.

LEGAL BASIS:
Nonprofit organization.

ELIGIBILITY:
Applicants must be student members of the
Mycological Society of America. In selecting
the recipient of the Fellowship, consideration
is given to scholastic merit, research ability
and promise shown as a future mycologist.

FINANCIAL DATA:
Amount of support per award:
Approximately $2,000 per fellowship; $1,000
for Myron P. Backus Award.

Total amount of support: Approximately
$15,000 annually.

COOPERATIVE FUNDING PROGRAMS: NAMA
Memorial Fellowship donated by The North
American Mycological Association.

APPLICATION INFORMATION:
Duration: One year. Nonrenewable.
Deadline: February 15.

PUBLICATIONS:
Mycologia, research journal; *Inoculum,*
newsletter.

ADDRESS INQUIRIES TO:
Secretary
(See address above.)

NATIONAL ALOPECIA AREATA FOUNDATION   [2295]

14 Mitchell Boulevard
San Rafael, CA 94903
(415) 472-3780
Fax: (415) 472-5343

E-MAIL ADDRESS:
info@naaf.org

WEB SITE ADDRESS:
www.naaf.org

FOUNDED: 1981

AREAS OF INTEREST:
Baldness, hair loss and alopecia areata.

TYPE:
Research grants.

YEAR PROGRAM STARTED: 1985

PURPOSE:
To support research to find an acceptable
treatment and studies that will lead to an
eventual cure for alopecia areata.

ELIGIBILITY:
Must be an Institute Review Board-approved
researcher who has submitted a proposal
about alopecia areata or hair biology. No
funding for established investigators.

FINANCIAL DATA:
Salaries only fellows, assistants, residents and
technicians.

Amount of support per award: $10,000 to
$50,000.

Total amount of support: $3,200,000 since
inception of program.

COOPERATIVE FUNDING PROGRAMS: Joint grants
with other organizations.

NUMBER OF APPLICANTS MOST RECENT YEAR:
9.

NUMBER OF AWARDS: 7.

APPLICATION INFORMATION:
Contact the Foundation for application
procedures.
Duration: One year.

ADDRESS INQUIRIES TO:
Jeanne Rappoport, Vice President
Administration and Meetings
(See address above.)

NATIONAL SCIENCE FOUNDATION   [2296]

Division of Molecular and Cellular Biosciences
4201 Wilson Boulevard, Room 655
Arlington, VA 22230
(703) 292-8440
Fax: (703) 292-9061

WEB SITE ADDRESS:
www.nsf.gov

FOUNDED: 1950

AREAS OF INTEREST:
Biochemistry, biophysics, genetics and cell
biology.

NAME(S) OF PROGRAMS:
- **Division of Molecular and Cellular Biosciences Programs**

TYPE:
Conferences/seminars; Project/program
grants; Research grants; Seed money grants.

These programs have the following clusters:
biomolecular systems, cellular systems, and
genes and genome systems.

Support for individual research projects,
research workshops, symposia and
conferences and for the purchase of scientific
equipment for research purposes. Support is
available in the following categories:

Cellular Systems: Supports research on the
structural and functional organization of
plant, animal and microbial cells and on
signaling pathways and regulation at the
cellular level. Cellular organization includes
the assembly and function of structural
elements in the cell such as the cytoskeleton,
membranes, organelles, intercellular
compartments, intranuclear structures and the
extracellular matrix (including walls). Also
included are both structural and dynamic
aspects of cellular and intracellular motility,
meiosis and mitosis and cell shape and cell
polarity. Related topics include the
mechanisms of endocytosis, exocytosis, and
intracellular trafficking of membranes and
macromolecules. Signaling and regulation
include intracellular and transmembrane
signal transduction mechanisms such as ion
channel activity and second messenger
cascades, cellular mechanisms of
self-recognition and defense and the control
of cell cycle progression and cell growth.

Biomolecular Systems: Supports research
aimed at understanding the structure,
function, dynamics and metabolism of
biological molecules. Biochemical and
biophysical approaches are used in the study
of proteins, nucleic acids, lipids,
carbohydrates and other cellular components.
Topics include, but are not limited to,
enzyme mechanism and regulation, structural
biology, protein synthesis, structure, function
and assembly of supramolecular complexes,
energy transduction, photosynthesis, electron
transfer, characterization of primary and
secondary metabolic pathways, membrane
structure and function, biogeochemical
cycles, degradation of polymers and
xenobiotic compounds and the synthesis and
properties of bimolecular materials.
Theoretical as well as in vivo and in vitro
experimental studies are considered in all
areas.

Genes and Genome Systems: Supports a
wide range of studies directed toward
answering significant questions of genetic
organization, recombination, transcription,
genome replication and function and
transmission of heritable information in all
organisms from viruses to plants and
animals. Such questions can be asked of
either the nuclear or organelle genome.
Specific areas include, but are not limited to,
mechanisms of gene regulation,
recombination, meiotic and mitotic
mechanisms, sex determination, interactions
at the genetic level between organisms and
molecular evolution of genes. Approaches to
the questions can utilize Mendelian genetics,
molecular genetics or biochemical methods
or, ideally, any combination which will be
optimally effective.

YEAR PROGRAM STARTED: 1992

PURPOSE:
To increase our store of knowledge in these
fields and enhance our understanding of the
scientific aspects of major problems
confronting the nation.

LEGAL BASIS:
National Science Foundation Act of 1950, Public Law 81-507, as amended.

ELIGIBILITY:
The principal recipients of scientific research project support are academic institutions and nonprofit research institutions. Grants may also be awarded to other types of institutions and to individuals. In these cases, preliminary inquiry should be made to the cognizant program officer before a proposal is submitted. Support may be provided to projects involving a single scientist or to projects covering the activities of a number of scientists. Awards are made for projects confined to a single disciplinary area and for projects which cross or merge disciplinary interests. Clinically oriented research is not supported.

FINANCIAL DATA:
Total amount of support: Approximately $124,000,000 for the year 2010.

APPLICATION INFORMATION:
Duration: Varies.
Deadline: Contact Foundation for specific dates.

PUBLICATIONS:
Brochures.

DIRECTORS:
Dr. Stephen Howell, Division Director

ADDRESS INQUIRIES TO:
Cognizant Program Officer

NATIONAL SCIENCE FOUNDATION [2297]
Division of Environmental Biology
4201 Wilson Boulevard, Room 635N
Arlington, VA 22230
(703) 292-8480
Fax: (703) 292-9064

E-MAIL ADDRESS:
pfirth@nsf.gov
sedaniel@nsf.gov

WEB SITE ADDRESS:
www.nsf.gov/bio/deb/about.jsp

FOUNDED: 1950

AREAS OF INTEREST:
Ecology, ecosystem science, population biology and systematic biology, and biodiversity inventories cluster.

NAME(S) OF PROGRAMS:
- **Division of Environmental Biology**

TYPE:
Conferences/seminars; Research grants; Training grants; Travel grants.

PURPOSE:
To increase our store of knowledge in these fields and enhance our understanding of the scientific aspects of major problems confronting the nation.

LEGAL BASIS:
National Science Foundation Act of 1950, Public Law 81-507, as amended.

ELIGIBILITY:
The principal recipients of scientific research project support are academic institutions and nonprofit research institutions. Grants may also be awarded to other types of institutions and to individuals. In these cases, preliminary inquiry should be made to the cognizant program officer before a proposal is submitted. Support may be provided to projects involving a single scientist or to

projects covering the activities of a number of scientists. Awards are made for projects confined to a single disciplinary area and for projects which cross or merge disciplinary interests.

FINANCIAL DATA:
Amount of support per award: $108,000 average.
Total amount of support: $115,000,000 for the fiscal year ended September 30, 2009.

NUMBER OF APPLICANTS MOST RECENT YEAR:
2,500.

NUMBER OF AWARDS: 500.

APPLICATION INFORMATION:
Duration: 12 to 60 months, depending on the scientific merit and requirements of the project.
Deadline: January 9 and July 9.

PUBLICATIONS:
Awards list; program description.

ADDRESS INQUIRIES TO:
Penny Firth, Deputy Division Director
(See address above.)

SOCIETY FOR DEVELOPMENTAL BIOLOGY [2298]
9650 Rockville Pike
Bethesda, MD 20814-3998
(301) 634-7815
Fax: (301) 634-7825

E-MAIL ADDRESS:
sdb@sdbonline.org

WEB SITE ADDRESS:
www.sdbonline.org

FOUNDED: 1939

AREAS OF INTEREST:
Developmental biology.

NAME(S) OF PROGRAMS:
- **Edwin G. Conklin Medal**
- **Developmental Biology-SDB Lifetime Achievement Award**
- **John Doctor Best Education Poster Award**
- **Viktor Hamburger Outstanding Educator Prize**
- **Latin American-Caribbean Scholarships**
- **Non-SDB Meeting Grants**
- **SDB Boot Camp for New Faculty**
- **SDB Travel Awards**
- **Teaching Faculty Travel Grants**

TYPE:
Awards/prizes; Conferences/seminars; Scholarships.

PURPOSE:
To further the study of development in all organisms and at all levels; to represent and promote communication among students of development; to promote the field of developmental biology.

ELIGIBILITY:
Must be a student or investigator studying in the field of developmental biology.

For the Latin American Award, student must study in Latin America or the Caribbean.

FINANCIAL DATA:
Amount of support per award: Latin American-Caribbean Scholarships: $2,000; John Doctor Best Education Poster Award:

$1,000; Teaching Faculty Travel Grants: $500; Student/Postdoctoral Travel Awards: Varies.
Total amount of support: Varies.

NUMBER OF AWARDS: Latin American-Caribbean Scholarships: 6.

APPLICATION INFORMATION:
Nomination instructions and application guidelines may be obtained from the Society's web site.
Duration: One-time award. Reapplication possible.

ADDRESS INQUIRIES TO:
Ida Chow, Executive Officer
(See address above.)

SOCIETY FOR THE STUDY OF AMPHIBIANS AND REPTILES
Department of Environmental Studies and Biology
Elon University, Campus Box 2015
Elon, NC 27244
(336) 278-6229

E-MAIL ADDRESS:
jkapfer@elon.edu

WEB SITE ADDRESS:
www.ssarherps.org/pages/GIH.php

TYPE:
Awards/prizes; Research grants. Awards are given in six categories: Conservation of Amphibians and/or Reptiles, Field Research, Laboratory Research, Herpetological Education, Travel and International Research.

See entry 2171 for full listing.

THE UNIVERSITY OF CALGARY
Faculty of Graduate Studies
Earth Sciences Building, Room 720
2500 University Drive, N.W.
Calgary AB T2N 1N4 Canada
(403) 220-4938
Fax: (403) 289-7635

E-MAIL ADDRESS:
gsaward@ucalgary.ca

WEB SITE ADDRESS:
www.grad.ucalgary.ca

TYPE:
Awards/prizes; Scholarships. Award for study in the fields of cellular, molecular, microbial or biochemical biology. Tenable at The University of Calgary, Department of Biological Sciences.

See entry 1904 for full listing.

THE WETLANDS INSTITUTE [2299]
1075 Stone Harbor Boulevard
Stone Harbor, NJ 08247-1424
(609) 368-1211
Fax: (609) 368-3871

E-MAIL ADDRESS:
research@wetlandsinstitute.org

WEB SITE ADDRESS:
www.wetlandsinstitute.org

FOUNDED: 1969

AREAS OF INTEREST:
Mid-Atlantic coastal organisms and environments.

NAME(S) OF PROGRAMS:
- **Wetlands Institute Summer Research**

TYPE:
Fellowships; Internships; Scholarships.
Summer fellowships for field research on
mid-Atlantic coastal organisms and
environments at the Wetlands Institute.

YEAR PROGRAM STARTED: 1969

PURPOSE:
To involve undergraduate students in a wide
variety of research projects pertaining to
coastal environments.

LEGAL BASIS:
Nonprofit organization that conducts research
and education.

ELIGIBILITY:
Applicants should have a minimum of one
year college education. A science major is
desired, but not required.

GEOGRAPHIC RESTRICTIONS:
United States.

FINANCIAL DATA:
Amount of support per award: Varies with
project.

NUMBER OF APPLICANTS MOST RECENT YEAR:
20.

NUMBER OF AWARDS: 5.

APPLICATION INFORMATION:
Duration: Minimum of 10 weeks, starting
last week of May.
Deadline: March 1.

IRS IDENTIFICATION NUMBER: 23-7046783

STAFF:
Roger Wood, Grant Specialist

ADDRESS INQUIRIES TO:
Cindy O'Connor, Executive Director or
Roger Wood, Grant Specialist
(See address above.)

WHITEHALL FOUNDATION, INC.   [2300]

125 Worth Avenue
Suite 220
Palm Beach, FL 33480
(561) 655-4474
Fax: (561) 655-1296

E-MAIL ADDRESS:
email@whitehall.org

WEB SITE ADDRESS:
www.whitehall.org

FOUNDED: 1937

AREAS OF INTEREST:
Exclusive focus on assisting basic research in
vertebrate (excluding clinical) and
invertebrate neurobiology in the U.S.

TYPE:
Grants-in-aid; Research grants. Research
grants are available to established scientists
of all ages working at accredited institutions
in the U.S.

The grants-in-aid program is designed for
researchers at the assistant professor level
who experience difficulty in competing for
research funds because they have not yet
become firmly established. Grants-in-aid will
also be made to senior scientists.

YEAR PROGRAM STARTED: 1937

PURPOSE:
To assist scholarly research in the life
sciences; to assist those dynamic areas of
basic biological research that are not heavily
supported by federal agencies or other
foundations with specialized missions.

LEGAL BASIS:
Not-for-profit corporation.

ELIGIBILITY:
Grants-in-aid: All applications will be judged
on the scientific merit and innovative aspects
of the proposal, as well as on past
performance and evidence of the applicant's
continued productivity.

Research grants: Applications will be judged
on the scientific merit and the innovative
aspects of the proposal, as well as on the
competence of the applicant.

The Foundation does not award funds to
investigators who have substantial existing or
potential support (even if it is for an
unrelated purpose), and applications may be
held in abeyance until the results of other
funding decisions are determined. In general,
the Foundation currently defines "substantial"
as approximately $200,000 per year
(including both direct and indirect expense
but excluding the principal investigator's
salary). The principal investigator must hold
no less than the position of assistant
professor, or the equivalent, in order to make
application.

GEOGRAPHIC RESTRICTIONS:
United States.

FINANCIAL DATA:
Amount of support per award: Research
Grants: $30,000 to $75,000 per year;
Grants-in-aid: Up to $30,000.

APPLICATION INFORMATION:
The first step in the proposal process is the
submission of a Letter of Intent, which
includes the following:
(1) cover page on institutional letterhead
including investigator's full name, academic
rank and institutional affiliation, complete
U.S. mail and e-mail addresses, telephone
and fax numbers, title of the project (not to
exceed 60 characters), type of grant
requested, and a table of all current and
pending funding including grant title, source,
total amount of direct and indirect costs per
year, length in years, percent effort expended
on the project and notification date if the
application is still pending and;
(2) research abstract of the proposed research
project (not to exceed two pages and 600
words). Investigator's last name must be
placed on the top right corner of each page.
Do not include any reprints, curriculum
vitaes, or letters of reference.

On the basis of this letter, the Whitehall
Foundation's scientific advisory staff will
determine whether or not the proposed
research project will continue to the
application process.

Letters of Intent will not be accepted via
e-mail.
Duration: Grants-in-aid: One year. Research
Grants: Up to three years; a renewal grant
with a maximum of two years is possible, but
it will be awarded on a competitive basis.

IRS IDENTIFICATION NUMBER: 13-5637595

ADDRESS INQUIRIES TO:
Whitehall Foundation, Inc.
P.O. Box 3423
Palm Beach, FL 33480

*PLEASE NOTE:
The Foundation encourages the use of
electronic mail. All correspondence and
reports should be sent to the e-mail address
above. The Letter of Intent must be
submitted in hard copy on institutional
letterhead.

WILSON ORNITHOLOGICAL SOCIETY   [2301]

Museum of Zoology
University of Michigan
1109 Geddes Avenue
Ann Arbor, MI 48109-1079
(734) 764-0457

E-MAIL ADDRESS:
dovec@si.edu

WEB SITE ADDRESS:
www.wilsonsociety.org/awards/wosawards.
html

FOUNDED: 1888

AREAS OF INTEREST:
Ornithology.

NAME(S) OF PROGRAMS:
● **Louis Agassiz Fuertes Award**
● **George A. Hall/Harold Mayfield Award**
● **Paul A. Stewart Award**
● **Student Travel Awards**
● **Alexander Wilson Student Presentation Award**

TYPE:
Grants-in-aid. Fuertes, Hall/Mayfield and
Stewart Awards provide for the promotion
and encouragement of field research on birds.
A research proposal is required.

Student Travel Awards provide funds for
students to attend the annual meeting.

Alexander Wilson Student Presentation
Award is given to the best student paper
presented at the annual meeting.

YEAR PROGRAM STARTED: 1947

PURPOSE:
To promote the scientific study of birds.

LEGAL BASIS:
Corporation.

ELIGIBILITY:
Each award requires a willingness of the
awardee to report results of the research as
an oral or poster paper at an annual meeting
of the Wilson Ornithological Society.

Louis Agassiz Fuertes Award: Available to
all ornithologists, although graduate students
and young professionals are preferred. Any
avian research is eligible.

George A. Hall/Harold Mayfield Award:
Limited to independent researchers without
access to funds and facilities available at
colleges, universities or governmental
agencies, and is restricted to
nonprofessionals, including high school
students. Any kind of avian research is
eligible.

Paul A. Stewart Awards: Preference will be
given to proposals for studies of bird
movements based on banding, analysis of
recoveries and returns of banded birds, with
an emphasis on economic ornithology.

Student Travel Awards: Students presenting
an oral paper or poster at WOS Annual
Meeting are invited to apply.

FINANCIAL DATA:
Amount of support per award: Fuertes
Award: $2,500; Hall/Mayfield Award: $1,000;
Stewart Award: $500.

NUMBER OF APPLICANTS MOST RECENT YEAR:
114.

NUMBER OF AWARDS: Fuertes Award: 2;
Hall/Mayfield Award: 1; Stewart Award: 8.

APPLICATION INFORMATION:
Application forms are obtainable from the
Chairman of the Awards Committee or from
the web site above.
Duration: One-time grant. Nonrenewable.
Deadline: February 1.

PUBLICATIONS:
*Wilson Journal of Ornithology; Wilson
Bulletin; Guide to Graduate Programs in
Ornithology; Manual of Ornithology.*

OFFICERS:
Dr. Dale Kennedy, President
Dr. Robert Beason, First Vice President
Dr. Robert L. Curry, Second Vice President
Melinda Clark, Treasurer
Dr. John Smallwood, Secretary
Dr. Clait E. Braun, Editor

ADDRESS INQUIRIES TO:
Carla Dove, Research Awards
(See address above.)

Environment

ACORN FOUNDATION [2302]
c/o Common Counsel Foundation
678 13th Street, Suite 100
Oakland, CA 94612
(510) 834-2995
Fax: (510) 834-2998

E-MAIL ADDRESS:
info@commoncounsel.org
grantsadmin@commoncounsel.org

WEB SITE ADDRESS:
www.commoncounsel.org

FOUNDED: 1978

AREAS OF INTEREST:
A sustainable ecological future and a healthy
global environment.

TYPE:
General operating grants.

YEAR PROGRAM STARTED: 1978

PURPOSE:
To advance community-based organizations
working for environmental conservation,
sustainability and environmental justice.

ELIGIBILITY:
The Foundation makes grants to grassroots
organizations. Organizational budget must be
$400,000 or less. The Foundation is
particularly interested in small and innovative
community-based projects that engage in
community organizing in order to:
(1) preserve and restore habitats supporting
biological diversity and wildlife;
(2) advocate for environmental justice,
particularly in low-income and indigenous
communities and;
(3) prevent or remedy toxic pollution.

GEOGRAPHIC RESTRICTIONS:
Western and southern United States and
Appalachia.

FINANCIAL DATA:
Amount of support per award: $5,000 to
$10,000.

NUMBER OF APPLICANTS MOST RECENT YEAR:
More than 100.

NUMBER OF AWARDS: 10 to 14 per year.

APPLICATION INFORMATION:
Organizations that meet the eligibility and
funding criteria are encouraged to submit a
letter of inquiry form.
Duration: 12 months.
Deadline: January 15 and June 15 for spring
and fall grantmaking meetings.

ADDRESS INQUIRIES TO:
Grants Administrator
(See address above.)

*PLEASE NOTE:
The Foundation is only able to invite full
proposals from approximately 10% of the
organizations that apply.

ALASKA CONSERVATION FOUNDATION [2303]
441 West Fifth Avenue
Suite 402
Anchorage, AK 99501-2340
(907) 276-1917
Fax: (907) 274-4145

E-MAIL ADDRESS:
acfinfo@alaskaconservation.org

WEB SITE ADDRESS:
www.alaskaconservation.org

FOUNDED: 1977

AREAS OF INTEREST:
Conservation, ecosystem and lands
protection, marine conservation, linking
conservation with the economy and
organizational effectiveness.

NAME(S) OF PROGRAMS:
● **ACF General Grants**
● **ACF Opportunity Grants**

TYPE:
Challenge/matching grants; General operating
grants; Internships; Project/program grants;
Technical assistance; Training grants.

YEAR PROGRAM STARTED: 1980

PURPOSE:
To build strategic leadership and support for
Alaskan efforts to take care of wild lands,
water and wildlife, which sustain diverse
cultures, healthy communities and prosperous
economies.

LEGAL BASIS:
501(c)(3) public foundation.

ELIGIBILITY:
Incorporate, tax-exempt organizations,
non-incorporated organizations and
individuals may apply for funding.

GEOGRAPHIC RESTRICTIONS:
Alaska.

FINANCIAL DATA:
Amount of support per award: General
Grants: Up to $25,000; Opportunity Grants:
Up to $2,500.

APPLICATION INFORMATION:
Contact the Program Officer to determine if
the project fits within the grantmaking
program. ACF will invite full proposals to
appropriate projects.
Deadline: General grant deadlines are two
times per year. Opportunity grant proposals
are considered on a monthly basis, generally
the last week of each month.

IRS IDENTIFICATION NUMBER: 92-0061466

ADDRESS INQUIRIES TO:
Grantmaking Committee
(See address above.)

ALASKA CONSERVATION FOUNDATION [2304]
441 West Fifth Avenue
Suite 402
Anchorage, AK 99501
(907) 276-1917
Fax: (907) 274-4145

E-MAIL ADDRESS:
grants@alaskaconservation.org

WEB SITE ADDRESS:
www.alaskaconservation.org

AREAS OF INTEREST:
Conservation, ecosystem and lands
protection, marine conservation, linking
conservation with the economy and
organizational effectiveness.

NAME(S) OF PROGRAMS:
● **Rapid Response Grant**

TYPE:
Awards/prizes; General operating grants;
Internships; Project/program grants.

YEAR PROGRAM STARTED: 1977

PURPOSE:
To allow for a timely response to
fast-breaking environmental issues of
statewide or national importance.

ELIGIBILITY:
Incorporated, tax-exempt organizations,
non-incorporated organizations, and
individuals may apply for funding.

GEOGRAPHIC RESTRICTIONS:
Alaska.

FINANCIAL DATA:
Amount of support per award: $2,500 to
$10,000.

APPLICATION INFORMATION:
Contact the Program Officer to determine if
the project fits within the grantmaking
program. ACF will invite full proposals to
appropriate projects. Rapid Response projects
must address an issue of statewide or
national importance. If invited, proposals to
the Rapid Response Fund should provide a
compelling narrative/justification, a clear
timeline, a detailed budget, and have a good
chance for success.

ADDRESS INQUIRIES TO:
Rapid Response Committee
(See address above.)

AMERICAN ACADEMY IN ROME [2305]
7 East 60th Street
New York, NY 10022
(212) 751-7200
Fax: (212) 751-7220

E-MAIL ADDRESS:
info@aarome.org

WEB SITE ADDRESS:
www.aarome.org

FOUNDED: 1894

AREAS OF INTEREST:
Landscape architecture.

NAME(S) OF PROGRAMS:
● **The Rome Prize Fellowship in
Landscape Architecture**

TYPE:
Awards/prizes; Fellowships; Residencies.
Provides a residential year at the American
Academy in Rome for an American

landscape architect for advanced study, travel and association with other fellows in the arts and humanities.

YEAR PROGRAM STARTED: 1920

PURPOSE:
To provide American landscape architects with a special opportunity for advanced study in Rome.

LEGAL BASIS:
Nonprofit, national organization.

ELIGIBILITY:
Applicants must hold an accredited degree in landscape architecture, or equivalent experience.

GEOGRAPHIC RESTRICTIONS:
United States.

FINANCIAL DATA:
Award consists of stipend, plus housing and meals allowance.
Amount of support per award: $26,000.
Total amount of support: $52,000.

NUMBER OF APPLICANTS MOST RECENT YEAR:
15.

NUMBER OF AWARDS: 2 annually.

APPLICATION INFORMATION:
Applications are submitted electronically.
Duration: One academic year.
Deadline: November 1. Announcement in April.

PUBLICATIONS:
Program announcement.

STAFF:
Adele Chatfield-Taylor, President
Shawn Miller, Program Director

ADDRESS INQUIRIES TO:
Program Director
(See address above.)

AMERICAN ALPINE CLUB [2306]

710 10th Street
Suite 100
Golden, CO 80401
(303) 384-0110
Fax: (303) 384-0111

E-MAIL ADDRESS:
grants@americanalpineclub.org
jmiller@americanalpineclub.org

WEB SITE ADDRESS:
www.americanalpineclub.org

FOUNDED: 1902

AREAS OF INTEREST:
Mountaineering, mountain environment and polar regions.

NAME(S) OF PROGRAMS:
● **McNeill-Nott Climbing Award**
● **Mountain Fellowship**
● **Research Grants**
● **Lyman Spitzer Cutting Edge Climbing Award**

TYPE:
Project/program grants; Research grants; Travel grants. Grants to support research in Arctic and alpine environments. Funds may also be used to assist in publication or other dissemination of the results of such research.

The Mountain Fellowship encourages young American climbers under 26 years of age to go into remote areas and seek out climbs more difficult than they might ordinarily be able to do.

YEAR PROGRAM STARTED: 1945

PURPOSE:
To encourage and broaden scientific research in mountains and the polar regions.

LEGAL BASIS:
Membership organization.

ELIGIBILITY:
Individuals engaged in appropriate research are eligible to apply.

FINANCIAL DATA:
Amount of support per award: Varies.
Total amount of support: Over $50,000 annually.

APPLICATION INFORMATION:
Duration: One-time grant. New application required for ongoing projects.
Deadline: McNeill-Nott Climbing Award and Lyman Spitzer Cutting Edge Climbing Award: January 1. Announcement within four to six weeks. Mountaineering Fund Grants: April 1 and November 1. Notification eight to 10 weeks after deadline. Research Grants: March 1.

PUBLICATIONS:
Application guidelines.

ADDRESS INQUIRIES TO:
Janet Miller, Grants Manager
E-mail: jmiller@americanalpineclub.org

AMERICAN WATER RESOURCES ASSOCIATION   [2307]

4 West Federal Street
Middleburg, VA 20118-1612
(540) 687-8390
Fax: (540) 687-8395

E-MAIL ADDRESS:
info@awra.org

WEB SITE ADDRESS:
www.awra.org

FOUNDED: 1964

AREAS OF INTEREST:
Water resources.

NAME(S) OF PROGRAMS:
● **Richard A. Herbert Memorial Educational Fund**

TYPE:
Scholarships.

YEAR PROGRAM STARTED: 1980

PURPOSE:
To advance multidisciplinary water resources management and research.

ELIGIBILITY:
Applicant must be a national AWRA member who is enrolled in a program related to water resources. May be a full-time undergraduate student working towards an undergraduate degree or a full-time graduate student.

The undergraduate scholarship will be awarded to the student most qualified by academic performance. Measures of academic performance include the cumulative grade point average, relevance of the student's curriculum to water resources, and leadership in extracurricular activities related to water resources. The graduate scholarship will be awarded to the student most qualified by academic and/or research performance.

FINANCIAL DATA:
Amount of support per award: $2,000 per award.

Total amount of support: $4,000.

NUMBER OF APPLICANTS MOST RECENT YEAR: 3 undergraduate and 14 graduate applications.

NUMBER OF AWARDS: 2.

APPLICATION INFORMATION:
Submit a title page and summary of academic interests and achievements, extracurricular interests, and career goals as they relate to the selection criteria. Summaries must be limited to two pages. Include three letters of reference, a transcript of all college courses (undergraduate and graduate), and the applicant's full name, permanent mailing address, e-mail address, and a phone number at which applicant may be reached.
Duration: One year.
Deadline: April 22.

ADDRESS INQUIRIES TO:
AWRA Scholarship Coordinator
(See address above.)

BEN & JERRY'S FOUNDATION

30 Community Drive
South Burlington, VT 05403-6828
(802) 846-1500
Fax: (802) 846-1610

WEB SITE ADDRESS:
www.benandjerrysfoundation.org

TYPE:
General operating grants; Project/program grants. Grants to nonprofit organizations which facilitate progressive social change by addressing the underlying conditions of societal and/or environmental problems.

See entry 1036 for full listing.

BONNEVILLE ENVIRONMENTAL FOUNDATION   [2308]

240 S.W. First Avenue
Portland, OR 97204-3503
(503) 248-1905
Fax: (503) 248-1908

E-MAIL ADDRESS:
info@b-e-f.org

WEB SITE ADDRESS:
www.b-e-f.org

FOUNDED: 1998

AREAS OF INTEREST:
Environmental conservation and the development of new sources of renewable energy.

NAME(S) OF PROGRAMS:
● **Model Watershed Program**
● **Renewable Energy Program**

TYPE:
Grants-in-aid. Model Watershed Program is intended to restore ecological integrity and native fish populations in watersheds across the western U.S.

Renewable Energy Program supports school solar projects and other renewable energy technologies that are taken up by utility and community-based renewable energy projects.

PURPOSE:
To support watershed restoration programs; to develop new sources of renewable energy.

ELIGIBILITY:
The Foundation does not fund residential projects.

FINANCIAL DATA:
Amount of support per award: Varies.

Total amount of support: $400,000 for each program for the year 2010.

APPLICATION INFORMATION:
Candidates interested in applying for Watershed Model Program grants are requested to submit a two- to three-page letter of inquiry or contact Todd Reeve, Vice President for Watershed Programs, at the telephone number above or e-mail treeve@b-e-f.org.

Candidates interested in applying for Renewable Energy Program grants are requested to submit a two- to three-page letter of inquiry or contact Dick Wanderscheid, Vice President of Renewable Energy Group, at the telephone number above or e-mail dwanderscheid@b-e-f.org.

STAFF:
Angus Duncan, President, Watershed Program
Dick Wanderscheid, Vice President for Renewable Energy Program
Todd Reeve, Vice President, Watershed Program
Robert Warren, Watershed Programs Manager

ADDRESS INQUIRIES TO:
For the Model Watershed Program:
Todd Reeve, Vice President
Watershed Program
E-mail: treeve@b-e-f.org
(See address above.)

For the Renewable Energy Program:
Dick Wanderscheid, Vice President for Renewable Energy Group
E-mail: dwanderscheid@b-e-f.org
(See address above.)

BRAINERD FOUNDATION [2309]

1601 Second Avenue
Suite 610
Seattle, WA 98101
(206) 448-0676
Fax: (206) 448-7222

E-MAIL ADDRESS:
info@brainerd.org

WEB SITE ADDRESS:
www.brainerd.org

FOUNDED: 1995

AREAS OF INTEREST:
Environment.

NAME(S) OF PROGRAMS:
● **Grassroots Fund Grants**
● **Opportunity Fund Grants**
● **Program Grants (Conservation Policy, Place-based Conservation, Conservation Capacity)**

TYPE:
General operating grants; Matching gifts; Project/program grants; Training grants.

YEAR PROGRAM STARTED: 1995

PURPOSE:
To protect the environment of the Northwest and build broad citizen support for conservation.

ELIGIBILITY:
Organizations must be nonprofit classified as 501(c)(3) public charities by the IRS or Canadian organizations deemed equivalent by the Foundation.

GEOGRAPHIC RESTRICTIONS:
British Columbia and Yukon Territory, Canada; Alaska, Idaho, Montana, Oregon and Washington, United States.

FINANCIAL DATA:
Grants may be used to cover costs associated with, but not limited to, grassroots outreach, media strategies, litigation, scientific and economic studies, computer networking, and organizational capacity building.
Amount of support per award: Program Grants: $15,000 to $50,000; Grassroots Fund Grants: Up to $10,000; Opportunity Fund Grants: Up to $3,000.

Total amount of support: $3,154,355 for the year 2008 (unaudited).

NUMBER OF APPLICANTS MOST RECENT YEAR:
180 for the year 2009.

NUMBER OF AWARDS: 100 for the year 2009.

REPRESENTATIVE AWARDS:
$40,000 to Montana Environmental Information Center, Helena, MT; $45,000 to Wildlife Conservation Society, Bozeman, MT; $75,000 to Resource Media, Seattle, WA; $25,000 to Conservation Voters for Idaho, Boise, ID; $40,000 to Salmon Valley Stewardship, Salmon, ID.

APPLICATION INFORMATION:
Proposals by invitation only. One- to three-page letters of inquiry are accepted on a rolling basis. Each inquiry is weighed on its merits and strategic value, and on how it fits with guidelines. If a program officer invites a full proposal, a specific deadline will be given.
Duration: One year. Occasionally two.

STAFF:
Ann Krumboltz, Executive Director
Jim Owens, Senior Program Officer

ADDRESS INQUIRIES TO:
See e-mail above.

BRUNSWICK PUBLIC FOUNDATION [2310]

One Northfield Court
Lake Forest, IL 60045
(847) 735-4344
Fax: (847) 735-4330

FOUNDED: 1998

AREAS OF INTEREST:
Environmental waterways.

TYPE:
Project/program grants.

PURPOSE:
To support community development primarily through contributions to preselected local United Way organizations; to support organizations that enhance the country's water resources for the recreational use by the public through proposals invited by the Foundation trustees.

ELIGIBILITY:
Grants are made to organizations that have tax-exempt status under Section 501(c)(3) of the Internal Revenue Code. Nonsectarian religious programs may apply. No grants are made to individuals.

FINANCIAL DATA:
Amount of support per award: $5,000 to $100,000.

Total amount of support: $325,000.

NUMBER OF AWARDS: 25.

APPLICATION INFORMATION:
Deadline: March 15, July 15 and October 15.

IRS IDENTIFICATION NUMBER: 36-4195390

STAFF:
Lisa DeBartolo

BOARD OF DIRECTORS:
Jim Hubbard
David Knight
B. Russell Lockridge

ADDRESS INQUIRIES TO:
Lisa DeBartolo, Coordinator
(See address above.)

*SPECIAL STIPULATIONS:
By invitation only.

THE BULLITT FOUNDATION [2311]

1212 Minor Avenue
Seattle, WA 98101
(206) 343-0807
Fax: (206) 343-0822

E-MAIL ADDRESS:
info@bullitt.org

WEB SITE ADDRESS:
www.bullitt.org

FOUNDED: 1952

AREAS OF INTEREST:
Environment.

NAME(S) OF PROGRAMS:
● **Ecosystem Services**
● **Energy Industry and Technology**
● **Leadership and Civil Engagement**
● **Urban Ecology**

TYPE:
Challenge/matching grants; Demonstration grants; Development grants; General operating grants; Matching gifts; Project/program grants; Seed money grants; Technical assistance; Training grants.

YEAR PROGRAM STARTED: 1952

PURPOSE:
To protect and restore the environment of the Pacific Northwest.

LEGAL BASIS:
Private foundation.

ELIGIBILITY:
Applicants must be organizations that have nonprofit tax status with clear, significant and achievable goals, as well as a cogent strategy to realize them. The trustees favor projects that avoid excessive reliance on any one source of funding. The Foundation cannot fund political elections or lobbying activities involving specific legislation. The Foundation does not fund university overhead costs or capital projects.

GEOGRAPHIC RESTRICTIONS:
Pacific Northwest, including Idaho, western Montana, Oregon and Washington state, coastal rainforests in Alaska and British Columbia, Canada.

FINANCIAL DATA:
Amount of support per award: Grants: $5,000 to $200,000; $35,000 average.

Total amount of support: $4,471,700 in grants for the year 2009.

Matching fund requirements: Employee and trustee donations will be matched.

NUMBER OF APPLICANTS MOST RECENT YEAR:
169 for the year 2009.

NUMBER OF AWARDS: 127 for the year 2009.

REPRESENTATIVE AWARDS:
$50,000 to Justice Alliance Education Fund;
$100,000 to Climate Solutions; $30,000 to
Duwamish River Cleanup Coalition; $25,000
to Ecotrust.

APPLICATION INFORMATION:
An organization must first submit a proposal
inquiry via the web site.

If invited, the organization must then submit
a proposal. To apply for a grant, an
organization must include:
(1) the Grant Request Cover Sheet, available
upon request, and attach it to proposal. Be as
clear as possible in identifying anticipated
results for the project year. Try to answer the
questions: "What is going to be better about
the environment as a result of the project?
How will the organization measure how
successful the project has been?" Include
measurable goals that directly relate to the
Foundation's environmental priorities;
(2) a brief project description (no longer than
five pages) defending the significance of the
initiative and prospects for success. Relate
the proposal to the Foundation's stated
priorities. Grants are made on an annual (not
multiyear) basis, so emphasize objectives for
the project year. Identify the methods and
criteria to be used to measure or determine
results. Videos or other tapes are not
encouraged unless necessary to describe the
project;
(3) a work plan and timetable for the
one-year funding period;
(4) a brief history of the accomplishments of
the applicant organization and why it is best
suited to address the stated need;
(5) the qualifications of those who will bear
primary responsibility for the success of the
initiative and the share of their time they will
devote to the project;
(6) a list of the officers and directors of the
organizations;
(7) a copy of the IRS determination letter
verifying the tax-exempt status of the
organization;
(8) a detailed budget of the project and the
general budget of the sponsoring
organization;
(9) an audited statement for the prior year or
the IRS 990 report and;
(10) a detailed funding plan for the financial
resources needed for the project, including
other prospective sources of support.

Duration: One year. Renewal possible but
not automatic; reapplication is necessary.

Deadline: Proposal inquiry: March 15 and
September 15.

PUBLICATIONS:
Guidelines.

IRS IDENTIFICATION NUMBER: 91-6027795

TRUSTEES AND OFFICERS:
Maggie Walker, Chairperson
Denis Hayes, President
Harriet Bullitt, Vice President
Phyllis Wise, Treasurer
Anne Fennessy, Secretary
Jabe Blumenthal
Rod Brown
Maud Daudon
Estella Leopold
Michael Parham
Douglass Raff

ADDRESS INQUIRIES TO:
Program Officer
(See e-mail or address above.)

LIZ CLAIBORNE AND ART ORTENBERG FOUNDATION [2312]
650 5th Avenue
15th Floor
New York, NY 10019
(212) 333-2536
Fax: (212) 956-3531

E-MAIL ADDRESS:
lcaof@lcaof.org

WEB SITE ADDRESS:
www.lcaof.org

FOUNDED: 1984

AREAS OF INTEREST:
Integration of conservation and development
in the rural landscape.

TYPE:
Challenge/matching grants; Development
grants; General operating grants;
Project/program grants; Research grants;
Seed money grants.

PURPOSE:
To conserve nature and relieve human
distress; to redress the breakdown in the
processes linking nature and humanity.

ELIGIBILITY:
The Foundation funds modest, carefully
designed field projects, primarily in
developing countries. No funding for general
support or to underwrite institutional
overhead. Local people should have a
substantial proprietary interest in the project.

GEOGRAPHIC RESTRICTIONS:
Developing countries and the Northern
Rockies region of the United States.

FINANCIAL DATA:
Amount of support per award: $10,000 to
$100,000.
Total amount of support: $4,200,000 for
fiscal year 2010.

REPRESENTATIVE AWARDS:
$142,000 to African Conservation Centre for
Amboseli Research and Conservation
Program in Kenya and Tanzania; $49,030 to
Wildlife Conservation Society for Tiger
Conservation Program in Cambodia; $90,000
to Panthera Corporation for Jaguar
Conservation Program in Brazil.

APPLICATION INFORMATION:
Submissions to the Foundation must include
a clearly stated project objective, anticipated
duration and cost, criteria that will be used to
determine the success of the proposed project
and detailed information concerning the
participation and/or proprietorship of local
communities and organizations.

Duration: One year. Must reapply for
continued support.

PUBLICATIONS:
The View from Airlie; *MONTANA: People
and the Economy*; brochure; *Next Year
Country-View from Red Lodge*; *9 Case
Studies on the Interior West of U.S.*

TRUSTEES:
Art Ortenberg

DIRECTORS:
Dr. William Conway
Dr. William deBuys
Dr. Robert Dewar
Dr. Grant Parker
Dr. Alison Richard
Dr. George Schaller
Dr. David Western

ADDRESS INQUIRIES TO:
James Murtaugh, Director
Lori Cohen, Project Coordinator
(See address above.)

COLUMBIA UNIVERSITY
Graduate School of Journalism
2950 Broadway
New York, NY 10027-7004
(212) 854-6468
Fax: (212) 854-3148

E-MAIL ADDRESS:
lsr21@columbia.edu

WEB SITE ADDRESS:
www.jrn.columbia.edu

TYPE:
Awards/prizes. Awarded for distinguished
excellence in environmental journalism.

See entry 2053 for full listing.

CONSERVATION AND RESEARCH FOUNDATION [2313]
P.O. Box 909
Shelburne, VT 05482-0909
(802) 985-4106

WEB SITE ADDRESS:
conservationresearch.wordpress.com

FOUNDED: 1953

AREAS OF INTEREST:
Conservation and enlightened use of
renewable natural resources, encouragement
of related research in the biological sciences
and promotion of methods to limit human
fertility.

NAME(S) OF PROGRAMS:
● **Research and Conservation Grants**

TYPE:
Challenge/matching grants; General operating
grants. Grants to organizations and
individuals engaged either in biological
research or in conservation activities that
might have a beneficial effect on
environmental quality.

YEAR PROGRAM STARTED: 1953

PURPOSE:
To promote the conservation of the Earth's
natural resources and deepen the
understanding of the intricate relationship
between people and the environment that
supports them; to promote methods of
limiting human reproduction.

LEGAL BASIS:
Public foundation.

ELIGIBILITY:
Appropriate background and credentials
required. With respect to research, normally
only those investigations that might, for one
reason or another, be ineligible to receive
funding from conventional granting agencies
will be considered.

Grants do not cover institutional overhead.

Foundation does not provide funding for
scholarships or fellowships.

FINANCIAL DATA:
Indirect costs usually not allowed.
Amount of support per award: Grants rarely
exceed $5,000.
Total amount of support: $29,500 for the
year 2009.

COOPERATIVE FUNDING PROGRAMS:
Occasionally required.

NUMBER OF APPLICANTS MOST RECENT YEAR:
18 for the year 2009.

NUMBER OF AWARDS: 11 for the year 2009.

REPRESENTATIVE AWARDS:
$7,500 to Population Media Center; $5,000 to Western Lands Project; $1,000 to Connecticut River Council.

APPLICATION INFORMATION:
Proposals accepted only by invitation. A letter of inquiry with one-page abstract of proposal and budget may be submitted.

PUBLICATIONS:
Annual report; policy statement.

IRS IDENTIFICATION NUMBER: 04-605-1843

OFFICERS:
Dr. Mary G. Wetzel, President
Myron Sopher, Treasurer
Dr. Philip M. Lintilhac, Secretary

TRUSTEES:
Dr. Tobias Baskin
Dr. Jon D. Erickson
Dr. Patricia Erickson
Richard H. Goodwin, Jr.
Jeffrey F. Griffin
Crea S. Lintilhac
Dr. Philip M. Lintilhac
Dr. Ernesto Mendez
Dr. Louise M. Tritton
Dr. Hubert W. Vogelmann
Dr. Thomas C. Vogelmann
Dr. Mary G. Wetzel
Alexander T. Wilson

ADDRESS INQUIRIES TO:
Philip M. Lintilhac, Secretary
(See address above.)

COOPERATIVE INSTITUTE FOR RESEARCH IN ENVIRONMENTAL SCIENCES (CIRES) [2314]
CIRES Building, Room 318
University of Colorado
Boulder, CO 80309-0216
(303) 492-1143
Fax: (303) 492-1149

E-MAIL ADDRESS:
info@cires.colorado.edu
dempsey@cires.colorado.edu

WEB SITE ADDRESS:
cires.colorado.edu/collaboration/fellowships

FOUNDED: 1967

AREAS OF INTEREST:
Physics, chemistry and dynamics of the earth system; global and regional environmental change; climate system monitoring, diagnostics, and modeling; development and application of remote sensing and in-situ measurement techniques for the earth and its atmosphere, cryosphere, ecosystems, and oceans.

NAME(S) OF PROGRAMS:
● **CIRES Visiting Fellowship Program in Environmental Sciences**

TYPE:
Fellowships. The program provides opportunities for interactions between CIRES scientists and visiting fellows to pursue common research interests. CIRES research includes theoretical studies, laboratory experimentation, and field investigations which may affect the enhancement of air and water quality and prediction of weather climate fluctuations.

YEAR PROGRAM STARTED: 1968

PURPOSE:
To provide support for scientists from around the world to visit CIRES and collaborate in a variety of research projects.

LEGAL BASIS:
Sponsored jointly by the University of Colorado and National Oceanic and Atmospheric Administration.

ELIGIBILITY:
Applicants must be Ph.D. scientists at all levels; faculty planning sabbatical leave and recent Ph.D. recipients are especially encouraged to apply. Priority is given to candidates with research experience at institutions outside the Boulder scientific community. The program is open to scientists of all countries. The University of Colorado is committed to diversity and equality in education and employment.

FINANCIAL DATA:
Amount of support per award: Stipend is flexible based on research experience.

APPLICATION INFORMATION:
Applicant must send a resume, publications list and a brief (two to four pages) description of the proposed research. In addition, candidates should request three letters of recommendation, to be sent directly to CIRES, from persons familiar with their qualifications. Postdoctoral-level applicants must also submit undergraduate and graduate transcripts.
Duration: One year. No renewal. Appointments can begin at any time during the year.
Deadline: December 31. Selection the following March.

ADDRESS INQUIRIES TO:
Karen Dempsey
Human Resources Coordinator
(See address above.)

THE ECOLOGY FOUNDATION [2315]
28 Mayflower Drive
Rochester, NY 14618
(585) 244-2012
Fax: (585) 244-2012

E-MAIL ADDRESS:
gttbst@aol.com

FOUNDED: 1999

AREAS OF INTEREST:
Ecology and energy efficiency.

TYPE:
Project/program grants. The Foundation funds workable, understandable ecological projects and ties performance expectations and support services to its grants, striving to prepare the inventor for the inevitable business aspects that follow once an invention approaches commercialization.

YEAR PROGRAM STARTED: 1999

PURPOSE:
To support research that explores the viability and potential commercialization of various inventions that will increase energy efficiency and ultimately reduce environmental problems facing mankind.

LEGAL BASIS:
501(c)(3) charitable foundation.

ELIGIBILITY:
Workable, understandable ecological projects.

FINANCIAL DATA:
Amount of support per award: Up to $700,000 (in increments).

APPLICATION INFORMATION:
Contact the Foundation.
Duration: One to three years. Renewable.

ADDRESS INQUIRIES TO:
Terry Thomas, President
(See address above.)

THE ENERGY FOUNDATION [2316]
301 Battery Street, 5th Floor
San Francisco, CA 94111
(415) 561-6700
Fax: (415) 561-6709

E-MAIL ADDRESS:
energyfund@ef.org

WEB SITE ADDRESS:
www.ef.org

FOUNDED: 1991

AREAS OF INTEREST:
Energy efficiency and renewable energy.

TYPE:
Project/program grants. Promotes energy efficiency and renewable energy. Grants awarded in areas involving power, buildings, transportation, and climate programs.

YEAR PROGRAM STARTED: 1991

PURPOSE:
To assist in a national, and ultimately a global, transition to a sustainable future by promoting energy efficiency and renewable energy.

LEGAL BASIS:
Public charity 501(c)(3).

ELIGIBILITY:
501(c)(3) organizations only. No grants to individuals or for-profit organizations. Projects must have broad regional or national implications. No grants to religious organizations, political parties or for development of technology. No research and development or demonstration grants.

GEOGRAPHIC RESTRICTIONS:
United States and China.

FINANCIAL DATA:
Amount of support per award: Varies.
Total amount of support: Approximately $60,000,000 in total grant payments for the year 2010.

NUMBER OF APPLICANTS MOST RECENT YEAR:
880 for the year 2008.

NUMBER OF AWARDS: 530 for the year 2008.

REPRESENTATIVE AWARDS:
$120,000 to Natural Resources Defense Council to advance energy efficiency and renewable programs for the electric industry in New Jersey; $75,000 to Renewable Energy Policy Project to analyze and promote policies to encourage photovoltaic energy; $50,000 to Coalition for Clean Air to continue to advocate for clean vehicles in California.

APPLICATION INFORMATION:
There is no fixed format for proposals. However, applications are available online. Applicant should include a statement of problem to be addressed, target audience, timeline, project budget, history of organization and intended mission and goals.

Duration: Typically one year. Renewal possible.

Deadline: Board meets three times a year in March, June and November. Announcement of grants follows meeting.

PUBLICATIONS:
Annual report.

IRS IDENTIFICATION NUMBER: 94-3126848

BOARD OF DIRECTORS:
Susan Tierney, Chairperson
Rosina Bierbaum
Mark Burget
Robert Crane
Larry Goulder
Denis Hayes
Eric Heitz
Khee Poh Lam
Alan Lloyd
Rose McKinney-James
Victor Rabinowitch
William Ruckelshaus
Phil Sharp
Noa Staryk
Michael Wang
Hongjun Zhang

OFFICERS AND STAFF:
Eric Heitz, President
Jiang Lin, Senior Vice President/Director, The China Sustainable Energy Program
Barbara Wagner, Senior Vice President and Chief Operating Officer
Charlotte Pera, Senior Vice President and Director for U.S. Programs
David Wooley, Vice President and Program Director
Jason Mark, Vice President and Deputy Director of U.S. Programs
Cathy Clagett, Director of Organizational Development
Craig Appel, Director of Partner Relations
Bentham Paulos, Program Director
Marcus Schneider, Program Director
John Wilson, Program Director
Jean Ku, Program Manager
David Tuft, Program Officer
Adam Atkinson-Lewis, Senior Program Associate
Cary Berkley, Senior Program Associate
Kimberly Williams, Senior Program Associate
Jane Bloch, Program Associate
Rachel Golden, Program Associate
Tom Strand, Information Technology Specialist
Katie McCormack, Portfolio Manager
Todd Foland, Grants Administrator
Erin Colling, Grants Assistant
Patrick Taylor, Grants Assistant

ADDRESS INQUIRIES TO:
Charlotte Pera, Senior Vice President
(See address above.)

ENVIRONMENTAL LAW INSTITUTE

2000 L Street, N.W.
Suite 620
Washington, DC 20036-4919
(202) 939-3800
Fax: (202) 939-3868

E-MAIL ADDRESS:
law@eli.org

WEB SITE ADDRESS:
www.eli.org

TYPE:
Scholarships. Tuition scholarships to annual Environmental Law Course.

See entry 2102 for full listing.

FISHAMERICA FOUNDATION   [2317]

225 Reinekers Lane, Suite 420
Alexandria, VA 22314
(703) 519-9691
Fax: (703) 519-1872

E-MAIL ADDRESS:
fishamerica@asafishing.org

WEB SITE ADDRESS:
www.fishamerica.org

FOUNDED: 1983

AREAS OF INTEREST:
Environment and conservation.

NAME(S) OF PROGRAMS:
● **Fisheries Conservation and Research Projects**

TYPE:
Challenge/matching grants; Project/program grants; Research grants; Seed money grants.

YEAR PROGRAM STARTED: 1983

PURPOSE:
To provide funding for on-the-ground projects aimed at enhancing fish populations, restoring fish habitat, improving water quality and advancing fisheries research to improve sportfishing success.

LEGAL BASIS:
Public foundation, 501(c)(3).

ELIGIBILITY:
Any nonprofit tax-exempt organization including conservation organizations, sporting clubs, civic groups, and local and state agencies can apply.

GEOGRAPHIC RESTRICTIONS:
United States and Canada.

FINANCIAL DATA:
Amount of support per award: Average $15,000 per grant.
Total amount of support: $686,880 for conservation and research projects for fiscal year 2010.
Matching fund requirements: Not required, but matching funds enhance applications.

NUMBER OF APPLICANTS MOST RECENT YEAR:
162.

NUMBER OF AWARDS: 27.

REPRESENTATIVE AWARDS:
$50,000 to Elizabeth River Project, Portsmouth, VA, to improve fisheries habitat along the Elizabeth River in the Chesapeake Bay watershed; $7,512 to Rural Human Services of Crescent City, CA, to improve fisheries habitat in the Lower Klamath watershed by installing instream habitat structures, stabilizing eroding streambanks, and revegetating the riparian buffer along Sultan Creek; $14,600 to Idaho Department of Fish and Game to improve fish habitat in the Little Salmon River watershed.

APPLICATION INFORMATION:
Applicants should submit application, letter of support from the appropriate state resource agency biologist, and evidence of nonprofit status.
Duration: One year.

PUBLICATIONS:
Guidelines and application.

IRS IDENTIFICATION NUMBER: 36-3219015

BOARD OF DIRECTORS:
Jeff Marble, Chairman
Gregg Wollner, Vice Chairman
Jim Hubbard, Treasurer
Dave Bulthuis, Secretary
Scott Frnka, At-Large
Thomas Dammrich
Bob Eakes
Tom Fote
John E. Frampton
Ken Hammond
Kirk Immens
John Jilling
Martin MacDonald
Dave Pfeiffer
Jeff Pontius
Dick Pool
Geoff Ratte
Paul Schluter
K.C. Walsh

ADDRESS INQUIRIES TO:
Grants Manager
(See address above.)

*SPECIAL STIPULATIONS:
Conservation projects must result in the on-the-ground restoration of fish habitat, enhancement of fish populations, and/or the improvement of water quality. Research projects must result in a regional or national impact in one of the following areas: fisheries management, water quality or fish habitat studies, fish stock enhancement studies, economic impact studies related to sportfishing, or tagging.

THE GARDEN CLUB OF AMERICA   [2318]

14 East 60th Street
New York, NY 10022
(212) 753-8287
Fax: (212) 753-0134

E-MAIL ADDRESS:
scholarships@gcamerica.org

WEB SITE ADDRESS:
www.gcamerica.org

FOUNDED: 1913

AREAS OF INTEREST:
Conservation, historic preservation and plant conservation.

NAME(S) OF PROGRAMS:
● **GCA Awards for Summer Environmental Studies**

TYPE:
Scholarships.

YEAR PROGRAM STARTED: 1964

PURPOSE:
To encourage studies and careers in the environmental field.

LEGAL BASIS:
Nonprofit, national organization.

ELIGIBILITY:
Open to a qualified undergraduate entering a summer program following the freshman, sophomore, and junior years.

FINANCIAL DATA:
Amount of support per award: $2,000.

NUMBER OF AWARDS: 4 or more.

APPLICATION INFORMATION:
Applications are available online.

Deadline: February 10.

PUBLICATIONS:
Program announcement.

ADDRESS INQUIRIES TO:
Connie Yates, Liaison
Scholarship Committee-Summer Studies
(See address above.)

THE GARDEN CLUB OF AMERICA [2319]

14 East 60th Street
New York, NY 10022
(212) 753-8287
Fax: (212) 753-0134

E-MAIL ADDRESS:
scholarships@gcamerica.org

WEB SITE ADDRESS:
www.gcamerica.org

FOUNDED: 1913

AREAS OF INTEREST:
Conservation, historic preservation and plant conservation, and tropical plant study.

NAME(S) OF PROGRAMS:
- **Catherine Beattie Fellowship**
- **The GCA Award in Coastal Wetland Studies**
- **The Loy McCandless Marks Scholarship in Tropical Ornamental Horticulture**

TYPE:
Fellowships. Beattie Fellowship: Research grant to a graduate student in the horticultural field to conduct field research on the biology and management of rare plants in conjunction with the programs of the Center for Plant Conservation headquartered at the Missouri Botanical Garden.

GCA Award in Coastal Wetland Studies: Seeks to promote wetland conservation through the support of young scientists in their field work and research.

Loy McCandless Marks Scholarship in Tropical Ornamental Horticulture: Affords a graduate student, or advanced undergraduate, an opportunity to study tropical ornamental horticulture at an appropriate foreign institution specializing in the study of tropical plants. Scholarship is given biennially in even years.

YEAR PROGRAM STARTED: 1983

PURPOSE:
Beattie Fellowship: To promote conservation of rare and endangered flora in the U.S.

The GCA Award in Coastal Wetland Studies: To promote wetlands conservation through the support of young scientists in their field work and research.

Loy McCandless Marks Scholarship in Tropical Ornamental Horticulture: To foster the study of tropical plants and their use in horticulture and landscape architecture.

LEGAL BASIS:
Nonprofit, national organization.

ELIGIBILITY:
Beattie Fellowship: Preference is given to graduate students whose projects focus on the endangered flora of the Carolinas and the southeastern U.S.

GCA Award in Coastal Wetland Studies: Graduate students.

Loy McCandless Marks Scholarship in Tropical Ornamental Horticulture: Graduate students and advanced undergraduates.

GEOGRAPHIC RESTRICTIONS:
United States.

FINANCIAL DATA:
Amount of support per award: Beattie Fellowship: Up to $4,000; GCA Award in Coastal Wetland Studies: $5,000; Loy McCandless Marks Scholarship in Tropical Ornamental Horticulture: $2,000.

NUMBER OF AWARDS: Beattie Fellowship, GCA Award in Coastal Wetland Studies and Loy McCandless Marks Scholarship in Tropical Ornamental Horticulture: 1 annually.

APPLICATION INFORMATION:
Further information and application forms are available from The Center for Plant Conservation at the address below.

Duration: One year.

Deadline: Beattie Fellowship: November 30; GCA Award in Coastal Wetland Studies: January 15; Loy McCandless Marks Scholarship in Tropical Ornamental Horticulture: January 15 in even years only.

PUBLICATIONS:
Program announcement.

ADDRESS INQUIRIES TO:
Beattie Fellowship:
Kathryn Kennedy
President and Executive Director
The Center for Plant Conservation
Missouri Botanical Garden
P.O. Box 299
St. Louis, MO 63166-0299

Loy McCandless Marks Scholarship and GCA Awards:
Connie Yates, Administrator
The Garden Club of America
(See address above.)

THE GARDEN CLUB OF AMERICA [2320]

14 East 60th Street
New York, NY 10022
(212) 753-8287
Fax: (212) 753-0134

E-MAIL ADDRESS:
scholarships@gcamerica.org

WEB SITE ADDRESS:
www.gcamerica.org

FOUNDED: 1913

AREAS OF INTEREST:
Horticulture, botany, landscape architecture and environmental studies.

NAME(S) OF PROGRAMS:
- **GCA Interchange Fellowship in Horticulture and Martin McLaren Scholarship**

TYPE:
Exchange programs; Fellowships. A graduate academic year in the U.S. for a British student and a work-study program for an American at universities and botanical gardens in the U.K. in fields related to horticulture, botany and landscape design.

YEAR PROGRAM STARTED: 1948

PURPOSE:
To foster British-American relations through the interchange of scholars in horticulture, botany, landscape architecture and environmental studies.

LEGAL BASIS:
Nonprofit, national organization.

ELIGIBILITY:
Open to men or women who are American citizens not older than 26 at the time of application. Applicants must have earned a B.A. or B.S. degree prior to the start of the Fellowship. They must be single and unaccompanied.

GEOGRAPHIC RESTRICTIONS:
United States.

FINANCIAL DATA:
The Fellowship covers the cost of tuition, travel expenses, board, lodging and incidental college expenses. It also provides an allowance for personal needs.

Amount of support per award: Varies.

COOPERATIVE FUNDING PROGRAMS: Sponsored jointly by the Garden Club of America and the Martin McLaren Scholarship in Horticulture, which is administered through the Institute of Horticulture.

NUMBER OF APPLICANTS MOST RECENT YEAR: 8.

NUMBER OF AWARDS: 2 annually.

APPLICATION INFORMATION:
Application form must be accompanied by: (1) one essay describing the applicant, including biographical data, how the applicant first became interested in horticulture, hobbies and special interests, travel in the U.S. and abroad, and applicant's ability to speak a foreign language; (2) one essay stating the reasons for applying for this scholarship, the specific field to be studied while in England, and what the applicant expects to gain and contribute, should he or she be awarded this scholarship; (3) copy of official college transcript and; (4) four letters of recommendation, including one from a college professor who knows the applicant well, and one from a personal reference (not a member of the applicant's family and not connected with the applicant's academic career). Please furnish names and addresses of those who are writing these recommendations.

Duration: 10-month program.

Deadline: February 1.

PUBLICATIONS:
Program announcement.

ADDRESS INQUIRIES TO:
Martin McLaren Scholarship:
Connie Yates, Administrator
The Garden Club of America
Interchange Fellowship
(See address above.)

Interchange Fellowship (funds British student):
Marjorie Noel
E-mail: mclarenscholarship@rhs.org.uk

THE GARDEN CLUB OF AMERICA [2321]

14 East 60th Street
New York, NY 10022
(212) 753-8287
Fax: (212) 753-0134

E-MAIL ADDRESS:
scholarships@gcamerica.org

WEB SITE ADDRESS:
www.gcamerica.org

FOUNDED: 1913

AREAS OF INTEREST:
Plant preservation and tropical botany.

NAME(S) OF PROGRAMS:
- **The Anne S. Chatham Fellowship in Medicinal Botany**
- **Garden Club of America Awards in Tropical Botany**
- **The Frances M. Peacock Scholarship for Native Bird Habitat**

TYPE:
Research grants. Anne S. Chatham Fellowship in Medicinal Botany: Grant to enable study in medicinal botany.

GCA Awards in Tropical Botany: Grants to enable field study in tropical botany.

Frances M. Peacock Scholarship for Native Bird Habitat: Financial assistance to college seniors and graduate students to study habitat-related issues that will benefit threatened or endangered bird species and lend useful information for land management decisions.

YEAR PROGRAM STARTED: 1983

PURPOSE:
Anne S. Chatham Fellowship in Medicinal Botany: To protect and preserve knowledge about the medicinal use of plants by providing research support in the field of ethnobotany.

GCA Awards in Tropical Botany: To promote the preservation of tropical forests by enlarging the body of botanists with field experience.

Frances M. Peacock Scholarship for Native Bird Habitat: To study areas in the U.S. that provide winter or summer habitat for threatened and endangered native birds.

LEGAL BASIS:
Nonprofit, national organization.

ELIGIBILITY:
Chatham Fellowship in Medicinal Botany: Open to Ph.D. candidates and recent Ph.Ds.

GCA Awards in Tropical Botany: Open to Ph.D. candidates who will be carrying on field work in the tropics as a part of their doctoral dissertation research. Preference will be given to applications from those graduate students indicating that they have a long-term commitment to conservation of the forests. Nationality is not a criterion.

Peacock Scholarship for Native Bird Habitat: College seniors and graduate students.

GEOGRAPHIC RESTRICTIONS:
United States.

FINANCIAL DATA:
Amount of support per award: Chatham Fellowship in Medicinal Botany: $4,000; GCA Awards in Tropical Botany: $5,500; Peacock Scholarship for Native Bird Habitat: $4,000.
Total amount of support: Varies each year depending on funds.

NUMBER OF APPLICANTS MOST RECENT YEAR:
15.

NUMBER OF AWARDS: Chatham Fellowship in Medicinal Botany: 1; GCA Awards in Tropical Botany: 2 annually; Peacock Scholarship for Native Bird Habitat: 1.

APPLICATION INFORMATION:
Applications should include:
(1) a curriculum vitae for the student, including graduate and undergraduate transcripts;

(2) a two-page outline of the proposed research and a letter of recommendation from the advisor, which should include an evaluation of the student's progress to date and plans for the future and;
(3) evidence of foreign language capability, if necessary for country of research.

Further information regarding the GCA Awards in Tropical Botany is available from the World Wildlife Fund at the address below.
Duration: One year.
Deadline: Chatham Fellowship in Medicinal Botany: February 1; GCA Awards in Tropical Botany and Peacock Scholarship for Native Bird Habitat: January 15.

PUBLICATIONS:
Program announcement.

STAFF:
Connie Yates, Administrator

ADDRESS INQUIRIES TO:
Awards in Tropical Botany:
Andrea Santy
World Wildlife Fund
1250 24th Street, N.W., Suite 500
Washington, DC 20037
Tel: (202) 778-9632

Chatham Fellowship:
Dr. Robert E. Magill
Missouri Botanical Garden
P.O. Box 299
St. Louis, MO 63166
Tel: (314) 577-9503

Peacock Scholarship:
Scott Sutcliffe
Cornell Lab of Ornithology
159 Sapsucker Woods Road
Ithaca, NY 14850
Fax: (607) 254-2415

GREAT BEAR FOUNDATION [2322]
P.O. Box 9383
Missoula, MT 59807
(406) 829-9378
Fax: (406) 829-9379

E-MAIL ADDRESS:
gbf@greatbear.org

WEB SITE ADDRESS:
www.greatbear.org

FOUNDED: 1982

AREAS OF INTEREST:
Wildlife conservation, with a special emphasis on bears.

TYPE:
Scholarships.

PURPOSE:
To promote the education and study of wildlife conservation.

LEGAL BASIS:
501(c)(3) U.S. nonprofit organization.

FINANCIAL DATA:
Amount of support per award: Varies by program.
Total amount of support: $2,000.

APPLICATION INFORMATION:
Contact the Foundation for application procedures.
Duration: One year. Renewal possible.

ADDRESS INQUIRIES TO:
Dr. Charles Jonkel, President
(See address above.)

GREAT LAKES PROTECTION FUND [2323]
1560 Sherman Avenue
Suite 880
Evanston, IL 60201
(847) 425-8150
Fax: (847) 424-9832

WEB SITE ADDRESS:
www.glpf.org

FOUNDED: 1989

AREAS OF INTEREST:
To identify, demonstrate and promote regional action to enhance the health of the Great Lakes ecosystem.

NAME(S) OF PROGRAMS:
- **Great Lakes Protection Fund**

TYPE:
Challenge/matching grants; Demonstration grants; Development grants; Project/program grants; Seed money grants.

YEAR PROGRAM STARTED: 1990

PURPOSE:
To support projects that identify, demonstrate and promote regional action to enhance the health of the Great Lakes ecosystem.

LEGAL BASIS:
Nonprofit, multi-state endowment.

ELIGIBILITY:
The Great Lakes Protection Fund can support a wide variety of applicants. Nonprofit organizations (including environmental organizations, trade associations, and universities), for-profit businesses, government agencies, and individuals are eligible for Fund support. Successful applicants must maintain open access to certain project data, records and information.

All applicants must comply with the Fund's guidelines, show that the proposed work has clear public benefit to the Great Lakes basin, and that any related financial benefits will accrue to the public good. Government agencies must show that Fund support is not being used to replace or duplicate public funds.

FINANCIAL DATA:
Amount of support per award: Varies.
Total amount of support: $2,000,000 for the year 2010.

REPRESENTATIVE AWARDS:
$435,000 over 24 months to the Delta Institute to develop a series of tools to track and measure the full extent of the environmental impacts associated with specific reduction actions. Working with 13 facilities in Michigan, the team expects to reduce water use by over 15 million gallons per day, to eliminate almost 3 million tons of solid waste, reduce CO_2 emissions by over 11,000 tons, reduce emissions of criteria air pollutants by 150,000 pounds, and reduce hazard chemical use by over 200,000 gallons each year. The tools developed will provide a more accurate account of how on-site energy efficiency actions translate into "real" air pollutant reductions at a power generating facility. In conjunction with a panel of Sustainability Institute Fellows, the team will verify these ecosystem impacts and identify third-party transactions to retire the benefits.

APPLICATION INFORMATION:
The first step is the submission of a brief proposal that summarizes the proposed

project. The following documents must be included:
(1) completed applicant cover sheet;
(2) preproposal document, no more than three pages, describing the environmental outcome, proposed work, key personnel and financial plan and;
(3) a resume of the project's manager (no more than two pages).

Preproposal documents can be submitted by e-mail to preproposal@glpf.org or send six copies addressed to Preproposal Application, Great Lakes Protection Fund, at the address above.
Duration: Multiyear.

PUBLICATIONS:
Annual report; guidelines for funding; summary papers.

STAFF:
Russell Van Herik, Executive Director
Robert Eder, Vice President and Director of Finance and Administration
David Rankin, Vice President and Director of Programs
Amy Elledge, Communication Administrator

BOARD MEMBERS:
Wendy Abrams
Richard Baird
Lori Boughton
Jason Culotta
Matthew Driscoll
Michael Elmendorf
Caren Glotfelty
Edwin J. Hammett
D. Scott Harrison
John Kilroy
Richard Meeusen
Craig Shaver
Debra Shore
Maureen Smyth

ADDRESS INQUIRIES TO:
David Rankin
Vice President and Director of Programs
(See address above.)

THE JACOB AND TERESE HERSHEY FOUNDATION [2324]

2121 San Felipe
Suite 124
Houston, TX 77019
(713) 529-7611
Fax: (713) 529-7613

E-MAIL ADDRESS:
judithboyce@jthershey.org
teresethershey@jthershey.org

FOUNDED: 1961

AREAS OF INTEREST:
Animal protection, conservation, environmental, open space and parks, environmental education, land acquisition and human population control.

TYPE:
Capital grants; Challenge/matching grants; Conferences/seminars; Demonstration grants; Development grants; General operating grants; Matching gifts; Project/program grants; Research grants; Seed money grants; Training grants. Land acquisition.

YEAR PROGRAM STARTED: 1961

PURPOSE:
To promote preservation and conservation of land, forests, streams, wetlands and habitat existing in a natural state and the defense of such resources; to establish, conserve and preserve parks and open space for public use; to help provide care facilities for animals and birds, both domestic and wild; to aid education efforts to promote environmental literacy and comprehension of the complexities of the web of life, particularly in primary and secondary schools, museums and through citizen nonprofit organizations with similar purpose; to promote efforts toward population control.

LEGAL BASIS:
Private foundation.

ELIGIBILITY:
Grants are made to organizations that have tax-exempt status under Section 501(c)(3) of the Internal Revenue Code. Grants are not made to medical or religious institutions or groups, or to individuals. No grants for galas or parties. Multiple funding sources are encouraged.

GEOGRAPHIC RESTRICTIONS:
Southwestern Colorado; Austin and Houston, Texas areas.

FINANCIAL DATA:
Amount of support per award: Generally, $500 to $5,000.
Total amount of support: $200,000 per year.

NUMBER OF APPLICANTS MOST RECENT YEAR:
110.

NUMBER OF AWARDS: 91.

APPLICATION INFORMATION:
Submit written applications only. No general solicitations or bulk mailings. Keep the application simple. One copy only.

Contact the Foundation for one-page grant guidelines.
Duration: One-time grants. May reapply.
Deadline: May 1 and October 1. Applicant will receive an acknowledgement of receipt of application, as well as the date of the meeting at which it will be considered. Organizations are only considered for grants once per year. Notices and grants are sent in July and December.

IRS IDENTIFICATION NUMBER: 74-6039126

EXECUTIVE DIRECTOR:
Judith Boyce

ADDRESS INQUIRIES TO:
Judith Boyce, Executive Director
(See address above.)

THE HUDSON RIVER FOUNDATION [2325]

17 Battery Place, Suite 915
New York, NY 10004
(212) 483-7667
Fax: (212) 924-8325

E-MAIL ADDRESS:
info@hudsonriver.org

WEB SITE ADDRESS:
www.hudsonriver.org

FOUNDED: 1981

AREAS OF INTEREST:
Environmental, ecological and public policy aspects of the Hudson River estuary.

NAME(S) OF PROGRAMS:
● **Hudson River Fund**
● **Hudson River Improvement Fund**
● **New York City Environmental Fund**

TYPE:
Capital grants; Fellowships; Research grants; Travel grants. The Hudson River Fund was created to meet the critical need for an independent institution to sponsor scientific research programs that would contribute to the development of sound public policy concerning the River's ecological system. The Hudson River Fund makes grants in five categories: Hudson River Research Grants, Travel Grants, Expedited Grants, Hudson River Graduate Fellowships, and Tibor T. Polgar Fellowships.

The Hudson River Improvement Fund supports projects to enhance public use and enjoyment of the Hudson River's natural, scenic and cultural resources. The emphasis of the Improvement Fund is on physical projects requiring capital construction, development, or improvement.

The New York City Environmental Fund proposes to foster "restoration, care, public enjoyment of, and education about New York City's natural resources."

YEAR PROGRAM STARTED: 1983

PURPOSE:
To make science integral to decision-making with regard to the Hudson River and its watershed; to support competent stewardship of this extraordinary resource.

LEGAL BASIS:
Private foundation.

ELIGIBILITY:
Research must be focused on Hudson River.

FINANCIAL DATA:
Amount of support per award: Graduate Fellowships: Up to $15,000 for one year, plus up to $1,000 toward supplies (doctoral students); up to $11,000 for one year, plus up to $1,000 for supplies (Master's students). Polgar Fellowships are $3,800, plus limited research funds. Sponsoring professors receive a $500 stipend for Polgar Fellowships only.

NUMBER OF APPLICANTS MOST RECENT YEAR:
80 for research grants.

NUMBER OF AWARDS: 9.

APPLICATION INFORMATION:
Contact Foundation for details.
Duration: One to two years.
Deadline: Contact the Foundation.

PUBLICATIONS:
Annual Program Plan; *Hudson River Fund: Call for Proposals.*

EXECUTIVE DIRECTOR:
Clay Hiles

THE EDMUND NILES HUYCK PRESERVE, INC.

P.O. Box 189
Rensselaerville, NY 12147
(518) 797-3440
Fax: (518) 797-3440

E-MAIL ADDRESS:
huyckpreserve@wildblue.net

WEB SITE ADDRESS:
www.huyckpreserve.org

TYPE:
Research grants. Stipends, housing and laboratory space for predoctoral and postdoctoral scientists conducting research on and utilizing the natural resources of The E.N. Huyck Preserve.

See entry 2285 for full listing.

ILLINOIS CLEAN ENERGY COMMUNITY FOUNDATION [2326]

2 North LaSalle Street, Suite 1140
Chicago, IL 60602
(312) 372-5191
Fax: (312) 372-5190

E-MAIL ADDRESS:
dobrien@illinoiscleanenergy.org

WEB SITE ADDRESS:
www.illinoiscleanenergy.org

FOUNDED: 1999

AREAS OF INTEREST:
Improving the environmental quality of life in the state of Illinois and natural habitat preservation.

TYPE:
Grants-in-aid; Project/program grants. The Foundation provides financial support in two principal ways:
(1) Grantmaking: The Foundation provides grants, loans and other financial support, on a competitive basis, in response to proposals submitted by organizations in accord with the Foundation's announced strategic priorities and the application process described below. The Foundation can provide several different types of financial support, including grants, loans and other investments.
(2) Direct Initiatives: The Foundation identifies strategic opportunities to undertake large-scale, high-impact projects and special initiatives that further its program objectives in energy efficiency, renewable energy and natural areas conservation.

YEAR PROGRAM STARTED: 2001

PURPOSE:
To invest in clean energy development and land preservation efforts, working with communities and citizens to improve environmental quality in Illinois; to support programs and projects that will improve energy efficiency, develop renewable energy resources and preserve and enhance natural areas and wildlife habitats throughout the state.

LEGAL BASIS:
Independent, nonprofit grantmaking institution.

ELIGIBILITY:
The Foundation provides funding to tax-exempt organizations, including governmental entities. The Foundation will not provide funding for remediation of environmentally impaired properties, technology research, promotion of proprietary products, reoccurring operating costs, political campaigns or lobbying, capital campaigns or support for an organization's endowment, or projects undertaken by individuals.

GEOGRAPHIC RESTRICTIONS:
Illinois.

FINANCIAL DATA:
Amount of support per award: $2,000 to $500,000.
Total amount of support: Approximately $13,000,000 in total grants awarded for the year 2010.

APPLICATION INFORMATION:
Duration: One to two years.

ADDRESS INQUIRIES TO:
Bob Romo, Senior Program Officer
(See address above.)

INTERNATIONAL CRANE FOUNDATION, INC.

E-11376 Shady Lane Road
Baraboo, WI 53913
(608) 356-9462
Fax: (608) 356-9465

E-MAIL ADDRESS:
cranes@savingcranes.org

WEB SITE ADDRESS:
www.savingcranes.org

TYPE:
Internships. Formal stipended internship programs in the fields of aviculture, crane ecology and conservation education.

See entry 2286 for full listing.

J. SEWARD JOHNSON, SR. 1963 CHARITABLE TRUST

100 Albany Street
Suite 200
New Brunswick, NJ 08901
(732) 524-1020
Fax: (732) 524-1019

TYPE:
Project/program grants; Research grants.

See entry 1392 for full listing.

LANDSCAPE ARCHITECTURE FOUNDATION [2327]

818 18th Street, N.W.
Suite 810
Washington, DC 20006
(202) 331-7070 ext. 14
Fax: (202) 331-7079

E-MAIL ADDRESS:
scholarships@lafoundation.org

WEB SITE ADDRESS:
www.lafoundation.org

FOUNDED: 1966

AREAS OF INTEREST:
The profession of landscape architecture.

NAME(S) OF PROGRAMS:
- **ASLA Council of Fellows Scholarship**
- **Dangermond Fellowship**
- **EDSA Minority Scholarship**
- **Hawaii Chapter David T. Woolsey Scholarship**
- **Steven G. King Play Environments Scholarship**
- **Landscape Forms Design for People Scholarship**
- **Olmsted Scholars Program**
- **Courtland Paul Scholarship**
- **Peridian International/Rae L. Price, FASLA Scholarship**
- **Rain Bird Intelligent Use of Water Scholarship**
- **Douglas Dockery Thomas Fellowship in Garden History and Design**

TYPE:
Fellowships; Internships; Scholarships. Awards for undergraduate and graduate students pursuing an education in landscape architecture.

PURPOSE:
To assist students enrolled in programs of landscape architecture.

LEGAL BASIS:
Nonprofit, tax-exempt foundation.

ELIGIBILITY:
Open to undergraduate and graduate students currently enrolled in a professional degree program in landscape architecture. Available to students in financial need who show promise and commitment to the profession.

GEOGRAPHIC RESTRICTIONS:
United States and Canada.

FINANCIAL DATA:
Amount of support per award: Olmsted Scholars Program: $25,000.
Total amount of support: $80,000.

APPLICATION INFORMATION:
Duration: One academic year.
Deadline: Douglas Dockery Thomas Fellowship: February 1. All others: February 15.

PUBLICATIONS:
Guidelines.

ADDRESS INQUIRIES TO:
Heather Whitlow, Director of Programs and Communications
(See address and e-mail above.)

THE LEF FOUNDATION

121 Circle Road
San Rafael, CA 94903
(415) 499-9591 (CA)
(617) 492-5333 (New England)
Fax: (617) 868-5603 (New England)

E-MAIL ADDRESS:
marina@lef-foundation.org

WEB SITE ADDRESS:
www.lef-foundation.org

TYPE:
Awards/prizes; Project/program grants; Seed money grants. Program development.

See entry 446 for full listing.

THE CHARLES A. AND ANNE MORROW LINDBERGH FOUNDATION [2328]

2150 Third Avenue North, Suite 310
Anoka, MN 55303
(763) 576-1596
Fax: (763) 576-1664

E-MAIL ADDRESS:
info@lindberghfoundation.org

WEB SITE ADDRESS:
www.lindberghfoundation.org

FOUNDED: 1977

AREAS OF INTEREST:
Aviation/aerospace, agriculture, conservation of animal resources, conservation of plant resources, general conservation, humanities/education, arts, intercultural communication, biomedical research, conservation of water resources, exploration, health and population sciences, adaptive technology, and waste minimization and management.

NAME(S) OF PROGRAMS:
- **The Lindbergh Grants Program**

TYPE:
Project/program grants; Research grants. The Jonathan Lindbergh Brown Grant will support projects in adaptive technology or biomedical research which seek to redress imbalance between an individual and his or her human environment.

YEAR PROGRAM STARTED: 1977

PURPOSE:
To promote and advance Charles A. and Anne Morrow Lindbergh's vision of a balance between our human/natural environment and technological advancement.

LEGAL BASIS:
Nonprofit organization with 501(c)(3) tax-exempt status.

ELIGIBILITY:
Awarded to individuals whose proposed projects represent a significant contribution toward the achievement of a balance between the advance of technology and preservation of our human/natural environment.

Citizens of all countries are eligible. The Foundation welcomes candidates who may or may not be affiliated with an academic or nonprofit institution. Grants are made to individuals and not to affiliated institutions for institutional programs.

Proposals will be evaluated on a competitive basis with emphasis on the proposed project's practical application of the advance of technology and our human/natural environment. Originality of the approach to solving the problem and the solution's ultimate practical application will be considered.

FINANCIAL DATA:
Amount of support per award: Up to $10,580 (a symbolic amount representing the cost of the "Spirit of St. Louis" in 1927).
Total amount of support: Varies.

NUMBER OF APPLICANTS MOST RECENT YEAR:
166.

NUMBER OF AWARDS: 8.

APPLICATION INFORMATION:
Formal application package may be requested from the Lindbergh Foundation (self-addressed, stamped envelope requested) or downloaded from the web site. Applications and endorser reports must be submitted in English. Five copies of a typewritten application, following the format provided, must be submitted. One PDF copy required as well.
Duration: One year.
Deadline: Second Thursday of June for funding to start the following year. Announcements are made by April 15 of each year.

PUBLICATIONS:
Annual report; application guidelines; previous Lindbergh Grant project summaries; newsletter.

IRS IDENTIFICATION NUMBER: 13-2882090

OFFICERS:
Larry Williams, Chairman and President
Gregg Maryniak, Vice Chairman
David Treinis, Vice Chairman
Reeve Lindbergh, Honorary Chairman
Daniel E. Stoltz, Treasurer
John Petersen, Secretary

STAFF:
Shelley L. Nehl, Managing Director/Grants Administrator

ADDRESS INQUIRIES TO:
Grants Administrator
(See address above.)

*SPECIAL STIPULATIONS:
The Foundation does not provide support for tuition, scholarships, fellowships or related travel.

MARSHALL COMMUNITY FOUNDATION

126 West Michigan Avenue
Suite 202
Marshall, MI 49068
(269) 781-2273
Fax: (269) 781-9747

E-MAIL ADDRESS:
info@marshallcf.org

WEB SITE ADDRESS:
www.marshallcf.org

TYPE:
Project/program grants.

See entry 1669 for full listing.

MONSANTO FUND   [2329]

800 North Lindbergh Boulevard, A2N
St. Louis, MO 63167
(314) 694-5322
Fax: (314) 694-7658

E-MAIL ADDRESS:
monsanto.fund@monsanto.com

WEB SITE ADDRESS:
www.monsantofund.org

FOUNDED: 1964

AREAS OF INTEREST:
Improving nutritional well-being through agriculture, science education, the environment and Monsanto communities.

TYPE:
Project/program grants.

PURPOSE:
To improve the Earth's ecosystem - including clean water, clean air, productive land and thriving biodiversity - and the well-being of her people by supporting projects in the focus areas.

ELIGIBILITY:
Applicants must be nonprofit 501(c)(3) or units of government 170(c)(1). Proposed projects must fit within one of the focus areas. Must be an experienced, established and reputable organization (not a start-up organization), financially sound with a diverse funding base, and be audited annually.

Grants are not given to religious organizations.

GEOGRAPHIC RESTRICTIONS:
United States.

FINANCIAL DATA:
Amount of support per award: Average $25,000.
Total amount of support: Approximately $13,900,000 for the year 2008.

APPLICATION INFORMATION:
Initially, applicant must submit a two- to three-page Preliminary Funding Request by regular mail.
Duration: One to two years.
Deadline: Preliminary Funding Request: January 1 and July 1.

ADDRESS INQUIRIES TO:
Lisa Bannon-Bergmann
Contributions Manager
(See address above.)

NATIONAL FISH AND WILDLIFE FOUNDATION   [2330]

1133 15th Street, N.W.
Suite 1100
Washington, DC 20005
(202) 857-0166
Fax: (202) 857-0162

E-MAIL ADDRESS:
info@nfwf.org

WEB SITE ADDRESS:
www.nfwf.org

FOUNDED: 1984

AREAS OF INTEREST:
Conservation of natural resources including fish, wildlife and plants.

TYPE:
Challenge/matching grants; Formula grants; Matching gifts; Project/program grants; Scholarships.

YEAR PROGRAM STARTED: 1986

PURPOSE:
To conserve natural resources through habitat protection, environmental education, natural resource management, species conservation and leadership training for conservation professionals.

LEGAL BASIS:
Private 501(c)(3) organization.

ELIGIBILITY:
Must be a 501(c)(3) organization. No grants to individuals.

FINANCIAL DATA:
With $40,000,000 in federal funds and $139,000,000 in private contributions and grantee matching funds, the Foundation's total conservation investments topped $179,000,000 for the year 2010.
Amount of support per award: Varies.
Matching fund requirements: At least 1:1, preference for higher leverage.

NUMBER OF APPLICANTS MOST RECENT YEAR:
Varies.

NUMBER OF AWARDS: Varies.

REPRESENTATIVE AWARDS:
$100,000 to Iowa Department of Natural Resources to restore 1,254 acres of bottomland hardwood forest in northeast Iowa on former agricultural lands. The project is working to reduce forest fragmentation, enhance water quality, and improve critical habitat for neo-tropical birds and other wildlife; $400,000 to Conservation Fund to reduce nutrient and sediment runoff entering Rockymarsh Run – a tributary to the Potomac River and ultimately the Chesapeake Bay; $87,800 to Environmental Defense to develop and implement 12 habitat restoration projects on 250 acres of private lands in New York, Maryland, and Pennsylvania. Restoration will help recover the federally endangered bog turtle population as well as other rare species that rely on fens and other shallow wetlands.

APPLICATION INFORMATION:
Information on application can be obtained from the address above.
Duration: Support usually lasts for one year. Renewals are on a case-by-case basis.
Deadline: Contact the Foundation for exact dates.

PUBLICATIONS:
Annual report; application guidelines.

IRS IDENTIFICATION NUMBER: 52-1384129

STAFF:
Claude Gascon, Ph.D., Executive Vice
President, Science, Evaluation and Programs
Jeff Trandahl, Executive Director

BOARD OF DIRECTORS:
Mark F. Rockefeller, Chairman
Patrick Durkin, Vice Chairman
Christopher M. James, Vice Chairman
Carl R. Kuehner, III, Vice Chairman
Steven E. Chancellor
Max C. Chapman, Jr.
J. Michael Cline
Lance Conn
Ray Dalio
Jennie Turner Garlington
Caroline Getty
Rowan Gould
J.J. Healy
George C. Hixon
Paul Tudor Jones, II
Wayne LaPierre
Dr. Jane Lubchenco
Don J. McGrath
Michael L. Meadows
Philip E. Moriarty
Ruth O. Mutch
Chad Pike
Amy Robbins
Jim Root
Stephen C. Schram
Federico Stubbe
John Tomke
Steven A. Williams

ADDRESS INQUIRIES TO:
Appropriate Partnership Office Director
(See address above.)

NATIONAL INSTITUTE OF ENVIRONMENTAL HEALTH SCIENCES [2331]

Division of Extramural Research and Training
111 T.W. Alexander Drive
Research Triangle Park, NC 27709
(919) 541-3289
Fax: (919) 541-2843

E-MAIL ADDRESS:
mastin@niehs.nih.gov

WEB SITE ADDRESS:
www.niehs.nih.gov

FOUNDED: 1966

AREAS OF INTEREST:
Environmental health sciences research.

NAME(S) OF PROGRAMS:
- **Environmental Health Sciences Research and Training Grants**

TYPE:
Conferences/seminars; Demonstration grants;
Development grants; Fellowships;
Project/program grants; Research grants;
Training grants. NIEHS pursues its mission
by supporting basic and applied research on
the consequences of the exposure of humans
to potentially toxic or harmful agents in the
environment.

Research of interest encompasses studies that
relate to the biological effects of
environmental chemicals and physical factors
including such agents as hazardous gases,
suspended particles, aerosols, industrial
by-products and intermediates, heavy metals,
trace elements, food additives, adulterants
and pesticides. Physical factors include noise,
light, heat, microwaves and other forms of
nonionizing radiation.

Research Training Programs support
individuals at both the predoctoral and
postdoctoral levels in the areas of
environmental toxicology, environmental
pathology, environmental mutagenesis and
environmental epidemiology.

YEAR PROGRAM STARTED: 1966

PURPOSE:
To support research and research training in
environmental health.

LEGAL BASIS:
Government agency authorized under Section
301(d), Public Health Services Act; 42
U.S.C. 241; 42 C.F.R. 52.

ELIGIBILITY:
Universities, research institutes and other
public or private institutions may apply on
behalf of qualified researchers. Small
businesses may apply for SBIR grants.

GEOGRAPHIC RESTRICTIONS:
United States.

FINANCIAL DATA:
Funds are provided, as available, for all
allowable expenses associated with approved
research projects.
Amount of support per award: Varies.
Total amount of support: Varies.

APPLICATION INFORMATION:
Duration: Total grant project periods may not
exceed five years and are renewable on a
competitive basis at the end of the project
period. Average project period length is
currently four years.
Deadline: Varies with the specific grant;
contact the Division of Extramural Research
and Training for program deadline dates.

PUBLICATIONS:
Fact book; special announcements.

STAFF:
Dr. Carol Shreffler, Health Science
Administrator

ADDRESS INQUIRIES TO:
J. Patrick Mastin, Ph.D.
Acting Deputy Director
(See address above.)

NATIONAL OCEANIC AND ATMOSPHERIC ADMINISTRATION [2332]

NOAA's Ocean Service
Estuarine Reserves Division
1305 East-West Highway N/ORM5
Silver Spring, MD 20910
(301) 713-3155 ext. 105
(301) 563-7105
Fax: (301) 713-4012

E-MAIL ADDRESS:
alison.krepp@noaa.gov

WEB SITE ADDRESS:
nerrs.noaa.gov

FOUNDED: 1970

AREAS OF INTEREST:
Restoration, nutrient dynamics, habitat
conservation, invasive species, biodiversity,
non-point source pollution, and economic,
sociological and/or anthropological research
applicable to estuarine ecosystem
management.

NAME(S) OF PROGRAMS:
- **NOAA/National Estuarine Research Reserves Graduate Research Fellowship Program**

TYPE:
Fellowships.

YEAR PROGRAM STARTED: 1997

PURPOSE:
The NERR Graduate Research Fellowships
provide Master's degree students and Ph.D.
candidates with an opportunity to conduct
research of local and national significance
that focuses on enhancing coastal zone
management. Fellows conduct their research
within a National Estuarine Research Reserve
and gain hands-on experience by
participating in their host reserve's research
and monitoring programs. Graduate Research
Fellowship projects are based on the
reserve's local needs, the reserve system's
national priorities and the student's interest.

LEGAL BASIS:
Coastal Zone Management Act.

ELIGIBILITY:
Applicant must be admitted to or enrolled in
a full-time Master's or doctoral program at a
U.S.-accredited university. A portion of the
research must be conducted within a NERR
site.

FINANCIAL DATA:
Amount of support per award: $20,000 per
year.
Matching fund requirements: 30% match of
total cost required.

NUMBER OF APPLICANTS MOST RECENT YEAR:
64 for fiscal year 2011.

NUMBER OF AWARDS: Varies.

APPLICATION INFORMATION:
Duration: One to three years.
Deadline: November 1.

PUBLICATIONS:
Application guidelines.

ADDRESS INQUIRIES TO:
Alison Krepp, Program Coordinator
(See address above.)

NATIONAL PARK FOUNDATION [2333]

1201 Eye Street, N.W.
Suite 550B
Washington, DC 20005
(202) 354-6460
Fax: (202) 371-2066

E-MAIL ADDRESS:
ask-nps@nationalparks.org

WEB SITE ADDRESS:
www.nationalparks.org

FOUNDED: 1967

AREAS OF INTEREST:
Youth engagement, community engagement
and conservation, and professional
engagement.

NAME(S) OF PROGRAMS:
- **Active Trails**
- **Albright-Wirth Grants Program**
- **America's Best Idea**
- **Electronic Field Trips**
- **The Junior Ranger Program**
- **Park Teachers Program**
- **Parks Climate Challenge**
- **Transportation Scholar**
- **Harry Yount National Park Ranger Award**

TYPE:
Block grants; Challenge/matching grants;
Research grants; Scholarships. Grants range
from small seed or start-up programs to
larger ones which continue successful

projects. Grants enable the parks to obtain additional cash and in-kind contributions, such as products, service or volunteer time.

The Albright-Wirth Employee Development Fund underwrites advanced skills training, graduate education and other professional development programs for Park Service employees.

The Harry Yount National Park Ranger Award recognizes a Ranger for leadership, exemplary skills and dedication to the Park Ranger profession.

YEAR PROGRAM STARTED: 1967

PURPOSE:
To help fund important conservation, preservation, and education efforts on-the-ground in the Parks.

LEGAL BASIS:
Nonprofit organization.

ELIGIBILITY:
All grants are made directly for projects in the national park system. Grants will fund educational projects, field training for volunteers and interns, resource conservation, historic preservation, interpretation programs for park visitors, outreach programs, and park projects conducted by park friends, cooperating associations or academic institutions.

The grants program will not fund the purchase of vehicles or maintenance equipment, new construction or large-scale improvements to buildings, infrastructure construction or maintenance of roads and utilities, base salaries of NPS staff, cost of professional conferences or attendance at them, grants or scholarships, advocacy or litigation, or the start-up costs of friends groups.

FINANCIAL DATA:
Amount of support per award: $5,000 to $25,000.
Total amount of support: Varies.
Matching fund requirements: Challenged grants 1:1.

APPLICATION INFORMATION:
Applications accepted only from national park units or organizations working in partnership with national parks. Complete information is available online.
Duration: Usually one year. Renewal applications permitted.
Deadline: Varies.

PUBLICATIONS:
Annual report.

IRS IDENTIFICATION NUMBER: 52-1086761

OFFICERS:
Hon. Ken Salazar, Chairman and Secretary of the Interior
Chris Sullivan, Vice Chairman
Charles Peck, Treasurer
John Jarvis, Secretary, Director National Park Service

STAFF:
Neil Mulholland, President and Chief Executive Officer
Celeste Regan, Chief Financial Officer

NATIONAL WILDLIFE FEDERATION [2334]

11100 Wildlife Center Drive
Reston, VA 20190
(703) 438-6265
(800) 247-7387
Fax: (703) 438-6468

E-MAIL ADDRESS:
cochranc@nwf.org

WEB SITE ADDRESS:
www.nwf.org

FOUNDED: 1936

AREAS OF INTEREST:
Conservation of wildlife and other natural resources.

NAME(S) OF PROGRAMS:
● **Conservation Internships**

TYPE:
Fellowships; Internships. National Wildlife Federation offers a variety of education internships in which the intern would assist with conservation education and outreach activities.

YEAR PROGRAM STARTED: 1989

PURPOSE:
To educate, inspire, and assist individuals and organizations to conserve wildlife and other natural resources.

LEGAL BASIS:
Nonprofit organization able to carry on a defined amount of lobbying.

ELIGIBILITY:
A background in ecology, the environment, educational programming or camp counseling is desirable. Applicants must be reliable, energetic and willing to accept responsibilities.

GEOGRAPHIC RESTRICTIONS:
United States.

FINANCIAL DATA:
Amount of support per award: $400 per week, plus core benefits.
Total amount of support: Varies.

NUMBER OF AWARDS: Varies.

APPLICATION INFORMATION:
Further information is available upon request to the Intern Program Coordinator.
Duration: 24 to 48 weeks.
Deadline: Varies.

ADDRESS INQUIRIES TO:
Courtney Cochran
Intern Program Coordinator
(See address above.)

NATIONAL WILDLIFE FEDERATION [2335]

11100 Wildlife Center Drive
Reston, VA 20190-5362
(703) 438-6265
Fax: (703) 438-6468

E-MAIL ADDRESS:
campus@nwf.org

WEB SITE ADDRESS:
www.nwf.org/campusecology/fellowships

FOUNDED: 1936

AREAS OF INTEREST:
Global warming impacts and solutions.

NAME(S) OF PROGRAMS:
● **Campus Ecology Fellowships**

TYPE:
Fellowships.

YEAR PROGRAM STARTED: 1973

PURPOSE:
To give well-qualified and highly motivated individuals substantive practical experience.

LEGAL BASIS:
Nonprofit organization able to carry on a defined amount of lobbying.

ELIGIBILITY:
Undergraduate or graduate students from any college or university in the U.S. may apply. Applications are invited from students in all disciplines and are not limited to environmental studies majors. Current and former employees of National Wildlife Federation and former NWF Campus Ecology Fellows are ineligible to apply. Former NWF interns are eligible to apply following one year from their final work date. Applications from students who have been nominated by a formal group or committee working on climate and other sustainability projects on campus will receive special consideration. A nomination process is especially encouraged where more than one student may be interested in applying for NWF's Campus Ecology Fellowship. The applicant must be enrolled in school throughout the duration of the 15-month grant period.

GEOGRAPHIC RESTRICTIONS:
United States.

FINANCIAL DATA:
Amount of support per award:
Undergraduates: Up to $2,000 to offset project expenses; Graduates: Up to $5,000.
Total amount of support: Varies.

COOPERATIVE FUNDING PROGRAMS: Kendeda Sustainability Fund of the Tides Foundation, Kendeda Fund, Nathan Cummings Foundation, Town Creek Foundation.

NUMBER OF APPLICANTS MOST RECENT YEAR:
Approximately 400.

NUMBER OF AWARDS: 15 for the year 2010.

APPLICATION INFORMATION:
Duration: 15 months.
Deadline: Varies.

PUBLICATIONS:
Program description.

OFFICERS:
Larry Schweiger, President and Chief Executive Officer

ADDRESS INQUIRIES TO:
Campus Ecology Fellowships
(See address above.)

NEW YORK SEA GRANT INSTITUTE [2336]

121 Discovery Hall
Stony Brook University
Stony Brook, NY 11794-5001
(631) 632-6905
Fax: (631) 632-6917

E-MAIL ADDRESS:
nyseagrant@notes.cc.sunysb.edu

WEB SITE ADDRESS:
www.nyseagrant.org

FOUNDED: 1971

AREAS OF INTEREST:
Coastal resource management, fisheries biology, contaminants and environmental quality, environmental processes and marine economics, seafood use and technology, recreation and tourism, human dimensions, marine aquaculture, youth education, biotech, and coastal processes.

TYPE:
Awards/prizes; Conferences/seminars; Development grants; Endowments; Fellowships; Internships; Project/program grants; Research grants; Scholarships; Technical assistance; Travel grants. Principally grants for laboratory and field studies, publications and communication and curriculum development.

YEAR PROGRAM STARTED: 1971

PURPOSE:
To foster the wise use and development of coastal resources through research, education and training.

LEGAL BASIS:
A cooperative research and education activity of the State University of New York and Cornell University, as well as NOAA's National Sea Grant College Program.

ELIGIBILITY:
Applicant must be a member of the faculty of an institution of higher learning or of a nonprofit organization. Projects must address issues relevant to New York state. In most cases, applicants are affiliated with New York institutions.

FINANCIAL DATA:
Amount of support per award: Varies.
Total amount of support: $2,500,000.
Matching fund requirements: Matching funds equal to 50% of funds requested must be provided by applicant from non-federal sources.

NUMBER OF APPLICANTS MOST RECENT YEAR:
Around 100 for most biennial solicitations.

NUMBER OF AWARDS: Approximately 20 per year.

APPLICATION INFORMATION:
Duration: One year. Continuation possible.
Deadline: Biennial with occasional out-of-cycle.

OFFICERS:
James W. Ammerman, Director
Helen Domske, Interim Associate Director
Cornelia G. Schlenk, Assistant Director

ADDRESS INQUIRIES TO:
James W. Ammerman, Director
(See address above.)

JESSIE SMITH NOYES FOUNDATION   [2337]
6 East 39th Street
12th Floor
New York, NY 10016
(212) 684-6577
Fax: (212) 689-6549

E-MAIL ADDRESS:
noyes@noyes.org

WEB SITE ADDRESS:
www.noyes.org

FOUNDED: 1947

AREAS OF INTEREST:
Sustainable agriculture, toxics, reproductive rights, environmental justice, and environment in New York City.

TYPE:
General operating grants; Project/program grants. Grants to tax-exempt institutions in the connected and overlapping areas of sustainable agriculture, toxics, reproductive rights, and New York City environment in order to achieve the Foundation's overall

goal, which is to promote a sustainable and just social and natural system by supporting grassroots organizations and movements committed to this goal.

PURPOSE:
To support programs that promote a sustainable and just social and natural system.

LEGAL BASIS:
Family foundation.

ELIGIBILITY:
The Foundation makes grants to tax-exempt organizations with 501(c)(3) classification from the IRS for work within the U.S. to individuals. It will not consider requests for endowments, capital construction, general fund-raising, deficit financing or scholarships, fellowships, loans or grants to individuals. The Foundation does not make grants for research or give support to conferences, seminars, media events, or workshops, unless they are an integral part of a broader program, does not generally make grants for college- and university-based programs, and does not provide support for the production and development of television and media programming.

GEOGRAPHIC RESTRICTIONS:
United States.

FINANCIAL DATA:
Amount of support per award: Varies.
Total amount of support: $2,590,000 for the year 2009.

NUMBER OF APPLICANTS MOST RECENT YEAR:
Approximately 350 letters of inquiry received each year.

NUMBER OF AWARDS: Approximately 100 per year.

REPRESENTATIVE AWARDS:
$25,000 to Alaska Community Action on Toxins, Anchorage, AK; $15,000 to Families United for Racial and Economic Equality, Brooklyn, NY; $25,000 to ACCESS/Women's Health Rights Coalition, Oakland, CA; $30,000 to National Campaign for Sustainable Agriculture, Pine Bush, NY.

APPLICATION INFORMATION:
The first step should be a letter of inquiry of no more than three pages. The Foundation welcomes the opportunity to meet with prospective grantees, but prefers to wait until after it receives a letter to determine if the meeting will be useful.

Letters of inquiry are reviewed by the program staff who determine if requests meet the Foundation's funding priorities. Those not meeting the priorities are declined. Requests that meet the priorities are given further consideration and a full proposal may be requested. Proposals should be submitted to the Foundation only upon request.
Duration: Varies.
Deadline: Letters of inquiry are accepted at any time. If a proposal is requested, it is assigned to one of the Foundation's three board meetings.

IRS IDENTIFICATION NUMBER: 13-5600408

OFFICERS:
Victor De Luca, President

STAFF:
Millie Buchanan, Program Officer
Wilma Montanez, Program Officer
Kolu Zigbi, Program Officer
Margaret Segall, Director of Administration

BOARD OF DIRECTORS:
Chitra Staley, Chairperson
Carol Kuhre, Vice Chairperson
Dorothy Anderson
George Beardsley
Jerry Beardsley
Betty Emarita
Ann Fritz
Jenifer Getz
Nicholas Jacangelo
Bruce Kahn
Ben Lovell
LaDonna Redmond
Belvie Rooks
Ann F. Wiener

ADDRESS INQUIRIES TO:
Victor De Luca, President
(See address above.)

PATAGONIA INC.   [2338]
P.O. Box 150
Ventura, CA 93002
(805) 643-8616
Fax: (805) 643-2367

E-MAIL ADDRESS:
inquires@patagonia.com

WEB SITE ADDRESS:
www.patagonia.com/enviro

AREAS OF INTEREST:
Preservation and protection of the natural environment.

NAME(S) OF PROGRAMS:
● **Environmental Grant Program**

TYPE:
General operating grants; Product donations; Project/program grants. Funds to help local groups working to protect local habitats and to force the government to abide by its own laws in regards to biodiversity and ecosystem protection.

YEAR PROGRAM STARTED: 1987

PURPOSE:
To assist groups who strive to preserve and restore the natural environment.

LEGAL BASIS:
Private corporation giving program.

ELIGIBILITY:
Applicants must be 501(c)(3) tax-exempt organizations. No grants for scientific research, video, television or media projects or more general environmental education efforts.

GEOGRAPHIC RESTRICTIONS:
United States, Canada, Europe, Japan and South America.

FINANCIAL DATA:
Company pledges one percent of yearly sales or 10% of pre-tax profits, whichever is higher, to grassroots environmental groups. Total amount varies yearly, thus grant distribution is based on the sales volume achieved for the previous six months, as grants are distributed twice yearly.
Amount of support per award: $3,000 to $8,000.

APPLICATION INFORMATION:
Duration: One year. Applicants must reapply for continued funding.
Deadline: Proposals must be submitted no later than April 30 or August 31. Grants distributed in September and January, respectively.

PUBLICATIONS:
Program guidelines.

ADDRESS INQUIRIES TO:
Lisa Myers
Environmental Programs Associate
(See address above.)

*PLEASE NOTE:
Phone calls are discouraged.

PEW FELLOWS PROGRAM IN MARINE CONSERVATION   [2339]

Pew Environment Group
901 E Street, N.W., 10th Floor
Washington, DC 20004
(202) 552-2297

WEB SITE ADDRESS:
www.pewmarinefellows.org

FOUNDED: 1988

AREAS OF INTEREST:
Marine conservation.

TYPE:
Fellowships.

YEAR PROGRAM STARTED: 1990

PURPOSE:
To support innovative, applied projects aimed at developing and implementing solutions to critical challenges facing the world's oceans.

LEGAL BASIS:
Private foundation.

ELIGIBILITY:
Applicant must work in the field of research, education, communications, advocacy or policy, and must be nominated.

FINANCIAL DATA:
Amount of support per award: $150,000 over three years, to be applied to a specific project.
Total amount of support: $750,000 per year.

NUMBER OF APPLICANTS MOST RECENT YEAR:
50.

NUMBER OF AWARDS: 5 individuals or teams.

REPRESENTATIVE AWARDS:
Dr. P. Dee Boersma, University of Washington; Noah T. Idechong, Palau Conservation Society; Derek C.G. Muir, Environment Canada.

APPLICATION INFORMATION:
Applications are by nomination only. Unsolicited applications are not accepted.
Duration: Three years.

PUBLICATIONS:
Program guidelines; newsletter.

ADDRESS INQUIRIES TO:
Polita Glynn, Program Manager
(See address above.)

*SPECIAL STIPULATIONS:
The Foundation does not accept unsolicited proposals.

RESOURCES FOR THE FUTURE   [2340]

1616 P Street, N.W.
Washington, DC 20036-1400
(202) 328-5000
Fax: (202) 939-3460

E-MAIL ADDRESS:
info@rff.org

WEB SITE ADDRESS:
www.rff.org

AREAS OF INTEREST:
Economics, policy sciences or issues relating to the environment and natural resources of energy.

NAME(S) OF PROGRAMS:
● **Joseph L. Fisher Dissertation Fellowships**
● **The Walter O. Spofford, Jr., Memorial Internship**

TYPE:
Awards/prizes; Fellowships; Internships. Joseph L. Fisher Dissertation Fellowships are in support of doctoral dissertation research on issues related to the environment, natural resources or energy.

The Walter O. Spofford, Jr., Memorial Internship is a paid internship for graduate students.

PURPOSE:
Joseph L. Fisher Dissertation Fellowships: To support graduate students in the final year of their dissertation research.

ELIGIBILITY:
Joseph L. Fisher Dissertation Fellowships: Candidates must have completed the preliminary examinations for the Doctorate not later than February 1 prior to the application deadline. Resources for the Future particularly encourages women and members of minority groups to apply. RFF's primary research disciplines are economics and other social sciences. Proposals originating in these fields will have the greatest likelihood of success. Proposals from the physical or biological sciences must have an immediate and obvious link to environmental policy matters.

The Walter O. Spofford, Jr., Memorial Internship: Candidates should be highly motivated and in the first or second year of graduate training in the social or natural sciences. Candidates should also have outstanding policy analysis and writing skills. They should also have a special interest in Chinese environmental issues.

FINANCIAL DATA:
Under the Tax Reform Act of 1986, most, if not all, of this stipend will probably be taxable income. This Fellowship is intended to be the principal source of support for graduate students in the final year of their dissertation research. The Fellowship will be reduced by the amount of any other financial assistance other than tuition support. Financial assistance must be disclosed to RFF. No additional support will be provided for travel, data acquisition, or other dissertation-related expenses.

If necessary, support for travel expenses and visa assistance can be provided for the Spofford Internship.
Amount of support per award: Joseph L. Fisher Dissertation Fellowships: $18,000 stipend for the academic year; Walter O. Spofford, Jr. Memorial Internship: $375 stipend per week.

APPLICATION INFORMATION:
Joseph L. Fisher Dissertation Fellowships: Graduate students interested in applying should submit the following:
(1) a completed application form;
(2) a cover letter;
(3) curriculum vitae;
(4) a graduate transcript;
(5) a one-page abstract of the dissertation;
(6) a technical summary of the dissertation not to exceed 2,500 words in length (not

including the bibliography);
(7) a letter from the department chair or other university official certifying the student's doctoral candidacy and;
(8) two letters of recommendation from faculty members on the student's dissertation committee.
The technical summary should describe clearly the aim of the dissertation, its significance in relation to the existing literature, and the research methods and data to be used. RFF cannot provide written evaluations of proposals.

The Walter O. Spofford, Jr., Memorial Internship: Students should submit a completed application form, a cover letter describing their areas of interest, a resume, and a recent transcript. Applicants must have proof of eligibility to be employed in the U.S. One letter of recommendation from a faculty member should be sent directly by the professor to RFF. Transcripts and recommendation letters should be sent either by e-mail to spofford-award@rff.org with the name of the applicant in the subject field, or by post mail to: Coordinator for Academic Programs-Spofford Award, Resources for the Future, at the address above.
Duration: Joseph L. Fisher Dissertation Fellowships: One year; The Walter O. Spofford, Jr., Memorial Internship: Summer.

*SPECIAL STIPULATIONS:
It is expected that Fellowship recipients will not engage in full-time employment during the period of Fellowship tenure.

RESOURCES FOR THE FUTURE   [2341]

1616 P Street, N.W.
Washington, DC 20036-1400
(202) 328-5000
Fax: (202) 939-3460

E-MAIL ADDRESS:
info@rff.org

WEB SITE ADDRESS:
www.rff.org

FOUNDED: 1952

AREAS OF INTEREST:
Research and public education in development, conservation, economics, the use of natural resources and in the quality of the environment.

NAME(S) OF PROGRAMS:
● **Gilbert F. White Postdoctoral Fellowship Program**

TYPE:
Awards/prizes; Fellowships; Internships; Research grants; Residencies; Visiting scholars. Resident fellowships in honor of Gilbert F. White, internationally known statesman of science, for postdoctoral research in one of three divisions: the Energy and Natural Resources Division, the Quality of the Environment Division, or the Center for Risk Management.

YEAR PROGRAM STARTED: 1980

PURPOSE:
To support research in areas related to natural resources, energy, or the environment.

LEGAL BASIS:
Private, nonprofit research organization.

ELIGIBILITY:
Open to individuals in any discipline who will have completed their doctoral

requirements by the beginning of the 2011-12 academic year. Selection criteria include the proposed research program and how it will fit with RFF work in progress. Teaching and/or research experience at the postdoctoral level is preferred, though not essential. Individuals holding positions in government, as well as at academic institutions, are eligible.

FINANCIAL DATA:
Fellows receive an annual stipend based upon their current salary, plus research support, office facilities at RFF, and an allowance of up to $1,000 for moving or living expenses. This stipend may be supplemented from other sources if the supplement does not divert the fellow from his or her research. Fellowships do not provide medical insurance or other RFF fringe benefits. Neither Social Security nor tax payments are deducted from the stipend.

Amount of support per award: Varies.

Total amount of support: Varies.

NUMBER OF APPLICANTS MOST RECENT YEAR:
12.

NUMBER OF AWARDS: 1.

APPLICATION INFORMATION:
No application form is required. Candidates should submit the following:
(1) brief letter of application and a curriculum vitae including educational background, professional experience and honors/awards received;
(2) list of publications and description of significant research completed, but not published;
(3) statement of proposed research (not more than 10 double-spaced pages) with hypothesis, objective, methods to be used, anticipated benefit, and how the work relates to current RFF research;
(4) project budget and;
(5) three letters of recommendation from fellow faculty members or colleagues.

With the exception of letters of recommendation, all materials should be sent electronically as Word documents to white-award@rff.org. Reference letters should be sent by mail to the Coordinator for Academic Programs-White Award at the address listed above.

Duration: 11 months.

Deadline: February. Announcement in April.

PUBLICATIONS:
Guidelines.

IRS IDENTIFICATION NUMBER: 53-0220900

OFFICERS:
Philip R. Sharp, President

ADDRESS INQUIRIES TO:
Mara Parrish, Human Resources
(See address above.)

RESOURCES FOR THE FUTURE   [2342]
1616 P Street, N.W.
Washington, DC 20036-1400
(202) 328-5088
Fax: (202) 939-3460

E-MAIL ADDRESS:
info@rff.org

WEB SITE ADDRESS:
www.rff.org

AREAS OF INTEREST:
Economics, policy sciences or issues relating to the environment and natural resources of energy.

NAME(S) OF PROGRAMS:
● **John V. Krutilla Research Stipend**

TYPE:
Research grants. Stipend can be used for summer salary support, to pay for research assistance, or for any other legitimate research expenses.

PURPOSE:
To provide research assistance.

ELIGIBILITY:
Open to young scholars who have a recently awarded doctoral degree (no more than five years beyond receipt of Ph.D.).

FINANCIAL DATA:
Amount of support per award: $5,500.

APPLICATION INFORMATION:
No application form is required. Individuals interested in applying should submit:
(1) a short description of the proposed research (no more than five typed pages, double-spaced; references do not count in the page total);
(2) a curriculum vitae and;
(3) one letter of recommendation that can comment on the candidate's past research and proposed project in specific terms; the letter of recommendation should be sent separately and should identify the name of the individual who is applying for the Krutilla research award.

All application materials must be sent electronically as Word documents to krutilla-award@rff.org. Mark the transmitted e-mail's subject as Krutilla Research Award.

Duration: One year.

Deadline: Last day of February. Announcement in April.

THE RUSSELL FAMILY FOUNDATION   [2343]
3025 Harborview Drive
Gig Harbor, WA 98335
(253) 858-5050
Fax: (253) 851-0460

E-MAIL ADDRESS:
info@trff.org

WEB SITE ADDRESS:
www.trff.org

FOUNDED: 1999

AREAS OF INTEREST:
Environmental sustainability.

TYPE:
Project/program grants. Grants focused regionally on Puget Sound, environmental education and green business practices.

PURPOSE:
To implement strategies that raise awareness and understanding of our environment and the importance of protecting it.

ELIGIBILITY:
Organizations must be 501(c)(3) or nonprofit entities such as public schools and school districts, and must be located in and/or provide services within the Puget Sound region. No grants to individuals.

GEOGRAPHIC RESTRICTIONS:
Western Washington state (Clallam, Jefferson, King, Kitsap, Mason, Pierce, San Juan, Skagit, Snohomish, Thurston and Whatcom Island counties).

FINANCIAL DATA:
Amount of support per award: Average grant: $30,000.

APPLICATION INFORMATION:
Submit letter of inquiry through Foundation's online grantmaking system.

Duration: One year. Renewal by reapplication.

Deadline: Letter of inquiry: February 14 and October 10.

ADDRESS INQUIRIES TO:
Linsey Sauer, Grants Manager
(See address above.)

SMITHSONIAN ENVIRONMENTAL RESEARCH CENTER   [2344]
647 Contees Wharf Road
Edgewater, MD 21037
(443) 482-2217
Fax: (443) 482-2380

E-MAIL ADDRESS:
sercintern@si.edu

WEB SITE ADDRESS:
www.serc.si.
edu/pro_training/internships/internships.aspx

FOUNDED: 1975

AREAS OF INTEREST:
Environmental research and environmental education.

NAME(S) OF PROGRAMS:
● **Professional Training**

TYPE:
Challenge/matching grants; Fellowships; Internships; Research grants. The Program enables undergraduate and graduate students to work on specific projects under the direction of the Center's professional staff and is tailored to provide the maximum educational benefit to each participant. Graduate students and undergraduates may conduct independent projects with the approval of the staff member with whom they plan to study.

Subject matter of the projects includes terrestrial and estuarine environmental research within the disciplines of mathematics, chemistry, microbiology, botany, zoology, and environmental education.

Fellowships are offered annually at the postdoctoral, predoctoral and graduate levels.

Internships are offered three times per year at the undergraduate levels, recent graduate, or beginning Master's student.

YEAR PROGRAM STARTED: 1972

PURPOSE:
To offer undergraduate- and graduate-level students a unique opportunity to gain exposure to and experience in environmental research.

LEGAL BASIS:
Research unit of the Smithsonian Institution.

ELIGIBILITY:
Applicants must be qualified students from academic institutions in the U.S. or abroad. The SERC will accept applications from interested individuals who are in a position to commit themselves fully to the completion of a project. Selection is based upon the student's academic credentials, extent of relevant training or experience, letters of

recommendation and the congruence of the student's expressed goals with those of the Professional Training Program.

FINANCIAL DATA:
Dorm space is available for $85 per week and does not include board. Space is limited.

Amount of support per award: Interns receive $450 per week.

Total amount of support: $45,000 postdoctoral/senior stipend; $30,000 predoctoral stipend; $6,500 graduate student; research allowances are additional.

NUMBER OF APPLICANTS MOST RECENT YEAR:
273 for the year 2010; 365 for the year 2011.

NUMBER OF AWARDS: 44 for the year 2010.

APPLICATION INFORMATION:
Application materials and additional information regarding fellowships can be obtained from the Smithsonian Institution Office of Fellowships and Grants, E-mail: siofg@ofg.si.edu.

Duration: Intern Appointments: Generally 10 to 16 weeks; Fellowships: One year, with renewal.

Deadline: Spring Session: November 15; Summer Session: February 1; Fall Session: June 1; Fellowships: January 15.

PUBLICATIONS:
Application guidelines.

STAFF:
Anson H. Hines, Director
Patrick Megonigal, Deputy Director
Daniel Gustafson, Jr., Fellowship Coordinator

ADDRESS INQUIRIES TO:
Daniel Gustafson, Jr.
Fellowship Coordinator
(See address above.)

SOIL AND WATER CONSERVATION SOCIETY [2345]

945 S.W. Ankeny Road
Ankeny, IA 50021-9763
(515) 289-2331
Fax: (515) 289-1227

E-MAIL ADDRESS:
swcs@swcs.org

WEB SITE ADDRESS:
www.swcs.org

AREAS OF INTEREST:
Soil, water and related natural resource management.

NAME(S) OF PROGRAMS:
● **Kenneth E. Grant Research Scholarship**

TYPE:
Research grants. Provides financial aid to members of the Society for graduate-level research on a specific conservation topic that will help the Society carry out its mission of fostering the science and the art of soil, water, and related natural resource management to achieve sustainability.

PURPOSE:
To foster the science and the art of soil, water and related natural resource management to achieve sustainability; to promote and practice an ethic recognizing the interdependence of people and the environment.

ELIGIBILITY:
Open to members of the Society who have demonstrated integrity, ability and

competence to complete the specified study topic. Applicants must be eligible for graduate work at an accredited institution and show reasonable need for financial assistance. Must be members of the Society for at least one year.

FINANCIAL DATA:
Amount of support per award: Up to $1,300.

APPLICATION INFORMATION:
Applicants must submit a proposal and evidence of their ability to meet eligibility requirements. There are no specific application forms.

Duration: One year.

Deadline: February 12.

SWEET WATER TRUST [2346]

One Short Street, Suite 2
Northampton, MA 01060
(617) 263-7776
Fax: (617) 263-7774

E-MAIL ADDRESS:
eendicott@sweetwatertrust.org

WEB SITE ADDRESS:
www.sweetwatertrust.org

FOUNDED: 1992

AREAS OF INTEREST:
Conservation of wild nature.

NAME(S) OF PROGRAMS:
● **Wild Land, Wild Waters Land Protection Program**

TYPE:
Project/program grants. Program is intended to conserve the natural ecosystems in the Northern Forest region (northern New England and the Adirondacks).

YEAR PROGRAM STARTED: 1992

PURPOSE:
To protect and acquire wildlands; to protect watersheds in the Northern Appalachian eco-region.

LEGAL BASIS:
Private trust.

ELIGIBILITY:
Eligible organizations must be IRS 501(c)(3) tax-exempt. Projects under consideration must be part of an overall conservation strategy of at least 10,000 acres.

GEOGRAPHIC RESTRICTIONS:
Northern New England states, neighboring forests of the Canadian provinces.

FINANCIAL DATA:
Amount of support per award: $1,000 to $1,000,000 for land acquisition.

Total amount of support: Approximately $750,000 annually.

NUMBER OF APPLICANTS MOST RECENT YEAR:
10.

APPLICATION INFORMATION:
First step to apply for funding is a preliminary e-mail inquiry, briefly explaining how the proposed project fits within the Trust's guidelines.

Duration: One year. Multiyear grants possible.

PUBLICATIONS:
Guidelines.

IRS IDENTIFICATION NUMBER: 04-3118545

OFFICERS AND TRUSTEES:
Eve Endicott, Executive Director
Walker Buckner, Trustee

ADDRESS INQUIRIES TO:
Eve Endicott, Executive Director
(See e-mail address above.)

*SPECIAL STIPULATIONS:
Trust does not accept unsolicited proposals.

THE ROBERT & PATRICIA SWITZER FOUNDATION [2347]

P.O. Box 293
Belfast, ME 04915-0293
(207) 338-5654
Fax: (207) 338-5655

E-MAIL ADDRESS:
erin@switzernetwork.org

WEB SITE ADDRESS:
www.switzernetwork.org

FOUNDED: 1987

AREAS OF INTEREST:
Environment.

NAME(S) OF PROGRAMS:
● **Switzer Environmental Fellowship Program**

TYPE:
Fellowships; Project/program grants. Annual fellowship to recognize environmental leaders who have the ability and determination to make a significant impact on environmental quality.

YEAR PROGRAM STARTED: 1987

PURPOSE:
To support highly talented graduate students in California and New England whose studies are directed toward improving environmental quality and who demonstrate leadership in their field.

ELIGIBILITY:
Applicants must meet the following criteria:
(1) be a U.S. citizen;
(2) be enrolled in an accredited institution in California or New England and;
(3) have strong academic qualifications.

Master's degree candidates must have completed at least one semester of course work.

Ph.D. candidates must have completed at least three years of doctoral work or passed their qualifying exams.

GEOGRAPHIC RESTRICTIONS:
California and New England.

FINANCIAL DATA:
Amount of support per award: $15,000, paid in two equal installments, the first in June and the second in late January or early February.

NUMBER OF APPLICANTS MOST RECENT YEAR:
350.

NUMBER OF AWARDS: 20 annually; 10 in California and 10 in New England.

APPLICATION INFORMATION:
Duration: One year.

Deadline: January 15.

ADDRESS INQUIRIES TO:
Erin Lloyd, Program Officer
(See address above.)

TOURISM CARES [2348]

275 Turnpike Street
Suite 307
Canton, MA 02021
(781) 821-5990 ext. 208
Fax: (781) 821-8949

E-MAIL ADDRESS:
carolynv@tourismcares.org

WEB SITE ADDRESS:
www.tourismcares.org/grants

FOUNDED: 2005

AREAS OF INTEREST:
Travel and tourism; hospitality; sustainable tourism; conservation, preservation or restoration; cultural heritage tourism; responsible tourism; educational programs and interpretive programs.

NAME(S) OF PROGRAMS:
● **Worldwide Grant Program**

TYPE:
Project/program grants. Grants to nonprofit, tax-exempt organizations.

As part of its mission, Tourism Cares distributes charitable grants to worthy tourism-related 501(c)(3) nonprofit organizations worldwide to conserve, preserve or restore sites of exceptional cultural, historic or natural significance. The program goals call for a balanced distribution to U.S. and non-U.S. recipients.

YEAR PROGRAM STARTED: 1999

PURPOSE:
To benefit society by preserving the travel experience for future generations by awarding academic, professional, and service-learning scholarships to students of travel, tourism, and hospitality; by giving grants to cultural, historic and natural tourism-related sites worldwide; and by organizing volunteer efforts to clean up and restore tourism-related sites in need of care and rejuvenation.

LEGAL BASIS:
Nonprofit, tax-exempt 501(c)(3) public charity.

ELIGIBILITY:
Grant recipients must be organizations classified as nonprofit and tax-exempt under Section 501(c)(3) of the U.S. Internal Revenue Code or, in the case of non-U.S. organizations, must function as the equivalent. Site must be a cultural, historic or natural tourism-related site of exceptional significance. The project or program must be "brick-and-mortar" capital improvements or educational programs that enhance the way the site is interpreted.

FINANCIAL DATA:
Amount of support per award: Typical grants are $10,000.

Total amount of support: Since their inception, the economic impact of the Tourism Cares grant programs, when combined with matching funds, totals more than $2,000,000.

Matching fund requirements: Preference is given to projects or programs with secured matching or challenge-grant funding from a source external to one's organization at the time of the grant request, but it is not a requirement.

NUMBER OF AWARDS: Varies.

APPLICATION INFORMATION:
Detailed application information can be obtained online.
Duration: 12 months.
Deadline: May vary; detailed information is available at the web site.

PUBLICATIONS:
e-newsletter.

IRS IDENTIFICATION NUMBER: 20-2013457

ADDRESS INQUIRIES TO:
Tourism Cares Grants Department
E-mail: grants@tourismcares.org

TOWN CREEK FOUNDATION, INC.   [2349]
121 North West Street
Easton, MD 21601
(410) 763-8171
Fax: (410) 763-8172

E-MAIL ADDRESS:
info@towncreekfdn.org

WEB SITE ADDRESS:
www.towncreekfdn.org

FOUNDED: 1981

AREAS OF INTEREST:
The environment and climate change.

TYPE:
General operating grants; Project/program grants.

YEAR PROGRAM STARTED: 1981

PURPOSE:
To seek a healthy natural and sustainable environment, through public education, citizen action and advocacy.

LEGAL BASIS:
Private, tax-exempt foundation.

ELIGIBILITY:
501(c)(3) tax-exempt organizations are eligible for support. The Foundation does not make grants to individuals, organizations considered to be "private foundations," primary and secondary schools, hospitals or health care institutions, religious organizations or capital and building fund campaigns. It does not make grants to colleges or universities except when some aspect of their work is an integral part of a program supported by the Foundation. It does not fund research, scholarship programs, conferences not part of a program supported by the Foundation, or publication of books and periodicals, or visual or performing arts.

GEOGRAPHIC RESTRICTIONS:
United States. Environmental focus: Mid-Atlantic region.

FINANCIAL DATA:
Amount of support per award: Average: $40,000 to $50,000.

Total amount of support: $2,181,000 for the year 2010.

NUMBER OF AWARDS: 50 for the year 2009.

REPRESENTATIVE AWARDS:
$40,000 to Apollo Alliance; $100,000 to Chesapeake Bay Foundation; $75,000 to Living on Earth.

APPLICATION INFORMATION:
Online application preferred. Guidelines are available online.
Duration: One year.
Deadline: Fall: Letter of Intent/Inquiry: November. Invited Proposals: December.

Spring: Letter of Intent/Inquiry: March. Invited Proposals: April.

IRS IDENTIFICATION NUMBER: 52-1227030

TRUSTEES AND OFFICERS:
Jennifer Stanley, President
Lisa A. Stanley, Vice President
Philip E.L. Dietz, Jr., Secretary and Treasurer

Donald Boesch
Betsy Taylor

ADDRESS INQUIRIES TO:
Cheryl Lee, Office Manager
(See address above.)

*PLEASE NOTE:
Letters of Inquiry should be submitted online.

U.S. DEPARTMENT OF AGRICULTURE   [2350]
1400 Independence Avenue, S.W.
Stop 0513
Washington, DC 20250-0510
(202) 720-6221
Fax: (202) 720-4619

E-MAIL ADDRESS:
robertstephenson@wdc.usda.gov

WEB SITE ADDRESS:
www.fsa.usda.gov

FOUNDED: 1933

AREAS OF INTEREST:
The conservation of the nation's soil, forest and water resources.

CONSULTING OR VOLUNTEER SERVICES:
Technical assistance is provided by federal and state agencies cooperating with this program.

NAME(S) OF PROGRAMS:
● **Emergency Conservation Program (ECP)**

TYPE:
Grants-in-aid. Cost-share assistance with agricultural producers to rehabilitate agricultural lands damaged by natural disasters. Assistance may also be provided for carrying out emergency water conservation measures during periods of severe drought.

YEAR PROGRAM STARTED: 1957

PURPOSE:
To provide assistance in restoring agricultural lands to their pre-disaster condition; to provide emergency water conservation measures where the producer is unable to do so without federal assistance.

LEGAL BASIS:
Government agency, authorized by P.L. 95-334, August 1978.

ELIGIBILITY:
Applicants are limited to agricultural producers, such as owners, landlords, tenants or sharecroppers of farms or ranches used to produce grains, row crops, livestock, vegetables, hay, orchards, vineyards, seed crops or other agricultural commodities commercially.

All landowners, regardless of race, sex, religion, marital status, disability, color, age or national origin, may apply for cost-sharing.

GEOGRAPHIC RESTRICTIONS:
United States.

FINANCIAL DATA:
Subject to periodic (usually annual) appropriations by Congress.

Amount of support per award: Maximum of $200,000 per person per disaster.

Matching fund requirements: Producers are required to contribute the difference between the cost-share amount and the total cost of each ECP practice.

ADDRESS INQUIRIES TO:
Contact the nearest FSA County Office where your land is located.

U.S. ENVIRONMENTAL PROTECTION AGENCY [2351]

Office of Enforcement and Compliance Assurance (2225A)
1200 Pennsylvania Avenue, N.W.
Washington, DC 20460
(202) 564-4147
Fax: (202) 564-0085

E-MAIL ADDRESS:
havinga.al@epa.gov

WEB SITE ADDRESS:
www.epa.gov/compliance/state/grants/fifra.html

FOUNDED: 1970

AREAS OF INTEREST:
Pesticides enforcement.

NAME(S) OF PROGRAMS:
- **Pesticide Enforcement Cooperative Agreements**

TYPE:
Grants-in-aid; Project/program grants.

YEAR PROGRAM STARTED: 1977

PURPOSE:
To develop and maintain comprehensive pesticide programs that address all aspects of pesticide enforcement and special pesticide initiatives; to sponsor cooperative surveillance monitoring and analytical procedures; to encourage regulatory activities within the states and tribes.

LEGAL BASIS:
Federal Insecticide, Fungicide and Rodenticide Act, as amended; P.L. 92-516; 7 U.S.C. 136 et seq. as amended by P.L. 94-140, Section 23(a) and 95-396.

ELIGIBILITY:
State agencies having pesticide enforcement responsibilities in each state, territory and possession of the U.S., including the District of Columbia and Indian tribes.

The applicant must supply evidence of legal authority to conduct pesticide enforcement activities and a workable program adopted for the agency.

Each application will be reviewed according to the following criteria:
(1) the need for the development, improvement and/or maintenance of a comprehensive pesticides enforcement program within the state;
(2) the relative amount of pesticide production, formulation and use in the state and the potential risk to human health and the environment from pesticide misuse or abuse;
(3) the potential of the cooperative agreement to have a long-term beneficial impact on human health and the environment resulting from the comprehensive enforcement program and;
(4) the past level and effectiveness of the state pesticide regulatory program.

FINANCIAL DATA:
Amount of support per award: Varies by state, territory and tribe.
Matching fund requirements: 15% state match.

NUMBER OF AWARDS: Approximately 78.

APPLICATION INFORMATION:
It is advisable to preapply by having an informal meeting with the regional program office concerning program preparation. Prior to approval of any grants, the official State Pesticides Regulatory Agency must coordinate local pesticide enforcement efforts. The standard application forms furnished by the federal agency and OMB Circular No. A-102 must be used for this program. Completed applications and other required forms should be submitted to the appropriate EPA Regional Office.
Duration: Usually 12 months.

ADDRESS INQUIRIES TO:
Al Havinga
(See address above.)

U.S. ENVIRONMENTAL PROTECTION AGENCY [2352]

Office of Superfund Remediation and Technology Innovation (5203P)
1200 Pennsylvania Avenue, N.W.
Washington, DC 20460
(703) 603-8835

E-MAIL ADDRESS:
singer.yolanda@epamail.epa.gov

WEB SITE ADDRESS:
www.epa.gov/superfund

FOUNDED: 1970

AREAS OF INTEREST:
Cleanup of hazardous waste releases into the environment.

NAME(S) OF PROGRAMS:
- **Hazardous Substance Response Trust Fund**

TYPE:
Project/program grants. Cooperative agreements to eligible states, tribes or local governments to help investigate, study and clean up uncontrolled hazardous waste sites as listed in the National Priorities List (40 CFR 300).

YEAR PROGRAM STARTED: 1981

PURPOSE:
To undertake removal actions at NPL and non-NPL sites to protect the public from the release of hazardous materials; to conduct preremedial activities to determine if sites require listing on the NPL; to perform remedial planning and remedial implementation actions in response to releases on the NPL; to clean up the hazardous waste sites that are found to pose the most imminent threat to human health; to support state involvement in the Superfund program.

LEGAL BASIS:
Comprehensive Environmental Response, Compensation and Liability Act of 1980 (Superfund) (P.L. 96-510), as amended by The Superfund Amendments and Reauthorization Act of 1986 (SARA) (P.L. 99-499), The Small Business Liability Relief and Brown Fields Revitalization Act (PL 107-118).

ELIGIBILITY:
States (and political subdivisions thereof), commonwealths, U.S. territories and possessions, and federally recognized Indian tribal governments, including intertribal consortia.

For remedial site planning, implementation and cleanup assistance, the site must appear on the National Priorities List of the National

Oil and Hazardous Substances Contingency Plan, where each is ranked in priority. Each project is examined and selected on a case-by-case basis depending on the site ranking, the availability of matching funds from the state, the availability of Trust funds, receipt of application and other criteria as determined by the EPA.

GEOGRAPHIC RESTRICTIONS:
United States and its territories, tribes and political subdivisions.

FINANCIAL DATA:
Amount of support per award: $1,000 to $80,000,000. Average $2,000,000. Median $200,000.
Total amount of support: Estimated $60,000,000 for fiscal year 2010.
Matching fund requirements: If the site was privately operated at the time of disposal, the state must share 10% of the costs for remedial action and the remaining 90% will be provided by the Fund. If the site was publicly operated at the time of disposal, the state must supply at least 50% of all response costs at the time of remedial action.

APPLICATION INFORMATION:
Applicants must use the standard application forms as furnished by the Federal Government and OMB Circular No. A-102.

ADDRESS INQUIRIES TO:
Yolanda Singer, Environmental Scientist Site Assessment Remedy Decision Branch
(See address above.)

U.S. SOCIETY ON DAMS

1616 17th Street, Suite 483
Denver, CO 80202
(303) 628-5430
Fax: (303) 628-5431

E-MAIL ADDRESS:
stephens@ussdams.org

WEB SITE ADDRESS:
www.ussdams.org

TYPE:
Scholarships.

See entry 2832 for full listing.

UNIVERSITY OF PITTSBURGH [2353]

Pymatuning Laboratory of Ecology
13142 Hartstown Road
Linesville, PA 16424
(814) 683-5813
Fax: (814) 683-2302

E-MAIL ADDRESS:
pymlab@pitt.edu

WEB SITE ADDRESS:
www.pitt.edu/~biology/pymatuning.htm

FOUNDED: 1949

AREAS OF INTEREST:
Ecology research.

NAME(S) OF PROGRAMS:
- **Leasure K. Darbaker Prize in Botany**
- **McKinley Research Fund**
- **Pape Research Fund**

TYPE:
Research grants. The Leasure K. Darbaker Prize in Botany is an annual award available for support of botanically related studies at the graduate or postdoctoral level.

The G. McKinley Research Fund and the Pape Research Fund of the Pittsburgh Foundation provide grants for support of graduate and postdoctoral research in ecology. Several are awarded each summer.

LEGAL BASIS:
Department of the University of Pittsburgh.

ELIGIBILITY:
Proposals are welcome at all academic graduate and postdoctoral levels for research in any area of ecology.

Awards are granted for work to be carried out at the facility in northwestern Pennsylvania.

FINANCIAL DATA:
Funds for travel, equipment, supplies, assistants and room and board at the laboratory may be included.
Amount of support per award: Darbaker Prize: $1,000 to $1,200; McKinley and Pape: Up to $3,000.

APPLICATION INFORMATION:
Application information can be found at the web site.
Deadline: February 7.

PUBLICATIONS:
Application guidelines.

ADDRESS INQUIRIES TO:
Dr. Rick Relyea, Director
(See address above.)

THE UNIVERSITY OF SYDNEY   [2354]
Scholarships Office
Level 5, Jane Foss Russell Building G02
The University of Sydney N.S.W. 2006
Australia
(02) 8627 8112
Fax: (02) 8627 8145

E-MAIL ADDRESS:
research.training@sydney.edu.au

WEB SITE ADDRESS:
www.sydney.edu.au/scholarships/research

FOUNDED: 1850

AREAS OF INTEREST:
Water conservation.

NAME(S) OF PROGRAMS:
● **Richard Claude Mankin Scholarship**

TYPE:
Scholarships. Postdoctoral award for research and postgraduate for research leading to a higher degree. Tenable at the University of Sydney.

YEAR PROGRAM STARTED: 1973

PURPOSE:
To promote research related to water conservation at the University of Sydney.

LEGAL BASIS:
University.

ELIGIBILITY:
Candidates may be of postgraduate or postdoctoral standing at the University of Sydney.

FINANCIAL DATA:
The scholarship does not cover tuition fees payable by international students.
Amount of support per award: $22,860 AUD per annum for the year 2011.

NUMBER OF AWARDS: 1 offered as vacancy occurs and funds are available.

APPLICATION INFORMATION:
Duration: Two years for Master's candidate. Up to three and one-half years for Ph.D. candidate.
Deadline: First week in January and first week in July.

VIRGINIA ENVIRONMENTAL ENDOWMENT   [2355]
3 James Center
1051 East Cary Street, Suite 1400
Richmond, VA 23219
(804) 644-5000
Fax: (804) 644-0603

E-MAIL ADDRESS:
info@vee.org

WEB SITE ADDRESS:
www.vee.org

FOUNDED: 1977

AREAS OF INTEREST:
Environmental improvement.

NAME(S) OF PROGRAMS:
● **Kanawha and Ohio River Valleys Program**
● **Virginia Mini-Grant Program**
● **Virginia Program**

TYPE:
Challenge/matching grants; Demonstration grants; Project/program grants; Research grants; Seed money grants; Research contracts. Provides grants to projects that demonstrate feasibility, innovation and appropriateness to the Endowment's purpose and priorities. Improvement of the quality of the environment in the Commonwealth of Virginia, especially water quality research and monitoring; land conservation; Chesapeake Bay conservation, research and education; and environmental education. Programs addressing water quality and the effects of water pollution on public health and the environment in the Kanawha River and Ohio River valleys of Kentucky and West Virginia.

YEAR PROGRAM STARTED: 1977

PURPOSE:
To improve the quality of the environment by using its capital to encourage all sectors to work together to prevent pollution, conserve natural resources and promote environmental literacy.

LEGAL BASIS:
Tax-exempt, grantmaking organization 501(c)(4).

ELIGIBILITY:
The Endowment makes grants to nonprofit, tax-exempt, charitable organizations and institutions as well as to governmental agencies. It encourages requests for specific projects that promise measurable results to improve the environment. Applicants should describe specifically how they propose to measure the success of a grant project. Grant funds are not provided for general support, overhead, indirect costs, capital projects, land purchases, building construction or renovation, endowments, lawsuits or to individuals.

GEOGRAPHIC RESTRICTIONS:
The state of Virginia and the Kanawha and Ohio River valleys of Kentucky and West Virginia.

FINANCIAL DATA:
Reviewed asset value: $15,094,703 as of March 31, 2010.
Amount of support per award: Varies.
Total amount of support: $247,951 for fiscal year ended March 31, 2010.
Matching fund requirements: At least a 1:1 match is normally required.

COOPERATIVE FUNDING PROGRAMS: The Endowment welcomes opportunities for collaboration.

NUMBER OF APPLICANTS MOST RECENT YEAR: 63.

NUMBER OF AWARDS: 26 for fiscal year ended March 31, 2010.

REPRESENTATIVE AWARDS:
$43,461 to University of Virginia, Charlottesville, VA, for V-PharmaCalc: A Tool to Predict Influent Pharmaceutical Concentrations to Virginia's Wastewater Treatment Plants, 15-month grant (matched by $70,800); $10,000 to James River Association, Richmond, VA, for Upper James River Riverkeeper Program (matched by $10,000 from the Campbell Foundation); $10,000 to Wetlands Watch, Inc., Norfolk, VA, for Adapting to Climate Change in Virginia (matched by $25,000).

APPLICATION INFORMATION:
Two copies of the complete proposal, signed by the organization's chief executive officer or board chairman, must be received by the deadline date. The Endowment does not review or comment on preliminary proposals. Applicants to the Virginia Mini-Grant Program should review the special guidelines and application materials for the Mini-Grant Program on the web site.

Each proposal must include the following information:
(1) a cover letter identifying the applicant, project title, grant request, matching funds, project schedule, and whether the proposal is being submitted to the Virginia Program, the Virginia Mini-Grant Program, or the Kanawha and Ohio River Valleys Program;
(2) a project description, limited to five pages, clearly stating the need for the project, goals and objectives and how they will be achieved, how project results will be measured, and relationship to other work being done in the field;
(3) a description of the organization, names and qualifications of key project staff, a list of the members of the governing board, the current operating budget, and a copy of the current tax-exempt ruling from the IRS, if applicable;
(4) a line-item budget for the proposed project showing total project costs, the amount and proposed allocation of grant funds requested from the Endowment, and all sources and amounts of matching funds, which must equal or exceed the requested grant;
(5) the project schedule, with specific beginning and ending dates for requested grant support and;
(6) a detailed plan for evaluating and disseminating project results, for continuing project activities, and for raising future financial support.

Proposals may not be submitted by facsimile or by e-mail.

For delivery by U.S. Mail, address to Gerald P. McCarthy, Executive Director, Virginia Environmental Endowment, P.O. Box 790, Richmond, VA 23218-0790. Package delivery goes to Gerald P. McCarthy, at the street address above.

Duration: Stipulated with specific projects. One year preferred.

Deadline: Kanawha and Ohio River Valleys Program: June 15; Virginia Program and Virginia Mini-Grant Program: June 15 and December 1. Proposals must be received by 5 P.M. (E.S.T.). Postmark date is not acceptable. Board decisions about proposals are normally made in April and October.

PUBLICATIONS:
Annual report, including guidelines.

IRS IDENTIFICATION NUMBER: 54-1041973

OFFICERS:
Dixon M. Butler, President
Robert B. Smith, Jr., Senior Vice President
Paul U. Elbling, Treasurer
Gerald P. McCarthy, Secretary

STAFF:
Gerald P. McCarthy, Executive Director

DIRECTORS:
Robin D. Baliles
Dixon M. Butler
William B. Cummings
Paul U. Elbling
Landon Hilliard
Anna L. Lawson
Frances A. Lewis
Nina Randolph
Robert B. Smith, Jr.

ADDRESS INQUIRIES TO:
Gerald P. McCarthy, Executive Director
(See address above.)

*SPECIAL STIPULATIONS:
No preliminary proposal reviews are provided; full proposals are required.

WEEDEN FOUNDATION [2356]
747 Third Avenue, 34th Floor
New York, NY 10017
(212) 888-1672
Fax: (212) 888-1354

E-MAIL ADDRESS:
weedenfdn@weedenfdn.org

WEB SITE ADDRESS:
www.weedenfdn.org

FOUNDED: 1963

AREAS OF INTEREST:
Biodiversity, population and environment, natural resource conservation and consumption.

NAME(S) OF PROGRAMS:
- **Consumption**
- **Domestic Biodiversity**
- **International Biodiversity**
- **Population**

TYPE:
General operating grants; Project/program grants.

YEAR PROGRAM STARTED: 1963

PURPOSE:
To address the adverse impact of exploding human population and overuse of natural resources on the biological fabric of the planet.

LEGAL BASIS:
Nonprofit, family foundation.

ELIGIBILITY:
Applicants must be nonprofit, tax-exempt organizations with 501(c)(3) status or international equivalent.

GEOGRAPHIC RESTRICTIONS:
Bolivia, Central Siberia, Chile and the Pacific Northwest.

FINANCIAL DATA:
Amount of support per award: Average: $15,000 to $25,000.
Total amount of support: Varies.

REPRESENTATIVE AWARDS:
$20,000 to IPAS; $20,000 to Center for a New American Dream; $20,000 to Forest Ethics; $20,000 to Natural Trails and Waters Coalition.

APPLICATION INFORMATION:
Applicants should submit a letter of inquiry, and the Foundation will request a full proposal, if interested.
Duration: One year. Renewal possible.
Deadline: Varies.

IRS IDENTIFICATION NUMBER: 94-6109313

STAFF:
Donald A. Weeden, Executive Director
Charmayne Palomba, Research Assistant

BOARD OF DIRECTORS:
Norm Weeden, Ph.D., President
John D. Weeden, Secretary and Treasurer
David Davies
Christina Roux
Alan Weeden
Donald E. Weeden
Leslie Weeden
William Weeden

ADDRESS INQUIRIES TO:
Donald A. Weeden, Executive Director
(See address above.)

WEGE FOUNDATION
P.O. Box 6388
Grand Rapids, MI 49516-6388
(616) 957-0480
Fax: (616) 957-0616

E-MAIL ADDRESS:
tmccarthy@wegefoundation.org

WEB SITE ADDRESS:
www.wegefoundation.org

TYPE:
Capital grants; Challenge/matching grants; Endowments; General operating grants; Internships; Matching gifts; Project/program grants; Scholarships.

See entry 432 for full listing.

THE WILDLIFE CONSERVATION SOCIETY [2357]
2300 Southern Boulevard
Bronx, NY 10460
(718) 220-5100
Fax: (718) 364-4275

E-MAIL ADDRESS:
fellowship@wcs.org

WEB SITE ADDRESS:
programs.wcs.org/grants
www.wcs.org

FOUNDED: 1895

AREAS OF INTEREST:
Wildlife conservation, wildlands, communities, threatened wildlife and ecosystems.

NAME(S) OF PROGRAMS:
- **Research Fellowship Program**

TYPE:
Awards/prizes; Fellowships; Project/program grants; Research grants. Awards small grants to field research projects leading to the conservation of threatened wildlife and wildlife habitat.

YEAR PROGRAM STARTED: 1993

PURPOSE:
To support individual research projects that lead to concrete advances in the understanding and conservation of wildlife or wildlands.

LEGAL BASIS:
Nonprofit organization.

ELIGIBILITY:
Project must demonstrate strong scientific merit, as well as direct relevance to wildlife conservation. No support for conferences, travel to scientific meetings, legal actions, construction of permanent field stations, tuition, salaries, overhead costs, major laboratory expenses, gene storage, vehicle purchase, captive breeding, or computer equipment. Stipends are not funded; however, investigators who have no other source of support may receive modest living expenses. Faculty and/or research advisors should not be listed as a principal investigator unless they plan to carry out the majority of the field work.

The program supports marine or terrestrial field research in Africa, Asia, and Latin America (including Mexico). While all applications to work in Asian, African, and Latin American countries are currently considered, the Society encourages applications from nationals from the following countries: Algeria, Argentina, Azerbaijan, Bolivia, Brazil, China, Colombia, Egypt, Georgia, India, Indonesia, Libya, Malaysia, Pakistan, Russia, Trinidad and Tobago, Turkey and Venezuela. Proposals are accepted for research in North America only from Native Americans and First Nation people. Must conduct work on Native lands or on issues of direct relevance to wildlife or on species governed by treated intertribal agreement.

FINANCIAL DATA:
Amount of support per award: $1,000 to $25,000. Average: $10,655.

APPLICATION INFORMATION:
Proposals can be submitted in English, Spanish or French, but the coversheet and abstract must be in English. Application and procedures are available online.
Duration: One year.
Deadline: March 15 and September 15. Final decisions are announced at the end of June and December.

PUBLICATIONS:
Application guidelines.

THE DEAN WITTER FOUNDATION
57 Post Street, Suite 510
San Francisco, CA 94104
(415) 981-2966
Fax: (415) 981-5218

E-MAIL ADDRESS:
admin@deanwitterfoundation.org

WEB SITE ADDRESS:
www.deanwitterfoundation.org

TYPE:
Challenge/matching grants; Fellowships; General operating grants; Internships;

Matching gifts; Professorships; Project/program grants; Research grants; Scholarships; Seed money grants.

See entry 2042 for full listing.

Medicine (multiple disciplines)

A-T CHILDREN'S PROJECT [2358]

5300 West Hillsboro Boulevard
Suite 105
Coconut Creek, FL 33073
(954) 481-6611
Fax: (954) 725-1153

E-MAIL ADDRESS:
grants@atcp.org
info@atcp.org

WEB SITE ADDRESS:
www.atcp.org

FOUNDED: 1993

AREAS OF INTEREST:
Research in the area of ATM (ataxia-telangiectasia mutated) biology.

TYPE:
Research grants.

YEAR PROGRAM STARTED: 1993

PURPOSE:
To accelerate first-rate, international scientific research in the area of ATM (ataxia-telangiectasia mutated) biology, especially ATM neurobiology; to help find a cure or life-improving treatments for children with ataxia-telangiectasia.

ELIGIBILITY:
Open to all ages and nationalities. Proposal for grant must have direct relevance to ataxia-telangiectasia.

FINANCIAL DATA:
Amount of support per award: Up to $75,000 per year.
Total amount of support: Varies.

APPLICATION INFORMATION:
A Letter of Intent is not required. However, prior to submission of a full-length proposal, applicants seeking Scientific Advisory Board input may submit a Letter of Intent directly to the Science Coordinator at cynthia@atcp.org. This letter, not to exceed two pages, should include a brief abstract describing the proposed research, specific aims and an estimated budget.

Applicants must submit an electronic copy of their proposal in either MSWord or PDF formats to grants@atcp.org. Also submit three copies to Dr. Cynthia Rothblum-Oviatt, Science Coordinator, at the address above.

Duration: One to two years.
Deadline: September 1 and March 1 of each calendar year.

ADDRESS INQUIRIES TO:
Dr. Cynthia Rothblum-Oviatt
Science Coordinator
E-mail: cynthia@atcp.org

ALBERTA INNOVATES HEALTH SOLUTIONS [2359]

Suite 1500
10104 - 103 Avenue, N.W.
Edmonton AB T5J 4A7 Canada
(780) 423-5727
Fax: (780) 429-3509

E-MAIL ADDRESS:
health@albertainnovates.ca

WEB SITE ADDRESS:
www.ahfmr.ab.ca
www.albertainnovates.ca

FOUNDED: 1980

AREAS OF INTEREST:
Supporting biomedical and health research at Alberta universities, affiliated institutions, and other medical and technology-related institutions.

NAME(S) OF PROGRAMS:
- **Clinical Fellowship**
- **Community Health Research Travel Grant**
- **Community Health Research Visiting Lecturer Award**
- **Conferences and Symposia**
- **Fast-track Fellowship**
- **Fast-track Studentship**
- **Forefront Internship Program**
- **Full-Time Fellowship**
- **Full-Time Studentship**
- **Health Research Career Renewal Award**
- **Health Research Full-Time Studentship**
- **Heritage Visiting Professorship**
- **Heritage Visiting Scientists (to or from Alberta)**
- **HYRS Program**
- **Interdisciplinary Team Grant**
- **Local Workshop, Retreat or Planning Session**
- **M.D./Ph.D. Studentship**
- **MBT/MBA Studentship Awards**
- **Part-Time Fellowship**
- **Part-Time Studentship**
- **Special Initiatives**
- **Summer Studentship**

TYPE:
Assistantships; Awards/prizes; Block grants; Capital grants; Challenge/matching grants; Conferences/seminars; Development grants; Fellowships; General operating grants; Grants-in-aid; Internships; Matching gifts; Product donations; Professorships; Project/program grants; Research grants; Residencies; Scholarships; Seed money grants; Technical assistance; Training grants; Travel grants; Visiting scholars; Research contracts. Interdisciplinary team grants. Awards for personnel support, equipment purchase, conferences and workshops.

YEAR PROGRAM STARTED: 1980

PURPOSE:
To promote research in medical and health sciences and implement means of using the scientific resources of the medical sciences in Alberta.

LEGAL BASIS:
Funding agency created by an act of the Alberta legislature.

ELIGIBILITY:
Most awards tenable only in Alberta.

GEOGRAPHIC RESTRICTIONS:
Alberta.

FINANCIAL DATA:
Grants are made on a year-round basis from interest revenue earned on an original endowment of $300,000,000.
Amount of support per award: Stipulated with individual awards.
Total amount of support: $77,000,000 for the fiscal year 2009-10.
Matching fund requirements: Stipulated with applicable awards.

COOPERATIVE FUNDING PROGRAMS: Alberta Heritage Foundation for Medical Research Endowment Fund.

NUMBER OF AWARDS: Over 800 for the fiscal year 2009-10.

APPLICATION INFORMATION:
Application forms and guidelines are available from the Research Services Offices of Alberta universities and from the Foundation.
Duration: Varies by program.
Deadline: Varies by program.

PUBLICATIONS:
Guidelines for Grants and Awards.

ADDRESS INQUIRIES TO:
Pamela Valentine
Vice President, Programs
(See address above.)

*SPECIAL STIPULATIONS:
Awards are to be held in Alberta, or if held outside Alberta, are to be sponsored by an Alberta university.

THE JOHN W. ALDEN TRUST

c/o Rackemann, Sawyer & Brewster
160 Federal Street, 15th Floor
Boston, MA 02110-1700
(617) 951-1108
Fax: (617) 542-7437

E-MAIL ADDRESS:
smonahan@rackemann.com

WEB SITE ADDRESS:
www.cybergrants.com/alden

TYPE:
Capital grants; Challenge/matching grants; Conferences/seminars; Demonstration grants; Development grants; Matching gifts; Project/program grants; Research grants; Scholarships; Seed money grants; Technical assistance; Training grants. Grants will normally be made for specific projects rather than general operating expenses.

See entry 1171 for full listing.

ALZHEIMER'S DRUG DISCOVERY FOUNDATION [2360]

57 West 57th Street
Suite 904
New York, NY 10019
(212) 901-8000
Fax: (212) 901-8010

E-MAIL ADDRESS:
hfillit@alzdiscovery.org

WEB SITE ADDRESS:
www.alzdiscovery.org

FOUNDED: 2004

AREAS OF INTEREST:
Drug discovery and development for Alzheimer's disease, related dementias and cognitive decline.

NAME(S) OF PROGRAMS:
- **Novel Approaches to Drug Discovery in Alzheimer's Disease**

TYPE:
Awards/prizes; Conferences/seminars; Research grants.

PURPOSE:
To promote the research and development of therapies to identify, treat and prevent cognitive decline, Alzheimer's disease and related dementias.

LEGAL BASIS:
Nonprofit Delaware corporation 501(c)(3) public charity.

ELIGIBILITY:
Applicant must be a university medical center or early-stage biotechnology company.

FINANCIAL DATA:
Amount of support per award: $150,000 to $300,000 per year.
Total amount of support: Varies.

NUMBER OF APPLICANTS MOST RECENT YEAR: 250.

NUMBER OF AWARDS: 37.

APPLICATION INFORMATION:
Duration: One to two years.
Deadline: Letters of intent accepted on an ongoing basis. Applications due quarterly.

ADDRESS INQUIRIES TO:
Adam Liebling, Senior Grants Manager
(See address above.)

AMERICAN ACADEMY OF FACIAL PLASTIC AND RECONSTRUCTIVE SURGERY (AAFPRS) [2361]

Educational and Research Foundation
for the AAFPRS
310 South Henry Street
Alexandria, VA 22314
(703) 299-9291
Fax: (703) 299-8898

E-MAIL ADDRESS:
matkins@aafprs.org

WEB SITE ADDRESS:
www.aafprs.org

FOUNDED: 1964

AREAS OF INTEREST:
Physician education in cosmetic and reconstructive surgery of the face, head and neck.

CONSULTING OR VOLUNTEER SERVICES:
Combined Otolaryngology Research Efforts (C.O.R.E.).

NAME(S) OF PROGRAMS:
● **Leslie Bernstein Resident Research Grants**

TYPE:
Research grants; Seed money grants. Cash award toward research by a resident member in facial plastic and reconstructive surgery.

YEAR PROGRAM STARTED: 1983

PURPOSE:
To stimulate resident research in projects that are well conceived and scientifically valid.

LEGAL BASIS:
Professional association of independent members.

ELIGIBILITY:
Applicant must be an AAFPRS member. Residents at any level may apply, even if the research work will be done during their fellowship year.

FINANCIAL DATA:
Grant money must be used for direct costs; only 10% of monies can be used for indirect cost.
Amount of support per award: $5,000.
Total amount of support: $10,000.

NUMBER OF APPLICANTS MOST RECENT YEAR:
12 for the year 2010.

NUMBER OF AWARDS: Up to 2.

APPLICATION INFORMATION:
Applicants must submit a letter of intent. Guidelines are available from AAFPRS.
Duration: One to two years.
Deadline: December 15. Announcement in August.

PUBLICATIONS:
Guidelines; application form.

IRS IDENTIFICATION NUMBER: 36-2952891

ADDRESS INQUIRIES TO:
Maria Atkins
Manager, Membership Services
(See address above.)

*SPECIAL STIPULATIONS:
All applicants are required to have sponsorship and oversight of the department chair or by an AAFPRS member as mentor. Applications must be submitted through C.O.R.E.

AMERICAN ACADEMY OF FACIAL PLASTIC AND RECONSTRUCTIVE SURGERY (AAFPRS) [2362]

Educational and Research Foundation
for the AAFPRS
310 South Henry Street
Alexandria, VA 22314
(703) 299-9291
Fax: (703) 299-8898

E-MAIL ADDRESS:
matkins@aafprs.org

WEB SITE ADDRESS:
www.aafprs.org

FOUNDED: 1964

AREAS OF INTEREST:
Physician education in cosmetic and reconstructive surgery of the face, head and neck.

CONSULTING OR VOLUNTEER SERVICES:
Combined Otolaryngology Research Efforts (C.O.R.E.).

NAME(S) OF PROGRAMS:
● **Leslie Bernstein Investigator Development Grant**

TYPE:
Project/program grants; Research grants; Seed money grants. Support for the work of a young faculty member conducting significant clinical or laboratory research in facial plastic surgery and training resident surgeons in research. Funded by a donation from Leslie Bernstein, M.D., D.D.S., to the AAFPRS Foundation.

YEAR PROGRAM STARTED: 1983

PURPOSE:
To support work of a young faculty member in Facial Plastic Surgery conducting significant clinical or laboratory research and involved in the training of resident surgeons in research.

LEGAL BASIS:
Professional association of independent members.

ELIGIBILITY:
Applicants must be Academy members. Research proposals are subject to the following conditions:
(1) a sponsor, either an Academy Fellow or the investigator's department chairman, is required;
(2) the parent institution must provide professional support and;
(3) the research plan must incorporate a resident or residents in the research activities.

FINANCIAL DATA:
Grant monies must be used for direct costs; only 10% can be used for indirect cost.
Amount of support per award: $15,000.
Total amount of support: $15,000.

NUMBER OF APPLICANTS MOST RECENT YEAR: 2 for the year 2010.

NUMBER OF AWARDS: 1 for the year 2010.

APPLICATION INFORMATION:
Applicants must submit a letter of intent. The official entry form must be completed and submitted with the proposal. Failure to comply with the particular requirements and format outlined in the guidelines may result in disqualification.
Duration: Three years.
Deadline: December 15 each year. Announcement in August.

PUBLICATIONS:
Grants and awards brochure.

IRS IDENTIFICATION NUMBER: 36-2952891

ADDRESS INQUIRIES TO:
Maria Atkins
Manager, Membership Services
(See address above.)

*SPECIAL STIPULATIONS:
Applications must be submitted through C.O.R.E.

AMERICAN ACADEMY OF FACIAL PLASTIC AND RECONSTRUCTIVE SURGERY (AAFPRS) [2363]

Educational and Research Foundation
for the AAFPRS
310 South Henry Street
Alexandria, VA 22314
(703) 299-9291
Fax: (703) 299-8898

E-MAIL ADDRESS:
matkins@aafprs.org

WEB SITE ADDRESS:
www.aafprs.org

FOUNDED: 1964

AREAS OF INTEREST:
Physician education in cosmetic and reconstructive surgery of the face, head and neck.

CONSULTING OR VOLUNTEER SERVICES:
Combined Otolaryngology Research Efforts (C.O.R.E.).

NAME(S) OF PROGRAMS:
● **Leslie Bernstein Research Grant**

TYPE:
Project/program grants; Research grants; Seed money grants. Research award for Academy members, funded by income from a donation by Leslie Bernstein, M.D., D.D.S., to the Academy's Foundation.

YEAR PROGRAM STARTED: 1988

PURPOSE:
To encourage original research projects which will advance facial plastic and reconstructive surgery.

LEGAL BASIS:
Professional association of independent members.

ELIGIBILITY:
Applicants must be AAFPRS members undertaking research that will advance facial plastic and reconstructive surgery. The primary criteria are that the research be original and have direct application to facial plastic surgery.

FINANCIAL DATA:
Grants may be used as seed money for research projects.
Amount of support per award: $25,000.
Total amount of support: $25,000.

NUMBER OF AWARDS: 1.

APPLICATION INFORMATION:
Proposals should be typed (double-spaced) and include the following information:
(1) investigator's curriculum vitae;
(2) brief statement of the specific aims of the investigator's research project, not to exceed 150 words;
(3) brief review of the significance of the work performed by the investigator and/or others, not to exceed two pages;
(4) a detailed description of research procedures including the experimental design, justification of sample size, outcome measures and methods of analysis including justification of each item;
(5) budget for the research award;
(6) description of facilities;
(7) certification of institutional conformity to the U.S. Government Guidelines for Human and Animal Experimentation and;
(8) application must be submitted through C.O.R.E. program.
Duration: Three years.
Deadline: December 15 for review. Announcement in August.

PUBLICATIONS:
Grants and awards brochure.

IRS IDENTIFICATION NUMBER: 36-2952891

ADDRESS INQUIRIES TO:
Maria Atkins
Manager, Membership Services
(See address above.)

AMERICAN ACADEMY OF FACIAL PLASTIC AND RECONSTRUCTIVE SURGERY (AAFPRS) [2364]

Educational and Research Foundation for the AAFPRS
310 South Henry Street
Alexandria, VA 22314
(703) 299-9291 ext. 234
Fax: (703) 299-8898

E-MAIL ADDRESS:
aholton@aafprs.org

WEB SITE ADDRESS:
www.aafprs.org

AREAS OF INTEREST:
Facial plastic and reconstructive surgery.

NAME(S) OF PROGRAMS:
- **Community Service Award**
- **John Dickinson Teacher of the Year Award**
- **Sir Harold Delf Gillies Award**
- **F. Mark Rafaty Memorial Award**
- **Residency Travel Award**
- **John Orlando Roe Award**
- **Ben Shuster Memorial Award**
- **Ira Tresley Research Award**
- **William Wright Award**

TYPE:
Awards/prizes; Fellowships; Travel grants. Community Service Award may be presented annually to an AAFPRS member who has distinguished himself/herself by providing and/or making possible free medical service to the poor in his/her community.

John Dickinson Teacher of the Year Award honors an AAFPRS fellow member for sharing knowledge about facial plastic and reconstructive surgery with the effective use of audiovisuals in any one year.

Sir Harold Delf Gillies Award is presented each year to the graduate fellow who submits the best basic science research paper written during fellowship.

The F. Mark Rafaty Memorial Award may be presented each year to an AAFPRS member who has made outstanding contributions to facial plastic and reconstructive surgery.

The Residency Travel Award is presented to the most outstanding paper in facial plastic and reconstructive surgery, primarily authored by a resident or medical student in training. The paper must be submitted by February 1 for consideration, and to be presented at the Annual Fall Meeting.

The John Orlando Roe Award is presented each year to the graduate fellow who submits the best clinical research paper written during fellowship.

The Ben Shuster Memorial Award is presented for the most outstanding research paper by a resident or fellow in training on any clinical work or research in facial plastic and reconstructive surgery delivered at a national meeting (or its equivalent) between March 1 and the following February 28. Each entrant must be the sole or senior author and an AAFPRS member.

The Ira Tresley Research Award recognizes the best original research in facial plastic surgery by an AAFPRS member who has been board-certified for at least three years. Papers presented at a national meeting (or its equivalent) between March 1 and the following February 28 are eligible for this award.

William Wright Award may be presented each year to an AAFPRS member who has made outstanding contributions to facial plastic and reconstructive surgery.

PURPOSE:
To support research in facial and reconstructive plastic surgery.

LEGAL BASIS:
Foundation.

ELIGIBILITY:
Applicants must be AAFPRS members, except medical students may apply for Resident Travel Award.

GEOGRAPHIC RESTRICTIONS:
United States.

FINANCIAL DATA:
Amount of support per award: $1,000; Residency Travel Award: $500.
Total amount of support: $5,000.

NUMBER OF AWARDS: Residency Travel Award: Up to 2; All others: 1.

APPLICATION INFORMATION:
Contact Foundation for application information.
Deadline: February 1.

PUBLICATIONS:
Application form.

STAFF:
Stephen C. Duffy, Executive Vice President
Ann K. Jenne, Director, Development and Humanitarian Programs
Lisa A. Sarrge, Director of Finance
Rita Chua Magness, Director, Marketing and Publications
Fatima E. Sanders, Manager, Fellowship Programs
Ollie Edwards, Manager, Meetings and Exhibits
Maria Atkins, Manager, Membership Services

ADDRESS INQUIRIES TO:
Michelle Busey, Administrative Assistant
(See address above.)

AMERICAN ACADEMY OF FAMILY PHYSICIANS FOUNDATION [2365]

11400 Tomahawk Creek Parkway
Leawood, KS 66211
(913) 906-6000
Fax: (913) 906-6095

E-MAIL ADDRESS:
pnaragon@aafp.org

WEB SITE ADDRESS:
www.aafpfoundation.org

FOUNDED: 1958

AREAS OF INTEREST:
Family physician practice and training.

NAME(S) OF PROGRAMS:
- **Joint AAFP/F-AAFP Grant Awards Program (JGAP)**
- **Pfizer Teacher Development Award**

TYPE:
Awards/prizes; Research grants; Scholarships; Seed money grants; Training grants. The AAFP/F, through the Joint Grant Awards Program, is primarily interested in supporting research projects conducted by family physicians on topics relevant to family medicine. Funds are available for both formal grant proposals as well as less formal applications for research stimulation studies.

The Pfizer Teacher Development Award provides community-based family physicians who are committed to teaching family medicine part-time a scholarship to attend skill-building opportunities and a stipend for their teaching center.

PURPOSE:
To strengthen research in family medicine.

LEGAL BASIS:
Foundation.

ELIGIBILITY:
The Joint Grant Awards Program seeks proposals requesting grant support for family medicine research. Those eligible to receive a grant include individual family physicians, family medicine organizations or associations, family medicine residency programs, departments of family medicine and educational and health care institutions

or organizations which will use the program support exclusively for research projects directly involving and impacting on family medicine. Examples of activities that will not normally be considered for grant support are designing a curriculum, supporting a seminar, or production of an instructional videotape. At least one investigator on the research team must be a member of AAFP.

For the Pfizer Teacher Development Award, eligible applicants must be AAFP members who are no more than seven years out of family medicine residency and who have entered or plan to enter part-time teaching of family medicine.

GEOGRAPHIC RESTRICTIONS:
Pfizer Teacher Development Award: United States.

FINANCIAL DATA:
Amount of support per award: Varies.

NUMBER OF AWARDS: 12 Joint Grant Awards and 13 Pfizer Teacher Development Awards for the year 2010.

APPLICATION INFORMATION:
All programs require application forms and/or letters of intent.

For the Pfizer Teacher Development Award, applicants must submit an application form and a curriculum vitae, a letter of verification of qualifications from applicant's family practice residency program director, a recommendation letter and reference form from two faculty members of the residency program, either full-time, part-time or voluntary members and a letter of verification from the administration of the program in which the applicant is teaching.
Duration: Varies.
Deadline: Joint Grant Awards: December 1 and June 1; Pfizer Teacher Development Award: May 1.

PUBLICATIONS:
Program announcement; application packet.

OFFICERS:
Richard G. Roberts, M.D., J.D., President
Mary Jo Welker, M.D., Vice President
Craig Doane, Executive Director

STAFF:
Susie Morantz, Senior Manager, Grants and Awards
Sondra Goodman, Grants and Programs Manager

ADDRESS INQUIRIES TO:
Susie Morantz
Senior Manager, Grants and Awards or
Sondra Goodman
Grants and Programs Manager
(See address above.)

AMERICAN AGING ASSOCIATION [2366]
Case Western Reserve University
Department of Pathology
2103 Cornell Road
Room 5125
Cleveland, OH 44106
(216) 368-3671
Fax: (216) 368-8964

E-MAIL ADDRESS:
americanaging@case.edu

WEB SITE ADDRESS:
www.americanaging.org

FOUNDED: 1970

AREAS OF INTEREST:
Biomedical gerontology.

NAME(S) OF PROGRAMS:
● **Paul Glenn Award**
● **Walter Nicolai Award in Biomedical Gerontology**

TYPE:
Awards/prizes; Conferences/seminars; Travel grants. One first prize and one runner-up for each award annually.

Paul Glenn Award: For meritorious research in the area of biomedical gerontology by a postdoctoral fellow.

Walter Nicolai Award: For meritorious basic biologic aging research by a graduate or medical student.

PURPOSE:
To promote biological aging research.

ELIGIBILITY:
Nominees must be graduate or medical students. Each nomination must have a sponsor. A nomination may be made by any member of a society associated with aging research. The sponsor may reside in the U.S., Canada or Mexico.

GEOGRAPHIC RESTRICTIONS:
North America.

FINANCIAL DATA:
Awards include a citation and cash prize.
Amount of support per award: $500 for first place and $250 for each runner-up.
Total amount of support: $1,500 annually.

NUMBER OF AWARDS: 2 for the Glenn Award, 2 for the Nicolai Award.

APPLICATION INFORMATION:
Nominations should include four copies of a six- to 10-page report of the research being nominated, sponsor's letter commenting on the significance of the work and candidate's curriculum vitae with current address.
Duration: One-time award.
Deadline: March 1.

PUBLICATIONS:
AGE, the Journal of the American Aging Association, quarterly; *Age News Quarterly.*

IRS IDENTIFICATION NUMBER: 23-7364654

OFFICERS:
Michael Forster, Ph.D., President
Kevin Perrot, Vice President
Julie Mattison, Ph.D., Secretary

ADDRESS INQUIRIES TO:
Peggy Harris, Business Administrator
(See address above.)

AMERICAN ASSOCIATION FOR HAND SURGERY [2367]
900 Cummings Center
Suite 221-U
Beverly, MA 01915
(978) 927-8330
Fax: (978) 524-8890

E-MAIL ADDRESS:
contact@handsurgery.org

WEB SITE ADDRESS:
www.handsurgery.org

AREAS OF INTEREST:
Hand surgery.

TYPE:
Research grants.

YEAR PROGRAM STARTED: 1970

PURPOSE:
To foster creativity and innovation in basic and/or clinical research in all areas pertinent to hand surgery.

ELIGIBILITY:
Open to residents, fellows, therapists and AAHS members. One of the co-investigators must be an AAHS member.

FINANCIAL DATA:
Amount of support per award: $10,000.

NUMBER OF AWARDS: 1 annually.

APPLICATION INFORMATION:
Applications can be requested from the Central Office or downloaded from the Association's web site.
Deadline: December 1.

AMERICAN COLLEGE OF LEGAL MEDICINE [2368]
1100 East Woodfield Road
Suite 520
Schaumburg, IL 60173-5125
(847) 969-0283
Fax: (847) 517-7229

E-MAIL ADDRESS:
info@aclm.org

WEB SITE ADDRESS:
www.aclm.org

FOUNDED: 1960

AREAS OF INTEREST:
Legal medicine.

NAME(S) OF PROGRAMS:
● **American College of Legal Medicine's Student Writing Competition in Law, Medicine and Bioethics**

TYPE:
Awards/prizes. The Hirsh Award is awarded to a law, dentistry, podiatry, nursing, pharmacy, health science, health care administration, or public health student.

PURPOSE:
To promote interdisciplinary cooperation and an understanding of issues where law and medicine converge.

ELIGIBILITY:
Must be a student at an accredited school of law, medicine, dentistry, podiatry, nursing, pharmacy, health science, health care, administration, or public health that has written an outstanding original paper on Legal Medicine.

FINANCIAL DATA:
Amount of support per award: Hirsh Award: $1,000 first prize, $500 second prize and $250 third prize.
Total amount of support: $1,750.

NUMBER OF AWARDS: 3.

APPLICATION INFORMATION:
Deadline: January 10, 2012. Announcements in August.

ADDRESS INQUIRIES TO:
Sue O'Sullivan, Administrative Director
(See address above.)

AMERICAN FEDERATION FOR AGING RESEARCH (AFAR) [2369]
55 West 39th Street
16th Floor
New York, NY 10018
(212) 703-9977
(888) 582-2327
Fax: (212) 997-0330

E-MAIL ADDRESS:
grants@afar.org

WEB SITE ADDRESS:
www.afar.org

FOUNDED: 1981

AREAS OF INTEREST:
Aging research.

NAME(S) OF PROGRAMS:
- **Rosalinde and Arthur Gilbert Foundation/AFAR New Investigator Awards in Alzheimer's Disease**
- **Julie Martin Mid-Career Awards in Aging Research**

TYPE:
Awards/prizes; Research grants. The Rosalinde and Arthur Gilbert Foundation/AFAR New Investigator Awards in Alzheimer's Disease supports research in areas in which more scientific investigation is needed to improve the prevention, diagnosis and treatment of Alzheimer's Disease.

The Julie Martin Mid-Career Award in Aging Research encourages outstanding midcareer scientists who have not been engaged in aging research but whose research is relevant and could lead to novel approaches to aging.

PURPOSE:
To support basic biomedical research that promotes healthier aging and advances the understanding of the aging process and its associated diseases and disorders; to encourage the training of new scientists and physicians in geriatric research and in the practice of geriatric medicine.

LEGAL BASIS:
Private foundation.

ELIGIBILITY:
Rosalinde and Arthur Gilbert Foundation/AFAR New Investigator Awards in Alzheimer's Disease: Junior faculty in the U.S. and Israel who conduct basic biology of aging research on the earliest precursors of Alzheimer's Disease.

Julie Martin Mid-Career Awards in Aging Research: Outstanding midcareer scientists whose research has the potential for high payoff in advancing the understanding of basic aging.

GEOGRAPHIC RESTRICTIONS:
United States.

FINANCIAL DATA:
Amount of support per award: Rosalinde and Arthur Gilbert Foundation/AFAR New Investigator Awards in Alzheimer's Disease: $75,000; Julie Martin Mid-Career Awards in Aging Research: $550,000.

NUMBER OF AWARDS: Rosalinde and Arthur Gilbert Foundation/AFAR New Investigator Awards in Alzheimer's Disease: Up to 5; Julie Martin Mid-Career Awards in Aging Research: 2.

APPLICATION INFORMATION:
Duration: Rosalinde and Arthur Gilbert Foundation/AFAR New Investigator Awards in Alzheimer's Disease: One to two years; Julie Martin Mid-Career Awards in Aging Research: Four years.

PUBLICATIONS:
Program announcement.

STAFF:
Stephanie Lederman, Executive Director
Nancy O'Leary, Director, Development
Odette van der Willik, Director, Grant Programs

Hattie Herman, Program Officer
Catherine Cullar, Administrative Manager

AMERICAN FEDERATION FOR AGING RESEARCH (AFAR) [2370]

55 West 39th Street
16th Floor
New York, NY 10018
(212) 703-9977
(888) 582-2327
Fax: (212) 997-0330

E-MAIL ADDRESS:
grants@afar.org

WEB SITE ADDRESS:
www.afar.org
www.beeson.org

FOUNDED: 1981

AREAS OF INTEREST:
Biomedical aging research.

NAME(S) OF PROGRAMS:
- **AFAR Research Grants**
- **Paul Beeson Career Development Awards in Aging Research Program**
- **Ellison Medical Foundation/AFAR Postdoctoral Fellows in Aging Research Program**
- **Glenn/AFAR Breakthroughs in Gerontology Awards**
- **Medical Student Training in Aging Research Program (MSTAR)**

TYPE:
Fellowships; Research grants; Scholarships; Training grants. The AFAR Research Grants are given to provide one to two years of support for junior faculty to do research that will serve as the basis for longer-term research efforts.

The Paul Beeson Career Development Awards in Aging Research Program is intended to bolster the current and severe shortage of academic physicians who have the combination of medical, academic and scientific training relative to caring for older people.

Ellison Medical Foundation/AFAR Postdoctoral Fellows in Aging Research Program addresses the current concerns about an adequate funding base for postdoctoral fellows (both M.Ds. and Ph.Ds.) who conduct research in the fundamental mechanisms of aging.

The Glenn/AFAR Breakthroughs in Gerontology Awards are to provide timely support to a small number of pilot research programs that may be of relatively high risk but which offer significant promise of yielding transforming discoveries in the fundamental biology of aging.

Medical Student Training in Aging Research Program (MSTAR) provides medical students, early in their training, with an enriching experience in aging-related research and geriatrics, under the mentorship of top experts in the field. Students participate in an eight- to 12-week structured research, clinical and didactic program in geriatrics.

PURPOSE:
To support basic biomedical research that promotes healthier aging and advances the understanding of the aging process and its associated diseases and disorders; to encourage the training of new scientists and physicians in geriatric research and in the practice of geriatric medicine.

LEGAL BASIS:
Private foundation.

ELIGIBILITY:
For the AFAR Research Grants, applicants must be junior faculty (M.Ds. and Ph.Ds.).

Paul Beeson Career Development Awards in Aging Research Program applicants are clinically trained individuals who are pursuing research careers in aging.

For the Ellison Medical Foundation/AFAR Postdoctoral Fellows in Aging Research Program, postdoctoral fellows at all levels of training are eligible.

For the Glenn/AFAR Breakthroughs in Gerontology Awards, qualified applicants must be full-time faculty members at the rank of assistant professor or higher who can demonstrate a strong record of independence.

The Medical Student Training in Aging Research Program (MSTAR) is intended for medical students and is built on the Medical Student Geriatric Scholars Program.

GEOGRAPHIC RESTRICTIONS:
United States.

FINANCIAL DATA:
Amount of support per award: AFAR Research Grants: Up to $100,000; Paul Beeson Career Development Awards in Aging Research: $200,000 per year; Ellison Medical Foundation/AFAR Postdoctoral Fellows in Aging Research Program: $45,218 to $59,402; Glenn/AFAR Breakthroughs in Gerontology Awards: Up to $200,000.

NUMBER OF AWARDS: AFAR Research Grants: Up to 15; Paul Beeson Career Development Awards in Aging Research: Up to 10; Ellison Medical Foundation/AFAR Postdoctoral Fellows in Aging Research Program: Up to 15; Glenn/AFAR Breakthroughs in Gerontology Awards: 2.

APPLICATION INFORMATION:
Application form required.
Duration: One to two years.
Deadline: Mid-December.

PUBLICATIONS:
Program announcement.

STAFF:
Stephanie Lederman, Executive Director
Nancy O'Leary, Director, Development
Odette van der Willik, Director, Grant Programs
Hattie Herman, Program Officer
Catherine Cullar, Administrative Manager

AMERICAN FOUNDATION FOR AGING RESEARCH [2371]

SUNY Albany - Biological Sciences
1400 Washington Avenue
Albany, NY 12222
(518) 437-4448

E-MAIL ADDRESS:
afar@agingresearchfoundation.org

WEB SITE ADDRESS:
www.agingresearchfoundation.org

FOUNDED: 1979

AREAS OF INTEREST:
Research in biology of aging and age-related diseases.

NAME(S) OF PROGRAMS:
- **Special Awards for Students in North Carolina**
- **Special Awards in Cancer and Neurobiology**

TYPE:
Fellowships; Scholarships. Undergraduate scholarships and graduate fellowships for students in M.S., Ph.D., D.V.M., D.D.S. and M.D. degree programs.

YEAR PROGRAM STARTED: 1979

PURPOSE:
To grant scholarships and fellowships to young scientists conducting cellular, molecular or genetic research on the aging process or age-related illnesses (i.e., cancer, Alzheimer's, diabetes).

LEGAL BASIS:
Nonprofit, tax-exempt, charitable, educational and scientific organization.

ELIGIBILITY:
U.S. citizenship is not required. However, applicants must be enrolled in a degree program at a U.S. institution. Each applicant must submit a preapplication (available on web site) to describe a project related to age-related disease or biology of aging.

GEOGRAPHIC RESTRICTIONS:
United States.

FINANCIAL DATA:
Awards in support of tuition and fees at the student's academic institute.
Amount of support per award: $500 to $2,000 per semester.
Total amount of support: $10,000 to $15,000.

NUMBER OF APPLICANTS MOST RECENT YEAR:
100.

NUMBER OF AWARDS: 5 to 15.

APPLICATION INFORMATION:
Contact Foundation to request a pre-application.
Duration: Renewals possible.
Deadline: Applications are reviewed on an ongoing basis.

PUBLICATIONS:
News from AFAR, newsletter.

IRS IDENTIFICATION NUMBER: 43-1217061

OFFICERS:
Paul F. Agris, President
Paul G. Wallace, Vice President

ADDRESS INQUIRIES TO:
See e-mail address above.

*SPECIAL STIPULATIONS:
Research must be done at U.S. institutions.

AMERICAN HEADACHE SOCIETY   [2372]
19 Mantua Road
Mount Royal, NJ 08061
(856) 423-0043
Fax: (856) 423-0082

E-MAIL ADDRESS:
ahshq@talley.com

WEB SITE ADDRESS:
www.americanheadachesociety.org

AREAS OF INTEREST:
Headache and face pain.

NAME(S) OF PROGRAMS:
● **American Headache Society/Allergan Headache Fellowship Award**

TYPE:
Awards/prizes; Fellowships.

PURPOSE:
To support the fellowship recipient for a 12-month period in honor of the progress being made towards headache being recognized as a board certified specialty.

ELIGIBILITY:
Contact AHS Headquarters for eligibility requirements.

GEOGRAPHIC RESTRICTIONS:
United States.

FINANCIAL DATA:
Amount of support per award: $40,000.
Total amount of support: $40,000.

NUMBER OF AWARDS: 1.

APPLICATION INFORMATION:
Contact AHS Headquarters for a complete application.
Duration: One year.
Deadline: February 1.

IRS IDENTIFICATION NUMBER: 43-6058456

ADDRESS INQUIRIES TO:
Linda McGillicuddy, Executive Director
(See address above.)

*SPECIAL STIPULATIONS:
A six-month update and final report is required.

AMERICAN HEADACHE SOCIETY   [2373]
19 Mantua Road
Mount Royal, NJ 08061
(856) 423-0043
Fax: (856) 423-0082

E-MAIL ADDRESS:
ahshq@talley.com

WEB SITE ADDRESS:
www.americanheadachesociety.org

AREAS OF INTEREST:
Headache and face pain.

NAME(S) OF PROGRAMS:
● **American Headache Society/Merck Headache Fellowship Award**

TYPE:
Awards/prizes; Fellowships.

PURPOSE:
To support the fellowship recipient during a 12-month period to obtain advanced clinical training in all aspects of headache diagnosis, management and prevention, and to pursue clinical research participation.

ELIGIBILITY:
Contact AHS Headquarters for eligibility requirements.

GEOGRAPHIC RESTRICTIONS:
United States.

FINANCIAL DATA:
Amount of support per award: $40,000.
Total amount of support: $40,000.

NUMBER OF AWARDS: 1.

APPLICATION INFORMATION:
Contact AHS Headquarters for a complete application.
Duration: One year.
Deadline: February 1.

IRS IDENTIFICATION NUMBER: 43-6058456

ADDRESS INQUIRIES TO:
Linda McGillicuddy, Executive Director
(See address above.)

*SPECIAL STIPULATIONS:
A six-month update and final report is required.

AMERICAN KIDNEY FUND   [2374]
6110 Executive Boulevard, Suite 1010
Rockville, MD 20852
(800) 638-8299
(866) 300-2900 (Spanish/English HelpLine)
Fax: (301) 881-0569

E-MAIL ADDRESS:
helpline@kidneyfund.org

WEB SITE ADDRESS:
www.kidneyfund.org

FOUNDED: 1971

AREAS OF INTEREST:
Treatment, prevention and cure of kidney disease.

NAME(S) OF PROGRAMS:
● **American Kidney Fund Regional Conference Series**
● **Clinical Scientist in Nephrology (CSN)**

TYPE:
Development grants; Fellowships; Project/program grants; Research grants; Training grants. The Clinical Scientist in Nephrology (CSN) program has the goal of improving the quality of care provided to kidney patients through enhancing the training of nephrologists who desire to pursue an academic career and whose primary professional commitment is to scholarship in the provision of patient care.

YEAR PROGRAM STARTED: 1989

PURPOSE:
To provide aid in the treatment, prevention and care of kidney disease.

ELIGIBILITY:
Applicant must be a nephrologist in a current academic setting. Contact AKF for further details.

GEOGRAPHIC RESTRICTIONS:
United States and its territories.

FINANCIAL DATA:
Amount of support per award: Up to $80,000 per year.
Total amount of support: Up to $160,000.

NUMBER OF APPLICANTS MOST RECENT YEAR:
11.

NUMBER OF AWARDS: 1.

APPLICATION INFORMATION:
Duration: One to two years.
Deadline: December 1.

ADDRESS INQUIRIES TO:
Jennifer St. Clair Russell
Director of Public
and Professional Education
(See address above.)

AMERICAN KIDNEY FUND   [2375]
6110 Executive Boulevard, Suite 1010
Rockville, MD 20852
(800) 638-8299
(866) 300-2900 (Spanish/English HelpLine)
Fax: (301) 881-0898

E-MAIL ADDRESS:
helpline@kidneyfund.org

WEB SITE ADDRESS:
www.kidneyfund.org

FOUNDED: 1971

AREAS OF INTEREST:
Treatment, prevention and cure of kidney disease.

NAME(S) OF PROGRAMS:
- **Patient Services Grants**

TYPE:
Grants-in-aid; Product donations. Medical Grants. Provides financial assistance to qualified dialysis patients who are referred by their physicians and social workers for treatment-specific expenses such as transportation, over-the-counter medicines, medication co-payments, kidney donor expenses and other necessities.

YEAR PROGRAM STARTED: 1971

PURPOSE:
To provide aid in the treatment, prevention, and cure of kidney disease.

ELIGIBILITY:
Based on income. Kidney dialysis and transplant patients living in the U.S. are eligible.

GEOGRAPHIC RESTRICTIONS:
United States and its territories.

FINANCIAL DATA:
Amount of support per award: $175 every six months ($350 per year).

NUMBER OF AWARDS: 63,500.

APPLICATION INFORMATION:
Contact the Fund at the toll-free number.
Duration: Renewable.

IRS IDENTIFICATION NUMBER: 23-7124261

ADDRESS INQUIRIES TO:
Janice Contreras
(See address above.)

AMERICAN MEDICAL ASSOCIATION FOUNDATION

515 North State Street
Chicago, IL 60654
(312) 464-4200
Fax: (312) 464-4142

E-MAIL ADDRESS:
amafoundation@ama-assn.org

WEB SITE ADDRESS:
www.amafoundation.org

TYPE:
Awards/prizes; Project/program grants; Research grants; Scholarships; Seed money grants. Excellence in Medicine Awards are given to recognize physicians and medical students who are improving the health of their communities and the lives of those who are most in need.

The Joan F. Giambalvo Memorial Scholarship is presented in conjunction with the AMA's Women Physicians Congress to provide a research grant to help researchers advance the progress of women in the medical profession and identify and address the needs of women physicians and medical students.

Health Literacy Initiative seeks to provide awareness among physicians and health care providers to understand healthy literacy and its impact on patient safety.

Healthy Communities/Healthy America awards grants to existing, physician-led free clinics that provide free or low-cost medical care to underserved and uninsured populations.

Healthy Living Grant Program provides grants to support healthy lifestyles projects in the areas of nutrition, physical fitness, prescription medication safety and violence prevention.

The Minority Scholars Awards are given in collaboration with the AMA Minority Affairs Consortium to first- and second-year medical students from historically underrepresented minority groups in the medical profession.

The Physicians of Tomorrow Scholarships are awarded to promising fourth-year medical students based on financial need and academic excellence.

In partnership with the AMA Alliance, the Scholars Fund distributes tuition assistance funds to medical schools across the country.

The Seed Grant Research Program provides medical students, physician residents and fellows with grants to help them conduct basic science or clinical research.

The Arthur N. Wilson, M.D. Scholarship is awarded to a medical student who is a graduate of a high school in southeast Alaska.

See entry 1775 for full listing.

AMERICAN MEDICAL TECHNOLOGISTS   [2376]

10700 West Higgins Road
Suite 150
Rosemont, IL 60018
(847) 823-5169
(800) 275-1268

E-MAIL ADDRESS:
mail@amt1.com

WEB SITE ADDRESS:
www.amt1.com

FOUNDED: 1939

AREAS OF INTEREST:
Students pursuing studies as medical technologist, medical laboratory technician, medical laboratory assistant, medical administrative specialist, medical assistant, dental assistant, or phlebotomist.

NAME(S) OF PROGRAMS:
- **AMT Student Scholarships**

TYPE:
Scholarships.

YEAR PROGRAM STARTED: 1969

PURPOSE:
To assist students to complete the training to work in clinical laboratories and doctors' offices.

LEGAL BASIS:
Incorporated in New Jersey in 1939 as a nonprofit organization.

ELIGIBILITY:
The following criteria apply:
(1) applicant must be a graduate of, or a senior in, an accredited high school (G.E.D. also acceptable);
(2) applicant must be enrolled in a school accredited by an accrediting agency recognized by the U.S. Department of Education and;
(3) applicant's course of study must lead to a career in one of the disciplines (medical technologist, medical laboratory technician, medical laboratory assistant, medical administrative specialist, medical assistant, dental assistant, or phlebotomist) certified by

the American Medical Technologists; applicants pursuing careers other than those certified by the American Medical Technologists will not be accepted.

Winners of the scholarship must furnish proof of being either a student in good standing or enrolled for entrance into the fall program of an accredited school. The award may only be used to defray tuition costs, and will be sent directly to the school of the recipient's choice. Applicant must provide evidence of financial need and career goals.

GEOGRAPHIC RESTRICTIONS:
United States.

FINANCIAL DATA:
Amount of support per award: $500.
Total amount of support: $2,500.

NUMBER OF APPLICANTS MOST RECENT YEAR:
75.

NUMBER OF AWARDS: 5 annually.

APPLICATION INFORMATION:
Detailed information is available online.
Deadline: Application form must be completed and received by April 1 to be considered for the current year's scholarship.

PUBLICATIONS:
Application form.

ADDRESS INQUIRIES TO:
Linda Halblander
Scholarship Program Coordinator
(See address above.)

*SPECIAL STIPULATIONS:
The award may only be used to defray tuition costs, and will be sent directly to the school of the recipient's choice.

AMERICAN MEDICAL WOMEN'S ASSOCIATION, INC.   [2377]

100 North 20th Street, 4th Floor
Philadelphia, PA 19103
(215) 320-3716
Fax: (215) 564-2175

E-MAIL ADDRESS:
associatedirector@amwa-doc.org

WEB SITE ADDRESS:
www.amwa-doc.org

FOUNDED: 1915

AREAS OF INTEREST:
Women physicians, women medical students and women's health.

NAME(S) OF PROGRAMS:
- **American Women's Hospitals Service (AWHS)**

TYPE:
Awards/prizes; Conferences/seminars; General operating grants; Project/program grants; Training grants; Travel grants. Support for clinics serving the poor in medically underserved areas, scholarships and loans to qualifying women medical students, and continuing medical education for physicians in areas related to women's health.

YEAR PROGRAM STARTED: 1915

PURPOSE:
To advance women in medicine and improve women's health through advocacy, leadership, education, expertise and mentoring, and strategic alliances.

LEGAL BASIS:
AMWA: 501(c)(6) corporation. AWHS: 501(c)(3) foundation.

ELIGIBILITY:
Open to women who are enrolled in accredited medical schools in the U.S.

GEOGRAPHIC RESTRICTIONS:
United States.

BOARD OF DIRECTORS:
Eliza Chin, M.D., M.P.H., President

ADDRESS INQUIRIES TO:
Sarah Hagy, Associate Director
(See address above.)

THE AMERICAN PORPHYRIA FOUNDATION [2378]

4900 Woodway Drive
Suite 780
Houston, TX 77056-1837
(713) 266-9617
Fax: (713) 840-9552

E-MAIL ADDRESS:
porphyrus@aol.com

WEB SITE ADDRESS:
www.porphyriafoundation.com

AREAS OF INTEREST:
Porphyria.

TYPE:
Research grants.

PURPOSE:
To improve the health and well-being of individuals and families affected by porphyria.

ELIGIBILITY:
Qualified investigators involved in porphyria research.

FINANCIAL DATA:
Amount of support per award: $5,000 to $10,000.

APPLICATION INFORMATION:
Send a two-page summary of proposed research and research experience to the Foundation.

PUBLICATIONS:
Newsletters.

ADDRESS INQUIRIES TO:
Desiree Lyon Howe, Executive Director
(See address above.)

AMERICAN ROENTGEN RAY SOCIETY [2379]

44211 Slatestone Court
Leesburg, VA 20176
(703) 729-3353
Fax: (703) 729-4839

E-MAIL ADDRESS:
info@arrs.org

WEB SITE ADDRESS:
www.arrs.org

FOUNDED: 1900

AREAS OF INTEREST:
Diagnostic radiology.

NAME(S) OF PROGRAMS:
● **ARRS Annual Scholarship Program**

TYPE:
Scholarships.

YEAR PROGRAM STARTED: 1992

PURPOSE:
To provide resources needed to acquire knowledge, skills and training in the areas

that are vital to radiology but have traditionally been outside the scope of diagnostic radiology.

ELIGIBILITY:
Candidates must have earned an M.D. or D.O. from an accredited institution. Also, must have completed all residencies or fellowship training or equivalent, full-time appointment as instructor, assistant professor or equivalent for no more than five years beyond training. Appointment must be in a department of radiology, nuclear medicine, ultrasound or radiation oncology.

FINANCIAL DATA:
Funds distributed to individual's institution.
Amount of support per award: $140,000.

APPLICATION INFORMATION:
Submission of a curriculum vitae, summary of qualifications, goals and purposes of the study, estimated budget, and a statement from department regarding applicant's goals and commitment ensuring applicant's return to faculty upon completion.
Duration: One to two years.
Deadline: November.

ADDRESS INQUIRIES TO:
Keri Sperry, Director
Communications and Development
(See address above.)

AMERICAN SOCIETY FOR CLINICAL PATHOLOGY [2380]

33 West Monroe, Suite 1600
Chicago, IL 60603
(312) 541-4978
Fax: (312) 541-4767

E-MAIL ADDRESS:
betty.sanders@ascp.org

WEB SITE ADDRESS:
www.ascp.org/scholarships

FOUNDED: 1922

AREAS OF INTEREST:
Laboratory medicine.

NAME(S) OF PROGRAMS:
● **ASCP Scholarships**

TYPE:
Scholarships.

PURPOSE:
To encourage and support individuals interested in laboratory professions.

LEGAL BASIS:
Professional society.

ELIGIBILITY:
ASCP Scholarships are offered to eligible final-year students in Medical Technologist (MT), Medical Laboratory Technician (MLT), Cytotechnologist (CT), Histotechnician (HT), Histotechnologist (HTL) and Pathologist Assistant (PA) programs. An applicant must be enrolled in an NAACLS- or CAAHEP-accredited program, in the final clinical year of education and a U.S. citizen or permanent U.S. resident. Applicants must also have a minimum 2.8 grade point average on a 4.0 scale.

Scholarship selection criteria include academic achievement, leadership abilities and community activities, professional goals, and endorsements from faculty and community leaders.

GEOGRAPHIC RESTRICTIONS:
United States.

FINANCIAL DATA:
Amount of support per award: $1,000.
Total amount of support: Approximately $50,000 per year.

NUMBER OF APPLICANTS MOST RECENT YEAR:
450.

NUMBER OF AWARDS: 50 for the year 2010.

APPLICATION INFORMATION:
Application form required.
Duration: One year. Nonrenewable.
Deadline: November 15, 2011.

PUBLICATIONS:
Announcement.

ADDRESS INQUIRIES TO:
Betty Sanders
Program Manager/ASCP Scholarships
(See address above.)

AMERICAN SOCIETY OF HEMATOLOGY [2381]

2021 L Street, N.W.
Suite 900
Washington, DC 20036
(202) 776-0544
Fax: (888) 719-7814

E-MAIL ADDRESS:
awards@hematology.org

WEB SITE ADDRESS:
www.hematology.org

FOUNDED: 1985

AREAS OF INTEREST:
Hematology, basic and clinical/translational research.

NAME(S) OF PROGRAMS:
● **ASH Scholar Award**
● **Fellow Scholar Award**
● **Junior Faculty Scholar Award**

TYPE:
Awards/prizes; Fellowships; Research grants; Scholarships.

PURPOSE:
To support hematologists who have chosen a career in research.

ELIGIBILITY:
Fellows must have more than two years, but less than six years, postdoctoral research training at the time of application. Junior Faculty applicants must be within the first two years of their initial tenure-track faculty appointment as Assistant Professor at the time of application.

GEOGRAPHIC RESTRICTIONS:
United States and Canada.

FINANCIAL DATA:
Amount of support per award: $150,000 for a Junior Faculty Scholar Award or $100,000 for a Fellow Scholar Award. These awards can be spread over two or three years with an annual maximum not to exceed $75,000 for junior faculty and $50,000 for fellows.
Total amount of support: Approximately $2,000,000 for the year 2010.

APPLICATION INFORMATION:
Duration: Two to three years.
Deadline: Mandatory Letter of Intent: Late April/early May; Application: Late August/early September.

ADDRESS INQUIRIES TO:
Elisa Shea, Awards Manager
(See address above.)

*SPECIAL STIPULATIONS:
A letter of intent is required before submission of full proposal.

AMERICAN SOCIETY OF HEMATOLOGY [2382]

2021 L Street, N.W.
Suite 900
Washington, DC 20036
(202) 776-0544
Fax: (888) 719-7814

E-MAIL ADDRESS:
awards@hematology.org

WEB SITE ADDRESS:
www.hematology.org

AREAS OF INTEREST:
Hematology.

NAME(S) OF PROGRAMS:
● **Trainee Research Award Program**

TYPE:
Awards/prizes. Each scholarship provides the medical school with funds to cover the expenses for students to complete a three-month program and travel support for students to attend the ASH annual meeting.

PURPOSE:
To provide medical students, residents, and selected undergraduates with an introduction to the specialty of hematology by encouraging them to take time during a summer or an equivalent period during their medical school curriculum to work on a project with a hematologist.

ELIGIBILITY:
Medical students, residents, and selected undergraduates in North America, Mexico and Canada.

GEOGRAPHIC RESTRICTIONS:
North America, Mexico and Canada.

FINANCIAL DATA:
Amount of support per award: $4,000 cash award and $1,000 travel stipend for annual meeting.
Total amount of support: $200,000 for the year 2010.

APPLICATION INFORMATION:
The institution is responsible for selecting student participants. Contact the Society for additional application information.
Deadline: Mid-March.

ADDRESS INQUIRIES TO:
Elisa Shea, Awards Manager
(See address above.)

AMERICAN SOCIETY OF HYPERTENSION [2383]

148 Madison Avenue
5th Floor
New York, NY 10016-6700
(212) 696-9099
Fax: (212) 696-0711

E-MAIL ADDRESS:
awards@ash-us.org

WEB SITE ADDRESS:
www.ash-us.org

AREAS OF INTEREST:
Hypertension and related cardiovascular disease.

TYPE:
Awards/prizes; Research grants.

PURPOSE:
To organize and conduct educational activities designed to promote and encourage the development, advancement, and exchange of scientific information in all aspects of research, diagnosis, and treatment of hypertension and related cardiovascular diseases.

GEOGRAPHIC RESTRICTIONS:
North America.

FINANCIAL DATA:
Amount of support per award: $500 to $10,000.

STAFF:
Ashley Buron, Program Coordinator
Scientific Meetings and Professional Affairs

ADDRESS INQUIRIES TO:
Ashley Buron, Program Coordinator
Scientific Meetings and Professional Affairs
(See address above.)

AMERICAN SOCIETY OF NEURORADIOLOGY/ EDUCATION AND RESEARCH FOUNDATION [2384]

2210 Midwest Road
Oak Brook, IL 60521
(630) 574-0220
Fax: (630) 574-0661

E-MAIL ADDRESS:
executive@asnr.org

WEB SITE ADDRESS:
www.asnr.org

AREAS OF INTEREST:
Neuroradiology.

TYPE:
Fellowships.

YEAR PROGRAM STARTED: 1962

PURPOSE:
To disseminate scientific and educational information about neuroradiology.

FINANCIAL DATA:
Amount of support per award: Up to $40,000.

APPLICATION INFORMATION:
Contact the Organization for application procedures.
Duration: One year. Some renewals.

ADDRESS INQUIRIES TO:
James B. Gantenberg, Executive Director
(See address above.)

AMERICAN VETERINARY MEDICAL ASSOCIATION [2385]

AVMA Governmental Relations Division
1910 Sunderland Place, N.W.
Washington, DC 20036
(800) 321-1473
Fax: (202) 842-4360

E-MAIL ADDRESS:
fellowship@avma.org

WEB SITE ADDRESS:
www.avma.org/grd

AREAS OF INTEREST:
Veterinary medicine.

NAME(S) OF PROGRAMS:
● **Congressional Science Fellowship**

TYPE:
Fellowships.

YEAR PROGRAM STARTED: 1988

PURPOSE:
To support AVMA members to serve as a congressional or executive branch fellow for one year in a personal or committee office of the U.S. Congress.

LEGAL BASIS:
Association.

ELIGIBILITY:
Applicants must be AVMA members and U.S. citizens who demonstrate special competence in an area of veterinary medicine, possess a broad professional background and exhibit an interest in applying scientific knowledge to solve societal/public policy problems.

Applicants must be articulate, literate, adaptable and capable of working on a wide range of policy issues.

GEOGRAPHIC RESTRICTIONS:
United States.

FINANCIAL DATA:
Amount of support per award: $74,000 plus expenses and up to $6,000 in health insurance premiums.

NUMBER OF APPLICANTS MOST RECENT YEAR:
20.

NUMBER OF AWARDS: 3 for the year 2011-12.

APPLICATION INFORMATION:
Applicants must submit:
(1) a letter of intent;
(2) a curriculum vitae;
(3) two letters of reference from professional colleagues;
(4) a letter of support from the applicant's local, state, specialty or allied veterinary medical organization and;
(5) a personal statement (not to exceed 750 words) describing the applicant's qualifications, commitment to veterinary medicine and why the fellowship is desired.
Duration: One year.
Deadline: Mid-February.

PUBLICATIONS:
Program announcement.

IRS IDENTIFICATION NUMBER: 36-6117739

STAFF:
Dotty Gray, Associate Director

ADDRESS INQUIRIES TO:
See e-mail address above.

ANIMAL ASSISTANCE FOUNDATION [2386]

1805 South Bellaire Street
Suite 400
Denver, CO 80222-4321
(303) 744-8396
Fax: (303) 744-7065

E-MAIL ADDRESS:
giesd@aaf-fd.org

WEB SITE ADDRESS:
www.aaf-fd.org

FOUNDED: 1975

AREAS OF INTEREST:
Animal welfare.

TYPE:
Capital grants; Challenge/matching grants; General operating grants; Project/program grants. Operating and service grants. The Foundation:
(1) offers charitable support through its grantmaking program to organizations that advance its goal of establishing Colorado as a model state for the care and humane treatment of animals;
(2) brings a scientific focus to the work of animal welfare through advocacy and funding for data collection;

(3) fosters a culture of stewardship for animals through education initiatives;
(4) celebrates animal contributions through the AAF's grantmaking focus of human-animal connection, whose main priorities are the unwanted horse, the link between human violence and animal abuse and animal-assisted therapies and;
(5) convenes community conversations on animal welfare.

YEAR PROGRAM STARTED: 1975

PURPOSE:
To provide leadership and support in improving animal welfare in the state of Colorado; to make Colorado exemplary in animal welfare and philanthropy for animal welfare.

LEGAL BASIS:
Private foundation.

ELIGIBILITY:
In considering grant requests, the Foundation values proposals that:
(1) advance its goal of establishing Colorado as a Model State for the care and humane treatment of animals;
(2) are located in Colorado or that have a direct impact on animals and their owners in Colorado;
(3) demonstrate collaboration within the community and;
(4) demonstrate a high potential for self-sufficiency and sustainability.

Grants are not given to individuals. Eligible applicants must be a unit of government or recognized as an IRS 501(c)(3) tax-exempt organization and must propose an activity compatible with the Foundation's mission. (Groups designated by the IRS as Type III supporting organizations, however, are not eligible to apply.) Religious organizations are not eligible.

The AAF will consider applications for general operating, pet sterilization, matching grant programs, capital requests, education for animal health, treatment and well-being, capital construction, and technical assistance.

The Foundation does not fund individuals, pets of individuals, debt retirement, indirect administrative costs, start-up costs, endowments or political campaigns.

GEOGRAPHIC RESTRICTIONS:
Colorado.

FINANCIAL DATA:
Amount of support per award: Typically $2,000 to $5,000.
Total amount of support: $659,082 in grants and $1,169,001 for total charitable purposes for the year 2009.
Matching fund requirements: Varies.

NUMBER OF APPLICANTS MOST RECENT YEAR: 104.

NUMBER OF AWARDS: 61 (38 Model State and 23 Service Grant recipients).

REPRESENTATIVE AWARDS:
$100,000 to Denver University; $25,000 to Humane Society of South Platte Valley.

APPLICATION INFORMATION:
If Foundation has indicated it will accept applicant's proposal, the following criteria must be met:
(1) Applications must be typed, computer-generated or legibly printed;
(2) Applicant must submit one original, unbound, and in a form that can be readily copied (unstapled or not in a folder or notebook);
(3) One electronic copy of the application (plus attachments) must be submitted;
(4) The Colorado Common Grant Application must be used and;
(5) In addition to the attachments required by the Colorado Common Grant Application, if applicant is required to be licensed by the Pet Animal Care Facilities Act, a copy of the current PACFA license and PACFA statistics for the most recent year must be included.

Send the original grant application and attachments via mail to the address above and also an electronic copy of the application and attachments to info@aaf-fd.org.

Duration: One to two years. Nonrenewable.

Deadline: Last Friday in March and September.

PUBLICATIONS:
Annual report.

IRS IDENTIFICATION NUMBER: 84-0715412

ADDRESS INQUIRIES TO:
Letters of inquiry and formal proposals should be addressed to:
Grant Committee: Application and Information
Animal Assistance Foundation
(See address or phone number above.)
E-mail: info@aaf-fd.org

*SPECIAL STIPULATIONS:
Eligible organizations are asked to submit only one proposal per year. If funded, programs are eligible to request for a second year's funding.

APLASTIC ANEMIA AND MDS INTERNATIONAL FOUNDATION [2387]
100 Park Avenue, Suite 108
Rockville, MD 20850
(301) 279-7202
(800) 747-2820
Fax: (301) 279-7205

E-MAIL ADDRESS:
help@aamds.org

WEB SITE ADDRESS:
www.aamds.org

FOUNDED: 1983

AREAS OF INTEREST:
Aplastic anemia, myelodysplastic syndrome (MDS) and paroxysmal nocturnal hemoglobinuria (PNH).

NAME(S) OF PROGRAMS:
● Established Researcher Award
● New Researcher Award

TYPE:
Research grants.

YEAR PROGRAM STARTED: 1983

PURPOSE:
To support research related to aplastic anemia, myelodysplastic syndrome (MDS) and paroxysmal nocturnal hemoglobinuria (PNH).

ELIGIBILITY:
Qualified investigators affiliated with appropriate institutions are eligible to apply.

FINANCIAL DATA:
Amount of support per award: $30,000 per year.

APPLICATION INFORMATION:
Applications must be submitted electronically.

Duration: Two years. Second-year funding pending approval by Medical Board.

Deadline: February 28.

STAFF:
Alice Houk, Director of Health Professional Programs

ADDRESS INQUIRIES TO:
Alice Houk
Director of Health Professional Programs
(See address above.)

ARTHRITIS NATIONAL RESEARCH FOUNDATION (ANRF) [2388]
200 Oceangate, Suite 830
Long Beach, CA 90802
(800) 588-2873
Fax: (562) 437-6057

E-MAIL ADDRESS:
hbelisle@curearthritis.org

WEB SITE ADDRESS:
www.curearthritis.org

FOUNDED: 1952

AREAS OF INTEREST:
Research related to arthritis.

NAME(S) OF PROGRAMS:
● ANRF Arthritis Research Grants

TYPE:
Fellowships; Research grants; Travel grants. ANRF Arthritis Research Grants are intended to support basic and clinical research focusing on rheumatic and related autoimmune diseases, such as osteoarthritis and rheumatoid arthritis.

YEAR PROGRAM STARTED: 1952

PURPOSE:
To support basic and clinical research related to arthritis.

ELIGIBILITY:
Applicants must hold an M.D. and/or Ph.D. degree or equivalent. Applicants need not be U.S. citizens, but must conduct their research at U.S. nonprofit institutions.

FINANCIAL DATA:
No overhead expenses funded.
Amount of support per award: $20,000 to $75,000.
Total amount of support: $975,000 for fiscal year 2010-11.

NUMBER OF APPLICANTS MOST RECENT YEAR: 59.

NUMBER OF AWARDS: 14.

APPLICATION INFORMATION:
A standard cover sheet and budget page are required and provided on the Foundation's web site. Application must be submitted online along with two hard copies, one original and one copy.

Duration: One year. May apply for second year of funding.

Deadline: January 18 or next business day.

IRS IDENTIFICATION NUMBER: 95-6043953

STAFF:
Helene Belisle, Executive Director

ADDRESS INQUIRIES TO:
See e-mail address above.

AUTISM SPEAKS [2389]

1060 State Road, 2nd Floor
Princeton, NJ 08540
(609) 228-7313
Fax: (609) 430-9163

E-MAIL ADDRESS:
jnew@autismspeaks.org

WEB SITE ADDRESS:
www.autismspeaks.org

FOUNDED: 1994

AREAS OF INTEREST:
Autism.

NAME(S) OF PROGRAMS:
- **Basic and Clinical Awards, Pilot and Full Levels**
- **Family Services Community Grants**
- **Global Public Health Initiative**
- **Predoctoral Fellowships**
- **Trailblazer**
- **Translational PostDoctoral Fellowships**
- **Treatment, Pilot and Full Levels**

TYPE:
Fellowships; Project/program grants; Research grants. Research grants relevant to understanding and improving the communication capabilities of individuals with autism, particularly those who are nonverbal or minimally verbal.

YEAR PROGRAM STARTED: 1994

PURPOSE:
To fund global biomedical research into the causes, prevention, treatment and cure for autism; to raise public awareness about autism and its effects on individuals, families and society.

LEGAL BASIS:
National nonprofit, tax-exempt organization.

ELIGIBILITY:
Science grants: Open to investigators at established research institutions.

GEOGRAPHIC RESTRICTIONS:
United States.

FINANCIAL DATA:
Amount of support per award: Varies.
Total amount of support: Varies.

NUMBER OF APPLICANTS MOST RECENT YEAR:
1,000.

NUMBER OF AWARDS: Varies.

APPLICATION INFORMATION:
All proposals must be submitted online via Autism Speaks grants administration site.
Duration: Varies.
Deadline: Varies.

IRS IDENTIFICATION NUMBER: 20-2329938

ADDRESS INQUIRIES TO:
Joan New, Senior Grants Administrator for Science
(See address above.)

Family Services: Serena Selkin
Grants Administrator
E-mail: sselkin@autismspeaks.org

BATTEN DISEASE SUPPORT AND RESEARCH ASSOCIATION [2390]

166 Humphries Drive
Reynoldsburg, OH 43068
(740) 927-4298
(800) 448-4570
Fax: (866) 648-8718

E-MAIL ADDRESS:
bdsra1@bdsra.org

WEB SITE ADDRESS:
www.bdsra.org

FOUNDED: 1987

AREAS OF INTEREST:
Batten Disease, NCL and Kufs Disease.

NAME(S) OF PROGRAMS:
- **Batten Disease Research Grant**

TYPE:
Fellowships; Research grants; Seed money grants.

YEAR PROGRAM STARTED: 1994

PURPOSE:
To maximize the opportunities of victims of Batten to lead as normal lives as possible; to provide a parent communication network, information and emotional support to families of persons with Batten Disease; to educate lay persons and professionals about the special needs of victims and their families; to act as a national registry for NCL researchers throughout the world.

ELIGIBILITY:
Applications will be reviewed based upon the quality of the proposed science, the probability of achieving the specific aims proposed and the likelihood of securing federal funding for continued research.

FINANCIAL DATA:
Total amount of support: Approximately $500,000 annually.

NUMBER OF APPLICANTS MOST RECENT YEAR:
24.

NUMBER OF AWARDS: 9.

APPLICATION INFORMATION:
Write or call the Foundation to determine the interest and appropriateness of a full proposal.
Duration: One to two years.
Deadline: May 15.

IRS IDENTIFICATION NUMBER: 91-1397792

STAFF:
Lance W. Johnston, Executive Director

ADDRESS INQUIRIES TO:
Lance W. Johnston, Executive Director
(See address above.)

*SPECIAL STIPULATIONS:
Grants must not be used to cover indirect or overhead costs.

BRIGHAM AND WOMEN'S HOSPITAL

75 Francis Street
Boston, MA 02115
(617) 732-8422
Fax: (617) 582-6112

WEB SITE ADDRESS:
www.brighamandwomens.
org/delandfellowship

TYPE:
Fellowships.

See entry 1517 for full listing.

BURROUGHS WELLCOME FUND [2391]

21 T.W. Alexander Drive
Research Triangle Park, NC 27709
(919) 991-5100
Fax: (919) 991-5160

E-MAIL ADDRESS:
info@bwfund.org

WEB SITE ADDRESS:
www.bwfund.org

FOUNDED: 1955

AREAS OF INTEREST:
Biomedical research.

NAME(S) OF PROGRAMS:
- **Career Awards at the Scientific Interface**
- **Career Awards for Medical Scientists**
- **Institutional Program Unifying Population and Laboratory Based Sciences**
- **Investigators in the Pathogenesis of Infectious Disease**
- **Preterm Birth Initiative**

TYPE:
Awards/prizes; Conferences/seminars; Research grants. Career Awards at the Scientific Interface bridge advanced postdoctoral training and the first three years of faculty service. These awards are intended to foster the early career development of researchers with backgrounds in the physical/mathematical/computational sciences whose work addresses biological questions.

Career Awards for Medical Scientists provide funds to bridge advanced postdoctoral/fellowship training and the early years of faculty service. This award addresses the ongoing problem of increasing the number of physician scientists and will help facilitate the transition to a career in research.

Institutional Program Unifying Population and Laboratory Based Sciences provide funds to unite the population and computational sciences and the laboratory-based biological sciences. The award supports the training of researchers working between existing research concentrations in population approaches to human health and in basic biological sciences.

Investigators in the Pathogenesis of Infectious Disease provide awards for opportunities for accomplished investigators at the assistant professor level to study pathogenesis, with a focus on the intersection of human and microbial biology. The program is intended to shed light on the overarching issues of how human hosts handle infectious challenge.

Preterm Birth Initiative brings together a diverse interdisciplinary group with expertise in genetics/genomics, immunology, microbiology and proteomics along with the more traditional areas of parturition research such as maternal fetal medicine, obstetrics and pediatrics to address the scientific issues related to preterm birth.

PURPOSE:
To advance the medical sciences by supporting research and other scientific and educational activities; to help scientists early in their careers develop as independent investigators; to advance fields in the basic medical sciences that are undervalued or in need of particular encouragement.

GEOGRAPHIC RESTRICTIONS:
United States and Canada.

FINANCIAL DATA:
Assets of approximately $750,000,000 for fiscal year 2008.

Amount of support per award: Career Awards at the Scientific Interface: $500,000; Career Awards for Medical Scientists: $700,000; Institutional Program Unifying Population and Laboratory Based Sciences: $2,500,000; Investigators in Pathogenesis of Infectious Disease: $500,000; Preterm Birth Initiative: Up to $600,000.

Total amount of support: Approximately $25,000,000 in grants awarded annually.

APPLICATION INFORMATION:
Duration: Preterm Birth Initiative: Four years. All others: Five years.

PUBLICATIONS:
FOCUS, newsletter; *Career Development Guides*, annual report.

IRS IDENTIFICATION NUMBER: 23-7225395

ADDRESS INQUIRIES TO:
Burroughs Wellcome Fund
P.O. Box 13901
Research Triangle Park, NC 27709-3901

BUSHROD H. CAMPBELL AND ADAH F. HALL CHARITY FUND   [2392]

c/o Hemenway & Barnes LLP
60 State Street
Boston, MA 02109
(617) 619-8257
Fax: (617) 227-0781

E-MAIL ADDRESS:
btaylor@hembar.com

FOUNDED: 1956

AREAS OF INTEREST:
Aid to the impoverished, aid to the elderly and population control.

TYPE:
Capital grants; General operating grants; Project/program grants. Made on a limited basis.

YEAR PROGRAM STARTED: 1956

PURPOSE:
To aid organizations devoted to providing aid to the elderly, population control and health care.

LEGAL BASIS:
Private foundation.

ELIGIBILITY:
Grants are made to tax-exempt organizations, with compelling need, located within Boston and neighboring communities, with the exception of organizations devoted to population control which can be located anywhere within the U.S. No grants to individuals.

Grants are contingent upon success of the project and wise expenditure of funds.

GEOGRAPHIC RESTRICTIONS:
Generally, Boston and neighboring communities.

FINANCIAL DATA:
Amount of support per award: $1,000 to $10,000. Average $5,000.
Total amount of support: $900,000 paid for fiscal year ended May 31, 2009 for all programs.

NUMBER OF APPLICANTS MOST RECENT YEAR:
140 for all programs.

APPLICATION INFORMATION:
A brief letter or telephone call is all that is needed to request an application and

guidelines. These two documents contain all the information necessary to submit a complete proposal.

Deadline: August 15, October 15, January 15 and April 15. Announcement by mail only subsequent to each meeting.

PUBLICATIONS:
Foundation brochure.

TRUSTEES:
Casimir de Rham, Jr.
Arthur B. Page
Curtis Prout

ADDRESS INQUIRIES TO:
Brenda Taylor, Administrator
(See address above.)

CANADIAN BLOOD SERVICES   [2393]

1800 Alta Vista Drive
Ottawa ON K1G 4J5 Canada
(613) 739-2408
Fax: (613) 739-2201

E-MAIL ADDRESS:
cilla.perry@blood.ca

WEB SITE ADDRESS:
www.blood.ca

AREAS OF INTEREST:
Research in transfusion science.

NAME(S) OF PROGRAMS:
● **Canadian Blood Services Trainee Awards Graduate Fellowship Program**
● **Canadian Blood Services Trainee Awards Postdoctoral Fellowship**

TYPE:
Fellowships.

PURPOSE:
To attract and support young investigators to initiate or continue training in the field of transfusion science; to foster careers related to transfusion science in Canada.

ELIGIBILITY:
Graduate Fellowship: Open to graduate students who are undertaking full-time research training leading to a Ph.D. degree. Students registering solely for a Master's degree will not be considered.

Postdoctoral Fellowship: Candidates must hold a recent Ph.D., M.D., D.D.S., D.V.M. or equivalent.

FINANCIAL DATA:
Amount of support per award: Graduate Fellowship: $21,000 per annum (CIHR guidelines); Postdoctoral Fellowship: $40,000 per annum (CIHR guidelines).
Total amount of support: Graduate Fellowship: Approximately $500,000; Postdoctoral Fellowship: Approximately $100,000.

NUMBER OF APPLICANTS MOST RECENT YEAR:
14 Graduate Fellowships and 5 Postdoctoral Fellowships for the year 2009.

NUMBER OF AWARDS: 10 Graduate Fellowships and 4 Postdoctoral Fellowships for the year 2009.

APPLICATION INFORMATION:
Candidates are required to submit application form GFP-01 for Graduate Fellowship or RD40 for Postdoctoral Fellowship.

Duration: Two years. Renewal to maximum of four years for Graduate Fellowship and three years for Postdoctoral Fellowship.

Deadline: Graduate Fellowship Program: May 17 and November 15; Postdoctoral Fellowship: July 2.

ADDRESS INQUIRIES TO:
Cilla Perry
Manager, Research and Development
(See address above.)

CANADIAN INSTITUTES OF HEALTH RESEARCH (CIHR)   [2394]

160 Elgin Street, 9th Floor
Address Locator 4809A
Ottawa ON K1A 0W9 Canada
(613) 954-1968
(888) 603-4178 (press 1)
Fax: (613) 954-1800

E-MAIL ADDRESS:
info@cihr-irsc.gc.ca

WEB SITE ADDRESS:
www.cihr-irsc.gc.ca

FOUNDED: 2000

AREAS OF INTEREST:
Basic, applied and clinical research in Canada in the health sciences.

NAME(S) OF PROGRAMS:
● **Canada Graduate Scholarships Master's Awards**

TYPE:
Awards/prizes; Scholarships. Intended to provide special recognition and support to students who are pursuing a Master's degree in a health-related field in Canada. These candidates are expected to have an exceptionally high potential for future research achievement and productivity.

YEAR PROGRAM STARTED: 2003

PURPOSE:
To help ensure a reliable supply of highly qualified personnel to meet the needs of Canada's knowledge economy.

LEGAL BASIS:
Government agency.

ELIGIBILITY:
The program is open to Canadian citizens and permanent residents. At the time of the CIHR deadline for application, candidates must have completed or be in the last year of a Bachelor's degree or have been registered for no more than 10 months as a full-time student in a Master's program. Only those students engaged in full-time Master's programs in which research is a major component are eligible for support. Awards will take effect only after the recipient has registered in a full-time Master's program.

Persons with a health professional degree who seek support for Master's research training are eligible to apply, but should also consult the guidelines for the CIHR Fellowships program. Those eligible for both have the option of applying to either program but not to both in the same year (i.e., September through August).

GEOGRAPHIC RESTRICTIONS:
Canada.

FINANCIAL DATA:
Amount of support per award: $17,500 (CAN).
Total amount of support: Estimated $3,815,000 for the year 2007.

NUMBER OF APPLICANTS MOST RECENT YEAR:
357 for the year 2007.

NUMBER OF AWARDS: 218 for the year 2007.

APPLICATION INFORMATION:
Duration: One year. Nonrenewable.
Deadline: February 1.

ADDRESS INQUIRIES TO:
Joane Delage, Program Coordinator
(See address above.)

*SPECIAL STIPULATIONS:
Awards must be taken up between July 1 and
October 1 following the offer of award and
must commence at the beginning of the
semesters, September 1 and January 1.

CANADIAN INSTITUTES OF HEALTH RESEARCH (CIHR)   [2395]

160 Elgin Street, 9th Floor
Address Locator 4809A
Ottawa ON K1A 0W9 Canada
(613) 954-1963
Fax: (613) 954-1800

E-MAIL ADDRESS:
dra@cihr-irsc.gc.ca
brd@irsc-cihr.gc.ca

WEB SITE ADDRESS:
www.cihr-irsc.gc.ca

FOUNDED: 1969

AREAS OF INTEREST:
Basic, applied and clinical research in
Canada in the health sciences.

NAME(S) OF PROGRAMS:
● **Frederick Banting and Charles Best Canada Graduate Scholarship-Doctoral Awards**

TYPE:
Scholarships.

PURPOSE:
To provide special recognition and support to
students who are pursuing a doctoral degree
in a health-related field in Canada.

ELIGIBILITY:
The program is open to Canadian citizens
and permanent residents of Canada. Only
those students engaged in full-time research
training in a Canadian graduate school are
eligible for support.

GEOGRAPHIC RESTRICTIONS:
Canada.

FINANCIAL DATA:
Amount of support per award: $30,000
(CAN) annual stipend, plus an annual
research allowance of $5,000.
Total amount of support: Varies.

NUMBER OF APPLICANTS MOST RECENT YEAR:
1,100.

NUMBER OF AWARDS: 180.

APPLICATION INFORMATION:
Duration: Three years.
Deadline: October 15.

CANADIAN INSTITUTES OF HEALTH RESEARCH (CIHR)   [2396]

160 Elgin Street, 9th Floor
Address Locator 4809A
Ottawa ON K1A 0W9 Canada
(613) 954-1968
(888) 603-4178 (press 1)
Fax: (613) 954-1800

E-MAIL ADDRESS:
info@cihr-irsc.gc.ca

WEB SITE ADDRESS:
www.cihr-irsc.gc.ca
www.vanier.gc.ca

FOUNDED: 1969

AREAS OF INTEREST:
Basic, applied and clinical research in
Canada in the health sciences.

NAME(S) OF PROGRAMS:
● **Doctoral Research Award: Vanier Canada Graduate Scholarships**

TYPE:
Awards/prizes; Training grants. Training
awards. The Vanier Canada Graduate
Scholarship program aims to attract and
retain world-class doctoral students by
supporting students who demonstrate a high
standard of scholarly achievement in graduate
studies in the social sciences and humanities,
natural sciences and engineering, and health,
as well as leadership skills.

YEAR PROGRAM STARTED: 1997

PURPOSE:
To support promising doctoral students.

LEGAL BASIS:
Government agency.

ELIGIBILITY:
Canadian citizens, permanent residents and
international students are eligible to be
nominated for a Vanier Canada Graduate
Scholarship.

GEOGRAPHIC RESTRICTIONS:
Canada.

FINANCIAL DATA:
Amount of support per award: $50,000
(CAN) per year.

COOPERATIVE FUNDING PROGRAMS: Natural
Sciences and Engineering Research Council
of Canada; Social Sciences and Humanities
Research Council of Canada

NUMBER OF APPLICANTS MOST RECENT YEAR:
Approximately 166 annually.

NUMBER OF AWARDS: 55 to 56.

APPLICATION INFORMATION:
The university must provide a nomination
letter for each student it wishes to nominate.
The letter must provide a high-level rationale
for the nomination, explaining why the
university is nominating the student for the
award, and how the institution will support
the nominee in the development of his or her
potential.
Duration: Three years maximum.
Nonrenewable.
Deadline: Typically October.

ADDRESS INQUIRIES TO:
Dominique Lalonde, Deputy Director
Doctoral Research Awards
(See address above.)

*SPECIAL STIPULATIONS:
Awards must be taken up within 12 months
of the date of offer.

CANADIAN INSTITUTES OF HEALTH RESEARCH (CIHR)   [2397]

160 Elgin Street, 9th Floor
Address Locator 4809A
Ottawa ON K1A 0W9 Canada
(613) 948-8199
Fax: (613) 954-1800

E-MAIL ADDRESS:
fellowships@cihr-irsc.gc.ca

WEB SITE ADDRESS:
www.cihr-irsc.gc.ca

FOUNDED: 1969

AREAS OF INTEREST:
Health research sciences.

NAME(S) OF PROGRAMS:
● **Fellowship Program**

TYPE:
Fellowships. Postdoctoral fellowships.

YEAR PROGRAM STARTED: 1969

PURPOSE:
To provide support for highly qualified
candidates to add to their experience by
engaging in research either in Canada or
abroad.

LEGAL BASIS:
Government agency.

ELIGIBILITY:
A candidate must hold, or be completing, a
Ph.D. or a health professional degree (or
equivalent). The health professional degree
must be in a regulated health profession such
as medicine, dentistry, pharmacy, optometry,
veterinary medicine, chiropractic, nursing or
rehabilitative science.

For those with a Ph.D. degree (or equivalent),
or a Ph.D. and health professional degree, the
maximum period of support is three years,
and candidates will only be eligible for
support until the end of their fifth year of
post-Ph.D. training.

For individuals that do not hold a health
professional degree, awards will take effect
only after the recipient has completed all
requirements of the Ph.D. program, including
the oral examination.

Candidates with more than three years of
post-Ph.D. research training by the
competition deadline are not eligible to
apply. Any interruption in a candidate's
post-Ph.D. research training will be taken
into account in determining eligibility.

An applicant may not hold more than three
years of federal award funding (e.g., SSHRC,
NSERC, CIHR) to undertake postdoctoral
studies. Recipients already holding a
postdoctoral award from a federal source for
a term of three years are not eligible to
apply.

Individuals wishing to undertake post-Ph.D.
research training in the same research
environment (e.g., same department,
supervisor or co-supervisor) in which they
received their Ph.D. are not eligible for an
award.

Candidates with a health professional degree
may propose a program of research leading
to a Master's or Ph.D. degree; however,
registration in a graduate program is not a
requirement.

FINANCIAL DATA:
Amount of support per award: $21,000 to
$55,000 (CAN) per year, plus $5,000
research allowance per year.
Total amount of support: $12,000,000.

NUMBER OF APPLICANTS MOST RECENT YEAR:
1,200 for the year 2010-11.

NUMBER OF AWARDS: 170 for the year 2010-11.

APPLICATION INFORMATION:
Guidelines will be made available to the
public in July.

Duration: One to five years, depending on degree held.

Deadline: February and October. See web site for exact dates.

PUBLICATIONS:
Annual Report of the President; Grants and Awards Guide.

STAFF:
Christine Sincennes, Team Lead

ADDRESS INQUIRIES TO:
Christine Sincennes, Team Lead
Research Capacity Development
(See address above.)

CANADIAN LIVER FOUNDATION

2235 Sheppard Avenue East
Suite 1500
Toronto ON M2J 5B5 Canada
(416) 491-3353
(800) 563-5483
Fax: (416) 491-4952

E-MAIL ADDRESS:
clf@liver.ca

WEB SITE ADDRESS:
www.liver.ca

TYPE:
Research grants.

See entry 2570 for full listing.

CANADIAN LIVER FOUNDATION   [2398]

2235 Sheppard Avenue East
Suite 1500
Toronto ON M2J 5B5 Canada
(416) 491-3353
(800) 563-5483
Fax: (416) 491-4952

E-MAIL ADDRESS:
clf@liver.ca

WEB SITE ADDRESS:
www.liver.ca

FOUNDED: 1969

AREAS OF INTEREST:
Research and education into the causes, diagnosis, prevention and treatment of diseases of the liver.

NAME(S) OF PROGRAMS:
• **Canadian Liver Foundation Graduate Studentships**

TYPE:
Scholarships.

PURPOSE:
To enable academically superior students to undertake full-time studies in a Canadian university in a discipline relevant to the Foundation's objectives.

LEGAL BASIS:
Registered Canadian charity.

ELIGIBILITY:
Candidates must be accepted into a full-time university graduate science program in a medically-related discipline related to a Master's or doctoral degree and hold a record of superior academic performance in studies relevant to the proposed training.

Candidates must be sponsored by a faculty supervisor with a record of productive medical research and sufficient, competitively

acquired research funding to ensure the satisfactory conduct of the student's research during the term of the award.

GEOGRAPHIC RESTRICTIONS:
Canada.

FINANCIAL DATA:
Amount of support per award: $20,000 per year.

NUMBER OF APPLICANTS MOST RECENT YEAR:
Approximately 15 for the year 2010.

NUMBER OF AWARDS: 4 for the year 2010.

APPLICATION INFORMATION:
Duration: Two academic years. Nonrenewable. Upon approval, transfer from an M.Sc. programme to a Ph.D. programme will permit the student to renew for the total of four years of support.
Deadline: March 31, for awards to become tenable the following September 1.

PUBLICATIONS:
Program description and guidelines.

STAFF:
Billie Potkonjak, National Director of Health Promotion and Patient Services

ADDRESS INQUIRIES TO:
Billie Potkonjak, National Director of Health Promotion and Patient Services
(See address above.)

CANADIAN LIVER FOUNDATION   [2399]

2235 Sheppard Avenue East
Suite 1500
Toronto ON M2J 5B5 Canada
(416) 491-3353
(800) 563-5483
Fax: (416) 491-4952

E-MAIL ADDRESS:
clf@liver.ca

WEB SITE ADDRESS:
www.liver.ca

FOUNDED: 1969

AREAS OF INTEREST:
Research and education into the causes, diagnosis, prevention and treatment of diseases of the liver.

NAME(S) OF PROGRAMS:
• **Summer Studentships**

TYPE:
Scholarships.

PURPOSE:
To provide an opportunity for a limited number of well-motivated students with records of strong academic performance to participate in liver-related research in Canada.

LEGAL BASIS:
Registered Canadian charity.

ELIGIBILITY:
Applicants must be registered at a Canadian institution in an undergraduate degree program.

GEOGRAPHIC RESTRICTIONS:
Canada.

FINANCIAL DATA:
Amount of support per award: $4,000 (CAN) for any three summer months (May through August).

NUMBER OF APPLICANTS MOST RECENT YEAR:
25.

NUMBER OF AWARDS: 11 for the year 2007.

APPLICATION INFORMATION:
Guidelines and application forms are available in hospitals and universities through the office of Research Administration, on the Foundation web site, or from the address above. A limit of two applications may be sponsored by a faculty supervisor, who must have a record of productive medical research related to the liver and adequate research funding, and who must be prepared to provide the student with direct supervision during the term of the award.
Duration: Each award will be for any three summer months (May to August).
Deadline: March 31.

PUBLICATIONS:
Program description and guidelines.

STAFF:
Billie Potkonjak, National Director of Health Promotion and Patient Services

ADDRESS INQUIRIES TO:
Billie Potkonjak, National Director of Health Promotion and Patient Services
(See address above.)

CANADIAN SOCIETY FOR MEDICAL LABORATORY SCIENCE   [2400]

33 Wellington Street North
Hamilton ON L8R 1M7 Canada
(905) 528-8642
Fax: (905) 528-4968

WEB SITE ADDRESS:
www.csmls.org

FOUNDED: 1937

AREAS OF INTEREST:
Continuing education and medical research.

TYPE:
Scholarships. Available to students involved in the clinical phase of their medical lab technology training program. Students must be enrolled in general medical laboratory technology, cytotechnology, or clinical genetics studies leading to CSMLS certification.

YEAR PROGRAM STARTED: 1937

ELIGIBILITY:
Applicants must be enrolled with the CSMLS as a student member and be a Canadian citizen or permanent resident.

GEOGRAPHIC RESTRICTIONS:
Canada.

FINANCIAL DATA:
Amount of support per award: $500 (CAN).
Total amount of support: $2,500 (CAN).

COOPERATIVE FUNDING PROGRAMS: Program is made possible by the generous support of Ortho-Clinical Diagnostics, LifeLabs Medical Laboratory Services, BD Biosciences and Cowan Insurance Brokers.

NUMBER OF AWARDS: 5.

APPLICATION INFORMATION:
Contact the Society.
Duration: Varies depending on award. Generally nonrenewable.
Deadline: October 1.

ADDRESS INQUIRIES TO:
Christine Nielsen, Executive Director
(See address above.)

*SPECIAL STIPULATIONS:
Must be a student enrolled in an accredited training program in Canada.

CHINESE AMERICAN MEDICAL SOCIETY [2401]

281 Edgewood Avenue
Teaneck, NJ 07666
(201) 833-1506
Fax: (201) 833-8252

E-MAIL ADDRESS:
hw5@columbia.edu

WEB SITE ADDRESS:
www.camsociety.org

FOUNDED: 1963

AREAS OF INTEREST:
Medicine.

NAME(S) OF PROGRAMS:
- **CAMS Scholarship Program**
- **Medical Student Summer Research Fellowship**

TYPE:
Research grants; Scholarships.

YEAR PROGRAM STARTED: 1973

PURPOSE:
To promote the scientific association of medical professionals of Chinese descent; to advance medical knowledge and scientific research with emphasis on aspects unique to the Chinese; to establish scholarships to medical dental students and to provide endowments to medical schools and hospitals of good standing; to promote the health status of Chinese Americans.

LEGAL BASIS:
A nonprofit, charitable, educational, and scientific society.

ELIGIBILITY:
Candidates must reside in the U.S. at the time of application, either as alien students or citizens of the U.S. Also, must be matriculated in an approved medical or dental school in the U.S. or Canada.

FINANCIAL DATA:
Amount of support per award: $3,200 to $4,000.

ADDRESS INQUIRIES TO:
Dr. Hsueh H. Wang, Executive Director
(See address above.)

COLLEGE OF PHYSICIANS OF PHILADELPHIA

Francis Clark Wood Institute
for the History of Medicine
19 South 22nd Street
Philadelphia, PA 19103-3097
(215) 399-2305
Fax: (215) 561-6477

E-MAIL ADDRESS:
sereda@collegeofphysicians.org

WEB SITE ADDRESS:
www.collegeofphysicians.org

TYPE:
Travel grants; Visiting scholars. This program allows scholars to conduct short-term research in the College's Library and/or Mutter Museum.

See entry 624 for full listing.

CUREPSP FOUNDATION FOR PSP/CBD AND RELATED BRAIN DISEASES

30 East Padonia Road
Suite 201
Timonium, MD 21093
(410) 785-7004
Fax: (410) 785-7009

E-MAIL ADDRESS:
bantum@curepsp.org

WEB SITE ADDRESS:
www.curepsp.org

TYPE:
Research grants.

See entry 2618 for full listing.

CYSTIC FIBROSIS CANADA [2402]

2221 Yonge Street
Suite 601
Toronto ON M4S 2B4 Canada
(416) 485-9149
(800) 378-2233 (Canada only)
Fax: (416) 485-0960; (416) 485-5707

E-MAIL ADDRESS:
info@cysticfibrosis.ca

WEB SITE ADDRESS:
www.cysticfibrosis.ca

FOUNDED: 1960

AREAS OF INTEREST:
Cystic fibrosis (CF).

NAME(S) OF PROGRAMS:
- **Small Conference Grants**

TYPE:
Conferences/seminars. Support for small conferences which focus on subjects of direct relevance to cystic fibrosis (medical/scientific conferences). Also, grants to facilitate the exchange of special expertise between larger, university-based cystic fibrosis clinics and smaller, more remote clinics (interclinic exchanges).

YEAR PROGRAM STARTED: 1961

PURPOSE:
To support small conferences which are focused on subjects of direct relevance to cystic fibrosis.

LEGAL BASIS:
Nonprofit.

ELIGIBILITY:
Applications will be accepted only from CF clinic directors and CCFF-funded investigators, where the applicant is a member of the conference organizing committee but not a speaker, and the priority would be conferences held in Canada. Subject to the availability of funds, grants are made on a first-come, first-served basis. Frequency of application from any particular individual or group should be reasonable.

GEOGRAPHIC RESTRICTIONS:
Canada.

FINANCIAL DATA:
Amount of support per award:
Medical/scientific conferences: Up to $2,500;
Interclinic exchanges: Normally up to $1,000.
Total amount of support: Varies.

APPLICATION INFORMATION:
Applications should be made in the form of a letter. For medical/scientific conferences, the application should indicate who is organizing and attending the conference and the specific topic(s) and purpose of the conference, along with an itemized budget for the request. For interclinic exchanges, the application should specify the proposed arrangements for, and the specific purpose of, the exchange.
Duration: Varies.

Deadline: Applications may be submitted at any time, but the Foundation should be consulted in advance with respect to the availability of funds.

PUBLICATIONS:
Grants and Awards Guide, English/French booklet.

ADDRESS INQUIRIES TO:
Manager, Research Programs
(See address above.)

THE DANA FOUNDATION [2403]

505 Fifth Avenue, Sixth Floor
New York, NY 10017
(212) 223-4040
Fax: (212) 317-8721

E-MAIL ADDRESS:
amarin@dana.org

WEB SITE ADDRESS:
www.dana.org

FOUNDED: 1950

AREAS OF INTEREST:
Science, health and education, with a current focus on immunology and neuroscience research, and in K-12 education, particularly the use of arts in education.

NAME(S) OF PROGRAMS:
- **Brain and Immuno-Imaging Program**
- **Clinical Neuroscience Research**
- **Neuroimmunology**

TYPE:
Awards/prizes; Challenge/matching grants; Project/program grants; Research grants. For the decade of the 1990s, the Foundation focused on brain research. In 2001, interests expanded to include research in immunology. Grants in these areas are made principally through competitive Clinical Hypotheses Programs in immuno-imaging, neuroimmunology, neuroimaging and brain-cardiovascular system interactions. These competitive grants programs support pilot testing of experimental and innovative ideas that in immunology and neuroscience research have the potential of advancing clinical applications. The Foundation also supports an invitational program in which leading scientists are invited to compete for research grants designed to improve immune system responses to biological agents.

The Foundation has supported advances in education throughout its history. Its current interest is focused primarily on professional development programs that foster improved teaching of the performing arts in public schools. Programs emphasize innovative training projects that are exported from, or imported to, New York City, Washington, DC, Los Angeles and their surrounding areas. Letters of intent are accepted on a rolling basis. Grantees are selected through a competitive process.

YEAR PROGRAM STARTED: 1950

PURPOSE:
To strengthen and improve the quality of science, health and education.

LEGAL BASIS:
Private, independent philanthropic foundation.

ELIGIBILITY:
The Foundation, in general, makes its grants in accordance with the following policies:
(1) it supports programs in science, health and education; carefully defined objectives in

each field guide its grantmaking;
(2) in many cases, it requires grantee institutions to share the cost of a project or raise matching funds;
(3) it makes no grants directly to individuals;
(4) it does not support annual operating budgets of organizations, deficit reduction, capital campaigns or individual sabbaticals and;
(5) it does not schedule meetings with applicants, other than by specific invitation initiated by the Foundation.

GEOGRAPHIC RESTRICTIONS:
United States.

FINANCIAL DATA:
Amount of support per award: $200,000 to $300,000.

Total amount of support: Varies by program.

Matching fund requirements: Most awards for matching grants require grant recipients to raise a significant portion of the financing necessary for the proposed project.

NUMBER OF APPLICANTS MOST RECENT YEAR:
500.

NUMBER OF AWARDS: Varies.

APPLICATION INFORMATION:
Clinical Neuroscience Research: Requests for Proposals (RFPs) for the Program are sent to the deans of all U.S. medical schools and other invited institutions.

Inquiries for grant support should be in the form of a two-page letter describing:
(1) goal(s) of the project;
(2) need the project would meet and its fit with the Foundation's priorities in health or education;
(3) means to be used to achieve the project's goal(s);
(4) capabilities of the institution to undertake the project and the qualifications of the project's proposed director and;
(5) estimated cost and proposed methods of financing the project, including the institution's intended contribution.

Letters of inquiry should be mailed to the Foundation. No proposals submitted by fax will be accepted. If the Foundation determines that an inquiry fits its interests, a full proposal will be requested. Supporting materials should not be submitted until requested. A full proposal should be accompanied by documents establishing the applicant's Internal Revenue Code 501(c)(3) tax-exempt status.

Duration: Up to three years. Renewals are rare.

Deadline: Varies.

PUBLICATIONS:
Annual report; *Dana Report*, newsletter; application guidelines.

IRS IDENTIFICATION NUMBER: 06-6036761

BOARD OF DIRECTORS:
Edward F. Rover, Chairman
Clark M. Whittemore, Jr., Secretary and Treasurer
Edward Bleier
Wallace L. Cook
Charles A. Dana, III
Steven E. Hyman, M.D.
LaSalle D. Leffall, Jr., M.D.
Hildegarde E. Mahoney
Ann McLaughlin-Korologos
Herbert J. Siegel

ADMINISTRATION:
Edward F. Rover, President

Jane Nevins, Vice President
Barbara E. Gill, Vice President, Communications
Burton M. Mirsky, Vice President, Finance

ADDRESS INQUIRIES TO:
Angie Marin, Grant Officer
(See address above.)

DERMATOLOGY FOUNDATION   [2404]
1560 Sherman Avenue
Suite 870
Evanston, IL 60201-4808
(847) 328-2256
Fax: (847) 328-0509

E-MAIL ADDRESS:
dfgen@dermatologyfoundation.org

WEB SITE ADDRESS:
www.dermatologyfoundation.org

FOUNDED: 1964

AREAS OF INTEREST:
Cancer and other diseases of the skin, hair and nails.

TYPE:
Fellowships; Project/program grants; Research grants. Research funding in the form of career development grants, fellowships, project/program grants and research grants for academic investigators in the early stages of their careers.

There are 12 research award categories. Career development awards include Physician Scientist, Dermatologic Surgery, Health Care Policy, Medical Dermatology, Psoriasis, Science of Human Appearance and Women's Health Issues. Dermatologist Investigator and Pediatric Dermatology Fellowships. Various Patient-Directed and Research Grants available.

YEAR PROGRAM STARTED: 1964

PURPOSE:
To advance the research careers of young individuals in dermatology and cutaneous biology, with the emphasis on research benefiting the dermatology community at large.

LEGAL BASIS:
Nonprofit charitable organization.

GEOGRAPHIC RESTRICTIONS:
United States.

FINANCIAL DATA:
Amount of support per award: Career development awards: Average $55,000; Fellowships: Average $30,000 to $45,000; Grants: Average $20,000.

Total amount of support: $3,100,000 in research funding for the year 2011.

NUMBER OF AWARDS: 67.

APPLICATION INFORMATION:
Forms are available only on the Foundation web site.

Duration: One year. Renewal possibilities vary.

Deadline: October 15. Announcement mid-winter at the annual meeting of the American Academy of Dermatology.

PUBLICATIONS:
Annual report; *Dermatology Focus*, scientific publication.

IRS IDENTIFICATION NUMBER: 04-6115524

OFFICERS:
Bruce U. Wintroub, M.D., Chairman, Board of Trustees
Richard L. Edelson, M.D., President
Michael D. Tharp, M.D., Vice President
Stuart R. Lessin, M.D., Secretary/Treasurer

ADDRESS INQUIRIES TO:
Sandra R. Benz, Executive Director
(See address above.)

PATRICK AND CATHERINE WELDON DONAGHUE MEDICAL RESEARCH FOUNDATION   [2405]
18 North Main Street
West Hartford, CT 06107
(860) 521-9011
Fax: (860) 521-9018

E-MAIL ADDRESS:
office@donaghue.org

WEB SITE ADDRESS:
www.donaghue.org

FOUNDED: 1991

AREAS OF INTEREST:
Medical and health research.

NAME(S) OF PROGRAMS:
● **Donaghue Program for Research Leadership**

TYPE:
Project/program grants; Research grants. Foundation grants support research to promote knowledge which will be of practical benefit to human life.

YEAR PROGRAM STARTED: 1991

PURPOSE:
To support health research grants in Connecticut.

LEGAL BASIS:
Charitable testamentary trust.

ELIGIBILITY:
Eligible organizations must be IRS 501(c)(3) tax-exempt. No grants to individuals or religious organizations. Applications are not accepted from outside Connecticut.

GEOGRAPHIC RESTRICTIONS:
Connecticut.

FINANCIAL DATA:
Total amount of support: Varies.

APPLICATION INFORMATION:
Duration: One to four years.
Deadline: Varies.

PUBLICATIONS:
Annual report; periodic newsletters; application guidelines and forms.

STAFF:
Lynne Garner, Ph.D., President and Trustee
Stacy Cloud, Grants Administrator

ADDRESS INQUIRIES TO:
Stacy Cloud, Grants Administrator
(See address above.)

EDWIN H. EDDY FAMILY FOUNDATION   [2406]
Wells Fargo Bank Minnesota
222 West Superior Street
Duluth, MN 55802
(218) 723-2615
Fax: (218) 722-9158

AREAS OF INTEREST:
Communicative disorders, research, rehabilitation and treatment.

TYPE:
Matching gifts; Project/program grants; Research grants; Scholarships; Technical assistance.

PURPOSE:
To promote medical research and rehabilitative medicine in the city of Duluth, MN, and the surrounding area.

LEGAL BASIS:
Private foundation.

ELIGIBILITY:
Grants are not made to individuals. A qualifying organization must have 501(c)(3) not-for-profit status.

Scholarships are provided for college seniors and students in an accredited graduate program of communication disorders at University of Minnesota, Duluth. Applicants for scholarships must be citizens or residents of the U.S. The award will be strictly scholarship and not traineeship. Only full-time students qualify. Applicants must meet a minimum overall grade point average (currently 3.3) to qualify for a scholarship.

GEOGRAPHIC RESTRICTIONS:
Duluth, Minnesota and the surrounding area.

FINANCIAL DATA:
Amount of support per award: Scholarships: $1,200 to senior-level students for the regular school year; $3,500 to graduate-level students.
Total amount of support: Approximately $200,000 annually.

NUMBER OF AWARDS: Varies.

APPLICATION INFORMATION:
Grant applicant organization must request guidelines, then submit a proposal which includes the IRS 501(c)(3) letter of determination.

Scholarship applicants must provide the Foundation a completed application form and a certified copy of the most recent transcript from present or previous institution attended.
Duration: Scholarships: One year. Renewable.

TRUSTEE:
Karl Wasson, Trustee

ADDRESS INQUIRIES TO:
Karl Wasson, Trustee
Edwin H. Eddy Family Foundation
(See address above.)

EMERGENCY MEDICINE FOUNDATION   [2407]
1125 Executive Circle
Irving, TX 75038-2522
(800) 798-1822 ext. 3216
Fax: (972) 580-2816

E-MAIL ADDRESS:
info@emfoundation.org

WEB SITE ADDRESS:
www.emfoundation.org

FOUNDED: 1972

AREAS OF INTEREST:
Emergency medicine research.

TYPE:
Fellowships; Research grants. Policy-based research awards in emergency medicine.

YEAR PROGRAM STARTED: 1972

PURPOSE:
To promote education and research in emergency medicine.

ELIGIBILITY:
Must be an emergency medicine researcher.

GEOGRAPHIC RESTRICTIONS:
United States.

FINANCIAL DATA:
Amount of support per award: $2,400 to $150,000.

NUMBER OF APPLICANTS MOST RECENT YEAR:
75.

APPLICATION INFORMATION:
Duration: One year.
Deadline: Varies.

ADDRESS INQUIRIES TO:
Holly Hull Miori, Development Manager
(See address above.)

FOUNDATION FOR ANESTHESIA EDUCATION AND RESEARCH   [2408]
200 First Street, S.W., WF6-674
Rochester, MN 55905
(507) 266-6866
Fax: (507) 284-0291

E-MAIL ADDRESS:
demulling.carol@mayo.edu

WEB SITE ADDRESS:
www.faer.org

AREAS OF INTEREST:
Anesthesiology, critical care, pain, and all areas of perioperative medicine.

NAME(S) OF PROGRAMS:
- **FAER Mentored Research Training Grant**
- **FAER Research Education Grant**
- **FAER Research Fellowship Grant**

TYPE:
Fellowships; Research grants; Training grants. These grants are designed to create opportunities for physicians to excel in an exceedingly competitive environment and to eventually acquire NIH funding.

PURPOSE:
To provide research grant funding for promising investigators to train in clinical, basic science and translational anesthesiology research.

ELIGIBILITY:
FAER Mentored Research Training Grant: Applicants must be instructors or assistant professors who are within 10 years of their initial appointment.

FAER Research Education Grant: Open to anesthesiology residents or faculty.

FAER Research Fellowship Grant: Open to anesthesiology residents after CA-1 training and six months of clinical scientist track.

A 20-member committee consisting of both clinical and basic science anesthesiologists reviews proposals. Clinical and outcomes projects are encouraged.

GEOGRAPHIC RESTRICTIONS:
United States.

FINANCIAL DATA:
Amount of support per award: $50,000 to $175,000.
Total amount of support: $2,000,000 annually.

NUMBER OF APPLICANTS MOST RECENT YEAR:
55.

NUMBER OF AWARDS: 14.

APPLICATION INFORMATION:
Deadline: February 15.

IRS IDENTIFICATION NUMBER: 52-1494164

ADDRESS INQUIRIES TO:
Denham S. Ward, M.D., Ph.D., President
(See address above.)

THE MICHAEL J. FOX FOUNDATION FOR PARKINSON'S RESEARCH   [2409]
Church Street Station
P.O. Box 780
New York, NY 10008
(212) 509-0995
Fax: (212) 509-2390

E-MAIL ADDRESS:
research@michaeljfox.org

WEB SITE ADDRESS:
www.michaeljfox.org

FOUNDED: 2000

AREAS OF INTEREST:
Medical research and Parkinson's disease.

TYPE:
Conferences/seminars; Research grants.

YEAR PROGRAM STARTED: 2000

PURPOSE:
To find a cure for Parkinson's disease through an aggressively funded research agenda; to ensure the development of improved therapies for those living with Parkinson's today.

LEGAL BASIS:
501(c)(3).

ELIGIBILITY:
Varies depending on research program.

FINANCIAL DATA:
Amount of support per award: Varies.
Total amount of support: Varies.

NUMBER OF APPLICANTS MOST RECENT YEAR:
624 for the year 2010.

NUMBER OF AWARDS: 142 for the year 2010.

APPLICATION INFORMATION:
The Foundation has implemented an electronic grant submission and review system that will enable research to be funded quickly and efficiently. Applicants should consult the Foundation web site for information.
Duration: Varies.
Deadline: Varies.

PUBLICATIONS:
Accelerating the Cure, newsletter; *Fox Flash*, e-newsletter; annual report; progress report.

IRS IDENTIFICATION NUMBER: 13-4141945

STAFF:
Deborah W. Brooks, Co-Founder
Katie Hood, Chief Executive Officer

BOARD OF DIRECTORS:
Michael J. Fox, Founder
George E. Prescott, Chairman
David Golub, Vice Chairman
Holly S. Andersen, M.D.
Eva Andersson-Dubin, M.D.
Jon Brooks
Barry J. Cohen
Donny Deutsch
David Einhorn
Karen Finerman
Nelle Fortenberry
Albert B. Glickman

Mark L. Hart, III
Skip Irving
Kathleen Kennedy
Morton M. Kondracke
Edwin A. Levy
Mark S. Lipschultz
Douglas I. Ostrover
Tracy Pollan
Ryan Reynolds
Frederick E. Rowe
Lily Safra
Curtis Schenker
Woody Shackleton
Fred G. Weiss

ADDRESS INQUIRIES TO:
Todd Sherer
Vice President, Research Programs
(See address above.)

THE PARKER B. FRANCIS FELLOWSHIP PROGRAM [2410]
VA Puget Sound Health Care System
1660 South Columbian Way, 151L
Seattle, WA 98108
(206) 764-2219
Fax: (206) 768-5289

E-MAIL ADDRESS:
dsnapp@u.washington.edu

WEB SITE ADDRESS:
www.francisfellowships.org

FOUNDED: 1951

AREAS OF INTEREST:
Research related to lung biology, pulmonary disease and respiratory medicine.

TYPE:
Fellowships. Awarded for postdoctoral lung research and training.

YEAR PROGRAM STARTED: 1975

PURPOSE:
To enable qualified postdoctoral candidates to devote the major part of their professional effort in research related to pulmonary disease.

LEGAL BASIS:
Private foundation.

ELIGIBILITY:
M.D. or Ph.D. candidates may hold any relevant doctoral degree (e.g., M.D., Ph.D., Sc.D., D.V.M., D.P.H.) and an aptitude and proficiency in research. Candidates must be citizens of the U.S., Canada or Mexico, or have documentation towards securing citizenship.

GEOGRAPHIC RESTRICTIONS:
North America.

FINANCIAL DATA:
Funds to be used for stipends and fringe benefits, with up to $2,000 per year as a travel allowance.
Amount of support per award: $156,000.

NUMBER OF AWARDS: 15 to 18.

APPLICATION INFORMATION:
Duration: Three years.
Deadline: October 10. Announcement in February.

PUBLICATIONS:
Annual report; application guidelines.

STAFF:
Deborah Snapp, Administrator

SCIENTIFIC ADVISORY COMMITTEE:
Qutayba Hamid, M.D., Ph.D.
Polly Parsons, M.D.

Usha Raj, M.D.
Dean Sheppard, M.D.
Julian Solway, M.D.
David S. Wilkes, M.D.

ADDRESS INQUIRIES TO:
Thomas R. Martin, M.D., Director
(See address above.)

*SPECIAL STIPULATIONS:
Only one application will be accepted from a department or division per year. Support is provided for only two Fellows in a department at any one time. E-mail inquiries preferred.

FRAXA RESEARCH FOUNDATION [2411]
45 Pleasant Street
Newburyport, MA 01950
(978) 462-1866
Fax: (978) 463-9985

E-MAIL ADDRESS:
info@fraxa.org

WEB SITE ADDRESS:
www.fraxa.org

FOUNDED: 1994

AREAS OF INTEREST:
Medical research aimed at the treatment of Fragile X Syndrome.

NAME(S) OF PROGRAMS:
● **FRAXA Grants and Fellowships**

TYPE:
Fellowships; Research grants; Research contracts.

YEAR PROGRAM STARTED: 1994

PURPOSE:
To promote research aimed at finding a specific treatment for Fragile X Syndrome; to provide funds for postdoctoral fellowships and investigator-initiated grants.

FINANCIAL DATA:
Amount of support per award: Up to $45,000 per year for fellowships. No limit on grants.

APPLICATION INFORMATION:
Application form, plus a one-page initial inquiry letter.
Duration: One year. Renewable.
Deadline: February 1.

PUBLICATIONS:
Newsletter.

IRS IDENTIFICATION NUMBER: 04-3222167

OFFICER:
Katherine Clapp, President

FRIENDS OF JOSE CARRERAS INTERNATIONAL LEUKEMIA FOUNDATION [2412]
1100 Fairview Avenue North
Suite D5-100
P.O. Box 19024
Seattle, WA 98109-1024
(206) 667-7108
Fax: (206) 667-6124

E-MAIL ADDRESS:
friendsjc@carreras-foundation.org

WEB SITE ADDRESS:
www.carreras-foundation.org

FOUNDED: 1990

AREAS OF INTEREST:
Leukemia and related hematologic diseases research.

NAME(S) OF PROGRAMS:
● **Research Fellowships**

TYPE:
Fellowships.

YEAR PROGRAM STARTED: 1990

PURPOSE:
To cure leukemia and allied diseases by providing funding for medical research to young investigators.

LEGAL BASIS:
501(c)(3).

ELIGIBILITY:
Candidates must hold an M.D. or Ph.D. degree and have completed at least three years postdoctoral training, but must be less than 10 years past their first doctoral degree when the award begins. There are no restrictions based on nationality, but only one application will be considered from each sponsoring institution. Candidates must be committed to the research goals of the Foundation, must be able to devote at least 60% of their time to the project and must have a sponsoring institution with the academic environment to provide adequate support for the proposed project.

FINANCIAL DATA:
Amount of support per award: $50,000 per year.

APPLICATION INFORMATION:
All applications must be typed, single-spaced, in English and must follow the format specified in the application packet. All forms must be completed and space restrictions adhered to. Request for application forms will not be considered after October 15. Application forms will not be sent by fax. Do not contact the Foundation for results. Reapplication by unsuccessful candidates will be necessary for the following year.
Duration: Three years.

ADDRESS INQUIRIES TO:
Karen Carbonneau, Administrator
(See address or e-mail above.)

FSH SOCIETY, INC. [2413]
64 Grove Street
BBRI Room 353
Watertown, MA 02472
(617) 658-7878
Fax: (617) 658-7879

E-MAIL ADDRESS:
nancy.vanzant@fshsociety.org

WEB SITE ADDRESS:
www.fshsociety.org

FOUNDED: 1991

AREAS OF INTEREST:
Facioscapulohumeral Muscular Dystrophy.

TYPE:
Conferences/seminars; Fellowships; Project/program grants; Research grants; Travel grants.

YEAR PROGRAM STARTED: 1998

PURPOSE:
To promote research on and disperse information on Facioscapulohumeral Muscular Dystrophy.

ELIGIBILITY:
Applications may be submitted by domestic or foreign for-profit and nonprofit organizations, public and private, such as

universities, colleges, hospitals, laboratories, units of state and local governments, and eligible agencies of the federal government.

FINANCIAL DATA:
Total amount of support: $30,000 to $45,000 per year.

NUMBER OF APPLICANTS MOST RECENT YEAR: 9.

NUMBER OF AWARDS: 5.

APPLICATION INFORMATION:
Duration: One year.
Deadline: February 1 and August 1.

PUBLICATIONS:
FSH Watch Newsletter; patient information on FSHD (English and Spanish).

IRS IDENTIFICATION NUMBER: 52-1762747

STAFF:
Daniel Paul Perez, President
Nancy Van Zant, Executive Director

ADDRESS INQUIRIES TO:
Nancy Van Zant, Executive Director
(See address above.)

GLAUCOMA RESEARCH FOUNDATION

251 Post Street, Suite 600
San Francisco, CA 94108
(415) 986-3162
Fax: (415) 986-3763

E-MAIL ADDRESS:
research@glaucoma.org

WEB SITE ADDRESS:
www.glaucoma.org

TYPE:
Research grants.

See entry 2674 for full listing.

THE GRAYSON-JOCKEY CLUB RESEARCH FOUNDATION [2414]

821 Corporate Drive
Lexington, KY 40503
(859) 224-2850
Fax: (859) 224-2853

E-MAIL ADDRESS:
ebowen@jockeyclub.com

WEB SITE ADDRESS:
www.grayson-jockeyclub.org

FOUNDED: 1940

AREAS OF INTEREST:
Race horses, veterinary medicine and research for all horses.

TYPE:
Research grants. Supports equine medical research.

PURPOSE:
To promote research in veterinary medicine and in the breeding, raising and handling of horses.

LEGAL BASIS:
Nonprofit foundation.

ELIGIBILITY:
The principal investigator should have some professional rank and salary from the institution involved, or hold some grade of Research Professorship with salary from the institution. Research interest must be relevant to the equine, particularly in regard to, but not limited to, cardiopulmonary disorders, infectious diseases, musculoskeletal disorders, and reproduction.

FINANCIAL DATA:
Amount of support per award: Average $50,000.
Total amount of support: Approximately $1,000,000 annually.

NUMBER OF APPLICANTS MOST RECENT YEAR: 60.

NUMBER OF AWARDS: 15.

APPLICATION INFORMATION:
Duration: One or two years.
Deadline: October 1. Announcement April 1.

PUBLICATIONS:
Application; guidelines; *Research Today*, newsletter.

OFFICERS:
Dell Hancock, Chairman
A. Gary Lavin, D.V.M., Vice Chairman
Edward L. Bowen, President
Nancy C. Kelly, Vice President of Development/Secretary
Laura Barillaro, Treasurer

ADDRESS INQUIRIES TO:
Edward L. Bowen, President
(See address above.)

HEALTH RESOURCES AND SERVICES ADMINISTRATION [2415]

Primary Care Medical Education Branch
Division of Medicine and Dentistry
5600 Fishers Lane, Room 9A-27
Rockville, MD 20857
(301) 443-1467
Fax: (301) 443-1945

WEB SITE ADDRESS:
bhpr.hrsa.gov/grants/default.htm

NAME(S) OF PROGRAMS:
● **Training in Primary Care Medicine and Dentistry**

TYPE:
Residencies; Training grants. Grants to assist in meeting the cost of planning, developing, operating or participating in approved graduate training programs in the fields of medicine and dentistry. The program assists residency programs in the promotion of physicians who are trained for and will enter the practice of medicine or dentistry.

YEAR PROGRAM STARTED: 1972

PURPOSE:
To improve and expand access to quality health care for all.

LEGAL BASIS:
Section 747(a) of the PHS Act, as amended by the Health Professions Education Extension Amendments of 1992, Public Law 102-408.

ELIGIBILITY:
Hospitals, accredited schools of medicine and osteopathy and/or public or private nonprofit entities providing health or educational programs are eligible.

GEOGRAPHIC RESTRICTIONS:
United States.

FINANCIAL DATA:
Grants may include support for the program only or support of both the program and trainees who plan to specialize or work in the practice of family medicine.
Total amount of support: $6,850,000 budgeted for fiscal year 2008.

NUMBER OF AWARDS: Approximately 112 for fiscal years 2008-10.

APPLICATION INFORMATION:
Applicants are required to apply for this funding opportunity electronically through www.grants.gov.
All applications are competitively reviewed and evaluated.
Duration: One to three years. Renewal permitted.

THE LARRY L. HILLBLOM FOUNDATION, INC. [2416]

755 Baywood Drive, Suite 180
Petaluma, CA 94954
(707) 762-6691
Fax: (707) 762-6694

E-MAIL ADDRESS:
som@llhf.org

WEB SITE ADDRESS:
www.llhf.org

AREAS OF INTEREST:
Medical research on diabetes mellitus and diseases associated with aging.

NAME(S) OF PROGRAMS:
● **Fellowship Research Grants**
● **Start-Up Research Grants**

TYPE:
Fellowships; Professorships; Project/program grants; Research grants; Research contracts. Fellowship Research Grants are intended to enable qualified institutions to provide postdoctoral research fellowship training to qualified applicants in one of the two areas of stated interest to the Foundation.

Start-Up Research Grants are offered to qualified institutions to enable them to select and assist qualified researchers to initiate independent research careers.

YEAR PROGRAM STARTED: 2000

PURPOSE:
To provide philanthropic support exclusively for charitable, religious, scientific, literary and educational purposes.

ELIGIBILITY:
Eligible organizations must have 501(c)(3) status.

GEOGRAPHIC RESTRICTIONS:
Primarily, California.

FINANCIAL DATA:
Amount of support per award: Fellowship Grants: Up to $60,000 per year; Start-Up Grants: Up to $70,000 per year.
Total amount of support: Varies.

NUMBER OF APPLICANTS MOST RECENT YEAR: 100.

NUMBER OF AWARDS: 26 for the year 2010-11.

APPLICATION INFORMATION:
Duration: Up to three years.
Deadline: Early January. Notification by June.

HIMSS FOUNDATION [2417]

230 East Ohio Street, Suite 500
Chicago, IL 60611-3270
(312) 915-9277
(312) 664-4467
Fax: (312) 915-9512

E-MAIL ADDRESS:
foundation@himss.org

WEB SITE ADDRESS:
www.himss.org

FOUNDED: 1961

AREAS OF INTEREST:
Health care information and management systems.

NAME(S) OF PROGRAMS:
● **HIMSS Foundation Scholarship Program**

TYPE:
Awards/prizes; Conferences/seminars; Fellowships; Internships; Research grants; Scholarships.

YEAR PROGRAM STARTED: 1986

PURPOSE:
To recognize students who have the potential to be future leaders in the health care information management systems industry.

ELIGIBILITY:
Applicant must be a student in an accredited degree granting institution, a junior when the scholarship is awarded, and a student member of the Healthcare Information and Management Systems Society. Previous winners are not eligible, although the undergraduate winner is eligible if pursuing a graduate degree.

FINANCIAL DATA:
An all-expense paid trip to the HIMSS annual conference is awarded in addition to grant.
Amount of support per award: $5,000.
Total amount of support: Varies.

NUMBER OF APPLICANTS MOST RECENT YEAR:
140.

NUMBER OF AWARDS: 8 to 11.

APPLICATION INFORMATION:
Duration: One year.
Deadline: Applications are accepted annually August 1 to October 31.

ADDRESS INQUIRIES TO:
Megan McGuirk
Program Manager, Professional Development
(See address above.)

MAXIMILIAN E. & MARION O. HOFFMAN FOUNDATION, INC.   [2418]
970 Farmington Avenue, Suite 203
West Hartford, CT 06107
(860) 521-2949
Fax: (860) 561-5082

E-MAIL ADDRESS:
kwhoffman@snet.net

AREAS OF INTEREST:
Education, medicine and the arts.

TYPE:
Project/program grants.

PURPOSE:
To provide funding to 501(c)(3) nonprofits conducting projects in education, medicine, and the arts.

LEGAL BASIS:
Nonprofit private foundation.

ELIGIBILITY:
Applicants must be 501(c)(3). No grants to individuals.

GEOGRAPHIC RESTRICTIONS:
United States, with preference to Connecticut.

FINANCIAL DATA:
Amount of support per award: Varies depending on needs and nature of the request.

APPLICATION INFORMATION:
Submit Letter of Inquiry with copy of 501(c)(3).
Duration: One year. Some multiyear grants. Renewal possible by reapplication.
Deadline: The Board of Directors meets four to six times a year to consider requests.

PUBLICATIONS:
Application form.

ADDRESS INQUIRIES TO:
Marion Barrak, President
(See address above.)

HOWARD HUGHES MEDICAL INSTITUTE   [2419]
Medical Research Fellows Program
1 Cloister Ct., Bldg. 60, Room 254
Bethesda, MD 20814-1460
(800) 424-9924
Fax: (240) 497-2314

E-MAIL ADDRESS:
medfellows@hhmi.org

WEB SITE ADDRESS:
www.hhmi.org/medstudent

FOUNDED: 1953

AREAS OF INTEREST:
Fundamental biomedical research and science education.

NAME(S) OF PROGRAMS:
● **Medical Research Fellows Program**

TYPE:
Fellowships.

YEAR PROGRAM STARTED: 1989

PURPOSE:
To strengthen and expand the pool of medically trained researchers.

LEGAL BASIS:
Medical research organization.

ELIGIBILITY:
Applicant must be enrolled in medical, dental or veterinary school in the U.S., not in a Ph.D. or M.D./Ph.D. or other combined professional degree/Ph.D. program. Applicant must plan to spend a year full-time in fundamental biomedical research.

FINANCIAL DATA:
Amount of support per award: $28,000 stipend, $5,500 research allowance, and $5,500 Fellow's allowance.

NUMBER OF APPLICANTS MOST RECENT YEAR:
244.

NUMBER OF AWARDS: 66 for the year 2012.

APPLICATION INFORMATION:
Online application requires the following information:
(1) educational background;
(2) prior research experience;
(3) research plan;
(4) mentor's endorsement and reference letters and;
(5) undergraduate academic transcript data.
Duration: One year.
Deadline: January. Announcement at the end of March.

IRS IDENTIFICATION NUMBER: 59-0735717

ADDRESS INQUIRIES TO:
Melanie Daub, Program Officer
(See address above.)

IMMUNE DEFICIENCY FOUNDATION
40 West Chesapeake Avenue
Suite 308
Towson, MD 21204
(866) 939-7568
Fax: (410) 321-0293

E-MAIL ADDRESS:
odavis@primaryimmune.org

WEB SITE ADDRESS:
www.usidnet.org

TYPE:
Travel grants; Visiting scholars.

See entry 2492 for full listing.

INTERNATIONAL ANESTHESIA RESEARCH SOCIETY (IARS)   [2420]
100 Pine Street
Suite 230
San Francisco, CA 94111
(415) 296-6900
Fax: (415) 296-6901

E-MAIL ADDRESS:
info@iars.org

WEB SITE ADDRESS:
www.iars.org

FOUNDED: 1922

AREAS OF INTEREST:
Anesthesia.

NAME(S) OF PROGRAMS:
● **Anesthesiology Teaching Recognition Awards**
● **Frontiers in Anesthesia Research Award**

TYPE:
Research grants. Education awards.

YEAR PROGRAM STARTED: 1995

PURPOSE:
To foster innovation and creativity by an individual researcher in the field of anesthesiology.

ELIGIBILITY:
Applicant must be a member of the IARS and must be a member in good standing in the sponsoring Department of Anesthesiology. Applicants are eligible for this award during the 15 years following their first academic appointment in anesthesiology (regardless of institution). The proposed area of investigation must have direct relevance to the specialty of Anesthesiology.

Candidates may have active peer review funding, but there can be no duplication with the proposal. There are no restrictions in budget categories other than institutional overhead which will not be paid as part of the Award.

FINANCIAL DATA:
Amount of support per award:
Anesthesiology Teaching Recognition Awards: $15,000; Frontiers in Anesthesia Research Award: $750,000, in three annual installments.

NUMBER OF APPLICANTS MOST RECENT YEAR:
Frontiers in Anesthesia Research Award: 20 for the year 2009.

NUMBER OF AWARDS: Anesthesiology Teaching Recognition Awards: 2 annually; Frontiers in Anesthesia Research Award: 1 biennially, in odd years.

APPLICATION INFORMATION:
Application can be submitted online.
Duration: Frontiers in Anesthesia Research Award: Three years.
Deadline: Frontiers in Anesthesia Research Award: October 2011.

PUBLICATIONS:
Anethesia & Analgesia, journal.

ADDRESS INQUIRIES TO:
Amanda Roberts, Program Coordinator
(See address above.)

INTERNATIONAL ANESTHESIA RESEARCH SOCIETY (IARS)   [2421]
100 Pine Street
Suite 230
San Francisco, CA 94111
(415) 296-6900
Fax: (415) 296-6901

E-MAIL ADDRESS:
info@iars.org

WEB SITE ADDRESS:
www.iars.org

FOUNDED: 1922

AREAS OF INTEREST:
Anesthesia.

NAME(S) OF PROGRAMS:
● **Clinical Scholar Research Awards**

TYPE:
Research grants.

YEAR PROGRAM STARTED: 1994

PURPOSE:
To further the understanding of clinical practice in anesthesiology and related sciences through clinical investigations.

ELIGIBILITY:
The principal applicant must be a member of the IARS and an investigator with research experience who has yet to establish a history of substantial funding, and be less than 10 years after completion of clinical training or Ph.D. Prior recipients of an IARS Clinical Scholar Research Award are not eligible to apply. In general, previous or current recipients of NIH R0-1 grants, or the equivalent, will not be eligible to apply. Exceptions to this rule are possible for individuals who have not previously received funding for clinical research.

Research must involve human subjects, in vivo or in vitro.

FINANCIAL DATA:
Amount of support per award: $80,000.
Total amount of support: $320,000.

NUMBER OF APPLICANTS MOST RECENT YEAR:
60.

NUMBER OF AWARDS: Up to 4 awarded annually.

APPLICATION INFORMATION:
Application must be submitted online.
Duration: Two years.
Deadline: December 1, 2011 for the 2012 awards.

PUBLICATIONS:
Anesthesia & Analgesia, journal.

ADDRESS INQUIRIES TO:
Amanda Roberts, Program Coordinator
(See address above.)

*SPECIAL STIPULATIONS:
Prior recipients of an IARS Clinical Scholar Research Award are not eligible for this award.

INTERNATIONAL COLLEGE OF SURGEONS   [2422]
1516 North Lake Shore Drive
Chicago, IL 60610-1694
(312) 787-1638
Fax: (312) 787-1683

E-MAIL ADDRESS:
max@icsglobal.org

WEB SITE ADDRESS:
www.icsglobal.org

AREAS OF INTEREST:
Medical research and surgery.

NAME(S) OF PROGRAMS:
● **ICS Scholarship**

TYPE:
Scholarships.

PURPOSE:
To support education and research.

ELIGIBILITY:
Open to surgeons around the world traveling to developed nations to further their education.

FINANCIAL DATA:
Amount of support per award: $500 to $2,000.

NUMBER OF APPLICANTS MOST RECENT YEAR:
15.

APPLICATION INFORMATION:
Send request to ICS.
Duration: Varies.

ADDRESS INQUIRIES TO:
Max Downham, Executive Director
(See address above.)

INTERNATIONAL FEDERATION OF BIOMEDICAL LABORATORY SCIENCE (IFBLS)   [2423]
P.O. Box 2830 LCD 1
Hamilton ON L8N 3N8 Canada
(905) 528-8642 ext. 8695
Fax: (905) 528-4968

E-MAIL ADDRESS:
communications@ifbls.org

WEB SITE ADDRESS:
www.ifbls.org

FOUNDED: 1954

AREAS OF INTEREST:
Medical laboratory science, improving training, education and status of medical laboratory technologists, standardization of training, and quality of medical laboratory science and services.

CONSULTING OR VOLUNTEER SERVICES:
Non-governmental organization in official relationship with the World Health Organization and the Council of Europe.

NAME(S) OF PROGRAMS:
● **IFBLS Award Program**

TYPE:
Awards/prizes; Conferences/seminars; Development grants; Project/program grants;

Scholarships; Travel grants; Visiting scholars. Prizes for biennial competition, usually by essay or project, to members only. Various prizes are offered by laboratory suppliers and pharmaceutical manufacturers in various fields of medical laboratory science.

YEAR PROGRAM STARTED: 1966

PURPOSE:
To promote medical laboratory technology all over the world by affording opportunities for medical laboratory technologists to meet to discuss problems of common professional interest in an international forum.

LEGAL BASIS:
International association.

ELIGIBILITY:
Competitors must be contributing members of a national association which is itself a contributing member of IFBLS.

FINANCIAL DATA:
Amount of support per award: Varies.
Total amount of support: Varies.

COOPERATIVE FUNDING PROGRAMS: Member society subscription donations.

APPLICATION INFORMATION:
Information is available from the Executive Office.
Deadline: December 31.

PUBLICATIONS:
IFBLS information pamphlet; *BLSI*; Code of Ethics; Qualification statement.

STAFF:
Janna Malseed, Office Administrator

*SPECIAL STIPULATIONS:
Membership in one of the national associations of IFBLS required.

INTERNATIONAL MYELOMA FOUNDATION (IMF)   [2424]
12650 Riverside Drive, Suite 206
North Hollywood, CA 91607-3421
(818) 487-7455
Fax: (818) 487-7454

E-MAIL ADDRESS:
theimf@myeloma.org

WEB SITE ADDRESS:
www.myeloma.org

FOUNDED: 1990

AREAS OF INTEREST:
Myeloma.

NAME(S) OF PROGRAMS:
● **Brian D. Novis Research Grants**

TYPE:
Internships; Research grants; Travel grants.

YEAR PROGRAM STARTED: 1995

PURPOSE:
To promote research into better treatments, management, prevention and a cure for myeloma.

LEGAL BASIS:
Nonprofit organization.

ELIGIBILITY:
Open to junior researchers or senior researchers working in the field of multiple myeloma. Junior researchers must have completed postdoctoral studies or clinical fellowships no later than August 1 of the application year and must have the ability to devote a minimum of 50% of his or her time

to research during the award year. Also, must provide a completed application with evidence of a meritorious research project.

FINANCIAL DATA:
Amount of support per award: Junior researchers: $50,000; Senior researchers: $80,000.

Total amount of support: Varies each year.

APPLICATION INFORMATION:
Applications can be downloaded from the Foundation's web site.

Duration: One year. Renewable upon reapplication.

Deadline: August 1 (postmarked) for the following year's program.

PUBLICATIONS:
Myeloma Today, newsletter.

STAFF:
Susie Novis, President
Lisa Paik, Vice President of Medical Meetings and CME Programs

ADDRESS INQUIRIES TO:
Lisa Paik, Vice President of Medical Meetings and CME Programs or Rachael Coffey
(See address above.)

THE IRWIN FOUNDATION [2425]

50 Crocker Boulevard
Suite 100
Mount Clemens, MI 48043
(586) 469-5050
Fax: (586) 469-0018

E-MAIL ADDRESS:
info@irwinfoundation.com

WEB SITE ADDRESS:
www.irwinfoundation.com

FOUNDED: 1995

AREAS OF INTEREST:
Aiding veterinary education.

NAME(S) OF PROGRAMS:
● **The Irwin Foundation Scholarship**

TYPE:
Grants-in-aid; Scholarships. The Foundation provides program assistance to veterinary schools including cash donations, purchase of equipment and service contributions (i.e., use of non-cash foundation assets). Since its inception, the Foundation has provided funding for scholarships in veterinary education. This program has expanded to assist future veterinary technicians.

PURPOSE:
To help veterinary schools and the students who attend them.

ELIGIBILITY:
Scholarship funding is limited to accredited schools within major universities. Scholarship recipients are chosen by the schools themselves. The Foundation does not particiate in, nor interfere with, the selection process.

FINANCIAL DATA:
Amount of support per award: $10,000 to $25,000.

Total amount of support: $25,000 per year.

APPLICATION INFORMATION:
Only universities may contact the Foundation for details.

Duration: One year.

ADDRESS INQUIRIES TO:
Sharon L. Potter, Director
(See address above.)

ROBERT WOOD JOHNSON FOUNDATION [2426]

Route One and College Road East
Princeton, NJ 08543-2316
(877) 843-7953
Fax: (609) 627-7582

E-MAIL ADDRESS:
mail@rwjf.org

WEB SITE ADDRESS:
www.rwjf.org

FOUNDED: 1972

AREAS OF INTEREST:
Childhood obesity, health insurance coverage, human capital, pioneer, public health, quality/equality, and vulnerable populations.

TYPE:
Project/program grants; Research grants. The Foundation supports training, education, research (excluding biomedical research) and projects that demonstrate the effective delivery of health care services. Rather than paying for individual care, the Foundation concentrates on health care systems and the conditions that promote better health.

Grantees include hospitals, medical, nursing, and public schools, professional associations, research organizations, state and local government agencies, and community groups.

The Foundation grants in seven areas:
(1) Childhood Obesity focuses on reversing the childhood obesity epidemic by 2015;
(2) Health Insurance Coverage focuses on ensuring that everyone in America has stable, affordable care coverage;
(3) Human Capital supports programs that assure the nation has a diverse, well-trained leadership and workforce in health and health care;
(4) Pioneer aims to spur potentially breakthrough improvements in the future of health and health care;
(5) Public Health supports programs that strengthen the practice of public health;
(6) Quality/Equality supports programs helping communities set and achieve ambitious goals to improve quality of health and;
(7) Vulnerable Populations supports ideas to help overcome longstanding health challenges.

YEAR PROGRAM STARTED: 1972

PURPOSE:
To improve the health and health care of all Americans; to improve health care - how it is delivered, how it is paid for, and how well it does for patients and their families.

LEGAL BASIS:
Private foundation.

ELIGIBILITY:
Preference is given to tax-exempt, public agencies under Section 501(c)(3). The Foundation does not fund general operating expenses or existing deficits, endowments or capital costs, basic biomedical research, drug therapies or devices research, international programs or institutions, direct support of individuals, or lobbying of any kind.

In addition, the Foundation rarely makes grants for conferences, unless they relate clearly to the Foundation's goals, or for

publications and media projects, except those that grow out of one of the Foundation's grant programs.

GEOGRAPHIC RESTRICTIONS:
United States.

FINANCIAL DATA:
Assets of approximately $10 billion.

Amount of support per award: Varies.

Total amount of support: Varies.

COOPERATIVE FUNDING PROGRAMS: Robert Wood Johnson Foundation Local Funding Partnerships.

NUMBER OF APPLICANTS MOST RECENT YEAR:
1,276.

REPRESENTATIVE AWARDS:
$18,734,344 to Sports4Kids to support National Expansion of Sports4Kids: A Program that Promotes Physical Activity and Play at Schools (phase 2); $15,959,747 to University of Illinois at Chicago Health Research and Policy Centers to support Bridging the Gap: Research Informing Practice and Policy for Healthy Youth Behavior; $8,563,940 to Kaiser Foundation Research Institute to support expediting the study of the genetic and environmental determinants of health.

APPLICATION INFORMATION:
Applicants should initiate the process of applying for an unsolicited grant by submitting a three-page online brief proposal using the application form provided on the Foundation's web site.

The Foundation accepts proposals online only.

Duration: Varies.

Deadline: Varies.

OFFICERS:
Hon. Thomas H. Kean, Chairman, Board of Trustees
Risa Lavizzo-Mourey, M.D., M.B.A., President and Chief Executive Officer
John R. Lumpkin, M.D., Senior Vice President and Director Health Care Group
James S. Marks, M.D., M.P.H., Senior Vice President and Director Health Group
Katherine Hatton, Vice President, General Counsel and Secretary
Robert G. Hughes, Ph.D., Vice President and Chief Learning Officer
David J. Morse, Vice President, Communications
David L. Waldman, Vice President, Human Resources and Administration
Albert O. Shar, Ph.D., Vice President, Information Technology
Peter Goodwin, Vice President, National Program Affairs
David Colby, Ph.D., Vice President, Research and Evaluation
Peggi Einhorn, Chief Financial Officer and Treasurer
Brian S. O'Neil, Chief Investment Officer
Robin E. Mockenhaupt, Chief of Staff
Mary E. Castria, Controller

ADDRESS INQUIRIES TO:
Lydia Ryba, Manager
Office of Proposal Management
P.O. Box 2316
Princeton, NJ 08543-2316

ROBERT J. KLEBERG, JR. AND HELEN C. KLEBERG FOUNDATION [2427]
700 North St. Mary's Street
Suite 1200
San Antonio, TX 78205
(210) 271-3691
Fax: (210) 299-1541

E-MAIL ADDRESS:
cathyf@alexventures.com

AREAS OF INTEREST:
Biomedical research, health and education.

TYPE:
Project/program grants; Research grants.

PURPOSE:
To provide financial support for research projects or actual programs in the area of biomedical research, education, health and welfare.

LEGAL BASIS:
Private foundation.

ELIGIBILITY:
Applicants must be IRS 501(c)(3) organizations. No grants to individuals. No grants for endowments, deficit financing, ongoing operating expenses, community organizations outside of Texas, indirect costs or overhead for research projects.

GEOGRAPHIC RESTRICTIONS:
United States.

FINANCIAL DATA:
Amount of support per award: Varies.
Total amount of support: Varies.

APPLICATION INFORMATION:
Applicants should send a proposal including background of the organization, description of the proposed project, detailed project budget, amount requested, evidence of tax-exempt status and a statement of approval of the request for funds signed by the chief administrator of the organization.
Duration: One year. Reapply for additional funding.
Deadline: First week in May and October for June and December meetings.

PUBLICATIONS:
Guidelines.

ADDRESS INQUIRIES TO:
Grant Coordinator
(See address above.)

THE JACOB AND VALERIA LANGELOTH FOUNDATION [2428]
275 Madison Avenue, 33rd Floor
New York, NY 10016
(212) 687-1133
Fax: (212) 687-8877

E-MAIL ADDRESS:
info@langeloth.org

WEB SITE ADDRESS:
www.langeloth.org

AREAS OF INTEREST:
Health care.

TYPE:
Demonstration grants; Project/program grants; Research grants.

PURPOSE:
To promote and support effective and creative programs, practices and policies related to healing from illness, accident, physical,

social or emotional trauma; to extend the availability of programs that promote healing to underserved populations.

ELIGIBILITY:
Grants are made to organizations that have tax-exempt status under Section 501(c)(3) of the Internal Revenue Code and that are health care providers, academic research institutions or community-based organizations. Grants are made nationwide, with a specific interest in New York state.

FINANCIAL DATA:
Amount of support per award: Varies.

APPLICATION INFORMATION:
Applications must be submitted online. Organizations may submit more than one application, but each project requires a separate registration and user name. The process involves the following steps:
(1) project registration;
(2) letter of intent invitation;
(3) letter of intent submission;
(4) proposal invitation and;
(5) proposal submission.
Applicants will be notified via e-mail at each step.
Duration: Up to three years.
Deadline: February 1 and August 1 for the letter of intent.

STAFF:
Scott Moyer, President
Andrea Fionda, Program Officer
Melissa Houston, Grants Manager

ADDRESS INQUIRIES TO:
Scott Moyer, President
(See address above.)

LEUKEMIA RESEARCH FOUNDATION
3520 Lake Avenue
Suite 202
Wilmette, IL 60091
(847) 424-0600
Fax: (847) 424-0606

E-MAIL ADDRESS:
info@lrfmail.org

WEB SITE ADDRESS:
www.leukemia-research.org

TYPE:
Research grants. The goal of the grant program is to support new investigators. It funds scientists and physicians around the world.

See entry 2598 for full listing.

LOWE SYNDROME ASSOCIATION [2429]
P.O. Box 864346
Plano, TX 75086-4346
(972) 733-1338

E-MAIL ADDRESS:
info@lowesyndrome.org

WEB SITE ADDRESS:
www.lowesyndrome.org

FOUNDED: 1982

AREAS OF INTEREST:
Medical research pertaining to Lowe Syndrome.

NAME(S) OF PROGRAMS:
● **The Leland McSpadden Memorial Fund for Medical and Scientific Research**

TYPE:
Research grants. Supports research leading to a better understanding of the metabolic basis of Lowe Syndrome, to better treatments of the major complications of Lowe Syndrome, to the prevention of Lowe Syndrome, and/or to a cure for Lowe Syndrome.

YEAR PROGRAM STARTED: 1983

PURPOSE:
To foster communication among families; to promote a better understanding of Lowe Syndrome and the potential of individuals with this condition; to provide information, and encourage and support medical research relating to Lowe Syndrome.

ELIGIBILITY:
Researchers of all types are invited to send applications, including but not limited to, universities, hospitals, and other nonprofit organizations with interest in research in areas specified by the Association.

FINANCIAL DATA:
Amount of support per award: Up to $25,000.

NUMBER OF APPLICANTS MOST RECENT YEAR:
1.

APPLICATION INFORMATION:
Duration: One year.
Deadline: Receipt of research proposals: When RFPs are issued.

ADDRESS INQUIRIES TO:
Deborah Jacobs, President
(See address above.)

LUPUS FOUNDATION OF AMERICA, INC. [2430]
2000 L Street, N.W., Suite 410
Washington, DC 20036
(202) 349-1153
(202) 349-1155
Fax: (202) 349-1156

E-MAIL ADDRESS:
dieguez@lupus.org

WEB SITE ADDRESS:
www.lupus.org/rfa

FOUNDED: 1977

AREAS OF INTEREST:
Lupus research.

NAME(S) OF PROGRAMS:
● **Basic, Clinical and Translational Research Grant Programs**
● **Gina Finzi Memorial Student Summer Fellowship Program**

TYPE:
Research grants. Summer Fellowship.

YEAR PROGRAM STARTED: 1977

ELIGIBILITY:
Applicants whose home institutions are in the U.S., Canada or Mexico may apply.

GEOGRAPHIC RESTRICTIONS:
North America.

FINANCIAL DATA:
No indirect costs.
Amount of support per award: Gina M. Finzi Memorial Student Summer Fellowships offer a $2,000 award. Other awards on varying topics (including neuropsychiatric lupus, pediatric lupus, reproductive issues in lupus, cutaneous lupus, stem cells in lupus research, and lupus nephritis) offer awards of $50,000 to $100,000.

APPLICATION INFORMATION:
Guidelines and form available at the Foundation web site.
Duration: Finzi Student Fellowships are for one summer. Other awards are for one year.
Deadline: Research Grants: April 30. Awarded October 1; Student Summer Fellowships: March 31. Awarded in May.

ADDRESS INQUIRIES TO:
Dario Dieguez, Jr., Ph.D.
Research Program Manager
(See address above.)

JOSIAH MACY JR. FOUNDATION [2431]

44 East 64th Street
New York, NY 10065
(212) 486-2424
Fax: (212) 644-0765

E-MAIL ADDRESS:
info@macyfoundation.org

WEB SITE ADDRESS:
www.macyfoundation.org

FOUNDED: 1930

AREAS OF INTEREST:
Health care, health professions education and medical education.

NAME(S) OF PROGRAMS:
● **Conference Programs**
● **Health Care Policy**
● **Minorities in Medicine**

TYPE:
Conferences/seminars; Demonstration grants; Development grants; Matching gifts; Project/program grants. Major interest in education for careers in medicine or medical science. Special programs on preparation of minority groups for health professions and teamwork among and between health professions.

YEAR PROGRAM STARTED: 1930

PURPOSE:
To fund activities in medical and other health professional education.

LEGAL BASIS:
Private foundation.

ELIGIBILITY:
Applicants must be qualified not-for-profit institutions with appropriate interests. No grants are made directly to individuals, nor for building, annual fund appeals or medical research.

GEOGRAPHIC RESTRICTIONS:
United States.

FINANCIAL DATA:
Amount of support per award: Varies based on need.
Matching fund requirements: Foundation matches gifts from full-time employees, directors and officers only to charitable organizations.

APPLICATION INFORMATION:
Letters of Inquiry should include:
(1) name of the sponsoring agency or institution;
(2) description of the project;
(3) names and qualifications of the persons who will be responsible for the project and;
(4) initial budget.

An important component of the letter of inquiry is the initial budget. For convenience, the Foundation has provided a brief form online to aid in judging expenses.

As a matter of policy, the Foundation does not accept submission of applications via e-mail or the Internet.
Duration: Varies.

PUBLICATIONS:
Annual report; conference proceedings.

STAFF:
Peter Goodwin, MBA, Chief Operating Officer and Treasurer
Karen A. Butler
Nicholas R. Romano
Stephen C. Schoenbaum, M.D.

BOARD OF DIRECTORS:
William H. Wright, II, Chairman
George E. Thibault, M.D., President
Lawrence K. Altman, M.D.
George Campbell, Jr., Ph.D.
Linda Cronenwett, Ph.D., R.N.
Harvey Fineberg, M.D., Ph.D.
Linda P. Fried, M.D.
John W. Frymoyer, M.D.
Henry P. Johnson
Judith B. Krauss, R.N.
Herbert Pardes, M.D.
Paul G. Ramsey, M.D.
George Erik Rupp, Ph.D.
Reed V. Tuckson, M.D., FACP

ADDRESS INQUIRIES TO:
Foundation President
(See address above.)

MAP INTERNATIONAL [2432]

4700 Glynco Parkway
Brunswick, GA 31525
(912) 265-6010
Fax: (912) 265-6170

E-MAIL ADDRESS:
bbohl@map.org

WEB SITE ADDRESS:
www.map.org

FOUNDED: 1954

AREAS OF INTEREST:
Community health development.

NAME(S) OF PROGRAMS:
● **MAP International Medical Fellowship**

TYPE:
Travel grants. Fellowship for medical education.

YEAR PROGRAM STARTED: 1971

PURPOSE:
To encourage lifelong involvement in global health issues by providing selected medical students firsthand exposure in a Christian context to the health, social and cultural characteristics of a developing world community.

LEGAL BASIS:
Nonprofit organization.

ELIGIBILITY:
Grants are available for senior medical students. Applicants must attend an approved medical school in North America.

FINANCIAL DATA:
Grant pays 100% of the lowest airfare to the country they will be serving.
Amount of support per award: Varies.
Total amount of support: Varies.

NUMBER OF APPLICANTS MOST RECENT YEAR:
17.

NUMBER OF AWARDS: 13.

APPLICATION INFORMATION:
Application form required. Contact organization for other application requirements.
Duration: Minimum eight weeks.
Deadline: March 1. Announcement May 2.

PUBLICATIONS:
Annual report (MAP International); application forms.

IRS IDENTIFICATION NUMBER: 36-2586390

ADDRESS INQUIRIES TO:
MAP Fellows Coordinator
(See address above.)

MARCH OF DIMES FOUNDATION [2433]

1275 Mamaroneck Avenue
White Plains, NY 10605
(914) 997-4555
Fax: (914) 997-4560

E-MAIL ADDRESS:
mkatz@marchofdimes.com;
researchgrants@marchofdimes.com

WEB SITE ADDRESS:
www.marchofdimes.com

FOUNDED: 1938

AREAS OF INTEREST:
Prevention of birth defects, the amelioration of their consequences and the improvement of the outcome of pregnancy.

NAME(S) OF PROGRAMS:
● **Research Grants Program**

TYPE:
Research grants. Grants for research in human birth defects.

The March of Dimes defines a birth defect as any abnormality of structure or function, whether inherited or acquired in utero and presenting in infancy or early childhood. Deviations from reproductive health of women and men as an underlying basis of birth defects (i.e., preconceptional events, perinatal course and premature births) are appropriate subjects for research support. The Foundation does not accept applications dealing with infertility.

YEAR PROGRAM STARTED: 1974

PURPOSE:
To support programs designed to gain new knowledge about the mechanisms that cause birth defects and to find ways of controlling or preventing them.

LEGAL BASIS:
Tax-exempt 501(c)(3) organization.

ELIGIBILITY:
In considering grant applications, the March of Dimes takes into account purpose of the research program and plan of study, qualifications, experience and abilities of the persons who are to supervise and participate in the proposed program, and facilities available.

Qualified scientists, with faculty appointments or equivalent, from universities, hospitals and research institutions are invited to submit applications for research grants directed at the prevention of birth defects. Research subjects appropriate for support include basic biological processes governing development, genetics, clinical studies, studies of reproductive health, environmental toxicology, and social and behavioral studies.

In social and behavioral sciences, the Foundation is interested in applications proposing research that advances the understanding of, and therefore the ability to prevent the cognitive and behavioral risks that affect outcomes of pregnancy, the perinatal period, and subsequent child development. Because change in behavior is an important component of several of its campaigns, the Foundation is interested in studies that address this method of prevention.

FINANCIAL DATA:
These grants do not cover the recipient's or other faculty salaries, but do provide salary support for technical help.

Amount of support per award: $60,225 to $157,593 per year; Average: $93,342; Median: $95,463.

NUMBER OF APPLICANTS MOST RECENT YEAR: 349 for the year 2009.

NUMBER OF AWARDS: 34 for the year 2009.

REPRESENTATIVE AWARDS:
$256,634 to Ka Yee Christina Lee, Ph.D., University of Chicago, for "Structure-Function Relationship in Lung Surfactant Systems;" $260,242 to Clifford J. Tabin, Ph.D., Harvard Medical School, for "The Role of Small RNA's in Regulating Vertebrate Limb Development."

APPLICATION INFORMATION:
Applicants should electronically submit the required administrative information and a Letter of Intent addressed to the Senior Vice President for Research and Global Programs summarizing the proposed studies via the Foundation's online system. The Letter of Intent must include the following information in this order:
(1) the objective;
(2) the relevance to birth defects or reproductive health;
(3) the hypothesis or hypotheses to be tested;
(4) preliminary data;
(5) a statement of the methods of procedure;
(6) a plan for evaluating the results;
(7) current financial support (list each current grant or contract for the conduct of this research; if no other grants, state "NONE") and;
(8) if this is a request for a renewal of a current Foundation grant or if one holds a Basil O'Connor Starter Scholar Research Award, it must include a summary of its progress.

The Letters of Intent will be evaluated by a scientific advisory committee, and applications will be invited from those whom the committee recommends.

Duration: Three years.

Deadline: Letter of Intent: April 30. Complete application: Beginning September 15. Applicants will be informed of the scientific advisory committee's decision no later than the following April 30. Funding initiated June 1.

PUBLICATIONS:
Program announcement; grants list.

ADDRESS INQUIRIES TO:
Michael Katz, M.D.
Senior Vice President for Research and Global Programs
(See address above.)

MARCH OF DIMES FOUNDATION   [2434]
1275 Mamaroneck Avenue
White Plains, NY 10605
(914) 997-4555
Fax: (914) 997-4560

E-MAIL ADDRESS:
mkatz@marchofdimes.com
researchgrants@marchofdimes.com

WEB SITE ADDRESS:
www.marchofdimes.com

FOUNDED: 1938

AREAS OF INTEREST:
Prevention of birth defects, the amelioration of their consequences and the improvement of the outcome of pregnancy.

NAME(S) OF PROGRAMS:
● **Prematurity Research Initiative (PRI)**

TYPE:
Research grants. The March of Dimes defines a birth defect as any abnormality of structure or function, whether inherited or acquired in utero, presenting in infancy or early childhood. Deviations from reproductive health as an underlying basis of birth defects are also included. Thus preconceptual events, prenatal course, and premature births are appropriate subjects for research support.

The Foundation seeks applications requesting grant support for projects relating to causes of prematurity. Research proposals of new paradigms based on strong conceptual frameworks are invited. The intent is to provide new insights into the large, and increasing, proportion of preterm deliveries in which the cause (and thus the means of prevention) remains elusive. The research proposals need to consider especially, but not be limited to, genetics, gene-environment interactions, and animal models. The Foundation encourages novel approaches.

YEAR PROGRAM STARTED: 1938

PURPOSE:
To provide new insights into the large, and increasing, proportion of preterm deliveries in which the cause (and thus the means of prevention) remains elusive.

LEGAL BASIS:
Tax-exempt 501(c)(3) organization.

ELIGIBILITY:
Applicants must be members of not-for-profit institutions.

GEOGRAPHIC RESTRICTIONS:
United States.

FINANCIAL DATA:
Grants do not cover the recipient's or other faculty salaries, but do provide salary support for technical help.

Amount of support per award: $110,070 to $168,554 per year; Average: $144,574; Median: $135,287.

APPLICATION INFORMATION:
Potential applicants should electronically submit the required administrative information and a Letter of Intent addressed to the Senior Vice President for Research and Global Programs summarizing the proposed studies via the Foundation's online system at researchgrants.marchofdimes.com/pri. The Letter of Intent must include the following information in this order:
(1) the objective;
(2) the major hypothesis to be tested and key specific aims;

(3) any preliminary data;
(4) a brief description of the study design including key outcome variables and the statistical framework that will be applied to the analysis;
(5) a plan for evaluating the results;
(6) projected time frame for the investigation;
(7) current financial support: list each current grant or contract for the conduct of this and any other research (If there are no other grants, state "NONE";) and;
(8) if this is a request for a renewal of a current March of Dimes grant, it must include a summary of its progress.

Please do not include References Cited with your Letter of Intent. This Letter of Intent may not be submitted by fax. The Letter of Intent will be evaluated and applications will be invited from those who are selected. The Foundation requests no telephone inquiries.

Duration: Three years.

Deadline: April 15. The Foundation's decision will be transmitted to the candidates no later than May 15. Those who are invited to apply will have to do so on or before July 15; the applicants will be informed of the decisions regarding their applications no later than January 1 of the following year, with funding initiated on March 1 of that year.

PUBLICATIONS:
Program policies and grants list.

ADDRESS INQUIRIES TO:
Michael Katz, M.D.
Senior Vice President for Research and Global Programs
(See address above.)

*PLEASE NOTE:
The Foundation does not accept applications dealing with infertility.

Please adhere to the instructions precisely. Any letter that does not follow this precise format will not be included in the review process.

MARCH OF DIMES FOUNDATION   [2435]
1275 Mamaroneck Avenue
White Plains, NY 10605
(914) 997-4555
Fax: (914) 997-4560

E-MAIL ADDRESS:
mkatz@marchofdimes.com
researchgrants@marchofdimes.com

WEB SITE ADDRESS:
www.marchofdimes.com

FOUNDED: 1938

AREAS OF INTEREST:
Prevention of birth defects, the amelioration of their consequences and the improvement of the outcome of pregnancy.

NAME(S) OF PROGRAMS:
● **Basil O'Connor Starter Scholar Research Awards**

TYPE:
Research grants. The March of Dimes defines a birth defect as any abnormality of structure or function, whether inherited or acquired in utero and presenting in infancy or early childhood. Deviations from reproductive health of women and men as an underlying basis of birth defects (i.e., preconceptional events, perinatal course and premature births) are appropriate subjects for research support.

YEAR PROGRAM STARTED: 1973

PURPOSE:
To support programs designed to gain new knowledge about the mechanisms that cause birth defects and to find ways of controlling them.

LEGAL BASIS:
Tax-exempt 501(c)(3) organization.

ELIGIBILITY:
Designed for young scientists just embarking on their independent research careers and is limited, therefore, to those holding recent faculty appointments. The applicants' research interests should be consonant with those of the Foundation.

March of Dimes takes into account the purpose of the research program and plan submitted, qualifications, experience and abilities of the persons who are to supervise and participate in the proposed program and the facilities available. Applicants must have no other major funding.

FINANCIAL DATA:
Grants do not cover the recipient's salary, but do provide salary support for technical help.
Amount of support per award: Up to $75,000 per year.

NUMBER OF APPLICANTS MOST RECENT YEAR:
158.

NUMBER OF AWARDS: 43.

REPRESENTATIVE AWARDS:
$30,000 to Anne L. Calof, Ph.D., University of Iowa, Iowa City, IA, for "Strategies for Identifying Genes that Regulate Neurogenesis in Mammals;" $7,000 to Piero Rinaldo, M.D., Yale University, New Haven, CT, for "The Role of Inborn Errors of Fatty Acid Oxidation as a Cause of Sudden Infant Death Syndrome;" $10,000 to John B. Thomas, Ph.D., The Salk Institute, La Jolla, CA, for "Transcriptional Regulation of Neural Cell Fate in Drosophila."

APPLICATION INFORMATION:
Deans, Chairs of Departments or Directors of Institutes/Centers should submit nominations for this award addressed to the Senior Vice President for Research and Global Programs. Additionally, the following information must be provided via the Foundation's online systems.
(1) title of the proposed research project;
(2) nominator's name, academic appointment, mailing address, telephone and fax numbers and e-mail address;
(3) candidate's name, academic appointment, mailing address, telephone and fax numbers and e-mail address;
(4) candidate's curriculum vitae in NIH format;
(5) an abstract of the proposed research and;
(6) the Letter of Nomination, submitted by post, fax or e-mail. If submitted by e-mail, it must include the file containing the Letter of Nomination as an attachment and be sent to BOCNominations@marchofdimes.com. The nomination letter should contain information about the candidate's faculty appointment, independence, and facilities available, including his or her laboratory space.

The submissions will be reviewed for appropriateness of the qualifications of the applicant. The Foundation's decision will be transmitted to the candidates, who may then submit a proposal. The scientific advisory committee will conduct the final review of the proposals in October, and the candidates will be informed of the decisions shortly thereafter.

Duration: Programs are approved for two years.
Deadline: Nominations: March 15. Proposals: Beginning June 30. Reviewed in October for February 1 funding cycle.

PUBLICATIONS:
Program announcement and grants list.

NATIONAL OFFICERS:
Gary D. Forsee, Chairman
Jennifer L. Howse, Ph.D., President
Nancy Lukitsh, Treasurer
Anna Eleanor Roosevelt, Secretary
Lisa Bellsey, Esq., Assistant Secretary
Jane Massey, Chief Operating Officer
Nancy Green, M.D., Medical Director

ADDRESS INQUIRIES TO:
Michael Katz, M.D.
Senior Vice President for Research and Global Programs
(See address above.)

*PLEASE NOTE:
The Foundation does not accept applications dealing with infertility.

*SPECIAL STIPULATIONS:
Applicants may not be recipients of a major grant (e.g., an RO1, or other grant exceeding $200,000 a year) at the time of application. Candidates may not simultaneously submit an application for any other March of Dimes research program. Those who have previously submitted an application to the March of Dimes are not eligible for a Basil O'Connor Award, but may apply for a regular research grant.

MAYO CLINIC [2436]
Mayo School of Graduate Medical Education
200 First Street, S.W.
Rochester, MN 55905
(507) 284-1196
Fax: (507) 538-3267

E-MAIL ADDRESS:
pathologyeducation@mayo.edu

WEB SITE ADDRESS:
www.mayo.edu/msgme

AREAS OF INTEREST:
Surgical and medical pathology, including bone and soft tissue pathology, cardiovascular pathology, cytopathology, and GI/liver pathology.

NAME(S) OF PROGRAMS:
● **Surgical Pathology Fellowships**

TYPE:
Fellowships. Available subspecialty fellowships include bone and soft tissue pathology, cardiovascular pathology, cytopathology, gastrointestinal pathology, hematopathology, neuropathology, pulmonary pathology and surgical pathology. Each fellowship will give ample opportunity to diagnose and work with a large diverse volume of tissue specimens. Fellows will assist Mayo's staff consultants with projects and will be encouraged to initiate and participate in clinical pathology and basic research studies for publication and presentation at national meetings. Fellows will also develop and present studies at conferences and seminars and may assist in teaching pathology residents, medical students and fellows from other departments. Each specialty fellowship consists of a one-year program except neuropathology, which is a two-year appointment. Combined fellowships are also possible.

PURPOSE:
To promote the belief that physicians need to work together, teach and learn from others and conduct research to provide sustained, excellent patient care.

LEGAL BASIS:
Hospital.

ELIGIBILITY:
Applicants must have a medical degree with U.S. or Canadian specialty training in anatomic pathology for all specialty fellowships.

FINANCIAL DATA:
Fellows will be permitted 15 days each year for vacation. Fellows will also receive a stipend and benefits package including a comprehensive medical care plan, short-term disability insurance, voluntary family life insurance, dental assistance plan, professional liability coverage and excess personal liability insurance. Since Fellows are encouraged to present research at regional and national meetings, Mayo will pay authorized expenses to attend that meeting within the U.S.
Amount of support per award: Varies depending on experience and fellowship.

NUMBER OF AWARDS: 1 in each specialty except for surgical pathology, which has 4 or more fellows.

APPLICATION INFORMATION:
To apply for a Mayo fellowship, applicants need to submit:
(1) a completed Mayo School of Graduate Medical Education application form;
(2) official college, graduate school and medical school transcripts;
(3) an official record of board scores;
(4) a dean's letter and two other letters of recommendation;
(5) curriculum vitae and personal statement;
(6) a valid ECFMG certificate if the applicant has graduated from a medical school outside of the U.S. or Canada and;
(7) a letter of recommendation from the residency program director.

If an applicant is considered for an appointment, they will be asked to visit Mayo Clinic Rochester for an interview with the program director and selected faculty. Interviews are conducted from January through March each year.
Duration: One year for specialties and two years for neuropathology.
Deadline: January 1 of the year preceding appointment.

PUBLICATIONS:
Brochure.

BENJAMIN AND MARY SIDDONS MEASEY FOUNDATION [2437]
P.O. Box 258
Media, PA 19063
(610) 566-5800
Fax: (610) 566-8197

FOUNDED: 1958

AREAS OF INTEREST:
Medical education in Philadelphia area processed through Phila Medical schools only.

NAME(S) OF PROGRAMS:
● **Medical Education Grants**

TYPE:
Challenge/matching grants; Fellowships;
Grants-in-aid.

YEAR PROGRAM STARTED: 1958

PURPOSE:
To advance medical education of physicians.

LEGAL BASIS:
1958 Trust Document.

ELIGIBILITY:
Grants are made through accredited medical
schools in the immediate Philadelphia, PA
area. Individual applications are not accepted
by the Foundation; institutions only.

GEOGRAPHIC RESTRICTIONS:
Philadelphia, Pennsylvania area.

FINANCIAL DATA:
Amount of support per award: $7,500 to
$500,000.
Total amount of support: $2,500,000 for the
year 2010.

NUMBER OF APPLICANTS MOST RECENT YEAR:
10.

APPLICATION INFORMATION:
Application is by letter. Organizations must
provide 501(c)(3) tax-exempt information.
Duration: One year. Nonrenewable.
Deadline: Two weeks prior to quarterly
meetings held in March, June, September and
December.

IRS IDENTIFICATION NUMBER: 23-6298781

STAFF:
James C. Brennan, Esq., Manager
M.S. Donaldson, Esq., Secretary

ADDRESS INQUIRIES TO:
James C. Brennan, Esq., Manager and
Counsel
(See address above.)

*SPECIAL STIPULATIONS:
No applications to Foundation directly.

MEDICAL LIBRARY ASSOCIATION

65 East Wacker Place
Suite 1900
Chicago, IL 60601-7298
(312) 419-9094
Fax: (312) 419-8950

E-MAIL ADDRESS:
mlapd2@mlahq.org

WEB SITE ADDRESS:
www.mlanet.org/awards

TYPE:
Fellowships; Scholarships. Awarded for study
and doctoral work in health sciences
librarianship.

Thomson Reuters/MLA Doctoral Fellowship
is awarded biennially. It was established by
the Institute for Scientific Information (ISI)
and is administered by the MLA.

See entry 773 for full listing.

NATIONAL ALOPECIA AREATA FOUNDATION

14 Mitchell Boulevard
San Rafael, CA 94903
(415) 472-3780
Fax: (415) 472-5343

E-MAIL ADDRESS:
info@naaf.org

WEB SITE ADDRESS:
www.naaf.org

TYPE:
Research grants.

See entry 2295 for full listing.

NATIONAL BRAIN TUMOR SOCIETY [2438]

124 Watertown Street
Suite 2D
Watertown, MA 02472
(617) 924-9997
Fax: (617) 924-9998

E-MAIL ADDRESS:
research@braintumor.org

WEB SITE ADDRESS:
www.braintumor.org

FOUNDED: 1981

AREAS OF INTEREST:
Brain tumor treatment.

CONSULTING OR VOLUNTEER SERVICES:
Research, advocacy/public policy, and patient
care.

NAME(S) OF PROGRAMS:
• **NBTF Brain Tumor Research Grants**

TYPE:
Awards/prizes; Project/program grants;
Research grants.

YEAR PROGRAM STARTED: 1981

PURPOSE:
To provide information and support for brain
tumor patients, family members, and health
care professionals; to support innovative
research into better treatment options and a
cure for brain tumors.

ELIGIBILITY:
For clinical grants, applicants must be
qualified research investigators with a Ph.D.
or higher level practicing neuroscience at
U.S. or Canadian medical centers. Quality of
Life researcher need not be Ph.D., but must
hold at least a Master's degree.

Grant monies cannot be used for general
administrative costs, debt reduction, or
indirect costs of the project.

GEOGRAPHIC RESTRICTIONS:
United States and Canada.

FINANCIAL DATA:
Total amount of support: $500,000 to
$750,000.

NUMBER OF APPLICANTS MOST RECENT YEAR:
100.

NUMBER OF AWARDS: 12.

APPLICATION INFORMATION:
Contact the Society for application form and
guidelines.
Duration: One year. Renewal possible.

IRS IDENTIFICATION NUMBER: 94-2876985

ADDRESS INQUIRIES TO:
Carrie Treadwell
Director of Research Grants
(See address above.)

NATIONAL CENTER FOR RESEARCH RESOURCES (NCRR) [2439]

Division of Research Infrastructure
One Democracy Plaza, Room 940
6701 Democracy Boulevard, MSC 4874
Bethesda, MD 20892-4874
(301) 435-0778
Fax: (301) 480-3770

WEB SITE ADDRESS:
www.ncrr.nih.gov

AREAS OF INTEREST:
Animal research facilities improvement
program.

NAME(S) OF PROGRAMS:
• **Grant for Repair, Renovation and Modernization of Existing Research Facilities**

TYPE:
Project/program grants.

PURPOSE:
To upgrade animal facilities to support the
conduct of PHS-supported biomedical and
behavioral research.

LEGAL BASIS:
Governmental agency.

ELIGIBILITY:
Any domestic public or private institution or
organization may apply if the institution has
one or more research projects currently
supported by the Public Health Service
(PHS) that involve the use of laboratory
animals.

Institutions and commercial firms providing
only services or products without
animal-related research component are not
eligible to apply.

This program will also not support requests
for equipment to be used for teaching
purposes and/or for housing non-research
animals.

FINANCIAL DATA:
Amount of support per award: $500,000
(direct costs).

NUMBER OF APPLICANTS MOST RECENT YEAR:
82 for the year 2008.

NUMBER OF AWARDS: 16 for the year 2008.

APPLICATION INFORMATION:
Applications should be submitted
electronically on Form 424, available at
www.grants.gov.
Deadline: May 28.

ADDRESS INQUIRIES TO:
Greg Farber, Director
(See address above.)

NATIONAL CENTER FOR RESEARCH RESOURCES (NCRR) [2440]

Office of Grants Management
6701 Democracy Boulevard, MSC 4874
Bethesda, MD 20892-4874
(301) 435-0844
(301) 435-0840
Fax: (301) 480-3777

E-MAIL ADDRESS:
athertoh@mail.nih.gov

WEB SITE ADDRESS:
www.ncrr.nih.gov

AREAS OF INTEREST:
Biomedical technology, clinical research,
comparative medicine and research

infrastructure. These areas create, develop and provide a comprehensive range of human, animal, technological and other resources to enable biomedical research advances. Such resources enable biomedical investigators the opportunity to study many diseases and disorders.

NAME(S) OF PROGRAMS:
- **Biomedical Technology Program**
- **Clinical Research**
- **Comparative Medicine**
- **Research Infrastructure**

TYPE:
Research grants. The National Center for Research Resources (NCRR), a component of the National Institutes of Health, supports critical research technologies and shared resources that facilitate biomedical research.

NCRR funding is intended primarily for the biomedical research community, not the general public.

YEAR PROGRAM STARTED: 1962

PURPOSE:
To assist academic and other institutions in developing and sustaining sophisticated technological capabilities vital to modern biomedical research.

LEGAL BASIS:
Section 301 of the Public Health Service Act, Public Law 78-410, as amended.

ELIGIBILITY:
For a given research support activity to qualify as a biomedical research technology resource, the activity must:
(1) emphasize a health-relevant technology which is in a dynamically evolving status;
(2) have service capabilities that exceed those which can be fully exploited by any one of the potential users and;
(3) have operating costs at a level which could not be justified by any one of the research efforts to be served.

FINANCIAL DATA:
Amount of support per award: Up to $650,000 (direct costs).

APPLICATION INFORMATION:
Official application materials are available upon request to NCRR.
Duration: Up to five years without reapplying.

PUBLICATIONS:
Annual report; application guidelines.

ADDRESS INQUIRIES TO:
Barbara M. Alving, M.D., Director
(See address above.)

NATIONAL HEART, LUNG AND BLOOD INSTITUTE (NHLBI)

National Institutes of Health
Grants Operations Branch, Room 7160
6701 Rockledge Drive, MSC-7926
Bethesda, MD 20892-7926
(301) 435-0144
Fax: (301) 480-3310

E-MAIL ADDRESS:
whitesa@nhlbi.nih.gov

WEB SITE ADDRESS:
www.nhlbi.nih.gov/funding/index.htm
www.grants.nhlbi.nih.gov

TYPE:
Conferences/seminars; Fellowships; Project/program grants; Research grants; Training grants; Loan forgiveness programs.

Career awards and other grant mechanisms to foster research on heart, vascular and lung diseases, and to develop scientists in these areas. Also, small business grants. Loan forgiveness programs are for research.

See entry 2554 for full listing.

THE NATIONAL HEMOPHILIA FOUNDATION [2441]

116 West 32nd Street, 11th Floor
New York, NY 10001
(212) 328-3727
Fax: (212) 328-3799

E-MAIL ADDRESS:
awang@hemophilia.org

WEB SITE ADDRESS:
www.hemophilia.org

FOUNDED: 1948

AREAS OF INTEREST:
Biochemistry, genetics, hematology, microbiology, orthopedics, psychiatry and other disciplines related to hemophilia and other bleeding disorders.

NAME(S) OF PROGRAMS:
- **Judith Graham Pool Postdoctoral Research Fellowships in Bleeding Disorders**

TYPE:
Development grants; Fellowships; Research grants. Support for research in clinical and/or basic sciences in areas relating to problems in hemophilia and other bleeding disorders.

Judith Graham Pool Postdoctoral Research Fellowships are designed to support research studies of high scientific merit and relevance to hemophilia. They are awarded through professional and graduate schools, or research institutions.

YEAR PROGRAM STARTED: 1972

PURPOSE:
To encourage and support hemophilia-related and other bleeding disorders research.

LEGAL BASIS:
Voluntary, nonprofit health organization.

ELIGIBILITY:
Applicants must have completed doctoral training and must enter the fellowship program from a doctoral, postdoctoral, internship or residency training program. This is not a research grant program for established investigators or faculty members.

GEOGRAPHIC RESTRICTIONS:
United States.

FINANCIAL DATA:
All money is to be used for salary and up to $750 for travel. No overhead is paid to any institution, except with the consent of the grantee and from his or her stipend.
Amount of support per award: $42,000 per year.
Total amount of support: Varies.

NUMBER OF AWARDS: 1.

APPLICATION INFORMATION:
Interested candidates must submit a Letter of Intent. This should be a brief letter identifying the researcher, their mentor, institution, and a decription of the proposed research project. Letters of intent should include an NIH-style curriculum vitae or biosketch for both candidate and mentor. After review, candidates may be invited to submit a full application.

Duration: Up to two years. Renewal contingent upon review of fellow's six-month progress report.
Deadline: Letter of Intent: December 20.

STAFF:
Val Bias, Chief Executive Officer
Neil Frick, Vice President, Clinical Research and Information Services
Angelina Wang, Director of Research and Medical Information

ADDRESS INQUIRIES TO:
Angelina Wang, Director of Research and Medical Information
(See address above.)

NATIONAL INSTITUTE OF ENVIRONMENTAL HEALTH SCIENCES

Division of Extramural Research and Training
111 T.W. Alexander Drive
Research Triangle Park, NC 27709
(919) 541-3289
Fax: (919) 541-2843

E-MAIL ADDRESS:
mastin@niehs.nih.gov

WEB SITE ADDRESS:
www.niehs.nih.gov

TYPE:
Conferences/seminars; Demonstration grants; Development grants; Fellowships; Project/program grants; Research grants; Training grants. NIEHS pursues its mission by supporting basic and applied research on the consequences of the exposure of humans to potentially toxic or harmful agents in the environment.

Research of interest encompasses studies that relate to the biological effects of environmental chemicals and physical factors including such agents as hazardous gases, suspended particles, aerosols, industrial by-products and intermediates, heavy metals, trace elements, food additives, adulterants and pesticides. Physical factors include noise, light, heat, microwaves and other forms of nonionizing radiation.

Research Training Programs support individuals at both the predoctoral and postdoctoral levels in the areas of environmental toxicology, environmental pathology, environmental mutagenesis and environmental epidemiology.

See entry 2331 for full listing.

NATIONAL INSTITUTE OF GENERAL MEDICAL SCIENCES [2442]

National Institutes of Health
45 Center Drive, MSC 6200
Bethesda, MD 20892-6200
(301) 496-7301
Fax: (301) 402-0224

E-MAIL ADDRESS:
info@nigms.nih.gov

WEB SITE ADDRESS:
www.nigms.nih.gov

FOUNDED: 1962

AREAS OF INTEREST:
Basic biomedical research.

NAME(S) OF PROGRAMS:
- **Center for Bioinformatics and Computational Biology**
- **Division of Cell Biology and Biophysics**

- **Division of Genetics and Developmental Biology**
- **Division of Minority Opportunities in Research**
- **Division of Pharmacology, Physiology, and Biological Chemistry**

TYPE:
Conferences/seminars; Development grants; Fellowships; Internships; Project/program grants; Research grants; Technical assistance; Training grants; Travel grants; Visiting scholars; Research contracts. Grants to support research on the structure and function of cells and cell organelles. Research to gain knowledge that will lead to the prevention, therapy and control of genetic diseases, as well as research to increase knowledge of drug action in order to increase safety of administration and diminish toxicity. Grants also given for research in biophysics and the physiological sciences and in certain clinical areas, particularly anesthesiology and trauma and burns. All of the research programs also support research training.

In addition, the Institute has special research and research training programs designed to increase the numbers and capabilities of minority scientists engaged in biomedical research.

YEAR PROGRAM STARTED: 1962

PURPOSE:
To support basic biomedical research that lays the foundation for advances in disease diagnosis, treatment, and prevention; to help provide the most critical element of good research: well-prepared scientists.

LEGAL BASIS:
Part of a government agency under the PHS Act, various sections, and various public laws.

ELIGIBILITY:
For Research Grants, applicants must be academic institutions, teaching hospitals, public agencies, nonprofit organizations and for-profit corporations.

National Research Service Awards for the above areas may be made to individuals for postdoctoral training or nonprofit institutions for the training of individuals at the predoctoral and postdoctoral level.

For Small Business Innovative Research Program, applicants must be qualified small businesses to stimulate technological innovation in areas of interest to the Institute.

FINANCIAL DATA:
Total amount of support: $2.051 billion for fiscal year 2010.

NUMBER OF AWARDS: 4,571 NIGMS-funded research grants for fiscal year 2010.

APPLICATION INFORMATION:
The appropriate application forms and instructions may be obtained from and submitted to:
The Division of Extramural Outreach and Information Resources
Office of Extramural Research
National Institutes of Health, Room 6207
6701 Rockledge Drive, MSC 7910
Bethesda, MD 20892-7910
Tel: (301) 435-0714
E-mail: grantsinfo@nih.gov.
Duration: Varies.
Deadline: Varies by program.

STAFF:
Ann Dieffenbach, Information Officer

ADDRESS INQUIRIES TO:
Office of Communications
and Public Liaison
(See address above.)

NATIONAL INSTITUTE OF GENERAL MEDICAL SCIENCES   [2443]
Division of Minority Opportunities in Research
45 Center Drive, Room 2AS-37
MSC 6200
Bethesda, MD 20892-6200
(301) 594-3900
Fax: (301) 480-2753

E-MAIL ADDRESS:
zlotnikh@nigms.nih.gov

WEB SITE ADDRESS:
www.nigms.nih.gov

FOUNDED: 1972

NAME(S) OF PROGRAMS:
- **Minority Biomedical Research Support Branch**

TYPE:
Development grants; Research grants; Technical assistance. Grants to assist eligible institutions to strengthen the institutions' biomedical research capabilities and provide opportunities to students to engage in biomedical or behavioral research and other activities in preparation for Ph.D. training in these areas.

YEAR PROGRAM STARTED: 1972

PURPOSE:
To increase the number of faculty, students, and investigators who are members of groups underrepresented in the biomedical and behavioral sciences who are engaged in research in these fields.

LEGAL BASIS:
Public Health Service Act of 1944 as amended, Section 301(c); U.S.C. 241.d.

ELIGIBILITY:
Applicant must be located in a state, the District of Columbia or a U.S. territory, and be a public or private university, four-year college or other institution offering undergraduate, graduate or health professional degrees with more than 50% minority enrollment, a public or private nonprofit four-year college or other institution offering undergraduate, graduate or health professional degrees, with a significant enrollment (but not necessarily more than 50%) derived from ethnic minorities, if the secretary of DHHS determines that the institution is committed to encouragement and assistance to ethnic minority faculty, students and investigators, or an Indian tribe with a recognized governing body which performs substantial government functions or an Alaska Regional Corporation (ARC) as defined in the Alaska Native Claims Settlement Act and located in a state, the District of Columbia, Puerto Rico, the Virgin Islands, the Canal Zone, Guam, American Samoa or the Trust Territory of the Pacific Islands.

GEOGRAPHIC RESTRICTIONS:
United States and its territories.

FINANCIAL DATA:
Amount of support per award: $135,000 to $2,000,000.

COOPERATIVE FUNDING PROGRAMS: Co-funding with other NIH Institutes.

APPLICATION INFORMATION:
Detailed information is available from the Branch Chief.
Duration: Typically three to four years.

ADDRESS INQUIRIES TO:
Dr. Hinda Zlotnik, Branch Chief
(See address above.)

NATIONAL INSTITUTE OF GENERAL MEDICAL SCIENCES   [2444]
Natcher Building, MSC 6200
45 Center Drive, 2AS-13A
Bethesda, MD 20892-6200
(301) 594-0828
Fax: (301) 480-2004

E-MAIL ADDRESS:
shapirob@nigms.nih.gov

WEB SITE ADDRESS:
www.nigms.nih.gov

AREAS OF INTEREST:
Basic biomedical research.

NAME(S) OF PROGRAMS:
- **Medical Scientist Training Program**

TYPE:
Training grants. The goal of this program is to prepare its graduates to function independently in both clinical practice and scientific research. MSTP has over 41 participating programs.

YEAR PROGRAM STARTED: 1964

PURPOSE:
To support research training leading to the combined M.D.-Ph.D. degree.

ELIGIBILITY:
Applicants must be U.S. citizens or permanent residents.

GEOGRAPHIC RESTRICTIONS:
United States.

FINANCIAL DATA:
Many institutions supplement the basic stipend provided by the MSTP grant. Trainees incur no payback obligation.
Amount of support per award: $21,000 stipend plus tuition allowance and modest sum for travel, equipment and supplies for the year 2011.
Total amount of support: Varies.

NUMBER OF AWARDS: 921.

APPLICATION INFORMATION:
Individuals who wish to enter the program should contact the program office at the participating institution(s) of their choice directly for curriculum information and admission requirements. Interested institutions should contact the NIGMS program director at participating institutions for information concerning the program. Institutions should include the standard Form 424.
Duration: Maximum six years, although the course of study for the combined degree may take longer. Continued support conditional upon annual review and availability of funds to the institution.
Deadline: January 25, May 25 and September 25. Grant awarded only once per year.

NATIONAL INSTITUTES OF HEALTH [2445]

Office of Extramural Research
9000 Rockville Pike
Bethesda, MD 20892
(301) 435-0714

E-MAIL ADDRESS:
grantsinfo@nih.gov

WEB SITE ADDRESS:
www.nih.gov

FOUNDED: 1930

AREAS OF INTEREST:
Biomedical research and improvement of human health.

NAME(S) OF PROGRAMS:
● **Ruth L. Kirschstein National Research Service Awards for Individual Postdoctoral Fellowships in Muscular Dystrophy Research (F32)**

TYPE:
Fellowships; Research grants; Training grants. Research supported through this funding opportunity will address basic, translational or clinical studies of the muscular dystrophies.

PURPOSE:
To provide support to promising applicants with the potential to become productive and successful independent research investigators in scientific health-related fields relevant to the programmatic interests of the National Institute of Arthritis and Musculoskeletal and Skin Diseases (NIAMS).

LEGAL BASIS:
Section 472 of the Public Health Service Act as amended (42 USC 289l-1).

ELIGIBILITY:
Applicant - Project Director/Principal Investigator (PD/PI) - must be citizen or noncitizen national of the U.S. or have been lawfully admitted to the U.S. for permanent residence.

Before the award can be activated, the candidate will have received a Ph.D., M.D., D.O., D.C., D.D.S., D.V.M., O.D., D.P.M., Sc.D., Eng.D., Dr.P.H., DNSc., N.D., Pharm.D., D.S.W., Psy.D., or equivalent doctoral degree from an accredited domestic or foreign institution.

GEOGRAPHIC RESTRICTIONS:
United States and its territories.

FINANCIAL DATA:
Amount of support per award: Varies.

NUMBER OF AWARDS: Varies.

APPLICATION INFORMATION:
Guidelines and detailed information are available on the NIH web site.
Duration: Varies.

NATIONAL INSTITUTES OF HEALTH [2446]

Office of Extramural Research (OER)
9000 Rockville Pike
Bethesda, MD 20892
(301) 435-0714
TTY: (301) 451-5936

E-MAIL ADDRESS:
grantsinfo@nih.gov

WEB SITE ADDRESS:
www.nih.gov

FOUNDED: 1887

AREAS OF INTEREST:
Biomedical research and improvement of human health.

NAME(S) OF PROGRAMS:
● **Mentored Clinical Scientist Research Career Development Award (Parent K08)**

TYPE:
Research grants. This program prepares qualified individuals for careers that have a significant impact on the health-related research needs of the nation.

PURPOSE:
To help ensure that a diverse pool of highly trained scientists are available in appropriate scientific disciplines to address the nation's biomedical, behavioral and clinical research needs.

LEGAL BASIS:
Public Health Service Act, Section 301(c).

ELIGIBILITY:
Eligible organizations include higher education institutions, nonprofits other than institutions of higher education, for-profit organizations , different domestic levels of government, Native American tribal organizations and faith-based or community-based organizations.

Eligible individuals (program director/principal investigator) must be a citizen or a noncitizen national of the U.S. or have been lawfully admitted for permanent residence. They must have a clinical doctoral degree (e.g., M.D., D.D.S., D.M.D., D.O., D.C., O.D., N.D., D.V.M., Pharm.D., or Ph.D. (in certain clinical disciplines). The K08 award may be used by candidates with different levels of prior research training and at different stages in their career development.

GEOGRAPHIC RESTRICTIONS:
United States.

APPLICATION INFORMATION:
Applications must be submitted electronically. Paper applications will not be accepted.
Duration: Up to five years.

NATIONAL INSTITUTES OF HEALTH [2447]

Office of Extramural Research
9000 Rockville Pike
Bethesda, MD 20892
(301) 435-0714
TTY: (301) 451-5936

E-MAIL ADDRESS:
grantsinfo@nih.gov

WEB SITE ADDRESS:
www.nih.gov

FOUNDED: 1930

AREAS OF INTEREST:
Biomedical research and improvement of human health.

NAME(S) OF PROGRAMS:
● **Ruth L. Kirschstein National Research Service Awards (NRSA) for Individual Senior Fellows (Parent F33)**

TYPE:
Fellowships. This program is intended to provide senior fellowship support to experienced scientists who wish to make major changes in the direction of their research careers or who wish to broaden their scientific background by acquiring new research capabilities as independent research investigators in scientific health-related fields relevant to the missions of the participating NIH Institutes and Centers.

PURPOSE:
To further biomedical research.

LEGAL BASIS:
An agency of the U.S. Public Health Service.

ELIGIBILITY:
Individuals with at least seven years of research experience beyond the Doctorate (individuals with Ph.D., M.D., O.D., associate professors, full professors, etc.) and who have progressed to the stage of independent investigator.

GEOGRAPHIC RESTRICTIONS:
United States.

NUMBER OF AWARDS: Varies.

APPLICATION INFORMATION:
Duration: Typically, up to two years.

NATIONAL INSTITUTES OF HEALTH [2448]

National Center for Research Resources
6701 Democracy Boulevard
Room 958, Building One
Bethesda, MD 20892
(301) 435-0772
Fax: (301) 480-3659

E-MAIL ADDRESS:
sig@mail.nih.gov

WEB SITE ADDRESS:
www.ncrr.nih.gov

FOUNDED: 1930

AREAS OF INTEREST:
Biomedical research and improvement of human health.

NAME(S) OF PROGRAMS:
● **Shared Instrumentation Grant Program**

TYPE:
Project/program grants.

YEAR PROGRAM STARTED: 1982

PURPOSE:
To provide research institutions the opportunity to obtain expensive (over $100,000 per item) commercially available instruments to be shared by groups of NIH-funded investigators.

LEGAL BASIS:
An agency of the U.S. Public Health Service.

ELIGIBILITY:
Federal agencies, foreign institutions and for-profit institutions are not eligible.

FINANCIAL DATA:
Amount of support per award: Applications are limited to instruments that cost at least $100,000 per instrument or system. Maximum award is $600,000.
Total amount of support: $42,000,000 for fiscal year 2010.

NUMBER OF APPLICANTS MOST RECENT YEAR: 342.

NUMBER OF AWARDS: 134 for the year 2010.

APPLICATION INFORMATION:
Form PHS-398 or SF424 (R&R) via www.grants.gov. Announcement in December issue of NIH *Guide to Grants and Contracts.*
Duration: One year. No renewals.
Deadline: Usually the last week in March.

ADDRESS INQUIRIES TO:
Shared Instrumentation Grant Program
(See address above.)

NATIONAL MEDICAL FELLOWSHIPS, INC. [2449]

347 Fifth Avenue, Suite 510
New York, NY 10016
(212) 483-8880
Fax: (212) 483-8897

E-MAIL ADDRESS:
nmf1@nmfonline.org

WEB SITE ADDRESS:
www.nmfonline.org

FOUNDED: 1946

AREAS OF INTEREST:
Minority medical students and health care of low-income and minority communities.

NAME(S) OF PROGRAMS:
- **Metropolitan Life Foundation Awards for Academic Excellence in Medicine**
- **National Medical Association Special Award Programs**
- **Need Based Scholarship Program**
- **NMF/GE Medical Scholar Program**
- **Aura E. Severinghaus Award**

TYPE:
Awards/prizes; Fellowships; Scholarships. In addition to its general scholarship program, NMF administers a number of special award and fellowship programs that recognize and encourage extraordinary accomplishments.

The General Scholarship Program offers need-based awards to students enrolled in the first or second year of medical school.

The Metropolitan Life Foundation Awards for Academic Excellence in Medicine are awarded to students who reside or attend school in designated cities and who demonstrate academic achievement, leadership, and financial need.

The National Medical Association Special Award Programs sponsor annual prizes that recognize achievement among African-American students.

NMF/GE Medical Scholar Program is an international program for 12 fourth-year minority students who demonstrate academic achievement and leadership, and who are selected for a medical elective in West Africa for a two-month period.

The Aura E. Severinghaus Award is presented to a senior of outstanding academic excellence and leadership attending the College of Physicians and Surgeons of Columbia University.

YEAR PROGRAM STARTED: 1946

PURPOSE:
To improve the health of low-income and minority communities by increasing the number of minority physicians and addressing the special needs of these communities.

LEGAL BASIS:
Nonprofit corporation.

ELIGIBILITY:
All programs are open to American citizens who are African-American, Hawaiian and Alaska Natives, Native American, or Hispanics, as specified for the individual program. Applicants must be enrolled in accredited M.D. and D.O. degree-granting programs in the U.S.

FINANCIAL DATA:
Amount of support per award: Varies.
Total amount of support: Varies.

NUMBER OF APPLICANTS MOST RECENT YEAR:
Varies.

NUMBER OF AWARDS: Varies.

APPLICATION INFORMATION:
Guidelines and official application materials are available upon request to National Medical Fellowships.
Duration: Varies by program.
Deadline: Varies by program.

OFFICERS:
Dr. Esther Dyer, President and Chief Executive Officer

BOARD OF DIRECTORS:
Arthur W. Kaemmer, M.D., Chairman
Miriam Graddick, Ph.D., Vice Chairman
Dr. Stephen Keith, Treasurer
Robert L.M. Hilliard, M.D., Secretary

ADDRESS INQUIRIES TO:
Programs Operations and Management
(See address above.)

THE NATIONAL ORGANIZATION FOR RARE DISORDERS [2450]

55 Kenosia Avenue
Danbury, CT 06813-1968
(203) 744-0100
Fax: (203) 798-2291

E-MAIL ADDRESS:
research@rarediseases.org

WEB SITE ADDRESS:
www.rarediseases.org

FOUNDED: 1983

AREAS OF INTEREST:
Rare "orphan" disease.

NAME(S) OF PROGRAMS:
- **Annual Roscoe Brady Lysosomal Storage Disease Fellowship Award**
- **Restricted Research Program**

TYPE:
Research grants; Seed money grants. Fellowship award provides grant to M.D. or M.D./Ph.D. to study new treatments or diagnostic tests for lysosomal storage diseases.

The Restricted Research Program provides seed money grants to academic scientists studying new treatments or diagnostic tests for rare diseases.

PURPOSE:
To promote the diagnosis, treatment and cure of rare disorders through programs of education, advocacy, service and research.

ELIGIBILITY:
Must be an academic scientist. IRB approval and a copy of informed consent is necessary if the study involves human, and NIH Recombinant DNA Advisory Committee review or waiver of review if human gene therapy is involved.

FINANCIAL DATA:
Overhead and indirect costs are not awarded.
Amount of support per award: Minimum $30,000.
Total amount of support: Varies.

NUMBER OF APPLICANTS MOST RECENT YEAR:
Approximately 25.

NUMBER OF AWARDS: 1 to 5.

APPLICATION INFORMATION:
Submit a letter of intent, curriculum vitae, one-page abstract, and a brief budget. Full proposals by invitation only. Requests for proposals announcements typically posted online in early March of each year.
Duration: One to two years.
Deadline: Typically early to mid-May.

ADDRESS INQUIRIES TO:
Stefanie Putkowski, R.N.
Research Program Administrator
The National Organization
for Rare Disorders
P.O. Box 1968
Danbury, CT 06813-1968

*SPECIAL STIPULATIONS:
Reports and communication must be written in English and adhere to the most recent guidelines set forth by the National Institutes of Health.

NATIONAL SOCIETY DAUGHTERS OF THE AMERICAN REVOLUTION [2451]

1776 D Street, N.W.
Washington, DC 20006-5303
(202) 879-3292

WEB SITE ADDRESS:
www.dar.org

FOUNDED: 1895

AREAS OF INTEREST:
Medicine and psychiatric nursing.

NAME(S) OF PROGRAMS:
- **Irene and Daisy MacGregor Memorial Scholarship**

TYPE:
Scholarships.

YEAR PROGRAM STARTED: 1991

PURPOSE:
To provide ways and means to aid students in attaining higher education.

LEGAL BASIS:
Incorporated historical society.

ELIGIBILITY:
Scholarships are awarded without regard to race, religion, sex or national origin. All four-year scholarships must be for consecutive years and are renewable only upon review and approval of annual transcript. Candidates must be U.S. citizens and must attend or plan to attend an accredited college or university in the U.S. No affiliation or relationship to DAR is required for qualification, but candidate must be sponsored by a local DAR Chapter. Awards are judged on the basis of academic excellence, commitment to field of study, as required, and financial need.

The MacGregor Memorial Scholarship is awarded to students of high scholastic standing and character who have been accepted into or are pursuing an approved course of study to become a medical doctor (not pre-med) at an approved, accredited medical school.

This MacGregor Memorial Scholarship is also available to students who have been accepted into or who are pursuing an approved course of study in the field of psychiatric nursing, graduate level, at medical schools, colleges or universities. There is a preference to females "if equally qualified."

FINANCIAL DATA:
Amount of support per award: $5,000 annually for up to four consecutive years, with a maximum of $20,000.

APPLICATION INFORMATION:
To obtain a scholarship application packet, send a self-addressed, stamped #10 business-size envelope to Office of the Reporter General, DAR Scholarship Committee, at the address listed above.

No affiliation or relationship with the NSDAR is necessary, unless specifically stated, to apply for a scholarship.

Included with the application packet is the list of DAR State Scholarship Chairmen. All scholarship applicants are required to have a letter of sponsorship from a chapter. Individuals interested in obtaining a letter of sponsorship from a local chapter are encouraged to contact the DAR State Chairman.

Duration: Up to four consecutive years. Annual transcript review required for renewal and award.

Deadline: April 15.

PUBLICATIONS:
American Spirit, magazine.

ADDRESS INQUIRIES TO:
Office of the Reporter General
DAR Scholarship Committee
(See address above.)

NORTH AMERICAN SPINE SOCIETY (NASS)   [2452]
8320 St. Moritz Drive
Spring Grove, IL 60081
(630) 230-3691
Fax: (630) 230-3791

E-MAIL ADDRESS:
kjames@spine.org

WEB SITE ADDRESS:
www.spine.org

FOUNDED: 1985

AREAS OF INTEREST:
Disorders and functions of the human spine.

NAME(S) OF PROGRAMS:
● **Clinical Traveling Fellowship**
● **Research Grant**
● **Research Traveling Fellowship**
● **Young Investigator Grants**

TYPE:
Fellowships; Research grants. Clinical Traveling Fellowship: At least one month to be spent in three to five different medical centers studying spine techniques.

Research Traveling Fellowship: At least five months at one medical center, other than the one in which the applicants currently practice. This Fellowship primarily covers the cost of travel and housing.

Research Grant: This grant is for investigative research on the spine.

Young Investigator Grant: This grant is for projects in basic science, clinical or translational.

YEAR PROGRAM STARTED: 1989

PURPOSE:
To advance quality spine care through education, research and advocacy; to encourage and support basic and clinical science that is performed with integrity and

with a goal towards improving quality spine care for patients and understanding underlying disorders.

ELIGIBILITY:
Qualified investigators are eligible to apply. Applicants for Fellowships must have the approval of the institution and recommendation of the department head where the research training will be conducted.

FINANCIAL DATA:
Amount of support per award: $50,000 to $100,000.

Total amount of support: Varies.

NUMBER OF APPLICANTS MOST RECENT YEAR:
151.

NUMBER OF AWARDS: Fellowships: 2; Research Grants: 3.

APPLICATION INFORMATION:
Contact the Organization for application procedures. Budget restrictions are available when requesting an application.

Duration: Two years.

Deadline: Letters of Proposals for Grants: First week in February. Invited Grants and Fellowships: First week in May.

ADDRESS INQUIRIES TO:
Karen James
Assistant Manager of Research
(See address above.)

ORTHOPAEDIC RESEARCH AND EDUCATION FOUNDATION   [2453]
6300 North River Road
Suite 700
Rosemont, IL 60018-4261
(847) 698-9980
Fax: (847) 698-7806

E-MAIL ADDRESS:
mcguire@oref.org

WEB SITE ADDRESS:
www.oref.org

FOUNDED: 1955

AREAS OF INTEREST:
Musculoskeletal research.

NAME(S) OF PROGRAMS:
● **OREF Clinical Research Award**

TYPE:
Awards/prizes.

YEAR PROGRAM STARTED: 1996

PURPOSE:
To award outstanding research related to clinical musculoskeletal disease or injury.

LEGAL BASIS:
Special-interest foundation, 501(c)(3).

ELIGIBILITY:
Individual applicants must be members of the AAOS, ORS, Canadian Orthopaedic Association, Canadian ORS or sponsored by a member. Applicants are generally nonprofit organizations.

FINANCIAL DATA:
Amount of support per award: $20,000.

Total amount of support: $20,000.

NUMBER OF APPLICANTS MOST RECENT YEAR:
6.

NUMBER OF AWARDS: 1.

APPLICATION INFORMATION:
Submission guidelines are available on the web site.

Duration: One year.

Deadline: July 1.

PUBLICATIONS:
Annual report; application guidelines.

ADDRESS INQUIRIES TO:
Jean McGuire, Vice President of Grants
(See address above.)

ORTHOPAEDIC RESEARCH AND EDUCATION FOUNDATION   [2454]
6300 North River Road
Suite 700
Rosemont, IL 60018-4261
(847) 698-9980
Fax: (847) 698-7806

E-MAIL ADDRESS:
mcguire@oref.org

WEB SITE ADDRESS:
www.oref.org

FOUNDED: 1955

AREAS OF INTEREST:
Orthopaedic research.

NAME(S) OF PROGRAMS:
● **Career Development Grants**

TYPE:
Research grants. Grants for scientific research in orthopaedic surgery.

YEAR PROGRAM STARTED: 1984

PURPOSE:
To encourage a commitment to scientific research in orthopaedic surgery.

LEGAL BASIS:
501(c)(3) special-interest foundation.

ELIGIBILITY:
Candidates must have completed residency in orthopaedic surgery and have demonstrated a sustained interest in research, as well as excellence in clinical training. Letters of nomination and support must offer convincing evidence of the candidate's potential to develop as an investigator.

GEOGRAPHIC RESTRICTIONS:
United States.

FINANCIAL DATA:
Amount of support per award: Up to $75,000 per year. Budget may include salary support.

Total amount of support: $450,000 for the year 2010.

NUMBER OF APPLICANTS MOST RECENT YEAR:
11 for the year 2010.

NUMBER OF AWARDS: 2 for the year 2010.

APPLICATION INFORMATION:
Duration: Up to three years, conditional upon annual review.

Deadline: October 1. Announcement the following February or March.

PUBLICATIONS:
Annual report; application guidelines.

ADDRESS INQUIRIES TO:
Jean McGuire, Vice President of Grants
(See address above.)

*SPECIAL STIPULATIONS:
Applicant must be working in the U.S. only.

ORTHOPAEDIC RESEARCH AND EDUCATION FOUNDATION [2455]

6300 North River Road
Suite 700
Rosemont, IL 60018-4261
(847) 698-9980
Fax: (847) 698-7806

E-MAIL ADDRESS:
mcguire@oref.org

WEB SITE ADDRESS:
www.oref.org

FOUNDED: 1955

AREAS OF INTEREST:
Orthopaedic surgery research.

NAME(S) OF PROGRAMS:
- **Resident Clinician-Scientist Training Grant**

TYPE:
Research grants. Grants to prepare residents for a career with research as a major component.

YEAR PROGRAM STARTED: 1961

PURPOSE:
To encourage the research interests and meritorious projects of residents and fellows in approved orthopaedic programs.

LEGAL BASIS:
501(c)(3) special-interest foundation.

ELIGIBILITY:
Candidates must be residents or fellows in approved orthopaedic programs.

GEOGRAPHIC RESTRICTIONS:
United States.

FINANCIAL DATA:
Grants provide funds for supplies and expenses, but not for resident salary or travel.
Amount of support per award: Up to $20,000.
Total amount of support: $140,000 for the year 2010.

NUMBER OF APPLICANTS MOST RECENT YEAR:
36 for the year 2010.

NUMBER OF AWARDS: 7 for the year 2010.

APPLICATION INFORMATION:
Applications are available on the web site from April until October 1.
Duration: One year.
Deadline: October 1. Announcement the following February or March.

PUBLICATIONS:
Annual report; application guidelines.

ADDRESS INQUIRIES TO:
Jean McGuire, Vice President of Grants
(See address above.)

*SPECIAL STIPULATIONS:
Resident must be working in the U.S.

OSTEOGENESIS IMPERFECTA FOUNDATION [2456]

804 West Diamond Avenue
Suite 210
Gaithersburg, MD 20878
(301) 947-0083
Fax: (301) 947-0456

E-MAIL ADDRESS:
bonelink@oif.org

WEB SITE ADDRESS:
www.oif.org

FOUNDED: 1970

AREAS OF INTEREST:
Osteogenesis imperfecta medical research.

NAME(S) OF PROGRAMS:
- **Clinical Seed Grants**
- **Michael Geisman Fellowships**
- **Seed Grants**

TYPE:
Fellowships; Research grants; Seed money grants. Clinical Seed Grants are designed to study people with osteogenesis imperfecta and their families.

Michael Geisman Fellowships: Applicants must be in academic institutions and the work must be done under the supervision of a mentor with training and experience in osteogenesis imperfecta (OI) or a related field.

Seed Grants are for basic or clinical studies with relevance to OI.

YEAR PROGRAM STARTED: 1970

PURPOSE:
To expand understanding and identify improved treatments for osteogenesis imperfecta.

LEGAL BASIS:
Nonprofit organization.

ELIGIBILITY:
Applicants for the fellowship must be postdoctoral fellows in academic institutions and the work must be done under the supervision of a mentor with appropriate training and experience in this or related field.

FINANCIAL DATA:
Amount of support per award: Clinical Seed Grants: Up to $120,000; Michael Geisman Fellowships: Up to $50,000 per year ($35,000 toward the investigator's salary and up to $15,000 per year for supplies); Seed Grants: Up to $60,000.

APPLICATION INFORMATION:
Applicants should submit an original application with 10 copies. The application should include an abstract for a lay audience, budget, education, previous research experience, professional training, publications and a research plan. Electronic submissions are accepted.
Duration: Clinical Seed Grants: One-time funding for two years; Michael Geisman Fellowships: One year with possible renewal; Seed Grants: One-time funding for one year.
Deadline: December 1.

PUBLICATIONS:
Annual report; application guidelines; bimonthly newsletter.

IRS IDENTIFICATION NUMBER: 23-7076021

ADDRESS INQUIRIES TO:
OIF Research Department
(See address above.)

OXALOSIS AND HYPEROXALURIA FOUNDATION [2457]

201 East 19th Street, Suite 12-E
New York, NY 10003
(212) 777-0470
(800) 643-8699
Fax: (212) 777-0471

E-MAIL ADDRESS:
kimh@ohf.org

WEB SITE ADDRESS:
www.ohf.org

FOUNDED: 1989

AREAS OF INTEREST:
Hyperoxaluria and oxalosis.

NAME(S) OF PROGRAMS:
- **OHF Research Grant**

TYPE:
Research grants. The Research Grant program assists investigators, new or established, who have research projects for which they need support.

PURPOSE:
To fund grants which will increase the understanding of hyperoxaluria and oxalosis and improve the clinical management and treatment of these diseases.

ELIGIBILITY:
Applications are accepted from anywhere in the world. There are no citizenship requirements.

FINANCIAL DATA:
Funds may be used for salaries for the investigators, technical assistance, special equipment, animals, supplies and travel.
Amount of support per award: Up to $160,000.

APPLICATION INFORMATION:
All applications must be made on the OHF forms. OHF prefers that applications be submitted electronically as an attachment and e-mailed to grantapp@ohf.org. Appendices, if included, may also be submitted electronically. Additionally, one original paper copy of the application must be submitted to the OHF Office address listed above. Applications or supporting material received after the deadline will not be considered, regardless of the date of postmark.
Duration: Up to two years.
Deadline: September 15.

ADDRESS INQUIRIES TO:
Kim Hollander, Executive Director
(See address above.)

OXNARD FOUNDATION [2458]

5 Royal St. George Road
Newport Beach, CA 92660
(949) 644-4160
Fax: (949) 644-4171

E-MAIL ADDRESS:
covlineage@gmail.com

AREAS OF INTEREST:
General medical research.

TYPE:
Matching gifts; Research grants.

PURPOSE:
To help continue medical research in the areas of concern for the Foundation.

ELIGIBILITY:
IRS 501(c)(3) tax-exempt organizations, schools and hospitals.

GEOGRAPHIC RESTRICTIONS:
California and New Mexico.

FINANCIAL DATA:
Amount of support per award: $35,000 to $50,000.
Total amount of support: Varies.

APPLICATION INFORMATION:
Applicants should first send a letter and include a copy of the IRS tax determination letter.

Duration: One year. Renewal by reapplication.

Deadline: Applications are reviewed at Board meetings in February, June and November.

ADDRESS INQUIRIES TO:
Christopher Veitch, President
(See address above.)

PHARMACEUTICAL RESEARCH AND MANUFACTURERS OF AMERICA FOUNDATION, INC. [2459]

950 F Street, N.W.
Suite 300
Washington, DC 20004
(202) 572-7756
Fax: (202) 572-7799

E-MAIL ADDRESS:
foundation@phrma.org

WEB SITE ADDRESS:
www.phrmafoundation.org

AREAS OF INTEREST:
Health outcomes and pharmaceutical research.

NAME(S) OF PROGRAMS:
● **Predoctoral Fellowships in Health Outcomes**

TYPE:
Fellowships.

YEAR PROGRAM STARTED: 2002

PURPOSE:
To support promising students during their thesis research.

ELIGIBILITY:
Full-time, in-residence Ph.D. candidates in the fields of health outcomes enrolled in U.S. schools of medicine, pharmacy, dentistry, or schools of public health are eligible to apply. Students must have completed two years of study and start their thesis research by the time the award is activated. Applicants must be U.S. citizens or permanent residents. Applications are to be submitted by an accredited U.S. school.

GEOGRAPHIC RESTRICTIONS:
United States.

FINANCIAL DATA:
Award is made to the university on behalf of the fellow. Annual stipend payable monthly for one to two years. $500 per year may be used for incidentals directly associated with thesis research preparation.

Amount of support per award: Maximum $50,000 ($25,000 per year).

NUMBER OF AWARDS: 2 budgeted.

APPLICATION INFORMATION:
Duration: Two years.

Deadline: Deadline and announcement date is available online.

PUBLICATIONS:
Brochure.

BOARD OF DIRECTORS:
Garry A. Neil, M.D., Chairman
John Castellani
Mikael Dolsten, M.D., Ph.D.
Ivan Gergel, M.D.
Glenn J. Gormley, M.D., Ph.D.
Howard G. Hutchinson, M.D.
Peter S. Kim, Ph.D.
John M. Leonard, M.D.
Jan M. Lundberg, Ph.D.

John Orloff, M.D.
Moncef Slaoui, Ph.D.

ADVISORY COMMITTEE:
J. Lynle Bootman, Ph.D., Sc.D.
Jean Paul Gagnon, Ph.D.
Geoff Makinson, Ph.D.
C. Daniel Mullins, Ph.D.
Nancy C. Santanello, M.D., M.S.
Sean D. Sullivan, Ph.D.

ADDRESS INQUIRIES TO:
Predoctoral Fellowships
in Health Outcomes
(See address above.)

PHARMACEUTICAL RESEARCH AND MANUFACTURERS OF AMERICA FOUNDATION, INC. [2460]

950 F Street, N.W.
Suite 300
Washington, DC 20004
(202) 572-7756
Fax: (202) 572-7799

E-MAIL ADDRESS:
foundation@phrma.org

WEB SITE ADDRESS:
www.phrmafoundation.org

AREAS OF INTEREST:
Informatics.

NAME(S) OF PROGRAMS:
● **Postdoctoral Fellowships in Informatics**

TYPE:
Fellowships.

YEAR PROGRAM STARTED: 2002

PURPOSE:
To support postdoctoral career development activities of individuals preparing to engage in research that will bridge the gap between experimental and computational approaches in genomic and biomedical studies.

ELIGIBILITY:
Applicants must hold a Ph.D. degree in the field of study logically or functionally related to the proposed postdoctoral activities, or expect to receive the Ph.D. before activating the award. Must also have firm commitment from an accredited U.S. university and be a U.S. citizen or permanent resident.

GEOGRAPHIC RESTRICTIONS:
United States.

FINANCIAL DATA:
Annual stipend made to the institution on behalf of the fellow.

Amount of support per award: Maximum $80,000 ($40,000 per year).

NUMBER OF AWARDS: 2 budgeted.

APPLICATION INFORMATION:
Applications are to be submitted at the Foundation web site.

Duration: One to two years.

Deadline: September 1. Announcement December 15.

PUBLICATIONS:
Brochure.

ADDRESS INQUIRIES TO:
Postdoctoral Fellowships in Informatics
(See address above.)

*SPECIAL STIPULATIONS:
Second year contingent upon progress report approved by the Foundation and submission of a financial report.

PHARMACEUTICAL RESEARCH AND MANUFACTURERS OF AMERICA FOUNDATION, INC. [2461]

950 F Street, N.W.
Suite 300
Washington, DC 20004
(202) 572-7756
Fax: (202) 572-7799

E-MAIL ADDRESS:
foundation@phrma.org

WEB SITE ADDRESS:
www.phrmafoundation.org

AREAS OF INTEREST:
Health outcomes, informatics, pharmacology/toxicology and pharmaceutics.

NAME(S) OF PROGRAMS:
● **Sabbatical Fellowships in Health Outcomes**
● **Sabbatical Fellowships in Informatics**
● **Sabbatical Fellowships in Pharmaceutics**
● **Sabbatical Fellowships in Pharmacology/Toxicology**

TYPE:
Fellowships.

YEAR PROGRAM STARTED: 2002

PURPOSE:
To provide support for individuals engaged in a multidisciplinary research training program that will create or extend their credentials in the fields of health outcomes, informatics, pharmacology/toxicology or pharmaceutics.

ELIGIBILITY:
Varies by program.

GEOGRAPHIC RESTRICTIONS:
United States.

FINANCIAL DATA:
Amount of support per award: $40,000.

Matching fund requirements: Matching funds must be provided by the institution.

NUMBER OF AWARDS: 1 budgeted for each program.

APPLICATION INFORMATION:
Applications are to be submitted at the Foundation web site.

Duration: One year.

Deadline: Pharmaceutics and Health Outcomes: October 1. All others: September 1. Announcement: December 15.

PUBLICATIONS:
Brochure.

ADDRESS INQUIRIES TO:
Sabbatical Fellowships
(See address above.)

PHARMACEUTICAL RESEARCH AND MANUFACTURERS OF AMERICA FOUNDATION, INC. [2462]

950 F Street, N.W.
Suite 300
Washington, DC 20004
(202) 572-7756
Fax: (202) 572-7799

E-MAIL ADDRESS:
foundation@phrma.org

WEB SITE ADDRESS:
www.phrmafoundation.org

AREAS OF INTEREST:
Pharmacology and toxicology.

NAME(S) OF PROGRAMS:
● **Postdoctoral Fellowship in Pharmacology/Toxicology**

TYPE:
Fellowships.

YEAR PROGRAM STARTED: 2002

PURPOSE:
To support postdoctoral career development activities of individuals prepared (or preparing) to engage in research that integrates information on molecular or cellular mechanisms of action with information on the effect of an agent in the intact organism.

ELIGIBILITY:
Applicants must hold a Ph.D. degree or appropriate terminal research doctorate in a field of study logically or functionally related to the proposed postdoctoral activities, or expect to receive the Ph.D. before activating the award. They must also have a firm commitment from an accredited U.S. university and be a U.S. citizen or permanent resident.

GEOGRAPHIC RESTRICTIONS:
United States.

FINANCIAL DATA:
Stipend is made to the institution on behalf of the fellow.
Amount of support per award: Maximum $80,000 ($40,000 per year).

NUMBER OF AWARDS: 2 budgeted.

APPLICATION INFORMATION:
Applications are to be submitted at the Foundation web site.
Duration: Two years.
Deadline: September 1. Announcement December 15.

PUBLICATIONS:
Brochure.

ADDRESS INQUIRIES TO:
Postdoctoral Fellowship in Pharmacology/Toxicology
(See address above.)

*SPECIAL STIPULATIONS:
Second year is contingent upon a progress report approved by the Foundation and submission of a financial report.

PHARMACEUTICAL RESEARCH AND MANUFACTURERS OF AMERICA FOUNDATION, INC.

950 F Street, N.W.
Suite 300
Washington, DC 20004
(202) 572-7756
Fax: (202) 572-7799

E-MAIL ADDRESS:
foundation@phrma.org

WEB SITE ADDRESS:
www.phrmafoundation.org

TYPE:
Project/program grants; Research grants; Seed money grants. Starter grants to support research in the fields of pharmacology, clinical pharmacology, drug toxicology, pharmaceutics, informatics and health outcomes.

See entry 2704 for full listing.

PHARMACEUTICAL RESEARCH AND MANUFACTURERS OF AMERICA FOUNDATION, INC.   [2463]

950 F Street, N.W.
Suite 300
Washington, DC 20004
(202) 572-7756
Fax: (202) 572-7799

E-MAIL ADDRESS:
foundation@phrma.org

WEB SITE ADDRESS:
www.phrmafoundation.org

FOUNDED: 1965

AREAS OF INTEREST:
Health outcomes.

NAME(S) OF PROGRAMS:
● **Postdoctoral Fellowship in Health Outcomes**

TYPE:
Fellowships. This program provides stipend to well-trained graduates from Pharm.D., M.D., and Ph.D. programs who seek to further develop and refine research skills through formal postdoctoral training.

YEAR PROGRAM STARTED: 2002

PURPOSE:
To encourage graduates from Ph.D. programs in health outcomes to continue their research skills through formal postdoctoral training.

LEGAL BASIS:
501(c)(3) organization.

ELIGIBILITY:
Applicant must be a graduate from Pharm.D., M.D. or Ph.D. program.

Before an individual is eligible to apply for a PHRMA Foundation award, he or she must first have a firm commitment from a U.S. university. Applications must be submitted by an accredited school in the U.S. and all applicants should either be a U.S. citizen or permanent resident.

GEOGRAPHIC RESTRICTIONS:
United States.

FINANCIAL DATA:
Amount of support per award: Maximum $110,000 ($55,000 per year).

NUMBER OF AWARDS: 1 budgeted.

APPLICATION INFORMATION:
Duration: Two years.
Deadline: Deadline and announcement date will be available online.

PUBLICATIONS:
Brochure.

IRS IDENTIFICATION NUMBER: 52-6063009

BOARD OF DIRECTORS:
Garry A. Neil, M.D., Chairman
John Castellani
Mikael Dolsten, M.D., Ph.D.
Ivan Gergel, M.D.
Glenn J. Gormley, M.D., Ph.D.
Howard G. Hutchinson, M.D.
Peter S. Kim, Ph.D.
John M. Leonard, M.D.
Jan M. Lundberg, Ph.D.
John Orloff, M.D.
Moncef Slaoui, Ph.D.

ADVISORY COMMITTEE:
J. Lynle Bootman, Ph.D., Sc.D.
Jean Paul Gagnon, Ph.D.
Geoff Makinson, Ph.D.
C. Daniel Mullins, Ph.D.

Nancy C. Santanello, M.D., M.S.
Sean D. Sullivan, Ph.D.

ADDRESS INQUIRIES TO:
Postdoctoral Fellowship in Health Outcomes
(See address above.)

DR. AND MRS. ARTHUR WILLIAM PHILLIPS CHARITABLE TRUST   [2464]

229 Elm Street
Oil City, PA 16301
(814) 676-2736
Fax: (814) 677-5701

FOUNDED: 1979

AREAS OF INTEREST:
Primarily medical centers, research and education.

TYPE:
Project/program grants.

PURPOSE:
To support many varied projects.

ELIGIBILITY:
Organizations must be:
(1) IRS 501(c)(3) tax-exempt;
(2) located in northwestern Pennsylvania;
(3) able to raise the balance of necessary funding from other sources and;
(4) able to show evidence of financial responsibility that will insure the completion and success of the project.

GEOGRAPHIC RESTRICTIONS:
Northwestern Pennsylvania.

FINANCIAL DATA:
Amount of support per award: Varies.
Total amount of support: Approximately $600,000.

APPLICATION INFORMATION:
Applications should be made in triplicate and include a short history of the organization, the need for the project, the annual budget for the project, other helpful financial budgetary information and a copy of their 501(c)(3).

IRS IDENTIFICATION NUMBER: 25-6201015

TRUSTEES:
Larry S. Adams
Edith Gilmore Letcher
Robert W. McFate

ADDRESS INQUIRIES TO:
Robert W. McFate, Trustee
(See address above.)

PLASTIC SURGERY FOUNDATION (PSF)   [2465]

ASPS/PSF
444 East Algonquin Road
Arlington Heights, IL 60005
(847) 228-9900
Fax: (847) 228-0628

E-MAIL ADDRESS:
research@plasticsurgery.org

WEB SITE ADDRESS:
www.plasticsurgery.org

AREAS OF INTEREST:
Any area (basic, translational, clinical and outcomes) of research related to plastic surgery sciences.

NAME(S) OF PROGRAMS:
- **National Endowment for Plastic Surgery Research Grant**
- **Pilot Research Grant**
- **Research Fellowship Grant**

TYPE:
Research grants. National Endowment for Plastic Surgery Research Grants encourage and support research projects which address clinically relevant issues facing the practice of plastic surgery. Applications must address a topic of importance to the current clinical practice of plastic surgery, and a clear, realistic path for application of acquired knowledge to the practice of plastic surgery must be described.

Pilot Research Grants promote plastic surgery advancement and innovation. These grants provide seed funding, and are intended to allow researchers to conduct preliminary studies related to plastic surgery science that set the stage for applications to external funding agencies. Studies that are a prelude to applications to the NIH are strongly encouraged.

Research Fellowship Grants encourage the research and academic career development for plastic surgery residents and junior faculty. The research fellowship is intended to supplement salary support during a mentored research experience. The PSF/KCI Wound Care Research Fellowship is for support of a research project focusing on wound care management. Funds may not be used for research project expenses.

PURPOSE:
To fund research that will eliminate problems in aesthetic surgery.

ELIGIBILITY:
National Endowment for Plastic Surgery Research Grant and Pilot Research Grant: Principal Investigator must be an active or candidate member of ASPS or obtain sponsorship from an active or candidate member of ASPS. Applicants must be M.D., D.O., or Ph.D. and hold a full-time position in a Department of Plastic Surgery or equivalent.

Research Fellowship Grant: Applicant must be an active or candidate member of ASPS or obtain sponsorship from an active or candidate member of ASPS. Applicants must be an M.D. or D.O. and hold a full-time position in a Department of Plastic Surgery. Applicants must be residents or within five years of initial faculty appointment. Resident applicants will devote 100% of their time to research training for a continuous 12-month period and may not be assigned to clinical rotations that satisfy residency requirements. Junior faculty applicants must have a minimum of 25% protected time for research.

FINANCIAL DATA:
Amount of support per award: National Endowment for Plastic Surgery Grant: Up to $50,000; Pilot Research Grant: Up to $10,000; PSF and PSF/KCI: Up to $50,000 for salary support.

APPLICATION INFORMATION:
Applications must be completed online. Further information is available online, or contact Research and Grants Associate at the phone number or e-mail address above.
Duration: 12 months.
Deadline: July 1 and December 1.

STAFF:
Jen McCormick, Research and Grants Associate

ADDRESS INQUIRIES TO:
Jen McCormick
Research and Grants Associate
(See address above.)

PLASTIC SURGERY FOUNDATION (PSF) [2466]

ASPS/PSF
444 East Algonquin Road
Arlington Heights, IL 60005
(847) 228-3356
Fax: (847) 228-0628

E-MAIL ADDRESS:
jmccormick@plasticsurgery.org

WEB SITE ADDRESS:
www.plasticsurgery.org

AREAS OF INTEREST:
Hand surgery, with preference on clinical/translational research with emphasis on clinical care.

NAME(S) OF PROGRAMS:
- **PSF/AFSH Hand Surgeon Scientist Award**

TYPE:
Awards/prizes. The award is designed to support young investigators who have demonstrated excellence in research by receiving extramural research funding in 2010 or later under one or more of the K08 or K23 career development awards from the NIH.

PURPOSE:
To ensure that young investigators in hand surgery have sufficient protected time to develop a productive career in academic surgery.

ELIGIBILITY:
Applicant must be young faculty member in a U.S. accredited plastic surgery program and must also be a member of the American Society for Surgery of the Hand. The applicant must demonstrate he or she has received a commitment from the NIH, with written proof at time of application.

FINANCIAL DATA:
Award is intended for salary support and will help supplement income lost due to time spent in research.
Amount of support per award: $75,000 per year.

APPLICATION INFORMATION:
Applications must be completed online. For more information, contact the Research Grants Coordinator at Tel: (847) 228-9900 or e-mail research@plasticsurgery.org.
Duration: Up to five years, subject to annual review.
Deadline: December 1.

ADDRESS INQUIRIES TO:
Jen McCormick
Research and Grants Associate
(See address above.)

POST-POLIO HEALTH INTERNATIONAL [2467]

4207 Lindell Boulevard
Suite 110
St. Louis, MO 63108-2930
(314) 534-0475
Fax: (314) 534-5070

E-MAIL ADDRESS:
director@post-polio.org

WEB SITE ADDRESS:
www.post-polio.org

FOUNDED: 1995

AREAS OF INTEREST:
Neuromuscular respiratory diseases and post-poliomyelitis.

NAME(S) OF PROGRAMS:
- **The Research Fund**

TYPE:
Research grants; Seed money grants. The Research Fund supports the work of researchers investigating the late effects of poliomyelitis and/or neuromuscular respiratory disease through one of two grants:

The Thomas Wallace Rogers Memorial Respiratory Research Grant: To study the cause(s) and treatment of neuromuscular respiratory insufficiency and the effects of long-term home mechanical ventilation.

The Post-Poliomyelitis Research Grant: This grant is to study the cause(s), treatment and management of the problem of the late effects of polio.

Only one of the above two is awarded every two years.

YEAR PROGRAM STARTED: 2000

PURPOSE:
To help support researchers, scientists, and clinicians worldwide to investigate the cause, treatment, and management of post-poliomyelitis and neuromuscular respiratory disease; to seek scientific information leading to eventual amelioration of the consequences of poliomyelitis and/or neuromuscular respiratory diseases.

LEGAL BASIS:
Not-for-profit organization.

ELIGIBILITY:
Applicants must be affiliated with an institution or organization. Citizens of all countries may apply. Applications, however, must be in English. Proposals will not be accepted via fax. The research may be quantitative and/or qualitative and follow sound and appropriate research standards relevant to the subject matter. The research findings must relate to improving the quality of life for people with disabilities. Preference will be given to innovative or original research. All requested information must be included. Incomplete applications will be disqualified.

FINANCIAL DATA:
Amount of support per award: $25,000.
Total amount of support: $25,000.

NUMBER OF APPLICANTS MOST RECENT YEAR: 13.

NUMBER OF AWARDS: 1.

REPRESENTATIVE AWARDS:
Dr. Zeev Meiner, M.D., "Characteristics of Poliomyelitis and Post-Polio Patients Among Jews and Arabs in Jerusalem;" Dr. Claire Kalpakjian, Ph.D., "The Role of Oral Glutathione in Improvement of Health Outcomes Among Persons with Late Effects of Poliomyelitis."

APPLICATION INFORMATION:
Proposals should be e-mailed in PDF format to the e-mail address above and one print copy of the application sent to the address above. There are two phases in the application process. Complete instructions are available on the Foundation's web site.

Duration: One year.

Deadline: Applications: March 5. The deadline is in two phases: Phase 1, March 5 (postmarked); Phase 2, September 24 (postmarked).

IRS IDENTIFICATION NUMBER: 34-0961952

ADDRESS INQUIRIES TO:
Joan L. Headley, Executive Director
(See address above.)

THE ELISABETH SEVERANCE PRENTISS FOUNDATION   [2468]

c/o PNC Bank
1900 East Ninth Street
Mailstop B7-YB13-03-1
Cleveland, OH 44114
(216) 222-2760
Fax: (216) 222-2410

E-MAIL ADDRESS:
john.baco@pnc.com

WEB SITE ADDRESS:
www.esprentissfoundation.org

FOUNDED: 1944

AREAS OF INTEREST:
Medical research, public health, hospital assistance for capital improvements, operation, management and administration.

TYPE:
Capital grants; Project/program grants. Project grants, educational support grants and building improvement grants in related medical areas.

YEAR PROGRAM STARTED: 1944

PURPOSE:
To promote and improve medical services, especially within Cuyahoga County (OH) for all individuals.

LEGAL BASIS:
Charitable foundation.

ELIGIBILITY:
Grant request must fall within restrictions of general purpose requirements, must not be for individuals for scholarships, fellowships, grants-in-aid or other personal purposes and must not be for redistribution by national foundations. Most favorable consideration will be given to those requests from applicants for purposes within the Cuyahoga County (OH) area. The Foundation strongly favors grant requests for specific projects over those requesting general operating support.

GEOGRAPHIC RESTRICTIONS:
Greater Cleveland, Ohio.

FINANCIAL DATA:
Amount of support per award:
Approximately $5,000 to $1,000,000.
Total amount of support: $4,169,968 for the year 2009.

APPLICATION INFORMATION:
There is no set form, but sufficient information and facts with supporting data should be given in the application to permit the Board of Managers to make a fair decision based on full and complete information. Applicant should also include six copies of each pertinent document being sent.

Duration: Support will continue, with annual installments, until requested grant has been satisfied. Grants are renewable.

Deadline: April 15 and October 15. Announcement after May and November semiannual board meetings.

BOARD OF DIRECTORS:
Quentin Alexander, President
Elisabeth H. Alexander
Pamela A. Alexander
Harry J. Bolwell
William R. Robertson

ADDRESS INQUIRIES TO:
Richard W. Mack, Secretary
(See address above.)

PULMONARY FIBROSIS FOUNDATION   [2469]

811 West Evergreen, Suite 204
Chicago, IL 60642
(888) 733-6741
Fax: (866) 587-9158

E-MAIL ADDRESS:
info@pulmonaryfibrosis.org

WEB SITE ADDRESS:
www.pulmonaryfibrosis.org

AREAS OF INTEREST:
Research of and treatment for pulmonary fibrosis.

NAME(S) OF PROGRAMS:
● **Clinical Research in Pulmonary Fibrosis Program**

TYPE:
Matching gifts. Supports postdoctoral research for studies in the clinical investigation of pulmonary fibrosis.

YEAR PROGRAM STARTED: 2000

PURPOSE:
To improve the quality of life of those affected by pulmonary fibrosis; to provide funding for research and treatment of pulmonary fibrosis.

ELIGIBILITY:
Researchers by invitation only.

FINANCIAL DATA:
Amount of support per award: Varies.
Total amount of support: Nearly $3,000,000 over the last 10 years.

IRS IDENTIFICATION NUMBER: 84-1558631

ADDRESS INQUIRIES TO:
Patti Tuomey, Chief Operating Officer
(See address above.)

RADIOLOGICAL SOCIETY OF NORTH AMERICA RESEARCH AND EDUCATION FOUNDATION   [2470]

820 Jorie Boulevard
Oak Brook, IL 60523-2251
(630) 571-7816
Fax: (630) 571-7837

E-MAIL ADDRESS:
swalter@rsna.org

WEB SITE ADDRESS:
www.rsna.org/foundation

FOUNDED: 1915

AREAS OF INTEREST:
Radiology.

NAME(S) OF PROGRAMS:
● **Research Seed Grant**

TYPE:
Seed money grants. Research Seed Grant support is available for any area of research related to the radiologic sciences.

PURPOSE:
To enable investigators to gain experience in defining objectives and testing hypotheses in preparation for major grant applications to corporations, foundations and governmental agencies.

ELIGIBILITY:
Applicants must be RSNA members at the time of application.

FINANCIAL DATA:
Research Seed Grant is to support the preliminary or pilot phase of scientific projects, not to supplement major funding already secured. No salary support for the principal investigator will be provided.
Amount of support per award: Up to $40,000.

NUMBER OF APPLICANTS MOST RECENT YEAR: 28.

NUMBER OF AWARDS: 6.

APPLICATION INFORMATION:
Applications are completed using the online Grant Application System. A printed, signed copy must be sent and received in the Foundation office on or before the posted deadline date.
Duration: One year.
Deadline: January 15.

ADDRESS INQUIRIES TO:
Scott Walter
Assistant Director, Grant Administration
(See address above.)

RADIOLOGICAL SOCIETY OF NORTH AMERICA RESEARCH AND EDUCATION FOUNDATION   [2471]

820 Jorie Boulevard
Oak Brook, IL 60523-2251
(630) 571-7816
Fax: (630) 571-7837

E-MAIL ADDRESS:
swalter@rsna.org

WEB SITE ADDRESS:
www.rsna.org/foundation

FOUNDED: 1915

AREAS OF INTEREST:
Radiology.

NAME(S) OF PROGRAMS:
● **Research Medical Student Grant**

TYPE:
Research grants. Research Medical Student Grant is for any area of research related to the radiologic sciences.

PURPOSE:
To make radiology research opportunities possible for medical students and to encourage them, early in their medical careers, to consider academic radiology as an important option for their future.

ELIGIBILITY:
Applicants must be RSNA members at the time of application.

FINANCIAL DATA:
Funds are intended to secure protected time for the recipient and may not be used for nonpersonnel research expenses.

Amount of support per award: $3,000.

Total amount of support: Approximately $75,000.

Matching fund requirements: $3,000 to be matched by the sponsoring department ($6,000 total) as a stipend for the medical student.

NUMBER OF APPLICANTS MOST RECENT YEAR: 36.

NUMBER OF AWARDS: 24.

APPLICATION INFORMATION:
Applications are completed using the online Grant Application System. A printed, signed copy must be sent and received in the Foundation office on or before the posted deadline date.

Duration: 10 weeks full-time (or equivalent).

Deadline: February 1.

ADDRESS INQUIRIES TO:
Scott Walter
Assistant Director, Grant Administration
(See address above.)

RADIOLOGICAL SOCIETY OF NORTH AMERICA RESEARCH AND EDUCATION FOUNDATION [2472]

820 Jorie Boulevard
Oak Brook, IL 60523-2251
(630) 571-7816
Fax: (630) 571-7837

E-MAIL ADDRESS:
swalter@rsna.org

WEB SITE ADDRESS:
www.rsna.org/foundation

FOUNDED: 1915

AREAS OF INTEREST:
Radiology.

NAME(S) OF PROGRAMS:
● **Education Scholar Grant**

TYPE:
Training grants. Any area of education related to the radiologic sciences.

PURPOSE:
To fund individuals in radiology or related disciplines who are seeking an opportunity to develop their expertise in radiologic education; to develop teachers in radiology who can share their knowledge with the radiology community.

ELIGIBILITY:
Applicants must be RSNA members at the time of application.

FINANCIAL DATA:
Educational Scholar Grant to be used as part-time salary support and for educational expenses.

Amount of support per award: Up to $75,000 per year; $150,000 maximum.

NUMBER OF APPLICANTS MOST RECENT YEAR: 36.

NUMBER OF AWARDS: 4.

APPLICATION INFORMATION:
Applications are completed using the online Grant Application System. A printed, signed copy must be sent and received in the Foundation office on or before the posted deadline date.

Duration: Up to two years.

Deadline: January 10.

ADDRESS INQUIRIES TO:
Scott Walter
Assistant Director, Grant Administration
(See address above.)

RADIOLOGICAL SOCIETY OF NORTH AMERICA RESEARCH AND EDUCATION FOUNDATION [2473]

820 Jorie Boulevard
Oak Brook, IL 60523-2251
(630) 571-7816
Fax: (630) 571-7837

E-MAIL ADDRESS:
swalter@rsna.org

WEB SITE ADDRESS:
www.rsna.org/foundation

FOUNDED: 1915

AREAS OF INTEREST:
Radiology.

NAME(S) OF PROGRAMS:
● **RSNA/AUR/APDR/SCARD Radiology Education Research Development Grant**

TYPE:
Research grants.

PURPOSE:
To encourage innovation and improvement in health sciences education by providing research opportunities to individuals in pursuit of advancing the science of radiology education; to help in building a critical mass of radiology education researchers and promote the careers of persons advancing the science of radiology education.

ELIGIBILITY:
Grants are awarded to any person, at any level of career development, affiliated with a radiology department. Applicants must be members of one or more of the sponsoring organizations.

FINANCIAL DATA:
Grants can be used to help cover the costs of research materials, research assistant support and limited primary investigator salary support.

Amount of support per award: Up to $10,000.

COOPERATIVE FUNDING PROGRAMS:
Co-sponsored by the Radiological Society of North America (RSNA), Association of University Radiologists (AUR), Association of Program Directors in Radiology (APDR), and Society of Chairmen of Academic Radiology Departments (SCARD).

NUMBER OF APPLICANTS MOST RECENT YEAR: 5.

NUMBER OF AWARDS: 2.

APPLICATION INFORMATION:
Contact the Foundation for application procedures.

Duration: One year.

Deadline: January 10.

ADDRESS INQUIRIES TO:
Scott Walter
Assistant Director, Grant Administration
(See address above.)

RADIOLOGICAL SOCIETY OF NORTH AMERICA RESEARCH AND EDUCATION FOUNDATION [2474]

820 Jorie Boulevard
Oak Brook, IL 60523-2251
(630) 571-7816
Fax: (630) 571-7837

E-MAIL ADDRESS:
swalter@rsna.org

WEB SITE ADDRESS:
www.rsna.org/foundation

FOUNDED: 1915

AREAS OF INTEREST:
Radiology.

NAME(S) OF PROGRAMS:
● **RSNA Research Scholar Grant**

TYPE:
Research grants.

PURPOSE:
To support junior faculty members who have completed the conventional resident/fellowship training programs but have not yet been recognized as independent investigators.

ELIGIBILITY:
Any area of research related to the radiologic sciences is eligible for Research Scholar Grant support. Applicants must be nominated by their department chair.

FINANCIAL DATA:
Amount of support per award: $150,000 ($75,000 per year).

NUMBER OF APPLICANTS MOST RECENT YEAR: 20.

NUMBER OF AWARDS: 6.

APPLICATION INFORMATION:
Applications may be obtained from the Foundation web site.

Duration: Two years.

Deadline: January 15.

ADDRESS INQUIRIES TO:
Scott Walter
Assistant Director, Grant Administration
(See address above.)

RADIOLOGICAL SOCIETY OF NORTH AMERICA RESEARCH AND EDUCATION FOUNDATION [2475]

820 Jorie Boulevard
Oak Brook, IL 60523-2251
(630) 571-7816
Fax: (630) 571-7837

E-MAIL ADDRESS:
swalter@rsna.org

WEB SITE ADDRESS:
www.rsna.org/foundation

FOUNDED: 1915

AREAS OF INTEREST:
Radiology.

NAME(S) OF PROGRAMS:
● **Research Resident/Fellow Grant**

TYPE:
Research grants. Grants will be awarded for diverse types of projects in the radiologic sciences including basic science and clinical research studies. This program is not intended to fund Ph.D. postdoctoral projects, nor to support those whose primary aim is to obtain practical experience in clinical radiology.

PURPOSE:
To provide young investigators not yet professionally established in the radiologic sciences an opportunity to gain further insight into scientific investigation and to develop competence in research techniques and methods.

ELIGIBILITY:
At the time of application, the applicant must:
(1) be an RSNA member;
(2) be a resident or fellow in a department of radiology, radiation oncology or nuclear medicine within a North American educational institution;
(3) have completed the internship year (PGY-1) and at least six months of specialty training in the radiologic sciences (PGY-2) for the resident grant, or be in the last year of, or have completed, the prescribed residency training for the fellow grant. (If awarded, applicant must be in a fellowship position during the period of grant support);
(4) be certified by the American Board of Radiology or equivalent, or on track for certification;
(5) not have been principal investigator on grant/contract amounts totaling more than $60,000 in a single calendar year (includes support from single or combined grants or contracts from any source including government, private or industrial/commercial sources);
(6) not be agent(s) of any for-profit, commercial company in the radiologic sciences (applies to applicant/co-principal investigator);
(7) not submit more than one research or education grant application to the RSNA Research and Education Foundation per year and;
(8) not have concurrent RSNA grants.

Acceptance of an award from another source for the same project is prohibited unless one source provides only salary support and the other source provides only support for non-personnel research expenses.

FINANCIAL DATA:
Funds may be used for salary and/or non-personnel research expenses.

Amount of support per award: $50,000 salary support for one-year Research Fellow project or $30,000 salary support for one-year Research Resident project.

NUMBER OF APPLICANTS MOST RECENT YEAR: 66.

NUMBER OF AWARDS: 24.

APPLICATION INFORMATION:
Applications are completed online using the Online Grant Application System. A printed, signed copy must be received in the Foundation office on or before the posted deadline date.

Duration: One year; however, residents may opt for a six-month, full-time research project.

Deadline: January 15.

ADDRESS INQUIRIES TO:
Scott Walter
Assistant Director, Grant Administration
(See address above.)

V. KANN RASMUSSEN FOUNDATION

c/o Rockefeller Brothers Fund
475 Riverside Drive, Suite 900
New York, NY 10115
(212) 812-4268
Fax: (212) 812-4299

E-MAIL ADDRESS:
info@vkrf.org

WEB SITE ADDRESS:
www.vkrf.org

TYPE:
Challenge/matching grants; General operating grants; Project/program grants.

See entry 2219 for full listing.

FANNIE E. RIPPEL FOUNDATION [2476]

14 Maple Avenue, Suite 200
Morristown, NJ 07960
(973) 540-0101
Fax: (973) 540-0404

E-MAIL ADDRESS:
pmacbain@rippelfoundation.org

WEB SITE ADDRESS:
rippelfoundation.org

FOUNDED: 1953

TYPE:
Project/program grants.

PURPOSE:
To seed innovation, catalyze change and create model processes that will lead to improvements in health.

LEGAL BASIS:
Private foundation.

ELIGIBILITY:
Organizations, associations, institutions and hospitals are eligible. No grants are made to individuals.

FINANCIAL DATA:
Amount of support per award: Varies.

Total amount of support: $3,000,000 to $4,000,000 per year.

NUMBER OF APPLICANTS MOST RECENT YEAR: Varies.

NUMBER OF AWARDS: Average 8 to 12 per year.

APPLICATION INFORMATION:
When a grant proposal is requested, the following materials are required:
(1) written project proposal, including problem statement, project objectives, planned measures of success and timeline;
(2) profiles or resumes of key staff members;
(3) project and agency budget;
(4) IRS determination letter of 501(c)(3) status;
(5) most recent 990 tax return and;
(6) most recent audited financial statement, with auditor's management letter.

IRS IDENTIFICATION NUMBER: 22-1559427

OFFICERS:
John D. Campbell, Chairman
Laura K. Landy, President and Chief Executive Officer
Abby O'Neill, Vice President
Chana Fitton, Treasurer
David Surrenda, Secretary

TRUSTEES:
John D. Campbell
Elizabeth Christopherson

Laura K. Landy
David Surrenda

ADDRESS INQUIRIES TO:
Patricia MacBain, Office Manager
(See address above.)

SAVOY FOUNDATION [2477]

230 Foch Street
St.-Jean-sur-Richelieu QC J3B 2B2 Canada
(450) 358-9779
Fax: (450) 346-1045

E-MAIL ADDRESS:
epilepsy@savoy-foundation.ca

WEB SITE ADDRESS:
www.savoy-foundation.ca

FOUNDED: 1971

AREAS OF INTEREST:
Epilepsy and medical research.

TYPE:
Fellowships; Research grants; Scholarships.

PURPOSE:
To promote research on epilepsy.

ELIGIBILITY:
Studentships will be awarded to meritorious applicants wishing to acquire training and pursue research in a biomedical discipline, the health sciences or social sciences related to epilepsy. To be eligible, the candidate must have a good university record (B.Sc., M.D. or equivalent diploma) and have ensured that a qualified researcher affiliated to a university and/or hospital will supervise his or her work. Concomitant registration in a graduate program (M.Sc. or Ph.D.) is encouraged.

Post-Doctoral and Clinical Research Fellowships will be awarded to scientists or medical specialists (Ph.D. or M.D.) wishing to carry out a full-time research project in the field of epilepsy.

Research Grants are available to clinicians and/or established scientists working on epilepsy or related subjects.

Studentships, fellowships, and grants are available to Canadian researchers, to foreign nationals or for projects conducted in Canada.

FINANCIAL DATA:
Amount of support per award: Studentships: $15,000 (CAN) per year. An annual sum of $1,000 will be allocated to the laboratory or institution as additional support for the research project. Post-Doctoral and Clinical Research Fellowships: $30,000. Research Grants: Up to $25,000.

Total amount of support: More than $350,000 (CAN) per year.

NUMBER OF APPLICANTS MOST RECENT YEAR: 35.

NUMBER OF AWARDS: 15.

APPLICATION INFORMATION:
Duration: Studentships: One year. Renewable for a maximum duration of four years; Post-Doctoral and Clinical Research Fellowships: One year. Nonrenewable; Research grants generally are not renewable.

Deadline: January 15 (postmark). If January 15 falls on a weekend or holiday, the Foundation will consider the next working day as the deadline.

EXECUTIVE COMMITTEE:
George M. Savoy, President

Caroline Savoy, Vice President/Secretary
Alain Barbeau, Secretary and Treasurer

ADDRESS INQUIRIES TO:
Caroline Savoy, Secretary
(See address above.)

SCLERODERMA
FOUNDATION   [2478]
300 Rosewood Drive, Suite 105
Danvers, MA 01923
(978) 463-5843 ext. 248
(800) 722-4673
Fax: (978) 463-5809

E-MAIL ADDRESS:
tsperry@scleroderma.org

WEB SITE ADDRESS:
www.scleroderma.org

FOUNDED: 1998

AREAS OF INTEREST:
Scleroderma.

NAME(S) OF PROGRAMS:
● **Scleroderma Foundation Research
  Grants**

TYPE:
Research grants.

YEAR PROGRAM STARTED: 1998

PURPOSE:
To support research in the area of
scleroderma.

ELIGIBILITY:
Applicants must be principal investigators.

GEOGRAPHIC RESTRICTIONS:
United States for new investigators;
international for established investigators.

FINANCIAL DATA:
Amount of support per award: $150,000.
Total amount of support: Up to $1,000,000
annually.

NUMBER OF APPLICANTS MOST RECENT YEAR:
43.

NUMBER OF AWARDS: 7.

APPLICATION INFORMATION:
Applicants must use the application form
following NIH guidelines.
Duration: Two to three years.
Deadline: September 15. Call to verify
deadline date. Notification in December for
program beginning January.

PUBLICATIONS:
Quarterly magazine; literature.

IRS IDENTIFICATION NUMBER: 52-1375827

STAFF:
Tracey O. Sperry, Director of Development
and Research

ADDRESS INQUIRIES TO:
Tracey O. Sperry
Director of Development and Research
(See address above.)

SMITH FAMILY AWARDS
PROGRAM FOR EXCELLENCE
IN BIOMEDICAL
RESEARCH   [2479]
95 Berkeley Street, Suite 208
Boston, MA 02116
(617) 279-2240 ext. 702

E-MAIL ADDRESS:
glockwood@nria.org

WEB SITE ADDRESS:
www.tmfgrants.org/smith

FOUNDED: 1991

AREAS OF INTEREST:
Basic biomedical research, physics, chemistry
and engineering.

TYPE:
Research grants.

YEAR PROGRAM STARTED: 1991

PURPOSE:
To provide research grants for newly
independent junior faculty.

ELIGIBILITY:
Refer to guidelines at the web site above.

GEOGRAPHIC RESTRICTIONS:
Massachusetts, Yale University and Brown
University.

FINANCIAL DATA:
Amount of support per award: $300,000;
$100,000 per year for three years.
Total amount of support: $1,500,000
annually.

COOPERATIVE FUNDING PROGRAMS: Principal
funding provided by the Richard and Susan
Smith Family Foundation with contributing
support from other donors.

NUMBER OF APPLICANTS MOST RECENT YEAR:
41 for the year 2010.

NUMBER OF AWARDS: 6 for funding cycle
2010-13.

REPRESENTATIVE AWARDS:
"Structure and Mechanism of the Human
RISC-Loading Complex;" "Exploring the
Function of Sleep in Neural Circuit
Formation;" "Hepatic Stellate Cells Instruct
Lymphoid Progenitors to Home to the
Thymus;" "Non-coding RNA as a Regulator
of Cell Fate through Functional Interaction
with Polycomb Group Proteins;" "Targeting
Hsp90 with Small Cyclic Peptides."

APPLICATION INFORMATION:
Information and forms are available on the
web site.
Duration: Three years. Nonrenewable.

PUBLICATIONS:
Application guidelines; directory of grant
recipients (online).

ADDRESS INQUIRIES TO:
Senior Program Officer
(See address above.)

SNM   [2480]
1850 Samuel Morse Drive
Reston, VA 20190-5316
(703) 708-9000
Fax: (703) 708-9015

E-MAIL ADDRESS:
grantinfo@snm.org

WEB SITE ADDRESS:
www.snm.org/grants

FOUNDED: 1969

AREAS OF INTEREST:
Nuclear medicine.

NAME(S) OF PROGRAMS:
● **Paul Cole Scholarships**
● **PDEF Mickey Williams Minority
  Student Scholarships**

TYPE:
Scholarships. Scholarships support education
of nuclear medicine technology students.

YEAR PROGRAM STARTED: 1969

PURPOSE:
To enhance the standards, further the
progress, encourage research and improve
practice in the field of nuclear medicine.

LEGAL BASIS:
Tax-exempt, nonprofit organization.

ELIGIBILITY:
Nuclear medicine technology students with a
grade point average of 2.5, on a 4.0 scale,
are eligible. Scholarships will be distributed
among the following C.A.H.E.A.- or
C.A.M.R.T.-approved Nuclear Medicine
Technology Programs: Baccalaureate
programs, Associate degree programs and
Certificate programs.

Applicants will be ranked according to their
personal statement of goals, prior academic
performance, current financial need and the
recommendation of the Training Program
Director. Weight will be given to applicants
who are not only academically capable but to
those whose financial situation is such that
without the scholarship they might not be
able to attend the training program.

The PDEF Mickey Williams Minority
Student Scholarship supports minority
students pursuing a two- or four-year degree
in nuclear medicine.

GEOGRAPHIC RESTRICTIONS:
United States and Canada.

FINANCIAL DATA:
The scholarship may be used for tuition, or
for other expenses if no tuition is charged.
Amount of support per award: Paul Cole
Scholarships: $1,000; PDEF Mickey
Williams Minority Student Scholarships:
$2,500.
Total amount of support: $22,000 for the
year 2010.

NUMBER OF APPLICANTS MOST RECENT YEAR:
100.

NUMBER OF AWARDS: Paul Cole Scholarships:
32 for the year 2009; Mickey Williams
Minority Student Scholarships: 3 for the year
2008.

APPLICATION INFORMATION:
The Program Director must submit, on behalf
of the applicant, the following:
(1) a completed application form which
identifies the training program and its type, a
statement of the applicant's goals, the
applicant's financial resources, and the
Program Director's signature;
(2) transcript of high school and/or college
and;
(3) a letter of acceptance into the Nuclear
Medicine program with the Program
Director's signature.
Duration: One year.
Deadline: Approximately January 15.
Announcement in March or April.

SNM   [2481]
1850 Samuel Morse Drive
Reston, VA 20190-5316
(703) 708-9000
Fax: (703) 708-9015

E-MAIL ADDRESS:
nmitchell@snm.org

WEB SITE ADDRESS:
www.snm.org/grants

FOUNDED: 1969

AREAS OF INTEREST:
Nuclear medicine.

NAME(S) OF PROGRAMS:
- **Pilot Research Grants**
- **SNM/Covidien Seed Grant**
- **Student Fellowship Awards**
- **Mark Tetalman Memorial Award**

TYPE:
Awards/prizes; Fellowships; Research grants; Seed money grants.

YEAR PROGRAM STARTED: 1969

PURPOSE:
To advance excellence in health care through education and research in nuclear medicine by the provision of grants and awards.

LEGAL BASIS:
Tax-exempt, nonprofit organization.

ELIGIBILITY:
Pilot Research Grants: Basic and clinical scientists in the early stages of their careers, employed by academic and research-oriented organizations in the U.S.
SNM/Covidien Seed Grant: Basic or clinical scientists employed by academic and research-oriented organizations.
Student Fellowship Awards: Students enrolled in medical, pharmacy, or graduate school, or undergraduate students demonstrating outstanding competence in nuclear medicine and/or molecular imaging research.
Mark Tetalman Memorial Award: Applicants must be 36 years old or younger as of July 1 of the application year and must have obtained certification in Nuclear Medicine or Nuclear Radiology, or have completed a Ph.D. program within the last seven years.

FINANCIAL DATA:
Amount of support per award: Pilot Research Grants and SNM/Covidien Seed Grant: $25,000; Student Fellowship Awards: $3,000 maximum for three-month fellowship; Mark Tetalman Memorial Award: $5,000.

APPLICATION INFORMATION:
Information concerning the criteria for the various grants and awards are available from the organization.
Duration: Varies.

OFFICERS:
Virginia Pappas, Chief Executive Officer
Alexander McEwan, M.D., President

THE SOCIETY FOR INVESTIGATIVE DERMATOLOGY   [2482]
526 Superior Avenue East
Suite 540
Cleveland, OH 44114-1999
(216) 579-9300
Fax: (216) 579-9333

E-MAIL ADDRESS:
sid@sidnet.org

WEB SITE ADDRESS:
www.sidnet.org

FOUNDED: 1938

AREAS OF INTEREST:
Skin biology, skin disease, and publication and results of skin research.

CONSULTING OR VOLUNTEER SERVICES:
Advocacy for biomedical research.

NAME(S) OF PROGRAMS:
- **Albert M. Kligman Fellowship Fund Award**

TYPE:
Awards/prizes; Conferences/seminars; Fellowships; Research grants; Travel grants. Awards will be used to support resident, fellow and medical student travel to the Society's annual meetings to present their scientific work.

YEAR PROGRAM STARTED: 1973

PURPOSE:
To encourage trainees to become skin scientists; to encourage the best and brightest young scholars to become members of the research community in dermatology and to participate in the activities of the Society.

LEGAL BASIS:
Tax-exempt.

ELIGIBILITY:
Applicants must hold the M.D. or Ph.D. Project must be skin-/skin disease-related. Preceptor is required. One year of work minimum.

FINANCIAL DATA:
No indirect costs.
Amount of support per award: $25,000.

NUMBER OF AWARDS: Approximately 20.

APPLICATION INFORMATION:
Information on application can be obtained from the address above.
Duration: One year.
Deadline: Contact the Society for exact dates.

IRS IDENTIFICATION NUMBER: 23-1361165

OFFICERS:
Tom Lawley, President

SOCIETY OF CARDIOVASCULAR ANESTHESIOLOGISTS
2209 Dickens Road
Richmond, VA 23230
(804) 282-0084
Fax: (804) 282-0090

E-MAIL ADDRESS:
sca@societyhq.com

WEB SITE ADDRESS:
www.scahq.org

TYPE:
Research grants.

See entry 2559 for full listing.

THE SOCIETY OF MEDICAL FRIENDS OF WINE   [2483]
511 Jones Place
Walnut Creek, CA 94597-3141
(925) 933-9691
Fax: (925) 933-9691

E-MAIL ADDRESS:
susanguerguy@sbcglobal.net

WEB SITE ADDRESS:
www.medicalfriendsofwine.org

FOUNDED: 1939

AREAS OF INTEREST:
Wine-related scientific research.

NAME(S) OF PROGRAMS:
- **Leonard D. Adams Research Award**

TYPE:
Awards/prizes. Award for published original research identifying substances in wine, ascertaining the effects of wine components

on living cells, tissues or organs or indicating appropriate clinical applications of wine in treatment or prevention of disease.

YEAR PROGRAM STARTED: 1961

PURPOSE:
To promote research on the relationship between wine and health.

LEGAL BASIS:
Corporation.

FINANCIAL DATA:
Amount of support per award: $2,000 biannually.

ADDRESS INQUIRIES TO:
Susan Guerguy, Executive Secretary
(See address above.)

TASTE AND SMELL CLINIC   [2484]
Center for Molecular Nutrition and Sensory Disorders
5125 MacArthur Boulevard, N.W., Suite 20
Washington, DC 20016
(202) 364-4180
Fax: (202) 364-9727

E-MAIL ADDRESS:
doc@tasteandsmell.com

WEB SITE ADDRESS:
www.tasteandsmell.com

FOUNDED: 1969

AREAS OF INTEREST:
Taste and smell, clinical treatment of patients with taste and smell disorders, growth factors in relationship to stem cell maturation and development, saliva, salivary diagnostics, salivary proteins, functional magnetic imaging of the brain, transcranial magnetic stimulation of the brain, nasal mucus physiology and pathology, and nasal mucus diagnostics.

CONSULTING OR VOLUNTEER SERVICES:
The Taste and Smell Dysfunction Foundation.

NAME(S) OF PROGRAMS:
- **Taste and Smell Disorders Internship Program**

TYPE:
Assistantships; Conferences/seminars; Exchange programs; Fellowships; Internships; Research grants; Scholarships; Training grants; Visiting scholars; Work-study programs. The Taste and Smell Disorders Internship Program is offered to provide internships and programs to evaluate and treat patients with taste and smell dysfunctions.

YEAR PROGRAM STARTED: 1975

PURPOSE:
To provide internships and other programs to evaluate and treat patients with taste and smell dysfunctions; to study salivary and nasal mucus proteins; to support biochemists and physicians interested in cognitive neurology who want to come work with the clinic.

LEGAL BASIS:
Private organization.

ELIGIBILITY:
Preference to individuals from the Washington, DC metropolitan area.

FINANCIAL DATA:
Amount of support per award: Varies depending on need and tasks required.
Total amount of support: $20,000 to $60,000 per year.

COOPERATIVE FUNDING PROGRAMS: Taste and Smell Dysfunction Foundation.

NUMBER OF APPLICANTS MOST RECENT YEAR: 3.

NUMBER OF AWARDS: 1.

APPLICATION INFORMATION:
Resume and three letters of recommendation from scientific mentors are required.
Duration: One year. Renewable for second and third year.
Deadline: June 30.

STAFF:
R.I. Henkin, Director
S. Holen, Staff Scientist
S.J. Potolicchio, Senior Scientist in Neurology
L.M. Levy, Senior Scientist in Neuro-radiology

ADDRESS INQUIRIES TO:
R.I. Henkin, Director
(See address above.)

THE THOMAS FOUNDATION   [2485]
201 West Big Beaver Road
Suite 600
Troy, MI 48084
(248) 528-1111
Fax: (248) 528-5129

FOUNDED: 1994

AREAS OF INTEREST:
Medical research, mainly in the area of diabetes, and social and educational programs.

TYPE:
Research grants.

YEAR PROGRAM STARTED: 1994

PURPOSE:
To administer funds for scientific, educational and charitable purposes.

LEGAL BASIS:
Private foundation.

ELIGIBILITY:
Eligible organizations must be IRS 501(c)(3) tax-exempt.

GEOGRAPHIC RESTRICTIONS:
Southeastern Michigan.

FINANCIAL DATA:
Amount of support per award: Varies.

APPLICATION INFORMATION:
Applicants may send a written proposal and must include a copy of the IRS tax determination letter.
Duration: One year. Renewal possible.

ADDRESS INQUIRIES TO:
Jay H. Brody, Esq.
(See address above.)

U.S. DEPARTMENT OF THE NAVY   [2486]
Manpower, Personnel, Training and Education Command
Building One, Tower 13, Room 13132
8901 Wisconsin Avenue
Bethesda, MD 20889-5611
(301) 295-1217
(301) 295-9950
Fax: (301) 319-4122

E-MAIL ADDRESS:
oh@med.navy.mil

WEB SITE ADDRESS:
www.med.navy.mil/sites/navmedmpte/accessions/Pages/default.aspx

FOUNDED: 1972

AREAS OF INTEREST:
Medicine, osteopathy, dentistry, optometry and physician assistant.

CONSULTING OR VOLUNTEER SERVICES:
Navy recruiting service.

NAME(S) OF PROGRAMS:
● **Navy Health Professions Scholarship Program (HPSP)**

TYPE:
Scholarships. This is an educational support program for individuals pursuing graduate degrees in professional medical programs and who have a desire to serve in the U.S. Navy following graduation.

YEAR PROGRAM STARTED: 1972

PURPOSE:
To provide officers for the Navy who are trained in these disciplines.

LEGAL BASIS:
Authorized by Public Law 92-426.

ELIGIBILITY:
Applicants must be:
(1) U.S. citizens (dual citizenship not permitted);
(2) physically qualified for a commission in the U.S. Navy and;
(3) accepted into an accredited school in the U.S., Canada or Puerto Rico.

Eligible degree programs include medicine-allopathic (M.D.) or osteopathic (D.O.), dentistry (D.D.S. or D.M.D.), optometry (O.D.), podiatry (D.P.M.), clinical psychology (Ph.D.-level program only) and physician assistant (P.A.-C.) (Master's-level program only).

GEOGRAPHIC RESTRICTIONS:
United States and Puerto Rico.

FINANCIAL DATA:
Amount of support per award: Scholarship includes full tuition (no upper limit) and allowable fees, reimbursement for all required books, supplies and equipment (some limits apply, $20,000 signing bonus (medicine and dentistry only), monthly stipend of $1,992, full pay and allowances of an ensign (O-1) for 45 days per year (about $4,500), and reimbursement for student's health insurance if required by school.
Total amount of support: Approximately $83,000,000 in tuition and stipends. Part of annual Congressional appropriation.

APPLICATION INFORMATION:
Guidelines are available on the web site.
Duration: One to four years, according to year level upon entry. Acceptance of the program requires continuous participation until graduation. Dental scholarships are the same as medical scholarships.

STAFF:
LCDR Marlene Sanchez, Head, Student Programs
Dr. Sandra Yerkes, Program Manager
Lt. Yolanda Adams, Assistant Program Manager
Mrs. Frances Smith, Registrar

ADDRESS INQUIRIES TO:
LCDR Marlene Sanchez
Head, Student Programs
Medical Department Accessions Directorate
U.S. Department of the Navy

Tel: (301) 295-1217
E-mail: marlene.sanchez@med.navy.mil
(See address above.)

*SPECIAL STIPULATIONS:
For Scholarship awardees, one year of active duty (not in training) is required for each year of the Scholarship, with a three-year minimum.

THE UNIVERSITY OF CALGARY
Faculty of Graduate Studies
Earth Sciences Building, Room 720
2500 University Drive, N.W.
Calgary AB T2N 1N4 Canada
(403) 220-4938
Fax: (403) 289-7635

E-MAIL ADDRESS:
gsaward@ucalgary.ca

WEB SITE ADDRESS:
www.grad.ucalgary.ca

TYPE:
Awards/prizes; Scholarships. Awards for study in the medical sciences. Tenable at The University of Calgary. Award endowed through a bequest of the late William H. Davies.

See entry 1903 for full listing.

THE UNIVERSITY OF SYDNEY
Scholarships Office
Level 5, Jane Foss Russell Building G02
The University of Sydney N.S.W. 2006
Australia
(02) 8627 8112
Fax: (02) 8627 8145

E-MAIL ADDRESS:
research.training@sydney.edu.au

WEB SITE ADDRESS:
www.sydney.edu.au/scholarships/research

TYPE:
Fellowships. Awarded for research and training in the diseases of domestic animals and their treatment in the University Veterinary Centre.

See entry 1707 for full listing.

THE UNIVERSITY OF SYDNEY   [2487]
Scholarships Office
Level 5, Jane Foss Russell Building G02
The University of Sydney N.S.W. 2006
Australia
(02) 8627 8112
Fax: (02) 8627 8145

E-MAIL ADDRESS:
research.training@sydney.edu.au

WEB SITE ADDRESS:
www.sydney.edu.au/scholarships/research

FOUNDED: 1850

AREAS OF INTEREST:
Medicine.

NAME(S) OF PROGRAMS:
● **Sydney Medical School Postgraduate Research Scholarships**

TYPE:
Scholarships. For research leading to a higher degree. Tenable in the Sydney Medical School at the University of Sydney.

PURPOSE:
To promote and encourage research in the medical sciences in the University of Sydney.

LEGAL BASIS:
University.

ELIGIBILITY:
Available to full-time research candidates, normally Ph.D., in any department or research unit associated with the Sydney Medical School at the University of Sydney. Applicants must be either Australian citizens or permanent residents of Australia.

GEOGRAPHIC RESTRICTIONS:
Australia.

FINANCIAL DATA:
Amount of support per award: $22,860 AUD per annum for the year 2011.

NUMBER OF AWARDS: Varies according to availability of funds.

APPLICATION INFORMATION:
Duration: One year. Renewal for second and third year subject to satisfactory progress.
Deadline: As advertised.

ADDRESS INQUIRIES TO:
Scholarships Officer
Sydney Medical School (A27)
The University of Sydney
N.S.W. 2006 Australia
E-mail: scholarships@med.usyd.edu.au

*PLEASE NOTE:
Very few awards are available and competition for them is extremely keen. They are awarded strictly on academic merit and only graduates with First Class Honours or equivalent qualifications (e.g., graduation magna cum laude) will be considered.

THE VALLEY FOUNDATION [2488]
16450 Los Gatos Boulevard, Suite 210
Los Gatos, CA 95032
(408) 358-4545
Fax: (408) 358-4548

E-MAIL ADDRESS:
admin@valley.org

WEB SITE ADDRESS:
www.valley.org

FOUNDED: 1984

AREAS OF INTEREST:
Medical services and health care for lower income households, the arts, senior citizens, education and research.

TYPE:
Project/program grants.

YEAR PROGRAM STARTED: 1984

PURPOSE:
To provide funding for nonprofit organizations in Santa Clara County, CA, with an emphasis in the medical field.

LEGAL BASIS:
Nonprofit foundation.

ELIGIBILITY:
Applicants must be tax-exempt charitable organizations. No grants to individuals or for religious purposes.

GEOGRAPHIC RESTRICTIONS:
Santa Clara County, California.

FINANCIAL DATA:
The Foundation prefers to avoid grants which provide more than one-half of an organization's total budget in a 12-month period, usually expecting community and applicant commitment to a project through local cost sharing.

Amount of support per award: $10,000 to $100,000.

REPRESENTATIVE AWARDS:
$100,000 to Opera San Jose to fund artist salaries for the inaugural season at the California Theatre; $100,000 to Walden West School Foundation to fund Science Learning Center project; $25,000 to Diabetes Society of Santa Clara Valley to fund diabetes educational camps.

APPLICATION INFORMATION:
Applicants are required to send, one month prior to submitting a full proposal with proper headings, full information of contact person, a preliminary one- to two-page letter of intent describing the general background and purpose of the sponsoring organization, the need to be addressed, the goals of the project and the total project budget. A full proposal will be requested if the proposed project falls within the Foundation's current areas of interest.
Duration: Varies, but multiple-year requests are discouraged. Organizations which have received funding must wait at least one full year before submitting another application. Organizations that did not make it to the full LOI full proposal cycle can reapply on the anniversary of their first LOI submission.

PUBLICATIONS:
Application guidelines.

IRS IDENTIFICATION NUMBER: 94-1584547

STAFF:
Vaskie Turner, Administrator

BOARD OF TRUSTEES:
Phillip R. Boyce, Chairman
Richard Sieve, M.D., Vice Chairman
Edgar G. LaVeque, Treasurer
Herbert Kain, M.D., Secretary
Arthur A. Basham, M.D.
Daniel P. Moore
Joseph Parisi

ADDRESS INQUIRIES TO:
Vaskie Turner, Administrator
(See address above.)

FRANKLIN H. AND RUTH L. WELLS FOUNDATION
3607 Rosemont Avenue, Suite 404
Camp Hill, PA 17011
(717) 763-1157

E-MAIL ADDRESS:
mgibbons989@verizon.net

TYPE:
Project/program grants; Seed money grants. Seed money grants are primarily for new programs.

See entry 1230 for full listing.

Allergy, immunology, infectious diseases

AMERICAN ACADEMY OF ALLERGY ASTHMA & IMMUNOLOGY [2489]
555 East Wells Street, Suite 1100
Milwaukee, WI 53202-3823
(414) 272-6071
Fax: (414) 272-6070

E-MAIL ADDRESS:
info@aaaai.org

WEB SITE ADDRESS:
www.aaaai.org

FOUNDED: 1943

AREAS OF INTEREST:
Allergy and immunology.

NAME(S) OF PROGRAMS:
● **Travel Grant Awards**

TYPE:
Travel grants. Travel funds to attend the Academy's annual scientific meeting.

PURPOSE:
To advance the knowledge and practice of allergy by discussion at meetings, by fostering the education of students and the public, by encouraging union and cooperation among those engaged in this field and by promoting and stimulating research and study in allergy.

LEGAL BASIS:
Nonprofit.

ELIGIBILITY:
Travel grants for the annual meeting are awarded to member fellows-in-training in the field of allergy and immunology. The grants will be awarded on the basis of merit as judged by the committee. Individuals with a faculty appointment will not be considered.

GEOGRAPHIC RESTRICTIONS:
United States and Canada.

FINANCIAL DATA:
Amount of support per award: Up to $800 for travel to the annual meeting for first year fellows-in-training; up to $650 for second- or third-year fellows-in-training; up to $1,100 for applicants who submit an abstract which is accepted for presentation.

APPLICATION INFORMATION:
Applicants who have not previously been awarded this grant should submit an application form, available on request from the Academy.
Deadline: Contact the Academy.

ADDRESS INQUIRIES TO:
Mariana Duran, Program Coordinator
(See address above.)

ARTHRITIS NATIONAL RESEARCH FOUNDATION (ANRF)
200 Oceangate, Suite 830
Long Beach, CA 90802
(800) 588-2873
Fax: (562) 437-6057

E-MAIL ADDRESS:
hbelisle@curearthritis.org

WEB SITE ADDRESS:
www.curearthritis.org

TYPE:
Fellowships; Research grants; Travel grants. ANRF Arthritis Research Grants are intended to support basic and clinical research focusing on rheumatic and related autoimmune diseases, such as osteoarthritis and rheumatoid arthritis.

See entry 2388 for full listing.

CANCER RESEARCH INSTITUTE

One Exchange Plaza
55 Broadway, Suite 1802
New York, NY 10006
(212) 688-7515
(800) 992-2623
Fax: (212) 832-9376

E-MAIL ADDRESS:
grants@cancerresearch.org

WEB SITE ADDRESS:
www.cancerresearch.org

TYPE:
Fellowships; Research grants; Training grants.

See entry 2590 for full listing.

CANCER RESEARCH INSTITUTE

One Exchange Plaza
55 Broadway, Suite 1802
New York, NY 10006
(212) 688-7515
(800) 992-2623
Fax: (212) 832-9376

E-MAIL ADDRESS:
grants@cancerresearch.org

WEB SITE ADDRESS:
www.cancerresearch.org

TYPE:
Awards/prizes; Research grants. Award supports tenure-track assistant professors or equivalent undertaking their first independent investigations in general immunology or tumor immunology.

See entry 2589 for full listing.

DYSTROPHIC EPIDERMOLYSIS BULLOSA RESEARCH ASSOCIATION OF AMERICA, INC. [2490]

16 East 41st Street, 3rd Floor
New York, NY 10017
(212) 868-1573
Fax: (212) 868-9296

E-MAIL ADDRESS:
staff@debra.org

WEB SITE ADDRESS:
www.debra.org

FOUNDED: 1980

AREAS OF INTEREST:
Research into the causes, treatment and cure of EB and other genetic disorders of the skin.

NAME(S) OF PROGRAMS:
● **DEBRA International Research Grants**

TYPE:
Research grants. Financial aid for EB families in crisis.

YEAR PROGRAM STARTED: 1980

PURPOSE:
To provide opportunity to advance research into the effects, causes, treatments and cure for epidermolysis bullosa.

ELIGIBILITY:
Peer-reviewed grants made to full-time or part-time researchers.

GEOGRAPHIC RESTRICTIONS:
United States.

FINANCIAL DATA:
Reimbursement of medical expenses according to DEBRA funds available.
Amount of support per award: Varies.
Total amount of support: Varies.

APPLICATION INFORMATION:
Guidelines may be obtained from the organization at the address above.
Duration: One to three years.
Deadline: March 15 and September 15.

IRS IDENTIFICATION NUMBER: 11-2519726

ADDRESS INQUIRIES TO:
Mary Sprague, Executive Director
(See address above.)

THE HEISER PROGRAM FOR RESEARCH IN LEPROSY AND TUBERCULOSIS [2491]

c/o New York Community Trust
909 Third Avenue
New York, NY 10022
(212) 686-0010
Fax: (212) 532-8528

E-MAIL ADDRESS:
lm@nyct-cfi.org

WEB SITE ADDRESS:
www.nycommunitytrust.org

FOUNDED: 1974

AREAS OF INTEREST:
Basic biomedical research on leprosy and tuberculosis.

NAME(S) OF PROGRAMS:
● **Postdoctoral Research Fellowships in Leprosy and Tuberculosis**
● **Research Grants in Leprosy**

TYPE:
Fellowships; Research grants.

YEAR PROGRAM STARTED: 1974

PURPOSE:
To support biomedical scientists in early postdoctoral training for research in leprosy and/or tuberculosis.

FINANCIAL DATA:
Amount of support per award: Small Research Grants: Up to $50,000; Postdoctoral Research Fellowships: $40,000 per year.

APPLICATION INFORMATION:
Application form can be obtained from the Heiser Program at the above address.
Duration: Small Research Grants: Varies; Postdoctoral Research Fellowships: One year. Renewable for a second year.
Deadline: March.

ADDRESS INQUIRIES TO:
Len McNally, Director
(See address above.)

IMMUNE DEFICIENCY FOUNDATION [2492]

40 West Chesapeake Avenue
Suite 308
Towson, MD 21204
(866) 939-7568
Fax: (410) 321-0293

E-MAIL ADDRESS:
odavis@primaryimmune.org

WEB SITE ADDRESS:
www.usidnet.org

AREAS OF INTEREST:
Immunodeficiency diseases.

NAME(S) OF PROGRAMS:
● **U.S. Immunodeficiency Network**

TYPE:
Travel grants; Visiting scholars.

YEAR PROGRAM STARTED: 2003

PURPOSE:
To improve the diagnosis and treatment of patients with primary immunodeficiency diseases through research and education.

ELIGIBILITY:
Open to researchers whose work focuses on identifying the causes and treatment of primary immunodeficiency diseases.

GEOGRAPHIC RESTRICTIONS:
United States.

FINANCIAL DATA:
Amount of support per award: Generally up to $2,000.
Total amount of support: $1,500,000.

ADDRESS INQUIRIES TO:
Onika Davis
USIDNET Registry Manager
(See address above.)

MAGIC JOHNSON FOUNDATION, INC.

9100 Wilshire Boulevard
Suite 700, East Tower
Beverly Hills, CA 90212
(310) 246-4400
Fax: (310) 246-1106

WEB SITE ADDRESS:
www.magicjohnson.org

TYPE:
Project/program grants; Scholarships; Technical assistance.

See entry 200 for full listing.

LOVELACE RESPIRATORY RESEARCH INSTITUTE [2493]

2425 Ridgecrest Drive, S.E.
Albuquerque, NM 87108
(505) 348-9400
Fax: (505) 348-4966

E-MAIL ADDRESS:
aescovedo@lrri.org

WEB SITE ADDRESS:
www.lrri.org

FOUNDED: 1947

AREAS OF INTEREST:
Respiratory diseases.

NAME(S) OF PROGRAMS:
● **Postdoctoral Training Program**

TYPE:
Fellowships. Training program in respiratory tract disease caused by environmental agents.

YEAR PROGRAM STARTED: 1947

PURPOSE:
To provide research into prevention, treatment and cure of respiratory disease.

LEGAL BASIS:
Private research organization.

ELIGIBILITY:
Programs are tailored to individuals. Laboratory research or pathogenesis of disease can focus on one of several disciplinary areas, including cell biology,

molecular biology, biochemistry, immunology, pathology, physiology, radiobiology or aerosol science, depending on interests and qualifications. Applicants must be U.S. citizens or permanent residents or eligible for a visa.

GEOGRAPHIC RESTRICTIONS:
United States.

FINANCIAL DATA:
Fellowship includes stipend and health insurance, relocation allowance, tuition and fees.
Amount of support per award: Varies.
Total amount of support: Varies.

NUMBER OF APPLICANTS MOST RECENT YEAR:
30.

NUMBER OF AWARDS: 4.

APPLICATION INFORMATION:
Application form required. Contact Institute for application guidelines.
Duration: One year. Renewable for second and third year.

ADDRESS INQUIRIES TO:
Amber Escovedo, SPHR
Human Resources Manager
(See address above.)

ROBERT MAPPLETHORPE FOUNDATION, INC.
477 Madison Avenue, 15th Floor
New York, NY 10022-5835
(212) 755-3025
Fax: (212) 941-4764

E-MAIL ADDRESS:
joree@mapplethorpe.org

WEB SITE ADDRESS:
www.mapplethorpe.org

TYPE:
Project/program grants. Assists in creation or expansion of photography departments in museums and other public institutions. Emphasis is on the acquisition of photographs or the support for study and exhibition facilities.

See entry 503 for full listing.

NATIONAL FOUNDATION FOR INFECTIOUS DISEASES   [2494]
4733 Bethesda Avenue, Suite 750
Bethesda, MD 20814
(301) 656-0003
Fax: (301) 907-0878

E-MAIL ADDRESS:
info@nfid.org

WEB SITE ADDRESS:
www.nfid.org

FOUNDED: 1973

AREAS OF INTEREST:
Research, education and prevention of infectious diseases.

NAME(S) OF PROGRAMS:
- **NFID Advanced Vaccinology Course Travel Grants**
- **NFID Traveling Professorship in Rural Areas**

TYPE:
Awards/prizes; Fellowships; Travel grants.

PURPOSE:
To support research leading to the causes, cures and prevention of infectious diseases; to encourage and sponsor public and professional educational programs.

LEGAL BASIS:
Nonprofit, tax-exempt foundation with 501(c)(3) status.

ELIGIBILITY:
NFID Advanced Vaccinology Course Travel Grant: Applicant must have made separate application to the course.
NFID Traveling Professorship in Rural Areas: Applicant must be board certified in infectious diseases and be a U.S. citizen.

FINANCIAL DATA:
NFID Advanced Vaccinology Course Travel Grant is meant to defray expenses related to attending the course, including registration, airfare, ground transportation, lodging, meals and incidentals. Grant payment for the NFID Traveling Professorship in Rural Areas may be used for travel expenses, handout production and supplies. Personal honorarium will not exceed $5,000 of the grant.
Amount of support per award: NFID Advanced Vaccinology Course Travel Grant: $4,000; NFID Traveling Professorship in Rural Areas: $10,000.

COOPERATIVE FUNDING PROGRAMS: NFID Advanced Vaccinology Course Travel Grant: sanofi pasteur, NFID Traveling Professorship in Rural Areas: NFID Steven R. Mostow Endowment for Outreach Programs.

APPLICATION INFORMATION:
Applicant must submit original application and two copies (four copies for Traveling Professorship) addressed to the Grants Manager at the address above.
Duration: NFID Traveling Professorship in Rural Areas: Five full working days, either continuous or intermittent, to be completed within one year of grant assignment.

IRS IDENTIFICATION NUMBER: 23-7198530

OFFICERS:
Leonard Novick, Executive Director
Susan J. Rehm, M.D., Medical Director

BOARD OF DIRECTORS:
George C. Hill, Ph.D., President
William Schaffner, M.D., President-Elect
Thomas M. File, Jr., M.D., Vice President
Larry K. Pickering, M.D., Treasurer
Patrick Joseph, M.D., Secretary

BOARD OF TRUSTEES:
C. Douglas Webb, Jr., Ph.D., Chairman

NATIONAL INSTITUTE OF ALLERGY AND INFECTIOUS DISEASES   [2495]
National Institutes of Health
6700-B Rockledge Drive
Room 2141, MSC 7610
Bethesda, MD 20892
(301) 496-7291
Fax: (301) 402-0369

E-MAIL ADDRESS:
mk74s@nih.gov

WEB SITE ADDRESS:
www.niaid.nih.gov

FOUNDED: 1948

NAME(S) OF PROGRAMS:
- **Division of AIDS (DAIDS)**

- **Division of Allergy, Immunology and Transplantation (DAIT)**
- **Division of Microbiology and Infectious Diseases (DMID) Research Programs**

TYPE:
Research grants. National research service awards (training) and research and development contracts. Research is funded in the areas listed below.

Recombinant DNA Research: To enhance understanding and control of infectious disease agents, synthesize biologically useful substances in more manageable cell systems and improve expertise in elimination of potential biohazards.

Hospital-Associated Infections: To enlarge our store of fundamental knowledge and to develop positive methods for prevention and treatment of these infections.

Sexually Transmitted Diseases: To undertake research which will provide much needed information relating to the biology and immunology of all sexually transmitted diseases.

Bacterial Vaccines: To develop and establish the safety and efficacy of bacterial vaccines.

Influenza and Other Acute Viral Respiratory Infections: To stimulate and support research to obtain information on the influenza virus and other respiratory viruses essential to development of more efficient vaccines.

Hepatitis: To isolate the etiological agents of this disease and to determine the best methods of growing hepatitis viruses for vaccine development and production.

Enteric Infectious Diseases: To study the etiology and pathogenesis of acute gastroenteritis.

Antibiotic Trials: To conduct controlled, prospective and multicentered studies designed to compare efficacy, safety, duration and costs with standard chemotherapeutic agents.

Antiviral Therapy: To support scientists conducting basic research on how drugs and other antiviral substances work in the cell and in animals.

Parasitic Diseases: To study parasitic antigens and host responses to parasitic infections with a goal of eventual vaccine development.

International Biomedical Research, joint research efforts - U.S.-Japan Cooperative Medical Science Program and the International Collaboration in Infectious Diseases Research (ICIDR).

LEGAL BASIS:
Public Health Service Act, Section 301; Public Law 78-410, as amended by the Small Business Innovation Act, Public Law 97-219; Public Health Service Act, Title IV, as amended by the Health Research Extension Act of 1985, Public Law 99-158.

ELIGIBILITY:
Universities, colleges, hospitals, laboratories and other public or private (profit and nonprofit) institutions, including state and local units of government, and individuals involved in appropriate research are eligible to make application for grant support of research by a named principal investigator.

FINANCIAL DATA:
Amount of support per award: Varies.

APPLICATION INFORMATION:
Duration: Grants: Three years average. Contracts negotiated on an individual basis.

Deadline: Grant proposals must be received seven to eight months prior to September, January or May council meetings. Contract deadlines are specified in the request announcements.

ADDRESS INQUIRIES TO:
Dr. Marvin R. Kalt, Director, DEA, NIAID (See address above.)

NATIONAL INSTITUTE OF ALLERGY AND INFECTIOUS DISEASES [2496]

National Institutes of Health
6700-B Rockledge Drive
Room 2141, MSC 7610
Bethesda, MD 20892
(301) 496-7291
Fax: (301) 402-0369

E-MAIL ADDRESS:
kaltmr@niaid.nih.gov

WEB SITE ADDRESS:
www.niaid.nih.gov/ncn/budget/default.htm

FOUNDED: 1955

AREAS OF INTEREST:
Allergy and infectious diseases.

NAME(S) OF PROGRAMS:
- **Clinical Investigator Awards**
- **Minority Research Enhancement Awards**
- **National Research Services Awards**
- **Physician Scientist Awards**
- **Research Career Awards**
- **Small Business Innovation Research Awards**

TYPE:
Awards/prizes. National research service awards (training) and research and development contracts. Support for preclinical and clinical research directly geared toward developing new treatments and potential vaccines for AIDS. These research activities also include the basic science foundation needed to advance drug and vaccine development, including studies in epidemiology, HIV pathogenesis and biostatistics research.

In the area of pathogenesis, the Institute funds programs that increase the understanding of the biology of HIV by multidisciplinary study of such aspects of the virus as its life cycle and its effects on the host.

YEAR PROGRAM STARTED: 1955

PURPOSE:
To decrease or prevent the spread of infection by HIV; to curb disease progression in people who are infected by the virus but do not have symptoms; to limit disease progression and mortality in people with AIDS while preserving a high quality of life.

LEGAL BASIS:
Public Health Service Act, Section 301; Public Law 78-410, as amended by the Small Business Innovation Act, Public Law 97-219; Public Health Service Act, Title IV, as amended by the Health Research Extension Act of 1985, Public Law 99-158.

ELIGIBILITY:
Universities, colleges, hospitals, laboratories and other public or private institutions (profit and nonprofit), including state and local units of government, and individuals involved in appropriate research are eligible to make application for grant support of research by a named principal investigator.

FINANCIAL DATA:
Total amount of support: Varies.

APPLICATION INFORMATION:
Duration: Grants: Four years average. Contracts negotiated on an individual basis.
Deadline: Grant proposals must be received seven to eight months prior to September, January or May council meetings. Contract deadlines are specified in the request announcements.

NIAID ENTERIC AND HEPATIC INFECTIOUS DISEASES RESEARCH GRANTS [2497]

National Institute of Allergy and Infectious Diseases
National Institutes of Health
Mailstop 7614, 6700-B Rockledge Drive
Bethesda, MD 20892
(301) 496-7075
Fax: (301) 493-0597

WEB SITE ADDRESS:
www.niaid.nih.gov/ncn/budget/default.htm

AREAS OF INTEREST:
Infection and disease caused by enteric and hepatic pathogens.

TYPE:
Conferences/seminars; Development grants; Fellowships; Project/program grants; Research grants; Training grants; Loan forgiveness programs; Research contracts. Research grants for investigator-oriented research.

PURPOSE:
To support investigator-initiated research of infection and diseases caused by enteric and hepatic pathogens.

ELIGIBILITY:
Applicants are not required to be a 501(c)(3) organization. Religious and foreign organizations are welcome.

APPLICATION INFORMATION:
Candidates must submit application at www.grants.gov.
Duration: Up to five years of support. Selected grants are renewable if grant recipients reapply.

ADDRESS INQUIRIES TO:
Dr. Leslye Johnson, Ph.D.
Division of Microbiology and Infectious Diseases
(See address above.)

Dentistry

THE AMERICAN ACADEMY OF ESTHETIC DENTISTRY [2498]

303 West Madison Street
Suite 2650
Chicago, IL 60606
(312) 981-6770
Fax: (312) 265-2908

E-MAIL ADDRESS:
info@estheticacademy.org

WEB SITE ADDRESS:
www.estheticacademy.org

FOUNDED: 1975

AREAS OF INTEREST:
Dentistry.

NAME(S) OF PROGRAMS:
- **AAED Esthetic Dentistry Research Grants**

TYPE:
Research grants.

YEAR PROGRAM STARTED: 1993

PURPOSE:
To promote the integration of dental esthetics into the total spectrum of oral health care.

ELIGIBILITY:
Applicant must be a graduate student or young untenured faculty at the instructor or assistant professor level at an accredited dental school.

GEOGRAPHIC RESTRICTIONS:
United States, Canada and Puerto Rico.

FINANCIAL DATA:
Amount of support per award: Up to $5,000.

NUMBER OF APPLICANTS MOST RECENT YEAR:
8.

NUMBER OF AWARDS: 1 per year.

APPLICATION INFORMATION:
Contact the Association for application procedures.
Duration: One year.
Deadline: May 28.

ADDRESS INQUIRIES TO:
Joe Jackson, Executive Director
(See address above.)

AMERICAN ACADEMY OF IMPLANT DENTISTRY RESEARCH FOUNDATION, INC. [2499]

211 East Chicago Avenue
Suite 750
Chicago, IL 60611
(312) 335-1550
Fax: (312) 335-9090

E-MAIL ADDRESS:
afshin@aaid.com

WEB SITE ADDRESS:
www.aaid.com

FOUNDED: 1979

AREAS OF INTEREST:
Dental implant research.

NAME(S) OF PROGRAMS:
- **Humanitarian Project Support**
- **Small Research Award**
- **Student Research Grant**

TYPE:
Awards/prizes; Project/program grants; Research grants. Humanitarian Project Support is available to those 501(c)(3) organizations who support the handicapped or disabled and medically-at-risk in need of dental implant.

Small Research Award provides limited support for meritorious dental implant research projects which determine the feasibility of a larger research project. This may be described as the conduct of pilot studies or venture research to develop and test new techniques and procedures, to carry out a small clinical or animal research project and to analyze existing data.

Student Research Grant is available for all graduate dental students. Research must be related to dental implant.

YEAR PROGRAM STARTED: 1981

PURPOSE:
To provide limited support for meritorious dental implant research projects.

LEGAL BASIS:
Research foundation.

ELIGIBILITY:
Investigators from any scientific discipline and at any stage of their career may apply for a Small Grant. These awards are appropriated for new investigators and those changing areas of research or resuming research careers.

Student Research Grant is available to postgraduate dental students for implant-related research studies.

FINANCIAL DATA:
Grants may be used for supplies, small items of equipment and salary for technical and support personnel.

Amount of support per award: Humanitarian Project Support: Up to $10,000; Small Research Award: Up to $25,000 (total project costs); Student Research Grant: Up to $2,500 per year.

NUMBER OF AWARDS: Small Research Award: 1 to 2; Student Research Grant: Up to 4.

APPLICATION INFORMATION:
Required documentation includes abstract of research plan, budget estimate, explanation of the project, including its specific aims, significance, experimental design and methods, sequence of events and time schedule and a complete bibliography, curriculum vitae and a list of all co-investigators and consultants.

Duration: Student Research Grant: Up to two years. Nonrenewable.

Deadline: Small Research Award: August 1. Student Research Grant: May 1.

PUBLICATIONS:
Guidelines.

OFFICERS:
John Minichetti, D.D.S., Chairman
Sharon Bennett, Chief Executive Officer

ADDRESS INQUIRIES TO:
F. Afshin Alavi, Chief Financial Officer
(See address above.)

AMERICAN ASSOCIATION FOR DENTAL RESEARCH   [2500]
1619 Duke Street
Alexandria, VA 22314-3406
(703) 548-0066
Fax: (703) 548-1883

E-MAIL ADDRESS:
sherren@iadr.org

WEB SITE ADDRESS:
www.aadronline.org

AREAS OF INTEREST:
Dental research.

NAME(S) OF PROGRAMS:
- **AADR/Johnson & Johnson Healthcare Products Hatton Competition**

TYPE:
Awards/prizes. For junior investigators (junior, senior and postdoctoral) who exhibit potential for a productive career in dental research.

PURPOSE:
To advance research and increase knowledge for the improvement of oral health; to

support and represent the oral health research community; to facilitate the communication and application of research findings.

ELIGIBILITY:
Applicants must be U.S. citizens or non-citizen nationals of the U.S. (or who have been lawfully admitted for permanent residence at the time of submission of the abstract - those with a "green card") or persons of other nationalities whose research is performed in the U.S. There is no age limit for entrants in the AADR competition.

FINANCIAL DATA:
Amount of support per award: First prize: $1,000; Second prize: $500.

Total amount of support: $4,500.

NUMBER OF AWARDS: 3 First Prizes and 3 Second Prizes.

APPLICATION INFORMATION:
Deadline: October 3, 2011.

ADDRESS INQUIRIES TO:
Sheri S. Herren
Awards, Fellowships and Grants Manager
(See address above.)

AMERICAN ASSOCIATION FOR DENTAL RESEARCH   [2501]
1619 Duke Street
Alexandria, VA 22314-3406
(703) 548-0066
Fax: (703) 548-1883

E-MAIL ADDRESS:
sherren@iadr.org

WEB SITE ADDRESS:
www.aadronline.org

AREAS OF INTEREST:
Basic and clinical research related to oral health.

NAME(S) OF PROGRAMS:
- **Student Research Fellowships**

PURPOSE:
To advance research and increase knowledge for the improvement of oral health; to support and represent the oral health research community; to facilitate the communication and application of research findings.

ELIGIBILITY:
Applicant must be enrolled in an accredited D.D.S./D.M.D. or hygiene program in a dental institution and must be sponsored by a faculty member. Students should not have received their degree, nor should they in the year of award. Applicant may have an advanced degree in a basic science subject.

GEOGRAPHIC RESTRICTIONS:
United States.

FINANCIAL DATA:
Amount of support per award: $3,000.

Total amount of support: $54,000 for the year 2009.

NUMBER OF AWARDS: 21 for the year 2010.

APPLICATION INFORMATION:
Proposals will follow the general format of the Public Health Service Grant Application Form PHS 398, which is to be used only as a guideline. Each proposal must include the following:
(1) objectives, describing what the research is intended to accomplish and the hypothesis to be tested;
(2) background and significance;
(3) preliminary data, if any;

(4) materials and methods, including statistical management of data;
(5) literature cited;
(6) resource information, facilities and equipment to be used for the research project;
(7) other support for applicant and sponsor and;
(8) for those projects involving Recombinant DNA/Recombinant DNA Molecules, an indication that the project adheres to the current NIH Guidelines for Research Involving Recombinant DNA Molecules.

The following documents must also be included:
(1) cover letter from the applicant's sponsor, indicating the dental school's and the sponsor's support of the proposed research;
(2) curriculum vitae, not to exceed two pages, outlining the student's career up to the time of application;
(3) copy of the sponsor's biographical sketch in NIH format, not to exceed two pages and;
(4) documentation that the project has been approved by the Institutional Review Board for projects involving human subjects or vertebrate animals.

Proposals longer than eight pages (PDF) and/or 2,800 words will not be considered.

Deadline: January 13, 2012.

ADDRESS INQUIRIES TO:
Sheri S. Herren
Awards, Fellowships and Grants Manager
(See address above.)

AMERICAN ASSOCIATION FOR DENTAL RESEARCH   [2502]
1619 Duke Street
Alexandria, VA 22314-3406
(703) 548-0066
Fax: (703) 548-1883

E-MAIL ADDRESS:
sherren@iadr.org

WEB SITE ADDRESS:
www.aadronline.org

AREAS OF INTEREST:
Clinical research in periodontology.

NAME(S) OF PROGRAMS:
- **William B. Clark Fellowship in Clinical Research**

PURPOSE:
To advance research and increase knowledge for the improvement of oral health; to support and represent the oral health research community; to facilitate the communication and application of research findings.

ELIGIBILITY:
Applicant must have completed first professional degree, should be appointed at an accredited dental school or academic research center in U.S., and must be a member of AADR.

GEOGRAPHIC RESTRICTIONS:
United States.

FINANCIAL DATA:
Amount of support per award: $5,000.

Total amount of support: $5,000.

APPLICATION INFORMATION:
Applicants must submit the following:
(1) letter stating their interest in applying for the award;
(2) three- to four-page (double-spaced) overview of their proposed areas of training, including how the experience will affect

future research to be conducted by the applicant;

(3) brief description of the facility which will provide the training and;

(4) letter of support from the proposed mentor.

Deadline: October 14, 2011.

ADDRESS INQUIRIES TO:
Sheri S. Herren
Awards, Fellowships and Grants Manager
(See address above.)

AMERICAN ASSOCIATION FOR DENTAL RESEARCH   [2503]

1619 Duke Street
Alexandria, VA 22314-3406
(703) 548-0066
Fax: (703) 548-1883

E-MAIL ADDRESS:
sherren@iadr.org

WEB SITE ADDRESS:
www.aadronline.org

AREAS OF INTEREST:
Dental research.

NAME(S) OF PROGRAMS:
• **William J. Gies Award**

TYPE:
Awards/prizes. For the best paper published in the *Journal of Dental Research* during the preceding year.

PURPOSE:
To advance research and increase knowledge for the improvement of oral health; to support and represent the oral health research community; to facilitate the communication and application of research findings.

GEOGRAPHIC RESTRICTIONS:
United States.

FINANCIAL DATA:
Amount of support per award: $1,000.
Total amount of support: $1,000.

APPLICATION INFORMATION:
Deadline: October 14, 2011.

ADDRESS INQUIRIES TO:
Sheri S. Herren
Awards, Fellowships and Grants Manager
(See address above.)

AMERICAN ASSOCIATION OF WOMEN DENTISTS   [2504]

216 West Jackson Boulevard, Suite 625
Chicago, IL 60606
(312) 263-1822
(800) 920-2293
Fax: (312) 750-1203

E-MAIL ADDRESS:
info@aawd.org

WEB SITE ADDRESS:
www.aawd.org

FOUNDED: 1921

AREAS OF INTEREST:
Dentistry.

NAME(S) OF PROGRAMS:
• **Colgate Research Scholarship**
• **Gillette Hayden Memorial Foundation**
• **Proctor & Gamble Research Award for Postdoctoral Students**
• **Smiles for Success Foundation**

TYPE:
Awards/prizes; Scholarships. Colgate Research Scholarships support AAWD member/junior or senior dental students who are involved in dental research.

Gillette Hayden Memorial Foundation provides low-cost loan programs for AAWD student members.

Proctor & Gamble Research Award for Postdoctoral Students provides a scholarship for research projects involving women's oral health.

Smiles for Success Foundation helps women in transition from welfare to work by providing low- or no- cost dental work.

PURPOSE:
To encourage women dental students who contribute to the school, to dentistry or dental health who are in need of financial assistance.

ELIGIBILITY:
Applicants must be dentists or junior/senior dental students.

FINANCIAL DATA:
Amount of support per award: Varies.
Total amount of support: Varies.

COOPERATIVE FUNDING PROGRAMS:
Scholarships are donated by Colgate Company and other organizations and members.

APPLICATION INFORMATION:
Contact the Association for detailed guidelines.
Duration: One year.
Deadline: Applications for Colgate Research Scholarship are accepted January to April. Applications for Proctor and Gamble Research Award are accepted April to August. Hayden Memorial and Smiles for Success Foundation applications are accepted year-round.

PUBLICATIONS:
Chronicle; *Women's Dental Journal*.

ADDRESS INQUIRIES TO:
Debbie Gidley, Executive Director
(See address above.)

AMERICAN DENTAL ASSISTANTS ASSOCIATION   [2505]

35 East Wacker Drive
Suite 1730
Chicago, IL 60601-2211
(312) 541-1550 ext. 200
Fax: (312) 541-1496

E-MAIL ADDRESS:
adaahelp@aol.com

WEB SITE ADDRESS:
www.dentalassistant.org

FOUNDED: 1923

AREAS OF INTEREST:
Dental assisting.

NAME(S) OF PROGRAMS:
• **Juliette A. Southard/Oral-B Laboratories Scholarship Program**

TYPE:
Scholarships. Tuition scholarships awarded to dental assisting students interested in furthering their education.

YEAR PROGRAM STARTED: 1946

PURPOSE:
To provide financial assistance for highly qualified applicants pursuing dental assisting education.

LEGAL BASIS:
Nonprofit professional organization.

ELIGIBILITY:
Applicants must be high school graduates or equivalent and enrolled in a dental assisting program. Candidates will be considered on the basis of academic achievement, ability, interest in dentistry and personal attributes. Must be a member of the ADAA.

GEOGRAPHIC RESTRICTIONS:
United States.

FINANCIAL DATA:
Amount of support per award: Varies.
Total amount of support: Varies.

APPLICATION INFORMATION:
Applicants for dental assisting scholarships must submit academic transcripts (high school and/or college), proof of acceptance into an accredited program and a letter of intent to pursue a long-range career in dental assisting. Two letters of reference are also required.
Duration: One year.
Deadline: March 31.

STAFF:
Lawrence H. Sepin, Executive Director

ADDRESS INQUIRIES TO:
Scholarship Committee
(See address above.)

AMERICAN DENTAL HYGIENISTS' ASSOCIATION INSTITUTE FOR ORAL HEALTH   [2506]

444 North Michigan Avenue
Suite 3400
Chicago, IL 60611
(312) 440-8900 ext. 244
(800) 735-4916
Fax: (312) 467-1806

E-MAIL ADDRESS:
institute@adha.net

WEB SITE ADDRESS:
www.adha.org/institute

FOUNDED: 1927

AREAS OF INTEREST:
Dental hygiene.

NAME(S) OF PROGRAMS:
• **ADHA Institute Dental Hygiene Scholarships**

TYPE:
Scholarships. The Graduate Scholarship Program awards licensed dental hygienists who are, or will be, enrolled as graduate students in a program leading to a Master's or doctoral degree in dental hygiene or dental hygiene education. There is also an undergraduate scholarship program.

YEAR PROGRAM STARTED: 1986

PURPOSE:
To invest in the future careers of dental hygiene students by ensuring that they will be of exceptional quality and dedication.

LEGAL BASIS:
501(c)(3) public charity, as described in Sections 509(1)(1)-170(b)(1)(A)(vi) of the Internal Revenue Code.

GEOGRAPHIC RESTRICTIONS:
United States.

FINANCIAL DATA:
Amount of support per award: $1,000 to $2,000.

Total amount of support: $60,000 for the year 2010.

APPLICATION INFORMATION:
Applications can only be downloaded from the web site.

Duration: Scholarships are awarded for a period of one academic year.

Deadline: May 1.

PUBLICATIONS:
Annual report.

ADDRESS INQUIRIES TO:
Star Jackson, Administrator
(See address above.)

HISPANIC DENTAL ASSOCIATION FOUNDATION [2507]

3085 Stevenson Drive, Suite 200
Springfield, IL 62703
(217) 529-6517
Fax: (217) 529-9120

E-MAIL ADDRESS:
hispanicdental@hdassoc.org

WEB SITE ADDRESS:
www.hdassoc.org

FOUNDED: 1990

AREAS OF INTEREST:
Oral health careers.

NAME(S) OF PROGRAMS:
• **Colgate-Palmolive Scholarship**
• **Proctor and Gamble Professional Oral Health Scholarship**
• **Dr. Juan D. Villarreal Scholarship**

TYPE:
Scholarships.

PURPOSE:
To encourage entry of Hispanics into oral health careers.

ELIGIBILITY:
Students must have permanent resident status in the U.S. and be a current student member of the Hispanic Dental Association.

Colgate-Palmolive Scholarships are open to student members of the Association who have been accepted into or are currently enrolled in an accredited Master's program in a dentistry-related field. Students must have an undergraduate or graduate degree in an oral health-related field (dental hygienist, dentistry, etc.) from the U.S. or abroad.

Proctor and Gamble Professional Oral Health Scholarships are open to student members of the Association who have been accepted into an accredited dental, dental hygiene, dental assisting or dental technician program.

Dr. Juan D. Villarreal Scholarships are open to student members of the Association who have been accepted into or are currently enrolled in an accredited dental school or dental hygiene program in the state of Texas. The student may be at any stage of the undergraduate program, first through fourth years.

GEOGRAPHIC RESTRICTIONS:
Dr. Juan D. Villarreal Scholarships: Texas.

FINANCIAL DATA:
Amount of support per award:
Colgate-Palmolive Scholarships: Up to

$10,000; Proctor and Gamble Professional Oral Health and Dr. Juan D. Villarreal Scholarships: Up to $1,000.

NUMBER OF AWARDS: Varies.

APPLICATION INFORMATION:
Application can be downloaded from the web site.

Duration: One year. Renewal possible by reapplication.

STAFF:
Rita Brummett, Associate Director

ADDRESS INQUIRIES TO:
Rita Brummett, Associate Director
(See address above.)

INTERNATIONAL ASSOCIATION FOR DENTAL RESEARCH [2508]

1619 Duke Street
Alexandria, VA 22314-3406
(703) 548-0066
Fax: (703) 548-1883

E-MAIL ADDRESS:
sherren@iadr.org

WEB SITE ADDRESS:
www.iadr.org

AREAS OF INTEREST:
Original research in the area of oral health, basic, clinical and applied studies.

NAME(S) OF PROGRAMS:
• **Colgate Oral Health Research Award**

YEAR PROGRAM STARTED: 1998

PURPOSE:
To advance research and increase knowledge for the improvement of oral health; to support and represent the oral health research community; to facilitate the communication and applications of research findings.

ELIGIBILITY:
The nominee must be a member of the Oral Health Research Group. Work considered for this award should have resulted in publications in scientific, peer-reviewed journals. Researchers who are currently under contract with Colgate-Palmolive Company are not eligible to participate.

FINANCIAL DATA:
Amount of support per award: $2,000.
Total amount of support: $2,000.

NUMBER OF AWARDS: 1.

APPLICATION INFORMATION:
Nominations must include a curriculum vitae that provides supporting evidence that the nominee has conducted original research. A letter of nomination should highlight the major reasons and specific research for which the individual is being nominated. Submit nominations electronically to Award Chair.

Deadline: Varies. Award is announced at the annual IADR General Session during the Oral Health Research Group business meeting.

ADDRESS INQUIRIES TO:
Frances Doherty Genco
Award Chairperson
E-mail: fgenco@gmail.com or
Sheri S. Herren
Awards, Fellowships and Grants Manager
(See e-mail address above.)

NATIONAL INSTITUTE OF DENTAL AND CRANIOFACIAL RESEARCH (NIDCR) [2509]

National Institutes of Health
6701 Democracy Boulevard, Room 688
Bethesda, MD 20892
(301) 496-4263
Fax: (301) 402-7033

E-MAIL ADDRESS:
friedenla@nidcr.nih.gov

WEB SITE ADDRESS:
www.nidcr.nih.gov

FOUNDED: 1948

AREAS OF INTEREST:
Dental, craniofacial health and research.

NAME(S) OF PROGRAMS:
• **Individual NRSA Postdoctoral Fellowships (F-32)**

TYPE:
Fellowships. Provides up to three years of support for trainees at academic institutions to broaden their scientific background or extend their potential for research in health-related areas.

YEAR PROGRAM STARTED: 1974

PURPOSE:
To develop individuals for careers in oral health research.

LEGAL BASIS:
Public Health Service Act as amended, Section 301c; 42 CFR 61; 42 U.S.C. 288a.

ELIGIBILITY:
Applicants must be citizens, non-citizen nationals or permanent residents of the U.S. at the time of the award and have a Ph.D., M.D., D.D.S., D.O., D.V.M. or equivalent degree prior to the beginning date of the proposed fellowship.

GEOGRAPHIC RESTRICTIONS:
United States.

FINANCIAL DATA:
Stipend level is based on number of years of postdoctoral experience. Additional funds are available for other training-related expenses.

Amount of support per award: Stipend levels are $37,740 to $52,068. Up to $7,850 per 12 months for institutional allowances.

Total amount of support: Varies.

APPLICATION INFORMATION:
Detailed information can be obtained from the Institute.

Duration: One, two or three years.

Deadline: April 8, August 8 and December 8.

ADDRESS INQUIRIES TO:
Leslie Frieden
Extramural Training Officer
(See address above.)

NATIONAL INSTITUTE OF DENTAL AND CRANIOFACIAL RESEARCH (NIDCR) [2510]

National Institutes of Health
6701 Democracy Boulevard, 6th Floor
Bethesda, MD 20892-4878
(301) 435-7908
Fax: (301) 480-8319

E-MAIL ADDRESS:
jatkinso@mail.nih.gov

WEB SITE ADDRESS:
www.nidcr.nih.gov

FOUNDED: 1948

AREAS OF INTEREST:
Multiple areas of research with the goal of improving oral and craniofacial health.

NAME(S) OF PROGRAMS:
- **AIDS**
- **Behavioral/Social Science Research**
- **Biotechnology/Regenerative Medicine**
- **Clinical Research/Clinical Trials**
- **Computational Science**
- **Conference Grants**
- **Epidemiology/Population Research**
- **Genetic Studies**
- **Health Literacy Research**
- **International Health**
- **Neurobiology/Pain**
- **Oral Cancer**
- **Oral Health Disparities Research**
- **Teeth and Bone**
- **Women's Health**

TYPE:
Conferences/seminars; Project/program grants; Research grants; Research contracts. Grants made to individual investigators for the support of clinical and nonclinical research projects bearing on oral health conditions.

YEAR PROGRAM STARTED: 1948

PURPOSE:
To develop methods for preventing and treating oral diseases and conditions through research related to oral and craniofacial health.

LEGAL BASIS:
Public Health Service Act as amended, Section 301c; 42 CFR 61; 42 U.S.C. 288a.

ELIGIBILITY:
Open to scientists at universities, hospitals, laboratories and other public, nonprofit or profit institutions. Applications are competitively rated on the basis of scientific merit and grants must be approved by the National Advisory Dental Research Council.

FINANCIAL DATA:
Grant funds may be used for salaries of professional and nonprofessional personnel, equipment, supplies, travel, other approved expenditures and indirect costs.
Amount of support per award: Varies.

APPLICATION INFORMATION:
Contact the Institute for detailed information.
Duration: Two to five years.
Deadline: Contact the Institute for exact dates.

OFFICERS:
Dr. Lawrence Tabak, Institute Director

NATIONAL INSTITUTE OF DENTAL AND CRANIOFACIAL RESEARCH (NIDCR) [2511]
National Institutes of Health
6701 Democracy Boulevard, Room 688
Bethesda, MD 20892
(301) 496-4263
Fax: (301) 402-7033

E-MAIL ADDRESS:
friedenla@nidcr.nih.gov

WEB SITE ADDRESS:
www.nidcr.nih.gov

FOUNDED: 1948

AREAS OF INTEREST:
Biomedical and behavioral research.

NAME(S) OF PROGRAMS:
- **Individual NRSA Senior Fellowship Award (F-33)**

TYPE:
Fellowships. Provides health research training for experienced scientists, enabling them to update their skills or make changes in the direction of their career.

YEAR PROGRAM STARTED: 1979

PURPOSE:
To provide opportunities for experienced scientists to make major changes in the direction of their research careers, to enlarge their scientific background, to acquire new research capabilities, or to enlarge their command of an allied research field.

LEGAL BASIS:
Section 472 of the Public Health Service Act as amended (42 U.S.C. 2981-1).

ELIGIBILITY:
Applicants must be citizens, non-citizen nationals or permanent residents of the U.S. at the time of the award. Applicants must be at least seven years beyond the qualifying doctoral degree and have a sponsoring institution and mentor.

GEOGRAPHIC RESTRICTIONS:
United States.

FINANCIAL DATA:
A stipend is provided. Additional funds are available for other training-related expenses.
Amount of support per award: Stipend of $52,068. Up to $7,850 per 12 months for institutional allowances.
Total amount of support: Varies.

NUMBER OF AWARDS: 3.

APPLICATION INFORMATION:
Detailed information can be obtained from the Institute.
Duration: Up to two years.
Deadline: April 8, August 8 and December 8.

ADDRESS INQUIRIES TO:
Leslie Frieden
Extramural Training Officer
(See address above.)

Internal medicine

AMERICAN SOCIETY FOR PARENTERAL AND ENTERAL NUTRITION, RHOADS RESEARCH FOUNDATION
8630 Fenton Street
Suite 412
Silver Spring, MD 20910
(301) 587-6315 ext. 132
Fax: (301) 587-2365

E-MAIL ADDRESS:
paulab@aspen.nutr.org

WEB SITE ADDRESS:
www.nutritioncare.org

TYPE:
Research grants; Seed money grants. Annual support for nutritional research.

See entry 2566 for full listing.

AMERICAN SOCIETY OF HEMATOLOGY [2512]
2021 L Street, N.W.
Suite 900
Washington, DC 20036
(202) 776-0544
Fax: (888) 719-7814

E-MAIL ADDRESS:
awards@hematology.org

WEB SITE ADDRESS:
www.hematology.org

AREAS OF INTEREST:
Scientific abstracts.

NAME(S) OF PROGRAMS:
- **Merit Awards**
- **Travel Awards**

TYPE:
Awards/prizes; Travel grants.

PURPOSE:
To offer need- and merit-based awards to select individuals in order to help defray annual meeting travel expenses.

ELIGIBILITY:
Travel Awards: Applicants must be undergraduate students, medical students, graduate students, resident physicians, and postdoctoral fellows who are both first author and presenter of an abstract.

Merit Awards are offered to the first authors/presenters of abstracts that receive the highest score in the categories of undergraduate student, medical student, graduate student, resident physician, and postdoctoral fellow.

FINANCIAL DATA:
Amount of support per award: $500.
Total amount of support: Varies.

APPLICATION INFORMATION:
Contact the Organization for application procedures.
Duration: One-time award.

ADDRESS INQUIRIES TO:
Elisa Shea, Awards Manager
(See address above.)

AMERICAN SOCIETY OF NEPHROLOGY [2513]
1510 H Street, N.W.
Suite 800
Washington, DC 20005
(202) 640-4660
Fax: (202) 637-9793

E-MAIL ADDRESS:
email@asn-online.org

WEB SITE ADDRESS:
www.asn-online.org

AREAS OF INTEREST:
Nephrology.

NAME(S) OF PROGRAMS:
- **The M. James Scherbenske Grant**

TYPE:
Research grants.

PURPOSE:
To provide bridge funding for investigators from R01 to R01 whose application was scored, but not funded.

ELIGIBILITY:
Applicant must have submitted a competitive renewal R01 application that was scored but not funded. Cannot have more than $100,000 of total extramural research funding (direct

costs) as a principal investigator, co-principal investigator, and/or collaborating investigator with paid percent effort. Applicant must be an active member of the ASN and hold an M.D., Ph.D., or equivalent degree. The applicant's membership must be current with dues fully paid no later than February 1 of the calendar year in which the application is submitted. Appointment to full-time faculty must be confirmed in writing by the Department Chair, indicating the date of first full-time faculty appointment, and providing assurance that the department will provide needed resources for conducting independent research (laboratory and office space, salary support, and protected research time of at least 75%). Additionally, applicants will be considered ineligible should they submit more than one ASN grant application during any particular grants cycle.

GEOGRAPHIC RESTRICTIONS:
North and Central America.

FINANCIAL DATA:
Total amount of support: $100,000.

APPLICATION INFORMATION:
Only online applications will be accepted. There are no font or margin specifications. No need to include a proposed budget with application.
Duration: One year.
Deadline: November, March and June.

ADDRESS INQUIRIES TO:
E-mail: grants@asn-online.org

AMERICAN SOCIETY OF NEPHROLOGY   [2514]
1510 H Street, N.W.
Suite 800
Washington, DC 20005
(202) 640-4660
Fax: (202) 637-9793

E-MAIL ADDRESS:
email@asn-online.org

WEB SITE ADDRESS:
www.asn-online.org

AREAS OF INTEREST:
Nephrology.

NAME(S) OF PROGRAMS:
• **ASN-AST John Merrill Grant in Transplantation**
• **Carl W. Gottschalk Research Scholar Grant**
• **Norman Siegel Research Scholar Grant**

TYPE:
Research grants.

PURPOSE:
To enhance and assist the study and practice of nephrology; to provide a forum for the promulgation of research; to meet the professional and continuing education needs of its members; to foster the independent careers of young investigators in biomedical research related to nephrology and transplantation.

ELIGIBILITY:
Merrill and Gottschalk Grants: Applicants must be active ASN members and hold an M.D., Ph.D., or equivalent degree. At the time of submission, the applicant's membership must be current and their dues paid. Appointment to full-time faculty must be confirmed in writing by the department chair, indicating the date of first full-time faculty appointment, and providing assurance

that the department will provide needed resources for conducting independent research. Additionally, applicants will be considered ineligible should they submit more than one ASN grant application during any particular grants cycle.

FINANCIAL DATA:
Amount of support per award: $100,000 per year.

APPLICATION INFORMATION:
Only online applications will be accepted.
Duration: Two years.
Deadline: Last Friday in January.

ADDRESS INQUIRIES TO:
E-mail: grants@asn-online.org

AMERICAN SOCIETY OF NEPHROLOGY   [2515]
1510 H Street, N.W.
Suite 800
Washington, DC 20005
(202) 640-4660
Fax: (202) 637-9793

E-MAIL ADDRESS:
email@asn-online.org

WEB SITE ADDRESS:
www.asn-online.org

AREAS OF INTEREST:
Nephrology.

NAME(S) OF PROGRAMS:
• **ASN Student Scholar Grant**

TYPE:
Fellowships.

PURPOSE:
To enable selected medical students with an interest in either basic or clinical research to engage in continuous full-time research.

ELIGIBILITY:
Applicants must be currently enrolled in a U.S. medical school and in good standing. Applicants already receiving other sources of stipend support are not eligible.

The mentor must be an ASN member and must submit a program of study for the applicant. An award period can be a summer, semester, academic year, or any other 10- to 52-week period of continuous full-time research.

GEOGRAPHIC RESTRICTIONS:
United States.

FINANCIAL DATA:
Amount of support per award: Stipend of $400 per week, plus $100 per week provided to the principal investigator's lab to cover expenses and up to $1,500 to attend the ASN meeting following the research period.

APPLICATION INFORMATION:
Only online applications will be accepted.
Duration: 10 to 52 weeks.
Deadline: December 16, 2011 for funding to start January to December 2012.

ADDRESS INQUIRIES TO:
E-mail: grants@asn-online.org

CANCER FEDERATION, INC.   [2516]
711 West Ramsey Street
Banning, CA 92220
(951) 849-4325
Fax: (951) 849-0156

E-MAIL ADDRESS:
info@cancerfed.org

WEB SITE ADDRESS:
www.cancerfed.org

FOUNDED: 1977

AREAS OF INTEREST:
Cancer.

TYPE:
Research grants; Scholarships. The Federation has five basic programs: research, biology, scholarships, publishing (books, a magazine, a newsletter, and other materials) and patient aid.

YEAR PROGRAM STARTED: 1977

PURPOSE:
To fund research in cancer immunology and scholarships; to serve cancer patients and their families; to provide patient aid.

LEGAL BASIS:
Member supported charity.

ELIGIBILITY:
Candidates must major in biology or natural sciences and conduct research at the following institutions: Allegheny General Hospital, Delaware State College, Hawaii Medical Center, Hektoen Research Institute, Houston Medical School, Loma Linda Medical School, Loyola University Medical School, Mount Sinai Medical Center, Oregon State University, Pacific University, Rutgers University, St. Jude's Children's Hospital, Sloan Kettering Cancer Center, University of Arizona, University of California (Irvine, Riverside, San Francisco and Santa Barbara), University of Delaware, University of Illinois, University of Pittsburgh, University of Texas (Dallas and San Antonio), University of Washington, and Western University of Health Sciences.

FINANCIAL DATA:
Amount of support per award: $250 to $500.
Total amount of support: $300,000.

NUMBER OF APPLICANTS MOST RECENT YEAR:
50.

NUMBER OF AWARDS: 60 scholarships.

APPLICATION INFORMATION:
Scholar is chosen by institution.
Duration: One year. Renewal possible by reapplication.
Deadline: Varies according to sponsoring institution.

PUBLICATIONS:
Challenge, magazine; *CF Newsletter*; *Four Women Against Cancer*; and several others.

IRS IDENTIFICATION NUMBER: 95-3133568

ADDRESS INQUIRIES TO:
John Steinbacher, Chief Executive Officer
P.O. Box 1298
Banning, CA 92220

*PLEASE NOTE:
The Foundation also gives scholarships to cancer (recovered) patients who are in college.

CHILDREN'S TUMOR FOUNDATION   [2517]
95 Pine Street
16th Floor
New York, NY 10005
(212) 344-6633
Fax: (212) 747-0004

E-MAIL ADDRESS:
mwong@ctf.org

WEB SITE ADDRESS:
www.ctf.org

NAME(S) OF PROGRAMS:
- **Drug Discovery Initiative Award**
- **NF Clinic Network (CTF-NFCN)**
- **Young Investigator Awards**

TYPE:
Research grants; Seed money grants; Travel grants; Research contracts. Clinic support grants.

PURPOSE:
To improve the health and well-being of individuals and families affected by the neurofibromatoses.

ELIGIBILITY:
Drug Discovery Initiative Award: Applicants should have an M.D., Ph.D., or equivalent degree and access to all resources needed. Applicants from academia and the private sector are welcome, and partnerships between the two are encouraged. Applications are welcomed from all qualified individuals worldwide.
NF Clinic Network: Any clinic in the U.S. that sees NF patients may apply to be a CTF-NFCN Affiliate Clinic.
Young Investigator Award: Open to graduate students, postdoctoral fellows and young investigators no more than four years past completion of their M.D./Ph.D. training. The Investigator can be a graduate student or postdoctoral fellow associated with the laboratory of a more senior researcher, who acts as the research sponsor.

FINANCIAL DATA:
Amount of support per award: Drug Discovery Initiative Award: Up to $50,000; NF Clinic Network: Up to $3,000 per year; Young Investigator Award: Commensurate with experience.
Total amount of support: Young Investigator Award: $50,000 to $100,000.

NUMBER OF AWARDS: Young Investigator Award: Approximately 8.

APPLICATION INFORMATION:
Applications may be submitted online.
Duration: Young Investigator Award: Up to two years.
Deadline: Drug Discovery Initiative Award: Throughout the year. NF Clinic Network: Applications are received and evaluated on a rolling basis. Young Investigator Award: Letter of intent: Mid-February. Full application: Early April.

IRS IDENTIFICATION NUMBER: 13-2298956

STAFF:
George Orsanakos, President
Kim Hunter-Schaedle, Chief Scientific Officer

ADDRESS INQUIRIES TO:
Min Wong, Research Program Director
(See address above.)

CYSTIC FIBROSIS CANADA [2518]

2221 Yonge Street
Suite 601
Toronto ON M4S 2B4 Canada
(416) 485-9149
(800) 378-2233 (Canada only)
Fax: (416) 485-0960

E-MAIL ADDRESS:
researchprograms@cysticfibrosis.ca

WEB SITE ADDRESS:
www.cysticfibrosis.ca

FOUNDED: 1960

AREAS OF INTEREST:
Cystic fibrosis.

TYPE:
Fellowships; General operating grants; Grants-in-aid; Research grants; Scholarships; Training grants; Travel grants. Studentships; Summer studentships; Senior scientist research training awards; Small conference grants.

A limited number of competitive fellowships are offered by the Organization each year for basic or clinical research training in areas of the biomedical or behavioral sciences pertinent to cystic fibrosis.

Research grants are intended to facilitate the scientific investigation of all aspects of cystic fibrosis.

Scholarships provide salary support for a limited number of exceptional investigators, offering them an opportunity to develop outstanding cystic fibrosis research programs, unhampered by heavy teaching or clinical loads.

A limited number of competitive studentships are offered by the Organization each year to: (1) highly qualified graduate students who are registered for a higher degree, and who are undertaking full-time research training in areas of the biomedical or behavioral sciences relevant to cystic fibrosis or; (2) highly qualified students who are registered in a joint M.D./M.Sc. or M.D./Ph.D. program.

YEAR PROGRAM STARTED: 1961

PURPOSE:
To further research on cystic fibrosis.

LEGAL BASIS:
Nonprofit organization.

ELIGIBILITY:
Research Grants: A principal investigator should hold a recognized, full-time faculty appointment in a relevant discipline at a Canadian university or hospital. Under exceptional circumstances, and at the discretion of the Research Subcommittee, research grant applications from other individuals may be evaluated on a case-by-case basis, with significant emphasis placed on the degree of independence of the applicant, and on the institutional commitments to this individual.

Scholarship applications are restricted to candidates who have received their first faculty appointment within the preceding five calendar years. Applicants must hold an M.D. or Ph.D. degree, and must be sponsored by the chairman of the appropriate department and by the dean of the faculty. A commitment should be provided by the nominating institution, stating that the institution intends to continue to support the Scholar following the completion of the award.

Fellowships: Individuals who hold M.D. or Ph.D. degrees are eligible to apply. Medical graduates should have already completed basic residency training, and must be eligible for Canadian licensure. Applications for clinical fellowships must have a strong research component in the proposed program. Fellowships are not awarded for residency-type clinical training. Applicants

who have already completed six or more years of postgraduate study or training are not eligible for the Foundation fellowships.

Studentships are awarded for studies at the Master's or doctoral level. If a student receiving support for studies leading to a Master's degree elects to continue to a Doctorate degree, he or she must reapply for an initial Foundation studentship at the doctoral level. Students are expected to spend at least 75% of their time on the research training described in their application. Awards are tenable only at Canadian universities.

GEOGRAPHIC RESTRICTIONS:
Canada.

FINANCIAL DATA:
Scholarship, Fellowship and Studentship awards follow prevailing Canadian rates.

APPLICATION INFORMATION:
Copies of the Organization's Grants and Awards Guide are available. Applications should be submitted on the forms provided by the Organization. The guidelines and application forms must be closely followed.
Duration: Varies.
Deadline: Varies.

PUBLICATIONS:
Annual report; *Grants and Awards Guide*, English/French booklet; application guidelines.

ADDRESS INQUIRIES TO:
Andrea Mackesy
Manager, Research Programs
(See address above.)

CYSTIC FIBROSIS CANADA [2519]

2221 Yonge Street
Suite 601
Toronto ON M4S 2B4 Canada
(800) 378-2233
(416) 485-9149
Fax: (416) 485-0960

E-MAIL ADDRESS:
info@cysticfibrosis.ca

WEB SITE ADDRESS:
www.cysticfibrosis.ca

FOUNDED: 1960

AREAS OF INTEREST:
Cystic fibrosis.

NAME(S) OF PROGRAMS:
- **Clinic Incentive Grants**

TYPE:
Grants-in-aid; Seed money grants. Clinic Incentive Grants are intended to enhance the standard of clinical care available to Canadians with cystic fibrosis, by providing funds to initiate a comprehensive program for cystic fibrosis patient care, research and teaching, or to strengthen an existing program.

YEAR PROGRAM STARTED: 1961

PURPOSE:
To help establish a comprehensive program for patient care, research, and teaching in cystic fibrosis.

LEGAL BASIS:
Nonprofit organization.

ELIGIBILITY:
Grants may be made to medical schools or hospitals in Canada. Program potential,

regional need, relative need of the institution for assistance and special medical and technical advantages will be considered.

GEOGRAPHIC RESTRICTIONS:
Canada.

FINANCIAL DATA:
Grant payments will be made at the beginning of each quarter. Limited funding is available for related travel.
Total amount of support: $1,776,200 for the year 2010-11.

APPLICATION INFORMATION:
Duration: One year. Grants are to be renegotiated annually.
Deadline: October 1.

ADDRESS INQUIRIES TO:
Ian D. McIntosh
Manager, Clinical Programs
(See address above.)

HISTIOCYTOSIS ASSOCIATION OF AMERICA   [2520]
332 North Broadway
Pitman, NJ 08071
(856) 589-6606
Fax: (856) 589-6614

E-MAIL ADDRESS:
association@histio.org

WEB SITE ADDRESS:
www.histio.org

FOUNDED: 1986

AREAS OF INTEREST:
Histiocytosis, hemophagocytic lymphohistiocytosis and other histiocytic disorders.

NAME(S) OF PROGRAMS:
● **Research Grant Program**

TYPE:
Project/program grants; Research grants; Seed money grants.

YEAR PROGRAM STARTED: 1989

PURPOSE:
To fund worthy scientific research projects; to educate physicians and scientists; to encourage and support symposia into histiocytic disorders; to directly participate in research projects; to encourage publication of scientific information.

ELIGIBILITY:
Must be a tax-exempt, nonprofit medical research organization with researchers working in the field of histiocytosis research.

FINANCIAL DATA:
Amount of support per award: Up to $50,000 for one-year grants.
Total amount of support: Varies.

NUMBER OF APPLICANTS MOST RECENT YEAR: 12.

NUMBER OF AWARDS: 9.

APPLICATION INFORMATION:
Application can be downloaded from the web site.
Duration: Up to one year.
Deadline: July 1.

IRS IDENTIFICATION NUMBER: 22-2827069

STAFF:
Jeffrey Toughill, Executive Director

ADDRESS INQUIRIES TO:
Jeffrey Toughill, Executive Director
(See address above.)

THE LEUKEMIA & LYMPHOMA SOCIETY   [2521]
1311 Mamaroneck Avenue
Suite 310
White Plains, NY 10605
(914) 821-8859
(914) 821-8843
Fax: (914) 821-8946

E-MAIL ADDRESS:
researchprograms@lls.org

WEB SITE ADDRESS:
www.lls.org

AREAS OF INTEREST:
Leukemia, lymphoma and myeloma.

NAME(S) OF PROGRAMS:
● **Career Development Program**

TYPE:
Fellowships; Research grants. The Career Development Program provides awards intended to meet the specific needs of investigators at different stages of their research careers. The five awards, Fellow, Scholar, Scholar in Clinical Research, Special Fellow and Special Fellow in Clinical Research, provide stipends to investigators, allowing them to devote themselves to research bearing on leukemia, lymphoma and myeloma.

PURPOSE:
To cure leukemia, lymphoma, Hodgkin's disease and myeloma; to improve the quality of life of patients and their families; to support individuals pursuing careers in basic or clinical research in leukemia, lymphoma and myeloma.

ELIGIBILITY:
Qualified investigators affiliated with appropriate institutions are eligible to apply. Applicants must have the approval of the institution and recommendation of the department head where the research training will be conducted. Ph.D. or M.D. status is required.

FINANCIAL DATA:
Amount of support per award: $165,000 for three years for Fellows; $550,000 for five years for Scholars and Scholars in Clinical Research; $195,000 for three years for Special Fellows and Special Fellows in Clinical Research.

APPLICATION INFORMATION:
Guidelines are available on the web site.
Duration: Renewable for up to five years at the level of Scholar and three years at the level of Special Fellow and Fellow.
Deadline: Preliminary application: September 15. Full application: October 1.

ADDRESS INQUIRIES TO:
Sammy Hattar
Director of Research Administration
(See address above.)

THE LEUKEMIA & LYMPHOMA SOCIETY   [2522]
1311 Mamaroneck Avenue
Suite 310
White Plains, NY 10605
(914) 821-8859
(914) 821-8843
Fax: (914) 821-8946

E-MAIL ADDRESS:
researchprograms@lls.org

WEB SITE ADDRESS:
www.lls.org

AREAS OF INTEREST:
Leukemia, lymphoma and myeloma.

NAME(S) OF PROGRAMS:
● **Translational Research Program**

TYPE:
Research grants. Translational Research Program is intended to encourage and provide support for new and novel clinical research. The goal of the program is to accelerate transfer of findings from the laboratory to clinical application.

PURPOSE:
To encourage and provide early-stage support for clinical research in leukemia, lymphoma, and myeloma, with the intention of developing innovative approaches to treatment, diagnosis or prevention; to support projects that translate laboratory findings to clinical application.

ELIGIBILITY:
Ph.D. or M.D. status is required. Candidates must be affiliated with a non-federal public or private nonprofit institution engaged in cancer-related research.

FINANCIAL DATA:
Amount of support per award: $200,000 annually.

COOPERATIVE FUNDING PROGRAMS: National Career Institutes; Academic, Public, Private, Partnership Program (AP4).

NUMBER OF APPLICANTS MOST RECENT YEAR: 203 for the year 2008.

NUMBER OF AWARDS: 42 for the year 2008.

APPLICATION INFORMATION:
Guidelines are available on the web site.
Duration: Three years. In special cases these may be renewed for two years.
Deadline: Preliminary application: March 1. Full application: March 15.

ADDRESS INQUIRIES TO:
Sammy Hattar
Director of Research Administration
(See address above.)

THE LEUKEMIA & LYMPHOMA SOCIETY   [2523]
1311 Mamaroneck Avenue
Suite 310
White Plains, NY 10605
(914) 821-8859
(914) 821-8843
Fax: (914) 821-8946

E-MAIL ADDRESS:
researchprograms@lls.org

WEB SITE ADDRESS:
www.lls.org

AREAS OF INTEREST:
Leukemia, lymphoma, Hodgkin's disease and myeloma.

NAME(S) OF PROGRAMS:
● **Marshall A. Lichtman Specialized Center of Research Program**

TYPE:
Research grants. The grant supports scientific core laboratories required by the component research programs, so as to provide access to key high technology to support facilities that might not otherwise be available to individual research programs.

PURPOSE:

To support research programs that are focused on any aspect of leukemia, lymphoma, Hodgkin's disease and myeloma in order to foster interactions, cooperation, and to enhance interdisciplinary research among the participants.

ELIGIBILITY:

Applications may be submitted by individuals holding an M.D., Ph.D., or equivalent degree, working in domestic or foreign nonprofit organizations, such as universities, colleges, hospitals or laboratories. Applications may be multi-institutional in nature. Applicants need not be U.S. citizens, and there are no restrictions on applicant age, race, gender or creed.

FINANCIAL DATA:

Expenses for administrative staff (including secretarial) costs cannot exceed one full-time equivalent for the Center per year. Travel costs for all investigators cannot exceed $10,000 per year for the Center. The aggregate of office supplies and telephone costs cannot exceed $6,000 per year for the Center.

Amount of support per award: Up to $1,250,000 annually.

NUMBER OF APPLICANTS MOST RECENT YEAR: 31 for the year 2008.

NUMBER OF AWARDS: 3 for the year 2008.

APPLICATION INFORMATION:

Guidelines are available on the web site.

Duration: Five years.

Deadline: Letter of Intent: November 1. Notification sent to those selected for full application submission by December 31. Application: March 15.

ADDRESS INQUIRIES TO:

Sammy Hattar
Director of Research Administration
(See address above.)

LYMPHOMA RESEARCH FOUNDATION [2524]

115 Broadway, 13th Floor
New York, NY 10006
(212) 349-2910
Fax: (212) 349-2886

E-MAIL ADDRESS:

researchgrants@lymphoma.org

WEB SITE ADDRESS:

www.lymphoma.org

FOUNDED: 2001

AREAS OF INTEREST:

Lymphoma research.

CONSULTING OR VOLUNTEER SERVICES:

Many volunteer-based Chapters throughout the country.

NAME(S) OF PROGRAMS:

- **Clinical Investigator - Career Development Awards**
- **Focus Area Grants: Follicular Lymphoma Research Grants**
- **Focus Area Grants: Mantle Cell Lymphoma Correlative Grants**
- **Postdoctoral Fellowships**

TYPE:

Fellowships; Research grants.

YEAR PROGRAM STARTED: 1992

PURPOSE:

To develop novel therapeutic strategies for the treatment of lymphoma.

LEGAL BASIS:

Nonprofit organization.

ELIGIBILITY:

Career Development Award applicants should be advanced fellows or junior faculty up to the level of assistant professor and must also possess at least two years of training in hematology and/or oncology, plus clinical experience managing patients with lymphoma. Applicants must be licensed physicians at a clinical research institution in the U.S. or Canada for the duration of the LRF Clinical Investigator Grant.

Focus Area Grant applicants should be licensed Senior Researchers. These are awarded to experienced researchers pursuing the development of novel and innovative treatments.

Postdoctoral Fellowship applicants must have completed two years of their fellowship, or not more than two years as a junior faculty instructor or assistant professor at the start of the award period, and hold an M.D., Ph.D., or equivalent degree. Applicants must be affiliated with a sponsoring institution in the U.S. or Canada for the duration of the LRF Grant. Citizenship is not required.

FINANCIAL DATA:

Amount of support per award: Career Development Awards: $75,000 per year; Focus Area Grants: Up to $250,000; Postdoctoral Fellowships: $50,000 in year one and $55,000 in year two.

Total amount of support: Varies.

NUMBER OF AWARDS: 12 grants for the year 2010.

APPLICATION INFORMATION:

E-mail the Foundation for application procedures.

Duration: Career Development Awards and Focus Area Grants: Three years; Postdoctoral Fellowships: Two years.

Deadline: Varies.

BOARD OF DIRECTORS:

Errol Cook, Chairman and Chief Executive Officer
Michael D. Ditzian, Executive Vice President
Tom Condon, Treasurer
Jerry Freundlich, Secretary
Dr. Morton Coleman, Chairman, Medical Affiliates Board New Jersey and New York
Dr. Richard I. Fisher, Chairman, Scientific Advisory Board
John Balan
Dr. Joseph R. Bertino
Heidi Dieter
Robert E. Fischer
Barbara Freundlich
Tom L. Harrison
Marie L. Matthews
Miriam Phalen
Steven J. Prince
Leonard M. Rosen
Michael Werner

ADDRESS INQUIRIES TO:

Mickey DiFabrizio
Research Department Coordinator
(See telephone number listed above.)

NATIONAL HEADACHE FOUNDATION [2525]

820 North Orleans, Suite 411
Chicago, IL 60610-3132
(312) 274-2650
(888) 643-5552
Fax: (312) 640-9049

E-MAIL ADDRESS:

info@headaches.org

WEB SITE ADDRESS:

www.headaches.org

FOUNDED: 1970

AREAS OF INTEREST:

Headache and pain.

TYPE:

Research grants. Support for research in the field of headache and pain.

YEAR PROGRAM STARTED: 1970

PURPOSE:

To provide education and information helpful to headache sufferers; to serve as an information resource to headache sufferers, their families and the physicians who treat them; to promote research into potential headache causes and treatments; to educate the public to the fact that headaches are a legitimate biological disorder and sufferers need understanding and continuity of care.

LEGAL BASIS:

Nonprofit organization.

ELIGIBILITY:

Investigators from departments of neurology and pharmacology are invited to apply. Submissions from other departments and individual investigators are also welcome. No funding for overhead, salaries, rent or indirect expenses. Grants may be used for data analysis, interpretation, reading of results, etc.

GEOGRAPHIC RESTRICTIONS:

United States.

FINANCIAL DATA:

Full or partial funding may be granted.

Amount of support per award: Varies depending on project.

NUMBER OF APPLICANTS MOST RECENT YEAR: 12.

NUMBER OF AWARDS: 9 for the year 2009-10.

REPRESENTATIVE AWARDS:

$15,000 to Beth Israel Deaconess Medical Center for Activity of Meningeal Sensory Neurons: Excitatory vs. Inhibitory Mechanisms in Sensitization; $15,000 to Northwestern Memorial Hospital for The Relation of Idiopathic Intracranial Hypertension (Pseudo tumor Cetebri) and Brain Quabain; $10,000 to Missouri State University for ATP and CGRP a Synergistic Mechanism Regulating Nociception in Trigeminal Ganglion Neurons; $10,000 to University of Iowa for Does Pregnancy Reduce Light Aversion in a Mouse Model of Migraine?; $10,000 to University of Missouri Kansas City for Novel Mechanism Underlying the Pathophysiology of Visual Impairment During Migraine Headaches; $10,000 to University of Porto, Portugal for Indentification of Generic Variants Associated with Increased Susceptibility of Migraine.

APPLICATION INFORMATION:

Applicants must submit abstract of research proposal on Foundation form as well as protocol and proposed budget. Proposed projects will be evaluated at the winter board meeting of the NHF.

Duration: One year.

Deadline: December 1. Announcement in March.

PUBLICATIONS:
Program announcement.

ADDRESS INQUIRIES TO:
Robert Dalton, Executive Director
(See address above.)

NATIONAL HEART, LUNG AND BLOOD INSTITUTE (NHLBI) [2526]

Division of Blood Diseases and Resources
National Institutes of Health
6701 Rockledge Drive, Suite 9030
Bethesda, MD 20892
(301) 435-0080
Fax: (301) 480-0867

E-MAIL ADDRESS:
pucies@nhlbi.nih.gov

WEB SITE ADDRESS:
www.nhlbi.nih.gov

FOUNDED: 1948

AREAS OF INTEREST:
Research on the causes, prevention, and treatment of nonmalignant blood diseases, including anemias, sickle cell disease, and thalassemia; premalignant processes such as myelodysplasia and myeloproliferative disorders; hemophilia and other abnormalities of hemostasis and thrombosis; and immune dysfunction.

NAME(S) OF PROGRAMS:
• **Blood Diseases and Resources Research**

TYPE:
Conferences/seminars; Demonstration grants; Fellowships; Grants-in-aid; Project/program grants; Training grants; Research contracts. Funding encompasses a broad spectrum of research ranging from basic biology to medical management of blood diseases.

YEAR PROGRAM STARTED: 1972

PURPOSE:
To develop programs that will reduce the morbidity and mortality caused by blood diseases, lead to the primary prevention of these diseases and ensure the availability of adequate supplies of safe and efficacious blood products.

LEGAL BASIS:
Public Health Service Act, Section 301(e) and Section 412; Public Law 78-410, as amended; 42 U.S.C. 241; 42 U.S.C. 287a; Public Health Service Act, Section 472; Public Law 78-410, as amended; 42 U.S.C. 289 1-1.

ELIGIBILITY:
Any nonprofit organization engaged in biomedical research and institutions (or companies) organized for profit may apply for grants with the exception of National Research Service Awards. Only citizens and non-citizen nationals are eligible for support by research training and career development programs. Other mechanisms are not restricted.

FINANCIAL DATA:
Grants may support salaries, equipment, supplies, travel and patient hospitalization as required to perform the research effort.
Amount of support per award: Varies by the type of grant.
Total amount of support: $450,000,000 for fiscal year 2010.

APPLICATION INFORMATION:
Duration: One to five years. Renewable through reapplication.

Deadline: Varies.

PUBLICATIONS:
Annual report.

DIRECTORS:
W. Keith Hoots, Director
Donna DiMichele, M.D., Deputy Director
Susan Pucie, Senior Program Analyst

RESEARCH STAFF:
Harvey Luksenburg, M.D., Branch Chief, Blood Diseases Branch
Simone Glynn, M.D., Chief, Transfusion Medicine and Cellular Therapeutics Branch
Donna DiMichele, Acting Chief, Thrombosis and Hemostasis Branch

ADDRESS INQUIRIES TO:
Division of Blood Diseases and Resources
(See address above.)

NEURO-DEVELOPMENTAL TREATMENT ASSOCIATION [2527]

1540 South Coast Highway
Suite 203
Laguna Beach, CA 92651
(800) 869-9295
Fax: (949) 376-3456

E-MAIL ADDRESS:
membership@ndta.org

WEB SITE ADDRESS:
www.ndta.org

AREAS OF INTEREST:
Neuro-Developmental Treatment.

TYPE:
Research grants.

PURPOSE:
To support the investigation of the effectiveness of Neuro-Developmental Treatment with pediatric and adult populations.

ELIGIBILITY:
Qualified investigators affiliated with appropriate institutions are eligible to apply. Applicants must have the approval of the institution and recommendation of the department head where the research training will be conducted.

FINANCIAL DATA:
The grant does not pay indirect, overhead or salary reimbursement costs.
Amount of support per award: Up to $5,000.

NUMBER OF AWARDS: Typically 1 annually.

APPLICATION INFORMATION:
Send requests for a grant application and guidelines to:
Janet Powell, Ph.D., OT
University of Washington
Division of Occupational Therapy
1959 Northeast Pacific Street, Box 356490
Seattle, WA 98195
E-mail: jmpowell@u.washington.edu.
Deadline: December 1.

ADDRESS INQUIRIES TO:
Mark Toof, Associate Director
(See address above.)

THE NEUROPATHY ASSOCIATION [2528]

60 East 42nd Street
Suite 942
New York, NY 10165
(212) 692-0662
Fax: (212) 692-0668

E-MAIL ADDRESS:
info@neuropathy.org
npires@neuropathy.org

WEB SITE ADDRESS:
www.neuropathy.org

FOUNDED: 1995

AREAS OF INTEREST:
Disorders of the peripheral nervous system.

CONSULTING OR VOLUNTEER SERVICES:
Volunteer services.

TYPE:
Research grants.

YEAR PROGRAM STARTED: 1995

PURPOSE:
To support research into the causes and treatment of peripheral neuropathies; to provide support through education and sharing information and experiences related to peripheral neuropathy.

LEGAL BASIS:
501(c)(3).

ELIGIBILITY:
Open to medical doctors working in a neurological research program in the area of neuropathy.

FINANCIAL DATA:
Amount of support per award: $40,000.

NUMBER OF APPLICANTS MOST RECENT YEAR: 12.

NUMBER OF AWARDS: 2.

APPLICATION INFORMATION:
Write or call the Foundation to determine the interest and appropriateness of a full proposal.
Duration: Up to two years.
Deadline: September.

ADDRESS INQUIRIES TO:
Natacha Pires
Director, Medical and Public Affairs
(See address above.)

THE SOCIETY FOR CARDIOVASCULAR ANGIOGRAPHY AND INTERVENTIONS

2400 N Street, N.W.
Suite 500
Washington, DC 20037-1153
(202) 741-9854
(800) 992-7224
Fax: (800) 863-5202

E-MAIL ADDRESS:
info@scai.org
rortega@scai.org

WEB SITE ADDRESS:
www.scai.org

TYPE:
Fellowships.

See entry 2558 for full listing.

Cardiovascular and pulmonary

AMERICAN COLLEGE OF CARDIOLOGY [2529]

2400 N Street, N.W.
Washington, DC 20037
(202) 375-6613
Fax: (202) 375-6848

E-MAIL ADDRESS:
kventura@acc.org

WEB SITE ADDRESS:
www.cardiosource.org/awards

AREAS OF INTEREST:
Cardiology.

NAME(S) OF PROGRAMS:
- **ACCF/Merck Research Fellowships in Cardiovascular Disease**

TYPE:
Fellowships.

PURPOSE:
To advance research in cardiovascular disease.

ELIGIBILITY:
Anyone currently in an adult cardiology fellowship training program recognized by the Accreditation Council for Graduate Medical Education or the American Osteopathic Association and who has the recommendation and agreement of their training program director and institution is eligible to apply. Preference is given to individuals who have had no more than two years of prior full-time experience either in clinical or basic research.

GEOGRAPHIC RESTRICTIONS:
United States and Canada.

FINANCIAL DATA:
Amount of support per award: $60,000.

NUMBER OF AWARDS: 4.

APPLICATION INFORMATION:
Guidelines and application form are available online.
Duration: One year.
Deadline: October 6.

ADDRESS INQUIRIES TO:
Kelly Evans Ventura, Associate Director
(See address above.)

AMERICAN COLLEGE OF CARDIOLOGY [2530]

2400 N Street, N.W.
Washington, DC 20037
(202) 375-6613
Fax: (202) 375-6848

E-MAIL ADDRESS:
kventura@acc.org

WEB SITE ADDRESS:
www.cardiosource.org/awards

AREAS OF INTEREST:
Cardiology.

NAME(S) OF PROGRAMS:
- **ACC Young Investigators Awards Competition**

TYPE:
Awards/prizes. Awarded in three categories:
(1) Clinical Investigations;
(2) Physiology, Pharmacology, and Pathology and;
(3) Molecular and Cellular Cardiology.

PURPOSE:
To encourage and recognize young scientific investigators of promise.

ELIGIBILITY:
Any physician or scientist presently in a residency or fellowship training program or who has been in such a program within the past three years, medical students, and Ph.D. candidates are eligible to apply.

FINANCIAL DATA:
Amount of support per award: First Place: $2,000; Second Place: $1,000.

APPLICATION INFORMATION:
Guidelines and application form are available online.
Deadline: October.

ADDRESS INQUIRIES TO:
Kelly Evans Ventura, Associate Director
(See address above.)

AMERICAN HEART ASSOCIATION [2531]

AHA National Center
7272 Greenville Avenue
Dallas, TX 75231-4596
(214) 360-6104
Fax: (214) 360-6124

E-MAIL ADDRESS:
apply@heart.org

WEB SITE ADDRESS:
my.americanheart.org

FOUNDED: 1948

AREAS OF INTEREST:
Research broadly related to cardiovascular disease and stroke, and research in clinical, basic science, bioengineering or biotechnology, and public health problems.

NAME(S) OF PROGRAMS:
- **Postdoctoral Fellowship**

TYPE:
Fellowships. Supports individuals before they are ready for some stage of independent research.

PURPOSE:
To help a trainee initiate a career in cardiovascular and stroke research while obtaining significant research results under the supervision of a sponsor or mentor.

ELIGIBILITY:
Applicants must:
(1) be a U.S. citizen or permanent resident;
(2) be individuals before they are ready for some stage of independent research;
(3) have M.D., Ph.D., D.O., D.V.M. (or equivalent) at activation and;
(4) have five years or less postdoctoral research experience at time of activation.

FINANCIAL DATA:
Amount of support per award: Varies per initiative for each geographical area.

APPLICATION INFORMATION:
Guidelines and application form are available on the web site.
Duration: Two years. Must reapply for third year.
Deadline: July.

ADDRESS INQUIRIES TO:
See e-mail address above.

AMERICAN HEART ASSOCIATION [2532]

AHA National Center
7272 Greenville Avenue
Dallas, TX 75231-4596
(214) 360-6104
Fax: (214) 360-6124

E-MAIL ADDRESS:
apply@heart.org

WEB SITE ADDRESS:
my.americanheart.org

FOUNDED: 1948

AREAS OF INTEREST:
Research broadly related to cardiovascular disease and stroke, and research in clinical, basic science, bioengineering or biotechnology, and public health problems.

NAME(S) OF PROGRAMS:
- **Predoctoral Fellowship**

TYPE:
Fellowships.

PURPOSE:
To help students initiate careers in cardiovascular and stroke research by providing research assistance and training.

ELIGIBILITY:
Applicants must meet the following criteria:
(1) be a U.S. citizen or permanent resident;
(2) be post-Baccalaureate, predoctoral M.D., Ph.D., D.O., D.V.M. (or equivalent) students seeking research training with a sponsor/mentor prior to embarking on a research career and;
(3) be a full-time student working toward their degree.

FINANCIAL DATA:
Amount of support per award: Varies per initiative for each geographical area.

APPLICATION INFORMATION:
Guidelines and application form are available on the web site.
Duration: One to two years. Must reapply for third year.
Deadline: July.

ADDRESS INQUIRIES TO:
See e-mail address above.

AMERICAN HEART ASSOCIATION [2533]

AHA National Center
7272 Greenville Avenue
Dallas, TX 75231-4596
(214) 360-6104
Fax: (214) 360-6124

E-MAIL ADDRESS:
apply@heart.org

WEB SITE ADDRESS:
my.americanheart.org

FOUNDED: 1948

AREAS OF INTEREST:
Research broadly related to cardiovascular disease and stroke, and clinical, basic science, bioengineering or biotechnology, and public health problems.

NAME(S) OF PROGRAMS:
- **Beginning Grant-in-Aid**

TYPE:
Grants-in-aid. Beginning grant-in-aid for all basic disciplines as well as epidemiological, community and clinical investigations that bear on cardiovascular and stroke problems.

PURPOSE:
To promote the independent status of promising beginning scientists.

ELIGIBILITY:
Applicant must:
(1) be a U.S. citizen or permanent resident;
(2) at time of application have M.D., Ph.D., D.O., D.V.M. or equivalent initiating independent research career;
(3) hold position of assistant professor (or equivalent) or higher at activation and;
(4) have faculty/staff appointment at activation and meet institutional requirements for grant submission at time of application.

GEOGRAPHIC RESTRICTIONS:
United States.

FINANCIAL DATA:
Amount of support per award: Varies per initiative for each geographical area.

APPLICATION INFORMATION:
Guidelines and application form are available on the web site.
Duration: Two years. Possible one to two years upon reapplication.
Deadline: July.

ADDRESS INQUIRIES TO:
See e-mail address above.

AMERICAN HEART ASSOCIATION [2534]
AHA National Center
7272 Greenville Avenue
Dallas, TX 75231-4596
(214) 360-6104
Fax: (214) 360-6124

E-MAIL ADDRESS:
apply@heart.org

WEB SITE ADDRESS:
my.americanheart.org

FOUNDED: 1948

AREAS OF INTEREST:
Research broadly related to cardiovascular disease and stroke, and research in clinical, basic science, bioengineering or biotechnology, and public health problems.

NAME(S) OF PROGRAMS:
● **Greater Southeast Affiliate Health Sciences Fellowship Program**

TYPE:
Fellowships. Provides opportunities for health science students to work for 10 consecutive weeks with a faculty/staff member on any project related to the mission of the AHA.

PURPOSE:
To encourage students to consider a future academic career in health science.

ELIGIBILITY:
Proposals are encouraged from all basic disciplines, including multidisciplinary efforts, as well as epidemiological and clinical disciplines that bear on cardiovascular and stroke problems.

Applicant must be predoctoral M.D., D.O., D.D.S., Pharm.D. (or equivalent) health science student. At the time of application, student must be a U.S. citizen, permanent resident, pending permanent resident or hold one of the following visas: E-3, F-1, H1-B, J-1, O-1 or TN.

Award must be completed at any accredited institution in Alabama, Florida, Georgia, Louisiana, Mississippi, Puerto Rico, Tennessee or U.S. Virgin Islands.

FINANCIAL DATA:
Amount of support per award: $4,500 per student.
Total amount of support: $13,500 per year.

NUMBER OF AWARDS: Up to 3 student fellows per institution per year.

APPLICATION INFORMATION:
Guidelines and application form are available on the web site.
Duration: Two years.

AMERICAN HEART ASSOCIATION [2535]
AHA National Center
7272 Greenville Avenue
Dallas, TX 75231-4596
(214) 360-6104
Fax: (214) 360-6124

E-MAIL ADDRESS:
apply@heart.org

WEB SITE ADDRESS:
my.americanheart.org/research

FOUNDED: 1948

AREAS OF INTEREST:
Research broadly related to cardiovascular disease and stroke, and research in clinical, basic science, bioengineering or biotechnology, and public health problems.

NAME(S) OF PROGRAMS:
● **Great Rivers Affiliate Student Undergraduate Research Fellowship**

TYPE:
Fellowships. Institutional award to qualified research institutions, within the Affiliate's geographic boundaries, that can offer a meaningful research experience to undergraduate students.

PURPOSE:
To encourage promising students, including women and members of minority groups underrepresented in the sciences, from all disciplines to consider research careers while supporting the highest quality scientific investigation broadly related to cardiovascular disease and stroke.

ELIGIBILITY:
Applicant must be a U.S. citizen or permanent resident, pending permanent resident, J-1, E-3, H1-B, TN, O-1, or F-1 visa. To be eligible, undergraduate students should be currently classified at the junior or senior academic status at the time of award activation. Students must be enrolled full-time in an undergraduate degree program, at the time of application, in either a four-year college or university, or a two-year institution with plans to transfer to a four-year college or university by the fall semester immediately following the summer program.

The award may be completed at any accredited institution in Delaware, Kentucky, Ohio, Pennsylvania or West Virginia.

FINANCIAL DATA:
Amount of support per award: $4,000 per student; $20,000 maximum per year for institution; $40,000 maximum for a two-year award.

NUMBER OF AWARDS: Up to 5 per institution.

APPLICATION INFORMATION:
Guidelines and application form are available on the web site.
Duration: One to two years.

AMERICAN HEART ASSOCIATION [2536]
AHA National Center
7272 Greenville Avenue
Dallas, TX 75231-4596
(214) 360-6104
Fax: (214) 360-6124

E-MAIL ADDRESS:
apply@heart.org

WEB SITE ADDRESS:
my.americanheart.org

FOUNDED: 1948

AREAS OF INTEREST:
Research broadly related to cardiovascular disease and stroke, and research in clinical, basic science, bioengineering or biotechnology, and public health problems.

NAME(S) OF PROGRAMS:
● **Grant-in-Aid Program**

TYPE:
Grants-in-aid. Offered through Founders and Western States Affiliates.

PURPOSE:
To encourage and adequately fund the most innovative and meritorious research projects from independent investigators.

ELIGIBILITY:
Proposals are encouraged from all basic disciplines, as well as epidemiological, behavioral, community and clinical investigations that bear on cardiovascular and stroke problems. At the time of application, the applicant must:
(1) hold a faculty/staff appointment of any rank (or equivalent), and must be conducting independent research. Not intended for individuals in research training or fellowship positions;
(2) hold an M.D., Ph.D., D.O., D.V.M. or equivalent post-Baccaulareate doctoral degree;
(3) meet institutional requirements for grant submission and;
(4) be a U.S. citizen, permanent resident, pending permanent resident or hold these visas: E-3, H1-B, J-1, O-1 or TN.

For the Founders Affiliate program, the award may be completed at any accredited institution in Connecticut, Maine, Massachusetts, New Hampshire, New Jersey, New York, Rhode Island or Vermont.

For the Western States Affiliate program, the award may be completed at any accredited institution in Alaska, Arizona, California, Hawaii, Idaho, Montana, Nevada, Oregon, Utah or Washington.

FINANCIAL DATA:
Amount of support per award: Founders Affiliate: $66,000 per year (including up to $30,000 for salary/fringe and 10% indirect cost); Western States Affiliate: $70,000 maximum per year (including up to $35,000 for salary/fringe and 10% indirect cost).

NUMBER OF APPLICANTS MOST RECENT YEAR:
Founders Affiliate: 113 reviewed.

NUMBER OF AWARDS: Founders Affiliate: 9.

APPLICATION INFORMATION:
Guidelines and application form are available on the web site.
Duration: Founders Affiliate: Three years; Western States Affiliate: Two years.

*SPECIAL STIPULATIONS:
At the time of award activation, the amount of other research funding available to the principal investigator may not exceed $250,000 annually. This includes direct funds, and does not include the PI salary/fringe and intramural funding.

AMERICAN HEART ASSOCIATION [2537]
AHA National Center
7272 Greenville Avenue
Dallas, TX 75231-4596
(214) 360-6104
Fax: (214) 360-6124

E-MAIL ADDRESS:
apply@heart.org

WEB SITE ADDRESS:
my.americanheart.org

FOUNDED: 1948

AREAS OF INTEREST:
Research broadly related to cardiovascular function and disease and stroke, or to related clinical, basic science, bioengineering or biotechnology, and public health problems, including multidisciplinary efforts.

NAME(S) OF PROGRAMS:
● **National Innovative Research Grant**

TYPE:
Research grants.

PURPOSE:
To support highly innovative, high-risk, high-reward research that could ultimately lead to critical discoveries or major advancements that will accelerate the field of cardiovascular and stroke research.

ELIGIBILITY:
At the time of application, the applicant must:
(1) hold an M.D., Ph.D., D.O. or equivalent doctoral degree;
(2) meet institutional requirements for grant submission;
(3) be a U.S. citizen, permanent resident, pending permanent resident, or have one of the following visas: E-3, H-1B, J-1, O-1 or TN and;
(4) at the time of award activation, have a faculty (or faculty equivalent) appointment. This award is not intended for postdoctoral fellows or others in research training positions.

Eligibility for the grant is not restricted based upon experience level or seniority. Seniority will not be used as a criterion in evaluating an application's merit.

FINANCIAL DATA:
Amount of support per award: $75,000 per year (including 10% indirect costs).

NUMBER OF APPLICANTS MOST RECENT YEAR:
183 for the year 2010.

NUMBER OF AWARDS: 19 for the year 2010.

APPLICATION INFORMATION:
Guidelines and application form are available on the web site.
Duration: Two years.

AMERICAN HEART ASSOCIATION [2538]
AHA National Center
7272 Greenville Avenue
Dallas, TX 75231-4596
(214) 360-6104
Fax: (214) 360-6124

E-MAIL ADDRESS:
apply@heart.org

WEB SITE ADDRESS:
my.americanheart.org

FOUNDED: 1948

AREAS OF INTEREST:
Research broadly related to cardiovascular function and disease and stroke, or related to clinical, basic science, bioengineering or biotechnology, and public health problems, including multidisciplinary efforts.

NAME(S) OF PROGRAMS:
● **National Established Investigator Award**

TYPE:
Research grants. Candidates for this award have a demonstrated commitment to cardiovascular or cerebrovascular science as indicated by prior publication history and scientific accomplishments. A candidate's career is expected to be in a rapid growth phase.

PURPOSE:
To support midcareer investigators with unusual promise and an established record of accomplishments.

ELIGIBILITY:
Proposals are encouraged from all basic disciplines as well as epidemiological, behavioral, community and clinical investigations that bear on cardiovascular and stroke problems.

At the time of application, the applicant must:
(1) have an M.D., Ph.D., D.O. or equivalent doctoral degree;
(2) be a faculty/staff member;
(3) meet institutional requirements for grant submission;
(4) have current national-level funding as a principal investigator (or co-PI) on an R01 grant or its equivalent;
(5) be a U.S. citizen or permanent resident and;
(6) at the time of award activation be at least four years, but no more than nine years, since the first faculty/staff appointment at the assistant professor level or equivalent (including, but not limited to, research assistant professor, research scientist, staff scientist, etc.). Instructor positions (or equivalent positions) do not count toward the four or nine years of eligibility.

Research awards are limited to nonprofit institutions, including medical, osteopathic and dental schools, veterinary schools, schools of public health, pharmacy schools, nursing schools, universities and colleges, public and voluntary hospitals and other nonprofit institutions that can demonstrate the ability to conduct the proposed research. Applications will not be accepted for work with funding to be administered through any federal institution or work to be performed by a federal employee, except for Veterans Administration employees.

Funding is prohibited for awards at non-U.S. institutions.

FINANCIAL DATA:
Amount of support per award: $80,000 per year (including up to 10% indirect costs).

APPLICATION INFORMATION:
Guidelines and application form are available on the web site.
Duration: Five years. No renewals.

AMERICAN HEART ASSOCIATION [2539]
AHA National Center
7272 Greenville Avenue
Dallas, TX 75231-4596
(214) 360-6104
Fax: (214) 360-6124

E-MAIL ADDRESS:
apply@heart.org

WEB SITE ADDRESS:
my.americanheart.org

FOUNDED: 1948

AREAS OF INTEREST:
Reducing disability and death from cardiovascular diseases and stroke; clinical, basic science, bioengineering/biotechnology, and public health problems; epidemiological, community and clinical investigations that bear on cardiovascular and stroke problems.

NAME(S) OF PROGRAMS:
● **National Clinical Research Program**
● **National Scientist Development Grant**

TYPE:
Awards/prizes; Development grants; Research grants. National Clinical Research Program is intended to encourage early career investigators who have appropriate and supportive mentoring relationships to engage in high-quality introductory and pilot clinical studies that will guide future strategies for reducing cardiovascular disease and stroke while fostering new research in clinical and translational science, and encouraging community- and population-based activities.

National Scientist Development Grant is intended to support highly promising beginning scientists in their progress toward independence by encouraging and adequately funding research projects that can bridge the gap between completion of research training and readiness for successful competition as an independent investigator.

YEAR PROGRAM STARTED: 1997

PURPOSE:
To support research activities broadly related to cardiovascular function and disease, stroke, or to related basic science, clinical, bioengineering/biotechnology and public health problems.

LEGAL BASIS:
Research association.

ELIGIBILITY:
Applicant must be U.S. citizen or permanent resident.

National Clinical Research Program: Open to health care professionals with a Master's or post-Baccalaureate doctoral degree, including M.P.H., R.N., Pharm.D., M.D., D.O. or Ph.D. Interdisciplinary research teams are eligible. Applicant must meet institutional requirements for grant submission at time of application.

National Scientist Development Grant: At the time of application, applicant must hold an M.D., Ph.D., D.O., D.V.M. or equivalent post-Baccalaureate doctoral degree and meet institutional requirements for grant submission. At the time of award activation, applicant must hold a faculty-staff position up to and including the rank of assistant professor (or equivalent). Applications may be submitted for review in the final year of a postdoctoral research fellowship or in the initial years of the first faculty/staff appointment. No more than four years can have elapsed since an applicant's first faculty/staff appointment (after receipt of doctoral degree) at the assistant professor level or its equivalent (including, but not limited to, research assistant professor, research scientist, staff scientist, etc.).

GEOGRAPHIC RESTRICTIONS:
United States.

FINANCIAL DATA:
Amount of support per award: National Clinical Research Program: Up to $50,000 per year for direct costs, plus $5,000 per year (10%) indirect costs, up to a maximum of $110,000 over two years. National Scientist Development Grant: Maximum $77,000 per year ($70,000 direct plus 10% indirect costs).

APPLICATION INFORMATION:
Guidelines and application form are available on the web site.
Duration: National Clinical Research Program: Two years. National Scientist Development Grant: Four years.
Deadline: July.

ADDRESS INQUIRIES TO:
See e-mail address above.

THE AMERICAN LEGION NATIONAL HEADQUARTERS
P.O. Box 1055
Indianapolis, IN 46206
(317) 630-1323
Fax: (317) 630-1369

E-MAIL ADDRESS:
acy@legion.org

WEB SITE ADDRESS:
www.legion.org

TYPE:
Scholarships. Scholarship grants for registered nurses.

See entry 2643 for full listing.

AMERICAN LUNG ASSOCIATION [2540]
14 Wall Street
New York, NY 10005
(212) 315-8700
Fax: (212) 315-8874

WEB SITE ADDRESS:
www.lungusa.org

FOUNDED: 1904

AREAS OF INTEREST:
Research and education for the prevention and control of lung disease.

NAME(S) OF PROGRAMS:
● **Dalsemer Research Grant**

TYPE:
Research grants.

PURPOSE:
To support research in interstitial lung disease.

LEGAL BASIS:
Nonprofit.

ELIGIBILITY:
At the time of application, applicant must: (1) hold a doctoral degree and be assured of a faculty appointment or equivalent with demonstrated institutional commitment (salary support, research space) by the start

of the award;
(2) have completed two years of postdoctoral research training;
(3) be U.S. citizens or foreign nationals holding one of the following visa immigration statuses: permanent resident (Green Card), exchange visitor (J-1), temporary worker in a specialty occupation (H-1, H-1B), Canadian or Mexican citizen engaging in professional activities (TC or TN), or temporary worker with extraordinary abilities in the sciences (O-1). Non-citizens must submit a notarized copy of proof of visa immigration status and;
(4) be employed by a U.S. institution.

Grantee organizations must be recognized academic or other nonprofit research entities.

Medical residents, those presently enrolled in a degree program (e.g., graduate students), and established investigators are not eligible to apply.

FINANCIAL DATA:
Amount of support per award: $40,000 per year.

NUMBER OF AWARDS: 1 to 2.

APPLICATION INFORMATION:
Duration: Up to two years.
Deadline: Varies.

PUBLICATIONS:
Program announcement.

AMERICAN LUNG ASSOCIATION [2541]
14 Wall Street
New York, NY 10005
(212) 315-8700
Fax: (212) 315-8874

E-MAIL ADDRESS:
nsaadi@lungusa.org

WEB SITE ADDRESS:
www.lungusa.org

FOUNDED: 1904

AREAS OF INTEREST:
Adult pulmonary medicine, lung biology, pediatric pulmonary medicine, and research and education for the prevention and control of lung disease.

NAME(S) OF PROGRAMS:
● **Senior Research Training Fellowships**

TYPE:
Fellowships.

YEAR PROGRAM STARTED: 1948

PURPOSE:
To prevent lung disease and promote lung health through research, education and advocacy.

LEGAL BASIS:
Nonprofit foundation.

ELIGIBILITY:
Applicants must be an M.D. or Ph.D. entering the fourth and fifth years of their research fellowship seeking further academic training as scientific investigators.

GEOGRAPHIC RESTRICTIONS:
United States.

FINANCIAL DATA:
Amount of support per award: $32,500 per year.

APPLICATION INFORMATION:
Contact the Association for details.
Duration: Up to two years.

Deadline: September.

PUBLICATIONS:
Program announcement.

AMERICAN LUNG ASSOCIATION [2542]
14 Wall Street
New York, NY 10005
(212) 315-8700
Fax: (212) 315-8874

E-MAIL ADDRESS:
nsaadi@lungusa.org

WEB SITE ADDRESS:
www.lungusa.org

FOUNDED: 1904

AREAS OF INTEREST:
Research and education for the prevention and control of lung disease.

NAME(S) OF PROGRAMS:
● **Biomedical Research Grants**

TYPE:
Research grants.

YEAR PROGRAM STARTED: 1921

PURPOSE:
To prevent lung disease and promote lung health through research, education and advocacy.

LEGAL BASIS:
Nonprofit foundation.

ELIGIBILITY:
Intended for investigators researching the mechanisms of lung disease and general lung biology.

FINANCIAL DATA:
Amount of support per award: $40,000 per year.

APPLICATION INFORMATION:
Contact the Association for details.
Duration: Up to two years.
Deadline: September.

PUBLICATIONS:
Program announcement.

AMERICAN LUNG ASSOCIATION [2543]
14 Wall Street
New York, NY 10005
(212) 315-8700
Fax: (212) 608-3219

E-MAIL ADDRESS:
nsaadi@lungusa.org

WEB SITE ADDRESS:
www.lungusa.org/research

FOUNDED: 1904

AREAS OF INTEREST:
Research and education for the prevention and control of lung disease.

NAME(S) OF PROGRAMS:
● **Lung Health Dissertation Grant**

TYPE:
Research grants.

LEGAL BASIS:
Nonprofit organization.

ELIGIBILITY:
Grant is intended for predoctoral support for students with an academic career focus and/or nurses pursuing a doctoral degree. Research areas of particular interest to the

Association include psychosocial, behavioral, health services, health policy, epidemiological, biostatistical and educational matters related to lung disease. Applicants must be matriculating in a full-time doctoral program. Individuals with an M.D. seeking a Ph.D. are not eligible.

Applicant must be a U.S. citizen or permanent resident or have a valid working visa. Research must be conducted in the U.S.

GEOGRAPHIC RESTRICTIONS:
United States.

FINANCIAL DATA:
Amount of support per award: Up to $21,000 ($16,000 stipend and $5,000 for research support).

NUMBER OF APPLICANTS MOST RECENT YEAR: 8 to 10 for the year 2010.

NUMBER OF AWARDS: 1.

APPLICATION INFORMATION:
Duration: Up to two years.

AMERICAN SOCIETY OF ECHOCARDIOGRAPHY [2544]
2100 Gateway Centre Boulevard
Suite 310
Morrisville, NC 27560
(919) 861-5574
Fax: (919) 882-9900

E-MAIL ADDRESS:
avanhoever@asecho.org

WEB SITE ADDRESS:
www.asecho.org

FOUNDED: 1975

AREAS OF INTEREST:
Cardiovascular diseases, cardiovascular ultrasound and echocardiography.

NAME(S) OF PROGRAMS:
● **Career Development Awards**
● **Echo Investigator Awards**

TYPE:
Research grants.

PURPOSE:
To support worthy research activities related to echocardiography.

ELIGIBILITY:
The applicant must hold the professional degree of M.D., Ph.D. or equivalent. Eligibility requirements and funding data for available awards can be found at the web site listed above.

FINANCIAL DATA:
Amount of support per award: Varies.

APPLICATION INFORMATION:
Application available from the Foundation.
Duration: One year. Renewal possible.

ADDRESS INQUIRIES TO:
Andrea Van Hoever
Vice President of Research
(See address above.)

AMERICAN SOCIETY OF ECHOCARDIOGRAPHY [2545]
2100 Gateway Centre Boulevard
Suite 310
Morrisville, NC 27560
(919) 861-5574
Fax: (919) 882-9900

E-MAIL ADDRESS:
avanhoever@asecho.org

WEB SITE ADDRESS:
www.asecho.org

FOUNDED: 1975

AREAS OF INTEREST:
Echocardiography, cardiovascular ultrasound and cardiovascular diseases.

NAME(S) OF PROGRAMS:
● **Cardiovascular Sonographer Research Award**

TYPE:
Research grants.

PURPOSE:
To support the growth and development of sonographer research.

ELIGIBILITY:
The applicant must be a sonographer holding echocardiography certification from ARDMS or CCI. Applicants are to identify a physician or scientist sponsor, and a supporting letter from their sponsor will be required defining the respective roles of applicant and sponsor in their proposed project. Applicants and their sponsors must be members of ASE. The award recipient and sponsor must hold a full-time position at the institution where the research is conducted and will have scientific responsibility for the conduct of the proposed research.

FINANCIAL DATA:
Amount of support per award: Varies.
Total amount of support: Varies.

APPLICATION INFORMATION:
Application available from the Foundation.
Duration: One year. Renewal possible on a case-by-case basis.
Deadline: Varies.

ADDRESS INQUIRIES TO:
Andrea Van Hoever
Vice President of Research
(See address above.)

AMERICAN SOCIETY OF NUCLEAR CARDIOLOGY [2546]
4340 East-West Highway
Suite 1120
Bethesda, MD 20814-4578
(301) 215-7575
Fax: (301) 215-7113

E-MAIL ADDRESS:
info@asnc.org

WEB SITE ADDRESS:
www.asnc.org

AREAS OF INTEREST:
Nuclear cardiology.

NAME(S) OF PROGRAMS:
● **American Society of Nuclear Cardiology Foundation Research Awards**

TYPE:
Research grants. Nuclear cardiology awards from any of the following areas: Basic or Applied Scientific Research, Cardiac PET and/or PET/CT Research, Cardiovascular Computed Tomography (CVCT) Research, Clinical Applications or Clinical Research, and Molecular Imaging Research.

PURPOSE:
To support basic and applied scientific research in nuclear cardiology in order to promote advances in the field and to promote nuclear cardiology as a career path for scientists.

ELIGIBILITY:
The applicant must, at the time of the award, be a candidate for a Ph.D. or equivalent degree, hold a Ph.D. or Ph.D. equivalent, or hold an M.D. or equivalent degree with a demonstrated track record in scientific research, or be within three years of having completed such degrees. If in a postdoctoral training program, the applicant must have an agreement with the director of the program to conduct the project. Priority will be given to applicants who have made a commitment to pursue scientific careers and to those with no other major external salary support.

FINANCIAL DATA:
Amount of support per award: $30,000.

COOPERATIVE FUNDING PROGRAMS: Astellas Pharma US, Inc.; Covidien; GE Healthcare (Medical Diagnostics).

NUMBER OF AWARDS: 3.

APPLICATION INFORMATION:
Contact the Organization for application procedures.
Duration: One-time award.
Deadline: Varies.

THE CANADIAN LUNG ASSOCIATION (CLA) [2547]
1750 Courtwood Crescent
Suite 300
Ottawa ON K2C 2B5 Canada
(613) 569-6411 ext. 262
Fax: (613) 569-8860

E-MAIL ADDRESS:
research@lung.ca

WEB SITE ADDRESS:
www.lung.ca

FOUNDED: 1958

AREAS OF INTEREST:
Prevention and control of lung disease including asthma, emphysema, chronic bronchitis, tuberculosis and lung cancer; air pollution and smoking.

NAME(S) OF PROGRAMS:
● **Canadian Thoracic Society Fellowship**
● **Canadian Thoracic Society Studentship**

TYPE:
Fellowships. The Society offers a number of fellowships and studentships to support research training in pulmonary disease.

YEAR PROGRAM STARTED: 1959

PURPOSE:
To permit physicians and those holding Doctorate degrees in the health sciences to be funded for a period of research training so they may contribute to Canadian work in the area of respiratory disease.

LEGAL BASIS:
Not-for-profit, incorporated.

ELIGIBILITY:
A candidate/applicant must hold, or be completing, a Ph.D. or a health professional degree (or equivalent). The health professional degree must be in a field such as medicine, dentistry, pharmacy, optometry, veterinary medicine, chiropractic, nursing or rehabilitative science. For individuals that do not hold a health professional degree, awards will take effect only after the recipient has completed all requirements of the Ph.D. program, including the oral examination.

These awards are normally held at Canadian institutions. Canadian citizens and permanent residents may apply for awards to be held outside Canada. Candidates who are neither Canadian citizens nor permanent residents may apply only for awards to be held in Canada.

FINANCIAL DATA:
Amount of support per award: Fellowships: $45,000 to $55,000 (CAN) per year; Studentships: $21,000 (CAN) per year.

Total amount of support: Varies.

COOPERATIVE FUNDING PROGRAMS: Partnerships include CIHR and the pharmaceutical industry (peer review only).

NUMBER OF APPLICANTS MOST RECENT YEAR: 33 for the year 2011.

NUMBER OF AWARDS: Approximately 6 each year.

APPLICATION INFORMATION:
Duration: One to two years. Competitive renewal.

Deadline: January 15.

PUBLICATIONS:
Canadian Respiratory Journal.

ADDRESS INQUIRIES TO:
The Canadian Thoracic Society
c/o Michelle McEvoy, Manager of Research
(See address above.)

THE CANADIAN LUNG ASSOCIATION (CLA)
1750 Courtwood Crescent
Suite 300
Ottawa ON K2C 2B5 Canada
(613) 569-6411
Fax: (613) 569-8860

E-MAIL ADDRESS:
info@lung.ca
research@lung.ca

WEB SITE ADDRESS:
www.lung.ca

TYPE:
Fellowships; Research grants. Fellowships are offered to registered nurses pursuing postgraduate education with a major component of the program involving respiratory nursing practice, physiotherapists pursuing postgraduate training with respiratory research as the major component, and respiratory therapists pursuing postgraduate education with a major component of the program involving respiratory therapy practice.

Grants for research and feasibility studies are offered to registered nurses undertaking research investigations related to nursing management of patients with respiratory disease and symptoms. Grants are also offered to physiotherapists undertaking investigations related to management of patients with respiratory disease. Respiratory therapists undertaking research investigations related to the management of patients with respiratory disease and symptoms may also qualify.

See entry 2646 for full listing.

THE CHEST FOUNDATION [2548]
3300 Dundee Road
Northbrook, IL 60062-2348
(847) 498-8308
Fax: (847) 498-5460

E-MAIL ADDRESS:
mlederer@chestnet.org

WEB SITE ADDRESS:
www.chestfoundation.org

FOUNDED: 1935

AREAS OF INTEREST:
All aspects of chest medicine and surgery.

NAME(S) OF PROGRAMS:
- **ACCP Young Investigator Award**
- **ACCP/Alfred Soffer Research Award**
- **Alpha-1 Foundation/CHEST Foundation Clinical Research Award in Alpha-1 Antitrypsin (AAT) Deficiency**
- **The American Society of Transplantation/CHEST Foundation Clinical Research Award in Lung Transplantation**
- **The Association of Specialty Professors/CHEST Foundation Geriatric Development Research Award**
- **The Roger C. Bone Advances in End-of-Life Care Award**
- **The CHEST Foundation Clinical Research Award in Women's Health**
- **The CHEST Foundation/LUNGevity Foundation Clinical Research Award in Lung Cancer**
- **Clinical Research Trainee Awards**
- **Humanitarian Project Development Grants**
- **Humanitarian Recognition Awards**

TYPE:
Awards/prizes; Development grants. Awards for abstracts on all aspects of chest medicine and surgery (circulation, respiration, thoracic-cardiovascular surgery, critical care and related disciplines) presented at the Annual Scientific Assembly held usually in late October each year.

ACCP Young Investigator Awards are given to investigators who are in residency or fellowship programs or who have completed their fellowship program within the last five years and whose abstracts are judged to describe outstanding original scientific research.

ACCP/Alfred Soffer Research Awards are given for the two papers judged best in scientific quality.

Clinical Research Trainee Awards are granted to six physicians enrolled in a subspecialty training program with the best proposal for a clinical research project.

Humanitarian Project Development Grants and Humanitarian Recognition Awards are granted to ACCP members who have demonstrated professional dedication to the community.

YEAR PROGRAM STARTED: 1996

PURPOSE:
To provide resources to advance the prevention and treatment of diseases of the chest: asthma, tuberculosis, end-of-life issues, smoking prevention and chronic obstructive pulmonary disease.

LEGAL BASIS:
Supporting organization.

ELIGIBILITY:
Investigators from outside the U.S. are welcome, provided abstracts and presentations are in English. Abstracts must be original and should not have been presented nationally or published elsewhere in manuscript form prior to the Annual Scientific Assembly.

The ACCP/Alfred Soffer Research Award is open to M.D. and non-M.D. investigators at all academic levels and to investigators in both basic and clinical research.

The ACCP Young Investigator Award is open to investigators who are in residency or fellowship programs or who have completed their fellowship programs within the last five years. Co-authors are permitted, but the presenting young investigator must be the primary contributor. An abstract in any area of chest medicine and surgery is eligible.

Clinical Research Awards are open to U.S. and Canadian ACCP members.

FINANCIAL DATA:
Amount of support per award: ACCP/Alfred Soffer Research Award: $1,000 each; ACCP Young Investigator Award: $1,000 each to defray travel costs; Clinical Research Trainee Awards: $10,000 each; Clinical Research Awards in partnership with other foundations and associations: $20,000 to $50,000 for one year.

Total amount of support: $500,000.

COOPERATIVE FUNDING PROGRAMS: Alpha-1 Foundation, The American Society of Transplantation, The Association of Specialty Professors, LUNGevity Foundation.

NUMBER OF APPLICANTS MOST RECENT YEAR: Abstracts: Over 400; Clinical Research: Over 50.

NUMBER OF AWARDS: ACCP/Alfred Soffer Research Award: 2; ACCP Young Investigator Award: 20; Clinical Research Trainee Awards: 6; Humanitarian Project Development Grants: 2; Humanitarian Recognition Awards: 5 to 10; All other awards in partnership with other foundations and associations: 1 each.

APPLICATION INFORMATION:
The winning abstracts are selected from those submitted to the College for the Annual International Scientific Assembly. Abstract submission forms are available from the Foundation. All abstracts submitted are automatically considered for the ACCP/Alfred Soffer Research Awards, but applicants must indicate if they would like to have their abstracts considered for one of the other awards.

Duration: One-time award.

Deadline: April 30.

PUBLICATIONS:
Call for Abstracts, brochure. Also in *Ads in CHEST,* monthly publication of The American College of Chest Physicians (ACCP).

IRS IDENTIFICATION NUMBER: 36-3286520

ADDRESS INQUIRIES TO:
Lee Ann Fulton, Project Manager
(See address above.)

*SPECIAL STIPULATIONS:
Award recipients are expected to attend the Annual International Scientific Assembly of the ACCP, which usually occurs at the end of October.

GREENBURG-MAY FOUNDATION
P.O. Box 5816
Miami Beach, FL 33154
(305) 864-8639

TYPE:
Development grants; Research grants. Social services.

See entry 2595 for full listing.

HEART AND STROKE FOUNDATION OF CANADA [2549]

222 Queen Street
Suite 1402
Ottawa ON K1P 5V9 Canada
(613) 569-4361
Fax: (613) 569-3278

E-MAIL ADDRESS:
research@hsf.ca

WEB SITE ADDRESS:
www.hsf.ca/research

FOUNDED: 1956

AREAS OF INTEREST:
Cardiovascular/cerebrovascular research.

NAME(S) OF PROGRAMS:
● **Grant-in-Aid**

TYPE:
Grants-in-aid. Grants to support projects of an experimental nature in cardiovascular/cerebrovascular research or development.

YEAR PROGRAM STARTED: 1958

PURPOSE:
To reduce the morbidity and mortality from cardiovascular/cerebrovascular disease in Canada.

LEGAL BASIS:
Nonprofit.

ELIGIBILITY:
Qualified investigators affiliated with appropriate institutions are eligible.

GEOGRAPHIC RESTRICTIONS:
Canada.

FINANCIAL DATA:
Amount of support per award: Varies, depending upon the needs and nature of the request and by provincial foundation.

APPLICATION INFORMATION:
Current guidelines and official application materials may be obtained online.
Duration: One to three years.
Deadline: Applications should be received in their complete form by September 1 for awards normally becoming effective on July 1 of the following year.

ADDRESS INQUIRIES TO:
Research Department
(See e-mail address above.)

HEART AND STROKE FOUNDATION OF CANADA [2550]

222 Queen Street
Suite 1402
Ottawa ON K1P 5V9 Canada
(613) 569-4361
Fax: (613) 569-3278

E-MAIL ADDRESS:
research@hsf.ca

WEB SITE ADDRESS:
www.hsf.ca/research

FOUNDED: 1956

AREAS OF INTEREST:
Cardiovascular and cerebrovascular research.

NAME(S) OF PROGRAMS:
● **New Investigator**

TYPE:
Awards/prizes; Scholarships. The New Investigator is the senior award offered by the Foundation.

YEAR PROGRAM STARTED: 1958

PURPOSE:
To reduce the morbidity and mortality from cardiovascular disease in Canada.

LEGAL BASIS:
Nonprofit.

ELIGIBILITY:
Individuals who have clearly demonstrated excellence during their predoctoral and postdoctoral training in cardiovascular or cerebrovascular research are eligible.

GEOGRAPHIC RESTRICTIONS:
Canada.

FINANCIAL DATA:
Amount of support per award: $60,000 (CAN) including employer's portion of fringe benefits.

APPLICATION INFORMATION:
Official application materials may be obtained from the web site.
Duration: Varies.
Deadline: September 1, to become tenable July 1 of the following year.

ADDRESS INQUIRIES TO:
Research Department
(See e-mail address above.)

HEART AND STROKE FOUNDATION OF CANADA [2551]

222 Queen Street
Suite 1402
Ottawa ON K1P 5V9 Canada
(613) 569-4361
Fax: (613) 569-3278

E-MAIL ADDRESS:
research@hsf.ca

WEB SITE ADDRESS:
www.hsf.ca/research

FOUNDED: 1956

AREAS OF INTEREST:
Cardiovascular and cerebrovascular research.

NAME(S) OF PROGRAMS:
● **Research Fellowship**

TYPE:
Fellowships.

YEAR PROGRAM STARTED: 1958

PURPOSE:
To attract and foster the young investigator to initiate and/or continue training and competence in scientific method in a chosen area of the cardiovascular and cerebrovascular fields.

LEGAL BASIS:
Nonprofit organization.

ELIGIBILITY:
Intended for applicants with a Ph.D. or M.D. degree with expertise in the behavioral sciences, epidemiology or related disciplines.

GEOGRAPHIC RESTRICTIONS:
Canada.

FINANCIAL DATA:
Amount of support per award: Up to $50,000 (CAN) per year.

APPLICATION INFORMATION:
Official application materials may be obtained from the web site.
Duration: Two to three years.
Deadline: November 1 for fellowships normally becoming tenable on July 1 of the following year.

ADDRESS INQUIRIES TO:
Research Department
(See e-mail address above.)

*PLEASE NOTE:
Applicants for research fellowship awards should note that if two unsuccessful applications for personnel support have been made, a subsequent application will be considered only if there has been a change in supervisor and/or institution.

HEART RHYTHM SOCIETY [2552]

1400 K Street, N.W., Suite 500
Washington, DC 20005
(202) 464-3400
Fax: (202) 464-3401

E-MAIL ADDRESS:
info@hrsonline.org

WEB SITE ADDRESS:
www.hrsonline.org

FOUNDED: 1979

AREAS OF INTEREST:
Fostering educational and scientific activities in the fields of cardiac pacing and electrophysiology through annual scientific sessions, regional educational courses, policy conferences, annual symposia and continuing education courses.

CONSULTING OR VOLUNTEER SERVICES:
Sponsors policy conferences.

NAME(S) OF PROGRAMS:
● **Michael Bilitch Fellowship in Cardiac Pacing and Electrophysiology**
● **Clinical Research Award in Honor of Mark Josephson and Hein Wellens**
● **Heart Rhythm Society Fellowship in Cardiac Pacing and Electrophysiology**
● **Michel Mirowski International Fellowship in Cardiac Pacing and Electrophysiology**
● **Kenneth M. Rosen Fellowship in Cardiac Pacing and Electrophysiology**
● **Max Schaldach Fellowship in Cardiac Pacing and Electrophysiology**
● **Young Investigator Awards**

TYPE:
Awards/prizes; Block grants; Fellowships; Project/program grants; Research grants; Travel grants. Awards for additional training in the fields of cardiac pacing and cardiac electrophysiology.

YEAR PROGRAM STARTED: 1982

PURPOSE:
To promote and advance the educational process of its membership and interested non-members.

LEGAL BASIS:
Tax-exempt, nonprofit educational organization.

ELIGIBILITY:
Applicants must be citizens of a country in North America, except for international fellowship.

GEOGRAPHIC RESTRICTIONS:
North America.

FINANCIAL DATA:
Amount of support per award: Bilitch, Mirowski, Rosen and NASPE Fellowships: $50,000; Young Investigator Awards: $1,000 for the two first-prize awards and four $500 honorable mention awards.

NUMBER OF AWARDS: 9.

APPLICATION INFORMATION:
Duration: One year. Renewable once in competition with other applicants.
Deadline: Young Investigator: December 9 with announcement in February. All other programs: August with announcement in January.

PUBLICATIONS:
Annual report.

IRS IDENTIFICATION NUMBER: 04-2694458

ADDRESS INQUIRIES TO:
Manager of Professional and Patient Education
(See address above.)

NATIONAL BLOOD FOUNDATION [2553]

8101 Glenbrook Road
Bethesda, MD 20814-2749
(301) 907-6977
Fax: (301) 907-6895

E-MAIL ADDRESS:
nbf@aabb.org

WEB SITE ADDRESS:
www.aabb.org/nbf

FOUNDED: 1983

AREAS OF INTEREST:
Blood banking, blood safety, transfusion medicine, tissue transplantation and cellular therapy.

NAME(S) OF PROGRAMS:
• **Scientific Research Grants Program**

TYPE:
Awards/prizes; Development grants; Seed money grants. Basic medical research grants.

The focus of the NBF's Scientific Research Grants Program is to support early career researchers in the field of transfusion medicine, to include aspects of immunology, hematology, tissue and transplantation medicine, cellular therapies, emerging infectious disease, immunohematology, donor health and recruitment and retention, and implementation of technological advances. Priority is given to young investigators and innovative new projects with the potential to have a practical impact on patients and donors in transfusion medicine.

YEAR PROGRAM STARTED: 1985

PURPOSE:
To actively support the leadership role of the AABB in establishing and promoting the highest standards of care for patients and donors by funding basic and applied scientific research, administrative research/projects, professional education in all aspects of blood banking, transfusion medicine and tissue transplantation.

LEGAL BASIS:
Nonprofit association.

ELIGIBILITY:
Each applicant/researcher must be a doctor (M.D. or Ph.D.) or transfusion medicine

professional. Priority will be given to innovative, new projects. Funding will not be given to any one investigator more than two times. Awards will not be made to increase the funding available for currently funded research projects.

FINANCIAL DATA:
Grant awards may not cover indirect costs. Equipment expenditures cannot exceed $8,000 per grant.
Amount of support per award: Up to $75,000.

NUMBER OF AWARDS: Varies.

APPLICATION INFORMATION:
Required application forms are available from the Foundation at the address above. Electronic submission required as Word document or pdf, size restrictions. Application fee of $150 if applicant is not an AABB individual member.
Duration: One to two years.
Deadline: December 30. Announcement in June for funds to be distributed in July.

PUBLICATIONS:
Application; program announcement.

IRS IDENTIFICATION NUMBER: 36-2384118

ADDRESS INQUIRIES TO:
Jeanne P. Luschin, MBA, Director
(See address above.)

NATIONAL HEART, LUNG AND BLOOD INSTITUTE (NHLBI) [2554]

National Institutes of Health
Grants Operations Branch, Room 7160
6701 Rockledge Drive, MSC-7926
Bethesda, MD 20892-7926
(301) 435-0144
Fax: (301) 480-3310

E-MAIL ADDRESS:
whitesa@nhlbi.nih.gov

WEB SITE ADDRESS:
www.nhlbi.nih.gov/funding/index.htm
www.grants.nhlbi.nih.gov

FOUNDED: 1948

AREAS OF INTEREST:
Diseases of the heart, blood vessels, lung and blood, sleep disorders, clinical use of blood and blood resources, and transfusion medicine.

TYPE:
Conferences/seminars; Fellowships; Project/program grants; Research grants; Training grants; Loan forgiveness programs. Career awards and other grant mechanisms to foster research on heart, vascular and lung diseases, and to develop scientists in these areas. Also, small business grants. Loan forgiveness programs are for research.

YEAR PROGRAM STARTED: 1948

PURPOSE:
To support research into the causes, improved diagnosis, treatment and prevention of cardiovascular diseases in arteriosclerosis, hypertension, cardiovascular disease, coronary heart disease, peripheral vascular disease, arrhythmias, heart failure and shock, congenital and rheumatic heart disease, cardiomyopathies and infections of the heart, circulatory assistance and AIDS.

LEGAL BASIS:
Public Health Service Act, Sections 301(c), 412 and 472.

ELIGIBILITY:
Any nonprofit or for-profit organization engaged in biomedical research may apply. An individual may apply for a fellowship award. Some restrictions may apply to foreign grantee institutions.

FINANCIAL DATA:
Amount of support per award: Varies by type of award.

APPLICATION INFORMATION:
Duration: Varies.
Deadline: Varies.

PUBLICATIONS:
NHLBI Fact Book; Annual Report of Director, NHLBI.

OFFICER:
Suzanne White, Chief Grants Management Officer

ADDRESS INQUIRIES TO:
Suzanne White
Chief Grants Management Officer
(See address above.)

NATIONAL HEART, LUNG AND BLOOD INSTITUTE (NHLBI) [2555]

Two Rockledge Centre, Suite 10042
6701 Rockledge Drive, MSC 7952
Bethesda, MD 20892-7952
(301) 435-0233
Fax: (301) 480-3547

E-MAIL ADDRESS:
kileyj@nhlbi.nih.gov

WEB SITE ADDRESS:
www.nhlbi.nih.gov

FOUNDED: 1948

AREAS OF INTEREST:
Pulmonary research, prevention, education and training programs in pulmonary diseases.

NAME(S) OF PROGRAMS:
• **Lung Diseases Research**

TYPE:
Project/program grants. Cooperative agreements.

YEAR PROGRAM STARTED: 1970

PURPOSE:
To use available knowledge and technology to solve specific disease problems of the lungs; to promote further studies on the structure and function of the lung; to achieve improvement in the prevention and treatment of lung diseases.

LEGAL BASIS:
Public Health Service Act, Section 301, 422 and 487, as amended, Public Laws 78-410 and 99-158, 42 U.S.C. 241, 42 U.S.C. 285, and 42 U.S.C. 288, as amended.

ELIGIBILITY:
Any nonprofit or for-profit organization engaged in biomedical research may apply for grants with the exception of NRSAs. An individual may apply for an NRSA or, in some cases, may qualify for a research grant if adequate facilities in which to perform the research are available.

Some grants are available to U.S. citizens or institutions only.

FINANCIAL DATA:
Grants may support salaries, equipment, supplies, travel, and patient hospitalization as required to perform the research effort.

Amount of support per award: $74,704 to $3,847,725; average $464,939.

Total amount of support: Estimated $600,000,000 for fiscal year 2010.

NUMBER OF AWARDS: Estimated 1,140 research grants and 100 National Research Service Awards for fiscal year 2010.

APPLICATION INFORMATION:
Research grant applications are submitted on designated forms to the Center for Scientific Review, National Institutes of Health, Bethesda, MD 20892. Forms for individual NRSA applications may be obtained from and submitted to the Office of Research Manpower, Center for Scientific Review, National Institutes of Health, Bethesda, MD 20892. For some special grant programs, applicants may be advised to submit directly to the Review Branch, Division of Extramural Affairs, National Heart, Lung, and Blood Institute, Bethesda, MD 20892. The standard application forms, as furnished by PHS and required by 45 CFR, Part 92, must be used for this program.

Duration: One to five years. Renewable.

Deadline: February 1, June 1 and October 1 (or as specified in RFA announcements).

PUBLICATIONS:
Annual Program Report.

STAFF:
Dr. James P. Kiley, Director, Division of Lung Diseases

ADDRESS INQUIRIES TO:
Dr. James P. Kiley, Director
Division of Lung Diseases
(See address above.)

THE POTTS MEMORIAL FOUNDATION [2556]

97 Patroon Street
Claverack, NY 12513
(518) 851-2292

FOUNDED: 1922

AREAS OF INTEREST:
Tuberculosis.

TYPE:
Fellowships; Grants-in-aid; Research grants; Seed money grants. At present, the program allows the Foundation to provide for the care, treatment and rehabilitation of persons afflicted with tuberculosis by methods selected by the trustees. This may include maintenance, operation of hospitals, research, vocational counseling and guidance, scholarships, subsidies for education and training, job placement, grants to hospitals and charitable institutions and the operation of sheltered workshops.

YEAR PROGRAM STARTED: 1922

PURPOSE:
To help people who are battling tuberculosis.

LEGAL BASIS:
Nonprofit corporation.

FINANCIAL DATA:
Amount of support per award: $1,000 to $30,000.

NUMBER OF APPLICANTS MOST RECENT YEAR:
Under 50.

NUMBER OF AWARDS: 10 or less.

APPLICATION INFORMATION:
A letter of request should be furnished in as much detail as possible, including a detailed budget, to the Foundation.

Duration: One year.

Deadline: 30 days prior to May 15 and October 15.

OFFICERS:
Brian Daggett, M.D., President
Kathleen A. McDonough, Ph.D., Vice President
Sidney D. Richter, Treasurer
Donna D. Klose, Secretary

TRUSTEES:
John Chan, M.D.
Joseph J. Fusco, M.D.
Richard Gullot, M.D.
Donna O'Hare, M.D.

ADDRESS INQUIRIES TO:
Donna D. Klose, Secretary
P.O. Box 1015
Hudson, NY 12534

THE SARNOFF CARDIOVASCULAR RESEARCH FOUNDATION [2557]

731 Walker Road
Suite G2
Great Falls, VA 22066
(703) 759-7600
(888) 472-7663
Fax: (703) 759-7838

E-MAIL ADDRESS:
dboyd@sarnofffoundation.org

WEB SITE ADDRESS:
www.sarnofffoundation.org

FOUNDED: 1981

AREAS OF INTEREST:
Cardiovascular research.

NAME(S) OF PROGRAMS:
- **Sarnoff Fellowship Program**
- **Sarnoff Scholar Fellow-to-Faculty Transition Award**

TYPE:
Awards/prizes; Fellowships. Research Fellowship and Award.

PURPOSE:
To give medical students the opportunity to spend a year conducting intensive work in a biomedical research laboratory; to provide financial support to former Sarnoff Fellows committed to pursuing a career in cardiovascular research.

ELIGIBILITY:
Sarnoff Fellowship Program is for medical students enrolled in any accredited medical school in the U.S. who have completed their second or third year of medical school. Applicants enrolled in an M.D./Ph.D. program are ineligible.

Sarnoff Scholar Fellow-to-Faculty Transition Award applicant must be a former Sarnoff Fellow pursuing a career in cardiovascular research. Applicants may apply during the second half of their post-residency training/fellowship program and/or overlapping with the first two junior faculty years.

GEOGRAPHIC RESTRICTIONS:
United States.

FINANCIAL DATA:
Amount of support per award: Fellowship: $28,500 stipend and $7,000 allowance for travel and moving expenses, health insurance and computer equipment; Scholar: $50,000 in direct costs per year for salary support,

$10,000 per year research supply budget and maximum of 10% indirect costs paid to the institution for handling the award.

NUMBER OF AWARDS: Fellowship: Up to 18 annually; Scholar: 1 annually.

APPLICATION INFORMATION:
Applicants to the Fellowship Program must submit the following:
(1) one-page personal statement describing scholarly interests and career plans;
(2) three-page essay on the applicant's cardiovascular topic of interest;
(3) completed application form and signed statement of confidentiality;
(4) official medical school transcript;
(5) curriculum vitae;
(6) recommendation from the applicant's sponsor;
(7) two additional recommendations and;
(8) any other material that the applicant determines is appropriate to support the application.

Duration: Fellowship: One year; Scholar: Two years.

Deadline: Fellowship: January 7, 2012.

ADDRESS INQUIRIES TO:
Dana Boyd, Executive Director
(See address above.)

THE SOCIETY FOR CARDIOVASCULAR ANGIOGRAPHY AND INTERVENTIONS [2558]

2400 N Street, N.W.
Suite 500
Washington, DC 20037-1153
(202) 741-9854
(800) 992-7224
Fax: (800) 863-5202

E-MAIL ADDRESS:
info@scai.org
rortega@scai.org

WEB SITE ADDRESS:
www.scai.org

FOUNDED: 1976

NAME(S) OF PROGRAMS:
- **SCAI/Cordis Fellowship Program for Interventional Cardiology**

TYPE:
Fellowships.

YEAR PROGRAM STARTED: 2005

PURPOSE:
To encourage meaningful investigation into invasive/interventional techniques; to foster new insights into patient care.

LEGAL BASIS:
Nonprofit medical specialty society.

ELIGIBILITY:
SCAI/Cordis: Applicants should be serving in an accredited invasive/interventional cardiology fellowship training program.

GEOGRAPHIC RESTRICTIONS:
United States and Canada.

FINANCIAL DATA:
Amount of support per award: $30,000.

NUMBER OF APPLICANTS MOST RECENT YEAR:
25.

NUMBER OF AWARDS: 2.

APPLICATION INFORMATION:
Detailed instructions and application form can be found on the Society web site.

Duration: One year.

PUBLICATIONS:
Application guidelines.

ADDRESS INQUIRIES TO:
Rebecca Ortega
Director of Program Development
Tel: (202) 741-9872

SOCIETY OF CARDIOVASCULAR ANESTHESIOLOGISTS   [2559]
2209 Dickens Road
Richmond, VA 23230
(804) 282-0084
Fax: (804) 282-0090

E-MAIL ADDRESS:
sca@societyhq.com

WEB SITE ADDRESS:
www.scahq.org

AREAS OF INTEREST:
Cardiothoracic and vascular anesthesia.

NAME(S) OF PROGRAMS:
- **Roizen & Anesthesia Research Foundation New Investigator Grant**
- **SCA Starter Grants**
- **SCA-IARS Mid-Career Grant**

TYPE:
Research grants.

PURPOSE:
To promote excellence in patient care
through education and research in
perioperative care for patients undergoing
cardiothoracic and vascular procedures.

ELIGIBILITY:
Grant applicants must be a member of
Society of Cardiovascular Anesthesiologists
and hold an M.D. or Ph.D. degree.

No part of the grant may be used for salary
support of the principal investigator (or
fellows or residents), travel or tuition
expenses of the principal investigator, patient
costs (except to pay for pertinent laboratory
studies), consultant costs, alterations or
renovations.

FINANCIAL DATA:
Amount of support per award: $25,000 to
$50,000 per year.

Total amount of support: Up to $100,000 per
recipient, depending on which grant is
applied for.

NUMBER OF APPLICANTS MOST RECENT YEAR:
17.

NUMBER OF AWARDS: Maximum of 5 each year.

APPLICATION INFORMATION:
Duration: Up to two years.
Deadline: March 3.

IRS IDENTIFICATION NUMBER: 72-0863580

ADDRESS INQUIRIES TO:
Heather Spiess, Executive Director
(See address above.)

Metabolism, gastroenterology, nephrology

AMERICAN DIABETES ASSOCIATION, INC.   [2560]
1701 North Beauregard Street
Alexandria, VA 22311
(703) 549-1500 ext. 2362
Fax: (703) 549-1715

E-MAIL ADDRESS:
grantquestions@diabetes.org

WEB SITE ADDRESS:
www.diabetes.org/research

FOUNDED: 1940

AREAS OF INTEREST:
Programs serving the needs of people with
diabetes, their families, researchers, clinicians
and the diabetic health care team.

CONSULTING OR VOLUNTEER SERVICES:
Various support and education programs
carried out at affiliate level. Research
program on national level.

NAME(S) OF PROGRAMS:
- **ADA-ASP Young Investigator Innovation Award in Geriatric Endocrinology**
- **ADA-TPNA Beta Cell Postdoctoral Fellowship**
- **ADA-TPNA Cardiovascular Complications in Diabetes Postdoctoral Fellowship**
- **Henry Becton Innovation Award**
- **Career Development Award**
- **Clinical Research Award**
- **Clinical Scholars Award**
- **Clinical Scientist Training Award**
- **Distinguished Clinical Scientist Award**
- **Innovation Award**
- **Junior Faculty Award**
- **Mentor-Based Minority Postdoctoral Fellowship**
- **Mentor-Based Postdoctoral Fellowship Program**
- **Research Award**

TYPE:
Fellowships; Research grants; Training
grants.

YEAR PROGRAM STARTED: 1955

PURPOSE:
To aid in the search for a cure and prevention
of diabetes; to help those with diabetes
complications.

LEGAL BASIS:
Nonprofit voluntary health organization.

ELIGIBILITY:
Applicants for all awards except the Clinical
Scholars and Clinical Scientist Training
Awards must have M.D., Ph.D., Pharm.D.,
D.P.M. or D.O. degrees or appropriate health
or science-related degrees, and must hold
full-time or clinical faculty positions or the
equivalent at university-affiliated institutions
within the U.S. or its possessions. For all
programs, applicants must be U.S. citizens or
permanent residents. For Career Development
Award, applicants must have an assistant
professor-level faculty appointment. For the
Junior Faculty Award, applicants can have
any level of faculty appointment. For the
Mentor-Based Minority Postdoctoral
Fellowship, underrepresented minorities are
defined as those minorities who are

underrepresented in the area of biomedical
and behavioral research. These minority
groups include African Americans, Hispanics,
Pacific Islanders, American Indian and
Alaskan Natives.

GEOGRAPHIC RESTRICTIONS:
United States.

FINANCIAL DATA:
Amount of support per award: ADA-ASP
Young Investigator Innovation Award:
$75,000 per year; Career Development
Awards: Approximately $150,000 per year;
Clinical Research Grants and Distinguished
Clinical Scientist Award: $200,000 per year;
Junior Faculty Award: Up to $120,000 per
year, plus up to $10,000 per year towards
repayment of the principal on loans for a
doctoral degree (M.D. or Ph.D.);
Mentor-Based Minority Postdoctoral
Fellowship and both ADA-TPNA
Postdoctoral Fellowships: $45,000 per year;
Mentor-Based Postdoctoral Fellowships:
Approximately $45,000 per year; Research
Awards: Approximately $100,000 per year.

NUMBER OF APPLICANTS MOST RECENT YEAR:
900 for fiscal year 2009.

APPLICATION INFORMATION:
Applicants for all grants must submit
application forms, a nontechnical description
of the research project of less than 200 words
and a scientific abstract of the proposal of no
more than 200 words.

Duration: Career Development Awards: Five
years. Nonrenewable; Clinical Research
Grants and Junior Faculty Award: Three
years; Innovation Awards: Two years;
Mentor-Based Minority Postdoctoral
Fellowship: Two to three years;
Mentor-Based Postdoctoral Fellowships: Four
years; Research Awards: Up to three years.

Deadline: ADA-ASP Innovation Awards,
Career Development Awards, Clinical
Research Grants, Junior Faculty Award,
Innovation Awards, and Research Awards:
January 15 and July 15. Henry Becton
Innovation, Clinical Scientist Training,
Medical Scholars, Distinguished Clinical
Scientist, and all Postdoctoral Fellowship
Awards: January 15.

PUBLICATIONS:
Annual reports.

OFFICERS:
George J. Huntley, C.P.A., Chairman of the
Board
Sue McLaughlin, B.S., C.D.E., President,
Health Care and Education
R. Paul Robertson, M.D., President, Medicine
and Science

ADDRESS INQUIRIES TO:
Magda Galindo, Research Program Manager
(See address above.)

AMERICAN GASTROENTEROLOGICAL ASSOCIATION (AGA)   [2561]
4930 Del Ray Avenue
Bethesda, MD 20814
(301) 222-4012
Fax: (301) 652-3890

E-MAIL ADDRESS:
awards@fdhn.org

WEB SITE ADDRESS:
www.gastro.org/fdhnfunding

FOUNDED: 1990

AREAS OF INTEREST:
Gastroenterology and related fields.

NAME(S) OF PROGRAMS:
- **AGA R. Robert and Sally D. Funderburg Research Award in Gastric Cancer**

TYPE:
Research grants. Recognition award for an established investigator working on novel approaches in gastric cancer, including the fields of gastric mucosal cell biology, regeneration and regulation of cell growth (not as they relate to peptic ulcer disease or repair), inflammation as precancerous lesions, genetics of gastric carcinoma, oncogenes in gastric epithelial malignancies, epidemiology of gastric cancer, etiology of gastric epithelial malignancies or clinical research in diagnosis or treatment of gastric carcinoma.

YEAR PROGRAM STARTED: 1990

PURPOSE:
To support an established investigator in the field of gastric biology which enhances our fundamental understanding of gastric cancer pathobiology in order to develop a cure for the disease.

LEGAL BASIS:
Nonprofit foundation.

ELIGIBILITY:
Candidates must hold faculty positions at accredited North American institutions. Candidates may not hold other exclusively salary support awards on a similar topic from other agencies. In recognition of their underrepresentation in gastroenterology-related fields, women and minorities are strongly encouraged to apply. Applicant must also be a member of the AGA.

Awardees will be selected based on the novelty, feasibility and significance of the proposal, attributes of the candidate and the likelihood that support will lead the applicant toward a research career in the field of gastric cancer biology. Preference will be given to novel approaches.

GEOGRAPHIC RESTRICTIONS:
North America.

FINANCIAL DATA:
Funds are to be used for the salary, support, equipment and supplies of the investigator, to promote his or her involvement in the field. No indirect costs will be allowed.

Amount of support per award: $50,000 per year.

NUMBER OF APPLICANTS MOST RECENT YEAR: 4 for the year 2009.

NUMBER OF AWARDS: 1.

APPLICATION INFORMATION:
Application forms can be obtained by writing to the National Office.

Duration: Two years.

Deadline: Early September.

PUBLICATIONS:
Announcements.

ADDRESS INQUIRIES TO:
Wykenna S.C. Vailor
Manager, Research Policy and Awards
(See address above.)

*SPECIAL STIPULATIONS:
Applicant must be an AGA member at the time of application submission.

AMERICAN GASTROENTEROLOGICAL ASSOCIATION (AGA) [2562]

4930 Del Ray Avenue
Bethesda, MD 20814
(301) 222-4012
Fax: (301) 652-3890

E-MAIL ADDRESS:
awards@fdhn.org

WEB SITE ADDRESS:
www.gastro.org/fdhnfunding

FOUNDED: 1990

AREAS OF INTEREST:
Gastroenterology and related fields.

NAME(S) OF PROGRAMS:
- **AGA Foundation Research Scholar Award**

TYPE:
Research grants. Awards for young investigators working in any area of gastroenterology, hepatology or in related areas.

YEAR PROGRAM STARTED: 1990

PURPOSE:
To provide salary support or, in special circumstances, research support to ensure that a major proportion of time is protected for research scholarship. The overall objective is to enable young investigators to develop independent productive research careers in gastroenterology-related fields.

LEGAL BASIS:
Nonprofit foundation.

ELIGIBILITY:
The applicant must hold a full-time faculty position at a North American university or professional institute at the time of application. Applicant also must be a member of the AGA. The award is not intended for fellows, but for young faculty who have demonstrated unusual promise and have some record of accomplishment in research. Emphasis will be on support of physician-investigators who have a high potential to develop independent productive research careers in gastroenterology and hepatology. Nonphysician candidates with a Ph.D. will also be considered. Established investigators are not appropriate candidates. Candidates must devote at least 70% of their effort to research related to the gastrointestinal tract or liver. Candidates should be early in their careers and, commonly, will have recently completed their fellowship training. In recognition of their underrepresentation in gastroenterology-related fields, one award is reserved for a minority candidate.

Applicants cannot hold or have held, prior to receiving the first payment of this award, an R01, R29, K-series award, VA career development award, or any award with similar objectives from non-federal sources. However, awards or grants obtained after receipt of the Research Scholar Award support by the RSA would be required to forfeit the remaining balance of award.

GEOGRAPHIC RESTRICTIONS:
North America.

FINANCIAL DATA:
Amount of support per award: $120,000 ($60,000 per year).

COOPERATIVE FUNDING PROGRAMS: Jointly sponsored by the American Gastroenterological Association and participating pharmaceutical corporations.

NUMBER OF APPLICANTS MOST RECENT YEAR:
41 for the year 2009.

NUMBER OF AWARDS: 6.

APPLICATION INFORMATION:
Application forms can be obtained by writing to the ADHF National Office.

Duration: Two years. Third year funding may be available under certain circumstances.

Deadline: Early September for awards to begin the following July.

ADDRESS INQUIRIES TO:
Wykenna S.C. Vailor
Manager, Research Policy and Awards
(See address above.)

*SPECIAL STIPULATIONS:
Applicant must be an AGA member at the time of application submission.

AMERICAN GASTROENTEROLOGICAL ASSOCIATION (AGA) [2563]

4930 Del Ray Avenue
Bethesda, MD 20814
(301) 222-4012
Fax: (301) 652-3890

E-MAIL ADDRESS:
awards@fdhn.org

WEB SITE ADDRESS:
www.gastro.org/fdhnfunding

FOUNDED: 1990

AREAS OF INTEREST:
Gastroenterology and related fields.

NAME(S) OF PROGRAMS:
- **AGA Foundation Student Research Fellowship Award**

TYPE:
Research grants. Financial support for individuals to obtain research experience by spending some time in an active research environment. The proposed subjects of investigation should be related to a problem in digestive disease or nutrition. This award is not intended to provide salary for lab technicians.

YEAR PROGRAM STARTED: 1990

PURPOSE:
To stimulate interest in research careers in digestive diseases by providing salary support for research projects.

LEGAL BASIS:
Nonprofit foundation.

ELIGIBILITY:
Candidates may be high school students or undergraduate students at accredited North American (U.S. or Canada) institutions and must be in full-time research with a preceptor for a minimum of 10 weeks. Candidates holding advanced degrees must be enrolled as undergraduate students. In recognition of their underrepresentation in gastroenterology-related fields, women and minorities are strongly encouraged to apply. Candidates may not hold similar salary support awards from other agencies, e.g., American Liver Foundation and/or Crohn's and Colitis Foundation.

The preceptor must be a full-time faculty member who directs a research project in a gastroenterology-related area at an accredited

North American institution. In addition, he/she must be an individual member of the AGA.

Awardees will be selected based on novelty, feasibility and significance of the proposal, attributes of the candidate, the record of the preceptor, evidence of institutional commitment and the laboratory environment.

GEOGRAPHIC RESTRICTIONS:
North America.

FINANCIAL DATA:
Amount of support per award: $2,500.

NUMBER OF APPLICANTS MOST RECENT YEAR:
52 for the year 2008.

NUMBER OF AWARDS: 22 for the year 2008.

APPLICATION INFORMATION:
Duration: 10 weeks minimum during the year.
Deadline: March for awards to begin the following July.

PUBLICATIONS:
Announcement.

ADDRESS INQUIRIES TO:
Wykenna S.C. Vailor
Manager, Research Policy and Awards
(See address above.)

*SPECIAL STIPULATIONS:
Applicants must be sponsored by a member of the AGA. The sponsor must be an AGA member at the time of application submission.

AMERICAN GASTROENTEROLOGICAL ASSOCIATION (AGA)   [2564]

4930 Del Ray Avenue
Bethesda, MD 20814
(301) 222-4012
Fax: (301) 652-3890

E-MAIL ADDRESS:
awards@fdhn.org

WEB SITE ADDRESS:
www.gastro.org/fdhnfunding

FOUNDED: 1990

AREAS OF INTEREST:
Gastroenterology and related fields.

NAME(S) OF PROGRAMS:
• **AGA Foundation Fellowship to Faculty Transition Award**

TYPE:
Research grants. Awards for current trainees in gastroenterology working in any area of gastrointestinal or liver function or their related diseases.

YEAR PROGRAM STARTED: 1990

PURPOSE:
To provide salary support for current trainees in gastroenterology-related fields so they may gain additional full-time research training in a basic science department to acquire modern laboratory skills in order to prepare them for independent research careers in digestive diseases.

LEGAL BASIS:
Nonprofit foundation.

ELIGIBILITY:
Applicants must be M.Ds. or M.D./Ph.Ds. currently in a gastroenterology-related fellowship at an accredited North American institution, who are clinically active and committed to academic careers and who will

have completed two years of research at the time of the start of this award. There are no restrictions to citizenship. Although the host institution may supplement the award, the applicant may not concurrently hold a similar training award or grant from another organization, such as the NIH, American Liver Foundation, Crohn's and Colitis Foundation, etc. Applicants must demonstrate how they will obtain the additional knowledge in the proposed project and how it may be used in their future research. In recognition of their underrepresentation in gastroenterology-related fields, women and minorities are strongly encouraged to apply.

Applicants must be an AGA member or be sponsored by an AGA member who directs a gastroenterology-related unit that is engaged in research training in a North American medical school, affiliated teaching hospital or research institute. A qualified sponsor may submit only one application. The sponsor must ensure that all requirements of the institution have been met regarding application for and receipt of research funds.

Each applicant must be co-sponsored by the director of a basic research laboratory or other comparable laboratory, who should be committed to the training and development of the awardee, be prepared to offer the resources of his or her laboratory and be able to spend the requisite time and effort necessary to guarantee a high-quality research and training experience.

GEOGRAPHIC RESTRICTIONS:
North America.

FINANCIAL DATA:
Amount of support per award: $40,000 per year.

NUMBER OF APPLICANTS MOST RECENT YEAR:
12 for the year 2008.

NUMBER OF AWARDS: Up to 4.

APPLICATION INFORMATION:
Applications and additional information can be obtained from the ADHF National Office at the address above.
Duration: Two years.
Deadline: Early September for the award period beginning the following July.

PUBLICATIONS:
Announcement.

ADDRESS INQUIRIES TO:
Wykenna S.C. Vailor
Manager, Research Policy and Awards
(See address above.)

*SPECIAL STIPULATIONS:
Applicant must be an AGA member at the time of application submission.

AMERICAN GASTROENTEROLOGICAL ASSOCIATION (AGA)   [2565]

4930 Del Ray Avenue
Bethesda, MD 20814
(301) 222-4012
Fax: (301) 652-3890

E-MAIL ADDRESS:
awards@fdhn.org

WEB SITE ADDRESS:
www.gastro.org/fdhnfunding

FOUNDED: 1990

AREAS OF INTEREST:
Gastroenterology and related fields.

NAME(S) OF PROGRAMS:
• **Elsevier Pilot Research Award**

TYPE:
Research grants. Research initiative grants for investigators to work in gastroenterology- or hepatology-related areas.

YEAR PROGRAM STARTED: 1990

PURPOSE:
To provide non-salary funds to new investigators starting their research careers to help them establish their independence; to support pilot projects that represent new research directions for established investigators, with the intent of stimulating research in gastroenterology- or hepatology-related areas by permitting investigators to obtain new data which can ultimately provide the basis for subsequent grant applications of more substantial funding and duration.

LEGAL BASIS:
Nonprofit foundation.

ELIGIBILITY:
Open to investigators with M.Ds. or Ph.Ds. (or equivalent), who must hold faculty positions at accredited North American institutions. They may not hold awards on a similar topic from other agencies. Applicant must also be a member of the AGA. In recognition of their underrepresentation in gastroenterology-related fields, women and minorities are strongly encouraged to apply.

Proposals will be selected on the basis of novelty, importance, feasibility, environment, commitment of the institution and overall likelihood that the projects will lead to more substantial, subsequent grant applications. For clinical projects, prior IRB approval must be obtained and that documentation must accompany submission of the application.

GEOGRAPHIC RESTRICTIONS:
North America.

FINANCIAL DATA:
Funds may be used for salary (for lab personnel and technicians only), supplies or equipment. Indirect costs are not allowed.
Amount of support per award: $25,000 per year.

NUMBER OF APPLICANTS MOST RECENT YEAR:
38 for the year 2008.

NUMBER OF AWARDS: 1.

APPLICATION INFORMATION:
Duration: One year.
Deadline: Mid-January.

ADDRESS INQUIRIES TO:
Wykenna S.C. Vailor
Manager, Research Policy and Awards
(See address above.)

*SPECIAL STIPULATIONS:
Applicant must be an AGA member at the time of application submission.

AMERICAN SOCIETY FOR PARENTERAL AND ENTERAL NUTRITION, RHOADS RESEARCH FOUNDATION [2566]

8630 Fenton Street
Suite 412
Silver Spring, MD 20910
(301) 587-6315 ext. 132
Fax: (301) 587-2365

E-MAIL ADDRESS:
paulab@aspen.nutr.org

WEB SITE ADDRESS:
www.nutritioncare.org

FOUNDED: 1975

AREAS OF INTEREST:
Metabolic issues and nutrition support therapy.

TYPE:
Research grants; Seed money grants. Annual support for nutritional research.

YEAR PROGRAM STARTED: 1992

PURPOSE:
To support research projects in nutrition support therapy and metabolic issues by young and new investigators.

LEGAL BASIS:
Nonprofit foundation.

ELIGIBILITY:
Applicants are encouraged from the fields of medicine, dietetics, nursing and pharmacy. Grants are only given to individuals. There are no citizenship requirements. A.S.P.E.N. membership is required.

FINANCIAL DATA:
Amount of support per award: Up to $25,000.
Total amount of support: Up to $100,000 annually.

NUMBER OF APPLICANTS MOST RECENT YEAR:
Up to 18 annually.

NUMBER OF AWARDS: Up to 3 at $25,000; 1 at $16,000; 2 at $5,000.

APPLICATION INFORMATION:
Application form required. Contact the Society for additional information.
Duration: One year. Renewal possible up to two years.
Deadline: September 8.

PUBLICATIONS:
Application guidelines.

ADDRESS INQUIRIES TO:
Paula Bowen
Research Program Administrator
(See address above.)

AMERICAN SOCIETY OF NEPHROLOGY [2567]

1510 H Street, N.W.
Suite 800
Washington, DC 20005
(202) 640-4660
Fax: (202) 637-9793

E-MAIL ADDRESS:
grants@asn-online.org

WEB SITE ADDRESS:
www.asn-online.org

AREAS OF INTEREST:
Nephrology and membranous nephropathy.

NAME(S) OF PROGRAMS:
● **ASN Researcher Travel Support**
● **ASN-ASP Junior Development Grant in Geriatric Nephrology**
● **Career Grants**
● **Halpin Foundation-ASN Research Grant**

TYPE:
Research grants; Travel grants. ASN-ASP Junior Development Grant in Geriatric Nephrology supports developing academic subspecialists interested in careers focused on the geriatric and gerontological aspects of nephrology during the early years of a first faculty appointment.

Halpin Foundation-ASN Research Grant provides funding for young faculty to foster evolution to an independent research career by providing transition funding toward successful application for an R01 grant.

ELIGIBILITY:
Applicants must be active members of the ASN.

FINANCIAL DATA:
Amount of support per award: ASN-ASP Junior Development Grant: $75,000 annually, plus $3,000 to be allocated for travel; Halpin Foundation-ASN Research Grant: $100,000 annually; Career Grants: $100,000 annually; ASN Researcher: $1,000.

COOPERATIVE FUNDING PROGRAMS: The Association of Subspecialty Professors (ASP) and Halpin Foundation.

APPLICATION INFORMATION:
Duration: ASN-ASP Junior Development and Halpin Foundation-ASN Research Grants: Two years. Progress report required for second-year renewal. Career Grants: Two years.

THE ELI AND EDYTHE BROAD FOUNDATION [2568]

Broad Medical Research Program
10900 Wilshire Boulevard, 12th Floor
Los Angeles, CA 90024-6532
(310) 954-5091
Fax: (310) 954-5092

E-MAIL ADDRESS:
info@broadmedical.org

WEB SITE ADDRESS:
www.broadmedical.org

FOUNDED: 2001

AREAS OF INTEREST:
Understanding and treating inflammatory bowel disease.

NAME(S) OF PROGRAMS:
● **Broad Medical Research Program**

TYPE:
Research grants; Seed money grants. Designed to stimulate innovative research that will lead to both the prevention and successful therapy of inflammatory bowel disease.

YEAR PROGRAM STARTED: 2001

PURPOSE:
To understand and treat inflammatory bowel disease.

ELIGIBILITY:
Grants will only be awarded to nonprofit organizations, such as universities, hospitals and research institutes.

FINANCIAL DATA:
Amount of support per award: Average $114,796 per year.
Total amount of support: $3,499,172.50 for the year 2010.

NUMBER OF APPLICANTS MOST RECENT YEAR:
99.

NUMBER OF AWARDS: 18 new awards.

APPLICATION INFORMATION:
Applicants should submit a brief Letter of Interest (up to three pages, not including attachments) as the initial request for funding. Investigators whose Letters of Interest fit the Program's criteria and areas of interest will be invited to submit a full grant application.

The following information is part of the three-page limit:
(1) title of the project;
(2) specific hypothesis or question to be investigated;
(3) methodology;
(4) data analysis and;
(5) anticipated outcomes.

Additionally, applicants are required to:
(1) state why the project fits the Program's criteria, including its relevance and likely benefits to patients with inflammatory bowel disease in the next several years;
(2) attach the investigator's curriculum vitae(s) or biographical sketch(es);
(3) briefly describe the laboratory or clinical environment;
(4) indicate the estimated total budget and the period for which funding is requested and;
(5) provide the principal investigator's e-mail and postal addresses.

Supportive information, such as references, preliminary data or recent publications, may be included. These will not be counted as part of the three-page limit.
Duration: Up to two years.

IRS IDENTIFICATION NUMBER: 95-4686318

ADDRESS INQUIRIES TO:
See e-mail address above.

CANADIAN DIABETES ASSOCIATION [2569]

National Life Building
522 University Avenue, Suite 1400
Toronto ON M5C 2R5 Canada
(416) 363-3373 ext. 7085
Fax: (416) 363-7465

E-MAIL ADDRESS:
myrtella.hodge@diabetes.ca

WEB SITE ADDRESS:
www.diabetes.ca

FOUNDED: 1953

AREAS OF INTEREST:
Medical research into the causes and cure of diabetes.

NAME(S) OF PROGRAMS:
● **Charles H. Best Research Fund**

TYPE:
Research grants. Support for ongoing research into better ways to treat diabetes and ultimately cure it.

YEAR PROGRAM STARTED: 1975

PURPOSE:
To promote the health of Canadians through diabetes research, education, service and advocacy.

LEGAL BASIS:
Nonprofit.

ELIGIBILITY:
Individuals and groups may apply for research programs in Canada only.

GEOGRAPHIC RESTRICTIONS:
Canada.

FINANCIAL DATA:
Total amount of support: Varies.
Matching fund requirements: Varies.

NUMBER OF APPLICANTS MOST RECENT YEAR:
170 for the 2011 competition.

NUMBER OF AWARDS: 24 operating grants and 16 personnel awards for the year 2010.

APPLICATION INFORMATION:
Guidelines and application form are available on the web site.

ADDRESS INQUIRIES TO:
Myrtella Hodge, Manager of Research (See address above.)

CANADIAN LIVER FOUNDATION   [2570]
2235 Sheppard Avenue East
Suite 1500
Toronto ON M2J 5B5 Canada
(416) 491-3353
(800) 563-5483
Fax: (416) 491-4952

E-MAIL ADDRESS:
clf@liver.ca

WEB SITE ADDRESS:
www.liver.ca

FOUNDED: 1969

AREAS OF INTEREST:
Research and education into the causes, diagnosis, prevention and treatment of diseases of the liver.

NAME(S) OF PROGRAMS:
● **Canadian Liver Foundation Operating Grant**

TYPE:
Research grants.

YEAR PROGRAM STARTED: 1970

PURPOSE:
To support research projects directed towards a defined objective, conducted by an investigator working alone or in collaboration with others.

LEGAL BASIS:
Registered Canadian charity.

ELIGIBILITY:
Hepatobiliary research investigators who hold an academic appointment in a Canadian university or affiliated institution are eligible to apply. Clinical investigators and basic scientists will be considered. These grants may be used to purchase materials, supplies and items of equipment costing less than $5,000, to buy and maintain animals, and to support travel costs (to a limit of $1,000).

GEOGRAPHIC RESTRICTIONS:
Canada.

FINANCIAL DATA:
Amount of support per award: Up to $60,000 per year for two years.
Total amount of support: Varies depending on the number of suitable candidates and the funds available.

NUMBER OF APPLICANTS MOST RECENT YEAR: 9 for the year 2010.

NUMBER OF AWARDS: 2 for the year 2010.

REPRESENTATIVE AWARDS:
Dr. Laura Arbour, University of British Columbia, "Genetic studies of primary biliary cirrhosis in First Nations peoples of the Pacific Northwest Coast;" Dr. Norman Kneteman, University of Alberta, "Transcriptional regulation of hepatic genes in response to hepatitis C infection and treatment with interferon alpha 2b;" Dr. Diana Mager, University of Alberta, "Altered

fat metabolism as a mechanism for hepatic steatosis in children with non-alcoholic fatty liver disease."

APPLICATION INFORMATION:
The applicant must designate the institution in which he or she holds an academic appointment. The institution is considered by the Foundation to be responsible for the provision of space, facilities, furniture and general services for the conduct of the research project described.
Duration: Two years.
Deadline: March 31, for awards to become tenable the following September 1.

PUBLICATIONS:
Program description and guidelines.

STAFF:
Billie Potkonjak, National Director of Health Promotion and Patient Services

ADDRESS INQUIRIES TO:
Billie Potkonjak, National Director of Health Promotion and Patient Services (See address above.)

CANADIAN LIVER FOUNDATION
2235 Sheppard Avenue East
Suite 1500
Toronto ON M2J 5B5 Canada
(416) 491-3353
(800) 563-5483
Fax: (416) 491-4952

E-MAIL ADDRESS:
clf@liver.ca

WEB SITE ADDRESS:
www.liver.ca

TYPE:
Scholarships.

See entry 2399 for full listing.

CANADIAN LIVER FOUNDATION
2235 Sheppard Avenue East
Suite 1500
Toronto ON M2J 5B5 Canada
(416) 491-3353
(800) 563-5483
Fax: (416) 491-4952

E-MAIL ADDRESS:
clf@liver.ca

WEB SITE ADDRESS:
www.liver.ca

TYPE:
Scholarships.

See entry 2398 for full listing.

COOLEY'S ANEMIA FOUNDATION, INC.   [2571]
330 7th Avenue
Suite 200
New York, NY 10001-5264
(212) 279-8090 ext. 201
(800) 522-7222
Fax: (212) 279-5999

E-MAIL ADDRESS:
info@cooleysanemia.org

WEB SITE ADDRESS:
www.cooleysanemia.org

FOUNDED: 1954

AREAS OF INTEREST:
Cooley's anemia and all thalassemias.

TYPE:
Fellowships; Research grants. Clinical grants. Research, public and professional education, patient care and public information. Basic and clinical research and fellowships.

YEAR PROGRAM STARTED: 1954

PURPOSE:
To provide impetus to benefit the advancement of knowledge and the quality of care in Cooley's anemia and other thalassemias.

LEGAL BASIS:
Federal tax-exempt, nonprofit, voluntary health agency.

FINANCIAL DATA:
Amount of support per award: Fellowships: $32,000; Clinical grants: Up to $40,000.

NUMBER OF APPLICANTS MOST RECENT YEAR: 30.

APPLICATION INFORMATION:
Duration: One year. Possibility for renewal for second year.
Deadline: First Monday in February.

PUBLICATIONS:
Lifeline Newsletter; screening material; educational pamphlets.

IRS IDENTIFICATION NUMBER: 11-1971539

OFFICERS:
Tony Viola, President

ADDRESS INQUIRIES TO:
Gina Cioffi, National Executive Director (See address above.)

CROHN'S AND COLITIS FOUNDATION OF AMERICA, INC.   [2572]
386 Park Avenue South
17th Floor
New York, NY 10016-8804
(212) 685-3440
(800) 932-2423
Fax: (212) 779-4098

E-MAIL ADDRESS:
grants@ccfa.org

WEB SITE ADDRESS:
www.ccfa.org

FOUNDED: 1967

AREAS OF INTEREST:
Research and education in inflammatory bowel disease (Crohn's disease and ulcerative colitis).

CONSULTING OR VOLUNTEER SERVICES:
Medical committees (consisting of physician volunteers) provide services in the areas of patient and professional education, research development, grants review, etc.

NAME(S) OF PROGRAMS:
● **CCFA Career Development Award**
● **CCFA Research Fellowship Award**
● **CCFA Senior Research Award**
● **CCFA Student Research Fellowship Awards**

TYPE:
Fellowships; Research grants; Training grants. Senior Research Award provides funds to enable established investigators to generate sufficient data to become competitive for funds from other sources, such as the National Institutes of Health.

Research Fellowship Awards and Career Development Awards encourage the early developmental stages of individuals with potential for a career of independent basic and/or clinical investigation in IBD.

Student Research Fellowship Awards are available for undergraduate, medical or graduate students (not yet engaged in thesis research) in accredited North American institutions to conduct full-time research with a mentor investigating a subject relevant to IBD.

YEAR PROGRAM STARTED: 1967

PURPOSE:
To fund research leading to understanding of and ultimate cure for Crohn's disease and ulcerative colitis.

LEGAL BASIS:
Nonprofit, special-interest foundation.

ELIGIBILITY:
For Career Development Awards, candidates must have at least five years of relevant postdoctoral experience prior to the beginning date of the awards and not in excess of 10 years beyond the attainment of their Doctorate degrees.

For Research Fellowship Awards, candidates must have had two years of relevant postdoctoral experience prior to the beginning date of the award.

For Research Training Awards, candidates must be sponsored by a public or private nonprofit institution or a government institution engaged in health care and health-related research within the U.S. and its possessions. Individuals who already are well established in the field are not considered eligible for these awards. Applicants must hold M.D. or Ph.D. degrees and be employed within the U.S. at the time of submission. Eligibility is not restricted by citizenship.

For Senior Research Award, applicants must be established researchers in the field of inflammatory bowel disease.

FINANCIAL DATA:
Amount of support per award: Career Development Award: $90,000 per year; Research Fellowship Award: $58,250 per year; Senior Research Award: $128,700 per year; Student Research Fellowship Award: $2,500.

COOPERATIVE FUNDING PROGRAMS:
NASPGHAN/CDHNF.

NUMBER OF AWARDS: Over 200.

REPRESENTATIVE AWARDS:
$5,396,724 to Subra Kugathasan, M.D., Emory University, Atlanta, GA, for "Risk stratification and identification of Immunogenetic markers of complicated disease course in pediatric Crohn's disease;" $2,715,000 to Jeffrey Gordon, M.D., Washington University School of Medicine, St. Louis, MO, for "CCFA Gut Microbiome Initiative."

APPLICATION INFORMATION:
Before submitting a Letter of Intent or Full Proposal, applicants are urged to view the online policies and instructions. After the Letter of Intent is submitted and approved, CCFA Research Grants Administration will send an e-mail to the applicant with a link to complete and submit a Full Proposal.
Duration: Senior Research Awards: One to three years.

Deadline: Student Research Fellowship Awards: March 15. Awards begin on or about June 15. Career Development Award, Research Fellowship Award and Senior Research Award: January 14 for July 1 start date and July 1 for January 1 start date.

PUBLICATIONS:
Annual report; *Inflammatory Bowel Diseases*; *Foundation Focus*; brochures.

STAFF:
Richard Geswell, President

OFFICERS AND TRUSTEES:
Gary Sinderbrand, Chairman
Michael Koss, Chairperson-Elect of the Board
Lloyd Mayer, M.D., Chairperson, National Scientific Advisory

FOUNDERS:
Henry D. Janowitz, M.D.
William D. Modell
Irwin M. Rosenthal

ADDRESS INQUIRIES TO:
Natasha Rampersaud
Director, Grants Administration
(See address above.)

CYSTIC FIBROSIS FOUNDATION [2573]
6931 Arlington Road
Bethesda, MD 20814
(301) 951-4422
(800) 344-4823
Fax: (301) 951-6378; (301) 841-2605

E-MAIL ADDRESS:
grants@cff.org

WEB SITE ADDRESS:
www.cff.org

FOUNDED: 1955

AREAS OF INTEREST:
Research, care and education programs to benefit patients with cystic fibrosis.

NAME(S) OF PROGRAMS:
- **CFF/NIH Funding Award**
- **Clinical Research Grants**
- **Leroy Matthews Physician/Scientist Award**
- **Pilot and Feasibility Awards**
- **Research Grants**
- **Harry Shwachman Clinical Investigator Award**
- **Special Research Awards**
- **Therapeutics Development Grants**

TYPE:
Fellowships; Research grants; Training grants. The CFF/NIH Award supports excellent CF-related research projects that have been submitted to and approved by the National Institutes of Health (NIH) but cannot be supported by available NIH funds.

Clinical Research Grants offer support to clinical research projects directly related to cystic fibrosis treatment and care.

Leroy Matthews Physician/Scientist Award provides support for outstanding, newly trained pediatricians and internists (M.D. and M.D./Ph.D.) to complete subspecialty training, develop into independent investigators, and initiate a research program.

Pilot and Feasibility Awards are for developing and testing new hypotheses and/or new methods and to support promising new investigators as they establish themselves in research areas relevant to CF.

Research Grants are intended to encourage the development of new information that contributes to the understanding of the basic etiology and pathogenesis of cystic fibrosis.

The Harry Shwachman Award provides the opportunity for clinically-trained physicians to develop into independent biomedical research investigators who are actively involved in CF-related areas. It is also intended to facilitate the transition from postdoctoral training to a career in academic medicine.

Special Research Awards direct research efforts toward specific areas of CF-related research.

Therapeutics Development Grants provide funds to businesses that will develop commercial products to benefit individuals with CF. Structured as a matching grants program, funds will be awarded only if they are matched by the recipient.

YEAR PROGRAM STARTED: 1955

PURPOSE:
To encourage clinical research into the cause, care and treatment of cystic fibrosis; to train specialists for careers in academic medicine.

LEGAL BASIS:
501(c)(3) organization, incorporated as a nonprofit, tax-exempt organization.

ELIGIBILITY:
Contact the Foundation at the address above for specific details on the various grant programs.

FINANCIAL DATA:
Amount of support per award: CFF/NIH Funding Award: $75,000 to $125,000 per year; Clinical Research Grants: Up to $80,000 per year (single-center) and up to $150,000 per year (multicenter); Leroy Matthews Physician/Scientist Award: $48,000 (stipend) plus $10,000 (research and development) for year one to $76,000 (stipend) plus $15,000 (research and development) for year six; Pilot and Feasibility Awards: Up to $40,000 per year; Research Grants: $90,000 per year; Harry Shwachman Clinical Investigator Award: Up to $76,000 per year plus $15,000 for supplies; Therapeutics Development Grants: Up to $100,000 per year for a maximum of two years for Component I and up to $750,000 per year for a maximum of two years for Component II.

APPLICATION INFORMATION:
Further information may be received from the Office of Grants Management.
Duration: CFF/NIH Funding Award: Up to two years (from CFF); Clinical Research Grants: Up to three years; Matthews Physician/Scientist Award: Up to six years; Pilot and Feasibility Awards: Up to two years; Research Grants: Two years with possible renewal for two additional years; Shwachman Clinical Investigator Award: Three years; Therapeutic Development Grants: Up to two years for both Components I and II.
Deadline: CFF/NIH Funding Award and Therapeutics Development Grants reviewed on an ongoing basis; Clinical Research Grants: June 1 for letter of intent, first Wednesday in September for application; Pilot and Feasibility Awards, Matthews Physician/Scientist Award, Research Grants and Shwachman Clinical Investigator Award: First Wednesday in September (application).

PUBLICATIONS:
Annual report; application form; guidelines.

STAFF:
Robert J. Beall, Ph.D., President and Chief
Executive Officer
Rich Mattingly, Chief Operating Officer

ADDRESS INQUIRIES TO:
Grants and Contracts Manager
(See address above.)

JUVENILE DIABETES RESEARCH FOUNDATION INTERNATIONAL   [2574]

26 Broadway
14th Floor
New York, NY 10004
(212) 785-9500
(800) 533-2873
Fax: (212) 785-9595

E-MAIL ADDRESS:
info@jdrf.org

WEB SITE ADDRESS:
www.jdrf.org

FOUNDED: 1970

AREAS OF INTEREST:
To support research into the causes,
treatment, prevention and cure of diabetes
and its complications.

NAME(S) OF PROGRAMS:
● **Regular Research Grant**

TYPE:
Project/program grants; Research grants.
Support for a variety of needs, such as
salaries for technical assistance, special
equipment, animals and supplies for scientific
investigations related to diabetes.

YEAR PROGRAM STARTED: 1973

PURPOSE:
To support scientific investigations of
diabetes.

LEGAL BASIS:
Incorporated not-for-profit voluntary health
agency.

ELIGIBILITY:
Grants are awarded to new or established
researchers. Proposal must be for a scientific
research project involving the cause,
treatment, prevention, and/or cure of diabetes
and its complications. Applicants must hold
an M.D., D.M.D., D.V.M., Ph.D. or
equivalent and have a full-time faculty
position or equivalent at a college, university,
medical school, company, or other research
facility.

FINANCIAL DATA:
Salary support plus fringe benefits for the
principal investigator may not exceed his or
her percentage effort on the project
multiplied by institutional base salary.
Indirect costs (excluding equipment) may not
exceed 10%. Funds may be used for salaries
for technical assistant, special equipment,
animals and supplies.
Amount of support per award: $165,000 per
year for three years, including indirect cost.

APPLICATION INFORMATION:
Application forms are available from the
address above. The current JDF or NIH
application may be used; however, for the
NIH the research plan must include two
abstracts (one written in scientific language
and one in lay language) and cannot exceed
10 pages. Applicants must submit a signed

original with 15 copies and include
information regarding all other sources of
support (current or pending) including title,
abstract, annual total amount of grant,
inclusive funding period and percentage
effort of the applicant. In addition, applicants
must include a detailed letter of intent
outlining the rationale for the request,
budgetary requirements, and curriculum vitae
of the principal investigator. Applications
from industry must also include the rationale
of how the proposed device/technology will
address an important issue in diabetes
management or research and the potential to
improve diabetes management or progress
toward prevention or cure of diabetes and its
complications.
Duration: One year with renewal by
application for up to two additional years.
Deadline: Applications open May 1. Online
applications due July 15, with review in
November. Notification in December for start
date of March 1.

PUBLICATIONS:
Annual report; policy statement; research
appropriations sheet; *Countdown Magazine.*

ADDRESS INQUIRIES TO:
Martin Duenas
Director Operations and Administration
(See address above.)

JUVENILE DIABETES RESEARCH FOUNDATION INTERNATIONAL   [2575]

26 Broadway
14th Floor
New York, NY 10004
(212) 785-9500
(800) 533-2873
Fax: (212) 785-9595

E-MAIL ADDRESS:
info@jdrf.org

WEB SITE ADDRESS:
www.jdrf.org

FOUNDED: 1970

AREAS OF INTEREST:
To support research into the causes,
treatment, prevention and cure of diabetes
and its complications.

NAME(S) OF PROGRAMS:
● **Postdoctoral Fellowships**

TYPE:
Fellowships. Postdoctoral fellowships to
attract qualified and promising scientists
entering their professional career into fields
of research in diabetes. The applicant is
required to work with a sponsor who can
provide a training environment most
conducive to beginning a career in
diabetes-relevant research. Fellowship
research may be conducted at foreign and
domestic, for-profit and nonprofit, public and
private organizations such as universities,
colleges, hospitals, laboratories, units of state
and local governments, and eligible agencies
of the federal government.

YEAR PROGRAM STARTED: 1973

PURPOSE:
To support advanced training in fields of
research directly related to diabetes.

LEGAL BASIS:
Incorporated not-for-profit voluntary health
agency.

ELIGIBILITY:
By the beginning of the period of support
sought, the applicant must have a doctoral
degree (M.D., D.M., D.V.M., Ph.D. or the
equivalent) for no more than five years
before the fellowship and may not have a
faculty appointment. Each applicant must be
sponsored by a scientist who is affiliated
full-time with an accredited institution and
who agrees to supervise that individual's
training. JDF welcomes applications from
women and members of minority groups
underrepresented in the sciences.

The applicant is responsible for selecting a
research mentor and for making arrangements
to work in this person's laboratory. The
designated mentor must be the senior
scientist who will directly supervise the
proposed research.

FINANCIAL DATA:
The stipend is dependent on the number of
years of relevant experience.
Amount of support per award: $41,068 to
$52,492 per year for two years with a
research allowance of $3,000 per year.

APPLICATION INFORMATION:
Application forms are available from the
address above. Applicants must submit a
signed original with 15 copies. The applicant
must include three letters of reference
assessing the scientific abilities and potential
of the applicant and a statement of career
goals with the relevance to diabetes-related
research. The sponsor must outline a specific
training program, confirm the space and
facilities for the research project, provide
information on all sources of grant support
(current or pending, federal or non-federal)
and must include the title, amounts, funding
periods and abstract pages of all current and
pending support.
Duration: One year. Renewable for a second
year with demonstration of suitable progress.
Deadline: September 1 and February 1. A
copy of the first two pages of the application
by August 15 and January 15, respectively.
Notification late November and May,
respectively.

PUBLICATIONS:
Annual report; policy statement; research
appropriations sheet; *Countdown Magazine.*

ADDRESS INQUIRIES TO:
Martin Duenas
Director Operations and Administration
(See address above.)

*SPECIAL STIPULATIONS:
Awardees will be required to attend an
annual JDF two-day meeting to present the
results of their work and produce a progress
report at the end of each funding year.
Awardees must spend at least 80% of time
and effort on the research project during the
period of the award.

JUVENILE DIABETES RESEARCH FOUNDATION INTERNATIONAL   [2576]

26 Broadway
14th Floor
New York, NY 10004
(212) 785-9500
(800) 533-2873
Fax: (212) 785-9595

E-MAIL ADDRESS:
info@jdrf.org

WEB SITE ADDRESS:
www.jdrf.org

FOUNDED: 1970

AREAS OF INTEREST:
Prevention and treatment of type I diabetes and its complications.

NAME(S) OF PROGRAMS:
- **Career Development Awards**

TYPE:
Development grants; Research grants; Training grants. Grants are awarded to promising scientists entering their professional career in the diabetes research field. In the five-year term, awardees will focus their research efforts in a subject directly related to JDRF's research mission goals and position themselves to work at the leading edge of diabetes research.

YEAR PROGRAM STARTED: 1979

PURPOSE:
To attract qualified and promising scientists early in their faculty careers and to give them the opportunity to establish themselves in areas that reflect the JDRF research mission goals.

LEGAL BASIS:
Charitable foundation.

ELIGIBILITY:
The individuals must be in a relatively early stage of their career who have demonstrated superior scholarship and show the greatest promise for future achievement in research, including either clinically relevant research or basic research. Ordinarily, their first degree (M.D., Ph.D., D.M.D., D.V.D. or equivalent) will have been received at least three, but not more than seven, years before the award. The applicant must hold an academic position including assistant professor or equivalent at the time of the award. At the inception of the award, however, the applicant must be a faculty member in a university, health science center, or comparable institution with strong, well-established research and training programs for the chosen area of interest.

FINANCIAL DATA:
Indirect costs cannot exceed 10%.
Amount of support per award: $150,000 per year; up to $65,000 of this may be requested for research allowance which can include a technician, supplies, equipment and travel up to $2,000 per year.

APPLICATION INFORMATION:
Application forms are available from the address above. Applicants must submit a signed original with 15 copies and include three letters of reference assessing the candidate's scientific abilities, assurance from the university of an academic commitment to the applicant and the research project, all other sources of funding (current, federal and non-federal), with the title, abstract, annual and total amount of support and inclusive funding periods of all current and pending grants.
Duration: One year. Renewable up to a maximum of four years pending satisfactory progress.
Deadline: Applications open May 1. Online applications due July 15, with review in November. Notification in December for start date of March 1.

PUBLICATIONS:
Annual report; policy statement; research appropriations sheet; *Countdown Magazine.*

ADDRESS INQUIRIES TO:
Martin Duenas
Director Operations and Administration
(See address above.)

THE KIDNEY FOUNDATION OF CANADA [2577]
5165 Sherbrooke Street West
Suite 300
Montreal QC H4A 1T6 Canada
(514) 369-4806
Fax: (514) 369-2472

E-MAIL ADDRESS:
research@kidney.ca

WEB SITE ADDRESS:
www.kidney.ca

FOUNDED: 1964

AREAS OF INTEREST:
Research that may further the current knowledge pertaining to the kidney and urinary tract.

NAME(S) OF PROGRAMS:
- **Biomedical Research Grant**

TYPE:
Research grants. Provides funds to defray the cost of research, including the purchase and maintenance of experimental animals, the purchase of materials, supplies and equipment and the payment of laboratory assistants.

YEAR PROGRAM STARTED: 1972

PURPOSE:
To acquire a greater understanding of kidney diseases and the importance of the role of the kidneys in the human body.

LEGAL BASIS:
Corporation.

ELIGIBILITY:
Applicants must be Canadian citizens or landed immigrants. Research must be conducted within Canada and funding is limited to individuals holding staff appointments at Canadian universities or other recognized Canadian academic institutions.

Grant applications for equipment only will not be considered.

GEOGRAPHIC RESTRICTIONS:
Canada.

FINANCIAL DATA:
Amount of support per award: Maximum $50,000 (CAN) per year.
Total amount of support: $100,000.

NUMBER OF APPLICANTS MOST RECENT YEAR:
76.

NUMBER OF AWARDS: 24.

APPLICATION INFORMATION:
Duration: Up to three years. Grants run from July 1 to June 30.
Deadline: October 15.

ADDRESS INQUIRIES TO:
Director, National Research Program
(See address above.)

THE KIDNEY FOUNDATION OF CANADA [2578]
5165 Sherbrooke Street West
Suite 300
Montreal QC H4A 1T6 Canada
(514) 369-4806
Fax: (514) 369-2472

E-MAIL ADDRESS:
research@kidney.ca

WEB SITE ADDRESS:
www.kidney.ca

FOUNDED: 1964

AREAS OF INTEREST:
Research that may further the current knowledge pertaining to the kidney and urinary tract.

NAME(S) OF PROGRAMS:
- **Allied Health Research Grant**

TYPE:
Research grants. Funds allocated to assist in defraying the cost of research, including the purchase and maintenance of experimental animals, the purchase of materials, supplies and equipment and the payment of laboratory assistants. Travel assistance is also available.

YEAR PROGRAM STARTED: 1972

PURPOSE:
To foster and encourage research relevant to clinical practice in the area of nephrology and urology by allied health professionals.

LEGAL BASIS:
Corporation.

ELIGIBILITY:
Open to Canadian citizens. The Foundation will consider only those applications which prove scientific excellence where there is clear, demonstrated relevance of the project and its outcomes to the mission of The Kidney Foundation and the primary investigator is an allied health professional (e.g., nurses, technicians, dieticians, social workers).

Funds are available for research conducted within Canada.

The majority of applicants/co-applicants must be allied health professionals.

Priority will be given to applications submitted where the primary investigation has a demonstrated commitment to nephrology, urology or organ donation.

Under no circumstance should the grant application exceed the amount of $50,000. An investigator may not hold more than $50,000 per year from The Kidney Foundation as an award from a single grant or from multiple grants where the applicant is listed as an investigator or as a co-investigator.

GEOGRAPHIC RESTRICTIONS:
Canada.

FINANCIAL DATA:
Amount of support per award: Up to $50,000 (CAN) per year.
Total amount of support: Varies.

APPLICATION INFORMATION:
Initial or renewal application must be made on the prescribed form and sent in 12 copies to The Kidney Foundation at the address above. Grant application must also include letters of intent to participate from collaborators who have a role in the research project. Additional documentation, in the future, may be requested from the applicant.
Duration: One year. Must reapply for renewal of second year. Grants run from July 1 to June 30.
Deadline: October 15.

ADDRESS INQUIRIES TO:
Director, National Research Program
(See address above.)

THE KIDNEY FOUNDATION OF CANADA [2579]

5165 Sherbrooke Street West
Suite 300
Montreal QC H4A 1T6 Canada
(514) 369-4806
Fax: (514) 369-2472

E-MAIL ADDRESS:
research@kidney.ca

WEB SITE ADDRESS:
www.kidney.ca

FOUNDED: 1964

AREAS OF INTEREST:
Research that may further the current knowledge pertaining to the kidney and urinary tract.

NAME(S) OF PROGRAMS:
● **Allied Health Doctoral Fellowship**

TYPE:
Fellowships. Designed to provide for full-time academic and research preparation at the doctoral level in Canada or abroad. The award is designed to encourage new students to enter doctoral programs, as well as support students currently enrolled in a program.

YEAR PROGRAM STARTED: 1991

PURPOSE:
To promote and enhance the development of nephrology/urology allied health investigators in Canada.

LEGAL BASIS:
Corporation.

ELIGIBILITY:
Open to nephrology/urology nurses and technicians, social workers, dietitians, transplant coordinators and other allied health professionals. Applicant must demonstrate commitment to the area of nephrology/urology with a minimum of two years direct clinic practice.

Applicant must intend to return to Canada, if studies are outside the country.

FINANCIAL DATA:
Amount of support per award: Up to $31,000 per year for fellowship, depending upon the applicant's qualifications.
Total amount of support: $56,000.

APPLICATION INFORMATION:
Applications must be made on the prescribed forms which are available from the National Office. The completed application must include a certified transcript of the applicant's postsecondary school academic records, a letter from the supervisor, dean or department chairperson outlining academic plan and possible research plans, a letter from the sponsoring institution confirming the acceptance of candidate by June 30 and two Assessment of Candidate forms from persons who can give an assessment of the applicant's ability.
Duration: One year. A second, third or fourth year may be obtained upon successful reapplication.
Deadline: March 15. Renewal possible.

PUBLICATIONS:
Guidelines; application form; annual report.

ADDRESS INQUIRIES TO:
Wim Wolfs, Director
National Research Program
(See address above.)

THE KIDNEY FOUNDATION OF CANADA [2580]

5165 Sherbrooke Street West
Suite 300
Montreal QC H4A 1T6 Canada
(514) 369-4806
Fax: (514) 369-2472

E-MAIL ADDRESS:
research@kidney.ca

WEB SITE ADDRESS:
www.kidney.ca

AREAS OF INTEREST:
Research into the incidence and cure of kidney and urinary tract disease, patient services and public education.

NAME(S) OF PROGRAMS:
● **Allied Health Scholarship**

TYPE:
Scholarships. To promote and enhance the development of nephrology/urology allied health investigators in Canada.

YEAR PROGRAM STARTED: 1991

PURPOSE:
To assist the student with a demonstrated interest in nephrology/urology in pursuing education at the Master's or doctoral level.

LEGAL BASIS:
Corporation.

ELIGIBILITY:
Open to nurses and technicians, social workers, dietitians, transplant coordinators, and other allied health professionals who demonstrate commitment to the area of nephrology, urology or organ donation. Applicants who demonstrate a minimum of two years direct clinical practice are eligible. Must have Canadian citizenship or landed immigrant status.

FINANCIAL DATA:
Amount of support per award: Up to $5,000 per year for full-time studies and $2,500 per year for part-time studies up to a maximum of $10,000 (CAN).

NUMBER OF AWARDS: Varies depending on funding.

APPLICATION INFORMATION:
Duration: One year. Must reapply for second year of funding.
Deadline: March 15.

PUBLICATIONS:
Guidelines; application forms; annual report.

ADDRESS INQUIRIES TO:
Wim Wolffs, Director, Research Program
(See address above.)

NATIONAL KIDNEY FOUNDATION [2581]

30 East 33rd Street
New York, NY 10016
(212) 889-2210
(800) 622-9010
Fax: (212) 779-0068

E-MAIL ADDRESS:
research@kidney.org

WEB SITE ADDRESS:
www.kidney.org

FOUNDED: 1950

AREAS OF INTEREST:
Function and diseases of the kidney.

NAME(S) OF PROGRAMS:
● **Research Fellowship Award**

TYPE:
Fellowships; Grants-in-aid; Research grants. Fellowships for research and training in the field of kidney function and disease. Current emphasis is on supporting research and training in academic nephrology on closely related fields.

YEAR PROGRAM STARTED: 1967

PURPOSE:
To support those aspects of kidney research and training which are not adequately financed by governmental agencies and to support training of individuals whose goal is a career in academic nephrology or related fields.

LEGAL BASIS:
Voluntary health agency.

ELIGIBILITY:
Applicants must have completed no more than 4.5 years of postdoctoral research training (after receipt of M.D., Ph.D., D.O., or equivalent degree) at the time of the activation of the award. For those applying for a second year (competitive renewal), applicants must have completed no more than 5.5 years of postdoctoral training. Individuals completing two years of training may be eligible for a third year of funding to gain additional training towards becoming an independent investigator, but that additional support will not be awarded to carry out the initial project proposal. Anyone who has ever held a faculty appointment at the level of assistant professor is ineligible.

FINANCIAL DATA:
Amount of support per award: $50,000 annual stipend for new awardees.
Total amount of support: Varies.

NUMBER OF AWARDS: 10 new research fellowships awarded each year.

APPLICATION INFORMATION:
Application available online.
Duration: Awards are made normally on an annual basis; however, fellows can reapply for a second year.
Deadline: First quarter of each calendar year.

OFFICERS:
Bill Cella, Chairman
Lynda Szczech, M.D., President

ADDRESS INQUIRIES TO:
Kristine Persinger, Grant Coordinator
(See address above.)

NATIONAL KIDNEY FOUNDATION [2582]

30 East 33rd Street
New York, NY 10016
(212) 889-2210
(800) 622-9010
Fax: (212) 779-0068

E-MAIL ADDRESS:
christinep@kidney.org

WEB SITE ADDRESS:
www.kidney.org

AREAS OF INTEREST:
Improvement in the treatment and prevention of kidney disease.

NAME(S) OF PROGRAMS:
● **Young Investigator Grant Program**

TYPE:
Development grants; Project/program grants; Research grants; Seed money grants.

YEAR PROGRAM STARTED: 1987

PURPOSE:
To support research in the fields of nephrology, urology and related disciplines by individuals who have completed fellowship training and who hold junior faculty positions at university-affiliated medical centers in the U.S.

LEGAL BASIS:
Voluntary health agency.

ELIGIBILITY:
Applications will be considered from individuals who will have completed research fellowship training in nephrology, urology or closely related fields prior to the start of the grant award and who intend to pursue research directly to these areas. At the time funding begins (July 1), the applicant must hold a full-time, junior faculty appointment in a university-affiliated medical center in the U.S. Customarily, the appropriate faculty rank is that of assistant professor.

Applications must be made prior to the end of the third year after initial faculty appointment. Because of the application deadline, for most individuals whose appointments commenced July 1, the last application deadline will fall in their third year at the junior faculty level.

These grants are intended to support research primarily by individuals holding M.D. or Ph.D. degrees who are commencing careers on the faculty of medical schools. In all cases, the applicant's research and career goals must be directed to the study of normal or abnormal kidney function or of diseases of the kidney and urinary tract.

GEOGRAPHIC RESTRICTIONS:
United States.

FINANCIAL DATA:
Amount of support per award: $50,000 per year.

NUMBER OF APPLICANTS MOST RECENT YEAR:
40.

NUMBER OF AWARDS: Varies.

APPLICATION INFORMATION:
Application form, letter of commitment from the applicant's department and three letters of recommendation are required.
Duration: Up to two years per annual review.
Deadline: December 1.

PUBLICATIONS:
Program announcement.

STAFF:
Dolph Chianchiano, Senior Vice President Health Policy and Research

ADDRESS INQUIRIES TO:
Christine Persinger
Research Program Manager
(See e-mail address above.)

NATIONAL KIDNEY FOUNDATION [2583]
30 East 33rd Street
New York, NY 10016
(212) 889-2210
(800) 622-9010
Fax: (212) 779-0068

E-MAIL ADDRESS:
christinep@kidney.org

WEB SITE ADDRESS:
www.kidney.org

FOUNDED: 1993

AREAS OF INTEREST:
Function and diseases of the kidney.

NAME(S) OF PROGRAMS:
- **Clinical Scientist Award**

TYPE:
Awards/prizes. Salary subsidy.

YEAR PROGRAM STARTED: 1993

PURPOSE:
To support investigators who have demonstrated outstanding clinical research potential to promote their continued success as independent investigators.

LEGAL BASIS:
Voluntary health agency.

ELIGIBILITY:
The intent of the award is to fund highly promising investigators during the early stages of their independent research careers. Applicants must hold an M.D. or equivalent domestic or foreign degree and must be full-time staff members of a department within an institution in the U.S. at the time of the award.

Applicants will generally have at least five, but not more than 10, years of postdoctoral research experience by the beginning of the award date. Clinical training received after the doctoral degree does not count as research experience. Candidate must have demonstrated independent research accomplishments at the time of application. Applicants must demonstrate that they have sufficient project funding to support the proposed work during the tenure of the award. This support may be from extramural or institutional sources.

Applicants must be citizens or permanent residents of the U.S. at the time of application.

GEOGRAPHIC RESTRICTIONS:
United States.

FINANCIAL DATA:
Amount of support per award: $50,000 per year.
Total amount of support: Varies.

NUMBER OF APPLICANTS MOST RECENT YEAR:
4.

NUMBER OF AWARDS: 3 per year maximum.

APPLICATION INFORMATION:
Applications will be reviewed by a committee designated by the National Kidney Foundation. Attention will be given to the general qualifications and prior training of the applicant, the quality and originality of the previous research, the scientific merit of the research proposed in the application, the independence of the applicant and the applicant's promise for continued productivity.
Duration: Three years, reviewed annually. No renewals.
Deadline: December 1.

STAFF:
Dolph Chianchiano, Senior Vice President Health Policy and Research

ADDRESS INQUIRIES TO:
Christine Persinger
Research Program Manager
(See e-mail address above.)

*SPECIAL STIPULATIONS:
Clinical Scientists are expected to devote a minimum of 75% of their time to research.

Awardees may devote up to 25% of their time to other professional activities. The awardee will be known as a Clinical Scientist of the National Kidney Foundation and should acknowledge this support in publications resulting from the proposed work.

Oncology

AMERICAN ASSOCIATION FOR CANCER RESEARCH [2584]
615 Chestnut Street, 17th Floor
Philadelphia, PA 19106
(215) 440-9300
Fax: (215) 440-9372

E-MAIL ADDRESS:
grants@aacr.org

WEB SITE ADDRESS:
www.aacr.org

FOUNDED: 1907

AREAS OF INTEREST:
Cancer.

NAME(S) OF PROGRAMS:
- **Career Development Awards**
- **Innovator Awards in Cancer Research**
- **Research Grants and Fellowships**
- **Scholar-in-Training Awards**

TYPE:
Awards/prizes; Fellowships; Research grants; Travel grants. AACR Career Development Awards in Cancer Research support research by junior investigators. These awards, which include an annual stipend, provide important transitional support for direct research expenses as researchers move from the ranks of early career scientists to faculty status.

AACR Research Fellowships in Basic, Clinical and Translational Research foster cancer research throughout the world by scientists currently at the postdoctoral or clinical research fellow level.

AACR Scholar-in-Training Awards enhance the education and training of graduate students, medical students and residents, clinical fellows or equivalent, and postdoctoral fellows by facilitating their attendance at the Annual Meeting and Special Conferences of the American Association for Cancer Research. These awards are presented to scientists in training who are presenters of abstracts that have been highly rated by AACR.

Innovator Awards in Cancer Research are designed to foster innovation and collaboration in cancer research and support independent investigators early in their careers. The awards provide the recipients with the recognition they need to further their careers and possibly leverage additional funding.

PURPOSE:
To facilitate communication and dissemination of knowledge among scientists and others dedicated to the cancer problem; to foster research in cancer and related biomedical sciences; to encourage presentation and discussion of new and important observations in the field; to foster public education, science education and training; to advance the understanding of cancer etiology, prevention, diagnosis and treatment throughout the world.

LEGAL BASIS:
Not-for-profit society.

ELIGIBILITY:
Grants are given to individuals. For some programs, applicants must be working at an academic institution in the U.S. No grants to religious organizations. AACR Associate Members and persons who are not yet members of AACR are eligible for awards.

Fellowship candidates must have completed a Ph.D., M.D., or other doctoral degree. Candidates must be working as a postdoctoral or clinical research fellow at an academic facility, teaching hospital, or research institution, and must be in their second, third, or fourth year of a cancer research fellowship at the beginning of the award year. Academic faculty holding the rank of adjunct professor, associate professor, assistant professor, or higher, graduate or medical students, medical residents, permanent national government employees, and employees of private industry are not eligible. Candidates must be nominated by a member of AACR and must be an AACR member or apply for membership by the time the fellowship application is submitted. AACR Associate Members may not serve as nominators.

Career Development Award candidates must be full-time, junior faculty at the time the grant term begins. Candidates must also have completed productive postdoctoral research and demonstrated independent, investigator-initiated research. Employees of a national government and employees of private industry are not eligible. Candidates must be nominated by a member of AACR and must be an AACR member or apply for membership by the time the application is submitted. AACR Associate Members may not serve as nominators.

FINANCIAL DATA:
For both Fellowship and Award recipients, free registration and support for travel expenses to the AACR Annual Meeting to accept the award is also provided.
Amount of support per award: Fellowships: $30,000 to $45,000 salary support per year; Career Development Awards: $50,000 to $75,000 per year for two years for salary or direct research expenses.
Total amount of support: Varies.

NUMBER OF APPLICANTS MOST RECENT YEAR:
Over 250.

NUMBER OF AWARDS: Scholar-in-Training: Approximately 250 per year; Awards and Fellowships: Approximately 30 per year.

APPLICATION INFORMATION:
Application form required.
Duration: Fellowships: One to three years; Awards: Two years.
Deadline: Scholar-in-Training: November of each year for Annual Meeting Awards, with notification the following February; Fellowships and Awards: Fall of each year, with notification the following February.

PUBLICATIONS:
Cancer Research, scientific journal; *Clinical Cancer Research,* journal; *Cell Growth and Differentiation,* journal; *Cancer Epidemiology, Biomarkers and Prevention,* journal.

ADDRESS INQUIRIES TO:
Deborah L. Crabtree
Program Administrator
(See address above.)

AMERICAN BRAIN TUMOR ASSOCIATION
2720 River Road
Des Plaines, IL 60018
(847) 827-9910
Fax: (847) 827-9918

E-MAIL ADDRESS:
info@abta.org

WEB SITE ADDRESS:
www.abta.org

TYPE:
Fellowships; Seed money grants; Training grants.

See entry 2612 for full listing.

AMERICAN CANCER SOCIETY, INC.   [2585]
250 Williams Street, N.W.
6th Floor
Atlanta, GA 30303-1002
(404) 329-7558
Fax: (404) 321-4669

E-MAIL ADDRESS:
grants@cancer.org

WEB SITE ADDRESS:
www.cancer.org/research

FOUNDED: 1946

AREAS OF INTEREST:
All forms of cancer and their cures.

NAME(S) OF PROGRAMS:
● **Postdoctoral Fellowship**

TYPE:
Fellowships. Fellowships to enable young investigators to qualify for independent careers in cancer research. Support is primarily intended for study in the U.S. However, programs may be undertaken in other countries when training objectives can best be attained by so doing.

YEAR PROGRAM STARTED: 1946

PURPOSE:
To speed the conquest of cancer by training and supporting personnel for cancer research.

LEGAL BASIS:
Nonprofit corporation.

ELIGIBILITY:
Applicants must be U.S. citizens or legal permanent residents. The latter must provide notarized evidence of their legal resident alien status. Applicants who hold doctoral degrees in appropriate disciplines are eligible to apply. Applicant shall have been awarded a doctoral degree prior to the activation of the grant.

GEOGRAPHIC RESTRICTIONS:
United States.

FINANCIAL DATA:
Amount of support per award: Award includes an annual stipend of $44,000 in the first year, $46,000 in the second and $48,000 in the third. Relocation travel expenses for fellow only and a fellowship allowance of up to $4,000 per year.

APPLICATION INFORMATION:
Official application materials are available on the Society's web site or upon request to the Grants Assistant.
Duration: Up to three years.
Deadline: Deadlines for receipt of completed materials are April 1, for approved grants to be activated on or after January 1, and October 15, for approved grants to be activated on July 1.

ADDRESS INQUIRIES TO:
Annette P. Jordan, Grants Assistant
(See address above.)

AMERICAN CANCER SOCIETY, INC.   [2586]
250 Williams Street, N.W.
6th Floor
Atlanta, GA 30303-1002
(404) 329-7558
Fax: (404) 321-4669

E-MAIL ADDRESS:
grants@cancer.org

WEB SITE ADDRESS:
www.cancer.org/research

FOUNDED: 1946

AREAS OF INTEREST:
Cancer and its cures.

NAME(S) OF PROGRAMS:
● **Institutional Research Grants**

TYPE:
Block grants. Grants for institutional cancer research projects. Support is available for integration of varied efforts in cancer research within the institution and preliminary testing of new and venturesome ideas for research on cancer by junior investigators without other national research support.

YEAR PROGRAM STARTED: 1957

PURPOSE:
To eliminate cancer as a major health problem by preventing cancer, saving lives and diminishing suffering from cancer through research, education, advocacy and service.

LEGAL BASIS:
Nonprofit corporation.

ELIGIBILITY:
Institutions of higher learning in the U.S. and its territories are eligible to apply for support of appropriate research to be conducted by qualified investigators.

GEOGRAPHIC RESTRICTIONS:
United States.

FINANCIAL DATA:
Allowable expenditures include stipends for graduate student and postdoctoral assistants and equipment costing less than $2,000, such as research supplies.
Amount of support per award: Average $90,000 per year.

APPLICATION INFORMATION:
Grant application materials become available January 1 and are available on the Society's web site.
Duration: One to three years. Renewable upon reapplication.
Deadline: April 1.

ADDRESS INQUIRIES TO:
Annette P. Jordan, Grants Assistant
(See address above.)

AMERICAN GASTROENTEROLOGICAL ASSOCIATION (AGA)

4930 Del Ray Avenue
Bethesda, MD 20814
(301) 222-4012
Fax: (301) 652-3890

E-MAIL ADDRESS:
awards@fdhn.org

WEB SITE ADDRESS:
www.gastro.org/fdhnfunding

TYPE:
Research grants. Recognition award for an established investigator working on novel approaches in gastric cancer, including the fields of gastric mucosal cell biology, regeneration and regulation of cell growth (not as they relate to peptic ulcer disease or repair), inflammation as precancerous lesions, genetics of gastric carcinoma, oncogenes in gastric epithelial malignancies, epidemiology of gastric cancer, etiology of gastric epithelial malignancies or clinical research in diagnosis or treatment of gastric carcinoma.

See entry 2561 for full listing.

AMERICAN INSTITUTE FOR CANCER RESEARCH [2587]

1759 R Street, N.W.
Washington, DC 20009
(202) 328-7744
Fax: (202) 328-7226

E-MAIL ADDRESS:
research@aicr.org

WEB SITE ADDRESS:
www.aicr.org

FOUNDED: 1982

AREAS OF INTEREST:
Food, nutrition, physical activity and the prevention and treatment of cancer; food, nutrition, physical activity and cancer survivorship.

NAME(S) OF PROGRAMS:
- **Investigator Initiated Grants (IIG)**
- **Matching Grants (MG)**
- **Postdoctoral Grant Awards (PDA)**

TYPE:
Research grants. The Investigator Initiated Research Grant program is open to researchers at not-for-profit universities, hospitals or research centers. The Institute encourages new research on dietary means of preventing and treating cancer, or improving the life of the cancer patient or survivor.

The Matching Grants program helps fund research projects with matching support from for-profit corporations.

The Postdoctoral Grant Awards have been developed to encourage new researchers to explore innovative research ideas.

PURPOSE:
To foster research on diet, nutrition and cancer and educate the public about the results.

ELIGIBILITY:
Institutions: Research grants are awarded to nonprofit institutions in the Americas. Grant applications will not be accepted from agencies of the federal government or agencies supported entirely by the federal government of any country. Proof of nonprofit status of the institution must be submitted with the grant application.

Investigators: The Principal Investigator must (for an IIG or MG application) have a Ph.D. or equivalent degree or M.D. degree and be a research staff or faculty member at a nonprofit academic or research institution at the minimum level of an assistant professor (or its equivalent) or higher. Applicants for a Postdoctoral Grant Award must have a Ph.D. or equivalent degree or M.D. degree no more than four years prior to date of application and be a research staff or faculty member at a nonprofit academic or research institution at a level no higher than assistant professor. The Principal Investigator at an institution in the U.S. must be a citizen of the U.S. or foreign national with a permanent residence visa that is valid for the duration of the grant award. In other countries, the Principal Investigator must meet the requirements of that country for permanent residency and employment.

GEOGRAPHIC RESTRICTIONS:
North, Central and South America and the Caribbean.

FINANCIAL DATA:
Amount of support per award: Investigator Initiated Grants (IIG): Up to $75,000 per year, plus 10% indirect costs; Postdoctoral Grant Awards (PDGA): Up to $38,000 per year; Matching Grants: Up to $75,000 per year.

NUMBER OF APPLICANTS MOST RECENT YEAR:
118.

NUMBER OF AWARDS: 26.

APPLICATION INFORMATION:
Online application form required.
Duration: One to two years. Postdoctoral Grant is not renewable. All other programs are renewable.

PUBLICATIONS:
Grant application package; recipients list; application form.

STAFF:
Susan Higginbotham, Ph.D., R.D., Director for Research

ADDRESS INQUIRIES TO:
Research Department
(See address above.)

ASSOCIATION FOR RESEARCH OF CHILDHOOD CANCER, INC. (AROCC) [2588]

P.O. Box 251
Buffalo, NY 14225-0251
(716) 681-4433

E-MAIL ADDRESS:
president@arocc.org

WEB SITE ADDRESS:
www.arocc.org

FOUNDED: 1971

AREAS OF INTEREST:
Pediatric cancer research and parent support.

TYPE:
Seed money grants. Pilot projects.

YEAR PROGRAM STARTED: 1971

PURPOSE:
To fund pediatric cancer research institutions in New York state to find better treatment, and eventually a cure, for the types of cancer that afflict children.

LEGAL BASIS:
Tax-exempt, not-for-profit corporation in New York state.

ELIGIBILITY:
Awarded to qualified investigators in pediatric cancer research.

FINANCIAL DATA:
Amount of support per award: Varies.
Total amount of support: Varies according to the financial restrictions of the Association.
Matching fund requirements: Depends on the nature of the project.

NUMBER OF APPLICANTS MOST RECENT YEAR:
30.

NUMBER OF AWARDS: 3 to 5 per year.

APPLICATION INFORMATION:
Application must be submitted on AROCC forms. All grants are evaluated by AROCC Medical Advisors.
Duration: One year average. Consideration for three years. Renewal is possible based on past progress supported by abstracts and publications.
Deadline: November 1. Announcement by June 30.

ADDRESS INQUIRIES TO:
Anne O'Donnell, President
(See address above.)

CANCER RESEARCH INSTITUTE [2589]

One Exchange Plaza
55 Broadway, Suite 1802
New York, NY 10006
(212) 688-7515
(800) 992-2623
Fax: (212) 832-9376

E-MAIL ADDRESS:
grants@cancerresearch.org

WEB SITE ADDRESS:
www.cancerresearch.org

FOUNDED: 1953

AREAS OF INTEREST:
General or tumor immunology.

NAME(S) OF PROGRAMS:
- **Investigator Award**

TYPE:
Awards/prizes; Research grants. Award supports tenure-track assistant professors or equivalent undertaking their first independent investigations in general immunology or tumor immunology.

YEAR PROGRAM STARTED: 1986

PURPOSE:
To further the development of immunological approaches to the diagnosis, treatment and prevention of cancer.

LEGAL BASIS:
Private, nonprofit organization.

ELIGIBILITY:
Applicant must be a tenure-track assistant professor or equivalent when award activates.

FINANCIAL DATA:
Award can be used at the recipient's discretion for salary, technical assistance, supplies and/or equipment.
Amount of support per award: $50,000 per year.
Total amount of support: $1,200,000 for fiscal year 2008.

NUMBER OF APPLICANTS MOST RECENT YEAR:
44 for the year 2009.

NUMBER OF AWARDS: 6 for the year 2009.

APPLICATION INFORMATION:
The application process consists of two steps:
(1) submission of a paper application form and five sets of attachments (curriculum vitae, bibliography, abstract of research proposal, four-page description of research program, appendices, and three letters of recommendation) and;
(2) submission of an online application form.
Duration: Four years.
Deadline: March 1.

PUBLICATIONS:
Program guidelines; applications.

IRS IDENTIFICATION NUMBER: 13-1837442

ADDRESS INQUIRIES TO:
Elizabeth Joyce, Grants Administrator
(See address above.)

CANCER RESEARCH INSTITUTE   [2590]
One Exchange Plaza
55 Broadway, Suite 1802
New York, NY 10006
(212) 688-7515
(800) 992-2623
Fax: (212) 832-9376

E-MAIL ADDRESS:
grants@cancerresearch.org

WEB SITE ADDRESS:
www.cancerresearch.org

FOUNDED: 1953

AREAS OF INTEREST:
General or tumor immunology.

NAME(S) OF PROGRAMS:
• **Irvington Institute Fellowship Program of the Cancer Research Institute**

TYPE:
Fellowships; Research grants; Training grants.

YEAR PROGRAM STARTED: 1971

PURPOSE:
To offer postdoctoral fellowships to qualified individuals in the formative stages of their career who wish to receive training in general or cancer immunology.

LEGAL BASIS:
Private, nonprofit organization.

ELIGIBILITY:
Applicants must have a doctoral degree and must conduct research under a sponsor who holds a formal appointment at the sponsoring institution. There are no nationality restrictions. Work may be carried out in the U.S. or abroad at nonprofit institutions and medical centers. Fellows with five or more years of postdoctoral experience are ineligible.

FINANCIAL DATA:
Amount of support per award: $45,000 stipend for the first year, $47,000 for the second year, and $49,000 for the third year. An institutional allowance of $1,500 per year is provided for the host institution to cover laboratory supplies, scientific travel and health insurance on behalf of the fellow.
Total amount of support: $3,839,396 for fiscal year 2008.

NUMBER OF APPLICANTS MOST RECENT YEAR:
245 for the year 2009.

NUMBER OF AWARDS: 31 for the year 2009.

APPLICATION INFORMATION:
Paper applications will not be accepted. Applicants must complete an electronic application form to be submitted with the following attachments:
(1) description of the applicant's background;
(2) list of other funding sources to which applications have been submitted;
(3) applicant's curriculum vitae and bibliography;
(4) abstract of research in non-technical English;
(5) outline of research proposal, not to exceed 10 pages;
(6) letter of introduction from sponsor;
(7) sponsor's curriculum vitae, bibliography and current support and;
(8) letter of recommendation from two individuals acquainted with applicant's work.
Duration: Three years.
Deadline: April 1 and October 1. Notification eight to 10 weeks after the deadline.

PUBLICATIONS:
Annual report; application guidelines.

IRS IDENTIFICATION NUMBER: 13-1837442

STAFF:
Jill O'Donnell-Tormey, Executive Director
Lynne Harmer, Director of Grants Administration

ADDRESS INQUIRIES TO:
Elizabeth Joyce, Administrator
(See address above.)

THE CANCER RESEARCH SOCIETY, INC.   [2591]
625 President Kennedy Avenue
Suite 402
Montreal QC H3A 3S5 Canada
(514) 861-9227
Fax: (514) 861-9220

E-MAIL ADDRESS:
grants@src-crs.ca

WEB SITE ADDRESS:
www.cancerresearchsociety.ca

FOUNDED: 1945

AREAS OF INTEREST:
Cancer research.

NAME(S) OF PROGRAMS:
• **Grants for Cancer Research**

TYPE:
Fellowships; General operating grants.

YEAR PROGRAM STARTED: 1946

PURPOSE:
To find the cause, cure and prevention of cancer.

LEGAL BASIS:
Nonprofit registered fund-raising corporation.

ELIGIBILITY:
Any qualified researcher who is associated with an accredited institution may apply, provided the research is done in Canada.

GEOGRAPHIC RESTRICTIONS:
Canada.

FINANCIAL DATA:
Amount of support per award: $60,000 per year.

COOPERATIVE FUNDING PROGRAMS: Canadian Institutes of Health Research and Canadian Breast Cancer Alliance.

NUMBER OF APPLICANTS MOST RECENT YEAR:
210 for the year 2010.

NUMBER OF AWARDS: 35 for the year 2010.

APPLICATION INFORMATION:
Duration: Two years. Renewal possible.
Deadline: February 15 for research grants.

BOARD OF DIRECTORS:
Mario Chevrette, Ph.D., President
Annick Bergeron, L.L.B., Vice President
Nathalie Labelle, C.A., B.A.A., Treasurer
Micheline Bouchard, Secretary
Mike G. Bouchard, L.L.B., MBA
Marie-Kym Brisson
Francois Des Rochers
Philippe P. Huneault
Lucie Jeannotte, Ph.D.
Heidi Lange, C.R.H.A.
Gail Snyder, M.A.
Dr. Denis Soulieres, M.D., M.Sc.

ADDRESS INQUIRIES TO:
Josee-France Villemure, Scientific Advisor
(See address above.)

CANCER RESEARCH UK   [2592]
Research Funding
61 Lincoln's Inn Fields
P.O. Box 123
London WC2A 3PX England
44 (020) 7242 0200
Fax: 44 (020) 7269 3100

WEB SITE ADDRESS:
science.cancerresearchuk.org

FOUNDED: 2002

AREAS OF INTEREST:
Research into the causes, diagnosis, treatment and prevention of cancer.

TYPE:
Fellowships; Project/program grants; Research grants; Training grants. There are various grant programs for cancer research including clinical trials. Funding includes research groups, fellowships, programs and project grants.

YEAR PROGRAM STARTED: 2002

PURPOSE:
To carry out world-class research to improve understanding of cancer and find out how to prevent, diagnose and treat different kinds of cancer; to ensure that the findings are used to improve the lives of all cancer patients; to help people to understand cancer, the progress being made and the choices each person can make; to work in partnership with others to achieve the greatest impact in the fight against cancer.

LEGAL BASIS:
Charity (public funded).

ELIGIBILITY:
Research should be conducted in the U.K. Awards are made to researchers in universities, medical schools and independent research organizations.

GEOGRAPHIC RESTRICTIONS:
United Kingdom.

FINANCIAL DATA:
Amount of support per award: Varies.
Total amount of support: GBP 333,000,000 for the year 2007-08.
Matching fund requirements: Varies.

NUMBER OF APPLICANTS MOST RECENT YEAR:
Over 800.

NUMBER OF AWARDS: Over 1,100 projects supported.

APPLICATION INFORMATION:
Contact a member of Research Funding for a discussion prior to sending an application. Application form available online.

Duration: Two to six years (longer for clinical trials).

PUBLICATIONS:
Scientific Yearbook; Annual Review.

THE JANE COFFIN CHILDS MEMORIAL FUND FOR MEDICAL RESEARCH [2593]

333 Cedar Street
New Haven, CT 06510
(203) 785-4612
Fax: (203) 785-3301

E-MAIL ADDRESS:
jccfund@yale.edu

WEB SITE ADDRESS:
www.jccfund.org

FOUNDED: 1937

AREAS OF INTEREST:
Cancer research.

TYPE:
Fellowships. Postdoctoral fellowships for studies in the medical and related sciences bearing on cancer.

YEAR PROGRAM STARTED: 1944

PURPOSE:
To further research into the causes, origins and treatment of cancer.

LEGAL BASIS:
Private foundation.

ELIGIBILITY:
Applicants must be U.S. or foreign citizens holding the M.D. or Ph.D. degree in the proposed field of study (or the equivalent in training and experience) and have no more than one year postdoctoral experience. The prior sponsorship of the laboratory at which they promise to work must be obtained.

Awards to foreign nationals will be made only for work in the U.S., whereas fellowships to American citizens are tenable in the U.S. or any foreign country.

FINANCIAL DATA:
Amount of support per award: $45,000 for the first year, $46,000 for the second year and $48,000 for the third year, with an additional allowance of $1,000 for each dependent child. A grant of $1,500 per year to be applied toward the cost of research is usually made available to the sponsoring laboratory each year.

Total amount of support: $3,200,000.

NUMBER OF APPLICANTS MOST RECENT YEAR:
320.

APPLICATION INFORMATION:
Official application materials are available online.

Duration: Two to three years.

Deadline: February 1 to be considered at late spring meetings.

IRS IDENTIFICATION NUMBER: 06-6034840

OFFICERS:
James E. Childs, Chairman
William G. Gridley, Jr., Vice Chairman
Hendon C. Pingeon, Treasurer

STAFF:
Dr. Randy Schekman, Science Director
Kim Roberts, Administrative Director

ADDRESS INQUIRIES TO:
Kim Roberts, Administrative Director
(See address above.)

RUTH ESTRIN GOLDBERG MEMORIAL FOR CANCER RESEARCH [2594]

653 Colonial Arms Road
Union, NJ 07083-7605
(908) 686-5508

E-MAIL ADDRESS:
goodfudgie@aol.com

WEB SITE ADDRESS:
regm-cancer-research.us

FOUNDED: 1949

AREAS OF INTEREST:
Cancer research.

TYPE:
Development grants; General operating grants; Project/program grants; Research grants; Seed money grants.

YEAR PROGRAM STARTED: 1949

PURPOSE:
To raise funds to support cancer research.

LEGAL BASIS:
Nonprofit.

ELIGIBILITY:
Applicant must be affiliated with an accredited institution in New Jersey, New York or Pennsylvania.

GEOGRAPHIC RESTRICTIONS:
Eastern United States.

FINANCIAL DATA:
Amount of support per award: $10,000 to $25,000 average, if available.

Total amount of support: Average $30,000 to $50,000.

NUMBER OF APPLICANTS MOST RECENT YEAR:
10.

NUMBER OF AWARDS: 2.

APPLICATION INFORMATION:
Those interested should request an application form and copy of the Memorial's policy governing grants.

Duration: One year. Renewal possible upon reapplication the following year.

Deadline: April 30. Announcement June 1.

ADDRESS INQUIRIES TO:
Rhoda Goodman
(See address above.)

GREENBURG-MAY FOUNDATION [2595]

P.O. Box 5816
Miami Beach, FL 33154
(305) 864-8639

FOUNDED: 1947

AREAS OF INTEREST:
Medical research, Parkinson's disease, with primary focus on research in cancer and heart disease, the aged, and Jewish institutions.

TYPE:
Development grants; Research grants. Social services.

PURPOSE:
To improve health conditions and expedite cures in many diseases through research.

ELIGIBILITY:
Eligible organizations must be IRS 501(c)(3) tax-exempt and be located in Florida or New York. No funding to individuals.

GEOGRAPHIC RESTRICTIONS:
Florida and New York.

FINANCIAL DATA:
Amount of support per award: Varies depending on project.

APPLICATION INFORMATION:
Applicants must submit a copy of their tax-exempt determination letter. Contact the Foundation for further guidelines.

ADDRESS INQUIRIES TO:
Isabel May, President
(See address above.)

SUSAN G. KOMEN FOR THE CURE [2596]

5005 LBJ Freeway
Suite 250
Dallas, TX 75244
(972) 701-2050
Fax: (972) 701-2121

E-MAIL ADDRESS:
malciati@komen.org

WEB SITE ADDRESS:
www.komen.org/grants

FOUNDED: 1982

AREAS OF INTEREST:
Breast cancer research.

CONSULTING OR VOLUNTEER SERVICES:
Through a Komen Affiliate; find a Komen Affiliate on the Organization's web site.

NAME(S) OF PROGRAMS:
- **Career Catalyst Research Grants**
- **Investigator Initiated Research Grants**
- **Post Baccalaureate Training in Disparities Research**
- **Postdoctoral Fellowships**
- **Promise Grants**

TYPE:
Fellowships; Research grants; Training grants.

YEAR PROGRAM STARTED: 1982

PURPOSE:
To support breast cancer research and awareness.

LEGAL BASIS:
Texas nonprofit corporation.

ELIGIBILITY:
Varies with each award or grant.

FINANCIAL DATA:
Amount of support per award: $150,000 to $7,500,000.

Total amount of support: Varies per program.

NUMBER OF APPLICANTS MOST RECENT YEAR:
1,400 pre-applications and 865 full applications.

NUMBER OF AWARDS: 139 grants awarded for the year 2008.

APPLICATION INFORMATION:
Duration: Three to five years.

Deadline: Varies.

PUBLICATIONS:
Annual report.

IRS IDENTIFICATION NUMBER: 75-1835298

ADDRESS INQUIRIES TO:
Sari DeLand
Research Project Manager
(See address above.)

THE LADIES AUXILIARY TO THE VETERANS OF FOREIGN WARS [2597]

National Headquarters
406 West 34th Street, 10th Floor
Kansas City, MO 64111
(816) 561-8655
Fax: (816) 931-4753

E-MAIL ADDRESS:
info@ladiesauxvfw.org

WEB SITE ADDRESS:
www.ladiesauxvfw.org

AREAS OF INTEREST:
Cancer research.

NAME(S) OF PROGRAMS:
• **Postdoctoral Cancer Research Fellowship**

TYPE:
Fellowships; Research grants. A two-year fellowship for full-time cancer research.

YEAR PROGRAM STARTED: 1947

PURPOSE:
To support cancer research; to present an opportunity for researchers to devote two years, full-time, to making new discoveries about cancer.

LEGAL BASIS:
Nonprofit.

ELIGIBILITY:
U.S. universities, hospitals and other institutions are invited to nominate one individual who meets the criteria. Candidates must:
(1) be U.S. citizens (the nominator does not have to be);
(2) be nominated by the person who will be supervising the lab in which the researcher will be working;
(3) be qualified in a specific cancer-related specialty and the proposed research project must be cancer-related;
(4) have earned a doctoral-level degree by July 1 of the year application is made; if candidate does not have the degree by the time of application, he or she must indicate the date expected on the application form no later than July 1 of the application year and;
(5) proposed research must be the principal professional responsibility of the recipient during the fellowship.

GEOGRAPHIC RESTRICTIONS:
United States.

FINANCIAL DATA:
The funds are to be used as a salary or stipend, which may cover fringe benefits. If the institution's normal postdoctoral salary is greater than $50,000 per year, it is acceptable for the institution to supplement the salary. If the normal salary is less than $50,000, the excess funds may be used for lab equipment or supplies. During the two-year term of this fellowship, the researcher may not receive other funding towards his or her salary except as just described. Funds must be used before the end of a 25-month period.
Amount of support per award: $100,000 ($50,000 per year for two years).
Total amount of support: $100,000.

NUMBER OF AWARDS: 1.

APPLICATION INFORMATION:
Applications will be reviewed by a panel of basic and clinical researchers in the oncology field. The application must include the following:

(1) completed Official Application Form for current year;
(2) NIH biographical sketch on candidate's training, experience, honors and list of candidate's published research;
(3) brief description of proposed research project including abstract, methods, procedures and significance;
(4) timeline for the project and expected results throughout study; specifically, the results anticipated to have been obtained after nine months of funding. This information will be used to review adequacy of progress;
(5) letter of recommendation from sponsor (and from co-mentor if another individual will contribute significantly to the training supervision);
(6) NIH biographical sketch on sponsor (and co-mentor, if applicable) and;
(7) brief description of lab funding available to support proposed project.
Items 2, 3 and 4 must not exceed 10 pages. (Excess will be viewed negatively by review panel.) Do not use type smaller than 11-point font.
Duration: Two years. Not renewable.
Deadline: Must be postmarked by March 1; no exceptions. The winner of the fellowship will be notified by June 1, and upon receipt of written acceptance $50,000 will be issued.

PUBLICATIONS:
Program announcement; application.

ADDRESS INQUIRIES TO:
Judy Millick, Administrator of Programs
Cancer Research Fellowship Program
(See address above.)

LEUKEMIA RESEARCH FOUNDATION [2598]

3520 Lake Avenue
Suite 202
Wilmette, IL 60091
(847) 424-0600
Fax: (847) 424-0606

E-MAIL ADDRESS:
info@lrfmail.org

WEB SITE ADDRESS:
www.leukemia-research.org

FOUNDED: 1946

AREAS OF INTEREST:
Curing leukemia, lymphoma and myelodysplastic syndromes.

NAME(S) OF PROGRAMS:
• **New Investigator Awards**

TYPE:
Research grants. The goal of the grant program is to support new investigators. It funds scientists and physicians around the world.

YEAR PROGRAM STARTED: 1946

PURPOSE:
To conquer leukemia, lymphoma and myelodysplastic syndromes by funding research into their causes and cures; to enrich the quality of life of those touched by these diseases.

ELIGIBILITY:
Preference will be given to applicants proposing new lines of investigation.

FINANCIAL DATA:
Amount of support per award: Up to $100,000.
Total amount of support: More than $1,000,000 annually.

NUMBER OF APPLICANTS MOST RECENT YEAR:
73 for the year 2010-11.

NUMBER OF AWARDS: Varies.

APPLICATION INFORMATION:
Applications will only be accepted electronically and should be e-mailed to grants@lrfmail.org. All applicants will receive a receipt via e-mail when their application is received. Hard copies of grant applications will not be accepted.

Applicants must use the 2011-12 application cover sheet. This form must be filled out in its entirety for an application to be accepted and assigned for review. The Medical Advisory Board will not consider applications which are incomplete.

Document format should be single-spaced, using a 12-point font throughout, on 8 1/2 by 11- inch paper. A concise one paragraph description of the project is to be included in the application as a separate page. This paragraph should be in extreme lay terminology, appropriate for an audience without scientific training. Explain terms which cannot be simplified.
Duration: One year. Funding cycle begins July 1.
Deadline: February.

IRS IDENTIFICATION NUMBER: 36-6102182

ADDRESS INQUIRIES TO:
Linda Kabot
Research Grants Administrator
(See address above.)

THE MILHEIM FOUNDATION FOR CANCER RESEARCH [2599]

c/o U.S. Bank
200 University Boulevard
Denver, CO 80206
(303) 316-5944
Fax: (303) 394-4902

WEB SITE ADDRESS:
milheim.org

FOUNDED: 1959

AREAS OF INTEREST:
Cancer research.

TYPE:
Research grants; Seed money grants. Grants to cancer research grantmaking organizations within the state of Colorado.

YEAR PROGRAM STARTED: 1959

PURPOSE:
To provide financial support for research work for the prevention, treatment and cure of cancer; to make known to the public the benefits and results of research sponsored by the Milheim Foundation.

LEGAL BASIS:
Special-interest foundation. Established under the last will and testament of Clara Milheim Wheeler.

GEOGRAPHIC RESTRICTIONS:
Colorado.

FINANCIAL DATA:
Amount of support per award: Varies.
Total amount of support: Varies.

APPLICATION INFORMATION:
Duration: One year, beginning in July.

ADDRESS INQUIRIES TO:
Sally Woods, Vice President
Private Client Reserve
E-mail: sally.woods@usbank.com

ONCOLOGY NURSING FOUNDATION [2600]

125 Enterprise Drive
Pittsburgh, PA 15275-1214
(412) 859-6298
Fax: (412) 859-6160

E-MAIL ADDRESS:
jbrown@ons.org

WEB SITE ADDRESS:
www.ons.org

FOUNDED: 1981

AREAS OF INTEREST:
Oncology nursing.

NAME(S) OF PROGRAMS:
● **Fellowship Program**
● **Small Grants Research Program**

TYPE:
Fellowships; Research grants.

YEAR PROGRAM STARTED: 1984

PURPOSE:
To support the professional development of oncology nurses around the world.

LEGAL BASIS:
National public, nonprofit, tax-exempt organization.

ELIGIBILITY:
An applicant must be a health professional actively involved in some aspect of cancer patient care, education or research. Membership in the Oncology Nursing Society is preferred but not required. Doctoral students are eligible. The Foundation does not fund completed projects or those nearing completion, tuition or conference registration fees, travel, the purchase of office equipment or institutional indirect costs.

FINANCIAL DATA:
Amount of support per award: Fellowships: $20,000; Small Grants: $10,000.
Total amount of support: $269,863 for the year 2010.

NUMBER OF APPLICANTS MOST RECENT YEAR: 50.

NUMBER OF AWARDS: Varies.

APPLICATION INFORMATION:
Applications must include:
(1) an e-mail address;
(2) $25 application fee (make checks payable to the Oncology Nursing Foundation);
(3) if a resubmission, attach a cover letter explaining the revisions to the application;
(4) title page with all signatures;
(5) an IRB or animal welfare committee approval letter;
(6) 500-word abstract;
(7) an eight-page project narrative describing purpose and specific aims, significance, background and review of literature, research design, experimental variables, instruments, facilities and resources;
(8) reference list;
(9) timetable;
(10) statement of scientific integrity;
(11) letters of support;
(12) form documenting the signature of the thesis or dissertation chairperson;
(13) biographical sketches (two-page limit) and;
(14) itemized budgets and budget narratives.
Duration: Research Fellowships: One year; Small Grants: Two years.
Deadline: Fellowships: July 1. Notification by September 15. Grants: October 1. Notification by January 1.

PUBLICATIONS:
Program announcement; applications; guidelines; *Recognition of Achievement: Awards, Grants, Honors, Scholarships.*

ADDRESS INQUIRIES TO:
Jenny Brown, Grants Specialist
Oncology Nursing Society Research Team
(See address above.)

THE ELSA U. PARDEE FOUNDATION [2601]

P.O. Box 2767
Midland, MI 48641-2767
(989) 832-3691
Fax: (989) 832-8842

WEB SITE ADDRESS:
www.pardeefoundation.org

FOUNDED: 1944

AREAS OF INTEREST:
Research for control and cure of cancer.

TYPE:
Research grants. Grants for research projects relating to the cure and control of cancer and for the treatment needs of cancer victims.

The Foundation supports activities in three major areas:
(1) innovative new cancer research projects;
(2) established, ongoing cancer programs and;
(3) Pardee Cancer Treatment Committees in six counties in central Michigan and one Texas county where the Dow Chemical Company has a presence. The Treatment Committees assist cancer victims with their treatment expenses.

PURPOSE:
To promote the control and cure of cancer.

LEGAL BASIS:
Private foundation.

ELIGIBILITY:
Grants are limited under the terms of the charter to the cure and control of cancer, and in general do not provide for building funds, equipment (except that used in a specific project), fellowships or fund-raising campaign contributions.

Priority is given to researchers at nonprofit institutions in the U.S. who are new to the field of cancer research, or to established research investigators examining new approaches to cancer cure.

FINANCIAL DATA:
Total assets of $75,426,678 as of December 31, 2009.

The Foundation provides more than $3,000,000 annually to support research directed towards the detection, treatment and cure of cancer.

Amount of support per award: Grants vary in amount, depending upon the needs and nature of the request.
Total amount of support: $4,146,956 in total grants for year ended December 31, 2009.

NUMBER OF APPLICANTS MOST RECENT YEAR: 128 in 2009.

NUMBER OF AWARDS: 23 grants funded in 2009.

REPRESENTATIVE AWARDS:
$51,823 to University of Alabama for a study of infiltrating suppressive gamma/delta T cells in glioblastoma; $103,844 to California Institute of Technology for the study of potent and specific killing of human cancer cells via triggered nanomechanical transduction; $149,188 to University of California for the study of p85 and FGFR3 signaling in multiple myeloma.

APPLICATION INFORMATION:
Grant applications may be submitted online at the Foundation web site.
Duration: Grants typically one year in duration.
Deadline: Grant applications are reviewed by the Medical Committee in April, August and November.

PUBLICATIONS:
Annual report; application guidelines.

OFFICERS AND TRUSTEES:
Gail E. Lanphear, President
Lisa J. Gerstacker, Vice President and Assistant Treasurer
Alan W. Ott, Treasurer
James A. Kendall, Secretary
W. James Allen, Assistant Treasurer and Assistant Secretary
Laurie G. Bouwman, Trustee
Mary M. Neely, Trustee
William D. Schuette, Trustee
Michael Woolhiser, Trustee

PREVENT CANCER FOUNDATION [2602]

1600 Duke Street, Suite 500
Alexandria, VA 22314
(703) 836-4412
Fax: (703) 836-4413

E-MAIL ADDRESS:
info@preventcancer.org

WEB SITE ADDRESS:
www.preventcancer.org

FOUNDED: 1985

AREAS OF INTEREST:
Cancer prevention and cancer early detection.

TYPE:
Fellowships; Research grants.
Grants/Fellowships are given for prevention and early detection of cancer through scientific research and education.

PURPOSE:
To support innovative projects in prevention and early detection of cancer through scientific research.

ELIGIBILITY:
Fellowships: Citizenship is unrestricted, but research must be conducted primarily in the U.S. Postdoctoral Fellows (graduate students who will have their doctoral degrees before the project start date) are eligible to apply. Individuals with academic or professional degrees (e.g., M.D., Phar.D., Ph.D.) who are conducting cancer prevention research under the guidance of a mentor are also eligible.

Grants: Citizenship is unrestricted, but research must be conducted primarily in the U.S. Researchers at the instructor or assistant professor level with relevant academic or professional degrees (e.g., M.D., Phar.D., Ph.D.) who are conducting cancer prevention research and researchers who are farther along in their careers and who are shifting their focus to cancer prevention are eligible to apply.

GEOGRAPHIC RESTRICTIONS:
United States.

FINANCIAL DATA:
Indirect costs will not be covered.

Amount of support per award: $40,000 per year.

APPLICATION INFORMATION:
Electronic submissions are required, along with the original sent by mail.

Duration: Two years.

Deadline: February 28 and September 14.

STAFF:
Jessica Abeita, Assistant Director of Research, Administration and Community Outreach

ADDRESS INQUIRIES TO:
Jessica Abeita, Assistant Director of Research, Administration and Community Outreach
(See address above.)

PROSTATE CANCER RESEARCH AND EDUCATION FOUNDATION (PC-REF) [2603]

6823 Deer Hollow Place
San Diego, CA 92120-1605
(619) 461-8181
(619) 906-4700
Fax: (619) 794-2100

E-MAIL ADDRESS:
info@pcref.org

WEB SITE ADDRESS:
www.pcref.org

FOUNDED: 1997

AREAS OF INTEREST:
Prostate cancer.

TYPE:
Seed money grants. The Foundation provides seed money to deserving researchers to help them generate preliminary results that are needed to obtain major grants in the field of prostate cancer.

PURPOSE:
To promote medical research and treatment regarding prostate cancer.

ELIGIBILITY:
The Foundation concentrates on projects that will help prostate cancer patients sooner rather than later. Grants are not made to individuals.

FINANCIAL DATA:
The Foundation funds direct expenses only, not overhead expenses.

Amount of support per award: Varies.

APPLICATION INFORMATION:
Duration: Varies. Renewal possible.

IRS IDENTIFICATION NUMBER: 91-1863748

ADDRESS INQUIRIES TO:
Dr. Israel Barken
Founder and Medical Director
(See address above.)

DAMON RUNYON CANCER RESEARCH FOUNDATION [2604]

One Exchange Plaza
55 Broadway, Suite 302
New York, NY 10006-3720
(212) 455-0520
Fax: (212) 455-0529

E-MAIL ADDRESS:
awards@damonrunyon.org

WEB SITE ADDRESS:
www.damonrunyon.org

FOUNDED: 1946

AREAS OF INTEREST:
All theoretical and experimental research that is relevant to the study of cancer and the search for cancer causes, mechanisms, therapies and prevention.

NAME(S) OF PROGRAMS:
- **Dale F. Frey Award for Breakthrough Scientists**
- **Damon Runyon Clinical Investigator Award**
- **Damon Runyon Fellowship Award**
- **Damon Runyon-Rachleff Innovation Award**

TYPE:
Conferences/seminars; Development grants; Fellowships; Project/program grants; Loan forgiveness programs. Dale F. Frey Award for Breakthrough Scientists provides additional funding to scientists completing a Damon Runyon Fellowship who are most likely to make paradigm-shifting breakthroughs. This funding is to accelerate their path to independence and their impact on cancer.

The Damon Runyon Clinical Investigator Award supports early career physician-scientists conducting patient-oriented research. The goal of this innovative program is to increase the number of physicians capable of moving seamlessly between the laboratory and the patient's bedside in search of breakthrough treatments.

The Damon Runyon Fellowship Award supports the training of the brightest postdoctoral scientists as they embark upon their research careers. This funding enables them to be trained by established investigators in leading research laboratories across the country.

The Damon Runyon-Rachleff Innovation Award supports the next generation of exceptionally creative thinkers with high risk/high reward ideas that have the potential to significantly impact our understanding of and/or approaches to the prevention, diagnosis or treatment of cancer, but lack sufficient preliminary data to obtain traditional funding.

YEAR PROGRAM STARTED: 1947

PURPOSE:
To advance cancer research through supporting the development of the most promising young talent in cancer research.

LEGAL BASIS:
501(c)(3) organization, classified as a publicly supported organization and not as a private foundation under Section 509(a)(1) of the IRS, incorporated in New York.

ELIGIBILITY:
Frey Award: Damon Runyon Fellows are eligible to apply in the third year of their Fellowship.

Clinical Investigator Award: Each applicant (who must be a U.S. citizen or permanent legal resident) must be nominated by his/her institution. Applications will only be accepted from institutions that have been invited to submit them by the Foundation.

For the Fellowship Award, applicants must have completed one or more of the following degrees or its equivalent: M.D., M.D./Ph.D., Ph.D., D.D.S., D.V.M.

Level I Funding is for basic and physician scientist applicants who must have received their degrees within the year prior to the FAC meeting at which their applications are to be considered.

Level II Funding is for physician scientists (M.D.) and clinical scientists (M.D., M.D./Ph.D., D.D.S., D.V.M. or the equivalent) who must have completed their residencies and clinical fellowship training within three years prior to the FAC meeting at which their applications are to be considered and be board-eligible.

The proposed investigation must be conducted at a university, hospital, or research institution. Foreign candidates may only apply to do research in the U.S.

Only candidates who are beginning their first full-time postdoctoral research fellowship are eligible.

Innovation Award: Institutional nominations are not required and there is no limit to the number of applications that can be received from a particular institution. Applicants (including non-U.S. citizens) must be conducting independent research at a U.S. research institution.

FINANCIAL DATA:
Awards are made to institutions for the support of the Fellow under direct supervision of the Sponsor.

Amount of support per award: Clinical Investigator Awards: $150,000 each year for three years. In addition, awardees may be eligible to retire up to $100,000 of their medical school debt.

Fellowship Award: Level I stipend: $50,000 per year for three years.
Level II stipend: $60,000 per year for three years.

A sum of $2,000 is awarded each year to the laboratory in which the Fellow is working, and can be used by the Fellow for his/her educational and scientific expenses. With a written request to the Foundation from the Fellow, the expense allowance may be used to defray the cost of health benefits. The Fellow determines how he/she would like to spend the money with approval from his/her mentor. It is not an allowance for institutional overhead, postdoctoral scholar registration fees or postdoctoral fellowship taxes. Institutions may not automatically deduct any fees from this allowance without the Fellow's approval.

Additionally, the Foundation also provides a Dependent Child Allowance of $1,000 per child per year. (There is no allowance for a spouse.) Eligible Fellows must provide a copy of the birth or adoption certificate for each child.

Total amount of support: Approximately $3,000,000 in Clinical Investigator Awards, approximately $4,400,000 in Fellowship Awards, and approximately $1,600,000 in Innovation Awards for fiscal year 2010.

NUMBER OF APPLICANTS MOST RECENT YEAR:
Clinical Investigator Awards: 50; Fellowship Awards: 324; Innovation Awards: 128.

NUMBER OF AWARDS: Clinical Investigator Awards: 5 new, 15 renewals; Fellowship Awards: 30 new, 59 renewals; Innovation Awards: 5 new, 6 renewals.

REPRESENTATIVE AWARDS:
Damon Runyon Clinical Investigator Award: Pierre P. Massion, M.D., "Proteomic approach of risk assessment of lung cancer," with David P. Carbone, M.D., Ph.D., Vanderbilt University Medical Center, Nashville, TN; Damon Runyon Postdoctoral

Fellowship: Amanda M. Jamieson, Ph.D., "Role of toll-like receptors in immunosurveillance of tumors," with Ruslan M. Medzhitov, Ph.D., Yale University, New Haven, CT.

APPLICATION INFORMATION:
For Fellowship Awards, applicants must include:
(1) application cover sheet with all required signatures;
(2) the sponsor's biographical sketch in NIH format and a list of current funding - please limit the sponsor's bibliography to five publications that are most relevant to the proposed research;
(3) sponsor's letter describing training plan for the candidate and percentage of proposal written by the candidate;
(4) the applicant's curriculum vitae, including a bibliography of all published works;
(5) a letter from the applicant describing his or her previous research and teaching experience - the letter must state that the applicant is committed to a career in cancer research;
(6) the research proposal, which shall not exceed five pages of single-spaced 12-point type with at least one-half inch margins, should include a summary of the research proposed, a brief background to the proposed research, specific research objectives/aims, the method of approach for the proposed research concisely described, the significance of the proposed research to the Foundation's goals, the relevance of his or her own background and the background and previous work of the sponsor and any other investigators to the proposed research, a written statement testifying adequate safety precautions as well as appropriate board or committee approval for projects that involve any biohazards, a list of references including the full title of each work cited, although the references are not included in the five-page limit, and figures or tables appended or incorporated into the text (not to exceed two extra pages);
(7) a copy of the applicant's degree certificate;
(8) the Summary of Research Form, not to exceed one page - not stapled to the application;
(9) if available, up to three different reprints of the applicant's publications and;
(10) three reference letters from qualified individuals, other than the sponsor, who can evaluate the candidate's qualifications for the proposed research project and assess the candidate's potential for successful independent cancer research.
Duration: Clinical Investigator, Fellowship and Innovation Awards: Three years. Frey Award: Up to two years.
Deadline: Clinical Investigator Award: March 1; Fellowship Award: March 15 and August 15 for consideration in May and November, respectively; Innovation Award: June 1 for preproposals. Frey Award: July 15.

PUBLICATIONS:
Annual report; award brochures.

BOARD OF DIRECTORS:
Alan M. Leventhal, Chairman
Leon G. Cooperman, Vice Chairman, Finance, and Treasurer
Michael L. Gordon, Vice Chairman, Board Development
David M. Livingston, M.D., Vice Chairman, Scientific Programs
Sanford W. Morhouse, Esq., Vice Chairman, Audit and Corporate Governance

David M. Beirne, Vice Chairman, Development and Communications
Steven J. Burakoff, M.D.
William L. Carroll, M.D.
Gary E. Earlbaum
Thomas J. Fahey, Jr., M.D.
Dale F. Frey
John A. Fry
Elaine V. Fuchs, Ph.D.
Richard B. Gaynor, M.D.
Margaret A. Gilliam
Todd R. Golub, M.D.
Scott Greenstein
Jay Ireland
Ronald Levy, M.D.
David G. Marshall
John H. Myers
Richard J. O'Reilly, M.D.
Katharine F. Plum
Andrew S. Rachleff
Karen D. Seitz
William R. Sellers, M.D.
Samuel C. Silverstein, M.D.

ADDRESS INQUIRIES TO:
Clare M. Cahill, Director
Award Programs Administration
(See address above.)

THE SKIN CANCER FOUNDATION   [2605]
149 Madison Avenue
Suite 901
New York, NY 10016
(212) 725-5176
Fax: (212) 725-5751

E-MAIL ADDRESS:
mstine@skincancer.org

WEB SITE ADDRESS:
www.skincancer.org

FOUNDED: 1979

AREAS OF INTEREST:
To promote skin cancer research.

NAME(S) OF PROGRAMS:
- **Melissa K. Bambino Memorial Award**
- **Dr. Alfred W. Kopf Research Grant Award**
- **Live Love and Laugh Research Award**
- **Dr. Marcia Robbins-Wilf Research Award**
- **Dr. Patricia Wexler Research Grant Award**

TYPE:
Research grants.

YEAR PROGRAM STARTED: 1981

PURPOSE:
To reduce the incidence, morbidity, and mortality of skin cancer.

LEGAL BASIS:
Nonprofit foundation.

ELIGIBILITY:
Applications must be for research projects relevant to skin cancer which address, at the basic science and clinical level, improved methods of prevention and detection of skin cancers.

GEOGRAPHIC RESTRICTIONS:
United States.

FINANCIAL DATA:
Amount of support per award: $10,000.

NUMBER OF AWARDS: 5 for the year 2008.

APPLICATION INFORMATION:
Duration: One year.

ADDRESS INQUIRIES TO:
Mary Stine, Executive Director
(See address above.)

*SPECIAL STIPULATIONS:
E-mail applications are not accepted. Because the amounts of the grants are small, the Foundation does not fund overhead or indirect costs.

LADY TATA MEMORIAL TRUST   [2606]
c/o Mr. J.D. Contractor
Tata Limited
18 Grosvenor Place
London SW1X 7HS England
(020) 7235 8281
Fax: (020) 7259 5996

E-MAIL ADDRESS:
daniel.catovsky@icr.ac.uk

WEB SITE ADDRESS:
www.icr.ac.uk/research/research_sections/
haemato_oncology/4480.shtml

FOUNDED: 1933

AREAS OF INTEREST:
Leukemia research.

TYPE:
Fellowships; Research grants; Scholarships. Annual awards for postgraduate scientists of any nationality to support programs of research likely to throw light on the nature of leukemia. One grant of a studentship for a student entering an M.Phil./Ph.D. program is available. The Trustees especially wish to encourage studies on the leukaemogenic agents and on the epidemiology, pathogenesis, immunology and genetic basis of leukemia. The work may be done in any country or in an institution where the candidate has been accepted.

YEAR PROGRAM STARTED: 1933

PURPOSE:
To support research in leukemia.

LEGAL BASIS:
Registered charity.

ELIGIBILITY:
Suitably qualified medical or science graduates of any nationality, who are accepted in the institution where the work is to be undertaken, may apply.

FINANCIAL DATA:
Stipends are paid in quarterly installments. Since amounts vary according to age, qualifications, experience and the scales appropriate to the institution where the applicant has been accepted, intending applicants should try to find out the range of salary that would be appropriate before they apply.
Amount of support per award: GBP 15,000 to 25,000.

Total amount of support: GBP 400,000.

NUMBER OF APPLICANTS MOST RECENT YEAR:
30.

NUMBER OF AWARDS: 10 to 12.

APPLICATION INFORMATION:
Application forms are available at the web site.

Duration: All awards are tenable for one year. Awards for two years may be given if considered by the Trust to be in best interests of a particular project.

Deadline: March 1. Announcements June 18.

OFFICERS:
D. Catovsky, Chairman, Scientific Advisory Committee

ADDRESS INQUIRIES TO:
Professor D. Catovsky
c/o Mr. J.D. Contractor
(See address above.)

*SPECIAL STIPULATIONS:
Holders of awards are expected to submit half-yearly reports on their progress to the Scientific Advisory Committee and to acknowledge the support of the Trust in their publication.

UNION FOR INTERNATIONAL CANCER CONTROL   [2607]
62 route de Frontenex
1207 Geneva Switzerland
+41 22 809 1843
Fax: +41 22 809 1810

E-MAIL ADDRESS:
fellows@uicc.org

WEB SITE ADDRESS:
www.uicc.org

FOUNDED: 1935

AREAS OF INTEREST:
Cancer research, clinical oncology, oncology nursing and voluntary cancer societies.

NAME(S) OF PROGRAMS:
- **American Cancer Society International Fellowships for Beginning Investigators (ACSBI)**
- **Asia Pacific Cancer Society Training Grants (APCASOT)**
- **Trish Greene International Cancer Nursing Training Workshops**
- **International Cancer Technology Transfer Fellowships (ICRETT)**
- **Training Workshops**
- **Yamagiwa-Yoshida Memorial International Cancer Study Grants (YY)**

TYPE:
Fellowships; Grants-in-aid; Research grants; Training grants. The UICC Fellowships Programme provides long-, medium- and short-term fellowships abroad to qualified investigators, clinicians, and nurses, who are actively engaged in cancer research, clinical oncology, or oncology nursing. Short-term scheme offers non-medical training opportunities in the Asia-Pacific region.

PURPOSE:
To enable qualified cancer investigators, doctors, nurses, cancer society staff or accredited volunteers to carry out specific research and clinical projects, or to obtain training in cancer society work in appropriate organizations abroad.

ELIGIBILITY:
Candidates must:
(1) possess appropriate professional qualifications and experience according to the specific fellowship applied for;
(2) be currently engaged in cancer research, clinical oncology practice, oncology nursing, or cancer society work;
(3) be on the staff payroll of a university, research laboratory or institute, hospital, oncology unit, or voluntary cancer society (or be accredited volunteers of such societies) to where they will return at the end of a fellowship and;
(4) have adequate fluency in a language that will permit effective communication at the host institute.
Candidates may submit application for only one fellowship scheme at a time. Applicants who have already obtained a UICC fellowship in the past may apply for further UICC awards only if they are members of the Association of UICC Fellows.

No distinction will be made among candidates on the basis of gender, ethnic origin, religious or political beliefs. Awards are made on the basis of scientific and expert evaluation of the application and the proposed work as set out by the candidate in the project description by reviewers of the highest international standing in their respective fields. Decisions are final and cannot be appealed.

Fellowships are conditional on Fellows returning to the home institutes at the end of the fellowship period. Awards are not granted for basic training courses, lectures, meetings, conferences, congresses or for visiting institutes. They cannot prolong or run concurrently with other awards and cannot be granted to candidates who are already physically present at the proposed host institute while their applications are under consideration. ICRETT Workshops, Trish Greene CNTW and APCASOT may not be financially supplemented. Those programs terminated early must notify UICC immediately and appropriate funds be reimbursed. All awards require an end-of-the-project report in English, within one month at the end of the project.

GEOGRAPHIC RESTRICTIONS:
APCASOT: Asia-Pacific region.

FINANCIAL DATA:
Amount of support per award: ACSBI: $45,000 average; APCASOT: $1,800 average; Trish Greene CNTW: $2,000 to $3,000 average; ICRETT: $3,400 average; Training Workshops: $3,000 average; YY: $10,000 average.

NUMBER OF AWARDS: ACSBI: 6 to 8; APCASOT: 5 to 10; Trish Greene CNTW: 5 to 15; ICRETT: 120 to 150; Training Workshops: 10 to 20; YY: 14 to 16.

APPLICATION INFORMATION:
Applications and all supporting documentation for ACSBI, YY, ICRETT, Trish Greene CNTW and APCASOT must be submitted in English. Applications may be submitted by fax or e-mail with originals also sent by airmail or courier service and will be acknowledged promptly. Candidates will be advised if items are missing. Those proposals that have undergone a review and selection process and were not approved for funding cannot be resubmitted. However, candidates are encouraged to submit new applications for new work programs.

Duration: Training workshops: Three to five days; Fellowships and grants: Up to 12 months.

Deadline: ACSBI: December 1. APCASOT: September 24. Trish Greene CNTW, ICRETT and Training Workshops: Applications accepted anytime. YY: January 15 and July 1.

ADDRESS INQUIRIES TO:
UICC Fellowships Department
(See address above.)

*SPECIAL STIPULATIONS:
UICC requires an end-of-the-project report in English within one month of the end of the project.

Rheumatology

ARTHRITIS FOUNDATION [2608]
1330 West Peachtree Street, N.W.
Suite 100
Atlanta, GA 30309
(404) 965-7537
Fax: (404) 872-8694

E-MAIL ADDRESS:
tkidd@arthritis.org

WEB SITE ADDRESS:
www.arthritis.org

FOUNDED: 1948

AREAS OF INTEREST:
The cause, prevention and cure of arthritis, the nation's number one crippling disease.

NAME(S) OF PROGRAMS:
- **Postdoctoral Fellowships**
- **Research Innovative Grants**

TYPE:
Fellowships; Research grants; Training grants. Postdoctoral Fellowships are intended to encourage qualified physicians and scientists to embark on careers in research related to the understanding of arthritis and the rheumatic diseases.

YEAR PROGRAM STARTED: 1951

PURPOSE:
To provide support for young investigators at the beginning of their research careers as they investigate questions related to arthritis and musculoskeletal diseases.

LEGAL BASIS:
Nonprofit organization.

ELIGIBILITY:
Qualified individuals holding an M.D., Ph.D., D.O., D.V.M., or equivalent degree from an accredited institution are eligible to apply.

GEOGRAPHIC RESTRICTIONS:
United States.

FINANCIAL DATA:
Fellowship provides salary support for the early years of the necessary training period. 90% of the time must be devoted to AF-funded project.
Amount of support per award: $150,000 over three years, paid at $50,000 annually, to be used as salary and fringe benefits.

NUMBER OF APPLICANTS MOST RECENT YEAR:
114.

NUMBER OF AWARDS: 19 for the year 2008.

APPLICATION INFORMATION:
Official application materials are available from the Foundation.

Duration: Two years, with renewal for a third year.
Deadline: Contact the Foundation for exact dates.

OFFICERS:
Cecile Perich, Chairperson
Dr. John Klippel, President

ADDRESS INQUIRIES TO:
Leigh Hoffner, Grants Specialist
(See address above.)

THE ARTHRITIS SOCIETY [2609]
393 University Avenue, Suite 1700
Toronto ON M5G 1E6 Canada
(416) 979-3353
Fax: (416) 979-1149

E-MAIL ADDRESS:
jwysocki@arthritis.ca

WEB SITE ADDRESS:
www.arthritis.ca

FOUNDED: 1948

AREAS OF INTEREST:
Arthritis medical and scientific research.

NAME(S) OF PROGRAMS:
- **The Arthritis Society Clinician Teacher Award**
- **The Arthritis Society Distinguished Senior Research Investigators**
- **The Arthritis Society Investigator Award**
- **The Arthritis Society National Research Initiative**
- **The Arthritis Society New Investigator Award**
- **The Arthritis Society Operating Grants**
- **The Arthritis Society Research Grants**

TYPE:
Fellowships; General operating grants; Research grants; Scholarships.

PURPOSE:
To search for the underlying causes and subsequent cures for arthritis; to promote the best possible care and treatment for people with arthritis.

LEGAL BASIS:
Registered charity.

ELIGIBILITY:
Applicants are restricted to Canadian citizens and permanent residents of Canada. Applicants for research grants must hold faculty appointments at Canadian medical schools. Specific requirements vary by program.

GEOGRAPHIC RESTRICTIONS:
Canada.

FINANCIAL DATA:
Amount of support per award: Varies.
Total amount of support: Varies.
Matching fund requirements: Varies.

NUMBER OF APPLICANTS MOST RECENT YEAR:
55 new for the year 2010.

NUMBER OF AWARDS: 11 new and 36 continuing for the year 2010.

APPLICATION INFORMATION:
Duration: Varies by program.
Deadline: Varies by program.

PUBLICATIONS:
Annual report; regulations.

BOARD MEMBERS:
Maureen Quigley, Chairperson
Ken Ready, Vice Chairperson

Steven McNair, President and Chief Executive Officer
Andrew Grant, Treasurer
Dr. Joanne Homik, Chairman of the Medical Advisory Committee
Dr. John Matyas, Chairman of Scientific Advisory Committee
Michael Whitcombe, Honourary Solicitor
Heather Howe, Director at Large
Chris Nelson, Director at Large
Kenneth Smith, Director at Large
Gordon Stevens, Director at Large
David West, Director at Large

ADDRESS INQUIRIES TO:
Julie Wysocki, Manager
Research and Career Development
(See address above.)

LUPUS FOUNDATION OF AMERICA, INC.
2000 L Street, N.W., Suite 410
Washington, DC 20036
(202) 349-1153
(202) 349-1155
Fax: (202) 349-1156

E-MAIL ADDRESS:
dieguez@lupus.org

WEB SITE ADDRESS:
www.lupus.org/rfa

TYPE:
Research grants. Summer Fellowship.

See entry 2430 for full listing.

NATIONAL INSTITUTE OF ARTHRITIS AND MUSCULOSKELETAL AND SKIN DISEASES [2610]
NIH, One Democracy Plaza
6701 Democracy Boulevard, Suite 800
Bethesda, MD 20892
(301) 594-5055
Fax: (301) 480-4543

WEB SITE ADDRESS:
www.niams.nih.gov

FOUNDED: 1986

AREAS OF INTEREST:
Muscle and exercise physiology.

NAME(S) OF PROGRAMS:
- **Muscle Biology Branch**

TYPE:
Fellowships; Grants-in-aid; Project/program grants; Research grants; Training grants; Research contracts. The Muscle Biology Program's interests include the mechanisms of action and contraction and excitation and relaxation of muscle, metabolism and energetics, muscle membranes (sarcoplasmic reticulum), muscle development, molecular architecture, biochemical and enzymatic studies of muscle proteins and chemomechanics. A major interest is musculoskeletal fitness and adaptive biology. This program also has an interest in muscle diseases and disorders including Duchenne muscular dystrophy.

YEAR PROGRAM STARTED: 1983

PURPOSE:
To make funds available to researchers doing work in the area of muscle and exercise physiology.

LEGAL BASIS:
Public Health Service Act, Sections 301(c), 433, 472; Public Law 93-604, as amended by Public Law 94-562.

ELIGIBILITY:
Applicants must be individuals and/or public and nonprofit institutions for research grants. Research contracts are awarded to public, commercial, industrial, hospital, nonprofit and educational institutions. Awardees must be citizens or have been admitted to the U.S. for permanent residence. Postdoctoral awardees must have a professional or scientific degree.

GEOGRAPHIC RESTRICTIONS:
United States.

FINANCIAL DATA:
Amount of support per award: Research Grants: $275,000 direct costs for two years; National Research Service Postdoctoral Awards: Varies; Career Awards: Up to $75,000.

APPLICATION INFORMATION:
Application is available online.
Duration: Up to five years for research grants. One to five years for contracts. Individual fellowships awarded for one to three years.
Deadline: Varies.

Neurology

ALZHEIMER'S ASSOCIATION, INC. [2611]
225 North Michigan Avenue
Suite 1700
Chicago, IL 60601-7633
(312) 335-5747
Fax: (312) 335-4034; (866) 699-1246

E-MAIL ADDRESS:
mary.epps-streeter@alz.org
grantsapp@alz.org

WEB SITE ADDRESS:
www.alz.org

FOUNDED: 1980

AREAS OF INTEREST:
Basic and applied research relevant to Alzheimer's disease and related disorders.

NAME(S) OF PROGRAMS:
- **Everyday Technologies for Alzheimer Care (ETAC)**
- **The Senator Mark Hatfield Award for Clinical Research in Alzheimer's Disease**
- **Investigator-Initiated Research Grants**
- **New Investigator Research Grants**
- **The Zenith Fellows Award Program**

TYPE:
Fellowships; Research grants; Seed money grants. Reducing the duration of disability and shortening the period of dependency is one of the missions of the Ronald and Nancy Reagan Research Institute of the Alzheimer's Association. During the last few years, research on the behavioral, social, clinical and environmental aspects of Alzheimer's disease has been making impressive progress.

Everyday Technologies for Alzheimer Care (ETAC) is a program of research support.

The Senator Mark Hatfield Award for Clinical Research in Alzheimer's Disease focuses on clinical research and support of new investigators.

Investigator-Initiated Research Grants concentrate on interventions for Alzheimer's disease.

New Investigator Research Grants fund investigators that are no more than 10 years past their doctoral degree. The funding will allow them to conduct preliminary research which will be the basis of later research grant applications to the National Institutes of Health or other funding agencies.

The Zenith Fellows Award is currently designed to provide major support for investigators who have made or who show promise of making significant contributions to Alzheimer's disease research.

YEAR PROGRAM STARTED: 1982

PURPOSE:
To target prevention of the devastating effects of Alzheimer's disease; to ensure effective treatments; to delay onset of Alzheimer's disabling symptoms.

LEGAL BASIS:
Private, voluntary health association.

ELIGIBILITY:
Public, private, domestic and foreign research laboratories, medical centers, hospitals and universities are eligible to apply, with the exception of state and federal government-appropriated laboratories and for-profit organizations, which are prohibited from serving as the applicant institution. However, state and federal government scientists can participate as collaborating scientists with research teams from other eligible applicant institutions. The award will be issued to the applicant institution, not to the investigator.

Each program has specific requirements. Therefore, contact the Association for additional information.

FINANCIAL DATA:
A maximum of 10% of expenses for overhead, not to exceed maximum funding level requested.

Amount of support per award: Everyday Technologies for Alzheimer Care (ETAC): Maximum $200,000; Senator Mark Hatfield: Maximum $225,000; Investigator-Initiated Research Grants: Maximum $240,000; New Investigator Research Grants: Maximum $100,000; Zenith Fellows Award Program: Maximum $100,000.

NUMBER OF AWARDS: Everyday Technologies for Alzheimer Care (ETAC): 4; Senator Mark Hatfield: 1; Investigator-Initiated Research Grants: 55; New Investigator Research Grants: 20; Zenith Fellows Award Program: 5.

APPLICATION INFORMATION:
Letter of Intent (LOI) must be submitted through the online application system and includes:
(1) name of the principal investigator;
(2) contact information for the principal investigator (complete mailing address, telephone number, fax number and e-mail address);
(3) institution(s) involved in the research proposal;
(4) title of the investigation;
(5) area of focus of the submission;

(6) grant competition for which applicant is applying and;
(7) brief rationale for the proposal.

Note: An investigator may submit more than one application during the research grant competition, but each application must be a separate and distinct research proposal (i.e., non-overlapping specific aims).

Duration: Varies.

Deadline: Contact the Association for exact dates.

PUBLICATIONS:
Annual report; application guidelines.

ADDRESS INQUIRIES TO:
Mary Epps-Streeter, Grants Operations
(See address above.)

AMERICAN BRAIN TUMOR ASSOCIATION   [2612]
2720 River Road
Des Plaines, IL 60018
(847) 827-9910
Fax: (847) 827-9918

E-MAIL ADDRESS:
info@abta.org

WEB SITE ADDRESS:
www.abta.org

AREAS OF INTEREST:
Brain tumor research.

NAME(S) OF PROGRAMS:
● **Basic Research Fellowship Awards**
● **Discovery Grants**
● **Translational Research Awards**

TYPE:
Fellowships; Seed money grants; Training grants.

PURPOSE:
To encourage talented scientists early in their careers to enter, or remain in, the field of brain tumor research; to facilitate the development of potentially important research studies.

ELIGIBILITY:
Applicant must be a Postdoctorate who intends to pursue a career in brain tumor research.

GEOGRAPHIC RESTRICTIONS:
United States and Canada.

FINANCIAL DATA:
Amount of support per award: Discovery Grants: $50,000, payable over a one-year period; Research Fellowships: $80,000, payable over a two-year period; Translational Research Awards: $75,000, payable over a one-year period.

NUMBER OF AWARDS: Varies.

APPLICATION INFORMATION:
Contact the Organization for application procedures. Applications accepted by invitation only for Discovery Grants.

Duration: Discovery Grants and Translational Research Awards: One year; Research Fellowships: Two years.

Deadline: Discovery Grants: Letters of Intent due early fall. Research Fellowships and Translational Research Awards: Applications are available in September and are due early January.

ADDRESS INQUIRIES TO:
Deneen Hesser, Director of Research and Patient Services
(See address above.)

AMERICAN EPILEPSY SOCIETY (AES)   [2613]
342 North Main Street
West Hartford, CT 06117-2507
(860) 586-7505 ext. 510
Fax: (860) 586-7550

E-MAIL ADDRESS:
info@aesnet.org

WEB SITE ADDRESS:
www.aesnet.org

FOUNDED: 1936

AREAS OF INTEREST:
Study and acquisition, dissemination and application of knowledge concerning epilepsy in all its phases including biological, clinical and social.

NAME(S) OF PROGRAMS:
● **The Grass Foundation - AES Young Investigator Travel Award**
● **Lennox and Lombroso Postdoctoral Research Fellowship**
● **Lennox and Lombroso Predoctoral Research Fellowship**
● **Postdoctoral Research Fellowship**
● **Predoctoral Research Fellowship**
● **Research and Training Workshops**
● **Research Infrastructure Awards**
● **Research Initiative Fund Grants**
● **Susan S. Spencer Clinical Research Training Fellowship in Epilepsy**

TYPE:
Awards/prizes; Fellowships; Research grants. The American Epilepsy Society is one of the oldest neurological professional organizations in the U.S. The Society, in partnership with other organizations, funds Research Grants and Fellowships that are awarded to individuals with a professional degree whose research impacts an aspect of the study of, and work toward the cure for, epilepsy. Some funding programs are for Society members only.

The Grass Foundation - AES Young Investigator Travel Award: This award recognizes and honors outstanding young investigators conducting research in basic or clinical neuroscience related to epilepsy; the Grass Foundation and the Society have combined resources to present this annual meeting poster travel award.

Lennox and Lombroso Postdoctoral Research Fellowship: This one-year fellowship, administered by the Epilepsy Foundation, is available to physicians or Ph.D. neuroscientists who desire postdoctoral research experience.

Lennox and Lombroso Predoctoral Research Fellowship: This one-year fellowship, administered by the Epilepsy Foundation, is offered to graduate students matriculating in a full-time doctoral (Ph.D.) program with an academic career focus, with dissertation research related to epilepsy.

Postdoctoral Research Fellowship: This one-year fellowship, administered by the Epilepsy Foundation, is available to physicians or Ph.D. neuroscientists who desire postdoctoral research experience.

Predoctoral Research Fellowship: This one-year fellowship, administered by the Epilepsy Foundation, is offered to graduate students matriculating in a full-time doctoral (Ph.D.) program with an academic career focus, with dissertation research related to epilepsy.

Research and Training Workshops: The Society, through the Research and Training Committee, provides funding for targeted workshops, intended for clinical or scientific audiences and on specific collaborative topics in neuroscience.

Research Infrastructure Awards: This is a program for the Society's members that provides an opportunity to obtain support for nationwide or international networks of clinical or basic science researchers focused on understanding the causes, consequences and treatment of epilepsy.

Research Initiative Fund Grants: This is a funding mechanism for the Society's members that will provide seed support to encourage innovative, collaborative research in all disciplines (clinical, social, basic science, etc.) associated with the epilepsy field.

Susan S. Spencer Clinical Research Training Fellowship in Epilepsy: A two-year fellowship to support clinical research training in the field of epilepsy.

YEAR PROGRAM STARTED: 1970

PURPOSE:
To promote interdisciplinary communications, scientific investigation and exchange of clinical information about epilepsy; to improve the quality of life for people with epilepsy; to provide those engaged in research with information and assistance of potential benefit in advancing their work.

LEGAL BASIS:
501(c)(3) organization.

ELIGIBILITY:
Details for the different programs can be found online.

FINANCIAL DATA:
Susan S. Spencer Clinical Research Training Fellowship in Epilepsy: Supplementation of the stipend with other grants or by the fellowship institution is permissible, but Fellows may not accept other fellowships, similar awards or have another source of support for more than 50 percent of their research salary while holding an AAN Foundation Clinical Research Training Fellowship. Only direct costs will be funded by this award.
Amount of support per award: Susan S. Spencer Clinical Research Training Fellowship in Epilepsy: Each Fellowship will consist of a commitment of $55,000 per year for two years, plus $10,000 per year for tuition to support formal education in clinical research methodology at the applicant's institution or elsewhere.
Total amount of support: Varies.

COOPERATIVE FUNDING PROGRAMS: The Society has formed alliances with other organizations that provide research funding, including the Grass Foundation, Epilepsy Foundation and other funding sources.

Susan S. Spencer Clinical Research Training Fellowship in Epilepsy is supported by the AAN Foundation, the American Epilepsy Society and the Epilepsy Foundation.

NUMBER OF APPLICANTS MOST RECENT YEAR:
Varies.

NUMBER OF AWARDS: Lennox and Lombroso Postdoctoral Research Fellowship and Postdoctoral Research Fellowship: 3 Postdoctoral Research Fellowships are funded every year, and every other year a fourth is funded by the Lennox and Lombroso fund.

Lennox and Lombroso Predoctoral Research Fellowship and Predoctoral Research Fellowship: A total of 4 are funded every year, with 1 of those funded by the Lennox and Lombroso fund.

APPLICATION INFORMATION:
Duration: One to two years.
Deadline: Varies.

IRS IDENTIFICATION NUMBER: 04-6112600

STAFF:
M. Suzanne C. Berry, M.B.A., CAE, Executive Director
Cheryl-Ann Tubby, IOM, CPP, Assistant Executive Director

ADDRESS INQUIRIES TO:
M. Suzanne C. Berry, M.B.A., CAE
Executive Director
(See address above.)

AMERICAN HEALTH ASSISTANCE FOUNDATION   [2614]

22512 Gateway Center Drive
Clarksburg, MD 20871
(301) 948-3244
Fax: (301) 948-4403

E-MAIL ADDRESS:
researchgrants@ahaf.org

WEB SITE ADDRESS:
www.ahaf.org

FOUNDED: 1973

AREAS OF INTEREST:
Alzheimer's disease research.

NAME(S) OF PROGRAMS:
• **Alzheimer's Disease Research**

TYPE:
Research grants. Awards for basic research into the causes and treatment of age-related and degenerative diseases.

YEAR PROGRAM STARTED: 1985

PURPOSE:
To develop treatments, preventions and cures for Alzheimer's disease.

LEGAL BASIS:
Nonprofit foundation.

ELIGIBILITY:
Grants are awarded on the basis of the proposal's scientific merit and its relevance to understanding the disease studied. No funds for large equipment, institutional overhead costs, construction or building expenses.

FINANCIAL DATA:
Amount of support per award: Fellows: Up to $100,000; Pilot studies: Up to $150,000; Standard award: Up to $400,000.
Total amount of support: Varies.

NUMBER OF AWARDS: 23 for fiscal year 2010.

APPLICATION INFORMATION:
Duration: Three-year projects, two-year pilot studies and two-year research fellowships.
Deadline: Contact the Foundation for exact dates.

PUBLICATIONS:
Annual report; clinical brochures; newsletters.

ADDRESS INQUIRIES TO:
See e-mail address above.

AMERICAN PARKINSON DISEASE ASSOCIATION, INC.   [2615]

135 Parkinson Avenue
Staten Island, NY 10305
(718) 981-8001
(800) 223-2732
Fax: (718) 981-4399

E-MAIL ADDRESS:
hduffy@apdaparkinson.org

WEB SITE ADDRESS:
www.apdaparkinson.org

FOUNDED: 1961

AREAS OF INTEREST:
Parkinson's disease, medical neurology and neuropathology.

NAME(S) OF PROGRAMS:
• **Medical Student Summer Fellowships**

TYPE:
Fellowships. To assist investigators in establishing careers in the research of Parkinson's disease.

YEAR PROGRAM STARTED: 1965

PURPOSE:
To enable medical students to perform supervised laboratory or clinical research designed to clarify our understanding of Parkinson's disease, its nature, manifestations, etiology or treatment.

LEGAL BASIS:
Not-for-profit organization.

ELIGIBILITY:
Applicant should be a full-time medical student in good academic standing in an approved U.S. medical school. The proposed research project must be performed in an academic medical center or recognized research institute in the U.S. and be sponsored by a full-time faculty member or established institute scientist. The project must be part of the sponsor's ongoing research and be performed under the sponsor's direct supervision. Either laboratory or clinical research or a combination of both may be acceptable; however, merely reviewing literature or preparing reports will not be deemed acceptable.

GEOGRAPHIC RESTRICTIONS:
United States.

FINANCIAL DATA:
Amount of support per award: $4,000.

NUMBER OF AWARDS: Varies.

APPLICATION INFORMATION:
The medical student should provide a brief description of the proposed work, not to exceed three pages, containing the following elements:
(1) title of the research study;
(2) location of where the study will be performed (i.e., department or laboratory);
(3) identify sponsor (include mailing address, phone number and e-mail address);
(4) background rationale including preliminary results of work completed by the sponsor;
(5) goals and objectives;
(6) investigative methods;
(7) data analysis method;
(8) significance of anticipated findings;
(9) institutional resources available and;
(10) description of study subjects (human or animal).

Application must be accompanied by a supporting letter from the sponsor, a letter of reference from another faculty member familiar with the student's previous academic performance, and a letter from the Dean's office assuring the student is in good academic standing.

Duration: Three months.

Deadline: January 31.

PUBLICATIONS:
Program announcement; guidelines.

ADDRESS INQUIRIES TO:
Heather Duffy, Associate Director of Scientific and Medical Affairs
(See address above.)

THE AMYOTROPHIC LATERAL SCLEROSIS ASSOCIATION [2616]

National Office
27001 Agoura Road, Suite 250
Calabasas Hills, CA 91301-5104
(818) 880-9007
Fax: (818) 880-9006

E-MAIL ADDRESS:
researchgrants@alsa-national.org

WEB SITE ADDRESS:
www.alsa.org

FOUNDED: 1971

AREAS OF INTEREST:
Amyotrophic lateral sclerosis (ALS) programs include research grants, patient services, public education and awareness, local chapter development, and advocacy.

CONSULTING OR VOLUNTEER SERVICES:
Local chapters are staffed by volunteers. The Association serves ALS patients and families by phone and letter through patient education programs, support groups, referrals to resources, equipment loans, etc. Provides education programs for health care community.

NAME(S) OF PROGRAMS:
● **Research Grant Program**

TYPE:
Awards/prizes; Conferences/seminars; Fellowships; Project/program grants; Research grants; Technical assistance; Research contracts. Grants, for a specified number of years, to neuroscientific researchers to pursue a project of relevance to Amyotrophic Lateral Sclerosis. Both basic and clinical research supported (including postdoctoral fellowships). The ALS Association forms partnerships on clinical trials.

YEAR PROGRAM STARTED: 1974

PURPOSE:
To find the cause and cure of amyotrophic lateral sclerosis; to support research vital to this goal.

LEGAL BASIS:
Nonprofit voluntary health agency under IRS 501(c)(3).

ELIGIBILITY:
Applicant should be a faculty member at a reputable scientific facility.

FINANCIAL DATA:
Amount of support per award: Multiyear grants: Maximum $80,000 per year; Starter grants: Maximum $40,000 for 12-month period; Postdoctoral fellows: Maximum $40,000 per year for two years.
Total amount of support: $5,000,000 per fiscal year.

NUMBER OF APPLICANTS MOST RECENT YEAR:
650 applications for grants for the year 2010.

NUMBER OF AWARDS: 45.

REPRESENTATIVE AWARDS:
$120,000 to Joseph Beckman, Ph.D., University of Alabama at Birmingham; $80,000 to Laura Dugan, M.D., Massachusetts General Hospital; $35,000 to Charles Epstein, M.D., University of California at San Francisco.

APPLICATION INFORMATION:
Request an abstract form from the e-mail address above. Submit a one-page abstract, via e-mail, describing the proposed project. An application form will be sent with the invitation to submit, after review and interest in abstract.

Duration: Two to three years; longer if justifiable. Renewable on occasion. Some starter grants for 12 months.

Deadline: Information available upon request to the e-mail address above.

PUBLICATIONS:
Research ALS Today, newspaper; miscellaneous ALS information and patient care brochures; *ALS Journal News*, monthly.

IRS IDENTIFICATION NUMBER: 13-3271855

OFFICERS:
Lucie Bruijn, Ph.D., Senior Vice President, Research and Development

ADDRESS INQUIRIES TO:
Lucie Bruijn, Ph.D., Senior Vice President Research and Development
(See address above.)

BENIGN ESSENTIAL BLEPHAROSPASM RESEARCH FOUNDATION INC.

637 North 7th Street
Suite 102
Beaumont, TX 77702
(409) 832-0788
Fax: (409) 832-0890

E-MAIL ADDRESS:
bebrf@blepharospasm.org

WEB SITE ADDRESS:
www.blepharospasm.org

TYPE:
Fellowships; Project/program grants; Research grants; Seed money grants.

See entry 2667 for full listing.

CEREBRAL PALSY INTERNATIONAL RESEARCH FOUNDATION   [2617]

186 Princeton Hightstown Road
Building 4, Second Floor
Princeton Junction, NJ 08550
(609) 452-1200
Fax: (609) 452-1201

E-MAIL ADDRESS:
jcarmosino@cpirf.org

WEB SITE ADDRESS:
www.cpirf.org

FOUNDED: 1955

NAME(S) OF PROGRAMS:
● **CPI Research Grants**

TYPE:
Research grants. Grants are awarded for pilot studies in areas which have a relationship to cerebral palsy. While most research in the central nervous system may be useful, the Foundation requires that research proposals

define clear and direct relevance to cerebral palsy. Currently, high priority is assigned to prevention of prematurity, decrease of perinatal neurologic morbidity, prevention of central nervous system infections of the newborn and to medical, surgical and bioengineering methods that may improve the functioning of persons with cerebral palsy addressing issues such as impaired mobility, impaired communication skills, swallowing, drooling and effects of aging on further diminution of function. However, any proposal designed to prevent cerebral palsy or to improve its treatment and management will be considered.

YEAR PROGRAM STARTED: 1955

PURPOSE:
To support research pilot studies in areas of etiology, pathology, prevention and therapy bearing directly on cerebral palsy and the disabilities associated with it.

LEGAL BASIS:
Private foundation.

ELIGIBILITY:
Tax-exempt universities and other organizations are eligible to apply on behalf of qualified individuals.

FINANCIAL DATA:
Amount of support per award: Up to $50,000 for one year; total of $100,000 for two years including indirect costs not in excess of 15% of each budgetary item, except for equipment.
Total amount of support: $827,477 for fiscal year 2010.

NUMBER OF APPLICANTS MOST RECENT YEAR:
40.

NUMBER OF AWARDS: 13.

APPLICATION INFORMATION:
Application form required. The grant review process usually takes about three months.
Duration: Up to two years.

STAFF:
Glenn R. Tringali, Chief Executive Officer
James A. Blackman, M.D., Medical Director
Jacqueline Carmosino, Manager of Administration

ADDRESS INQUIRIES TO:
Jacqueline Carmosino
Manager of Administration
(See address above.)

CUREPSP FOUNDATION FOR PSP/CBD AND RELATED BRAIN DISEASES   [2618]

30 East Padonia Road
Suite 201
Timonium, MD 21093
(410) 785-7004
Fax: (410) 785-7009

E-MAIL ADDRESS:
bantum@curepsp.org

WEB SITE ADDRESS:
www.curepsp.org

FOUNDED: 1990

AREAS OF INTEREST:
Progressive supranuclear palsy and corticobasal degeneration.

TYPE:
Research grants.

YEAR PROGRAM STARTED: 1997

PURPOSE:
To provide support for basic and clinical research in progressive supranuclear palsy and corticobasal degeneration.

ELIGIBILITY:
Qualified investigators affiliated with appropriate institutions are eligible to apply. Applicants must have the approval of the institution where the research training will be conducted. Ph.D. or M.D. status is required.

FINANCIAL DATA:
There is a $8,000 maximum for durable equipment and $300 maximum for publication costs.
Amount of support per award: Varies.

NUMBER OF APPLICANTS MOST RECENT YEAR:
10.

NUMBER OF AWARDS: 4 to 5 per year.

APPLICATION INFORMATION:
Duration: Varies.

ADDRESS INQUIRIES TO:
Lawrence I. Golbe, M.D.
Chairperson, Scientific Advisory Board and Director of Research
The Society for PSP
Department of Neurology
UMDNJ-Robert Wood Johnson
Medical School
97 Paterson Street
New Brunswick, NJ 08901
Tel: (732) 235-7729
Fax: (732) 235-7041
E-mail: golbe@umdnj.edu

*SPECIAL STIPULATIONS:
Studies designed primarily to investigate related conditions such as Alzheimer's disease or Parkinson's disease are eligible if they include patients with PSP (or samples from such patients) and may be expected to increase our knowledge of PSP and CBD.

DYSAUTONOMIA FOUNDATION, INC. [2619]

315 West 39th Street
Suite 701
New York, NY 10018
(212) 279-1066
Fax: (212) 279-2066

E-MAIL ADDRESS:
info@famdys.org

WEB SITE ADDRESS:
www.familialdysautonomia.org

FOUNDED: 1951

AREAS OF INTEREST:
Familial dysautonomia.

CONSULTING OR VOLUNTEER SERVICES:
Dysautonomia Treatment and Evaluation Center at New York University Medical Center, 530 First Avenue, Suite 9Q, New York, NY 10016, under the direction of Felicia B. Axelrod, M.D.

NAME(S) OF PROGRAMS:
● **Dysautonomia Research Program**

TYPE:
Project/program grants; Research grants; Seed money grants. In addition to support for research and clinical study, the Foundation also provides financial support to the Dysautonomia Treatment and Evaluation Center at NYU and the Israeli FD Center in Jerusalem.

YEAR PROGRAM STARTED: 1955

PURPOSE:
To fund research into control and/or cure for familial dysautonomia; to stimulate and promote medical research into familial dysautonomia (an inherited disease of the autonomic nervous system); to provide information to lay and medical public.

LEGAL BASIS:
Nonprofit, tax-exempt corporation.

ELIGIBILITY:
Researcher connected with a recognized medical and/or teaching institution may apply.

FINANCIAL DATA:
Amount of support per award: Varies, depending upon the needs and nature of the request.
Total amount of support: Varies.

NUMBER OF APPLICANTS MOST RECENT YEAR:
15.

NUMBER OF AWARDS: 6.

REPRESENTATIVE AWARDS:
Yang Xu, Construction of Mouse Models for Familial Dysautonomia; Jesper Svejstrup, IKAP and Its Role as a Component of the Elongator Complex; James F. Gusella and Susan A. Slaugenhaupt, Screening for FD Drugs in Patient Cell Cultures; Susan A. Slaugenhaupt and Robin Reed, Investigation of the mRNA Splicing Defect That Causes FD.

APPLICATION INFORMATION:
Application forms are supplied upon request. Researchers must check online to see if the Foundation is soliciting research application before submitting.
Duration: One year with option to apply for ongoing research and/or renewal. Renewal application (with progress report) is required each year.
Deadline: Contact the Foundation.

IRS IDENTIFICATION NUMBER: 13-6145280

STAFF:
David Brenner, Executive Director

DYSTONIA MEDICAL RESEARCH FOUNDATION [2620]

One East Wacker Drive
Suite 2810
Chicago, IL 60601-1905
(312) 755-0198 ext. 107
Fax: (312) 803-0138

E-MAIL ADDRESS:
dystonia@dystonia-foundation.org

WEB SITE ADDRESS:
www.dystonia-foundation.org

FOUNDED: 1976

AREAS OF INTEREST:
Dystonia.

NAME(S) OF PROGRAMS:
● **Discretionary Grants**
● **Research Grants**

TYPE:
Fellowships; Project/program grants; Research grants. Research Grants to be used for hypothesis-driven dystonia-related research. Typically, studies focus on genetics, human brain tissue, anatomy and physiology of the basal ganglia and relevant brain circuitry.

YEAR PROGRAM STARTED: 1976

PURPOSE:
To fund research into the cause of, treatments and a cure for, dystonia.

LEGAL BASIS:
Private foundation.

ELIGIBILITY:
For all programs, all nonprofit institutions or organizations within the U.S., Canada and those foreign countries where supervision of grant administration is possible are eligible. For all investigations involving humans, approval by the institution's human subject protection committee is necessary. If research proposals involve human brain tissue, the Foundation will make every effort to obtain appropriate tissue from affected individuals and from controls. No support for medical care of dystonia patients, construction or alternations. Investigators must have M.D. or Ph.D. degrees.

FINANCIAL DATA:
Support cannot be used for indirect costs, new construction or renovation of existing facilities, consultant fees or travel costs unless specified in the original grant application.
Amount of support per award: Research Grants: Up to $75,000 per year; Two-Year Fellowships: Up to $50,000 per year.
Total amount of support: Varies.

APPLICATION INFORMATION:
Application form required for all programs. The principal investigator should submit a letter of recommendation with the proposal.
Duration: One or two years.
Deadline: Contact the Foundation for exact dates.

PUBLICATIONS:
Guidelines.

IRS IDENTIFICATION NUMBER: 95-3378526

ADDRESS INQUIRIES TO:
Janet Hieshetter, Executive Director
(See address above.)

EPILEPSY FOUNDATION OF AMERICA

8301 Professional Place East
Landover, MD 20785-8301
(301) 459-3700
Fax: (301) 577-4941

E-MAIL ADDRESS:
grants@efa.org

WEB SITE ADDRESS:
www.epilepsyfoundation.org

TYPE:
Fellowships. Offers qualified individuals an opportunity to develop expertise in the area of epilepsy research relative to the health sciences through a three-month training experience with involvement in an epilepsy research project in either a clinical or laboratory setting.

See entry 1974 for full listing.

EPILEPSY FOUNDATION OF AMERICA

8301 Professional Place East
Landover, MD 20785-8301
(301) 459-3700
Fax: (301) 577-4941

E-MAIL ADDRESS:
grants@efa.org

WEB SITE ADDRESS:
www.epilepsyfoundation.org

TYPE:
Fellowships. Awards for postdoctoral study through a one-year training experience in the area of epilepsy research. Appropriate fields of study for applications in the behavioral sciences include sociology, social work, psychology, anthropology, nursing, political science and others relevant to epilepsy research or practice.

See entry 1975 for full listing.

EPILEPSY FOUNDATION OF AMERICA   [2621]

8301 Professional Place East
Landover, MD 20785
(800) 332-1000
Fax: (301) 577-2684

E-MAIL ADDRESS:
grants@efa.org
info@efa.org

WEB SITE ADDRESS:
www.epilepsyfoundation.org

FOUNDED: 1968

AREAS OF INTEREST:
Epilepsy research and training.

TYPE:
Research grants.

PURPOSE:
To support basic and clinical research in the biological and behavioral sciences that will advance the understanding, treatment and prevention of epilepsy.

LEGAL BASIS:
Private foundation.

ELIGIBILITY:
This program supports newly independent faculty members entering the field of epilepsy research. Postdoctoral fellows and established investigators (associate professor level or above) are ineligible.

GEOGRAPHIC RESTRICTIONS:
United States.

FINANCIAL DATA:
Amount of support per award: $50,000 per year.

NUMBER OF AWARDS: 8.

APPLICATION INFORMATION:
Application forms and guidelines can be obtained from the address above.
Duration: One or two years.
Deadline: Contact the Foundation for exact dates.

EPILEPSY FOUNDATION OF AMERICA   [2622]

8301 Professional Place East
Landover, MD 20785
(800) 332-1000
Fax: (301) 577-2684

E-MAIL ADDRESS:
grants@efa.org
info@efa.org

WEB SITE ADDRESS:
www.epilepsyfoundation.org

FOUNDED: 1968

AREAS OF INTEREST:
Epilepsy research and training.

NAME(S) OF PROGRAMS:
- **Postdoctoral Research Fellowships**
- **Predoctoral Research Training Fellowships**
- **Research and Training Fellowships for Clinicians**

TYPE:
Fellowships. Awards offer qualified individuals the opportunity to develop expertise in clinical epilepsy research through a one-year clinical training experience and involvement in a clinical epilepsy research project. Research may be either basic or clinical, but there must be an equal emphasis on clinical training and clinical epileptology.

The Postdoctoral Research Fellowships are intended to develop academic physicians and scientists committed to research related to epilepsy. The program emphasizes individuals who will be trained in research in epilepsy rather than those who use epilepsy as a tool for research in other fields. Applications will be considered equally from individuals interested in acquiring experience either in basic laboratory research or in the conduct of human clinical studies.

The Predoctoral Research Training Fellowship proposes to support predoctoral students with dissertation research related to epilepsy, thus strengthening their interest in establishing epilepsy research as a career direction. Applications from all fields of epilepsy research, from basic to human, are encouraged.

The Research and Training Fellowships for Clinicians aim to develop academic clinicians to teach patient care of persons with epilepsy and advance knowledge about epilepsy through research. Applications will be considered equally from individuals interested in acquiring experience in the conduct of human clinical studies and who plan to study epilepsy as a human disorder. Research projects may be in the area of basic laboratory research or clinical research; however, there must be a substantial clinical training component of the program. Emphasis is placed on individuals who will be trained in research in epilepsy rather than use epilepsy as a tool in their research in other fields.

YEAR PROGRAM STARTED: 1981

LEGAL BASIS:
Private foundation.

GEOGRAPHIC RESTRICTIONS:
United States.

FINANCIAL DATA:
Amount of support per award: Postdoctoral Research Fellowships: $45,000 stipend; Predoctoral Research Training Fellowships: $20,000 stipend; Research and Training Fellowships for Clinicians: $50,000 stipend.

NUMBER OF APPLICANTS MOST RECENT YEAR: 131.

NUMBER OF AWARDS: 43.

APPLICATION INFORMATION:
Application forms and guidelines are available online.
Duration: One year.

THE GRASS FOUNDATION [2623]

P.O. Box 3101
Eugene, OR 97403
(541) 346-3540
Fax: (541) 346-4548

E-MAIL ADDRESS:
info@grassfoundation.org

WEB SITE ADDRESS:
www.grassfoundation.org

FOUNDED: 1955

AREAS OF INTEREST:
Research and education in neuroscience.

NAME(S) OF PROGRAMS:
- **Grass Fellowships in Neuroscience**

TYPE:
Fellowships; Research grants. Summer research support for independent research projects in neurobiology at the Marine Biological Laboratories, Woods Hole, MA.

YEAR PROGRAM STARTED: 1955

PURPOSE:
To encourage young investigators in the field of neurobiology.

LEGAL BASIS:
Private foundation.

ELIGIBILITY:
Applicants must be late predoctoral or early postdoctoral investigators who are qualified in neurobiological research. Preference will be given to applicants with no more than three years postdoctoral and with no prior research experience at MBL. Fellow must have proper visa.

FINANCIAL DATA:
The Grass Foundation pays traveling expenses, reasonable living expenses while at MBL and certain laboratory costs. There is a modest drawing account for personal expenses. Expenses of the spouse or domestic partner and dependent children are likewise paid.

APPLICATION INFORMATION:
Application materials may be obtained from the Foundation's web site.
Duration: 14 weeks.
Deadline: December 10. Announcement by March 1.

SELECTION COMMITTEE:
S. Adamo, Ph.D.
C.E. Carr, Ph.D.
G.W. Davis, Ph.D.
B. Grafstein, Ph.D.
H.J. Grass, M.D.
R.R. Hoy, Ph.D.
D.B. Kelley, Ph.D.
K. Khodakhah, Ph.D.
R.F. Larkin, C.P.A.
J.L. Noebels, M.D., Ph.D.
A.R. Segal, Esq.
J.C. Weeks, Ph.D.
S. Zottoli, Ph.D.

ADDRESS INQUIRIES TO:
Janis C. Weeks, Ph.D., President
(See address above.)

HUNTINGTON'S DISEASE SOCIETY OF AMERICA, INC.   [2624]

505 Eighth Avenue, Suite 902
New York, NY 10018
(212) 242-1968
Fax: (212) 239-3430

E-MAIL ADDRESS:
hdsainfo@hdsa.org

WEB SITE ADDRESS:
www.hdsa.org

FOUNDED: 1967

AREAS OF INTEREST:
Research into Huntington's disease.

NAME(S) OF PROGRAMS:
- **Huntington's Disease Research Fellowships and Grants**

TYPE:
Fellowships; Research grants.

YEAR PROGRAM STARTED: 1986

PURPOSE:
To support and stimulate research into the cause, prevention and treatment of Huntington's disease.

LEGAL BASIS:
Nonprofit, tax-exempt voluntary health agency.

ELIGIBILITY:
Candidates for fellowships must have a Ph.D., M.D. or equivalent. These awards are designed to help promising young postdoctoral investigators in the early stages of their careers, rather than to assist in the support of well-established individuals to whom more general sources of funds may be available.

Grant awards are provided as seed monies for new or innovative research projects in the hope that they will develop sufficiently to attract funding from other sources. Grants are available to all investigators in support of basic or clinical research related to Huntington's disease.

The medical school or university must agree to supply adequate laboratory facilities.

FINANCIAL DATA:
Amount of support per award: Varies.
Total amount of support: Varies.

NUMBER OF APPLICANTS MOST RECENT YEAR:
40.

NUMBER OF AWARDS: 5.

APPLICATION INFORMATION:
Duration: Details are available online.

PUBLICATIONS:
Annual report; application guidelines; *Toward a Cure, The Marker.*

IRS IDENTIFICATION NUMBER: 13-3349872

ADDRESS INQUIRIES TO:
Louise Vetter, Chief Executive Officer
(See address above.)

THE MCKNIGHT ENDOWMENT FUND FOR NEUROSCIENCE [2625]

The McKnight Foundation
710 South Second Street, Suite 400
Minneapolis, MN 55401
(612) 333-4220
Fax: (612) 332-3833

E-MAIL ADDRESS:
info@mcknight.org

WEB SITE ADDRESS:
www.mcknight.org/neuroscience

FOUNDED: 1987

AREAS OF INTEREST:
Neuroscience.

NAME(S) OF PROGRAMS:
- **McKnight Neuroscience Scholar Award**

TYPE:
Awards/prizes; Research grants.

YEAR PROGRAM STARTED: 1987

PURPOSE:
To encourage neuroscientists in the early stages of their careers to focus on disorders of learning and memory.

LEGAL BASIS:
Nonprofit.

ELIGIBILITY:
Applicants must hold an M.D. and/or Ph.D. degree, have completed formal postdoctoral training and be in the early stages of an independent research career. Applicants should show evidence of a commitment to a continuing career in neuroscience.

GEOGRAPHIC RESTRICTIONS:
United States.

FINANCIAL DATA:
Awards are made to the sponsoring institution and are to be used for salary and direct costs.
Amount of support per award: $75,000 per year.

NUMBER OF AWARDS: Up to 6 annually.

APPLICATION INFORMATION:
Application forms and guidelines are available September 15.
Duration: Three years.
Deadline: January 2. Announcement by May 15.

OFFICER:
Kate Wolford, President

ADDRESS INQUIRIES TO:
Eileen Mahler, Program Manager
(See address above.)

MONTREAL NEUROLOGICAL INSTITUTE [2626]

3801 University Street
Room 636
Montreal QC H3A 2B4 Canada
(514) 398-1903
(514) 398-5205
Fax: (514) 398-8248

E-MAIL ADDRESS:
robert.dunn@mcgill.ca

WEB SITE ADDRESS:
www.mni.mcgill.ca

FOUNDED: 1934

AREAS OF INTEREST:
Neurology, neurosurgery and neuroscience.

NAME(S) OF PROGRAMS:
- **Jeanne Timmins Costello Fellowships**
- **Preston Robb Fellowship**

TYPE:
Exchange programs; Fellowships. Awards for research and study in the fields of clinical and basic neurosciences.

PURPOSE:
To provide the recipient with the experience of going from laboratory bench to the patient's bedside by exploiting the strengths of the Institute in basic and clinical science.

LEGAL BASIS:
University, research institute.

ELIGIBILITY:
For the Costello Fellowship, candidates must have an M.D. or Ph.D. degree. Those candidates with M.D. degrees will ordinarily have completed clinical studies in neurology or neurosurgery. Research themes at the MNI include neuroanatomy, neurochemistry, neurogenetics, molecular genetics, neuroimaging, neuroimmunology, epilepsy, neuromuscular disease, neuro-oncology, molecular and cellular biology and neuropsychology.

For the Robb Fellowship, candidates must have an M.D. degree with clinical studies in neurology or neurosurgery.

FINANCIAL DATA:
Amount of support per award: $40,000 per year.

NUMBER OF AWARDS: Jeanne Timmins Costello Fellowships: 4; Preston Robb Fellowship: 1.

APPLICATION INFORMATION:
Application form and guidelines are available online from July 31 to October 31.
Duration: One year. Renewal possible for one additional year.
Deadline: November 2.

PUBLICATIONS:
Annual report.

ADDRESS INQUIRIES TO:
Robert Dunn, Associate Director
(See address above.)

MULTIPLE SCLEROSIS SOCIETY OF CANADA [2627]

175 Bloor Street East
Suite 700, North Tower
Toronto ON M4W 3R8 Canada
(416) 922-6065
Fax: (416) 922-7538

E-MAIL ADDRESS:
msresearchgrants@mssociety.ca

WEB SITE ADDRESS:
www.mssociety.ca

FOUNDED: 1948

AREAS OF INTEREST:
Neurology, immunology, virology, pathology and biochemistry.

NAME(S) OF PROGRAMS:
- **Research Studentship**

TYPE:
Research grants. Studentships offered at the Master's and Ph.D. levels.

PURPOSE:
To find the cause and cure of multiple sclerosis.

LEGAL BASIS:
Charitable organization.

ELIGIBILITY:
Applicant must be a Canadian citizen, landed immigrant, or person holding a Canadian student visa who is going to school at a recognized Canadian research institute, or a Canadian citizen or landed immigrant who is going to school at a recognized foreign research institute.

FINANCIAL DATA:
Amount of support per award: Master's: $18,000 (CAN) per year; Ph.D.: $20,000 (CAN) per year.
Total amount of support: Varies.

NUMBER OF APPLICANTS MOST RECENT YEAR: 64 for the year 2010-11.

NUMBER OF AWARDS: 30 for the year 2010-11.

APPLICATION INFORMATION:
Applications are only accepted online.
Duration: One year beginning July 1. Renewal possible for up to three additional years.
Deadline: October 1. Announcement the following March 1.

ADDRESS INQUIRIES TO:
Research and Programs Department
(See e-mail address above.)

MULTIPLE SCLEROSIS SOCIETY OF CANADA   [2628]
175 Bloor Street East
Suite 700, North Tower
Toronto ON M4W 3R8 Canada
(416) 922-6065
Fax: (416) 922-7538

E-MAIL ADDRESS:
msresearchgrants@mssociety.ca

WEB SITE ADDRESS:
www.mssociety.ca

FOUNDED: 1948

AREAS OF INTEREST:
Neurology, immunology, virology, pathology and biochemistry.

NAME(S) OF PROGRAMS:
- **Biomedical Research Grants**
- **Clinical and Population Health Research Grants**

TYPE:
Research grants.

PURPOSE:
To find the cause and cure of multiple sclerosis.

LEGAL BASIS:
Charitable organization.

ELIGIBILITY:
Applicants must carry out research at a recognized Canadian research institute (e.g., university or hospital).

FINANCIAL DATA:
Amount of support per award: $10,000 to $100,000 (CAN) average per year.
Total amount of support: Varies.

NUMBER OF APPLICANTS MOST RECENT YEAR: 53 for the year 2010-11.

NUMBER OF AWARDS: 27 for the year 2010-11.

APPLICATION INFORMATION:
Applications are only accepted online.
Duration: Up to three years, beginning April 1.
Deadline: October 1. Announcement the following March 1.

ADDRESS INQUIRIES TO:
Research and Programs Department
(See e-mail address above.)

MULTIPLE SCLEROSIS SOCIETY OF CANADA   [2629]
175 Bloor Street East
Suite 700, North Tower
Toronto ON M4W 3R8 Canada
(416) 922-6065
Fax: (416) 922-7538

E-MAIL ADDRESS:
msresearchgrants@mssociety.ca

WEB SITE ADDRESS:
www.mssociety.ca

FOUNDED: 1948

AREAS OF INTEREST:
Neurology, immunology, virology, pathology and biochemistry.

NAME(S) OF PROGRAMS:
- **Postdoctoral Fellowship**

TYPE:
Fellowships.

PURPOSE:
To find the cause and cure of multiple sclerosis.

LEGAL BASIS:
Charitable organization.

ELIGIBILITY:
Applicant must be a Canadian citizen, landed immigrant or person holding a Canadian student visa who is working at a recognized Canadian research institute, or a Canadian citizen or landed immigrant who is working at a recognized foreign research institute.

FINANCIAL DATA:
Amount of support per award: $39,000 (CAN) per year.
Total amount of support: Varies.

NUMBER OF APPLICANTS MOST RECENT YEAR: 49 for the year 2010-11.

NUMBER OF AWARDS: 35 for the year 2010-11.

APPLICATION INFORMATION:
Applications are only accepted online through www.mscanadagrants.ca.
Duration: One year beginning July 1. Renewal possible for an additional two years.
Deadline: October 1. Announcement the following March 1.

ADDRESS INQUIRIES TO:
Research and Programs Department
(See e-mail address above.)

MULTIPLE SCLEROSIS SOCIETY OF CANADA   [2630]
175 Bloor Street East
Suite 700, North Tower
Toronto ON M4W 3R8 Canada
(416) 922-6065
Fax: (416) 922-7538

E-MAIL ADDRESS:
msresearchgrants@mssociety.ca

WEB SITE ADDRESS:
www.mssociety.ca

FOUNDED: 1948

AREAS OF INTEREST:
Neurology, immunology, virology, pathology and biochemistry.

NAME(S) OF PROGRAMS:
- **Donald Paty Career Development Awards**

TYPE:
Training grants. Funding for the salary of an investigator starting his or her career as an independent researcher.

PURPOSE:
To find the cause and cure of multiple sclerosis.

LEGAL BASIS:
Charitable organization.

ELIGIBILITY:
Candidates must hold the award at a recognized Canadian research institute (e.g., university or hospital).

FINANCIAL DATA:
Amount of support per award: $50,000 (CAN) per year.
Total amount of support: Varies.

NUMBER OF APPLICANTS MOST RECENT YEAR: 4 for the year 2010-11.

NUMBER OF AWARDS: 2 for the year 2010-11.

APPLICATION INFORMATION:
Applications are only accepted online.
Duration: Normally awarded for three years, beginning July 1.
Deadline: October 1. Announcement the following March 1.

ADDRESS INQUIRIES TO:
Research and Programs Department
(See e-mail address above.)

MUSCULAR DYSTROPHY ASSOCIATION   [2631]
3300 East Sunrise Drive
Tucson, AZ 85718
(520) 529-5496
Fax: (520) 529-5454

E-MAIL ADDRESS:
research@mdausa.org

WEB SITE ADDRESS:
www.mdausa.org

FOUNDED: 1950

AREAS OF INTEREST:
Research into diseases of the neuromuscular system.

NAME(S) OF PROGRAMS:
- **Neuromuscular Disease Research**

TYPE:
Research grants; Training grants. Translational Research Grants. Basic scientific and clinical research grants are offered.

MDA supports research into diseases of the neuromuscular system to develop effective treatments for the muscular dystrophies and related diseases which include spinal muscular atrophy and other motor neuron diseases, inflammatory myopathies, metabolic myopathies, diseases of the neuromuscular junction, certain peripheral neuropathies and basic research increasing general knowledge in the neuromuscular field.

YEAR PROGRAM STARTED: 1950

PURPOSE:
To find the causes of, and treatments for, neuromuscular diseases.

LEGAL BASIS:
Nonprofit, voluntary health agency.

ELIGIBILITY:
An applicant must be a professional or faculty member at an appropriate educational, medical or research institution and be qualified to conduct and supervise a program of original research, have access to institutional resources necessary to conduct the proposed research project and hold a Doctor of Medicine, Doctor of Philosophy, Doctor of Science or equivalent degree.

Proposals from applicants outside the U.S. will be considered only for projects of highest priority to MDA and when, in addition to the applicant's having met the eligibility requirements noted above, one or more of the following conditions exist: the applicant's country of residence has inadequate sources of financial support for biomedical research, collaboration with an MDA-supported U.S. investigator is required to conduct the project, or an invitation to submit an application has been extended by MDA.

FINANCIAL DATA:
Funding levels for Primary Research Grants are unlimited. Overhead limited to a maximum of 10% of the total direct costs of the grant requested.

Amount of support per award: Development Grants: Up to $60,000 per year.

Total amount of support: Varies.

NUMBER OF APPLICANTS MOST RECENT YEAR:
500.

NUMBER OF AWARDS: 80 for the year 2010.

APPLICATION INFORMATION:
Guidelines are available on the web site.

Duration: One, two or three years.

Deadline: For Neuromuscular Disease Research, applications must be requested by December 15 and submitted by January 15 for funding to commence the following July 1. Applications must be requested by June 15 and submitted by July 15 for funding to commence the following February 1.

OFFICERS:
Jerry Lewis, National Chairman
R. Rodney Howell, M.D., Chairman of the Board
Gerald C. Weinberg, President and Chief Executive Officer
Suzanne Lowden, Treasurer
Timmi Masters, Secretary

STAFF:
Gail Schmertz Kerner, Executive Vice President and General Counsel
Kevin Moran, Executive Vice President-Business Development
Pete Morgan, Executive Vice President-Field Organization
Valerie A. Cwik, M.D., Executive Vice President-Research and Medical Director
Michelle Morgan, Senior Vice President-Health Care Services
Stephen Evans, Vice President-Finance
Jim Brown, Vice President-Public Relations

ADDRESS INQUIRIES TO:
Research Department
(See address above.)

MYASTHENIA GRAVIS FOUNDATION OF AMERICA, INC. [2632]

355 Lexington Avenue
15th Floor
New York, NY 10017
(212) 297-2156
(800) 541-5454
Fax: (212) 370-9047

E-MAIL ADDRESS:
mgfa@myasthenia.org

WEB SITE ADDRESS:
www.myasthenia.org

FOUNDED: 1952

AREAS OF INTEREST:
Myasthenia gravis and related neuromuscular conditions.

CONSULTING OR VOLUNTEER SERVICES:
Nationwide Chapter Network.

NAME(S) OF PROGRAMS:
● **Nurses Research Fellowship**

TYPE:
Fellowships; Research grants. Awards for research pertaining to problems faced by myasthenia gravis patients.

YEAR PROGRAM STARTED: 1988

PURPOSE:
To create an effective communications, service and human relations network for myasthenics, their families and friends; to educate both the lay and professional community about myasthenia gravis; to stimulate and support scientific inquiry, interchange and research in the quest for improved treatment techniques and a cure.

LEGAL BASIS:
Nonprofit corporate foundation.

ELIGIBILITY:
Candidates must be currently licensed as registered professional nurses. Fellowships are limited to U.S. or Canadian citizens or holders of bona fide permanent visas for training in U.S. institutions.

FINANCIAL DATA:
Amount of support per award: Up to $5,000.

NUMBER OF APPLICANTS MOST RECENT YEAR:
1.

NUMBER OF AWARDS: 1.

APPLICATION INFORMATION:
Candidates should submit four copies of cover letter stating that he or she is applying for the Nurses Research Fellowship, proposed budget, curriculum vitae, research proposal and letters of approval to conduct research by appropriate parties (i.e., institution, physicians and educational facilities).

Duration: One year.

Deadline: April 1.

PUBLICATIONS:
Guidelines.

IRS IDENTIFICATION NUMBER: 13-5672224

ADDRESS INQUIRIES TO:
Tor Holtan, Chief Executive Officer
(See address above.)

NATIONAL ATAXIA FOUNDATION [2633]

2600 Fernbrook Lane, Suite 119
Minneapolis, MN 55447
(763) 553-0020
Fax: (763) 553-0167

E-MAIL ADDRESS:
naf@ataxia.org

WEB SITE ADDRESS:
www.ataxia.org

FOUNDED: 1957

AREAS OF INTEREST:
Cause and treatment of ataxia.

NAME(S) OF PROGRAMS:
● **National Ataxia Foundation Fellowship Award**
● **National Ataxia Foundation Research Grant Program**
● **National Ataxia Foundation Young Investigator Award**

TYPE:
Fellowships; Research grants; Seed money grants. Young investigator award.

YEAR PROGRAM STARTED: 1978

PURPOSE:
To support research into hereditary and sporadic ataxia, as well as treatment, services, and education of the disorder.

LEGAL BASIS:
Nonprofit 501(c)(3) organization.

ELIGIBILITY:
Individuals and organizations, including religious, can apply.

FINANCIAL DATA:
Amount of support per award: Fellowship Award: Up to $35,000; Research Grant Program: Up to $30,000; Young Investigator Award: $35,000 to $50,000.

Total amount of support: Over $900,000 for the year 2009.

NUMBER OF APPLICANTS MOST RECENT YEAR:
Varies.

NUMBER OF AWARDS: Varies.

APPLICATION INFORMATION:
Letter of Intent must be submitted one month prior to application deadlines.

Duration: Research Grant and Research Fellowship: One year. Renewals by reapplication each year for continuing support. Young Investigator Award: One year.

Deadline: Research Grant: August 15; Research Fellowship: September 15; Young Investigator: September 1.

PUBLICATIONS:
Annual report; application guidelines.

IRS IDENTIFICATION NUMBER: 41-0832903

ADDRESS INQUIRIES TO:
Michael Parent, Executive Director
(See address above.)

NATIONAL HEADACHE FOUNDATION

820 North Orleans, Suite 411
Chicago, IL 60610-3132
(312) 274-2650
(888) 643-5552
Fax: (312) 640-9049

E-MAIL ADDRESS:
info@headaches.org

WEB SITE ADDRESS:
www.headaches.org

TYPE:
Research grants. Support for research in the field of headache and pain.

See entry 2525 for full listing.

NATIONAL INSTITUTE OF NEUROLOGICAL DISORDERS AND STROKE   [2634]

Building 31, Room 8A34
9000 Rockville Pike
Bethesda, MD 20892
(301) 435-7726
Fax: (301) 402-6276

E-MAIL ADDRESS:
frushouk@ninds.nih.gov

WEB SITE ADDRESS:
www.ninds.nih.gov

FOUNDED: 1950

AREAS OF INTEREST:
Neurological disorders, including multiple sclerosis and amyotrophic lateral sclerosis, movement disorders, such as the dystonias and Tourette's syndrome and degenerative and dementing disorders such as Parkinson's, Huntington's and Alzheimer's diseases, stroke, spinal cord injury, neural regeneration and plasticity, coma, chronic pain, head injury, peripheral nerve injury, tumors of the nervous system, brain edema and manipulative therapy, and convulsive, developmental and neuromuscular disorders.

NAME(S) OF PROGRAMS:
• **NINDS Extramural Research Grants**

TYPE:
Assistantships; Conferences/seminars; Fellowships; Project/program grants; Research grants; Training grants; Research contracts. Support for research, including neurological science basic research, which explores the fundamental structure and function of the brain and the nervous system, research to understand the causes and origins of pathological conditions of the nervous system with the goal of prevention of these disorders, research on the natural course of neurological disorders, research training in the basic neurological sciences and mechanisms associated with stroke and other cerebrovascular disorders, effects of trauma to the nervous system, neuroplasticity and regeneration and tumors of neural and sensory tissues.
Research may include:
(1) improved methods of disease prevention;
(2) new methods of diagnosis and treatment;
(3) clinical trials;
(4) drug development;
(5) development of neural prostheses for stroke and paraplegia;
(6) epidemiological research and;
(7) research training in the clinical sciences.

PURPOSE:
To support research on neurological diseases and stroke.

LEGAL BASIS:
PHS Act, Section 301, Section 431 and Section 433; Public Law 78-410, as amended; (42 U.S.C. 241), (42 U.S.C. 289C). PHS Act, Section 472; Public Law 78-410, as amended; (42 U.S.C. 289L-1).

ELIGIBILITY:
Research grants are available to any public or private nonprofit university, college, hospital, laboratory, or other institution, including state and local units of government, or to any individual. National Research Service Awards for the above areas may be made to individuals or to non-federal public and private nonprofit institutions for the training of individuals at the pre- and postdoctoral levels.

FINANCIAL DATA:
Grants may be used for any usual research expenses including salaries, equipment supplies, travel to scientific meetings, patient care, publications, etc.
Amount of support per award: Approximately $400,000.
Total amount of support: $1.5 billion estimated for fiscal year 2010.

NUMBER OF AWARDS: Approximately 4,000.

APPLICATION INFORMATION:
Application forms may be requested from the Division of Research Grants, National Institutes of Health, Bethesda, MD 20892.
Duration: One to five years. Renewal applications may be submitted.
Deadline: November 1, March 1, and July 1. Awards are announced throughout the year.

ADDRESS INQUIRIES TO:
Director, Division of Extramural Activities
NINDS, NIH MSC 9531
6001 Executive Boulevard
Rockville, MD 20892

NATIONAL MULTIPLE SCLEROSIS SOCIETY   [2635]

733 Third Avenue
New York, NY 10017-3288
(212) 986-3240
Fax: (212) 986-7981

E-MAIL ADDRESS:
nat@nmss.org

WEB SITE ADDRESS:
www.nationalmssociety.org

FOUNDED: 1946

AREAS OF INTEREST:
Multiple sclerosis.

NAME(S) OF PROGRAMS:
• **Postdoctoral Fellowships Program in Multiple Sclerosis Research**

TYPE:
Fellowships. Postdoctoral fellowships for advanced training leading to an academic career involving clinical or fundamental research related to multiple sclerosis and allied neurological disorders.

YEAR PROGRAM STARTED: 1955

PURPOSE:
To support investigators for whom further assistance may be critical in obtaining the training required for a research or academic career, or for whom the additional training will increase research or teaching potential in areas related to multiple sclerosis.

LEGAL BASIS:
Voluntary health agency, tax status 501(c)(3).

ELIGIBILITY:
Qualified investigators holding a doctoral level degree in medicine or appropriate biological fields are eligible to apply. Candidates must select their own training institutions and make all necessary arrangements for the conduct of proposed training or study program. Awards are based upon the applicant's professional status, training and experience.

FINANCIAL DATA:
Candidates must request all funds required, including cost of travel to and from the institution providing training.
Amount of support per award: Varies.

Total amount of support: $2,656,500 for the year 2008.

NUMBER OF APPLICANTS MOST RECENT YEAR: 65 for the year 2008.

NUMBER OF AWARDS: 24 for the year 2008.

APPLICATION INFORMATION:
Before submitting a proposal for fellowship support, the investigator must consult the Research Programs Department by phone or e-mail to determine whether the research plan is appropriate and relevant to the mission of the Society.
Duration: Up to three years.
Deadline: August 12.

OFFICERS OF THE BOARD:
Weyman Johnson, Chairman
Joyce Nelson, President and Chief Executive Officer
Richard Mengel, Treasurer
Craig Lynch, Secretary

ADDRESS INQUIRIES TO:
Jennifer Stark, Ph.D.
Director of Research Training Programs
Tel: (212) 476-0462
E-mail: jennifer.stark@nmss.org

NATIONAL MULTIPLE SCLEROSIS SOCIETY   [2636]

Research and Medical Programs
733 Third Avenue
New York, NY 10017-3288
(212) 986-3240
Fax: (212) 986-7981

E-MAIL ADDRESS:
nat@nmss.org

WEB SITE ADDRESS:
www.nationalmssociety.org

FOUNDED: 1946

AREAS OF INTEREST:
Multiple sclerosis.

NAME(S) OF PROGRAMS:
• **National Multiple Sclerosis Society Research Grants Program**

TYPE:
Fellowships; Research grants; Training grants. Grants for fundamental or applied research in scientific areas pertinent to multiple sclerosis. Grants are available for clinical or nonclinical studies, providing they show a reasonable relevance to the Society's interests.

YEAR PROGRAM STARTED: 1947

PURPOSE:
To support research into the cause, prevention, alleviation and cure of multiple sclerosis.

LEGAL BASIS:
Voluntary health agency, tax status 501(c)(3).

ELIGIBILITY:
Qualified investigators affiliated with appropriate institutions are eligible to apply. Institutions are the official recipients of grants.

FINANCIAL DATA:
The principal investigator and the grantee institution will be advised of the exact amount and duration of the grant award. Grant funds may be requested for professional and nonprofessional personnel, permanent equipment, consumable supplies, travel and other expenditures and indirect costs.
Amount of support per award: Varies.

Total amount of support: $27,686,000 for the year 2008.

NUMBER OF APPLICANTS MOST RECENT YEAR: 245 for the year 2008.

NUMBER OF AWARDS: 62 for the year 2008.

APPLICATION INFORMATION:
Before submitting a proposal for research support, investigators must consult the Research Programs Department by phone or e-mail to determine whether the research plan is appropriate and relevant to the Society's goals.
Duration: Maximum of five years.
Deadline: August 3.

OFFICERS OF THE BOARD:
Weyman Johnson, Chairman
Joyce Nelson, President and Chief Executive Officer
Richard Mengel, Treasurer
Craig Lynch, Secretary

ADDRESS INQUIRIES TO:
Eileen Madray
E-mail: eileen.madray@nmss.org

NEUROSURGERY RESEARCH AND EDUCATION FOUNDATION [2637]

5550 Meadowbrook Drive
Rolling Meadows, IL 60008
(847) 378-0500
(888) 566-AANS
Fax: (847) 378-0600

E-MAIL ADDRESS:
info@aans.org

WEB SITE ADDRESS:
www.aans.org

FOUNDED: 1982

AREAS OF INTEREST:
Neurosurgery.

NAME(S) OF PROGRAMS:
● **Research Fellowships**
● **Young Clinician Investigator Award**

TYPE:
Awards/prizes; Fellowships; Research grants.

YEAR PROGRAM STARTED: 1983

PURPOSE:
To advance the neurosciences.

LEGAL BASIS:
Private foundation.

ELIGIBILITY:
Applicants for the Research Fellowship must be M.Ds. who have been accepted into or who are in an approved residency training program in neurological surgery in North America.

Applicants for the Young Clinician Investigator Award must be neurosurgeons who are full-time faculty in North American teaching institutions in the early years of their careers. Those who accept grants from other sources for the same project are ineligible.

GEOGRAPHIC RESTRICTIONS:
North America.

FINANCIAL DATA:
Amount of support per award: $40,000.

NUMBER OF APPLICANTS MOST RECENT YEAR: 50.

NUMBER OF AWARDS: 10 for the year 2009.

APPLICATION INFORMATION:
Applicants must provide a proposal, budget, a current curriculum vitae and three letters of reference. Electronic applications are accepted.
Duration: One year beginning July 1.
Deadline: Approximately October 31. Call for exact deadline. Announcement by end of March.

ADDRESS INQUIRIES TO:
Julie A. Quattrocchi, Grants Coordinator
(See address above.)

*SPECIAL STIPULATIONS:
Individuals who accept a grant from another source (NIH or private) for the same project will be ineligible for either award.

PARKINSON'S DISEASE FOUNDATION, INC. [2638]

1359 Broadway, Suite 1509
New York, NY 10018
(212) 923-4700
Fax: (212) 923-4778

E-MAIL ADDRESS:
info@pdf.org

WEB SITE ADDRESS:
www.pdf.org

FOUNDED: 1957

AREAS OF INTEREST:
Basic and clinical research toward finding the cause and a cure for Parkinson's disease.

CONSULTING OR VOLUNTEER SERVICES:
Information and referral service to Parkinson's disease patients and caregivers.

NAME(S) OF PROGRAMS:
● **International Research Grants Award**
● **Postdoctoral Fellowship**

TYPE:
Fellowships; Research grants.

PURPOSE:
To help establish an independent laboratory research program in Parkinson's disease.

LEGAL BASIS:
Nonprofit organization.

ELIGIBILITY:
Contact the Foundation.

FINANCIAL DATA:
The Postdoctoral Fellowship does not pay indirect or overhead costs and requires the grant recipient to account for all expenditures. The second year's funding is dependent upon submission of a satisfactory report covering the first year's work.
Amount of support per award: International Research Grants Award: Up to $75,000, plus 10% indirect expenses; Postdoctoral Fellowships: Up to $42,500 for basic science or up to $55,000 for clinical neurology, plus $5,000 research allowance.
Total amount of support: Approximately $1,000,000.

APPLICATION INFORMATION:
Applications must be submitted online. Applicants for the Postdoctoral Fellowship must also submit the investigator's curriculum vitae, an outline of work to be undertaken and a detailed budget.
Duration: International Research Grants Award: One year. Renewal possible for second year. Fellowships: One year. No renewals.

PUBLICATIONS:
Annual reports; research reports; application guidelines.

ADDRESS INQUIRIES TO:
Research
(See address above.)

PARKINSON'S DISEASE FOUNDATION, INC. [2639]

1359 Broadway, Suite 1509
New York, NY 10018
(212) 923-4700
(800) 457-6676
Fax: (212) 923-4778

E-MAIL ADDRESS:
vholt@pdf.org
grants@pdf.org

WEB SITE ADDRESS:
www.pdf.org

FOUNDED: 1957

AREAS OF INTEREST:
Basic and clinical research toward finding the cause and cure for Parkinson's disease.

CONSULTING OR VOLUNTEER SERVICES:
Information and referral service to Parkinson's disease patients and caregivers; counseling.

NAME(S) OF PROGRAMS:
● **Summer Student Fellowship**

TYPE:
Fellowships. Supports medical students and undergraduates for study under the supervision of an established investigator.

PURPOSE:
To seek the cause and cure of Parkinson's disease.

LEGAL BASIS:
Nonprofit organization.

ELIGIBILITY:
Undergraduate, graduate and medical students are eligible.

FINANCIAL DATA:
Amount of support per award: Up to $3,000.
Total amount of support: $1,900,000 annually.

NUMBER OF APPLICANTS MOST RECENT YEAR: 160.

APPLICATION INFORMATION:
Duration: 10 weeks.
Deadline: Varies.

PUBLICATIONS:
Annual reports; research reports; application guidelines and forms.

STAFF:
Robin Anthony Elliott, Executive Director, Assistant Treasurer and Assistant Secretary

BOARD OF DIRECTORS:
Page Morton Black, Chairman of the Board
Lewis P. Rowland, M.D., President
Timothy A. Pedley, M.D., Vice President
Stephen Ackerman, Treasurer
Isobel Robins Konecky, Secretary
Stanley Fahn, M.D., Scientific Director

DIRECTORS:
Constance Woodruff Atwell, Ph.D.
Karen Elizabeth Burke, M.D., Ph.D.
Margo Catsimatidis
Barbara Costikyan
Peter Dorn
Stephen B. Flood, Esq.
Sara Belk Gambrell
Daniel Gersen, Esq.
Arlene Levine

Marshall Loeb
Howard DeWitt Morgan
Alma Rangel
Marie D. Schwartz
Domna Stanton, Ph.D.
Sandra Feagan Stern, Ed.D.
Melvin S. Taub
Martin Tuchman

ADDRESS INQUIRIES TO:
Valerie Holt, Executive Assistant and
Research Grants Administrator or
James Beck, Ph.D., Research Director
(See address above.)

CHRISTOPHER AND DANA REEVE FOUNDATION [2640]
636 Morris Turnpike, Suite 3A
Short Hills, NJ 07078
(973) 379-2690
(800) 225-0292
Fax: (973) 912-9433

E-MAIL ADDRESS:
information@christopherreeve.org

WEB SITE ADDRESS:
www.paralysis.org
www.christopherreeve.org

FOUNDED: 1982

AREAS OF INTEREST:
Developing effective treatments for paralysis
and other sequelae resulting from spinal cord
injury and central nervous system (CNS)
disorders; improving the quality of life for
individuals living with paralysis.

NAME(S) OF PROGRAMS:
● **Quality of Life Grants**

TYPE:
Research grants; Seed money grants. Provide
funding to organizations nationwide that help
improve opportunities, access and day-to-day
quality of life for individuals with paralysis.
The program recognizes the unique and
numerous needs of these individuals and the
importance of providing services that enable
them to participate in all areas of life. The
awards fulfill a variety of needs for recipient
organizations.

PURPOSE:
To support exemplary organizations that
provide valuable services to individuals with
paralysis and their quality of life and health.

LEGAL BASIS:
Not-for-profit organization.

ELIGIBILITY:
Well-established investigators and qualified
postdoctoral scientists may apply.

Quality of Life Grants are awarded to
501(c)(3) organizations in three categories:
Actively Achieving, Bridging Barriers and
Caring and Coping.

FINANCIAL DATA:
Amount of support per award: Up to
$25,000.

COOPERATIVE FUNDING PROGRAMS: Some
Quality of Life Grants are funded through a
cooperative agreement with the Centers for
Disease Control and Prevention.

NUMBER OF APPLICANTS MOST RECENT YEAR:
Approximately 620.

NUMBER OF AWARDS: 200.

APPLICATION INFORMATION:
Applicants with questions about the relevance
of their work to the Foundation's program

should send a preproposal letter or e-mail of
one to one-and-one-half pages describing the
proposed research (aims, brief description of
methods, perceived relevance of research to
the Association's priorities, etc.), to insure
that the development of a full proposal is
warranted. This should be done no later than
six to eight weeks prior to the application
deadline.

Quality of Life grants are awarded twice
yearly and all applications must be submitted
online through the Reeve Foundation web
site. Potential applicants may call to discuss
proposed project if unsure of relevance to
Foundation's funding goals.
Duration: One year.
Deadline: March 1 and September 1.

PUBLICATIONS:
Guidelines; application form.

IRS IDENTIFICATION NUMBER: 22-2939536

ADDRESS INQUIRIES TO:
Donna Valente, Director
Tel: (973) 467-8270 ext. 7211
E-mail: dvalente@christopherreeve.org

*SPECIAL STIPULATIONS:
Prior grant recipients must wait two grant
cycles upon receiving grant to reapply for
funding.

TOURETTE SYNDROME ASSOCIATION, INC. [2641]
42-40 Bell Boulevard
Suite 205
Bayside, NY 11361-2820
(718) 224-2999
Fax: (718) 279-9596

E-MAIL ADDRESS:
ts@tsa-usa.org

WEB SITE ADDRESS:
www.tsa-usa.org

FOUNDED: 1972

AREAS OF INTEREST:
Education, research and services relating to
Tourette Syndrome and relevant scientific
fields, such as biochemistry, neuroanatomy,
neurophysiology, genetics, molecular biology,
epidemiology, psychiatry, psychology,
neuropsychology, neurology, neuroimaging,
neuropathology, pharmacology and/or animal
models.

NAME(S) OF PROGRAMS:
● **Tourette Syndrome Research and
Training Grants**

TYPE:
Demonstration grants; Development grants;
Fellowships; General operating grants;
Research grants; Seed money grants;
Technical assistance. Research and training
grants available for Ph.D. and M.D.
researchers in the following categories:
(1) proposals in basic neuroscience
specifically relevant to Tourette Syndrome;
(2) clinical studies related to the etiology,
pathophysiology and treatment of Tourette
Syndrome and;
(3) one-year training postdoctoral
fellowships.

YEAR PROGRAM STARTED: 1984

PURPOSE:
To support significant basic and clinical
research in Tourette Syndrome.

LEGAL BASIS:
Not-for-profit organization.

ELIGIBILITY:
Open to Ph.D. and M.D. investigators from
all areas of science who can contribute to the
understanding of the genetics, pathogenesis,
pathophysiology and the treatment of
Tourette Syndrome. Investigators already
studying Tourette Syndrome and those
currently working in areas of science that can
be applied to the problems of Tourette
Syndrome are invited to apply.

FINANCIAL DATA:
These designated award levels can include
indirect costs no greater than 10%. However,
the total grant award cannot exceed $75,000
inclusive of any indirect costs.
Amount of support per award: Basic
neuroscience and clinical studies: $5,000 to
$75,000; One-year training postdoctoral
fellowships: $15,000 to $40,000, depending
on level of experience.
Total amount of support: Varies.

NUMBER OF APPLICANTS MOST RECENT YEAR:
80.

NUMBER OF AWARDS: 20.

REPRESENTATIVE AWARDS:
$74,779 to Bradley Schlaggar, M.D., Ph.D.,
Washington University School of Medicine,
St. Louis, MO, for "Functional Connectivity
of Executive Control Networks in Tourette
Syndrome;" $75,000 to Rolf Joho, Ph.D.,
University of Texas, Southwestern Medical
Center, Dallas, TX, for "KV3 Potassium
Channels and Tourette Syndrome."

APPLICATION INFORMATION:
Guidelines, general interests and forms are
available from the Association.

For preliminary screening, a letter of intent
briefly describing the scientific basis and
relevance of the proposed project is
requested. The approximate project funding
level should be included. Inquirers will be
promptly informed as to whether to proceed
with a full application.
Duration: One to two years. Competitive
renewals only.
Deadline: Letters of intent are due in late
September. Final proposals due in December
each year. Awards are announced in March.

PUBLICATIONS:
Application packet; brochure.

OFFICERS:
Kenneth D. Moelis, Chairperson
Nancy Thomas-Baker, First Vice Chairperson
Reid Ashinoff, Second Vice Chairperson
Dennis Squilla, Third Vice Chairperson
Michael Wolff, Fourth Vice Chairperson
Donald Nowill, Treasurer
Viktoria Holm-Kramer, Secretary

ADVISORY BOARD:
Peter J. Hollenbeck, Ph.D., Co-Chairperson
Jonathan W. Mink, M.D., Ph.D.,
Co-Chairperson
Jill B. Becker, Ph.D.
Kevin M. Biglan, M.D., Ph.D.
Maja Bucan, Ph.D.
S. Barak Caine, Ph.D.
Marian DiFiglia, Ph.D.
Kirk A. Frey, M.D., Ph.D.
Tamara Hershey, Ph.D.
David E. Housman, Ph.D.
Joseph Jankovic, M.D.
C.J. Malanga, M.D., Ph.D.
Francis McMahon, M.D.
Jane S. Paulsen, Ph.D.
John P. Rice, Ph.D.
Susan R. Sesack, Ph.D.
David A. Silbersweig, M.D.

Neal R. Swerdlow, M.D., Ph.D.
Robert S. Turner, Ph.D.
Jean-Paul Vonsattel, M.D.
John T. Walkup, M.D.
Steven Zalcman, Ph.D.

ADDRESS INQUIRIES TO:
Peter J. Hollenbeck, Ph.D., Co-Chairperson
Jonathan W. Mink, M.D., Ph.D.,
Co-Chairperson
TSA Scientific Advisory Board
(See address above.)

Nursing

AMERICAN ASSOCIATION FOR THE HISTORY OF NURSING, INC. [2642]

10200 West 44th Avenue
Suite 304
Wheat Ridge, CO 80033
(303) 422-2685
Fax: (303) 422-8894

E-MAIL ADDRESS:
dstumph@resourcenter.com

WEB SITE ADDRESS:
www.aahn.org

FOUNDED: 1978

AREAS OF INTEREST:
Nursing historical research.

NAME(S) OF PROGRAMS:
- **Competitive Student Research Award**
- **Postdoctoral Award to Honor the Nurse Cadet Corps**

TYPE:
Awards/prizes; Research grants. Research awards.

PURPOSE:
To encourage and support research in nursing history.

ELIGIBILITY:
Competitive Student Research Award: Student must be an AAHN member enrolled in an accredited Master's or doctoral program. Proposals must focus on a significant question in the history of nursing and the research advisor will be doctorally prepared with scholarly activity in the field of nursing history and prior experience in guidance of research training.

Postdoctoral Award: Applicant must be an AAHN member with a doctoral degree. Proposals will be judged for scholarly merit and significance to the field of nursing history.

FINANCIAL DATA:
Amount of support per award: Competitive Student Research Award: $2,000; Postdoctoral Award: $3,000.
Total amount of support: $5,000.

NUMBER OF APPLICANTS MOST RECENT YEAR: 8 to 12.

NUMBER OF AWARDS: 3.

APPLICATION INFORMATION:
Deadline: Spring.

ADDRESS INQUIRIES TO:
David L. Stumph, IOM, CAE
(See address above.)

THE AMERICAN LEGION NATIONAL HEADQUARTERS [2643]

P.O. Box 1055
Indianapolis, IN 46206
(317) 630-1323
Fax: (317) 630-1369

E-MAIL ADDRESS:
acy@legion.org

WEB SITE ADDRESS:
www.legion.org

FOUNDED: 1919

NAME(S) OF PROGRAMS:
- **Eight and Forty Lung and Respiratory Disease Nursing Scholarship Fund**

TYPE:
Scholarships. Scholarship grants for registered nurses.

YEAR PROGRAM STARTED: 1957

PURPOSE:
To allow registered nurses to further their education at the graduate level in the area of pediatric lung and respiratory diseases.

ELIGIBILITY:
Applicant must be a registered nurse, in adequate health and a U.S. citizen. Applicant must also have freedom to pursue full-time employment, have qualities of leadership and be able to attend classes full- or part-time at an accredited school of nursing.

FINANCIAL DATA:
Amount of support per award: Up to $5,000.

NUMBER OF APPLICANTS MOST RECENT YEAR: 57.

APPLICATION INFORMATION:
Application forms may be obtained from the address above.
Duration: One school year.
Deadline: May 15. Announcement July 1.

PUBLICATIONS:
Brochure.

ADDRESS INQUIRIES TO:
Eight and Forty Scholarships
(See address above.)

AMERICAN NURSES FOUNDATION, INC. [2644]

8515 Georgia Avenue
Suite 400 West
Silver Spring, MD 20910
(301) 628-5227
Fax: (301) 628-5354

E-MAIL ADDRESS:
anf@ana.org

WEB SITE ADDRESS:
www.anfonline.org
www.nursingworld.org/anf

FOUNDED: 1955

AREAS OF INTEREST:
Nursing research.

NAME(S) OF PROGRAMS:
- **Nursing Research Grants**

TYPE:
Research grants.

YEAR PROGRAM STARTED: 1955

PURPOSE:
To support research conducted by nurse investigators.

LEGAL BASIS:
Not-for-profit corporation under section 501(c)(3) of the Internal Revenue Code.

ELIGIBILITY:
Applicant must be an R.N. with a minimum of a Baccalaureate degree in nursing.

FINANCIAL DATA:
Total funding is dependent, in part, on the participation of external sponsors.
Amount of support per award: $3,000 minimum; $25,000 average award.
Total amount of support: Varies.

NUMBER OF APPLICANTS MOST RECENT YEAR: 115.

NUMBER OF AWARDS: Varies.

APPLICATION INFORMATION:
The application packet is available beginning February 1. Interested individuals can contact the Foundation.
Duration: One year. No renewals.
Deadline: May 2 (postmark). Award announcement: August 31.

PUBLICATIONS:
Annual report; newsletter; research publications.

OFFICERS:
Margaret L. Zalon, Ph.D., R.N., President
Patricia W. Underwood, Ph.D., R.N., Vice President
Patricia R. Messmer, Ph.D., R.N., Treasurer
Barbara K. Reck, B.S., Secretary

ADDRESS INQUIRIES TO:
Director
(See address above.)

*PLEASE NOTE:
Some of the grants are restricted to a particular field of study.

ASSOCIATION OF WOMEN'S HEALTH, OBSTETRIC AND NEONATAL NURSES (AWHONN) [2645]

2000 L Street, N.W.
Suite 740
Washington, DC 20036
(202) 261-2400
Fax: (202) 728-0575

E-MAIL ADDRESS:
researchprograms@awhonn.org

WEB SITE ADDRESS:
www.awhonn.org

FOUNDED: 1969

AREAS OF INTEREST:
Women's health, obstetrics, neonatal nursing, novice researchers, and childbearing and newborns.

NAME(S) OF PROGRAMS:
- **AWHONN Research Grants Program**

TYPE:
Research grants.

YEAR PROGRAM STARTED: 1993

PURPOSE:
To promote the advancement of nursing research among members.

ELIGIBILITY:
Applicant must be current member at the time of application and at time of selection and funding. Researchers who are currently principal investigators on a federally funded grant, or who have already received an AWHONN-funded research grant, are not

eligible. Current members of the Research Advisory Panel are ineligible for the duration of their committee service.

GEOGRAPHIC RESTRICTIONS:
Canada and United States.

FINANCIAL DATA:
Amount of support per award: $5,000 to $10,000.

NUMBER OF APPLICANTS MOST RECENT YEAR:
15 for 2010.

NUMBER OF AWARDS: 3 for 2010.

REPRESENTATIVE AWARDS:
Hill Rom - Celeste Phillips Family Centered Maternity Care Award; March of Dimes Saving Babies Together Award; AWHONN Novice Researcher Award.

APPLICATION INFORMATION:
Duration: One year.
Deadline: November 1.

PUBLICATIONS:
Journal of Obstetric, Gynecologic and Neonatal Nursing.

ADDRESS INQUIRIES TO:
Research Coordinator
E-mail: researchprograms@awhonn.org

THE CANADIAN LUNG ASSOCIATION (CLA)   [2646]
1750 Courtwood Crescent
Suite 300
Ottawa ON K2C 2B5 Canada
(613) 569-6411
Fax: (613) 569-8860

E-MAIL ADDRESS:
info@lung.ca
research@lung.ca

WEB SITE ADDRESS:
www.lung.ca

FOUNDED: 1977

AREAS OF INTEREST:
Respiratory health.

NAME(S) OF PROGRAMS:
● **The Canadian Respiratory Health Professionals Fellowships and Grants**

TYPE:
Fellowships; Research grants. Fellowships are offered to registered nurses pursuing postgraduate education with a major component of the program involving respiratory nursing practice, physiotherapists pursuing postgraduate training with respiratory research as the major component, and respiratory therapists pursuing postgraduate education with a major component of the program involving respiratory therapy practice.

Grants for research and feasibility studies are offered to registered nurses undertaking research investigations related to nursing management of patients with respiratory disease and symptoms. Grants are also offered to physiotherapists undertaking investigations related to management of patients with respiratory disease. Respiratory therapists undertaking research investigations related to the management of patients with respiratory disease and symptoms may also qualify.

PURPOSE:
To build research capacity in respiratory health; to support research excellence; to assist future researchers in their professional

development in congruence with the mission of the Association; to increase the number of nurses with expertise in the clinical practice of respiratory nursing and as leaders in advancing knowledge, which will result in improved quality of care in respiratory nursing.

LEGAL BASIS:
Not-for-profit, incorporated.

ELIGIBILITY:
For Fellowships, an applicant must be a Canadian citizen or a permanent Canadian resident, a Registered Nurse, Registered Physiotherapist or Registered Respiratory Therapist, be enrolled or accepted for full-time studies in a graduate program at the Master's or Doctorate level and be a member of CRHP.

For Research Grants, the principal investigator must be a Canadian citizen or a permanent Canadian resident, a Registered Nurse, a Registered Physiotherapist or Registered Respiratory Therapist, hold an appointment in, or have an affiliation with, a health care agency, education institution, or other organization in Canada that can administer the funds in an approved manner and be a member of CRHP.

FINANCIAL DATA:
Amount of support per award: Varies.
Total amount of support: Varies.

NUMBER OF APPLICANTS MOST RECENT YEAR:
Approximately 20.

NUMBER OF AWARDS: Approximately 10 each year.

APPLICATION INFORMATION:
Duration: One year.
Deadline: Contact the Foundation for exact dates.

PUBLICATIONS:
Brochure; newsletters.

OFFICERS:
Lloyd Sutherland, Chairperson, The Canadian Lung Association
Darrel Melvin, CRHP Transition Team Co-chair
Peter Vavougios, CRHP Transition Team Co-chair
Cheryl Winger, CRHP Transition Team Co-chair

ADDRESS INQUIRIES TO:
The Canadian Respiratory Health Professionals
c/o Ann Van Dam
The Canadian Lung Association
(See address above.)

FOUNDATION FOR NEONATAL RESEARCH AND EDUCATION (FNRE)   [2647]
East Holly Avenue
P.O. Box 56
Pitman, NJ 08071-0056
(856) 256-2343
Fax: (856) 589-7463

E-MAIL ADDRESS:
barbara.bates@ajj.com

WEB SITE ADDRESS:
www.inurse.com/fnre

FOUNDED: 1984

AREAS OF INTEREST:
Neonatal nursing.

TYPE:
Research grants; Scholarships.

YEAR PROGRAM STARTED: 1992

PURPOSE:
To support research and education in neonatal nursing.

LEGAL BASIS:
Nonprofit.

ELIGIBILITY:
Members of the FNRE Research Review Committee and the FNRE Board members are not eligible for research grants.

Applicant must be principal investigator of the project. If the principal investigator has limited research experience, it is expected that the application will reflect appropriate nursing research consultation.

FINANCIAL DATA:
Amount of support per award: Varies.
Total amount of support: Varies.

NUMBER OF AWARDS: 1 to 2.

APPLICATION INFORMATION:
Applications must include:
(1) application form;
(2) budget;
(3) curriculum vitae/biographical sketch;
(4) abstract;
(5) research plan;
(6) reference;
(7) appendices;
(8) IRB approval and;
(9) conflict of interest disclosure.

Ten copies of the grant proposal must be submitted.
Duration: One year. Extensions requested in writing may be granted.
Deadline: May 1. Award notifications will be mailed by September.

FOUNDATION OF THE NATIONAL STUDENT NURSES' ASSOCIATION, INC.   [2648]
45 Main Street
Suite 606
Brooklyn, NY 11201-1075
(718) 210-0705
Fax: (718) 797-1186

E-MAIL ADDRESS:
lauren@nsna.org
nsna@nsna.org

WEB SITE ADDRESS:
www.nsna.org

FOUNDED: 1969

AREAS OF INTEREST:
Nursing education.

TYPE:
Scholarships. Scholarships based on academic achievement, financial need and involvement in nursing student organizations and community activities related to health care. Additional criteria may be required by some sponsors.

PURPOSE:
To provide aid to nursing students.

LEGAL BASIS:
501(c)(3) charitable foundation.

ELIGIBILITY:
Applicants must be U.S. citizens or students with an Alien Registration number. They must also be currently enrolled in state-approved schools of nursing or pre-nursing in Associate degree, Baccalaureate, diploma, generic Doctorate,

and generic Master's programs. Funds are not available for graduate study unless it is for a first degree in nursing. Graduating high school seniors are not eligible. Monies are awarded in the spring to be used in the next academic year and summer school. Monies can only be used for nursing or pre-nursing in one of the above-mentioned programs. No monies can be used for graduate education unless leading to a first degree in nursing. If applicant is matriculating into a nursing program, letter of acceptance must accompany this application. Proof of enrollment will be required at time of award. Current Association Board of Directors and Association Nominating and Elections Committee members are not eligible.

FINANCIAL DATA:
Amount of support per award: Scholarships: $1,000 to $2,500.
Total amount of support: Over $125,000 annually in the general scholarship program.

NUMBER OF APPLICANTS MOST RECENT YEAR: 700.

NUMBER OF AWARDS: 66.

APPLICATION INFORMATION:
Applications are available on the NSNA web site from May until the following January. Each completed application, when filed, must be accompanied by a $10 processing fee.

Applicants must submit a copy of their recent nursing school and college transcripts, or grade report. NSNA members must submit proof of their membership. Registered nurses in Baccalaureate programs and licensed practical/vocational nurses in programs leading to registered nurse licensure must submit a copy of their license to be considered for the Career Mobility Scholarships.
Duration: One year. Scholarships are awarded in the spring.
Deadline: January 13, 2012.

ADDRESS INQUIRIES TO:
Scholarship Program Committee
(See address above.)

*PLEASE NOTE:
The scholarships are based on academic achievement, financial need, and involvement in nursing student organizations and community activities related to health care. Additional criteria may be required by some sponsors.

HELENE FULD HEALTH TRUST [2649]
HSBC Bank USA, N.A.
452 Fifth Avenue, 6th Floor
New York, NY 10018
(212) 525-2418
Fax: (646) 366-3828

E-MAIL ADDRESS:
marianne.caskran@hsbcpb.com

WEB SITE ADDRESS:
www.fuld.org

FOUNDED: 1935

AREAS OF INTEREST:
Nursing education and nursing students.

TYPE:
Endowments. Financial aid to nursing students remains a priority. The Trust will seek opportunities to establish endowed scholarships at select nursing schools through an invitational process.

YEAR PROGRAM STARTED: 1969

PURPOSE:
To support and promote the health, welfare and education of student nurses.

LEGAL BASIS:
Private foundation.

ELIGIBILITY:
The Trust will not accept unsolicited grant requests for financial aid. Acknowledging the increased complexity of and sophisticated knowledge required for health care delivery, the Trust will give preference to programs that offer B.S.N. degrees and higher.

GEOGRAPHIC RESTRICTIONS:
United States.

FINANCIAL DATA:
Amount of support per award: $500,000 up.
Total amount of support: Approximately $4,000,000 annually.

NUMBER OF AWARDS: Approximately 3,000.

APPLICATION INFORMATION:
Contact the Trust for details.
Duration: Up to three years.

IRS IDENTIFICATION NUMBER: 13-6309307

ADDRESS INQUIRIES TO:
Marianne Caskran, Grants Administrator
(See address above.)

INDEPENDENCE FOUNDATION [2650]
Offices at the Bellevue
200 South Broad Street, Suite 1101
Philadelphia, PA 19102
(215) 985-4009
Fax: (215) 985-3989

E-MAIL ADDRESS:
ssherman@independencefoundation.org

WEB SITE ADDRESS:
www.independencefoundation.org

FOUNDED: 1932

AREAS OF INTEREST:
Community-based, nurse-managed health care, health promotion, family planning and comprehensive health care services where issues of quality, access and cost are taken into consideration; culture, arts and legal aid and assistance to the disadvantaged; visual and performing arts.

NAME(S) OF PROGRAMS:
- **Individual Artists Fellowship/Performing and Visual Arts**
- **New Theater Works Initiative**
- **Public Interest Law Fellowships**

TYPE:
Challenge/matching grants; Fellowships; General operating grants; Project/program grants.

YEAR PROGRAM STARTED: 1993

PURPOSE:
To encourage and support nursing; to have a valuable impact on the quality of health care services; to strengthen nursing education's focus on community-based care in both Philadelphia and surrounding Pennsylvania counties.

LEGAL BASIS:
Private foundation.

ELIGIBILITY:
No grants to individuals.

GEOGRAPHIC RESTRICTIONS:
Philadelphia and four surrounding counties of Bucks, Chester, Delaware and Montgomery.

FINANCIAL DATA:
Unaudited net assets of $68,182,100 for the year ended December 31, 2009.
Amount of support per award: Multiyear grants: $250 to $200,000.
Total amount of support: $3,956,117 in unaudited grants for the year ended December 31, 2009.
Matching fund requirements: Match of contributions by individual new donors or increase in contributions by current individual donors (nongovernmental/nonfoundation funds).

NUMBER OF AWARDS: 128.

REPRESENTATIVE AWARDS:
Culture and the Arts: $5,000 to Headlong Dance Theater, Philadelphia, PA, for general operating support; Health and Human Services: $10,000 to Overbrook School for the Blind, Philadelphia, PA, for project support; Public Interest Law: $10,000 to Homeless Advocacy Project, Philadelphia, PA, for general operating support.

APPLICATION INFORMATION:
Each year the Foundation sends out RFP (Requests for Proposal) under the following categories: Nurse Managed Health Care Initiatives, Health and Human Services, Legal Aid Initiatives, Culture and Arts Initiatives, Public Interest Law Fellowship Program and Individual Artist Fellowship Program.

Contact the Foundation for the RFP packets and submission deadlines.
Duration: Varies.
Deadline: Varies.

PUBLICATIONS:
Annual report; application guidelines.

IRS IDENTIFICATION NUMBER: 23-1352110

DIRECTORS AND OFFICERS:
Hon. Phyllis W. Beck, Chairperson
Susan E. Sherman, President and Chief Executive Officer
Andre Dennis, Esq., Vice President
Barton Silverman, Director
Andrea Mengel, Secretary

ADDRESS INQUIRIES TO:
Susan E. Sherman
President and Chief Executive Officer
(See address above.)

MYASTHENIA GRAVIS FOUNDATION OF AMERICA, INC.
355 Lexington Avenue
15th Floor
New York, NY 10017
(212) 297-2156
(800) 541-5454
Fax: (212) 370-9047

E-MAIL ADDRESS:
mgfa@myasthenia.org

WEB SITE ADDRESS:
www.myasthenia.org

TYPE:
Fellowships; Research grants. Awards for research pertaining to problems faced by myasthenia gravis patients.

See entry 2632 for full listing.

NATIONAL BLACK NURSES ASSOCIATION, INC. [2651]

8630 Fenton Street
Suite 330
Silver Spring, MD 20910
(301) 589-3200
Fax: (301) 589-3223

E-MAIL ADDRESS:
info@nbna.org

WEB SITE ADDRESS:
www.nbna.org

AREAS OF INTEREST:
HIV/AIDS, cardiovascular disease, women and children's health, cancer, substance abuse, and violence in African American communities.

NAME(S) OF PROGRAMS:
- **Martha R. Dudley LVN/LPN Scholarship**
- **Mayo Foundations Scholarship**
- **NBNA Board of Directors Scholarship**
- **Nursing Spectrum Scholarship**
- **Dr. Lauranne Sams Scholarship**

TYPE:
Scholarships.

PURPOSE:
To advance nursing practice, improve health care for all Americans, particularly the unserved and the underserved, and shape health policy for the access and delivery of health care services.

LEGAL BASIS:
Nonprofit professional association.

ELIGIBILITY:
Awards are given primarily to African Americans enrolled at any level in a nursing program (AD, BSN or LPN/LVN). Applicant must be in good standing at the time of application and be a member of NBNA.

GEOGRAPHIC RESTRICTIONS:
United States.

FINANCIAL DATA:
Amount of support per award: $1,000 to $5,000.

NUMBER OF AWARDS: 10.

APPLICATION INFORMATION:
Each chapter must submit completed scholarship application forms filled out by each candidate it recommends. Applications must be accompanied with two letters of recommendation. Letters from the school of nursing and a nurse in the area will suffice for candidates who have no local chapter in the area.

Duration: One year. Nonrenewable.

Deadline: April 15. Awards are presented at the August conference.

BOARD OF DIRECTORS:
Dr. Debra A. Toney, President

ADDRESS INQUIRIES TO:
Scholarships Committee
(See address above.)

NATIONAL INSTITUTE OF NURSING RESEARCH [2652]

31 Center Drive, Room 5B-10
Bethesda, MD 20892-2178
(301) 496-0207
Fax: (301) 480-8845

E-MAIL ADDRESS:
info@ninr.nih.gov

WEB SITE ADDRESS:
www.ninr.nih.gov

FOUNDED: 1986

AREAS OF INTEREST:
Health of individuals, families, communities and populations.

CONSULTING OR VOLUNTEER SERVICES:
For potential principal investigators.

NAME(S) OF PROGRAMS:
- **Career Development Grants**
- **Research Grants**
- **Research Training Grants**
- **Small Business Innovation Research Grants**

TYPE:
Fellowships; Project/program grants; Research grants; Training grants. Funds may be used for salaries, consultation, equipment, travel and other usual costs, subject to federal regulations applicable to the grant. Fellowships are for postdoctoral research training; predoctoral support is also available.

YEAR PROGRAM STARTED: 1986

PURPOSE:
To support nursing research, research training at pre- and postdoctoral levels, and research related to patient care, the promotion of health, the prevention of disease and the mitigation of the effects of acute and chronic illnesses and disabilities.

LEGAL BASIS:
Public Health Service Act, Sections 301, 483, 484, and 487, as amended by Public Law 99-158.

ELIGIBILITY:
Applicant may be a for-profit organization, a nonprofit organization, a public or private institution such as a university, college, hospital and laboratory, a unit of state government, a unit of local government, an eligible agency of the federal government, a foreign institution, a domestic institution, a faith-based or community-based organization, an Indian/Native American tribal government (federally recognized), an Indian/Native American tribal government (other than federally recognized), or an Indian/Native American tribally designated organization.

GEOGRAPHIC RESTRICTIONS:
United States.

FINANCIAL DATA:
Amount of support per award: Varies based on type of grant and duration.

Total amount of support: Varies.

COOPERATIVE FUNDING PROGRAMS: Co-funding of research project grants with other NIH Institutes and Centers.

APPLICATION INFORMATION:
Deadline: Applications are accepted at any time for inclusion in one of the three annual review cycles beginning February 1, June 1 and October 1. Renewals: March 1, July 1 and November 1.

PUBLICATIONS:
Investigators' publications.

STAFF:
Brian Albertini, Grants Manager

ADDRESS INQUIRIES TO:
Doug Hussey, Chief, Office of Science Policy and Public Liaison
(See address above.)

NATIONAL SOCIETY DAUGHTERS OF THE AMERICAN REVOLUTION [2653]

1776 D Street, N.W.
Washington, DC 20006-5303
(202) 879-3292

WEB SITE ADDRESS:
www.dar.org

FOUNDED: 1895

AREAS OF INTEREST:
Nursing.

NAME(S) OF PROGRAMS:
- **Madeline Pickett Cogswell Nursing Scholarship**
- **Caroline E. Holt Nursing Scholarship**

TYPE:
Scholarships. Awarded to students who are enrolled or currently attending an accredited school of nursing.

PURPOSE:
To provide ways and means to help students to attain higher education; to perpetuate the memory and spirit of men and women who achieved American Independence by acquisition and protection of historical spots and erection of monuments; to carry out injunction of Washington in his farewell address to the American people; to maintain institutions of American Freedom; to aid liberty.

LEGAL BASIS:
Incorporated historical society.

ELIGIBILITY:
Scholarships are awarded without regard to race, religion, sex or national origin. Candidates must be U.S. citizens and must attend an accredited college or university in the U.S. Awards are judged on the basis of academic excellence, commitment to field of study, as required, and financial need.

Applicants for the Cogswell Nursing Scholarship must be members, descendents of members or eligible for membership in NSDAR. DAR member number must be on the application.

No affiliation or relationship to DAR is required for qualification for the Holt Nursing Scholarship, but candidate must be sponsored by a local DAR Chapter.

GEOGRAPHIC RESTRICTIONS:
United States.

FINANCIAL DATA:
Amount of support per award: $1,000.

Total amount of support: Varies.

NUMBER OF AWARDS: Varies.

APPLICATION INFORMATION:
To obtain a scholarship application packet, send a self-addressed, stamped #10 business-size envelope to Office of the Reporter General, DAR Scholarship Committee, at the address listed above.

Included with the application packet is the list of DAR State Scholarship Chairmen. All scholarship applicants are required to have a letter of sponsorship from a chapter. Individuals interested in obtaining a letter of sponsorship from a local chapter are encouraged to contact the DAR State Chairman.

Duration: One academic year. Nonrenewable.

Deadline: February 15.

PUBLICATIONS:
American Spirit, magazine.

ADDRESS INQUIRIES TO:
Office of the Reporter General
DAR Scholarship Committee
(See address above.)

*PLEASE NOTE:
Awards are placed on deposit with the
college or university. Any unused portion
shall be returned to the National Society.

NATIONAL SOCIETY DAUGHTERS OF THE AMERICAN REVOLUTION

1776 D Street, N.W.
Washington, DC 20006-5303
(202) 879-3292

WEB SITE ADDRESS:
www.dar.org

TYPE:
Scholarships.

See entry 2451 for full listing.

NURSES' EDUCATIONAL FUNDS, INC.   [2654]

304 Park Avenue South, 11th Floor
New York, NY 10010
(212) 590-2443
Fax: (212) 590-2446

E-MAIL ADDRESS:
info@n-e-f.org

WEB SITE ADDRESS:
www.n-e-f.org

FOUNDED: 1954

AREAS OF INTEREST:
Graduate nursing studies.

TYPE:
Fellowships; Scholarships. Fellowships and
scholarships for registered nurses seeking a
Master's in nursing or Doctorate degree in
nursing or a related field.

YEAR PROGRAM STARTED: 1914

PURPOSE:
To increase the supply of nurses qualified for
administrative, supervisory, teaching or
research positions and clinical specialization
in nursing.

LEGAL BASIS:
Private foundation.

ELIGIBILITY:
Registered nurses who are U.S. citizens, or
who have officially declared intention of
becoming citizens, are eligible to apply if
they have been accepted into a Master's
program, or applying to a Master's program
of nursing education accredited by NLNAC
or CCNE, or enrolled full-time or part-time
in a doctoral program in a field related to
nursing. Applicants must be able to present
proof of membership in a professional
nursing association.

GEOGRAPHIC RESTRICTIONS:
United States.

FINANCIAL DATA:
Amount of support per award: Scholarships
and fellowships vary in amount, according to
the funds available.
Total amount of support: Varies.

NUMBER OF APPLICANTS MOST RECENT YEAR:
130.

NUMBER OF AWARDS: Varies.

APPLICATION INFORMATION:
Official application materials are available
upon request to the NEF or can be
downloaded from the web site.
Duration: One academic year. Nonrenewable.
Deadline: March 1.

PUBLICATIONS:
Newsletter.

BOARD OF DIRECTORS:
Cynthia Sculco, R.N., Ed.D., President
Joan M. Arnold, R.N., Ph.D., Vice President
Henry B. Spencer, Treasurer
Rita Reis Wieczorek, R.N., P.N.P., Secretary
M. Elizabeth Carnegie, R.N., D.P.A.
Mary Shaffer Collins, Ph.D., R.N.
Kathleen M. Dirschel, R.N., Ph.D.
Jeanette Ives Erickson, M.S., R.N.
Harriet R. Feldman, R.N., Ph.D.
M. Louise Fitzpatrick, R.N., Ed.D.
Barbara Hazard, R.N., Ph.D.
Barbara Heller, R.N., Ed.D.
Rona F. Levin, R.N., Ph.D.
Margaret L. McClure, R.N., Ed.D.
Afaf Meleis, R.N., Ph.D.
Thelma Schorr, R.N., B.S.N.
Ursula Springer, Ph.D.
Madeleine Sugimoto, R.N., M.Ed.
Barbara L. Tate, R.N., Ed.D.

ADDRESS INQUIRIES TO:
Esu Manzano
NEF Manager and Scholarship Coordinator
(See address above.)

REHABILITATION NURSING FOUNDATION   [2655]

4700 West Lake Avenue
Glenview, IL 60025
(847) 375-4710
Fax: (847) 375-6481

E-MAIL ADDRESS:
info@rehabnurse.org

WEB SITE ADDRESS:
www.rehabnurse.org

AREAS OF INTEREST:
Rehabilitation nursing.

NAME(S) OF PROGRAMS:
● **RNF Fellow Research Grant**
● **RNF New Investigator Research Grant**
● **Sigma Theta Tau/RNF Research Grant**

TYPE:
Research grants.

PURPOSE:
To promote and advance professional
rehabilitation nursing practice through
education, advocacy, collaboration, and
research to enhance the quality of life for
those affected by disability and chronic
illness.

ELIGIBILITY:
The principal investigator for the research
project must be a registered nurse who is
active in rehabilitation or who demonstrates
interest in and significant contributions to
rehabilitation nursing. Graduate student
researchers are eligible for funding.

FINANCIAL DATA:
Amount of support per award: RNF Fellow
Research Grant: Up to $10,000 per year;
RNF New Investigator Research Grant:
$10,000; Sigma Theta Tau/RNF Research
Grant: $4,500.

NUMBER OF AWARDS: RNF Fellow Research
Grant: Up to 2; Others: 1 each.

APPLICATION INFORMATION:
All applicants must:
(1) complete a Summary Data Form;
(2) submit a typed, 250- to 350-word abstract
defining the research problem, stating the
significance of the research, and presenting
the research methodology and plan for
analysis;
(3) have the institution or agency named in
the proposal complete the Administrative
Approval Form to indicate acknowledgment
and approval of the research project and;
(4) complete the Research Grant Checklist to
verify inclusion of all required materials and
include it as part of the application.

All forms and material can be downloaded
from the web site.
Deadline: Proposals must be postmarked by
February 1.

ADDRESS INQUIRIES TO:
Susan Floutsakos, Account Manager
(See address above.)

SIGMA THETA TAU INTERNATIONAL   [2656]

Honor Society of Nursing
550 West North Street
Indianapolis, IN 46202
(317) 634-8171 (Local)
(888) 634-7575 (U.S./Canada)
Fax: (317) 634-8188

E-MAIL ADDRESS:
research@stti.iupui.edu

WEB SITE ADDRESS:
www.nursingsociety.org

FOUNDED: 1922

AREAS OF INTEREST:
Nursing.

NAME(S) OF PROGRAMS:
● **Rosemary Berkel Crisp Research
  Award**
● **Doris Bloch Research Award**
● **Virginia Henderson Clinical Research
  Grant**
● **Small Grants**
● **Joan K. Stout, R.N., Research Grant**

TYPE:
Research grants.

YEAR PROGRAM STARTED: 1936

PURPOSE:
To encourage qualified nurses to contribute to
the advancement of nursing through research.

LEGAL BASIS:
Incorporated.

ELIGIBILITY:
Applicants must meet the following
requirements:
(1) be a registered nurse with a current
license;
(2) hold a Master's or doctoral degree or be
enrolled in a doctoral program;
(3) be ready to implement research project
when funding is received and;
(4) complete the project within one year of
funding.

For the Rosemary Berkel Crisp Research
Award, applicant must be a member of
Sigma Theta Tau International. Some
preference will be given to applicants
residing in Arkansas, Illinois, Kentucky,
Missouri and Tennessee.

For the Virginia Henderson Clinical Research
Grant, applicant must be a member of Sigma
Theta Tau International and be actively

involved in some aspect of health care delivery, education or research in a clinical setting.

FINANCIAL DATA:
Amount of support per award: $5,000 maximum.
Total amount of support: Varies.

NUMBER OF AWARDS: 10 to 15 Small Grants.

APPLICATION INFORMATION:
Duration: For approved research time.
Deadline: Joan K. Stout, R.N., Research Grant: July 1. All others: December 1.

PUBLICATIONS:
Guidelines; applications.

NATIONAL OFFICERS:
Karen H. Morin, R.N., D.S.N., President
Suzanne Prevost, R.N., Ph.D., President-Elect
Gwen Sherwood, R.N., Ph.D., Vice President
Richard Ricciardi, Ph.D., FAANP, Treasurer
Beverly S. Reigel, R.N., Ph.D., Secretary
Patricia E. Thompson, R.N., Ed.D., Chief Executive Officer

ADDRESS INQUIRIES TO:
Grants Coordinator
(See address above.)

U.S. DEPARTMENT OF HEALTH AND HUMAN SERVICES   [2657]
HRSA/BHPr, Division of Nursing
Parklawn Building, Room 9-61
5600 Fishers Lane
Rockville, MD 20857
(301) 443-5688
Fax: (301) 443-0791

WEB SITE ADDRESS:
www.bhpr.hrsa.gov/nursing

AREAS OF INTEREST:
Nursing education and practice.

TYPE:
Project/program grants; Training grants.

YEAR PROGRAM STARTED: 1965

PURPOSE:
To improve nursing practice and education through projects that increase the knowledge and skills of nursing personnel, enhance their effectiveness in primary care delivery, increase the number of qualified professional nurses and increase nursing workforce diversity.

LEGAL BASIS:
Amendment to Public Health Service Act, Title VIII, Section 820 by "The Health Professions Education Partnership Act of 1998" Public Law 105-392, Subtitle B.

ELIGIBILITY:
Eligible entities are schools of nursing, nursing centers, academic health centers, state or local governments, and other public or private nonprofit entities appropriate by the Secretary that submit an application in accordance with Section 802.

GEOGRAPHIC RESTRICTIONS:
United States.

FINANCIAL DATA:
Amount of support per award: Grants vary in amount, depending on the needs and nature of the project.
Total amount of support: Varies.

APPLICATION INFORMATION:
Duration: Varies according to project.

ADDRESS INQUIRIES TO:
Division of Nursing, BHPr/HRSA
Nursing Education and Practice Branch
Parklawn Building, Room 9-36
5600 Fishers Lane
Rockville, MD 20857

VIRGINIA DEPARTMENT OF HEALTH   [2658]
Office of Minority Health and Public Health Policy
109 Governor Street, 10th Floor
Suite 1016-East
Richmond, VA 23219
(804) 864-7431
Fax: (804) 864-7440

E-MAIL ADDRESS:
incentiveprograms@vdh.virginia.gov

WEB SITE ADDRESS:
www.vdh.virginia.gov

NAME(S) OF PROGRAMS:
- **Commonwealth of Virginia Nurse Educator Scholarship Program**
- **Mary Marshall Nursing Scholarship/Practical Nurse Program**
- **Mary Marshall Nursing Scholarship/Registered Nurse Program**
- **Nurse Practitioner/Nurse Midwife Scholarship Program**

TYPE:
Scholarships. Awarded to eligible students enrolled in undergraduate or graduate nursing programs at schools of nursing approved by the Virginia State Board of Nursing to assist with their professional education.

Undergraduate nursing programs are defined as those leading to a licensed practical nurse, an Associate degree, diploma, or Baccalaureate degree in nursing.

YEAR PROGRAM STARTED: 1950

PURPOSE:
To provide the citizens of the state with more skilled and greater nursing care coverage.

LEGAL BASIS:
Funding is appropriated by the General Assembly of Virginia under code 23-35.9-23-35.13; code 32.1-122.6-01; and Title 32.1, Chapter 6, 32.1-122.6-02.

ELIGIBILITY:
Criteria vary for the different scholarships. Because of the strict nature of these criteria, it is vital that the applicant contact the Department for full particulars.

GEOGRAPHIC RESTRICTIONS:
Virginia.

FINANCIAL DATA:
Amount of scholarships varies, depending upon amount appropriated by the General Assembly, amount collected by the Board of Nursing and the number of qualified applicants. There are strict conditions attached to these scholarships. (They are not outright gifts; require service in the Commonwealth of Virginia.)
Amount of support per award: Varies each year.

NUMBER OF APPLICANTS MOST RECENT YEAR: 250.

NUMBER OF AWARDS: 140.

APPLICATION INFORMATION:
Applications are available online. Application period is June 1 to July 31 for the nurse educator scholarship. Required data for

application include most current transcript of grades (or last school attended if not currently enrolled), verification of need from the Financial Aid Officer and recommendation of the Director of the School of Nursing.
Duration: Each scholarship is awarded for a single year. Upon reapplication, scholarships may be awarded for succeeding years to a maximum of four years.
Deadline: July 31 for applicants to the nurse educator scholarships.

PUBLICATIONS:
Guidelines.

OFFICER:
Aileen Edwards Harris, M.S.A., Healthcare Workforce Manager

ADDRESS INQUIRIES TO:
Nursing Scholarships
(See address above.)

Obstetrics and gynecology

CENTRAL ASSOCIATION OF OBSTETRICIANS AND GYNECOLOGISTS   [2659]
15 North Main
Minot, ND 58703
(701) 838-8323
Fax: (701) 852-8733

E-MAIL ADDRESS:
rhickel@caog.org

WEB SITE ADDRESS:
www.caog.org

FOUNDED: 1929

AREAS OF INTEREST:
Obstetrics and gynecology, including investigative and/or clinical work.

NAME(S) OF PROGRAMS:
- **Annual Central Prize Award**
- **Central Poster Award**
- **Community Hospital Award**
- **President's Certificate of Merit Award**
- **Young Investigator's Award**

TYPE:
Awards/prizes. The Annual Central Prize Award, President's Certificate of Merit Award and Central Poster Awards are presented annually for manuscripts demonstrating outstanding investigative or clinical work in the field of obstetrics and gynecology.

The Community Hospital Award is presented annually for clinical study or research in the field of obstetrics and gynecology to members located in community hospitals who are not full-time faculty in medical schools. Preference for this award will be given to papers concerning gynecologic endoscopy or any other diagnostic or therapeutic procedures which enhance the quality of care of gynecologic or obstetric patients.

The Young Investigator's Award is presented annually for clinical study or research in the field of obstetrics and gynecology to residents, fellows, and clinicians residing in the geographic confines of the Central Association.

YEAR PROGRAM STARTED: 1929

PURPOSE:
To encourage original work in obstetrics and gynecology.

LEGAL BASIS:
Nonprofit medical organization.

ELIGIBILITY:
Those eligible to compete are accredited physicians, teachers, research workers and medical students whose work was done within the geographic area of the Association.

For the Community Hospital Award, at least one author must be a member of the Central Association. Manuscripts must be written expressly for this competition and they must be original, not having been previously presented or published. Manuscripts will be considered for both the general program and the award unless the author specifically requests otherwise in writing.

GEOGRAPHIC RESTRICTIONS:
Alabama, Arizona, Arkansas, Colorado, Idaho, Illinois, Indiana, Iowa, Kansas, Kentucky, Louisiana, Michigan, Minnesota, Mississippi, Missouri, Montana, Nebraska, Nevada, New Mexico, North Dakota, Ohio, Oklahoma, South Dakota, Tennessee, Texas, Utah, West Virginia, Wisconsin and Wyoming.

FINANCIAL DATA:
Amount of support per award: Annual Central Prize Award: $2,000; Central Poster Award: $500 each; Community Hospital Award: $1,000; President's Certificate of Merit Award: $1,500; Young Investigator's Award: $750.

Total amount of support: $6,250 annually.

NUMBER OF APPLICANTS MOST RECENT YEAR: 50.

NUMBER OF AWARDS: Annual Central Prize Award, Community Hospital Award, President's Certificate of Merit, and Young Investigator's Award: 1 of each annually. Central Poster Award: 2 annually.

APPLICATION INFORMATION:
For consideration for these awards, an online abstract must be submitted. The abstract maximum length is 800 words.

Duration: One year. Nonrenewable.

Deadline: Mid-March each year. Award winners notified early May.

OFFICERS AND TRUSTEES:
Christine Comstock, M.D., President
Gayle Olson, M.D., President Elect I
John Calkins, M.D., President Elect II
Barbara Parilla, M.D., Vice President
Kirk Ramin, M.D., Secretary-Treasurer
David Lewis, M.D., Assistant
Secretary-Treasurer
Diana Curran, M.D.
Stephen Fortunato, M.D.
Harriette Hampton, M.D.
Stephen Locher, M.D.
J. Coffy Pieternelle, M.D.
Carl Smith, M.D.

ADDRESS INQUIRIES TO:
Rochelle Hickel
(See address above.)

REPRODUCTIVE SCIENTIST DEVELOPMENT PROGRAM [2660]

1466 Fourth Avenue
Building MRIV, Room 223
Box 0922
San Francisco, CA 94143-0922
(415) 476-9047
Fax: (415) 476-9596

E-MAIL ADDRESS:
minasim@obgyn.ucsf.edu

WEB SITE ADDRESS:
www.rsdp.org

FOUNDED: 1986

AREAS OF INTEREST:
Obstetric-gynecologic academic investigative careers in fundamental biomedical science.

NAME(S) OF PROGRAMS:
● **Reproductive Scientist Development Program**

TYPE:
Research grants. National postdoctoral career development program grant for full-time basic research under the mentorship of internationally recognized senior scientists.

YEAR PROGRAM STARTED: 1988

PURPOSE:
To train obstetrician-gynecologists committed to academic investigative careers in fundamental biomedical science.

ELIGIBILITY:
Candidates must be seeking a career in academic obstetrics and gynecology research and meet the following criteria:
(1) possess M.D. or D.O. degree;
(2) be a U.S. citizen, non-citizen national, verification as a permanent citizen at time of award;
(3) have completed a four-year internship and residency in obstetrics-gynecology approved by the Accreditation Council for Graduate Medical Education or the Royal College of Physicians and Surgeons of Canada and;
(4) submit a research proposal as part of application.

GEOGRAPHIC RESTRICTIONS:
United States.

FINANCIAL DATA:
Amount of support per award: The Foundation provides $20,000 to $25,000 annually to co-fund a position with the NIH.

Total amount of support: $75,000 salary and $25,000 supplies.

APPLICATION INFORMATION:
Applicant must submit a letter of intent to the RSDP office indicating the name of the Department of Ob/Gyn sponsor, name and address of proposed scientific mentor, and a brief description of the research project. This will be reviewed by the Executive Committee for appropriateness, and feedback will be provided to potential applicants.

Duration: Two to three years.

Deadline: Letter of intent: August 15. Application: October 1.

ADDRESS INQUIRIES TO:
Maro Minasi
Program Administrator
(See address above.)

U.S. DEPARTMENT OF HEALTH AND HUMAN SERVICES [2661]

Maternal and Child Health Bureau
Parklawn Building, Room 18-31
5600 Fishers Lane
Rockville, MD 20857
(301) 443-2204
Fax: (301) 443-9354

WEB SITE ADDRESS:
www.mchb.hrsa.gov
www.hrsa.gov

FOUNDED: 1936

AREAS OF INTEREST:
Health of mothers and children.

NAME(S) OF PROGRAMS:
● **Maternal and Child Health Services Block Grant**

TYPE:
Block grants. The Title V Block Grant Program has as a general purpose the improvement of the health of all mothers and children in the nation. The Block Grant Program has three components: Formula Block Grants to 59 states and other political jurisdictions, Special Projects of Regional and National Significance (SPRANS), and Community Integrated Service Systems (CISS) Grants.

PURPOSE:
To improve the health of all mothers and children; to create federal-state partnerships to develop service systems in U.S. communities that can meet the critical challenges facing maternal and child health.

LEGAL BASIS:
Title V, Section 501, of the Social Security Act, as amended by Public Law 101-239.

ELIGIBILITY:
State health agencies.

GEOGRAPHIC RESTRICTIONS:
United States and its territories.

FINANCIAL DATA:
Amount of support per award: Grants vary in amount, depending upon the number of children at the poverty level in the state.

Total amount of support: Approximately $560,000,000.

Matching fund requirements: The Title V Block Grant Program requires that every four dollars of federal Title V money must be matched by at least three dollars of state and local money.

COOPERATIVE FUNDING PROGRAMS: NICHD, CDC, Department of Education, ADAMHA and other inter-agency agreements.

NUMBER OF AWARDS: 59.

APPLICATION INFORMATION:
Apply online at www.grants.gov.

Duration: One to two years. Must reapply annually.

Deadline: July 15.

ADDRESS INQUIRIES TO:
Maternal and Child Health Bureau
(See address above.)

Ophthalmology and otolaryngology

THE ALCON FOUNDATION, INC. [2662]

6201 South Freeway
Fort Worth, TX 76134-2099
(817) 293-0450
Fax: (817) 615-3811

E-MAIL ADDRESS:
sara.woodward@alconlabs.com

WEB SITE ADDRESS:
www.alcon.com

AREAS OF INTEREST:
Ophthalmology and vision care.

TYPE:
Project/program grants. Grants to organizations and institutions improving ophthalmic education and skills in vision-related issues.

YEAR PROGRAM STARTED: 1962

LEGAL BASIS:
Corporate foundation.

ELIGIBILITY:
Eligible organizations must be 501(c)(3) nonprofit entities. Grants are awarded for community activities of interest to Alcon employees in communities where Alcon has a facility. Generally, grants awarded outside of Alcon communities are for organizations with a national focus on eyecare.

NUMBER OF APPLICANTS MOST RECENT YEAR:
Over 1,000.

NUMBER OF AWARDS: 350 for the year 2010.

REPRESENTATIVE AWARDS:
$30,000 to Prevent Blindness Texas; $5,000 to Jubilee Theatre; $16,000 to Association for Research in Vision and Ophthalmology; $20,000 to Fort Worth Symphony Orchestra.

APPLICATION INFORMATION:
Only online application will be accepted.
Duration: One year.

ADDRESS INQUIRIES TO:
Sara Woodward, President
(See address above.)

AMERICAN ACADEMY OF OPTOMETRY [2663]
6110 Executive Boulevard
Suite 506
Rockville, MD 20852
(301) 984-1441 ext. 3082
Fax: (301) 984-4737

E-MAIL ADDRESS:
helenv@aaoptom.org

WEB SITE ADDRESS:
www.aaopt.org

FOUNDED: 1922

AREAS OF INTEREST:
Vision science and vision care.

NAME(S) OF PROGRAMS:
● **Julius F. Neumueller Award in Optics**

TYPE:
Awards/prizes.

YEAR PROGRAM STARTED: 1969

PURPOSE:
To advance optometric education in optics.

LEGAL BASIS:
Tax-exempt corporation.

ELIGIBILITY:
Applicant must be a student pursuing an O.D. degree in a school of optometry recognized by the AOA Council on Optometric Education and must submit a paper, not to exceed 3,000 words, on Geometrical Optics, Physical Optics, Ophthalmic Optics or Optics of the Eye.

GEOGRAPHIC RESTRICTIONS:
Primarily United States and Canada.

FINANCIAL DATA:
Amount of support per award:
Approximately $750.
Total amount of support: Approximately $750 annually.

NUMBER OF APPLICANTS MOST RECENT YEAR:
10.

NUMBER OF AWARDS: 1.

APPLICATION INFORMATION:
Each school may submit two papers each year to the Chairman of the Awards Committee, which are judged by selected members of the American Academy of Optometry.
Duration: One-time award.
Deadline: April 2. Award announcement September 1.

ADDRESS INQUIRIES TO:
Helen Viksnins, Director
Education and Member Relations
(See address above.)

AMERICAN DIABETES ASSOCIATION, INC.
1701 North Beauregard Street
Alexandria, VA 22311
(703) 549-1500 ext. 2362
Fax: (703) 549-1715

E-MAIL ADDRESS:
grantquestions@diabetes.org

WEB SITE ADDRESS:
www.diabetes.org/research

TYPE:
Fellowships; Research grants; Training grants.

See entry 2560 for full listing.

AMERICAN HEALTH ASSISTANCE FOUNDATION [2664]
22512 Gateway Center Drive
Clarksburg, MD 20871
(301) 948-3244
Fax: (301) 948-4403

E-MAIL ADDRESS:
researchgrants@ahaf.org

WEB SITE ADDRESS:
www.ahaf.org

FOUNDED: 1978

AREAS OF INTEREST:
Glaucoma research.

NAME(S) OF PROGRAMS:
● **National Glaucoma Research Program**

TYPE:
Research grants. Support for basic research into the causes and potential treatments of glaucoma.

YEAR PROGRAM STARTED: 1978

PURPOSE:
To develop treatments, preventions and cures for glaucoma.

LEGAL BASIS:
Nonprofit foundation.

ELIGIBILITY:
Grants are awarded on the basis of the proposal's scientific merit and its relevance to understanding the disease studied. No funds for large equipment, institutional overhead costs, construction or building expenses.

FINANCIAL DATA:
Amount of support per award: Up to $50,000 per year.
Total amount of support: Varies.

NUMBER OF AWARDS: 13 for fiscal year 2010.

APPLICATION INFORMATION:
Duration: Up to two years.

PUBLICATIONS:
Annual report; newsletters; clinical brochures.

ADDRESS INQUIRIES TO:
See e-mail address above.

AMERICAN HEALTH ASSISTANCE FOUNDATION
22512 Gateway Center Drive
Clarksburg, MD 20871
(301) 948-3244
Fax: (301) 948-4403

E-MAIL ADDRESS:
drg@ahaf.org

WEB SITE ADDRESS:
www.ahaf.org

TYPE:
Research grants.

See entry 1512 for full listing.

AMERICAN OPTOMETRIC FOUNDATION [2665]
6110 Executive Boulevard
Suite 506
Rockville, MD 20852
(301) 984-1441 ext. 3086
Fax: (301) 984-4737

E-MAIL ADDRESS:
loiss@aaoptom.org

WEB SITE ADDRESS:
www.aaopt.org

FOUNDED: 1947

AREAS OF INTEREST:
Optometric research and education.

NAME(S) OF PROGRAMS:
● **Accuvue Eye Health Program**
● **Award of Excellence**
● **William C. Ezell Fellowship**
● **Vision Service Plan Research Grant**
● **Vistakon® Contact Lens Residency Award**
● **Vistakon® Pediatric Residency Award**

TYPE:
Awards/prizes; Fellowships; Project/program grants; Research grants; Scholarships. Scholarships for individuals pursuing an O.D. degree and fellowships for graduate students.

YEAR PROGRAM STARTED: 1952

PURPOSE:
To encourage teaching careers in optometry and to further vision research, both basic and clinical.

LEGAL BASIS:
IRS tax status 501(c)(3).

ELIGIBILITY:
Applicants must be postgraduate students (i.e., those who have received the Doctor of Optometry [O.D.] degree) and must be entering or continuing a full-time academic program toward the Master's or Ph.D. degree. They must also be planning on a career in teaching and/or research at an optometric school or college.

GEOGRAPHIC RESTRICTIONS:
Canada, Puerto Rico and United States.

FINANCIAL DATA:
Full fellowships are available in amounts of up to $8,000, plus travel grants to ARVO and American Academy of Optometry's annual meetings.

Amount of support per award: Varies.

Total amount of support: Varies.

NUMBER OF APPLICANTS MOST RECENT YEAR:
Ezell Fellowships: 46; Other awards: 30.

NUMBER OF AWARDS: 12.

APPLICATION INFORMATION:
Prospective applicants may obtain detailed
information regarding application procedures
from the optometric schools/colleges or the
administrative offices of the AOF.

Duration: Fellowships are awarded for a
period of one year and may be renewed two
times. The maximum period of support for
any one fellowship is three years.

Deadline: Applications must be submitted by
March of each year.

PUBLICATIONS:
Application guidelines/criteria.

DIRECTORS:
Anthony J. Adams, O.D., Ph.D., FAAO,
President
Joseph Molinari, O.D., M.Ed.,
Secretary-Treasurer
Lois Schoenbrun, C.A.E., FAAO, Executive
Director, AAO
Mark Bullimore, Ph.D., FAAO, Development
Director
Catherine Amos, O.D., FAAO
Joseph Barr
Philip Keefer
David Kirschen, O.D., Ph.D., FAAO

AMERICAN
SPEECH-LANGUAGE-HEARING
FOUNDATION   [2666]

2200 Research Boulevard
Rockville, MD 20850-3289
(301) 296-8703
Fax: (301) 296-8567

E-MAIL ADDRESS:
foundationprograms@asha.org

WEB SITE ADDRESS:
www.ashfoundation.org

FOUNDED: 1946

AREAS OF INTEREST:
Communication sciences and disorders.

NAME(S) OF PROGRAMS:
● **Louis M. DiCarlo Award for Recent
  Clinical Achievement**
● **Graduate Student Scholarship for a
  Minority Student**
● **Graduate Student Scholarship for
  International/Minority Students**
● **Graduate Student Scholarship for
  Students with a Disability**
● **Graduate Student Scholarships**
● **Frank R. Kleffner Lifetime Career
  Award**
● **New Century Scholars Doctoral
  Scholarship**
● **New Century Scholars Program
  Research Grant**
● **Research Grants for New Investigators**
● **Student Research Grant in Audiology**
● **Student Research Grant in Early
  Childhood Language Development**
● **Rolland J. Van Hattum Award**

TYPE:
Awards/prizes; Project/program grants;
Research grants; Scholarships. Louis M.
DiCarlo Award for Clinical Achievement
recognizes individuals demonstrating

outstanding achievement in the advancement
of knowledge in clinical practice within the
past three years.

Graduate Student Scholarships are available
to students demonstrating outstanding
academic achievement in communication
sciences and disorders. These include general
scholarships, scholarships for students with
disabilities, and scholarships for international
and minority students.

Frank R. Kleffner Lifetime Career Award
recognizes outstanding lifetime achievement
in clinical science and practice.

New Century Scholars Research Grants are
awarded to individuals committed to
teacher-investigator careers in the university
or college environment or in external
research institutes or laboratories.

New Investigator Research Grants are
awarded to new scientists to pursue research
in audiology or speech-language pathology.

Student Research Grant in Clinical or
Rehabilitative Audiology supports a proposed
one-year study to conduct research in
audiology.

Student Research Grant in Early Childhood
Language supports a proposed one-year study
to conduct research in early childhood
language development.

Rolland J. Van Hattum Award recognizes
professionals demonstrating significant
contribution to the delivery of audiology
and/or speech pathology services in the
schools.

YEAR PROGRAM STARTED: 1979

PURPOSE:
To further education in speech, language and
hearing through the provision of financial
assistance; to recognize and support research
and similar endeavors which contribute to the
advancement of knowledge and improvement
of practice in serving children and adults
with speech, language, or hearing disorders;
to identify and facilitate new directions in the
field of communication sciences and
disorders through support of such vehicles as
conferences, publications and other activities.

LEGAL BASIS:
501(c)(3) Association.

FINANCIAL DATA:
Amount of support per award: Research
Grants: $2,000 to $10,000, depending on
grant type; Scholarships: $2,000 to $10,000.

Total amount of support: Varies.

NUMBER OF APPLICANTS MOST RECENT YEAR:
Approximately 300 for all programs.

NUMBER OF AWARDS: 40.

APPLICATION INFORMATION:
Guidelines are available from the Foundation.
Required documentation for scholarships
includes application form, academic
documentation, faculty recommendation
committee report, and student essay.
Applications for research grants require a
research proposal.

Duration: One year. Nonrenewable.

Deadline: Usually May or June. Awards
presented in November.

PUBLICATIONS:
Annual report; program and application
guidelines; fact sheet.

IRS IDENTIFICATION NUMBER: 52-6055761

BOARD OF TRUSTEES:
Jon F. Miller, President

ADDRESS INQUIRIES TO:
Project Assistant
(See address above.)

BENIGN ESSENTIAL
BLEPHAROSPASM RESEARCH
FOUNDATION INC.   [2667]

637 North 7th Street
Suite 102
Beaumont, TX 77702
(409) 832-0788
Fax: (409) 832-0890

E-MAIL ADDRESS:
bebrf@blepharospasm.org

WEB SITE ADDRESS:
www.blepharospasm.org

FOUNDED: 1981

AREAS OF INTEREST:
Benign essential blepharospasm, Meige
syndrome, hemifacial spasm and related
disorders and infirmities of the facial
musculature.

TYPE:
Fellowships; Project/program grants;
Research grants; Seed money grants.

YEAR PROGRAM STARTED: 1985

PURPOSE:
To undertake, promote, develop and carry on
the search for the cause and cure for benign
essential blepharospasm and other related
disorders and infirmities of the facial
musculature.

LEGAL BASIS:
Foundation.

ELIGIBILITY:
Research proposals must relate specifically to
benign essential blepharospasm and Meige to
include new treatments, pathophysiology and
genetics, photophobia and dry eye.

FINANCIAL DATA:
Amount of support per award: $10,000 to
$150,000.

Total amount of support: $150,000.

NUMBER OF APPLICANTS MOST RECENT YEAR:
9.

NUMBER OF AWARDS: 5 for the year 2010.

APPLICATION INFORMATION:
Duration: One to two years. Extensions have
been granted.

Deadline: August 31.

PUBLICATIONS:
Program announcement; application
guidelines; brochure.

IRS IDENTIFICATION NUMBER: 74-2193322

BOARD OF DIRECTORS:
Mary Lou Koster Thompson, President
Glynda Lucas, Vice President
Emil Weaver, Treasurer
Mary Smith, Secretary

CANADIAN NATIONAL
INSTITUTE FOR THE
BLIND   [2668]

1929 Bayview Avenue
Toronto ON M4G 3E8 Canada
(416) 486-2500 ext. 7622
Fax: (416) 480-7000

E-MAIL ADDRESS:
shampa.bose@cnib.ca

WEB SITE ADDRESS:
www.cnib.ca

FOUNDED: 1918

AREAS OF INTEREST:
Ophthalmic subspecialties and vision research.

NAME(S) OF PROGRAMS:
• **CNIB/Baker Grant**

TYPE:
Challenge/matching grants; Fellowships; Matching gifts; Research grants; Seed money grants; Training grants. Priority is given to a person assured of academic posting in Canada on completion of training.

YEAR PROGRAM STARTED: 1961

PURPOSE:
To promote research and vision health; to enhance independence for people with vision loss.

LEGAL BASIS:
Charitable organization.

ELIGIBILITY:
Graduate Canadian ophthalmologists and optometrists returning to a teaching position in Canada or to practice in underserved areas are eligible to apply. Travel costs will not be funded. If fellowship funding is received from any other source, the CNIB Fellowship must be declined or returned.

FINANCIAL DATA:
Total amount of support: Approximately $208,000 for the year 2009-10.

NUMBER OF APPLICANTS MOST RECENT YEAR: 23.

NUMBER OF AWARDS: 6 fellowships and 10 research grants.

APPLICATION INFORMATION:
Application must be submitted electronically.
Duration: One year. Applicants must reapply for additional or ongoing training assistance and must submit new references from the center in which they are presently doing their extra training.
Deadline: December 1. Grant payments will begin July 1 of the following year.

PUBLICATIONS:
Guidelines.

ADDRESS INQUIRIES TO:
Ms. Shampa Bose, Grants Administrator
(See address above.)

DEAFNESS RESEARCH FOUNDATION   [2669]
363 Seventh Avenue, 10th Floor
New York, NY 10001-3904
(212) 257-6140
Fax: (212) 257-6139

E-MAIL ADDRESS:
grants@drf.org

WEB SITE ADDRESS:
www.drf.org

FOUNDED: 1958

AREAS OF INTEREST:
Research concerning the causes, treatment and prevention of hearing loss and related ear and balance disorders.

NAME(S) OF PROGRAMS:
• **DRF Grants for Research Projects**

TYPE:
Conferences/seminars; Research grants; Seed money grants; Travel grants. Limited in

amount and term, grants are awarded as seed funding in support of projects directed by new investigators or for promising new studies in areas of demonstrable basic science or clinical importance. It does include grant support for new research by established investigators.

Specifically, applications will be considered for research directed to any aspect of the ear; that is, investigation of the function, physiology, biochemistry, genetics, anatomy or pathology. Basic and applied research is welcome.

YEAR PROGRAM STARTED: 1958

PURPOSE:
To make a lifetime of hearing health possible for all people through quality research and public education.

LEGAL BASIS:
Nonprofit public voluntary organization.

ELIGIBILITY:
Applications are accepted from all U.S. institutions, including universities, hospitals and nonprofit tax-exempt institutions, public or private.

The DRF review committees will consider the subject of the research, the quality of its design, its potential for significant advance in basic knowledge or clinical application, the available facilities and personnel at the institution in which the research will be carried out and the qualifications of the investigators.

In accepting a research grant, the institution and the principal investigator are responsible for using grant funds only for those purposes set forth in the application and approved in the DRF award letter.

GEOGRAPHIC RESTRICTIONS:
United States.

FINANCIAL DATA:
Grant funds may be budgeted and used for direct costs of carrying out approved projects, including equipment purchases and supplies. Grant funds may not be used for the salary of principal investigator or co-investigator, travel, living expenses, printing costs, overhead costs exceeding 10% of project costs or public information/education programs.
Amount of support per award: Regardless of the indirect amount, the DRF award will not exceed $25,000.
Total amount of support: $457,696.62 for the year 2009.

NUMBER OF APPLICANTS MOST RECENT YEAR:
Approximately 25.

NUMBER OF AWARDS: 18 for the year 2009-10.

APPLICATION INFORMATION:
New Project applications and Second-Year applications must be submitted using the current forms available on the DRF web site.
Duration: One calendar year. Possible renewal for second-year grant support.
Deadline: December 1 for first-year applications. Principal investigators are notified in June.

PUBLICATIONS:
Hearing Health Magazine.

IRS IDENTIFICATION NUMBER: 13-1882107

STAFF:
Andrea Kardonsky-Boidman, Chief Operating Officer

Liz Saldana, Chief Development Officer
Elissa Freedberg, Foundation Grants Manager
Trisha Donaldson-Pitter, Grants and Programs Coordinator

ADDRESS INQUIRIES TO:
Trisha Donaldson-Pitter
Grants and Programs Coordinator
(See address above.)

EYE BANK ASSOCIATION OF AMERICA   [2670]
1015 18th Street, N.W.
Suite 1010
Washington, DC 20036
(202) 775-4999
Fax: (202) 429-6036

E-MAIL ADDRESS:
info@restoresight.org

WEB SITE ADDRESS:
www.restoresight.org

FOUNDED: 1961

AREAS OF INTEREST:
Restoration of sight through eye banks.

NAME(S) OF PROGRAMS:
• **EBAA Research Grants**

TYPE:
Research grants.

PURPOSE:
To provide support for proposals specifically concerned with issues related to eye banking and corneal transplantation.

ELIGIBILITY:
Must be a physician, including corneal surgeon and other eye care specialist, basic scientist, including biomedical and social scientists, or eye-bank technician, nurse, fellow, ophthalmology fellow or medical student that is supervised by a physician.

FINANCIAL DATA:
Amount of support per award: Generally $3,000 to $5,000.

NUMBER OF AWARDS: Varies.

APPLICATION INFORMATION:
Application form describing goals, background, methods and materials, and budgetary analysis must be completed. Applications should be typed and returned to the offices of the EBAA after approval by the appropriate eye bank or other nonprofit institution.

Applicants in training, eye-bank technicians, and nurses must submit a letter from the scientific supervisor regarding their capabilities of carrying out the proposed research study. Applicants who are not Paton Society members or who are not affiliated with an EBAA eye bank must submit a letter of support from a Paton Society member or the medical director of an EBAA eye bank; this letter must address the applicant's capabilities for carrying out the research and the available facilities. A curriculum vitae of the principal investigator and/or scientific supervisor should be enclosed.

Submit one original and 12 copies of the completed application. Faxed copies are not acceptable. Do not exceed the space allowed for describing the proposal or the application may be not considered for funding.
Duration: One year. Renewal possible.
Deadline: Early March.

FIGHT FOR SIGHT, INC. [2671]

381 Park Avenue South
Suite 809
New York, NY 10016
(212) 679-6060
Fax: (212) 679-4466

E-MAIL ADDRESS:
janice@fightforsight.org

WEB SITE ADDRESS:
www.fightforsight.org

FOUNDED: 1946

AREAS OF INTEREST:
Ophthalmology and visual sciences.

NAME(S) OF PROGRAMS:
● **Fight for Sight Grant-in-Aid**

TYPE:
Grants-in-aid. Support for research that may
lead to advances in preventing blindness,
treatment and cure of visual disorders,
restoring vision and preserving sight.

YEAR PROGRAM STARTED: 1953

PURPOSE:
To provide seed money for pilot projects for
young, unfunded faculty.

LEGAL BASIS:
501(c)(3) corporation.

ELIGIBILITY:
Investigators who have access to suitable
research facilities are eligible to apply.
Special consideration will be given to pilot
projects. Awards will be given to the
beginning investigator who has not yet had
the opportunity to demonstrate fully his or
her proficiency in ophthalmic research and
therefore is unlikely to receive support from
other sources.

With few exceptions, work to be performed
in the U.S. or Canada.

GEOGRAPHIC RESTRICTIONS:
United States and Canada.

FINANCIAL DATA:
Funds are to be used to defray costs of
equipment, consumable supplies and
personnel (excluding applicant).
Amount of support per award: Up to
$20,000.

APPLICATION INFORMATION:
Duration: One year.
Deadline: February 1. Start date between
July 1 and September 1.

PUBLICATIONS:
Brochure.

ADDRESS INQUIRIES TO:
Janice Benson, Assistant Director
(See address above.)

FIGHT FOR SIGHT, INC. [2672]

381 Park Avenue South
Suite 809
New York, NY 10016
(212) 679-6060
Fax: (212) 679-4466

E-MAIL ADDRESS:
janice@fightforsight.org

WEB SITE ADDRESS:
www.fightforsight.org

FOUNDED: 1946

AREAS OF INTEREST:
Ophthalmology and visual sciences.

NAME(S) OF PROGRAMS:
● **Fight for Sight Postdoctoral Fellowship**

TYPE:
Fellowships; Grants-in-aid; Research grants;
Seed money grants. Stipend to support
individuals with a Doctorate who are
interested in academic careers involving basic
or clinical research in ophthalmology or
visual sciences.

YEAR PROGRAM STARTED: 1953

PURPOSE:
To assist research and treatment aimed at
eliminating blinding eye diseases and sight
impairment.

LEGAL BASIS:
501(c)(3) corporation.

ELIGIBILITY:
Physicians or scientists holding a Doctorate
and who are interested in academic careers
involving fundamental or clinical research in
ophthalmology or its related sciences are
eligible to apply. If at the time of filing the
applicant does not as yet have a Doctorate, it
is required that a cover letter be submitted
together with the application advising that the
Doctorate will be conferred by the designated
commencement date.

GEOGRAPHIC RESTRICTIONS:
United States and Canada.

FINANCIAL DATA:
Amount of support per award: Stipend up to
$20,000.

NUMBER OF APPLICANTS MOST RECENT YEAR:
130.

NUMBER OF AWARDS: Approximately 15 to 20.

APPLICATION INFORMATION:
Applications are available online. Completed
applications should include:
(1) application face pages and related
information completed online and including
information about the applicant, his or her
education and training, institution and
sponsor;
(2) a research proposal of no more than six
single-spaced pages, not including references;
(3) letters of support from a sponsor,
departmental chair, and a third reference.
These letters should include an evaluation of
the student, the role of the mentor in
advising the applicant during the project, the
training plan, any extracurricular training the
student will receive and other information
helpful to the committee in evaluating the
mentor, the laboratory and the institutional
resources in support of a FFS Postdoctoral
Award. They should specifically address the
suitability of the applicant's training, his or
her academic achievements and, most
importantly, his or her potential to develop
into an independent eye and vision researcher
and/or leader in academic ophthalmology;
(4) an NIH-style biosketch of the applicant
and sponsor and;
(5) supplemental information, including
relevant awards, previous research experience
and academic or career goals.
Duration: One year.
Deadline: February 1. Start date is between
July 1 and September 1.

PUBLICATIONS:
Brochure.

ADDRESS INQUIRIES TO:
Janice Benson, Assistant Director
(See address above.)

*SPECIAL STIPULATIONS:
Research work to be performed in the U.S.
or Canada.

THE GLAUCOMA FOUNDATION [2673]

80 Maiden Lane, Suite 700
New York, NY 10038-4778
(212) 285-0080
Fax: (212) 651-1888

E-MAIL ADDRESS:
info@glaucomafoundation.org

WEB SITE ADDRESS:
www.glaucomafoundation.org

FOUNDED: 1984

AREAS OF INTEREST:
Glaucoma.

TYPE:
Research grants.

PURPOSE:
To fund research to determine the causes of
glaucoma; to improve methods of treatment,
and ultimately to develop cures for the
various kinds of glaucoma.

ELIGIBILITY:
Applicants must have a full-time faculty
position or the equivalent. Applicant must
also demonstrate the Principal Investigator's
understanding of glaucoma or his or her
collaboration with an investigator who has
experience in glaucoma research. If
collaboration is warranted, a letter of support
from the glaucoma researcher must be
included in the application.

FINANCIAL DATA:
Amount of support per award: $40,000.

NUMBER OF APPLICANTS MOST RECENT YEAR:
20.

APPLICATION INFORMATION:
Contact the Foundation for application
information.
Duration: One year. Renewable.
Deadline: March 1 and September 1.

ADDRESS INQUIRIES TO:
Scott Christensen, President
(See address above.)

GLAUCOMA RESEARCH FOUNDATION [2674]

251 Post Street, Suite 600
San Francisco, CA 94108
(415) 986-3162
Fax: (415) 986-3763

E-MAIL ADDRESS:
research@glaucoma.org

WEB SITE ADDRESS:
www.glaucoma.org

AREAS OF INTEREST:
Research and education pertaining to
glaucoma.

NAME(S) OF PROGRAMS:
● **Shaffer Fund for Innovative Glaucoma
Research**

TYPE:
Research grants.

PURPOSE:
To protect the sight and independence of
people with glaucoma through research and
education; to provide funding for such
research.

ELIGIBILITY:
Applicants must hold a graduate degree.

FINANCIAL DATA:
Amount of support per award: $15,000 to $40,000.

NUMBER OF APPLICANTS MOST RECENT YEAR:
30.

NUMBER OF AWARDS: 4.

APPLICATION INFORMATION:
The Foundation does not accept unsolicited requests for grant applications. Researchers interested in applying for a grant are asked to submit a Preliminary Proposal Form. After review, successful applicants will receive a grant application.
Duration: One year.

ADDRESS INQUIRIES TO:
Thomas Brunner
Chief Executive Officer and President
(See address above.)

HEED OPHTHALMIC FOUNDATION   [2675]
Cleveland Clinic, Desk i-30
9500 Euclid Avenue
Cleveland, OH 44195
(216) 445-8145
Fax: (216) 444-8968

E-MAIL ADDRESS:
gutmanf@ccf.org

WEB SITE ADDRESS:
www.heed.org

AREAS OF INTEREST:
Diseases and surgery of the eye or research in opthalmology.

NAME(S) OF PROGRAMS:
● **Heed Fellowship**

TYPE:
Fellowships.

PURPOSE:
To provide assistance to men and women who desire to further their education or to conduct research in opthalmology.

ELIGIBILITY:
Open to U.S. citizens who are graduates of an institution approved by the AMA.

FINANCIAL DATA:
Amount of support per award: $10,000 for the year 2010.
Total amount of support: $140,000 for the year 2010.

NUMBER OF APPLICANTS MOST RECENT YEAR:
14.

NUMBER OF AWARDS: 14 for the year 2010.

APPLICATION INFORMATION:
Applicants are required to submit:
(1) a one-page statement setting forth the applicant's major ophthalmic interest, professional aims and objectives, and noting qualifications deserving of particular consideration;
(2) a letter of recommendation from the Chair of Ophthalmology who supervised residency training;
(3) a letter from the preceptor of the applicant's fellowship program describing the program, including a statement that a minimum of 20% of the fellowship will be spent in research;
(4) two additional letters of recommendation from physicians who have supervised the applicant;
(5) a letter of acceptance of the applicant at the institution where the fellowship is to be

taken (this may be a copy of the applicant's match letter) and;
(6) a letter of recommendation from the Chairman of the department who has offered an academic appointment (optional).

Do not send curriculum vitae.

Facsimiles of application materials or letters of recommendation will not be accepted.
Duration: One year. Nonrenewable.
Deadline: January 15.

ADDRESS INQUIRIES TO:
Dr. Froncie Gutman, Secretary/Treasurer
(See address above.)

NATIONAL EYE INSTITUTE   [2676]
National Institutes of Health
5635 Fishers Lane, Suite 1300
MSC 9300
Bethesda, MD 20892
(301) 451-2020
Fax: (301) 402-0528

E-MAIL ADDRESS:
2020@nei.nih.gov

WEB SITE ADDRESS:
www.nei.nih.gov

FOUNDED: 1968

AREAS OF INTEREST:
Vision research, cooperative clinical trials for evaluation, diagnosis and therapy of ocular diseases, and epidemiologic and risk factor studies of ocular diseases.

NAME(S) OF PROGRAMS:
● **Cooperative Clinical Research Grants**
● **Small Business Innovation Research Awards**

TYPE:
Conferences/seminars; Development grants; Fellowships; Research grants; Training grants; Research contracts. Research Project Grants support individual investigators whose work is aimed at discovering means of improving the prevention, diagnosis and treatment of blinding and disabling eye and vision disorders.

Small Business Innovation Research Awards aim to stimulate technological innovations, to use small business to meet federal research-development needs that may ultimately lead to commercial products or services and to foster and encourage participation by minority and disadvantaged persons in technological innovations.

Areas of study include vision research, retinal diseases, corneal diseases, cataract, glaucoma, visual impairment and its rehabilitation, strabismus, amblyopic and visual processing.

YEAR PROGRAM STARTED: 1968

PURPOSE:
To gain new knowledge about normal and abnormal functioning of the eye and visual system; to support research aimed at improving the prevention, diagnosis and treatment of eye disease and disorders of vision. These are essential for progress against the major causes of blindness and visual disability.

ELIGIBILITY:
Research grants are available to any public or private university, college, hospital, laboratory, or other institution, including state

and local units of government and federal institutions; eligibility is no longer restricted to nonprofit organizations.

FINANCIAL DATA:
Amount of support per award: Grants vary in amount, depending upon the needs and nature of the request.

APPLICATION INFORMATION:
Those interested in applying are encouraged to contact the NEI staff prior to submitting applications.
Duration: Small Business Innovation Research Award: Six months to two years. All others: Varies.
Deadline: Varies according to award.

IRS IDENTIFICATION NUMBER: 52-0858115

STAFF:
Paul Sieving, M.D., Director, NEI
Richard Fisher, Associate Director for Science Policy and Legislation

ADDRESS INQUIRIES TO:
Jerome Wujek, Ph.D.
Research Resources Officer
(See address above.)

NATIONAL EYE INSTITUTE   [2677]
5635 Fishers Lane, Suite 1300
Bethesda, MD 20892
(301) 451-2020
Fax: (301) 496-9997

E-MAIL ADDRESS:
wwd@nei.nih.gov

WEB SITE ADDRESS:
www.nei.nih.gov

AREAS OF INTEREST:
Vision research, cooperative clinical trials for evaluation, diagnosis and therapy of ocular diseases, and epidemiologic and risk factor studies of ocular diseases.

NAME(S) OF PROGRAMS:
● **Center Core Grants**

TYPE:
Research grants; Research contracts.

PURPOSE:
To support centralized resources and facilities shared by investigators with existing NINDS-funded research projects; to enrich the effectiveness of ongoing research; to promote new research directions.

FINANCIAL DATA:
Amount of support per award: Applicants may request up to $500,000 per year in direct costs.
Matching fund requirements: Cost sharing is not required to be eligible for this program. However, it is strongly encouraged for applicant organizations to make appropriate and needed commitments to the Center in order to maximize the effectiveness and utility of the shared resources.

APPLICATION INFORMATION:
Contact NEI for details.
Duration: Maximum project period of five years.

ADDRESS INQUIRIES TO:
Hemin R. Chin, Ph.D.
(See address above.)

NATIONAL INSTITUTES OF HEALTH [2678]

Extramural Outreach and
Information Resources
6705 Rockledge Drive, Suite 350
Bethesda, MD 20892
(301) 451-4225
Fax: (301) 480-0146

E-MAIL ADDRESS:
nihtrain@nih.gov

WEB SITE ADDRESS:
grants.nih.gov/training/nrsa.htm

NAME(S) OF PROGRAMS:
• **National Research Service Awards
(NRSAs)**

TYPE:
Fellowships; Training grants. Support for
research training.

LEGAL BASIS:
Government agency.

FINANCIAL DATA:
Amount of support per award: $21,600
stipend at predoctoral level and up to
$53,112 at the postdoctoral level.

APPLICATION INFORMATION:
Application forms required. Contact the
Institute.
Duration: Postdoctoral awards: One to three
years. Predoctoral award: One to five years.
Deadline: April 8, August 8 and December
8.

ADDRESS INQUIRIES TO:
Extramural Outreach and
Information Resources
(See address above.)

NATIONAL MARFAN FOUNDATION [2679]

22 Manhasset Avenue
Port Washington, NY 11050
(516) 883-8712 ext. 17
Fax: (516) 883-8040

E-MAIL ADDRESS:
research@marfan.org

WEB SITE ADDRESS:
www.marfan.org

FOUNDED: 1981

AREAS OF INTEREST:
Marfan syndrome communication, research
and accurate information.

NAME(S) OF PROGRAMS:
• **National Marfan Foundation Research
Grant**

TYPE:
Awards/prizes; Fellowships; Research grants.
Basic and clinical research related to the
Marfan syndrome and related connective
tissue disorders. Areas include basic
translational and clinical research in genetics,
cardiology, ophthalmology and orthopaedic
issues of the Marfan syndrome.

PURPOSE:
To provide financial support for investigators,
scientists and physicians studying any or all
disciplines involved in Marfan syndrome
research.

ELIGIBILITY:
The principal investigator must hold an M.D.,
D.O., Ph.D., Sc.D., D.D.S., D.V.M. or
equivalent degree. The investigator must have
proven ability to pursue independent research
publications in peer-reviewed journals.

FINANCIAL DATA:
Amount of support per award: $50,000 to
$100,000.
Total amount of support: $150,000 for the
year 2010.

NUMBER OF APPLICANTS MOST RECENT YEAR:
10 for the year 2009.

NUMBER OF AWARDS: 2 for the year 2009.

APPLICATION INFORMATION:
Duration: One or two years.
Deadline: April.

ADDRESS INQUIRIES TO:
Josephine Grima, Ph.D., Vice President
Research and Government Relations
(See address above.)

RESEARCH FUND OF THE AMERICAN OTOLOGICAL SOCIETY, INC. [2680]

Johns Hopkins University, School of Medicine
Department of Otolaryngology-Head & Neck
Surgery
601 North Caroline Street, JHOC 6255
Baltimore, MD 21287-0910
(410) 955-7381
Fax: (410) 955-0035

E-MAIL ADDRESS:
jcarey@jhmi.edu

WEB SITE ADDRESS:
www.americanotologicalsociety.
org/information.html

FOUNDED: 1926

AREAS OF INTEREST:
Otosclerosis, Meniere's disease and related
ear disorders.

NAME(S) OF PROGRAMS:
• **AOS Clinician-Scientist Award**
• **Clinical Trial**
• **Research Grants**
• **Research Training Fellowship**

TYPE:
Fellowships; Research grants. AOS
Clinician-Scientist Award: For salary support
of a new clinician-scientist, at the assistant
professor level, in order to facilitate
development into an independent otologic
investigator. Department chair guarantees at
least 50% time commitment in research.

Clinical Trial: Study must be related to
otosclerosis or Meniere's disease.

Research Grants: Should be related to
otosclerosis or Meniere's disease.

Research Training Fellowship: For physicians
only (residents and medical students).
Fellowship will support one to two years of
full-time research conducted outside of
residency training.

YEAR PROGRAM STARTED: 1926

PURPOSE:
To encourage research in otosclerosis,
Meniere's disease and related ear disorders.

LEGAL BASIS:
Private foundation.

ELIGIBILITY:
Applicant must be a U.S. citizen or
permanent U.S. resident, graduate of
ACGME-approved otolaryngology residency
program, and must hold or be approved for a
full-time university faculty appointment.
Preference will be given to candidates who
are currently enrolled in or have completed a

neurotology fellowship program. Research
conducted during the Clinician-Scientist
Award can be on any topic related to ear
disorders.

Research must be conducted in U.S. or
Canadian institutions.

GEOGRAPHIC RESTRICTIONS:
United States and Canada.

FINANCIAL DATA:
Amount of support per award: AOS
Clinician-Scientist Award: Up to $80,000 for
salary and research support; Clinical Trial:
$66,000 maximum per year; Research
Grants: $55,000 maximum per year;
Research Training Fellowship: $35,000
stipend and $5,000 for supplies.

APPLICATION INFORMATION:
For the Clinical Trial and Research Grant
Awards, a description of the relationship
between the research study and otosclerosis
or Meniere's disease is an integral part of the
application. Applications for the Research
Training Fellowship must be accompanied by
sponsoring institution documentation stating
that facilities and faculty are appropriate for
requested research.

To obtain continued support, an application
must be submitted annually along with a
progress report.
Duration: One to two years. Application may
be made for continued support.
Deadline: Postmarked by January 31.

STAFF:
John P. Carey, M.D., Executive Secretary

ADDRESS INQUIRIES TO:
John P. Carey, M.D., Executive Secretary
(See address above.)

Osteopathy

AMERICAN OSTEOPATHIC FOUNDATION [2681]

142 East Ontario Street, Suite 1450
Chicago, IL 60611-2864
(312) 202-8232
Fax: (312) 202-8216

E-MAIL ADDRESS:
vheck@aof-foundation.org

WEB SITE ADDRESS:
www.aof-foundation.org

FOUNDED: 1949

AREAS OF INTEREST:
Osteopathic medical education and research.

TYPE:
Awards/prizes; Scholarships. Grants.

PURPOSE:
To assist and encourage osteopathic medical
students, researchers and physicians; to
ensure the ideals of osteopathic medicine by
initiating and supporting programs that
enhance the profession, advance the quality
of people's health, and recognize excellence
in the areas of education and research.

LEGAL BASIS:
Private foundation.

ELIGIBILITY: [1]
Applicants must be in their second through
last year at an AOA-accredited U.S. college
of osteopathic medicine.

FINANCIAL DATA:
Amount of support per award: Varies.

APPLICATION INFORMATION:
Applications or nomination forms are available January 1 on the Foundation web site.
Duration: 12 months starting June 1.
Deadline: Varies.

PUBLICATIONS:
Application; brochure.

ADDRESS INQUIRIES TO:
Vicki L. Heck
Associate Director of Communications
(See address above.)

AMERICAN OSTEOPATHIC FOUNDATION [2682]
142 East Ontario Street, Suite 1450
Chicago, IL 60611-2864
(312) 202-8232
(312) 202-8234
Fax: (312) 202-8216

E-MAIL ADDRESS:
vheck@aof-foundation.org

WEB SITE ADDRESS:
www.aof-foundation.org

FOUNDED: 1949

AREAS OF INTEREST:
Osteopathic medical education and research.

NAME(S) OF PROGRAMS:
● **Outstanding Resident of the Year Award**

TYPE:
Awards/prizes.

PURPOSE:
To recognize outstanding osteopathic physicians.

LEGAL BASIS:
Private foundation.

ELIGIBILITY:
Osteopathic physicians currently in the second through last year of an AOA-approved residency program are eligible. Applications will be accepted only after nomination by the residency director and endorsement of that nomination by the trainer. Only one nomination per residency program will be accepted.

FINANCIAL DATA:
Awardees also receive a travel grant to attend the Annual Convention.
Amount of support per award: $5,000.

APPLICATION INFORMATION:
Only online applications are accepted.

ADDRESS INQUIRIES TO:
Vicki Heck
Associate Director of Communications
(See address above.)

AMERICAN OSTEOPATHIC FOUNDATION
142 East Ontario Street, Suite 1450
Chicago, IL 60611-2864
(312) 202-8232
(312) 202-8234
Fax: (312) 202-8216

E-MAIL ADDRESS:
vheck@aof-foundation.org

WEB SITE ADDRESS:
www.aof-foundation.org

TYPE:
Scholarships. Awarded annually to one rising second-year student at each of the accredited U.S. colleges of osteopathic medicine.
See entry 1776 for full listing.

FOUNDATION FOR OSTEOPATHIC EMERGENCY MEDICINE [2683]
142 East Ontario Street
Suite 1500
Chicago, IL 60611
(312) 587-3709
(312) 587-1765
Fax: (312) 587-9951

E-MAIL ADDRESS:
swhitmer@foem.org

WEB SITE ADDRESS:
www.foem.org

FOUNDED: 1998

AREAS OF INTEREST:
Osteopathic emergency medicine.

NAME(S) OF PROGRAMS:
● **Investigator Grant**
● **David A. Kuchinski Memorial Research Grant**
● **Resident Research Grant**
● **Young Investigator Grant**

TYPE:
Awards/prizes; Research grants.

YEAR PROGRAM STARTED: 1998

PURPOSE:
To assist osteopathic emergency physicians in their research endeavors.

LEGAL BASIS:
501(c)(3).

ELIGIBILITY:
Grants are made to individuals or organizations that have tax-exempt status under Section 501(c)(3) of the Internal Revenue Code.

GEOGRAPHIC RESTRICTIONS:
United States.

FINANCIAL DATA:
Amount of support per award: Investigator Grant and Young Investigator Grant: $1,000 to $3,000; Kuchinski Memorial Research Grant: Varies; Resident Research Grant: $500 to $3,000.

NUMBER OF APPLICANTS MOST RECENT YEAR: 3 for the year 2010.

NUMBER OF AWARDS: 1 for the year 2010.

APPLICATION INFORMATION:
Contact the Foundation for application procedures.
Deadline: July 1. Reviewed in April, July and October.

PUBLICATIONS:
Research Beacon.

ADDRESS INQUIRIES TO:
Stephanie Whitmer
Director of Development
(See address above.)

MAINE OSTEOPATHIC ASSOCIATION [2684]
693 Western Avenue, Suite 1
Manchester, ME 04351
(207) 623-1101
Fax: (207) 623-4228

E-MAIL ADDRESS:
info@mainedo.org

WEB SITE ADDRESS:
www.mainedo.org

FOUNDED: 1912

AREAS OF INTEREST:
Osteopathic medicine.

NAME(S) OF PROGRAMS:
● **Doctors for Maine's Future Scholarship Program**

TYPE:
Scholarships. The program is a tuition subsidy for eligible students who enroll in a qualifying Maine-based medical school program.

LEGAL BASIS:
Nonprofit physician membership organization.

ELIGIBILITY:
Any Maine resident who will enroll in a participating institution.

GEOGRAPHIC RESTRICTIONS:
Maine.

FINANCIAL DATA:
Amount of support per award: $1,000.

NUMBER OF AWARDS: Varies.

APPLICATION INFORMATION:
Application form is available at the Association web site.
Deadline: May.

STAFF:
Angela Westhoff, Executive Director

NATIONAL INSTITUTE OF ARTHRITIS AND MUSCULOSKELETAL AND SKIN DISEASES [2685]
National Institutes of Health
6701 Democracy Boulevard, Suite 800
Bethesda, MD 20892-6500
(301) 594-5055
Fax: (301) 480-4543

WEB SITE ADDRESS:
www.niams.nih.gov

AREAS OF INTEREST:
Arthritis and musculoskeletal diseases; bone biology.

NAME(S) OF PROGRAMS:
● **Bone Biology Program**
● **Bone Diseases Program**

TYPE:
Awards/prizes; Conferences/seminars; Fellowships; Grants-in-aid; Project/program grants; Research grants; Training grants; Research contracts. National Research Service Postdoctoral Awards and Career Development Awards.

LEGAL BASIS:
Public Health Service Act, Sections 301(c), 433, 472; Public Law 93-604, as amended by Public Law 94-562.

GEOGRAPHIC RESTRICTIONS:
United States.

FINANCIAL DATA:
Amount of support per award: $250,000 average for research grants; $150,000 average for training grants; $100,000 average for career development awards; $30,000 average for the fellowships.
Total amount of support: Varies.

APPLICATION INFORMATION:
Duration: Up to five years for research grants.
Deadline: Varies.

ADDRESS INQUIRIES TO:
William J. Sharrock, Ph.D., Director
(See address above.)

NEW JERSEY OSTEOPATHIC EDUCATION FOUNDATION [2686]

One Distribution Way
Suite 201
Monmouth Junction, NJ 08852-3001
(732) 940-9000 ext. 303
Fax: (732) 940-8899

E-MAIL ADDRESS:
njaops@njosteo.com

WEB SITE ADDRESS:
www.njosteo.com

FOUNDED: 1901

AREAS OF INTEREST:
Osteopathic education.

TYPE:
Scholarships. For students pursuing osteopathic medical education. A first-year scholarship will be awarded to New Jersey residents accepted to the fall class of any approved college of osteopathic medicine.

YEAR PROGRAM STARTED: 1965

PURPOSE:
To provide the means to promote education in the field of osteopathic medicine.

LEGAL BASIS:
Not-for-profit corporation.

ELIGIBILITY:
Applicants must be residents of New Jersey having completed four years of pre-medical education and entering their first year in an osteopathic college. Applicants must have a 3.0 grade point average on a 4.0 scale or be in the upper 25% of his or her class. Selections are based on class standing, financial need, high motivation and professional promise. Students accepting scholarships must agree to become members of the New Jersey Association of Osteopathic Physicians and Surgeons and the American Osteopathic Association.

GEOGRAPHIC RESTRICTIONS:
New Jersey.

FINANCIAL DATA:
The scholarship sum will be paid directly to the college to cover part of the first year's tuition.
Amount of support per award: $4,000 to $7,000.

NUMBER OF AWARDS: Approximately 7 each year.

APPLICATION INFORMATION:
To apply for a scholarship, qualified students must:
(1) submit a completed NJOEF scholarship application;
(2) provide four named references, at least one of whom is an osteopathic physician;
(3) provide four completed reference evaluation forms;
(4) supply MCAT scores with confirmation code;
(5) supply pre-med college transcripts directly from the college;
(6) compose an essay sharing his or her

desire to become an osteopathic physician (why osteopathic medicine?) and;
(7) supply the prior year's tax return or that of the parent/guardian, if the student is claimed as a dependent.
Duration: One year.
Deadline: April 30.

IRS IDENTIFICATION NUMBER: 22-6088562

ADDRESS INQUIRIES TO:
Scholarship Program
(See address above.)

Pediatrics

ACADEMIC PEDIATRIC ASSOCIATION [2687]

6728 Old McLean Village Drive
McLean, VA 22101
(703) 556-9222
Fax: (703) 556-8729

E-MAIL ADDRESS:
info@academicpeds.org

WEB SITE ADDRESS:
www.academicpeds.org

FOUNDED: 1960

AREAS OF INTEREST:
General pediatrics.

NAME(S) OF PROGRAMS:
● **Young Investigator Grant Program**

TYPE:
Project/program grants; Research grants.

YEAR PROGRAM STARTED: 1994

PURPOSE:
To provide financial support to teaching, research and health care delivery projects in general pediatrics.

ELIGIBILITY:
The principal investigator of any proposal submitted must be a member of the APA or have submitted an application for membership. Preference will be given to new investigators, including those in training. Preference will be given to proposals that have the potential of leading to projects of a larger or longer-term nature.

FINANCIAL DATA:
Amount of support per award: Generally, up to $10,000.

NUMBER OF AWARDS: 3 to 4.

APPLICATION INFORMATION:
Applicants must submit a two-page proposal. Only electronic submissions as an e-mail attachment are accepted. The proposals should contain a brief overview of the project including purpose, methods, evaluation and estimated budget. A curriculum vitae for the principal investigator must also be included with the proposal. Budget requests should not include overhead or salary for the principal investigator if they are full-time faculty. The review panel will identify those that warrant further elaboration. Re-submitted proposals can be no more than 10 pages in length including tables and appendices. They must contain background, hypothesis, description of key personnel, detailed budget with justification and methods.
Duration: One year. Renewal possible.

ADDRESS INQUIRIES TO:
Connie Mackay
Young Investigator Grant
(See address above.)

AMERICAN ACADEMY OF PEDIATRICS [2688]

Department of Membership
141 Northwest Point Boulevard
Elk Grove Village, IL 60007
(847) 434-4000
(800) 433-9016 ext. 7864
Fax: (847) 434-8000

E-MAIL ADDRESS:
membership@aap.org

WEB SITE ADDRESS:
www.aap.org/ypn

FOUNDED: 1930

AREAS OF INTEREST:
Pediatric training.

NAME(S) OF PROGRAMS:
● **American Academy of Pediatrics Residency Scholarships**

TYPE:
Residencies; Scholarships. Stipend for the support of pediatric residents.

YEAR PROGRAM STARTED: 1982

PURPOSE:
To enable young physicians to complete their pediatric training.

LEGAL BASIS:
Nonprofit organization.

ELIGIBILITY:
Applicant must have completed, or will have completed by July 1, a qualifying approved internship (PL-0) and have a definite commitment for a first-year pediatric residency (PL-1) accredited by the Residency Review Committee for Pediatrics. In addition, applicant must be a pediatric resident or chief resident (categorical pediatrics or combined-training program) in a training program and have made a definite commitment for another year of residency (not fellowship) in a U.S. or Canadian program accredited by the Residency Review Committee for Pediatrics, as well as have a real need for financial assistance.

GEOGRAPHIC RESTRICTIONS:
United States and Canada.

FINANCIAL DATA:
Amount of support per award: $1,000, $1,500, $3,000 and $5,000.
Total amount of support: Varies.

APPLICATION INFORMATION:
Official application materials are available upon request in November. Applications must be supported by a form from the Department Head or the Chief of Service or the Residency Program Director addressing the financial need, commitment to pediatrics and performance in the program.
Duration: One year. Possible renewals.
Deadline: Last Friday in February.

ADDRESS INQUIRIES TO:
Kimberley VandenBrook
Residency Scholarship Coordinator
(See address above.)

THE CANADIAN FOUNDATION FOR THE STUDY OF INFANT DEATHS [2689]

60 James Street, Suite 403
St. Catherines ON L2R 7E7 Canada
(905) 688-8884
(800) END-SIDS (Canada)
Fax: (905) 688-3300

E-MAIL ADDRESS:
sidsinfo@sidscanada.org

WEB SITE ADDRESS:
www.sidscanada.org

FOUNDED: 1973

AREAS OF INTEREST:
Sudden Infant Death Syndrome.

CONSULTING OR VOLUNTEER SERVICES:
Self-Help Peer Support.

NAME(S) OF PROGRAMS:
- **Dr. Sydney Segal Research Grants**

TYPE:
Fellowships; Research grants. Studentships. Awarded toward the study of any discipline (medical, nursing, psychological, biological, sociological) which is concerned with the causes and effects of Sudden Infant Death Syndrome. Grants are awarded on three levels: studentship, fellowship, and special project.

YEAR PROGRAM STARTED: 1973

PURPOSE:
To enable students to pursue full-time higher degree studies at a university in Canada researching Sudden Infant Death Syndrome.

LEGAL BASIS:
Private foundation.

ELIGIBILITY:
Applications at the studentship level are invited from graduate students who are undertaking full-time training in research in the health sciences leading to an M.Sc. or Ph.D. degree or the equivalent. Limited funding at the fellowship level is available. Applications are invited from suitably qualified persons who are undertaking higher level training into Sudden Infant Death Syndrome.

Grants are awarded only to those working at Canadian institutions.

GEOGRAPHIC RESTRICTIONS:
Canada.

FINANCIAL DATA:
Amount of support per award: $10,000 to $35,000 (CAN) maximum.
Total amount of support: Approximately $100,000 (CAN) annually.

APPLICATION INFORMATION:
Application form required. Applications for studentship level grants are to be endorsed by the Dean of the Faculty/Director of the School as well as by the head of the department. Photocopies will be accepted. Applications available online.
Duration: One year for all levels.
Deadline: June 1. Renewal requests require reapplication.

PUBLICATIONS:
Application form.

*PLEASE NOTE:
Funding at the fellowship level is very limited.

CEREBRAL PALSY INTERNATIONAL RESEARCH FOUNDATION

186 Princeton Hightstown Road
Building 4, Second Floor
Princeton Junction, NJ 08550
(609) 452-1200
Fax: (609) 452-1201

E-MAIL ADDRESS:
jcarmosino@cpirf.org

WEB SITE ADDRESS:
www.cpirf.org

TYPE:
Research grants. Grants are awarded for pilot studies in areas which have a relationship to cerebral palsy. While most research in the central nervous system may be useful, the Foundation requires that research proposals define clear and direct relevance to cerebral palsy. Currently, high priority is assigned to prevention of prematurity, decrease of perinatal neurologic morbidity, prevention of central nervous system infections of the newborn and to medical, surgical and bioengineering methods that may improve the functioning of persons with cerebral palsy addressing issues such as impaired mobility, impaired communication skills, swallowing, drooling and effects of aging on further diminution of function. However, any proposal designed to prevent cerebral palsy or to improve its treatment and management will be considered.

See entry 2617 for full listing.

DYSAUTONOMIA FOUNDATION, INC.

315 West 39th Street
Suite 701
New York, NY 10018
(212) 279-1066
Fax: (212) 279-2066

E-MAIL ADDRESS:
info@famdys.org

WEB SITE ADDRESS:
www.familialdysautonomia.org

TYPE:
Project/program grants; Research grants; Seed money grants. In addition to support for research and clinical study, the Foundation also provides financial support to the Dysautonomia Treatment and Evaluation Center at NYU and the Israeli FD Center in Jerusalem.

See entry 2619 for full listing.

FIRST CANDLE/SIDS ALLIANCE [2690]

1314 Bedford Avenue
Suite 210
Baltimore, MD 21208
(410) 653-8226
(800) 221-7437
Fax: (410) 653-8709

E-MAIL ADDRESS:
info@firstcandle.org

WEB SITE ADDRESS:
www.firstcandle.org

FOUNDED: 1962

AREAS OF INTEREST:
Medical research into the cause and prevention of Sudden Infant Death Syndrome, counseling and information

projects which aid parents and educate the public about SIDS and SIDS-related issues and education of relevant professionals on SIDS and about care for infants at-risk.

CONSULTING OR VOLUNTEER SERVICES:
Local chapters provide voluntary peer support to parents and National Office provides consulting services in the management of specialized services, seminars to health professionals, review of SIDS medical research proposals and clearinghouse for literature and films on SIDS and related issues.

NAME(S) OF PROGRAMS:
- **Professional Research**

TYPE:
Conferences/seminars; Research grants. Professional medical research for SIDS, stillbirths and related issues.

YEAR PROGRAM STARTED: 1963

PURPOSE:
To promote infant health and survival during the prenatal period through two years of age by means of advocacy, education and research; to provide SIDS and other infant death bereavement services.

LEGAL BASIS:
Not-for-profit corporation.

ELIGIBILITY:
Applicant reviews are made on an individual basis by the First Candle/SIDS Alliance and the Alliance Medical and Scientific Advisory Council.

FINANCIAL DATA:
Amount of support per award: Grants vary in amount depending upon proposals.
Total amount of support: Varies.

NUMBER OF AWARDS: 6 per year average.

APPLICATION INFORMATION:
Letters soliciting Foundation interest prior to submission of proposals are welcome.

IRS IDENTIFICATION NUMBER: 52-1591162

ADDRESS INQUIRIES TO:
Susan Gerber-Berning
Chief Executive Officer
(See address above.)

CHARLES H. HOOD FOUNDATION, INC. [2691]

95 Berkeley Street, Suite 208
Boston, MA 02116
(617) 695-9439

WEB SITE ADDRESS:
www.tmfgrants.org/hood

FOUNDED: 1942

AREAS OF INTEREST:
Child health research.

NAME(S) OF PROGRAMS:
- **Child Health Research Awards Program**

TYPE:
Research grants. Medical research grants that are relevant to child health. Projects must be hypothesis-driven clinical, basic science, public health, health services research or epidemiology.

YEAR PROGRAM STARTED: 1942

PURPOSE:
To improve the health and quality of life for children through grant support of New England-based pediatric researchers.

LEGAL BASIS:
Private family foundation.

ELIGIBILITY:
Investigators working in tax-exempt academic, medical and research institutions in New England are eligible. Grants must have relevance to child health. Investigators must be within five years of their first faculty appointment. In addition to basic science research, grants are also given to researchers in public health, epidemiology, clinical research and health services research.

GEOGRAPHIC RESTRICTIONS:
New England.

FINANCIAL DATA:
Amount of support per award: $75,000 per year for two years (inclusive of 10% overhead).
Total amount of support: $1,500,000 over two years.

NUMBER OF APPLICANTS MOST RECENT YEAR:
51.

NUMBER OF AWARDS: 10 new grants for the year 2010.

REPRESENTATIVE AWARDS:
Renee Boynton-Jarrett, M.D., Sc.D., Boston University School of Medicine, "A Nested Case-Control Study of Genetic and Psychosocial Determinants of Early Puberty;" Steven Hatch, M.D., University of Massachusetts Medical School, "Maternally Derived Anti-Dengue Antibodies and the Risk of DHF in Infants;" Rebekah Mannix, M.D., M.P.H., Children's Hospital Boston, "The Effect of Age on Outcome after Traumatic Brain Injury in Apolipoprotein E4 Carriers."

APPLICATION INFORMATION:
Application guidelines, instructions and forms are available on the web site.
Duration: Two years.
Deadline: Spring and Fall for Child Health Research Grants. Funding begins on July 1 and January 1. Deadlines and guidelines change each cycle.

IRS IDENTIFICATION NUMBER: 04-3507847

OFFICERS:
John O. Parker, President and Treasurer
Neil Smiley, Vice President
Raymond Considine, Secretary and Executive Director
John Parker, Jr., Clerk

TRUSTEES:
Jeffrey Boutwell, Ph.D.
Barbara Bula

HUMAN GROWTH FOUNDATION [2692]
997 Glen Cove Avenue, Suite 5
Glen Head, NY 11545
(516) 671-4041
(800) 451-6434
Fax: (516) 671-4055

E-MAIL ADDRESS:
hgf1@hgfound.org

WEB SITE ADDRESS:
www.hgfound.org

FOUNDED: 1965

AREAS OF INTEREST:
Growth disorders and pediatrics.

NAME(S) OF PROGRAMS:
● **Small Grants for Research in Field of Short Stature**

TYPE:
Research grants.

YEAR PROGRAM STARTED: 1965

PURPOSE:
To help medical science better understand the process of growth and to help individuals with growth-related disorders, their families and health care professionals through education, research and advocacy.

ELIGIBILITY:
Applicants must be involved in research of the human growth process. Special consideration will be given to young investigators and to projects dealing with psychological, social, and educational aspects of dwarfism and its treatment and to new approaches to diagnosis and management, as well as clinical and basic research in the mechanisms of statural growth disorders of children including chondrodystrophies, genetic, or psychological causes.

FINANCIAL DATA:
Amount of support per award: $10,000 to $15,000.

NUMBER OF APPLICANTS MOST RECENT YEAR:
Over 40.

NUMBER OF AWARDS: Up to 3.

APPLICATION INFORMATION:
Application and guidelines are available from the Foundation. Applicants must first provide a Letter of Intent. Grant applications must be in NIH format.
Duration: One-time funding.
Deadline: Letter of Intent: May 15. Final application: September 1.

ADDRESS INQUIRIES TO:
Patricia D. Costa, Executive Director
(See address above.)

NATIONAL LEUKEMIA RESEARCH ASSOCIATION [2693]
585 Stewart Avenue
Suite LL-18
Garden City, NY 11530
(516) 222-1944
Fax: (516) 222-0457

E-MAIL ADDRESS:
info@childrensleukemia.org

WEB SITE ADDRESS:
www.childrensleukemia.org

FOUNDED: 1965

AREAS OF INTEREST:
Pediatric medicine and leukemia.

NAME(S) OF PROGRAMS:
● **Children's Leukemia Research Grants**

TYPE:
Research grants. Support for research efforts into the causes and cure of leukemia. Patient aid to families in need while meeting the expenses incurred in leukemia treatment.

YEAR PROGRAM STARTED: 1965

PURPOSE:
To work towards a cure for leukemia and to provide patient aid.

ELIGIBILITY:
Grants are given to individuals for leukemia research. There are no citizenship requirements. Organizations do not have to be nonprofit. Grants are available for start-up funding for laboratory or clinical investigations in leukemia. Although the

association prefers to fund new investigators, applications from established investigators for new initiatives are also solicited.

FINANCIAL DATA:
Amount of support per award: Up to $20,000 per year.

APPLICATION INFORMATION:
Application form required. Contact Association for other requirements.
Duration: One year. Renewal for a second year is considered if other funding for promising projects has not been obtained.
Deadline: June 30.

ADDRESS INQUIRIES TO:
Allan Weinberg, Executive Director
(See address above.)

SICKKIDS FOUNDATION
525 University Avenue, 14th Floor
Toronto ON M5G 2L3 Canada
(416) 813-6166 ext. 2354
(800) 661-1083
Fax: (416) 813-7311

E-MAIL ADDRESS:
national.grants@sickkidsfoundation.com

WEB SITE ADDRESS:
www.sickkidsfoundation.com/grants

TYPE:
Awards/prizes; Conferences/seminars; Project/program grants; Research grants. Grants for research for subspecialty training of career physicians and scientists to equip them for work in child health disciplines that are underdeveloped in Canada.

See entry 1562 for full listing.

SOCIETY FOR PEDIATRIC DERMATOLOGY [2694]
8365 Keystone Crossing, Suite 107
Indianapolis, IN 46240
(317) 202-0224
Fax: (317) 205-9481

E-MAIL ADDRESS:
spd@hp-assoc.com

WEB SITE ADDRESS:
www.pedsderm.net

FOUNDED: 1975

AREAS OF INTEREST:
Pediatric dermatology.

NAME(S) OF PROGRAMS:
● **Pilot Project Award**
● **William Reston Research Award**

TYPE:
Research grants; Seed money grants. Research grants for investigators on the faculty and postdoctoral levels.

PURPOSE:
To foster research in pediatric dermatology.

LEGAL BASIS:
Medical society.

ELIGIBILITY:
Applicants must have completed training in pediatrics or dermatology and be active in the investigation of pediatric dermatology. Importance of the project and feasibility within the timeframe available are selection criteria.

FINANCIAL DATA:
Amount of support per award: William Reston Research Award: Up to $20,000; Pilot Project Award: Up to $7,500.

Total amount of support: Varies.

NUMBER OF AWARDS: 1 of each annually.

APPLICATION INFORMATION:
Application form required. Notices also placed in various medical, dermatology and pediatrics publications.
Duration: One year.
Deadline: Mid-April. Notification about mid-May.

ADDRESS INQUIRIES TO:
Awards and Goals Committee
(See address above.)

THRASHER RESEARCH FUND [2695]
Gateway Tower West, Suite 1650
15 West South Temple Street
Salt Lake City, UT 84101
(801) 240-4753
Fax: (801) 240-1625

E-MAIL ADDRESS:
martinezaf@thrasherresearch.org

WEB SITE ADDRESS:
www.thrasherresearch.org

FOUNDED: 1977

AREAS OF INTEREST:
Pediatric medical research, with emphasis on clinical/translational research with potential findings that would be clinically applicable in a short period of time in the prevention, diagnosis and/or treatment of pediatric medical problems.

TYPE:
Research grants. Grants for support of research that addresses problems in children's health in areas of critical illnesses that have been insufficiently researched or investigated. The Fund assumes that significant solutions to children's health problems remain undiscovered and invites a broad array of applications designed to remedy these deficiencies.

YEAR PROGRAM STARTED: 1977

PURPOSE:
To provide grants for pediatric medical research that addresses problems in children's health that are significant in terms of either magnitude or severity.

LEGAL BASIS:
Private organization.

ELIGIBILITY:
The Fund supports medical research that seeks to prevent or cure children's critical illnesses, injuries and disabilities. Projects should:
(1) be scientifically sound and culturally appropriate;
(2) document methods and practices that have sustainable benefits;
(3) have specific aims and a well-designed methodology and;
(4) evaluate the significance of impact on children's health.

Funding is limited to research. The Fund does not award grants for general operations, construction or renovation of buildings or facilities, nor does the Fund award grants for general donations, loans, student aid, scholarships, educational programs or support of other funds or institutions.

The Fund excludes research using human fetal tissue, stem cell research, or behavioral science research.

FINANCIAL DATA:
Financial support may be provided for supplies, minor equipment and technical personnel assistance related to a specific Fund-sponsored project. Principal investigators in need of salary support for a specific project may apply for 20% support, based on federal guidelines.
Amount of support per award: $5,000 to $500,000. Typically $100,000 to $300,000.
Total amount of support: Varies.

NUMBER OF APPLICANTS MOST RECENT YEAR: 100.

NUMBER OF AWARDS: 25.

APPLICATION INFORMATION:
Application guidelines are available on the Fund's web site. Potential applicants are encouraged to contact Fund staff prior to a formal submission to determine the potential fit of a project with current Fund interests.
Duration: Three years.

PUBLICATIONS:
Brochure; application information.

STAFF:
A. Dean Byrd, Ph.D., MBA, President
R. Justin Brown, M.P.H., Research Manager
Megan Duncan, M.P.H., Research Manager
Aaron V. Pontsler, M.S., MBA, Research Manager

U.S. DEPARTMENT OF HEALTH AND HUMAN SERVICES
Maternal and Child Health Bureau
Parklawn Building, Room 18-31
5600 Fishers Lane
Rockville, MD 20857
(301) 443-2204
Fax: (301) 443-9354

WEB SITE ADDRESS:
www.mchb.hrsa.gov
www.hrsa.gov

TYPE:
Block grants. The Title V Block Grant Program has as a general purpose the improvement of the health of all mothers and children in the nation. The Block Grant Program has three components: Formula Block Grants to 59 states and other political jurisdictions, Special Projects of Regional and National Significance (SPRANS), and Community Integrated Service Systems (CISS) Grants.

See entry 2661 for full listing.

Pharmacology

AMERICAN ASSOCIATION OF COLLEGES OF PHARMACY [2696]
1727 King Street, Floor 2
Alexandria, VA 22314
(703) 739-2330
Fax: (703) 836-8982

E-MAIL ADDRESS:
vlau@aacp.org

WEB SITE ADDRESS:
www.aacp.org

FOUNDED: 1942

AREAS OF INTEREST:
Pharmaceutical education.

NAME(S) OF PROGRAMS:
- **New Pharmacy Faculty Research Awards**

TYPE:
Research grants.

YEAR PROGRAM STARTED: 1985

PURPOSE:
To provide start-up funds for new faculty members to assist in establishing a research program. These grants assist new faculty in establishing themselves as independent investigators.

LEGAL BASIS:
Nonprofit foundation, tax-exempt under the IRS code.

ELIGIBILITY:
Applicants must have earned terminal degrees in their disciplines (Pharm.D., Ph.D.), hold a regular full-time academic faculty appointment in a school or college of pharmacy, hold the rank of assistant professor, and be in the first to fifth year of their academic appointment.

Only one proposal per investigator will be accepted for review. Previous recipients of AACP NIP grants are not eligible to reapply. Faculty members who presently have NIH funding (grants, contracts) or funding from any other disciplinary society are not eligible to apply. Applicants to the NIP program must be members of AACP, starting their academic careers at U.S. colleges and schools of pharmacy that are accredited by ACPE and whose institution is a regular institutional member of AACP.

Successful applicants must submit two copies of a final report, plus two copies of any reprints of abstracts/papers published in refereed journals that result from the NIP-supported project, upon completion of the research, and interim reports for research continuing longer than one year on the disposition of funds and the progress in achieving the goals of the research.

GEOGRAPHIC RESTRICTIONS:
United States.

FINANCIAL DATA:
In addition to grant monies, each award winner will receive $1,000 for required travel to the AACP Annual Meeting.
Amount of support per award: Up to $10,000.
Total amount of support: Up to $150,000 for the year 2008.

NUMBER OF APPLICANTS MOST RECENT YEAR: 40 for the year 2008.

NUMBER OF AWARDS: Up to 15.

APPLICATION INFORMATION:
Initial Letter of Intent must be submitted electronically.

Application material may be found at the AACP web site. Proposals must consist of the following eight parts:
(1) title page with signatures of department chair and dean;
(2) abstract page;
(3) research narrative;
(4) budget page;
(5) biographical sketch form;
(6) animal research approval letter, if applicable;
(7) human subjects research approval letter, if

applicable, and;

(8) other supporting documentation, if applicable.

Application material must be submitted electronically in a single PDF file to Diane Drakeley, E-mail: ddrakely@aacp.org, by the deadline date. Complete applications will not be accepted if no Letter of Intent has been submitted.

Duration: One year.

Deadline: Letter of Intent: Mid-August; Full Proposal: Mid-September.

PUBLICATIONS:
Program announcement.

OFFICERS:
Lucinda Maine, Executive Vice President and Chief Executive Officer

ADDRESS INQUIRIES TO:
Vincent Lau, Vice President, Research and Graduate Affairs
(See address above.)

AMERICAN FOUNDATION FOR PHARMACEUTICAL EDUCATION   [2697]

One Church Street, Suite 400
Rockville, MD 20850
(301) 738-2160
Fax: (301) 738-2161

E-MAIL ADDRESS:
info@afpenet.org

WEB SITE ADDRESS:
www.afpenet.org

FOUNDED: 1942

AREAS OF INTEREST:
Pharmaceutical education.

NAME(S) OF PROGRAMS:
● **Phi Lambda Sigma-GlaxoSmithKline-AFPE First Year Graduate Scholarship**
● **Rho Chi-Schering Plough-AFPE First Year Graduate Scholarship**

TYPE:
Scholarships. Phi Lambda Sigma-GlaxoSmithKline-AFPE First Year Graduate Scholarship encourages outstanding Phi Lambda Sigma members to pursue the Ph.D. in a college of pharmacy graduate program.

Rho Chi-Schering Plough-AFPE First Year Graduate Scholarship encourages outstanding Rho Chi Honor Society members to pursue the Ph.D. in a college of pharmacy graduate program.

YEAR PROGRAM STARTED: 1985

PURPOSE:
To encourage outstanding Rho Chi and Phi Lambda Sigma members to continue their education in a graduate program for the Ph.D. in a college of pharmacy.

LEGAL BASIS:
Nonprofit foundation, tax-exempt under the IRS code.

ELIGIBILITY:
Phi Lambda Sigma-GlaxoSmithKline-AFPE Scholarship: Applicants must be in the final year of a pharmacy B.S. or Pharm.D. program and be a member of Phi Lambda Sigma. U.S. citizenship or permanent resident status is required.

Rho Chi-Schering Plough-AFPE Scholarship: An applicant must be a senior pharmacy student enrolled in a dual-degree pathway leading to a professional degree in pharmacy and the Ph.D., or first-year graduate students, entering a graduate Ph.D. program in an accredited school or college of pharmacy as a full-time student. Applicants must be in the final year of professional studies or have completed professional studies. U.S. citizenship or permanent resident status is required. Applicants must be members of the Rho Chi Honor Society.

GEOGRAPHIC RESTRICTIONS:
United States.

FINANCIAL DATA:
Phi Lambda Sigma-GlaxoSmithKline-AFPE: The scholarship may be used for any purpose decided by the awardee and faculty sponsor that will enable the student to have a successful program, i.e., student stipend, laboratory supplies, books, materials, travel, etc., related to the program of graduate study. None of the funds shall be used for indirect costs by the institution. Funding will be provided in two equal stipends on September 1 and February 1.

Amount of support per award: $7,500.

Total amount of support: $15,000.

NUMBER OF APPLICANTS MOST RECENT YEAR:
25.

NUMBER OF AWARDS: 1 of each.

APPLICATION INFORMATION:
For the Phi Lambda Sigma Award, the following information should be sent to Mary Euler, Executive Director of Phi Lambda Sigma Leadership Society, c/o University of Charleston School of Pharmacy, 2300 MacCorkle, S.E., Charleston, WV 25304; Tel: (304) 357-4860; E-mail: exec.director@philambdasigma.org:
(1) letters of recommendation from two college faculty members who are acquainted with the student and his or her potential for graduate study;
(2) name of the graduate school the student plans to attend (if known);
(3) a one- to two-page statement by applicant elaborating reasons for wishing to attend graduate school;
(4) a list of special honors, awards and accomplishments in high school and college reflecting achievement and ability to succeed in graduate school and;
(5) an official transcript of all collegiate grades and copies of GRE, SAT and other national achievement test scores.

For the Rho Chi Scholarship, application forms are available from Rho Chi Faculty Advisors or the Secretary of Rho Chi. Required information should be sent to: The Rho Chi Society National Office, UNC School of Pharmacy, 3210 Kerr Hall, CB No. 7360, Chapel Hill, NC 27599-7360; Tel: (919) 843-9001; E-mail: rhochi@unc.edu. The packet should include the following:
(1) a completed application form;
(2) a one-page description of present academic status including all previous scholarships and fellowships and memberships in professional, scientific, scholastic and honor societies;
(3) a one-page account of involvement in professional and extracurricular activities, list of proposed expenses for the year; if married, include spouse and family expenses; list all sources and amounts of income;
(4) name of university to be attended and planned field of study;
(5) graduate record examination scores;
(6) a one- to two-page statement describing career goals;
(7) official transcripts from all colleges or universities attended and;
(8) letters of reference from three individuals who are directly familiar with the applicant and can speak specifically to educational achievements and capacity for graduate study.

Duration: One academic year.

Deadline: February 1. Notification by April 15.

PUBLICATIONS:
Program announcement.

OFFICERS:
Robert M. Bachman, President

ADDRESS INQUIRIES TO:
Yona Mead, Grants Manager
(See address above.)>

AMERICAN FOUNDATION FOR PHARMACEUTICAL EDUCATION   [2698]

One Church Street, Suite 400
Rockville, MD 20850
(301) 738-2160
Fax: (301) 738-2161

E-MAIL ADDRESS:
afpe@att.net

WEB SITE ADDRESS:
www.afpenet.org

FOUNDED: 1942

AREAS OF INTEREST:
Pharmaceutical education.

NAME(S) OF PROGRAMS:
● **Kappa Epsilon-AFPE-Nellie Wakeman First Year Graduate Fellowship**

TYPE:
Fellowships.

PURPOSE:
To encourage an outstanding pharmacy school graduate to pursue an advanced degree in the pharmaceutical sciences.

ELIGIBILITY:
An applicant must be in the final year of a pharmacy college B.S. or Pharm.D. program or have completed a pharmacy degree. Consideration is given to those who need financial assistance to further their education in pharmacy. At the time of application, the Kappa Epsilon member must be in good financial standing with the KE Fraternity and planning to pursue a Doctor of Philosophy (Ph.D.) degree, a Master's degree, or a combined Residency/Master's degree program at a U.S. college or school of pharmacy. Applicants may apply annually and receive up to three years of financial support.

FINANCIAL DATA:
The funds may be used for any purpose decided by the awardee and faculty sponsor that will enable the student to have a successful program, e.g., student stipend, laboratory supplies, books, materials, travel related to the program of study. None of the funds shall be used for indirect costs by the institution.

Amount of support per award: $4,000.

Total amount of support: $4,000.

NUMBER OF AWARDS: 1.

APPLICATION INFORMATION:
Applications can be downloaded from the web site. Applications must include:

(1) a completed application form (application and reference forms available from a Kappa Epsilon faculty advisor or the Kappa Epsilon Executive Office, Tel: (913) 262-2749);
(2) a letter of recommendation from the faculty advisor and one other faculty member familiar with the applicant (both faculty members are to complete a letter of reference form) and;
(3) official transcripts of all collegiate grades, undergraduate and graduate.
Applications should be sent to the Kappa Epsilon Executive Office: 7700 Shawnee Mission Parkway, Suite 201, Overland Park, KS 66202.

Duration: One year.

Deadline: All application materials must be received by February 15. Notification by March.

ADDRESS INQUIRIES TO:
Yona Mead, Grants Manager
(See address above.)

AMERICAN INSTITUTE OF THE HISTORY OF PHARMACY [2699]
University of Wisconsin School of Pharmacy
Rennebohm Hall
777 Highland Avenue
Madison, WI 53705-2222
(608) 262-5378

E-MAIL ADDRESS:
gia@aihp.org

WEB SITE ADDRESS:
www.aihp.org

AREAS OF INTEREST:
History of pharmacy.

NAME(S) OF PROGRAMS:
● **Fischelis Grants for Research in the History of American Pharmacy**
● **History of Pharmacy Thesis Research Grants-in-Aid**

TYPE:
Grants-in-aid; Research grants.

PURPOSE:
To contribute to the understanding of the development of civilization by fostering the creation, preservation and dissemination of knowledge concerning the history and related humanistic aspects of the pharmaceutical field.

ELIGIBILITY:
For grants-in-aid, applicants must be Ph.D. students in good standing at an institution of the U.S. Students need not be American citizens, nor does the research topic have to be related to American history. Thesis research must be clearly related to some aspect of pharmaceutical history or some other humanistic investigation that utilizes a pharmaco-historical approach.

For Fischelis Grants, applicants do not have to be U.S. citizens, but must attend American institutions.

FINANCIAL DATA:
Grants-in-Aid only cover direct costs of research attributable to supplies and other expenses that cannot be reimbursed by the degree-granting institution itself. These can include computer time and programming, obtaining a photocopy or microform of essential sources, travel and maintenance at a site away from the home university. Ineligible expenses include routine typing of the manuscript, living expenses at the home university, publication of research results or routine illustrations for the manuscript.

Amount of support per award: Fischelis Grants: Varies; Grants-in-Aid: Up to $2,500.

APPLICATION INFORMATION:
Application forms required for both programs. For Grants-in-Aid, application must be no longer than four pages and must include identifying information of the graduate student, educational background, faculty reference information, thesis topic and description, estimate of expenses, statement of other financial support applied for and other information considered important to the proper consideration of the application.

Deadline: February 1.

ADDRESS INQUIRIES TO:
Beth D. Fisher
Director of Curatorial Affairs
(See address above.)

AMERICAN SOCIETY OF REGIONAL ANESTHESIA AND PAIN MEDICINE [2700]
520 North Northwest Highway
Park Ridge, IL 60068
(847) 825-7246
Fax: (847) 825-5658

E-MAIL ADDRESS:
n.bradle@asahq.org

WEB SITE ADDRESS:
www.asra.com

AREAS OF INTEREST:
Anesthesia and pain medicine.

NAME(S) OF PROGRAMS:
● **ASRA Carl Koller Memorial Research Grant**

TYPE:
Research grants; Seed money grants.

PURPOSE:
To support research related to any aspect of local anesthetics and regional anesthesia and their application to surgery, obstetrics and pain control; to encourage anesthesiologists and other researchers who are interested in the field.

ELIGIBILITY:
The applicant must be a member of the ASRA.

FINANCIAL DATA:
Amount of support per award: $500 to $50,000.
Total amount of support: Up to $75,000 biennially.

NUMBER OF APPLICANTS MOST RECENT YEAR:
20 for the year 2010.

NUMBER OF AWARDS: 2 for the year 2010.

APPLICATION INFORMATION:
The application, which must be written by the applicant, should be accompanied by a complete narrative research protocol. The research proposal must be concerned with an original idea or concept. The research must be carried out primarily by the applicant.

Deadline: September 1 of even-numbered years.

ADDRESS INQUIRIES TO:
Julie Kahlfeldt, Executive Director
Chairperson, Research Committee
(See address above.)

PHARMACEUTICAL RESEARCH AND MANUFACTURERS OF AMERICA FOUNDATION, INC. [2701]
950 F Street, N.W.
Suite 300
Washington, DC 20004
(202) 572-7756
Fax: (202) 572-7799

E-MAIL ADDRESS:
foundation@phrma.org

WEB SITE ADDRESS:
www.phrmafoundation.org

AREAS OF INTEREST:
Pharmacology and clinical pharmacology.

NAME(S) OF PROGRAMS:
● **The Paul Calabresi Medical Student Research Fellowship**

TYPE:
Fellowships.

PURPOSE:
To generate interest in research careers in pharmacology, including clinical pharmacology, among medical and dental students.

ELIGIBILITY:
Candidates must be enrolled in a U.S. medical/dental school and have finished at least one year of the school curriculum. Must be U.S. citizen or permanent resident and have firm commitment from an accredited U.S. school.

GEOGRAPHIC RESTRICTIONS:
United States.

FINANCIAL DATA:
Amount of support per award: Maximum stipend $18,000.

NUMBER OF AWARDS: 2 budgeted.

APPLICATION INFORMATION:
Applications are to be submitted online by an accredited U.S. school. The following information will be requested on the application:
(1) registration information including basic contact information, as well as information on citizenship;
(2) an extended letter containing the candidate's name, personal data, education and training, a curriculum vitae, information regarding prior research experience, and a bibliography, if available. The name of the immediate supervisor of the student must be stated and their relation to the project indicated. The supervisor's curriculum vitae and bibliography are to be submitted in NIH format/PHS 398. Limit document to no more than three pages and;
(3) a description of the proposed research, including the background, aims, methods, significance and facilities available. Please type, single space, font size 12-point or larger and number pages. This portion should be five pages not including the bibliography. The candidate must state how the fellowship will assist them in making a choice on the type of career in pharmacology or clinical pharmacology they will pursue. This letter should outline the chronology of the student's medical/dental education indicating exactly where in the process from matriculation to graduation the fellowship falls. The candidate should list any other support they are receiving.

Duration: Three months to two years.
Deadline: February 1. Announcement May 15.

ADDRESS INQUIRIES TO:
The Paul Calabresi Medical Student Research Fellowship
(See address above.)

*SPECIAL STIPULATIONS:
Commitment must be full-time. Student may undertake this investigative effort at their own school or another institution.

PHARMACEUTICAL RESEARCH AND MANUFACTURERS OF AMERICA FOUNDATION, INC. [2702]

950 F Street, N.W.
Suite 300
Washington, DC 20004
(202) 572-7756
Fax: (202) 572-7799

E-MAIL ADDRESS:
foundation@phrma.org

WEB SITE ADDRESS:
www.phrmafoundation.org

FOUNDED: 1965

AREAS OF INTEREST:
Pharmaceutics.

NAME(S) OF PROGRAMS:
- **Postdoctoral Fellowships in Pharmaceutics**

TYPE:
Fellowships.

YEAR PROGRAM STARTED: 1992

PURPOSE:
To encourage more qualified graduates from Ph.D. programs in pharmaceutics to obtain postdoctoral research training in the area of pharmaceutics.

LEGAL BASIS:
501(c)(3) organization.

ELIGIBILITY:
Applicants must either hold a Ph.D. degree in a field of study logically or functionally related to the proposed postdoctoral activities or expect to receive such a degree before activating the fellowship. Suitable facilities for the necessary training and research must be available to the applicant. U.S. citizenship or permanent residency in the U.S. is required. Applicant must have firm commitment from an accredited U.S. university.

GEOGRAPHIC RESTRICTIONS:
United States.

FINANCIAL DATA:
The award is made to the institution on behalf of the Fellow. The program provides no other subsidies (travel, tuition, fringe benefit costs, etc.) and indirect costs are not paid to the institution.
Amount of support per award: Maximum $80,000 ($40,000 per year).

NUMBER OF APPLICANTS MOST RECENT YEAR:
10.

NUMBER OF AWARDS: 2 budgeted.

APPLICATION INFORMATION:
Applications are to be submitted online by an accredited U.S. school.
Duration: Two years.
Deadline: October 1 for awards beginning January through December of the following year. Announcement December 15.

PUBLICATIONS:
Brochure.

IRS IDENTIFICATION NUMBER: 52-6063009

BOARD OF DIRECTORS:
Garry A. Neil, M.D., Chairman
John Castellani
Mikael Dolsten, M.D., Ph.D.
Ivan Gergel, M.D.
Glenn J. Gormley, M.D., Ph.D.
Howard G. Hutchinson, M.D.
Peter S. Kim, Ph.D.
John M. Leonard, M.D.
Jan M. Lundberg, Ph.D.
John Orloff, M.D.
Moncef Slaoui, Ph.D.

ADVISORY COMMITTEE:
William J. Curatolo, Ph.D., Chairman
Bradley D. Anderson, Ph.D.
Michael J. Hageman, Ph.D.
Charles Russell Middaugh, Ph.D.
Patrick J. Sinko, Ph.D., R.Ph.

ADDRESS INQUIRIES TO:
Postdoctoral Fellowships in Pharmaceutics
(See address above.)

*SPECIAL STIPULATIONS:
The second year of this award is contingent upon a progress report approved by the Foundation and submission of a financial report.

PHARMACEUTICAL RESEARCH AND MANUFACTURERS OF AMERICA FOUNDATION, INC. [2703]

950 F Street, N.W.
Suite 300
Washington, DC 20004
(202) 572-7756
Fax: (202) 572-7799

E-MAIL ADDRESS:
foundation@phrma.org

WEB SITE ADDRESS:
www.phrmafoundation.org

FOUNDED: 1965

AREAS OF INTEREST:
Pharmaceutics.

NAME(S) OF PROGRAMS:
- **Predoctoral Fellowships in Pharmaceutics**

TYPE:
Fellowships. Support for full-time research for promising students in the field of pharmaceutics during their thesis research.

YEAR PROGRAM STARTED: 1987

PURPOSE:
To support promising students in the area of pharmaceutics during their thesis research.

LEGAL BASIS:
501(c)(3) organization.

ELIGIBILITY:
Applicants must be full-time, in-residence Ph.D. candidates in the field of pharmaceutics who are enrolled in schools of pharmacy and who expect to complete the requirements for the Ph.D. in two years or less from the time the fellowship begins. The program seeks to support advanced students who will have completed the bulk of their pre-thesis requirements (generally two years of study) and are starting their thesis research by the time the award is activated. Students just starting in graduate school should not apply. Applicants must be U.S. citizens or

permanent residents and have a firm commitment from an accredited U.S. university.

GEOGRAPHIC RESTRICTIONS:
United States.

FINANCIAL DATA:
The award is made to the university on behalf of the Fellow and provides a stipend, payable monthly, which includes up to $500 for incidentals directly associated with the thesis research.
Amount of support per award: Maximum $40,000 ($20,000 per year), which includes up to $500 per year for expenses associated with thesis research.

NUMBER OF APPLICANTS MOST RECENT YEAR:
25.

NUMBER OF AWARDS: 3 budgeted.

APPLICATION INFORMATION:
Applications are to be submitted on the Foundation web site.
Duration: Two years.
Deadline: October 1 for awards beginning January through August of the following year. Announcement December 15.

PUBLICATIONS:
Brochure.

IRS IDENTIFICATION NUMBER: 52-6063009

BOARD OF DIRECTORS:
Garry A. Neil, M.D., Chairman
John Castellani
Mikael Dolsten, M.D., Ph.D.
Ivan Gergel, M.D.
Glenn J. Gormley, M.D., Ph.D.
Howard G. Hutchinson, M.D.
Peter S. Kim, Ph.D.
John M. Leonard, M.D.
Jan M. Lundberg, Ph.D.
John Orloff, M.D.
Moncef Slaoui, Ph.D.

ADVISORY COMMITTEE:
William J. Curatolo, Ph.D., Chairman
Bradley D. Anderson, Ph.D.
Michael J. Hageman, Ph.D.
Charles Russell Middaugh, Ph.D.
Patrick J. Sinko, Ph.D., R.Ph.

ADDRESS INQUIRIES TO:
Predoctoral Fellowships in Pharmaceutics
(See address above.)

PHARMACEUTICAL RESEARCH AND MANUFACTURERS OF AMERICA FOUNDATION, INC. [2704]

950 F Street, N.W.
Suite 300
Washington, DC 20004
(202) 572-7756
Fax: (202) 572-7799

E-MAIL ADDRESS:
foundation@phrma.org

WEB SITE ADDRESS:
www.phrmafoundation.org

FOUNDED: 1965

AREAS OF INTEREST:
Pharmacology, clinical pharmacology, drug toxicology, pharmaceutics, informatics and health outcomes.

NAME(S) OF PROGRAMS:
- **Research Starter Grants in Health Outcomes**
- **Research Starter Grants in Informatics**

- **Research Starter Grants in Pharmaceutics**
- **Research Starter Grants in Pharmacology/Toxicology**

TYPE:
Project/program grants; Research grants; Seed money grants. Starter grants to support research in the fields of pharmacology, clinical pharmacology, drug toxicology, pharmaceutics, informatics and health outcomes.

YEAR PROGRAM STARTED: 1972

PURPOSE:
To offer financial support to individuals beginning their independent research careers at the faculty level.

LEGAL BASIS:
501(c)(3) organization.

ELIGIBILITY:
Applicant must be a U.S. citizen or permanent resident. Those holding the academic rank of instructor or assistant professor and investigators at the doctoral level with equivalent positions are eligible to apply, providing their proposed research is neither directly nor indirectly subsidized to any significant degree by an extramural support mechanism.

GEOGRAPHIC RESTRICTIONS:
United States.

FINANCIAL DATA:
Funds are generally unrestricted, to provide resources directly related to the proposed research. Funds may not be used as salary support for the applicant nor for indirect costs to the institution. No more than $500 per year may be used for travel to professional meetings.
Amount of support per award: $60,000.
Total amount of support: Varies.

APPLICATION INFORMATION:
Duration: One year.
Deadline: Pharmacology/Toxicology and Informatics: September 1 for awards beginning January 1 of the following year. Pharmaceutics and Health Outcomes: October 1 for awards beginning January 1 of the following year. Announcements December 15.

PUBLICATIONS:
Brochure.

IRS IDENTIFICATION NUMBER: 52-6063009

BOARD OF DIRECTORS:
Garry A. Neil, M.D., Chairman
John Castellani
Mikael Dolsten, M.D., Ph.D.
Ivan Gergel, M.D.
Glenn J. Gormley, M.D., Ph.D.
Howard G. Hutchinson, M.D.
Peter S. Kim, Ph.D.
John M. Leonard, M.D.
Jan M. Lundberg, Ph.D.
John Orloff, M.D.
Moncef Slaoui, Ph.D.

ADVISORY COMMITTEE:
Daniel Acosta, Jr., Ph.D.
James W. Aiken, Ph.D.
Terry L. Bowlin, Ph.D.
Sue Piper Duckles, Ph.D.
Salvatore J. Enna, Ph.D.
Robert A. Kramer, Ph.D.
George R. Lenz, Ph.D., MBA
Harry LeVine, III, Ph.D.
Darryle D. Schoepp, Ph.D.
Patricia Seymour, Ph.D.

James J. Starling, Ph.D.
Stephanie W. Watts, Ph.D.
Megan Yao, Ph.D.

ADDRESS INQUIRIES TO:
Research Starter Grants
(See address above.)

PHARMACEUTICAL RESEARCH AND MANUFACTURERS OF AMERICA FOUNDATION, INC.   [2705]
950 F Street, N.W.
Suite 300
Washington, DC 20004
(202) 572-7756
Fax: (202) 572-7799

E-MAIL ADDRESS:
foundation@phrma.org

WEB SITE ADDRESS:
www.phrmafoundation.org

FOUNDED: 1965

AREAS OF INTEREST:
Pharmacology or toxicology.

NAME(S) OF PROGRAMS:
- **Predoctoral Fellowships in Pharmacology/Toxicology**

TYPE:
Fellowships. Support for full-time research for promising students in the fields of pharmacology or toxicology during their thesis research.

YEAR PROGRAM STARTED: 1978

PURPOSE:
To support promising students during their thesis research.

LEGAL BASIS:
501(c)(3) organization.

ELIGIBILITY:
Applicants must be full-time, in-residence Ph.D. candidates in the fields of pharmacology or toxicology who are enrolled in schools of medicine, dentistry, or veterinary medicine and who expect to complete the requirements for the Ph.D. in two years or less from the time the fellowship begins. The program seeks to support advanced students who will have completed the bulk of their pre-thesis requirements (generally two years of study) and are starting their thesis research by the time the award is activated. Students just starting in graduate school should not apply. Applicant must be a U.S. citizen or a permanent resident and must have a firm commitment from an accredited U.S. university.

GEOGRAPHIC RESTRICTIONS:
United States.

FINANCIAL DATA:
The award is made to the university on behalf of the Fellow and provides a stipend which includes up to $500 a year for incidentals directly associated with the thesis research.
Amount of support per award: Maximum $40,000 ($20,000 per year).

NUMBER OF APPLICANTS MOST RECENT YEAR:
40.

NUMBER OF AWARDS: 6.

APPLICATION INFORMATION:
Applications should be submitted to the Foundation by the appropriate representatives of the schools.

Duration: Two years.
Deadline: September 1 for awards beginning January through August of the following year. Announcement December 15.

PUBLICATIONS:
Brochure.

IRS IDENTIFICATION NUMBER: 52-6063009

BOARD OF DIRECTORS:
Garry A. Neil, M.D., Chairman
John Castellani
Mikael Dolsten, M.D., Ph.D.
Ivan Gergel, M.D.
Glenn J. Gormley, M.D., Ph.D.
Howard G. Hutchinson, M.D.
Peter S. Kim, Ph.D.
John M. Leonard, M.D.
Jan M. Lundberg, Ph.D.
John Orloff, M.D.
Moncef Slaoui, Ph.D.

ADVISORY COMMITTEE:
Daniel Acosta, Jr., Ph.D.
James W. Aiken, Ph.D.
Terry L. Bowlin, Ph.D.
Sue Piper Duckles, Ph.D.
Salvatore J. Enna, Ph.D.
Robert A. Kramer, Ph.D.
George R. Lenz, Ph.D., MBA
Harry LeVine, III, Ph.D.
Darryle D. Schoepp, Ph.D.
Patricia Seymour, Ph.D.
James J. Starling, Ph.D.
Stephanie W. Watts, Ph.D.
Megan Yao, Ph.D.

ADDRESS INQUIRIES TO:
Predoctoral Fellowships
in Pharmacology/Toxicology
(See address above.)

PHI DELTA CHI PHARMACY FRATERNITY   [2706]
116 North Lafayette Street
Suite B
South Lyon, MI 48178
(800) 732-1883

E-MAIL ADDRESS:
office@phideltachi.org

WEB SITE ADDRESS:
www.phideltachi.org

FOUNDED: 1883

AREAS OF INTEREST:
Leadership development and professional/service projects.

CONSULTING OR VOLUNTEER SERVICES:
Leadership development.

NAME(S) OF PROGRAMS:
- **Rand P. Hollenback Scholarship Program**

TYPE:
Scholarships.

YEAR PROGRAM STARTED: 1970

PURPOSE:
To improve scholarship within a Phi Delta Chi Chapter and/or School of Pharmacy.

LEGAL BASIS:
Professional fraternity.

ELIGIBILITY:
Phi Delta Chi membership required.

FINANCIAL DATA:
Amount of support per award: $100 to $150.
Total amount of support: $375.

NUMBER OF APPLICANTS MOST RECENT YEAR: 50.

NUMBER OF AWARDS: 3.

APPLICATION INFORMATION:
Selection is based on reports from Phi Delta Chi Chapters.
Duration: One-time award.
Deadline: May 31 of each year. Announcement in August of the following year.

PUBLICATIONS:
The Communicator.

OFFICERS:
Brandon Sucher, President
Lindsay Watson, Vice President for Alumni Affairs
Amy Valdez, Vice President for Collegiate Affairs
Michael Nelson, Vice President for Communications
Jennifer Esch, Vice President for Student Affairs
Kenny Walkup, Executive Director
Song C. You

ADDRESS INQUIRIES TO:
Kenny Walkup, Executive Director
(See address above.)

THE UNIVERSITY OF SYDNEY [2707]

Scholarships Office
Level 5, Jane Foss Russell Building G02
The University of Sydney N.S.W. 2006
Australia
(02) 8627 8112
Fax: (02) 8627 8145

E-MAIL ADDRESS:
research.training@sydney.edu.au

WEB SITE ADDRESS:
www.syndey.edu.au/scholarships/research

FOUNDED: 1850

AREAS OF INTEREST:
Pharmacy.

NAME(S) OF PROGRAMS:
● **Elizabeth Wunsch Postgraduate Research Scholarship in Pharmacy**

TYPE:
Scholarships.

YEAR PROGRAM STARTED: 1982

PURPOSE:
To promote and encourage research work within the Faculty of Pharmacy at the University of Sydney.

LEGAL BASIS:
University.

ELIGIBILITY:
Open to graduates of the University of Sydney or any other university who are eligible to enroll in a higher degree in the Faculty of Pharmacy on a topic approved by the Head of the Department.

FINANCIAL DATA:
The scholarship does not cover tuition fees payable by international students.
Amount of support per award: $22,860 AUD per annum for the year 2011.

NUMBER OF AWARDS: 1 offered as vacancy occurs and funds are available.

APPLICATION INFORMATION:
Duration: Master's research degree: Two years; Ph.D. degree: Three years.

ADDRESS INQUIRIES TO:
Faculty of Pharmacy
The University of Sydney
N.S.W. 2006 Australia
Tel: (02) 9036 7243
Fax: (02) 9351 4391
E-mail: maree.williams@sydney.edu.au

*PLEASE NOTE:
Very few awards are available and competition for them is extremely keen. They are awarded strictly on academic merit and only graduates with First Class Honours or equivalent qualifications (e.g., graduation magna cum laude) will be considered.

*SPECIAL STIPULATIONS:
Scholarships are tenable at the University of Sydney. Holder is required to enroll for a higher degree.

Physical medicine and rehabilitation

AMERICAN BURN ASSOCIATION [2708]

625 North Michigan Avenue
Suite 2550
Chicago, IL 60611
(312) 642-9260
Fax: (312) 642-9130

E-MAIL ADDRESS:
info@ameriburn.org

WEB SITE ADDRESS:
www.ameriburn.org

AREAS OF INTEREST:
Thermal injury.

NAME(S) OF PROGRAMS:
● **Education Exchange Program**
● **International Education Exchange Program**
● **Visiting Professor Program**

TYPE:
Exchange programs; Professorships; Travel grants.

PURPOSE:
To support efforts that address the problems of burn injuries and burn victims; to provide care and rehabilitation to burn patients, conduct burn-related research, educate burn team members, develop and implement burn injury prevention programs, fight fires and address the psychosocial needs of burn victims.

ELIGIBILITY:
Institutions of higher learning in the U.S. and its territories are eligible to apply for support of appropriate research to be conducted by qualified investigators.

GEOGRAPHIC RESTRICTIONS:
United States and Canada.

FINANCIAL DATA:
Amount of support per award: $1,500 to $2,000, depending on the award.

NUMBER OF AWARDS: 1 each annually.

APPLICATION INFORMATION:
Applicants must submit a brief letter outlining the purpose of the grant.

ADDRESS INQUIRIES TO:
John Krichbaum, Executive Director
(See address above.)

AMERICAN GERIATRICS SOCIETY [2709]

The Empire State Building
350 Fifth Avenue, Suite 801
New York, NY 10118
(212) 308-1414
Fax: (212) 832-8646

E-MAIL ADDRESS:
info@americangeriatrics.org

WEB SITE ADDRESS:
www.americangeriatrics.org

AREAS OF INTEREST:
Problems of the aged.

NAME(S) OF PROGRAMS:
● **Clinical Student Research Award**
● **Clinician of the Year**
● **Edward Henderson Student Award**
● **Dennis W. Jahnigen Memorial Award**
● **Merck/AGS New Investigator Awards**
● **Nascher/Manning Award**
● **Outstanding Scientific Achievement for Clinical Investigation Award**
● **Scientist-in-Training Research Award**

TYPE:
Awards/prizes. The AGS Student Research Award is presented to the student who submitted the most outstanding student abstract for the AGS Annual Meeting.

Clinician of the Year was established to recognize the great contributions of practitioners to the delivery of quality health care to older people, and the importance of the geriatrics clinician in our health care delivery system.

Edward Henderson Student Award is presented to a medical student interested in pursuing a career in geriatrics who has demonstrated excellence in the field.

Dennis W. Jahnigen Memorial Award is given annually to an AGS member who has provided leadership to train students in geriatrics and has contributed significantly to the progress of geriatrics education in health professions schools.

Merck/AGS New Investigator Awards are presented to individuals whose original research, as presented in a submitted abstract, reflects new and relevant research in geriatrics.

Nascher/Manning Award recognizes distinguished, lifelong achievement in clinical geriatrics, including medicine, psychiatry, and all other related disciplines.

Outstanding Scientific Achievement for Clinical Investigation Award recognizes outstanding achievement in clinical research addressing health care problems of older adults by an investigator who is actively involved in direct patient care.

PURPOSE:
To encourage and promote the field of geriatrics and to stress the importance of medical research in the field of aging; to recognize individuals whose outstanding work in geriatrics education, research and clinical practice contribute to the delivery of high quality care for older people.

FINANCIAL DATA:
Amount of support per award: Clinical Student Research Award, Edward Henderson Student Award and Scientist-in-Training Research Award: $500; Clinician of the Year: $2,000; Dennis W. Jahnigen Memorial Award, Nascher/Manning Award and Outstanding Scientific Achievement for

Clinical Investigation Award: travel expenses to attend the AGS meeting; Merck/AGS New Investigator Awards: $1,500.

APPLICATION INFORMATION:
To request an application, fax or e-mail Dennise McAlpin at the address above. Application is posted on the Society web site by mid-August.

Duration: Nascher/Manning Award: Biannual; All other awards: Annual.

Deadline: December 5, 2011.

ADDRESS INQUIRIES TO:
Dennise McAlpin
Manager of Professional Education
(See address above.)

AMERICAN KINESIOTHERAPY ASSOCIATION, INC. [2710]
118 College Drive, Box No. 5142
Hattiesburg, MS 39406
(800) 296-2582
Fax: 601-266-4445

E-MAIL ADDRESS:
info@akta.org

WEB SITE ADDRESS:
www.akta.org

FOUNDED: 1946

AREAS OF INTEREST:
Kinesiotherapy, including adaptive physical education.

NAME(S) OF PROGRAMS:
● **AKTA Lou Montalvano Memorial Scholarship**

TYPE:
Scholarships. Award for students in AKTA-accredited kinesiotherapy programs.

PURPOSE:
To recognize academic excellence and career planning through funding for educational needs.

LEGAL BASIS:
Incorporated, nonprofit organization.

ELIGIBILITY:
Candidate must be currently enrolled in an AKTA-accredited kinesiotherapy program in a university and have definite intentions to pursue certification and a career in kinesiotherapy. Candidate must be a current member of the AKTA. Past AKTA scholarship winners are ineligible to apply for further AKTA scholarships.

Scholarship committee reserves the right to withhold awarding of the scholarship if no qualified applicants emerge.

FINANCIAL DATA:
Amount of support per award: Usually $500.
Total amount of support: $500.

NUMBER OF AWARDS: 1 annually.

APPLICATION INFORMATION:
Application process includes college transcripts and three letters of recommendation. Further information is available from the Association.

Duration: One year.

Deadline: August 31.

ADDRESS INQUIRIES TO:
Arthur Morris, R.K.T.
AKTA Scholarship Committee Chairman
Tel: (541) 261-5899
E-mail: arthur.morris@va.gov
(See address above.)

THE AMERICAN ORTHOPAEDIC SOCIETY FOR SPORTS MEDICINE (AOSSM) [2711]
6300 North River Road
Suite 500
Rosemont, IL 60018
(877) 321-3500 (IL only)
(847) 292-4900
Fax: (847) 292-4905

E-MAIL ADDRESS:
bart@aossm.org

WEB SITE ADDRESS:
www.sportsmed.org

FOUNDED: 1972

AREAS OF INTEREST:
Sports medicine.

NAME(S) OF PROGRAMS:
● **AOSSM Young Investigator Grant**

TYPE:
Awards/prizes; Research grants. Grant is intended to encourage junior researchers.

PURPOSE:
To increase the knowledge of and improve the care of sports-related injuries and disease.

ELIGIBILITY:
Grants will be awarded to the principal investigators who fulfill the following criteria:
(1) has not received any peer-reviewed external funding nor any external funding greater than $15,000;
(2) must be an orthopaedic surgeon who has graduated from an approved residency program or is a resident currently in an approved program;
(3) must document and play the primary role in the proposed investigation and;
(4) must stay at the parent institution while completing the project.

FINANCIAL DATA:
Amount of support per award: $40,000 over a 24-month period.
Total amount of support: $40,000 annually.

NUMBER OF AWARDS: 2.

APPLICATION INFORMATION:
Online submission only.

Duration: Two years.

Deadline: Pre-review deadline: August 15. Final deadline: December 1.

ADDRESS INQUIRIES TO:
Barton J. Mann, Director of Research
(See address above.)

CHILDREN'S BRAIN TUMOR FOUNDATION
274 Madison Avenue
Suite 1004
New York, NY 10016
(212) 448-9494
Fax: (212) 448-1022

E-MAIL ADDRESS:
info@cbtf.org

WEB SITE ADDRESS:
www.cbtf.org

TYPE:
Research grants. Basic science research grants for pediatric brain and spinal cord tumors.

See entry 1181 for full listing.

FOUNDATION FOR PHYSICAL THERAPY, INC. [2712]
1111 North Fairfax Street
Alexandria, VA 22314-1488
(800) 875-1378 ext. 8505
Fax: (703) 706-8536

E-MAIL ADDRESS:
foundation@apta.org

WEB SITE ADDRESS:
www.foundationforphysicaltherapy.org

FOUNDED: 1979

AREAS OF INTEREST:
Physical therapy.

NAME(S) OF PROGRAMS:
● **Doctoral Opportunities for Clinicians and Scholars (DOCS) I and II**
● **Florence P. Kendall Doctoral Scholarships**
● **New Investigator Fellowship Training Initiative (NIFTI)**
● **NIFTI in Health Services Research**

TYPE:
Fellowships; Scholarships. Fellowships for postdoctoral physical therapy research. Scholarships for physical therapists who intend to pursue physical therapy research as a career.

YEAR PROGRAM STARTED: 1998

PURPOSE:
To provide scholarships that support physical therapists who wish to continue their doctoral coursework and enter the dissertation phase; to provide fellowships that support developing researchers and improve their competitiveness in securing external funding for future research.

LEGAL BASIS:
Foundation.

ELIGIBILITY:
Must be U.S. citizen or permanent resident. Scholarship applicants must be physical therapists or physical therapist assistants pursuing a doctoral degree in physical therapy or a related field with a research focus related to the clinical practice of physical therapy. Applicants must demonstrate a commitment to research.

Fellowship applicants must be physical therapists or physical therapist assistants who have completed Doctorate, or the professional education degree in physical therapy for those already holding a post-professional doctoral degree in the last five years.

One year of teaching is expected for each year of support.

FINANCIAL DATA:
Amount of support per award: Maximum of $15,000 for scholarships; $78,000 for fellowships.

Total amount of support: PODS I Scholarships: $7,500 annually for a maximum of three years (must reapply each year); PODS II Scholarships: Up to $15,000 annually for a maximum of two years (must reapply each year); Florence P. Kendall Doctoral Scholarships: $5,000; Fellowships: A two-year award totaling $78,000; NIFTI in Health Services Research: $70,000 in salary support the first year and $76,000 the second year.

Matching fund requirements: NIFTI in Health Services Research: Half of the salary support to be provided by the sponsoring institution.

NUMBER OF APPLICANTS MOST RECENT YEAR:
80 for the year 2009.

NUMBER OF AWARDS: 26 scholarships for the year 2009.

APPLICATION INFORMATION:
Applicants must check the online eligibility guidelines, review the application instructions, then submit the online application.
Duration: Scholarships: One year; Fellowships: Two years.
Deadline: Mid-January for Program of Doctoral Studies (PODS) Scholarships and New Investigator Fellowship Training Initiative (NIFTI) Fellowships; Mid-August for Florence P. Kendall Doctoral Scholarships.

IRS IDENTIFICATION NUMBER: 13-6161225

ADDRESS INQUIRIES TO:
Scientific Program Administrator
(See address above.)

FOUNDATION FOR PHYSICAL THERAPY, INC. [2713]
1111 North Fairfax Street
Alexandria, VA 22314-1488
(703) 706-8505
(800) 875-1378 ext. 8505
Fax: (703) 706-8587

E-MAIL ADDRESS:
foundation@apta.org

WEB SITE ADDRESS:
www.foundationforphysicaltherapy.org

FOUNDED: 1979

AREAS OF INTEREST:
Physical therapy research, investigative studies that add to or refine the body of clinical knowledge on which physical therapy practice is based, and intervention projects involving therapeutic procedures and modalities.

TYPE:
Research grants.

YEAR PROGRAM STARTED: 1998

PURPOSE:
To add to or refine the body of clinical knowledge on which physical therapy practice is based and to evaluate patient interventions.

LEGAL BASIS:
Foundation.

ELIGIBILITY:
Awards are made to qualified physical therapists and physical therapist assistants or groups of investigators. Must be a U.S. citizen or permanent resident. Projects must be sponsored by a U.S. institution or organization. No funds will be approved to finance cost overruns or deficits on existing projects or to finance projects already in progress.

FINANCIAL DATA:
Amount of support per award: $40,000 per year.
Total amount of support: $80,000 for the year 2011.

NUMBER OF APPLICANTS MOST RECENT YEAR: 7 for the year 2010.

NUMBER OF AWARDS: 2 for the year 2010.

APPLICATION INFORMATION:
Application guidelines and access to the online application system are available on the Foundation's web site.
Duration: One to two years.
Deadline: Proposals are due mid-August.

PUBLICATIONS:
Application guidelines.

IRS IDENTIFICATION NUMBER: 13-6161225

ADDRESS INQUIRIES TO:
Scientific Program Administrator
(See address above.)

INTERNATIONAL ORDER OF ALHAMBRA [2714]
4200 Leeds Avenue
Baltimore, MD 21229-5496
(410) 227-4545
Fax: (800) 478-2946

E-MAIL ADDRESS:
reid003@verizon.net

WEB SITE ADDRESS:
www.orderalhambra.org

FOUNDED: 1904

AREAS OF INTEREST:
Scholarships for those interested in teaching special education.

NAME(S) OF PROGRAMS:
● **Scholarship and Charity Fund**

TYPE:
Grants-in-aid; Scholarships.

YEAR PROGRAM STARTED: 1970

PURPOSE:
To further education in the field of the developmentally disabled.

LEGAL BASIS:
A nonprofit 501(c)(3) fraternal organization of Catholic men dedicated to assisting persons developmentally disabled by mental retardation.

ELIGIBILITY:
Applicant should be entering the junior or senior year of college or postgraduate study. Postgraduate study applies to students in colleges in California, Virginia and Canada. Applicants must be majoring in special education, which involves the mentally, physically or emotionally handicapped person, and must be eligible to teach special education upon graduation.

GEOGRAPHIC RESTRICTIONS:
United States and Canada.

FINANCIAL DATA:
Amount of support per award: Up to $500 per semester to a total of $2,000.

NUMBER OF AWARDS: 70 per year.

APPLICATION INFORMATION:
Students may only apply for one semester per application. Further information is available from the address above or the local Order of Alhambra in each state where applicant resides or attends school.
Duration: One semester. Renewable by reapplication.
Deadline: February 1 and July 1.

ADDRESS INQUIRIES TO:
Roger Reid, Executive Director
(See address above.)

RUTH JACKSON ORTHOPAEDIC SOCIETY [2715]
6300 North River Road
Suite 727
Rosemont, IL 60018
(847) 698-1626
Fax: (847) 823-0536

E-MAIL ADDRESS:
rjos@aaos.org

WEB SITE ADDRESS:
www.rjos.org

FOUNDED: 1983

AREAS OF INTEREST:
Orthopaedic surgery, musculoskeletal health and osteoporosis.

NAME(S) OF PROGRAMS:
● **Jacquelin Perry, MD Resident Research Award**
● **RJOS Traveling Fellowships**

TYPE:
Awards/prizes; Conferences/seminars; Research grants; Travel grants.

PURPOSE:
To encourage, promote and advance the science and medical art and practice of orthopaedic surgery amongst women; to promote women's musculoskeletal health through scientific, educational and charitable activities.

ELIGIBILITY:
Resident Research Award: Applicant must be a current resident in an accredited orthopaedic surgical residency and must be the primary investigator. Clinical and basic research projects are eligible.

APPLICATION INFORMATION:
Deadline: October 1.

PUBLICATIONS:
Newsletter.

IRS IDENTIFICATION NUMBER: 52-1398991

ADDRESS INQUIRIES TO:
Stella Gauthier, Society Coordinator
(See address above.)

NATIONAL AMBUCS, INC. [2716]
4285 Regency Court
High Point, NC 27265
(336) 852-0052 ext. 17
Fax: (336) 852-6830

E-MAIL ADDRESS:
scholars@ambucs.org

WEB SITE ADDRESS:
www.ambucs.org

FOUNDED: 1948

AREAS OF INTEREST:
Physical therapy, occupational therapy, speech-language pathology and hearing audiology.

NAME(S) OF PROGRAMS:
● **AMBUCS Scholars-Scholarships for Therapists**

TYPE:
Scholarships. AMBUCS Scholars is the largest private single source of educational grants for therapists in America. The goal of this program is to provide financial assistance to needy students studying therapy, which in return places trained individuals in the therapy community to help people with disabilities.

YEAR PROGRAM STARTED: 1955

PURPOSE:
To financially assist students studying for qualification in one of the therapy professions.

LEGAL BASIS:
Private nonprofit association.

ELIGIBILITY:
Applicant must be a citizen of the U.S., document financial need, document good scholastic standing and be accepted at the junior or senior undergraduate or graduate level in an accredited program by the appropriate health therapy profession authority in occupational therapy, physical therapy, speech-language pathology or hearing audiology.

FINANCIAL DATA:
Amount of support per award: $500 to $1,500, plus one two-year scholarship (awarded annually) of $6,000.

COOPERATIVE FUNDING PROGRAMS: Funding for this scholarship program is provided entirely by individual AMBUCS chapters and private donations.

NUMBER OF APPLICANTS MOST RECENT YEAR:
1,246 for the year 2010.

NUMBER OF AWARDS: Approximately 400 scholarships each year.

APPLICATION INFORMATION:
Applications must be submitted electronically. If the student is being sponsored by a local chapter, the student should give the local chapter a copy of the completed application, along with the most current IRS Form 1040, a narrative statement, and enrollment certification.
Duration: One academic year.
Deadline: Applications accepted from mid-January to April 15 only.

ADDRESS INQUIRIES TO:
Janice Blankenship
AMBUCS Scholarship Coordinator
AMBUCS Resource Center
P.O. Box 5127
High Point, NC 27262
E-mail: ambucs@ambucs.org

*PLEASE NOTE:
These scholarships do not cover therapist assistant, special education, psychology, or art, respiratory, music or recreational therapy.

NATIONAL ASSOCIATION OF HEALTH SERVICES EXECUTIVES (NAHSE) [2717]
NAHSE National Office
1050 Connecticut Avenue, N.W.
10th Floor
Washington, DC 20036
(202) 772-1030
Fax: (202) 772-1072

E-MAIL ADDRESS:
nahsehq@nahse.org

WEB SITE ADDRESS:
www.nahse.org

AREAS OF INTEREST:
Health care.

TYPE:
Scholarships.

PURPOSE:
To promote the advancement and development of Black health care leaders and elevate the quality of health care services rendered to minority and underserved communities.

ELIGIBILITY:
Applicant must:
(1) be either enrolled or accepted in an accredited college or university program, pursuing a B.S., M.S. or Doctorate degree, majoring in computer science, management of information technology or information management, or provide proof of intent to pursue a major in one of the above areas of study;
(2) be able to demonstrate financial need;
(3) be an active NAHSE member;
(4) have a minimum academic grade point average of 3.0 or above on a scale of 4.0 and;
(5) submit a position paper examining new information and technology trends and their effects on healthcare.

To retain the scholarship for the second year, the recipient must maintain a 3.0 grade point average and produce a position paper on new technologies and present the position paper to an FCG or NAHSE panel.

FINANCIAL DATA:
Amount of support per award: $2,500.
Total amount of support: $7,500 for the year 2011.

NUMBER OF APPLICANTS MOST RECENT YEAR:
12.

NUMBER OF AWARDS: 3.

APPLICATION INFORMATION:
Deadline: September 1.

ADDRESS INQUIRIES TO:
Beverly Glover, Coordinator
(See address above.)

NATIONAL INSTITUTE OF ARTHRITIS AND MUSCULOSKELETAL AND SKIN DISEASES
NIH, One Democracy Plaza
6701 Democracy Boulevard, Suite 800
Bethesda, MD 20892
(301) 594-5055
Fax: (301) 480-4543

WEB SITE ADDRESS:
www.niams.nih.gov

TYPE:
Fellowships; Grants-in-aid; Project/program grants; Research grants; Training grants; Research contracts. The Muscle Biology Program's interests include the mechanisms of action and contraction and excitation and relaxation of muscle, metabolism and energetics, muscle membranes (sarcoplasmic reticulum), muscle development, molecular architecture, biochemical and enzymatic studies of muscle proteins and chemomechanics. A major interest is musculoskeletal fitness and adaptive biology. This program also has an interest in muscle diseases and disorders including Duchenne muscular dystrophy.

See entry 2610 for full listing.

NATIONAL SOCIETY DAUGHTERS OF THE AMERICAN REVOLUTION [2718]
1776 D Street, N.W.
Washington, DC 20006-5303
(202) 879-3292
Fax: (202) 879-3348

WEB SITE ADDRESS:
www.dar.org

FOUNDED: 1895

AREAS OF INTEREST:
Occupational and physical therapy.

NAME(S) OF PROGRAMS:
● **Occupational/Physical Therapy Scholarship**

TYPE:
Scholarships. Awarded to students who are in financial need and have been accepted or are attending an accredited school of occupational or physical therapy (including art, music, or physical therapy).

PURPOSE:
To provide ways and means to aid students in attaining higher education.

LEGAL BASIS:
Incorporated historical society.

ELIGIBILITY:
Scholarships are awarded without regard to race, religion, sex or national origin. Candidates must be U.S. citizens and must be enrolled in an accredited school of occupational or physical therapy in the U.S. No affiliation or relationship to DAR is required for qualification, but candidate must be sponsored by a local DAR Chapter.

Candidate must be majoring in occupational therapy or physical therapy and must be in financial need.

Awards are judged on the basis of academic excellence, commitment to field of study, as required, and need.

GEOGRAPHIC RESTRICTIONS:
United States.

FINANCIAL DATA:
Amount of support per award: $1,000.

NUMBER OF AWARDS: Varies.

APPLICATION INFORMATION:
To obtain a scholarship application packet, send a self-addressed, stamped #10 business-size envelope to the Office of the Reporter General, DAR Scholarship Committee, at the address listed above.

Included with the application packet is the list of DAR State Scholarship Chairmen. All scholarship applicants are required to have a letter of sponsorship from a chapter. Individuals interested in obtaining a letter of sponsorship from a local chapter are encouraged to contact the DAR State Chairman. A letter of acceptance into the occupational therapy program or the transcript stating the applicant is in the occupational therapy program must be included with the application.
Deadline: February 15.

PUBLICATIONS:
American Spirit, magazine.

ADDRESS INQUIRIES TO:
Office of the Reporter General
DAR Scholarship Committee
(See address above.)

PHYSIOTHERAPY FOUNDATION OF CANADA [2719]
955 Green Valley Crescent
Suite 270
Ottawa ON K2C 3V4 Canada
(613) 686-1818
(888) 285-4136
Fax: (613) 564-1577

E-MAIL ADDRESS:
foundation@physiotherapy.ca

WEB SITE ADDRESS:
www.physiotherapyfoundation.ca

FOUNDED: 1982

AREAS OF INTEREST:
Canadian research and scholarship in physiotherapy.

NAME(S) OF PROGRAMS:
- **Alberta Research Award**
- **Constance Beattie Memorial Fund Bursary Program**
- **Alun Morgan Memorial Research Fund in Orthopaedic Physiotherapy**
- **PFC Research Grants**
- **B.E. Schnurr Memorial Fund Research Grant**
- **Ann Collins Whitmore Memorial Fund Awards**
- **Ann Collins Whitmore Memorial Fund Student Awards**

TYPE:
Fellowships; Research grants; Scholarships. Beattie Memorial Fund Bursary Program is to provide support for continuing education courses that are relevant to applicants' career goals.

Alun Morgan Memorial Research Fund provides support for physiotherapy research projects that deal with the management of musculoskeletal problems in Canada.

PFC Research Grants seek to encourage the development of new technology and treatment methods, develop methods for the prevention and early recognition of physical disabilities, evaluate the effectiveness and efficiency of both new and existing treatment methods, and encourage epidemiological studies on the incidence and prevalence of physical disabilities.

Schnurr Memorial Fund Research Grant and Alberta Research Award provide for physiotherapy research projects, with special encouragement made for projects from Alberta.

Ann Collins Whitmore Memorial Fund Awards are for physiotherapists enrolled in a Ph.D. or Master's program.

Ann Collins Whitmore Memorial Fund Student Awards competition is designed to encourage young researchers and is open to students pursuing a Baccalaureate degree in physiotherapy at one of the accredited university programs in Canada.

YEAR PROGRAM STARTED: 1983

PURPOSE:
To develop the science of physiotherapy and expand knowledge and skills of individual physiotherapists.

LEGAL BASIS:
Public foundation.

GEOGRAPHIC RESTRICTIONS:
Canada.

FINANCIAL DATA:
Amount of support per award: Beattie Memorial Fund Bursary Program: Up to $1,500; Morgan Memorial Research Fund and Schnurr Memorial Fund Research Grant: Up to $5,000; PFC Research Grants: $2,500; Whitmore Memorial Fund: Up to $4,000.
Total amount of support: $1,300,000 since inception.

NUMBER OF APPLICANTS MOST RECENT YEAR:
15.

NUMBER OF AWARDS: 15.

APPLICATION INFORMATION:
Applicant must use authorized application form.
Duration: One year. Renewal possible with reapplication.
Deadline: Beattie Memorial Fund, Alun Morgan Memorial Research Fund, Schnurr Memorial Fund and Whitmore Memorial Fund: February 15.

STAFF:
Chantal Dompierre, Executive Director

GOVERNING BOARD:
Robert Dykes, President
Stephen Martin, Treasurer

ADDRESS INQUIRIES TO:
Chantal Dompierre, Executive Director
(See address above.)

PVA SPINAL CORD RESEARCH FOUNDATION [2720]
801 Eighteenth Street, N.W.
Washington, DC 20006
(202) 416-7652
Fax: (202) 416-7641

E-MAIL ADDRESS:
foundations@pva.org

WEB SITE ADDRESS:
www.pva.org

FOUNDED: 1976

AREAS OF INTEREST:
Basic and applied research in spinal cord injury and diseases.

NAME(S) OF PROGRAMS:
- **Spinal Cord Injury Research Grants and Fellowships**

TYPE:
Awards/prizes; Conferences/seminars; Demonstration grants; Development grants; Fellowships; Project/program grants; Research grants; Seed money grants. The PVA Research Foundation funds research projects and fellowships relevant to spinal cord injury and diseases, in addition to sponsoring basic research that will increase scientific knowledge leading to a cure for spinal cord injury. The Foundation also funds research that deals with applied medical, psychological and technological areas of importance to persons with spinal cord injury or disease.

YEAR PROGRAM STARTED: 1976

PURPOSE:
To promote research to find better treatments and cures for paralysis; to support efforts to improve the quality of life of individuals with spinal cord dysfunction until cures are found.

LEGAL BASIS:
Tax-exempt corporation under sections 170(c) and 501(c)(3) of the Internal Revenue Code. Incorporated in the District of Columbia as a nonprofit organization.

ELIGIBILITY:
New faculty and fellows in a field related to spinal cord injury or diseases may submit a proposal for consideration. Postdoctoral fellowship proposals are considered for funding. Grants are based on the proposal submitted. Funding consideration on proposals submitted to the Foundation must pass a merit and relevance review by a Scientific Advisory Board and independent peer reviewers.

GEOGRAPHIC RESTRICTIONS:
United States and Canada.

FINANCIAL DATA:
Fringe benefits limited to 40%. Indirect cost limited to eight percent.
Amount of support per award: Fellowships: Maximum $50,000 per year; Basic science, clinical, design development: Maximum $75,000 per year.

NUMBER OF APPLICANTS MOST RECENT YEAR:
70.

NUMBER OF AWARDS: 13.

APPLICATION INFORMATION:
All application submissions must be made at the Foundation web site.

Completed application includes the following components:
(1) title page not exceeding 75 characters;
(2) applicant/principal investigator;
(3) institution and contacts;
(4) letters of reference (required for fellowships; optional for others);
(5) abstract;
(6) organization assurances;
(7) proposal narrative (20-page maximum, including references) and supporting documents (including biosketches and budget) and;
(8) signature page(s).

Specific instructions for completing each component are included with the templates for each component. All applicants must use templates as appropriate for their application to ensure uniformity of presentation for reviewers.

As the final step in submission, print, secure necessary signature(s), and send the original Signature Page(s) to the Foundation office. The signed Signature Page must be submitted by the deadline for submission of grant applications to make your application complete.
Duration: One to two years.
Deadline: September 1.

PUBLICATIONS:
Annual report; application guidelines.

IRS IDENTIFICATION NUMBER: 52-1064398

DIRECTORS AND OFFICERS:
Maurice L. Jordan, Deputy Executive Director
Gene A. Crayton, Chairman and President
John Ring, Treasurer
Thomas Stripling, Secretary
Peter Axelson, M.S., M.E.
John C. Bollinger
Rory Cooper, Ph.D.
Kenneth Clark Curley, M.D.
Donald J. Eastmead, M.D.
Ivenhoe T. Richey, II

ADDRESS INQUIRIES TO:
Barbara Zupnik, Grants Portfolio Manager
(See address above.)

SISTER KENNY REHABILITATION INSTITUTE
800 East 28th Street
Mail Route 12101
Minneapolis, MN 55407-3799
(612) 863-4872
Fax: (612) 863-8942

E-MAIL ADDRESS:
diana.kommer@allina.com

WEB SITE ADDRESS:
www.allina.com/ahs/ski.nsf

TYPE:
Awards/prizes. Prize money awards and ribbon awards to disabled artists at annual art show.

See entry 606 for full listing.

SOCIETY OF CRITICAL CARE MEDICINE [2721]
500 Midway Drive
Mount Prospect, IL 60056
(847) 493-6440
Fax: (847) 493-6441

E-MAIL ADDRESS:
pglover@sccm.org

WEB SITE ADDRESS:
www.sccm.
org/sccm/membership/grants/grants+home.
htm

AREAS OF INTEREST:
Critical care medicine.

NAME(S) OF PROGRAMS:
● **Norma J. Shoemaker Grant**
● **Vision Grant**

TYPE:
Research grants. Recipients receive financial rewards, prestige and recognition within the field of critical care medicine.

PURPOSE:
To promote excellence in critical care teaching and research for the improved care of the critically ill and injured.

ELIGIBILITY:
SCCM membership is required for research grants. Entries are judged by individually selected committees with expertise in the field associated with each grant.

FINANCIAL DATA:
Amount of support per award: Vision Grant: $50,000; Norma J. Shoemaker Grant: $15,000.

NUMBER OF AWARDS: 2 grants.

APPLICATION INFORMATION:
Deadline: Vision Grant: September 1; Norma J. Shoemaker Grant: September 15.

ADDRESS INQUIRIES TO:
Trish Glover, Program Development Manager (See e-mail address above.)

U.S. DEPARTMENT OF EDUCATION [2722]
OSERS Rehabilitation Services Administration
555 12th Street, S.W.
PCP Building, Room 5069
Washington, DC 20202-2647
(202) 245-7343

E-MAIL ADDRESS:
kerrie.clark@ed.gov

WEB SITE ADDRESS:
www.ed.gov.offices/OSERS/programs

FOUNDED: 1978

AREAS OF INTEREST:
Priorities are established annually for certain programs.

NAME(S) OF PROGRAMS:
● **Rehabilitation Service Projects**

TYPE:
Project/program grants. Project grants (contracts) are awarded for American Indians,

projects with industry, special projects and demonstrations, migrant workers and recreational services. Grants must substantially contribute to solution of vocational rehabilitation problems common to special groups of individuals with severe disabilities. For example, projects to prepare disabled individuals for gainful employment in the competitive labor market and payment to cover cost of establishing programs to expand or improve rehabilitation services for the severely disabled.

YEAR PROGRAM STARTED: 1978

PURPOSE:
To provide funds to state vocational rehabilitation agencies and public nonprofit organizations for projects and demonstrations which hold promise of expanding and otherwise improving services to individuals with severe disabilities.

LEGAL BASIS:
Rehabilitation Act of 1973, Public Law 93-112, as amended by Public Law 98-221, sections 121, 303(a)(1), 304, 305 and 611, 29 U.S.C. 701 and Public Law 99-506.

ELIGIBILITY:
Projects with industry employers and other organizations and all other public or private nonprofit institutions or organizations are eligible for support. Grants cannot be made directly to individuals. Migrant worker projects are funded by grants to state rehabilitation agencies and nonprofit public and private agencies, including territories/possessions and American Indian services for governing bodies of Indians. Also states, public and nonprofit agencies and organizations may apply. Beneficiary eligibility includes physically, mentally or emotionally disabled persons, with emphasis on those with the most severe disabilities.

FINANCIAL DATA:
Amount of support per award: Grants vary in amount depending on type of program.

Matching fund requirements: 20% for Projects with Industry and 10% for Migratory Worker and Indian Programs.

APPLICATION INFORMATION:
Official application forms may be obtained from the address above. An applicant should consult the office or official designated as the single point of contact in his or her state for more information on the process the state requires to be followed in applying for assistance, if the state has selected the program for review.

Duration: Most programs fund five-year projects.

Deadline: Grant applications are usually due February through June. Dates are published in the *Federal Register*.

Psychiatry, psychology, mental health

AMERICAN ACADEMY OF CHILD AND ADOLESCENT PSYCHIATRY [2723]
3615 Wisconsin Avenue, N.W.
Washington, DC 20016-3007
(202) 966-7300 ext. 117
Fax: (202) 969-2891

E-MAIL ADDRESS:
apartner@aacap.org

WEB SITE ADDRESS:
www.aacap.org

FOUNDED: 1953

AREAS OF INTEREST:
Child and adolescent psychiatry.

NAME(S) OF PROGRAMS:
● **Robinson-Cunningham Award**
● **Jeanne Spurlock Research Fellowship in Substance Abuse and Addiction for Minority Medical Students**

TYPE:
Awards/prizes; Conferences/seminars; Fellowships; Research grants; Travel grants. The Robinson-Cunningham Award recognizes a paper on some aspect of child and adolescent psychiatry started during residency and completed within three years of graduation. Preference will be given to independent work. If the research is done as part of a collaborative team, the resident or recently trained child and adolescent psychiatrist should be the first author or principal investigator. The selected author will be invited to attend the AACAP Annual Meeting. A certificate will be awarded with a $200 honorarium.

Jeanne Spurlock Research Fellowship in Substance Abuse and Addiction for Minority Medical Students Program, supported by the National Institute on Drug Abuse (NIDA), includes a $3,500 fellowship for work during the summer with a child and adolescent psychiatrist research-mentor, plus five days at the AACAP Annual Meeting.

YEAR PROGRAM STARTED: 1994

PURPOSE:
To increase the number of minority child and adolescent psychiatrists trained in research.

LEGAL BASIS:
Nonprofit organization.

GEOGRAPHIC RESTRICTIONS:
United States.

FINANCIAL DATA:
Amount of support per award: $200 to $3,500, depending on award.
Total amount of support: Varies.

NUMBER OF APPLICANTS MOST RECENT YEAR:
11.

NUMBER OF AWARDS: Robinson-Cunningham: 1; Jeanne Spurlock Research: Up to 3.

APPLICATION INFORMATION:
Programs require either an application form, letter of intent or nomination.
Duration: Eight to twelve weeks.
Deadline: Varies.

PUBLICATIONS:
Program announcement; *Research Notes*, newsletter.

ADDRESS INQUIRIES TO:
Ashley Partner
Training and Education Manager
(See address above.)

AMERICAN GROUP PSYCHOTHERAPY ASSOCIATION, INC. [2724]
25 East 21st Street, 6th Floor
New York, NY 10010
(212) 477-2677
Fax: (212) 979-6627

E-MAIL ADDRESS:
dfeirman@agpa.org

WEB SITE ADDRESS:
www.agpa.org

FOUNDED: 1942

AREAS OF INTEREST:
Group psychotherapy.

CONSULTING OR VOLUNTEER SERVICES:
Volunteer Program provided at Annual
Conferences for local students. Specific
duties are required in lieu of payment for
events at Annual Conferences.

NAME(S) OF PROGRAMS:
● **The Anne Alonso Scholarship**
● **Donald T. Brown Memorial
  Scholarship**
● **The Barry Bukatman, M.D. Memorial
  AGPA Scholarship**
● **Josephine M. Cunningham-Tervalon
  Scholarship**
● **Durkin/Glatzer Scholarship**
● **Ruth Hochberg Scholarship**
● **International Scholarship**
● **Susanne Jensen Scholarship**
● **Saul Scheidlinger Scholarship**
● **Mary M. Tanenbaum Scholarship**
● **The Wilkenfeld Psychiatric Resident
  Scholarship**

TYPE:
Scholarships; Travel grants; Visiting scholars.
Special rates for students in addition to the
volunteer program.

PURPOSE:
To enable professionals and other interested
people to attend these professional meetings
who would not otherwise be able to do so
due to lack of funds.

LEGAL BASIS:
Incorporated, nonprofit, professional
association.

ELIGIBILITY:
Financial need and proximity to location of
annual meetings are considered.

For the Durkin-Glatzer Scholarship,
applicants must be women entering or
re-entering the field of group psychotherapy.

Josephine M. Cunningham Scholarship is for
minority women.

Susanne Jensen Scholarship is for a
foreign-born woman working or training in
the U.S. as a group psychotherapist.

FINANCIAL DATA:
Amount of support per award: Tuition for
Annual Meeting and travel stipend for
Alonso Scholarship, Cunningham
Scholarship, Durkin-Glatzer Scholarship,
Hochberg Scholarship, and Wilkenfeld
Scholarship; $250 for Donald T. Brown
Fellowship.
Total amount of support: $8,000 to $25,000.

NUMBER OF AWARDS: 1 of each award or
program.

APPLICATION INFORMATION:
Current application guidelines are available
by contacting AGPA.
Duration: Two days for the Institute; three
days for Conference.
Deadline: November.

PUBLICATIONS:
*International Journal of Group
Psychotherapy; The Group Circle,* newsletter.

OFFICERS:
Jeffrey Kleinberg, Ph.D., CGP, President

Kathleen H. Ulman, Ph.D., President-Elect
Darryl L. Pure, Ph.D., Treasurer
Carol A. Vaughan, LCSW, Secretary

STAFF:
Marsha S. Block, CAE, CFRE, Chief
Executive Officer

ADDRESS INQUIRIES TO:
Diane Feirman, CAE
Public Affairs Director
(See address above.)

AMERICAN PSYCHIATRIC
ASSOCIATION [2725]
1000 Wilson Boulevard, Suite 1825
Arlington, VA 22209-3901
(703) 907-8667
Fax: (703) 907-7852

E-MAIL ADDRESS:
omna@psych.org

WEB SITE ADDRESS:
www.psych.org

FOUNDED: 1844

AREAS OF INTEREST:
Continuing study of psychiatry, working for
more effective application of psychiatric
knowledge to combat mental illnesses and
promote mental health of all citizens.

NAME(S) OF PROGRAMS:
● **APA Fellowship for Residents**

TYPE:
Awards/prizes; Fellowships. Program
enabling psychiatric residents to participate
actively in the deliberations of APA councils,
committees and task forces. Fellows become
active members of the group to which they
are assigned and attend its meetings
throughout the year. This has usually
included some subsidizing of their attendance
at the annual meetings held in May each
year.

YEAR PROGRAM STARTED: 1968

PURPOSE:
To provide a useful learning experience for
both the residents and the Association's
leadership.

LEGAL BASIS:
Nonprofit foundation.

ELIGIBILITY:
Candidates are nominated by Directors of
Residency Training Programs. To be eligible
for the APA Fellowship for Residents,
residents must be APA members (MIT) or
have applied for membership, must be in
their PGY-II year of psychiatric residency
training at the time of nomination and must
have passed a national or state board
examination (e.g., USMLE 1,2,3 or state
medical board leading to eligibility for state
licensure). Candidates are not required to be
U.S. citizens or graduates of a U.S. medical
school.

GEOGRAPHIC RESTRICTIONS:
United States and Canada.

NUMBER OF APPLICANTS MOST RECENT YEAR:
40.

NUMBER OF AWARDS: 10.

APPLICATION INFORMATION:
Duration: Two-year fellowship program. No
renewals.
Deadline: March 23. Announcement in June.

PUBLICATIONS:
Brochure.

AMERICAN PSYCHOLOGICAL
ASSOCIATION [2726]
Government Relations Office
Public Interest Directorate
750 First Street, N.E.
Washington, DC 20002-4242
(202) 336-6104
Fax: (202) 336-6063

E-MAIL ADDRESS:
delmore@apa.org

WEB SITE ADDRESS:
www.apa.org/about/gr/fellows

FOUNDED: 1892

AREAS OF INTEREST:
Professional organization to advance
psychology as a science and profession and
as a means of promoting health, education
and human welfare.

NAME(S) OF PROGRAMS:
● **APA Congressional Fellowship
  Program**

TYPE:
Fellowships. Program provides trained
scientists and practitioners an opportunity for
enhanced understanding of and involvement
in the federal policy-making process by
serving as Congressional staff in Washington,
DC.

YEAR PROGRAM STARTED: 1974

PURPOSE:
To provide an opportunity for psychologists
to participate in the policy-making process.

LEGAL BASIS:
Nonprofit professional organization.

ELIGIBILITY:
Doctoral degree in psychology and APA
membership required. Two years of
postdoctoral experience is preferred.
Individuals with sabbatical funds are eligible.
Must be U.S. citizen and willing to relocate
to Washington, DC.

GEOGRAPHIC RESTRICTIONS:
United States.

FINANCIAL DATA:
Amount of support per award: For the year
2010-11: $60,000 to $75,000, depending on
years of postdoctoral experience. Up to
$3,750 is allocated per Fellow for relocation
to the Washington, DC area and for travel
expenses during the year. An additional
monthly stipend of $375 is provided for
health insurance and/or other
fellowship-related expenses.

COOPERATIVE FUNDING PROGRAMS: Fellowship
is sponsored by the APA in cooperation with
the American Association for the
Advancement of Science.

NUMBER OF AWARDS: Up to 3.

APPLICATION INFORMATION:
Coversheet, curriculum vitae, three letters of
reference and a statement of interest are
required.
Duration: September through August (12
months). Nonrenewable.
Deadline: Early January. Announcement in
March.

STAFF:
Micah Haskell-Hoehl, Program Administrator

ADDRESS INQUIRIES TO:
Micah Haskell-Hoehl, Program Administrator
APA Congressional Fellowship Program
Tel: (202) 336-5935
E-mail: mhaskell-hoehl@apa.org

AMERICAN PSYCHOLOGICAL
ASSOCIATION   [2727]
Minority Fellowship Program/APA
750 First Street, N.E.
Washington, DC 20002-4242
(202) 336-6127
Fax: (202) 336-6012

E-MAIL ADDRESS:
mfp@apa.org

WEB SITE ADDRESS:
www.apa.org/mfp

FOUNDED: 1892

AREAS OF INTEREST:
Psychology.

NAME(S) OF PROGRAMS:
● **MFP Mental Health Services
  Fellowship**

TYPE:
Fellowships. Fellowship is geared to those
pursuing careers as practitioners and as
researchers specializing in the delivery of
mental health services to ethnic minority
populations. Students specializing in clinical,
school and counseling psychology are
encouraged to apply.

YEAR PROGRAM STARTED: 1974

PURPOSE:
To increase the knowledge of issues related
to ethnic minority mental health; to improve
the quality of mental health treatment
delivered to ethnic minority populations; to
provide financial support and professional
guidance to individuals pursuing doctoral
degrees in psychology.

LEGAL BASIS:
Nonprofit.

ELIGIBILITY:
Applicants are required to be:
(1) citizens or noncitizen nationals of the
U.S.;
(2) enrolled full-time in a doctoral degree
program in psychology (Ph.D. or Psy.D.);
Mental Health Services applicants must be
enrolled in an APA-accredited program;
(3) a member of an underrepresented ethnic
minority group (including, but not limited to,
African-American, Alaskan Native, Asian
American, Latino/Hispanic, Native American
and Pacific Islander) and;
(4) able to demonstrate a commitment to a
career in psychology and skilled in the
prevention, treatment or study of problems
affecting ethnic minority populations.

Person receiving Fellowship from MFP
cannot be the recipient of federal funds.

FINANCIAL DATA:
Amount of support per award: Follows
NRSA guidelines.

COOPERATIVE FUNDING PROGRAMS: Funding for
services training is made available through
the Substance Abuse and Mental Health
Services Administration allocations.

APPLICATION INFORMATION:
Applications are available October 1 to
January 15. Guidelines are available online.
Duration: One academic year. Renewable for
up to two additional years.

Deadline: January 15. Announcement by
April.

PUBLICATIONS:
Program brochure.

ADDRESS INQUIRIES TO:
Andrew Austin-Dailey, Director
Minority Fellowship Program
(See address above.)

AMERICAN PSYCHOLOGICAL
ASSOCIATION
Minority Fellowship Program/APA
750 First Street, N.E.
Washington, DC 20002-4242
(202) 336-6127
Fax: (202) 336-6012

E-MAIL ADDRESS:
mfp@apa.org

WEB SITE ADDRESS:
www.apa.org/pi/mfp

TYPE:
Fellowships. Geared to those pursuing careers
in substance abuse treatment and prevention
as practitioners and as researchers
specializing in the delivery of mental health
services to ethnic minority populations.

See entry 1026 for full listing.

AMERICAN PSYCHOSOMATIC
SOCIETY   [2728]
6728 Old McLean Village Drive
McLean, VA 22101
(703) 556-9222
Fax: (703) 556-8729

E-MAIL ADDRESS:
info@psychosomatic.org

WEB SITE ADDRESS:
www.psychosomatic.org

FOUNDED: 1942

AREAS OF INTEREST:
Psychosomatic medicine.

NAME(S) OF PROGRAMS:
● **American Psychosomatic Society
  Scholar Awards**
● **Herbert Weiner Early Career Award
  for Contributions to Psychosomatic
  Society**

TYPE:
Awards/prizes; Scholarships.

PURPOSE:
To support individuals who show substantial
promise in continuing study in psychosomatic
medicine.

LEGAL BASIS:
Not-for-profit organization.

ELIGIBILITY:
APS Scholar Award: Awarded to
students/trainees enrolled in medical,
graduate or undergraduate school or those in
residencies, internships or postdoctoral
fellowships. Applicants must submit an
abstract for APS meeting and be an active
member of APS.

Herbert Weiner Early Career Award for
Contributions to Psychosomatic Medicine:
Nominees must be fewer than 10 years past
their final academic degree and must be
members of the American Psychosomatic
Society.

FINANCIAL DATA:
Amount of support per award: APS Scholar
Award: Monetary assistance for hotel
accommodations, travel and conference fees;
Herbert Weiner Early Career Award: $1,000,
plaque and an opportunity to present the
research for which the award was given
during the annual meeting of the society.

NUMBER OF AWARDS: APS Scholar Award: 10
to 24; Herbert Weiner Early Career Award: 1.

APPLICATION INFORMATION:
Nominations must include a 500 to
1,000-word justification for the nomination,
an updated curriculum vitae and reprints of
the two to six publications of the work for
which the nomination is being made. Two- to
three-page proposal of the project and a copy
of the curriculum vitae are due June 1st of
each year.
Duration: One-time award.
Deadline: APS Scholar Awards: November 1;
Herbert Weiner Early Career Award:
December 1.

PUBLICATIONS:
Award announcement.

IRS IDENTIFICATION NUMBER: 11-1866747

ADDRESS INQUIRIES TO:
Award Committee
(See address above.)

ANNA-MONIKA
FOUNDATION   [2729]
Central Institute of Mental Health
J-5
D-68159 Mannheim Germany
49 621 1703 2002
Fax: 49 621 1703 2005

E-MAIL ADDRESS:
susanne.ratzka@zi-mannheim.de

WEB SITE ADDRESS:
www.anna-monika-stiftung.com

FOUNDED: 1965

AREAS OF INTEREST:
Biochemistry, neurophysiology,
neuropathology, psychopharmacology,
psychiatry, depression and psychosomatic
illnesses.

NAME(S) OF PROGRAMS:
● **The Anna-Monika Foundation Prize**

TYPE:
Awards/prizes. Prizes for research papers
investigating the biological substrate and
functional disturbances of depression.
Prize-winning lectures will be published in
Pharmacopsychiatry.

YEAR PROGRAM STARTED: 1966

PURPOSE:
To support international pioneering research
in the area of depression research.

LEGAL BASIS:
Private foundation, authorized by the state of
Nordrhein-Westfalen, Germany.

ELIGIBILITY:
As far as possible, the papers describing the
studies should feature information about the
recent advances and the knowledge that
should be helpful in promoting treatment and
open new paths of scientific progress in
depression. Papers published in the last two
years in an international scientific
peer-reviewed journal may be submitted.
Papers may be written in German, French or
English.

FINANCIAL DATA:
Total amount of support: EUR 25,000.

NUMBER OF AWARDS: Maximum of 3 biennially in odd-numbered years.

APPLICATION INFORMATION:
A maximum of three publications (in sets of four copies) plus a short summary (approximately 600 words) emphasizing the relevance and importance of the research are required. Submit the papers to the address above.
Deadline: March 31.

OFFICER:
Prof. Dr. Andreas Meyer-Lindenberg, M.D., Ph.D., Chairman of the Board and Director

ADDRESS INQUIRIES TO:
Prof. Dr. Andreas Meyer-Lindenberg
Chairman of the Board and Director
(See address above.)

THE ANXIETY DISORDERS ASSOCIATION OF AMERICA [2730]

8730 Georgia Avenue, Suite 600
Silver Spring, MD 20910
(240) 485-1001
Fax: (240) 485-1035

E-MAIL ADDRESS:
smenase@adaa.org

WEB SITE ADDRESS:
www.adaa.org

FOUNDED: 1980

AREAS OF INTEREST:
Anxiety disorders.

NAME(S) OF PROGRAMS:
● **Junior Faculty Research Grants**

TYPE:
Conferences/seminars; Project/program grants; Research grants; Seed money grants; Travel grants.

YEAR PROGRAM STARTED: 1999

PURPOSE:
To promote the prevention and cure of anxiety disorders and to improve the lives of all people who suffer from them; to increase the pool of independent investigators with interest and expertise in anxiety disorders research.

LEGAL BASIS:
Nonprofit association.

PUBLICATIONS:
Guidelines.

ADDRESS INQUIRIES TO:
Sarah Gerfen, Business Manager
(See address above.)

THE ARC OF THE UNITED STATES [2731]

1660 L Street, N.W.
Suite 301
Washington, DC 20036
(202) 534-3727
Fax: (202) 534-3731

E-MAIL ADDRESS:
ldavis@thearc.org

WEB SITE ADDRESS:
www.thearc.org

FOUNDED: 1950

AREAS OF INTEREST:
Prevention or improvement of mental retardation/developmental disabilities.

NAME(S) OF PROGRAMS:
● **Research Matters! Award**

TYPE:
Awards/prizes. Rewards an individual (or individuals) who has contributed in significant ways to research that enhances the well-being of persons with intellectual and developmental disabilities and their families, or that prevents such conditions and/or related effects.

PURPOSE:
To prevent or improve mental retardation.

ELIGIBILITY:
Selection is based on the importance of the research discovery to people with intellectual and developmental disabilities and their families, its practical significance and impact for people with disabilities, its relationship to research topics identified as priorities in the *National Goals and Research for People with Intellectual and Developmental Disabilities* report of 2006, and the history of work in the specified research area over a number of years that leads to a significant research conclusion.

FINANCIAL DATA:
Amount of support per award: $1,000.

APPLICATION INFORMATION:
Submit nomination electronically to Leigh Ann Davis at the e-mail address above.
Deadline: July 1.

ADDRESS INQUIRIES TO:
Leigh Ann Davis
Assistant Director of Professional and Family Services
(See address above.)

ASSOCIATION FOR APPLIED PSYCHOPHYSIOLOGY AND BIOFEEDBACK [2732]

10200 West 44th Avenue
Suite 304
Wheat Ridge, CO 80033-2840
(303) 422-8436
Fax: (303) 422-8894

E-MAIL ADDRESS:
aapb@resourcenter.com

WEB SITE ADDRESS:
www.aapb.org

FOUNDED: 1969

AREAS OF INTEREST:
Biofeedback and psychophysiology.

NAME(S) OF PROGRAMS:
● **Student Travel Scholarship Program**

TYPE:
Travel grants.

PURPOSE:
To advance the development, dissemination and utilization of knowledge about applied psychophysiology and biofeedback to improve health and the quality of life through research, education and practice.

ELIGIBILITY:
Must be a full-time student pursuing a professional or doctoral degree in a health-related field.

FINANCIAL DATA:
Amount of support per award: $400.
Total amount of support: Varies.

NUMBER OF AWARDS: Varies.

APPLICATION INFORMATION:
Contact the Organization for application procedures.
Deadline: October 1 for presentation. January 1 for scholarship application.

ASSOCIATION FOR BEHAVIORAL AND COGNITIVE THERAPIES [2733]

305 Seventh Avenue
16th Floor
New York, NY 10001
(212) 647-1890
Fax: (212) 647-1865

E-MAIL ADDRESS:
mjeimer@abct.org

WEB SITE ADDRESS:
www.abct.org

AREAS OF INTEREST:
Behavior therapy and cognitive behavior therapy.

NAME(S) OF PROGRAMS:
● **Virginia Roswell Dissertation Award**

TYPE:
Awards/prizes.

PURPOSE:
To explore the application of behavioral and cognitive sciences to understanding human behavior, developing interventions to enhance the human condition, and promoting the appropriate utilization of these interventions.

ELIGIBILITY:
Applicant must be an AABT student member who has already had their dissertation proposal approved and be investigating an area of direct relevance to behavior therapy or cognitive behavior therapy.

FINANCIAL DATA:
Amount of support per award: $1,000.

NUMBER OF AWARDS: 1.

APPLICATION INFORMATION:
All candidates must be nominated. Contact the Organization for nomination procedures.
Deadline: April.

ADDRESS INQUIRIES TO:
M.J. Eimer, Executive Director
(See address above.)

ASSOCIATION FOR BEHAVIORAL AND COGNITIVE THERAPIES [2734]

305 Seventh Avenue
16th Floor
New York, NY 10001
(212) 647-1890
Fax: (212) 647-1865

E-MAIL ADDRESS:
mjeimer@abct.org

WEB SITE ADDRESS:
www.abct.org

AREAS OF INTEREST:
Behavior therapy and cognitive sciences.

NAME(S) OF PROGRAMS:
● **President's New Researcher Award**

TYPE:
Awards/prizes.

PURPOSE:
To explore the application of behavioral and cognitive sciences to understanding human

behavior, developing interventions to enhance the human condition, and promoting the appropriate utilization of these interventions.

ELIGIBILITY:
Must be authored by an individual with five years or less post-training experience and have been published in the last two years or currently in press.

FINANCIAL DATA:
Amount of support per award: $500.

APPLICATION INFORMATION:
Contact the Organization for application procedures.
Deadline: August 10.

ADDRESS INQUIRIES TO:
M.J. Eimer, Executive Director
(See address above.)

AUTISM SPEAKS
1060 State Road, 2nd Floor
Princeton, NJ 08540
(609) 228-7313
Fax: (609) 430-9163

E-MAIL ADDRESS:
jnew@autismspeaks.org

WEB SITE ADDRESS:
www.autismspeaks.org

TYPE:
Fellowships; Project/program grants; Research grants. Research grants relevant to understanding and improving the communication capabilities of individuals with autism, particularly those who are nonverbal or minimally verbal.

See entry 2389 for full listing.

BRAIN & BEHAVIOR RESEARCH FOUNDATION [2735]
60 Cutter Mill Road
Suite 404
Great Neck, NY 11021
(516) 829-0091
Fax: (516) 487-6930

E-MAIL ADDRESS:
grants@bbrfoundation.org

WEB SITE ADDRESS:
www.bbrfoundation.org

FOUNDED: 1987

AREAS OF INTEREST:
Mental health, brain and behavior disorders.

NAME(S) OF PROGRAMS:
- **Distinguished Investigator Grant**
- **Independent Investigator Grant**
- **Young Investigator Grant**

TYPE:
Research grants. Distinguished Investigator Grant supports senior investigators (professor or equivalent level) who maintain a laboratory and who propose an innovative and new direction in their research with a one-year grant to encourage pursuit of innovative projects in schizophrenia, affective disorders, or other serious mental illnesses.

Independent Investigator Grant is intended for the scientist at the academic level of associate professor or equivalent, who has won national competitive support as a principal investigator. The program is intended to facilitate innovative research opportunities.

Young Investigator Grant enables promising investigators to either extend their research fellowship training or to begin careers as independent research faculty.

PURPOSE:
To raise and distribute funds for scientific research into the causes, cures, treatments and prevention of severe psychiatric brain disorders.

LEGAL BASIS:
Private, not-for-profit organization.

ELIGIBILITY:
Applicant must hold a doctoral-level degree and be affiliated with a university or research institution. For the Distinguished Investigator Grant, applicant must be a full professor (or professional equivalent) who maintains a laboratory. For the Independent Investigator Grant, applicant must be at associate professor level with national competitive support as a principal investigator. For the Young Investigator Grant, applicant must be advanced postdoctoral fellow through assistant professor (or equivalent) to either extend research fellowship training or to begin career as independent research faculty. Basic and/or clinical investigators are supported, but research must be relevant to schizophrenia, major affective disorders or other serious mental illnesses.

FINANCIAL DATA:
Amount of support per award: Distinguished Investigator: Up to $100,000 for one year; Independent Investigator: $50,000 per year for two years; Young Investigator: Up to $30,000 per year for up to two years.

NUMBER OF APPLICANTS MOST RECENT YEAR:
Distinguished Investigator: 201; Independent Investigator: 217; Young Investigator: 1,032 for the year 2010.

NUMBER OF AWARDS: Distinguished Investigator: 15; Independent Investigator: 42; Young Investigator: 214 for the year 2010.

APPLICATION INFORMATION:
Duration: Distinguished Investigator Grant: One year; Independent Investigator Grant: Two years; Young Investigator Grant: One or two years.
Deadline: Distinguished Investigator Grant: May 15; Independent Investigator Grant: March 5; Young Investigator Grant: January 25.

IRS IDENTIFICATION NUMBER: 31-1020010

STAFF:
Benita F. Shobe, President and Chief Executive Officer
Greg Corsico, Vice President, Development
Lou Innamorato, Vice President, Finance and Chief Financial Officer
Laura Wells, Vice President, Marketing and Communications
Lorraine Divone, Production Director
Diane Magnuson, Associate Director, Corporate and Foundation Development
Faith Rothblatt, Associate Director of Development
Meredith Klein, Associate Director of Major Gifts
Barbara Wheeler, Manager, Communications and Media Relations
Abbey Chakalis, Manager, Special Events
Josh Okun, Manager, Web Services
Doris Ip, Research Grants Manager
Jessica Mavaro, Database Coordinator
Laura Terio, C.S.W., Resource Specialist
John Bayat, Senior Accountant
Mike Kirsic, Senior Accountant

Sho Tin Chen, Associate, Research Grants
Grace Nagaur, Associate, Research Grants
Sharon Weinberg, Donor Management Associate

ADDRESS INQUIRIES TO:
Grants Management
(See address above.)

JAMES MCKEEN CATTELL FUND [2736]
Duke University, Department of Psychology & Neuroscience
Box 90086
9 Flowers Drive
Durham, NC 27708-0086
(919) 660-5713
(919) 660-5638
(919) 660-5712
Fax: (919) 660-5726

E-MAIL ADDRESS:
williams@psych.duke.edu

WEB SITE ADDRESS:
www.cattell.duke.edu

FOUNDED: 1941

NAME(S) OF PROGRAMS:
- **James McKeen Cattell Fund Fellowships for Psychologists**

TYPE:
Fellowships. The fellowship provides funds to supplement the regular sabbatical allowance provided by the recipients' home institutions.

YEAR PROGRAM STARTED: 1942

PURPOSE:
To promote scientific research and the dissemination of knowledge with the object of obtaining results beneficial to the development of the science of psychology.

LEGAL BASIS:
Tax-exempt foundation.

ELIGIBILITY:
The awards are available to psychologists who are faculty members at colleges and universities in the United States and Canada and are eligible, according to the regulations of their own institutions, for a sabbatical leave or its equivalent.

GEOGRAPHIC RESTRICTIONS:
United States and Canada.

FINANCIAL DATA:
Amount of support per award: Up to $37,500.

NUMBER OF APPLICANTS MOST RECENT YEAR:
Approximately 35.

NUMBER OF AWARDS: 1 to 6 per year.

APPLICATION INFORMATION:
Fellowship application is available at the Fund web site.
Deadline: December 1.

TRUSTEES AND OFFICERS:
Peter A. Ornstein, Managing Trustee
Christina L. Williams, Secretary-Treasurer
Marcia K. Johnson
Robert W. Levenson
Scott E. Maxwell

ADDRESS INQUIRIES TO:
Dr. Christina L. Williams
Secretary-Treasurer
(See address above.)

CENTRE FOR ADDICTION AND MENTAL HEALTH [2737]

33 Russell Street
Toronto ON M5S 2S1 Canada
(416) 535-8501
Fax: (416) 979-4704

WEB SITE ADDRESS:
www.camh.net

AREAS OF INTEREST:
Addiction and mental health.

NAME(S) OF PROGRAMS:
● **Postdoctoral Training Programme in Addiction and Mental Health**

TYPE:
Fellowships.

PURPOSE:
To provide Fellows with a comprehensive training program in the fields of addiction and mental health with training in research techniques.

ELIGIBILITY:
Candidates must have a Ph.D. or M.D. (or equivalent) at the time of taking up the appointment. Preference is given to Canadian citizens and permanent residents. Other successful applicants must obtain an appropriate visa.

FINANCIAL DATA:
Total amount of support: Approximately $50,000 annually.

NUMBER OF AWARDS: 3.

APPLICATION INFORMATION:
Duration: One year. May reapply.

ADDRESS INQUIRIES TO:
Manager, Research Finance Services
(See address above.)

COUNCIL ON SOCIAL WORK EDUCATION

1701 Duke Street, Suite 200
Alexandria, VA 22314-3457
(703) 683-8080
Fax: (703) 683-8099

E-MAIL ADDRESS:
gmeeks@cswe.org

WEB SITE ADDRESS:
www.cswe.org/mfp

TYPE:
Fellowships. Awards for minority doctoral level studies in social work, specializing in mental health and substance abuse-related education, research, policy and leadership.

See entry 1042 for full listing.

DEPARTMENT OF VETERANS AFFAIRS [2738]

Associated Health Education Office (14)
Office of Academic Affiliations
810 Vermont Avenue, N.W.
Washington, DC 20420
(202) 461-9493
Fax: (202) 461-9855

E-MAIL ADDRESS:
robert.zeiss@va.gov

WEB SITE ADDRESS:
www.psychologytraining.va.gov

FOUNDED: 1946

NAME(S) OF PROGRAMS:
● **VA Psychology Training Program**

TYPE:
Fellowships; Internships. Stipends for internship and postdoctoral training in clinical or counseling psychology. Provides one year of supervised training in the skills and techniques of these specialty areas. Participants have no obligation to remain with the VA after completion of training.

YEAR PROGRAM STARTED: 1946

PURPOSE:
To provide a source of highly qualified psychologists who are interested in the direct delivery of professional services in federal, state, and community facilities; to provide internship training to students enrolled in doctoral programs in clinical or counseling psychology from those schools accredited by the American Psychological Association; to provide postdoctoral fellowships to graduates of clinical or counseling psychology doctoral programs and internships that are accredited by the American Psychological Association.

LEGAL BASIS:
Federal agency.

ELIGIBILITY:
Applicant must be a U.S. citizen. Prospective intern must be enrolled in an academic graduate program leading to the doctoral degree in clinical or counseling psychology from an APA-accredited program. Prospective postdoctoral fellow must have completed a doctoral program and internship in clinical or counseling psychology accredited by the APA.

FINANCIAL DATA:
Amount of support per award: $23,974 and up for full-time interns, $42,239 and up for full-time postdoctoral fellows for the first year and $44,522 and up for full-time postdoctoral fellows for the second year.
Total amount of support: Varies.

NUMBER OF AWARDS: 477 intern positions at 97 sites and 266 postdoctoral fellow positions at 58 sites for academic year 2011-12.

APPLICATION INFORMATION:
Interested persons should contact the Director of Psychology Training at the VA Medical Center they are interested in.
Duration: One year. Occasionally two years for postdoctoral fellowships.
Deadline: November.

ADDRESS INQUIRIES TO:
Chief of Psychology Service or Director of Psychology Training at a local VA Medical Center

ALBERT ELLIS INSTITUTE [2739]

45 East 65th Street
New York, NY 10065
(212) 535-0822
Fax: (212) 249-3582

E-MAIL ADDRESS:
krisdoyle@albertellis.org

WEB SITE ADDRESS:
www.albertellis.org

FOUNDED: 1968

AREAS OF INTEREST:
Psychotherapy.

CONSULTING OR VOLUNTEER SERVICES:
Work-study positions offered.

NAME(S) OF PROGRAMS:
● **Postgraduate Clinical Fellowship Training Program at the Albert Ellis Institute**

TYPE:
Fellowships; Internships; Work-study programs. Postdoctoral fellowships and internships in cognitive behavior therapy for a comprehensive program, featuring intensive supervision of individual and group clients seen at the Institute's clinic, seminars and workshops.

YEAR PROGRAM STARTED: 1969

PURPOSE:
To train professionals in cognitive behavioral and Rational Emotive Behavior Therapy.

LEGAL BASIS:
Not-for-profit organization.

ELIGIBILITY:
Applicant must have a Ph.D. in psychology, M.D., M.S.W. or R.N. and be eligible for New York state certification or license in the field.

FINANCIAL DATA:
Amount of support per award: $9,000 per year.

NUMBER OF APPLICANTS MOST RECENT YEAR: 30.

NUMBER OF AWARDS: 4 for the 2010 academic year.

APPLICATION INFORMATION:
Application form required. On a separate page, state the reasons for wishing to enter the Fellowship Training Program, future plans in psychology, and curriculum vitae. Personal interviews are necessary.
Duration: Two years.
Deadline: January 15.

ADDRESS INQUIRIES TO:
Dr. Kristene Doyle
Associate Executive Director
(See address above.)

*PLEASE NOTE:
Training takes place in New York City.

EMERGENCY MENTAL HEALTH AND TRAUMATIC STRESS SERVICES BRANCH [2740]

One Choke Cherry, Room 6-1101
Rockville, MD 20857
(800) 308-3515
Fax: (240) 276-1890

WEB SITE ADDRESS:
www.samhsa.gov
mentalhealth.samhsa.gov/cmhs/emergencyservices

AREAS OF INTEREST:
Emergency mental health and crisis counseling.

NAME(S) OF PROGRAMS:
● **Crisis Counseling Assistance and Training Program**

TYPE:
Project/program grants. Grants to address the various dimensions of mental health crises affecting victims of presidentially declared major disasters. Support is available for development of training models and other psychological material for the delivery of crisis intervention services/outreach.

YEAR PROGRAM STARTED: 1974

PURPOSE:
To provide supplemental support to victims of major disasters and their families in emergency mental health and crisis intervention.

LEGAL BASIS:
Section 416 of The Robert T. Stafford Disaster Relief and Emergency Assistance Act (Public Law 100-707).

ELIGIBILITY:
Must be presidentially declared major disaster. U.S. territories and federally recognized tribes are also eligible.

FINANCIAL DATA:
Amount of support per award: Grants given according to justifiable need. Amounts vary in accordance with existing resources in stricken community.
Total amount of support: Varies.

COOPERATIVE FUNDING PROGRAMS: Program funding is supplemental when existing programs are inadequate to meet the needs of the community.

APPLICATION INFORMATION:
Duration: Nine months; renewal possible upon approval of CMHS and SAMHSA. Extension of grant possible in limited circumstances.
Deadline: 60 days following the disaster.

INTERNATIONAL OCD FOUNDATION   [2741]
112 Water Street, Suite 501
Boston, MA 02109
(617) 973-5801
Fax: (617) 973-5803

E-MAIL ADDRESS:
info@ocfoundation.org

WEB SITE ADDRESS:
www.ocfoundation.org

FOUNDED: 1986

AREAS OF INTEREST:
Obsessive-compulsive disorders and obsessive compulsive spectrum disorder.

NAME(S) OF PROGRAMS:
● **OCF Research Awards**

TYPE:
Research grants.

YEAR PROGRAM STARTED: 1994

PURPOSE:
To disseminate information and to fund research for the ultimate causes and cures for obsessive-compulsive disorders.

ELIGIBILITY:
Investigators whose research focuses on the nature, causes and treatment of OCD and related disorders are eligible to apply. Senior investigators may also ask for grant funding for projects that would provide pilot data for future larger scale federal grant applications.

FINANCIAL DATA:
Awards do not cover indirect or travel costs.
Amount of support per award: Varies.
Total amount of support: Varies.

NUMBER OF APPLICANTS MOST RECENT YEAR:
50.

NUMBER OF AWARDS: 5.

APPLICATION INFORMATION:
Applicants should request application guidelines.

Duration: One to two years.
Deadline: January.

PUBLICATIONS:
OCD Newsletter.

IRS IDENTIFICATION NUMBER: 22-2894564

STAFF:
Jeff Szymanski, Ph.D., Executive Director
Michael Spigler, Program Director

ADDRESS INQUIRIES TO:
Victor Sulkowski, Administrative Assistant
(See address above.)

THE KLINGENSTEIN THIRD GENERATION FOUNDATION   [2742]
787 Seventh Avenue
6th Floor
New York, NY 10019-6016
(212) 492-6179
Fax: (212) 492-7007

E-MAIL ADDRESS:
sally@ktgf.org

WEB SITE ADDRESS:
www.ktgf.org

FOUNDED: 1993

AREAS OF INTEREST:
Child and adolescent depression and ADHD.

TYPE:
Fellowships; Research grants. The Foundation funds research and other programs related to childhood and adolescent ADHD and depression. All funding is directed towards two research fellowship programs and the medical student training program. The Foundation does not accept general applications for project or research funding.

YEAR PROGRAM STARTED: 1993

PURPOSE:
To address the need for further research in pediatric ADHD and pediatric depression, and the need to cultivate more child and adolescent psychiatrists and psychologists.

LEGAL BASIS:
Family foundation.

ELIGIBILITY:
The Foundation is prohibited from making grants to political action groups and from lobbying the government, and makes no grants to individuals.

FINANCIAL DATA:
Amount of support per award: $30,000 per year.

NUMBER OF AWARDS: Up to 4.

APPLICATION INFORMATION:
Contact the Foundation for application details.
Duration: Two years.
Deadline: January.

BOARD OF TRUSTEES:
Andrew D. Klingenstein, President
Susan Klingenstein, Vice President
Thomas D. Klingenstein, Treasurer
Nancy K. Simpkins, Secretary
Sally Klingenstein Martell, Executive Director
Kathy Klingenstein
Amy Pollinger

ADVISORY COMMITTEE:
Thomas F. Anders, M.D.
Virginia Q. Anthony

William R. Beardslee, M.D.
David Brent, M.D.
Kiki Chang, M.D.
Anne Glowinski, M.D.
Laurence Greenhill, M.D.
Jeffrey H. Newcorn, M.D.

*PLEASE NOTE:
The Foundation does not accept unsolicited applications.

DELLA MARTIN FOUNDATION   [2743]
333 South Hope Street
43rd Floor
Los Angeles, CA 90071
(213) 617-4143
Fax: (213) 620-1398

FOUNDED: 1975

AREAS OF INTEREST:
Mental health research.

TYPE:
Endowments; Fellowships. Foundation has endowed four university chairs for mental health research.

YEAR PROGRAM STARTED: 1975

PURPOSE:
To promote research into causes of and cures for mental illness.

LEGAL BASIS:
Nonprofit foundation.

ELIGIBILITY:
For southern California tax-exempt organizations only. No grants are made to individuals.

GEOGRAPHIC RESTRICTIONS:
Southern California.

FINANCIAL DATA:
Total amount of support: $250,000 annually.
Matching fund requirements: Generally 1:1.

NUMBER OF APPLICANTS MOST RECENT YEAR:
20.

NUMBER OF AWARDS: 1 annually.

REPRESENTATIVE AWARDS:
$250,000 to University of California, Irvine to establish postgraduate research fellowship.

APPLICATION INFORMATION:
Send brief letter to the Foundation describing grant request.

IRS IDENTIFICATION NUMBER: 23-7444954

TRUSTEES:
Laurence K. Gould, Jr.
James A. Lonergan
Allen W. Mathias, Jr., M.D.
Barbara B. Morgan
Jane H. Roney
Thomas R. Sheppard
Philip A. Swan

ADDRESS INQUIRIES TO:
Laurence K. Gould, Jr., Trustee
(See address above.)

NATIONAL INSTITUTE OF MENTAL HEALTH   [2744]
Neuroscience Center Building
6001 Executive Boulevard
Room 6147, MSC 9609
Bethesda, MD 20892-9609
(301) 443-3367
Fax: (301) 480-1956

E-MAIL ADDRESS:
nimhreferral@mail.nih.gov

WEB SITE ADDRESS:
www.nimh.nih.gov

FOUNDED: 1948

AREAS OF INTEREST:
Basic neuroscience, genetics, basic behavioral science aimed at understanding mental disorders, research training, resource and technology development and drug discovery; translational research on the mechanisms of adult psychopathology and the development of novel treatment approaches for adult mental disorders; integrated research and research training that translates knowledge from basic/behavioral science into a better understanding of pediatric psychopathology and the development of novel treatment and prevention strategies; research on mechanisms and interventions on the interrelationship of physical and mental health; mental health research on AIDS that includes studies that range from the molecular and cellular basis of HIV/AIDS CNS infection to the domestic and international dissemination of effective preventative interventions; research that evaluates the effectiveness of treatment and preventive mental health interventions and mental health services research.

TYPE:
Development grants; Fellowships; Project/program grants; Research grants; Training grants; Research contracts.

YEAR PROGRAM STARTED: 1948

PURPOSE:
To support innovative science that will profoundly transform the diagnosis, treatment and prevention of mental disorders, paving the way for a cure; to reduce the burden of mental illness and behavioral disorders through research on mind, brain and behavior.

LEGAL BASIS:
Government agency.

FINANCIAL DATA:
Amount of support per award: Grants and awards vary in amount, depending upon the program and type of funding mechanism.
Total amount of support: Varies.

APPLICATION INFORMATION:
Application materials are available on NIMH web site. Prospective applicants should contact NIMH staff prior to submission to ensure the area of research that they investigate is within NIMH priorities.
Duration: Varies.
Deadline: Varies.

ADDRESS INQUIRIES TO:
Dr. Jean Noronha
(See address above.)

NATIONAL INSTITUTE OF MENTAL HEALTH

Division of Adult Translational Research and Treatment Development (DATR)
6001 Executive Boulevard, Room 7123, MSC 9632
Bethesda, MD 20892-9632
(301) 443-4863

E-MAIL ADDRESS:
bcuthber@mail.nih.gov

WEB SITE ADDRESS:
www.nimh.nih.
gov/about/organization/datr/index.shtml

TYPE:
Fellowships; Internships; Project/program grants; Research grants; Technical assistance; Training grants; Visiting scholars; Research contracts.
See entry 1988 for full listing.

NATIONAL SCIENCE FOUNDATION [2745]

Division of Behavioral and Cognitive Sciences
4201 Wilson Boulevard, Room 995
Arlington, VA 22230
(703) 292-7023
Fax: (703) 292-9083

WEB SITE ADDRESS:
www.nsf.gov

FOUNDED: 1950

AREAS OF INTEREST:
Social behavior and social development.

NAME(S) OF PROGRAMS:
● **Social Psychology Program**

TYPE:
Research grants. Support for laboratory and field research in all areas of human social behavior including social cognition, attitude formation and change, and social influence. The Program includes research on social, personality and emotional development in children and adults. Research to improve the conceptual and methodological base of social and developmental psychology is encouraged.

YEAR PROGRAM STARTED: 1972

PURPOSE:
To initiate and support scientific research and programs to strengthen research potential.

LEGAL BASIS:
National Science Foundation Act of 1950.

ELIGIBILITY:
Applicants may be colleges and universities on behalf of their staff members, nonprofit, nonacademic research institutions, such as independent museums, observatories, research laboratories, stock centers and similar organizations, private profit organizations, in exceptional circumstances, rarely, foreign institutions utilizing U.S. currency and, under special circumstances, unaffiliated U.S. scientists.

GEOGRAPHIC RESTRICTIONS:
United States.

FINANCIAL DATA:
Support may cover salaries, research assistantships, staff benefits if a direct cost, permanent equipment, travel, publication costs, computer costs and certain other direct and indirect costs.
Amount of support per award: Average $120,000 per year.
Total amount of support: Budget: $6,000,000.

NUMBER OF APPLICANTS MOST RECENT YEAR:
Approximately 120.

APPLICATION INFORMATION:
A proposal should include title and description of proposed research, information about the institution, principal investigator and business administrator, desired effective date of grant, duration of support, endorsement, facilities, personnel, current support and pending applications and budget.
Duration: Research grants may be awarded for periods of up to five years. Most grants are for two or three years.

Deadline: Target dates are January 15 and July 15.

STAFF:
Kellina Craig-Henderson, Program Director
Brett Pelham, Program Director

ADDRESS INQUIRIES TO:
Kellina Craig-Henderson, Program Director
Brett Pelham, Program Director
(See address above.)

NATIONAL SCIENCE FOUNDATION [2746]

Division of Behavioral & Cognitive Sciences
4201 Wilson Boulevard, Room 905
Arlington, VA 22230
(703) 292-7238
Fax: (703) 292-9068

WEB SITE ADDRESS:
www.nsf.gov

FOUNDED: 1950

NAME(S) OF PROGRAMS:
● **Perception, Action & Cognition Program**

TYPE:
Research grants. Supports research on perception, action and cognition including the development of these capacities. Emphasis is on research strongly grounded in theory. Research topics include vision, audition, haptics, attention, memory, reasoning, written and spoken discourse, motor control, and developmental issues in all topic areas. The program encompasses a wide range of theoretical perspectives such as symbolic computation, connectionism, ecological, nonlinear dynamics, complex systems, and a variety of methodologies including both experimental studies and modeling. Research involving acquired or developmental deficits is appropriate if the results speak to basic issues of cognition, perception or action.

YEAR PROGRAM STARTED: 1976

PURPOSE:
To initiate and support scientific research and programs to strengthen research potential.

LEGAL BASIS:
National Science Foundation Act of 1950.

ELIGIBILITY:
Applicants may be colleges and universities on behalf of their staff members, nonprofit, nonacademic research institutions, such as independent museums, observatories, research laboratories, stock centers and similar organizations, private profit organizations, in exceptional circumstances, rarely, foreign institutions utilizing U.S. currency and, under special circumstances, unaffiliated U.S. scientists.

GEOGRAPHIC RESTRICTIONS:
United States.

FINANCIAL DATA:
Support may cover salaries, research assistantships, staff benefits if a direct cost, permanent equipment, travel, publication costs, computer costs and certain other direct and indirect costs.
Amount of support per award:
Approximately $120,000 per year.
Total amount of support: $350,000.

APPLICATION INFORMATION:
A proposal should include information about the institution, principal investigator and business administrator, title and description of proposed research, desired effective date

of grant, duration of support, endorsement, facilities, personnel, current support and pending applications and budget.

Duration: 12 to 60 months, depending on the scientific merit and requirements of the project.

Deadline: February 1 and August 1.

STAFF:
Betty Tuller, Director

ADDRESS INQUIRIES TO:
Betty Tuller, Director
(See address above.)

PARAPSYCHOLOGY FOUNDATION, INC.   [2747]
P.O. Box 1562
New York, NY 10021
(212) 628-1550
Fax: (212) 628-1559

E-MAIL ADDRESS:
info@parapsychology.org

WEB SITE ADDRESS:
www.parapsychology.org

AREAS OF INTEREST:
Parapsychology.

NAME(S) OF PROGRAMS:
● **Eileen J. Garrett Scholarship**

TYPE:
Scholarships. Assists students attending an accredited college or university in pursuing the academic study of the science of parapsychology.

PURPOSE:
To promote research in parapsychology.

ELIGIBILITY:
Open to nationals of any country.

FINANCIAL DATA:
Amount of support per award: $3,000.

NUMBER OF AWARDS: 1.

APPLICATION INFORMATION:
Applicants must submit samples of writings on the subject with an application form from the Foundation. Letters of reference from three individuals who are familiar with the applicant's work and/or studies in parapsychology are required.

Duration: One year.

Deadline: July 15, for notification on August 1.

PARAPSYCHOLOGY FOUNDATION, INC.   [2748]
P.O. Box 1562
New York, NY 10021
(212) 628-1550
Fax: (212) 628-1559

E-MAIL ADDRESS:
office@parapsychology.org

WEB SITE ADDRESS:
www.parapsychology.org

AREAS OF INTEREST:
Parapsychology and psychic phenomena.

NAME(S) OF PROGRAMS:
● **Frances P. Bolton Fellowship**

TYPE:
Fellowships.

PURPOSE:
To further write up and polish the data amassed during the preparation of a doctoral dissertation/thesis.

ELIGIBILITY:
Awarded to a person who obtained their Ph.D. on the basis of a dissertation/thesis which dealt with some aspect of parapsychological phenomena.

FINANCIAL DATA:
Amount of support per award: $3,000.

APPLICATION INFORMATION:
Applications must be accompanied by a copy of the doctoral dissertation/thesis.

Deadline: February 15. Award notification March 1.

ADDRESS INQUIRIES TO:
Lisette Coly, Executive Director
(See address above.)

PARAPSYCHOLOGY FOUNDATION, INC.   [2749]
P.O. Box 1562
New York, NY 10021
(212) 628-1550
Fax: (212) 628-1559

E-MAIL ADDRESS:
office@parapsychology.org

WEB SITE ADDRESS:
www.parapsychology.org

AREAS OF INTEREST:
Parapsychology and psychic phenomena.

NAME(S) OF PROGRAMS:
● **Charles T. and Judith A. Tart Student Incentive Award**

TYPE:
Awards/prizes. Incentive award for research proposal.

YEAR PROGRAM STARTED: 2001

ELIGIBILITY:
Student must demonstrate a strong commitment to work within parapsychology. Open to undergraduate, graduate and postgraduate students who have in mind a specific research proposal which may be experimental, experiential, clinical, historical, survey- or questionnaire-based, archival, bibliographic, literary or any other type of investigation a student may propose.

FINANCIAL DATA:
Amount of support per award: $500.

APPLICATION INFORMATION:
Application must be in English and should be accompanied by two letters of reference, a one- to two-page description of the project that includes purpose, method, materials and duration of the project, and a one-page budget.

Deadline: November 15. Award notification on or around December 1.

ADDRESS INQUIRIES TO:
Lisette Coly, Executive Director
(See address above.)

PARAPSYCHOLOGY FOUNDATION, INC.   [2750]
P.O. Box 1562
New York, NY 10021
(212) 628-1550
Fax: (212) 628-1559

E-MAIL ADDRESS:
office@parapsychology.org

WEB SITE ADDRESS:
www.parapsychology.org

AREAS OF INTEREST:
Parapsychology and psychic phenomena.

NAME(S) OF PROGRAMS:
● **Robert R. Coly Prize**

TYPE:
Awards/prizes. Essay competition.

YEAR PROGRAM STARTED: 2004

PURPOSE:
To understand the complexities of parapsychology and help conceptualize its future.

ELIGIBILITY:
Incoming and current undergraduate college and university students who have sufficient interest in the field, even if they are not in a parapsychology degree program.

FINANCIAL DATA:
Amount of support per award: $1,000.

APPLICATION INFORMATION:
Application must be in English and include the following:
(1) copy of high school/college transcript;
(2) letters of recommendation (English only) from individuals who know their abilities and interest in parapsychology and;
(3) 1,000 to 1,500-word essay, written in English, addressing the topic "The Challenge of Parapsychology."

Deadline: November 15. Award notification on or around December 1.

ADDRESS INQUIRIES TO:
Lisette Coly, Executive Director
(See address above.)

PSI CHI, THE NATIONAL HONOR SOCIETY IN PSYCHOLOGY   [2751]
825 Vine Street
Chattanooga, TN 37403
(423) 756-2044
Fax: (423) 265-1529

E-MAIL ADDRESS:
psichi@psichi.org

WEB SITE ADDRESS:
www.psichi.org

FOUNDED: 1929

AREAS OF INTEREST:
Psychology.

CONSULTING OR VOLUNTEER SERVICES:
Honor society for psychology majors in four-year universities.

NAME(S) OF PROGRAMS:
● **Psi Chi/APA Edwin B. Newman Graduate Research Award**

TYPE:
Awards/prizes.

PURPOSE:
To give recognition to a graduate student for research in the field of psychology.

LEGAL BASIS:
Honor society.

ELIGIBILITY:
Awarded to graduate student submitting the best overall empirical study.

FINANCIAL DATA:
Award includes travel expense to attend the annual APA Convention.

Amount of support per award: Average: $1,000.

NUMBER OF AWARDS: 1.

APPLICATION INFORMATION:
Duration: One-time award.

Deadline: February 1.

PUBLICATIONS:
Eye on Psi Chi, magazine; *Journal of Undergraduate Research.*

ADDRESS INQUIRIES TO:
Melissa Strickland
Director of Finance/Awards
(See address above.)

SCOTTISH RITE CHARITABLE FOUNDATION OF CANADA [2752]

4 Queen Street South
Hamilton ON L8P 3R3 Canada
(905) 522-0033
Fax: (905) 522-3716

E-MAIL ADDRESS:
grantsandawards@srcf.ca
info@srcf.ca

WEB SITE ADDRESS:
www.srcf.ca

FOUNDED: 1970

AREAS OF INTEREST:
Biomedical research into intellectual impairment.

NAME(S) OF PROGRAMS:
● **Scottish Rite Charitable Foundation Major Research Grants**

TYPE:
Research grants. SRCFC grants support biomedical research into intellectual impairment focused on:
(1) the causes and eventual cure of intellectual impairment, such as autism and Down syndrome, especially as it affects children;
(2) the causes and eventual cure of Alzheimer's Disease and;
(3) research into other forms of intellectual impairment.

The focus should be on the causes and cure of the disease as opposed to the active treatment or palliative care.

YEAR PROGRAM STARTED: 1970

PURPOSE:
To provide financial support to researchers studying developmental disabilities.

LEGAL BASIS:
Nonprofit.

ELIGIBILITY:
The following criteria apply:
(1) applications are invited from researchers who hold, or have a firm offer of, at least a three-year academic appointment at a Canadian university or similar appointment at a Canadian research hospital;
(2) applicant must be a Canadian citizen and a permanent resident of Canada;
(3) special consideration will be given to applicants who have received their doctoral degree within the past five years;
(4) research projects must be endorsed by the research services department or equivalent of the university, hospital or research institute and;
(5) research must be carried out within Canada.

GEOGRAPHIC RESTRICTIONS:
Canada.

FINANCIAL DATA:
Amount of support per award: Up to $35,000 per year.

NUMBER OF AWARDS: Approximately 10 new and renewals per year.

APPLICATION INFORMATION:
The research proposals submitted should be accompanied by an explanation of the relationship of the research to the areas of priority, a proposed budget, published papers of the applicant relevant to the proposed research and the time lines of the research. Applications should be submitted to the Chair of the Awards Committee at the address above.

Duration: One, two or three years. Renewal contingent on a progress report of the work and research results.

Deadline: April 30 each year.

OFFICERS:
Allard B. Loopstra, President

ADDRESS INQUIRIES TO:
The Awards Committee
(See address above.)

SOCIETY OF BIOLOGICAL PSYCHIATRY [2753]

Mayo Clinic - Jacksonville
Research-Birdsall 310
4500 San Pablo Road
Jacksonville, FL 32224
(904) 953-2842
Fax: (904) 953-7117

E-MAIL ADDRESS:
maggie@sobp.org

WEB SITE ADDRESS:
www.sobp.org

FOUNDED: 1945

AREAS OF INTEREST:
Biological psychiatry, neuropsychopharmacology and clinical neuroscience.

NAME(S) OF PROGRAMS:
● **A.E. Bennett Research Awards**

TYPE:
Awards/prizes. Awards for recent, unpublished research papers in the field of biological psychiatry.

YEAR PROGRAM STARTED: 1958

PURPOSE:
To promote research in biological psychiatry.

LEGAL BASIS:
Nonprofit foundation.

ELIGIBILITY:
Applicants must be qualified investigators with appropriate interests. Preference is given to investigators 35 years of age or less who have not been engaged in research for greater than 10 years following award of their terminal degree or the end of formal clinical/fellowship training, whichever is later. Membership in the Society is not required.

FINANCIAL DATA:
Amount of support per award: $1,500 each for the best clinical paper and the best basic science paper submitted.

Total amount of support: $3,000 annually.

NUMBER OF APPLICANTS MOST RECENT YEAR: 10.

NUMBER OF AWARDS: 2 each year.

APPLICATION INFORMATION:
Completed manuscripts should be submitted in quadruplicate.

Duration: One year.

Deadline: Manuscripts must be received by January 14.

OFFICERS:
Husseini Manji, M.D., President
Elliott Richelson, M.D., Treasurer
David R. Rubinow, M.D., Executive Secretary

STAFF:
Maggie Peterson, MBA, Executive Director

COUNCIL MEMBERS:
Jeffrey A. Lieberman, M.D.
Harold A. Sackeim, Ph.D.
Alan F. Schatzberg, M.D.

ADDRESS INQUIRIES TO:
Maggie Peterson, MBA, Executive Director
(See address and e-mail above.)

SOCIETY OF BIOLOGICAL PSYCHIATRY [2754]

Mayo Clinic - Jacksonville
Research-Birdsall 310
4500 San Pablo Road
Jacksonville, FL 32224
(904) 953-2842
Fax: (904) 953-7117

E-MAIL ADDRESS:
maggie@sobp.org

WEB SITE ADDRESS:
www.sobp.org

FOUNDED: 1945

AREAS OF INTEREST:
Biological psychiatry, neuropsychopharmacology and clinical neuroscience.

NAME(S) OF PROGRAMS:
● **Ziskind-Somerfeld Research Award**

TYPE:
Awards/prizes. Award for recent, unsubmitted, unpublished research paper in the field of biological psychiatry.

YEAR PROGRAM STARTED: 1991

PURPOSE:
To stimulate investigations in biological psychiatry by senior investigators.

LEGAL BASIS:
Nonprofit.

ELIGIBILITY:
Candidates must be at least 35 years of age at time of submission, must continue to be actively involved in the area of research described in the submission and must be a member in good standing of the Society of Biological Psychiatry.

FINANCIAL DATA:
Amount of support per award: $2,500.

Total amount of support: $2,500 annually.

NUMBER OF APPLICANTS MOST RECENT YEAR: 5.

NUMBER OF AWARDS: 1 each year.

APPLICATION INFORMATION:
No application submission is required for the award. The Society provides a list of the top 10 articles to the Ziskind-Somerfeld Award Committee to review and make a final award selection.

Duration: One-time award.

Deadline: Announcement in May.

ADDRESS INQUIRIES TO:
Maggie Peterson, Executive Director
(See address above.)

SOCIETY OF BIOLOGICAL PSYCHIATRY   [2755]

Mayo Clinic - Jacksonville
Research-Birdsall 310
4500 San Pablo Road
Jacksonville, FL 32224
(904) 953-2842
Fax: (904) 953-7117

E-MAIL ADDRESS:
maggie@sobp.org

WEB SITE ADDRESS:
www.sobp.org

FOUNDED: 1945

AREAS OF INTEREST:
Biological psychiatry,
neuropsychopharmacology and clinical
neuroscience.

NAME(S) OF PROGRAMS:
● **Lilly Fellowship Awards**

TYPE:
Travel grants.

YEAR PROGRAM STARTED: 1991

PURPOSE:
To assist in defraying the cost of attending
the Society's Annual Meeting.

LEGAL BASIS:
Nonprofit organization.

ELIGIBILITY:
Applicants must be medical graduates in their
third, fourth or fifth year of residency or in a
bona fide research training program or
subspecialty training program within four
years of leaving a general psychiatry
residency training program. Selection is made
upon the basis of past excellence and
potential for professional growth in activities
pertaining to academic biological psychiatry
or clinical neuroscience.

FINANCIAL DATA:
Amount of support per award: $1,500.

Total amount of support: $15,000 annually.

NUMBER OF APPLICANTS MOST RECENT YEAR:
75.

APPLICATION INFORMATION:
Letter of nomination by Department
Chairperson or Training Director, current
curriculum vitae, and a one-page statement of
career interests and objectives should be
submitted to the Chairperson of the Lilly
Fellowship Awards Committee at the address
above.

Duration: One-time award.

Deadline: Letters of recommendation and all
supporting materials must be received by
January 18.

ADDRESS INQUIRIES TO:
Maggie Peterson, Executive Director
(See address above.)

VAN AMERINGEN FOUNDATION, INC.   [2756]

509 Madison Avenue
Room 2010
New York, NY 10022
(212) 758-6221

WEB SITE ADDRESS:
www.vanamfound.org

FOUNDED: 1950

AREAS OF INTEREST:
Mental illness and mental health.

TYPE:
General operating grants; Project/program
grants; Seed money grants. Grants for
projects and activities in areas of social
welfare, with particular emphasis on mental
health.

YEAR PROGRAM STARTED: 1950

PURPOSE:
To promote mental health through preventive
medicine, research, treatment and
rehabilitation.

LEGAL BASIS:
Private foundation.

ELIGIBILITY:
Tax-exempt organizations with appropriate
interests are eligible. No grants are made to
individuals.

GEOGRAPHIC RESTRICTIONS:
Metropolitan New York area and
Philadelphia.

FINANCIAL DATA:
Amount of support per award: Up to
$50,000, according to the needs and nature of
the project.

Total amount of support: Approximately
$4,000,000 for the year 2009.

NUMBER OF APPLICANTS MOST RECENT YEAR:
520.

NUMBER OF AWARDS: 89.

APPLICATION INFORMATION:
No formal application forms are required.
Proposals may be submitted in the form of a
short descriptive letter, enclosing such
pertinent background as tax status
documentation and the organization's annual
reports and financial statements. Proposals
may be submitted to the president at the
address above.

Deadline: Notification by December 1 for
March Board meeting, April 1 for June
meeting and July 1 for November meeting.

PUBLICATIONS:
Annual report; guidelines.

DIRECTORS:
Henry van Ameringen, President and
Treasurer
George Rowe, Jr., Vice President and
Secretary
Judith Beck
Alexandra Herzan
Christina K. Kind
Kenneth A. Kind
Patricia Kind
Andrew Kindfuller
Valerie Kind-Rubin
Laura K. McKenna
Clarence Sundram

ADDRESS INQUIRIES TO:
Henry van Ameringen, President
(See address above.)

TECHNOLOGY AND INDUSTRY

Technology and industry

AIR & WASTE MANAGEMENT ASSOCIATION (A&WMA)   [2757]

One Gateway Center, 3rd Floor
420 Fort Duquesne Boulevard
Pittsburgh, PA 15222
(412) 904-6006
Fax: (412) 232-3450

E-MAIL ADDRESS:
sgylptis@awma.org

WEB SITE ADDRESS:
www.awma.org

FOUNDED: 1907

AREAS OF INTEREST:
Air quality, waste management and/or
environmental management/policy/law.

NAME(S) OF PROGRAMS:
● **Scholarship Endowment Trust Fund**

TYPE:
Scholarships.

PURPOSE:
To provide monies for students with interest
in the area of air quality, waste management
and/or environmental management/policy/law.

ELIGIBILITY:
Must be a full-time graduate student pursuing
studies in the area of air quality, waste
management and/or environmental
management/policy/law.

FINANCIAL DATA:
Amount of support per award: $2,000 to
$7,500.
Total amount of support: Approximately
$26,000 annually.

NUMBER OF APPLICANTS MOST RECENT YEAR:
50.

NUMBER OF AWARDS: Approximately 10.

APPLICATION INFORMATION:
Applications must be completed online.
Duration: One year. Renewal possible by
reapplying.
Deadline: December 1.

ADDRESS INQUIRIES TO:
Stephanie Gylptis, Director of Education
(See address above.)

AIR TRAFFIC CONTROL ASSOCIATION (ATCA)   [2758]

1101 King Street, Suite 300
Alexandria, VA 22314
(703) 299-2430
Fax: (703) 299-2437

E-MAIL ADDRESS:
brian.courter@atca.org

WEB SITE ADDRESS:
www.atca.org

FOUNDED: 1956

AREAS OF INTEREST:
Air traffic control and aviation.

TYPE:
Scholarships. Scholarships to promising
young men and women enrolled in programs
leading to careers in aviation or air traffic
control and scholarships for dependents of air
traffic controllers pursuing a degree.

PURPOSE:
To promote careers in air traffic control or
aviation disciplines.

LEGAL BASIS:
Private, 501(c)(3) charity.

FINANCIAL DATA:
Amount of support per award: $3,000 to
$6,000.
Total amount of support: Varies.

NUMBER OF APPLICANTS MOST RECENT YEAR:
450.

NUMBER OF AWARDS: 8 to 12.

APPLICATION INFORMATION:
Duration: One year.
Deadline: May 1.

ADDRESS INQUIRIES TO:
Brian Courter
Meetings and Programs Coordinator
(See address above.)

AMERICAN GROUND WATER TRUST   [2759]

50 Pleasant Street
Suite 2
Concord, NH 03301-4073
(603) 228-5444
Fax: (603) 228-6557

E-MAIL ADDRESS:
trustinfo@agwt.org

WEB SITE ADDRESS:
www.agwt.org

FOUNDED: 1986

AREAS OF INTEREST:
Ground water education and protection.

NAME(S) OF PROGRAMS:
● **AMTROL Scholarship**
● **Baroid Scholarship**
● **Thomas M. Stetson Scholarship**

TYPE:
Awards/prizes; Scholarships.

YEAR PROGRAM STARTED: 1986

PURPOSE:
To provide education outreach to inform the
public about the optimal utilization and
protection of ground water for the benefit of
mankind.

LEGAL BASIS:
501(c)(3) nonprofit organization.

ELIGIBILITY:
Applicants must be U.S. citizens, apply
during their senior year in high school, and
be enrolled the following year in an
undergraduate program relevant to the ground
water industry.

GEOGRAPHIC RESTRICTIONS:
United States.

FINANCIAL DATA:
Amount of support per award: $1,000 to
$2,500.

NUMBER OF APPLICANTS MOST RECENT YEAR:
40 eligible candidates.

NUMBER OF AWARDS: 3.

APPLICATION INFORMATION:
Applicant must submit only one application
to be considered for all scholarships.
Completed application form must be
countersigned by a teacher at the applicant's
high school and accompanied by two letters
of recommendation. A 500-word essay and a
300-word description of the applicant's high
school ground water project and/or practical
environmental work experience must

---

accompany the application. Documentary
evidence of scholastic achievements and
references will be requested from finalists.
Duration: One academic year.
Deadline: June 1 of each year. The Trust will
write to all applicants (successful and
unsuccessful) at the end of August.

IRS IDENTIFICATION NUMBER: 23-7244958

STAFF:
Andrew W. Stone, Executive Director
Jacqueline Daoust, Policy Analyst

ADDRESS INQUIRIES TO:
Andrew W. Stone, Executive Director
(See address above.)

AMERICAN INSTITUTE OF BAKING   [2760]

1213 Bakers Way
Manhattan, KS 66502
(785) 537-4750
(800) 633-5137
Fax: (785) 537-1493

E-MAIL ADDRESS:
kembers@aibonline.org

WEB SITE ADDRESS:
www.aibonline.org

FOUNDED: 1919

AREAS OF INTEREST:
Research and education in baking, cereal
science, food plant sanitation, nutrition and
safety education.

NAME(S) OF PROGRAMS:
● **Course in Baking Science and
Technology**

TYPE:
Scholarships.

YEAR PROGRAM STARTED: 1922

PURPOSE:
To build new talent into the baking industry
at an advanced level.

LEGAL BASIS:
Nonprofit corporation, tax-exempt 501(c)(3).

ELIGIBILITY:
Applicants must meet the following entrance
requirements:
(1) high school diploma or GED and;
(2) two years of baking experience or passing
grade (overall score of 70% or higher) in
AIB's Science of Baking Correspondence
Course or have attained AIB-Certified Baker
status or other formal education in food
science considered equivalent by AIB's
Admissions.

A score of 400 on the TOEIC or 75 in the
TOEFL is required from English as a second
language students. A score of 550 on the
TOEIC is highly recommended.

FINANCIAL DATA:
Amount of support per award: $750 to
$12,000.
Total amount of support: $41,000.

NUMBER OF APPLICANTS MOST RECENT YEAR:
20.

NUMBER OF AWARDS: 20 per year.

APPLICATION INFORMATION:
Transcripts and letters of recommendation are
required. Send for admissions packet and/or
scholarships brochure.
Duration: 16 weeks.
Deadline: Applications submitted before May
1 and November 1 receive priority
consideration.

PUBLICATIONS:
Brochure; admissions packet.

IRS IDENTIFICATION NUMBER: 36-2166946

OFFICERS:
James Munyon, President
Gary Skrdlant, Treasurer and Secretary

ADDRESS INQUIRIES TO:
Ken Embers
Manager of Career Development
(See address above.)

AMERICAN SOCIETY FOR ENOLOGY AND VITICULTURE

1784 Picasso Avenue, Suite D
Davis, CA 95618-0551
(530) 753-3142
Fax: (530) 753-3318

E-MAIL ADDRESS:
society@asev.org

WEB SITE ADDRESS:
www.asev.org

TYPE:
Scholarships. Awards for undergraduate or
graduate students enrolled in enology or
viticulture or in a curriculum which
emphasizes a science basic to the wine and
grape industry and who intend to pursue a
career in research for the wine or grape
industry after graduation from college or
university.

See entry 2248 for full listing.

THE AMERICAN SOCIETY FOR NONDESTRUCTIVE TESTING, INC.   [2761]

1711 Arlingate Lane
Columbus, OH 43228-0518
(614) 274-6003
(800) 222-2768
Fax: (614) 274-6899

E-MAIL ADDRESS:
jsullivan@asnt.org

WEB SITE ADDRESS:
www.asnt.org

FOUNDED: 1941

AREAS OF INTEREST:
Nondestructive testing.

NAME(S) OF PROGRAMS:
● **ASNT Fellowship Award**

TYPE:
Fellowships. Nondestructive evaluation and
testing (NDE/NDT) is the science of
examining components and systems in a
manner that does not impair their further
usefulness. NDE/NDT is a complex,
multidisciplinary field offering exciting career
opportunities. Current areas for applying new
and advanced nondestructive testing
technology include power plant life
extension, aging aircraft and deteriorating
civil engineering structures.

YEAR PROGRAM STARTED: 1981

PURPOSE:
To advance the examination of objects with
technology that does not affect the object's
future usefulness; to identify up to three
ABET-accredited educational institutions that
may receive one of the awards for NDT
postgraduate research.

LEGAL BASIS:
Nonprofit organization.

ELIGIBILITY:
ABET-accredited academic institutions with
graduate educational research programs are
invited to submit proposals. Proposals are
evaluated based on their soundness of
approach, value of potential contribution,
potential for successful completion,
qualifications of potential student recipient,
qualifications of advisor, adequacy of
program of study, and adequacy of facilities.

FINANCIAL DATA:
Amount of support per award: $15,000.
Total amount of support: Up to $75,000.

APPLICATION INFORMATION:
The proposal, with all support materials,
should not exceed 20 one-sided sheets. It
must include a title page, table of contents,
research proposal, program of study, research
facilities, budget, research advisor, and
recipient. The educational facility must
submit a written report on the completed
study within 24 months of the program's
initiation. This report must be in a format
suitable for publication in the Society's
technical journal, *Materials Evaluation*. In
addition, the postgraduate student must
present his findings at an ASNT national
conference. No more than one proposal per
faculty member.
Duration: One year.
Deadline: October 15.

ADDRESS INQUIRIES TO:
Stephanie Dille, ASNT Executive Assistant
ASNT Headquarters
(See address above.)

*SPECIAL STIPULATIONS:
ASNT expects that funds from the ASNT
Fellowship Award will be used for support of
the student and the student's research, not for
overhead or indirect institution expenses.

APICS EDUCATIONAL AND RESEARCH FOUNDATION, INC.   [2762]

8430 West Bryn Mawr Avenue
Suite 1000
Chicago, IL 60631-3439
(800) 444-2742 (customer service)
(773) 867-1777
Fax: (773) 639-3115

E-MAIL ADDRESS:
jstults@apics.org

WEB SITE ADDRESS:
www.apics.org/education/erfoundation

FOUNDED: 1965

AREAS OF INTEREST:
Applied resource management,
manufacturing, service industries, production
and inventory management.

NAME(S) OF PROGRAMS:
● **George and Marion Plossl Doctoral
Dissertation Competition**

TYPE:
Awards/prizes; Conferences/seminars;
Fellowships; Project/program grants;
Research grants. Plossl Doctoral Dissertation
Competition is in the area of business
management.

Grants are also available at the postdoctoral,
academic-practitioner level in the field of
business.

YEAR PROGRAM STARTED: 1965

PURPOSE:
To further develop the APICS body of
knowledge; to develop professional efficiency
in production and inventory management.

LEGAL BASIS:
Tax-exempt 501(c)(3) organization.

ELIGIBILITY:
The Plossl Doctoral Dissertation Competition
is for doctoral students.

The program is a competition, not a
scholarship. Applicants must be currently
matriculated students in a business program.
High school students are not eligible.

FINANCIAL DATA:
Amount of support per award: $2,500.
Total amount of support: $2,500 annually.

NUMBER OF APPLICANTS MOST RECENT YEAR:
8.

NUMBER OF AWARDS: 1.

APPLICATION INFORMATION:
Application must include:
(1) project planning description;
(2) planned progress report dates;
(3) total itemized expenses;
(4) planned method for publication or
presentation and;
(5) qualifications of applicant.
Duration: Duration of project.
Deadline: June 1.

PUBLICATIONS:
Guidelines.

STAFF:
John Stults, Director of Corporate
Partnerships

ADDRESS INQUIRIES TO:
John Stults
Director of Corporate Partnerships
(See address above.)

AWS FOUNDATION, INC.   [2763]

550 N.W. LeJeune Road
Miami, FL 33126
(305) 443-9353
Fax: (305) 443-7559

E-MAIL ADDRESS:
vpinsky@aws.org

WEB SITE ADDRESS:
www.aws.org

FOUNDED: 1989

AREAS OF INTEREST:
Welding and materials joining.

NAME(S) OF PROGRAMS:
● **Howard E. and Wilma J. Adkins
Memorial Scholarship**
● **Airgas-Jerry Baker Scholarship**
● **Airgas-Terry Jarvis Memorial
Scholarship**
● **Arsham Amirikian Engineering
Scholarship**
● **D. Fred and Marian L. Bovie
Scholarship**
● **John C. Lincoln Memorial Scholarship**

TYPE:
Scholarships. Howard E. and Wilma J.
Adkins Memorial Scholarship is awarded to a
full-time college junior or senior pursuing a
minimum four-year degree in welding
engineering or welding engineering
technology.

Airgas-Jerry Baker Scholarship is awarded to
a full-time college undergraduate pursuing a
minimum four-year degree in welding

engineering or welding engineering technology; however, priority will be given to welding engineering students.

Airgas-Terry Jarvis Memorial Scholarship is awarded to a full-time college undergraduate pursuing a minimum four-year degree in welding engineering or welding engineering technology; however, priority will be given to welding engineering students.

Arsham Amirikian Engineering Scholarship is awarded to a college undergraduate pursuing a minimum four-year degree in civil engineering or welding engineering.

D. Fred and Marian L. Bovie Scholarship is awarded to a full-time college undergraduate pursuing a minimum four-year degree in welding engineering at The Ohio State University.

John C. Lincoln Memorial Scholarship is awarded to a college undergraduate pursuing a minimum four-year degree in welding engineering or welding engineering technology. Priority will be given to welding engineering students.

PURPOSE:
To promote education in welding engineering.

ELIGIBILITY:
Howard E. and Wilma J. Adkins Memorial Scholarship: U.S. citizens with a 3.2 grade point average in engineering, scientific and technical subjects, with a 2.8 overall grade point average.

Airgas-Jerry Baker Scholarship and Airgas-Terry Jarvis Memorial Scholarship: U.S. or Canadian citizens/residents who maintain a minimum overall grade point average of 2.8 with a 3.0 in engineering courses. Essay required: "Why I want to pursue a career with an industrial gas or welding equipment distributor?"

Arsham Amirikian Engineering Scholarship: Applicant must be a U.S. citizen or resident and have a minimum 3.0 overall grade point average.

D. Fred and Marian L. Bovie Scholarship: U.S. citizen or resident welding engineering student at The Ohio State University with a 3.0 overall grade point average. Electrical engineering students at The Ohio State University may be considered if there is no qualified welding engineering applicant at The Ohio State University.

John C. Lincoln Memorial Scholarship: U.S. citizen or resident with a 2.5 overall grade point average.

GEOGRAPHIC RESTRICTIONS:
Canada and United States.

FINANCIAL DATA:
Amount of support per award: Howard E. and Wilma J. Adkins Memorial Scholarship, Airgas-Jerry Baker Scholarship, Airgas-Terry Jarvis Memorial Scholarship and Arsham Amirikian Engineering Scholarship: $2,500; D. Fred and Marian L. Bovie Scholarship: $3,000; John C. Lincoln Memorial Scholarship: $3,500.

APPLICATION INFORMATION:
Duration: Howard E. and Wilma J. Adkins Memorial Scholarship: One year. May reapply for second year. Airgas-Jerry Baker Scholarship, Airgas-Terry Jarvis Memorial Scholarship, Arsham Amirikian Engineering Scholarship, D. Fred and Marian L. Bovie

Scholarship, and John C. Lincoln Memorial Scholarship: One year. Renewable up to three additional years by reapplication.
Deadline: February 15.

ADDRESS INQUIRIES TO:
Vicki L. Pinsky, Manager
(See address above.)

AWS FOUNDATION, INC.   [2764]

550 N.W. LeJeune Road
Miami, FL 33126
(305) 443-9353
Fax: (305) 443-7559

E-MAIL ADDRESS:
vpinsky@aws.org

WEB SITE ADDRESS:
www.aws.org

FOUNDED: 1989

AREAS OF INTEREST:
Welding and materials joining.

NAME(S) OF PROGRAMS:
- **Jack R. Barckhoff Welding Management Scholarship**
- **Edward J. Brady Memorial Scholarship**
- **William A. and Ann M. Brothers Scholarship**
- **Don and Shirley Hastings Scholarship**
- **Donald F. Hastings Scholarship**
- **William B. Howell Memorial Scholarship**

TYPE:
Scholarships. Jack R. Barckhoff Welding Management Scholarship is awarded to a college junior pursuing a minimum four-year degree in welding engineering at The Ohio State University. Applicants will be expected to enroll and complete the two-hour course in Total Welding Management at The Ohio State University. Applicants must also complete an essay on how they see their role once they have graduated in improving the world of welding and the welding industry in the U.S., and how they will use their education to improve the U.S. competitive position in welding and manufacturing.

Edward J. Brady Memorial Scholarship is awarded to a college undergraduate pursuing a minimum four-year degree in welding engineering or welding engineering technology. Priority will be given to welding engineering students.

William A. and Ann M. Brothers Scholarship is awarded to a full-time college undergraduate pursuing a minimum four-year degree in welding or a related program.

Don and Shirley Hastings Scholarship is awarded to a college undergraduate pursuing a minimum four-year degree in welding engineering or welding engineering technology. Priority will be given to welding engineering students.

Donald F. Hastings Scholarship is awarded to a college undergraduate pursuing a minimum four-year degree in welding engineering or welding engineering technology. Priority will be given to welding engineering students.

William B. Howell Memorial Scholarship is awarded to a full-time college undergraduate pursuing a minimum four-year degree in a welding program at an accredited university.

PURPOSE:
To promote education in welding engineering.

ELIGIBILITY:
For all scholarships, applicants must be U.S. citizens/residents and have a minimum 2.5 grade point average.

Jack R. Barckhoff Welding Management Scholarship: Applicant must attend The Ohio State University.

William A. and Ann M. Brothers Scholarship: Priority will be given to those individuals residing or attending school in the state of Ohio.

Don and Shirley Hastings Scholarship: Priority will be given to those individuals who reside or attend school in the states of California, Iowa or Ohio.

Donald F. Hastings Scholarship: Priority will be given to those individuals who reside or attend school in California or Ohio.

William B. Howell Memorial Scholarship: Priority will be given to those individuals who reside or attend school in Florida, Michigan or Ohio.

GEOGRAPHIC RESTRICTIONS:
United States.

FINANCIAL DATA:
Amount of support per award: Jack R. Barckhoff Welding Management Scholarship, Edward J. Brady Memorial Scholarship, Don and Shirley Hastings Scholarship, Donald F. Hastings Scholarship and William B. Howell Memorial Scholarship: $2,500; William A. and Ann M. Brothers Scholarship: $3,500.

NUMBER OF AWARDS: Jack R. Barckhoff Welding Management Scholarship: 2.

APPLICATION INFORMATION:
Edward J. Brady Memorial Scholarship: Application must include a letter of reference indicating previous hands-on welding experience and a 300 to 500-word essay on "Why I Want to Pursue a Career in Welding."
Duration: Jack R. Barckhoff Welding Management Scholarship: One year, with up to two years of scholarship support by reapplication; Edward J. Brady Memorial Scholarship, William A. and Ann M. Brothers Scholarship, Don and Shirley Hastings Scholarship, Donald F. Hastings Scholarship and William B. Howell Memorial Scholarship: One year, with up to four years of scholarship support by reapplication.
Deadline: February 15.

ADDRESS INQUIRIES TO:
Vicki L. Pinsky, Manager
(See address above.)

AWS FOUNDATION, INC.   [2765]

550 N.W. LeJeune Road
Miami, FL 33126
(305) 443-9353
Fax: (305) 443-7559

E-MAIL ADDRESS:
vpinsky@aws.org

WEB SITE ADDRESS:
www.aws.org

FOUNDED: 1989

AREAS OF INTEREST:
Welding and materials joining.

NAME(S) OF PROGRAMS:
- **Matsuo Bridge Company Ltd. of Japan Scholarship**
- **Miller Electric Manufacturing Company Scholarships**

- **Past Presidents Scholarship**
- **Robert L. Peaslee-Detroit Brazing and Soldering Scholarship**
- **Praxair International Scholarship**
- **James A. Turner, Jr. Memorial Scholarship**

TYPE:
Scholarships. Matsuo Bridge Company Ltd. of Japan Scholarship is for a college junior, senior, or graduate student pursuing a minimum four-year degree in civil engineering, welding engineering, welding engineering technology or a related discipline.

Miller Electric Mfg. Co. Scholarships program is for college students who will be seniors in a four-year Bachelor's degree program in welding engineering or welding engineering technology; however, priority will be given to welding engineering technology students. Priority will be given to Ferris State University students.

Past Presidents Scholarship is for a student in a four-year program in welding engineering, welding engineering technology, or an engineering program with an emphasis on welding, or a graduate student pursuing a Master's or Doctorate in engineering and/or management.

Robert L. Peaslee-Detroit Brazing and Soldering Scholarship is for a college junior or senior pursuing a minimum four-year degree, or a graduate student, in welding engineering, welding engineering technology, or materials joining science with an emphasis on brazing or soldering applications.

Praxair International Scholarship is for a full-time college student pursuing a minimum four-year degree in welding engineering or welding engineering technology; however, priority will be given to welding engineering students. Applicant must demonstrate leadership abilities through clubs, organizations, extracurricular academic activities, community involvement, etc.

James A. Turner, Jr. Memorial Scholarship is for a student pursuing a Bachelor's degree in business that will lead to a management career in welding store operations or welding distributorship.

PURPOSE:
To promote education in welding engineering.

ELIGIBILITY:
Matsuo Bridge Company Ltd. of Japan Scholarship: Applicant must be a U.S. citizen with a 3.0 overall grade point average; preference given to students from California, Oregon, Texas and Washington.

Miller Electric Mfg. Co. Scholarships: Applicant must be a U.S. citizen with a minimum 3.0 overall grade point average. Preference is given to students who exhibit a strong interest in welding equipment and have prior work experience in the welding equipment field.

Past Presidents Scholarship: Applicant must be a U.S. citizen and write a 300- to 500-word essay on their career aspirations. Applicant must have demonstrated leadership qualities, i.e., community involvement, AWS Section or other professional society participation, industry leadership, and be an AWS member.

Robert L. Peaslee-Detroit Brazing and Soldering Scholarship: Applicant may be a citizen of any country and plan to attend a university in the U.S. or Canada; U.S. citizens will receive priority. Minimum grade point average of 3.0 in engineering courses.

Praxair International Scholarship: Applicant must be a U.S. or Canadian citizen with a minimum overall grade point average of 2.5.

James A. Turner, Jr. Memorial Scholarship: Applicant must be employed at least 10 hours per week at a welding store operation or welding distributorship.

GEOGRAPHIC RESTRICTIONS:
United States.

FINANCIAL DATA:
Amount of support per award: Matsuo Bridge Company Ltd. of Japan Scholarship: $2,500. Miller Electric Mfg. Co. Scholarships: $3,000 each. Past Presidents Scholarship: $2,500. Robert L. Peaslee-Detroit Brazing and Soldering Scholarship: $2,500. Praxair International Scholarship: $2,500. James A. Turner, Jr. Memorial Scholarship: $3,500.

NUMBER OF AWARDS: Miller Electric Mfg. Co. Scholarships: 2.

APPLICATION INFORMATION:
Past Presidents Scholarship: One or more recommendation letters must come from community members, local AWS Section Officers, and/or AWS District Director, attesting to leadership capability; one or more recommendation letters must come from faculty (if a student), or from employer (if employed).

Robert L. Peaslee-Detroit Brazing and Soldering Scholarship: Personal statement must include at least one paragraph on applicant's interest in brazing or soldering, any courses taken in related subjects, and any other information that would help the Selection Committee in selecting a recipient. Also, include a description of applicant's impressions of any experience he or she has had involving soldering or brazing.

Duration: Miller Electric Mfg. Co. Scholarships: One-time award; Robert L. Peaslee-Detroit Brazing and Soldering Scholarship: Maximum of two years per award; Praxair International Scholarship and James A. Turner, Jr. Memorial Scholarship: Award recipients may reapply with a maximum of four years per award.

Deadline: February 15.

ADDRESS INQUIRIES TO:
Vicki L. Pinsky, Manager
(See address above.)

AWS FOUNDATION, INC. [2766]

550 N.W. LeJeune Road
Miami, FL 33126
(305) 443-9353 ext. 212
(800) 443-9353 ext. 212
Fax: (305) 443-7559

E-MAIL ADDRESS:
rwma@aws.org
vpinsky@aws.org

WEB SITE ADDRESS:
www.aws.org/rwma

FOUNDED: 1935

AREAS OF INTEREST:
Resistance welding processes.

NAME(S) OF PROGRAMS:
- **Resistance Welding Manufacturing Alliance Scholarship**

TYPE:
Scholarships.

YEAR PROGRAM STARTED: 2005

PURPOSE:
To encourage the highest standards of ethics in the resistance welding industry; to encourage education pertaining to the resistance welding processes.

ELIGIBILITY:
Applicant must:
(1) be a Junior level student in a four-year program and working towards a degree in welding engineering or welding engineering technology;
(2) have a minimum 3.0 overall grade point average and;
(3) be a U.S. or Canadian citizen and plan to attend an academic institution in the U.S. or Canada.

FINANCIAL DATA:
Awards are for tuition and fees only and will be paid directly to the academic institution.
Amount of support per award: $2,500.
Total amount of support: $2,500.

NUMBER OF AWARDS: 1.

APPLICATION INFORMATION:
Candidates must submit the following:
(1) a completed application form;
(2) an essay of 500 words or less about why the student wishes to become involved in the resistance welding industry;
(3) a letter of recommendation from an academic advisor or faculty member using the RWMA Scholarship Recommendation form;
(4) a second letter of recommendation from another party, such as an employer, using the RWMA Scholarship Recommendation form and;
(5) a personal statement.
Duration: One year. Renewal possible.
Deadline: February 15.

ADDRESS INQUIRIES TO:
Vicki L. Pinsky, Manager
(See address above.)

CHARLES BABBAGE INSTITUTE [2767]

University of Minnesota
211 Elmer L. Anderson Library
222 21st Avenue South
Minneapolis, MN 55455
(612) 624-5050
Fax: (612) 625-8054

E-MAIL ADDRESS:
cbi@umn.edu

WEB SITE ADDRESS:
www.cbi.umn.edu

FOUNDED: 1978

AREAS OF INTEREST:
History of computers and information technology.

NAME(S) OF PROGRAMS:
- **The Adelle and Erwin Tomash Fellowship in the History of Information Technology**

TYPE:
Fellowships.

YEAR PROGRAM STARTED: 1978

PURPOSE:
To advance the professional development of historians of information technology.

LEGAL BASIS:
University and research association.

ELIGIBILITY:
Open to graduate students whose dissertation addresses some aspect of the history of computers and information technology. Topics may be chosen from the technical history of hardware or software, economic or business aspects of the information technology industry or other topics in the social, institutional or legal history of computing. Theses that consider technical issues in their socio-economic context are especially encouraged.

Priority will be given to students who have completed all requirements for the doctoral degree except the research and writing of the dissertation.

The fellowship may be held at the home academic institution, the Babbage Institute or any other location where there are appropriate research facilities.

FINANCIAL DATA:
Amount of support per award: $14,000 stipend.
Total amount of support: $14,000.

NUMBER OF APPLICANTS MOST RECENT YEAR:
5.

NUMBER OF AWARDS: 1.

APPLICATION INFORMATION:
Applicants should send biographical data and a research plan. The plan should contain a statement and justification of the research problem, a discussion of procedure for research and writing, information on availability of research materials and evidence of faculty support for the project. Applicants should arrange for three letters of reference and certified transcripts of college credits to be sent directly to the Institute. There is no special application form. A one-page flyer describing the fellowship is available.
Duration: One academic year.
Deadline: January 15.

PUBLICATIONS:
Newsletter.

ADDRESS INQUIRIES TO:
Jeffrey Yost, Associate Director
Charles Babbage Institute
(See address above.)

COIN-OP CARES CHARITABLE AND EDUCATION FOUNDATION [2768]
c/o Amusement & Music Operators Association
600 Spring Hill Ring Road, Suite 111
West Dundee, IL 60118
(847) 428-7699
(800) 937-2662
Fax: (847) 428-7719

E-MAIL ADDRESS:
amoa@amoa.com

WEB SITE ADDRESS:
www.amoa.com

FOUNDED: 1948

AREAS OF INTEREST:
Higher education.

NAME(S) OF PROGRAMS:
● **Wayne E. Hesch Memorial Scholarships**

TYPE:
Scholarships. Designed to provide financial support to students who are, or plan or hope to be, engaged in the profession.

PURPOSE:
To provide leadership for the amusement, music, entertainment and vending industry; to protect and promote the industry interests.

ELIGIBILITY:
Open to individuals in need of financial assistance who are attending or plan to attend an institution of higher education and have a 3.0 grade point average on a 4.0 scale.

FINANCIAL DATA:
Amount of support per award: $1,000 each.
Total amount of support: $50,000 annually.

NUMBER OF AWARDS: 50 for the year 2010.

APPLICATION INFORMATION:
Duration: One year.
Deadline: January 15. Selection in late March. Announcement in April.

ADDRESS INQUIRIES TO:
Maggie Kapinos, Program Coordinator
(See address above.)

EARLY AMERICAN INDUSTRIES ASSOCIATION, INC. [2769]
P.O. Box 524
Hebron, MD 21830-0524
(410) 749-1965

WEB SITE ADDRESS:
www.eaiainfo.org

FOUNDED: 1933

AREAS OF INTEREST:
To encourage study and better understanding of early American industries in the home, shop, on the farm and the sea; to discover, identify, classify, preserve and exhibit obsolete tools, implements and mechanical devices used in early America, craft practices, and industrial technology.

NAME(S) OF PROGRAMS:
● **Research Grants Program**

TYPE:
Research grants. These are not scholarship or internship grants.

YEAR PROGRAM STARTED: 1977

PURPOSE:
To preserve and present historic trades, crafts and tools, and to interpret their impact on the present generation.

LEGAL BASIS:
Nonprofit corporation.

ELIGIBILITY:
Applicants may be sponsored by an institution or engaged in self-directed projects. Projects must relate to the purposes of the Association. Grants can supplement existing aid. These are not scholarship, fellowship or internship funds. A grant may not be used to pay for salaries, historical artifacts, software or equipment in whole or in part.

GEOGRAPHIC RESTRICTIONS:
United States.

FINANCIAL DATA:
A project report including a statement of expenditures must be filed by recipients.
Amount of support per award: Up to $2,000.
Total amount of support: $6,000 for the year 2009.

NUMBER OF APPLICANTS MOST RECENT YEAR:
7.

NUMBER OF AWARDS: 3 for the year 2009.

APPLICATION INFORMATION:
Application is available online, and must be completed and mailed to the above address.
Duration: One year. Nonrenewable.
Deadline: March 15 annually. Announcements in April annually.

PUBLICATIONS:
The Chronicle, quarterly journal; *Shavings*, newsletter for members; application guidelines; E.A.I.A. brochure.

OFFICERS:
John H. Verrill, Executive Director

ADDRESS INQUIRIES TO:
John H. Verrill
Executive Director
(See address above.)

FEDERAL HIGHWAY ADMINISTRATION [2770]
National Highway Institute
1310 North Courthouse Road, Suite 300
Arlington, VA 22201
(703) 235-0500
Fax: (703) 235-0593

E-MAIL ADDRESS:
henry.murdaugh@dot.gov

WEB SITE ADDRESS:
www.nhi.fhwa.dot.gov

AREAS OF INTEREST:
Transportation-related disciplines.

NAME(S) OF PROGRAMS:
● **Dwight David Eisenhower Transportation Fellowship Program**

TYPE:
Fellowships; Internships; Research grants; Technical assistance. Dwight David Eisenhower Transportation Fellowship Program's objectives are to attract the nation's brightest minds to the field of transportation, to enhance the careers of transportation professionals by encouraging them to seek advanced degrees, and to retain top talent in the transportation industry of the U.S. This Program encompasses all areas of transportation. The Program has seven award categories:
(1) Eisenhower Graduate (GRAD) Fellowships enable students to pursue master's degrees or doctorates in transportation-related fields at the university of their choice;
(2) Eisenhower Grants for Research (GRF) Fellowships acquaint undergraduate and graduate students with transportation research, development and technology transfer activities at the U.S. Department of Transportation facilities;
(3) Eisenhower Historically Black Colleges and Universities (HBCU) Fellowships provide HBCU students with additional opportunities to enter careers in transportation. The Fellowships also serve as a feeder for other Eisenhower fellowships;
(4) Eisenhower Hispanic Serving Institutions (HSI) Fellowships provide HSI students with additional opportunities to enter careers in transportation. The Fellowships also serve as a feeder for other Eisenhower fellowships;
(5) Eisenhower Tribal College Fellowships (TC) identify transportation-related activities and provide student fellowship opportunities at tribal colleges. The Fellowships also serve as a feeder for other Eisenhower fellowships;

(6) Eisenhower Intern Fellowships (EIF) and;
(7) Eisenhower People with Disabilities (PWD) Fellowships.

YEAR PROGRAM STARTED: 1983

PURPOSE:
To attract the nation's brightest minds to the field of transportation; to enhance the careers of transportation professionals by encouraging them to seek advanced degrees; to retain top talent in the transportation industry of the U.S.

LEGAL BASIS:
Government agency.

ELIGIBILITY:
Applicants must be enrolled in transportation-related disciplines (e.g., engineering, computer science, physics, transportation planning) at accredited universities.

GEOGRAPHIC RESTRICTIONS:
United States.

FINANCIAL DATA:
Award may include an allowance for tuition, stipend and travel expenses for the student to attend the annual Transportation Research Board (TRB) conference held in Washington, DC every January.
Amount of support per award: $1,500 to $102,000.
Total amount of support: $2,200,000 per year.

NUMBER OF AWARDS: Approximately 200 per year.

APPLICATION INFORMATION:
Undergraduate applicants must submit applications through their faculty advisors and be nominated for awards by their respective universities. Graduate applicants must apply to the Arlington, VA office. Further information is available from the Administration.
Duration: Minimum three months during the summer. Maximum three years of funding, with five years to complete the course.
Deadline: Graduate: Mid-February; Undergraduate: April 1.

PUBLICATIONS:
Application guidelines, brochures.

ADDRESS INQUIRIES TO:
Henry Murdaugh, Program Manager
(See address above.)

FOUNDATION FOR TECHNOLOGY EDUCATION
1914 Association Drive
Suite 201
Reston, VA 20191-1539
(703) 860-2100
Fax: (703) 860-0353
E-MAIL ADDRESS:
tmacdonald@iteea.org
WEB SITE ADDRESS:
www.iteea.org
TYPE:
Scholarships. The scholarship is for an undergraduate student majoring in technology education teacher preparation.
See entry 1803 for full listing.

FOUNDATION FOR TECHNOLOGY EDUCATION
1914 Association Drive
Suite 201
Reston, VA 20191-1539
(703) 860-2100
Fax: (703) 860-0353
E-MAIL ADDRESS:
tmacdonald@iteea.org
WEB SITE ADDRESS:
www.iteea.org
TYPE:
Grants-in-aid.
See entry 1649 for full listing.

FOUNDATION FOR TECHNOLOGY EDUCATION
1914 Association Drive
Suite 201
Reston, VA 20191-1539
(703) 860-2100
Fax: (703) 860-0353
E-MAIL ADDRESS:
tmacdonald@iteea.org
WEB SITE ADDRESS:
www.iteea.org
TYPE:
Scholarships.
See entry 1650 for full listing.

FOUNDATION FOR TECHNOLOGY EDUCATION
1914 Association Drive
Suite 201
Reston, VA 20191-1539
(703) 860-2100
Fax: (703) 860-0353
E-MAIL ADDRESS:
tmacdonald@iteea.org
WEB SITE ADDRESS:
www.iteea.org
TYPE:
Scholarships.
See entry 1804 for full listing.

THE FOUNDATION OF FLEXOGRAPHIC TECHNICAL ASSOCIATION   [2771]
900 Marconi Avenue
Ronkonkoma, NY 11779-7212
(631) 737-6020
Fax: (631) 737-6813
E-MAIL ADDRESS:
srubin@flexography.org
WEB SITE ADDRESS:
www.flexography.org
FOUNDED: 1958
AREAS OF INTEREST:
Flexographic printing.
NAME(S) OF PROGRAMS:
● **Flexographic Technical Association Scholarship**
TYPE:
Scholarships.
PURPOSE:
To support education in the study of flexography.

ELIGIBILITY:
Must be enrolled in a qualified school offering a study of flexography. Must have grade point average of 3.0 or better.
FINANCIAL DATA:
Amount of support per award: $3,000 per year.
Total amount of support: Varies.
NUMBER OF AWARDS: Varies.
APPLICATION INFORMATION:
Contact the Organization for application procedures.
Duration: One year. Renewable upon reapplication.
Deadline: Usually March of each year.
ADDRESS INQUIRIES TO:
Shelley Rubin
Educational Program Coordinator
(See address above.)

GREAT MINDS IN STEM   [2772]
3900 Whiteside Street
Los Angeles, CA 90063
(323) 262-0997
E-MAIL ADDRESS:
kbbarrera@greatmindsinstem.org
WEB SITE ADDRESS:
www.greatmindsinstem.org
AREAS OF INTEREST:
Science, technology, computer science, engineering and math.
NAME(S) OF PROGRAMS:
● **HENAAC Scholars Program**
TYPE:
Scholarships.
YEAR PROGRAM STARTED: 2000
PURPOSE:
To provide undergraduate and graduate scholarships to students majoring in science, technology, computer science, engineering and math.
ELIGIBILITY:
Applicants must be enrolled in an undergraduate or graduate engineering or science program at a college or university and must be planning to pursue a career in either area. Selection is based on academic standing, financial need, career potential and character.
GEOGRAPHIC RESTRICTIONS:
United States.
FINANCIAL DATA:
Amount of support per award: $500 to $3,000.
Total amount of support: Varies.
NUMBER OF APPLICANTS MOST RECENT YEAR: 600.
NUMBER OF AWARDS: 150 for the year 2010.
APPLICATION INFORMATION:
Application form required. If requesting an application in writing, send a self-addressed, stamped envelope. Absolutely no faxes will be accepted.
Duration: One academic year. Renewal possible.
Deadline: April 30.
ADDRESS INQUIRIES TO:
Kathy Borunda Barrera, Manager
HENAAC Scholars Program
(See address above.)

HIMSS FOUNDATION

230 East Ohio Street, Suite 500
Chicago, IL 60611-3270
(312) 915-9277
(312) 664-4467
Fax: (312) 915-9512

E-MAIL ADDRESS:
foundation@himss.org

WEB SITE ADDRESS:
www.himss.org

TYPE:
Awards/prizes; Conferences/seminars;
Fellowships; Internships; Research grants;
Scholarships.

See entry 2417 for full listing.

IEEE

IEEE History Center
Rutgers University
39 Union Street
New Brunswick, NJ 08901-8538
(732) 562-5468
Fax: (732) 932-1193

E-MAIL ADDRESS:
ieee-history@ieee.org

WEB SITE ADDRESS:
www.ieee.org/history_center

TYPE:
Fellowships; Internships. Fellowship in
Electrical History: Award for one year of
full-time doctoral or postdoctoral work in the
history of electrical engineering and
technology at a college or university of
recognized standing.

Internship in Electrical History: Two-month
internship for graduate research.

See entry 637 for full listing.

INSTITUTE OF FOOD TECHNOLOGISTS FOUNDATION [2773]

Scholarship Department
525 West Van Buren Street, Suite 1000
Chicago, IL 60607
(312) 604-0284
Fax: (312) 416-7919

E-MAIL ADDRESS:
akproctor@ift.org

WEB SITE ADDRESS:
www.ift.org

FOUNDED: 1939

AREAS OF INTEREST:
Food science and technology.

NAME(S) OF PROGRAMS:
● **Freshman Scholarships**
● **Graduate Scholarships**
● **Junior/Senior Scholarships**
● **Sophomore Scholarships**

TYPE:
Scholarships. Graduate Scholarships support
advanced study in the field of food science
and technology. Junior/Senior Scholarships
and Freshman/Sophomore Scholarships
encourage undergraduate enrollment in food
science and technology.

YEAR PROGRAM STARTED: 1950

PURPOSE:
To encourage and support outstanding
research in food science/technology including
such areas as food packaging, flavor

chemistry, new food ingredients and
products; to recognize scholastic
achievement.

LEGAL BASIS:
Nonprofit 501(c)(3) foundation.

ELIGIBILITY:
Graduate Scholarship applicants must be
enrolled in graduate studies at the time the
scholarship becomes effective, or a current
graduate student continuing a course of study
leading to an M.S. and/or Ph.D. degree.
Applicant must also be a person with an
above-average interest and aptitude in
research, enrolled in any educational
institution which is conducting fundamental
investigations for the advancement of food
science and technology and pursuing a
research program in the area of food
science/technology. Applicant must have a
3.0 grade point average. Research in such
disciplines as genetics, horticulture, nutrition,
microbiology, biochemistry, engineering,
chemistry, etc., is not eligible unless it is
directly related to the student's research
program in food science.

Junior/Senior Scholarship applicants must be
a sophomore, junior or senior pursuing an
approved program in food science or
technology in an educational institution, or a
sophomore student who plans to transfer to
such a program. Sophomore students
planning to transfer to an approved program
to complete their degree must do so by the
effective date of the scholarship.

Sophomore Scholarship applicants can be any
freshman who is, or at the time the
scholarship becomes effective will be,
enrolled in an approved program who has
maintained at least a 3.0 grade point average
on a scale of 4.0 for the first term of study
and who has the recommendation of both the
department head and a faculty member
familiar with the student's work.

Freshman Scholarship applicants must be
enrolling in an approved program in food
science or food technology or previous
graduates entering college for the first time in
such an IST-approved program.

Undergraduate scholarship program
applicants must be enrolled in a food
science/technology department or program
which offers curricula and options meeting
the IFT Undergraduate Curriculum Standards
for Degrees in Food Science, and graduate
students' research must be in the area of food
science.

Age, sex, race, religion and sexual orientation
are not conditions of eligibility for any of the
awards. Scholarship winners must become a
member of the IFT Student Association in
order to receive their award.

GEOGRAPHIC RESTRICTIONS:
United States, Canada and Mexico.

FINANCIAL DATA:
Amount of support per award: $1,000 to
$5,000.
Total amount of support: $160,000 for the
academic year 2009-10.

COOPERATIVE FUNDING PROGRAMS: The
scholarships are sponsored by numerous
companies, organizations and individuals.

NUMBER OF APPLICANTS MOST RECENT YEAR:
Approximately 300.

NUMBER OF AWARDS: 39 Graduate, 43
Junior/Senior, 15 Sophomore and 16
Freshman Scholarships for the academic year
2008-09.

APPLICATION INFORMATION:
Official application materials are available
from the department head of an educational
institution offering an IFT-approved program
in food science and technology, upon request
to the Institute, or by access of the Institute's
web site. Completed applications must be
submitted directly to the department head,
who will forward them to the Institute.

Duration: One year.

Deadline: February 19 for Graduate
Scholarships and Junior/Senior Scholarships;
March 15 for Sophomore and Freshman
Scholarships.

STAFF:
Anna K. Proctor, Coordinator

ADDRESS INQUIRIES TO:
Anna K. Proctor, Coordinator
(See address and e-mail above.)

THE INTERNATIONAL EXECUTIVE HOUSEKEEPERS ASSOCIATION [2774]

1001 Eastwind Drive
Suite 301
Westerville, OH 43081-3361
(614) 895-7166
Fax: (614) 895-1248

E-MAIL ADDRESS:
excel@ieha.org

WEB SITE ADDRESS:
www.ieha.org

FOUNDED: 1930

AREAS OF INTEREST:
Directors of housekeeping, environmental
service and facilities management.

NAME(S) OF PROGRAMS:
● **330-Hour Self Study Program**

TYPE:
Scholarships.

YEAR PROGRAM STARTED: 1960

PURPOSE:
To provide a professional organization for
executive housekeepers, directors of
environmental services, managers within the
housekeeping or custodial activities, and
suppliers of custodial goods and services.

ELIGIBILITY:
Must be a member or have a family member
that is a member of IEHA and be working
towards any degree program at a university
or college, in a certification program or
engaged in self-study.

FINANCIAL DATA:
Amount of support per award: $800 to
$1,500 per year.

NUMBER OF APPLICANTS MOST RECENT YEAR:
14.

NUMBER OF AWARDS: 10 for the year 2009.

APPLICATION INFORMATION:
Application may be requested from the
e-mail address above.

Deadline: Must be postmarked by January
10.

ADDRESS INQUIRIES TO:
Beth Risinger, Chief Executive Officer
(See address above.)

INTERNATIONAL FOOD SERVICE EXECUTIVES ASSOCIATION, INC. (IFSEA)   [2775]

4955 Miller Street, Suite 107
Wheat Ridge, CO 80033
(800) 893-5499

E-MAIL ADDRESS:
michelle@ifsea.com

WEB SITE ADDRESS:
www.ifsea.com

FOUNDED: 1901

AREAS OF INTEREST:
Food service field.

NAME(S) OF PROGRAMS:
● **Worthy Goal Scholarship**

TYPE:
Scholarships. Tuition scholarships.

YEAR PROGRAM STARTED: 1939

PURPOSE:
To give needed assistance to qualified young
people in furthering their careers in the food
service field.

LEGAL BASIS:
Tax-exempt, nonprofit.

ELIGIBILITY:
Students must be enrolled as or accepted as a
full-time student in a food service-related
major at a two or four-year college/university.

GEOGRAPHIC RESTRICTIONS:
United States.

FINANCIAL DATA:
Amount of support per award: $250 to
$1,500.
Total amount of support: $24,000 for the
year 2007-08.

NUMBER OF AWARDS: 20.

APPLICATION INFORMATION:
Scholarship application is available at the
Association web site.
Duration: One year. Renewable.
Deadline: February 1.

MICROSCOPY SOCIETY OF AMERICA   [2776]

12100 Sunset Hills Road
Suite 130
Reston, VA 20190
(703) 234-4115
(800) 538-3672
Fax: (703) 435-4390

E-MAIL ADDRESS:
associationmanagement@microscopy.org

WEB SITE ADDRESS:
www.microscopy.org

FOUNDED: 1942

AREAS OF INTEREST:
Microscopy.

NAME(S) OF PROGRAMS:
● **MSA Awards for Microscopists in
Developing Countries**

TYPE:
Awards/prizes; Conferences/seminars. Awards
to encourage attendance at the MSA Annual
Meeting by microscopists working in
developing countries who will travel to the
meeting. Several awards include free full
registration and attendance to the
proceedings.

PURPOSE:
To encourage microscopists who work in
developing countries to attend the
Microscopy Society of America's meeting.

LEGAL BASIS:
Nonprofit society.

ELIGIBILITY:
Applicants must be traveling from the
developing country to the nation to the
meeting and not be on extended visits to the
U.S. Preference will be given to applicants
who submit papers for presentation at the
meeting.

FINANCIAL DATA:
Amount of support per award: Average $295.
Total amount of support: Varies.

NUMBER OF APPLICANTS MOST RECENT YEAR: 2
to 3.

NUMBER OF AWARDS: Up to 10.

APPLICATION INFORMATION:
Applications consist of a completed Advance
Registration Form. If payment is included, it
will be assumed applicant will attend the
meeting even if application is denied. If
payment is not included, it will be assumed
applicant will be unable to attend the meeting
if no award is granted and the submitted
paper, if any, will be withdrawn.

A letter outlining the circumstances of the
applicant and stating the reasons for
requesting the award should also be included.
Duration: One-time award for attendance.
Deadline: February 15. Announcement
March 31.

PUBLICATIONS:
Proceedings.

ADDRESS INQUIRIES TO:
Peter Doherty, Managing Director
Scholarships and Award Inquiry
(See address above.)

PRINT AND GRAPHICS SCHOLARSHIP FOUNDATION   [2777]

200 Deer Run Road
Sewickley, PA 15143
(412) 741-6860
Fax: (412) 741-2311

E-MAIL ADDRESS:
pgsf@printing.org

WEB SITE ADDRESS:
www.printing.org/pgsf

FOUNDED: 1956

AREAS OF INTEREST:
Graphic communications and graphic arts;
printing technology and management.

NAME(S) OF PROGRAMS:
● **PGSF Undergraduate Awards**

TYPE:
Scholarships. Awarded to students who plan
to major and have a career in graphic
communications, printing technology, printing
management or publishing.

YEAR PROGRAM STARTED: 1956

PURPOSE:
To encourage eligible students to enter the
field of graphic communications in the
printing and publishing industries.

LEGAL BASIS:
Nonprofit foundation.

ELIGIBILITY:
Applicants must be high school seniors who
will graduate in January or June of current
year or high school graduates. Grants are
usually restricted to colleges and universities
offering two-year and four-year degree
programs recognized by the graphic
communications industry. A limited number
of awards also are available for students
already enrolled in two-year or four-year
college programs and for sons and daughters
of employees of scholarship sponsors.
Financial need is not a criterion for selection.

Applicant must be a full-time student and
must have and maintain a 3.0 grade point
average or higher.

GEOGRAPHIC RESTRICTIONS:
United States.

FINANCIAL DATA:
Awards are paid directly to colleges for
payment of tuition, fees and other charges.
Amount of support per award: $500 to
$5,000.

NUMBER OF APPLICANTS MOST RECENT YEAR:
1,500.

NUMBER OF AWARDS: Approximately 200
four-year scholarships annually.

APPLICATION INFORMATION:
Application must include two letters of
recommendation.
Duration: Renewable for up to four years
(unless otherwise specified).
Deadline: March 1 for high school students
and April 1 for students already enrolled in
college. Decisions are announced in July or
August.

PUBLICATIONS:
Annual reports; newsletter; career brochures.

IRS IDENTIFICATION NUMBER: 25-1668339

ADDRESS INQUIRIES TO:
Bernadine Eckert
Scholarship Administrator
(See address above.)

*SPECIAL STIPULATIONS:
Candidates must be pursuing a career in
graphic communications or printing and must
maintain a 3.0 grade point average.

PRINT AND GRAPHICS SCHOLARSHIP FOUNDATION   [2778]

200 Deer Run Road
Sewickley, PA 15143
(412) 741-6860
Fax: (412) 741-2311

E-MAIL ADDRESS:
pgsf@printing.org

WEB SITE ADDRESS:
www.printing.org/pgsf

FOUNDED: 1956

AREAS OF INTEREST:
Graphic communications, printing
technology, printing management and
publishing.

TYPE:
Fellowships. For advanced study relating to
the printing, publishing and packaging
industries. Support is provided for research
and study in engineering, chemistry, physics,
mathematics, industrial education or such
business technology areas as systems
analysis, operations research and marketing

research, provided the area of study has potential application in the printing, publishing and packaging industries.

YEAR PROGRAM STARTED: 1956

PURPOSE:
To strengthen the print and graphics industry through scholarship assistance.

LEGAL BASIS:
Nonprofit organization.

ELIGIBILITY:
Applicants must be students who plan to major and have a career in graphic communications, printing technology, printing management or publishing. Must have and maintain a 3.0 grade point average or higher, submit two recommendations, and be a full-time student.

FINANCIAL DATA:
Amount of support per award: $500 to $5,000.

NUMBER OF AWARDS: Varies.

APPLICATION INFORMATION:
Duration: One academic year. Renewable.
Deadline: February 15.

ADDRESS INQUIRIES TO:
Bernadine Eckert, Administrator
(See address above.)

SEMICONDUCTOR RESEARCH CORPORATION   [2779]
1101 Slater Road
Brighton Hall, Suite 120
Durham, NC 27703
(919) 941-9418
Fax: (919) 941-9450

E-MAIL ADDRESS:
steve.hillenius@src.org

WEB SITE ADDRESS:
www.src.org

FOUNDED: 1982

AREAS OF INTEREST:
Silicon integrated circuit technology, design, semiconductor manufacturing sciences, materials, processes and phenomena.

NAME(S) OF PROGRAMS:
- **Advanced Device Structures**
- **CAD Tools**
- **Environmental Safety and Health**
- **Factory Operations**
- **IC and System Design**
- **Interconnect and Packaging**
- **Materials and Processes**
- **Metrology**
- **Mixed Signal/Analog**
- **Modeling and Simulation**
- **Patterning**
- **Reliability**
- **TCAD**
- **Test and Testability**

TYPE:
Assistantships; Awards/prizes; Conferences/seminars; Demonstration grants; Fellowships; Research grants; Scholarships; Research contracts. Primarily research contracts. Also student design contests.

YEAR PROGRAM STARTED: 1982

PURPOSE:
To restore applied research base for the semiconductor industry.

LEGAL BASIS:
Nonprofit corporation.

ELIGIBILITY:
University faculty worldwide (except export-control countries).

FINANCIAL DATA:
Amount of support per award: Up to $2,000,000. Typically $50,000 to $100,000 per year.

NUMBER OF APPLICANTS MOST RECENT YEAR:
Approximately 600.

NUMBER OF AWARDS: Approximately 350.

APPLICATION INFORMATION:
The SRC prefers a brief white paper before submission of unsolicited proposals. Solicitations are used for new programs. Contact the Corporation for detailed information.
Duration: One to three years. Renewable.
Deadline: Varies by project.

ADDRESS INQUIRIES TO:
Executive Vice President
Research Operations
P.O. Box 12053
Research Triangle Park, NC 27709

SOCIETY OF MANUFACTURING ENGINEERS (SME) EDUCATION FOUNDATION   [2780]
One SME Drive
Dearborn, MI 48121
(313) 425-3300
Fax: (313) 425-3411

E-MAIL ADDRESS:
foundation@sme.org

WEB SITE ADDRESS:
www.smeef.org

FOUNDED: 1932

AREAS OF INTEREST:
Manufacturing and industrial engineering technology, machining technology, robotics, automated systems and technology.

NAME(S) OF PROGRAMS:
- **Caterpillar Scholars Award**
- **Connie and Robert T. Gunter Scholarship**
- **Clinton J. Helton Manufacturing Scholarship**
- **Kalamazoo Chapter No. 116-Roscoe Douglas Scholarship**
- **Lucille B. Kaufman Women's Scholarship**
- **E. Wayne Kay Scholarships**
- **St. Louis Chapter No. 17 Scholarship**
- **Myrtle and Earl Walker Scholarship**
- **William E. Weisel Scholarship**

TYPE:
Scholarships. Support for full-time students seeking careers in manufacturing or industrial engineering technology or closely related fields.

YEAR PROGRAM STARTED: 1982

LEGAL BASIS:
Professional society.

ELIGIBILITY:
Applicants must reside in the U.S. or Canada, be a full-time student pursuing a degree in manufacturing engineering, manufacturing engineering technology, or a closely related engineering field of study, and must attend an accredited institution in the U.S. or Canada. Applicants must have a minimum 2.5 grade point average.

GEOGRAPHIC RESTRICTIONS:
United States and Canada.

FINANCIAL DATA:
Amount of support per award: Varies according to scholarship.
Total amount of support: Over $400,000.

APPLICATION INFORMATION:
Applicants are required to submit only one application package consisting of one original. Application includes:
(1) scholarship cover sheet;
(2) student statement letter regarding student's career objectives;
(3) resume;
(4) original official transcript and;
(5) recommendations from two faculty and/or current or former employer.
Duration: One year. Students may reapply for undergraduate scholarships.
Deadline: February 1. Announcements in May and June.

PUBLICATIONS:
Program announcement.

BOARD OF DIRECTORS:
Khalil S. Taraman, President
Brian Ruestow, Vice President/Secretary
Peter F. Mackie, Treasurer
Kenneth Vedra, Assistant Treasurer
F. Brian Holmes
Barbara W. Kaufman
Dr. Irving Pressley McPhail
Glen H. Pearson
Pamela J. Ruschau
Mike Sayen
William R. Segar
Edward M. Swallow
Bill Tacon
William Taylor
Albert Wavering
Robert T. Williams

ADDRESS INQUIRIES TO:
Scholarship Coordinator
(See address above.)

TRANSPORTATION ASSOCIATION OF CANADA FOUNDATION   [2781]
2323 St. Laurent Boulevard
Ottawa ON K1G 4J8 Canada
(613) 736-1350
Fax: (613) 736-1395

E-MAIL ADDRESS:
foundation@tac-atc.ca

WEB SITE ADDRESS:
www.tac-foundation.ca

FOUNDED: 2003

AREAS OF INTEREST:
Transportation.

NAME(S) OF PROGRAMS:
- **TAC Foundation Scholarships and Bursaries**

TYPE:
Scholarships. Awards are provided for the study of road and transportation sciences, such as highway engineering, transport economics and administration.

YEAR PROGRAM STARTED: 2004

PURPOSE:
To encourage studies by Canadians in the field of transportation.

LEGAL BASIS:
Foundation.

ELIGIBILITY:
Applicants must be Canadian citizens or landed immigrants in Canada who are

enrolled in a university or college and pursuing studies full-time in some aspect of transportation.

FINANCIAL DATA:
Amount of support per award: $1,000 to $10,000.
Total amount of support: Over $120,000 annually.

NUMBER OF APPLICANTS MOST RECENT YEAR:
Approximately 125.

NUMBER OF AWARDS: 39 for the year 2010.

APPLICATION INFORMATION:
Duration: One year. Winners may reapply.
Deadline: Second week of February.

ADDRESS INQUIRIES TO:
Executive Director
(See address above.)

THE UNIVERSITY OF CALGARY

Faculty of Graduate Studies
Earth Sciences Building, Room 720
2500 University Drive, N.W.
Calgary AB T2N 1N4 Canada
(403) 220-4938
Fax: (403) 289-7635

E-MAIL ADDRESS:
gsaward@ucalgary.ca

WEB SITE ADDRESS:
www.grad.ucalgary.ca

TYPE:
Awards/prizes; Scholarships. Graduate scholarship for study in all areas relevant to the petroleum industry. Tenable at The University of Calgary. Award endowed through a bequest of the late Corinne Patteson.

See entry 1901 for full listing.

Aeronautics and astronautics

AIRCRAFT ELECTRONICS ASSOCIATION (AEA)   [2782]

3570 N.E. Ralph Powell Road
Lee's Summit, MO 64064
(816) 347-8400
Fax: (816) 347-8405

E-MAIL ADDRESS:
info@aea.net

WEB SITE ADDRESS:
www.aea.net/scholarship

AREAS OF INTEREST:
Avionics and aircraft electronics.

NAME(S) OF PROGRAMS:
- **David Arver Memorial Scholarship**
- **Dutch and Ginger Arver Scholarship**
- **Johnny Davis Memorial Scholarship**
- **Duncan Aviation Scholarship**
- **Field Aviation Company Scholarship**
- **Garmin - Jerry Smith Memorial Scholarship**
- **Garmin Scholarship**
- **Lowell Gaylor Memorial Scholarship**
- **Bud Glover Memorial Scholarship**
- **Leon Harris/Les Nichols Memorial Scholarship**
- **L-3 Avionics Systems Scholarship**
- **Mid-Continent Instrument Scholarship**

- **Rockwell Collins Scholarship**
- **Lee Tarbox Memorial Scholarship**

TYPE:
Scholarships.

PURPOSE:
To provide funding for students seeking higher education in the fields of avionics and aircraft electronics.

LEGAL BASIS:
Nonprofit.

ELIGIBILITY:
For the Bud Glover Memorial Scholarship, Mid-Continent Instruments Scholarships, and the Lowell Gaylor Memorial Scholarship, applicants can be anyone who plans to or is enrolled in an avionics program in an accredited U.S. or Canadian school.

Applicants for the Leon Harris/Les Nichols Memorial Scholarship may not be currently enrolled in the avionics program at Spartan.

Applicants for the Field Aviation Company Scholarship must attend an accredited vocational school located in Canada.

Applicants for Lee Tarbox Memorial, Garmin Scholarship, Johnny Davis Memorial and the Garmin-Jerry Smith Memorial Scholarships must be high school or vocational/technical school/college students who plan to or are attending an accredited vocational or technical school in an avionics or aviation-related program.

The Scholarships are not available to obtain pilot licenses.

GEOGRAPHIC RESTRICTIONS:
North America.

FINANCIAL DATA:
Amount of support per award: $1,000 to $30,000, depending on award.
Total amount of support: Varies.

NUMBER OF APPLICANTS MOST RECENT YEAR:
400.

NUMBER OF AWARDS: 15.

APPLICATION INFORMATION:
Duration: One year.
Deadline: February 15.

ADDRESS INQUIRIES TO:
Educational Foundation
(See address above.)

THE AMERICAN HISTORICAL ASSOCIATION

400 A Street, S.E.
Washington, DC 20003
(202) 544-2422
Fax: (202) 544-8307

E-MAIL ADDRESS:
rtownsend@historians.org

WEB SITE ADDRESS:
www.historians.org

TYPE:
Fellowships. The Association annually funds at least one fellow for a period of six months to one year, to undertake a proposed research project related to aerospace history. The Fellowship is supported by the National Aeronautics and Space Administration (NASA).

See entry 616 for full listing.

AMERICAN INSTITUTE OF AERONAUTICS AND ASTRONAUTICS   [2783]

1801 Alexander Bell Drive
Suite 500
Reston, VA 20191
(703) 264-7500
Fax: (703) 264-7551

E-MAIL ADDRESS:
stephenb@aiaa.org

WEB SITE ADDRESS:
www.aiaa.org

FOUNDED: 1977

AREAS OF INTEREST:
Arts, sciences, and technology of aeronautics and astronautics.

NAME(S) OF PROGRAMS:
- **American Institute of Aeronautics and Astronautics Undergraduate Scholarship Program**

TYPE:
Scholarships. Graduate awards are also offered.

YEAR PROGRAM STARTED: 1977

PURPOSE:
To encourage original research; to further dissemination of new knowledge; to foster the professional development of those engaged in scientific and engineering activities; to improve public understanding of the profession and its contributions; to foster education in engineering and science; to promote communication among engineers and scientists and with other professional groups; to stimulate outstanding professional accomplishments.

ELIGIBILITY:
The AIAA requirements are as follows:
(1) applicant must be a student member to apply;
(2) applicant's scholastic plan shall be such as to provide entry into some field of science or engineering encompassed by the technical activities of AIAA;
(3) applicant shall be enrolled in an accredited college or university in the U.S.;
(4) applicant shall not have or subsequently receive any other scholarship award which combined with the AIAA award would provide a stipend greater than the tuition plus direct educational expenses (such as books, lab fees, room, board, etc.) estimated by the educational institute he or she plans to attend;
(5) sophomore and junior students who receive one of these awards are eligible for yearly continuation of these awards (until completion of their senior year) provided they maintain a 3.3 (B+) grade point average on a scale of 4.0. Continuation, however, is not automatic. Students must reapply each year;
(6) financial background will not be a factor for eligibility;
(7) student must have a college grade point average of at least a 3.3 on a 4.0 scale and;
(8) student must have completed one semester or quarter of full-time academic college work.

FINANCIAL DATA:
Amount of support per award: The program presents yearly scholarship awards as follows: $2,000 each to one or more college sophomores; $2,000 each to one or more college juniors; $2,000 each to one or more college seniors. Two $2,500 scholarships will be given each year.

NUMBER OF APPLICANTS MOST RECENT YEAR:
142.

NUMBER OF AWARDS: 30.

APPLICATION INFORMATION:
Form and guidelines are available on the web
site.
Deadline: Applications must be received by
January 31.

ADDRESS INQUIRIES TO:
Student Programs Liaison
(See address above.)

AMERICAN METEOROLOGICAL SOCIETY [2784]
45 Beacon Street
Boston, MA 02108-3693
(617) 226-3907
Fax: (617) 742-8718

E-MAIL ADDRESS:
dfernandez@ametsoc.org

WEB SITE ADDRESS:
www.ametsoc.org

FOUNDED: 1919

AREAS OF INTEREST:
Meteorology, atmospheric, hydrologic and
oceanic sciences.

NAME(S) OF PROGRAMS:
- AMS Freshman Undergraduate Scholarship Program
- AMS Graduate Fellowship in the History of Science
- AMS Graduate Fellowships
- AMS Undergraduate Named Scholarships
- AMS/Industry Minority Scholarship
- The Father James B. Macelwane Annual Awards in Meteorology

TYPE:
Fellowships; Scholarships. AMS Freshman
Undergraduate Scholarship Program awards
funding to high school seniors entering their
freshman year of undergraduate study in the
fall.

AMS Graduate Fellowship in the History of
Science is awarded to a student wishing to
complete a dissertation on the history of the
atmospheric and related oceanic or
hydrologic sciences.

AMS Graduate Fellowships are designed to
attract students entering their first year of
graduate study in the fall who wish to pursue
advanced degrees in the atmospheric and
related oceanic and hydrologic sciences.

AMS/Industry Minority Scholarships award
funding to high school minority students who
have been traditionally underrepresented in
the sciences, especially Hispanic, Native
American and Black/African American
students.

AMS Undergraduate Named Scholarships are
directed to students entering their final year
of undergraduate study in the fall.

The Father James B. Macelwane Annual
Awards in Meteorology are intended to
stimulate interest in meteorology among
college students through the submission of
original student papers concerned with some
phase of the atmospheric sciences.

YEAR PROGRAM STARTED: 1965

PURPOSE:
To stimulate interest in meteorology among
college students and to recognize academic

excellence and achievement; to stimulate
careers in atmospheric and related oceanic
and hydrologic sciences.

LEGAL BASIS:
Nonprofit organization.

ELIGIBILITY:
Candidates must be U.S. citizens or hold
permanent resident status.

AMS encourages applications from women,
minorities and disabled students who are
traditionally underrepresented in the
atmospheric and related oceanic and
hydrologic sciences.

AMS Freshman Undergraduate Scholarship
Program makes awards on the basis of
academic excellence.

AMS Graduate Fellowship in the History of
Science: Candidate must be a graduate
student in good standing who proposes to
complete a dissertation on the history of the
atmospheric, or related oceanic or hydrologic
sciences.

AMS Graduate Fellowships: Applicants must
be entering their first year of graduate study
in the fall pursuing an advanced degree in
the atmospheric and related oceanic and
hydrologic sciences. Prospective candidates
from the fields of chemistry, computer
sciences, engineering, environmental
sciences, mathematics or physics who intend
to pursue careers in the atmospheric or
related oceanic or hydrologic sciences are
also encouraged to apply.

AMS/Industry Minority Scholarships:
Funding to high school minority students
who have been traditionally underrepresented
in the sciences, especially Hispanic, Native
American and Black/African American
students. Minority students must be entering
their freshman year of undergraduate study in
the fall at a four-year U.S. accredited
institution, and must plan to pursue a career
in the atmospheric or related oceanic or
hydrologic sciences.

AMS Undergraduate Named Scholarships:
Candidates must be entering their final
undergraduate year in the fall and majoring
in the atmospheric or related oceanic or
hydrologic sciences and/or must show clear
intent to make atmospheric or related
sciences their career.

Father James B. Macelwane Annual Awards
in Meteorology: Student must be enrolled as
an undergraduate at the time the paper is
written. No more than two students from any
one institution may enter papers in any one
contest.

GEOGRAPHIC RESTRICTIONS:
United States.

FINANCIAL DATA:
Amount of support per award: AMS
Freshman Undergraduate Scholarship
Program: $2,500 per year (freshman and
sophomore years); AMS Graduate Fellowship
in the History of Science: $15,000 stipend;
AMS Graduate Fellowships: $24,000 stipend;
AMS/Industry Minority Scholarships: $3,000
per year (freshman and sophomore years);
AMS Undergraduate Named Scholarships:
Varies; Father James B. Macelwane Annual
Awards in Meteorology: $1,000 stipend and
partial travel support to the AMS Annual
Meeting.
Total amount of support: Varies.

NUMBER OF APPLICANTS MOST RECENT YEAR:
340.

NUMBER OF AWARDS: 55.

APPLICATION INFORMATION:
Those interested should apply online at the
Society's web site. When writing for an
application package, specify which
application is being requested, and what year
of academic study applicant will be entering
in the fall. Submit a complete application
form, written letters of reference and official
transcripts.
Duration: AMS Freshman Undergraduate
Scholarship Program: Up to two years; AMS
Graduate History of Science Fellowship: One
year; AMS/Industry Minority: Two years;
AMS/Industry/Government Graduate
Fellowships: Nine months.
Deadline: February 10, 2012.

PUBLICATIONS:
Program announcement.

OFFICERS:
Dr. Keith L. Seitter, Executive Director

ADDRESS INQUIRIES TO:
Donna Fernandez, Development and
Student Programs Manager
(See address/phone/e-mail above) or

Stephanie Armstrong
Director of Development
Tel: (617) 226-3906 or 3907
E-mail: armstrong@ametsoc.org

*SPECIAL STIPULATIONS:
Applicants must review program
requirements before applying.

AVIATION DISTRIBUTORS AND MANUFACTURERS ASSOCIATION (ADMA) [2785]
100 North 20th Street
Fourth Floor
Philadelphia, PA 19103-1443
(215) 564-3484
Fax: (215) 564-2175

E-MAIL ADDRESS:
adma@fernley.com

WEB SITE ADDRESS:
www.adma.org

FOUNDED: 1943

AREAS OF INTEREST:
Aviation and pilot education, mechanics and
maintenance.

NAME(S) OF PROGRAMS:
- ADMA Scholarship Programs

TYPE:
Scholarships.

ELIGIBILITY:
Applicant must be one of following:
(1) third- or fourth-year B.S. candidate with
Aviation Management major, emphasis in
General Aviation, Airway Science
Management, Aviation Maintenance or
Airway Science Maintenance Management;
(2) third- or fourth-year B.S. candidate with
major in Professional Pilot with any of the
following emphasis: General Aviation, Flight
Engineer, Airway Science A/C Systems
Management or;
(3) second-year student in A/P education
program (two-year accredited aviation
technical school).

Applicant must also have 3.0 grade point
average or higher.

GEOGRAPHIC RESTRICTIONS:
United States.

FINANCIAL DATA:
Amount of support per award: $3,000.
Total amount of support: $9,000.

NUMBER OF AWARDS: 3.

APPLICATION INFORMATION:
Detailed information is available from the Association.
Duration: One year. Renewable by reapplication.

ADDRESS INQUIRIES TO:
Meg Taft, Executive Director
(See address above.)

AVIATION INSURANCE ASSOCIATION (AIA)   [2786]
400 Admiral Boulevard
Kansas City, MO 64106
(816) 221-8488
Fax: (816) 472-7765

E-MAIL ADDRESS:
mandie@robstan.com

WEB SITE ADDRESS:
www.aiaweb.org

AREAS OF INTEREST:
Aviation insurance.

NAME(S) OF PROGRAMS:
● **AIA Scholarship**

TYPE:
Scholarships.

PURPOSE:
To help students with an interest in aviation insurance to continue on to higher education.

LEGAL BASIS:
Nonprofit association.

ELIGIBILITY:
Applicants must have completed at least 30 college credits, of which 15 must be in aviation. Applicant must have a minimum 2.5 grade point average on a 4.0 scale, be a U.S. citizen, and submit a letter describing activities, indicating leadership qualities, goals, and reason for applying.

FINANCIAL DATA:
Amount of support per award: $2,500.

NUMBER OF AWARDS: 3.

APPLICATION INFORMATION:
Applicants must submit five sets of the following documents to be considered a scholarship candidate:
(1) completed AIA Scholarship application;
(2) letter describing activities, indicating leadership qualities, goals, rolls and reason for applying;
(3) at least one letter of recommendation from an employer or instructor;
(4) latest transcript(s) from all universities and colleges attended and;
(5) any FAA certificates.
Duration: One-time award.
Deadline: February 28.

ADDRESS INQUIRIES TO:
Mandie Bannwarth, Executive Director
(See address above.)

MCDONNELL CENTER FOR THE SPACE SCIENCES   [2787]
Washington University, Campus Box 1105
One Brookings Drive
St. Louis, MO 63130-4899
(314) 935-5332
Fax: (314) 935-4134

E-MAIL ADDRESS:
trecia@physics.wustl.edu

WEB SITE ADDRESS:
mcss.wustl.edu

FOUNDED: 1974

AREAS OF INTEREST:
Space sciences.

NAME(S) OF PROGRAMS:
● **McDonnell Astronaut Fellowships**
● **McDonnell Graduate Fellowships**

TYPE:
Fellowships. These fellowships are funded by a gift from the McDonnell Douglas Foundation to Washington University and provide tuition remission plus stipend for graduate students interested in pursuing research in the space sciences who are enrolled in the Washington University Departments of Physics or Earth and Planetary Sciences.

PURPOSE:
To support graduate students in the space sciences.

LEGAL BASIS:
University.

ELIGIBILITY:
All applicants for admission to graduate school in physics or earth and planetary sciences are considered for the McDonnell Graduate Fellowships if they are interested in pursuing research in the space sciences and note it on their application forms; only U.S. citizens are considered for the McDonnell Astronaut Fellowships.

GEOGRAPHIC RESTRICTIONS:
United States.

FINANCIAL DATA:
Amount of support per award: Varies.

APPLICATION INFORMATION:
Application materials for the individual graduate school programs may be obtained at the web site.
Duration: Three years.
Deadline: January 15. Announcement by April 1.

ADDRESS INQUIRIES TO:
Ramanath Cowsik, Director
(See address above.)

NATIONAL BUSINESS AVIATION ASSOCIATION   [2788]
1200 18th Street, N.W.
Suite 400
Washington, DC 20036-2527
(202) 783-9000
Fax: (202) 331-8364

E-MAIL ADDRESS:
info@nbaa.org
scholarships@nbaa.org

WEB SITE ADDRESS:
www.nbaa.org/scholarships

AREAS OF INTEREST:
Aviation.

NAME(S) OF PROGRAMS:
● **William M. Fanning Maintenance Scholarship**
● **Flight Attendant Scholarship**
● **International Operators Scholarship**

TYPE:
Scholarships. The William M. Fanning Maintenance Scholarship is for those who are pursuing careers as maintenance technicians.

The Flight Attendant Scholarship is dedicated to promoting education and training as a means to increase professionalism for business aviation flight attendants.

The International Operators Scholarship is dedicated to promoting education and training to increase safety and professionalism.

PURPOSE:
To help students continue their education in aviation and advance in that field.

LEGAL BASIS:
Nonprofit association.

ELIGIBILITY:
Contact the Association for details.

GEOGRAPHIC RESTRICTIONS:
United States.

FINANCIAL DATA:
Amount of support per award: Fanning Maintenance Scholarship: $2,500; International Operators Scholarship: $5,000.
Total amount of support: Varies.

NUMBER OF AWARDS: Fanning Maintenance Scholarship: 2.

APPLICATION INFORMATION:
Applications are available at the Association web site.
Duration: One-time award.
Deadline: Fanning Maintenance Scholarship: July 30; Flight Attendant Scholarship: March 31; International Operators Scholarship: January 31.

STAFF:
Jay Evans, Director, Operations

ADDRESS INQUIRIES TO:
E-mail: scholarships@nbaa.org

*PLEASE NOTE:
Awards will be made to U.S. citizens without regard to sex, race, religion or national origin.

NATIONAL BUSINESS AVIATION ASSOCIATION   [2789]
1200 18th Street, N.W.
Suite 400
Washington, DC 20036-2527
(202) 783-9000
Fax: (202) 331-8364

E-MAIL ADDRESS:
info@nbaa.org

WEB SITE ADDRESS:
www.nbaa.org/scholarships

AREAS OF INTEREST:
Aviation and business aviation.

NAME(S) OF PROGRAMS:
● **Lawrence Ginocchio Scholarship**
● **Schedulers & Dispatchers Scholarship**
● **UAA Janice K. Barden Scholarship**
● **USAIG PDP Scholarship**

TYPE:
Scholarships. Janice K. Barden Scholarship is presented to undergraduates who are studying aviation-related curricula.

Lawrence Ginocchio Scholarship honors individuals whose strength of character inspired a high standard. Applicants must be students at NBAA/UAA Member programs.

USAIG PDP Scholarship is awarded by the U.S. Aircraft Insurance Group (USAIG) to an applicant enrolled full-time in a university offering the NBAA Professional Development Program (PDP).

PURPOSE:
To help students continue their education in aviation and advance in that field.

LEGAL BASIS:
Nonprofit association.

ELIGIBILITY:
Contact the Association for details.

FINANCIAL DATA:
Amount of support per award: Janice K. Barden and USAIG PDP Scholarships: $1,000 each; Lawrence Ginocchio Scholarship: $4,500.

Total amount of support: Janice K. Barden Scholarship: $5,000; Lawrence Ginocchio Scholarship: $22,500; USAIG PDP Scholarship: $1,000.

NUMBER OF AWARDS: Janice K. Barden and Lawrence Ginocchio Scholarships: 5 each; USAIG PDP Scholarship: 1.

APPLICATION INFORMATION:
Contact the Association for guidelines.
Deadline: Varies.

STAFF:
Jay Evans, Director, Operations

ADDRESS INQUIRIES TO:
Jay Evans, Director, Operations
(See address above.)
E-mail: jevans@nbaa.org

NATIONAL BUSINESS AVIATION ASSOCIATION [2790]
1200 18th Street, N.W.
Suite 400
Washington, DC 20036-2527
(202) 783-9000
(202) 783-9250
Fax: (202) 331-8364

E-MAIL ADDRESS:
info@nbaa.org

WEB SITE ADDRESS:
www.nbaa.org/scholarships

AREAS OF INTEREST:
Aviation.

NAME(S) OF PROGRAMS:
● **Donald A. Baldwin Sr. Business Aviation Management Scholarship**

TYPE:
Scholarships. Promotes professional development in business aviation.

YEAR PROGRAM STARTED: 2007

PURPOSE:
To benefit individuals seeking to become NBAA Certified Aviation Managers (CAMs).

FINANCIAL DATA:
Amount of support per award: $1,225 per recipient.

APPLICATION INFORMATION:
Applicants must submit their resume, a 250-word essay explaining their plans for a career in business aviation, two letters of recommendation in support, and meet minimum qualifications to take the CAM exam.

ADDRESS INQUIRIES TO:
Jay Evans, Director, Operations
(See address above.)

PROFESSIONAL AVIATION MAINTENANCE ASSOCIATION FOUNDATION (PAMA) [2791]
400 North Washington Street
Suite 300
Alexandria, VA 22314
(703) 778-4647
(866) 865-7262
Fax: (703) 683-0018

E-MAIL ADDRESS:
hq@pama.org
info@pama.org

WEB SITE ADDRESS:
www.pama.org

FOUNDED: 1972

AREAS OF INTEREST:
Aviation maintenance.

NAME(S) OF PROGRAMS:
● **PAMA Student Scholarship Program**

TYPE:
Awards/prizes; Scholarships.

YEAR PROGRAM STARTED: 1980

PURPOSE:
To recognize and reward qualified Airframe and Powerplant students who have selected aviation maintenance as a career.

LEGAL BASIS:
Association.

ELIGIBILITY:
Students must be currently enrolled in FAR Part 147-certified educational institution in pursuit of Airframe & Powerplant (A&P) license. Students must have completed 25% of the required curriculum with a "B" average or equivalent. Students must need financial aid and must be recommended for the scholarship by a school instructor.

FINANCIAL DATA:
Award may be used for tuition, fees, books, or supplies directly related to the A&P program.
Amount of support per award: $1,000 to each recipient.
Total amount of support: Varies.

COOPERATIVE FUNDING PROGRAMS: The program operates on donations from regular, associate, student, educational, and corporate PAMA members and those raised at PAMA's Annual Chili Cook Off.

NUMBER OF AWARDS: Approximately 5.

APPLICATION INFORMATION:
Candidates meeting eligibility requirements are invited to submit the appropriate form and documentation July 1 through October 31.
Duration: One year.
Deadline: Postmarked by November 30. Notification in late December.

PUBLICATIONS:
PAMA Mx newsletter; application guidelines; PAMF brochure.

ADDRESS INQUIRIES TO:
PAMA Scholarships
(See address above.)

RTCA [2792]
1150 18th Street, N.W.
Suite 905
Washington, DC 20036
(202) 833-9339
Fax: (202) 833-9434

E-MAIL ADDRESS:
hmoses@rtca.org

WEB SITE ADDRESS:
www.rtca.org

FOUNDED: 1935

AREAS OF INTEREST:
Aviation electronics, telecommunications, and other closely allied fields such as determination of common operational requirements, state-of-the-art developments and applications, other problems associated with air traffic control, navigation, communications, and efficient utilization of airports and airspace.

NAME(S) OF PROGRAMS:
● **The William E. Jackson Award**

TYPE:
Awards/prizes. Award for a paper by an outstanding graduate student in aviation electronics or telecommunications, in memory of William E. Jackson, an outstanding pioneer in the development and implementation of the present airways, air traffic control, and aviation communication systems.

YEAR PROGRAM STARTED: 1975

PURPOSE:
To honor an outstanding graduate student in aviation electronics or telecommunications.

LEGAL BASIS:
Nonprofit, 501(c)(3) organization.

ELIGIBILITY:
Open to any graduate student earning a degree in the field of aviation electronics or telecommunication systems. There are no restrictions as to race, creed, color, religious affiliation, national origin or citizenship. The sole basis for selection will be the written report, which must be in English.

FINANCIAL DATA:
The recipient will travel at the expense of RTCA to the location of the award presentation. Complimentary registration for any RTCA business meeting taking place concurrently is also awarded.
Amount of support per award: $4,000.

NUMBER OF APPLICANTS MOST RECENT YEAR: 10.

NUMBER OF AWARDS: 1.

APPLICATION INFORMATION:
Submissions must be in the form of a thesis, project report, or paper in a technical journal. The work must have been completed no earlier than three years before the submission deadline and only those in English and without publication restrictions will be considered. Joint authors may submit if both or all qualify as students and candidates for undergraduate or graduate degrees in this field. Joint authors would share the award. In addition to the paper, candidates must submit two copies (one paper copy and one electronic submission) of each of the following: a one- to two-page summary of the written material, a biographical sketch of the candidate, and a letter of endorsement from the candidate's instructor, professor, or departmental head. Submit material to the address above.
Deadline: September 30.

OFFICERS:
Harold E. Moses, Program Director

ADDRESS INQUIRIES TO:
William E. Jackson Award Committee
(See address above.)

SMITHSONIAN NATIONAL AIR AND SPACE MUSEUM   [2793]

Smithsonian Institution
Independence Avenue at Sixth Street, S.W.
Room 3313, MRC 312
Washington, DC 20013-7012
(202) 633-2648
Fax: (202) 786-2447

E-MAIL ADDRESS:
nasm-fellowships@si.edu

WEB SITE ADDRESS:
www.nasm.si.edu

FOUNDED: 1946

AREAS OF INTEREST:
Aeronautics.

NAME(S) OF PROGRAMS:
- **Guggenheim Fellowship**
- **Charles A. Lindbergh Chair in Aerospace History**
- **Postdoctoral Earth and Planetary Sciences Fellowships**
- **A. Verville Fellowship**

TYPE:
Fellowships. The Guggenheim Fellowship is a competitive three- to 12-month in-residence fellowship for pre- or postdoctoral research in aviation and space history.

The A. Verville Fellowship is a competitive nine- to 12-month in-residence fellowship intended for analysis of major trends, developments, and accomplishments in the history of aviation or space studies.

All candidates are encouraged to pursue programs of research and writing that support publication of works that are scholarly in tone and substance, and/or addressed to an audience with broad interests. Each fellow will work closely with staff members who share similar interests.

PURPOSE:
To promote research into, and writing about, the history of aviation and space flight.

ELIGIBILITY:
All applicants must be able to write and converse fluently in English. Additional information is available online.

FINANCIAL DATA:
Amount of support per award: Guggenheim Fellowship: $30,000 for predoctoral candidates and $45,000 for postdoctoral candidates; Verville Fellowship: $55,000.

NUMBER OF AWARDS: 1 each.

APPLICATION INFORMATION:
Instructions and forms for each program are available on the web site.
Deadline: January 15.

PUBLICATIONS:
Brochure; application package.

ADDRESS INQUIRIES TO:
Collette Williams, Fellowship Program Coordinator

VERTICAL FLIGHT FOUNDATION   [2794]

217 North Washington Street
Alexandria, VA 22314
(703) 684-6777
Fax: (703) 739-9279

E-MAIL ADDRESS:
staff@vtol.org

WEB SITE ADDRESS:
www.vtol.org

FOUNDED: 1967

AREAS OF INTEREST:
Support of scientific and educational activities related to VTOL (Vertical Take-Off and Landing) flight.

NAME(S) OF PROGRAMS:
- **Vertical Flight Foundation Engineering Scholarships**

TYPE:
Scholarships. Annual scholarships to undergraduate senior, Master's or Ph.D. students interested in pursuing careers in some technical aspect of helicopter or vertical flight engineering.

YEAR PROGRAM STARTED: 1967

PURPOSE:
To acquire the best technical experts for the vertical flight industry.

LEGAL BASIS:
Independent, charitable trust.

ELIGIBILITY:
The VFF scholarships will be awarded to undergraduate senior, Master's and Ph.D. students studying for a career in the helicopter or vertical flight industry.

The scholarships are merit-based and are awarded in two categories: undergraduate and graduate. Individuals will be eligible once for one of the final two years of undergraduate studies and once for a year of graduate study. Applicants must be in school through the full academic year following receipt of the scholarship. To be eligible for a scholarship, an applicant must be a full-time student at an accredited school of engineering.

Applicants need not be members of the American Helicopter Society.

FINANCIAL DATA:
Amount of support per award: $2,000 to $4,000, depending upon endowment earnings.

NUMBER OF APPLICANTS MOST RECENT YEAR: 100.

NUMBER OF AWARDS: 13.

APPLICATION INFORMATION:
Detailed instructions are available at the web site. Applicants can also download a copy of the application form.
Duration: One academic year.
Deadline: February 1. Notification by April 15.

PUBLICATIONS:
Applications.

IRS IDENTIFICATION NUMBER: 23-6428319

ADDRESS INQUIRIES TO:
Kay Brackins, Student Liaison
(See address above.)

Engineering

ADSC: THE INTERNATIONAL ASSOCIATION OF FOUNDATION DRILLING   [2795]

8445 Freeport Parkway
Suite 325
Irving, TX 75063
(469) 359-6000
Fax: (459) 359-6007

E-MAIL ADDRESS:
ymaloney@adsc-iafd.com

WEB SITE ADDRESS:
www.adsc-iafd.com

FOUNDED: 1972

AREAS OF INTEREST:
Civil, geotechnical and structural engineering.

TYPE:
Scholarships.

PURPOSE:
To promote the foundation drilling and anchored earth retention industry.

ELIGIBILITY:
Must be a graduate student studying civil engineering.

GEOGRAPHIC RESTRICTIONS:
United States or Canada.

FINANCIAL DATA:
Amount of support per award: Maximum $3,000; $1,500 per semester. Part-time scholarship program: Maximum $3,000; $500 per semester.
Total amount of support: Approximately $42,000 annually.

NUMBER OF AWARDS: Minimum of 14 per year.

APPLICATION INFORMATION:
Applicants must submit a brief letter outlining personal goals, two letters of recommendation and a copy of their transcript with application. Further information and application may be obtained from the Association.
Duration: One year.
Deadline: Contact the Association for deadline.

ADDRESS INQUIRIES TO:
Yolanda Maloney, Executive Assistant
(See address above.)

AGC EDUCATION AND RESEARCH FOUNDATION   [2796]

2300 Wilson Boulevard, Suite 400
Arlington, VA 22201
(703) 837-5342
Fax: (703) 837-5451

E-MAIL ADDRESS:
patricianm@agc.org

WEB SITE ADDRESS:
www.agcfoundation.org

FOUNDED: 1968

AREAS OF INTEREST:
Construction and civic interest in improving the quality of educational programs for students specifically in the area of construction and construction research.

NAME(S) OF PROGRAMS:
- **James L. Allhands Essay Competition**
- **Graduate Scholarships**
- **Outstanding Educator Award**
- **Undergraduate Scholarship Program in Construction**

TYPE:
Project/program grants; Scholarships. Field study support.

YEAR PROGRAM STARTED: 1968

PURPOSE:
To improve the science of construction through the funding of scholarships and construction research projects.

LEGAL BASIS:
501(c)(3).

ELIGIBILITY:
Undergraduate scholarships are available to college sophomores and juniors enrolled or planning to enroll in a full-time, four- or five-year ABET or ACCE-accredited construction or civil engineering program. High school seniors and college freshman are not eligible.

Graduate awards are available to college seniors enrolled in an undergraduate construction or civil engineering degree program, or others possessing an undergraduate degree in construction or civil engineering. The applicant must be enrolled, or planning to enroll, in a graduate-level construction or civil engineering degree program as a full-time student. All candidates must be U.S. citizens or permanent U.S. residents.

GEOGRAPHIC RESTRICTIONS:
United States.

FINANCIAL DATA:
Amount of support per award: Allhands Essay Competition: First Prize $1,000 and an expense-paid trip to the AGC Convention; Graduate Scholarships: Up to $7,500; Outstanding Educator Award: $5,000 scholarship and an expense-paid trip to the AGC Convention, plus two $2,500 scholarships for students of the educator; Undergraduate Scholarships: $2,500 per year renewable to a maximum of $7,500.

Total amount of support: $300,000 for all programs.

NUMBER OF AWARDS: Over 100 scholarships are awarded each year.

APPLICATION INFORMATION:
Application is posted online after July 1.

Deadline: November 1.

IRS IDENTIFICATION NUMBER: 52-6083465

BOARD OF DIRECTORS:
Paul W. Diederich, President
Thomas J. Burleson, Vice President
John F. Kelley, III, Treasurer
Monique Valentine, Secretary
Russell F. Agosta
Robert L. Bowen
Larry C. Gaskins
B. Scott Holloway
Lee Kearney
Mark Knight
Roger Liska
Francis W. Madigan, Jr.
Daniel W. O'Brien
Barry Paceley
J. David Pepper
Frederick H. Poppe
Kenneth F. Robson
Norman J. Walton
Peter K.W. Wert

ADDRESS INQUIRIES TO:
Melinda Patrician, Director
(See address above.)

AMERICAN CHEMICAL SOCIETY
1155 16th Street, N.W.
Washington, DC 20036-4800
(202) 872-6283
Fax: (202) 776-8008

E-MAIL ADDRESS:
awards@acs.org

WEB SITE ADDRESS:
www.acs.org/awards

TYPE:
Awards/prizes.

See entry 2190 for full listing.

AMERICAN CONGRESS ON SURVEYING AND MAPPING (ACSM) [2797]
6 Montgomery Village Avenue
Suite 403
Gaithersburg, MD 20879
(240) 632-9716 ext. 109
Fax: (240) 632-1321

E-MAIL ADDRESS:
ilse.genovese@acsm.net

WEB SITE ADDRESS:
www.acsm.net

FOUNDED: 1941

AREAS OF INTEREST:
Geodetic surveying.

NAME(S) OF PROGRAMS:
- **American Association for Geodetic Surveying Graduate Fellowship Award**

TYPE:
Fellowships. Annual fellowship award to support graduate study in a program with a significant focus on geodetic surveying or geodesy at a school of the recipient's choice.

PURPOSE:
To recognize outstanding graduate students committed to the pursuit of knowledge in geodetic surveying, thus enhancing the ability of the profession to better serve the needs of society.

LEGAL BASIS:
Nonprofit educational organization.

ELIGIBILITY:
Nominees must be members of American Congress on Surveying and Mapping and should be enrolled in or accepted by a graduate program with a significant focus on geodetic surveying or geodesy. Preference will be given to applicants having at least two years of employment experience in the surveying profession.

GEOGRAPHIC RESTRICTIONS:
United States, Canada and South America.

FINANCIAL DATA:
Amount of support per award: $2,000 and an appropriate citation to be presented at the annual meeting.

Total amount of support: $2,000 annually.

COOPERATIVE FUNDING PROGRAMS: Provided by the American Association for Geodetic Surveying and administered by ACSM.

NUMBER OF AWARDS: 1 annually.

APPLICATION INFORMATION:
Required documentation includes:
(1) a completed application form;
(2) proof of membership in ACSM (this will be checked);
(3) a brief yet complete statement indicating

educational objectives, future plans of study or research, professional activities and financial need;
(4) at least three letters of recommendation (at least two from faculty members familiar with the student's work);
(5) a complete original official transcript through May of the year prior to when the award will be presented (the others may be copies) and;
(6) Do not send applications by fax or e-mail. Include one set of original transcripts. Mail all documents in one package. In addition, send unofficial transcripts for the fall semester when available.

Duration: One academic year.

Deadline: Varies.

PUBLICATIONS:
ACSM Bulletin, a bimonthly magazine; one quarterly Journal.

ADDRESS INQUIRIES TO:
Ilse Genevose
Communications Director
(See address above.)

AMERICAN CONGRESS ON SURVEYING AND MAPPING (ACSM) [2798]
6 Montgomery Village Avenue
Suite 403
Gaithersburg, MD 20879
(240) 632-9716 ext. 109
Fax: (240) 632-1321

E-MAIL ADDRESS:
ilse.genovese@acsm.net

WEB SITE ADDRESS:
www.acsm.net

FOUNDED: 1941

AREAS OF INTEREST:
Geodetic surveying.

NAME(S) OF PROGRAMS:
- **AAGS Joseph F. Dracup Scholarship Award**

TYPE:
Scholarships. The award is intended for students enrolled in four-year degree programs in surveying or in closely related degree programs.

PURPOSE:
To promote study in the surveying and mapping professions.

LEGAL BASIS:
Nonprofit educational organization.

ELIGIBILITY:
Nominees must be members of the American Congress on Surveying and Mapping. Student applicants must be enrolled in four-year degree programs in surveying or in closely related degree programs such as geomatics or surveying engineering. Preference will be given to applicants from programs with a significant focus on geodetic surveying.

GEOGRAPHIC RESTRICTIONS:
United States, Canada and South America.

FINANCIAL DATA:
Amount of support per award: $2,000 and an appropriate citation to be presented at the annual meeting.

Total amount of support: $2,000 annually.

COOPERATIVE FUNDING PROGRAMS: Provided by the American Association for Geodetic Surveying and administered by ACSM.

NUMBER OF APPLICANTS MOST RECENT YEAR: 33.

NUMBER OF AWARDS: 1 annually.

APPLICATION INFORMATION:
Required documentation includes:
(1) a completed application form;
(2) proof of membership in ACSM (this will be checked);
(3) a brief yet complete statement indicating educational objectives, future plans of study or research, professional activities and financial need;
(4) at least three letters of recommendation (at least two from faculty members familiar with the student's work);
(5) a complete original official transcript through May of the year prior to when the award will be presented (the others may be copies) and;
(6) Do not send applications by fax or e-mail. Include one set of original transcripts. Mail all documents in one package. In addition, send unofficial transcripts for the fall semester when available.
Duration: One academic year.

PUBLICATIONS:
ACSM Bulletin, a bimonthly magazine; one quarterly Journal.

ADDRESS INQUIRIES TO:
Ilse Genovese
Communications Director
(See address above.)

AMERICAN CONGRESS ON SURVEYING AND MAPPING (ACSM) [2799]

6 Montgomery Village Avenue
Suite 403
Gaithersburg, MD 20879
(240) 632-9716 ext. 109
Fax: (240) 632-1321

E-MAIL ADDRESS:
ilse.genovese@acsm.net

WEB SITE ADDRESS:
www.acsm.net

FOUNDED: 1941

AREAS OF INTEREST:
Surveying and surveying technology.

NAME(S) OF PROGRAMS:
- **The Berntsen International Scholarship in Surveying**
- **The Berntsen International Scholarship in Surveying Technology**

TYPE:
Scholarships. Berntsen International Scholarship in Surveying: Annual scholarship award for undergraduate study in four-year degree programs in surveying or in closely related degree programs such as geomatics or surveying engineering.

Berntsen International Scholarship in Surveying Technology: For students enrolled in two-year degree programs in surveying technology.

PURPOSE:
To provide financial assistance to students pursuing two- or four-year degree programs in surveying, surveying technology or closely related fields.

LEGAL BASIS:
Nonprofit, educational organization.

ELIGIBILITY:
The Berntsen International Scholarship in Surveying: Student applicants must be enrolled in four-year degree programs in surveying or in closely related degree programs such as geomatics or surveying engineering.

The Berntsen International Scholarship in Surveying Technology: Student applicants must be enrolled in two-year degree programs in surveying technology.

GEOGRAPHIC RESTRICTIONS:
United States.

FINANCIAL DATA:
Amount of support per award: Berntsen International Scholarship in Surveying: $1,500; Berntsen International Scholarship in Surveying Technology: $500.

COOPERATIVE FUNDING PROGRAMS:
Scholarships are made possible by Berntsen International, Inc., of Madison, WI.

NUMBER OF APPLICANTS MOST RECENT YEAR: 30.

NUMBER OF AWARDS: 1 each annually.

APPLICATION INFORMATION:
Required documentation includes:
(1) a completed application form;
(2) proof of membership in ACSM (this will be checked);
(3) a brief yet complete statement indicating educational objectives, future plans of study or research, professional activities and financial need;
(4) at least three letters of recommendation (at least two from faculty members familiar with the student's work);
(5) a complete original official transcript through May of the year prior to when the award will be presented (the others may be copies) and;
(6) Do not send applications by fax or e-mail. Include one set of original transcripts. Mail all documents in one package. In addition, send unofficial transcripts for the fall semester when available.
Duration: One academic year.
Deadline: Varies.

PUBLICATIONS:
ACSM Bulletin, a bimonthly magazine; one quarterly Journal.

STAFF:
Ilse Genevose, Communications Director

ADDRESS INQUIRIES TO:
Ilse Genovese
Communications Director
(See address above.)

AMERICAN CONGRESS ON SURVEYING AND MAPPING (ACSM) [2800]

6 Montgomery Village Avenue
Suite 403
Gaithersburg, MD 20879
(240) 632-9716 ext. 109
Fax: (240) 632-1321

E-MAIL ADDRESS:
ilse.genovese@acsm.net

WEB SITE ADDRESS:
www.acsm.net

FOUNDED: 1941

AREAS OF INTEREST:
Surveying.

NAME(S) OF PROGRAMS:
- **The Schonstedt Scholarship in Surveying**

TYPE:
Scholarships. For students enrolled in four-year degree programs in surveying or in closely related degree programs such as geomatics or surveying engineering.

PURPOSE:
To encourage and recognize students committed to a career in surveying.

LEGAL BASIS:
Nonprofit educational organization.

ELIGIBILITY:
The Schonstedt Scholarship is for students enrolled in four-year degree programs in surveying or in closely related degree programs such as geomatics or surveying engineering. Preference will be given to applicants with junior or senior standing.

GEOGRAPHIC RESTRICTIONS:
United States, Canada and South America.

FINANCIAL DATA:
Amount of support per award: $1,500.
Total amount of support: $1,500 annually.

COOPERATIVE FUNDING PROGRAMS: Scholarship is made possible by a donation from the Schonstedt Instrument Company of Kearneysville, WV.

NUMBER OF APPLICANTS MOST RECENT YEAR: 33.

NUMBER OF AWARDS: 1 annually.

APPLICATION INFORMATION:
Required documentation includes:
(1) a completed application form;
(2) proof of membership in ACSM (this will be checked);
(3) a brief yet complete statement indicating educational objectives, future plans of study or research, professional activities and financial need;
(4) at least three letters of recommendation (at least two from faculty members familiar with the student's work) and;
(5) a complete original official transcript through May of the year prior to when the award will be presented (the others may be copies) and;
(6) Do not send applications by fax or e-mail. Include one set of original transcripts. Mail all documents in one package. In addition, send unofficial transcripts for the fall semester when available.
Duration: One academic year.
Deadline: Varies.

PUBLICATIONS:
ACSM Bulletin, a bimonthly magazine; one quarterly Journal.

ADDRESS INQUIRIES TO:
Ilse Genovese
Communications Director
(See address above.)

AMERICAN CONGRESS ON SURVEYING AND MAPPING (ACSM) [2801]

6 Montgomery Village Avenue
Suite 403
Gaithersburg, MD 20879
(240) 632-9716 ext. 113
Fax: (240) 632-1321

E-MAIL ADDRESS:
ilse.genovese@acsm.net

WEB SITE ADDRESS:
www.acsm.net

FOUNDED: 1941

AREAS OF INTEREST:
Surveying.

NAME(S) OF PROGRAMS:
- **NSPS Board of Governors Scholarship**
- **The NSPS Scholarships**

TYPE:
Scholarships.

PURPOSE:
To recognize outstanding surveying students; to encourage qualified candidates to pursue an undergraduate degree in surveying.

LEGAL BASIS:
Nonprofit foundation.

ELIGIBILITY:
NSPS Board of Governors Scholarship applicants must be enrolled in studies in surveying or in closely related degree programs and entering their junior year of study in a four-year degree program of their choice (either full- or part-time) and must have maintained a minimum 3.0 grade point average.

The NSPS Scholarships are awarded to students enrolled in four-year degree programs in surveying or in closely related degree programs such as geomatics or surveying engineering. The Scholarships are intended to recognize outstanding students enrolled full-time in undergraduate surveying programs.

GEOGRAPHIC RESTRICTIONS:
United States.

FINANCIAL DATA:
Amount of support per award: $1,000.
Total amount of support: $3,000 annually.

COOPERATIVE FUNDING PROGRAMS: Scholarship is made possible by the National Society of Professional Surveyors.

NUMBER OF AWARDS: NSPS Board of Governors Scholarship: 1; The NSPS Scholarships: 2.

APPLICATION INFORMATION:
Applicants must submit (in the following order):
(1) a completed application form;
(2) proof of membership in ACSM (this will be checked);
(3) a brief yet complete statement indicating educational objectives, future plans of study or research, professional activities and financial need;
(4) at least three letters of recommendation (at least two from faculty members familiar with the student's work);
(5) a complete original official transcript through May of the year prior to when the award will be presented (the others may be copies) and;
(6) Do not send applications by fax or e-mail. Include one set of original transcripts. Mail all documents in one package. In addition, send unofficial transcripts for the fall semester when available.
Duration: One academic year.
Deadline: Varies.

ADDRESS INQUIRIES TO:
Ilse Genovese
Communications Director
(See address above.)

AMERICAN INSTITUTE OF CHEMICAL ENGINEERS (AICHE) [2802]

3 Park Avenue, 19th Floor
New York, NY 10016
(203) 702-7660
Fax: (203) 775-5177

E-MAIL ADDRESS:
awards@aiche.org

WEB SITE ADDRESS:
www.aiche.org

FOUNDED: 1908

AREAS OF INTEREST:
Chemical engineering.

NAME(S) OF PROGRAMS:
- **Computing in Chemical Engineering Award**

TYPE:
Awards/prizes.

YEAR PROGRAM STARTED: 1987

PURPOSE:
To recognize outstanding contributions in the application of computing and systems technology to chemical engineering.

LEGAL BASIS:
Nonprofit.

ELIGIBILITY:
Nominees are not required to be members of the division or the Institute.

GEOGRAPHIC RESTRICTIONS:
United States.

FINANCIAL DATA:
Amount of support per award: $3,000 and a plaque.

COOPERATIVE FUNDING PROGRAMS: Sponsored by The Dow Chemical Company and Mitsubishi Chemical Company.

APPLICATION INFORMATION:
Nominations must include a brief professional history of the nominee and specify how the nominee meets the criteria of the award. Three to five supporting letters, citing specific contributions and the reasons for their value, are required. Eight copies of the nomination form should be submitted to the designated division award committee chair. Electronic submission is preferred. Nominations will remain active for three years.
Duration: One-time award.
Deadline: April 15.

PUBLICATIONS:
Awards announcement; award nomination form.

ADDRESS INQUIRIES TO:
Professor Francis J. Doyle, III
University of California, Santa Barbara
Department of Chemical Engineering
Tel: (805) 893-8133
E-mail: doyle@engineering.ucsb.edu

AMERICAN INSTITUTE OF CHEMICAL ENGINEERS (AICHE) [2803]

3 Park Avenue, 19th Floor
New York, NY 10016
(203) 702-7660
Fax: (203) 775-5177

E-MAIL ADDRESS:
awards@aiche.org

WEB SITE ADDRESS:
www.aiche.org

FOUNDED: 1908

AREAS OF INTEREST:
Chemical engineering.

NAME(S) OF PROGRAMS:
- **Minority Scholarship Awards for College Students**

TYPE:
Scholarships.

YEAR PROGRAM STARTED: 1994

PURPOSE:
To encourage minority undergraduate study of chemical engineering.

LEGAL BASIS:
Nonprofit.

ELIGIBILITY:
Nominations are accepted from AIChE student chapters or chemical engineering clubs. Nominees must be AIChE national student members at the time of nomination, undergraduates in chemical engineering during the academic year, and members of a disadvantaged minority group that is underrepresented in chemical engineering. Chapters may nominate a student who will complete the chemical engineering Baccalaureate degree requirements in mid-year, but such nominees, if successful, will receive prorated awards. The selection of winners will be based on the nominee's academic record, participation in AIChE student and professional activities, career objectives, and financial need.

GEOGRAPHIC RESTRICTIONS:
United States.

FINANCIAL DATA:
Amount of support per award: $1,000.

NUMBER OF AWARDS: 10.

APPLICATION INFORMATION:
Duration: One-time award. No students may apply again.
Deadline: June 15.

PUBLICATIONS:
AIChExtra; awards nomination form.

AMERICAN NUCLEAR SOCIETY (ANS) [2804]

555 North Kensington Avenue
LaGrange Park, IL 60526
(708) 352-6611
Fax: (708) 352-0499

E-MAIL ADDRESS:
outreach@ans.org

WEB SITE ADDRESS:
www.ans.org

FOUNDED: 1954

AREAS OF INTEREST:
Nuclear science, nuclear engineering or nuclear-related field.

NAME(S) OF PROGRAMS:
- **Delayed Education for Women Scholarship**
- **John and Muriel Landis Scholarships**

TYPE:
Scholarships. Delayed Education for Women Scholarship is designed for women in a nuclear-related field whose formal studies have been delayed or interrupted for at least one year.

Landis Scholarships are administered by the ANS NEED Committee, and are awarded to undergraduate and graduate students who have greater-than-average financial need.

PURPOSE:
To encourage mature women whose formal studies in the field of nuclear science, nuclear engineering, or a nuclear-related field have been delayed or interrupted for at least one year; to provide financial aid to students with greater-than-average need.

ELIGIBILITY:
Delayed Education for Women Scholarship: Applicants must have experienced a minimum of a one-year delay or interruption of their undergraduate studies and must be entering a four-year curriculum. Those at graduate level of education can also apply. Applicants must also have proven academic ability as well as demonstrated financial need. An applicant must be a U.S. citizen or possess a permanent resident visa, be enrolled in a U.S. college or university, and must be sponsored by an ANS local section, division, student branch, committee or organization member. More than one applicant can be sponsored by any of these organizations. Those applying must be enrolled in a course of study relating to a degree in nuclear science or nuclear engineering in a U.S. institution. Applicants must be mature women whose undergraduate studies in nuclear science, nuclear engineering, or a nuclear-related field have been delayed.

Landis Scholarships: Applicants must be undergraduates or graduates who are U.S. citizens or permanent residents. The student must be enrolled in a course of study relating to a degree in nuclear science or nuclear engineering in a U.S. institution. The applicant also must have greater-than-average financial need. Consideration is given to conditions or experiences that render the student disadvantaged (poor high school/undergraduate preparation, etc.). Qualified high school seniors are eligible to apply for this scholarship.

GEOGRAPHIC RESTRICTIONS:
United States.

FINANCIAL DATA:
Scholarship funds may be used by the student to defray any bona fide education costs including tuition, books, room and board.

Amount of support per award: $5,000.

COOPERATIVE FUNDING PROGRAMS: Delayed Education for Women Scholarship: Sponsored jointly by the NEED and Professional Women in the ANS Committees.

NUMBER OF AWARDS: Delayed Education for Women Scholarship: 1; Landis Scholarships: Up to 8.

APPLICATION INFORMATION:
Separate applications are required. Forms can be downloaded at the web site.

Duration: One year. Nonrenewable.

Deadline: February 1.

ADDRESS INQUIRIES TO:
Scholarship Coordinator
(See address above.)

AMERICAN NUCLEAR SOCIETY (ANS)   [2805]
555 North Kensington Avenue
LaGrange Park, IL 60526
(708) 352-6611
Fax: (708) 352-0499

E-MAIL ADDRESS:
outreach@ans.org

WEB SITE ADDRESS:
www.ans.org

FOUNDED: 1954

AREAS OF INTEREST:
Nuclear science, nuclear engineering or nuclear-related field.

NAME(S) OF PROGRAMS:
● **Angelo F. Bisesti Memorial Scholarship**
● **Robert G. Lacy Memorial Scholarship**

TYPE:
Scholarships. Scholarship awards for undergraduate students who have completed two or more years in a course of study leading to a degree in nuclear science, nuclear engineering or a nuclear-related field.

PURPOSE:
To support higher education in the nuclear science field.

ELIGIBILITY:
An applicant must be a U.S. citizen or possess a permanent resident visa, be enrolled in a U.S. college or university, and must be sponsored by an ANS local section, division, student branch, committee or organization member. More than one applicant can be sponsored by any of these organizations.

FINANCIAL DATA:
Amount of support per award: $2,000.

NUMBER OF AWARDS: 1 each.

APPLICATION INFORMATION:
Scholarship application, transcript, letter of recommendation and three confidential reference forms must all be mailed together as a complete packet to ANS Headquarters, to the attention of Scholarship Coordinator. Application should be mailed at least seven days prior to the deadline. If all of the above forms are not included in the same packet, it will be considered an incomplete application. An incomplete packet could delay the scholarship application process. Please send a self-addressed, stamped envelope for a mail request.

Applicants must include the current year in school, the college or university he or she will be attending, and the intended major.

Duration: One year. Nonrenewable.

Deadline: February 1.

ADDRESS INQUIRIES TO:
Scholarship Coordinator
(See address above.)

AMERICAN NUCLEAR SOCIETY (ANS)   [2806]
555 North Kensington Avenue
LaGrange Park, IL 60526
(708) 352-6611
Fax: (708) 352-0499

E-MAIL ADDRESS:
outreach@ans.org

WEB SITE ADDRESS:
www.ans.org

FOUNDED: 1954

AREAS OF INTEREST:
Nuclear science, nuclear engineering or nuclear-related field.

NAME(S) OF PROGRAMS:
● **ANS Graduate Scholarships**
● **Everitt P. Blizard Scholarship**
● **Robert A. Dannels Memorial Graduate Scholarship**
● **Verne R. Dapp Memorial Scholarship**
● **Walter Meyer Scholarship**
● **James F. Schumar Scholarship**

TYPE:
Scholarships. Blizard Scholarship is for students pursuing graduate studies in the field of radiation protection and shielding.

Dapp and Meyer Scholarships are for full-time graduate students in a program leading to an advanced degree in nuclear science or nuclear engineering. The Dapp is awarded in odd-numbered years. The Meyer is awarded in even-numbered years.

Schumar Scholarship is for a student pursuing graduate studies in materials science and technology for nuclear applications.

PURPOSE:
To support higher education in the field of nuclear science.

ELIGIBILITY:
An applicant must be a U.S. citizen or possess a permanent resident visa, be enrolled in a U.S. university and must be sponsored by an ANS local section, division, student branch, committee or organization member. More than one applicant can be sponsored by any of these organizations.

The Dannels Scholarship is for a graduate-level course of study leading toward a degree in mathematics and computation. Only U.S. citizens or persons possessing a permanent resident visa are eligible. Nomination of handicapped persons is encouraged.

The Dapp Scholarship is awarded on the graduate level toward a degree in nuclear engineering at an accredited institution in the U.S. The nominee must be an ANS Student Section member. Only U.S. citizens or persons possessing a permanent resident visa are eligible.

GEOGRAPHIC RESTRICTIONS:
United States.

FINANCIAL DATA:
Scholarship funds may be used to defray any bona fide education costs including tuition, books, room and board.

Amount of support per award: Blizard, Dapp, Meyer, Schumar and ANS Graduate Scholarships: $3,000 each; Dannels Scholarship: $3,500.

NUMBER OF AWARDS: Blizard, Dapp, Meyer, Schumar and Dannels: 1 each; ANS Graduate Scholarships: Up to 29.

APPLICATION INFORMATION:
Scholarship application, transcript, letter of recommendation and three confidential reference forms must all be mailed together as a complete packet to ANS Headquarters, to the attention of Scholarship Coordinator. Application should be mailed at least seven days prior to the deadline. If all of the above forms are not included in the same packet, it will be considered an incomplete application. An incomplete packet could delay the scholarship application process. Please send a self-addressed, stamped envelope for a mail request.

Applicants must include the current year in school, the college or university he or she will be attending, and the intended major.

Duration: One year. Nonrenewable.

Deadline: February 1.

ADDRESS INQUIRIES TO:
Scholarship Coordinator
(See address above.)

AMERICAN NUCLEAR SOCIETY (ANS) [2807]

555 North Kensington Avenue
LaGrange Park, IL 60526
(708) 352-6611
Fax: (708) 352-0499

E-MAIL ADDRESS:
outreach@ans.org

WEB SITE ADDRESS:
www.ans.org

FOUNDED: 1954

AREAS OF INTEREST:
Nuclear science, nuclear engineering and nuclear-related field.

NAME(S) OF PROGRAMS:
● **Pittsburgh Local Section Scholarship**

TYPE:
Scholarships. Two Pittsburgh Local Section Scholarships: one for a graduate student (studying nuclear science and technology) and one for an undergraduate student (studying nuclear science and technology) who either have some affiliation with western Pennsylvania or who attend school at a nearby university within the region.

PURPOSE:
To support higher education in nuclear science.

ELIGIBILITY:
An applicant must be a U.S. citizen or possess a permanent resident visa, be enrolled in a U.S. college or university, and must be sponsored by an ANS local section, division, student branch, committee or organization member. More than one applicant can be sponsored by any of these organizations.

GEOGRAPHIC RESTRICTIONS:
Western Pennsylvania.

FINANCIAL DATA:
Scholarship funds may be used to defray any bona fide education costs including tuition, books, room and board.

Amount of support per award:
Undergraduate: $2,000; Graduate: $3,500.

NUMBER OF AWARDS: Undergraduate and Graduate: 1 each.

APPLICATION INFORMATION:
Scholarship application, transcript, letter of recommendation and three confidential reference forms must all be mailed together as a complete packet to ANS Headquarters, to the attention of Scholarship Coordinator. Application should be mailed at least seven days prior to the deadline. If all of the above forms are not included in the same packet, it will be considered an incomplete application. An incomplete packet could delay the scholarship application process. Please send a self-addressed, stamped envelope for a mail request.

Applicants must include the current year in school, the college or university he or she will be attending, and the intended major.

Duration: One year. Nonrenewable.

Deadline: February 1.

ADDRESS INQUIRIES TO:
Scholarship Coordinator
(See address above.)

AMERICAN NUCLEAR SOCIETY (ANS) [2808]

555 North Kensington Avenue
LaGrange Park, IL 60526
(708) 352-6611
Fax: (708) 352-0499

E-MAIL ADDRESS:
outreach@ans.org

WEB SITE ADDRESS:
www.ans.org

FOUNDED: 1954

AREAS OF INTEREST:
Nuclear science, nuclear engineering or nuclear-related fields.

NAME(S) OF PROGRAMS:
● **Decommissioning, Decontamination and Reutilization (DD&R) Scholarship**

TYPE:
Scholarships. For an undergraduate student in the engineering or science discipline that is associated with either decommissioning/decontamination of nuclear facilities, management/characterization of nuclear waste or restoration of the environment.

ELIGIBILITY:
Applicant must be at junior or senior undergraduate level and must be a U.S. citizen or permanent resident. He or she must be enrolled in a course of study relating to a degree in nuclear science or nuclear engineering in a U.S. institution. Additional criteria to be met include:
(1) the student must be enrolled in a curriculum of engineering or science that is associated either with decommissioning/decontamination of nuclear facilities, management/characterization of nuclear waste, restoration of the environment, or nuclear engineering;
(2) the scholarship is limited to U.S. citizens who are enrolled in U.S. schools;
(3) the student will join the American Nuclear Society (ANS);
(4) the student will designate the ANS DDR Division as one of his or her professional divisions and;
(5) he or she will commit to provide student support to the ANS DDR Division at the next ANS meeting after receipt of the scholarship award. (DDR will provide funding for the student's travel to the ANS meeting, including student registration, reasonable transportation, food and lodging.)

FINANCIAL DATA:
Scholarship funds may be used by the student to defray any bona fide education costs including tuition, books, room and board.

Amount of support per award: $3,000.

NUMBER OF AWARDS: 1 annually.

APPLICATION INFORMATION:
Applicant must submit a brief description of long and short-term professional objectives. Scholarship application, transcript, letter of recommendation and three confidential reference forms must all be mailed together as a complete packet to ANS Headquarters, to the attention of Scholarship Coordinator. If all of the above forms are not included in the same packet, it will be considered an incomplete application. An incomplete packet could delay the scholarship application process. Please send a self-addressed, stamped envelope for a mail request.

Applicants must include the current year in school, the college or university he or she will be attending and the intended major.

Duration: One year. Nonrenewable.

Deadline: February 1.

ADDRESS INQUIRIES TO:
Scholarship Coordinator
(See address above.)

AMERICAN NUCLEAR SOCIETY (ANS) [2809]

555 North Kensington Avenue
LaGrange Park, IL 60526
(708) 352-6611
Fax: (708) 352-0499

E-MAIL ADDRESS:
outreach@ans.org

WEB SITE ADDRESS:
www.ans.org

FOUNDED: 1954

AREAS OF INTEREST:
Nuclear science, nuclear engineering or nuclear-related field.

NAME(S) OF PROGRAMS:
● **Raymond DiSalvo Scholarship**
● **Robert T. Liner Scholarship**
● **Operations and Power Division Scholarship**
● **Charles (Tommy) Thomas Memorial Scholarship**

TYPE:
Scholarships. Award for a full-time undergraduate student in a program leading to a degree in nuclear science or nuclear engineering at an accredited institution in the U.S.

ELIGIBILITY:
Applicant must be a U.S. citizen or possess a permanent resident visa.

Academic accomplishments must be substantiated by transcript. Applicants must be sponsored by an ANS local section, division, student branch, committee or organization member.

Charles (Tommy) Thomas Memorial Scholarship: Undergraduate of at least junior year status pursuing a degree in a discipline preparing them for a career dealing with the environmental aspects of nuclear science or nuclear engineering.

GEOGRAPHIC RESTRICTIONS:
United States.

FINANCIAL DATA:
Scholarship funds may be used by the student to defray any bona fide education costs including tuition, fees, books, room and board.

Amount of support per award: Raymond DiSalvo and Robert T. Liner Scholarships: $2,000; Operations and Power Division Scholarship: $2,500; Charles (Tommy) Thomas Memorial Scholarship: $3,000.

NUMBER OF AWARDS: 1 each.

APPLICATION INFORMATION:
Scholarship application, transcript, letter of recommendation and three confidential

reference forms must all be mailed together as a complete packet to ANS Headquarters, to the attention of Scholarship Coordinator. Application should be mailed at least seven days prior to the deadline. If all of the above forms are not included in the same packet, it will be considered an incomplete application. An incomplete packet could delay the scholarship application process.

Additionally, a brief essay is required for the Thomas Memorial Scholarship describing how the applicant perceives environmental science- and engineering-related topics fitting into the nuclear field and how he or she plans to contribute to the field during the course of their professional career.

Duration: One year. Nonrenewable.

Deadline: February 1.

ADDRESS INQUIRIES TO:
Scholarship Coordinator
(See address above.)

AMERICAN NUCLEAR SOCIETY (ANS)

555 North Kensington Avenue
LaGrange Park, IL 60526
(708) 352-6611
Fax: (708) 352-0499

E-MAIL ADDRESS:
outreach@ans.org

WEB SITE ADDRESS:
www.ans.org

TYPE:
Scholarships. Scholarship award to recognize one outstanding undergraduate student or one graduate student pursuing a career in radioanalytical chemistry or analytical applications of nuclear science.

See entry 2191 for full listing.

AMERICAN NUCLEAR SOCIETY (ANS) [2810]

555 North Kensington Avenue
LaGrange Park, IL 60526
(708) 352-6611
Fax: (708) 352-0499

E-MAIL ADDRESS:
outreach@ans.org

WEB SITE ADDRESS:
www.ans.org

FOUNDED: 1954

AREAS OF INTEREST:
Nuclear science, nuclear engineering or nuclear-related fields.

NAME(S) OF PROGRAMS:
- **ANS Undergraduate Scholarships**
- **Joseph R. Dietrich Memorial Scholarship**
- **Alan F. Henry/Paul A. Greebler Memorial Graduate Scholarship**
- **John R. Lamarsh Memorial Scholarship**

TYPE:
Scholarships.

ELIGIBILITY:
Applicants must have completed a minimum of two complete academic years in a four-year nuclear engineering program and must be U.S. citizens or possess a permanent resident visa. Academic accomplishments must be substantiated by transcript. Applicant

must be sponsored by an ANS local section, division, student branch, committee or organization member.

Henry/Greebler Scholarship: Must be a full-time graduate student of a North American university engaged in Master's or Ph.D. research in the area of nuclear reactor physics or radiation transport. Students of all nationalities are eligible.

FINANCIAL DATA:
Scholarship funds may be used by the student to defray any bona fide education costs including tuition, fees, room and board.
Amount of support per award: ANS Undergraduate, Joseph R. Dietrich Memorial and John R. Lamarsh Memorial Scholarships: $2,000; Alan F. Henry/Paul A. Greebler Memorial Graduate Scholarship: $3,500.

NUMBER OF AWARDS: ANS Undergraduate Scholarships: Up to 21; Dietrich, Greebler and Lamarsh Memorial Scholarships: 1 each.

APPLICATION INFORMATION:
Applications are available on the web site or from the ANS headquarters. Please send a self-addressed, stamped envelope for a mail request. Applicants must include the current year in school, the college or university he or she will be attending and the intended major.

Duration: One year. Nonrenewable.

Deadline: February 1.

ADDRESS INQUIRIES TO:
Scholarship Coordinator
(See address above.)

AMERICAN PUBLIC POWER ASSOCIATION (APPA) [2811]

1875 Connecticut Avenue, N.W.
Suite 1200
Washington, DC 20009-5715
(202) 467-2994
Fax: (202) 467-2992

E-MAIL ADDRESS:
deed@publicpower.org

WEB SITE ADDRESS:
www.publicpower.org

FOUNDED: 1980

AREAS OF INTEREST:
Engineering, mathematics and computer science.

NAME(S) OF PROGRAMS:
- **DEED Scholarship**

TYPE:
Internships; Research grants; Scholarships.

YEAR PROGRAM STARTED: 1980

PURPOSE:
To promote the involvement of students studying in energy-related disciplines in the public power industry; to provide host utilities with technical assistance.

ELIGIBILITY:
Open to students conducting research on a project approved by the sponsoring utility who will then submit a final report on the project, describing the activities, cost, bibliography, achievements, problems, results and recommendations. Applicants will not be discriminated against on the basis of sex, race, religion, national origin or citizenship.

FINANCIAL DATA:
Amount of support per award: $4,000.
Total amount of support: Up to $40,000 per year.

APPLICATION INFORMATION:
Applications must be sent from a DEED member utility and must be dated on the last page by an authorized individual at the utility.
Deadline: February 15 and October 15.

ADDRESS INQUIRIES TO:
Khadija Pounsel, DEED Assistant
(See address above.)

AMERICAN SOCIETY FOR ENGINEERING EDUCATION [2812]

1818 N Street, N.W., Suite 600
Washington, DC 20036
(202) 331-3552
Fax: (202) 463-1401

E-MAIL ADDRESS:
sffp@asee.org

WEB SITE ADDRESS:
www.asee.org/sffp

AREAS OF INTEREST:
Science, engineering and mathematics.

NAME(S) OF PROGRAMS:
- **USAF Summer Faculty Fellowship Program**

TYPE:
Fellowships. Research fellowship.

PURPOSE:
To complement research efforts and build critical links between Air Force scientists and counterparts in the academic community.

ELIGIBILITY:
Must be a full-time faculty member of an accredited Baccalaureate-granting U.S. college, university or technical institution, and have earned a Ph.D. in science or engineering. No other employment or remuneration is permitted during the period of the award, eight to 12 weeks between April 29 to September 30.

GEOGRAPHIC RESTRICTIONS:
United States.

FINANCIAL DATA:
Amount of support per award: Assistant Professor: $1,300 per week; Associate Professor: $1,500 per week; Full Professor: $1,700 per week.
Total amount of support: Varies.

NUMBER OF APPLICANTS MOST RECENT YEAR: 265.

NUMBER OF AWARDS: 100.

APPLICATION INFORMATION:
Each applicant must get approval to apply to a program from the Advisor before uploading his or her proposal. Application opens August 1. Applications, curriculum vitae and references must be submitted electronically.

Duration: One summer.

Deadline: Late November.

ADDRESS INQUIRIES TO:
Jessica Sabo, Program Manager
(See address above.)

AMERICAN SOCIETY FOR ENGINEERING EDUCATION [2813]

1818 N Street, N.W., Suite 600
Washington, DC 20036-2479
(202) 331-3500
Fax: (202) 265-8504

E-MAIL ADDRESS:
projects@asee.org

WEB SITE ADDRESS:
www.asee.org

FOUNDED: 1893

AREAS OF INTEREST:
Engineering education programs and scientific research in government and industry.

NAME(S) OF PROGRAMS:
- **Department of Defense National Defense Science and Engineering Graduate Fellowship Program (NDSEG)**
- **Office of Naval Research-ASEE Summer Faculty and Sabbatical Leave Program**
- **Summer Research Opportunity Program**

TYPE:
Awards/prizes; Fellowships; Professorships; Research grants; Visiting scholars.

YEAR PROGRAM STARTED: 1964

ELIGIBILITY:
The Department of Defense National Defense Science and Engineering Graduate Fellowship Program is for students at or near the beginning of their graduate study in science or engineering. Applicants must be citizens or nationals of the U.S.

Office of Naval Research-ASEE Summer Faculty and Sabbatical Leave Programs are for U.S. citizens and legal permanent residents who hold teaching or research appointments at U.S. colleges and universities.

FINANCIAL DATA:
Amount of support per award: Varies.
Total amount of support: Varies.

NUMBER OF AWARDS: NDSEG: Approximately 200 new awards for the year 2010.

AMERICAN SOCIETY FOR ENGINEERING EDUCATION [2814]

1818 N Street, N.W., Suite 600
Washington, DC 20036
(202) 350-5763
(202) 331-3558
Fax: (202) 265-8504

E-MAIL ADDRESS:
postdocs@asee.org

WEB SITE ADDRESS:
www.asee.org/nrl

FOUNDED: 1893

AREAS OF INTEREST:
Engineering education programs, scientific research in government, industry and the military.

NAME(S) OF PROGRAMS:
- **Naval Research Laboratory (NRL) Postdoctoral Fellowship Program**

TYPE:
Fellowships. Offered at Naval research and development centers and laboratories. NRL is charged with developing technologies that will support Naval Forces in meeting future operational needs. Scientists and fellows working at NRL pursue research on subjects including, but not limited to, processing, biomedicine, logistics, command control and intelligence, training and oceanography.

YEAR PROGRAM STARTED: 2002

PURPOSE:
To significantly increase the involvement of creative and highly trained scientists and engineers from academia and industry in scientific and technical areas of interest and relevance to the Navy.

LEGAL BASIS:
Special interest society.

ELIGIBILITY:
Applicants must be U.S. citizens and permanent residents and must be eligible for a Department of Defense security clearance of "Secret." In most cases, participants will be permitted to do research pending completion of the security clearance. All appointments are contingent upon fellows obtaining the appropriate level of security clearance. Prior to appointment, participants must present evidence of having received the Ph.D., Sc.D. or other earned research doctoral degree recognized in U.S. as equivalent to the Ph.D. within seven years of the date of application or must present acceptable evidence of having completed all formal academic requirements for one of these degrees. No support to applicants who received prior postdoctoral appointment under any program at the same Navy laboratory. No appointments or denials based on grounds of race, creed, color, national origin, age or sex.

GEOGRAPHIC RESTRICTIONS:
United States.

FINANCIAL DATA:
Awards include stipend, insurance, relocation expenses and travel.
Amount of support per award: Up to $73,000.
Total amount of support: Varies.

NUMBER OF AWARDS: Approximately 40 new appointments each year.

APPLICATION INFORMATION:
Applicants should contact the research facility of interest to develop a suitable research proposal. Proposals developed closely with the proposed host facility stand the greatest chance of success in the selection process. A proposal should be no more than 10 pages, be concise, and address a problem of mutual interest to the applicant and Navy research facility.
Duration: One year. Renewable for a second and third year with satisfactory performance and availability of funds.

PUBLICATIONS:
Program announcement.

STAFF:
Shannon Koonce, Program Manager

ADDRESS INQUIRIES TO:
NRL Postdoctoral Program
Contracts/Grants Office
(See address above.)

THE AMERICAN SOCIETY FOR NONDESTRUCTIVE TESTING, INC.

1711 Arlingate Lane
Columbus, OH 43228
(614) 274-6003
(800) 222-2768
Fax: (614) 274-6899

E-MAIL ADDRESS:
sdille@asnt.org

WEB SITE ADDRESS:
www.asnt.org

TYPE:
Scholarships.

See entry 1777 for full listing.

AMERICAN SOCIETY OF CIVIL ENGINEERS [2815]

1801 Alexander Bell Drive
Reston, VA 20191-4400
(703) 295-6300 ext. 6106
(800) 548-2723
Fax: (703) 295-6132

E-MAIL ADDRESS:
student@asce.org

WEB SITE ADDRESS:
www.asce.org

FOUNDED: 1852

AREAS OF INTEREST:
Civil engineering.

NAME(S) OF PROGRAMS:
- **O.H. Ammann Research Fellowship in Structural Engineering**
- **Trent R. Dames and William W. Moore Fellowship**
- **Freeman Fellowship**
- **Jack E. Leisch Memorial National Graduate Fellowship**
- **J. Waldo Smith Hydraulic Fellowship**
- **Samuel Fletcher Tapman ASCE Student Chapter Scholarship**
- **Arthur S. Tuttle Memorial Scholarship**

TYPE:
Fellowships; Grants-in-aid; Research grants; Scholarships. Scholarships, fellowships and grants for research; undergraduate and graduate studies in civil engineering fields from ASCE endowments, operation or other funds.

J. Waldo Smith Hydraulic Fellowship is awarded triannually, Trent R. Dames and William W. Moore Fellowships are awarded biannually, and all others are awarded annually.

YEAR PROGRAM STARTED: 1924

PURPOSE:
To aid and encourage research and studies in civil engineering.

LEGAL BASIS:
Incorporated professional organization.

ELIGIBILITY:
Qualified engineers or engineering undergraduate or graduate students with appropriate interests are eligible to apply. Undergraduate students must be enrolled at an ABET-accredited university, be a member of an ASCE student chapter and also be a national student member. (A list of schools that have student chapters is available from the address above.) Membership applications may be submitted along with scholarship applications.

FINANCIAL DATA:
Amount of support per award: $2,000 to $10,000.

APPLICATION INFORMATION:
Application forms are available to members only (exception: Trent R. Dames and William W. Moore Fellowship). Application for membership may be requested and included in scholarship application. Details should be requested from the Society.

PUBLICATIONS:
Scholarships/Fellowships brochure.

OFFICERS:
Pat Natale, Executive Director
Jim O'Brien, Managing Director of
Professional and Educational Activities

ADDRESS INQUIRIES TO:
Ping Wei
Director of Educational Activities
(See address above.)

AMERICAN SOCIETY OF HEATING, REFRIGERATING AND AIR-CONDITIONING ENGINEERS, INC.   [2816]

1791 Tullie Circle, N.E.
Atlanta, GA 30329
(404) 636-8400
Fax: (404) 321-5478

E-MAIL ADDRESS:
mvaughn@ashrae.org

WEB SITE ADDRESS:
www.ashrae.org

FOUNDED: 1894

AREAS OF INTEREST:
Engineering, environmental technology,
technical assistance, public health and
conservation.

CONSULTING OR VOLUNTEER SERVICES:
Cooperative research with government
agencies and other organizations by
supplying ASHRAE expertise, usually in the
form of an advisory committee.

NAME(S) OF PROGRAMS:
● **ASHRAE Research Grants**

TYPE:
Research contracts. Institutional grants for
basic research and technical studies
concerned with the arts and sciences of
heating, refrigeration, air conditioning and
ventilation.

YEAR PROGRAM STARTED: 1912

PURPOSE:
To increase the amount and accuracy of
fundamental information in the fields of
heating, refrigeration, air
conditioning/ventilation and related areas and
to make this information available.

LEGAL BASIS:
Organization exempt under 501(c)(3) of the
Internal Revenue Code.

ELIGIBILITY:
Accredited institutions of higher learning
may apply with appropriate proposals.

FINANCIAL DATA:
Amount of support per award: $5,000 to
$250,000 per year.
Total amount of support: $2,900,000 for the
year 2010-11.

NUMBER OF AWARDS: 60 for the year 2010-11.

APPLICATION INFORMATION:
Applications take the form of a proposal with
detailed information concerning its
preparation available upon request to the
Manager of Research at the address above.
Duration: Support is for up to three years,
with the possibility of extension.
Deadline: Applications may be submitted
throughout the year; however, proposals are
usually acted upon only in January and June.

ADDRESS INQUIRIES TO:
Michael R. Vaughn, Manager of Research
and Technical Services
(See address above.)

AMERICAN SOCIETY OF HEATING, REFRIGERATING AND AIR-CONDITIONING ENGINEERS, INC.   [2817]

1791 Tullie Circle, N.E.
Atlanta, GA 30329
(404) 636-8400
Fax: (404) 321-5478

E-MAIL ADDRESS:
mvaughn@ashrae.org

WEB SITE ADDRESS:
www.ashrae.org

FOUNDED: 1894

AREAS OF INTEREST:
Engineering, environmental technology,
technical assistance, public health and
conservation.

NAME(S) OF PROGRAMS:
● **ASHRAE Graduate Grant-in-Aid Program**

TYPE:
Grants-in-aid; Research grants. Support for
projects of original research concerned with
the arts and sciences of heating, refrigeration,
air-conditioning/ventilation and related areas.

YEAR PROGRAM STARTED: 1968

PURPOSE:
To stimulate interest in the areas of heating,
refrigeration, air-conditioning and ventilation
through the encouragement of original
research in these fields.

LEGAL BASIS:
Organization exempt under 501(c)(3) of the
Internal Revenue Code.

ELIGIBILITY:
Qualified graduate engineering students
capable of carrying out appropriate and
scholarly research are eligible to apply.

FINANCIAL DATA:
Amount of support per award: $10,000.
Total amount of support: $210,000 for the
year 2010-11.

NUMBER OF APPLICANTS MOST RECENT YEAR:
35.

NUMBER OF AWARDS: 20 for the year ended
June 2010.

APPLICATION INFORMATION:
Prospective applicants should complete the
official Grant-in-Aid application containing
the following:
(1) significance of proposed research;
(2) outline or plan of procedure;
(3) approximate budget and extent to which
the applicant's institution will support the
work;
(4) plans for seeking other funds for this or
related work;
(5) anticipated plans for publication of
research results;
(6) student's name and qualifications and;
(7) faculty advisor's and institution's
qualifications to do the work.
Duration: Grants are usually awarded for a
maximum period of one year.
Deadline: Applications should be submitted
by or before December 15, for consideration
at review meeting held in January.

OFFICERS:
Gordon Holness, President
Lynn Bellenger, President-Elect
Jeff Littleton, Executive Vice President and
Secretary

ADDRESS INQUIRIES TO:
Michael R. Vaughn, Manager of
Research and Technical Services
(See address above.)

THE AMERICAN SOCIETY OF MECHANICAL ENGINEERS AUXILIARY, INC.   [2818]

3 Park Avenue, MS-RB
New York, NY 10016-5990
(212) 591-7650
Fax: (212) 591-7739

E-MAIL ADDRESS:
bigleyr@asme.org

WEB SITE ADDRESS:
www.asme.org/about-asme/scholarship-and-
loans/the-asme-auxiliary,-inc-

FOUNDED: 1923

AREAS OF INTEREST:
Mechanical engineering students.

NAME(S) OF PROGRAMS:
● **ASME/Auxiliary FIRST Clarke Scholarship**
● **Allen J. Baldwin Scholarship**
● **Berna Lou Cartwright Scholarship**
● **Sylvia W. Farny Scholarship**
● **Agnes Malakate Kezios Scholarship**
● **Elisabeth M. and Winchell M. Parsons Scholarship**
● **Rice-Cullimore Scholarship**
● **Marjorie Roy Rothermel Scholarship**
● **Charles B. Scharp Scholarship**
● **Student Loan Fund**

TYPE:
Scholarships. Student loans. ASME Auxiliary
FIRST Clarke Scholarship is for incoming
freshman enrolling in a mechanical
engineering program.

Baldwin, Cartwright, Farny, Kezios and
Scharp Scholarships are for undergraduate
students in mechanical engineering.

Parsons and Rothermel Scholarships are for
graduate students with a degree in
mechanical engineering, to be used to pursue
a Master's degree in mechanical engineering.

Rice-Cullimore Scholarship is for foreign
students at the graduate level.

Student Loan Fund is for juniors, seniors or
graduate students enrolled as degree
candidates in good standing.

YEAR PROGRAM STARTED: 1924

PURPOSE:
To give financial assistance to mechanical
engineering students.

LEGAL BASIS:
Incorporated organization.

ELIGIBILITY:
Applicants must be U.S. citizens, enrolled in
a degree program in a school with accredited
mechanical engineering curriculum and
members of the ASME for Cartwright and
Rothermel Scholarships and Student Loans.
Applicants must be foreign students, selected
in their home country, who meet the
requirements of the sponsor in their home
country who holds a contract with the
International Institute of Education for the
Rice-Cullimore Scholarship.

FINANCIAL DATA:
Amount of support per award: All
Scholarships (Baldwin, Cartwright, Farny,
Kezios, Rice-Cullimore, Rothermel and
Scharp): $2,000; Student Loans: $5,000
maximum.
Total amount of support: Varies.

NUMBER OF APPLICANTS MOST RECENT YEAR:
Undergraduate Scholarships: 16; Rothermel:
5; Student Loans: 3.

NUMBER OF AWARDS: Undergraduate
Scholarships: 4; Rothermel: 1; Student
Loans: 3.

APPLICATION INFORMATION:
Duration: One year.
Deadline: Scholarships: March 15.
Notification April 15.

PUBLICATIONS:
Application guidelines; scholarship forms;
applications.

OFFICERS:
Karen Malesky, President
Kay Simmons, Executive Vice President
Stella Seiders, Treasurer
Janet Watson, Recording Secretary
Vatsala Menon, Corresponding Secretary

ADDRESS INQUIRIES TO:
RuthAnn Bigley, Coordinator, Governance
(See address above.)

AMERICAN SOCIETY OF NAVAL
ENGINEERS (ASNE)   [2819]
1452 Duke Street
Alexandria, VA 22314-3458
(703) 836-6727
Fax: (703) 836-7491

E-MAIL ADDRESS:
mobrien@navalengineers.org

WEB SITE ADDRESS:
www.navalengineers.org

FOUNDED: 1888

AREAS OF INTEREST:
Naval Engineering includes all arts and
sciences as applied in the research,
development, design, construction, operation,
maintenance and logistic support of surface
and sub-surface ships and marine craft, naval
maritime auxiliaries, aviation and space
systems, combat systems, command control,
electronics and ordnance systems, ocean
structures and associated shore facilities,
which are used by naval and other military
forces and civilian maritime organizations for
the defense and well-being of the Nation.

CONSULTING OR VOLUNTEER SERVICES:
Volunteer Services.

NAME(S) OF PROGRAMS:
● **ASNE Scholarship Program**

TYPE:
Scholarships. Stipend for tuition, fees and
expenses to follow a full-time or co-op
program of study that applies to naval
engineering, such as naval architecture,
marine engineering, ocean engineering,
mechanical engineering, structural
engineering, electrical engineering, electronic
engineering and the physical sciences, as
well as other programs leading to careers
with civilian and military maritime
organizations supporting and developing
work and life at sea.

YEAR PROGRAM STARTED: 1979

PURPOSE:
To encourage college students to enter the
field of naval engineering; to support naval
engineers seeking advanced education in the
field.

LEGAL BASIS:
Nonprofit professional society.

ELIGIBILITY:
Support will be limited to the last year of
undergraduate education or one year of
graduate education in an accredited college
or university. Candidates must be U.S.
citizens and must have demonstrated or
expressed a genuine interest in a career in
naval engineering. Graduate students must be
members of ASNE and may apply at time of
application.

Selection criteria will be based on academic
record, work history, professional promise
and interest in naval engineering,
extracurricular activities, recommendations of
college faculty, employers and other character
references. Demonstrated financial need is
not a requirement, but it may be taken into
consideration by the Scholarship Committee.

A scholarship leading to an undergraduate
degree will not be continued for enrollment
in a graduate program; however, a student
may apply for a new award for graduate
study. A scholarship will not be awarded to a
doctoral candidate or to a person already
having an advanced degree.

GEOGRAPHIC RESTRICTIONS:
United States.

FINANCIAL DATA:
The award will be in the form of a check for
the first academic period payable jointly to
the awardee and the college or university that
the student will attend. Transcripts showing
satisfactory performance constitute the basis
for further awards for subsequent academic
periods.
Amount of support per award:
Undergraduate: $3,000; Graduate: $4,000.

NUMBER OF AWARDS: Varies.

APPLICATION INFORMATION:
Duration: One year.
Deadline: March 31. Notification by early
May.

PUBLICATIONS:
Naval Engineers Journal.

IRS IDENTIFICATION NUMBER: 53-0229465

OFFICERS:
Capt. Dennis K. Kruse, USN (Ret.),
Executive Director

SCHOLARSHIP COMMITTEE:
Andrew T. Geyer, Chairman

ADDRESS INQUIRIES TO:
ASNE Scholarship Committee
(See address above.)

AMERICAN SOCIETY OF
SAFETY ENGINEERS   [2820]
1800 East Oakton Street
Des Plaines, IL 60018-2187
(847) 699-2929
Fax: (847) 296-3769

E-MAIL ADDRESS:
customerservice@asse.org

WEB SITE ADDRESS:
www.asse.org

FOUNDED: 1911

AREAS OF INTEREST:
Occupational safety and health.

NAME(S) OF PROGRAMS:
● **Edgar Monsanto Queeny Safety
Professional of the Year Award**

TYPE:
Awards/prizes. Cash honorarium to
Society-selected award winners from
Monsanto Co.

YEAR PROGRAM STARTED: 1980

PURPOSE:
To recognize exemplary achievements in
Safety, Health and Environmental (SHE)
Education.

LEGAL BASIS:
Not-for-profit professional society.

ELIGIBILITY:
Nominee must be a professional member or
member of the Society, and not have received
this award within the past five years. U.S.
members must be active, dues-paying
members of a chapter. Nominee cannot be
running opposed for national ASSE
Executive Committee office or currently
serving on the national Technical and
Professional Recognition Committee.

FINANCIAL DATA:
Amount of support per award: $1,500
honorarium.

NUMBER OF APPLICANTS MOST RECENT YEAR:
1.

NUMBER OF AWARDS: 1 each year.

APPLICATION INFORMATION:
Nominations must be submitted in writing to
the ASSE Technical and Professional
Recognition Committee Chairman,
postmarked no later than November 1, to be
considered that same year. Individual
members, chapters, regions, practice
specialty, councils or the Society Board of
Directors may submit them. Must be
accompanied by a letter of endorsement from
the nominating colleague (Chapter, Regional
Operating Committees, Practice Specialty,
Councils or the Society Board of Directors),
as well as the immediate employment
supervisor, a single-page resume, plus a
petition listing the nominee's achievements.
Submit seven copies.
Deadline: November 1. Award announcement
in early March.

ADDRESS INQUIRIES TO:
Dennis Hudson
Director, Professional Affairs
(See address above.)

ASM MATERIALS EDUCATION
FOUNDATION
9639 Kinsman Road
Materials Park, OH 44073-0002
(440) 338-5151 ext. 5533
(800) 336-5152 ext. 5533
Fax: (440) 338-4634

E-MAIL ADDRESS:
jeane.deatherage@asminternational.org

WEB SITE ADDRESS:
www.asmfoundation.org

TYPE:
Scholarships.

See entry 2845 for full listing.

CANADIAN SOCIETY FOR CHEMICAL ENGINEERING [2821]

130 Slater Street
Suite 550
Ottawa ON K1P 6E2 Canada
(613) 232-6252 ext. 223
Fax: (613) 232-5862

E-MAIL ADDRESS:
awards@cheminst.ca

WEB SITE ADDRESS:
www.cheminst.ca

FOUNDED: 1945

AREAS OF INTEREST:
Chemical engineering.

NAME(S) OF PROGRAMS:
● **The CSChE Chemical Engineering Local Section Scholarships**
● **SNC-LAVALIN Plant Design Competition**

TYPE:
Scholarships. The CSChE Chemical Engineering Local Section Scholarships are offered to undergraduate students in chemical engineering about to enter the final year of studies at a Canadian university and will be made for leadership qualities and demonstrated contributions to the Canadian Society for Chemical Engineering, such as participation in student chapters. Two scholarships will be given annually.

The SNC-LAVALIN Plant Design Competition is offered to students enrolled in undergraduate chemical engineering programs at Canadian universities.

PURPOSE:
To promote undergraduate study in chemical engineering and provide financial support for that study.

LEGAL BASIS:
Special interest society.

ELIGIBILITY:
Local Section Scholarships: Applicants must be members of the Canadian Society for Chemical Engineering.

Applicants for the SNC-LAVALIN Plant Design Competition must be individuals and groups of undergraduate students registered in chemical engineering programs in Canadian universities during the current academic year. To minimize the number of projects to be judged, each chemical engineering department may submit no more than two entries.

GEOGRAPHIC RESTRICTIONS:
Canada.

FINANCIAL DATA:
Amount of support per award: Chemical Engineering Local Section: $2,000 each; SNC-LAVALIN Plant Design Competition: $1,000 to the team with the best design.

NUMBER OF AWARDS: 1 per scholarship or award.

APPLICATION INFORMATION:
For the scholarships, applications should contain evidence of academic standing, description of work to be undertaken, letters of reference, and evidence of contributions to the Society.

Entries for the SNC-LAVALIN Plant Design Competition should contain five CD copies of the following:
(1) a short summary, including a simplified flowsheet of the process;
(2) a copy of the final report submitted to the university at the end of the project;
(3) a list of students who performed the work, with their permanent addresses and phone numbers;
(4) the name of the collaborating organization and the engineers who assisted the students and;
(5) a brief description of the assistance provided by that organization.

The entry should be accompanied by a letter from the head of the department of chemical engineering indicating that the information is not confidential and that the summary may be published in *Canadian Chemical News*.

Deadline: Local Section Scholarships: April 30; SNC-LAVALIN Competition: May 15.

PUBLICATIONS:
Announcement.

ADDRESS INQUIRIES TO:
Gale Thirlwall, Awards Manager
(See address above.)

GEORGE WASHINGTON UNIVERSITY [2822]

Department of Electrical and Computer Engineering
801 22nd Street, N.W., Room 607
Washington, DC 20052
(202) 994-6083
Fax: (202) 994-0227

E-MAIL ADDRESS:
zaghloul@gwu.edu

WEB SITE ADDRESS:
www.ece.seas.gwu.edu

FOUNDED: 1821

AREAS OF INTEREST:
Electrical engineering, computer engineering and telecommunications.

NAME(S) OF PROGRAMS:
● **Graduate Teaching Assistantships**

TYPE:
Assistantships. Merit-based awards for graduate studies at George Washington University.

PURPOSE:
To attract high quality graduate students.

LEGAL BASIS:
University.

ELIGIBILITY:
Usually for currently enrolled students. Some fellowships are limited to U.S. citizens. Must have a grade point average of 3.5 on a possible scale of 4.0 and have taken the Graduate Record Examination.

GEOGRAPHIC RESTRICTIONS:
United States.

FINANCIAL DATA:
Amount of support per award: Varies.
Total amount of support: Varies.

APPLICATION INFORMATION:
Graduate students should submit an application for admission to the School of Engineering and Applied Science.
Duration: One academic year. Must reapply for additional funding.

ADDRESS INQUIRIES TO:
Dr. Mona Zaghloul, Chairperson
(See address above.)

GREAT MINDS IN STEM

3900 Whiteside Street
Los Angeles, CA 90063
(323) 262-0997

E-MAIL ADDRESS:
kbbarrera@greatmindsinstem.org

WEB SITE ADDRESS:
www.greatmindsinstem.org

TYPE:
Scholarships.

See entry 2772 for full listing.

INSTITUTE OF INDUSTRIAL ENGINEERS (IIE) [2823]

3577 Parkway Lane, Suite 200
Norcross, GA 30092
(770) 449-0461
Fax: (770) 441-3295

E-MAIL ADDRESS:
bcameron@iienet.org

WEB SITE ADDRESS:
www.iienet.org

FOUNDED: 1948

AREAS OF INTEREST:
The design, improvement and installation of integrated systems of people, material, information, equipment and energy, incorporating specialized knowledge and skills from the mathematical, physical and social sciences, together with the principles and methods of engineering analysis and design to specify, predict and evaluate the results to be obtained from such systems.

NAME(S) OF PROGRAMS:
● **John S.W. Fargher Scholarship**
● **C.B. Gambrell Undergraduate Scholarship**
● **Dwight D. Garden Scholarship**
● **Gilbreth Memorial Fellowship**
● **IIE Council of Fellows Undergraduate Scholarship**
● **John L. Imhoff Scholarship**
● **Harold and Inge Marcus Scholarship**
● **Marvin Mundel Memorial Scholarship**
● **Benjamin Willard Niebel Scholarship**
● **Presidents Scholarship**
● **A.O. Putnam Memorial Scholarship**
● **E.J. Sierleja Memorial Fellowship**
● **Society for Health Systems Scholarship**
● **United Parcel Service Scholarship for Female Students**
● **United Parcel Service Scholarship for Minority Students**
● **Lisa Zaken Award of Excellence**

TYPE:
Fellowships; Scholarships. The Institute supports the advancement of engineering education and research through scholarships and fellowships to recognize and support these types of endeavors.

PURPOSE:
To recognize academic excellence and campus leadership.

LEGAL BASIS:
Nonprofit, international professional membership society.

ELIGIBILITY:
Candidates must be active Institute members enrolled full-time in graduate or undergraduate industrial engineering programs. The nominee's scholastic ability, character, leadership, service, and financial need are all considered.

Membership is not required for the Imhoff Scholarship.

FINANCIAL DATA:
Amount of support per award: Varies per award.

APPLICATION INFORMATION:
Students may not apply directly for scholarships, except for the IIE Council of Fellows award. They must be nominated by their department head or faculty advisor. Nominations must be mailed to the Institute. Call for nominations are sent out at the beginning of each school year in the fall.
Deadline: December 1 (postmark).

STAFF:
Don Greene, Executive Director

ADDRESS INQUIRIES TO:
Bonnie Cameron
Headquarters Operations Administrator
(See address above.)

THE JAMES F. LINCOLN ARC WELDING FOUNDATION [2824]
22801 St. Clair Avenue
Cleveland, OH 44117
(216) 481-8100
Fax: (216) 486-1751

E-MAIL ADDRESS:
innovate@lincolnelectric.com

WEB SITE ADDRESS:
www.lincolnelectric.com
www.jflf.org

FOUNDED: 1936

AREAS OF INTEREST:
Engineering, welded design and fabrication.

NAME(S) OF PROGRAMS:
- **Awards for Achievement in Arc Welded Design, Engineering and Fabrication: College Division**

TYPE:
Awards/prizes. Awards to recognize and reward achievement by engineering and technology students (graduate and undergraduate) in solving design, engineering or fabricating problems involving the knowledge or application of arc welding.

YEAR PROGRAM STARTED: 1956

PURPOSE:
To recognize outstanding work in the welding design and fabrication field.

LEGAL BASIS:
Private corporate foundation.

ELIGIBILITY:
Graduate or undergraduate students enrolled in college or university programs leading to a Bachelor's, Master's or doctoral degree may submit papers completed within a one-year period, ending June 15 of the year of the contest. Papers should represent students' work on design, engineering or fabrication problems relating to any type of building, bridge or other generally stationary structure, any type of machine, product or mechanical apparatus or arc welding research, testing, procedure or process development.

Students to participate in the Undergraduate Division must be enrolled in a four-year or longer curriculum leading to a Bachelor's degree. Students to participate in the Graduate Division must be enrolled in a graduate program leading to a Master's or Doctorate degree. Qualified students may apply individually or jointly in groups of not more than five. Undergraduate students compete for 17 awards, and graduate students compete for 12 awards.

FINANCIAL DATA:
Amount of support per award: $25 to $1,000.

NUMBER OF AWARDS: Varies.

APPLICATION INFORMATION:
Official application materials are available upon request to the Secretary. Any number of entries may be submitted from one school, but no student may participate in more than one entry.
Duration: One year.

EXECUTIVE STAFF:
Roy Morrow, President
Carl Peters, Executive Director
Lori Hurley, Secretary

TRUSTEES AND OFFICERS:
David Manning, Chairman
Duane Miller, Trustee

ADDRESS INQUIRIES TO:
Roy Morrow, President
(See address above.)

LOS ALAMOS NATIONAL LABORATORY
P.O. Box 1663
MS-P125
Los Alamos, NM 87545
(505) 664-6947 ext. 05004
Fax: (505) 606-5901

E-MAIL ADDRESS:
hrstaffing-postdocs@lanl.gov

WEB SITE ADDRESS:
www.lanl.gov/science/postdocs

TYPE:
Fellowships. The Distinguished Postdoctoral Fellowships provide the opportunity for the recipients to collaborate with LANL scientists and engineers on staff-initiated research. Candidates for these awards must display extraordinary ability in scientific research and show clear and definite promise of becoming outstanding leaders in the research they pursue.

See entry 1949 for full listing.

NATIONAL ACTION COUNCIL FOR MINORITIES IN ENGINEERING, INC. (NACME)
440 Hamilton Avenue
Suite 302
White Plains, NY 10601-1813
(914) 539-4010
Fax: (914) 539-4032

E-MAIL ADDRESS:
scholars@nacme.org

WEB SITE ADDRESS:
www.nacme.org

TYPE:
Block grants; Endowments; Fellowships; Scholarships. NACME encourages students to consider engineering as a career and to pursue the requisite preparation in mathematics and science. It motivates high school students and channels them to engineering schools and provides scholarship support and leadership development seminars to its university scholars. The retention of minority students in engineering is a priority issue for NACME.

See entry 1063 for full listing.

THE NATIONAL GEM CONSORTIUM
1430 Duke Street
Alexandria, VA 22314
(703) 562-3646
Fax: (202) 207-2518

E-MAIL ADDRESS:
info@gemfellowship.org

WEB SITE ADDRESS:
www.gemfellowship.org

TYPE:
Conferences/seminars; Fellowships; Internships; Matching gifts. All-expense fellowship for graduate study (tuition and stipend) and paid summer work experience in a scientific or engineering environment.

See entry 1067 for full listing.

NATIONAL RESEARCH COUNCIL OF CANADA
1200 Montreal Road, Building M-58
Ottawa ON K1A 0R6 Canada
(613) 993-1947
Fax: (613) 941-6283

E-MAIL ADDRESS:
info@nrc-cnrc.gc.ca
racoordinator.hrb@nrc-cnrc.gc.ca

WEB SITE ADDRESS:
careers-carrieres.nrc-cnrc.gc.ca
www.nrc-cnrc.gc.ca

TYPE:
Assistantships. Research Associates will be appointed to the staff of the National Research Council on a term basis and will be offered salaries and benefits currently available to members of the continuing staff.

See entry 1954 for full listing.

NATIONAL SCIENCE FOUNDATION [2825]
Directorate for Engineering
Office of Assistant Director
4201 Wilson Boulevard, Room 505
Arlington, VA 22230
(703) 292-8300
(703) 292-8301
Fax: (703) 292-9013

WEB SITE ADDRESS:
www.nsf.gov

FOUNDED: 1950

AREAS OF INTEREST:
Chemical, biochemical and thermal engineering, mechanics, structures and materials engineering, electrical, communications and systems engineering, design, manufacturing and computer engineering, emerging engineering systems, cross-disciplinary research, engineering research centers, civil and environment engineering, earthquake engineering and small business innovation research.

NAME(S) OF PROGRAMS:
- **Directorate for Engineering Grants Program**

TYPE:
Assistantships; Conferences/seminars; Fellowships; Internships; Project/program grants; Research grants; Travel grants; Visiting scholars.

YEAR PROGRAM STARTED: 1984

PURPOSE:
To strengthen U.S. engineering education and research; to focus on areas relevant to national problems by supporting research across the entire range of engineering disciplines and by identifying areas where results are expected to have timely applications.

LEGAL BASIS:
Government agency.

ELIGIBILITY:
Proposals may be submitted by colleges, universities, profit and nonprofit organizations and by state, local or regional governments. Industry, state and local governments and other organizations are eligible to participate. Joint proposals are encouraged.

NSF does not make loans or grants to develop or promote any business venture, technical assistance, pilot plant efforts, research requiring security classification, the development of products for commercial marketing or market research for a particular product or invention.

GEOGRAPHIC RESTRICTIONS:
United States and its territories.

FINANCIAL DATA:
Amount of support per award: $2,000 to $5,000,000. Average $63,000.

APPLICATION INFORMATION:
Informal inquiry to the Directorate for Engineering may be made to determine whether or not a potential project would qualify for support.
Duration: One to five years. Average is approximately 30 months.
Deadline: Proposals may be submitted at any time. Approximately six to eight months are required for consideration of formal proposals.

PUBLICATIONS:
Grants for Research and Education in Science and Engineering; Publications of the National Science Foundation; Guide to Programs.

STAFF:
Dr. Cora Marrett, Acting Deputy Director
Dr. Thomas W. Peterson, Assistant Director, Engineering
Joanne Culbertson, Senior Advisor for Planning and Technology Evaluation

ADDRESS INQUIRIES TO:
Directorate for Engineering
(See address above.)

OAK RIDGE INSTITUTE FOR SCIENCE AND EDUCATION [2826]
P.O. Box 117
Oak Ridge, TN 37831-0117
(865) 574-7798
Fax: (865) 576-1609

E-MAIL ADDRESS:
ruth.keller@orau.org
science.education@orau.org

WEB SITE ADDRESS:
orise.orau.gov/sep/catalog.htm
see.orau.org

FOUNDED: 1946

AREAS OF INTEREST:
Energy-related disciplines and technologies.

NAME(S) OF PROGRAMS:
• **Professional Internship Program**

TYPE:
Internships. Full- and part-time appointments are available for a period of three to 12 months. Assignments afford students the opportunity to apply and practice theories and methods learned in the classroom. Program participants are assigned individual projects that relate to their academic majors, career goals, and the ongoing research and development missions of the facility. They make recommendations or reports regarding their findings or solutions to a staff member of the facility who provides guidance and advice, serves as their research advisor, and reviews their findings.

YEAR PROGRAM STARTED: 1950

PURPOSE:
To provide hands-on research training for students seeking associate, Baccalaureate, or graduate degrees in appropriate disciplines relating to science and engineering education, training and management systems, energy and environment systems, and medical sciences.

LEGAL BASIS:
Government agency.

ELIGIBILITY:
Applicants must be U.S. citizens or permanent residents, at least 18 years of age, and have a cumulative grade point average of 2.50 or higher. Appointments are tenable at the following facilities including the National Energy Technology Laboratory (NETL), Pittsburgh, PA and Savannah River Site, Aiken, SC.

GEOGRAPHIC RESTRICTIONS:
United States.

FINANCIAL DATA:
Amount of support per award: $384 to $850 per week.
Total amount of support: Varies.

NUMBER OF APPLICANTS MOST RECENT YEAR:
300.

APPLICATION INFORMATION:
Contact ORISE for general information and application guidelines.
Duration: Three to 18 months continuously. Renewals possible.
Deadline: February 15, June 1 and October 1.

PUBLICATIONS:
Program announcement; ORISE Resource Guide.

ADDRESS INQUIRIES TO:
Ruth Keller
Science and Engineering Education, MS 36
(See address above.)

PRECAST/PRESTRESSED CONCRETE INSTITUTE [2827]
200 West Adams Street
Suite 2100
Chicago, IL 60606
(312) 786-0300
Fax: (312) 621-1114

E-MAIL ADDRESS:
rbecker@pci.org

WEB SITE ADDRESS:
www.pci.org

AREAS OF INTEREST:
Research, design and construction of buildings, bridges and other structures using precast/prestressed concrete.

NAME(S) OF PROGRAMS:
• **Daniel P. Jenny Research Fellowships**

TYPE:
Fellowships.

YEAR PROGRAM STARTED: 1972

PURPOSE:
To support graduate students in civil engineering interested in research related to precast and prestressed concrete.

LEGAL BASIS:
Nonprofit trade association.

ELIGIBILITY:
Student applicants must be graduate students in civil engineering interested in research related to precast/prestressed concrete and enrolled in a U.S., Canadian or Mexican university. Religious organizations are ineligible.

GEOGRAPHIC RESTRICTIONS:
United States, Canada and Mexico.

FINANCIAL DATA:
Amount of support per award: $20,000.

NUMBER OF AWARDS: Up to 5.

APPLICATION INFORMATION:
Contact the Institute for application.
Duration: One to two years.
Deadline: Proposals solicited the first week of January. Deadline generally mid-March. Decision by end of April and announcement in May for following academic year.

ADDRESS INQUIRIES TO:
Roger Becker, Managing Director
Research and Development
(See address above.)

THE ROYAL SOCIETY OF CANADA [2828]
170 Waller Street
Ottawa ON K1N 9B9 Canada
(613) 991-9779
Fax: (613) 991-6996

E-MAIL ADDRESS:
awards@rsc-src.ca

WEB SITE ADDRESS:
www.rsc-src.ca

FOUNDED: 1975

AREAS OF INTEREST:
Engineering or applied sciences.

NAME(S) OF PROGRAMS:
• **The Bancroft Award**
• **The Sir John William Dawson Medal**
• **The McLaughlin Medal**
• **The McNeil Medal**
• **The Miroslaw Romanowski Medal**
• **The Rutherford Memorial Medals**
• **The John L. Synge Award**
• **The Alice Wilson Award**

TYPE:
Awards/prizes. The Bancroft Award is given for publication, instruction and research in the earth sciences that have conspicuously contributed to public understanding and appreciation of the subject.

The Sir John William Dawson Medal is made for important and sustained contributions in two domains of interest to RSC or in interdisciplinary research.

The McLaughlin Medal is awarded for important research of sustained excellence in any branch of the medical sciences.

The McNeil Medal for the Public Awareness of Science is awarded to a candidate who has demonstrated outstanding ability to promote and communicate science to students and the public (in the broadest sense of the latter term) within Canada.

The Miroslaw Romanowski Medal is awarded for significant contributions to the resolution of scientific aspects of environmental problems or for important improvements to the quality of an ecosystem in all aspects - terrestrial, atmospheric and aqueous - brought about by scientific means.

The Rutherford Memorial Medals are awarded for outstanding research in any branch of physics and chemistry.

The John L. Synge Award is given for outstanding research in any of the branches of the mathematical sciences.

The Alice Wilson Award is given to a woman of outstanding academic qualifications who is entering a career in scholarship or research at the postdoctoral level.

YEAR PROGRAM STARTED: 1975

PURPOSE:
To annually recognize Canadian citizens for contributions to engineering or applied sciences.

LEGAL BASIS:
Nonprofit.

ELIGIBILITY:
Awarded only to Canadian citizens or Canadian residents living in Canada for three years preceding the date of nomination.

GEOGRAPHIC RESTRICTIONS:
Canada.

FINANCIAL DATA:
Amount of support per award: The Bancroft and Synge Awards: A diploma and $2,500. The Dawson Medal: Silver medal and $2,500. The McLaughlin and Rutherford Memorial Medals: Gold-plated silver medal and $2,500. The McNeil Medal: Bronze medal and $1,500. The Romanowski Medal: Bronze Medal and $3,000. The Wilson Award: A diploma and $1,000.

APPLICATION INFORMATION:
Duration: The Bancroft Award and The Dawson Medal: Every two years. The McLaughlin, McNeil, Romanowski and Rutherford Memorial Medals and The Wilson Award : Every year. The Synge Award: Irregular intervals.
Deadline: December 1.

ADDRESS INQUIRIES TO:
Sarah Pouliot
Officer of Recognition
(See address above.)

THE SOCIETY OF NAVAL ARCHITECTS AND MARINE ENGINEERS [2829]
601 Pavonia Avenue, Suite 400
Jersey City, NJ 07306
(201) 499-5056
Fax: (201) 798-4975

E-MAIL ADDRESS:
efaustino@sname.org

WEB SITE ADDRESS:
www.sname.org

FOUNDED: 1893

AREAS OF INTEREST:
Naval architecture, marine engineering, ocean engineering or marine industry-related fields.

NAME(S) OF PROGRAMS:
- **Graduate Scholarships**
- **Undergraduate Scholarships**

TYPE:
Scholarships. The Society annually awards both graduate and undergraduate scholarships to encourage study in naval architecture, marine engineering, ocean engineering or marine industry-related fields.

Graduate Scholarships are made for one year of study leading to a Master's in naval architecture, marine engineering, ocean engineering or in fields directly related to the marine industry.

Undergraduate Scholarships are administered by schools offering undergraduate programs on grants given to the schools.

YEAR PROGRAM STARTED: 1933

PURPOSE:
To encourage young men and women to enter the fields of naval architecture, marine engineering, ocean engineering or marine industry-related fields as a career by aiding them to pursue courses of study in these specialties and to provide the incentive and attractions for such a career.

LEGAL BASIS:
Technical Society.

ELIGIBILITY:
Society scholarships are based soley on merit, not financial need.

Graduate Scholarships: Open to U.S., Canadian, or international applicants. Awards are made for one year of study leading to a Master's degree in naval architecture, marine engineering, ocean engineering or in fields directly related to the marine industry. Society membership is required by October 1 of year prior to application. Applicants must not receive their Master's prior to October 1 of the year in which they are applying for their scholarship. Graduate scholarships are awarded to an individual only once. Non-U.S. or Canadian citizens must plan to study in U.S. or Canadian schools.

Undergraduate Scholarships: Open to citizens of the U.S. and Canada. Study must be toward a degree in naval architecture, marine engineering, ocean engineering or marine industry-related fields at one of the following schools: California Maritime Academy, Florida Atlantic University, Florida Institute of Technology, Maine Maritime Academy, Massachusetts Institute of Technology, Memorial University of Newfoundland, SUNY Maritime College, Texas A&M University/College Station, University of British Columbia, University of California/Berkeley, University of Michigan, University of New Orleans, Virginia Polytechnic Institute or Webb Institute. The applicant must be entering his or her junior or senior year and must be a member in the Society four months prior to making an application. Scholarship awardees may repeat as an undergraduate recipient and subsequently apply for a graduate scholarship.

FINANCIAL DATA:
Amount of support per award: Graduate Scholarships: Up to $20,000 per year; Undergraduate Scholarships: Up to $2,000 per year.

NUMBER OF AWARDS: Graduate Scholarships: At least 6 annually.

APPLICATION INFORMATION:
Graduate Scholarships: Application may be downloaded from the Society web site or may be obtained by written request to the attention of the Chairperson, Scholarships Committee, at the address above. Applicants are required to provide GRE scores regardless of graduate school admission requirements.

Undergraduate Scholarships: Requests are made directly to above selected schools. The schools present their nominations in biographical form for each applicant and include a statement from the student indicating his or her career goals and why he or she is interested in the marine field. Selection of the recipients is made by the colleges in accordance with their established procedures.
Duration: Graduate Scholarships: One year. No renewals. Undergraduate Scholarships: One year. Awardee may repeat as an undergraduate recipient and subsequently apply for a Graduate Scholarship.
Deadline: Graduate Scholarships: Application and attachments prior to February 1; supporting documents by February 15. Graduate Scholarships selected in April; Undergraduate Scholarships approved in June.

SCHOLARSHIP COMMITTEE:
Dr. Walter MacLean, Chairman

ADDRESS INQUIRIES TO:
Erlinda Faustino, Scholarships Coordinator
(See address above.)

SOCIETY OF WOMEN ENGINEERS
120 South La Salle Street
Suite 1515
Chicago, IL 60603
(312) 596-5223
Fax: (312) 596-5252

E-MAIL ADDRESS:
hq@swe.org

WEB SITE ADDRESS:
www.swe.org

TYPE:
Awards/prizes; Conferences/seminars; Scholarships. Support for undergraduate and graduate engineering studies including women who have been out of the engineering job market for a minimum of two years and who will return to school for an engineering program.

See entry 1161 for full listing.

THE TAU BETA PI ASSOCIATION, INC. [2830]
508 Dougherty Engg Building
1512 Middle Drive
Knoxville, TN 37996-2215
(865) 546-4578
Fax: (865) 546-4579

E-MAIL ADDRESS:
tbp@tbp.org

WEB SITE ADDRESS:
www.tbp.org

FOUNDED: 1885

AREAS OF INTEREST:
Engineering.

NAME(S) OF PROGRAMS:
- **Raymond A. and Ina C. Best Fellowship for MBA**
- **Graduate Fellowship in Engineering**
- **Tau Beta Pi Undergraduate Scholarship**

TYPE:
Fellowships; Scholarships. The Fellowship awards are for one academic year of study in engineering for qualified graduate students.

The scholarships are awarded for senior year of full-time undergraduate study.

YEAR PROGRAM STARTED: 1928

PURPOSE:
To support the advancement of engineering education and the profession.

LEGAL BASIS:
Corporation.

ELIGIBILITY:
Candidate must be a member of Tau Beta Pi.

FINANCIAL DATA:
Fellows having other graduate study financial aid that is more than $20,000 in excess of tuition may be awarded Tau Beta Pi Fellowships without stipend. Persons supported by a salary from industry, government or other sources may not be entitled to the stipend.

Amount of support per award: Fellowships: $10,000; Scholarships: $2,000.

Total amount of support: $450,000 to $550,000 per year.

NUMBER OF APPLICANTS MOST RECENT YEAR: 646.

NUMBER OF AWARDS: 28 fellowships and 102 scholarships for the year 2010-11.

APPLICATION INFORMATION:
Application forms are available November 1 for the following academic year.

Duration: One academic year. Fellowships may be renewable upon application. Scholarships are not renewable.

Deadline: Fellowships: January 31 postmark; Scholarships: March 1 postmark.

PUBLICATIONS:
The Bent of Tau Beta Pi, quarterly magazine.

IRS IDENTIFICATION NUMBER: 62-0479545

OFFICERS:
James D. Froula, P.E., Executive Director
D. Stephen Pierre, P.E., Director of Fellowships

EXECUTIVE COUNCIL:
Dr. Larry A. Simonson, President
Solange C. Dao, Vice President
Dr. Jonathan F. K. Earle, Councillor
Jason A. Huggins, Councillor
Norman Pih, Councillor

ADDRESS INQUIRIES TO:
James D. Froula, P.E.
Executive Director
(See address above.)

U.S. DEPARTMENT OF ENERGY [2831]
P.O. Box 10940, MS-922-273
Pittsburgh, PA 15236
(412) 386-4781
Fax: (412) 386-5917

E-MAIL ADDRESS:
flenory@netl.doe.gov

WEB SITE ADDRESS:
www.grants.gov

FOUNDED: 1979

AREAS OF INTEREST:
Computational energy sciences, material science and novel materials for sensing or monitoring in extreme environments of fossil energy systems.

NAME(S) OF PROGRAMS:
- **University Coal Research Program**

TYPE:
Assistantships; Project/program grants; Research grants.

YEAR PROGRAM STARTED: 1980

PURPOSE:
To foster the highest quality fundamental research on coal at the university level; to ensure the continued training of researchers in the areas of fossil energy.

LEGAL BASIS:
Government agency.

ELIGIBILITY:
Open to U.S. colleges and universities only.

GEOGRAPHIC RESTRICTIONS:
United States.

FINANCIAL DATA:
Amount of support per award: Maximum DOE funding for grant applications submitted by one or two universities is $300,000 for a 36-month performance period.

Matching fund requirements: No matching fund requirements; however, cost-sharing and/or industrial collaboration is encouraged.

REPRESENTATIVE AWARDS:
$297,219 to Steven Ceccio of the University of Michigan, in collaboration with researchers at the University of Florida, for a grant entitled "A Study of Horizontal Gas Jets in a Bubbling Fluidized Bed of Non-Spherical Particles;" $299,819 to Liang-Shih Fan of Ohio State University for a grant entitled "Process/Equipment Co-Simulation on Syngas Chemical Looping Process;" $299,974 to Inga H. Musselman of University of Texas at Dallas for a grant entitled "Novel Zeolitic Imidazolate Framework/Polymer Membranes for Hydrogen Separations in Coal Processing;" $300,000 to Peter K. Liaw of the University of Tennessee for a grant entitled "Computational & Experimental Design of Fe-Based Superalloys for Elevated-Temperature Applications."

APPLICATION INFORMATION:
Duration: 36 months. No renewals.

OFFICERS:
Fred M. Glaser, Headquarters Portfolio Manager, University Coal Research Program

ADDRESS INQUIRIES TO:
Paula B. Flenory, Program Manager
University Coal Research Program
National Energy Technology Laboratory
(See address above.)

U.S. SOCIETY ON DAMS [2832]
1616 17th Street, Suite 483
Denver, CO 80202
(303) 628-5430
Fax: (303) 628-5431

E-MAIL ADDRESS:
stephens@ussdams.org

WEB SITE ADDRESS:
www.ussdams.org

AREAS OF INTEREST:
Dams and water resources.

NAME(S) OF PROGRAMS:
- **USSD Scholarship**

TYPE:
Scholarships.

PURPOSE:
To advance the technology of dam engineering, construction, operation, maintenance and dam safety; to foster socially and environmentally responsible water resources projects; to promote awareness of the role of dams in the beneficial and sustainable development of the nation's water resources.

ELIGIBILITY:
Open to U.S. college or university graduate students whose research studies have a potential for developing practical solutions to design and construction problems. Applicants must be U.S. citizens enrolled in U.S. academic institutions which have programs related to dams.

GEOGRAPHIC RESTRICTIONS:
United States.

FINANCIAL DATA:
Amount of support per award: $10,000; two finalists receive $1,000.

Total amount of support: $12,000 for the year 2010.

NUMBER OF AWARDS: 3 for the year 2010.

APPLICATION INFORMATION:
Applicants must submit a proposal describing a specific research topic. The proposed research work should be original and innovative. The proposed research can be part of an ongoing research project. Applicants are encouraged to submit proposals in topics that are related to their graduate research work. The application package must include the application form, a description of the proposed research work, an official set of academic transcripts and two letters of recommendation, one of which must be from the applicant's academic advisor.

ADDRESS INQUIRIES TO:
Dr. Enrique E. Matheu
U.S. Department of Homeland Security
3700 Massachusetts Avenue, N.W.
Washington, DC 20016
Tel: (703) 235-5638
E-mail: enrique.matheu@dhs.gov

THE UNIVERSITY OF SYDNEY [2833]
Scholarships Office
Level 5, Jane Foss Russell Building G02
The University of Sydney N.S.W. 2006
Australia
(02) 8627 8112
Fax: (02) 8627 8145

E-MAIL ADDRESS:
research.training@sydney.edu.au

WEB SITE ADDRESS:
www.sydney.edu.au/scholarships/research

FOUNDED: 1850

AREAS OF INTEREST:
Civil and mining engineering, electrical engineering, mechanical and mechatronic engineering.

NAME(S) OF PROGRAMS:
- **Civil and Mining Engineering Foundation Scholarship**
- **William John Padbury Scholarship**

- **Norman I. Price Scholarship in Electrical Engineering**
- **Peter Nicol Russell Postgraduate Scholarship in Mechanical and Mechatronic Engineering**
- **William Girling Watson Travelling Scholarship**

TYPE:
Scholarships. Awarded for research leading to a higher degree. Tenable at the University of Sydney.

PURPOSE:
To promote and encourage research and study in various fields of engineering.

LEGAL BASIS:
University.

ELIGIBILITY:
Open to graduates of the University of Sydney or to any other person eligible for admission to full-time candidature for a higher degree by research in the Faculty of Engineering and Information Technologies at the University of Sydney.

FINANCIAL DATA:
This scholarship does not cover tuition fees payable by international students.
Amount of support per award: Varies.

NUMBER OF AWARDS: 1 offered as vacancy occurs.

APPLICATION INFORMATION:
Duration: One year. May be renewed for a second year in the case of a Master's degree, and for a third year for a Ph.D.

ADDRESS INQUIRIES TO:
Faculty of Engineering and Information Technologies
The University of Sydney
N.S.W. 2006 Australia
Tel: (02) 9351 8719
Fax: (02) 9351 7082
E-mail:
engineering.postgraduate@sydney.edu.au

THE UNIVERSITY OF SYDNEY

Scholarships Office
Level 5, Jane Foss Russell Building G02
The University of Sydney N.S.W. 2006
Australia
(02) 8627 8112
Fax: (02) 8627 8145

E-MAIL ADDRESS:
research.training@sydney.edu.au

WEB SITE ADDRESS:
www.sydney.edu.au/scholarships/research

TYPE:
Scholarships. Awarded for research leading to a higher degree. Tenable at the University of Sydney.

See entry 2264 for full listing.

Home economics and nutrition

AMERICAN ASSOCIATION OF FAMILY AND CONSUMER SCIENCES (AAFCS)

400 North Columbus Street
Suite 202
Alexandria, VA 22314-2752
(703) 706-4600
(800) 424-8080
Fax: (703) 706-4663

E-MAIL ADDRESS:
staff@aafcs.org

WEB SITE ADDRESS:
www.aafcs.org/programs/index.html

TYPE:
Fellowships. AAFCS awards fellowships to individuals who have exhibited the potential to make contributions to the family and consumer sciences profession.

See entry 1007 for full listing.

AMERICAN ASSOCIATION OF FAMILY AND CONSUMER SCIENCES (AAFCS) [2834]

400 North Columbus Street
Suite 202
Alexandria, VA 22314-2752
(703) 706-4600
(800) 424-8080
Fax: (703) 706-4663

E-MAIL ADDRESS:
grants@aafcs.org

WEB SITE ADDRESS:
www.aafcs.org

FOUNDED: 1909

AREAS OF INTEREST:
Family and consumer sciences.

NAME(S) OF PROGRAMS:
- **Excellence in Extension Grant**

TYPE:
Seed money grants. For programs designed to enhance the well-being of families, to support the work of the Association, and to expand the Cooperative Extension program initiatives. Creative and innovative Cooperative Extension research, demonstration, or staff development proposals that address both the current and relevant issues in AAFCS or Extension are invited.

YEAR PROGRAM STARTED: 1962

PURPOSE:
To enhance the well-being of families; to expand the Cooperative Extension program efforts.

LEGAL BASIS:
501(c)(3) nonprofit charity.

ELIGIBILITY:
Those eligible to apply for the grant include:
(1) individuals or teams employed by Cooperative Extension with family and consumer sciences program responsibilities and;
(2) AAFCS communities, committees, commissions, councils, affiliates or units whose proposal is an Extension program that reflects best practices in curriculum development, delivery methods and learning outcomes. Collaborative efforts are encouraged.

Members of the AAFCS Board of Directors, Awards and Recognition Committee, and Development Committee are not eligible to apply during their terms of office. AAFCS staff members are not eligible to apply during their periods of employment with the Association.

The grant will be presented on a biannual basis when a qualified recipient is identified.

FINANCIAL DATA:
Monetary awards. No indirect costs will be paid by AAFCS.

Amount of support per award: $5,000 and a commemorative certificate. Also, the project leader will receive up to $1,000 of support for one year of AAFCS membership and participation in the AAFCS Annual Conference & Exposition, where the grant award will be presented.

Matching fund requirements: Each proposal must show a dollar-for-dollar match. Either cash or an in-kind match is acceptable.

NUMBER OF AWARDS: No more than 1 recipient (or recipient group) in years when applications are invited.

APPLICATION INFORMATION:
Duration: One year (October 1 to the following September 30).
Deadline: January 15.

PUBLICATIONS:
Brochure.

ADDRESS INQUIRIES TO:
Awards and Grants Department
(See address above.)

AMERICAN ASSOCIATION OF FAMILY AND CONSUMER SCIENCES (AAFCS) [2835]

400 North Columbus Street
Suite 202
Alexandria, VA 22314-2752
(703) 706-4600
(800) 424-8080
Fax: (703) 706-4663

E-MAIL ADDRESS:
awards@aafcs.org

WEB SITE ADDRESS:
www.aafcs.org

FOUNDED: 1909

AREAS OF INTEREST:
Family and consumer sciences.

NAME(S) OF PROGRAMS:
- **National Teacher of the Year Award**

TYPE:
Awards/prizes. Recognizes exemplary teachers who utilize cutting-edge methods, techniques and activities to provide the stimulus for and give visibility to family and consumer sciences elementary and secondary education.

YEAR PROGRAM STARTED: 1972

PURPOSE:
To provide leadership and support for professionals whose work assists individuals, families and communities in making informed decisions about their well-being, relationships and resources to achieve optimal quality of life.

LEGAL BASIS:
501(c)(3) nonprofit charity.

ELIGIBILITY:
National-level competitors for this award must have been chosen as an Affiliate Teacher of the Year (through competitions run at the affiliate level); each affiliate may enter no more than one Affiliate Teacher of the Year into the national competition per year and the nomination must be submitted by the Affiliate President. An Affiliate Teacher of the Year who is eligible for the National Teacher of the Year Award:
(1) is employed as a full-time family and consumer sciences teacher of grades

kindergarten through 12 at the time the nomination is submitted;

(2) is an AAFCS member at the time of nomination and for at least three consecutive years prior to nomination and;

(3) created and runs a family and consumer sciences program that focuses on one of the following five program areas: (a) career awareness/job skill training; (b) consumer education/family finance; (c) creative dimensions/alternative program designs; (d) family life/personal and social development and; (e) nutrition education/diet and health.

Members of the AAFCS Board of Directors, Awards and Recognition Committee, and Development Committee are not eligible for nomination during their terms of office. AAFCS staff members are not eligible for nomination during their periods of employment with the Association.

Award recipient must attend the AAFCS Annual Conference & Expo for presentation and recognition.

FINANCIAL DATA:
Amount of support per award: A commemorative plaque and a $2,500 award, plus up to $1,000 of support for one year of AAFCS membership and participation in the AAFCS Annual Conference & Expo.

NUMBER OF AWARDS: Up to 3 merit finalists, from whom 1 National Teacher of the Year is selected.

APPLICATION INFORMATION:
Detailed guidelines and instructions are available from the Association.

ADDRESS INQUIRIES TO:
See e-mail address above.

THE AMERICAN DIETETIC ASSOCIATION FOUNDATION   [2836]

120 South Riverside Plaza, 20th Floor
Chicago, IL 60606
(312) 899-4793
Fax: (312) 899-4796

WEB SITE ADDRESS:
www.eatright.org

FOUNDED: 1966

AREAS OF INTEREST:
Food, nutrition, dietetics and food service management.

TYPE:
Awards/prizes; Fellowships; Grants-in-aid; Research grants; Scholarships.

YEAR PROGRAM STARTED: 1966

PURPOSE:
To further progress in the educational and scientific advancement of dietetics.

LEGAL BASIS:
Public, not-for-profit foundation.

ELIGIBILITY:
Applicant has to be a member of the ADA to qualify for its scholarships and (in general) for its awards as well.

GEOGRAPHIC RESTRICTIONS:
Primarily United States.

FINANCIAL DATA:
Amount of support per award: Scholarships: $1,000 to $5,000.
Total amount of support: Over $320,000.

COOPERATIVE FUNDING PROGRAMS:
Collaborative Consumer Research Program.

NUMBER OF APPLICANTS MOST RECENT YEAR:
1,000.

NUMBER OF AWARDS: 200.

APPLICATION INFORMATION:
One common application form is used for all scholarships. Scholarship applications are available online to ADA members.

Awards applications are available by request to the ADA Foundation: Tel: (312) 899-4803; E-mail: epuga@eatright.org.

Deadline: Scholarships: February 15. Announcement in June; Awards, Fellowships and Grants: February 1.

PUBLICATIONS:
Annual report.

IRS IDENTIFICATION NUMBER: 36-6150906

AMERICAN SOCIETY FOR NUTRITION   [2837]

9650 Rockville Pike
Suite L-5100
Bethesda, MD 20814-3990
(301) 634-7051
Fax: (301) 634-7892

E-MAIL ADDRESS:
kdunn@nutrition.org

WEB SITE ADDRESS:
www.nutrition.org

FOUNDED: 1928

AREAS OF INTEREST:
Nutrition research.

NAME(S) OF PROGRAMS:
● **Predoctoral Fellowships in Nutrition Research**

TYPE:
Fellowships.

YEAR PROGRAM STARTED: 1982

PURPOSE:
To promote nutrition research by young scientists.

LEGAL BASIS:
Tax-exempt, nonprofit organization.

ELIGIBILITY:
Available to U.S. or Canadian citizens. Applicants must be members of the American Society for Nutrition (ASN) and must be enrolled in a graduate program which is listed in the ASN Directory of Graduate Programs.

GEOGRAPHIC RESTRICTIONS:
United States and Canada.

FINANCIAL DATA:
Amount of support per award: $5,000.

NUMBER OF APPLICANTS MOST RECENT YEAR:
50.

NUMBER OF AWARDS: 10.

APPLICATION INFORMATION:
Candidates must submit research proposals, application forms and evidence of registration in a program of study at a registered institution.
Duration: One year.
Deadline: December 1. Announcement in July.

IRS IDENTIFICATION NUMBER: 31-1507752

ADDRESS INQUIRIES TO:
Katrina Dunn, Programs Manager
(See address above.)

CENTER FOR SCIENCE IN THE PUBLIC INTEREST   [2838]

1220 L Street, N.W.
Suite 300
Washington, DC 20005
(202) 332-9110
Fax: (202) 265-4954

E-MAIL ADDRESS:
coday@cspinet.org

WEB SITE ADDRESS:
www.cspinet.org

FOUNDED: 1971

AREAS OF INTEREST:
Consumer advocacy on nutrition, diet and health.

NAME(S) OF PROGRAMS:
● **Public Interest Internships**

TYPE:
Internships. Stipends allow interns to work on specific projects under the direction of a Project Director or the Executive Director.

YEAR PROGRAM STARTED: 1978

PURPOSE:
To provide interns with direct, practical experience; to provide the Center with extra assistance.

LEGAL BASIS:
501(c)(3).

ELIGIBILITY:
Students in undergraduate, graduate, law and medical schools are eligible to apply. Requirements vary depending on specific internship applied for.

Must work out of the Washington, DC office.

FINANCIAL DATA:
Amount of support per award: Undergraduate interns are paid a hourly wage of $8.25 per hour and graduate students $9.25 per hour.

NUMBER OF APPLICANTS MOST RECENT YEAR:
250.

NUMBER OF AWARDS: 4 per year.

APPLICATION INFORMATION:
Cover letter should indicate preferred dates. Application materials should include the following:

(1) cover letter indicating issues of interest, future plans, and the dates that applicant is available;

(2) resume (experience with advocacy groups is not required, but would be advantageous);

(3) writing sample (a popularly written piece is preferred over a technical report);

(4) two letters of recommendation from instructors or employers that address applicant's academic/work ability and character and;

(5) official transcript of courses with grades.

Duration: 10 weeks. Renewal possible.

Deadline: Applicants are advised to follow the application guidelines and apply as soon as possible. Applications are taken on a rolling basis until all positions have been filled.

PUBLICATIONS:
Status report; general brochure; publications list; Nutrition Action Healthletter.

OFFICERS:
Michael F. Jacobson, Ph.D., Chief Executive Officer

ADDRESS INQUIRIES TO:
Intern Coordinator
(See address above.)

DIETITIANS OF CANADA   [2839]
480 University Avenue
Suite 604
Toronto ON M5G 1V2 Canada
(416) 596-0857
Fax: (416) 596-0603

E-MAIL ADDRESS:
diana.sheh@dietitians.ca

WEB SITE ADDRESS:
www.dietitians.ca

FOUNDED: 1935

AREAS OF INTEREST:
Dietetics and nutrition.

NAME(S) OF PROGRAMS:
- **Graduate Awards in Dietetics**
- **Research Grants in Dietetics**
- **Undergraduate Awards in Dietetics**

TYPE:
Awards/prizes; Research grants.

YEAR PROGRAM STARTED: 1966

PURPOSE:
To encourage members in graduate studies;
to promote and support dietetic research.

LEGAL BASIS:
Incorporated under Canada Corporations Act.

ELIGIBILITY:
For Graduate Awards, applicants must be DC
members registered in a graduate program in
dietetics.

For the Research Awards, applicants must be
practicing dietitians who are delivering direct
or indirect client/patient public care or
service. One of the investigators must be a
DC member.

For Undergraduate Awards, applicants must
be enrolled in final year of Bachelor's degree
program and student member of DC.

GEOGRAPHIC RESTRICTIONS:
Canada.

FINANCIAL DATA:
Amount of support per award: Research
Grants: $5,000 maximum small grants;
$5,000 to $20,000 large grants.
Total amount of support: Varies.

APPLICATION INFORMATION:
Completed application form, statement of
purpose for graduate study, academic
transcript, and four recommendations are
required.
Duration: One year. Large grants: One to
two years.
Deadline: Student Awards: February 1.
Announcement in July; Research Grant
Proposals: March 1.

PUBLICATIONS:
*Canadian Journal of Dietetic Practice and
Research (Revue Canadienne de la Pratique
et de la Recherche en Dietetique).*

ADDRESS INQUIRIES TO:
Awards Committee or
CFDR Research Grants
(See address above.)

FOOD AND DRUG LAW INSTITUTE (FDLI)
1155 15th Street, N.W., Suite 800
Washington, DC 20005-2706
(202) 371-1420
Fax: (202) 371-0649

E-MAIL ADDRESS:
pubsdept@fdli.org

WEB SITE ADDRESS:
www.fdli.org

TYPE:
Awards/prizes. The subject matter of the
competition is an in-depth analysis of a
current issue relevant to the food and drug
field, including a relevant case law, legislative
history and other authorities, particularly
where the U.S. Food and Drug
Administration is involved.

There are two categories of prizes:
(1) papers of 40 pages or less (including
appendices and footnotes) and;
(2) papers of more than 40 pages, but less
than 101 pages.

See entry 2103 for full listing.

INTERNATIONAL ASSOCIATION FOR FOOD PROTECTION   [2840]
6200 Aurora Avenue
Suite 200W
Des Moines, IA 50322
(515) 276-3344
(800) 369-6337
Fax: (515) 276-8655

E-MAIL ADDRESS:
info@foodprotection.org

WEB SITE ADDRESS:
www.foodprotection.org

FOUNDED: 1911

AREAS OF INTEREST:
Food science and research.

NAME(S) OF PROGRAMS:
- **Harold Barnum Industry Award**
- **Food Safety Innovation Award**
- **Harry Haverland Citation Award**
- **International Service Award**
- **Elmer Marth Educator Award**
- **Sanitarian Award**
- **Student Travel Scholarship Award**
- **Maurice Weber Laboratorian Award**

TYPE:
Awards/prizes; Travel grants. Cash awards
and plaques to outstanding members.

YEAR PROGRAM STARTED: 1973

PURPOSE:
To recognize and reward outstanding member
contributions in the specified award area.

LEGAL BASIS:
Nonprofit, incorporated professional
association.

ELIGIBILITY:
Nominees must be members of the
International Association for Food Protection.

FINANCIAL DATA:
Amount of support per award: $1,500 and
plaque.

NUMBER OF AWARDS: 1 of each award annually.

IRS IDENTIFICATION NUMBER: 35-0894354

OFFICERS:
Vicki Lewandowski, President
Lee-Ann Jaykus, President-Elect

Isabel Walls, Vice President
Katherine M.J. Swanson, Secretary

ADDRESS INQUIRIES TO:
David W. Tharp, Executive Director
(See address above.)

KAPPA OMICRON NU HONOR SOCIETY   [2841]
4990 Northwind Drive
Suite 140
East Lansing, MI 48823-5031
(517) 351-8335
Fax: (517) 351-8336

E-MAIL ADDRESS:
dmitstifer@kon.org

WEB SITE ADDRESS:
www.kon.org

FOUNDED: 1912

AREAS OF INTEREST:
Home economics, family and consumer
sciences, and human sciences.

NAME(S) OF PROGRAMS:
- **Marjorie M. Brown Dissertation
  Fellowship**
- **Ruth E. Hawthorne Research Grant**
- **Kappa Omicron Phi/Hettie Margaret
  Anthony Fellowship**
- **LeaderShape Institute Award**
- **Eileen C. Maddex Fellowship**
- **National Alumni Chapter Fellowship**
- **National Alumni Chapter Grant**
- **National Scholar Program**
- **New Initiatives Grant**
- **Omicron Nu Research Fellowship**

TYPE:
Fellowships; Project/program grants;
Research grants; Scholarships. Awarded to
members for graduate or postgraduate study
and research in home economics or one of its
specializations at colleges or universities with
strong research programs and supporting
disciplines for the chosen major or topic.

YEAR PROGRAM STARTED: 1969

PURPOSE:
To promote research and graduate study in
home economics by recognizing and
encouraging scholastic excellence.

LEGAL BASIS:
Nonprofit corporation, 501(c)(3) status.

ELIGIBILITY:
Applicant must be a member of Kappa
Omicron Nu who has demonstrated
scholarship, research and leadership potential.

FINANCIAL DATA:
Amount of support per award: $150 to
$10,000 per year.
Total amount of support: $35,000 for the
year 2009.

NUMBER OF APPLICANTS MOST RECENT YEAR:
6.

NUMBER OF AWARDS: Doctoral Fellowships: 2;
Master's Fellowships: 2; Research Grant: 1;
Leadership Award: 1; Scholar Grants: 50 for
the year 2009.

APPLICATION INFORMATION:
Duration: One academic year. Nonrenewable.
Deadline: Research and Project Grants:
February 15. Announcement April 15;
Doctoral Fellowships: January 15.
Announcement April 1; Master's
Fellowships: April 1. Announcement May 15.

PUBLICATIONS:
Brochure.

IRS IDENTIFICATION NUMBER: 38-1245233

BOARD OF DIRECTORS:
Deborah Tippett, Chairperson
Barbara Frazier, First Vice Chairperson
Kathleen O'Rourke, Second Vice
Chairperson
Cynthia Smith, Secretary

EXECUTIVE DIRECTOR:
Dr. Dorothy I. Mitstifer

ADDRESS INQUIRIES TO:
Dr. Dorothy I. Mitstifer, Executive Director
(See address above.)

NATIONAL CATTLEMAN'S BEEF ASSOCIATION [2842]
9110 East Nichols Avenue
Centennial, CO 80112-3450
(830) 569-0046
Fax: (303) 770-6921

E-MAIL ADDRESS:
smcneill@beef.org

WEB SITE ADDRESS:
www.beefresearch.org

FOUNDED: 1922

AREAS OF INTEREST:
Human nutrition, the relationship between
nutrients in beef and health (including amino
acids, vitamins and minerals), diet and
health.

NAME(S) OF PROGRAMS:
● **Nutrition Research**

TYPE:
Grants-in-aid; Research grants; Research
contracts. Research contracts and
grants-in-aid for experimental projects in the
areas of:
(1) beef as part of a balanced diet;
(2) parity studies;
(3) health benefits of beef lipids and;
(4) contribution of beef nutrients to total diet.

Proposals solicited via specific RFPs (request
for proposals).

YEAR PROGRAM STARTED: 1923

PURPOSE:
To gain further knowledge of the value of
beef in our diets; to develop research
technology that can be applied to the areas
noted above.

LEGAL BASIS:
Professional, nonprofit association.

ELIGIBILITY:
Open to qualified institutions (including
universities, medical centers, nonprofit
organizations and/or contract research
laboratories) with appropriate interests.

GEOGRAPHIC RESTRICTIONS:
United States.

FINANCIAL DATA:
Amount of support per award: $20,000 to
$50,000 for one year to $200,000 to
$400,000 for multiyear awards. Most are
$50,000 to $100,000.

COOPERATIVE FUNDING PROGRAMS:
Occasionally federally funded programs are
underway that can be facilitated with other
funds to expand the scope of the work.

APPLICATION INFORMATION:
Official application materials are available
upon request to NCBA at the address above,
after it has been established that the proposal
would be of mutual interest.

Duration: Support is provided for one to two
years depending upon the project.
Deadline: Varies for RFPs.

PUBLICATIONS:
Annual research report.

OFFICERS AND STAFF:
Mandy Carr, Ph.D., Executive Director, Beef
Safety Research
Shalene McNeill, Ph.D., Executive Director,
Nutrition Research

ADDRESS INQUIRIES TO:
Shalene McNeill, Ph.D.
Executive Director, Nutrition Research
(See address above.)

NATIONAL DAIRY COUNCIL [2843]
10255 West Higgins Road
Suite 900
Rosemont, IL 60018-5616
(847) 803-2000
Fax: (847) 803-2077

E-MAIL ADDRESS:
chris.cifelli@rosedmi.com

WEB SITE ADDRESS:
www.nationaldairycouncil.org

FOUNDED: 1915

AREAS OF INTEREST:
Independent research to aid in the ongoing
discovery of information about dairy foods'
important role in a healthy lifestyle. This
research provides insights to industry for new
dairy product innovation.

NAME(S) OF PROGRAMS:
● **Nutrition Research Program**

TYPE:
Research contracts. The National Dairy
Council is the nutrition research, education
and communications arm of Dairy
Management Inc. On behalf of U.S. dairy
farmers, the National Dairy Council provides
science-based nutrition information to, and in
collaboration with, a variety of stakeholders
committed to fostering a healthier society,
including health professionals, educators,
school nutrition directors, academia, industry,
consumers and media. The National Dairy
Council comprises a staff of nutrition science
researchers, registered dietitians and
communications experts dedicated to
educating the public on the health benefits of
consuming milk and milk products
throughout a person's lifespan.

YEAR PROGRAM STARTED: 1941

PURPOSE:
To disseminate nutrition programs, materials
and research to support government
recommendations for improved nutrition for
Americans, including consumption of at least
three servings of nutrient-rich low-fat or
fat-free milk and milk products a day, in
partnership with its network of state and
regional dairy councils.

LEGAL BASIS:
Nonprofit educational-scientific institution
under IRS 501(c)(3).

ELIGIBILITY:
Qualified investigators associated with
accredited institutions of higher learning are
eligible for support. Applicants must hold a
Ph.D., M.D., D.D.S., D.V.M. or other degree,
with experience demonstrating ability to
conduct the proposed research.

Funds are not available for alteration of
facilities or purchase of permanent
equipment.

FINANCIAL DATA:
Amount of support per award: Administered
research contracts vary in amount, depending
upon the needs and nature of the request.
Total amount of support: Varies.

COOPERATIVE FUNDING PROGRAMS: If research
interests of additional organizations coincide,
cooperative projects are preferred to enhance
efficiency of funds utilized and to benefit the
researcher through a broader base of support.

APPLICATION INFORMATION:
The National Dairy Council invites
submission of two-page pre-proposals in the
beginning of each calendar year, typically
early February. Applications which meet the
needs of the research program, which are
stated in the guidelines for pre-proposal
submission, will be reviewed. Approximately
two to three weeks following the submission
deadline, all applicants will receive notice of
the outcome of this screening process.
Applicants whose pre-proposals generated
interest will receive further information and
materials for submission of a detailed full
research application to the program. Full
proposals will be due approximately six to
eight weeks later. All full proposals will be
peer-reviewed for scientific merit by the
Nutrition Research Scientific Advisory
Committee, which is comprised of expert
scientists from academia, government and
industry. For information on the research
program and research topics of interest in the
next solicitation, please send a letter
requesting the information and a
self-addressed label to the address above or
contact the NDC research office.
Duration: Projects supported on a yearly
basis for up to three years.
Deadline: Preproposal: Typically February.
Full proposal: Typically April.

PUBLICATIONS:
Guidelines for application and administration.

ADMINISTRATION:
Christopher J. Cifelli, Ph.D., Director,
Nutrition Research

ADDRESS INQUIRIES TO:
Christopher J. Cifelli, Ph.D.
Director, Nutrition Research
(See address above.)

THE NATIONAL RESTAURANT ASSOCIATION EDUCATIONAL FOUNDATION [2844]
175 West Jackson Boulevard
Suite 1500
Chicago, IL 60604-2702
(800) 765-2122 ext. 6738
Fax: (312) 566-9733

E-MAIL ADDRESS:
scholars@nraef.org

WEB SITE ADDRESS:
www.nraef.org/scholarships

FOUNDED: 1987

AREAS OF INTEREST:
Foodservice education and training.

NAME(S) OF PROGRAMS:
● **National Restaurant Association
Educational Foundation (NRAE)
Scholarship Program**

TYPE:
Scholarships. Provides scholarships for students who are pursuing an education and career in the foodservice industry.

YEAR PROGRAM STARTED: 1987

PURPOSE:
To encourage and support students pursuing an education and career in the foodservice industry.

LEGAL BASIS:
Not-for-profit organization.

ELIGIBILITY:
All applicants must be:
(1) U.S. citizen or permanent resident alien;
(2) accepted and/or enrolled in a foodservice-related postsecondary program and;
(3) submit a completed application packet postmarked by the deadline date.

GEOGRAPHIC RESTRICTIONS:
United States and its territories.

FINANCIAL DATA:
Amount of support per award: Undergraduate Scholarships: $2,500.

NUMBER OF AWARDS: Approximately 400.

APPLICATION INFORMATION:
Duration: Varies depending upon the award.

PUBLICATIONS:
Awards brochure.

ADDRESS INQUIRIES TO:
Scholarships
(See address above.)

SHARE OUR STRENGTH
1730 M Street, N.W.
Suite 700
Washington, DC 20036
(202) 393-2925
(800) 969-4767
Fax: (202) 347-5868

E-MAIL ADDRESS:
grants@strength.org

WEB SITE ADDRESS:
www.strength.org

TYPE:
Project/program grants. Grants are focused on increasing participation in the federal nutrition programs, including summer meals, after school meals, SNAP, WIC, school breakfast, and on nutrition education.

See entry 1613 for full listing.

USDA FOOD AND NUTRITION SERVICE
Child Nutrition Division
3101 Park Center Drive, Room 640
Alexandria, VA 22302
(703) 305-2590
Fax: (703) 305-2879

WEB SITE ADDRESS:
www.fns.usda.gov/cnd

TYPE:
Formula grants; Grants-in-aid; Project/program grants. Reimbursement for the support of food service in schools, child and adult care institutions to improve nutrition.

The Child and Adult Care Food Program helps child care facilities and institutions serve nutritious meals and snacks to pre-school and school-age children. To participate, facilities and institutions must be licensed or approved to provide child care services. They must also meet certain other eligibility requirements. The program operates in nonresidential day care centers, settlement houses, outside-school-hours care centers, family day care homes, institutions providing day care for handicapped children and others. Participating facilities and institutions get cash assistance, USDA-donated foods and technical guidance. In child care centers, the amount of cash assistance varies according to the family size and income of children served. In day care homes, the amount of cash assistance is based on a food service payment rate. Similar benefits are also now available to adult day care centers which serve functionally impaired adults or persons 60 years of age or older.

The National School Lunch Program makes well-planned nutritious meals available to school children. Any public or nonprofit private schools of high school grade or under and licensed public or nonprofit private residential child care institutions are eligible to participate in the National School Lunch and School Breakfast Programs. Schools that participate are required to provide free and reduced-price meals to children unable to pay the full price. Eligibility is based on application information submitted by a parent or guardian. The household income limit for free lunches is set at or below 130% of the federal poverty level and for reduced price lunches household income must be above 130% or at or below 185% of the federal poverty level. Children from households not eligible for free or reduced-price meals must pay the school's full price charge for lunch. Cash and donated commodities are provided to participating schools and institutions according to the number of meals served.

The School Breakfast Program makes nutritious breakfasts available to school children under the same eligibility guidelines and general requirements as the National School Lunch Program.

The Special Milk Program for Children makes it possible for all children attending a participating school or institution to purchase milk at a reduced price or receive it free, if they are eligible. Reimbursement is provided for each half-pint of milk served under the program. Schools and institutions that participate in other federal child nutrition programs authorized under the National School Lunch Act or the Child Nutrition Act of 1966 may not participate in the Special Milk Program for Children, except for split-session kindergarten programs conducted in schools in which the children do not have access to the other meal program.

The Summer Food Service Program for Children helps communities serve meals to needy children when school is not in session. The program is sponsored by public or private nonprofit school food authorities or local, municipal, county or state governments. Public or private nonprofit residential camps, other private nonprofit organizations, colleges and universities which participate in the National Youth Sports Program also may be sponsors. The program operates in areas in which at least 50% of the children meet the income criteria for free and reduced-price school meals. USDA reimburses sponsors for operating costs of food services up to a specified maximum rate for each meal served. In addition, sponsors receive some reimbursement for planning, operating and supervising expenses.

See entry 1229 for full listing.

Mining and metallurgy

ASM MATERIALS EDUCATION FOUNDATION   [2845]
9639 Kinsman Road
Materials Park, OH 44073-0002
(440) 338-5151 ext. 5533
(800) 336-5152 ext. 5533
Fax: (440) 338-4634

E-MAIL ADDRESS:
jeane.deatherage@asminternational.org

WEB SITE ADDRESS:
www.asmfoundation.org

FOUNDED: 1913

AREAS OF INTEREST:
Materials science and engineering in related fields such as metallurgy, metallurgical engineering, polymeric engineering, ceramic engineering, advanced composites engineering and engineering of electronic materials.

NAME(S) OF PROGRAMS:
- **ASM Foundation Scholarships**
- **ASM Outstanding Scholars**
- **Edward J. Dulis Scholarship**
- **John M. Haniak Scholarship**
- **George A. Roberts Scholarship**
- **Lucille and Charles A. Wert Scholarship**
- **William Park Woodside Founder's Scholarship**

TYPE:
Scholarships.

YEAR PROGRAM STARTED: 1953

PURPOSE:
To encourage and support capable students with interest and potential in the field of metallurgy and materials science.

LEGAL BASIS:
501(c)(3) educational charity.

ELIGIBILITY:
Applicant must be a student member of ASM International and have an intended or declared major in metallurgy/materials science engineering. Applicants majoring in related science or engineering disciplines will be considered if they demonstrate a strong academic emphasis and interest in materials science. Applicant must also be at the sophomore level or above. Open to U.S. and international students.

G.A. Roberts and W.P. Woodside Scholarship candidates must have a junior or senior standing in the fall at a North American university, have proof of financial need, and must be a citizen of the U.S., Canada or Mexico and attending school in one of these countries. University must have an accredited science and engineering program leading to a Bachelor's degree.

Applicants are eligible for ASM Scholar or ASM Outstanding Scholar award a total of two times.

Criteria for selection include the student's academic achievement, interest in the field, and personal qualities. Financial need is not a factor, except for the G.A. Roberts and W.P. Woodside Scholarships.

GEOGRAPHIC RESTRICTIONS:
United States.

FINANCIAL DATA:
Amount of support per award: $1,500 to full tuition.

NUMBER OF AWARDS: 15 scholarships are awarded annually through the ASM International Foundation.

APPLICATION INFORMATION:
Required are completed scholarship application (Part One), two letters of recommendation, transcript of college academic records, a photograph, and an individual statement that is no longer than two typewritten pages. For G.A. Roberts and W.P. Woodside Scholarships only, applicants should complete Part Two of the application form, including a personal statement and a financial aid officer contact, along with previous requirements.

Duration: One academic year.

Deadline: Application and materials must be sent by May 1. Award winners will be notified by mail by July 15.

IRS IDENTIFICATION NUMBER: 34-6541397

OFFICERS:
Charles R. Hayes, Executive Director and Secretary

ADDRESS INQUIRIES TO:
ASM Foundation Undergraduate Scholarship Program
(See e-mail and web site above.)

*SPECIAL STIPULATIONS:
Must have completed one year of undergraduate work.

INSTITUTE OF MATERIALS, MINERALS AND MINING   [2846]
Danum House, South Parade
Doncaster DN1 2DY England
44 (0) 1302 320486
Fax: 44 (0) 1302 380900

E-MAIL ADDRESS:
graham.woodrow@iom3.org

WEB SITE ADDRESS:
www.iom3.org

FOUNDED: 1892

AREAS OF INTEREST:
Mining and metallurgy.

NAME(S) OF PROGRAMS:
● **Centenary Scholarship**
● **Stanley Elmore Fellowship Fund**
● **G. Vernon Hobson Bequest**
● **Mining Club Award**
● **Edgar Pam Fellowship**
● **The Tom Seaman Travelling Scholarship**
● **Bosworth Smith Trust Fund**

TYPE:
Awards/prizes; Fellowships; Research grants; Scholarships; Training grants; Travel grants. The Centenary Scholarship is restricted to first- or second-year undergraduates in student membership of the Institute and will be awarded for projects, visits, etc., in furtherance of applicants' career development.

Stanley Elmore Fellowship Fund offers fellowships (normally two for one year) applicable at a U.K. university for research into all branches of extractive metallurgy and mineral processing and, in special cases, for expenditure related to such research.

The G. Vernon Hobson Bequest awards are given for the advancement of teaching and practice of geology as applied to mining. One or more awards may be made for travel, research or other objects in accordance with the terms of the Bequest.

The Mining Club Award will be offered to British subjects 21 to 35 years of age who are actively engaged (in full- or part-time postgraduate study or in employment) in the minerals industry, as defined by the Institute, for travel purposes (for example, to study mineral industry operations in the U.K. or overseas, to present a paper at an international minerals industry conference or to assist the applicant in attending a full-time course of study related to the minerals industry outside the U.K.), or for any other similar purpose that may be regarded as being within the spirit of the award.

The Edgar Pam Fellowship is awarded for postgraduate study in subjects within the Institute's fields of interest, which range from exploration geology to extractive metallurgy. Those eligible for the award are young graduates, domiciled in Australia, Canada, New Zealand, South Africa and the U.K., who wish to undertake advanced study or research in the U.K.

The Tom Seaman Travelling Scholarship is awarded annually to a member, not older than 35 years of age, who is training or has been trained for a career in mining and/or related technologies. The scholarship shall be to assist the study for an aspect of engineering in the minerals industry, with the intention of advancing the associated standards or techniques.

The Bosworth Smith Trust Fund is given for the assistance of postgraduate research in metal mining, non-ferrous extraction metallurgy or mineral dressing. Applications will be considered for grants towards working expenses, the cost of visits to mines and plants in connection with such research, and purchase of apparatus.

ELIGIBILITY:
Applicants should note that, in general, preference will be given to members of the Institution (student membership is required for the Centenary Scholarship). Recipients of the awards will be required to submit summary reports of the ways in which such awards have been used for publication.

In judging the applications received for each award, the Institute will take into account academic excellence and scholarship. The application must, therefore, specify academic ability. Candidates merely seeking assistance for financial hardship will not be considered.

Applicants for awards must ensure that the particular fund from which support is being sought is relevant to their field(s) of interest. Applications not in accordance with the specified terms and conditions of the various funds, those which are received after March 31, and those for which the appropriate letters of support have not been received by that date will not be submitted to the awards committee.

APPLICATION INFORMATION:
Application form required. Applications not in accordance with the specified terms and conditions of the various funds, those which are received after the closing date each year, and those for which the appropriate levels of support have not been received by that date, will not be accepted for consideration.

Deadline: March 31.

PUBLICATIONS:
Guidelines.

ADDRESS INQUIRIES TO:
Dr. G.J.M. Woodrow
Deputy Chief Executive
(See address above.)

INTERNATIONAL CENTRE FOR DIFFRACTION DATA   [2847]
12 Campus Boulevard
Newtown Square, PA 19073-3273
(610) 325-9814
Fax: (610) 325-9823

E-MAIL ADDRESS:
info@icdd.com

WEB SITE ADDRESS:
www.icdd.com

AREAS OF INTEREST:
The science of crystallography.

NAME(S) OF PROGRAMS:
● **The Ludo Frevel Crystallography Scholarship Award**

TYPE:
Scholarships.

PURPOSE:
To encourage promising graduate students to pursue crystallographically oriented research.

ELIGIBILITY:
Applicant should be a graduate student seeking a degree with major interest in crystallography, crystal structure analysis, crystal morphology, modulated structures, correlation of atomic structures with physical properties, systematic classification of crystal structures, phase identification and materials characterization. There are no restrictions on country, race, age or sex.

Funds are not to be used for travel.

FINANCIAL DATA:
The scholarship stipend is to be used by the graduate student to help defray tuition and laboratory fees. A portion of the stipend may be applied to registration fees to accredited scientific meetings related to crystallography.

Amount of support per award: $2,500.

NUMBER OF APPLICANTS MOST RECENT YEAR: 45.

NUMBER OF AWARDS: 10.

APPLICATION INFORMATION:
The following information must be prepared in advance of applying online:
(1) a description of the candidate's proposed research (limit two pages), including purpose and rationale for the research, proposed methodology to be used in the study, and references and/or descriptions of the scientific background for the proposed research and;
(2) a curriculum vitae, including educational preparation (institutions, dates, degrees obtained and in progress, and particularly pertinent coursework), awards/honors received, any research publications and/or presentations given, any work experience (dates, employers, positions), and professional activities and memberships.

Duration: One year. Renewals possible. Renewal applications will be considered on a competitive basis in conjunction with all applications that have been submitted up to the closing date.

Deadline: October 26.

ADDRESS INQUIRIES TO:
Theresa Kozul, Conference Assistant
(See address above.)

MINERALOGICAL ASSOCIATION OF CANADA   [2848]

490, rue de la Couronne
Quebec QC G1K 9A9 Canada
(418) 653-0333
Fax: (418) 653-0777

E-MAIL ADDRESS:
office@mineralogicalassociation.ca

WEB SITE ADDRESS:
www.mineralogicalassociation.ca

FOUNDED: 1955

AREAS OF INTEREST:
Mineralogy.

NAME(S) OF PROGRAMS:
- **Leonard G. Berry Medal**
- **Hawley Award**
- **MAC Foundation Scholarship**
- **MAC Travel/Research Grants**
- **The Mineralogical Association of Canada Ann Sabina Award**
- **Peacock Medal**
- **Student Award Prizes**
- **Young Scientist Award**

TYPE:
Awards/prizes; Grants-in-aid; Research grants; Scholarships; Travel grants.

PURPOSE:
To promote and advance the knowledge of mineralogy and the allied disciplines of crystallography, petrology, geochemistry and mineral deposits.

LEGAL BASIS:
Nonprofit scientific and charitable organization.

ELIGIBILITY:
The Leonard G. Berry Medal is awarded for distinguished service to the Mineralogical Association of Canada.

The Hawley Award is presented to the author(s) of what is judged to be the best paper published in the preceding year's volume of *The Canadian Mineralogist.*

The MAC Foundation Scholarship is awarded to a graduate student involved in an M.Sc. or Ph.D. thesis program in the fields of mineralogy, crystallography, petrology, geochemistry or mineral deposits.

The MAC Travel/Research Grants are given to assist honours undergraduate and graduate students in the mineral sciences.

The Mineralogical Association of Canada Ann Sabina Award is given to the winner of the best self-collected mineral collection at the Annual Show of the Central Canadian Federation of Mineralogical Societies.

The Peacock Medal is awarded annually for excellence in research to a scientist who has made outstanding contributions to the mineralogical sciences in Canada.

Student Award Prizes are given to university students in mineralogy. The Association presents a MAC publication to the top student in the introductory mineralogy course at each Canadian university.

The Young Scientist Award is given to a young scientist who has made a significant international research contribution in a promising start to a scientific career.

GEOGRAPHIC RESTRICTIONS:
Canada.

FINANCIAL DATA:
Amount of support per award: Varies depending on award.
Total amount of support: $22,000.

NUMBER OF APPLICANTS MOST RECENT YEAR:
MAC Travel/Research Grants: 20.

NUMBER OF AWARDS: 12.

APPLICATION INFORMATION:
Contact the Association.

PUBLICATIONS:
The Canadian Mineralogist.

STAFF:
Robert F. Martin, Editor

ADDRESS INQUIRIES TO:
Pierrette Tremblay, Award Coordinator
(See address above.)

Indexes

Entry Listing by Chapter

Subject Index

A

Academic and Career Success: 1192

Academic Medicine. *See* Medicine, Academic

Accounting: 1625, 1743, 1772, 1847, 1848, 2011, 2012, 2020, 2021; *see also* Business; Financial Management

Acoustics: 2166; *see also* Noise

Acquired Immunodeficiency Syndrome (AIDS): 200, 343, 503, 1072, 1354, 1529, 1942, 2111, 2479, 2496, 2526

Acting. *See* Theatre

Actuarial Science: 2222, 2223, 2224, 2229, 2230; *see also* Insurance

Administration. *See* Arts Administration; Business Administration; Educational Administration; Health Administration; Library Administration; Management; Museum Administration; Public Administration

Adolescence. *See* Child Welfare and Health; Youth Adoption; Children, Adoption and Foster Care

Adult Education. *See* Education, Adult

Advertising: 632, 1048, 2017, 2018, 2046; *see also* Business; Public Relations

Aerodynamics: 2814

Aeronautics: 1966, 2782, 2783, 2785, 2786, 2788, 2789, 2792, 2793, 2794

Aerospace Sciences: 2165, 2166, 2186, 2187, 2188, 2314, 2328, 2782, 2785, 2786, 2788, 2789, 2791, 2792, 2793; *see also* Engineering; Sciences; Technology, Aerospace

Aerospace Sciences, History: 616, 1962

Africa: 207, 435, 949, 961, 981, 982, 1642, 2152, 2357; *see also* History, African; Literature, African; also specific nations

Africa, Research and Study in: 949

African-American Studies. *See* Minority Studies; Race Relations; also any discipline that may be given African-American emphasis

African Americans: 425, 435, 639, 772, 1046, 1082, 1088, 1093, 1095, 1316, 1495, 2651; *see also* America; Inner-City; Minority Studies; Race Relations; Urban Affairs; also any discipline that may be given African American emphasis or be of concern to African Americans

African Americans, Eligibility of: 1022, 1025, 1026, 1027, 1042, 1048, 1063, 1067, 1069, 1084, 1088, 1089, 1090, 1091, 1094, 1096, 1097, 1098, 1369, 1646, 1675, 1730, 2014, 2114, 2203, 2222, 2272, 2273, 2289, 2449, 2727, 2770; *see also* Minority Group Members, Eligibility of

Aged: 29, 32, 66, 86, 170, 175, 181, 192, 198, 201, 217, 220, 225, 226, 240, 247, 251, 275, 289, 304, 319, 325, 326, 331, 337, 349, 1061, 1073, 1200, 1244, 1247, 1251, 1270, 1301, 1336, 1338, 1355, 1360, 1366, 1373, 1409, 1410, 1437, 1450, 1454, 1467, 1515, 1524, 1531, 1548, 1550, 1565, 1573, 1576, 1580, 1587, 1595, 1604, 1609, 2261, 2360, 2366, 2369, 2370, 2371, 2392, 2403, 2476, 2488, 2614, 2709; *see also* Geriatrics and Gerontology

Agricultural Cooperatives. *See* Cooperatives, Rural and Consumer

Agricultural Economics: 2251, 2253, 2257, 2259, 2350

Agricultural Sciences: 169, 175, 888, 969, 1941, 2257, 2264, 2328, 2329, 2337, 2350, 2843; *see also* Animal Sciences; Food Technology; Nutrition

Agricultural Sciences, Education: 223, 612, 1214, 1279, 1840, 2073, 2246, 2248, 2252, 2257, 2258, 2265, 2267

Agricultural Sciences, Research and Study Abroad: 899, 1000, 2200, 2249, 2263, 2265

Air Pollution: 1532, 2314, 2329, 2757; *see also* Environmental Studies

Alabama: 256, 454, 750, 1265, 1318, 1337, 1514, 1765, 1766, 1767, 1926

Alaska: 265, 455, 1072, 2157, 2303

Alaskan Natives. *See* American Indians and Alaskan Natives

Albania: 873; *see also* Slavic and East Europe

Alcohol Abuse and Alcoholism: 1052, 1224, 1258, 1510, 1552, 1564; *see also* Behavioral Sciences; Medicine

Allergy: 2489, 2493, 2497; *see also* Immunology

Alpine Area: 2306

Alzheimer's Disease: 28, 2360, 2595, 2611, 2614, 2634, 2752

America: 808, 2081, 2136, 2222, 2247; *see also* Economics; History, American; Literature, American; Minority Studies; Political Science

American Indian and Alaskan Native Community Development: 1115, 1116, 1122, 1124, 1479, 1686, 1971; *see also* Minority Community and Institutional Development; Minority-Owned Businesses; Small Business Development

American Indians and Alaskan Natives: 720, 770, 772, 898, 1076, 1082, 1103, 1117, 1123, 1127, 1128, 1845, 1846; *see also* Minority Studies; Race Relations; also any discipline that may be given American Indian emphasis or be of concern to American Indians

American Indians and Alaskan Natives, Eligibility of: 1022, 1025, 1026, 1027, 1042, 1043, 1063, 1067, 1069, 1084, 1100, 1101, 1102, 1104, 1105, 1106, 1107, 1108, 1109, 1110, 1111, 1112, 1113, 1114, 1115, 1117, 1119, 1120, 1121, 1124, 1125, 1126, 1128, 1506, 1572, 1686, 1704, 1730, 1892, 2014, 2114, 2203, 2222, 2272, 2273, 2289, 2443, 2449, 2727, 2770; *see also* Minority-Group Members, Eligibility of

American Indians and Alaskan Natives, Employment: 1115, 1121, 2095; *see also* Equal Employment Opportunity; Labor

Amyotrophic Lateral Sclerosis (ALS): 2616, 2631, 2634

Anatomy: 2400, 2641

Anesthesiology: 2408, 2420, 2421, 2442

Animal Cruelty: 99, 220, 225, 264, 1468, 1475, 1946, 2009, 2242, 2324, 2386

Animal Sciences: 224, 1345, 1707, 1927, 1941, 1981, 2171, 2236, 2237, 2242, 2244, 2257, 2269, 2285, 2297, 2385, 2414, 2425; *see also* Veterinary Sciences

Animal Welfare: 46, 321

Antarctica: 1957

Anthropology: 393, 418, 428, 430, 476, 681, 887, 888, 920, 1876, 1920, 1929, 1931, 1962, 1971, 1978, 1979, 2146, 2147, 2148, 2150, 2151, 2152, 2153, 2154, 2155, 2156, 2212, 2270, 2276; *see also* Behavioral Sciences; History; Sociology

Anthropology, Research and Study Abroad: 960, 2157

Applied Sciences: 4, 989

Appraisal: 2013

Apprenticeships. *See* In-Service Training Projects

Aquatic Ecology. *See* Ecology, Aquatic

Arboriculture: 2262; *see also* Forestry

Archaeology: 381, 394, 664, 665, 888, 935, 1157, 1920, 1937, 1971, 2146, 2149, 2153, 2212

Archaeology, Research and Study Abroad: 382, 383, 384, 386, 408, 460, 876, 919, 921, 933, 934, 936, 940, 941, 942, 949, 963, 1731, 1780

Architecture: 370, 404, 431, 436, 437, 438, 439, 441, 442, 443, 444, 445, 446, 447, 450, 451, 452, 470, 492, 501, 508, 516, 522, 545, 610, 650, 656, 1086, 1134, 1919, 1920; *see also* Arts; Landscape Design; Urban and Regional Planning

Architecture, Research and Study Abroad: 375, 383, 441, 449, 450, 453, 610, 936

Arctic: 1732, 1959, 2306

Area Studies: 685, 686, 701, 702, 874, 878, 879, 880, 881, 882, 883, 900, 902, 903, 904, 908, 909, 912, 930, 944, 973, 975, 992, 994, 995, 1830, 1978; *see also* Africa; America; Asia; Atlantic Community; Canada; Europe; Geography; Latin and South America; Mediterranean Area; Middle East; NATO Member Countries; Orient; Pacific Area; Slavic and East Europe; also specific states, U.S. regions, or nations

Argentina: 1819

Arizona: 21, 143, 147, 461, 580, 786, 1101, 1112, 1248, 1299, 1437, 2327

Arkansas: 89, 209, 510, 1249, 1356, 1446

Armaments: 2814; *see also* Defense Projects and Research; International Security; National Security

Armed Services Personnel and Dependents, Eligibility of: 1798, 1850; *see also* Veterans, Eligibility or; Veterans' Children and Dependents, Eligibility of

Arms Control: 65, 300, 885, 907, 913

Art Criticism: 594; *see also* Literary Criticism

Art Galleries: 503, 514, 603; *see also* Exhibitions; Museums

Art History: 234, 375, 376, 386, 399, 404, 406, 418, 428, 430, 431, 436, 460, 476, 514, 523, 547, 577, 584, 587, 589, 591, 594, 920, 936, 999, 1914, 1920, 1962, 1971

Art Therapy: 2718

Arthritis. *See* Rheumatology and Rheumatic Diseases

Arts: 1, 2, 3, 5, 6, 7, 8, 12, 13, 14, 17, 18, 19, 20, 24, 30, 31, 32, 34, 35, 42, 43, 44, 52, 53, 57, 59, 60, 61, 62, 66, 74, 79, 80, 81, 86, 87, 91, 92, 96, 98, 99, 100, 104, 105, 107, 109, 113, 114, 115, 118, 120, 126, 127, 135, 137, 140, 142, 145, 147, 148, 149, 151, 155, 161, 164, 166, 167, 168, 169, 172, 180, 184, 191, 192, 195, 198, 203, 208, 212, 213, 215, 217, 220, 222, 226, 229, 231, 235, 240, 241, 246, 249, 251, 254, 255, 256, 257, 258, 259, 260, 265, 266, 273, 275, 279, 280, 283, 284, 289, 290, 296, 298, 306, 310, 312, 316, 321, 322, 324, 337, 339, 340, 342, 343, 345, 347, 351, 353, 359, 364, 366, 367, 369, 371, 373, 398, 409, 412, 429, 432, 434, 446, 447, 454, 455, 456, 459, 461, 463, 464, 465, 466, 467, 468, 469, 471, 473, 477, 478, 479, 481, 482, 484, 485, 488, 490, 491, 492, 493, 494, 495, 496, 497, 498, 501, 502, 503, 504, 505, 506, 508, 509, 510, 511, 512, 513, 514, 515, 516, 517, 519, 520, 521, 522, 524, 525, 526, 527, 528, 529, 531, 532, 533, 534, 535, 536, 537, 538, 539, 544, 545, 546, 549, 550, 551, 555, 556, 557, 571, 573, 600, 603, 611, 634, 683, 720, 748, 768, 808, 952, 965, 998, 1033, 1050,

Equal Employment Opportunity: 228, 254, 311, 1275, 2095; *see also* Labor

Equal Rights. *See* Human Rights

Equipment Grants: 70, 131, 219, 236, 336, 1323, 1961, 2296, 2815; *see also* Construction and Facilities Projects; specific fields of interest

Essays: 914; *see also* Nonfiction

Ethics: 23, 1363, 1922, 1956, 2239; *see also* Human Values; Legal Ethics; Medical Ethics

Ethnology: 376, 418, 430, 488, 1085, 1103, 2157, 2352; *see also* Anthropology; Sociology

Eurasia and East Europe 904, 981, 982

Europe: 578, 953, 970, 992, 994; *see also* Area Studies; History, European; Languages; Literature; Slavic and East Europe; Social Sciences; also specific nations

European Integration: 887

Evolution: 2146, 2292, 2297

Exchange Programs. *See* Cultural Exchange Programs; Educational Exchange Programs; International Projects and Seminars; International Study and Research Programs; Scientific Exchange Programs

Exhibitions: 467, 481, 505, 537, 599, 606, 2769; *see also* Cultural Events, Community; Museums; also specific disciplines

Experimental and Pilot Programs. *See* specific disciplines

Exploration and Field Research: 1937, 1943, 1957, 2211, 2212, 2243, 2299, 2306, 2328, 2336

F

Faculty Development: 901

Faculty, Study and Research Programs: 167, 400, 413, 415, 416, 421, 426, 689, 881, 883, 1678, 1706, 1716, 1749, 2018, 2026, 2168, 2291, 2561, 2562, 2565, 2696, 2736, 2813; *see also* Education, Teacher Preparation

Faculty, Study and Research Programs Abroad: 980, 994, 995, 1705; *see also* specific disciplines

Families in Crisis: 1164, 1213, 1228

Family Development: 5, 52, 149, 169, 870, 1180, 1450, 1481

Family Life: 52, 149, 150, 153, 173, 275, 278, 290, 1036, 1154, 1180, 1190, 1201, 1210, 1277, 1291, 1301, 1362, 1372, 1386, 1423, 1441, 1488, 1524, 1576, 1601, 1609, 2834, 2835, 2841

Family Planning: 195, 300, 1133, 1285, 1553, 1617, 2337, 2650; *see also* Genetics; Population Studies; Reproduction Research; Social Sciences; Social Welfare

Family Practice. *See* Medicine, Family Practice

Family Services: 60, 93, 128, 155, 171, 283, 1218, 1220, 1341, 1391, 1438, 1520, 1556, 1576, 1583, 1606, 1617; *see also* Social Services

Farm Safety and Health: 1214

Fashion: 476, 1889

Fats and Proteins. *See* Biological Sciences; Food Technology; Nutrition

Fiction: 705, 706, 714, 720, 725, 727, 728, 730, 734, 735, 740, 742, 744, 746, 1034; *see also* Literature; Manuscript Prizes, Poetry and Fiction; Publication Prizes, Creative Writing; Writers and Writing

Field Research. *See* Exploration and Field Research

Film: 377, 409, 446, 474, 485, 492, 494, 501, 508, 515, 530, 547, 576, 1006, 1165, 1640, 2056, 2059, 2089, 2111; *see also* Creative Arts

Film, Directing: 494, 571, 1165, 2056

Filmmaking: 532, 555

Finance: 202, 884, 2030, 2031, 2034, 2037, 2042, 2070, 2133, 2229, 2230; *see also* Business; Economics

Financial Assistance. *See* Emergency Financial Assistance

Financial Counseling: 2838

Financial Management: 22, 2011, 2012; *see also* Accounting

Fine Arts: 48, 138, 355, 447, 455, 461, 462, 468, 473, 502, 503, 505, 517, 525, 527, 529, 536, 545, 551, 556, 576, 580, 581, 582, 591, 595, 596, 598, 599, 600, 603, 611, 1117, 1399, 1579, 1920; *see also* Arts; Creative Arts; Decorative Arts; Design; Graphic Arts; Humanities; Painting; Photography; Sculpture

Fine Arts, Publication: 447, 503, 523, 594; *see also* Publication Prizes, History and Humanities

Fine Arts, Research and Study: 393, 436, 451, 590, 593, 594, 595, 596, 604, 610, 1117, 1919

Fine Arts, Research and Study Abroad: 375, 408, 480, 578, 605, 610

Fine Arts, Workshops and Residencies: 583, 593, 594

Finland: 945, 957, 1005; *see also* Scandinavia

Fire Control: 1352, 2162

Fire Department Administration: 1402, 1820

Fire Prevention and Research: 1052, 1352, 1820, 2162, 2708

Fish and Game Management: 1685, 1953, 2274, 2317, 2336; *see also* Animal Sciences; Conservation; Ecology, Aquatic; Marine Biology; Wildlife

Fitness. *See* Physical Fitness

Flemish Studies. *See* Arts; Europe; History, European

Floriculture: 2247, 2253, 2285; *see also* Botany; Horticulture

Florida: 60, 126, 257, 289, 299, 479, 784, 1073, 1092, 1130, 1211, 1301, 1303, 1534, 1538, 1559, 1612, 1647, 1719, 1797, 1801, 1802, 1874, 1875, 2595

Folk Arts: 462, 467, 471, 479, 485, 488, 491, 493, 500, 517, 520, 522, 524, 526, 531, 537, 546, 551, 556; *see also* Crafts; Creative Arts

Folk Studies. *See* Ethnology

Folklore: 878

Food Service. *See* Restaurant Management and Food Service

Food Technology: 173, 207, 893, 1928, 1941, 2566, 2587, 2760, 2773, 2840; *see also* Nutrition

Foreign Faculty Study Programs: 1012; *see also* Foreign Nationals, Eligibility of; Travel Grants, Foreign Faculty and Researchers; also specific nations

Foreign Languages. *See* Languages

Foreign Nationals, Eligibility of: 15, 16, 380, 426, 433, 436, 437, 484, 589, 622, 625, 715, 788, 789, 797, 805, 815, 817, 829, 833, 835, 893, 894, 906, 915, 919, 921, 931, 942, 957, 963, 967, 999, 1000, 1001, 1006, 1007, 1008, 1010, 1012, 1013, 1014, 1015, 1016, 1065, 1149, 1500, 1554, 1830, 1948, 1962, 1993, 2064, 2104, 2105, 2153, 2154, 2163, 2166, 2174, 2187, 2282, 2287, 2288, 2593, 2604, 2606, 2672, 2818; *see also* Foreign Faculty Study Programs; Travel Grants, Foreign Faculty and Researchers; Travel Grants, Foreign Students; Women, Foreign Nationals, Eligibility of; also specific nations

Foreign Policy Studies: 22, 883, 2123

Forest and Range Resources: 2256, 2321, 2350; *see also* Conservation; Ecology; Environmental Studies; Resource Development and Management

Forestry: 370, 969, 1479, 2256, 2262

Forestry, Education: 2260

France: 421, 437, 480, 668, 950, 984, 989, 1819

Franco-American Relations: 407, 668

Fraternal Organizations, Eligibility Limited to Members of: 1816, 2423, 2830, 2839

Freedom: 293, 1592, 1617, 2087, 2111, 2135

Funeral Service: 1944

G

Gardens. *See* Horticulture; Landscape Design

Gastroenterology: 2495, 2561, 2562, 2563, 2564, 2565, 2568, 2572, 2573

Gay and Lesbian Issues: 257, 1031, 1032, 1033, 1034, 1036, 1038, 1039, 1049, 1050, 1051, 1054, 1068, 1072, 1096, 1154, 1299, 1354, 1479, 1529, 2241; *see also* Acquired Immunodeficiency Syndrome (AIDS); Minority Affairs

Genetics: 224, 1512, 2238, 2239, 2287, 2296, 2297, 2371, 2389, 2410, 2429, 2433, 2434, 2435, 2441, 2442, 2495, 2518, 2573, 2620, 2624, 2631, 2641, 2664, 2676, 2679, 2744; *see also* Biological Sciences; Birth Defects; Medical Research; Reproduction Research

Genocide Studies: 681

Geochemistry: 2170, 2217

Geodesy: 2217, 2798; *see also* Earth Sciences; Engineering; Mathematics

Geographic Information Systems/Land Information Systems 2160, 2161, 2285, 2798

Geography: 887, 1943, 1966, 1971, 1985, 2204, 2205, 2206, 2207, 2212, 2314; *see also* Area Studies; Earth Sciences; Social Sciences

Geology: 4, 1911, 1957, 1959, 2202, 2203, 2208, 2211, 2212, 2217, 2218, 2276, 2686; *see also* Earth Sciences; Mineral Sciences

Geophysics: 1911, 1936, 1949, 1957, 1959, 1966, 2175, 2203, 2217, 2218, 2220, 2314; *see also* Earth Sciences; Physical Sciences; Physics

Georgia: 158, 271, 353, 369, 485, 765, 1271, 1292, 1296, 1337

Geospatial Sciences: 2160

Geriatrics and Gerontology: 170, 1520, 1550, 1573, 2238, 2360, 2366, 2369, 2370, 2371, 2392, 2416, 2709; *see also* Aged

Germany: 631, 681, 693, 920, 923, 953, 966, 967, 1005, 1729, 1737, 1739, 1771, 1819

Gerontology. *See* Geriatrics and Gerontology

Glaciology: 1957, 1959; *see also* Earth Sciences; Geology

Government: 65, 144, 168, 196, 202, 293, 311, 884, 1218, 1285, 1989, 1992, 2077, 2116, 2117, 2118, 2119, 2122, 2123, 2129, 2133, 2135, 2136, 2141, 2143, 2144, 2145; *see also* Community Government; Political Science; Public Administration

Government, Internships: 1089, 1125, 2113, 2120, 2128, 2131, 2132, 2134, 2137, 2140, 2142, 2335, 2726

Graphic Arts: 489, 590, 2046; *see also* Arts; Creative Arts; Design; Fine Arts; Visual Arts

Graphic Communications: 2777, 2778

Great Britain. *See* England; Ireland; Scotland

Greece: 382, 383, 386, 460, 934, 935, 936, 937, 938, 939, 940, 941, 1024, 1044

1413, 1436, 1460, 1469, 1604, 1633, 1729, 1751, 1784, 1876, 1971, 1973, 1996, 1997, 2000, 2075, 2091, 2126, 2133; *see also* Arts; Social Sciences; specific disciplines

Humanities, Curriculum Development 395, 540, 1678

Humanities, International Cooperative Programs: 902

Humanities, Publication, Exhibition, and Public Information Projects: 395, 410, 419, 506, 1470; *see also* Publication Prizes, History and Humanities

Humanities, Related to Other Disciplines: 378, 397, 433, 1937, 1956

Humanities, Research and Study: 376, 378, 389, 390, 391, 392, 393, 397, 400, 402, 406, 412, 413, 415, 416, 417, 418, 420, 421, 422, 424, 425, 426, 429, 433, 434, 619, 622, 873, 874, 879, 882, 908, 1069, 1784, 1910, 1919, 1922, 1937, 1995, 1996, 1997, 1998, 1999, 2000, 2001, 2091, 2150

Humanities, Research and Study Abroad 385, 398, 408, 421, 423, 909, 919, 921, 924, 931, 933, 938, 940, 942, 960, 962, 963, 990, 1000, 1745, 1788

Humanities, Teaching Methods: 1199

Humanities, Workshops and Seminars: 379, 397, 416, 421, 1678

Humor: 721

Hungary: 873

Hunger: 217, 218, 223, 317, 356, 1240, 1251, 1390, 1400, 1582, 1593, 1594, 1613, 1618; *see also* Disadvantaged; Poverty Programs, Social Welfare

Huntington's Disease: 2624, 2634; *see also* Neuromuscular Disorders

Hydrology: 2217, 2325, 2784

I

Iberia: 694, 912; *see also* Europe; specific nations

Iceland: 945

Ichthyology: 1929, 2276

Idaho: 188, 265, 491, 1072, 1615, 2308

Illinois: 1, 36, 84, 115, 116, 122, 135, 138, 151, 237, 263, 294, 306, 317, 326, 349, 357, 492, 859, 1073, 1259, 1260, 1283, 1284, 1390, 1425, 1524, 1818, 1831, 1945, 1972, 2326

Illustration: 264, 541, 741, 745; *see also* Graphic Arts

Immigrant Resettlement: 1045, 1056, 1413, 1466, 1736

Immigration Studies. *See* Ethnology

Immunology: 200, 331, 1058, 2166, 2296, 2400, 2478, 2489, 2492, 2493, 2495, 2496, 2510, 2568, 2589, 2590, 2606; *see also* Microbiology

In-Service Training Projects: 753, 906, 953, 1048, 1933, 2017, 2057, 2067, 2084, 2096, 2334, 2739, 2836; *see also* specific disciplines

India: 237, 690, 928, 951, 991, 1759, 1819

Indiana: 30, 230, 493, 769, 1313, 1332, 1390, 1485, 1773, 1883, 1972, 2252

Industrial Arts and Education: 2777, 2778, 2823; *see also* Education, Technical; Education, Vocational

Industrial Development: 2769

Industrial Relations: 1825

Industry and Industrial Research: 2024, 2094, 2192, 2196, 2198, 2200, 2779; *see also* Technology, Industrial

Infectious Diseases: 2491, 2494, 2495, 2497, 2695; *see also* Immunology; Microbiology

Information Sciences: 258, 753, 756, 757, 758, 773, 778, 888, 1020, 1477, 1501, 1958, 2011, 2047, 2417, 2767; *see also* Communications; Computer Sciences; Educational Media; Libraries and Librarianship

Inner-City: 32, 151, 263, 335, 1199, 1222, 1223, 1383, 1445; *see also* Community Development; Urban Affairs

Instructional Materials: 916, 1718; *see also* Communications; Curriculum Development; Education; Educational Media

Instrumentation, Biomedical: 2448

Insurance: 2023, 2222; *see also* Business; Finance

Interdisciplinary Research and Study: 391, 893, 894, 1937, 1956, 2233; *see also* Humanities, Related to Other Disciplines; Medicine, Related to Other Disciplines; Sciences, Related to Other Disciplines

Interior Design: 440, 513

Internal Medicine. *See* Medicine, Internal

International Development: 25, 898, 906, 999, 1002, 1348, 1387, 1388, 1597; *see also* Developing Nations

International Education. *See* Education, Comparative

International Exchange. *See* Cultural Exchange Programs; Educational Exchange Programs; International Study and Research Programs

International Law. *See* Law, International

International Market. *See* Trade

International Projects and Seminars: 994, 1739, 1764, 2039, 2155, 2156; *see also* Humanities, International Cooperative Programs; Medicine, International Cooperative Programs; Scientific Research and Development, International Cooperative Programs; Social Sciences, International Cooperative Programs

International Relations and International Affairs: 65, 93, 144, 150, 193, 681, 701, 877, 885, 888, 889, 890, 891, 892, 893, 894, 895, 896, 897, 900, 902, 905, 906, 907, 910, 912, 913, 914, 915, 980, 985, 992, 994, 995, 999, 1086, 1149, 1596, 1600, 1825, 1866, 1913, 2055, 2138, 2139; *see also* Area Studies; Economics, International: Environment, International; Law, International; Political Science, International; Social Sciences; also specific nations and disciplines of international concern

International Security: 65, 237, 879, 880, 881, 1992

International Study and Research Programs: 375, 385, 423, 433, 690, 775, 880, 884, 887, 896, 897, 901, 904, 906, 908, 909, 911, 916, 918, 920, 922, 924, 925, 926, 927, 928, 929, 930, 934, 945, 946, 947, 948, 949, 950, 951, 953, 954, 955, 956, 957, 958, 959, 960, 961, 962, 964, 966, 968, 969, 970, 971, 972, 973, 974, 975, 977, 979, 981, 982, 983, 985, 988, 990, 991, 992, 993, 994, 995, 996, 997, 998, 999, 1000, 1001, 1003, 1004, 1005, 1019, 1149, 1387, 1388, 1707, 1736, 1738, 1745, 1764, 1788, 1819, 1825, 2039, 2099, 2100, 2174, 2200, 2243, 2265, 2305, 2320, 2328, 2707, 2833; *see also* specific disciplines, research and study abroad

International Travel: 878, 906, 928, 994; *see also* Travel Grants, Foreign Faculty and Researchers

Internships. *See* In-Service Training Projects

Interracial Cooperation. *See* Race Relations

Inventory. *See* Materials Handling

Iowa: 495, 1073, 1205, 1243, 1365, 1390, 1741

Ireland: 715, 900, 1819

Islam: 921; *see also* Religion

Israel: 217, 307, 482, 867, 871, 875, 919, 934, 964, 1004, 1006, 1019, 1037, 1045, 1060, 1080, 1190, 1391, 1745, 2263

Italian-American Relations: 613, 617, 1079

Italy: 375, 383, 398, 589, 613, 638, 788, 938, 990, 1003, 1079, 1819, 1843

Italy, Eligibility Limited to Descendants of: 1079, 1797, 1843

J

Japan: 484, 901, 908, 971, 972, 978, 1005, 1017, 1739, 1819; *see also* Orient

Japanese-American Relations: 891, 902, 910, 916, 2128

Japanese Studies: 891, 901, 1751, 1822

Jazz: 515, 561, 562, 567; *see also* Music

Jewish Life: 28, 105, 161, 226, 482, 630, 681, 685, 686, 687, 688, 864, 867, 871, 929, 1037, 1045, 1060, 1080, 1190, 1289, 1361, 1450, 1663, 1831; *see also* Judaism

Job Preparedness: 111, 147, 349, 1184, 1262, 1451, 1624; *see also* Labor, Employment and Training

Journalism: 73, 119, 164, 196, 243, 370, 723, 884, 953, 1050, 1068, 1782, 1871, 1874, 2050, 2052, 2055, 2058, 2062, 2063, 2064, 2065, 2066, 2068, 2069, 2070, 2073, 2078, 2079, 2080, 2081, 2082, 2083, 2085, 2091, 2125, 2135; *see also* Communications; News Reporting: Public Relations; Publications; Writers and Writing

Journalism, Education: 40, 215, 1064, 1655, 1871, 2054, 2057, 2061, 2064, 2076, 2077, 2079, 2082, 2084, 2086, 2089, 2091

Journalism, Internships: 2044, 2049, 2057, 2067, 2084, 2113, 2133

Journalism, Medical and Health: 1775, 2067

Journalism, Religious: 1083, 2088

Journalism, Scientific: 2044, 2045, 2054, 2074, 2231

Judaism: 28, 161, 217, 307, 403, 482, 685, 686, 716, 717, 722, 862, 864, 867, 871, 956, 1056, 1060, 1074, 1289, 1391, 1462, 1471, 1529, 1824; *see also* Religion

Judicial Administration: 1500, 2117, 2142

Judicial Reform: 1504

Junior Colleges: 867; *see also* Education; Education, Higher, Research, Project, and General Support

Justice: 106, 144, 201, 229, 1275, 1290, 1321, 1413, 1501, 1591, 1592, 1593, 1982, 2079; *see also* Criminal Justice; Judicial Reform; Juvenile Justice; Law; Law Enforcement

Juvenile Delinquency: 1502, 1504, 1505, 1508; *see also* Children; Youth

Juvenile Justice: 301, 1486, 1504, 1505, 1508

K

Kansas: 209, 510, 1101, 1112, 1160, 1369, 1542, 1619

Kentucky: 186, 496, 1073, 1150, 1357, 2252, 2355

Korea: 950, 1739, 1829

Massachusetts: 37, 61, 82, 128, 274, 288, 305, 335, 410, 449, 506, 557, 641, 642, 643, 644, 733, 1139, 1171, 1198, 1200, 1255, 1263, 1323, 1347, 1371, 1396, 1472, 1473, 1474, 1502, 1556, 1560, 1565, 1583, 1588, 1609, 1616, 1655, 1695, 1836, 1837, 2392, 2479

Materials Handling: 2762

Materials Science: 949, 1019, 1936, 1949, 1966, 2172, 2831, 2845, 2846

Maternal Health Care: 197, 2661; *see also* Health; Medical and Health Services

Mathematics: 4, 190, 328, 1077, 1078, 1193, 1690, 1947, 1955, 1965, 1966, 2044, 2170, 2225, 2226, 2227, 2228, 2772, 2811, 2812; *see also* Computer Sciences; Sciences; Statistics

Mathematics, Education: 190, 1069, 1102, 1114, 1134, 1138, 1140, 1195, 1466, 1624, 1690, 1711, 1718, 1725, 1919, 1920, 1955, 1963, 2222, 2223, 2224, 2228, 2229, 2778

Mathematics, Research and Study: 1084, 1933, 1934, 1949, 2223, 2224, 2230, 2812

Mathematics, Research and Study Abroad: 958, 1004, 1019

Measurement Sciences: 2164, 2831

Mechanical Arts. *See* Industrial Arts and Education

Media. *See* Communications; also specific media forms

Media Arts: 468, 471, 477, 479, 492, 493, 494, 496, 500, 534, 546, 1049, 2048, 2085, 2089; *see also* Arts

Medical Administration. *See* Health Administration

Medical and Health Practitioners: 36, 1145, 1511, 1523, 1530, 1769, 2365, 2579, 2580, 2657, 2681, 2682; *see also* Medical and Health Services; Midwifery; Nursing

Medical and Health Services: 1, 18, 55, 58, 59, 66, 120, 170, 195, 200, 201, 262, 283, 285, 292, 331, 338, 353, 1076, 1305, 1450, 1464, 1511, 1517, 1521, 1544, 1561, 1562, 1566, 1567, 1568, 1570, 1578, 1611, 1614, 1619, 1677, 1769, 1820, 2328, 2375, 2392, 2426, 2468, 2476, 2478, 2652, 2695, 2717, 2744; *see also* Health Care Facilities; Hospitals

Medical Conference, Symposia, and Workshops: 1769, 1775, 2489, 2725

Medical Costs: 1511, 1517, 1521, 1567, 1769, 1775, 2426, 2693

Medical Education and Training: 170, 197, 200, 319, 362, 405, 1112, 1134, 1145, 1163, 1202, 1527, 1548, 1558, 1562, 1774, 1775, 1776, 1836, 1916, 1917, 1919, 1963, 2369, 2370, 2376, 2382, 2401, 2402, 2415, 2431, 2432, 2437, 2444, 2445, 2447, 2449, 2451, 2468, 2486, 2493, 2494, 2541, 2543, 2552, 2585, 2608, 2641, 2649, 2681, 2684, 2686, 2688, 2719, 2744; *see also* Midwifery; Nursing Education; specific diseases and areas of medicine by name

Medical Education and Training, Armed Services: 2486

Medical Education and Training, Outside of U.S.: 1667, 1903, 2394, 2395, 2396, 2398, 2399, 2487, 2607

Medical Ethics: 2239; *see also* Bioethics

Medical Facilities, Construction Grants 2488; *see also* Construction and Facilities Projects; Hospitals, Construction and Facilities Projects

Medical Journalism. *See* Journalism, Medical and Health

Medical Library: 773, 774, 1013, 1062; *see also* Library Science, Education; Library Services and Collection Utilization

Medical Research: 81, 99, 107, 121, 122, 123, 166, 236, 245, 262, 276, 289, 318, 321, 324, 331, 361, 362, 366, 405, 624, 1171, 1360, 1366, 1381, 1397, 1437, 1458, 1512, 1525, 1546, 1555, 1562, 1634, 1733, 1735, 1964, 1966, 1968, 2166, 2238, 2240, 2275, 2282, 2295, 2321, 2358, 2359, 2361, 2362, 2363, 2364, 2366, 2367, 2369, 2370, 2371, 2372, 2373, 2378, 2381, 2383, 2387, 2388, 2390, 2391, 2404, 2405, 2406, 2409, 2411, 2413, 2419, 2420, 2421, 2422, 2424, 2427, 2429, 2433, 2434, 2435, 2436, 2438, 2442, 2445, 2446, 2450, 2452, 2453, 2454, 2455, 2456, 2457, 2458, 2459, 2461, 2464, 2467, 2469, 2476, 2477, 2478, 2482, 2484, 2485, 2488, 2491, 2492, 2494, 2495, 2496, 2497, 2511, 2512, 2514, 2520, 2524, 2525, 2540, 2541, 2542, 2543, 2546, 2553, 2555, 2556, 2559, 2560, 2565, 2566, 2568, 2569, 2572, 2574, 2576, 2577, 2578, 2579, 2580, 2582, 2583, 2587, 2589, 2590, 2595, 2596, 2597, 2598, 2600, 2604, 2605, 2612, 2614, 2615, 2616, 2618, 2619, 2620, 2624, 2631, 2640, 2641, 2664, 2665, 2668, 2669, 2670, 2674, 2676, 2677, 2687, 2689, 2692, 2693, 2694, 2695, 2700, 2703, 2704, 2705, 2711, 2720, 2728, 2735; *see also* diseases and areas of medicine by name

Medical Research, Outside U.S.: 978, 998, 1017, 1729, 1771, 2282, 2359, 2397, 2400, 2487, 2491, 2570, 2593

Medical Research, Supplies and Equipment: 2435, 2440, 2448, 2586, 2669; *see also* Sciences, Equipment and Facilities

Medical Technology: 851, 1511, 1775, 2376, 2380, 2423, 2440, 2480, 2687, 2695; *see also* Dental Laboratory Technology

Medicine: 5, 7, 52, 104, 139, 143, 179, 214, 227, 272, 306, 313, 344, 354, 365, 368, 965, 1260, 1517, 1564, 1633, 1682, 1683, 1917, 2375, 2407, 2408, 2414, 2418, 2419, 2422, 2427, 2429, 2431, 2444, 2453, 2454, 2455, 2464, 2467, 2478, 2483, 2488, 2493, 2525, 2567, 2616, 2617, 2633, 2638, 2648, 2687, 2699, 2715, 2728; *see also* Biomedical Sciences and Research; Health; Hospitals; Surgery; also diseases and areas of medicine by name

Medicine, Academic: 1771, 1775, 2368, 2391, 2463, 2541, 2543, 2564, 2573, 2660

Medicine, Diagnostic: 204, 2377, 2604

Medicine, Experimental: 2166

Medicine, Family Practice: 2365, 2415

Medicine, History: 624, 1145, 2699; *see also* Sciences, History

Medicine, Internal: 2483, 2524, 2525, 2572, 2685

Medicine, International Cooperative Programs: 1729, 2432, 2495

Medicine, Organ Transplant: 2579

Medicine, Preventive: 200, 1534, 2369, 2370, 2409, 2442, 2587, 2604, 2689, 2695

Medicine, Public Information Projects: 200, 1511, 1545, 1562, 2488, 2695; *see also* Community Education

Medicine, Publication: 2400, 2444, 2728; *see also* Journalism, Medical and Health; Manuscript Prizes, Medical and Health Sciences; Publication Prizes, Medical and Health Sciences

Medicine, Related to Other Disciplines: 2488, 2544, 2545, 2610, 2711

Medieval Studies: 388, 645, 664; *see also* History; Humanities; Literature

Mediterranean Area: 384

Memory. *See* Learning Process and Memory

Mental and Emotional Health: 32, 55, 122, 249, 361, 861, 1042, 1212, 1248, 1461, 1478, 1480, 1520, 1589, 1610, 1756, 1988, 2723, 2729, 2731, 2735, 2737, 2741, 2742, 2743, 2744, 2756

Mental Health Services: 109, 309, 1026, 1037, 1413, 1450, 1530, 1619, 2737, 2740, 2744, 2756; *see also* Medical and Health Services

Mental Retardation: 356, 1059, 1171, 1483, 2714, 2731, 2752

Metabolism and Metabolic Disorders: 2296, 2433, 2434, 2435, 2518, 2569, 2582, 2583, 2610

Metallurgy: 1938, 1939, 1965, 1966, 2845, 2846, 2847, 2848; *see also* Materials Sciences; Physical Sciences; Technology, Mining

Meteorology: 1957, 1959, 2212, 2784; *see also* Atmospheric Sciences; Climatology

Mexican-Americans. *See* Spanish-Speaking Americans

Mexicans, Eligibility of: 886, 1022, 2845

Mexico: 156, 237, 886, 950, 1345, 2038, 2157, 2773

Michigan: 49, 75, 88, 118, 165, 207, 246, 269, 327, 351, 367, 412, 508, 1057, 1073, 1152, 1194, 1236, 1237, 1272, 1297, 1327, 1358, 1370, 1382, 1385, 1394, 1395, 1414, 1435, 1480, 1494, 1598, 1658, 1715, 1923, 2252, 2485

Microbiology: 1904, 2166, 2240, 2272, 2273, 2289, 2290, 2410, 2441, 2493, 2495, 2510; *see also* Biological Sciences

Middle East: 919, 921, 942, 961, 963, 981, 982; *see also* Area Studies; History; Languages; Literature; Social Sciences; also specific nations

Midwestern States: 125, 202, 421, 1073, 2659; *see also* states by name

Military History: 614, 665, 676, 677, 678, 679, 680; *see also* History

Military Sciences: 2115, 2814; *see also* Defense Projects and Research

Mineral Sciences: 2210, 2848; *see also* Geology; Materials Sciences; Sciences

Minimal Brain Dysfunction. *See* Learning Disabilities

Mining. *See* Technology, Mining

Minnesota: 41, 111, 120, 223, 239, 251, 347, 361, 409, 481, 739, 777, 1166, 1167, 1243, 1244, 1245, 1264, 1269, 1277, 1339, 1344, 1363, 1415, 1431, 1443, 1449, 1482, 1526, 1597

Minority Affairs: 136, 168, 192, 240, 269, 346, 362, 1031, 1032, 1036, 1049, 1068, 1174, 1270, 1588, 1596, 1682, 1722, 2449, 2803; *see also* Equal Educational Opportunity; Equal Employment Opportunity; Poverty Programs; Race Relations; Social Welfare; Urban Affairs; also specific minority groups

Minority Community and Institutional Development: 138, 1488, 1552, 1642; *see also* Community Development

Minority-Group Members, Eligibility of: 439, 752, 753, 759, 795, 827, 855, 1022, 1025, 1026, 1027, 1035, 1036, 1042, 1048, 1053, 1062, 1063, 1065, 1067, 1069, 1075, 1077, 1078, 1083, 1084, 1086, 1091, 1092, 1130, 1528, 1625, 1643, 1644, 1730, 1772, 1785, 1829, 1915, 1936, 2014, 2026, 2037, 2044, 2108, 2114, 2203, 2222, 2272, 2273, 2289, 2327, 2431, 2442, 2443, 2449, 2666, 2681, 2727, 2770, 2823, 2834; *see also* specific minority groups

Minority-Group Members, Employment: 228; *see also* Equal Employment Opportunity; Labor, Employment and Training; also specific minority groups

Minority-Owned Businesses: 1116; *see also* Business Development Assistance

Minority Studies: 425, 435, 1082, 1085, 1127, 1642, 1972; *see also* American Indians and Alaskan Natives; Asian-Americans; Blacks; Spanish-Speaking Americans; specific minority groups

Mississippi: 57, 89, 172, 207, 1356, 1656

Missouri: 58, 133, 209, 510, 1073, 1160, 1216, 1217, 1321, 1369, 1374, 1447, 1838, 1839

Molecular Biology: 245, 1904, 2289, 2296, 2410, 2581, 2612, 2616, 2676, 2677

Molecular Physics: 2164, 2181, 2233

Money and Banking. *See* Banking
Mongolia: 903
Montana: 265, 1072, 1417, 1490, 1615, 2308
Morocco: 1819
Morphology: 2699
Mortuary Education. *See* Funeral Service; Thanatology
Motion Pictures. *See* Film
Multidisciplinary Studies. *See* Interdisciplinary Research and Study
Multiple Sclerosis: 2627, 2628, 2629, 2630, 2634, 2635, 2636; *see also* Neuromuscular Disorders
Muscle Diseases: 2610, 2685; *see also* Neuromuscular Disorders
Muscular Atrophy: 2686
Muscular Dystrophy: 2631
Museology: 768
Museum Administration: 665, 682, 683, 775; *see also* Historic Site Administration
Museum Education: 597, 646, 681, 775, 781, 1117
Museums: 47, 74, 96, 107, 115, 138, 181, 220, 252, 285, 451, 462, 473, 476, 485, 503, 522, 546, 584, 591, 681, 768, 770, 771, 772; *see also* Cultural Affairs; Historic Preservation and Restoration; Libraries and Librarianship
Museums, Acquisitions: 503
Museums, Collection Utilization and Maintenance: 503, 587, 768, 770, 771, 772
Music: 3, 104, 138, 148, 278, 306, 372, 400, 409, 461, 462, 473, 474, 479, 485, 492, 493, 500, 508, 515, 518, 520, 522, 524, 534, 545, 546, 548, 556, 561, 573, 610, 793, 804, 808, 813, 819, 822, 828, 830, 878, 920, 966, 1006, 1399, 1869, 2157; *see also* Choir; Opera; Performing Arts
Music, Competitions: 562, 790, 791, 792, 794, 796, 797, 798, 805, 806, 807, 814, 815, 816, 817, 818, 821, 823, 824, 827, 828, 829, 830, 831, 833, 834, 836, 837, 838, 842, 844
Music, Composition: 375, 470, 501, 511, 518, 520, 543, 555, 788, 789, 790, 791, 792, 793, 798, 801, 807, 808, 812, 814, 820, 821, 823, 824, 825, 826, 830, 831, 833, 837, 2050
Music, Conducting: 788, 793, 808
Music, Education: 540, 562, 788, 795, 799, 803, 809, 810, 814, 816, 824, 826, 828, 832, 833, 835, 840, 841, 843, 1920
Music, Festivals: 801, 825
Music, History: 687, 688, 813
Music, Instrumentalists: 788, 797, 799, 800, 802, 803, 805, 806, 811, 814, 815, 816, 817, 821, 824, 829, 833, 834, 838, 841, 842, 843
Music, Lyricists and Vocalists: 788, 797, 808, 819, 824, 827, 833, 836, 839, 843; *see also* Choir; Opera
Music, Publication: 796
Music, Research and Study Abroad: 480, 610, 788, 810
Music, Therapy: 826, 2718
Music, Workshops and Residencies: 475, 511, 530, 543, 800, 825, 828
Myasthenia Gravis: 2631, 2632
Mycology: 2294; *see also* Botany

N

Narcotics: 1392
National Security: 879, 880, 881, 981, 982, 983, 1148, 1992; *see also* Defense Projects and Research
Native American Art 518
Native Americans. *See* American Indians and Alaskan Natives
NATO Member Countries: 1018
Natural History: 2334
Natural Resources: 24, 149, 193, 223, 1358, 1479, 1480, 2323, 2324, 2340, 2341, 2352, 2759; *see also* Conservation; Energy Resources and Utilization; Environmental Studies; Forest and Range Resources; Land Use Management; Mineral Sciences; Petroleum Studies; Resource Development and Management; Water Resources
Natural Sciences: 74, 265, 962, 978, 1077, 1078, 1732, 1925, 1937, 2044, 2045, 2173, 2268, 2344; *see also* Physical Sciences; Sciences
Natural Sciences, Education: 1112, 1138, 2240
Near East: 930, 956; *see also* Area Studies; History; Languages; Literature; Social Sciences; also specific nations
Nebraska: 98, 260, 277, 282, 510, 516, 1496
Nephrology: 2374, 2375, 2513, 2514, 2515, 2567, 2577, 2578, 2579, 2580, 2581, 2582, 2583
Netherlands: 821, 1819
Neurobiology: 2289, 2300, 2510, 2624, 2735
Neurological Research: 2479, 2517, 2527, 2528, 2611, 2613, 2615, 2617, 2620, 2624, 2626, 2628, 2630, 2632, 2633, 2634
Neurological Research Training: 2622, 2627, 2629, 2635, 2639
Neurology: 2389, 2484, 2525, 2610, 2612, 2614, 2616, 2618, 2619, 2620, 2638, 2641, 2667

Neuromuscular Disorders: 2621, 2624, 2631, 2632, 2633, 2634, 2635, 2636, 2638, 2639, 2641; *see also* specific diseases
Neurophysiology: 2639
Neuropsychiatry: 2754, 2755
Neurosciences: 245, 1026, 1550, 2170, 2360, 2371, 2384, 2403, 2410, 2479, 2484, 2612, 2613, 2615, 2618, 2620, 2623, 2624, 2625, 2638, 2640, 2676, 2677, 2730, 2735, 2744, 2754, 2755
Neurosurgery: 2422, 2612, 2626, 2637; *see also* Surgery
Nevada: 304, 517, 532, 1446, 1664
New England States. *See* Eastern States; also states by name
New Hampshire: 519, 733, 779, 1200, 1256, 1583
New Jersey: 33, 52, 187, 197, 290, 520, 569, 651, 652, 653, 654, 655, 780, 1088, 1218, 1223, 1243, 1439, 1488, 1807, 1808, 1809, 1810, 1811, 1812, 1850, 1851, 2686
New Mexico: 207, 209, 580, 746, 1076, 1101, 1112, 1345, 1423, 2458
New York: 5, 50, 52, 78, 125, 166, 187, 201, 205, 268, 307, 315, 332, 409, 419, 463, 521, 522, 523, 569, 573, 579, 656, 657, 1045, 1174, 1177, 1187, 1198, 1293, 1300, 1310, 1325, 1338, 1346, 1360, 1424, 1478, 1538, 1724, 1763, 1792, 1852, 1853, 1854, 1855, 1856, 1859, 1884, 1885, 2017, 2131, 2132, 2133, 2134, 2241, 2325, 2337, 2588, 2595
New Zealand: 951, 1819
News Reporting: 1871, 2044, 2049, 2051, 2053, 2055, 2061, 2062, 2063, 2065, 2069, 2080, 2081, 2082, 2084; *see also* Journalism
Newspaper: 417, 2044, 2045, 2051, 2057, 2062, 2065, 2069, 2070, 2081, 2083, 2084; *see also* Communications; Journalism; Publications
Nigeria: 237
Nonfiction: 704, 706, 720, 725, 737, 746, 2062; *see also* Journalism; Literature; Manuscript Prizes, Nonfiction; Publication Prizes; Writers and Writing; also specific disciplines
Nonprofit Organizations. *See* areas of interest to nonprofit organizations
North Carolina: 39, 92, 124, 126, 142, 206, 273, 299, 314, 524, 782, 1207, 1308, 1495, 1607, 1637, 1690, 1701, 1755, 1858
North Dakota: 525, 1120, 1264
Norway: 945, 980, 999; *see also* Scandinavia
Novel: 734; *see also* Publication Prizes, Creative Writing; Writers and Writing
Nuclear Medicine: 2480, 2481
Nuclear Proliferation: 907, 917; *see also* Arms Control
Nuclear Sciences: 1933, 1934, 2191, 2233, 2804, 2805, 2806, 2808, 2809, 2810; *see also* Energy Resources and Utilization; Engineering; Physical Sciences; Radiology and Radiation Sciences; Sciences
Numismatics: 379, 618, 619
Nurse-Midwifery. *See* Midwifery
Nursery Schools. *See* Preschool Education and Care
Nursing: 1523, 1657, 2600, 2607, 2642, 2647, 2648, 2649, 2651; *see also* Hospitals; Medicine
Nursing Education: 319, 1758, 1854, 1864, 2451, 2486, 2600, 2642, 2643, 2646, 2648, 2649, 2650, 2651, 2653, 2654, 2657, 2658; *see also* Medical Education and Training
Nursing Research: 2600, 2632, 2642, 2644, 2645, 2646, 2647, 2649, 2652, 2655, 2656
Nutrition: 207, 218, 275, 317, 370, 899, 1007, 1229, 1390, 1613, 1618, 1941, 2044, 2103, 2329, 2483, 2509, 2518, 2563, 2566, 2695, 2834, 2835, 2836, 2839, 2843; *see also* Agricultural Sciences; Dietetics; Food Technology; Home Economics; Medicine
Nutrition Research: 2566, 2587, 2837, 2838, 2842, 2843

O

OAS Member Countries: 906
Obstetrics and Gynecology: 2391, 2617, 2645, 2659, 2660
Occupational Safety and Health: 147, 162, 1154, 2092, 2239, 2760, 2820; *see also* Health; Industry and Industrial Research
Occupational Therapy: 365, 2716, 2718; *see also* Handicapped; Health; Rehabilitation
Ocean Engineering: 1953, 1969, 2214, 2215, 2332, 2819, 2829
Ocean Management and Marine Policy: 1953, 2214, 2215, 2332, 2339; *see also* Environmental Studies
Oceanography: 1019, 1392, 1952, 1953, 1957, 1966, 1969, 2165, 2170, 2212, 2214, 2215, 2218, 2328, 2332, 2336, 2339, 2784, 2814; *see also* Earth Sciences; Physical Sciences
Ohio: 83, 90, 139, 141, 162, 168, 189, 233, 266, 271, 526, 783, 1221, 1233, 1286, 1288, 1289, 1317, 1357, 1366, 1429, 1444, 1469, 1480, 1492, 1548, 1714, 1861, 1862, 2242, 2252, 2468
Oklahoma: 209, 318, 459, 510, 527, 580, 1101, 1112, 1428, 1446, 1754
Oncology. *See* Cancer
Opera: 520, 562, 564, 810, 826, 827, 836, 839, 844; *see also* Music; Performing Arts

Ophthalmology: 1512, 2219, 2664, 2667, 2668, 2671, 2672, 2674, 2675, 2676, 2677, 2678; *see also* Visual Disorders
Optics: 2662, 2668
Optometry: 365, 2486, 2662, 2663, 2665, 2668, 2673, 2675
Oregon: 71, 85, 255, 265, 528, 1072, 1261, 1273, 1432, 1596, 1615, 2308
Organ Transplant. *See* Medicine, Organ Transplant
Orient: 400; *see also* Area Studies; Asia; History; Languages; Literature; also specific nations
Ornithology: 1929, 2276, 2301, 2321; *see also* Zoology
Orphanages. *See* Children, Adoption and Foster Care
Orthopaedics. *See* Podiatry and Orthopaedics
Osteopathy: 365, 1776, 2415, 2486, 2681, 2682, 2683, 2684, 2685, 2686
Otology: 2680

P

Pacific Area: 893, 894, 2607; *see also* Area Studies; History; Languages; Literature; also specific nations
Pacific Islanders, Eligibility of: 1027, 1069, 1124, 1704, 1730, 2272, 2273
Pain: 1208, 2525; *see also* Neurology
Painting: 469, 470, 501, 508, 512, 532, 539, 547, 578, 586, 590, 594, 599, 603, 609, 775, 1006; *see also* Arts; Creative Arts; Fine Arts
Painting, Workshops and Residencies: 375, 543, 555, 583, 607
Pakistan: 874
Paleobiology: 1962, 2297
Paleontology: 1929, 1931, 2146, 2212, 2217, 2270, 2276; *see also* Geology
Parapsychology: 2747, 2748, 2749, 2750
Parasitology: 2166, 2289, 2495
Parkinson's Disease: 2409, 2615, 2634, 2638, 2639
Parks and Recreation. *See* Recreation
Pathology: 2423, 2436, 2497, 2570, 2581; *see also* Cytopathology: related sciences
Pathology, Plant. *See* Plant Physiology and Pathology
Peace. *See* International Relations and International Affairs
Pediatric Nursing: 2643
Pediatrics: 1561, 2391, 2404, 2541, 2617, 2645, 2687, 2688, 2689, 2690, 2691, 2692, 2693, 2694; *see also* Child Welfare and Health
Pennsylvania: 117, 140, 173, 179, 214, 247, 290, 297, 330, 331, 372, 529, 1087, 1096, 1219, 1230, 1268, 1282, 1351, 1354, 1375, 1412, 1436, 1438, 1463, 1864, 1873, 2252, 2437, 2464, 2650, 2807
Penology. *See* Correctional Institutions and Procedures
Performing Arts: 47, 104, 123, 176, 186, 192, 239, 252, 278, 285, 315, 323, 377, 398, 446, 454, 455, 461, 462, 464, 467, 468, 471, 473, 474, 477, 479, 480, 481, 485, 488, 496, 498, 500, 502, 505, 506, 510, 515, 516, 517, 518, 519, 520, 524, 525, 526, 527, 528, 529, 530, 532, 534, 536, 537, 544, 545, 551, 556, 560, 561, 573, 574, 600, 793, 794, 799, 802, 809, 810, 811, 812, 818, 823, 827, 834, 835, 838, 839, 844, 1091, 1151, 1257, 1399, 1419, 1640, 1781, 1806; *see also* Arts; Cultural Affairs; Dance; Music; Theatre
Performing Arts, Research and Study Abroad: 946
Performing Arts, Workshops and Residencies: 572
Periodontology: 2502, 2509
Pesticides: 2351
Petroleum Sciences: 1901, 2158, 2202, 2221, 2352; *see also* Earth Sciences
Pharmacy and Pharmacology: 365, 1067, 2360, 2375, 2410, 2419, 2442, 2461, 2462, 2581, 2641, 2696, 2699, 2701, 2702, 2703, 2704, 2705; *see also* Morphology
Pharmacy and Pharmacology, Education: 1, 1728, 2697, 2698, 2701, 2706, 2707
Philanthropy: 149, 207, 214, 230, 277, 288, 323, 666, 875, 1200, 1222, 1249, 1250, 1269, 1287, 1290, 1292, 1298, 1313, 1318, 1337, 1355, 1357, 1457, 1582, 1658, 1701, 2386
Philology. *See* Linguistics
Philosophy: 344, 430, 431, 664, 681, 692, 719, 748, 940, 1865, 1920, 1971; *see also* Humanities; Political Philosophy
Philosophy, Classical. *See* Classical Studies
Philosophy, Renaissance. *See* Renaissance Studies
Philosophy, Research and Study: 393, 418
Philosophy, Research and Study Abroad: 408
Photogrammetry: 2160, 2161; *see also* Photography; Surveying
Photography: 456, 485, 501, 503, 515, 532, 539, 543, 547, 555, 562, 579, 588, 590, 607, 608, 2083; *see also* Creative Arts; Fine Arts; Visual Arts
Physical Education: 1543, 2710
Physical Fitness: 218, 1543, 2587
Physical Sciences: 328, 412, 1926, 1937, 1951, 1957, 1965, 2187, 2233, 2479, 2776, 2826; *see also* Chemistry; Materials Sciences; Natural Sciences; Nuclear Sciences; Physics; also specific physical sciences

Physical Sciences, Education: 1069, 1112, 1138, 1148, 1919, 1936, 1955, 2163, 2232
Physical Sciences, Research and Study: 1084, 1933, 1934, 2015, 2164, 2166, 2169, 2233
Physical Sciences, Research and Study Abroad: 1000, 1004, 1729, 2163
Physical Therapy: 365, 2712, 2713, 2716, 2718, 2719; *see also* Rehabilitation
Physics: 1004, 1019, 1879, 1920, 1936, 1949, 1952, 1957, 1959, 1965, 1966, 2169, 2170, 2187, 2231, 2234, 2235, 2240, 2314, 2344, 2778, 2826; *see also* Mathematics; Nuclear Sciences; Physical Sciences
Physiology: 224, 1948, 2166, 2289, 2296, 2299, 2410, 2442, 2484, 2581; *see also* Biological Sciences; related sciences
Physiotherapy: 2646
Planetology: 2182, 2187
Plant Physiology and Pathology: 1936, 2253, 2289; *see also* Botany
Plastic Surgery: 2361, 2362, 2363, 2364, 2422, 2465, 2466
Playwrights: 501, 530, 565, 568, 569, 570, 571, 572, 575, 722, 739; *see also* Drama; Literature; Theatre; Writers and Writing
Podiatry and Orthopaedics: 365, 1087, 2441, 2453, 2454, 2455, 2679, 2685, 2711, 2715
Poetry: 513, 532, 555, 691, 706, 708, 714, 720, 723, 724, 725, 729, 731, 732, 738, 742, 746, 749, 1034; *see also* Literature; Manuscript Prizes, Poetry and Fiction; Publication Prizes, Creative Writing; Writers and Writing
Poetry, Publication Support: 723, 724
Poetry, Translation: 699, 705, 708, 731
Poland: 873, 973, 974, 975, 976
Poland, Eligibility Limited to Descendants of: 1830
Police. *See* Law Enforcement
Policy Analysis: 237, 916, 1643, 1992, 1994
Political History: 376, 621, 631, 1896, 2121, 2123, 2124, 2125, 2144
Political Philosophy: 418, 430, 692, 2136; *see also* Political Science
Political Science: 4, 93, 202, 221, 293, 640, 681, 887, 888, 892, 920, 1896, 1971, 1978, 1979, 2077, 2114, 2122, 2123, 2125, 2130, 2135, 2139, 2141, 2157; *see also* Area Studies; Government; International Relations and International Affairs; Social Sciences
Political Science, Education: 1155, 1168, 1866, 1920, 1989, 2013, 2114, 2143
Political Science, International: 877, 884, 893, 895, 953, 980, 1002, 1825, 2123, 2130
Political Science, Internships: 1089, 1125, 2113, 2115, 2116, 2118, 2126, 2128, 2133, 2134, 2137
Political Science, Research and Study Abroad: 960, 993, 999
Pollution. *See* Air Pollution; Environmental Pollution; Water Pollution
Population Planning: 93, 283, 899, 2239, 2324, 2392
Population Studies: 47, 93, 176, 195, 237, 893, 894, 1553, 2239, 2356, 2391; *see also* Developing Nations, Population Studies; Family Planning; Social Sciences; Sociology
Portugal: 694, 695, 876; *see also* Iberia
Poverty Programs: 27, 95, 144, 168, 202, 246, 251, 274, 326, 875, 1055, 1118, 1147, 1186, 1200, 1219, 1251, 1275, 1286, 1329, 1372, 1383, 1411, 1445, 1453, 1560, 1563, 1565, 1572, 1582, 1586, 1588, 1596, 1605, 1613, 1972, 2095; *see also* Community Development; Equal Educational Opportunity; Equal Employment Opportunity; Minority Affairs; Race Relations; Social Welfare
Pre-Collegiate Education: 308
Presbyterianism: 865, 1870
Preschool Education and Care: 101, 157, 1186, 1195, 1203, 1218, 1223, 1225, 1366, 1492, 1636, 1710; *see also* Child Welfare and Health
Press: 2082, 2087
Print Media: 500, 2050, 2065, 2071, 2082; *see also* Communications; Journalism; Magazines; Newspaper; Publications
Printing and Publishing Industry: 501, 557, 709, 2771, 2777, 2778
Printmaking: 470, 532, 547, 586, 599, 603, 2771; *see also* Crafts
Production Planning: 2350, 2762
Professional Development: 1070, 1174, 1660, 1887, 2032
Prosthetics. *See* Orthotics and Prosthetics
Protestantism: 103, 181, 238, 854, 856, 857
Psychiatry: 1260, 2441, 2451, 2641, 2723, 2725, 2729, 2730, 2735, 2741, 2743, 2744, 2753, 2754, 2755; *see also* Mental and Emotional Health; Psychology
Psychical Manifestations: 2748, 2749, 2750
Psychology: 4, 393, 428, 960, 1019, 1260, 1643, 1644, 1971, 1978, 2003, 2004, 2005, 2006, 2007, 2008, 2139, 2157, 2410, 2641, 2726, 2728, 2730, 2732, 2733, 2734, 2735, 2736, 2741, 2751; *see also* Behavioral Sciences; Child Psychology; Mental and Emotional Health; Psychiatry; Social Psychology; Social Sciences
Psychology, Education: 1920, 2727, 2738
Psychology, Experimental: 2010
Psychology, Internships: 2738
Psychology, Organizational: 2010

Psychology, Research and Study: 1980, 2003, 2004, 2005, 2006, 2007, 2008

Psychotherapy: 2724, 2739

Public Administration: 27, 370, 1168, 2125, 2132, 2137, 2140, 2141; *see also* Government; Law Enforcement; Political Science

Public Affairs: 8, 51, 113, 130, 219, 254, 255, 366, 884, 953, 1086, 1137, 1170, 1633, 1762, 2022, 2139; *see also* Civic Affairs

Public Art 518, 526

Public Assistance: 1596, 1637

Public Broadcasting: 108

Public Health: 177, 322, 370, 888, 899, 1026, 1090, 1110, 1336, 1346, 1386, 1411, 1448, 1518, 1520, 1538, 1542, 1544, 1545, 1548, 1549, 1553, 1558, 1610, 1775, 1942, 2325, 2351, 2352, 2359, 2531, 2532, 2533, 2534, 2535, 2536, 2537, 2538, 2708, 2732; *see also* Environmental Studies; Health; entries beginning with Medical and Medicine; Social Welfare

Public Information Programs: 51, 913, 1224, 1620, 1621, 1622, 1623, 1992, 2054; *see also* Communications; Community Education; Cultural Events, Community; Humanities, Publication, Exhibition, and Public Information Projects; Medicine, Public Information Projects; Sciences, Public Information and Citizen Involvement Projects; Publication Prizes, Public Information

Public Policy: 75, 145, 193, 884, 952, 953, 1218, 1257, 1273, 1497, 1548, 1572, 1585, 1586, 1892, 1893, 1930, 1973, 2082, 2111, 2122, 2138, 2139, 2141, 2726

Public Policy Research: 136, 210, 374, 895, 1168, 1666, 2325, 2341

Public Service: 193, 364, 1060, 1094, 1509, 2128, 2145; *see also* Public Administration; Social Services

Public Welfare. *See* Social Welfare

Publication Assistance: 292, 657, 659, 709, 738, 901, 1137, 1780, 1971, 2769; *see also* specific fields

Publication Prizes, Creative Writing: 711, 714, 716, 717, 718, 721, 723, 727, 729, 730, 732, 733, 734, 736, 740, 743, 2050

Publication Prizes, Education: 1661, 2065

Publication Prizes, History and Humanities: 407, 482, 484, 523, 613, 614, 620, 625, 630, 633, 635, 636, 645, 654, 661, 670, 675, 700, 703, 704, 711, 715, 716, 717, 718, 737, 848, 870, 2062, 2066, 2068, 2144, 2151

Publication Prizes, Medical and Health Sciences: 2275, 2366, 2728

Publication Prizes, Public Information: 2051, 2052, 2053, 2065, 2070

Publication Prizes, Sciences: 636, 703, 737, 2045, 2152, 2192, 2231

Publication Prizes, Social Sciences: 2151

Publications: 482, 876, 1631, 2050, 2066; *see also* Fiction; Journalism; Literature; Magazines; Manuscript Completion; Manuscript Prizes; Newspaper; Novel; Playwrights; Poetry; Translation; Writers and Writing; also specific fields

Publishing Industry. *See* Printing and Publishing Industry

Puerto Rican Community Development. *See* Minority Community and Institutional Development; Minority-Owned Businesses; Small Business Development

Puerto Ricans. *See* Spanish-Speaking Americans; also any discipline that may be given Puerto Rican emphasis

Puerto Ricans, Eligibility of: 1022, 1042, 1067, 1069, 2014; *see also* Minority-Group Members, Eligibility of

Pulmonary Diseases. *See* Respiratory and Pulmonary Diseases

Purchasing: 2024

R

Race Relations: 27, 138, 1037, 1088, 1156, 1199, 1293, 1298, 1415, 1600, 1972, 1991, 2062, 2803; *see also* Equal Educational Opportunity; Equal Employment Opportunity; Human Relations; Minority Affairs; Poverty Programs; Social Welfare

Racial Equity: 207

Radio and Television: 485, 691, 1006, 2044, 2045, 2048, 2056, 2062, 2066, 2071, 2072, 2073, 2075, 2086; *see also* Broadcast Media; Communications; Educational Media; Social Sciences; Technology, Telecommunications

Radiology and Radiation Sciences: 2166, 2379, 2384, 2470, 2471, 2472, 2473, 2474, 2475, 2558; *see also* Medicine; Nuclear Sciences; Physical Sciences

Range Resources. *See* Forest and Range Resources

Rape. *See* Sexual Abuse

Reading: 395, 1284, 1660, 1661, 2065, 2746; *see also* Education and entries beginning with Education or Educational

Real Estate: 2013; *see also* Appraisal; Business; Finance

Recreation: 4, 30, 140, 220, 321, 342, 1093, 1173, 1217, 1250, 1316, 1366, 1368, 1395, 1404, 1411, 1461, 1476, 1494, 1543, 1574, 1669, 1680, 1715, 2324, 2333, 2334; *see also* Athletics; Community Development; Sports; Urban and Regional Planning

Refrigeration: 2816, 2817

Regional Planning. *See* Urban and Regional Planning

Rehabilitation: 5, 52, 1052, 1202, 1366, 1683, 2406, 2556, 2617, 2640, 2655, 2708, 2710, 2712, 2715, 2720; *see also* Corrective Therapy; Education, Special; Handicapped; Narcotics; Occupational Therapy; Physical Therapy; Vocational Rehabilitation

Relief Organizations: 875, 1270, 1349; *see also* Community Funds; Community Services; Emergency Grants

Religion: 3, 43, 45, 49, 54, 57, 64, 85, 97, 120, 127, 154, 174, 180, 213, 229, 230, 238, 270, 275, 312, 324, 344, 351, 368, 393, 418, 430, 681, 845, 846, 849, 850, 851, 861, 866, 868, 870, 871, 872, 1074, 1159, 1179, 1259, 1271, 1289, 1340, 1346, 1491, 1527, 1564, 1585, 1844, 1922, 2126, 2157; *see also* Catholicism; Christianity; Islam; Journalism, Religious; Judaism; Lutheranism; Protestantism

Religion, Comparative: 853

Religion, History: 394, 627, 628, 847, 848, 850, 857, 862

Religion - Interfaith 1300

Religion, Research and Study Abroad: 845, 946, 956, 1781

Religious Denominations, Eligibility Limited to Members of: 856, 857, 858, 863, 865, 866, 871, 1289, 1576, 1869, 1870

Religious Education: 108, 234, 241, 352, 850, 852, 853, 855, 856, 861, 863, 864, 865, 1074, 1527, 1667, 1869

Religious Institutions: 124, 125, 213, 304, 306, 352, 851, 866, 1437; *see also* Construction and Facilities Projects

Remote Sensing: 2160, 2161, 2314

Renaissance Studies: 388, 398, 402, 421, 1003; *see also* Arts; History; Literature; Philosophy

Renal Diseases. *See* Nephrology

Reproduction Research: 1553, 1948, 2287, 2434, 2435, 2660; *see also* Biological Sciences; Family Planning; Genetics; Medicine; Population Studies

Research: 15, 145, 167, 237, 413, 541, 666, 900, 901, 962, 970, 987, 1039, 1447, 1532, 1728, 1775, 2015, 2026, 2146, 2187, 2192, 2205, 2213, 2262, 2360, 2389, 2407, 2434, 2435, 2439, 2450, 2488, 2553, 2678, 2679, 2761; *see also* Educational Research; Medical Research; Scientific Research and Development; Technological Research; also specific fields of interest

Research Training: 1554, 1706, 1995, 1996, 1999, 2001, 2164, 2362, 2547, 2563, 2564, 2575, 2579, 2580, 2678, 2702; *see also* specific disciplines

Residential Artist or Scholar Programs: 375, 376, 380, 390, 392, 399, 418, 420, 422, 425, 433, 467, 475, 487, 491, 511, 530, 543, 593, 594, 622, 660, 853, 919, 1003, 1876, 1962, 2150, 2305; *see also* specific disciplines

Resource Development and Management: 113, 131, 893, 912, 1937, 1953, 2256, 2333, 2335, 2336, 2341, 2345; *see also* Developing Nations, Resource Development; Energy Resources and Utilization; Environmental Studies; also specific resources

Respiratory and Pulmonary Diseases: 1547, 2410, 2493, 2495, 2540, 2541, 2542, 2543, 2547, 2548, 2555, 2646

Respiratory and Pulmonary Diseases, Research Training: 2493, 2541, 2543, 2643, 2646

Restaurant Management and Food Service: 1229, 1818, 2032, 2775, 2836, 2844

Restoration. *See* Historic Preservation and Restoration

Rheumatology and Rheumatic Diseases: 361, 2388, 2478, 2608, 2609, 2685

Rhode Island: 70, 76, 309, 346, 411, 531, 733, 2140

Rockefeller Organizations: 666

Romania: 873

Rural Development: 207, 1199, 1423, 1470, 1486, 1993, 2261, 2266; *see also* Agricultural Sciences; Cooperatives, Rural and Consumer; Sociology; Urban and Regional Planning

Russia: 884, 904, 950, 970, 1348; *see also* other former republics of the U.S.S.R.

Russian Studies. *See* Slavic and East Europe

S

Sabbatical. *See* Faculty, Study and Research Programs

Safety. *See* Occupational Safety and Health; Social Welfare; Traffic Engineering and Safety

Sanitation: 2840; *see also* Engineering; Environmental Pollution; Health; Solid Waste Management, Wastewater Management

Scandinavia: 578, 945, 952; *see also* Europe; specific nations

Schools. *See* entries beginning with Education and Educational

Science, Communications: 2054, 2071

Sciences: 3, 8, 12, 13, 26, 49, 54, 57, 69, 85, 118, 227, 250, 261, 272, 280, 323, 339, 344, 354, 412, 497, 636, 960, 965, 1110, 1193, 1300, 1530, 1633, 1690, 1757, 1928, 1940, 1947, 1948, 1950, 1954, 2213, 2228, 2240, 2812, 2813; *see also* specific sciences

Organization and Program Index

The Organization and Program Index alphabetically lists grant programs in upper-lower case and funding organizations in upper case. In addition, programs also are listed following the organizations which sponsor them.

ALLEN (THE PAUL G.) FAMILY FOUNDATION: 13
ALLENDE (THE ISABEL) FOUNDATION
  Esperanza Grants: 1133
  Paula Scholarships: 1768
Allhands (James L.) Essay Competition: 2796
ALLIANCE FOR YOUNG ARTISTS & WRITERS (THE)
  Scholastic Art and Writing Awards (The): 456
Allied Health Doctoral Fellowship: 2579
Allied Health Research Grant: 2578
Allied Health Scholarship: 2580
Allons en France: 989
Allport (The Gordon) Intergroup Relations Prize: 2008
ALLSTATE FOUNDATION (THE): 1575
Alonso (The Anne) Scholarship: 2724
ALPHA SIGMA NU
  Alpha Sigma Nu Book Award: 703
Alpha Sigma Nu Book Award: 703
Alpha-1 Foundation/CHEST Foundation Clinical Research Award in
  Alpha-1 Antitrypsin (AAT) Deficiency: 2548
ALSC/Bound-to-Stay-Bound Books Scholarship: 1730
ALSC/Frederic G. Melcher Scholarship: 1730
Altenhofen (Robert E.) Memorial Scholarship: 2160
ALTERNATIVES RESEARCH AND DEVELOPMENT FOUNDATION
  Alternatives Research Grant Program: 1927
  Cave (William and Eleanor) Award: 1927
Alternatives Research Grant Program: 1927
ALTMAN FOUNDATION: 1238
ALTRIA GROUP, INC.: 14
Alumni Grant: 515
ALZHEIMER'S ASSOCIATION, INC.
  Everyday Technologies for Alzheimer Care (ETAC): 2611
  Hatfield (The Senator Mark) Award for Clinical Research in
  Alzheimer's Disease: 2611
  Investigator-Initiated Research Grants: 2611
  New Investigator Research Grants: 2611
  Zenith Fellows Award Program (The): 2611
Alzheimer's Disease Research: 2614
ALZHEIMER'S DRUG DISCOVERY FOUNDATION
  Novel Approaches to Drug Discovery in Alzheimer's Disease: 2360
AMARILLO AREA FOUNDATION: 1239
Amateur Achievement Award: 2180
Ambassador of Hope Award (The): 1564
Ambassadorial Scholarships: 986
AMBUCS Scholars-Scholarships for Therapists: 2716
AMERICA THE BEAUTIFUL FUND
  Operation Green Plant: 1240
America's Best Idea: 2333
AMERICA-ISRAEL CULTURAL FOUNDATION
  Scholarship Program for Israelis: 1006
AMERICAN ACADEMY IN BERLIN (THE)
  Berlin Prize Fellowship: 920
AMERICAN ACADEMY IN ROME
  Rome Prize Fellowships: 375
  Rome Prize Fellowship in Landscape Architecture (The): 2305
AMERICAN ACADEMY OF ALLERGY ASTHMA & IMMUNOLOGY
  Travel Grant Awards: 2489
AMERICAN ACADEMY OF ARTS AND LETTERS
  Rodgers (The Richard) Awards: 790
AMERICAN ACADEMY OF CHILD AND ADOLESCENT
PSYCHIATRY
  Robinson-Cunningham Award: 2723
  Spurlock (Jeanne) Research Fellowship in Substance Abuse and
  Addiction for Minority Medical Students: 2723
AMERICAN ACADEMY OF ESTHETIC DENTISTRY (THE)
  AAED Esthetic Dentistry Research Grants: 2498
AMERICAN ACADEMY OF FACIAL PLASTIC AND
RECONSTRUCTIVE SURGERY (AAFPRS)
  Bernstein (Leslie) Investigator Development Grant: 2362
  Bernstein (Leslie) Research Grant: 2363
  Bernstein (Leslie) Resident Research Grants: 2361
  Community Service Award: 2364
  Dickinson (John) Teacher of the Year Award: 2364
  Gillies (Sir Harold Delf) Award: 2364
  Rafaty (F. Mark) Memorial Award: 2364
  Residency Travel Award: 2364
  Roe (John Orlando) Award: 2364
  Shuster (Ben) Memorial Award: 2364
  Tresley (Ira) Research Award: 2364
  Wright (William) Award: 2364

AMERICAN ACADEMY OF FAMILY PHYSICIANS FOUNDATION
  Joint AAFP/F-AAFP Grant Awards Program (JGAP): 2365
  Pfizer Teacher Development Award: 2365
AMERICAN ACADEMY OF IMPLANT DENTISTRY RESEARCH
FOUNDATION, INC.
  Humanitarian Project Support: 2499
  Small Research Award: 2499
  Student Research Grant: 2499
AMERICAN ACADEMY OF OPTOMETRY
  Neumueller (Julius F.) Award in Optics: 2663
AMERICAN ACADEMY OF PEDIATRICS
  American Academy of Pediatrics Residency Scholarships: 2688
American Academy of Pediatrics Residency Scholarships: 2688
AMERICAN ACADEMY OF RELIGION
  Collaborative Research Grants: 845
  Individual Research Grants: 845
  International Dissertation Research Grant: 845
  Regional Development Grants: 846
AMERICAN ACCORDION MUSICOLOGICAL SOCIETY
  Annual Symposium Festival: 791
AMERICAN AGING ASSOCIATION
  Glenn (Paul) Award: 2366
  Nicolai (Walter) Award in Biomedical Gerontology: 2366
AMERICAN ALPINE CLUB
  McNeill-Nott Climbing Award: 2306
  Mountain Fellowship: 2306
  Research Grants: 2306
  Spitzer (Lyman) Cutting Edge Climbing Award: 2306
AMERICAN ANTIQUARIAN SOCIETY (AAS)
  AAS American Society for Eighteenth Century Studies Fellowship: 376
  AAS Fellowship for Creative and Performing Artists and Writers: 377
  AAS National Endowment for the Humanities Fellowships: 376
  AAS-Northeast Modern Language Association Fellowship: 376
  American Historical Print Collectors Fellowship: 376
  Botein (Stephen) Fellowships: 376
  Drawn to Art Fellowship (The): 376
  Last (Jay and Deborah) Fellowship: 376
  Legacy Fellowship (The): 376
  Peterson (Kate B. and Hall J.) Fellowships: 376
  Reese Fellowship (The): 376
  Tracy (Joyce A.) Fellowship: 376
AMERICAN ARCHITECTURAL FOUNDATION (THE)
  Hunt (The Richard Morris) Fellowship: 437
American Art Program: 234
AMERICAN ASSOCIATION FOR CANCER RESEARCH
  Career Development Awards: 2584
  Innovator Awards in Cancer Research: 2584
  Research Grants and Fellowships: 2584
  Scholar-in-Training Awards: 2584
AMERICAN ASSOCIATION FOR DENTAL RESEARCH
  AADR/Johnson & Johnson Healthcare Products Hatton Competition:
  2500
  Clark (William B.) Fellowship in Clinical Research: 2502
  Gies (William J.) Award: 2503
  Student Research Fellowships: 2501
American Association for Geodetic Surveying Graduate Fellowship
  Award: 2797
AMERICAN ASSOCIATION FOR HAND SURGERY: 2367
AMERICAN ASSOCIATION FOR THE ADVANCEMENT OF
SCIENCE
  AAAS Kavli Science Journalism Awards: 2045
  Mass Media Science and Engineering Fellows Program: 2044
AMERICAN ASSOCIATION FOR THE HISTORY OF NURSING, INC.
  Competitive Student Research Award: 2642
  Postdoctoral Award to Honor the Nurse Cadet Corps: 2642
AMERICAN ASSOCIATION OF COLLEGES OF PHARMACY
  New Pharmacy Faculty Research Awards: 2696
AMERICAN ASSOCIATION OF FAMILY AND CONSUMER
SCIENCES (AAFCS)
  Excellence in Extension Grant: 2834
  National and International Fellowships: 1007
  National Teacher of the Year Award: 2835
AMERICAN ASSOCIATION OF LAW LIBRARIES
  Library Degree for Law School Graduates: 751
  Library Degree for Non-Law School Graduates: 751
  Library School Graduates Attending Law School: 751
  Library School Graduates Seeking a Non-Law Degree: 751
  Strait (George A.) Minority Stipend Scholarship Endowment: 752
AMERICAN ASSOCIATION OF PETROLEUM GEOLOGISTS
FOUNDATION
  AAPG Foundation Grants-in-Aid: 2202

AMERICAN OPTOMETRIC FOUNDATION
  Accuvue Eye Health Program: 2665
  Award of Excellence: 2665
  Ezell (William C.) Fellowship: 2665
  Vision Service Plan Research Grant: 2665
  Vistakon® Contact Lens Residency Award: 2665
  Vistakon® Pediatric Residency Award: 2665
AMERICAN ORCHID SOCIETY
  American Orchid Society Grants for Orchid Research: 2271
American Orchid Society Grants for Orchid Research: 2271
AMERICAN ORIENTAL SOCIETY
  Hackney (Louise Wallace) Fellowship: 577
AMERICAN ORTHOPAEDIC SOCIETY FOR SPORTS MEDICINE
  (AOSSM) (THE)
  AOSSM Young Investigator Grant: 2711
AMERICAN OSTEOPATHIC FOUNDATION: 2681
  McCaughan (Russell C.), D.O., Education Scholarship: 1776
  Outstanding Resident of the Year Award: 2682
AMERICAN PARKINSON DISEASE ASSOCIATION, INC.
  Medical Student Summer Fellowships: 2615
AMERICAN PHILOSOPHICAL SOCIETY
  Franklin Research Grants: 15
  Lewis and Clark Fund for Exploration and Field Research (The): 16
  Library Resident Research Fellowships (The): 380
  Phillips Fund Grants for Native American Research: 1103
AMERICAN PLANNING ASSOCIATION
  Abrams (Charles) Scholarship Program: 1241
  McManus (Judith) Fellowship: 1025
AMERICAN POLITICAL SCIENCE ASSOCIATION
  APSA Minority Fellows Program: 2114
  Congressional Fellowship Program: 2113
AMERICAN PORPHYRIA FOUNDATION (THE): 2378
AMERICAN PSYCHIATRIC ASSOCIATION
  APA Fellowship for Residents: 2725
AMERICAN PSYCHOLOGICAL ASSOCIATION
  APA Congressional Fellowship Program: 2726
  Mental Health and Substance Abuse Services Fellowship: 1026
  MFP Mental Health Services Fellowship: 2727
AMERICAN PSYCHOSOMATIC SOCIETY
  American Psychosomatic Society Scholar Awards: 2728
  Weiner (Herbert) Early Career Award for Contributions to
  Psychosomatic Society: 2728
American Psychosomatic Society Scholar Awards: 2728
AMERICAN PUBLIC POWER ASSOCIATION (APPA)
  DEED Scholarship: 2811
AMERICAN RESEARCH CENTER IN EGYPT, INC.
  Fellowships for Research in Egypt: 930
AMERICAN RESEARCH INSTITUTE IN TURKEY, INC.
  ARIT Fellowship Program: 931
  Bogazici University Summer Language Program for Intensive Advanced
  Turkish Language Study: 932
  NEH Fellowships for Research in Turkey: 933
AMERICAN ROENTGEN RAY SOCIETY
  ARRS Annual Scholarship Program: 2379
AMERICAN SCHLAFHORST FOUNDATION: 17
AMERICAN SCHOOL OF CLASSICAL STUDIES AT ATHENS (THE)
  Advanced Fellowships: 936
  Bikakis (The Harry) Fellowship: 937
  Broneer (Oscar) Traveling Fellowship: 938
  CAORC Multi-Country Research Fellowships: 460
  Cotsen Traveling Fellowship for Research in Greece: 939
  Frantz (M. Alison) Fellowship in Post-Classical Studies at the
  Gennadius Library: 935
  Hirsch (The Jacob) Fellowship in Archaeology: 935
  Medieval Greek Summer Session at the Gennadius Library: 940
  National Endowment for the Humanities Fellowships: 934
  Wiener Laboratory Fellowships: 941
  Wiener Laboratory Post-Doctoral Research Fellowship: 941
  Wiener Laboratory Research Associateships: 941
  Wiener Laboratory Travel Grants: 941
AMERICAN SCHOOLS OF ORIENTAL RESEARCH (ASOR)
  Heritage Fellowships: 942
  Mesopotamian Fellowship: 942
  Platt Fellowships: 942
AMERICAN SOCIETY FOR CLINICAL PATHOLOGY
  ASCP Scholarships: 2380
American Society for Eighteenth-Century Studies Fellowships: 658
AMERICAN SOCIETY FOR ENGINEERING EDUCATION
  Department of Defense National Defense Science and Engineering
  Graduate Fellowship Program (NDSEG): 2813
  Naval Research Laboratory (NRL) Postdoctoral Fellowship Program:

2814
  Office of Naval Research-ASEE Summer Faculty and Sabbatical Leave
  Program: 2813
  Summer Research Opportunity Program: 2813
  USAF Summer Faculty Fellowship Program: 2812
AMERICAN SOCIETY FOR ENOLOGY AND VITICULTURE: 2248
AMERICAN SOCIETY FOR HEALTHCARE RISK MANAGEMENT:
  1513
AMERICAN SOCIETY FOR MASS SPECTROMETRY
  ASMS Research Awards in Mass Spectrometry: 2159
AMERICAN SOCIETY FOR MICROBIOLOGY
  ASM Robert D. Watkins Graduate Research Fellowships: 2273
  ASM/CDC Postdoctoral Research Fellowship Program: 2272
  Undergraduate Research Fellowship (URF): 2272
AMERICAN SOCIETY FOR NONDESTRUCTIVE TESTING, INC.
  (THE)
  ASNT Faculty Grant Award: 1626
  ASNT Fellowship Award: 2761
  Engineering Undergraduate Award: 1777
  Oliver (Robert B.) Scholarship: 1777
AMERICAN SOCIETY FOR NUTRITION
  Predoctoral Fellowships in Nutrition Research: 2837
AMERICAN SOCIETY FOR PARENTERAL AND ENTERAL
  NUTRITION, RHOADS RESEARCH FOUNDATION: 2566
AMERICAN SOCIETY FOR THEATRE RESEARCH
  ASTR Collaborative Research Award (The): 560
  Biennial Banes (Sally) Publication Prize: 560
  Brockett (Oscar G.) Essay Award: 560
  Chinoy (Helen Krich) Dissertation Research Fellowships: 560
  Co-sponsored Events Awards: 560
  Cohen (Selma Jeanne) Conference Presentation Award: 560
  Distinguished Scholar Award: 560
  Grants for Researchers with Heavy Teaching Loads: 560
  Hewitt (Barnard) Award: 560
  Hill (Errol) Award: 560
  Kahan (Gerald) Scholar's Prize: 560
  Keller (David) Travel Grants: 560
  Marshall (Thomas F.) Graduate Student Awards: 560
  McNamara (The Brooks) Publishing Subvention: 560
  Research Fellowships: 560
  Targeted Research Areas Grants: 560
AMERICAN SOCIETY OF CIVIL ENGINEERS
  Ammann (O.H.) Research Fellowship in Structural Engineering: 2815
  Dames (Trent R.) and Moore (William W.) Fellowship: 2815
  Freeman Fellowship: 2815
  Leisch (Jack E.) Memorial National Graduate Fellowship: 2815
  Smith (J. Waldo) Hydraulic Fellowship: 2815
  Tapman (Samuel Fletcher) ASCE Student Chapter Scholarship: 2815
  Tuttle (Arthur S.) Memorial Scholarship: 2815
AMERICAN SOCIETY OF COMPOSERS, AUTHORS AND
  PUBLISHERS (ASCAP)
  ASCAP Deems Taylor Awards: 704
AMERICAN SOCIETY OF ECHOCARDIOGRAPHY
  Cardiovascular Sonographer Research Award: 2545
  Career Development Awards: 2544
  Echo Investigator Awards: 2544
AMERICAN SOCIETY OF HEATING, REFRIGERATING AND
  AIR-CONDITIONING ENGINEERS, INC.
  ASHRAE Graduate Grant-in-Aid Program: 2817
  ASHRAE Research Grants: 2816
AMERICAN SOCIETY OF HEMATOLOGY
  ASH Scholar Award: 2381
  Fellow Scholar Award: 2381
  Junior Faculty Scholar Award: 2381
  Merit Awards: 2512
  Trainee Research Award Program: 2382
  Travel Awards: 2512
AMERICAN SOCIETY OF HYPERTENSION: 2383
AMERICAN SOCIETY OF INTERIOR DESIGNERS EDUCATIONAL
  FOUNDATION
  ASID Foundation Legacy Scholarship for Graduate Students: 440
  ASID Foundation Legacy Scholarship for Undergraduates: 440
  Eno (Irene Winifred) Grant: 440
  Polsky (Joel) Academic Achievement Award: 440
  Polsky (Joel) Prize: 440
AMERICAN SOCIETY OF MECHANICAL ENGINEERS AUXILIARY,
  INC. (THE)
  ASME/Auxiliary FIRST Clarke Scholarship: 2818
  Baldwin (Allen J.) Scholarship: 2818
  Cartwright (Berna Lou) Scholarship: 2818
  Farny (Sylvia W.) Scholarship: 2818

References in index are to entry numbers.

Rose Architectural Fellowship: 443
Rouse (Jim and Patty) Awards for Excellence in Community
    Revitalization: 1581
Enterprise Journalism Fellowships: 1871
ENTOMOLOGICAL FOUNDATION (THE)
    Beck (Stan) Fellowship: 2278
    LaFage (Jeffery P.) Graduate Student Research Award: 2280
    Richardson (Henry and Sylvia) Research Grant: 2279
    Undergraduate Scholarship Program: 2281
Entry Track: 491
Environment: 155, 176, 311
Environment and Communities: 290
Environment Program: 123
Environment Program (The): 1597
Environment Program Grant: 205
Environmental and Natural Resources Management Program: 193
Environmental Grant Program: 2338
Environmental Health Sciences Research and Training Grants: 2331
ENVIRONMENTAL LAW INSTITUTE
    Continuing Legal Education Scholarship Program: 2102
Environmental Program (The): 1474
Environmental Public Policy and Conflict Resolution Fellowships: 1893
Environmental Safety and Health: 2779
Epidemiology/Population Research: 2510
EPILEPSY FOUNDATION OF AMERICA: 2621
    Behavioral Sciences Postdoctoral Fellowship: 1975
    Behavioral Sciences Student Fellowships: 1974
    Health Sciences Student Fellowships: 1974
    Postdoctoral Research Fellowships: 2622
    Predoctoral Research Training Fellowships: 2622
    Research and Training Fellowships for Clinicians: 2622
EPISCOPAL CHURCH FOUNDATION
    ECF Fellowship Partners Program: 854
EPPLEY FOUNDATION FOR RESEARCH, INC. (THE): 1940
ERDAS Internship: 2160
ERION FOUNDATION: 134
ERNST & YOUNG FOUNDATION: 2021
Escue (Walter H.) Memorial Scholarship: 785
Esperanza Grants: 1133
ESSEX COUNTY COMMUNITY FOUNDATION
    Arts Forum: 1347
    Essex County Youth-at-Risk: 1347
    First Jobs: 1347
    Greater Lawrence Summer Fund: 1347
    Hunger Project (The): 1347
    Women's Fund of Essex County (The): 1347
Essex County Youth-at-Risk: 1347
Established Researcher Award: 2387
Ethnic Studies Fellowships: 1085
ETS Postdoctoral Fellowship Award Program: 1644
EURASIA FOUNDATION: 1348
Eurasia/South Asia Teaching Excellence and Achievement Program
    (TEA): 970
Eurasian Undergraduate Exchange Program (UGRAD): 970
Europe and Global Challenges: 427
EVANGELICAL LUTHERAN CHURCH IN AMERICA
    Educational Grant Program: 855
Event Grants: 1535
Everest (D.C.) Fellowship: 684
Everyday Technologies for Alzheimer Care (ETAC): 2611
Excellence in Education Program: 1319
Excellence in Extension Grant: 2834
Excellence in Medicine: 1775
Executive Fellowship Program: 2119
Executive Suites Program: 249
EXELON CORPORATION
    Corporate Giving Program: 135
Exemplary Research in Social Studies: 1983
Exhibitions Abroad Support Program: 1822
Expanding Opportunities for Participation in the Arts: 545
Expeditions: 518
Exploring Program: 1668
Express Grant: 1461
External Faculty Fellowships: 426
EXXONMOBIL CORPORATION: 136
EYE BANK ASSOCIATION OF AMERICA
    EBAA Research Grants: 2670
EZ (Empowerment Zone) Consulting Grants: 656
Ezell (William C.) Fellowship: 2665

F

FACES Grant: 483
Factory Operations: 2779
Faculty of Law Graduate Scholarship: 1912
Faculty Research Participation Program: 2168
FAER Mentored Research Training Grant: 2408
FAER Research Education Grant: 2408
FAER Research Fellowship Grant: 2408
Fagg (The John E.) Prize: 614
FAIR OAKS FOUNDATION: 1349
Fairbank (The John K.) Prize in East Asian History: 614
Fairchild (The Sherman) Foundation Fellowships: 592
FAIRFIELD COUNTY COMMUNITY FOUNDATION: 1350
FALK FOUNDATION: 1046
Family Services Community Grants: 2389
Fanning (William M.) Maintenance Scholarship: 2788
Fargher (John S.W.) Scholarship: 2823
FARGO-MOORHEAD AREA FOUNDATION: 137
FARM AID: 2251
Farm Kids for College Scholarships: 2258
Farny (Sylvia W.) Scholarship: 2818
Farrar (Marjorie M. and Lancelot L.) Awards: 668
Fast-track Fellowship: 2359
Fast-track Studentship: 2359
FATS AND PROTEINS RESEARCH FOUNDATION, INC.: 1941
FDI Postdoctoral Fellowship: 1642
FDI Predoctoral Dissertation Fellowship: 1642
Feddie Award (The): 2077
FEDERAL HIGHWAY ADMINISTRATION
    Eisenhower (Dwight David) Transportation Fellowship Program: 2770
Federal Work-Study: 1890
FEDERATION OF AMERICAN CONSUMERS AND TRAVELERS
    Classroom and Community Grants: 1645
    Community and Business Project Grants: 2022
    Continuing Education Scholarships: 1645
FEINSTEIN FOUNDATION (THE)
    Feinstein $1 Million Giveaway to Fight Hunger: 1582
Feinstein $1 Million Giveaway to Fight Hunger: 1582
Feis (The Herbert) Award: 614
Feitelson (Dina) Research Award: 1661
Felix (Robert) Memorial Scholarship: 2262
Fellow Scholar Award: 2381
Fellowship and Scholarship Program for Writers: 707
Fellowship for U.S.-Based Study: 1781
Fellowship in Aerospace History: 616
Fellowship of the Flanders House: 965
Fellowship Program: 131, 978, 2397, 2600
Fellowship Program at the Woodrow Wilson International Center for
    Scholars: 433
Fellowship Program for Journalists: 2083
Fellowship Research Grants: 1973, 2416
Fellowships: 415, 491, 531
Fellowships and Project Grants in Byzantine Studies, Pre-Columbian
    Studies and Garden and Landscape Studies: 399
Fellowships at the Albright Institute of Archaeological Research in
    Jerusalem: 919
Fellowships for American Indians or Alaskan Natives: 1100
Fellowships for Independent Study on the Italian Renaissance: 1003
Fellowships for Minorities in Management: 2014
Fellowships for Research in Egypt: 930
Fellowships in Art Conservation: 587
Fellowships in Science, Technology and International Security: 885
FELS (SAMUEL S.) FUND
    Arts and Culture: 1351
    Community Concerns: 1351
    Public Education: 1351
Ferrell (Robert H.) Book Prize: 671
Festivals DC: 478
Feynman (Richard P.) Postdoctoral Fellowship in Theory and Computing:
    1949
Field Aviation Company Scholarship: 2782
FIELD FOUNDATION OF ILLINOIS: 138
Field of Interest Funds: 1304, 1415
Field of Interest Grant Program: 1386
Field of Interest Grants: 1319
Fielding (Carole) Student Grants: 2089
FIELDSTONE FOUNDATION (THE): 401
Fight for Sight Grant-in-Aid: 2671
Fight for Sight Postdoctoral Fellowship: 2672

G

Gallagher (John J. and Anna H.) Fellowship: 1925
Gallatin Fellowships: 1002
Gallery Program: 477
GAMBLE FOUNDATION (THE): 1651
Gambrell (C.B.) Undergraduate Scholarship: 2823
GANNETT FOUNDATION: 152
Gannett Foundation Scholarship: 1064
GARDEN CLUB OF AMERICA (THE)
  Beattie (Catherine) Fellowship: 2319
  Chatham (The Anne S.) Fellowship in Medicinal Botany: 2321
  Garden Club of America Awards in Tropical Botany: 2321
  GCA Award in Coastal Wetland Studies (The): 2319
  GCA Awards for Summer Environmental Studies: 2318
  GCA Interchange Fellowship in Horticulture and Martin McLaren Scholarship: 2320
  Grosscup (Katharine M.) Scholarships: 2252
  Marks (The Loy McCandless) Scholarship in Tropical Ornamental Horticulture: 2319
  Peacock (The Frances M.) Scholarship for Native Bird Habitat: 2321
Garden Club of America Awards in Tropical Botany: 2321
Garden (Dwight D.) Scholarship: 2823
Garden State Historic Preservation Trust Fund (GSHPTF): 651
Garfield (Eugene) Doctoral Dissertation Fellowship: 758
Garfield (The Eugene)/ALISE Doctoral Dissertation Competition: 757
Garmin - Jerry Smith Memorial Scholarship: 2782
Garmin Scholarship: 2782
Garrett (Eileen J.) Scholarship: 2747
Garrett Scholarship: 785
Garvin (Mildred Barry) Prize: 654
Gates Millennium Scholars Program: 1131
GATX CORPORATION
  Dollars-for-Doers: 153
  Employee Matching Gifts: 153
Gaul (Harvey) Music Composition Contest: 831
Gauss (Christian) Award: 737
Gaver (Mary V.) Scholarship: 1730
Gay & Lesbian Fund for Colorado: 1050
GAY & LESBIAN FUND FOR COLORADO (THE), A PROGRAM OF THE GILL FOUNDATION
  Gay & Lesbian Fund for Colorado: 1050
Gaylor (Lowell) Memorial Scholarship: 2782
GCA Award in Coastal Wetland Studies (The): 2319
GCA Awards for Summer Environmental Studies: 2318
GCA Interchange Fellowship in Horticulture and Martin McLaren Scholarship: 2320
Geach (Portia) Memorial Award: 469
GEFFEN (THE DAVID) FOUNDATION: 1529
GEICO Life Scholarship: 1806
GEICO Public Service Awards: 1052
Geiger Memorial Fellowship: 667
Geiser (Emmett and Elsie) Scholarship: 1324
Geisman (Michael) Fellowships: 2456
Gelfand-Armin (Lawrence) Rappaport Fellowship: 669
GELLERT (CARL) AND CELIA BERTA GELLERT FOUNDATION: 154
GELLERT (THE FRED) FAMILY FOUNDATION
  Arts and Humanities: 155
  Education: 155
  Environment: 155
  Health: 155
  Youth, Seniors & Family Service: 155
GEM M.S. Engineering Fellowship (The): 1067
GEM Ph.D. Engineering Fellowship (The): 1067
GEM Ph.D. Science Fellowship (The): 1067
GENERAL BOARD OF HIGHER EDUCATION AND MINISTRY, THE UNITED METHODIST CHURCH
  Harkness (Georgia) Scholarships: 856
General College Scholarship Program: 1131
GENERAL COMMISSION ON ARCHIVES AND HISTORY OF THE UNITED METHODIST CHURCH
  Ness (John Harrison) Memorial Award: 857
General Endowment Fund: 1295
General Fellowship Program: 926
General Grant Program: 1
General Operating Support: 531
General Operating Support Grants: 520, 653
General Program: 237
General Program Support Grants: 520
General Program Support Grants Program: 479

General Project Grants: 519
GENERAL SERVICE FOUNDATION
  Colorado Program: 156
  Human Rights and Economic Justice: 156
  Reproductive Justice: 156
Genetic Studies: 2510
Gentile (Major Don S.) Scholarship: 1894
GeoEye Award: 2160
Geography Grants: 188
GEOLOGICAL SOCIETY OF AMERICA, INC. (THE)
  GSA Research Grants: 2208
GEORGE FOUNDATION (THE): 157
GEORGE WASHINGTON UNIVERSITY
  Graduate Teaching Assistantships: 2822
GEORGE WASHINGTON UNIVERSITY-ENGLISH DEPARTMENT
  Visiting Lecturer in Creative Writing: 713
GEORGETOWN UNIVERSITY
  Doctoral Program in Chemistry: 2197
GEORGIA COUNCIL FOR THE ARTS
  Arts Services: 485
  Community Arts Development: 485
  Traditional Arts: 485
GEORGIA LIBRARY ASSOCIATION
  Beard Scholarship: 765
  Hubbard Scholarship: 765
GEORGIA POWER FOUNDATION, INC.: 158
GEORGIA-PACIFIC FOUNDATION: 159
GERBER FOUNDATION (THE): 1194
GERMAN ACADEMIC EXCHANGE SERVICE
  DAAD Scholarship Programs for Study and Research in Germany: 966
German Chancellor Fellowship: 923
GERMAN HISTORICAL INSTITUTE
  Doctoral and Postdoctoral Fellowships: 631
Gershoy (The Leo) Award: 614
GETTY (J. PAUL) TRUST, GETTY FOUNDATION: 584
GHEENS FOUNDATION: 160
Giambalvo (Joan F.) Memorial Scholarship: 1775
Gies (William J.) Award: 2503
GIFFORD (THE ROSAMOND) CHARITABLE CORPORATION: 1360
Gifted Young Pianists Concerto Competition: 818
Gilbert Grants: 1837
Gilbert (Rosalinde and Arthur) Foundation/AFAR New Investigator Awards in Alzheimer's Disease: 2369
Gilbreth Memorial Fellowship: 2823
GILL FOUNDATION
  Gill Foundation General Fund: 1051
Gill Foundation General Fund: 1051
Gillette (The R.L.) Scholarship: 1023
Gillies (Sir Harold Delf) Award: 2364
Ginocchio (Lawrence) Scholarship: 2789
girlsBEST: 1167
GLAUCOMA FOUNDATION (THE): 2673
GLAUCOMA RESEARCH FOUNDATION
  Shaffer Fund for Innovative Glaucoma Research: 2674
GLAXOSMITHKLINE: 1530
GLBT Community Projects Fund: 257
Glenn (Paul) Award: 2366
Glenn/AFAR Breakthroughs in Gerontology Awards: 2370
Global: 74
Global Development: 176
GLOBAL FUND FOR WOMEN
  Assisting Women's Groups Globally: 1146
Global Network for Women's and Children's Health Research: 1561
Global Philanthropy Program: 335
Global Public Health Initiative: 2389
GLOECKNER (THE FRED C.) FOUNDATION, INC.: 2253
Gloeckner (M. Louise Carpenter, M.D.) Summer Research Fellowship: 1145
Glover (Bud) Memorial Scholarship: 2782
GoGirlGo! Grant Program: 1169
Gold Fund for Health: 1537
GOLDBERG (RUTH ESTRIN) MEMORIAL FOR CANCER RESEARCH: 2594
Goldberg (The Samuel) & Sons Foundation Prize for Jewish Fiction by Emerging Writers: 630
Golden Key Graduate Scholarship Award (The): 1806
GOLDEN KEY INTERNATIONAL HONOUR SOCIETY
  Business Achievement Awards: 1806
  Community Service Award: 1806
  Education Achievement Awards: 1806
  Engineering/Technology Achievement Awards: 1806

Jenkins Foundation: Improving the Health of Greater Richmond (The): 1291
JENNINGS (MARTHA HOLDEN) FOUNDATION
   Grants-to-Educators Program: 1714
   Open Grants: 1714
Jenny (Daniel P.) Research Fellowships: 2827
Jensen (Susanne) Scholarship: 2724
Jensen (The Walter J.) Fellowship for French Language, Literature and Culture: 984
Jerome Fellowships: 739
JEROME FOUNDATION, INC.: 409
Jessup Fellowship: 2268
JEWEL-OSCO: 1390
JEWETT (GEORGE FREDERICK) FOUNDATION: 195
JEWISH BOOK COUNCIL
   National Jewish Book Award-American Jewish Studies: 716
   National Jewish Book Award-Anthologies and Collections: 716
   National Jewish Book Award-Biography, Autobiography and Memoir: 716
   National Jewish Book Award-Children's and Young Adult Literature: 716
   National Jewish Book Award-Contemporary Jewish Life: 716
   National Jewish Book Award-Education and Jewish Identity: 716
   National Jewish Book Award-Fiction: 716
   National Jewish Book Award-History: 716
   National Jewish Book Award-Holocaust: 716
   National Jewish Book Award-Illustrated Children's Book: 716
   National Jewish Book Award-Jewish Family Literature: 716
   National Jewish Book Award-Modern Jewish Thought and Experience: 716
   National Jewish Book Award-Poetry: 716
   National Jewish Book Award-Scholarship: 716
   National Jewish Book Award-Sephardic Culture: 716
   National Jewish Book Award-Visual Arts: 716
   National Jewish Book Award-Women's Studies: 716
   National Jewish Book Award-Writing Based on Archival Materials: 716
   Rohr (Sami) Prize for Jewish Literature: 717
JEWISH COMMUNAL SERVICE ASSOCIATION OF NORTH AMERICA
   Graduate Student Network: 1663
   Outstanding Journal Article: 1663
   Professional Development Programs: 1663
   Young Professional Award: 1663
JEWISH COMMUNITY FOUNDATION OF LOS ANGELES
   Capital Grants: 1391
   Cutting Edge Grants: 1391
   Israel Grants: 1391
   Los Angeles Collaborative Grants: 1391
JEWISH FAMILY AND CHILDREN'S SERVICES: 1824
JEWISH HEALTHCARE FOUNDATION OF PITTSBURGH (THE): 1540
Jewish Life and Values: 105
Jewson (Ruth) Award: 1601
JFK LIBRARY FOUNDATION
   Kennedy Library Archival Internships: 196
JFNY Grant for Japanese Studies: 901
JFNY Grant Program - Arts and Culture: 901
JILA
   Postdoctoral Research Associateships: 2164
   Visiting Fellowships: 2164
JOHNS HOPKINS CENTER FOR ALTERNATIVES TO ANIMAL TESTING (THE): 1541
Johns (Hyland) Grant: 2262
Johnson (Alvin H.) AMS 50 Dissertation Fellowships: 795
JOHNSON & JOHNSON FAMILY OF COMPANIES: 197
JOHNSON CONTROLS FOUNDATION: 198
JOHNSON FOUNDATION, INC. (THE): 199
JOHNSON (J. SEWARD, SR.) 1963 CHARITABLE TRUST: 1392
Johnson (Lyndon B.) School of Public Affairs: 1762
JOHNSON (THE LYNDON BAINES) FOUNDATION: 2129
Johnson (Magic) Foundation HIV/AIDS Grant: 200
JOHNSON (MAGIC) FOUNDATION, INC.
   Johnson (Magic) Foundation HIV/AIDS Grant: 200
   Michaels (Taylor) Scholarship: 200
JOHNSON (ROBERT WOOD) FOUNDATION: 2426
JOHNSON (WALTER S.) FOUNDATION
   High Risk & Adjudicated Youth: 1664
   School Reform: 1664
   Youth Development: 1664
Joint AAFP/F-AAFP Grant Awards Program (JGAP): 2365
JONES (DAISY MARQUIS) FOUNDATION: 201

JONES (THE FLETCHER) FOUNDATION: 1750
Joseph-Armand Bombardier Canada Graduate Scholarships-Master's Scholarships: 2001
JOSLYN (THE CARL W. AND CARRIE MAE) CHARITABLE TRUST: 1590
JOURNAL OF THE AMERICAN MEDICAL ASSOCIATION
   Fishbein (Morris) Fellowship in Medical Editing: 2067
Journalism Awards Program: 2061
Journalism Foundation: 1871
Journalism Grants: 1446
Journalism Program: 215, 243
Journalist of the Year Award: 1068
JOYCE FOUNDATION (THE): 202
JPMORGAN CHASE FOUNDATION (THE): 203
Judaic and Related Studies Postdoctoral Fellowships: 956
Judicial Administration Fellowship Program: 2117
Junior Faculty Award: 2560
Junior Faculty Research Grants: 2730
Junior Faculty Scholar Award: 2381
Junior Fellowship: 927
Junior Fellowships: 387, 447
Junior Library Guild-Sister Sally Daly Grant: 763
Junior Ranger Program (The): 2333
Junior/Senior Scholarships: 2773
Juvenile Accountability Block Grants Program: 1508
JUVENILE DIABETES RESEARCH FOUNDATION INTERNATIONAL
   Career Development Awards: 2576
   Postdoctoral Fellowships: 2575
   Regular Research Grant: 2574
Juvenile Justice and Delinquency Prevention Allocation to States: 1505
Juvenile Justice and Delinquency Prevention Program: 1504

K

Kabis (Dorothy) Internship: 1155
Kagiwada (David Tamotsu) Memorial Fund: 852
Kahan (Gerald) Scholar's Prize: 560
KAHANOFF FOUNDATION (THE): 1393
Kalamazoo Chapter No. 116-Roscoe Douglas Scholarship: 2780
KALAMAZOO COMMUNITY FOUNDATION: 1394
Kanawha and Ohio River Valleys Program: 2355
KANSAS HEALTH FOUNDATION
   Recognition Grants: 1542
KANTOR (ALICE AND JULIUS) CHARITABLE TRUST: 204
KANTZLER FOUNDATION (THE): 1395
KAPLAN (THE J.M.) FUND, INC.
   City Life Grant: 205
   Discretionary Grants: 205
   Environment Program Grant: 205
   Furthermore Grant: 205
   Historic Preservation Grant: 205
   Migrations Grant: 205
Kaplan-Goodkind Memorial Scholarship Fund: 840
Kappa Epsilon-AFPE-Nellie Wakeman First Year Graduate Fellowship: 2698
KAPPA OMICRON NU HONOR SOCIETY
   Brown (Marjorie M.) Dissertation Fellowship: 2841
   Hawthorne (Ruth E.) Research Grant: 2841
   Kappa Omicron Phi/Hettie Margaret Anthony Fellowship: 2841
   LeaderShape Institute Award: 2841
   Maddex (Eileen C.) Fellowship: 2841
   National Alumni Chapter Fellowship: 2841
   National Alumni Chapter Grant: 2841
   National Scholar Program: 2841
   New Initiatives Grant: 2841
   Omicron Nu Research Fellowship: 2841
Kappa Omicron Phi/Hettie Margaret Anthony Fellowship: 2841
KAPPA TAU ALPHA
   Mott (Frank Luther) KTA Research/Book Award: 2068
Kashiwahara (Ken) Scholarship: 2086
KAUFMAN (LOUIS G.) ENDOWMENT FUND: 1715
Kaufman (Lucille B.) Women's Scholarship: 2780
Kay (E. Wayne) Scholarships: 2780
KAZANJIAN (THE CALVIN K.) ECONOMICS FOUNDATION, INC.: 2025
KCC JAPAN EDUCATION EXCHANGE
   Graduate Fellowships: 1751
Keats (Ezra Jack) Children's Literature Research Fellowship Program: 747
Keats (Ezra Jack)/Kerlan Collection Memorial Fellowship: 745

References in index are to entry numbers.

NATIONAL ENDOWMENT FOR THE ARTS: 514
NATIONAL ENDOWMENT FOR THE HUMANITIES
  Fellowships: 415
  Grants for Teaching and Learning Resources: 1678
  Office of Challenge Grants: 414
  Preservation and Access: 417
  Public Programs: 2075
  Research Program: 413
  Seminars and Institutes Program: 416
  Summer Stipends: 415
National Endowment for the Humanities Fellowships: 422, 934
National Endowment for the Humanities (NEH) Fellowship: 921
National Established Investigator Award: 2538
NATIONAL EYE INSTITUTE
  Center Core Grants: 2677
  Cooperative Clinical Research Grants: 2676
  Small Business Innovation Research Awards: 2676
NATIONAL FARMER'S ORGANIZATION
  Farm Kids for College Scholarships: 2258
NATIONAL FASTENER DISTRIBUTORS ASSOCIATION: 1679
NATIONAL FEDERATION OF MUSIC CLUBS
  Award Program for Summer Music Festivals and Music Centers: 825
  Bullock (Dorothy Dann) Music Therapy Award: 826
  NFMC Competitions and Awards: 824
NATIONAL FEDERATION OF REPUBLICAN WOMEN
  Kabis (Dorothy) Internship: 1155
  National Pathfinders Scholarship: 1155
  Rendel (Betty) Scholarship: 1155
NATIONAL FEDERATION OF STATE POETRY SOCIETIES, INC.
  Meudt (The Edna) Memorial Award & The Florence Kahn Memorial
  Award: 723
  NFSPS College University Level Poetry Competition Awards: 723
NATIONAL FEDERATION OF THE BLIND
  National Federation of the Blind Scholarship Program: 1066
National Federation of the Blind Scholarship Program: 1066
NATIONAL FISH AND WILDLIFE FOUNDATION: 2330
NATIONAL FOOTBALL LEAGUE CHARITIES
  Medical Research Grant: 1680
  Player Foundation Grant: 1680
  Pro Bowl Grants: 1680
NATIONAL FOSTER PARENT ASSOCIATION
  NFPA Scholarship: 1209
NATIONAL FOUNDATION FOR ADVANCEMENT IN THE ARTS
  Alumni Grant: 515
  In the Studio/Out of the Studio: 515
  YoungArts Miami: 515
  YoungArts New York: 515
  YoungArts Week: 515
NATIONAL FOUNDATION FOR INFECTIOUS DISEASES
  NFID Advanced Vaccinology Course Travel Grants: 2494
  NFID Traveling Professorship in Rural Areas: 2494
NATIONAL GEM CONSORTIUM (THE)
  GEM M.S. Engineering Fellowship (The): 1067
  GEM Ph.D. Engineering Fellowship (The): 1067
  GEM Ph.D. Science Fellowship (The): 1067
  Grad Lab: 1067
  Graduate and Faculty Development Program: 1067
NATIONAL GEOGRAPHIC SOCIETY
  National Geographic Society Committee for Research and Exploration:
  2212
National Geographic Society Committee for Research and Exploration:
  2212
National Glaucoma Research Program: 2664
National Guard Grant: 1883
NATIONAL HEADACHE FOUNDATION: 2525
NATIONAL HEALTH SERVICE CORPS (NHSC)
  National Health Service Corps Scholarship Program: 1549
National Health Service Corps Scholarship Program: 1549
National Heart Council (NHC): 1677
NATIONAL HEART, LUNG AND BLOOD INSTITUTE (NHLBI): 2554
  Blood Diseases and Resources Research: 2526
  Lung Diseases Research: 2555
NATIONAL HEMOPHILIA FOUNDATION (THE)
  Pool (Judith Graham) Postdoctoral Research Fellowships in Bleeding
  Disorders: 2441
NATIONAL HIGHWAY TRAFFIC SAFETY ADMINISTRATION
  State and Community Highway Safety Program Section 402: 1602
NATIONAL HISTORICAL PUBLICATIONS AND RECORDS
  COMMISSION: 648
National History Day Prize in Women's History, Junior Division: 626
NATIONAL HOME LIBRARY FOUNDATION: 778

NATIONAL HUMANITIES CENTER
  National Humanities Center Fellowships: 418
National Humanities Center Fellowships: 418
National Innovative Research Grant: 2537
NATIONAL INSTITUTE FOR LABOR RELATIONS RESEARCH
  Future Teacher Scholarship: 1842
  Ruggles (The William B.) Journalism Scholarship: 2076
NATIONAL INSTITUTE OF ALLERGY AND INFECTIOUS DISEASES
  Clinical Investigator Awards: 2496
  Division of AIDS (DAIDS): 2495
  Division of Allergy, Immunology and Transplantation (DAIT): 2495
  Division of Microbiology and Infectious Diseases (DMID) Research
  Programs: 2495
  Minority Research Enhancement Awards: 2496
  National Research Services Awards: 2496
  Physician Scientist Awards: 2496
  Research Career Awards: 2496
  Small Business Innovation Research Awards: 2496
NATIONAL INSTITUTE OF ARTHRITIS AND MUSCULOSKELETAL
  AND SKIN DISEASES
  Bone Biology Program: 2685
  Bone Diseases Program: 2685
  Muscle Biology Branch: 2610
NATIONAL INSTITUTE OF DENTAL AND CRANIOFACIAL
  RESEARCH (NIDCR)
  AIDS: 2510
  Behavioral/Social Science Research: 2510
  Biotechnology/Regenerative Medicine: 2510
  Clinical Research/Clinical Trials: 2510
  Computational Science: 2510
  Conference Grants: 2510
  Epidemiology/Population Research: 2510
  Genetic Studies: 2510
  Health Literacy Research: 2510
  Individual NRSA Postdoctoral Fellowships (F-32): 2509
  Individual NRSA Senior Fellowship Award (F-33): 2511
  International Health: 2510
  Neurobiology/Pain: 2510
  Oral Cancer: 2510
  Oral Health Disparities Research: 2510
  Teeth and Bone: 2510
  Women's Health: 2510
NATIONAL INSTITUTE OF ENVIRONMENTAL HEALTH SCIENCES
  Environmental Health Sciences Research and Training Grants: 2331
NATIONAL INSTITUTE OF GENERAL MEDICAL SCIENCES
  Center for Bioinformatics and Computational Biology: 2442
  Division of Cell Biology and Biophysics: 2442
  Division of Genetics and Developmental Biology: 2442
  Division of Minority Opportunities in Research: 2442
  Division of Pharmacology, Physiology, and Biological Chemistry: 2442
  Medical Scientist Training Program: 2444
  Minority Biomedical Research Support Branch: 2443
NATIONAL INSTITUTE OF JUSTICE
  Research Grants: 1501
NATIONAL INSTITUTE OF MENTAL HEALTH: 2744
  Research Training and Career Development Program: 1988
  Traumatic Stress Research Program: 1988
NATIONAL INSTITUTE OF NEUROLOGICAL DISORDERS AND
  STROKE
  NINDS Extramural Research Grants: 2634
NATIONAL INSTITUTE OF NURSING RESEARCH
  Career Development Grants: 2652
  Research Grants: 2652
  Research Training Grants: 2652
  Small Business Innovation Research Grants: 2652
NATIONAL INSTITUTE OF STANDARDS AND TECHNOLOGY
  Manufacturing Extension Partnership: 2094
NATIONAL INSTITUTE ON AGING
  Aging Research: 1550
NATIONAL INSTITUTE ON ALCOHOL ABUSE AND ALCOHOLISM
  Academic Career Awards (K07): 1551
  Career Enhancement Award for Stem Cell Research (K18): 1551
  Independent Scientist Awards (K02): 1551
  Mentored Patient-Oriented Research Career Development Award (K23):
  1551
  Mentored Quantitative Research Career Development Award (K25):
  1551
  Midcareer Investigator Award in Patient-Oriented Research (K24): 1551
  Scientist Development Awards for Mentored Clinical (K08): 1551

RESEARCH CORPORATION FOR SCIENCE ADVANCEMENT
Cottrell Scholar Awards: 2169
Multi-Investigator Cottrell College Science Awards: 2169
Scialog: Solar Energy Conversion: 2169
Single Investigator Cottrell College Science Awards: 2169
Research Fellowship: 901, 2551
Research Fellowship Award: 2581
Research Fellowship Grant: 2465
Research Fellowship Program: 2357
Research Fellowships: 560, 2412, 2637
Research Fellowships in American History and Culture: 639
Research Fellowships in Art History: 587
Research Fieldwork: 1500
Research Fund (The): 2467
RESEARCH FUND OF THE AMERICAN OTOLOGICAL SOCIETY,
INC.
AOS Clinician-Scientist Award: 2680
Clinical Trial: 2680
Research Grants: 2680
Research Training Fellowship: 2680
Research Grant: 2144, 2452
Research Grant in Crystallography, Mineral Physics or Chemistry and
Mineralogy: 2210
Research Grant Program: 1698, 2520, 2616
Research Grants: 623, 1501, 2201, 2306, 2573, 2620, 2652, 2680
Research Grants and Fellowships: 2584
Research Grants for New Investigators: 2666
Research Grants in Dietetics: 2839
Research Grants in Leprosy: 2491
Research Grants Program: 2433, 2769
Research in Remote Sensing of the Earth and Environment Grants: 2216
Research Infrastructure: 2440
Research Infrastructure Awards: 2613
Research Initiative Fund Grants: 2613
Research Innovative Grants: 2608
Research Institute: 949
Research Inventory Grants: 410
Research Library Program: 398
Research Matters! Award: 2731
Research Medical Student Grant: 2471
Research Program: 413
Research Resident/Fellow Grant: 2475
Research Seed Grant: 2470
Research Starter Grants in Health Outcomes: 2704
Research Starter Grants in Informatics: 2704
Research Starter Grants in Pharmaceutics: 2704
Research Starter Grants in Pharmacology/Toxicology: 2704
Research Studentship: 2627
Research Support Grants: 447
Research Training and Career Development Program: 1988
Research Training Fellowship: 2680
Research Training Grants: 2652
Research Travel Award: 668
Research Travel Grant Program: 2123
Research Travel Grants: 628
Research Traveling Fellowship: 2452
Residencies at Ragdale Foundation: 530
Residency Partnership Program: 800
Residency Travel Award: 2364
Resident Clinician-Scientist Training Grant: 2455
Resident Research Grant: 2683
Resident Scholar Fellowships: 2150
Resident Scholars Program: 853
Resistance Welding Manufacturing Alliance Scholarship: 2766
RESOURCES FOR THE FUTURE
Fisher (Joseph L.) Dissertation Fellowships: 2340
Krutilla (John V.) Research Stipend: 2342
Spofford (The Walter O., Jr.) Memorial Internship: 2340
White (Gilbert F.) Postdoctoral Fellowship Program: 2341
Responsive Grants: 255
Responsive Grants Program: 1614
Reston (William) Research Award: 2694
Restricted Research Program: 2450
Retired and Senior Volunteer Program (RSVP): 1580
RETIREMENT RESEARCH FOUNDATION (THE)
Accessible Faith Program: 1073
Core Grants Program: 1073
Organizational Capacity Building Initiative: 1073
REVSON (THE CHARLES H.) FOUNDATION: 307

REYNOLDS (DONALD W.) FOUNDATION
Aging and Quality of Life: 1446
Capital Grants: 1446
Cardiovascular Clinical Research: 1446
Journalism Grants: 1446
REYNOLDS (J.B.) FOUNDATION: 1447
REYNOLDS (KATE B.) CHARITABLE TRUST
Health Care Division: 1607
Poor and Needy Division: 1607
REYNOLDS (Z. SMITH) FOUNDATION, INC.: 308
RGK FOUNDATION: 1448
Rho Chi-Schering Plough-AFPE First Year Graduate Scholarship: 2697
RHODE ISLAND FOUNDATION/RHODE ISLAND COMMUNITY
FOUNDATION (THE): 309
RHODE ISLAND STATE COUNCIL ON THE ARTS
Fellowships: 531
Folk Arts Apprenticeships: 531
General Operating Support: 531
Project Grants: 531
RIBA Research Trusts Awards: 450
Ribbon of Hope: 1690
Rice-Cullimore Scholarship: 2818
Richardson (Henry and Sylvia) Research Grant: 2279
RICHARDSON (SID W.) FOUNDATION: 310
RICHARDSON (SID W.) MEMORIAL FUND: 1872
RICHARDSON (SMITH) FOUNDATION, INC.
Domestic Public Policy Program: 1992
International Security and Foreign Policy Program: 1992
Richmond Eye and Ear Fund: 1291
Ridgway (General and Mrs. Matthew B.) Research Grant: 677
Rieck (Donald A.) Research Grant: 1640
RIGHTEOUS PERSONS FOUNDATION: 1074
RILEY (THE MABEL LOUISE) FOUNDATION : 1695
Rinehart School of Sculpture (MFA): 590
RIPPEL (FANNIE E.) FOUNDATION: 2476
Rippon (John W.) Research Award: 2294
Risling (David) Emergency Aid Scholarships: 1104
Rittenhouse Award: 774
Rivera (Geraldo) Scholarship: 1064
RJOS Traveling Fellowships: 2715
RNF Fellow Research Grant: 2655
RNF New Investigator Research Grant: 2655
Robb (Preston) Fellowship: 2626
Robbins-Wilf (Dr. Marcia) Research Award: 2605
ROBERTS (FOREST) THEATRE
Panowski (Mildred and Albert) Playwriting Award: 572
Roberts (George A.) Scholarship: 2845
Roberts (Summerfield G.) Award: 673
Robeson (The Paul) Fund for Independent Media: 2059
Robins, Kaplan, Miller and Ciresi Foundation for Children: 1415
Robinson (Helen M.) Grant: 1661
ROBINSON (JACKIE) FOUNDATION
Education and Leadership Development Program: 1075
Robinson (Jacqueline) Regional Competition Awards: 1093
Robinson (The James Harvey) Prize: 614
Robinson (Samuel) Essay Contest: 1870
Robinson-Cunningham Award: 2723
ROCHE FOUNDATION (THE): 1720
ROCHESTER AREA COMMUNITY FOUNDATION: 1158
ROCHESTER AREA FOUNDATION: 1449
ROCK ISLAND ARSENAL MUSEUM
Maguire (Richard C.) Scholarship: 665
ROCKEFELLER ARCHIVE CENTER
Grants-in-Aid for Research at the Rockefeller Archive Center: 666
ROCKEFELLER FAMILY FUND
Citizen Participation and Government Accountability: 311
Economic Justice for Women: 311
Environment: 311
Institutional Responsiveness: 311
Rockwell Collins Scholarship: 2782
ROCKWELL FUND, INC.
Operating Funds: 312
Program/Project Support: 312
Rodgers (The Richard) Awards: 790
Rodriguez (Michael and Maggie) Scholarship: 1064
Roe (John Orlando) Award: 2364
Rogers (Frank Bradway) Information Advancement Award: 774
Rogerson (Clark T.) Research Award: 2294
Rohr (Sami) Prize for Jewish Literature: 717
Roizen & Anesthesia Research Foundation New Investigator Grant: 2559
Rolex Awards for Enterprise Program: 313

ROLEX SA
  Rolex Awards for Enterprise Program: 313
Romanell-Phi Beta Kappa Professorship in Philosophy (The): 1865
Romani (The George T. and Margaret W.) Fellowships: 388
Romanowski (The Miroslaw) Medal: 2828
Rome Prize Fellowship in Landscape Architecture (The): 2305
Rome Prize Fellowships: 375
Roosevelt (Theodore) Memorial Grants: 1929
Rorison (Harmon Chadbourn) Fellowship: 407
Rose Architectural Fellowship: 443
ROSE COMMUNITY FOUNDATION: 1450
Rosen (Kenneth M.) Fellowship in Cardiac Pacing and Electrophysiology:
  2552
ROSENBERG (HENRY AND RUTH BLAUSTEIN) FOUNDATION:
  1451
Rosenblith (Walter A.) New Investigator Award: 1532
Rosewood Family Scholarship Program: 1092
ROSS FOUNDATION: 1452
Rossiter (Margaret W.) History of Women in Science Prize: 636
ROSWELL ARTIST-IN-RESIDENCE PROGRAM: 602
Roswell (Virginia) Dissertation Award: 2733
ROTARY CLUB OF BRYN MAWR (THE)
  Cabell (Harry H.) Scholarship Program: 1873
ROTARY FOUNDATION OF ROTARY INTERNATIONAL (THE)
  Ambassadorial Scholarships: 986
  Rotary Peace Fellowships: 985
Rotary Peace Fellowships: 985
Rotch Travelling Scholarship: 449
ROTCH TRAVELLING SCHOLARSHIP IN ARCHITECTURE
  Rotch Travelling Scholarship: 449
  Rotch Travelling Studio: 449
Rotch Travelling Studio: 449
Roth (Lois) Award for a Translation of a Literary Work: 696
Roth (Richard J.) Journalism Fellowship: 2133
Rothermel (Marjorie Roy) Scholarship: 2818
Rouse (Jim and Patty) Awards for Excellence in Community
  Revitalization: 1581
Rousseau (Theodore) Fellowships: 775
Rowe (The Leo S.) Pan American Fund: 1014
Rowley Fund/Ministerial Education Fund: 852
ROYAL INSTITUTE OF BRITISH ARCHITECTS
  RIBA Research Trusts Awards: 450
ROYAL SOCIETY OF CANADA (THE)
  Bancroft Award (The): 2828
  Dawson (The Sir John William) Medal: 2828
  McLaughlin Medal (The): 2828
  McNeil Medal (The): 2828
  Romanowski (The Miroslaw) Medal: 2828
  Rutherford Memorial Medals (The): 2828
  Synge (The John L.) Award: 2828
  Wilson (The Alice) Award: 2828
ROYAL SOCIETY OF EDINBURGH (THE)
  Royal Society of Edinburgh Scottish Government Personal Research
  Fellowships: 987
Royal Society of Edinburgh Scottish Government Personal Research
  Fellowships: 987
ROYAL TOWN PLANNING INSTITUTE (THE)
  Pepler (George) International Award: 1993
Rozelle (Pete and Carrie) Award: 1673
RSNA Research Scholar Grant: 2474
RSNA/AUR/APDR/SCARD Radiology Education Research Development
  Grant: 2473
RTCA
  Jackson (The William E.) Award: 2792
Ruckes (The Paul and Ellen) Scholarship: 1023
Ruggles (The William B.) Journalism Scholarship: 2076
Runaway and Homeless Youth Grants Program: 1227
RUNNING STRONG FOR AMERICAN INDIAN YOUTH: 1122
RUNYON (DAMON) CANCER RESEARCH FOUNDATION
  Frey (Dale F.) Award for Breakthrough Scientists: 2604
  Runyon (Damon) Clinical Investigator Award: 2604
  Runyon (Damon) Fellowship Award: 2604
  Runyon-Rachleff (Damon) Innovation Award: 2604
Runyon (Damon) Clinical Investigator Award: 2604
Runyon (Damon) Fellowship Award: 2604
Runyon-Rachleff (Damon) Innovation Award: 2604
Rural Housing Grants (Section 504): 2261
RURAL HOUSING SERVICE
  Rural Housing Grants (Section 504): 2261

RURITAN NATIONAL FOUNDATION
  Build Your Dollars Grant: 1696
  Educational Grant Program: 1696
  Operation We Care: 1608
RUSSELL FAMILY FOUNDATION (THE): 2343
  Jane's Fellowship Program: 1453
RUSSELL (JOSEPHINE G.) TRUST: 1560
Russell (Peter Nicol) Postgraduate Scholarship in Mechanical and
  Mechatronic Engineering: 2833
Rutherford Memorial Medals (The): 2828

S

Sabbatical Fellowships in Health Outcomes: 2461
Sabbatical Fellowships in Informatics: 2461
Sabbatical Fellowships in Pharmaceutics: 2461
Sabbatical Fellowships in Pharmacology/Toxicology: 2461
SACHS FOUNDATION
  Financial Aid for Education of Black Residents of Colorado: 1097
Sacred in Opera: 827
Sacred Sites Program: 656
Safe and Drug Free Schools Program: 1224
Safe Passage: Youth Transitioning from Foster Care: 257
SAGE (RUSSELL) FOUNDATION: 1994
Sager (The Louis and Fannie) Memorial Scholarship: 1848
SAGES Program (The): 2006
SAGINAW COMMUNITY FOUNDATION: 1454
Saguaro Fund: 1049
SAIGH FOUNDATION (THE): 1216
SAILORS' SNUG HARBOR OF BOSTON: 1609
ST. ANDREW'S SOCIETY OF THE STATE OF NEW YORK
  Scholarship Program for Graduate Study in Scotland: 988
SAINT CROIX VALLEY FOUNDATION
  Health and Wellness Grant: 1455
  Music Education Grant: 1455
  Nonprofit Management Assistance Grants: 1455
  Valley Arts Initiative Grant: 1455
St. Louis Chapter No. 17 Scholarship: 2780
ST. LOUIS RAMS FOUNDATION: 1217
SAINT LUKE'S EPISCOPAL HEALTH CHARITIES: 1610
ST. PETERSBURG TIMES FUND, INC.
  Barnes Scholarship: 1875
  Career Journalism Scholarship: 1874
SAINT-GOBAIN CORPORATION FOUNDATION: 1456
Salinas (Maria Elena) Scholarship: 1064
SALISBURY COMMUNITY FOUNDATION: 314
Saloutos (Theodore) Book Award: 612
Salvatori Fellowship: 2127
SAMLA Studies Award: 700
Sams (Dr. Lauranne) Scholarship: 2651
SAMUELS (THE FAN FOX AND LESLIE R.) FOUNDATION, INC.
  Performing Arts: 315
SAN ANGELO AREA FOUNDATION: 1457
SAN ANGELO SYMPHONY SOCIETY
  Sorantin Young Artist Award: 834
SAN ANTONIO AREA FOUNDATION
  Discretionary Grant Process: 1458
SAN DIEGO ART INSTITUTE
  Annual International Juried Award Exhibition: 603
  Southern California Regional Juried Award: 603
  Youth Art: 603
SAN DIEGO FOUNDATION (THE): 1459
SAN FRANCISCO CONSERVATORY OF MUSIC
  Performance Scholarships in Music for Students in Bachelor and Master
  of Music Programs: 835
SAN FRANCISCO FOUNDATION (THE)
  Art Awards: 532
  Bay Area Grants Program: 316
  Cadogan Fine Arts Fellowships: 604
  Community Leadership Awards: 1460
  Murphy Fine Arts Fellowships: 604
SAN FRANCISCO OPERA CENTER
  Adler Fellowships: 836
  Merola Opera Program: 836
  Schwabacher Debut Recitals: 836
Sanitarian Award: 2840
SANTA BARBARA FOUNDATION
  Express Grant: 1461
  Strategy Grant: 1461

SANTA BARBARA MISSION ARCHIVE-LIBRARY
  Geiger Memorial Fellowship: 667
Santa Cruz Community Foundation: 1299
SANTA FE COMMUNITY FOUNDATION: 1076
SAR Prize: 700
SARA LEE FOUNDATION: 317
SARKEYS FOUNDATION: 318
SARNOFF CARDIOVASCULAR RESEARCH FOUNDATION (THE)
  Sarnoff Fellowship Program: 2557
  Sarnoff Scholar Fellow-to-Faculty Transition Award: 2557
Sarnoff Fellowship Program: 2557
Sarnoff Scholar Fellow-to-Faculty Transition Award: 2557
Sarton Medal: 636
SAVOY FOUNDATION: 2477
SCA Starter Grants: 2559
SCA-IARS Mid-Career Grant: 2559
SCAC (FRENCH CULTURAL AND EDUCATIONAL OFFICE)
  Allons en France: 989
  Chateaubriand Fellowships Program: 989
  Green Connection: 989
  Partner University Fund (PUF) (The): 989
  Rencontres Internationales de Jeunes (RIJ): 989
  Teacher Training in France: 989
  Teaching Assistant Program in France: 989
  Verne (Jules) Program: 989
Scaglione (Aldo and Jeanne) Prize for a Translation of a Literary Work:
  696
Scaglione (Aldo and Jeanne) Prize for a Translation of a Scholarly Study
  of Literature: 696
Scaglione (Aldo and Jeanne) Prize for Comparative Literary Studies: 696
Scaglione (Aldo and Jeanne) Prize for French and Francophone Studies:
  696
Scaglione (Aldo and Jeanne) Prize for Italian Studies: 696
Scaglione (Aldo and Jeanne) Prize for Slavic Studies: 696
Scaglione (Aldo and Jeanne) Prize for Studies in Germanic Languages
  and Literatures: 696
Scaglione (Aldo and Jeanne) Publication Award for a Manuscript in
  Italian Literary Studies: 696
SCAI/Cordis Fellowship Program for Interventional Cardiology: 2558
SCAIFE (SARAH) FOUNDATION, INC.: 2138
Scarborough (William Sanders) Prize: 696
Schaar (Ruby Yoshino) Playwright Award: 568
Schaffer (Rita) Young Investigator Award: 2275
Schaldach (Max) Fellowship in Cardiac Pacing and Electrophysiology:
  2552
Schallek Fellowship: 645
Scharp (Charles B.) Scholarship: 2818
Schecter (Abe) Graduate Scholarship: 2086
Schedulers & Dispatchers Scholarship: 2789
Scheidlinger (Saul) Scholarship: 2724
Scherbenske (The M. James) Grant: 2513
Schimke (Mary McEwen) Scholarship: 1163
Schizophrenia Grants: 361
Schlundt (The Esther) Fund: 769
Schmitt (Bernadotte) Grant: 614
Schneeberger (Jimmy) Scholarship Fund: 1303
Schnurr (B.E.) Memorial Fund Research Grant: 2719
Scholar Awards: 245
Scholar in Residence Grants: 410
Scholar's Award: 2144
Scholar-in-Training Awards: 2584
Scholarly Paper Competition: 827
Scholars Fund: 1775
Scholars-in-Residence: 425
Scholarship and Charity Fund: 2714
Scholarship Endowment Trust Fund: 2757
Scholarship Funds: 89, 1304
Scholarship Program: 361
Scholarship Program for Graduate Study in Scotland: 988
Scholarship Program for Israelis: 1006
Scholarship Program for Young Pianists: 802
Scholarships for Academic Excellence: 1852
Scholarships for Children and Spouses of Deceased or Disabled Veterans
  and Servicemembers: 1801
Scholarships for Disadvantaged Students: 1657
Scholarships for Finnish Studies and Research: 957
Scholarships for Professional Training as School Media Specialists: 783
Scholarships for Study in Library Service: 780
Scholarships for Summer Music Courses: 788
Scholarships in Library Science: 750

Scholastic Art and Writing Awards (The): 456
SCHOLL (DR.) FOUNDATION: 319
SCHOMBURG CENTER FOR RESEARCH IN BLACK CULTURE
  (THE)
  Scholars-in-Residence: 425
Schonstedt Scholarship in Surveying (The): 2800
School at Jacob's Pillow (The): 567
School Breakfast Program (The): 1229
School Bus Grants: 508
SCHOOL FOR ADVANCED RESEARCH
  Advanced Seminar Program: 2150
  Resident Scholar Fellowships: 2150
  Staley (J.I.) Prize: 2151
  Summer Scholar Fellowships: 1876
School of Social Science Fellowships: 1979
SCHOOL OF THE MUSEUM OF FINE ARTS, BOSTON
  Traveling Fellowship Award: 605
School Partnership Projects: 516
School Reform: 1664
Schork (Kurt) Awards in International Journalism: 2063
SCHOTT FOUNDATION FOR PUBLIC EDUCATION (THE): 1697
Schroepfer Medal Award: 2192
SCHUMANN FUND FOR NEW JERSEY (THE): 1218
Schumar (James F.) Scholarship: 2806
SCHUSTERMAN (CHARLES AND LYNN) FAMILY FOUNDATION:
  1462
Schutze (Katherine J.) Memorial Scholarship for Women Seminary
  Students: 852
SCHWAB (CHARLES AND HELEN) FOUNDATION
  Foundation Initiative Grants: 320
SCHWAB (CHARLES) FOUNDATION
  Schwab Moneywise^^99: 2034
Schwab Moneywise^^99: 2034
Schwabacher Debut Recitals: 836
Schwartz (Frances M.) Fellowship: 618
Scialog: Solar Energy Conversion: 2169
Science for Peace and Security Programme: 1018
Science in Society Awards: 2074
Science Undergraduate Laboratory Internships: 1933
Science, Technology and Society: 1956
Scientific Research Grants Program: 2553
Scientific Research Grants/Proposal Writing Contest: 1945
Scientist Development Awards for Mentored Clinical (K08): 1551
Scientist Development Awards for Mentored Research (K01): 1551
Scientist-in-Training Research Award: 2709
SCLERODERMA FOUNDATION
  Scleroderma Foundation Research Grants: 2478
Scleroderma Foundation Research Grants: 2478
ScotiaMcLeod Scholarship: 1905
SCOTT (KENNETH A.) CHARITABLE TRUST: 2242
Scottish Rite Charitable Foundation Major Research Grants: 2752
SCOTTISH RITE CHARITABLE FOUNDATION OF CANADA
  Scottish Rite Charitable Foundation Major Research Grants: 2752
SCOVILLE (HERBERT, JR.) PEACE FELLOWSHIP PROGRAM: 907
SCRANTON AREA FOUNDATION: 1463
SCRIPPS (THE ELLEN BROWNING) FOUNDATION: 321
Scudder (Vida Dutton) Fellowship: 1162
SCUOLA NORMALE SUPERIORE
  Graduate School Scholarships for Study in Italy: 990
SDB Boot Camp for New Faculty: 2298
SDB Travel Awards: 2298
SDE Fellowship Program: 1960
Seaman (The Tom) Travelling Scholarship: 2846
Seattle ASWA Chapter Scholarship: 2020
SEATTLE FOUNDATION (THE)
  Community Grantmaking Program: 322
SEAVER INSTITUTE (THE): 323
SEAY (GEORGE J. AND EFFIE L.) MEMORIAL TRUST: 1611
Security and Defence Forum Internship Program: 2115
Seed Grant Research Program: 1775
Seed Grants: 2456
SEG Scholarship Program: 2220
Segal (Dr. Sydney) Research Grants: 2689
SEGAL (THE GEORGE AND HELEN) FOUNDATION: 533
SELBY (WILLIAM G. AND MARIE) FOUNDATION: 1612
Selected Professions Fellowships: 1134
SELF FAMILY FOUNDATION (THE): 1464
SEMICONDUCTOR RESEARCH CORPORATION
  Advanced Device Structures: 2779
  CAD Tools: 2779
  Environmental Safety and Health: 2779

Factory Operations: 2779
IC and System Design: 2779
Interconnect and Packaging: 2779
Materials and Processes: 2779
Metrology: 2779
Mixed Signal Analog: 2779
Modeling and Simulation: 2779
Patterning: 2779
Reliability: 2779
TCAD: 2779
Test and Testability: 2779
Seminar, Workshop and Conference Support: 927
Seminars and Institutes Program: 416
Senior Adult Scholarship Program: 1765
Senior Companion Program: 1580
Senior Fellowship: 927
Senior Fellowships: 447
Senior Research Fellowship Program: 2263
Senior Research Training Fellowships: 2541
Senior Scholar Award: 2238
Senior Scientist Awards (K05): 1551
Sequoyah Graduate Scholarships: 1106
Sessa (Frank B.) Scholarship for Continuing Education of a Beta Phi Mu
  Member: 758
751 Yale Legacy Fund Award: 1041
SEVENTEEN MAGAZINE
  SEVENTEEN'S Annual Fiction Contest: 740
SEVENTEEN'S Annual Fiction Contest: 740
Severinghaus (Aura E.) Award: 2449
SEYBERT FOUNDATION (THE): 1219
SFCA Grants Programs: 488
SFU Graduate Fellowships: 2036
SFU Teaching Assistantships: 2035
Shackford (M.A. Cartland) Medical Fellowship: 1163
Shaffer Fund for Innovative Glaucoma Research: 2674
SHAFR Dissertation Completion Fellowships: 671
SHAFR Summer Institute: 671
Shankar-Spiegel Award for the Best Dissertation Proposal in
  Direct/Interactive Marketing: 2018
SHARE OUR STRENGTH
  No Kid Hungry: 1613
Shared Instrumentation Grant Program: 2448
SHASTA REGIONAL COMMUNITY FOUNDATION
  McConnell Foundation Fund (The): 1465
  Redding Rancheria Community Fund: 1465
SHASTRI INDO-CANADIAN INSTITUTE (SICI)
  India Studies Fellowship Competition: 991
Shaughnessy (Mina P.) Prize: 697
Shaw Foundation Grants: 1502
SHAW (GARDINER HOWLAND) FOUNDATION
  Grantee Workshops: 1502
  Participating Foundation of Grantmakers for Public Safety: 1502
  Shaw Foundation Grants: 1502
Shaw (Harriet A.) Fellowship: 1162
Shaw (The Peter) Memorial Award: 1753
Shea (The John Gilmary) Prize: 848
SHEAFER (EMMA A.) CHARITABLE TRUST: 573
Shelter Medicine Programs: 1981
Sheltering Arms Fund: 1291
Shelton (Perc H.) and Gladys A. Pospisil Shelton Foundation Advised
  Fund Grants: 188
SHERIDAN (THOMAS B. AND ELIZABETH M.) FOUNDATION: 1721
Shklar (Eugene and Daymel) Fellowships in Ukrainian Studies: 767
Shoemaker (Norma J.) Grant: 2721
Short-Term Research Fellowship: 642, 901
Short-Term Research Fellowships: 392
Short-Term Residencies/Arts Education: 520
Short-Term Travel Grants: 970
SHRIVER (EUNICE KENNEDY) NATIONAL INSTITUTE OF CHILD
  HEALTH AND HUMAN DEVELOPMENT
  Child Development and Behavior Branch: 1561
  Endocrinology, Nutrition and Growth Branch: 1561
  Global Network for Women's and Children's Health Research: 1561
  Obstetric and Pediatric Pharmacology Branch: 1561
  Pediatric, Adolescent and Maternal AIDS Branch: 1561
SHUBERT FOUNDATION, INC. (THE): 574
Shultz (Louis J. and Mary Ellen) Scholarship: 1324
Shuster (Ben) Memorial Award: 2364
Shwachman (Harry) Clinical Investigator Award: 2573
Sibley (Mary Isabel) Fellowship: 1157

SICKKIDS FOUNDATION
  Community Conference Grants Program: 1562
  New Investigator Research Grants: 1562
Sidney Awards: 2062
Siegel (Norman) Research Scholar Grant: 2514
Sierleja (E.J.) Memorial Fellowship: 2823
SIERRA HEALTH FOUNDATION
  Conference and Convening Program: 1614
  Grizzly Creek Ranch Camp and Conference Center: 1614
  Health Leadership Program: 1614
  Responsive Grants Program: 1614
SIGMA ALPHA IOTA MUSIC FRATERNITY
  Inter-American Music Awards: 837
SIGMA DELTA EPSILON/GRADUATE WOMEN IN SCIENCE
  SDE Fellowship Program: 1960
Sigma Pi Sigma Undergraduate Research Awards: 2234
SIGMA THETA TAU INTERNATIONAL
  Berkel Crisp (Rosemary) Research Award: 2656
  Bloch (Doris) Research Award: 2656
  Henderson (Virginia) Clinical Research Grant: 2656
  Small Grants: 2656
  Stout, R.N. (Joan K.), Research Grant: 2656
Sigma Theta Tau/RNF Research Grant: 2655
SIGMA XI: THE SCIENTIFIC RESEARCH SOCIETY
  Grants-in-Aid of Research: 1961
SILICON VALLEY COMMUNITY FOUNDATION: 1466
Silver Apple Award Scholarships: 2017
Silver (Dorothy) Playwriting Award Competition: 722
Simkins (Francis B.) Award: 675
SIMMONS FAMILY FOUNDATION: 324
Simmons (The John) Short Fiction Award: 744
SIMON FRASER UNIVERSITY
  SFU Graduate Fellowships: 2036
  SFU Teaching Assistantships: 2035
Simon (William E.) Fellowship for Noble Purpose: 2127
Simpson (Carole) Scholarship: 2086
SIMS (J. MARION) FOUNDATION: 325
Simulation Fellowship Program: 2165
Simunovich Family Agricultural Scholarship (The): 1324
Single Investigator Cottrell College Science Awards: 2169
Sioussat (Helen J.)/Fay Wells Scholarship: 2048
SIRAGUSA FOUNDATION (THE): 326
SISTER FUND (THE): 1159
SISTER KENNY REHABILITATION INSTITUTE
  Sister Kenny Rehabilitation Institute International Art Show by Artists
    with Disabilities: 606
Sister Kenny Rehabilitation Institute International Art Show by Artists
    with Disabilities: 606
SISTERS OF ST. JOSEPH HEALTHCARE FOUNDATION: 1563
SKELLY (GERTRUDE E.) CHARITABLE FOUNDATION: 1758
SKILLBUILDERS FUND: 1160
SKILLMAN FOUNDATION (THE): 327
SKIN CANCER FOUNDATION (THE)
  Bambino (Melissa K.) Memorial Award: 2605
  Kopf (Dr. Alfred W.) Research Grant Award: 2605
  Live Love and Laugh Research Award: 2605
  Robbins-Wilf (Dr. Marcia) Research Award: 2605
  Wexler (Dr. Patricia) Research Grant Award: 2605
SKOWHEGAN SCHOOL OF PAINTING AND SCULPTURE: 607
SLADEN (THE PERCY) MEMORIAL FUND
  Sladen (Percy) Memorial Fund Grants: 2243
Sladen (Percy) Memorial Fund Grants: 2243
Slagle (Allogan) Memorial Scholarship: 1108
Slim (H. Colin) Award: 796
SLOAN (ALFRED P.) FOUNDATION: 328
  Minority Ph.D. Program: 1077
  Sloan Indigenous Graduate Partnership: 1078
  Sloan Research Fellowships: 2170
Sloan Indigenous Graduate Partnership: 1078
Sloan Research Fellowships: 2170
Small Business Innovation Research Awards: 2496, 2676
Small Business Innovation Research Grants: 2652
Small Business Innovation Research Program: 1552
Small Conference Grants: 2402
Small Grant Program: 363
Small Grant Support: 527
Small Grants: 2092, 2656
Small Grants for Research in Field of Short Stature: 2692
Small Grants Research Program: 2600
Small Projects Program: 478
Small Research Award: 2499

SOCIETY OF ARCHITECTURAL HISTORIANS
  Tompkins (Sally Kress) Fellowship: 452
SOCIETY OF BIOLOGICAL PSYCHIATRY
  Bennett (A.E.) Research Awards: 2753
  Lilly Fellowship Awards: 2755
  Ziskind-Somerfeld Research Award: 2754
SOCIETY OF CARDIOVASCULAR ANESTHESIOLOGISTS
  Roizen & Anesthesia Research Foundation New Investigator Grant:
    2559
  SCA Starter Grants: 2559
  SCA-IARS Mid-Career Grant: 2559
SOCIETY OF CHILDREN'S BOOK WRITERS AND ILLUSTRATORS
  Freeman (Don) Memorial Grant-in-Aid: 741
  Work-In-Progress Grants: 741
SOCIETY OF CRITICAL CARE MEDICINE
  Shoemaker (Norma J.) Grant: 2721
  Vision Grant: 2721
SOCIETY OF DAUGHTERS OF THE U.S. ARMY
  Society of Daughters of the United States Army Scholarships: 1878
Society of Daughters of the United States Army Scholarships: 1878
SOCIETY OF EXPLORATION GEOPHYSICISTS
  SEG Scholarship Program: 2220
SOCIETY OF MANUFACTURING ENGINEERS (SME) EDUCATION
  FOUNDATION
  Caterpillar Scholars Award: 2780
  Gunter (Connie and Robert T.) Scholarship: 2780
  Helton (Clinton J.) Manufacturing Scholarship: 2780
  Kalamazoo Chapter No. 116-Roscoe Douglas Scholarship: 2780
  Kaufman (Lucille B.) Women's Scholarship: 2780
  Kay (E. Wayne) Scholarships: 2780
  St. Louis Chapter No. 17 Scholarship: 2780
  Walker (Myrtle and Earl) Scholarship: 2780
  Weisel (William E.) Scholarship: 2780
SOCIETY OF MEDICAL FRIENDS OF WINE (THE)
  Adams (Leonard D.) Research Award: 2483
SOCIETY OF NAVAL ARCHITECTS AND MARINE ENGINEERS
  (THE)
  Graduate Scholarships: 2829
  Undergraduate Scholarships: 2829
SOCIETY OF PHYSICS STUDENTS
  Sigma Pi Sigma Undergraduate Research Awards: 2234
  Society of Physics Students Leadership Scholarship: 1879
  White (Marsh W.) Awards: 2235
Society of Physics Students Leadership Scholarship: 1879
Society of Professional Journalists: 1871
SOCIETY OF WOMEN ENGINEERS
  Society of Women Engineers Scholarship Program: 1161
Society of Women Engineers Scholarship Program: 1161
Software Donations: 258
SOIL AND WATER CONSERVATION SOCIETY
  Grant (Kenneth E.) Research Scholarship: 2345
Solie (Ruth A.) Award: 796
SOMMERHOCHSCHULE-UNIVERSITY OF VIENNA
  International Summer Program (Summer Campus Strobl/St.
    Wolfgang/Austria): 992
Sonenfeld (Alexandra Apostolides) Memorial Scholarship: 1144
SONS OF ITALY FOUNDATION
  National Leadership Grant Competition: 1079
SONS OF THE REPUBLIC OF TEXAS (THE)
  Presidio La Bahia Award: 674
  Roberts (Summerfield G.) Award: 673
SONY USA FOUNDATION, INC.: 1722
Sophomore Scholarships: 2773
Sorantin Young Artist Award: 834
SOROS (THE PAUL & DAISY) FELLOWSHIPS FOR NEW
  AMERICANS : 1880
SOSLAND FOUNDATION (THE): 1080
SOSS (Season Support): 535
Sousa/Ostwald Award: 792
SOUTH ATLANTIC MODERN LANGUAGE ASSOCIATION
  Graduate Student Essay Prize: 700
  Harper Fund Award: 700
  SAMLA Studies Award: 700
  SAR Prize: 700
SOUTH CAROLINA ARTS COMMISSION
  Artist Fellowship Program: 534
SOUTH CAROLINA HIGHER EDUCATION TUITION GRANTS
  COMMISSION
  South Carolina Tuition Grants Program: 1881
South Carolina Tuition Grants Program: 1881

SOUTH DAKOTA ARTS COUNCIL
  Artist Grants: 535
  Artist-in-Schools: 535
  Arts Organization Challenge Grants: 535
  Professional Development: 535
  Project Grants: 535
  SOSS (Season Support): 535
  Technical Assistance: 535
  Touring Arts: 535
Southard (Juliette A.)/Oral-B Laboratories Scholarship Program: 2505
Southern Arizona HIV/AIDS Consortia: 1299
Southern California Regional Juried Award: 603
SOUTHERN HISTORICAL ASSOCIATION
  Mitchell (H.L.) Award: 675
  Owsley (Frank L. and Harriet C.) Award: 675
  Rawley (James A.) Award: 675
  Simkins (Francis B.) Award: 675
  Sydnor (Charles S.) Award: 675
  Wall (Bennett H.) Award: 675
SOUTHFIELD COMMUNITY FOUNDATION (THE): 1467
SOUTHWEST FLORIDA COMMUNITY FOUNDATION
  Leadership Seminar Series: 1468
SOWERS CLUB OF NEBRASKA FOUNDATION: 333
SPACE TELESCOPE SCIENCE INSTITUTE
  Hubble Fellowship Program: 2187
Speakers in the Humanities Program: 419
Special Awards for Students in North Carolina: 2371
Special Awards in Cancer and Neurobiology: 2371
Special Emphasis Research Career Award (SERCA): 2092
Special Grant Program in the Chemical Sciences: 2195
SPECIAL HOPE FOUNDATION (THE): 1081
Special Initiatives: 2359
Special Milk Program for Children (The): 1229
Special Presenter Initiatives: 509
Special Project Challenge Grant: 1316
Special Project Funds: 1304
Special Project Grants: 520, 1544
Special Projects: 525
Special Projects Program: 1021
Special Research Awards: 2573
Special Scholarship Endowment Grants: 1857
Specific Cultural Projects Grants Program: 479
Spectrum Initiative Scholarship Program: 1730
Speech Pathology (Master's): 1514
SPENCER FOUNDATION
  Dissertation Fellowship Program: 1698
  Research Grant Program: 1698
Spencer (Susan S.) Clinical Research Training Fellowship in Epilepsy:
  2613
Spinal Cord Injury Research Grants and Fellowships: 2720
Spitzer (Lyman) Cutting Edge Climbing Award: 2306
Spofford (The Walter O., Jr.) Memorial Internship: 2340
SPRAGUE (SETH) EDUCATIONAL AND CHARITABLE
  FOUNDATION: 334
Spring Meadow Nursery Scholarship: 1817
SPSSI Grants-in-Aid: 2002
Spurlock (Jeanne) Research Fellowship in Substance Abuse and Addiction
  for Minority Medical Students: 2723
SSHRC Postdoctoral Fellowships: 1997
SSRC/JSPS Long-Term Fellowship: 908
SSRC/JSPS Short-Term Fellowship: 908
Stable Homes, Stable Families: 1192
STACEY (THE JOHN F. AND ANNA LEE) SCHOLARSHIP FUND:
  609
Stahl (Steven A.) Research Grant: 1661
Staley (J.I.) Prize: 2151
Standard Research Grants: 1623
Stanfield and D'Orlando Art Scholarship: 539
STANFORD HUMANITIES CENTER
  External Faculty Fellowships: 426
Stanley Drama Award: 575
STARK COMMUNITY FOUNDATION: 1469
Starrett (Agnes Lynch) Poetry Prize: 738
STARS Residencies: 506
Start Schools: 471
Start-Up Research Grants: 2416
Starter Grants: 1981
State and Community Highway Safety Program Section 402: 1602
State & Tribal Grant Programs: 1228
State Arts Resources: 524
State Community Development Block Grant Program: 1484

Geographical Index

American Society of Neuroradiology/Education and Research Foundation: 2384

American Society of Regional Anesthesia and Pain Medicine: 2700

American Society of Safety Engineers: 2820

Aon Foundation: 1172

APICS Educational and Research Foundation, Inc.: 2762

Appraisal Institute Education Trust: 2013

Argonne National Laboratory: 1933, 1934

Association for Library and Information Science Education: 756, 757

Baxter International Foundation (The): 36

Blair (William) and Company Foundation: 1259

Blowitz-Ridgeway Foundation: 1260

Boeing Company (The): 53

Brunswick Foundation, Inc.: 1267

Brunswick Public Foundation: 2310

Caterpillar Corporate Giving Program: 1274

Catholic Library Association: 763

Charleston Area Charitable Foundation: 1280

CHEST Foundation (The): 2548

Chicago Board of Trade Foundation: 1522

Chicago Community Trust (The): 1283

Chicago Sun-Times Charity Trust: 1284

Chicago Tribune Foundation: 73

Civic Orchestra of Chicago: 803

Coin-Op Cares Charitable and Education Foundation: 2768

Coleman Foundation, Inc. (The): 84

Community Foundation of the Fox River Valley: 1320

Community Memorial Foundation: 1524

Coordinating Council for Women in History, Inc. (The): 626

Crossroads Fund: 1972

Deere (John) Foundation: 110

Dermatology Foundation: 2404

Dirksen Congressional Center (The): 2121

Donnelley (Gaylord and Dorothy) Foundation: 115

Donnelley (R.R.): 116

Duchossois Family Foundation (The): 122

Dystonia Medical Research Foundation: 2620

Evangelical Lutheran Church in America: 855

Exelon Corporation: 135

Federation of American Consumers and Travelers: 1645, 2022

Field Foundation of Illinois: 138

Foundation for Osteopathic Emergency Medicine: 2683

Foundation of the American College of Healthcare Executives (The): 1528

Fry (Lloyd A.) Foundation: 151

GATX Corporation: 153

Graham Foundation for Advanced Studies in the Fine Arts: 445

Great Lakes Protection Fund: 2323

Hermann (Grover) Foundation: 1585

HIMSS Foundation: 2417

Hispanic Dental Association Foundation: 2507

Illinois Arts Council: 492

Illinois Clean Energy Community Foundation: 2326

Illinois Restaurant Association Educational Foundation, Inc.: 1818

Illinois State Academy of Science: 1945

Immanuel Bible Foundation: 859

Institute for the International Education of Students (IES): 1819

Institute of Food Technologists Foundation: 2773

International College of Surgeons: 2422

International Foundation for Ethical Research, Inc.: 1946

Jackson (Ruth) Orthopaedic Society: 2715

Jewel-OSCO: 1390

Journal of the American Medical Association: 2067

Joyce Foundation (The): 202

KCC Japan Education Exchange: 1751

Kraft Foods, Inc.: 218

Leukemia Research Foundation: 2598

Levie (Marcus and Theresa) Educational Fund: 1831

MacArthur (John D. and Catherine T.) Foundation: 237

MacArthur (Roderick) Foundation: 1592

McCormick Foundation: 243

McDonald (Ronald) House Charities: 1204

Medical Library Association: 1013, 1062, 250, 773, 774

Millard (Adah K.) Charitable Trust: 260

Motorola Mobility Foundation (The): 263

National Black MBA Association: 1422

National Council of Teachers of English Research Foundation: 1676

National Dairy Council: 2843

National Fastener Distributors Association: 1679

National Headache Foundation: 2525

National Restaurant Association Educational Foundation (The): 2032, 2844

Neurosurgery Research and Education Foundation: 2637

Newberry Library (The): 1119, 420, 421, 422, 423, 424, 658

North American Spine Society (NASS): 2452

Northern Trust Company (The): 1425

Orthopaedic Research and Education Foundation: 2453, 2454, 2455

Pick (The Albert, Jr.) Fund: 294

Plastic Surgery Foundation (PSF): 2465, 2466

Playboy Foundation (The): 2111

Precast/Prestressed Concrete Institute: 2827

Pulmonary Fibrosis Foundation: 2469

Radiological Society of North America Research and Education Foundation: 2470, 2471, 2472, 2473, 2474, 2475

Ragdale Foundation: 530

Regenstein Foundation (The): 306

Rehabilitation Nursing Foundation: 2655

Retirement Research Foundation (The): 1073

Rock Island Arsenal Museum: 665

Rotary Foundation of Rotary International (The): 985, 986

Sara Lee Foundation: 317

Scholl (Dr.) Foundation: 319

Siragusa Foundation (The): 326

Society of Actuaries (SOA): 2229, 2230

Society of Architectural Historians: 452

Society of Critical Care Medicine: 2721

Society of Women Engineers: 1161

Spencer Foundation: 1698

Stern (Irvin) Foundation: 1471

Tree Research & Education Endowment Fund: 2262

University of Illinois at Urbana-Champaign: 610

USG Foundation, Inc.: 357

VietNow National: 1708

Woods Fund of Chicago: 1497

Zonta International Foundation: 1170, 2043, 2188

Indiana

American Conservatory of Music: 793

American Legion Auxiliary - Department of Indiana: 1773

American Legion National Headquarters (The): 2643

Ball Brothers Foundation: 30

Ball (George and Frances) Foundation: 31

Central Indiana Community Foundation: 1276

Christian Church (Disciples of Christ): 852

Community Foundation of Muncie and Delaware County, Inc. (The): 1313

Community Foundation of Saint Joseph County: 1316

Consortium of College and University Media Centers: 1640

Contemporary Music Festival: 807

Cummins Foundation (The): 106

Cushwa Center for the Study of American Catholicism: 627, 628

Dearborn Community Foundation, Inc.: 1332

DePauw University Key Club International Bonner/Wright Scholarship: 1334

Hancock County Community Foundation: 1379

Health Foundation of Greater Indianapolis (The): 1533, 1584

History of Science Society: 635, 636

Indiana Arts Commission: 493

Indiana Library Federation: 769

Lawrence County Community Foundation: 1401

Lilly Endowment Inc.: 230

Lincoln Financial Foundation: 231

Mongolia Society, Inc. (The): 903

Monsanto Company/National Association of Farm Broadcasters: 1840

National Collegiate Athletic Association (The): 1841

National Federation of Music Clubs: 824, 825, 826

Percussive Arts Society: 830

Pulliam Journalism Fellowship: 2084

Sigma Theta Tau International: 2656

Society for Pediatric Dermatology: 2694

State Student Assistance Commission of Indiana: 1883

Unity Foundation of LaPorte County (The): 1485

Wabash Center for Teaching and Learning in Theology and Religion (The): 872

Iowa

American Association of University Women Educational Foundation: 1008, 1134, 1135, 1136, 1137

Carver (Roy J.) Charitable Trust: 1735

Cowles (Gardner and Florence Call) Foundation: 1741

Greater Cedar Rapids Community Foundation (The): 1365
Hoover (Herbert) Presidential Library Association, Inc.: 2125
International Association for Food Protection: 2840
Iowa Arts Council: 495
McElroy (R.J.) Trust: 1205
National Farmer's Organization: 2258
P.E.O. Sisterhood: 1015
Pioneer Hi-Bred, A DuPont Business: 1214
Principal Financial Group Foundation Inc.: 298
Quill and Scroll Foundation: 2085
Soil and Water Conservation Society: 2345
University of Iowa (The): 744

Kansas

American Academy of Family Physicians Foundation: 2365
American Association of Zoo Keepers: 2269
American Institute of Baking: 2760
Child Language Doctoral Program: 1791
Hutchinson Community Foundation: 490
Jellison Benevolent Society: 1662
Kansas Health Foundation: 1542
Pi Gamma Mu, International Honor Society in Social Science: 1866
Pritchett Trust: 1215
SkillBuilders Fund: 1160
United Methodist Health Ministry Fund: 1619
Wichita Community Foundation: 1493

Kentucky

Brown (James Graham) Foundation, Inc.: 56
Community Foundation of Louisville, Inc. (The): 472
Cooke (V.V.) Foundation: 97
Foundation for the Tri-State Community, Inc.: 1357
Gheens Foundation: 160
Grayson-Jockey Club Research Foundation (The): 2414
Humana Foundation (The): 186
Kentucky Arts Council: 496
Kentucky Foundation for Women: 1150
Presbyterian Church (U.S.A.): 1869, 1870, 865

Louisiana

Baton Rouge Area Foundation: 466
Booth-Bricker Fund (The): 54
Brown (The Joe W. and Dorothy Dorsett) Foundation: 57
Greater New Orleans Foundation (The): 1373
Historic New Orleans Collection (The): 633, 634
Honor Society of Phi Kappa Phi (The): 1816
Louisiana Division of the Arts, Department of Culture, Recreation and
    Tourism: 499, 500
National Taxidermists Association: 1071
Woolf (William C.) Foundation: 1498
Zigler (Fred B. and Ruth B.) Foundation: 1709

Maine

American Musicological Society: 795, 796
Burnham (The Margaret E.) Charitable Trust: 59
Central Maine Power Company: 69
Great Bay Foundation (The): 1583
Hannaford Charitable Foundation: 1654
Haystack Mountain School of Crafts: 489
Jackson Laboratory (The): 2287
King (Stephen and Tabitha) Foundation: 212
Libra Foundation: 229
Libra Future Fund: 2027
Maine Arts Commission: 502
Maine Initiatives: 1593
Maine Osteopathic Association: 2684
Morton-Kelly Charitable Trust (The): 1418
Mount Desert Island Biological Laboratory: 2291
Mulford (The Clarence E.) Trust: 264
Oak Grove School Foundation: 1691
Switzer (The Robert & Patricia) Foundation: 2347

Maryland

Abell Foundation, Inc. (The): 2
ABMRF/The Foundation for Alcohol Research: 1510
Agency for Healthcare Research and Quality (AHRQ): 1511

American Academy of Optometry: 2663
American Congress on Surveying and Mapping (ACSM): 2797, 2798,
    2799, 2800, 2801
American Foundation for Pharmaceutical Education: 1728, 2697, 2698
American Gastroenterological Association (AGA): 2561, 2562, 2563,
    2564, 2565
American Health Assistance Foundation: 1512, 2614, 2664
American Institute of Physics: 2231
American Kidney Fund: 2374, 2375
American Nurses Foundation, Inc.: 2644
American Optometric Foundation: 2665
American Society for Nutrition: 2837
American Society for Parenteral and Enteral Nutrition, Rhoads Research
    Foundation: 2566
American Society of Nuclear Cardiology: 2546
American Speech-Language-Hearing Foundation: 2666
Ames (The Kathryn) Foundation: 875
AMVETS: 1778, 1779
Anxiety Disorders Association of America (The): 2730
Aplastic Anemia and MDS International Foundation: 2387
ASPRS - The Imaging and Geospatial Information Society: 2160, 2161
Association on American Indian Affairs: 1104, 1105, 1106, 1107, 1108,
    1109, 1110, 1111
Baker (The William G., Jr.) Memorial Fund: 465
Baltimore Community Foundation: 32
Biomedical Engineering Society: 2275
Blaustein (Jacob and Hilda) Foundation: 1037
Blaustein (Morton K. and Jane) Foundation: 50
Building and Fire Research Laboratory: 2162
Business Solutions Association Educational Foundation: 1635
Campbell Foundation, Inc.: 1178
Casey (The Annie E.) Foundation: 1180
Centers for Medicare & Medicaid Services: 1521
Colonial Players, Inc. Theater-in-the-Round: 565
Commonweal Foundation, Inc.: 1183
Community Foundation of Frederick County, MD, Inc. (The): 1306
Community Foundation of the Eastern Shore: 1319
Constellation Energy Group: 95
CurePSP Foundation for PSP/CBD and Related Brain Diseases: 2618
Cystic Fibrosis Foundation: 2573
Early American Industries Association, Inc.: 2769
Ellison Medical Foundation (The): 2238
Emergency Mental Health and Traumatic Stress Services Branch: 2740
England (Lois & Richard) Family Foundation: 1190
Enterprise Community Partners: 1581, 443
Entomological Foundation (The): 2278, 2279, 2280, 2281
Epilepsy Foundation of America: 1974, 1975, 2621, 2622
First Candle/SIDS Alliance: 2690
Fogarty (John E.) International Center: 2282
Foundation for Spirituality and Medicine (The): 1527
Freeman (Carl M.) Foundation: 483
Goldseker Foundation: 1362
Grace (W. R.) Foundation, Inc.: 163
Health Resources and Services Administration: 1657, 2415
Higginson (Corina) Trust: 178
Hughes (Howard) Medical Institute: 1712, 2283, 2419
Immune Deficiency Foundation: 1058, 2492
International Association of Ice Cream Distributors and Vendors: 1659
International Order of Alhambra: 2714
Johns Hopkins Center for Alternatives to Animal Testing (The): 1541
Kerr (Grayce B.) Fund, Inc.: 210
Knott (Marion I. and Henry J.) Foundation, Inc.: 216
Leidy (The John J.) Foundation: 1403
Loats Foundation, Inc. (The): 232
Marriott International, Inc.: 242
Maryland Higher Education Commission: 1835
Maryland Institute College of Art: 590
Maryland State Arts Council: 505
Mid Atlantic Arts Foundation: 509
NASDAQ OMX Educational Foundation, Inc. (The): 2030
National Black Nurses Association, Inc.: 2651
National Blood Foundation: 2553
National Center for Research Resources (NCRR): 2439, 2440
National Center on Minority Health and Health Disparities: 1065
National Coalition of Black Meeting Planners (NCBMP): 1675
National Council for the Social Studies: 1983, 1984, 1985, 1986, 1987
National Emergency Medicine Association: 1677
National Eye Institute: 2676, 2677
National Federation of the Blind: 1066
National Foundation for Infectious Diseases: 2494

Massachusetts

Michigan

Berrien Community Foundation: 44
Bishop (A.G.) Charitable Trust: 49
Capital Region Community Foundation: 1272
Children's Literature Association: 712
Chrysler Foundation (The): 75
Community Foundation for Northeast Michigan: 1297
Community Foundation for Southeast Michigan: 88
Community Foundation of Greater Rochester: 1309
Community Foundation of the Holland/Zeeland Area (The): 91
Consumers Energy Foundation: 96
Cook Family Foundation: 1327
DeVos (Richard and Helen) Foundation: 1335
Dickinson Area Community Foundation: 1336
Dow (The Herbert H. and Grace A.) Foundation: 118
Earhart Foundation: 1973
Ford (Gerald R.) Presidential Library: 2123, 2124
Ford Motor Company Fund & Community Services: 145
Fremont Area Community Foundation (The): 1358
Frey Foundation: 149
Gerber Foundation (The): 1194
Graduate Education Opportunity Program: 1053
Grand Haven Area Community Foundation: 1364
Grand Rapids Community Foundation: 165
Great Lakes Colleges Association New Writers Awards: 714
Greater Lansing Foundation (The): 1370
Hess (William G. and Myrtle E.) Charitable Trust: 1057, 1658
Hillsdale County Community Foundation: 1382
Hudson-Webber Foundation: 1385
Irwin Foundation (The): 2425
Kalamazoo Community Foundation: 1394
Kantzler Foundation (The): 1395
Kappa Omicron Nu Honor Society: 2841
Kaufman (Louis G.) Endowment Fund: 1715
Kellogg (W.K.) Foundation: 207
Keweenaw Community Foundation: 1398
Kresge Foundation (The): 219
Les Cheneaux Community Foundation (The): 1404
Livingston Awards: 2069
M & M Area Community Foundation: 1408
Marshall Community Foundation: 1669
McGregor Fund: 246
Metro Health Foundation: 1598
Michigan Council for Arts and Cultural Affairs: 508
Michigan Gateway Community Foundation: 1414
Michigan Society of Fellows: 412
Michigan State University: 979
Michigan Women's Foundation: 1152
Monroe-Brown Foundation: 1752
Mott (Charles Stewart) Foundation: 1420
Pardee (The Elsa U.) Foundation: 2601
Petoskey-Harbor Springs Area Community Foundation: 1435
Phi Delta Chi Pharmacy Fraternity: 2706
Roberts (Forest) Theatre: 572
Saginaw Community Foundation: 1454
Skillman Foundation (The): 327
Society of Manufacturing Engineers (SME) Education Foundation: 2780
Southfield Community Foundation (The): 1467
Steelcase Foundation: 337
Thomas Foundation (The): 2485
Towsley (The Harry A. and Margaret D.) Foundation: 351
University of Michigan: 2091
Upjohn (W.E.) Institute for Employment Research: 2097
Wege Foundation: 432
Wickes (Harvey Randall) Foundation: 1494
Wilson (Matilda R.) Fund: 367
Wilson Ornithological Society: 2301
Winship Memorial Scholarship Foundation: 1923
Woman's National Farm and Garden Association (The): 2267

Minnesota

American Swedish Institute (The): 943, 944
Ameriprise Financial: 1242
Andersen Corporate Foundation (The): 1243
Andersen (Elmer L. and Eleanor J.) Foundation: 19
Andersen (Fred C. and Katherine B.) Foundation: 1244
Andersen (Hugh J.) Foundation: 1245
Arts Midwest: 561
Athwin Foundation: 24
Babbage (Charles) Institute: 2767

Bremer (Otto) Foundation: 1264
Butler (Patrick and Aimee) Family Foundation: 1269
Central Minnesota Community Foundation: 1277
Collegeville Institute for Ecumenical and Cultural Research: 853
Davis (Edwin W. and Catherine M.) Foundation: 109
Dell (Roger L. and Agnes C.) Charitable Trust: 1333
Deluxe Corporation Foundation: 111
Driscoll Foundation (The): 120
Duluth Superior Area Community Foundation: 1339
Ecolab Foundation: 1344
Eddy (Edwin H.) Family Foundation: 2406
Edwards (Ray) Memorial Trust: 1526
Forecast Public Artworks: 481
Foundation for Anesthesia Education and Research: 2408
Fuller (H.B.) Company Foundation: 1193
Graco Foundation (The): 1363
Hallett Charitable Trusts (The): 1746
Jerome Foundation, Inc.: 409
Land O'Lakes Foundation: 223, 224
Lindbergh (The Charles A. and Anne Morrow) Foundation: 2328
Marbrook Foundation: 239
Mardag Foundation: 240
Mayo Clinic: 2436
McKnight Endowment Fund for Neuroscience (The): 2625
McKnight Foundation (The): 1597
Medtronic Foundation: 251
Minneapolis Foundation (The): 1415
Minnesota Department of Education: 777
National Association of Geoscience Teachers: 2211
National Ataxia Foundation: 2633
National Council on Family Relations: 1601
Northwest Minnesota Foundation (The): 1426
Ordean Foundation (The): 1431
Phillips (Jay and Rose) Family Foundation of Minnesota: 1605
Playwrights' Center (The): 739
Porter (Irwin Andrew) Foundation: 296
RBC Foundation-U.S.A.: 1443
Rochester Area Foundation: 1449
Sigma Delta Epsilon/Graduate Women in Science: 1960
Sister Kenny Rehabilitation Institute: 606
SUPERVALU Foundation: 1618
3M Foundation, Inc.: 347
U.S. Bancorp Foundation: 1482
University of Minnesota: 541, 745
University of Oslo International Summer School: 999
Wasie Foundation (The): 361
Women's Foundation of Minnesota: 1166, 1167
Xcel Energy Foundation: 373

Mississippi

Agricultural History Society: 612
American Kinesiotherapy Association, Inc.: 2710
Foundation for the Mid South: 1356
Hardin (The Phil) Foundation: 1656
Hearin (Robert M.) Foundation: 172
University of Southern Mississippi (The): 747

Missouri

Aircraft Electronics Association (AEA): 2782
Aviation Insurance Association (AIA): 2786
BlueScope Foundation North America (The): 51
Brown Shoe Company, Inc. Charitable Trust: 58
Center for Plant Conservation: 2249
Community Foundation of the Ozarks: 1321
Consortium for Graduate Study in Management: 2014
Dula (The Caleb C. and Julia W.) Educational and Charitable Foundation: 125
Emerson: 133
Greater Kansas City Community Foundation and Affiliated Trusts (The): 1369
Green (Allen P. and Josephine B.) Foundation: 1374
Investigative Reporters and Editors: 2066
Kappa Tau Alpha: 2068
Knights of Columbus Vatican Film Library at St. Louis University: 719
Ladies Auxiliary to the Veterans of Foreign Wars (The): 2597
Lutheran Foundation of St. Louis: 861
McDonnell Center for the Space Sciences: 2787
McDonnell (James S.) Foundation: 245
Mid-America Arts Alliance: 510

North Carolina

Museum of Early Southern Decorative Arts (MESDA): 597
NAMTA Foundation for the Visual Arts: 598
National AMBUCS, Inc.: 2716
National Humanities Center: 418
National Institute of Environmental Health Sciences: 2331
North Carolina Arts Council: 524
North Carolina Association of Educators: 1755
North Carolina Community Foundation: 273
North Carolina GlaxoSmithKline Foundation: 1690
North Carolina Library Association: 782
North Carolina State Education Assistance Authority/College Foundation
   of North Carolina: 1858
Outer Banks Community Foundation: 1433
Progress Energy: 299
Reynolds (Kate B.) Charitable Trust: 1607
Reynolds (Z. Smith) Foundation, Inc.: 308
Salisbury Community Foundation: 314
Semiconductor Research Corporation: 2779
Sigma Alpha Iota Music Fraternity: 837
Sigma Xi: The Scientific Research Society: 1961
Society for the Study of Amphibians and Reptiles: 2171
Triangle Community Foundation: 1701
U.S. Army Research Office: 1965
United Arts Council of Raleigh and Wake County, Inc.: 540
Winston-Salem Foundation (The): 1495

North Dakota

Central Association of Obstetricians and Gynecologists: 2659
Fargo-Moorhead Area Foundation: 137
North Dakota Council on the Arts: 525
North Dakota State Board for Indian Scholarships: 1120

Ohio

Akron Community Foundation: 1233
American Aging Association: 2366
American Ceramic Society (The): 457
American Classical League (The): 689
American Society for Nondestructive Testing, Inc. (The): 1626, 1777,
   2761
ASM Materials Education Foundation: 2845
Batten Disease Support and Research Association: 2390
Bingham (The William) Foundation: 48
Cleveland Foundation (The): 1286
Cleveland Institute of Music: 804
Cliffs Foundation (The): 79
Codrington (The George W.) Charitable Foundation: 83
Columbus Foundation (The): 1288
Columbus Jewish Foundation: 1289
Community Foundation of Delaware County: 1304
Community Foundation of Lorain County (The): 1312
Community Foundation of Mount Vernon & Knox County (The): 90
Community Foundation of Shelby County (The): 1317
Corbin (The Mary S. and David C.) Foundation: 99
Eaton Corporation: 129
Educational Foundation for Women in Accounting (The): 2020
Firman Fund: 139
FirstEnergy: 1711
FirstEnergy Foundation: 141
Goodyear Tire & Rubber Company (The): 162
Greater Cincinnati Foundation (The): 1366
Gund (The George) Foundation: 168
HCR Manor Care Foundation: 1531
Heed Ophthalmic Foundation: 2675
Herb Society of America, Inc. (The): 2254
Iddings Benevolent Trust: 189
International Executive Housekeepers Association (The): 2774
Invent Now: 1947
Jennings (Martha Holden) Foundation: 1714
Kettering Fund (The): 1397
Kroger Company Foundation (The): 1400
Lincoln (The James F.) Arc Welding Foundation: 2824
Lubrizol Foundation (The): 233
Mandel Jewish Community Center of Cleveland (The): 722
Marcus (Jacob Rader) Center of the American Jewish Archives: 862
Marietta Community Foundation: 1410
Morgan (The Burton D.) Foundation: 2029
Mt. Sinai Health Care Foundation: 1548
Muskingum County Community Foundation: 1421
National Mole Day Foundation: 2199

Nationwide Foundation: 266
Nordson Corporation Foundation (The): 271
O'Neill (William J. and Dorothy K.) Foundation: 275
Ohio Arts Council: 526
Ohio Board of Regents: 1861, 1862
Ohio Educational Library Media Association: 783
Ohio National Guard Scholarship Program: 1863
OMNOVA Solutions Foundation: 1429
Parents Without Partners: 1694
Parker Hannifin Corporation Foundation: 286
Prentiss (The Elisabeth Severance) Foundation: 2468
Reinberger Foundation (The): 1444
Scott (Kenneth A.) Charitable Trust: 2242
Society for Historians of American Foreign Relations: 669, 670, 671
Society for Investigative Dermatology (The): 2482
Stark Community Foundation: 1469
Tait (The Frank M.) Foundation: 1221
Toledo Community Foundation: 1480
White (Thomas H.) Foundation: 1492
Wolfe Associates, Inc.: 368
World Piano Competition, Inc. (The): 841

Oklahoma

American Association of Petroleum Geologists Foundation: 2202
American Fidelity Foundation: 459
Bernsen (The Grace and Franklin) Foundation: 43
Bureau of Indian Education: 1113
Cherokee Nation of Oklahoma: 1115
Kerr Foundation, Inc. (The): 209
Mabee (The J.E. and L.E.) Foundation, Inc.: 236
Noble (Samuel Roberts) Foundation, Inc.: 1754
Oklahoma Arts Council: 527
Oklahoma City Community Foundation, Inc.: 1428
Sarkeys Foundation: 318
Schusterman (Charles and Lynn) Family Foundation: 1462
Society of Exploration Geophysicists: 2220
Stacey (The John F. and Anna Lee) Scholarship Fund: 609

Oregon

American Tinnitus Association (ATA): 1932
Bonneville Environmental Foundation: 2308
Carpenter Foundation (The): 1273
Collins Foundation (The): 85
Grass Foundation (The): 2623
Intel Foundation: 190
Jackson Foundation (The): 192
Lamb Foundation: 222
McDowell (Verne Catt) Corporation: 863
McKenzie River Gathering Foundation: 1596
Meyer Memorial Trust: 255
Oregon Arts Commission: 528
Oregon Community Foundation (The): 1432

Pennsylvania

Academy of Natural Sciences of Philadelphia (The): 1925, 2268
ADCO Foundation: 1727
Air & Waste Management Association (A&WMA): 2757
Alcoa Foundation: 9
Allegheny Foundation: 12
Alternatives Research and Development Foundation: 1927
American Association for Cancer Research: 2584
American Institute for Yemeni Studies: 926
American Medical Women's Association, Inc.: 2377
American Philosophical Society: 1103, 15, 16, 380
American Research Institute in Turkey, Inc.: 931, 932, 933
Aviation Distributors and Manufacturers Association (ADMA): 2785
Barra Foundation: 34
Bayer USA Foundation: 1935
Berks County Community Foundation: 1257
Berwind Corporation: 46
BNY Mellon Foundation of Southwestern Pennsylvania (The): 1262
Buhl Foundation (The): 1268
Center for Advanced Judaic Studies: 956
Centers for Disease Control and Prevention (CDC): 2092
Chatham University: 1790
Chester County Community Foundation: 1282
College of Physicians of Philadelphia: 624

Personnel Index

References in index are to entry numbers.

References in index are to entry numbers.

D

D'Amato, Catherine: 1263
D'Amico, Jessica: 1636
D'Amico, Julia: 311
D'Angelo, Leah: 311
D'Aquino, Tom: 1516
D'Arcy, Christine: 528
D'Arcy, Stephen R.: 1385
D'Elia, Lorraine: 154
D'Olier, H. Mitchell: 67
Dabashi, Hamid: 1978
Dadelahi, Samin: 1499
Daft, Douglas N.: 2028
Daggett, Brian, M.D.: 2556
Daggett, Christopher J.: 113, 1218
Dajani, Virginia: 790
Dalberto, Michel: 805
Dalio, Ray: 2330
DallaGrana, Rebecca: 535
Dalton, Sharon C.: 6
Daly, Charles U.: 202
Daly, James J.: 1266
Dammrich, Thomas: 2317
Damonte, Dirk: 25
Damonti, John L.: 55
Dana, Charles A., III: 2403
Daniel, Clifton Truman: 2144
Daniels, Dianne J.: 1629
Daniels, John W., Jr.: 1372
Dankenbring, James R.: 861
Dankers, Paul: 1416
Dao, Solange C.: 2830
Daoust, Jacqueline: 2759
Dardess, Margaret B.: 1690
Darling, Linda: 931, 932, 933
Darnieder, Gregory M.: 294
Daswani, Nico: 463
Daucher, Lynn: 1515
Daudet, Y., Prof.: 2105
Daudon, Maud: 2311
Daughtry, Deborah K.: 93
Daum, Paul L.: 2253
Davenport, Jessica: 845
David, Hal: 704, 798
Davidson, Betsy: 205
Davidson, Bradford: 205
Davidson, George A.: 1438
Davidson, Gretchen D.: 240
Davidson, Gwen: 465
Davidson, H.: 1589
Davidson, Joan K.: 205
Davidson, Marty: 1656
Davidson, Matthew: 205
Davidson, Peter: 205
Davidson, Suzanne Schwartz: 691
Davies, David: 2356
Davies, Matthew, Ph.D.: 949
Davis, Chastity: 1425
Davis, Dee: 27
Davis, Frank: 64
Davis, G.W., Ph.D.: 2623
Davis, Haley T.: 108
Davis, Holbrook R.: 108
Davis, J.H. Dow: 108
Davis, Jack: 460, 934, 935, 936, 937, 938
Davis, Joel P.: 108
Davis, John L.: 109
Davis, Karen: 1578
Davis, Leigh Evans: 1378
Davis, Leroy: 127
Davis, Martha: 1054
Davis, Marty: 583
Davis, Maynard K.: 108
Davis, Michael: 749
Davis, Paula: 2121
Davis, Robert: 36
Davis, Sara: 176
Davis, Scott: 1120
Davis, Stephanie L.: 1568
Davis, Thomas H., Jr.: 1318

Davis, Toni E.: 1863
Day, Betty: 1637
Day, Martha: 1218
Day, Susan C., M.D.: 1219
Dayton, Charles: 19
Dayton, Eric: 311
Dayton, John: 183
de Groote, Jacques: 948
de Hoyos, Debora: 1819
de Jonge Oudraat, Chantal, Ph.D.: 915
de Leon de Vega, Sonia Marie: 1270
De Luca, Victor: 2337
de Main, John: 844
De Maio, Stephen: 844
de Rham, Casimir, Jr.: 2392
de Sandi, Alfredo Jimenez: 2064
De Scherer, Richard K.: 1568
Deacon, Bob, Prof.: 977
Dean, Victoria Seaver: 323
Deatherage, Marie: 255
Deaver, Carolyn J.: 62
DeBartolo, Lisa: 1267, 2310
DeBruyne, Terry: 255
deBuys, William, Dr.: 2312
Decherd, Robert W.: 40
Decker, Charlie: 333
DeCourcey, Jim: 1273
Dedecker, Clotilde Perez-Bode: 1293
Dedrick, Chris: 1640
Deen, R.B., Jr.: 1656
DeFrantz, Anita L.: 1543
Dehli, Joyce: 2050
Dekker, Hans: 187
del Sol, Carlos M.: 63
DeLano, Mike: 1717
DelaTorre, Rodrigo: 1012
Delkoski, M.P.: 347
Dellinger, Robert J.: 297
DeMars, Bruce, Adm.: 182
Demopoulos, Harry B.: 123
Demyan, Kirk C.: 1354
Dendas, Ronald C., M.S.: 1558
Dendy, Richard: 977
Denham, Robert E.: 237
Denis, Melisa A.: 2026
Dennis, Andre, Esq.: 2650
Denson, Gloria: 2261
Denson-Low, Wanda K.: 53
Denyer, Mary C.: 977
DePillis, Mark S., Esq.: 1087
Depolo, Gary L.: 45
Deromedi, Sandy: 530
Des Landes, Claude: 474
Des Rochers, Francois: 2591
DeSantis, Daniel: 148
DeShazo, Ambassador Peter: 1012
DeShazo, Nikki, Hon.: 1475
Desmond, Amy B.: 571
Detrick, Robert, Dr.: 2217
Deutsch, Donny: 2409
Deverman, Jim: 2121
Devine, Michael J.: 2144
DeVita, M. Christine: 359
Devonish, Carrolle Perry: 117
Dew, Patti: 1372
Dewar, Robert, Dr.: 2312
Dezelan, Annette: 530
Diamond, Linda: 123
Diamond, Marla: 2267
Diamonstein-Spielvogel, Barbaralee, Dr.: 522
Diaz, Fred: 75
Diaz, Junot: 2050
DiCarlo, Mary: 2262
DiChiera, Cristina: 531
Dick, Stacy: 307
Dick, Sylvia Looney: 353
Dickson, Alan: 1355
Dicovitsky, Gary: 899
DiDomenico, Greg: 1524
DiDomenico, Rebecca: 93

Diederich, Paul W.: 2796
Diedericks, Janet: 294
Diefenderfer, Jeannie: 1154
Dieffenbach, Ann: 2442
Dien, Laurie: 1213
Dienes, Keith R.: 2233
Dieter, Heidi: 2524
Diethrick, June C.: 1281
Dietz, Philip E.L., Jr.: 2349
DiFiglia, Marian, Ph.D.: 2641
Diggs, James C.: 297
Dillaber, Michael: 1318
Dillingham, John A.: 2144
Dillon, Brenda: 1770
Dillon, Diane: 420, 421, 422, 423, 424, 658, 1119
Dillon, Douglas K.: 2253
DiMichele, Donna: 2526
DiMichele, Donna, M.D.: 2526
Dinges, Stan: 333
Dinkel, Jay: 1256
Dinovitz, Dino: 2061
Dinsmoor, Dorothy: 2195
Dion, Ernest E.: 1200
Dirschel, Kathleen M., R.N., Ph.D.: 2654
Dirzo, Rodolfo: 74
Dishman, J. Dallas, Ph.D.: 1529
DiSilvestro, Anthony: 63
DiTrapani, Joseph: 1079
Ditz, Christine A.: 1281
Ditzian, Michael D.: 2524
Divelbiss, Terry: 90
Divola, Julie: 1486
Divone, Lorraine: 2735
Dixon, Edith R.: 1087
Dixon, George W.: 1087
Dixon, Jack E., Ph.D.: 1712, 2283
Dixon-Reeves, Regina, Ph.D.: 151
Doan, Ruth A.: 118
Doane, Craig: 2365
Dobey, Lisa: 342
Dodd, Julie: 2085
Dodge, Holly: 359
Dodge, Stuart: 1097
Dodson, David: 27
Dodson, Paulette: 317
Doerfler, Ron: 2061
Doggett, W.B.: 129
Doherty, Peter: 2290
Dohrer, Kim: 2009
Dolan, Paul: 1285
Doll, Francisco J.: 170
Dolsten, Mikael, M.D., Ph.D.: 2459, 2463, 2702, 2703, 2704, 2705
Domaschko, Jane V.: 1366
Dombeck, Mike: 199
Dompierre, Chantal: 2719
Domske, Helen: 2336
Donahey, Robert W.: 275
Donahue, Brian: 621
Donaldson, M.S., Esq.: 2437
Donaldson, Phil: 1243
Donaldson-Pitter, Trisha: 2669
Donlon, Marcia: 1544
Donnelley, Ceara: 115
Donnelley, Elliott R.: 115
Donnelley, Laura: 115
Donnelley, Shawn M.: 115
Donovan, Thomas J.: 1256
Doolan, Victor: 2624
Doppstadt, Eric: 144
Dorhout, Peter K.: 2169
Dorn, Holbrook: 1633
Dorn, Peter: 2639
Dotson, Alphonse A.: 538
Doughty, Heather: 529
Douglas, Carolyn: 1318
Douglass, Sally: 127
Dow, Frances, Dr.: 977
Dow, Michael L.: 118
Dowding, Alyssa C.: 282

References in index are to entry numbers.

References in index are to entry numbers.

References in index are to entry numbers.

References in index are to entry numbers.

References in index are to entry numbers.

Rackoff, Nancy L.: 1438
Radtke, Neila: 566
Rae, Nancy: 75
Raff, Douglass: 2311
Raj, Usha, M.D.: 2410
Rajneri, Nelida: 2064
Rake, Michael, Sir: 2028
Rall, Ronald D., Rev. Dr.: 861
Rallo, Eduardo: 1466
Ralston, Craig S.: 1097
Ramakrishnan, Ramanath I.: 1063
Ramer, Bruce: 1074
Ramey, Samuel: 839
Ramin, Kirk, M.D.: 2659
Ramirez, Marcos: 401
Ramirez, Margarita: 1591
Ramm, Russell: 1942
Ramme, Leslie: 1279
Ramos, Lydia: 2085
Ramos, Yulian: 307
Ramos-Chertok, Maria: 241
Ramous, Olga: 1992
Ramsey, Paul G., M.D.: 2431
Randall, Gail T.: 10
Randall, Shirley: 1149
Randel, Don Michael: 252
Randle, Kathryn A.: 851
Randolph, Nina: 2355
Randolph, Wendy W.: 81
Random, Cindee: 851
Randt, Virginia: 2061
Rangel, Alma: 2639
Ranieri, Gualberto: 75
Rankin, David: 2323
Ranney, George A., Jr.: 138
Rao, Ennio: 700
Raphael, Cathy: 1154
Rapoport, Nessa: 307
Rapp, Marcia L.: 165
Rapson, Judith: 721
Rashford, John, Dr.: 115
Rasmussen, Ronn J.: 96
Rassler, Bridget I.: 1558
Rath, Tom: 1713
Ratte, Geoff: 2317
Rauch, Lawrence: 1391
Raudenbush, Stephen: 1698
Rauzi, Robert L.: 90
Raver, Cybele: 1698
Rawlinson, Rex: 1634
Ray, Adele Richardson: 1992
Ray, Gilbert T.: 1748
Rayburn, James, Dr.: 1926
Raymond, Carolyn M.: 247
Rayner, Laurie MacCallum: 395
Read, Mary B.: 1372
Ready, Ken: 2609
Rebmann, David: 1717
Reck, Barbara K., B.S.: 2644
Rede, George: 2085
Redmond, Jerry: 1243
Redmond, LaDonna: 2337
Redwood, Rene: 1154
Reed, Cynthia: 309
Reed, Kaye: 2148
Reed, Linda: 675
Reed, Page Branton: 2144
Reed, Reginald C.: 2026
Reeve, Todd: 2308
Regalado, Cristina M.: 1520
Regan, Celeste: 2333
Regan, Mary B.: 524
Regenstein, Susan: 306
Regetz, Sue Korte: 1485
Regions Bank: 256
Regnery, Alfred S.: 293, 2135
Regulska, Joanna: 904
Rehm, Susan J., M.D.: 2494
Reich, Paul: 255
Reiche, Nancy: 1323

Reid, Don: 721
Reid, Rosalind: 2054
Reid-Smith, Randall: 549
Reider, Corinne H.: 170
Reidy, James J.: 2233
Reierson, Gary: 853
Reigel, Beverly S., R.N., Ph.D.: 2656
Reill, Peter H.: 389, 390, 391, 392
Reilly, William K.: 283
Reimers, Fernando: 1012
Reinhart, A. Kevin: 931, 932, 933
Reisman, Barbara: 1218
Reitman, Robert S.: 1492
Rembe, Toni: 1486
Rendleman, Patricia P.: 314
Rennie, Renate: 912
Rentschler, Suzanne: 493
Renzer, David: 704
Resnick, Stewart A.: 584
Restrick, Nicole: 908, 910
Reuben-Cooke, Wilhelmina, J.D.: 124
Reveley, W. Taylor, III: 252
Revere, Elspeth: 237
Revson, Charles H., Jr.: 307
Reyes, Danielle: 1413
Reynolds, Angela M.: 1046
Reynolds, Neil: 863
Reynolds, Robert: 241
Reynolds, Ryan: 2409
Rhodus, G. Tomas, Jr.: 249
Ricciardi, Lawrence R.: 252
Riccio, Michael: 1693
Riccliardi, Richard, Ph.D., FAANP: 2656
Rice, Don: 2218
Rice, Gwendolyn M.: 294
Rice, John H.: 1351
Rice, John P., Ph.D.: 2641
Rice, Joseph A.: 167
Rice, Mabel L., Dr.: 1791
Rich, Harry: 450
Rich, Harvey: 226
Richard, Alison, Dr.: 2312
Richard, Frances: 820
Richard, Michael D.: 1204
Richards, Arnold, Dr.: 685, 686
Richards, Cecile: 144
Richardson, Elaina: 475
Richardson, Emily R.: 1607
Richardson, M. Catherine: 1360
Richardson, Peter L.: 1992
Richardson, Sarah Beinecke: 300
Richardson, Stuart S.: 1992
Richardson, Susan J.: 1607
Richardson, Tanyelle Hawkins: 2039
Richardson, William C.: 2097
Richelson, Elliott, M.D.: 2753
Richey, Ivenhoe T., II: 2720
Richland, Scott H.: 1391
Richmond, Marsha: 636
Richter, Sidney D.: 2556
Rickman, Tom: 558
Riddick, Cheryl: 1301
Ridley, Kristin R.: 1363
Riecker, Charles: 118
Riecker, Margaret Ann: 118, 351
Riehl, Margie: 216
Riehl, Michael: 216
Rieser, Len: 1351
Rifkind, Richard A.: 167
Rightmire, Karen A.: 372
Riley, Angela: 1127
Riley, Emily C.: 94
Riley, Heather A.: 54
Rinehart, Marsha: 90
Ring, John: 2720
Rishel, Jane: 115
Riskin, Steven M.: 93
Rist, Ray C.: 1978
Ritchie, Bruce: 1640
Ritchie, Robert C.: 406

Rivard, David: 1117
Rivera, Ron, C.P.A.: 1235
Rivera-Torres, Nancy: 1196
Rivers, Robert L.: 1088
Rivlin, Alice M., Ph.D.: 62
Rizzo, Robert: 317
Roach, Michele C.: 851
Robb, Lynda J.: 778
Robb, Walter: 426
Robbins, Amy: 2330
Robbins, Curtis: 1293
Robbins, Marlena: 1918
Robbins, N. Clay: 230
Robers, Frank: 1429
Roberts, Carla A.: 1358
Roberts, David E.: 1131
Roberts, Donald D.: 101
Roberts, Katherine Osborn: 1568
Roberts, Kenneth L.: 1359
Roberts, Kim: 2593
Roberts, Richard G., M.D., J.D.: 2365
Robertson, R. Paul, M.D.: 2560
Robertson, Wilhemina E.: 104
Robertson, William R.: 2468
Robins, Elizabeth: 2605
Robins, Perry, M.D.: 2605
Robinson, Barbara: 491
Robinson, Barbara Paul: 170
Robinson, Eugene: 2050
Robinson, Irwin: 704
Robinson, Irwin Z.: 798
Robinson, Jean A.: 1268
Robinson, John: 74
Robinson, John H.: 66
Robinson, Marty: 1307
Robinson, Ronald E.: 293, 2135
Robinson, Russell M., II: 124
Robison, Annette S.: 45
Robson, Kenneth F.: 2796
Rocha, Martha: 1164
Rockefeller, David, Jr.: 464
Rockefeller, Emily: 311
Rockefeller, John D., IV, Sen.: 902
Rockefeller, Justin: 311
Rockefeller, Mark F.: 2330
Rockefeller, Rebecca: 311
Rockefeller, Wendy: 311
Roddey, James C.: 1438
Rodgers, Brooke: 216
Rodgers, Daniel T.: 629
Rodgers, Jonathan: 577
Rodgers, Mary: 798
Rodgers, Mary Anne: 283
Rodgers, Patrick: 216
Rodgers-Edmonds, Catherine: 861
Rodriguez, Jose: 2026
Rodriguez, Ray: 215
Roedel, Paul R.: 372
Roeder, Susan: 1243
Rogalski, Shannon: 1546
Roger, David K.: 179
Rogers, Anne: 410
Rogers, Brian: 529
Rogers, James E.: 1355
Rogers, John W., Jr.: 215
Rogers, Julie L.: 1413
Rogers, Karen: 1372
Rogers, Karen H.: 124
Rogers, Lucy: 1166
Rogers, Margot M.: 202
Rogers, Mary Beth: 1448
Rogers, Sally J.: 1568
Rogers, Sarah: 445
Rohman, John M.: 502
Rohwer, Milton W.: 149
Rojas, Fernando: 908, 910
Romano, Irene: 935
Romano, Nicholas R.: 2431
Romberger, Stacey: 1354
Romero, Raul R.: 1131
Roney, Jane H.: 2743

References in index are to entry numbers.

References in index are to entry numbers.